2012/13

THE DIRECTORY OF

GRANT MAKING TRUSTS

RESEARCH TEAM: TOM TRAYNOR, ANNA ADAMS, JESSICA CARVER, CATRIONA CHRONNELL, JUDE DOHERTY, SUSANNE HOLLYWELL, SARAH JOHNSTON, LUCY LERNELIUS-TONKS, DENISE LILLYA, JENNY MCINTYRE, JONNY MORRIS, EMMA WESTON

22ND EDITION

DIRECTORY OF SOCIAL CHANGE

Published by
Directory of Social Change
24 Stephenson Way
London NW1 2DP
Tel: 08450 77 77 07; Fax: 020 7391 4804
email publications@dsc.org.uk
www.dsc.org.uk
from whom further copies and a full publications catalogue are available.

Directory of Social Change Northern Office
Federation House, Hope Street, Liverpool L1 9BW
Policy & Research 0151 708 0136; email: research@dsc.org.uk

Directory of Social Change is a Registered Charity no. 800517

First published by Charities Aid Foundation 1968
Second edition 1971
Third edition 1974
Fourth edition 1975
Fifth edition 1977
Sixth edition 1978
Seventh edition 1981
Eighth edition 1983
Ninth edition 1985
Tenth edition 1987
Eleventh edition 1989
Twelfth edition 1991
Thirteenth edition 1993
Fourteenth edition 1995
Fifteenth edition 1997
Sixteenth edition 1999
Seventeenth edition published by Directory of Social Change 2001
Eighteenth edition 2003
Nineteenth edition 2005
Twentieth edition 2007
Twenty-first edition 2010
Twenty-second edition 2012

ISBN 978 1 906294 56 4

British Library Cataloguing in Publication Data
A catalogue record for this book is available from the British Library

Cover design by Kate Bass
Text designed by Eugenie Dodd Typographics, London
Typeset by Marlinzo Services, Frome
Printed and bound in Great Britain by CPI Group, Croydon

FSC
www.fsc.org
MIX
Paper from
responsible sources
FSC® C013604

Contents

Contents

Foreword

Time has become an increasingly precious commodity for many charities and, without the right access and tools, valuable hours and days can easily be spent researching and writing funding applications which may have little or no chance of success. The *Directory of Grant Making Trusts* (DGMT) is a key resource for identifying the most appropriate funders that have money available to invest, enabling charities to focus on providing vital services and delivering on their charitable aims.

Trusts and foundations also play an important role in making the task of identifying available funding as simple as possible for charities. Being transparent about what is and is not funded, ensuring application processes are straightforward and being supportive can all make a significant difference to charities when requesting investment and/or support.

Economic upheaval and immense change in the voluntary sector look set to continue again this year. Resources such as the DGMT are necessary for charities to ensure that they remain informed about the funding on offer. Findings from our recent Funding Environment survey reveal that small to medium-sized charities are finding it significantly harder to secure funding, particularly to support much-needed, vital core costs, which 88% of respondents claim that they need more than any other type of funding. This directory will go some way to identifying those funders which offer this type of support for charities.

Despite the continued economic turmoil, our experience has also been that many small to medium-sized charities are adapting to the challenging new environment of fewer resources and increased needs, and we are optimistic that this will continue in 2012. We will continue to support core costs and hope that other funders will do the same so that organisations can remain proactive, resilient and resourceful, whilst still being focused on serving those most in need and the communities in which they live.

Linda Kelly, Chief Executive
Lloyds TSB Foundation for England and Wales

Introduction

This book covers the largest 2,500 grant-making trusts in the UK that give grants to organisations. The amounts given by individual funders range from £25,000 in total each year up to £551.5 million. The combined giving of all these trusts totals over £3.6 billion a year. The top 150 are listed at the end of this introduction and include the Big Lottery Fund and Awards for All, as well as more traditional grant-making trusts.

Charities Aid Foundation published the first edition of the *Directory of Grant Making Trusts* (DGMT) in 1968 and it has been researched and published by the Directory of Social Change since 2001. Over this time the title has gained a notable reputation as a comprehensive guide to UK grant-making trusts and their funding policies. It is designed to provide a bridge between the foundation and fundraising communities in the UK. Today it is hard to imagine the difficulties which must have been encountered in trying to obtain funds from trusts before the DGMT brought together so many of them in one place.

The DGMT is a key source of information on how trusts see themselves and their grantmaking. Each entry aims to reflect the trust's own view of its policies, priorities and exclusions. Other guides include independent, sometimes critical comment on and analysis of trust activities. The DGMT does not. Rather, it is the trusts' guide to grant-making trusts.

Since the last edition of this book was published the UK has emerged out of one of the worst recessions in living memory. Charities have been hit hard, and many have not survived. As economic uncertainty continues, it could be argued that the need for good-quality information on grant-making trusts has never been greater. Many of the funders here will have recently reviewed how they make grants and to whom, and some will have reduced the amount that they give or refocused their efforts to support beneficiaries with which they have an existing relationship.

Potential fundraisers should, however, remain optimistic. While many trusts have disappeared from this edition for one reason or another, there are over 100 trusts that are new to this edition; so the money is still out there. And whilst some funders may have reduced the amount that they give in grants each year, others have maintained and even increased their funding. It is interesting to note that the total amount of grants represented in this edition is comparable with the figure for the last edition, so there has not been the overall dramatic reduction in funding from grant-making trusts and foundations that many predicted. However, the need to focus on well-targeted applications to relevant funders has never been more important, and this book will help you in that endeavour.

During the latter part of 2011 we surveyed all of the funders in this book. Over a quarter responded to our questionnaire, and we have used the information that they provided to inform our research and enhance their entries. As a new element to this edition, we have also included indexes for 'core costs', 'salaries' and the 'replacement of statutory funding', based on the responses to our question about the types of grants that these trusts and foundations will consider. We hope that you will find this useful, but please remember that each of those funders listed will have other eligibility criteria which you must fulfil for your application to be considered – simply applying to these funders without further consideration of their focus, geographical area of benefit or other application criteria is likely to waste your time, effort and money!

We value the opinions of our readers on all aspects of this directory. We are always looking to improve the guide and would welcome any feedback – positive or negative – which could be useful for future editions. Please contact us at: Research Team, Directory of Social Change, Federation House, Hope Street, Liverpool L1 9BW, telephone 0151 708 0136 or email us at: dgmt@dsc.org.uk with any comments you would like to make.

The trusts we have listed This directory aims to include the majority of UK-based trusts that are capable of giving at least £25,000 a year to organisations. Every trust was sent a questionnaire giving them the opportunity to update key information about how they operate.

Many of the trusts are extremely helpful and provide comprehensive information on their current policies via their websites and published material. However, not all trusts are so open. Where a trust does not make this information available, their details have been updated, where possible, using the information on file at the Charity Commission or the Office of the Scottish Charity Regulator. In addition, all contact details were checked. Trusts have been included in the index under the relevant headings according to their own published guidelines. We have placed those trusts for which we do not have such information available under what we believe are the most suitable categories based on the information in their annual reports and accounts.

Some trusts continue to state their wish not to be included in this book. However, we believe that trust directories provide an invaluable bridge between the trust community and the rest of the voluntary sector, and that trusts in receipt of public funds through tax relief should not attempt to draw a veil of secrecy over their activities. Consequently, we have declined requests from trusts to be excluded from this directory.

In general we have included:

- trusts with a grant-making capacity of at least £25,000 per year which make grants to charities and voluntary organisations, including Big Lottery Fund and Awards for All (which operate like grant-making trusts).

We have excluded:

- trusts which fund individuals only;
- trusts which fund one organisation exclusively;
- trusts which have a grant-making capacity or an income of less than £25,000 (smaller local trusts are included on www.trustfunding.org.uk);
- trusts which have ceased to exist or are being wound down with remaining funds fully committed.

We continue to include trusts which state that they do not respond to unsolicited applications. We believe that their inclusion benefits fundraisers by giving a broader overview of the grant-making community, and that the information could be important in supporting relationship fundraising activity. We feel it benefits the trusts in helping them to communicate that they do not wish to receive applications, which fundraisers might not know if they identified the trust through other avenues. In this way we are working towards achieving one of our Great Giving campaign goals of reducing the number of ineligible applications that are submitted to trusts (please visit www.dsc.org.uk for more information).

Acknowledgements

We would like to thank Linda Kelly, Chief Executive of the Lloyds TSB Foundation for England and Wales, for contributing the foreword to this edition.

We would also like to thank all those trusts which make their information openly available, and all those who replied to our questionnaire.

How to use the DGMT

The directory starts with three indexes:

- trusts by geographical area
- trusts by field of interest and type of beneficiary
- trusts by grant type.

There is a listing of the top 150 trusts by grant total at the end of this introduction. All of these lists are in alphabetical order.

Using these indexes, users should end up with a shortlist of trusts whose funding policies match their needs.

Trusts by geographical area

This index enables you to see which trusts will consider applications from a charity or project in a particular geographical area. It contains two separate listings:

LIST OF GEOGRAPHICAL AREA HEADINGS

This is a complete list of all the geographical area headings used in the DGMT. The page numbers relate to the second listing.

LIST OF TRUSTS BY GEOGRAPHICAL AREA

These pages list trusts under the geographical areas from which they will consider applications for funding.

Trusts by field of interest and type of beneficiary

This index enables you to see which trusts are likely to fund projects doing a particular type of work to benefit a particular type of person. It lists trusts according to:

- the type of activity or work they are willing to fund – their 'fields of interest';
- who they want to benefit – their preferred 'beneficiaries'.

These pages contain two separate listings:

CATEGORISATION OF FIELDS OF INTEREST AND TYPES OF BENEFICIARY

This lists all of the headings used in the DGMT to categorise fields of interest and types of beneficiary. This listing should help you match your project with one – or more – of the categories used. The page numbers relate to the second listing.

LIST OF TRUSTS BY FIELD OF INTEREST AND TYPE OF BENEFICIARY

These pages list trusts under the fields of interest and types of beneficiary they have indicated they have a preference for or might be willing to support.

The index is structured hierarchically. This means that the general heading comes first, followed by more specific subject areas. For example, *Education and training* is split into eight sub-headings, including *Higher education*; *Informal, continuing and adult education*; *Primary and secondary school education*; and so on. Some of these are then split further. For example, *Primary and secondary school education* contains a further four categories including *Faith schools* and *Special needs schools*.

So, if your project falls under a specific heading such as *Special needs schools*, it may also be worth looking at the trusts which have expressed a general interest in funding primary and secondary education and, above that, education and training.

Trusts by type of grant

This index enables you to see which trusts will consider making the types of grant you are looking for. Trusts are listed under the types of grant that they have indicated they are willing to make. These pages contain two separate listings:

LIST OF GRANT TYPES

This lists all of the headings used in the DGMT to categorise grant types. Page numbers relate to the second listing.

LIST OF TRUSTS BY GRANT TYPE

These pages list trusts under the types of grant that they are willing to make.

The largest trusts

At the end of these sections, we have listed the largest 150 trusts by grant total in alphabetical order. Between them they account for around £3 billion, or about 83% of the funds available in the book. Please do not use this simply as a mailing list: these trusts cover a wide range of specialist interests and many of them will never fund your work.

We recommend that you read each entry carefully and compile your own list of major trusts relevant to you. You can then set this list alongside the other lists generated from the other indexes in the directory. We believe this is the most effective way of ensuring that you do not omit any major trusts.

How to use the DGMT
Key steps

STEP 1

Define the project, programme or work for which you are seeking funding.

▼

STEP 2

Geographical area: find the area most local to your requirements. Note down the names of the trusts listed here.

▼

STEP 3

Field of interest and type of beneficiary: identify the categories that match your project. Note down the names of the trusts listed here.

▼

STEP 4

Type of grant: identify the type of grant you are looking for. Note down the names of the trusts listed here.

▼

STEP 5

Compare the three lists of trusts to produce a list of those whose funding policies most closely match the characteristics of the project for which you are seeking funding.

▼

STEP 6

If your trust list is **too short** you could include trusts that have a general interest in funding your area.

▼

STEP 7

Look up entries for the trusts identified, study their details carefully and pay close attention to 'What is funded' and 'What is not funded'.

▼

STEP 8

Look at the list of the **top 150 trusts**. Look up entries for the trusts identified, study their details carefully and again pay close attention to 'What is funded' and 'What is not funded'.

Checklist

STEP 1 **The following checklist will help you assemble the information you need.**

- What is the geographical location of the people who will benefit from any funding received?
- What facilities or services will the funding provide?
- What are the characteristics which best describe the people who will benefit from any funding received?
- What type of grant are you looking for?

EXAMPLE *Funding is being sought for a project in Merseyside to enable unemployed young people to take part in an employment training scheme.*

- *The geographical location is: England → North West → **Merseyside***
- *The service to be provided is: **Vocational training***
- *The key characteristic of the people to benefit is that they are: **Unemployed***
- *The type of grant being sought is: **Project support***

STEP 2 **Look up the area where your project is based in the list of geographical area headings on page 2.**

- Turn to the relevant pages in the list of trusts by geographical area and note down the names of the trusts which have stated that they will consider funding projects in your area.

EXAMPLE *Look up the area most local to your requirements (Merseyside) in the list of geographical area headings. Then turn to the relevant page in the list of trusts by geographical area and look up the names of the trusts listed under Merseyside. You may want to look at the trusts listed under the broader region (North West) as well. Note down the names so that they can be compared with the lists through the indexes by type of grant and by field of interest and type of beneficiary.*

It is also worth looking at trusts listed under England, as a trust listed under a more general heading may be just as willing to fund activity in a specific region as another which states that it has a specific interest in that region.

STEP 3 Using the 'Field of interest and type of beneficiary' category on page 44, identify all the categories that match the project, programme or work for which you are seeking funding.

Turn to the relevant pages in the list of trusts by field of interest and type of beneficiary and look up the headings identified.

Note down the names of the trusts that appear under these headings so that you can compare them with the names identified through the indexes by geographical area and by type of grant.

EXAMPLE *With a project to provide training for work, you will probably look first under the main heading 'Education and training'. Under this heading you will find the sub-heading 'Informal, continuing and adult education' and under this you will find the heading 'Vocational education and training'. Note down the page numbers beside 'Informal, continuing and adult education' and 'Vocational education and training'. Trusts that have expressed an interest in funding vocational training may represent your best prospects, but trusts with a more general interest in funding informal education and training might be worth approaching – particularly if they like to fund projects in your area.*

If you look under 'Beneficial groups' you will find 'People who are poor, on low incomes', which is under 'Social and economic circumstances' and 'Disadvantaged and socially excluded people'. Note down this page number too.

STEP 4 Look up the type of grant that you are seeking in 'Trusts by type of grant' on page 158.

Turn to the relevant pages in the list of trusts by type of grant and note down the names of the trusts which will consider giving the type of grant that you are seeking. Compare these names with those that you identified through the indexes by geographical area and by field of interest and type of beneficiary.

EXAMPLE *Look up the type of grant you are seeking in the list of grant types (in this case 'Project support'). Then turn to the relevant page of the list of trusts by type of grant and look at the names of the trusts listed under 'Project support'. Note down the names of all these trusts.*

STEP 5 Compare the lists of trust names produced via steps 2, 3 and 4, and make a list of all the trusts which appear on more than one list. This will produce a list of trusts whose funding policies most closely match the characteristics of the project for which you are seeking funding.

STEP 6 **If the list turns out to be too short it can easily be adjusted.**

EXAMPLE *You find that you have ended up with a list of five trusts. Going back to step 3, you could include the trusts which come under 'Education and training', or, going back to step 2, you could include trusts which will consider funding projects in the North West.*

STEP 7 **Look up the entries for the trusts identified and study their details carefully, paying particular attention to 'Where funding can be given', 'What is funded' and 'What is not funded'.**

If you feel that there is a good match between the characteristics of the project for which you require support and the funding policies of the trust identified, you could submit an application.

STEP 8 **Look at the list of the top 150 trusts.**

Check that you have not missed any of the major funders because you have made your search too specific. Some of the largest foundations give to a wide range of organisations and projects, and they tend to give the largest grants. They are also the most over-subscribed.

Look up the entries for each trust and study their details carefully, paying particular attention to 'Where funding can be given', 'What is funded' and 'What is not funded'. If you feel that there is a good match between the characteristics of the project for which you require support and the funding policies of the trust identified, you could submit an application.

However, make sure that there is a good reason for writing to any trust that you select: do not just send off indiscriminate applications to the whole list!

A typical trust entry

A complete entry should contain information under the headings listed below. An explanation of the information which should appear in these fields is given alongside.

CC NO
Charity registration number

WHERE FUNDING CAN BE GIVEN
The village, town, borough, parish or other geographical area the trust is prepared to fund

WHAT IS FUNDED
Details of the types of project or activity the trust plans to fund

WHAT IS NOT FUNDED
The types of projects or causes the trust will definitely not fund, e.g. expeditions, scholarships

SAMPLE GRANTS
The main grants given by the trust in the last financial year

TRUSTEES
Names of the trustees

PUBLICATIONS
Titles of publications the trust has produced which are of interest to grant seekers

WHO TO APPLY TO
The name and address of the person to whom applications should be sent

ESTABLISHED
Year established

WHO CAN BENEFIT
The kinds of people, animals, etc., the trust wishes to ultimately benefit

TYPE OF GRANT
The types of grant or loan the trust is prepared to give, e.g. one-off, recurring, running costs

RANGE OF GRANTS
The smallest, largest and typical size of grant normally given

FINANCES
The most recent financial information, including the total amount of grants given

OTHER INFORMATION
Any other information which might be useful to grant seekers

HOW TO APPLY
Useful information to those preparing their grant application

■ **The Fictitious Trust**

CC NO 123456   **ESTABLISHED** 1993
WHERE FUNDING CAN BE GIVEN UK.
WHO CAN BENEFIT Charities benefiting children.
WHAT IS FUNDED Education and training.
WHAT IS NOT FUNDED No grants to individuals.
TYPE OF GRANT One-off, capital, running costs.
RANGE OF GRANTS £250–£5,000.
SAMPLE GRANTS A school (£5,000); a university (£1,000); a school library (£800); a school (£600); a grammar school, a further education college and for classroom equipment (£500 each); a university appeal (£400); and a wheelchair ramp (£250).
FINANCES Year 2011 Income £55,000 Grants £50,000 Assets £800,000
TRUSTEES Peter Brown, Chair; Mrs Mary Brown; Alistair Johnson; Lord Great; Lady Good.
PUBLICATIONS The Fictitious Trust – The First 20 Years.
OTHER INFORMATION This trust recently merged with the Fictional Trust.
HOW TO APPLY In writing to the address below. An sae should be enclosed if an acknowledgement is required.
WHO TO APPLY TO A Grant, Secretary, The Old Barn, Main Street, New Town ZC48 2QQ Tel 020 7123 4567 Fax 020 7123 4567 email trust@fictitioustrust.co.uk Website www.fictitioustrust.co.uk

A list of the top 150 trusts by grant total

This is a list of the largest 150 trusts by grant total in alphabetical order. Between them they account for around £3 billion, or about 83% of the funds available in the book. Please do not use this simply as a mailing list: these trusts cover a wide range of specialist interests and many of them will never fund your work.

We recommend that you read each entry carefully and compile your own list of major trusts relevant to you. You can then set this list alongside the other lists generated from the other indexes in the directory. We believe this is the most effective way of ensuring that you do not omit any major trusts.

The 29th May 1961 Charitable Trust

ABF The Soldiers' Charity

Achisomoch Aid Company Limited

Action Medical Research

Age UK

Aid to the Church in Need (UK)

The Alice Trust

Allchurches Trust Ltd

Arthritis Research UK

Arts Council England

The Arts Council of Northern Ireland

The Arts Council of Wales

Asthma UK

AW Charitable Trust

Awards for All

The Baily Thomas Charitable Fund

The Barclay Foundation

The Baring Foundation

BBC Children in Need

BibleLands

The Big Lottery Fund

The Birmingham Community Foundation

The Liz and Terry Bramall Charitable Trust

The British Gas (Scottish Gas) Energy Trust

The Audrey and Stanley Burton 1960 Charitable Trust

The Barrow Cadbury Trust and the Barrow Cadbury Fund

CAFOD

The Childwick Trust

Christian Aid

The City Bridge Trust

The Clore Duffield Foundation

The Clothworkers' Foundation

The Coalfields Regeneration Trust

Colyer-Fergusson Charitable Trust

The Community Foundation for Northern Ireland

Cumbria Community Foundation

Diabetes UK

The Dollond Charitable Trust

The Dulverton Trust

The Dunhill Medical Trust

The Charles Dunstone Charitable Trust

EDF Energy Trust

The John Ellerman Foundation

Entindale Ltd

The Eranda Foundation

Euro Charity Trust

The Exilarch's Foundation

Esmée Fairbairn Foundation

The Thomas Farr Charitable Trust

The February Foundation

Allan and Nesta Ferguson Charitable Settlement

The Fidelity UK Foundation

The Football Foundation

Forever Manchester (The Community Foundation for Greater Manchester)

The Foyle Foundation

The Freemasons' Grand Charity

The Thomas Freke and Lady Norton Charity

The Fuserna Foundation

The Gatsby Charitable Foundation

J Paul Getty Jr Charitable Trust

Global Charities

The Goldsmiths' Company Charity

The M and R Gross Charities Limited

Paul Hamlyn Foundation

The Headley Trust

The Helping Foundation

The Hemby Trust

The Hintze Family Charitable Foundation

The Jabbs Foundation

The Jerusalem Trust

The Elton John Aids Foundation

The Kay Kendall Leukaemia Fund

Kent Community Foundation

Keren Association

Maurice and Hilda Laing Charitable Trust

The LankellyChase Foundation

The Leeds Community Foundation

Leukaemia and Lymphoma Research

The Leverhulme Trust

The Linbury Trust

Lloyds TSB Foundation for England and Wales

The Trust for London

The London Community Foundation

The London Marathon Charitable Trust

The Lord's Taverners

John Lyon's Charity

Man Group plc Charitable Trust

Mayfair Charities Ltd

The Mercers' Charitable Foundation

Community Foundation for Merseyside

The Monument Trust

Muslim Hands

The National Art Collections Fund

The Northern Rock Foundation

The Nuffield Foundation

Oxfam (GB)

Pears Foundation

The Jack Petchey Foundation

Porticus UK

The David and Elaine Potter Foundation

The Prince of Wales's Charitable Foundation

Quartet Community Foundation

Rachel Charitable Trust

The Rank Foundation

The Joseph Rank Trust

The Sigrid Rausing Trust

The Robertson Trust

The Joseph Rowntree Charitable Trust

The Joseph Rowntree Foundation

Royal British Legion

The Rufford Foundation

Santander UK Foundation Limited

The Scottish Community Foundation

Seafarers UK (King George's Fund for Sailors)

The Samuel Sebba Charitable Trust

The Severn Trent Water Charitable Trust Fund

The Shetland Charitable Trust

Ruth Smart Foundation

The Henry Smith Charity

The Sobell Foundation

St James's Place Foundation

The Stewards' Company Limited

The Strasser Foundation

Tearfund

Tesco Charity Trust

The Sir Jules Thorn Charitable Trust

The Tolkien Trust

The Tudor Trust

Community Foundation Serving Tyne and Wear and Northumberland

The Underwood Trust

United Utilities Trust Fund

UnLtd (Foundation for Social Entrepreneurs)

'v'

John and Lucille van Geest Foundation

The Variety Club Children's Charity

The Vodafone (Group) Foundation

The Volant Charitable Trust

Voluntary Action Fund

Wales Council for Voluntary Action

The Waterloo Foundation

The Wates Foundation

The Wellcome Trust

The Westminster Foundation

The Garfield Weston Foundation

Wirral Mayor's Charity

The Maurice Wohl Charitable Foundation

The Charles Wolfson Charitable Trust

The Wolfson Family Charitable Trust

The Wolfson Foundation

The Zochonis Charitable Trust

Other publications and resources

The following publications and resources may also be of interest to readers of the DGMT. They are all available directly from the Directory of Social Change by ringing 08450 77 77 07 or visiting our website at www.dsc.org.uk.

The Guide to Grants for Individuals in Need
Directory of Social Change

This best-selling funding guide gives details of a wide range of funds and other support available for the relief of individual poverty and hardship. It remains a key reference book for social workers, as well as the individuals themselves and those concerned with their welfare.

- Details on national and local charitable trusts which collectively give over £300 million a year towards the relief of individual poverty and hardship.

- Essential advice on applications for each source: eligibility; types of grants given; annual grant total; contact details.

- An example of how to make an effective application, and advice on finding the right sources to apply to.

The Educational Grants Directory
Directory of Social Change

This best-selling guide gives details on a wide range of funds and other support available to schoolchildren and students in need, up to and including first degree level. It is a key reference book for educational social workers, student welfare officers, teachers and advice agencies, and the individuals themselves and their families. It includes:

- Sources of funding for children and students up to and including first degree level from trusts that collectively give around £50 million each year.

- Essential advice and information on applications for each source including eligibility, types of grants given, annual grant total and contact details.

- An example of how to make an effective application, and advice on finding the right sources to apply to.

The Guide to UK Company Giving
Directory of Social Change

This invaluable guide includes details of around 600 companies in the UK that give a combined total of around £360 million in cash donations to voluntary and community organisations. It contains:

- Essential information on who to contact with each company.

- Details information on cash donations, sponsorship, staff volunteering and gifts in kind.

The Guide to the Major Trusts Volumes 1 & 2 Directory of Social Change	The in-depth research and independent comment that these flagship titles offer has made them an essential reference guide for all fundraisers. These guides are the only source of independent critical analysis of trusts in practice. Volume 1: concentrates on the 400 largest trusts that give over £300,000 a year. Volume 2: complements volume 1 to provide a further 1,200 trusts that generally give between £30,000 and £300,000 each year, with some giving considerably more.
www.trustfunding.org.uk	Packed with information on more than 4,500 UK grant-making trusts, this successful and popular tool for fundraisers lists trusts that collectively give over £3.6 billion each year. ■ Search by geographical area, name of trust, type of grant or by keyword search. ■ Choose to receive notification when information on a particular trust or trusts are updated. ■ Receive monthly bulletins that keep you informed of news and updates.
www.grantsfor individuals.org.uk	*A Guide to Grants for Individuals in Need* and *The Educational Grants Directory* come together in this database. It contains over 3,500 trusts and foundations that give to individuals for educational and welfare purposes. Collectively they give over £350 million each year. ■ Search by geographical area, name of trust, type of grant or by keyword search. ■ Choose to receive notification when information on a particular trust or trusts is updated. ■ Receive monthly bulletins that keep you informed of news and updates.
www.companygiving. org.uk	This database contains all those companies in *The Guide to UK Company Giving*, as well as newly discovered company giving and support. Around 600 companies are featured, giving over £360 million in cash donations. Entries contain full details on the various giving methods (cash donations, in-kind support, employee-led support, sponsorship and commercially-led support), and describe both what the company is prepared to fund and the organisations it has supported in the past. ■ Search by geographical area, name of company, type of grant or keyword. ■ Choose to receive notification when information on a particular company or companies is updated. ■ Receive monthly bulletins that keep you informed of news and updates.

www.government funding.org.uk

This database is an essential tool for anyone looking for information on statutory funding. Continually updated, it provides details on over £2.3 billion of funding from local, regional, national and European sources.

- Receive notification of funding rounds before they open.
- Use funder ratings for an independent and unique insight into what to expect from over 200 local, regional, national and European sources.
- Search by type of grant, e.g. small grants, loans and contracts.

DSC also offers a range of specialist funding guides. These guides provide essential tailored reference points for fundraisers working in specific areas.

They include:

The Youth Funding Guide
The Sports Funding Guide
The Environmental Funding Guide
The Government Funding Guide

And, finally, a trusted source of fundraising advice.
The Complete Fundraising Handbook

Trusts by geographical area

This index contains two separate listings:

Geographical area headings: This lists all of the geographical area headings used in the DGMT.

Trusts by geographical area: This lists the trusts appearing in the DGMT under the geographical area for which they have expressed a funding preference.

Trusts by geographical area

The index contains two separate listings:

Geographical area headings
This lists all of the geographical area headings used in DGMT.

Trusts by geographical area
This lists the trusts appearing in the DGMT under the geographical areas for which they have expressed a funding preference

Type of place

■ Developing world

The A B Charitable Trust
Anglo American Group Foundation
The Ardwick Trust
The AS Charitable Trust
Veta Bailey Charitable Trust
The Balmore Trust
The Baring Foundation
The Body Shop Foundation
H E and E L Botteley Charitable Trust
The Bower Trust
Buckland Charitable Trust
Burdens Charitable Foundation
The Audrey and Stanley Burton 1960 Charitable Trust
Henry T and Lucy B Cadbury Charitable Trust
The Canning Trust
The Casey Trust
Christadelphian Samaritan Fund
Chrysalis Trust
The Conscience Trust
The Gershon Coren Charitable Foundation
Michael Cornish Charitable Trust
The Evan Cornish Foundation
The Cumber Family Charitable Trust
The Dorfred Charitable Trust
Dromintee Trust
The Eagle Charity Trust
The Gilbert and Eileen Edgar Foundation
The Ellerdale Trust
The Ericson Trust
Euro Charity Trust
Allan and Nesta Ferguson Charitable Settlement
The Donald Forrester Trust
The Anna Rosa Forster Charitable Trust
The Four Winds Trust
Sydney E Franklin Deceased's New Second Charity
The Jill Franklin Trust
The Fulmer Charitable Trust
The Fuserna Foundation
The Galanthus Trust
The Angela Gallagher Memorial Fund
Global Care
The Constance Green Foundation
H C D Memorial Fund
The Haramead Trust
Miss K M Harbinson's Charitable Trust
Hasluck Charitable Trust
The Headley Trust

Philip Henman Trust
The Joanna Herbert-Stepney Charitable Settlement (also known as The Paget Charitable Trust)
The Innocent Foundation
The Jephcott Charitable Trust
The Cyril and Eve Jumbo Charitable Trust
The Kirby Laing Foundation
The Beatrice Laing Trust
The Langley Charitable Trust
The Leonard Trust
The Linbury Trust
The Enid Linder Foundation
Paul Lunn-Rockliffe Charitable Trust
The Lyndhurst Trust
The Mahavir Trust (also known as the K S Mehta Charitable Trust)
The Marianne Foundation
Mariapolis Limited
The John Mason Family Trust
The Mirianog Trust
Peter John Murray Trust (PJM Trust)
Network for Social Change
Mr and Mrs F E F Newman Charitable Trust
Alice Noakes Memorial Charitable Trust
The Father O'Mahoney Memorial Trust
The Parthenon Trust
Pears Foundation
The Pilkington Charities Fund
The Col W W Pilkington Will Trusts The General Charity Fund
Prairie Trust
The W L Pratt Charitable Trust
Ranworth Trust
The Eleanor Rathbone Charitable Trust
The Reed Foundation
The Rhododendron Trust
The Sir Cliff Richard Charitable Trust
The River Farm Foundation
The Rivers Charitable Trust
Robyn Charitable Trust
The Rock Foundation
The Roddick Foundation
The Sir James Roll Charitable Trust
The Rothera Charitable Settlement
The RRAF Charitable Trust
The Rufford Small Grants Foundation
Ryklow Charitable Trust 1992 (also known as A B Williamson Charitable Trust)
The Saga Charitable Trust
The Alan and Babette Sainsbury Charitable Fund

The Shanti Charitable Trust
Rita and David Slowe Charitable Trust
The W F Southall Trust
St Francis's Leprosy Guild
The Peter Stebbings Memorial Charity
The Stone Family Foundation
The Gay and Keith Talbot Trust
C B and H H Taylor 1984 Trust
Tearfund
The Loke Wan Tho Memorial Foundation
The Tinsley Foundation
The Tisbury Telegraph Trust
The Tolkien Trust
The Tresillian Trust
Ulting Overseas Trust
The United Society for the Propagation of the Gospel
The Valentine Charitable Trust
The Van Neste Foundation
The Vardy Foundation
The Verdon-Smith Family Charitable Settlement
The Vodafone (Group) Foundation
War on Want
Zephyr Charitable Trust

■ Areas of social deprivation

The 29th May 1961 Charitable Trust
Access Sport
The Alchemy Foundation
The Pat Allsop Charitable Trust
Viscount Amory's Charitable Trust
The Anson Charitable Trust
The Archer Charitable Trust
AstonMansfield Charitable Trust
The Austin Bailey Trust
The Barbour Foundation
The Bartlett Taylor Charitable Trust
The Bay Tree Charitable Trust
The John Beckwith Charitable Trust
The Bellinger Donnay Trust
Bergqvist Charitable Trust
P G and N J Boulton Trust
John and Susan Bowers Fund
The Liz and Terry Bramall Charitable Trust
The Harold and Alice Bridges Charity
Bristol Archdeaconry Charity
The Burden Trust
The Arnold Burton 1998 Charitable Trust
Edward Cadbury Charitable Trust

CAFOD (Catholic Agency for
  Overseas Development)
Calouste Gulbenkian
  Foundation
The Calpe Trust
Christian Aid
The Church Urban Fund
Stephen Clark 1957
  Charitable Trust
The E Alec Colman Charitable
  Fund Ltd
The Coltstaple Trust
The Cotton Trust
The Cray Trust
The Hamilton Davies Trust
The Digbeth Trust
The Drapers' Charitable Fund
The Dulverton Trust
The Ellis Campbell Foundation
The Elmgrant Trust
Samuel William Farmer Trust
The Farmers' Company
  Charitable Fund
The A M Fenton Trust
The Earl Fitzwilliam Charitable
  Trust
The Football Association
  National Sports Centre
  Trust
The Forest Hill Charitable Trust
The Forte Charitable Trust
The Hugh Fraser Foundation
Generations Charitable Trust
Gloucestershire Community
  Foundation
The Alfred Haines Charitable
  Trust
The Peter Harrison Foundation
The Heart of England
  Community Foundation
The Heritage of London Trust
  Ltd
The Hilden Charitable Fund
R G Hills Charitable Trust
The Horne Trust
The Hunter Foundation
The Soli and Leah Kelaty Trust
  Fund
The Kiawah Charitable Trust
The William Leech Charity
The Marie Helen Luen
  Charitable Trust
The Lynn Foundation
Marr-Munning Trust
Mercury Phoenix Trust
Millennium Stadium Charitable
  Trust
The Millhouses Charitable
  Trust
The Morel Charitable Trust
Muslim Hands
Nazareth Trust Fund
The Norda Trust
The Northern Rock Foundation
The Odin Charitable Trust
The David and Elaine Potter
  Foundation

The Bishop Radford Trust
The Ripple Effect Foundation
Mrs L D Rope Third Charitable
  Settlement
The Rufford Foundation
The J S and E C Rymer
  Charitable Trust
Santander UK Foundation
  Limited
The SMB Charitable Trust
The Lady Tangye Charitable
  Trust
The Westcroft Trust
The Harold Hyam Wingate
  Foundation
The Wood Family Trust
The Matthews Wrightson
  Charity Trust
The Wyndham Charitable Trust

....

■ Urban areas, inner cities

Access Sport
The Alchemy Foundation
The Pat Allsop Charitable Trust
Viscount Amory's Charitable
  Trust
The Anson Charitable Trust
The Archer Trust
AstonMansfield Charitable
  Trust
The Austin Bailey Trust
The Barbour Foundation
The Bartlett Taylor Charitable
  Trust
The Bay Tree Charitable Trust
The John Beckwith Charitable
  Trust
The Bellinger Donnay Trust
Bergqvist Charitable Trust
The Oliver Borthwick Memorial
  Trust
P G and N J Boulton Trust
John and Susan Bowers Fund
The Liz and Terry Bramall
  Charitable Trust
The Harold and Alice Bridges
  Charity
Bristol Archdeaconry Charity
The Burden Trust
The Arnold Burton 1998
  Charitable Trust
Edward Cadbury Charitable
  Trust
CAFOD (Catholic Agency for
  Overseas Development)
Calouste Gulbenkian
  Foundation
The Calpe Trust
Christian Aid
The Church Urban Fund
Stephen Clark 1957
  Charitable Trust
The E Alec Colman Charitable
  Fund Ltd

The Coltstaple Trust
The Cotton Trust
The Cray Trust
The Hamilton Davies Trust
The Digbeth Trust
The Drapers' Charitable Fund
The Dulverton Trust
The Ellis Campbell Foundation
The Elmgrant Trust
Samuel William Farmer Trust
The Farmers' Company
  Charitable Fund
The A M Fenton Trust
The Earl Fitzwilliam Charitable
  Trust
The Football Association
  National Sports Centre
  Trust
The Forest Hill Charitable Trust
The Forte Charitable Trust
The Hugh Fraser Foundation
Generations Charitable Trust
Gloucestershire Community
  Foundation
The Alfred Haines Charitable
  Trust
The Peter Harrison Foundation
The Heart of England
  Community Foundation
The Heritage of London Trust
  Ltd
The Hilden Charitable Fund
R G Hills Charitable Trust
The Horne Trust
The Hunter Foundation
The Soli and Leah Kelaty Trust
  Fund
The Kiawah Charitable Trust
The William Leech Charity
The Marie Helen Luen
  Charitable Trust
The Lynn Foundation
Marr-Munning Trust
Mercury Phoenix Trust
The Millhouses Charitable
  Trust
The Morel Charitable Trust
Muslim Hands
Nazareth Trust Fund
The Norda Trust
The Northern Rock Foundation
The Odin Charitable Trust
The David and Elaine Potter
  Foundation
The Bishop Radford Trust
The Ripple Effect Foundation
The Rufford Foundation
The J S and E C Rymer
  Charitable Trust
Santander UK Foundation
  Limited
The SMB Charitable Trust
The Lady Tangye Charitable
  Trust
The Westcroft Trust
The Harold Hyam Wingate
  Foundation

The Wood Family Trust
The Matthews Wrightson
   Charity Trust
The Wyndham Charitable Trust

....

■ Rural areas

Access Sport
The Alchemy Foundation
The Pat Allsop Charitable Trust
Viscount Amory's Charitable
   Trust
The Anson Charitable Trust
The Archer Trust
AstonMansfield Charitable
   Trust
The Austin Bailey Trust
The Barbour Foundation
The Bartlett Taylor Charitable
   Trust
The Bay Tree Charitable Trust
The John Beckwith Charitable
   Trust
The Bellinger Donnay Trust
Bergqvist Charitable Trust
P G and N J Boulton Trust
John and Susan Bowers Fund
The Liz and Terry Bramall
   Charitable Trust
The Harold and Alice Bridges
   Charity
Bristol Archdeaconry Charity
The Burden Trust
The Arnold Burton 1998
   Charitable Trust
Edward Cadbury Charitable
   Trust
CAFOD (Catholic Agency for
   Overseas Development)
Calouste Gulbenkian
   Foundation
The Calpe Trust
Christian Aid
The Church Urban Fund
Stephen Clark 1957
   Charitable Trust
The Coalfields Regeneration
   Trust
The E Alec Colman Charitable
   Fund Ltd
The Coltstaple Trust
The Cotton Trust
The Cray Trust
The Hamilton Davies Trust
The Digbeth Trust
The Drapers' Charitable Fund
The Dulverton Trust
The Ellis Campbell Foundation
The Elmgrant Trust
Samuel William Farmer Trust
The Farmers' Company
   Charitable Fund
The A M Fenton Trust
The Earl Fitzwilliam Charitable
   Trust

The Football Association
   National Sports Centre
   Trust
The Forest Hill Charitable Trust
The Forte Charitable Trust
The Hugh Fraser Foundation
The Angela Gallagher Memorial
   Fund
Generations Charitable Trust
Gloucestershire Community
   Foundation
The Alfred Haines Charitable
   Trust
The Peter Harrison Foundation
The Heart of England
   Community Foundation
The Heritage of London Trust
   Ltd
The Hilden Charitable Fund
R G Hills Charitable Trust
The Horne Trust
The Hunter Foundation
The Soli and Leah Kelaty Trust
   Fund
The Kiawah Charitable Trust
The William Leech Charity
The Marie Helen Luen
   Charitable Trust
The Lynn Foundation
Marr-Munning Trust
Mercury Phoenix Trust
The Millhouses Charitable
   Trust
The Morel Charitable Trust
Muslim Hands
Nazareth Trust Fund
The Norda Trust
The Northern Rock Foundation
The Odin Charitable Trust
The David and Elaine Potter
   Foundation
The Bishop Radford Trust
The Ripple Effect Foundation
The Rufford Foundation
The J S and E C Rymer
   Charitable Trust
Santander UK Foundation
   Limited
Schroder Charity Trust
The SMB Charitable Trust
The Lady Tangye Charitable
   Trust
The Westcroft Trust
The Harold Hyam Wingate
   Foundation
The Wood Family Trust
The Matthews Wrightson
   Charity Trust
The Wyndham Charitable Trust

Worldwide

4 Charity Foundation
The Acacia Charitable Trust
Achiezer Association Ltd
Achisomoch Aid Company
   Limited
The Sylvia Adams Charitable
   Trust
Adenfirst Ltd
Aid to the Church in Need (UK)
The Ajahma Charitable Trust
The Alborada Trust
The Alexis Trust
The Altajir Trust
Altamont Ltd
AM Charitable Trust
The Amalur Foundation Limited
The Anchor Foundation
Andor Charitable Trust
The Henry Angest Foundation
Anglo American Group
   Foundation
The Apax Foundation
The John M Archer Charitable
   Trust
The Archer Trust
The Ardeola Charitable Trust
The Ardwick Trust
Armenian General Benevolent
   Union London Trust
The Armenian Relief Society of
   Great Britain Trust
Arsenal Charitable Trust
The Arthur Ronald Dyer
   Charitable Trust
The Arts Council of Northern
   Ireland
The Ove Arup Foundation
The Associated Country
   Women of the World
   (ACWW)
Astellas European Foundation
B W Charitable Trust
The Scott Bader
   Commonwealth Ltd
The Bagri Foundation
The Baker Charitable Trust
The C Alma Baker Trust
The Andrew Balint Charitable
   Trust
The George Balint Charitable
   Trust
The Paul Balint Charitable
   Trust
The Batchworth Trust
Bay Charitable Trust
The Bay Tree Charitable Trust
BCH Trust
The Beacon Trust
Bear Mordechai Ltd
Beauland Ltd
The Beaverbrook Foundation
The Becker Family Charitable
   Trust
The Victoria and David
   Beckham Children's Charity

The John Beckwith Charitable
Trust
The Beit Trust
The Ruth Berkowitz Charitable
Trust
BHST
BibleLands
The Bisgood Charitable Trust
(registered as Miss Jeanne
Bisgood's Charitable Trust)
The Bertie Black Foundation
The Neville and Elaine Blond
Charitable Trust
The Boltons Trust
The Linda and Gordon
Bonnyman Charitable Trust
Salo Bordon Charitable Trust
P G and N J Boulton Trust
The A H and E Boulton Trust
The Breadsticks Foundation
The Brendish Family
Foundation
Bridgepoint Inspire
British Institute at Ankara
British Ornithologists' Union
The Britto Foundation
The Bromley Trust
The Rory and Elizabeth Brooks
Foundation
Mrs E E Brown Charitable
Settlement
Brown-Mellows Trust
Brushmill Ltd
Buckingham Trust
Buckland Charitable Trust
The Bulldog Trust Limited
The Clara E Burgess Charity
The Arnold Burton 1998
Charitable Trust
The Derek Butler Trust
The Noel Buxton Trust
The James Caan Foundation
P H G Cadbury Charitable
Trust
The G W Cadbury Charitable
Trust
The William A Cadbury
Charitable Trust
CAFOD (Catholic Agency for
Overseas Development)
Calleva Foundation
Calouste Gulbenkian
Foundation
The Calpe Trust
Carlee Ltd
The Casey Trust
The Elizabeth Casson Trust
The Caswell Family Charitable
Trust
The Catholic Charitable Trust
Catholic Foreign Missions
The CBD Charitable Trust
The CH (1980) Charitable
Trust
Charitworth Limited
The Worshipful Company of
Chartered Accountants

General Charitable Trust
(also known as CALC)
Chasdei Tovim Me'oros
The Checkatrade Foundation
Childs Charitable Trust
The Childwick Trust
Christian Response to Eastern
Europe
Chrysalis Trust
Church of Ireland Priorities
Fund
The Cleevely Family Charitable
Trust
Closehelm Ltd
The Cobalt Trust
The Vivienne and Samuel
Cohen Charitable Trust
The Bernard Coleman
Charitable Trust
The E Alec Colman Charitable
Fund Ltd
Col-Reno Ltd
The Coltstaple Trust
Comic Relief
The Community Foundation for
Northern Ireland
The Cookson Charitable Trust
Michael Cornish Charitable
Trust
The Evan Cornish Foundation
The Michael Cowan
Foundation
Cowley Charitable Foundation
The Craps Charitable Trust
Criffel Charitable Trust
The R D Crusaders Foundation
The Cumber Family Charitable
Trust
Itzchok Meyer Cymerman Trust
Ltd
The Daiwa Anglo-Japanese
Foundation
Oizer Dalim Trust
The Wilfrid Bruce Davis
Charitable Trust
The De Laszlo Foundation
The Debmar Benevolent Trust
The Djanogly Foundation
The DM Charitable Trust
The Dollond Charitable Trust
The Dorfred Charitable Trust
Double 'O' Charity Ltd
The Doughty Charity Trust
The Dugdale Charitable Trust
The Duis Charitable Trust
The Dulverton Trust
Dushinsky Trust Ltd
Mildred Duveen Charitable
Trust
EAGA Partnership Charitable
Trust
Edupoor Limited
The Edith Maud Ellis 1985
Charitable Trust
The Emilienne Charitable Trust
Entindale Ltd
The Ericson Trust

The Esfandi Charitable
Foundation
The Estelle Trust
Joseph Ettedgui Charitable
Foundation
Euro Charity Trust
The Patrick Evans Foundation
The William and Christine
Eynon Charity
The Matthew Eyton Animal
Welfare Trust
The Fairstead Trust
The Family Rich Charities Trust
The February Foundation
Federation of Jewish Relief
Organisations
Allan and Nesta Ferguson
Charitable Settlement
The Fidelity UK Foundation
Fisherbeck Charitable Trust
The Mrs Yvonne Flux
Charitable Trust
The Follett Trust
The Forest Hill Charitable Trust
The Donald Forrester Trust
The Anna Rosa Forster
Charitable Trust
The Forte Charitable Trust
The Four Winds Trust
Sydney E Franklin Deceased's
New Second Charity
The Jill Franklin Trust
The Michael and Clara
Freeman Charitable Trust
Friends of Biala Ltd
Friends of Boyan Trust
Maurice Fry Charitable Trust
Mejer and Gertrude Miriam
Frydman Foundation
The Fuserna Foundation
The G D Charitable Trust
The Galanthus Trust
The Angela Gallagher Memorial
Fund
The Gatsby Charitable
Foundation
Generations Charitable Trust
Global Care
The GMW Charitable Trust
The Everard and Mina
Goodman Charitable
Foundation
The Hemraj Goyal Foundation
The Great Britain Sasakawa
Foundation
The Green Room Charitable
Trust
Philip and Judith Green Trust
The Wiles Greenworld
Charitable Trust
H and T Clients Charitable
Trust
H C D Memorial Fund
The Doris Louise Hailes
Charitable Trust
Paul Hamlyn Foundation
The Helen Hamlyn Trust

Hampton Fuel Allotment
Charity
The Doughty Hanson
Charitable Foundation
The Haramead Trust
Miss K M Harbinson's
Charitable Trust
The Hargrave Foundation
The Maurice Hatter Foundation
The Hawerby Trust
The Headley Trust
May Hearnshaw's Charity
The Charlotte Heber-Percy
Charitable Trust
Help the Hospices
The Christina Mary Hendrie
Trust for Scottish and
Canadian Charities
Philip Henman Trust
The Hill Charitable Trust
Hille Pandana
Hinduja Foundation
The Holbeck Charitable Trust
Sir Harold Hood's Charitable
Trust
The Hope Trust
The Horizon Foundation
The Hospital Saturday Fund
The Reta Lila Howard
Foundation
The Daniel Howard Trust
The Howe Family Foundation
HTA Sheba Foundation UK
Human Relief Foundation
Humanitarian and Charitable
One Trust (HACOT)
The Humanitarian Trust
The Huntingdon Foundation
John Huntingdon's Charity
The Hutton Foundation
The Huxham Charitable Trust
Infinity Capital Trust
The Inland Waterways
Association
The Innocent Foundation
International Spinal Research
Trust
Investream Charitable Trust
The Ireland Fund of Great
Britain
The Irish Youth Foundation
(UK) Ltd (incorporating The
Lawlor Foundation)
Irshad Trust
The Isaacs Charitable Trust
The Jabbs Foundation
The Marjory Jameson Trust
The Barbara Joyce Jarrald
Charitable Trust
Jay Education Trust
JCA Charitable Foundation
The Nick Jenkins Foundation
The Jephcott Charitable Trust
The Norman Joels Charitable
Trust
The Joffe Charitable Trust

The Elton John Aids
Foundation
The Muriel Jones Foundation
The J E Joseph Charitable
Fund
The Josh Charitable Trust
The Cyril and Eve Jumbo
Charitable Trust
Jusaca Charitable Trust
The Bernard Kahn Charitable
Trust
The Kalou Foundation
The Ian Karten Charitable
Trust
The Kasner Charitable Trust
The Kaufman Charitable Trust
The Soli and Leah Kelaty Trust
Fund
The Kennedy Charitable
Foundation
Kermaville Ltd
The Kessler Foundation
The Kiawah Charitable Trust
The Eric and Margaret Kinder
Charitable Trust
King Sturge Charitable Trust
Ernest Kleinwort Charitable
Trust
Kollel and Co. Limited
The Neil Kreitman Foundation
Kupath Gemach Chaim
Bechesed Viznitz Trust
The K P Ladd Charitable Trust
Maurice and Hilda Laing
Charitable Trust
The David Laing Foundation
The Kirby Laing Foundation
The Martin Laing Foundation
The Beatrice Laing Trust
The Lambert Charitable Trust
The Langdale Trust
The Langley Charitable Trust
Largsmount Ltd
Laslett's (Hinton) Charity
Lauchentilly Charitable
Foundation 1988
The Lauffer Family Charitable
Foundation
Mrs F B Laurence Charitable
Trust
The Law Society Charity
The Kennedy Leigh Charitable
Trust
The Leigh Trust
The Lennox and Wyfold
Foundation
The Erica Leonard Trust
The Leverhulme Trust
The Joseph Levy Charitable
Foundation
Lewis Family Charitable Trust
The Liebreich Foundation
Lifeline 4 Kids
The Lightbridge Foundation
The Limbourne Trust
The Linbury Trust

Lindale Educational
Foundation
Lindenleaf Charitable Trust
The Enid Linder Foundation
Jack Livingstone Charitable
Trust
The Charles Lloyd Foundation
The Locker Foundation
The Lolev Charitable Trust
The Lotus Foundation
The Lower Green Foundation
Henry Lumley Charitable Trust
Paul Lunn-Rockliffe Charitable
Trust
Lord and Lady Lurgan Trust
The Sir Jack Lyons Charitable
Trust
The Lyras Family Charitable
Trust
The Madeline Mabey Trust
The Mactaggart Third Fund
The SV and PE Magee Family
Charitable Trust
The Brian Maguire Charitable
Trust
The Mahavir Trust (also known
as the K S Mehta
Charitable Trust)
Malbin Trust
The Mallinckrodt Foundation
The Manoukian Charitable
Foundation
Marbeh Torah Trust
Marchig Animal Welfare Trust
The Marianne Foundation
Mariapolis Limited
Michael Marks Charitable
Trust
The Hilda and Samuel Marks
Foundation
Marmot Charitable Trust
Marr-Munning Trust
The Mears Foundation
Melodor Ltd
Melow Charitable Trust
The Menzies Charity
Foundation
Mercaz Torah Vechesed
Limited
Brian Mercer Charitable Trust
Mercury Phoenix Trust
T and J Meyer Family
Foundation Limited
Mi Yu Foundation
The Millward Charitable Trust
The Minos Trust
The Esmé Mitchell Trust
The Moonpig Foundation
The Henry Moore Foundation
The Peter Moores Foundation
Diana and Allan Morgenthau
Charitable Trust
Vyoel Moshe Charitable Trust
Brian and Jill Moss Charitable
Trust
The Mount Everest Foundation
The Edwina Mountbatten Trust

The Mountbatten Memorial Trust

Peter John Murray Trust (PJM Trust)

Muslim Hands

MW (CL) Foundation

MW (GK) Foundation

MW (HO) Foundation

MW (RH) Foundation

MYR Charitable Trust

The Naggar Charitable Trust

The Eleni Nakou Foundation

Nathan Charitable Trust

Nazareth Trust Fund

The Nchima Trust

The NDL Foundation

Ner Foundation

Network for Social Change

Mr and Mrs F E F Newman Charitable Trust

NJD Charitable Trust

Alice Noakes Memorial Charitable Trust

Nominet Charitable Foundation

The Northmoor Trust

The Norton Rose Charitable Foundation

Novi Most International

The Father O'Mahoney Memorial Trust

The Sir Peter O'Sullevan Charitable Trust

The Oakdale Trust

The Ogle Christian Trust

The Oikonomia Trust

The Old Broad Street Charity Trust

The Olga Charitable Trust

Onaway Trust

Open Gate

The O'Sullivan Family Charitable Trust

The Ouseley Trust

Oxfam (GB)

Panahpur (previously Panahpur Charitable Trust)

Panton Trust

The Paphitis Charitable Trust

The Paragon Trust

The Park House Charitable Trust

The Parthenon Trust

Ambika Paul Foundation

The Payne Charitable Trust

Pears Foundation

The Pell Charitable Trust

Peltz Trust

Pendragon Charitable Trust

The Persson Charitable Trust (formerly Highmoore Hall Charitable Trust)

The Persula Foundation

The Pervez Musharraf Foundation

The Pharsalia Charitable Trust

The Polehanger Trust

The J S F Pollitzer Charitable Settlement

The Polonsky Foundation

The Popocatepetl Trust

Edith and Ferdinand Porjes Charitable Trust

The John Porter Charitable Trust

The Porter Foundation

The J E Posnansky Charitable Trust

The David and Elaine Potter Foundation

The Praebendo Charitable Foundation

Prairie Trust

The Premier League Charitable Fund

Premierquote Ltd

Premishlaner Charitable Trust

The Tom Press Charitable Foundation

The Foundation of Prince William and Prince Harry

Private Equity Foundation

The Puebla Charitable Trust

The Puri Foundation

The Pyne Charitable Trust

The Queen Anne's Gate Foundation

Quothquan Trust

R J M Charitable Trust

Rachel Charitable Trust

The Ragdoll Foundation

The Rainford Trust

The Peggy Ramsay Foundation

The Joseph and Lena Randall Charitable Trust

The Joseph Rank Trust

Ranworth Trust

The Rashbass Family Trust

The Eleanor Rathbone Charitable Trust

The Sigrid Rausing Trust

The Rayne Trust

The Eva Reckitt Trust Fund

The Rehoboth Trust

Relief Fund for Romania Limited

Reuben Brothers Foundation

The Rhododendron Trust

C B Richard Ellis Charitable Trust

Ridgesave Limited

Robyn Charitable Trust

The Rock Foundation

The Roddick Foundation

Romeera Foundation

The Gerald Ronson Foundation

Rowanville Ltd

The Rowland Family Foundation

The Joseph Rowntree Charitable Trust

The RRAF Charitable Trust

The Rubin Foundation

William Arthur Rudd Memorial Trust

The Rufford Foundation

The Rufford Small Grants Foundation

Ryklow Charitable Trust 1992 (also known as A B Williamson Charitable Trust)

S F Foundation

The Jeremy and John Sacher Charitable Trust

The Michael Harry Sacher Trust

The Raymond and Beverley Sackler 1988 Foundation

The Ruzin Sadagora Trust

Erach and Roshan Sadri Foundation

The Saga Charitable Trust

The Alan and Babette Sainsbury Charitable Fund

Saint Sarkis Charity Trust

The Sammermar Trust

The Hon. M J Samuel Charitable Trust

The Samworth Foundation

The Sandhu Charitable Foundation

The Sands Family Trust

The Annie Schiff Charitable Trust

The Schmidt-Bodner Charitable Trust

Schroder Charity Trust

The Schroder Foundation

The Scotshill Trust

Scott (Eredine) Charitable Trust

Seafarers UK (King George's Fund for Sailors)

The Helene Sebba Charitable Trust

The Samuel Sebba Charitable Trust

The Seedfield Trust

SEM Charitable Trust

The Ayrton Senna Foundation

Shaara Ezra – The Moses Foundation

The Shanley Charitable Trust

The Shekinah Legacy

The Archie Sherman Cardiff Foundation

The Archie Sherman Charitable Trust

The Barnett and Sylvia Shine No 2 Charitable Trust

Shlomo Memorial Fund Limited

The Shoe Zone Trust

The Simpson Education and Conservation Trust

Sino-British Fellowship Trust

Rita and David Slowe Charitable Trust

Ruth Smart Foundation

The SMB Charitable Trust

The N Smith Charitable
  Settlement
The Stanley Smith UK
  Horticultural Trust
The Sobell Foundation
Social Business Trust (Scale-
  Up)
The Solo Charitable
  Settlement
Dr Richard Solomon's
  Charitable Trust
Songdale Ltd
R H Southern Trust
Spears-Stutz Charitable Trust
The Spero Foundation
St Francis's Leprosy Guild
St James' Trust Settlement
C E K Stern Charitable Trust
The Sigmund Sternberg
  Charitable Foundation
Stevenson Family's Charitable
  Trust
The Stewards' Company
  Limited (incorporating the J
  W Laing Trust and the J W
  Laing Biblical Scholarship
  Trust)
The Andy Stewart Charitable
  Foundation
The Sir Halley Stewart Trust
The Stone Family Foundation
The Strawberry Charitable
  Trust
Sueberry Ltd
The Suva Foundation Limited
The Sylvanus Charitable Trust
The Hugh Symons Charitable
  Trust
The Tabeel Trust
Tadlus Limited
The Tajtelbaum Charitable
  Trust
The Gay and Keith Talbot Trust
C B and H H Taylor 1984 Trust
Tearfund
Thackray Medical Research
  Trust
The West Charitable Trust
The Loke Wan Tho Memorial
  Foundation
The Elspeth J Thompson
  Charitable Trust
The Thornton Trust
The Three Oaks Trust
Mrs R P Tindall's Charitable
  Trust
The Tinsley Foundation
The Tory Family Foundation
The Tresillian Trust
The True Colours Trust
The Trust for Education
The Tudor Trust
The TUUT Charitable Trust
TVML Foundation
Trustees of Tzedakah
Ulting Overseas Trust
The Ulverscroft Foundation

The United Society for the
  Propagation of the Gospel
The David Uri Memorial Trust
The Vail Foundation
The Albert Van Den Bergh
  Charitable Trust
Veneziana Fund
Roger Vere Foundation
The Scurrah Wainwright Charity
War on Want
G R Waters Charitable Trust
  2000
Weatherley Charitable Trust
Webb Memorial Trust
The Weinberg Foundation
The Weinstein Foundation
The Weinstock Fund
The Joir and Kato Weisz
  Foundation
The Weldon UK Charitable
  Trust
The Wessex Youth Trust
The Westcroft Trust
The Melanie White Foundation
  Limited
The Williams Family Charitable
  Trust
The H D H Wills 1965
  Charitable Trust
Dame Violet Wills Charitable
  Trust
The Winton Charitable
  Foundation
The Witzenfeld Foundation
The Maurice Wohl Charitable
  Foundation
The Charles Wolfson
  Charitable Trust
The Wolfson Family Charitable
  Trust
The Wolfson Foundation
Women's World Day of Prayer
  (NCWWDPEWNI)
Woodlands Foundation Limited
Woodlands Green Ltd
ME Woolfe Charitable Trust
The Joan Wyatt Charitable
  Trust
Wychdale Ltd
Yankov Charitable Trust
The Dennis Alan Yardy
  Charitable Trust
The John Young Charitable
  Settlement
Suha Yusuf Charitable Trust
Zephyr Charitable Trust
The Zochonis Charitable Trust
The Zolfo Cooper Foundation
Zurich Community Trust (UK)
  Limited

....

■ Europe

Aid to the Church in Need (UK)
The Apax Foundation

Armenian General Benevolent
  Union London Trust
The Arts Council of Northern
  Ireland
The Scott Bader
  Commonwealth Ltd
The Andrew Balint Charitable
  Trust
The George Balint Charitable
  Trust
The Paul Balint Charitable
  Trust
British Institute at Ankara
British Ornithologists' Union
The William A Cadbury
  Charitable Trust
Calouste Gulbenkian
  Foundation
The Catholic Charitable Trust
Christian Response to Eastern
  Europe
Church of Ireland Priorities
  Fund
The Community Foundation for
  Northern Ireland
EAGA Partnership Charitable
  Trust
The Edith Maud Ellis 1985
  Charitable Trust
The Ericson Trust
The February Foundation
The Fidelity UK Foundation
The Headley Trust
The Hospital Saturday Fund
The Reta Lila Howard
  Foundation
The Huxham Charitable Trust
The Inland Waterways
  Association
The Ireland Fund of Great
  Britain
The Irish Youth Foundation
  (UK) Ltd (incorporating The
  Lawlor Foundation)
The Elton John Aids
  Foundation
The Kennedy Charitable
  Foundation
Lauchentilly Charitable
  Foundation 1988
The Leverhulme Trust
The Lyras Family Charitable
  Trust
Marchig Animal Welfare Trust
Marr-Munning Trust
The Mears Foundation
The Esmé Mitchell Trust
The Henry Moore Foundation
The Eleni Nakou Foundation
Mr and Mrs F E F Newman
  Charitable Trust
Novi Most International
The Father O'Mahoney
  Memorial Trust
The Old Broad Street Charity
  Trust
Open Gate

The Ouseley Trust
Oxfam (GB)
Private Equity Foundation
Rachel Charitable Trust
The Peggy Ramsay Foundation
The Joseph Rank Trust
Relief Fund for Romania
Limited
The Joseph Rowntree
Charitable Trust
William Arthur Rudd Memorial
Trust
Saint Sarkis Charity Trust
The Sylvanus Charitable Trust
C B and H H Taylor 1984 Trust
Veneziana Fund
Webb Memorial Trust
The H D H Wills 1965
Charitable Trust

....

■ **Republic of Ireland**

The Arts Council of Northern
Ireland
The William A Cadbury
Charitable Trust
Calouste Gulbenkian
Foundation
Church of Ireland Priorities
Fund
The Community Foundation for
Northern Ireland
The Edith Maud Ellis 1985
Charitable Trust
The Hospital Saturday Fund
The Reta Lila Howard
Foundation
The Inland Waterways
Association
The Ireland Fund of Great
Britain
The Irish Youth Foundation
(UK) Ltd (incorporating The
Lawlor Foundation)
The Elton John Aids
Foundation
The Kennedy Charitable
Foundation
Lauchentilly Charitable
Foundation 1988
The Esmé Mitchell Trust
Mr and Mrs F E F Newman
Charitable Trust
The Ouseley Trust
The Peggy Ramsay Foundation
The Joseph Rank Trust
C B and H H Taylor 1984 Trust
The H D H Wills 1965
Charitable Trust

....

■ **Asia**

4 Charity Foundation
The Acacia Charitable Trust
Achiezer Association Ltd

The Sylvia Adams Charitable
Trust
Aid to the Church in Need (UK)
The Altajir Trust
The Apax Foundation
The Ardwick Trust
The Scott Bader
Commonwealth Ltd
The Andrew Balint Charitable
Trust
The George Balint Charitable
Trust
The Paul Balint Charitable
Trust
BHST
BibleLands
The Bertie Black Foundation
The Breadsticks Foundation
The Brendish Family
Foundation
British Institute at Ankara
The Britto Foundation
Mrs E E Brown Charitable
Settlement
The James Caan Foundation
The CH (1980) Charitable
Trust
Charitworth Limited
Chasdei Tovim Me'oros
Closehelm Ltd
The Vivienne and Samuel
Cohen Charitable Trust
Col-Reno Ltd
The Craps Charitable Trust
Itzchok Meyer Cymerman Trust
Ltd
The Daiwa Anglo-Japanese
Foundation
The Wilfrid Bruce Davis
Charitable Trust
The Debmar Benevolent Trust
The Djanogly Foundation
The DM Charitable Trust
The Dollond Charitable Trust
The Doughty Charity Trust
Dushinsky Trust Ltd
Euro Charity Trust
The Family Rich Charities Trust
The February Foundation
Federation of Jewish Relief
Organisations
Mejer and Gertrude Miriam
Frydman Foundation
The Everard and Mina
Goodman Charitable
Foundation
The Great Britain Sasakawa
Foundation
Paul Hamlyn Foundation
The Helen Hamlyn Trust
The Daniel Howard Trust
The Humanitarian Trust
Investream Charitable Trust
The Isaacs Charitable Trust
JCA Charitable Foundation
The Nick Jenkins Foundation

The Norman Joels Charitable
Trust
The Elton John Aids
Foundation
The J E Joseph Charitable
Fund
The Josh Charitable Trust
The Bernard Kahn Charitable
Trust
The Ian Karten Charitable
Trust
The Kasner Charitable Trust
Kermaville Ltd
The Kessler Foundation
The Kiawah Charitable Trust
The Neil Kreitman Foundation
Kupath Gemach Chaim
Bechesed Viznitz Trust
The Lambert Charitable Trust
Largsmount Ltd
The Lauffer Family Charitable
Foundation
The Kennedy Leigh Charitable
Trust
The Leverhulme Trust
The Joseph Levy Charitable
Foundation
Lewis Family Charitable Trust
Jack Livingstone Charitable
Trust
The Locker Foundation
The Sir Jack Lyons Charitable
Trust
Marbeh Torah Trust
Marchig Animal Welfare Trust
The Hilda and Samuel Marks
Foundation
Marr-Munning Trust
The Mears Foundation
Melodor Ltd
Melow Charitable Trust
Mercaz Torah Vechesed
Limited
MYR Charitable Trust
Ner Foundation
NJD Charitable Trust
The Father O'Mahoney
Memorial Trust
Open Gate
Oxfam (GB)
Ambika Paul Foundation
The Payne Charitable Trust
Peltz Trust
The Pervez Musharraf
Foundation
The Polonsky Foundation
The John Porter Charitable
Trust
The Porter Foundation
The Puri Foundation
The Rayne Trust
The Rehoboth Trust
Rowanville Ltd
The Ruzin Sadagora Trust
The Scotshill Trust
The Helene Sebba Charitable
Trust

The Samuel Sebba Charitable
    Trust
SEM Charitable Trust
The Shekinah Legacy
The Archie Sherman Cardiff
    Foundation
The Archie Sherman Charitable
    Trust
The Shoe Zone Trust
Sino-British Fellowship Trust
The Sobell Foundation
The Solo Charitable
    Settlement
Songdale Ltd
Tadlus Limited
The Tajtelbaum Charitable
    Trust
TVML Foundation
Trustees of Tzedakah
The Vail Foundation
The Witzenfeld Foundation
The Maurice Wohl Charitable
    Foundation
The Charles Wolfson
    Charitable Trust
The Wolfson Family Charitable
    Trust
The Wolfson Foundation
Woodlands Foundation Limited

....

■ Africa

The Sylvia Adams Charitable
    Trust
Aid to the Church in Need (UK)
The Scott Bader
    Commonwealth Ltd
The Beit Trust
The Breadsticks Foundation
British Ornithologists' Union
The Noel Buxton Trust
The Childwick Trust
Comic Relief
The Dugdale Charitable Trust
The Dulverton Trust
The Estelle Trust
Euro Charity Trust
The February Foundation
The Gatsby Charitable
    Foundation
Philip and Judith Green Trust
The Headley Trust
The Nick Jenkins Foundation
The Joffe Charitable Trust
The Elton John Aids
    Foundation
The Kiawah Charitable Trust
The Lauffer Family Charitable
    Foundation
The Leverhulme Trust
Marchig Animal Welfare Trust
Marr-Munning Trust
The Mears Foundation
The Nchima Trust
The Father O'Mahoney
    Memorial Trust

Open Gate
Oxfam (GB)
The Samworth Foundation
The Scotshill Trust
SEM Charitable Trust
The Archie Sherman Cardiff
    Foundation
The Sir Halley Stewart Trust
Mrs R P Tindall's Charitable
    Trust
The True Colours Trust
The Trust for Education
The Tudor Trust
The Scurrah Wainwright Charity
The Zochonis Charitable Trust

....

■ Americas and the West Indies

Aid to the Church in Need (UK)
The Apax Foundation
The Scott Bader
    Commonwealth Ltd
The Beaverbrook Foundation
British Ornithologists' Union
The Catholic Charitable Trust
Col-Reno Ltd
The Michael Cowan
    Foundation
The Christina Mary Hendrie
    Trust for Scottish and
    Canadian Charities
The Huntingdon Foundation
The Neil Kreitman Foundation
The Lauffer Family Charitable
    Foundation
The Leverhulme Trust
Marchig Animal Welfare Trust
Marr-Munning Trust
The Henry Moore Foundation
The Peter Moores Foundation
MYR Charitable Trust
The Father O'Mahoney
    Memorial Trust
Open Gate
Oxfam (GB)
The Polonsky Foundation
The Helene Sebba Charitable
    Trust
The Archie Sherman Cardiff
    Foundation
St James' Trust Settlement
The Sylvanus Charitable Trust
TVML Foundation
G R Waters Charitable Trust
    2000

....

■ Australasia

The C Alma Baker Trust
The Josh Charitable Trust
The Lauffer Family Charitable
    Foundation
Marchig Animal Welfare Trust
The Mount Everest Foundation

Open Gate
The Archie Sherman Cardiff
    Foundation

United Kingdom

The 1970 Trust
The 1989 Willan Charitable Trust
The 29th May 1961 Charitable Trust
4 Charity Foundation
The A B Charitable Trust
The Aberbrothock Skea Trust
The Aberdeen Endowments Trust
The Aberdeenshire Educational Trust Scheme
ABF The Soldiers' Charity (formerly the Army Benevolent Fund)
Brian Abrams Charitable Trust
Eric Abrams Charitable Trust
The Acacia Charitable Trust
Access Sport
Achiezer Association Ltd
The ACT Foundation
Action Medical Research
The Company of Actuaries' Charitable Trust Fund
The Sylvia Adams Charitable Trust
The Adamson Trust
The Victor Adda Foundation
The Adint Charitable Trust
The Adnams Charity
AF Trust Company
Age Scotland (formerly Age Concern Scotland and Help the Aged)
Age UK (formerly Help the Aged and Age Concern)
The AIM Foundation
The Green and Lilian F M Ainsworth and Family Benevolent Fund
The Sylvia Aitken Charitable Trust
The Alabaster Trust
Alba Charitable Trust
The Albion Trust
D G Albright Charitable Trust
The Alchemy Foundation
Aldgate and All Hallows' Barking Exhibition Foundation
The Aldgate Freedom Foundation
The Alice Trust
All Saints Educational Trust
Allchurches Trust Ltd
The H B Allen Charitable Trust
The Alliance Family Foundation
Angus Allnatt Charitable Foundation
The Pat Allsop Charitable Trust
The Almond Trust
Almondsbury Charity
The Altajir Trust
Alvor Charitable Trust
Amabrill Limited

The Ammco Trust
Sir John and Lady Amory's Charitable Trust
Viscount Amory's Charitable Trust
The Ampelos Trust
The AMW Charitable Trust
The Andrew Anderson Trust
The André Christian Trust
Anguish's Educational Foundation
The Animal Defence Trust
The Eric Anker-Petersen Charity
The Annandale Charitable Trust
The Anson Charitable Trust
The Apax Foundation
Ambrose and Ann Appelbe Trust
The Appletree Trust
The John Apthorp Charitable Trust
The Arbib Foundation
Archbishop of Wales' Fund for Children
The Architectural Heritage Fund
The Ardwick Trust
The Argentarius Foundation
The Argus Appeal
Armenian General Benevolent Union London Trust
The John Armitage Charitable Trust
The Armourers' and Brasiers' Gauntlet Trust
The Arnold Foundation
Arsenal Charitable Trust
The Artemis Charitable Trust
Arthritis Research UK
The Arts and Entertainment Charitable Trust
Arts Council England
The Arts Council of Wales
The AS Charitable Trust
Ashburnham Thanksgiving Trust
A J H Ashby Will Trust
The Ashden Trust
The Ashendene Trust
The Ashley Family Foundation (formerly The Laura Ashley Foundation)
The Norman C Ashton Foundation
The Ashworth Charitable Trust
The Ian Askew Charitable Trust
The Association of Colleges Charitable Trust
The Association of Friends of Essex Churches
Asthma UK
AstonMansfield Charitable Trust
The Astor Foundation
The Astor of Hever Trust

The Aurelius Charitable Trust
The Lord Austin Trust
Autonomous Research Charitable Trust
The Avenue Charitable Trust
The John Avins Trustees
The Avon and Somerset Police Community Trust
AW Charitable Trust
Awards for All
The Aylesford Family Charitable Trust
The BAA Communities Trust
Harry Bacon Foundation
The BACTA Charitable Trust
The Scott Bader Commonwealth Ltd
Veta Bailey Charitable Trust
The Austin Bailey Trust
The Baily Thomas Charitable Fund
The Baird Trust
The Roy and Pixie Baker Charitable Trust
The Balcombe Charitable Trust
The Andrew Balint Charitable Trust
The George Balint Charitable Trust
The Paul Balint Charitable Trust
The Albert Casanova Ballard Deceased Trust
The Ballinger Charitable Trust
Balmain Charitable Trust
The Balmore Trust
The Balney Charitable Trust
The Baltic Charitable Fund
The Bamford Charitable Foundation
The Banbury Charities
William P Bancroft (No 2) Charitable Trust and Jenepher Gillett Trust
The Band Trust
The Barbers' Company General Charities
The Barbour Foundation
The Barcapel Foundation
Barchester Healthcare Foundation
The Barclay Foundation
The Baring Foundation
Peter Barker-Mill Memorial Charity
Barleycorn Trust
Lord Barnby's Foundation
Barnes Workhouse Fund
The Barnsbury Charitable Trust
The Barnstaple Bridge Trust
The Barnwood House Trust
The Misses Barrie Charitable Trust
Barrington Family Charitable Trust
The Charity of William Barrow

Stephen J Barry Charitable
Trust
The Bartlett Taylor Charitable
Trust
The Worshipful Company of
Basketmakers' Charitable
Trust
The Paul Bassham Charitable
Trust
D H and L H Baylin Charitable
Trust
The Louis Baylis (Maidenhead
Advertiser) Charitable Trust
BBC Children in Need
BC Partners Foundation
B-CH 1971 Charitable Trust
The Bearder Charity
The James Beattie Charitable
Trust
The Jack and Ada Beattie
Foundation
The Beaufort House Trust
Limited
The Beaverbrook Foundation
The Beccles Town Lands
Charity
The Becketts and Sargeants
Educational Foundation
The Victoria and David
Beckham Children's Charity
The Peter Beckwith Charitable
Trust
The Bedford Charity (The
Harpur Trust)
The Bedfordshire and
Hertfordshire Historic
Churches Trust
The Bedfordshire and Luton
Community Foundation
The David and Ruth Behrend
Fund
The Bellahouston Bequest
Fund
Bellasis Trust
The Bellhouse Foundation
The Bellinger Donnay Trust
Belljoe Tzedoko Ltd
The Benfield Motors Charitable
Trust
The Benham Charitable
Settlement
The Hervey Benham Charitable
Trust
Maurice and Jacqueline
Bennett Charitable Trust
Michael and Leslie Bennett
Charitable Trust
The Gerald Bentall Charitable
Trust
Bergqvist Charitable Trust
The Berkshire Community
Foundation
The Bestway Foundation
Thomas Betton's Charity for
Pensions and Relief-in-Need
BHST
The Mason Bibby 1981 Trust

The Bideford Bridge Trust
The Big Lottery Fund
The Billmeir Charitable Trust
Percy Bilton Charity
The Bingham Trust
The Bintaub Charitable Trust
The Birmingham Community
Foundation
The Birmingham District
Nursing Charitable Trust
The Birmingham Hospital
Saturday Fund Medical
Charity and Welfare Trust
Birmingham International
Airport Community Trust
The Lord Mayor of
Birmingham's Charity
Birthday House Trust
The Michael Bishop
Foundation
The Bishop's Development
Fund
The Sydney Black Charitable
Trust
The Bertie Black Foundation
Sir Alec Black's Charity
Blackheart Foundation (UK)
Limited
Isabel Blackman Foundation
The BlackRock (UK) Charitable
Trust
The Herbert and Peter
Blagrave Charitable Trust
The Blair Foundation
The Blanchminster Trust
The Sir Victor Blank Charitable
Settlement
Blatchington Court Trust
The Blueberry Charitable Trust
The Bluston Charitable
Settlement
The Nicholas Boas Charitable
Trust
The Body Shop Foundation
The Bonamy Charitable Trust
The John and Celia Bonham
Christie Charitable Trust
The Charlotte Bonham-Carter
Charitable Trust
Bonhomie United Charity
Society
BOOST Charitable Trust
The Booth Charities
The Boots Charitable Trust
The Bordon and Liphook
Charity
The Oliver Borthwick Memorial
Trust
The Boshier-Hinton Foundation
The Bothwell Charitable Trust
H E and E L Botteley
Charitable Trust
The Harry Bottom Charitable
Trust
Sir Clive Bourne Family Trust
The Anthony Bourne
Foundation

Bourneheights Limited
Community Foundation for
Bournemouth, Dorset and
Poole
The Bower Trust
The Bowerman Charitable
Trust
John and Susan Bowers Fund
The Bowland Charitable Trust
The William Brake Charitable
Trust
The Liz and Terry Bramall
Charitable Trust
The Tony Bramall Charitable
Trust
The Bransford Trust
The Breadsticks Foundation
The Breast Cancer Research
Trust
The Brendish Family
Foundation
The Harold and Alice Bridges
Charity
Briggs Animal Welfare Trust
The Brighton District Nursing
Association Trust
Bristol Archdeaconry Charity
The Bristol Charities
John Bristow and Thomas
Mason Trust
Britannia Foundation
The British Council for
Prevention of Blindness
The British Dietetic
Association General and
Education Trust Fund
The British Gas (Scottish Gas)
Energy Trust
British Heart Foundation
British Humane Association
British Institute at Ankara
British Record Industry Trust
The Britten-Pears Foundation
The Britto Foundation
The J and M Britton Charitable
Trust
The Charles and Edna
Broadhurst Charitable Trust
The Roger Brooke Charitable
Trust
The David Brooke Charity
The Charles Brotherton Trust
Joseph Brough Charitable
Trust
The Swinfen Broun Charitable
Trust
Mrs E E Brown Charitable
Settlement
Bill Brown's Charitable
Settlement
R S Brownless Charitable
Trust
Brownsword Charitable
Foundation
T B H Brunner's Charitable
Settlement

The Jack Brunton Charitable
Trust
The Bruntwood Charity
The Bryant Trust
The Buckinghamshire
Foundation
The Buckinghamshire Historic
Churches Trust
The Buckinghamshire Masonic
Centenary Fund
The Buffini Chao Foundation
The Rosemary Bugden
Charitable Trust
The E F Bulmer Benevolent
Fund
The BUPA Foundation
The Burden Trust
Burdens Charitable Foundation
The Burdett Trust for Nursing
The Burry Charitable Trust
The Audrey and Stanley Burton
1960 Charitable Trust
The Burton Breweries
Charitable Trust
The Geoffrey Burton Charitable
Trust
Consolidated Charity of Burton
upon Trent
Butchers' Company General
Charities
The Noel Buxton Trust
Ann Byrne Charitable Trust
C and F Charitable Trust
The C Charitable Trust
The James Caan Foundation
C J Cadbury Charitable Trust
Edward Cadbury Charitable
Trust
Henry T and Lucy B Cadbury
Charitable Trust
The Christopher Cadbury
Charitable Trust
The Richard Cadbury
Charitable Trust
The William A Cadbury
Charitable Trust
The Cadbury Foundation
The Edward and Dorothy
Cadbury Trust
The George Cadbury Trust
The Barrow Cadbury Trust and
the Barrow Cadbury Fund
The Cadogan Charity
CAF (Charities Aid Foundation)
The Callander Charitable Trust
Calouste Gulbenkian
Foundation
Calypso Browning Trust
The Cambridgeshire
Community Foundation
The Cambridgeshire Historic
Churches Trust
The Camelia Trust
The Campden Charities
Trustee
The Frederick and Phyllis Cann
Trust

The Canning Trust
M R Cannon 1998 Charitable
Trust
H and L Cantor Trust
Cardy Beaver Foundation
The Carew Pole Charitable
Trust
The D W T Cargill Fund
The Carlsson Family
Foundation
The Carlton House Charitable
Trust
The Worshipful Company of
Carmen Benevolent Trust
The Richard Carne Trust
The Carnegie Dunfermline
Trust
The Carnegie Trust for the
Universities of Scotland
The Carpenter Charitable Trust
The Carpenters' Company
Charitable Trust
The Carr-Gregory Trust
The Carrington Charitable
Trust
The Carron Charitable
Settlement
The Leslie Mary Carter
Charitable Trust
Carter's Educational
Foundation
The Carvill Trust
Cash for Kids Radio Clyde
Sir John Cass's Foundation
The Castanea Trust
The Castang Foundation
The Catalyst Charitable Trust
(formerly the Buckle Family
Charitable Trust)
The Catholic Trust for England
and Wales
The Cattanach Charitable Trust
The Joseph and Annie Cattle
Trust
The Thomas Sivewright Catto
Charitable Settlement
The Wilfrid and Constance
Cave Foundation
The Cayo Foundation
Elizabeth Cayzer Charitable
Trust
The B G S Cayzer Charitable
Trust
The Cazenove Charitable Trust
Celtic Charity Fund
The Cemlyn-Jones Trust
CfBT Education Trust
The CH (1980) Charitable
Trust
R E Chadwick Charitable Trust
The Amelia Chadwick Trust
The Pamela Champion
Foundation
Champneys Charitable
Foundation
The Chapman Charitable Trust

John William Chapman's
Charitable Trust
The Charities Advisory Trust
Charitworth Limited
The Charter 600 Charity
The Chasah Trust
Chasdei Tovim Me'oros
The Chelsea Building Society
Charitable Foundation
The Chelsea Square 1994
Trust
The Cheruby Trust
The Cheshire Provincial Fund
of Benevolence
Chest, Heart and Stroke
Scotland
The Chetwode Foundation
Chevioty Asset Management
Charitable Trust
The Malcolm Chick Charity
Child Growth Foundation
Children's Liver Disease
Foundation
The Children's Research Fund
The Childwick Trust
The Chippenham Borough
Lands Charity
The Chipping Sodbury Town
Lands Charity
CHK Charities Limited
The Chownes Foundation
The Chrimes Family Charitable
Trust
The Christabella Charitable
Trust
Christadelphian Samaritan
Fund
Christian Aid
The Church and Community
Fund
The Church Burgesses
Educational Foundation
Church Burgesses Trust
Church of Ireland Priorities
Fund
The Church Urban Fund
City and County of Swansea
Welsh Church Act Fund
The City Bridge Trust (formerly
known as Bridge House
Trust)
The City Educational Trust
Fund
CLA Charitable Trust
Stephen Clark 1957
Charitable Trust
J A Clark Charitable Trust
The Hilda and Alice Clark
Charitable Trust
The Roger and Sarah Bancroft
Clark Charitable Trust
The Clarke Charitable
Settlement
The Cleary Foundation
The Cleopatra Trust
Lord Clinton's Charitable Trust
The Clore Duffield Foundation

Miss V L Clore's 1967
Charitable Trust
Closehelm Ltd
The Clothworkers' Foundation
Richard Cloudesley's Charity
The Clover Trust
The Robert Clutterbuck
Charitable Trust
Clydpride Ltd
The Francis Coales Charitable
Foundation
The Coalfields Regeneration
Trust
The John Coates Charitable
Trust
Coats Foundation Trust
The Cobtree Charity Trust Ltd
The Denise Cohen Charitable
Trust
The Vivienne and Samuel
Cohen Charitable Trust
The John S Cohen Foundation
The R and S Cohen
Foundation
The Colchester Catalyst
Charity
John Coldman Charitable Trust
The Cole Charitable Trust
The Colefax Charitable Trust
The John and Freda Coleman
Charitable Trust
The George Henry Collins
Charity
The Sir Jeremiah Colman Gift
Trust
Col-Reno Ltd
The Colt Foundation
Colwinston Charitable Trust
Colyer-Fergusson Charitable
Trust
Comic Relief
The Comino Foundation
Community Foundation for
Calderdale
The Community Foundation for
Northern Ireland
The Compton Charitable Trust
The Douglas Compton James
Charitable Trust
The Congleton Inclosure Trust
The Congregational and
General Charitable Trust
The Conscience Trust
The Conservation Foundation
The Consolidated Charities for
the Infirm Merchant
Taylors' Company
The Cook and Wolstenholme
Charitable Trust
Gordon Cook Foundation
The Ernest Cook Trust
The Cooks Charity
The Catherine Cookson
Charitable Trust
Harold and Daphne Cooper
Charitable Trust
Mabel Cooper Charity

The Alice Ellen Cooper Dean
Charitable Foundation
The Co-operative Foundation
The Marjorie Coote Animal
Charity Trust
The Marjorie Coote Old
People's Charity
The Helen Jean Cope Trust
The J Reginald Corah
Foundation Fund
The Gershon Coren Charitable
Foundation
The Corinthian Trust
Edwin Cornforth 1983 Charity
Trust
Cornwall Community
Foundation
The Cornwall Historic
Churches Trust
The Duke of Cornwall's
Benevolent Fund
The Cornwell Charitable Trust
The Sidney and Elizabeth
Corob Charitable Trust
The Corona Charitable Trust
The Costa Family Charitable
Trust (formerly the Morgan
Williams Charitable Trust)
The Cotton Industry War
Memorial Trust
The Cotton Trust
Country Houses Foundation
County Durham Community
Foundation
The Augustine Courtauld Trust
Coutts Charitable Trust
The General Charities of the
City of Coventry
Coventry Building Society
Charitable Foundation
The John Cowan Foundation
The Michael Cowan
Foundation
The Sir Tom Cowie Charitable
Trust
The Sir William Coxen Trust
Fund
The Lord Cozens-Hardy Trust
The Craignish Trust
The Craps Charitable Trust
Michael Crawford Children's
Charity
The Cray Trust
Creative Scotland
The Crescent Trust
Cripplegate Foundation
The Violet and Milo Cripps
Charitable Trust
The Harry Crook Foundation
The Cross Trust
The Croydon Relief in Need
Charities
The Mayor of Croydon's
Charity Fund
The Peter Cruddas Foundation
Cruden Foundation Ltd

The Ronald Cruickshank's
Foundation
The Cuby Charitable Trust
Cullum Family Trust
The Culra Charitable Trust
Cumberland Building Society
Charitable Foundation
Cumbria Community
Foundation
The Cunningham Trust
The Harry Cureton Charitable
Trust
The D J H Currie Memorial
Trust
The Dennis Curry Charitable
Trust
The Raymond Curtis Charitable
Trust
The Manny Cussins
Foundation
The Cutler Trust (the
Worshipful Company of
Makers of Playing Cards)
The Cwmbran Trust
Itzchok Meyer Cymerman Trust
Ltd
The D G Charitable Settlement
The D'Oyly Carte Charitable
Trust
Roald Dahl's Marvellous
Children's Charity
The Daily Prayer Union
Charitable Trust Ltd
The Daisy Trust
The Daiwa Anglo-Japanese
Foundation
The Dr and Mrs A Darlington
Charitable Trust
Baron Davenport's Charity
The Davidson (Nairn)
Charitable Trust
The Davidson Family
Charitable Trust
The Alderman Joe Davidson
Memorial Trust
Michael Davies Charitable
Settlement
The Gwendoline and Margaret
Davies Charity
The Hamilton Davies Trust
The Wilfrid Bruce Davis
Charitable Trust
Davis-Rubens Charitable Trust
The Dawe Charitable Trust
The De Clermont Charitable
Company Ltd
The Helen and Geoffrey De
Freitas Charitable Trust
Peter De Haan Charitable
Trust
The Leopold De Rothschild
Charitable Trust
The Deakin Charitable Trust
William Dean Countryside and
Educational Trust
The Debmar Benevolent Trust
The Delius Trust

The Dellal Foundation
The Delves Charitable Trust
The Demigryphon Trust
The Denman Charitable Trust
The Denton Charitable Trust
The Denton Wilde Sapte
  Charitable Trust
The Earl of Derby's Charitable
  Trust
The Derbyshire Churches and
  Chapels Preservation Trust
Derbyshire Community
  Foundation
The J N Derbyshire Trust
Devon Community Foundation
The Devon Educational Trust
The Devon Historic Churches
  Trust
The Duke of Devonshire's
  Charitable Trust
The Sandy Dewhirst Charitable
  Trust
The Laduma Dhamecha
  Charitable Trust
Diabetes UK
Alan and Sheila Diamond
  Charitable Trust
David and Rose Diamond Trust
The Dibden Allotments Fund
The Gillian Dickinson Trust
The Dickon Trust
The Digbeth Trust
The Dinwoodie Settlement
Disability Aid Fund (The Roger
  and Jean Jefcoate Trust)
Dischma Charitable Trust
The Djanogly Foundation
The DLM Charitable Trust
The DM Charitable Trust
Louise Dobson Charitable
  Trust
The Derek and Eileen Dodgson
  Foundation
The Dollond Charitable Trust
Domepride Ltd
The Dorcas Trust
The Dorema Charitable Trust
The Dorset Historic Churches
  Trust
The Dorus Trust
The Doughty Charity Trust
The R M Douglas Charitable
  Trust
The Drapers' Charitable Fund
The Drayson Foundation
Dromintee Trust
The Dugdale Charitable Trust
The Dulverton Trust
The P B Dumbell Charitable
  Trust
The Dumbreck Charity
Dunard Fund
Ronald Duncan Literary
  Foundation
The Dunhill Medical Trust
The Houghton Dunn Charitable
  Trust

The Dunn Family Charitable
  Trust
The W E Dunn Trust
The Charles Dunstone
  Charitable Trust
Annette Duvollet Charitable
  Trust
The Dwek Family Charitable
  Trust
The Dyers' Company
  Charitable Trust
The James Dyson Foundation
EAGA Partnership Charitable
  Trust
The Eagle Charity Trust
Audrey Earle Charitable Trust
The Earley Charity
Earls Colne and Halstead
  Educational Charity
The Earmark Trust
East London Community
  Foundation
Eastern Counties Educational
  Trust Limited
The Sir John Eastwood
  Foundation
The Ebenezer Trust
The EBM Charitable Trust
The Ecology Trust
Eden Arts Trust
EDF Energy Trust (EDFET)
The Gilbert and Eileen Edgar
  Foundation
Gilbert Edgar Trust
Edinburgh Children's Holiday
  Fund
The Edinburgh Trust, No 2
  Account
Edinburgh Voluntary
  Organisations' Trust Funds
Educational Foundation of
  Alderman John Norman
Dr Edwards Bishop King's
  Fulham Endowment Fund
The W G Edwards Charitable
  Foundation
The William Edwards
  Educational Charity
The Elephant Trust
The George Elias Charitable
  Trust
The Gerald Palmer Eling Trust
  Company
The Wilfred and Elsie Elkes
  Charity Fund
The Maud Elkington Charitable
  Trust
Ellador Ltd
The Ellerdale Trust
The John Ellerman Foundation
The Ellinson Foundation Ltd
The Edith Maud Ellis 1985
  Charitable Trust
The Ellis Campbell Foundation
James Ellis Charitable Trust
The Elm House Trust
The Elmgrant Trust

The Elmley Foundation
Elshore Ltd
The Vernon N Ely Charitable
  Trust
The Embleton Trust
The Emerton-Christie Charity
EMI Music Sound Foundation
The Emmandjay Charitable
  Trust
Empath UK
The Worshipful Company of
  Engineers Charitable Trust
  Fund
The Englefield Charitable Trust
The English Schools' Football
  Association
The Enkalon Foundation
The Epigoni Trust
Epilepsy Research UK
The Equilibrium Foundation
The Equitable Charitable Trust
The Equity Trust Fund
The Eranda Foundation
The Ericson Trust
The Ernest Hecht Charitable
  Foundation
The Erskine Cunningham Hill
  Trust
Essex Community Foundation
The Essex Fairway Charitable
  Trust
The Essex Heritage Trust
Essex Provincial Charity Fund
The Essex Youth Trust
The Estelle Trust
Euro Charity Trust
The Alan Evans Memorial Trust
Sir John Evelyn's Charity
The Eventhall Family
  Charitable Trust
The Everard Foundation
The Eveson Charitable Trust
The Beryl Evetts and Robert
  Luff Animal Welfare Trust
The Execution Charitable Trust
The Mayor of Exeter's Appeal
  Fund
The Exilarch's Foundation
Extonglen Limited
F C Charitable Trust
The F P Limited Charitable
  Trust
The Faber Charitable Trust
Esmée Fairbairn Foundation
The Fairway Trust
The Fairwind Trust
Faisaltex Charitable Trust
Famos Foundation Trust
The Lord Faringdon Charitable
  Trust
Samuel William Farmer Trust
The Farmers' Company
  Charitable Fund
The Thomas Farr Charitable
  Trust
Walter Farthing (Trust) Limited
Farthing Trust

The Fassnidge Memorial Trust
Joseph Fattorini Charitable
   Trust 'B' Account
The Fawcett Charitable Trust
The February Foundation
The John Feeney Charitable
   Trust
The George Fentham
   Birmingham Charity
The A M Fenton Trust
Elizabeth Ferguson Charitable
   Trust Fund
The Fidelity UK Foundation
The Bluff Field Charitable Trust
The Doris Field Charitable
   Trust
Fife Council/Common Good
   Funds and Trusts
The Fifty Fund
Dixie Rose Findlay Charitable
   Trust
Finnart House School Trust
Gerald Finzi Charitable Trust
Firtree Trust
The Margaret Fisher Charitable
   Trust
The Sir John Fisher Foundation
The Fishmongers' Company's
   Charitable Trust
Marc Fitch Fund
The Fitton Trust
The Earl Fitzwilliam Charitable
   Trust
Bud Flanagan Leukaemia Fund
The Rose Flatau Charitable
   Trust
The Ian Fleming Charitable
   Trust
The Joyce Fletcher Charitable
   Trust
The Roy Fletcher Charitable
   Trust
Florence's Charitable Trust
The Flow Foundation
The Gerald Fogel Charitable
   Trust
The Football Association
   National Sports Centre
   Trust
The Football Association Youth
   Trust
The Football Foundation
The Forbes Charitable
   Foundation
The Forces Trust (Working
   Name)
Ford Britain Trust
The Oliver Ford Charitable
   Trust
Fordeve Ltd
The Lady Forester Trust
The Foresters' Fund for
   Children
The Foresters' Charity
   Stewards UK Trust

Forever Manchester (The
   Community Foundation for
   Greater Manchester)
Gwyneth Forrester Trust
The Fort Foundation
Lord Forte Foundation
Foundation for Management
   Education
The Foyle Foundation
The Isaac and Freda Frankel
   Memorial Charitable Trust
The Elizabeth Frankland Moore
   and Star Foundation
The Gordon Fraser Charitable
   Trust
The Hugh Fraser Foundation
The Joseph Strong Frazer Trust
The Louis and Valerie
   Freedman Charitable
   Settlement
The Freemasons' Grand
   Charity
The Thomas Freke and Lady
   Norton Charity
The Charles S French
   Charitable Trust
The Anne French Memorial
   Trust
The Freshfield Foundation
The Freshgate Trust
   Foundation
The Friarsgate Trust
The Friends Hall Farm Street
   Trust
The Friends of Kent Churches
Friends of Muir Group
Friends of Wiznitz Limited
Friends Provident Charitable
   Foundation
The Frognal Trust
T F C Frost Charitable Trust
The Patrick Frost Foundation
Mejer and Gertrude Miriam
   Frydman Foundation
The Fuellers Charitable Trust
   Fund
The Fulmer Charitable Trust
Worshipful Company of
   Furniture Makers Charitable
   Fund
Gableholt Limited
The Galbraith Trust
The Gale Family Charitable
   Trust
The Gamlen Charitable Trust
The Gamma Trust
The Gannochy Trust
The Ganzoni Charitable Trust
The Worshipful Company of
   Gardeners of London
The Samuel Gardner Memorial
   Trust
The Garnett Charitable Trust
Garrick Charitable Trust
Garvan Limited
Gatwick Airport Community
   Trust

The Robert Gavron Charitable
   Trust
Jacqueline and Michael Gee
   Charitable Trust
The General Nursing Council
   for England and Wales
   Trust
J Paul Getty Jr Charitable Trust
The Gibbs Charitable Trust
Simon Gibson Charitable Trust
The G C Gibson Charitable
   Trust
Lady Gibson's Charitable Trust
The Harvey and Hilary Gilbert
   Charitable Trust
The Girdlers' Company
   Charitable Trust
The B and P Glasser
   Charitable Trust
The Glass-House Trust
The Glastonbury Trust Limited
Global Charities (formerly
   GCap Charities)
Gloucestershire Community
   Foundation
The Gloucestershire Historic
   Churches Trust
Worshipful Company of
   Glovers of London Charity
   Fund
GMC Trust
The GNC Trust
The Meir Golda Trust
The Sydney and Phyllis
   Goldberg Memorial
   Charitable Trust
The Golden Bottle Trust
Golden Charitable Trust
The Jack Goldhill Charitable
   Trust
The Goldmark Trust
The Goldsmiths' Arts Trust
   Fund
The Goldsmiths' Company
   Charity
The Golsoncott Foundation
Golubovich Foundation
The Good Neighbours Trust
Nicholas and Judith
   Goodison's Charitable
   Settlement
The Everard and Mina
   Goodman Charitable
   Foundation
The Goodman Foundation
Mike Gooley Trailfinders
   Charity
Leonard Gordon Charitable
   Trust
The Gosling Foundation
   Limited
The Gough Charitable Trust
The Gould Charitable Trust
The Grace Charitable Trust
A B Grace Trust
The Graff Foundation

A and S Graham Charitable
Trust
The Grahame Charitable
Foundation Limited
Grampian Police Diced Cap
Charitable Fund
The Granada Foundation
Grand Charitable Trust of the
Order of Women
Freemasons
The Grand Order of Water
Rats' Charities Fund
The Grange Farm Centre Trust
Grantham Yorke Trust
GrantScape
The J G Graves Charitable
Trust
The Gray Trust
The Great Britain Sasakawa
Foundation
The Great Stone Bridge Trust
of Edenbridge
The Great Torrington Town
Lands Charity
The Constance Green
Foundation
The Philip Green Memorial
Trust
Philip and Judith Green Trust
Mrs H R Greene Charitable
Settlement
Greenham Common
Community Trust Limited
Naomi and Jeffrey Greenwood
Charitable Trust
Greggs Foundation (formerly
Greggs Trust)
The Gretna Charitable Trust
The Greys Charitable Trust
Grimmitt Trust
The Grocers' Charity
The M and R Gross Charities
Limited
The Grove Charitable Trust
The GRP Charitable Trust
The David and Marie Grumitt
Foundation
The Bishop of Guildford's
Foundation
The Guildry Incorporation of
Perth
The Walter Guinness
Charitable Trust
The Gunter Charitable Trust
The Gur Trust
Dr Guthrie's Association
The H and J Spack Charitable
Trust
The H and M Charitable Trust
The H P Charitable Trust
The Hackney Parochial
Charities
The Hadfield Trust
The Hadley Trust
The Hadrian Trust
The Alfred Haines Charitable
Trust

The Hale Trust
E F and M G Hall Charitable
Trust
The Edith Winifred Hall
Charitable Trust
Robert Hall Charity
The Hamamelis Trust
Hamilton Wallace Trust
Paul Hamlyn Foundation
Sue Hammerson's Charitable
Trust
The Hammonds Charitable
Trust
The Hampshire and Islands
Historic Churches Trust
Hampshire and Isle of Wight
Community Foundation
The Hampstead Wells and
Campden Trust
The W A Handley Charitable
Trust
Beatrice Hankey Foundation
Ltd
The Hanley Trust
The Kathleen Hannay
Memorial Charity
Lord Hanson Foundation
Harbo Charities Limited
The Harborne Parish Lands
Charity
The Harbour Charitable Trust
The Harbour Foundation
The Harding Trust
William Harding's Charity
The Hare of Steep Charitable
Trust
The Harebell Centenary Fund
The Kenneth Hargreaves
Charitable Trust
The Harris Charitable Trust
The Harris Charity
The Harris Family Charitable
Trust
The Edith Lilian Harrison 2000
Foundation
The Harrison and Potter Trust
The John Harrison Charitable
Trust
The Peter Harrison Foundation
The Spencer Hart Charitable
Trust
The Hartley Charitable Trust
The N and P Hartley Memorial
Trust
The Alfred And Peggy Harvey
Charitable Trust
William Geoffrey Harvey's
Discretionary Settlement
The Edward Harvist Trust Fund
Haskel Family Foundation
Hasluck Charitable Trust
The Hathaway Trust
The M A Hawe Settlement
The Hawthorne Charitable
Trust
The Dorothy Hay-Bolton
Charitable Trust

The Haymills Charitable Trust
The Charles Hayward
Foundation
Headley-Pitt Charitable Trust
Heagerty Charitable Trust
The Heart of England
Community Foundation
The Heathcoat Trust
Heathside Charitable Trust
The Hedera Charitable Trust
Percy Hedley 1990 Charitable
Trust
The Hedley Denton Charitable
Trust
The Hedley Foundation
The H J Heinz Company
Limited Charitable Trust
The Hellenic Foundation
The Michael and Morven Heller
Charitable Foundation
The Simon Heller Charitable
Settlement
Help the Homeless
The Helping Foundation
The Hemby Trust
The Christina Mary Hendrie
Trust for Scottish and
Canadian Charities
The Henley Educational Charity
The Tim Henman Charitable
Foundation
Esther Hennell Charitable
Trust
The G D Herbert Charitable
Trust
The Joanna Herbert-Stepney
Charitable Settlement (also
known as The Paget
Charitable Trust)
The Anne Herd Memorial Trust
The Herefordshire Community
Foundation
The Herefordshire Historic
Churches Trust
The Heritage of London Trust
Ltd
The Hertfordshire Community
Foundation
The Hesed Trust
The Hesslewood Children's
Trust (Hull Seamen's and
General Orphanage)
The Bernhard Heuberger
Charitable Trust
Hexham and Newcastle
Diocesan Trust (1947)
The P and C Hickinbotham
Charitable Trust
The Rosalind Hicks Charitable
Trust
The Higgs Charitable Trust
Alan Edward Higgs Charity
The High Sheriff's Police Trust
for the County of West
Midlands (Building Blocks)
Highcroft Charitable Trust
The Hilden Charitable Fund

The Derek Hill Foundation

The Charles Littlewood Hill Trust

The Hillingdon Community Trust

The Hillingdon Partnership Trust

R G Hills Charitable Trust

Hinchley Charitable Trust

Lady Hind Trust

Stuart Hine Trust

The Hinrichsen Foundation

The Hintze Family Charitable Foundation

The Hitchin Educational Foundation

The Henry C Hoare Charitable Trust

The Eleemosynary Charity of William Hobbayne

Hobson Charity Limited

Hockerill Educational Foundation

Matthew Hodder Charitable Trust

The Sir Julian Hodge Charitable Trust

The Jane Hodge Foundation

The J G Hogg Charitable Trust

The Holden Charitable Trust

John Holford's Charity

The Hollands-Warren Fund

The Hollick Family Charitable Trust

The Holliday Foundation

The Dorothy Holmes Charitable Trust

The Holmes Family Trust (Sheffield)

The Holst Foundation

P H Holt Foundation

The Edward Holt Trust

The Holywood Trust

The Homelands Charitable Trust

The Homestead Charitable Trust

Mary Homfray Charitable Trust

Hope for Youth (formerly Women Caring Trust)

HopMarket Charity

The Cuthbert Horn Trust

The Antony Hornby Charitable Trust

The Horne Foundation

The Horne Trust

The Worshipful Company of Horners' Charitable Trusts

The Hornsey Parochial Charities

The Hospital of God at Greatham

The Hospital Saturday Fund

The Sir Joseph Hotung Charitable Settlement

Houblon-Norman/George Fund

The House of Industry Estate

The Reta Lila Howard Foundation

The Daniel Howard Trust

The Clifford Howarth Charity Trust

The Hudson Foundation

The Huggard Charitable Trust

The Geoffrey C Hughes Charitable Trust

The Hull and East Riding Charitable Trust

Hulme Trust Estates (Educational)

The Humanitarian Trust

The Humberside Charitable Health Trust

The Michael and Shirley Hunt Charitable Trust

The Albert Hunt Trust

The Hunter Foundation

Miss Agnes H Hunter's Trust

The Huntingdon Foundation

Huntingdon Freemen's Charity

Hurdale Charity Limited

The Nani Huyu Charitable Trust

The P Y N and B Hyams Trust

The Hyde Charitable Trust – Youth Plus

The Idlewild Trust

The Iliffe Family Charitable Trust

Impetus Trust

The Indigo Trust

The Ingram Trust

The Inland Waterways Association

The Inlight Trust

The Inman Charity

The Inner London Magistrates Court Poor Box and Feeder Charity

The International Bankers Charitable Trust (The Worshipful Company of International Bankers)

The Inverforth Charitable Trust

Investream Charitable Trust

The Ireland Fund of Great Britain

The Irish Youth Foundation (UK) Ltd (incorporating The Lawlor Foundation)

The Ironmongers' Foundation

The Charles Irving Charitable Trust

Irwin Trust

The ISA Charity

The Isaacs Charitable Trust

The J Isaacs Charitable Trust

The Isle of Anglesey Charitable Trust

Isle of Dogs Community Foundation

The ITF Seafarers Trust

J A R Charitable Trust

The J J Charitable Trust

The J R S S T Charitable Trust

Elizabeth Jackson Charitable Trust

Jacobs Charitable Trust

The Ruth and Lionel Jacobson Trust (Second Fund) No 2

Jaffe Family Relief Fund

John James Bristol Foundation

The Susan and Stephen James Charitable Settlement (also known as the Stephen James Charitable Trust)

The James Trust

The Jarman Charitable Trust

The John Jarrold Trust

The Jeffrey Charitable Trust

Rees Jeffreys Road Fund

The Nick Jenkins Foundation

The Jenour Foundation

The Jerusalem Trust

Jerwood Charitable Foundation

Jesus Hospital Charity

Jewish Child's Day

The Jewish Youth Fund

The JMK Charitable Trust

The Joanies Trust

The Harold Joels Charitable Trust

The Jonathan Joels Charitable Trust

The Nicholas Joels Charitable Trust

The Norman Joels Charitable Trust

The Elton John Aids Foundation

The Michael John Trust

The Lillie Johnson Charitable Trust

The Johnson Foundation

The Johnson Group Cleaners Charity

The Johnnie Johnson Trust

The Johnson Wax Ltd Charitable Trust

The Joicey Trust

The Jones 1986 Charitable Trust

Dezna Robins Jones Charitable Foundation

The Marjorie and Geoffrey Jones Charitable Trust

The Jordan Charitable Foundation

The Joron Charitable Trust

The J E Joseph Charitable Fund

The Lady Eileen Joseph Foundation

The Josh Charitable Trust

JTH Charitable Trust

The Judith Trust

The Anton Jurgens Charitable Trust

The Bernard Kahn Charitable Trust

The Stanley Kalms Foundation

The Karenza Foundation
The Boris Karloff Charitable
Foundation
The Ian Karten Charitable
Trust
The Kasner Charitable Trust
The Kass Charitable Trust
The Kathleen Trust
The Michael and Ilse Katz
Foundation
The Katzauer Charitable
Settlement
The C S Kaufman Charitable
Trust
The Geoffrey John Kaye
Charitable Foundation
The Emmanuel Kaye
Foundation
The Caron Keating Foundation
The Kelly Family Charitable
Trust
Kelsick's Educational
Foundation
The KempWelch Charitable
Trust
The Kay Kendall Leukaemia
Fund
William Kendall's Charity (Wax
Chandlers' Company)
The Kennel Club Charitable
Trust
Kent Community Foundation
The Nancy Kenyon Charitable
Trust
Keren Association
Kermaville Ltd
E and E Kernkraut Charities
Limited
The Peter Kershaw Trust
The Kessler Foundation
Keswick Hall Trust
The Ursula Keyes Trust
The Robert Kiln Charitable
Trust
The King Henry VIII Endowed
Trust Warwick
The King/Cullimore Charitable
Trust
The King's Fund
The Kingsbury Charity
The Mary Kinross Charitable
Trust
Kinsurdy Charitable Trust
Kirkley Poor's Lands Estate
The Richard Kirkman
Charitable Trust
Kirschel Foundation
Robert Kitchin (Saddlers'
Company)
The Marina Kleinwort
Charitable Trust
The Sir James Knott Trust
The Kobler Trust
The Kohn Foundation
The KPMG Foundation
The Kreditor Charitable Trust
The Kreitman Foundation

The Neil Kreitman Foundation
The Heinz, Anna and Carol
Kroch Foundation
Kupath Gemach Chaim
Bechesed Viznitz Trust
The Kyte Charitable Trust
The Late Sir Pierce Lacy
Charity Trust
John Laing Charitable Trust
The Christopher Laing
Foundation
The Lambert Charitable Trust
Community Foundation for
Lancashire
Lancashire Environmental
Fund
Duchy of Lancaster Benevolent
Fund
The Lancaster Foundation
LandAid Charitable Trust
The Jack Lane Charitable Trust
The Allen Lane Foundation
The Langtree Trust
The LankellyChase Foundation
The Lanvern Foundation
The R J Larg Family Charitable
Trust
Largsmount Ltd
The Lark Trust
Lauchentilly Charitable
Foundation 1988
Laufer Charitable Trust
The Lauffer Family Charitable
Foundation
The Kathleen Laurence Trust
The Edgar E Lawley Foundation
The Herd Lawson and Muriel
Lawson Charitable Trust
The Lawson Beckman
Charitable Trust
The Raymond and Blanche
Lawson Charitable Trust
The Carole and Geoffrey
Lawson Foundation
The Mason Le Page Charitable
Trust
The Leach Fourteenth Trust
The David Lean Foundation
The Leathersellers' Company
Charitable Fund
The Leche Trust
The Arnold Lee Charitable
Trust
The William Leech Charity
The Lord Mayor of Leeds
Appeal Fund
Leeds Building Society
Charitable Foundation
The Leeds Community
Foundation
Leicester Charity Link (formerly
The Leicester Charity
Organisation Society)
Leicestershire Historic
Churches Trust
The Kennedy Leigh Charitable
Trust

Morris Leigh Foundation
Mrs Vera Leigh's Charity
The P Leigh-Bramwell Trust 'E'
The Erica Leonard Trust
The Leonard Trust
The Mark Leonard Trust
Lesley Lesley and Mutter Trust
Leukaemia and Lymphoma
Research
The Leverhulme Trade
Charities Trust
The Leverhulme Trust
Lord Leverhulme's Charitable
Trust
The Joseph Levy Charitable
Foundation
Lewis Family Charitable Trust
The John Spedan Lewis
Foundation
The Sir Edward Lewis
Foundation
John Lewis Partnership
General Community Fund
The Lewis Ward Trust
Liberum Foundation
Lichfield Conduit Lands
The Thomas Lilley Memorial
Trust
Limoges Charitable Trust
Lincolnshire Community
Foundation
The Lincolnshire Old Churches
Trust
The Lind Trust
The Linden Charitable Trust
The Linmardon Trust
The Ruth and Stuart Lipton
Charitable Trust
The Lister Charitable Trust
Frank Litchfield Charitable
Trust
The Andrew and Mary
Elizabeth Little Charitable
Trust
The Second Joseph Aaron
Littman Foundation
The George John and Sheilah
Livanos Charitable Trust
Liverpool Charity and Voluntary
Services
Liverpool Sailors' Home Trust
Jack Livingstone Charitable
Trust
The Elaine and Angus Lloyd
Charitable Trust
The Lloyd Fund
Lloyd's Charities Trust
Lloyds TSB Foundation for
England and Wales
Lloyds TSB Foundation for
Northern Ireland
Lloyds TSB Foundation for the
Channel Islands
Llysdinam Charitable Trust
Localtrent Ltd
The Loftus Charitable Trust

The Trust for London (formerly
the City Parochial
Foundation)
London Catalyst (formerly The
Metropolitan Hospital-
Sunday Fund)
The London Community
Foundation (formerly Capital
Community Foundation)
The London Law Trust
London Legal Support Trust
The London Marathon
Charitable Trust
The William and Katherine
Longman Trust
The Lord's Taverners
The Loseley and Guildway
Charitable Trust
The Lowy Mitchell Foundation
The C L Loyd Charitable Trust
LSA Charitable Trust
The Marie Helen Luen
Charitable Trust
Robert Luff Foundation Ltd
Lady Lumley's Educational
Foundation
C F Lunoe Trust Fund
The Ruth and Jack Lunzer
Charitable Trust
Lord and Lady Lurgan Trust
The Lyndhurst Trust
The Lynn Foundation
The Lynwood Trust
John Lyon's Charity
The Lyons Charitable Trust
The Sir Jack Lyons Charitable
Trust
The Joy and Malcolm Lyons
Foundation
Sylvanus Lyson's Charity
The M and C Trust
The M D and S Charitable
Trust
The M K Charitable Trust
The E M MacAndrew Trust
The R S Macdonald Charitable
Trust
Macdonald-Buchanan
Charitable Trust
The Macfarlane Walker Trust
The Mackay and Brewer
Charitable Trust
The Mackintosh Foundation
The MacRobert Trust
Ian Mactaggart Trust
James Madison Trust
The Magdalen and Lasher
Charity
Magdalen Hospital Trust
The Magen Charitable Trust
Mageni Trust
The Makin Charitable Trust
Man Group plc Charitable
Trust
Manchester Airport Community
Trust Fund

The Manchester Guardian
Society Charitable Trust
Lord Mayor of Manchester's
Charity Appeal Trust
Mandeville Trust
The Manifold Charitable Trust
W M Mann Foundation
R W Mann Trust
The Leslie and Lilian Manning
Trust
Maranatha Christian Trust
Marbeh Torah Trust
The Marcela Trust
Marchig Animal Welfare Trust
The Stella and Alexander
Margulies Charitable Trust
Market Harborough and The
Bowdens Charity
The Marks Family Foundation
The Ann and David Marks
Foundation
The Hilda and Samuel Marks
Foundation
J P Marland Charitable Trust
The Michael Marsh Charitable
Trust
The Marsh Christian Trust
The Charlotte Marshall
Charitable Trust
The Jim Marshall Charitable
Trust
The D G Marshall of
Cambridge Trust
Marshall's Charity
Marshgate Charitable
Settlement
Sir George Martin Trust
John Martin's Charity
The John Mason Family Trust
The Mason Porter Charitable
Trust
The Nancie Massey Charitable
Trust
The Mathew Trust
Matliwala Family Charitable
Trust
The Matt 6.3 Charitable Trust
The Violet Mauray Charitable
Trust
The Maxell Educational Trust
The Maxwell Family Foundation
Evelyn May Trust
Mayfair Charities Ltd
The Mayfield Valley Arts Trust
Mazars Charitable Trust
The Robert McAlpine
Foundation
The McDougall Trust
The A M McGreevy No 5
Charitable Settlement
The McKenna Charitable Trust
Martin McLaren Memorial
Trust
The Helen Isabella McMorran
Charitable Foundation
D D McPhail Charitable
Settlement

The Mears Foundation
The James Frederick and Ethel
Anne Measures Charity
The Medlock Charitable Trust
The Anthony and Elizabeth
Mellows Charitable
Settlement
Melow Charitable Trust
Meningitis Trust
Menuchar Ltd
Mercaz Torah Vechesed
Limited
The Mercers' Charitable
Foundation
The Merchant Taylors'
Company Charities Fund
The Merchant Venturers'
Charity
The Merchants' House of
Glasgow
The Mersey Docks and
Harbour Company
Charitable Fund
Community Foundation for
Merseyside
The Zachary Merton and
George Woofindin
Convalescent Trust
The Tony Metherell Charitable
Trust
The Metropolitan Drinking
Fountain and Cattle Trough
Association
London Masonic Charitable
Trust
Mickleham Charitable Trust
Gerald Micklem Charitable
Trust
The Masonic Province of
Middlesex Charitable Trust
Midhurst Pensions Trust
The Migraine Trust
Miles Trust for the Putney and
Roehampton Community
Millennium Stadium Charitable
Trust
The Hugh and Mary Miller
Bequest Trust
The Miller Foundation
The Millfield House Foundation
The Millfield Trust
The Millhouses Charitable
Trust
The Millichope Foundation
The Mills Charity
The Clare Milne Trust
Milton Keynes Community
Foundation
The Edgar Milward Charity
The Keith and Joan
Mindelsohn Charitable
Trust
The Peter Minet Trust
Minge's Gift and the Pooled
Trusts
Minton Charitable Trust

The Mirfield Educational
Charity
The Mirianog Trust
The Laurence Misener
Charitable Trust
The Mishcon Family Charitable
Trust
The Misselbrook Trust
The Brian Mitchell Charitable
Settlement
The Mitchell Charitable Trust
The Esmé Mitchell Trust
Keren Mitzvah Trust
The Mizpah Trust
The Mobbs Memorial Trust Ltd
The Modiano Charitable Trust
The Moette Charitable Trust
The Mole Charitable Trust
The Monatrea Charitable Trust
The D C Moncrieff Charitable
Trust
Monmouthshire County Council
Welsh Church Act Fund
The Montague Thompson
Coon Charitable Trust
The Colin Montgomerie
Charitable Foundation
The Monument Trust
George A Moore Foundation
The Henry Moore Foundation
The Nigel Moores Family
Charitable Trust
John Moores Foundation
The Peter Moores Foundation
The Morel Charitable Trust
The Morgan Charitable
Foundation
The Mr and Mrs J T Morgan
Foundation
The Oliver Morland Charitable
Trust
S C and M E Morland's
Charitable Trust
The Bernard Morris Charitable
Trust
The Morris Charitable Trust
The Willie and Mabel Morris
Charitable Trust
The Peter Morrison Charitable
Foundation
G M Morrison Charitable Trust
The Stanley Morrison
Charitable Trust
Moshal Charitable Trust
The Moshulu Charitable Trust
The Moss Charitable Trust
The Robert and Margaret
Moss Charitable Trust
Moss Family Charitable Trust
The Mothercare Charitable
Foundation
Moto in the Community Trust
J P Moulton Charitable
Foundation
The Mount Everest Foundation
Mountbatten Festival of Music
The MSE Charity

The Mugdock Children's Trust
The Mulberry Trust
The Edith Murphy Foundation
Murphy-Neumann Charity
Company Limited
The John R Murray Charitable
Trust
The Mushroom Fund
The Music Sales Charitable
Trust
The Mutual Trust Group
MYA Charitable Trust
MYR Charitable Trust
The Kitty and Daniel Nabarro
Charitable Trust
The Nadezhda Charitable Trust
The Janet Nash Charitable
Settlement
The National Art Collections
Fund
The National Churches Trust
(formerly the Historic
Churches Preservation
Trust with the Incorporated
Church Building Society)
The National Manuscripts
Conservation Trust
The Nationwide Foundation
Needham Market and Barking
Welfare Charities
The Worshipful Company of
Needlemakers' Charitable
Fund
The Neighbourly Charitable
Trust
The James Neill Trust Fund
Nemoral Ltd
Ner Foundation
Nesswall Ltd
The New Appeals Organisation
for the City and County of
Nottingham
New Court Charitable Trust
Newby Trust Limited
The Newcomen Collett
Foundation
Mr and Mrs F E F Newman
Charitable Trust
The Frances and Augustus
Newman Foundation
Newpier Charity Ltd
Alderman Newton's
Educational Foundation
The NFU Mutual Charitable
Trust
The Night Garden Charity
The Chevras Ezras Nitzrochim
Trust
NJD Charitable Trust
The Noon Foundation
The Norda Trust
Norie Charitable Trust
Normalyn Charitable Trust
The Norman Family Charitable
Trust
The Duncan Norman Trust
Fund

The Normanby Charitable Trust
The North British Hotel Trust
The North West Cancer
Research Fund
North West London Community
Foundation
The Northampton Municipal
Church Charities
The Northampton Queen's
Institute Relief in Sickness
Fund
The Earl of Northampton's
Charity
The Northcott Devon
Foundation
The Northcott Devon Medical
Foundation
The Northern Rock Foundation
The Northumberland Village
Homes Trust
The Northumbria Historic
Churches Trust
The Northwood Charitable
Trust
The Norton Foundation
The Norwich Church of England
Young Men's Society
The Norwich Historic Churches
Trust Ltd
The Norwich Town Close
Estate Charity
The Norwood and Newton
Settlement
The Noswad Charity
The Notgrove Trust
The Nottingham General
Dispensary
The Nottingham Gordon
Memorial Trust for Boys
and Girls
Nottinghamshire Community
Foundation
The Nottinghamshire Historic
Churches Trust
The Nottinghamshire Miners'
Welfare Trust Fund
The Nuffield Foundation
The Oak Trust
The Oakley Charitable Trust
The Oakmoor Charitable Trust
The Odin Charitable Trust
The Ofenheim Charitable Trust
Ogilvie Charities Deed No.2
(including the Charity of
Mary Catherine Ford Smith)
Oglesby Charitable Trust
Oizer Charitable Trust
The Old Broad Street Charity
Trust
The Old Enfield Charitable
Trust
Old Possum's Practical Trust
The John Oldacre Foundation
The Oldham Foundation
Open Gate
The Ormsby Charitable Trust
Orrin Charitable Trust

The Ouseley Trust
The Owen Family Trust
Oxfam (GB)
City of Oxford Charity
The Oxfordshire Community
    Foundation
The P F Charitable Trust
The Doris Pacey Charitable
    Foundation
Padwa Charitable Foundation
The Pallant Charitable Trust
The Palmer Foundation
Eleanor Palmer Trust
The Panacea Society
The James Pantyfedwen
    Foundation
The Park Charitable Trust
The Frank Parkinson
    Agricultural Trust
The Samuel and Freda
    Parkinson Charitable Trust
Arthur James Paterson
    Charitable Trust
The Constance Paterson
    Charitable Trust
Miss M E Swinton Paterson's
    Charitable Trust
The Patrick Charitable Trust
The Jack Patston Charitable
    Trust
Ambika Paul Foundation
Paycare Charity Trust (formerly
    known as Patients' Aid
    Association Hospital and
    Medical Charities Trust)
The Payne Charitable Trust
The Harry Payne Trust
The Peacock Charitable Trust
The Susanna Peake Charitable
    Trust
The David Pearlman Charitable
    Foundation
The Pedmore Sporting Club
    Trust Fund
The Dowager Countess
    Eleanor Peel Trust
Pegasus (Stanley) Trust
Peltz Trust
The Pennycress Trust
The Performing Right Society
    Foundation
B E Perl Charitable Trust
The Jack Petchey Foundation
The Petplan Charitable Trust
The Philips and Rubens
    Charitable Trust
The Phillips Charitable Trust
The Phillips Family Charitable
    Trust
Philological Foundation
The David Pickford Charitable
    Foundation
The Bernard Piggott Trust
The Pilgrim Trust
The Cecil Pilkington Charitable
    Trust

The Elise Pilkington Charitable
    Trust
The Pilkington Charities Fund
The Austin and Hope
    Pilkington Trust
The Sir Harry Pilkington Trust
The Col W W Pilkington Will
    Trusts The General Charity
    Fund
Miss A M Pilkington's
    Charitable Trust
The DLA Piper Charitable Trust
The Worshipful Company of
    Plaisterers Charitable Trust
The Platinum Trust
G S Plaut Charitable Trust
    Limited
Polden-Puckham Charitable
    Foundation
The Poling Charitable Trust
The George and Esme Pollitzer
    Charitable Settlement
The Pollywally Charitable Trust
The Polonsky Foundation
The Ponton House Trust
The Mayor of Poole's Appeal
    Fund
The John Porter Charitable
    Trust
The Porter Foundation
Porticus UK
The Portishead Nautical Trust
The Portrack Charitable Trust
The Mary Potter Convent
    Hospital Trust
The Powell Foundation
The W L Pratt Charitable Trust
The Douglas Prestwich
    Charitable Trust
The William Price Charitable
    Trust
The Lucy Price Relief-in-Need
    Charity
Sir John Priestman Charity
    Trust
The Primrose Trust
The Prince of Wales's
    Charitable Foundation
Princess Anne's Charities
The Priory Foundation
Prison Service Charity Fund
Private Equity Foundation
The Privy Purse Charitable
    Trust
The Proven Family Trust
The Provincial Grand Charity of
    the Province of Derbyshire
PSA Peugeot Citroen Charity
    Trust
The Richard and Christine
    Purchas Charitable Trust
The Puri Foundation
Mr and Mrs J A Pye's
    Charitable Settlement
Quartet Community Foundation
    (formerly the Greater Bristol
    Foundation)

Queen Mary's Roehampton
    Trust
The Queen's Silver Jubilee
    Trust
Quercus Trust
R S Charitable Trust
The R V W Trust
The Monica Rabagliati
    Charitable Trust
Rachel Charitable Trust
The Mr and Mrs Philip
    Rackham Charitable Trust
Richard Radcliffe Charitable
    Trust
The Radcliffe Trust
The Bishop Radford Trust
The Peggy Ramsay Foundation
The Rank Foundation
The Joseph Rank Trust
The Fanny Rapaport Charitable
    Settlement
The Ratcliff Foundation
The Ratcliff Pension Charity
The Ratcliffe Charitable Trust
The E L Rathbone Charitable
    Trust
The Ravensdale Trust
The Rayden Charitable Trust
The Roger Raymond Charitable
    Trust
The Rayne Foundation
The Rayne Trust
The John Rayner Charitable
    Trust
The Sir James Reckitt Charity
The Red Arrows Trust
Red Hill Charitable Trust
The Red Rose Charitable Trust
The C A Redfern Charitable
    Foundation
The Reed Foundation
Richard Reeve's Foundation
The Rehoboth Trust
The Max Reinhardt Charitable
    Trust
REMEDI
The Rest Harrow Trust
The Joan K Reynell Charitable
    Trust
The Nathaniel Reyner Trust
    Fund
The Rhondda Cynon Taff
    Welsh Church Acts Fund
Daisie Rich Trust
The Sir Cliff Richard Charitable
    Trust
The Clive Richards Charity
The Violet M Richards Charity
The Richmond Parish Lands
    Charity
Ridgesave Limited
The Ripple Effect Foundation
The Sir John Ritblat Family
    Foundation
The River Farm Foundation
The River Trust
The Rivers Charitable Trust

Riverside Charitable Trust Limited

Rix-Thompson-Rothenberg Foundation

Thomas Roberts Trust

The Robertson Trust

Edwin George Robinson Charitable Trust

Robyn Charitable Trust

The Rochester Bridge Trust

The Rock Solid Trust

The Rofeh Trust

Richard Rogers Charitable Settlement

Rokach Family Charitable Trust

The Helen Roll Charitable Trust

The Sir James Roll Charitable Trust

The Roman Research Trust

The C A Rookes Charitable Trust

Mrs L D Rope Third Charitable Settlement

Rosa – the UK fund for women and girls

The Rosca Trust

Alexandra Rose Charities

The Rose Foundation

The Cecil Rosen Foundation

Rosetrees Trust

The Rothera Charitable Settlement

The Rothermere Foundation

The Rotherwick Foundation

The Rothley Trust

The Roughley Charitable Trust

Mrs Gladys Row Fogo Charitable Trust

Rowanville Ltd

The Christopher Rowbotham Charitable Trust

The Rowing Foundation

The Rowlands Trust

The Joseph Rowntree Charitable Trust

The Joseph Rowntree Foundation

Joseph Rowntree Reform Trust Limited

Royal Artillery Charitable Fund

Royal British Legion

Royal Docks Trust (London)

Royal Masonic Trust for Girls and Boys

The Royal Scots Benevolent Society

The Alfred and Frances Rubens Charitable Trust

William Arthur Rudd Memorial Trust

The Rugby Group Benevolent Fund Limited

The Russell Trust

The J S and E C Rymer Charitable Trust

S O Charitable Trust

The Raymond and Beverley Sackler 1988 Foundation

The Sackler Trust (formerly Dr Mortimer and Theresa Sackler Foundation)

The Ruzin Sadagora Trust

The Saddlers' Company Charitable Fund

The Jean Sainsbury Animal Welfare Trust

The Sainsbury Family Charitable Trusts

Saint Luke's College Foundation

The Saintbury Trust

The Saints and Sinners Trust

The Salamander Charitable Trust

The Salt Foundation

The Salt Trust

Salters' Charitable Foundation

The Andrew Salvesen Charitable Trust

Basil Samuel Charitable Trust

Coral Samuel Charitable Trust

The Peter Samuel Charitable Trust

The Camilla Samuel Fund

The Samworth Foundation

The Sandra Charitable Trust

Santander UK Foundation Limited

The Sants Charitable Trust

Jimmy Savile Charitable Trust

The Scarfe Charitable Trust

The Schapira Charitable Trust

The R H Scholes Charitable Trust

The Schreib Trust

The Schreiber Charitable Trust

The Scotshill Trust

The Francis C Scott Charitable Trust

The Frieda Scott Charitable Trust

Sir Samuel Scott of Yews Trust

The Sir James and Lady Scott Trust

The Scott Trust Foundation

The Storrow Scott Will Trust

The Scottish Arts Council

Scottish Coal Industry Special Welfare Fund

The Scottish Community Foundation

The Scottish International Education Trust

The Scouloudi Foundation

Seamen's Hospital Society

The Searchlight Electric Charitable Trust

The Searle Charitable Trust

The Helene Sebba Charitable Trust

The Samuel Sebba Charitable Trust

Leslie Sell Charitable Trust

Sellata Ltd

SEM Charitable Trust

The Seneca Trust

The Seven Fifty Trust

The Severn Trent Water Charitable Trust Fund

sfgroup Charitable Fund for Disabled People

SFIA Educational Trust Limited

The Cyril Shack Trust

The Jean Shanks Foundation

The Shanti Charitable Trust

ShareGift (The Orr Mackintosh Foundation)

The Linley Shaw Foundation

The Sheepdrove Trust

The Sheffield and District Hospital Services Charitable Fund

The Shekinah Legacy

The Sheldon Trust

The P and D Shepherd Charitable Trust

The Sylvia and Colin Shepherd Charitable Trust

The Archie Sherman Cardiff Foundation

The Archie Sherman Charitable Trust

The R C Sherriff Trust

The Shetland Charitable Trust

SHINE (Support and Help in Education)

The Bassil Shippam and Alsford Trust

The Shipwrights' Company Charitable Fund

The Shirley Foundation

The Shoe Zone Trust

The J A Shone Memorial Trust

The Barbara A Shuttleworth Memorial Trust

The Sickle Foundation

The Mary Elizabeth Siebel Charity

David and Jennifer Sieff Charitable Trust

The Julius Silman Charitable Trust

The Leslie Silver Charitable Trust

The Simpson Foundation

The Huntly and Margery Sinclair Charitable Trust

Sino-British Fellowship Trust

The Skelton Bounty

The Charles Skey Charitable Trust

Skipton Building Society Charitable Foundation

The John Slater Foundation

Sloane Robinson Foundation

The Mrs Smith and Mount Trust

The Amanda Smith Charitable Trust

The E H Smith Charitable Trust
The Smith Charitable Trust
The Henry Smith Charity
The Leslie Smith Foundation
The Martin Smith Foundation
Stanley Smith General
    Charitable Trust
Philip Smith's Charitable Trust
The R C Snelling Charitable
    Trust
The Snowball Trust
The Sobell Foundation
Solev Co Ltd
Solihull Community Foundation
The Solo Charitable
    Settlement
David Solomons Charitable
    Trust
Friends of Somerset Churches
    and Chapels
Songdale Ltd
The E C Sosnow Charitable
    Trust
The Souter Charitable Trust
The South Square Trust
The Stephen R and Philippa H
    Southall Charitable Trust
The W F Southall Trust
The Southdown Trust
The Southover Manor General
    Education Trust
The Southwold Trust
The Sovereign Health Care
    Charitable Trust
Spar Charitable Fund
Sparks Charity (Sport Aiding
    Medical Research For Kids)
Sparquote Limited
The Spear Charitable Trust
The Worshipful Company of
    Spectacle Makers' Charity
The Jessie Spencer Trust
The Ralph and Irma Sperring
    Charity
The Moss Spiro Will Charitable
    Foundation
Split Infinitive Trust
The Spoore, Merry and Rixman
    Foundation
Spring Harvest
Rosalyn and Nicholas Springer
    Charitable Trust
Springfields Employees'
    Medical Research and
    Charity Trust Fund
Springrule Ltd
The Spurrell Charitable Trust
The Geoff and Fiona Squire
    Foundation
St Andrew's Conservation
    Trust
St Christopher's College
    Educational Trust
St Gabriel's Trust
St Hilda's Trust
St James' Trust Settlement
St James's Place Foundation

Sir Walter St John's
    Educational Charity
St Katharine and Shadwell
    Trust
The St Laurence Relief In
    Need Trust
St Michael's and All Saints'
    Charities
St Monica Trust Community
    Fund
The Late St Patrick White
    Charitable Trust
St Teilo's Trust
The Stafford Trust
The Stanley Foundation Ltd
The Stanton Ballard Charitable
    Trust
The Staples Trust
The Star Charitable Trust
The Peter Stebbings Memorial
    Charity
The Steel Charitable Trust
The Steinberg Family
    Charitable Trust
The Hugh Stenhouse
    Foundation
Stervon Ltd
The Stevenage Community
    Trust
The June Stevens Foundation
The Steventon Allotments and
    Relief-in-Need Charity
The Stewards' Charitable Trust
The Sir Halley Stewart Trust
The Stewarts Law Foundation
The Leonard Laity Stoate
    Charitable Trust
The Stobart Newlands
    Charitable Trust
The Edward Stocks-Massey
    Bequest Fund
The Stokenchurch Educational
    Charity
The Stoller Charitable Trust
The M J C Stone Charitable
    Trust
The Stone-Mallabar Charitable
    Foundation
The Samuel Storey Family
    Charitable Trust
Peter Stormonth Darling
    Charitable Trust
Peter Storrs Trust
The Strangward Trust
The Strasser Foundation
Stratford upon Avon Town
    Trust
Strathclyde Police Benevolent
    Fund
The W O Street Charitable
    Foundation
The A B Strom and R Strom
    Charitable Trust
The Sudborough Foundation
The Suffolk Foundation
The Suffolk Historic Churches
    Trust

The Alan Sugar Foundation
Sugarworld Trust
Summary Limited
The Summerfield Charitable
    Trust
The Bernard Sunley Charitable
    Foundation
Surrey Community Foundation
The Surrey Historic Buildings
    Trust Ltd
Sussex Community Foundation
The Sussex Historic Churches
    Trust
The Adrienne and Leslie
    Sussman Charitable Trust
The Sutasoma Trust
Sutton Coldfield Municipal
    Charities
The Sutton Trust
Swan Mountain Trust
Swansea and Brecon Diocesan
    Board of Finance Limited
The John Swire (1989)
    Charitable Trust
The Swire Charitable Trust
The Hugh and Ruby Sykes
    Charitable Trust
The Charles and Elsie Sykes
    Trust
The Sylvanus Charitable Trust
The Stella Symons Charitable
    Trust
T and S Trust Fund
Tadlus Limited
The Tajtelbaum Charitable
    Trust
The Talbot Trusts
The Talbot Village Trust
Tallow Chandlers Benevolent
    Fund
Talteg Ltd
The Tangent Charitable Trust
The Lady Tangye Charitable
    Trust
The David Tannen Charitable
    Trust
The Tanner Trust
The Lili Tapper Charitable
    Foundation
The Mrs A Lacy Tate Trust
The Taurus Foundation
The Tay Charitable Trust
C B and H H Taylor 1984 Trust
Humphrey Richardson Taylor
    Charitable Trust
The Connie and Albert Taylor
    Charitable Trust
The Cyril Taylor Charitable
    Trust
The Taylor Family Foundation
A P Taylor Trust
Rosanna Taylor's 1987 Charity
    Trust
The Tedworth Charitable Trust
Tees Valley Community
    Foundation
Tegham Limited

The Templeton Goodwill Trust
Tesco Charity Trust
The Thames Wharf Charity
The Thistle Trust
The David Thomas Charitable Trust
The Arthur and Margaret Thompson Charitable Trust
The Maurice and Vivien Thompson Charitable Trust
The Thompson Family Charitable Trust
The Thompson6 Charitable Trust
The Len Thomson Charitable Trust
The Sue Thomson Foundation
The Sir Jules Thorn Charitable Trust
The Thornton Foundation
The Three Guineas Trust
The Thriplow Charitable Trust
Mrs R P Tindall's Charitable Trust
The Tisbury Telegraph Trust
TJH Foundation
The Tobacco Pipe Makers and Tobacco Trade Benevolent Fund
The Tolkien Trust
Tollemache (Buckminster) Charitable Trust
Tomchei Torah Charitable Trust
The Tompkins Foundation
Toni and Guy Charitable Foundation Limited
The Torah Temimah Trust
Toras Chesed (London) Trust
Tottenham Grammar School Foundation
The Tower Hill Trust
The Towry Law Charitable Trust (also known as the Castle Educational Trust)
The Toy Trust
The Mayor of Trafford's Charity Fund
Annie Tranmer Charitable Trust
The Constance Travis Charitable Trust
The Treeside Trust
The Triangle Trust (1949) Fund
The True Colours Trust
Truedene Co. Ltd
The Truemark Trust
Truemart Limited
Trumros Limited
The Trust for Education
Trust Sixty Three
The Trusthouse Charitable Foundation
The James Tudor Foundation
Tudor Rose Ltd
The Tudor Trust
The Tufton Charitable Trust

The R D Turner Charitable Trust
The Douglas Turner Trust
The Florence Turner Trust
Miss S M Tutton Charitable Trust
TVML Foundation
Two Ridings Community Foundation
Community Foundation Serving Tyne and Wear and Northumberland
Trustees of Tzedakah
UKI Charitable Foundation
Ulster Garden Villages Ltd
Ultach Trust
Ulverston Town Lands Charity
The Underwood Trust
The Union of Orthodox Hebrew Congregation
United Utilities Trust Fund
Unity Theatre Trust
UnLtd (Foundation for Social Entrepreneurs)
The Michael Uren Foundation
Uxbridge United Welfare Trust
'v'
The Vail Foundation
Vale of Glamorgan – Welsh Church Fund
The Valentine Charitable Trust
The Valiant Charitable Trust
John and Lucille van Geest Foundation
The Van Neste Foundation
Mrs Maud Van Norden's Charitable Foundation
The Vandervell Foundation
The Vardy Foundation
The Variety Club Children's Charity
Veneziana Fund
The William and Patricia Venton Charitable Trust
The Verdon-Smith Family Charitable Settlement
Victoria Homes Trust
The Nigel Vinson Charitable Trust
The William and Ellen Vinten Trust
The Vintners' Company Charitable Foundation
Vintners' Gifts Charity
Vision Charity
Vivdale Ltd
The Viznitz Foundation
The Vodafone (Group) Foundation
The Volant Charitable Trust
Voluntary Action Fund
Wade's Charity
The Scurrah Wainwright Charity
The Wakefield and Tetley Trust
Wakeham Trust
The Community Foundation in Wales

Wales Council for Voluntary Action
Robert and Felicity Waley-Cohen Charitable Trust
The Walker Trust
The Thomas Wall Trust
Wallace and Gromit's Children's Foundation
Wallington Missionary Mart and Auctions
The F J Wallis Charitable Settlement
Walton on Thames Charity
Sir Siegmund Warburg's Voluntary Settlement
The Ward Blenkinsop Trust
The George Ward Charitable Trust
The Barbara Ward Children's Foundation
The John Warren Foundation
The Waterloo Foundation
G R Waters Charitable Trust 2000
The Waterways Trust
The Wates Foundation
Blyth Watson Charitable Trust
The Howard Watson Symington Memorial Charity
John Watson's Trust
The Weavers' Company Benevolent Fund
Webb Memorial Trust
The David Webster Charitable Trust
The William Webster Charitable Trust
The James Weir Foundation
The Barbara Welby Trust
The Weldon UK Charitable Trust
The Wellcome Trust
Welsh Church Fund Dyfed area (Carmarthenshire, Ceredigion and Pembrokeshire)
The Welton Foundation
The West Derby Wastelands Charity
West London Synagogue Charitable Fund
The West Yorkshire Police Community Fund
Mrs S K West's Charitable Trust
The Westminster Foundation
The Garfield Weston Foundation
The Barbara Whatmore Charitable Trust
The Whitaker Charitable Trust
The Colonel W H Whitbread Charitable Trust
The Simon Whitbread Charitable Trust
White Stuff Foundation

The Whitecourt Charitable
Trust
A H and B C Whiteley
Charitable Trust
The Norman Whiteley Trust
The Whitley Animal Protection
Trust
The Whittlesey Charity
The Lionel Wigram Memorial
Trust
The Richard Wilcox Welfare
Charity
The Felicity Wilde Charitable
Trust
The Wilkinson Charitable
Foundation
The Will Charitable Trust
The Kay Williams Charitable
Foundation
The Williams Charitable Trust
Williams Serendipity Trust
The H D H Wills 1965
Charitable Trust
The Dame Violet Wills Will
Trust
The Wilmcote Charitrust
Sumner Wilson Charitable
Trust
David Wilson Foundation
The Wilson Foundation
J and J R Wilson Trust
The Community Foundation for
Wiltshire and Swindon
The Benjamin Winegarten
Charitable Trust
The Harold Hyam Wingate
Foundation
The Francis Winham
Foundation
Anona Winn Charitable Trust
Wirral Mayor's Charity
The Witzenfeld Foundation
The Michael and Anna Wix
Charitable Trust
The Wixamtree Trust
The Woburn 1986 Charitable
Trust
The Maurice Wohl Charitable
Foundation
The Charles Wolfson
Charitable Trust
The Wolfson Family Charitable
Trust
The Wolfson Foundation
The Wolseley Charitable Trust
The James Wood Bequest
Fund
The Wood Family Trust
The Woodcock Charitable Trust
The F Glenister Woodger Trust
Woodlands Foundation Limited
Woodlands Trust
Woodroffe Benton Foundation
The Woodward Charitable
Trust
The A and R Woolf Charitable
Trust

Worcester Municipal Charities
(incorporating Worcester
Consolidated Municipal
Charity and Worcester
Municipal Exhibitions
Foundation)
The Worcestershire and
Dudley Historic Churches
Trust
The Fred and Della Worms
Charitable Trust
The Wragge and Co. Charitable
Trust
The Diana Edgson Wright
Charitable Trust
The Matthews Wrightson
Charity Trust
Miss E B Wrightson's
Charitable Settlement
Wychville Ltd
The Wyndham Charitable Trust
The Wyseliot Charitable Trust
The Xerox (UK) Trust
The Yapp Charitable Trust
The Yardley Great Trust
The W Wing Yip and Brothers
Foundation
The York Children's Trust
Yorkshire Agricultural Society
Yorkshire Building Society
Charitable Foundation
The South Yorkshire
Community Foundation
The Yorkshire Dales
Millennium Trust
The Yorkshire Historic
Churches Trust
The William Allen Young
Charitable Trust
The John K Young Endowment
Fund
Youth Music
The Marjorie and Arnold Ziff
Charitable Foundation
Stephen Zimmerman
Charitable Trust
The Zochonis Charitable Trust
Zurich Community Trust (UK)
Limited

UK

England

AF Trust Company
The John Armitage Charitable
Trust
Arts Council England
Barchester Healthcare
Foundation
The Baring Foundation
Birthday House Trust
The Boshier-Hinton Foundation
The Bothwell Charitable Trust
H E and E L Botteley
Charitable Trust
The British Gas (Scottish Gas)
Energy Trust
The Catholic Trust for England
and Wales
The Malcolm Chick Charity
The Church and Community
Fund
The Church Urban Fund
CLA Charitable Trust
Country Houses Foundation
The Sir William Coxen Trust
Fund
David and Rose Diamond Trust
The DM Charitable Trust
The Doughty Charity Trust
The James Dyson Foundation
The English Schools' Football
Association
The Ernest Hecht Charitable
Foundation
The Football Foundation
Gwyneth Forrester Trust
The Joseph Strong Frazer Trust
The Freemasons' Grand
Charity
The General Nursing Council
for England and Wales
Trust
The Goodman Foundation
Leonard Gordon Charitable
Trust
Lady Hind Trust
The Hintze Family Charitable
Foundation
The J Isaacs Charitable Trust
The Nick Jenkins Foundation
The Karenza Foundation
The Ian Karten Charitable
Trust
Keswick Hall Trust
Lloyds TSB Foundation for
England and Wales
Lord and Lady Lurgan Trust
Marshall's Charity
Marshgate Charitable
Settlement
The McKenna Charitable Trust
Moss Family Charitable Trust
Moto in the Community Trust
MYR Charitable Trust

The National Churches Trust (formerly the Historic Churches Preservation Trust with the Incorporated Church Building Society)
The Noon Foundation
The Norwood and Newton Settlement
The Ouseley Trust
The Worshipful Company of Plaisterers Charitable Trust
The John Rayner Charitable Trust
Alexandra Rose Charities
Royal British Legion
The Raymond and Beverley Sackler 1988 Foundation
The R H Scholes Charitable Trust
The Severn Trent Water Charitable Trust Fund
Skipton Building Society Charitable Foundation
The Sobell Foundation
The Leonard Laity Stoate Charitable Trust
TJH Foundation
Toni and Guy Charitable Foundation Limited
'v'
Robert and Felicity Waley-Cohen Charitable Trust
The Barbara Ward Children's Foundation
The Waterways Trust
A H and B C Whiteley Charitable Trust
The Francis Winham Foundation
The Yapp Charitable Trust
Youth Music

....

■ Greater London

Arsenal Charitable Trust
The Ashendene Trust
The Bellinger Donnay Trust
Bergqvist Charitable Trust
Butchers' Company General Charities
The Chapman Charitable Trust
The City Bridge Trust (formerly known as Bridge House Trust)
The Consolidated Charities for the Infirm Merchant Taylors' Company
Coutts Charitable Trust
The Charles S French Charitable Trust
The Worshipful Company of Gardeners of London
The Goldsmiths' Company Charity
The Grange Farm Centre Trust
The Hale Trust

The Helping Foundation
The Heritage of London Trust Ltd
The Antony Hornby Charitable Trust
The Worshipful Company of Horners' Charitable Trusts
The Inner London Magistrates Court Poor Box and Feeder Charity
The J E Joseph Charitable Fund
William Kendall's Charity (Wax Chandlers' Company)
The King's Fund
Robert Kitchin (Saddlers' Company)
The Mason Le Page Charitable Trust
The Trust for London (formerly the City Parochial Foundation)
London Catalyst (formerly The Metropolitan Hospital-Sunday Fund)
The London Community Foundation (formerly Capital Community Foundation)
London Legal Support Trust
The London Marathon Charitable Trust
Man Group plc Charitable Trust
London Masonic Charitable Trust
The Masonic Province of Middlesex Charitable Trust
The Peter Minet Trust
The Music Sales Charitable Trust
The Earl of Northampton's Charity
Ogilvie Charities Deed No.2 (including the Charity of Mary Catherine Ford Smith)
The David Pickford Charitable Foundation
sfgroup Charitable Fund for Disabled People
SHINE (Support and Help in Education)
The Mrs Smith and Mount Trust
T and S Trust Fund
Tallow Chandlers Benevolent Fund
The Cyril Taylor Charitable Trust
The Taylor Family Foundation
The Vintners' Company Charitable Foundation
Vintners' Gifts Charity
The Wates Foundation
Woodlands Trust

■ Barking and Dagenham

The Association of Friends of Essex Churches
East London Community Foundation
Ford Britain Trust
The Jack Petchey Foundation

■ Barnet

Maurice and Jacqueline Bennett Charitable Trust
The Bintaub Charitable Trust
Elshore Ltd
Finnart House School Trust
The Grove Charitable Trust
The Edward Harvist Trust Fund
The Bernhard Heuberger Charitable Trust
Highcroft Charitable Trust
Jesus Hospital Charity
Jewish Child's Day
The Jonathan Joels Charitable Trust
John Lyon's Charity
North West London Community Foundation
Eleanor Palmer Trust
Sparquote Limited

■ Bexley

Ford Britain Trust

■ Brent

The Edward Harvist Trust Fund
The Kingsbury Charity
John Lyon's Charity
North West London Community Foundation
The W Wing Yip and Brothers Foundation

■ Camden

The British Council for Prevention of Blindness
Sir John Cass's Foundation
Michael Crawford Children's Charity
The Grahame Charitable Foundation Limited
The Hampstead Wells and Campden Trust
The Edward Harvist Trust Fund
J A R Charitable Trust
The Harold Joels Charitable Trust
The Lowy Mitchell Foundation
John Lyon's Charity
Mayfair Charities Ltd
The Nuffield Foundation
Philological Foundation
Richard Reeve's Foundation
Sparquote Limited

The Will Charitable Trust

■ City of London

Aldgate and All Hallows'
  Barking Exhibition
  Foundation
The Aldgate Freedom
  Foundation
Sir John Cass's Foundation
The Denton Wilde Sapte
  Charitable Trust
The Girdlers' Company
  Charitable Trust
The B and P Glasser
  Charitable Trust
The Spencer Hart Charitable
  Trust
The Sir Joseph Hotung
  Charitable Settlement
John Lyon's Charity
The Modiano Charitable Trust
The Worshipful Company of
  Needlemakers' Charitable
  Fund
Richard Reeve's Foundation
St Katharine and Shadwell
  Trust
The Tobacco Pipe Makers and
  Tobacco Trade Benevolent
  Fund
The Wakefield and Tetley Trust

■ City of Westminster

The Avenue Charitable Trust
The Nicholas Boas Charitable
  Trust
Sir John Cass's Foundation
The R and S Cohen
  Foundation
Dischma Charitable Trust
The Edinburgh Trust, No 2
  Account
The Glass-House Trust
The Graff Foundation
The M and R Gross Charities
  Limited
The H and J Spack Charitable
  Trust
The Edward Harvist Trust Fund
The Simon Heller Charitable
  Settlement
The Hollick Family Charitable
  Trust
The P Y N and B Hyams Trust
The J J Charitable Trust
Jacobs Charitable Trust
The Jerusalem Trust
The Nicholas Joels Charitable
  Trust
The Stanley Kalms Foundation
The Boris Karloff Charitable
  Foundation
Largsmount Ltd

The Ruth and Stuart Lipton
  Charitable Trust
John Lyon's Charity
Nemoral Ltd
Philological Foundation
Basil Samuel Charitable Trust
ShareGift (The Orr Mackintosh
  Foundation)
Sparquote Limited
The Woodward Charitable
  Trust

■ Croydon

The Croydon Relief in Need
  Charities
The Mayor of Croydon's
  Charity Fund
The W Wing Yip and Brothers
  Foundation

■ Ealing

The Eleemosynary Charity of
  William Hobbayne
John Lyon's Charity
North West London Community
  Foundation
Sparquote Limited

■ Enfield

North West London Community
  Foundation
The Old Enfield Charitable
  Trust
Sparquote Limited

■ Greenwich

Sir John Cass's Foundation
Sir John Evelyn's Charity
Ford Britain Trust

■ Hackney

Sir John Cass's Foundation
East London Community
  Foundation
Friends of Wiznitz Limited
The Gur Trust
The Hackney Parochial
  Charities
The Harbour Foundation
The Hornsey Parochial
  Charities
Hurdale Charity Limited
MYA Charitable Trust
The Jack Petchey Foundation
St Katharine and Shadwell
  Trust

■ Hammersmith and

Fulham

Sir John Cass's Foundation
The Daisy Trust
Dr Edwards Bishop King's
  Fulham Endowment Fund
The Girdlers' Company
  Charitable Trust
John Lyon's Charity
Sparquote Limited

■ Haringey

The Hornsey Parochial
  Charities
North West London Community
  Foundation
Sparquote Limited
Tottenham Grammar School
  Foundation

■ Harrow

Amabrill Limited
The Samuel Gardner Memorial
  Trust
The Edward Harvist Trust Fund
The Geoffrey John Kaye
  Charitable Foundation
John Lyon's Charity
North West London Community
  Foundation

■ Havering

The Association of Friends of
  Essex Churches
East London Community
  Foundation
Ford Britain Trust
The Jack Petchey Foundation

■ Hillingdon

The Fassnidge Memorial Trust
The Hillingdon Community
  Trust
The Hillingdon Partnership
  Trust
North West London Community
  Foundation
A P Taylor Trust
Uxbridge United Welfare Trust

■ Islington

Sir John Cass's Foundation
Richard Cloudesley's Charity
Cripplegate Foundation
Richard Reeve's Foundation
Sparquote Limited

■ Kensington and Chelsea

ABF The Soldiers' Charity
  (formerly the Army
  Benevolent Fund)

The Campden Charities
  Trustee
Sir John Cass's Foundation
Grand Charitable Trust of the
  Order of Women
  Freemasons
Lord Hanson Foundation
John Lyon's Charity
Sparquote Limited

■ Lambeth

Sir John Cass's Foundation
Sir Walter St John's
  Educational Charity

■ Lewisham

Sir John Cass's Foundation
Sir John Evelyn's Charity

■ Merton

The Vernon N Ely Charitable
  Trust

■ Newham

The Association of Friends of
  Essex Churches
AstonMansfield Charitable
  Trust
Sir John Cass's Foundation
East London Community
  Foundation
Ford Britain Trust
The Jack Petchey Foundation
Royal Docks Trust (London)
St Katharine and Shadwell
  Trust

■ Redbridge

The Association of Friends of
  Essex Churches
East London Community
  Foundation
Ford Britain Trust
The Jack Petchey Foundation

■ Richmond upon Thames

Barnes Workhouse Fund
The Richmond Parish Lands
  Charity

■ Southwark

The Sir Victor Blank Charitable
  Settlement
Sir John Cass's Foundation
The Girdlers' Company
  Charitable Trust
The ITF Seafarers Trust
The McDougall Trust

The Newcomen Collett
  Foundation
The Wakefield and Tetley Trust

■ Sutton

Barleycorn Trust
Firtree Trust
The Lynwood Trust
Humphrey Richardson Taylor
  Charitable Trust
Wallington Missionary Mart
  and Auctions

■ Tower Hamlets

Aldgate and All Hallows'
  Barking Exhibition
  Foundation
Sir John Cass's Foundation
East London Community
  Foundation
The Girdlers' Company
  Charitable Trust
Isle of Dogs Community
  Foundation
The Palmer Foundation
The Jack Petchey Foundation
The Ratcliff Pension Charity
St Katharine and Shadwell
  Trust
The Tower Hill Trust
The Wakefield and Tetley Trust

■ Waltham Forest

The Association of Friends of
  Essex Churches
East London Community
  Foundation
The Jack Petchey Foundation

■ Wandsworth

Sir John Cass's Foundation
Miles Trust for the Putney and
  Roehampton Community
Sir Walter St John's
  Educational Charity

....
**■ South Eastern
England**

The Ammco Trust
The Bellinger Donnay Trust
The Chapman Charitable Trust
The Chelsea Square 1994
  Trust
The Essex Fairway Charitable
  Trust
The GNC Trust
E F and M G Hall Charitable
  Trust
The Dorothy Hay-Bolton
  Charitable Trust

The Antony Hornby Charitable
  Trust
The Leach Fourteenth Trust
The Earl of Northampton's
  Charity
Red Hill Charitable Trust
sfgroup Charitable Fund for
  Disabled People
The Mrs Smith and Mount
  Trust
The Taylor Family Foundation

■ Berkshire

The Ashendene Trust
The Louis Baylis (Maidenhead
  Advertiser) Charitable Trust
Bergqvist Charitable Trust
The Berkshire Community
  Foundation
The Herbert and Peter
  Blagrave Charitable Trust
The Colefax Charitable Trust
The Earley Charity
The Gilbert and Eileen Edgar
  Foundation
The Gerald Palmer Eling Trust
  Company
Greenham Common
  Community Trust Limited
The Henley Educational Charity
The Iliffe Family Charitable
  Trust
The JMK Charitable Trust
The Johnson Wax Ltd
  Charitable Trust
The Spoore, Merry and Rixman
  Foundation
The St Laurence Relief In
  Need Trust
The Vodafone (Group)
  Foundation
The Wates Foundation

■ Buckinghamshire

The Alice Trust
The Louis Baylis (Maidenhead
  Advertiser) Charitable Trust
Bergqvist Charitable Trust
The Buckinghamshire
  Foundation
The Buckinghamshire Historic
  Churches Trust
The Buckinghamshire Masonic
  Centenary Fund
William Harding's Charity
London Legal Support Trust
The Jim Marshall Charitable
  Trust
Milton Keynes Community
  Foundation
The Mobbs Memorial Trust Ltd
The Powell Foundation
The Stokenchurch Educational
  Charity

The Wates Foundation

■ **East Sussex**

The Argus Appeal
Isabel Blackman Foundation
The Brighton District Nursing
Association Trust
The Derek and Eileen Dodgson
Foundation
Gatwick Airport Community
Trust
The Hale Trust
Stuart Hine Trust
The Magdalen and Lasher
Charity
The Moss Charitable Trust
The Poling Charitable Trust
The Rotherwick Foundation
The Southover Manor General
Education Trust
Sussex Community Foundation
The Sussex Historic Churches
Trust
The Mrs A Lacy Tate Trust
The Wates Foundation

■ **Hampshire**

The BAA Communities Trust
The Herbert and Peter
Blagrave Charitable Trust
Bonhomie United Charity
Society
The Bordon and Liphook
Charity
The Colefax Charitable Trust
The John and Freda Coleman
Charitable Trust
The Dibden Allotments Fund
The Dugdale Charitable Trust
The Ellis Campbell Foundation
Ford Britain Trust
Greenham Common
Community Trust Limited
The Walter Guinness
Charitable Trust
The Hampshire and Islands
Historic Churches Trust
Hampshire and Isle of Wight
Community Foundation
The James Trust
The Johnson Wax Ltd
Charitable Trust
The Emmanuel Kaye
Foundation
The Leonard Trust
Gerald Micklem Charitable
Trust
The Moss Charitable Trust
The William Price Charitable
Trust
The Rotherwick Foundation

■ **Isle of Wight**

Hampshire and Isle of Wight
Community Foundation

■ **Kent**

The Charity of William Barrow
The Coalfields Regeneration
Trust
The Cobtree Charity Trust Ltd
The Cole Charitable Trust
Colyer-Fergusson Charitable
Trust
The Friends of Kent Churches
Gatwick Airport Community
Trust
The Great Stone Bridge Trust
of Edenbridge
The Hale Trust
R G Hills Charitable Trust
Matthew Hodder Charitable
Trust
The Hollands-Warren Fund
Kent Community Foundation
London Legal Support Trust
The David Pickford Charitable
Foundation
The Rochester Bridge Trust
The Rothermere Foundation

■ **Oxfordshire**

The Arbib Foundation
The Ashendene Trust
The Banbury Charities
The Louis Baylis (Maidenhead
Advertiser) Charitable Trust
Bergqvist Charitable Trust
The Henley Educational Charity
Elizabeth Jackson Charitable
Trust
The Robert and Margaret
Moss Charitable Trust
City of Oxford Charity
The Oxfordshire Community
Foundation
The Sants Charitable Trust
St Michael's and All Saints'
Charities
The Stanton Ballard Charitable
Trust
The Steventon Allotments and
Relief-in-Need Charity
The Vodafone (Group)
Foundation
The Wates Foundation

■ **Surrey**

John Bristow and Thomas
Mason Trust
The John and Freda Coleman
Charitable Trust
The John Cowan Foundation
T F C Frost Charitable Trust

Gatwick Airport Community
Trust
The Bishop of Guildford's
Foundation
The Hale Trust
The Ingram Trust
The Johnson Wax Ltd
Charitable Trust
The Erica Leonard Trust
London Legal Support Trust
The Masonic Province of
Middlesex Charitable Trust
The R C Sherriff Trust
Surrey Community Foundation
The Surrey Historic Buildings
Trust Ltd
Humphrey Richardson Taylor
Charitable Trust
Walton on Thames Charity
The Wates Foundation

■ **West Sussex**

The Argus Appeal
The BAA Communities Trust
The Derek and Eileen Dodgson
Foundation
The Dugdale Charitable Trust
Gatwick Airport Community
Trust
The Hale Trust
The Moss Charitable Trust
The Poling Charitable Trust
The Southover Manor General
Education Trust
Sussex Community Foundation
The Sussex Historic Churches
Trust
The Wates Foundation
The F Glenister Woodger Trust

....

■ **South Western**
England

The Chelsea Square 1994
Trust
The Cornwell Charitable Trust
The Joyce Fletcher Charitable
Trust
The Garnett Charitable Trust
The GNC Trust
The Leach Fourteenth Trust
The Norman Family Charitable
Trust
The Oldham Foundation
sfgroup Charitable Fund for
Disabled People
The Verdon-Smith Family
Charitable Settlement

■ **Avon**

Almondsbury Charity
The Avon and Somerset Police
Community Trust
Bristol Archdeaconry Charity

The Bristol Charities
The J and M Britton Charitable
Trust
M R Cannon 1998 Charitable
Trust
The Chipping Sodbury Town
Lands Charity
The Harry Crook Foundation
The Denman Charitable Trust
John James Bristol Foundation
The Merchant Venturers'
Charity
The Portishead Nautical Trust
Quartet Community Foundation
(formerly the Greater Bristol
Foundation)
The Rock Solid Trust
The Ralph and Irma Sperring
Charity
The Wates Foundation
The Dame Violet Wills Will
Trust

■ **Cornwall and the Scilly Isles**

The Blanchminster Trust
Cornwall Community
Foundation
The Cornwall Historic
Churches Trust
The Heathcoat Trust
The Michael and Ilse Katz
Foundation
The Clare Milne Trust

■ **Devon**

The H B Allen Charitable Trust
The Albert Casanova Ballard
Deceased Trust
The Barnstaple Bridge Trust
The Bideford Bridge Trust
Lord Clinton's Charitable Trust
The Dr and Mrs A Darlington
Charitable Trust
Devon Community Foundation
The Devon Educational Trust
The Devon Historic Churches
Trust
The Mayor of Exeter's Appeal
Fund
The Great Torrington Town
Lands Charity
The Heathcoat Trust
The Rosalind Hicks Charitable
Trust
Lesley Lesley and Mutter Trust
The Clare Milne Trust
The Northcott Devon
Foundation
The Northcott Devon Medical
Foundation
Saint Luke's College
Foundation

The Dame Violet Wills Will
Trust

■ **Dorset**

Community Foundation for
Bournemouth, Dorset and
Poole
The Dorset Historic Churches
Trust
The Margaret Fisher Charitable
Trust
The Moss Charitable Trust
The Mayor of Poole's Appeal
Fund
The Talbot Village Trust
Mrs R P Tindall's Charitable
Trust
The Valentine Charitable Trust
The Wates Foundation

■ **Gloucestershire**

The Barnwood House Trust
Gloucestershire Community
Foundation
The Gloucestershire Historic
Churches Trust
The Charles Irving Charitable
Trust
Elizabeth Jackson Charitable
Trust
The Jack Lane Charitable Trust
The Langtree Trust
Sylvanus Lyson's Charity
The Notgrove Trust
Quartet Community Foundation
(formerly the Greater Bristol
Foundation)
St Monica Trust Community
Fund
The Summerfield Charitable
Trust
The Wates Foundation

■ **Somerset**

The Avon and Somerset Police
Community Trust
The Hilda and Alice Clark
Charitable Trust
Quartet Community Foundation
(formerly the Greater Bristol
Foundation)
Friends of Somerset Churches
and Chapels
St Monica Trust Community
Fund
The Wates Foundation

■ **Wiltshire**

The Bellinger Donnay Trust
The Herbert and Peter
Blagrave Charitable Trust

The Chippenham Borough
Lands Charity
The Thomas Freke and Lady
Norton Charity
The Fulmer Charitable Trust
The Walter Guinness
Charitable Trust
The Jack Lane Charitable Trust
St Monica Trust Community
Fund
Mrs R P Tindall's Charitable
Trust
The Vodafone (Group)
Foundation
The Community Foundation for
Wiltshire and Swindon

■ **West Midlands region**

The Jack and Ada Beattie
Foundation
The Lord Mayor of
Birmingham's Charity
The Michael Bishop
Foundation
The Bransford Trust
The E F Bulmer Benevolent
Fund
The Coalfields Regeneration
Trust
Coventry Building Society
Charitable Foundation
The W E Dunn Trust
The GNC Trust
The Pedmore Sporting Club
Trust Fund
The Rugby Group Benevolent
Fund Limited
sfgroup Charitable Fund for
Disabled People
The Connie and Albert Taylor
Charitable Trust
The Wilmcote Charitrust
The Yardley Great Trust

■ **Herefordshire**

The Elmley Foundation
The Eveson Charitable Trust
The Herefordshire Community
Foundation
The Herefordshire Historic
Churches Trust
The Jordan Charitable
Foundation

■ **Shropshire**

Baron Davenport's Charity
The P B Dumbell Charitable
Trust
The Roy Fletcher Charitable
Trust
The Lady Forester Trust
The Maxell Educational Trust

Pegasus (Stanley) Trust
The Walker Trust

■ **Staffordshire**

The Bamford Charitable
　Foundation
Britannia Foundation
The Swinfen Broun Charitable
　Trust
The Burton Breweries
　Charitable Trust
Consolidated Charity of Burton
　upon Trent
The Clarke Charitable
　Settlement
Baron Davenport's Charity
The Wilfred and Elsie Elkes
　Charity Fund
The Alfred Haines Charitable
　Trust
Lichfield Conduit Lands
The Michael Marsh Charitable
　Trust
Open Gate
The Strasser Foundation
The Vodafone (Group)
　Foundation

■ **Warwickshire**

The Aylesford Family
　Charitable Trust
Birmingham International
　Airport Community Trust
Baron Davenport's Charity
The Dumbreck Charity
The William Edwards
　Educational Charity
The Alfred Haines Charitable
　Trust
The Heart of England
　Community Foundation
Alan Edward Higgs Charity
Elizabeth Jackson Charitable
　Trust
The King Henry VIII Endowed
　Trust Warwick
The Michael Marsh Charitable
　Trust
The Harry Payne Trust
The Lucy Price Relief-in-Need
　Charity
PSA Peugeot Citroen Charity
　Trust
The C A Rookes Charitable
　Trust
The Snowball Trust
Stratford upon Avon Town
　Trust
Woodlands Trust

■ **West Midlands**

The Lord Austin Trust
The John Avins Trustees

The Aylesford Family
　Charitable Trust
The James Beattie Charitable
　Trust
The Birmingham Community
　Foundation
The Birmingham District
　Nursing Charitable Trust
Birmingham International
　Airport Community Trust
The Charles Brotherton Trust
The Bryant Trust
The William A Cadbury
　Charitable Trust
Christadelphian Samaritan
　Fund
The Cole Charitable Trust
The George Henry Collins
　Charity
The Cook and Wolstenholme
　Charitable Trust
The General Charities of the
　City of Coventry
Baron Davenport's Charity
The Digbeth Trust
The P B Dumbell Charitable
　Trust
The Dumbreck Charity
The Eveson Charitable Trust
The John Feeney Charitable
　Trust
The George Fentham
　Birmingham Charity
The Friends Hall Farm Street
　Trust
Grantham Yorke Trust
Grimmitt Trust
The Alfred Haines Charitable
　Trust
The Harborne Parish Lands
　Charity
The Heart of England
　Community Foundation
Alan Edward Higgs Charity
The High Sheriff's Police Trust
　for the County of West
　Midlands (Building Blocks)
Elizabeth Jackson Charitable
　Trust
The Jarman Charitable Trust
The London Marathon
　Charitable Trust
The Michael Marsh Charitable
　Trust
The James Frederick and Ethel
　Anne Measures Charity
The Keith and Joan
　Mindelsohn Charitable
　Trust
The Payne Charitable Trust
The Harry Payne Trust
The Bernard Piggott Trust
PSA Peugeot Citroen Charity
　Trust
The Roughley Charitable Trust
The Sheldon Trust
The Snowball Trust

Solihull Community Foundation
Sutton Coldfield Municipal
　Charities
C B and H H Taylor 1984 Trust
Woodlands Trust
The W Wing Yip and Brothers
　Foundation

■ **Worcestershire**

Baron Davenport's Charity
The Dumbreck Charity
The Elmley Foundation
The Eveson Charitable Trust
HopMarket Charity
The Michael Marsh Charitable
　Trust
John Martin's Charity
The Harry Payne Trust
Worcester Municipal Charities
　(incorporating Worcester
　Consolidated Municipal
　Charity and Worcester
　Municipal Exhibitions
　Foundation)
The Worcestershire and
　Dudley Historic Churches
　Trust

....

■ **East Midlands**

The Bamford Charitable
　Foundation
The Jack and Ada Beattie
　Foundation
The Becketts and Sargeants
　Educational Foundation
Bergqvist Charitable Trust
The Bingham Trust
The Michael Bishop
　Foundation
The Boots Charitable Trust
Britannia Foundation
The Burton Breweries
　Charitable Trust
The Frederick and Phyllis Cann
　Trust
Carter's Educational
　Foundation
The Clarke Charitable
　Settlement
The Coalfields Regeneration
　Trust
The Compton Charitable Trust
The Douglas Compton James
　Charitable Trust
The Helen Jean Cope Trust
The J Reginald Corah
　Foundation Fund
Coventry Building Society
　Charitable Foundation
The Derbyshire Churches and
　Chapels Preservation Trust
Derbyshire Community
　Foundation
The J N Derbyshire Trust

The W E Dunn Trust
The Maud Elkington Charitable
 Trust
The Everard Foundation
The Fifty Fund
Ford Britain Trust
The GNC Trust
The Gray Trust
The Hartley Charitable Trust
The Joanna Herbert-Stepney
 Charitable Settlement (also
 known as The Paget
 Charitable Trust)
The Hesed Trust
Elizabeth Jackson Charitable
 Trust
Leicester Charity Link (formerly
 The Leicester Charity
 Organisation Society)
Leicestershire Historic
 Churches Trust
Lincolnshire Community
 Foundation
The Lincolnshire Old Churches
 Trust
The London Marathon
 Charitable Trust
Market Harborough and The
 Bowdens Charity
The New Appeals Organisation
 for the City and County of
 Nottingham
Alderman Newton's
 Educational Foundation
The Northampton Municipal
 Church Charities
The Northampton Queen's
 Institute Relief in Sickness
 Fund
The Nottingham General
 Dispensary
The Nottingham Gordon
 Memorial Trust for Boys
 and Girls
Nottinghamshire Community
 Foundation
The Nottinghamshire Historic
 Churches Trust
The Nottinghamshire Miners'
 Welfare Trust Fund
Open Gate
The Jack Patston Charitable
 Trust
The Mary Potter Convent
 Hospital Trust
The Provincial Grand Charity of
 the Province of Derbyshire
The Puri Foundation
The Rugby Group Benevolent
 Fund Limited
The Samworth Foundation
sfgroup Charitable Fund for
 Disabled People
The Shoe Zone Trust
The Mary Elizabeth Siebel
 Charity
The Strangward Trust

The Vodafone (Group)
 Foundation
The George Ward Charitable
 Trust
The John Warren Foundation
The Wates Foundation
The Howard Watson Symington
 Memorial Charity
The Wilmcote Charitrust
David Wilson Foundation
The Wilson Foundation

■ **Derbyshire**

The Bamford Charitable
 Foundation
The Bingham Trust
Britannia Foundation
The Burton Breweries
 Charitable Trust
The Clarke Charitable
 Settlement
The Helen Jean Cope Trust
The Derbyshire Churches and
 Chapels Preservation Trust
Derbyshire Community
 Foundation
Open Gate
The Provincial Grand Charity of
 the Province of Derbyshire
The Samworth Foundation

■ **Leicestershire**

The Burton Breweries
 Charitable Trust
The Helen Jean Cope Trust
The J Reginald Corah
 Foundation Fund
The Maud Elkington Charitable
 Trust
The Everard Foundation
The Joanna Herbert-Stepney
 Charitable Settlement (also
 known as The Paget
 Charitable Trust)
The Hesed Trust
Leicester Charity Link (formerly
 The Leicester Charity
 Organisation Society)
Leicestershire Historic
 Churches Trust
Market Harborough and The
 Bowdens Charity
Alderman Newton's
 Educational Foundation
Open Gate
The Jack Patston Charitable
 Trust
The Samworth Foundation
The Shoe Zone Trust
The George Ward Charitable
 Trust
The Howard Watson Symington
 Memorial Charity
David Wilson Foundation

■ **Lincolnshire**

Lincolnshire Community
 Foundation
The Lincolnshire Old Churches
 Trust
The John Warren Foundation

■ **Northamptonshire**

The Becketts and Sargeants
 Educational Foundation
Bergqvist Charitable Trust
The Frederick and Phyllis Cann
 Trust
The Compton Charitable Trust
The Douglas Compton James
 Charitable Trust
The Maud Elkington Charitable
 Trust
Ford Britain Trust
Elizabeth Jackson Charitable
 Trust
The London Marathon
 Charitable Trust
The Northampton Municipal
 Church Charities
The Northampton Queen's
 Institute Relief in Sickness
 Fund
The John Warren Foundation
The Wilson Foundation

■ **Nottinghamshire**

The Boots Charitable Trust
Carter's Educational
 Foundation
The Helen Jean Cope Trust
The J N Derbyshire Trust
The Fifty Fund
The Gray Trust
The Hartley Charitable Trust
The New Appeals Organisation
 for the City and County of
 Nottingham
The Nottingham General
 Dispensary
The Nottingham Gordon
 Memorial Trust for Boys
 and Girls
Nottinghamshire Community
 Foundation
The Nottinghamshire Historic
 Churches Trust
The Nottinghamshire Miners'
 Welfare Trust Fund
Open Gate
The Mary Potter Convent
 Hospital Trust
The Puri Foundation
The Samworth Foundation
The Mary Elizabeth Siebel
 Charity
The Vodafone (Group)
 Foundation
The John Warren Foundation

The Wates Foundation

....

■ **Eastern**

The Adnams Charity
Anguish's Educational
  Foundation
The Association of Friends of
  Essex Churches
The BAA Communities Trust
The Beccles Town Lands
  Charity
The Bedford Charity (The
  Harpur Trust)
The Bedfordshire and
  Hertfordshire Historic
  Churches Trust
The Bedfordshire and Luton
  Community Foundation
The Hervey Benham Charitable
  Trust
Bergqvist Charitable Trust
Ann Byrne Charitable Trust
The Cambridgeshire
  Community Foundation
The Cambridgeshire Historic
  Churches Trust
The Chapman Charitable Trust
The Christabella Charitable
  Trust
The Colchester Catalyst
  Charity
The Cole Charitable Trust
The Harry Cureton Charitable
  Trust
The D J H Currie Memorial
  Trust
Earls Colne and Halstead
  Educational Charity
The Ebenezer Trust
Educational Foundation of
  Alderman John Norman
Essex Community Foundation
The Essex Heritage Trust
Essex Provincial Charity Fund
The Essex Youth Trust
Walter Farthing (Trust) Limited
Farthing Trust
Ford Britain Trust
The Charles S French
  Charitable Trust
The Anne French Memorial
  Trust
The Ganzoni Charitable Trust
The GNC Trust
The Grange Farm Centre Trust
Robert Hall Charity
The Hertfordshire Community
  Foundation
The Hitchin Educational
  Foundation
The House of Industry Estate
Huntingdon Freemen's Charity
The John Jarrold Trust
Kirkley Poor's Lands Estate
London Legal Support Trust

The D G Marshall of
  Cambridge Trust
The Masonic Province of
  Middlesex Charitable Trust
The Mills Charity
The D C Moncrieff Charitable
  Trust
The Mothercare Charitable
  Foundation
The Music Sales Charitable
  Trust
Needham Market and Barking
  Welfare Charities
The Neighbourly Charitable
  Trust
The Norwich Historic Churches
  Trust Ltd
The Norwich Town Close
  Estate Charity
Ogilvie Charities Deed No.2
  (including the Charity of
  Mary Catherine Ford Smith)
The Jack Patston Charitable
  Trust
The Jack Petchey Foundation
The Mr and Mrs Philip
  Rackham Charitable Trust
Red Hill Charitable Trust
The Rosca Trust
sfgroup Charitable Fund for
  Disabled People
The R C Snelling Charitable
  Trust
The Southwold Trust
The Stevenage Community
  Trust
The Strangward Trust
The Suffolk Foundation
The Suffolk Historic Churches
  Trust
Trust Sixty Three
The John Warren Foundation
The Whittlesey Charity
The A and R Woolf Charitable
  Trust

■ **Bedfordshire**

The Bedford Charity (The
  Harpur Trust)
The Bedfordshire and
  Hertfordshire Historic
  Churches Trust
The Bedfordshire and Luton
  Community Foundation
Bergqvist Charitable Trust
The Hitchin Educational
  Foundation
The House of Industry Estate
The Neighbourly Charitable
  Trust
Trust Sixty Three
The John Warren Foundation

■ **Cambridgeshire**

The Cambridgeshire
  Community Foundation
The Cambridgeshire Historic
  Churches Trust
The Cole Charitable Trust
The Harry Cureton Charitable
  Trust
Farthing Trust
Robert Hall Charity
Huntingdon Freemen's Charity
The D G Marshall of
  Cambridge Trust
The Jack Patston Charitable
  Trust
The Whittlesey Charity

■ **Essex**

The Association of Friends of
  Essex Churches
The BAA Communities Trust
The Hervey Benham Charitable
  Trust
The Christabella Charitable
  Trust
The Colchester Catalyst
  Charity
The D J H Currie Memorial
  Trust
Earls Colne and Halstead
  Educational Charity
The Ebenezer Trust
Essex Community Foundation
The Essex Heritage Trust
Essex Provincial Charity Fund
The Essex Youth Trust
Walter Farthing (Trust) Limited
Ford Britain Trust
The Charles S French
  Charitable Trust
The Grange Farm Centre Trust
London Legal Support Trust
Ogilvie Charities Deed No.2
  (including the Charity of
  Mary Catherine Ford Smith)
The Jack Petchey Foundation
The Rosca Trust

■ **Hertfordshire**

The Bedfordshire and
  Hertfordshire Historic
  Churches Trust
Bergqvist Charitable Trust
The Hertfordshire Community
  Foundation
The Hitchin Educational
  Foundation
London Legal Support Trust
The Masonic Province of
  Middlesex Charitable Trust
The Mothercare Charitable
  Foundation
The Stevenage Community
  Trust

Trust Sixty Three

The A and R Woolf Charitable Trust

■ **Norfolk**

Anguish's Educational Foundation

Ann Byrne Charitable Trust

Educational Foundation of Alderman John Norman

The Anne French Memorial Trust

The John Jarrold Trust

The D C Moncrieff Charitable Trust

The Norwich Historic Churches Trust Ltd

The Norwich Town Close Estate Charity

The Mr and Mrs Philip Rackham Charitable Trust

The R C Snelling Charitable Trust

■ **Suffolk**

The Adnams Charity

The Beccles Town Lands Charity

The Anne French Memorial Trust

The Ganzoni Charitable Trust

Kirkley Poor's Lands Estate

The Mills Charity

The D C Moncrieff Charitable Trust

The Music Sales Charitable Trust

Needham Market and Barking Welfare Charities

Ogilvie Charities Deed No.2 (including the Charity of Mary Catherine Ford Smith)

The Southwold Trust

The Suffolk Foundation

The Suffolk Historic Churches Trust

■ **North West**

The Mason Bibby 1981 Trust

The Booth Charities

The Bowland Charitable Trust

The Harold and Alice Bridges Charity

Britannia Foundation

The Charles and Edna Broadhurst Charitable Trust

The Charles Brotherton Trust

The Camelia Trust

The Cheshire Provincial Fund of Benevolence

The Chrimes Family Charitable Trust

The Coalfields Regeneration Trust

The Congleton Inclosure Trust

Cumberland Building Society Charitable Foundation

Cumbria Community Foundation

The Hamilton Davies Trust

The Earl of Derby's Charitable Trust

Eden Arts Trust

The Ellerdale Trust

The Eventhall Family Charitable Trust

The Fairway Trust

Faisaltex Charitable Trust

Famos Foundation Trust

Forever Manchester (The Community Foundation for Greater Manchester)

The Fort Foundation

The Galbraith Trust

The GNC Trust

A B Grace Trust

The Granada Foundation

The Hadfield Trust

The Harris Charity

The Helping Foundation

The Hemby Trust

John Holford's Charity

The Edward Holt Trust

Hulme Trust Estates (Educational)

The Johnson Foundation

The Johnson Group Cleaners Charity

The J E Joseph Charitable Fund

Kelsick's Educational Foundation

The Peter Kershaw Trust

The Ursula Keyes Trust

Community Foundation for Lancashire

Duchy of Lancaster Benevolent Fund

The Herd Lawson and Muriel Lawson Charitable Trust

Liverpool Charity and Voluntary Services

Liverpool Sailors' Home Trust

The Makin Charitable Trust

Manchester Airport Community Trust Fund

The Manchester Guardian Society Charitable Trust

Lord Mayor of Manchester's Charity Appeal Trust

The Ann and David Marks Foundation

The John Mason Family Trust

Matliwala Family Charitable Trust

The Mersey Docks and Harbour Company Charitable Fund

Community Foundation for Merseyside

John Moores Foundation

The Mushroom Fund

The North West Cancer Research Fund

The Northern Rock Foundation

Oglesby Charitable Trust

The Oldham Foundation

The Payne Charitable Trust

The Pilkington Charities Fund

The Proven Family Trust

The Fanny Rapaport Charitable Settlement

The Ravensdale Trust

The Nathaniel Reyner Trust Fund

The Christopher Rowbotham Charitable Trust

The Francis C Scott Charitable Trust

The Frieda Scott Charitable Trust

The Sir James and Lady Scott Trust

sfgroup Charitable Fund for Disabled People

SHINE (Support and Help in Education)

The J A Shone Memorial Trust

The Skelton Bounty

Springfields Employees' Medical Research and Charity Trust Fund

The Edward Stocks-Massey Bequest Fund

T and S Trust Fund

The Mayor of Trafford's Charity Fund

Ulverston Town Lands Charity

United Utilities Trust Fund

The Vodafone (Group) Foundation

The West Derby Wastelands Charity

The Norman Whiteley Trust

Wirral Mayor's Charity

The W Wing Yip and Brothers Foundation

The Yorkshire Dales Millennium Trust

The Zochonis Charitable Trust

■ **Cheshire**

Britannia Foundation

The Cheshire Provincial Fund of Benevolence

The Congleton Inclosure Trust

The Hamilton Davies Trust

John Holford's Charity

The Ursula Keyes Trust

Manchester Airport Community Trust Fund

John Moores Foundation

The Proven Family Trust

The Christopher Rowbotham
   Charitable Trust
The Vodafone (Group)
   Foundation

■ **Cumbria**

The Harold and Alice Bridges
   Charity
Cumberland Building Society
   Charitable Foundation
Cumbria Community
   Foundation
Eden Arts Trust
The Hadfield Trust
Kelsick's Educational
   Foundation
The Herd Lawson and Muriel
   Lawson Charitable Trust
The Northern Rock Foundation
The Payne Charitable Trust
The Proven Family Trust
The Francis C Scott Charitable
   Trust
The Frieda Scott Charitable
   Trust
Ulverston Town Lands Charity
The Norman Whiteley Trust
The Yorkshire Dales
   Millennium Trust

■ **Greater Manchester**

The Booth Charities
The Camelia Trust
The Cheshire Provincial Fund
   of Benevolence
The Hamilton Davies Trust
Famos Foundation Trust
Forever Manchester (The
   Community Foundation for
   Greater Manchester)
The Helping Foundation
The Edward Holt Trust
Hulme Trust Estates
   (Educational)
The J E Joseph Charitable
   Fund
The Peter Kershaw Trust
Duchy of Lancaster Benevolent
   Fund
Manchester Airport Community
   Trust Fund
The Manchester Guardian
   Society Charitable Trust
Lord Mayor of Manchester's
   Charity Appeal Trust
The Ann and David Marks
   Foundation
The Christopher Rowbotham
   Charitable Trust
The Sir James and Lady Scott
   Trust
SHINE (Support and Help in
   Education)
The Skelton Bounty

T and S Trust Fund
The Mayor of Trafford's Charity
   Fund
The W Wing Yip and Brothers
   Foundation
The Zochonis Charitable Trust

■ **Lancashire**

The Harold and Alice Bridges
   Charity
Cumberland Building Society
   Charitable Foundation
Faisaltex Charitable Trust
The Fort Foundation
The Galbraith Trust
A B Grace Trust
The Harris Charity
Community Foundation for
   Lancashire
Duchy of Lancaster Benevolent
   Fund
Matliwala Family Charitable
   Trust
Community Foundation for
   Merseyside
John Moores Foundation
The Christopher Rowbotham
   Charitable Trust
The Francis C Scott Charitable
   Trust
The Skelton Bounty
Springfields Employees'
   Medical Research and
   Charity Trust Fund
The Edward Stocks-Massey
   Bequest Fund
The Yorkshire Dales
   Millennium Trust

■ **Merseyside**

The Mason Bibby 1981 Trust
The Charles and Edna
   Broadhurst Charitable Trust
The Charles Brotherton Trust
The Camelia Trust
The Cheshire Provincial Fund
   of Benevolence
The Chrimes Family Charitable
   Trust
The Ellerdale Trust
The Hemby Trust
The Johnson Foundation
The Johnson Group Cleaners
   Charity
Duchy of Lancaster Benevolent
   Fund
Liverpool Charity and Voluntary
   Services
Liverpool Sailors' Home Trust
The Makin Charitable Trust
The Mersey Docks and
   Harbour Company
   Charitable Fund

Community Foundation for
   Merseyside
John Moores Foundation
The Mushroom Fund
The Pilkington Charities Fund
The Proven Family Trust
The Ravensdale Trust
The Nathaniel Reyner Trust
   Fund
The J A Shone Memorial Trust
The Skelton Bounty
The West Derby Wastelands
   Charity
Wirral Mayor's Charity

....

■ **Yorkshire and the
   Humber**

The Norman C Ashton
   Foundation
The Bearder Charity
The Benfield Motors Charitable
   Trust
The Bishop's Development
   Fund
The Charles Brotherton Trust
The Jack Brunton Charitable
   Trust
The Audrey and Stanley Burton
   1960 Charitable Trust
M R Cannon 1998 Charitable
   Trust
The Joseph and Annie Cattle
   Trust
John William Chapman's
   Charitable Trust
The Church Burgesses
   Educational Foundation
Church Burgesses Trust
The Coalfields Regeneration
   Trust
Community Foundation for
   Calderdale
The Marjorie Coote Animal
   Charity Trust
The Marjorie Coote Old
   People's Charity
The Elm House Trust
The A M Fenton Trust
The Freshgate Trust
   Foundation
The GNC Trust
The Constance Green
   Foundation
The Harrison and Potter Trust
The Hartley Charitable Trust
The N and P Hartley Memorial
   Trust
The Hesslewood Children's
   Trust (Hull Seamen's and
   General Orphanage)
The Hull and East Riding
   Charitable Trust
The Humberside Charitable
   Health Trust

Duchy of Lancaster Benevolent
Fund
The Lord Mayor of Leeds
Appeal Fund
The Leeds Community
Foundation
The Lincolnshire Old Churches
Trust
Lady Lumley's Educational
Foundation
The Mayfield Valley Arts Trust
The Mirfield Educational
Charity
The James Neill Trust Fund
Open Gate
Sir John Priestman Charity
Trust
The J S and E C Rymer
Charitable Trust
The Salt Foundation
sfgroup Charitable Fund for
Disabled People
The Sylvia and Colin Shepherd
Charitable Trust
Split Infinitive Trust
The Talbot Trusts
Two Ridings Community
Foundation
Wade's Charity
The Scurrah Wainwright Charity
The West Yorkshire Police
Community Fund
The York Children's Trust
Yorkshire Agricultural Society
The South Yorkshire
Community Foundation
The Yorkshire Dales
Millennium Trust
The Yorkshire Historic
Churches Trust

■ **Humberside, East Riding**

The Joseph and Annie Cattle
Trust
The Hesslewood Children's
Trust (Hull Seamen's and
General Orphanage)
The Hull and East Riding
Charitable Trust
The Humberside Charitable
Health Trust
The Lincolnshire Old Churches
Trust
The J S and E C Rymer
Charitable Trust
sfgroup Charitable Fund for
Disabled People

■ **North Yorkshire**

The Charles Brotherton Trust
The Jack Brunton Charitable
Trust
M R Cannon 1998 Charitable
Trust

The Marjorie Coote Animal
Charity Trust
The Elm House Trust
Lady Lumley's Educational
Foundation
Sir John Priestman Charity
Trust
The Sylvia and Colin Shepherd
Charitable Trust
Two Ridings Community
Foundation
The York Children's Trust
The Yorkshire Dales
Millennium Trust

■ **South Yorkshire**

John William Chapman's
Charitable Trust
The Church Burgesses
Educational Foundation
Church Burgesses Trust
The Marjorie Coote Old
People's Charity
The Freshgate Trust
Foundation
The Mayfield Valley Arts Trust
The James Neill Trust Fund
Open Gate
The Talbot Trusts
The South Yorkshire
Community Foundation

■ **West Yorkshire**

The Norman C Ashton
Foundation
The Bearder Charity
The Benfield Motors Charitable
Trust
The Bishop's Development
Fund
The Charles Brotherton Trust
The Audrey and Stanley Burton
1960 Charitable Trust
Community Foundation for
Calderdale
The Constance Green
Foundation
The Harrison and Potter Trust
Duchy of Lancaster Benevolent
Fund
The Lord Mayor of Leeds
Appeal Fund
The Leeds Community
Foundation
The Mirfield Educational
Charity
The Salt Foundation
Wade's Charity
The West Yorkshire Police
Community Fund

■ **North East**

The 1989 Willan Charitable
Trust
The Roy and Pixie Baker
Charitable Trust
The Ballinger Charitable Trust
The Barbour Foundation
The Benfield Motors Charitable
Trust
Joseph Brough Charitable
Trust
M R Cannon 1998 Charitable
Trust
The Coalfields Regeneration
Trust
The Catherine Cookson
Charitable Trust
County Durham Community
Foundation
The Sir Tom Cowie Charitable
Trust
Cumberland Building Society
Charitable Foundation
The Gillian Dickinson Trust
The Dickon Trust
The Ellinson Foundation Ltd
The Elm House Trust
The GNC Trust
Greggs Foundation (formerly
Greggs Trust)
The Hadrian Trust
The W A Handley Charitable
Trust
The Hedley Denton Charitable
Trust
Hexham and Newcastle
Diocesan Trust (1947)
The Hospital of God at
Greatham
The Sir James Knott Trust
The William Leech Charity
The Leslie and Lilian Manning
Trust
The Millfield House Foundation
The Northern Rock Foundation
The Northumberland Village
Homes Trust
The Northumbria Historic
Churches Trust
Sir John Priestman Charity
Trust
The Rothley Trust
The Christopher Rowbotham
Charitable Trust
S O Charitable Trust
The Storrow Scott Will Trust
sfgroup Charitable Fund for
Disabled People
The Sylvia and Colin Shepherd
Charitable Trust
St Hilda's Trust
T and S Trust Fund
Tees Valley Community
Foundation

Community Foundation Serving
Tyne and Wear and
Northumberland
The William Webster
Charitable Trust
Yorkshire Agricultural Society

■ Cleveland

The Barbour Foundation
The Hadrian Trust
Hexham and Newcastle
Diocesan Trust (1947)
The Hospital of God at
Greatham
The Sir James Knott Trust
The Northern Rock Foundation
The Northumbria Historic
Churches Trust
Tees Valley Community
Foundation
Yorkshire Agricultural Society

■ Durham

The Barbour Foundation
Joseph Brough Charitable
Trust
M R Cannon 1998 Charitable
Trust
County Durham Community
Foundation
The Sir Tom Cowie Charitable
Trust
The Gillian Dickinson Trust
The Hadrian Trust
Hexham and Newcastle
Diocesan Trust (1947)
The Hospital of God at
Greatham
The Sir James Knott Trust
The William Leech Charity
The Northern Rock Foundation
The Northumbria Historic
Churches Trust
Sir John Priestman Charity
Trust
Yorkshire Agricultural Society

■ Northumberland

The Barbour Foundation
Joseph Brough Charitable
Trust
Cumberland Building Society
Charitable Foundation
The Gillian Dickinson Trust
The Hadrian Trust
The W A Handley Charitable
Trust
Hexham and Newcastle
Diocesan Trust (1947)
The Hospital of God at
Greatham
The Sir James Knott Trust
The William Leech Charity

The Northern Rock Foundation
The Northumbria Historic
Churches Trust
The Christopher Rowbotham
Charitable Trust
St Hilda's Trust
Community Foundation Serving
Tyne and Wear and
Northumberland
Yorkshire Agricultural Society

■ Tyne & Wear

The Barbour Foundation
Joseph Brough Charitable
Trust
The Sir Tom Cowie Charitable
Trust
The Gillian Dickinson Trust
The Ellinson Foundation Ltd
The Hadrian Trust
The W A Handley Charitable
Trust
Hexham and Newcastle
Diocesan Trust (1947)
The Hospital of God at
Greatham
The Sir James Knott Trust
The William Leech Charity
The Northern Rock Foundation
The Northumbria Historic
Churches Trust
Sir John Priestman Charity
Trust
The Christopher Rowbotham
Charitable Trust
S O Charitable Trust
St Hilda's Trust
T and S Trust Fund
Community Foundation Serving
Tyne and Wear and
Northumberland

Northern Ireland

Church of Ireland Priorities
Fund
The Community Foundation for
Northern Ireland
The Enkalon Foundation
The Garnett Charitable Trust
The GNC Trust
The Goodman Foundation
Hope for Youth (formerly
Women Caring Trust)
Lloyds TSB Foundation for
Northern Ireland
Lord and Lady Lurgan Trust
The Esmé Mitchell Trust
John Moores Foundation
Royal British Legion
Ulster Garden Villages Ltd
Ultach Trust
Victoria Homes Trust
The Vodafone (Group)
Foundation

Scotland

The Aberbrothock Skea Trust
The Aberdeen Endowments
Trust
The Aberdeenshire Educational
Trust Scheme
Age Scotland (formerly Age
Concern Scotland and Help
the Aged)
The AMW Charitable Trust
The BAA Communities Trust
The Baird Trust
Barchester Healthcare
Foundation
The Bellahouston Bequest
Fund
The Benfield Motors Charitable
Trust
The British Gas (Scottish Gas)
Energy Trust
The Callander Charitable Trust
The Carnegie Dunfermline
Trust
The Carnegie Trust for the
Universities of Scotland
Cash for Kids Radio Clyde
The Cattanach Charitable Trust
Chest, Heart and Stroke
Scotland
The Coalfields Regeneration
Trust
The Craignish Trust
The Cray Trust
Creative Scotland
The Cross Trust
Cumberland Building Society
Charitable Foundation
The Cunningham Trust
The Davidson (Nairn)
Charitable Trust
The Dickon Trust
Edinburgh Children's Holiday
Fund
Edinburgh Voluntary
Organisations' Trust Funds
The Ellis Campbell Foundation
The Erskine Cunningham Hill
Trust
Fife Council/Common Good
Funds and Trusts
The Gannochy Trust
The GNC Trust
Grampian Police Diced Cap
Charitable Fund
The Guildry Incorporation of
Perth
Dr Guthrie's Association
The Christina Mary Hendrie
Trust for Scottish and
Canadian Charities
The Anne Herd Memorial Trust
The Holywood Trust
Miss Agnes H Hunter's Trust
The Jeffrey Charitable Trust
The Jordan Charitable
Foundation

JTH Charitable Trust
The Ian Karten Charitable
Trust
The Kelly Family Charitable
Trust
The Late Sir Pierce Lacy
Charity Trust
The Andrew and Mary
Elizabeth Little Charitable
Trust
The R S Macdonald Charitable
Trust
The Mackintosh Foundation
W M Mann Foundation
The Nancie Massey Charitable
Trust
The Mathew Trust
The Merchants' House of
Glasgow
The Stanley Morrison
Charitable Trust
Moto in the Community Trust
The Mugdock Children's Trust
The North British Hotel Trust
The Northwood Charitable
Trust
Miss M E Swinton Paterson's
Charitable Trust
The Ponton House Trust
The Robertson Trust
Mrs Gladys Row Fogo
Charitable Trust
The Scottish Arts Council
Scottish Coal Industry Special
Welfare Fund
The Scottish Community
Foundation
The Scottish International
Education Trust
The Shetland Charitable Trust
The Hugh Stenhouse
Foundation
Strathclyde Police Benevolent
Fund
The Templeton Goodwill Trust
The Arthur and Margaret
Thompson Charitable Trust
The Len Thomson Charitable
Trust
Voluntary Action Fund
John Watson's Trust
A H and B C Whiteley
Charitable Trust
J and J R Wilson Trust
The James Wood Bequest
Fund
The John K Young Endowment
Fund

■ **Central**

The Callander Charitable Trust
Mrs Gladys Row Fogo
Charitable Trust
The James Wood Bequest
Fund

■ **Grampian Region**

The Aberbrothock Skea Trust
The Aberdeen Endowments
Trust
The Aberdeenshire Educational
Trust Scheme
The BAA Communities Trust
Grampian Police Diced Cap
Charitable Fund

■ **Highlands & Islands**

The Davidson (Nairn)
Charitable Trust
The Jordan Charitable
Foundation
The Mackintosh Foundation
The Shetland Charitable Trust

■ **Lothians Region**

The BAA Communities Trust
The Benfield Motors Charitable
Trust
Edinburgh Children's Holiday
Fund
Edinburgh Voluntary
Organisations' Trust Funds
The Kelly Family Charitable
Trust
The Ponton House Trust
Mrs Gladys Row Fogo
Charitable Trust
The John K Young Endowment
Fund

■ **Southern Scotland**

The Callander Charitable Trust
Cumberland Building Society
Charitable Foundation
The Holywood Trust

■ **Strathclyde**

The BAA Communities Trust
The Bellahouston Bequest
Fund
Cash for Kids Radio Clyde
The Andrew and Mary
Elizabeth Little Charitable
Trust
The Merchants' House of
Glasgow
The Stanley Morrison
Charitable Trust
Strathclyde Police Benevolent
Fund
The Templeton Goodwill Trust
The James Wood Bequest
Fund

■ **Tayside & Fife**

The Aberbrothock Skea Trust
The Carnegie Dunfermline
Trust
The Ellis Campbell Foundation
Fife Council/Common Good
Funds and Trusts
The Guildry Incorporation of
Perth
The Late Sir Pierce Lacy
Charity Trust
The Mathew Trust
The Northwood Charitable
Trust
The Arthur and Margaret
Thompson Charitable Trust

Wales

Archbishop of Wales' Fund for
Children
The John Armitage Charitable
Trust
The Arts Council of Wales
The Austin Bailey Trust
Barchester Healthcare
Foundation
The Baring Foundation
Birthday House Trust
The Boshier-Hinton Foundation
H E and E L Botteley
Charitable Trust
The Bower Trust
The British Gas (Scottish Gas)
Energy Trust
The Catholic Trust for England
and Wales
The Cemlyn-Jones Trust
The Chapman Charitable Trust
The Chrimes Family Charitable
Trust
The Church and Community
Fund
City and County of Swansea
Welsh Church Act Fund
CLA Charitable Trust
The Coalfields Regeneration
Trust
Colwinston Charitable Trust
The Cwmbran Trust
The DM Charitable Trust
The James Dyson Foundation
The Ernest Hecht Charitable
Foundation
Ford Britain Trust
Gwyneth Forrester Trust
The Joseph Strong Frazer Trust
The Freemasons' Grand
Charity
The General Nursing Council
for England and Wales
Trust
The GNC Trust
The Goodman Foundation
Leonard Gordon Charitable
Trust

Lady Hind Trust
The Hintze Family Charitable
  Foundation
The Jane Hodge Foundation
The J Isaacs Charitable Trust
The Isle of Anglesey Charitable
  Trust
The Nick Jenkins Foundation
Dezna Robins Jones Charitable
  Foundation
The Karenza Foundation
The Ian Karten Charitable
  Trust
Keswick Hall Trust
Lloyds TSB Foundation for
  England and Wales
Llysdinam Charitable Trust
Lord and Lady Lurgan Trust
Marshall's Charity
Marshgate Charitable
  Settlement
The McKenna Charitable Trust
Millennium Stadium Charitable
  Trust
Monmouthshire County Council
  Welsh Church Act Fund
The Mr and Mrs J T Morgan
  Foundation
Moto in the Community Trust
The National Churches Trust
  (formerly the Historic
  Churches Preservation
  Trust with the Incorporated
  Church Building Society)
The Noon Foundation
The North West Cancer
  Research Fund
The Norwood and Newton
  Settlement
The Ouseley Trust
The James Pantyfedwen
  Foundation
The Payne Charitable Trust
The Bernard Piggott Trust
The Rhondda Cynon Taff
  Welsh Church Acts Fund
Alexandra Rose Charities
Royal British Legion
The Severn Trent Water
  Charitable Trust Fund
Skipton Building Society
  Charitable Foundation
The Sobell Foundation
St Teilo's Trust
The Leonard Laity Stoate
  Charitable Trust
Swansea and Brecon Diocesan
  Board of Finance Limited
TJH Foundation
Toni and Guy Charitable
  Foundation Limited
Vale of Glamorgan – Welsh
  Church Fund
The Community Foundation in
  Wales
Wales Council for Voluntary
  Action

Robert and Felicity Waley-
  Cohen Charitable Trust
The Barbara Ward Children's
  Foundation
The Waterways Trust
Welsh Church Fund Dyfed
  area (Carmarthenshire,
  Ceredigion and
  Pembrokeshire)
A H and B C Whiteley
  Charitable Trust
The Yapp Charitable Trust

■ North Wales

The Cemlyn-Jones Trust
The Chrimes Family Charitable
  Trust
The Isle of Anglesey Charitable
  Trust
The North West Cancer
  Research Fund
The Payne Charitable Trust
The Bernard Piggott Trust

■ Mid and West Wales

The North West Cancer
  Research Fund
Swansea and Brecon Diocesan
  Board of Finance Limited
Welsh Church Fund Dyfed
  area (Carmarthenshire,
  Ceredigion and
  Pembrokeshire)

■ South Wales

The Austin Bailey Trust
City and County of Swansea
  Welsh Church Act Fund
The Cwmbran Trust
Ford Britain Trust
Monmouthshire County Council
  Welsh Church Act Fund
The Rhondda Cynon Taff
  Welsh Church Acts Fund
Swansea and Brecon Diocesan
  Board of Finance Limited
Vale of Glamorgan – Welsh
  Church Fund

Channel Islands

The Freemasons' Grand
  Charity
The Hampshire and Islands
  Historic Churches Trust
Lloyds TSB Foundation for the
  Channel Islands
Lord and Lady Lurgan Trust

Trusts by field of interest and type of beneficiary

This index contains two separate listings:

Categorisation of fields of interest and type of beneficiary: This lists all of the headings used in the DGMT to categorise fields of interest and types of beneficiary.

Trusts by field of interest and type of beneficiary: This lists trusts under the fields of interest and types of beneficiary for which they have expressed a funding preference.

Trusts by field of interest and type of beneficiary

These pages contain two separate listings:

Categorisation of fields of interest and type of beneficiary
This lists all of the headings used in the DGMT to categorise fields of interest and types of beneficiary

Trusts by field of interest and type of beneficiary
This lists trusts under the fields of interest and types of beneficiary for which they have expressed a funding preference

Arts, culture, sport and recreation 50

Arts and culture 53

Access to the arts 56

Amateur and community arts 56

Community arts 56

Eisteddfodau 56

Participation in the arts 56

Art and culture of specific countries 56

Greek art and culture 56

Japanese art and culture 56

Portugese art and culture 56

Scottish and Gaelic art and culture 56

Arts management, policy and planning 56

Combined arts 56

Crafts 56

Disability arts 57

Libraries 57

Literature 57

Museums and galleries 57

Performing arts 57

Dance 58

Music 58

Theatre 58

Visual arts 58

Fine art 58

Public art/ Sculpture 58

Heritage and the built environment 59

Arts and the envrionment 60

Architecture 60

Landscape 60

Heritage 60

Maintenance and preservation of buildings 60

Religious buildings 61

Restoration and maintenance of inland waterways 62

Built environment – education and research 62

Humanities 62
Archaeology 62

History 62

International understanding 62

Philosophy and ethics 62

Media and communications 63

Recreation and sport 63
Parks and open spaces 64

Recreation facilities 64

Sports for people with a disability 64

Sports 64

Development, housing and employment 65
Community and economic development 66

Housing 66

Specific industries 67

Education and training 67
Higher education 72

Informal, continuing and adult education 73

Vocational education and training 73

Integrated education 73

Management of schools 73

Particular subjects, curriculum development 73

Arts education and training 74

Business education 74

Citizenship, personal and social education 74

Domestic/ lifeskills education 74

Hospitality education 74

Literacy education 74

Religious education 74

Science education 75

Sports education 75

Technology, engineering and computer education 75

Pre-school education, nursery schools 75

Primary and secondary school education 75

Faith schools 76

Public and independent schools 76

Special needs schools 76

State schools 76

Teacher training 76

Environment and animals 77
Agriculture and fishing 79

Farming and food production 79

Fishing and fisheries 79

Forestry 79

Horticulture 79

Animal care 80

Animal conservation 80

Climate change 80

Countryside 80

Environmental education and research 81

Natural environment 81

Flora and fauna 82

Water resources 82

Wild places, wilderness 82

Pollution abatement and control 82

Sustainable environment 82

Energy issues 82

Loss of environment 83

Transport 83

General charitable purposes 83

Health 92
Alternative, complementary medicine 97

Health care 97

Health training 99

Medical equipment 99

Medical institutions 99

Nursing 100

Primary health care 100

Therapy 100

Health education/ prevention/ development 100

Health promotion 100

History of medicine 100

Medical research 100

Philanthropy and the voluntary sector 103
Voluntarism 103

Community participation 103

Voluntary sector capacity building 103

Religious activities 103
Christianity 108

Christian causes 110

Christian churches 110

Christian social thought 111

Ecumenicalism 111

Missionary work, evangelism 111

Hinduism 112

Inter-faith activities 112

Islam 112

Judaism 112

Jewish causes, work 114

Orthodox Judaism 115

Religious understanding 115

Rights, law and conflict 115
Citizen participation 116

Conflict resolution 116

Legal advice and services 116

Rights, equality and justice 116

Human rights 117

Civil liberties 117

Cultural equity 117

Disability rights 117

Economic justice 117

Racial justice 117

Social justice 117

Women's rights 117

Young people's rights 117

Science and technology 118
Engineering/ technology 118

Life sciences 118

Physical/earth sciences 118

Social sciences, policy and research 118
Economics 118

Political science 118

Physical/earth sciences 119

Social welfare 119
Community care services 125

Services for and about children and young people 127

Services for and about older people 128

Services for and about vulnerable people/people who are ill 129

Services for carers 129

Services for victims of crime 130

Services for women 130

Community centres and activities 130

Community and social centres 130

Community organisations 130

Arts, culture, sport and recreation

The 29th May 1961 Charitable Trust
The A B Charitable Trust
Access Sport
The Victor Adda Foundation
The Alice Trust
Allchurches Trust Ltd
Angus Allnatt Charitable Foundation
The Ammco Trust
The AMW Charitable Trust
Andor Charitable Trust
The Eric Anker-Petersen Charity
The Architectural Heritage Fund
The Armourers' and Brasiers' Gauntlet Trust
Arsenal Charitable Trust
The Arthur Ronald Dyer Charitable Trust
Arts Council England
The Arts Council of Northern Ireland
The Arts Council of Wales
The Ove Arup Foundation
A J H Ashby Will Trust
The Ashden Trust
The Ashendene Trust
The Ashley Family Foundation (formerly The Laura Ashley Foundation)
The Association of Friends of Essex Churches
The Astor Foundation
The Astor of Hever Trust
The Aurelius Charitable Trust
B W Charitable Trust
The Baird Trust
The Roy and Pixie Baker Charitable Trust
The Ballinger Charitable Trust
The Barcapel Foundation
The Baring Foundation
Barrington Family Charitable Trust
The John Beckwith Charitable Trust
The Bedford Charity (The Harpur Trust)
The Bedfordshire and Hertfordshire Historic Churches Trust
The Bellahouston Bequest Fund
The Hervey Benham Charitable Trust
Bergqvist Charitable Trust
The Big Lottery Fund
Birmingham International Airport Community Trust
Blackheart Foundation (UK) Limited

The Nicholas Boas Charitable Trust
BOOST Charitable Trust
The Bowerman Charitable Trust
John and Susan Bowers Fund
The Liz and Terry Bramall Charitable Trust
British Institute at Ankara
The Britten-Pears Foundation
The Rory and Elizabeth Brooks Foundation
Brown-Mellows Trust
T B H Brunner's Charitable Settlement
The Buckinghamshire Historic Churches Trust
The Rosemary Bugden Charitable Trust
The Audrey and Stanley Burton 1960 Charitable Trust
The Arnold Burton 1998 Charitable Trust
The Derek Butler Trust
C J Cadbury Charitable Trust
Edward Cadbury Charitable Trust
P H G Cadbury Charitable Trust
The William A Cadbury Charitable Trust
The Edward and Dorothy Cadbury Trust
The Barrow Cadbury Trust and the Barrow Cadbury Fund
Calouste Gulbenkian Foundation
The Cambridgeshire Historic Churches Trust
The Carnegie Dunfermline Trust
The Carpenters' Company Charitable Trust
The Carr-Gregory Trust
Carter's Educational Foundation
Elizabeth Cayzer Charitable Trust
The Cemlyn-Jones Trust
The Checkatrade Foundation
The Chipping Sodbury Town Lands Charity
Stephen Clark 1957 Charitable Trust
J A Clark Charitable Trust
The Clore Duffield Foundation
Miss V L Clore's 1967 Charitable Trust
The Robert Clutterbuck Charitable Trust
The Francis Coales Charitable Foundation
The John Coates Charitable Trust
The Denise Cohen Charitable Trust

The John S Cohen Foundation
The R and S Cohen Foundation
The Bernard Coleman Charitable Trust
Colwinston Charitable Trust
Colyer-Fergusson Charitable Trust
The Congleton Inclosure Trust
The Ernest Cook Trust
Country Houses Foundation
The Craignish Trust
Creative Scotland
The Crescent Trust
The Cross Trust
Cruden Foundation Ltd
The D J H Currie Memorial Trust
The D'Oyly Carte Charitable Trust
The Daiwa Anglo-Japanese Foundation
The Gwendoline and Margaret Davies Charity
The Hamilton Davies Trust
The Helen and Geoffrey De Freitas Charitable Trust
Peter De Haan Charitable Trust
The De Laszlo Foundation
The Leopold De Rothschild Charitable Trust
The Deakin Charitable Trust
The Delius Trust
The Denton Wilde Sapte Charitable Trust
The Derbyshire Churches and Chapels Preservation Trust
The Devon Historic Churches Trust
The Gillian Dickinson Trust
Dischma Charitable Trust
The Djanogly Foundation
The Dorset Historic Churches Trust
The Drapers' Charitable Fund
The Duis Charitable Trust
The Dulverton Trust
Dunard Fund
Ronald Duncan Literary Foundation
The Houghton Dunn Charitable Trust
The Dyers' Company Charitable Trust
The Earmark Trust
Eden Arts Trust
The Gilbert and Eileen Edgar Foundation
The Edinburgh Trust, No 2 Account
The Elephant Trust
The John Ellerman Foundation
The Ellis Campbell Foundation
The Elmgrant Trust
The Elmley Foundation

The Vernon N Ely Charitable Trust
The English Schools' Football Association
The Equity Trust Fund
The Eranda Foundation
The Ericson Trust
The Essex Heritage Trust
The Alan Evans Memorial Trust
Esmée Fairbairn Foundation
The Fairway Trust
The Family Rich Charities Trust
The Lord Faringdon Charitable Trust
Samuel William Farmer Trust
The February Foundation
The John Feeney Charitable Trust
Fife Council/Common Good Funds and Trusts
Gerald Finzi Charitable Trust
The Sir John Fisher Foundation
Fisherbeck Charitable Trust
The Fishmongers' Company's Charitable Trust
Marc Fitch Fund
The Joyce Fletcher Charitable Trust
The Follett Trust
The Football Association National Sports Centre Trust
The Football Association Youth Trust
The Football Foundation
Ford Britain Trust
The Donald Forrester Trust
The Fort Foundation
The Foyle Foundation
The Jill Franklin Trust
The Gordon Fraser Charitable Trust
The Hugh Fraser Foundation
The Joseph Strong Frazer Trust
The Thomas Freke and Lady Norton Charity
The Freshgate Trust Foundation
The Friends of Kent Churches
Friends of Muir Group
The Frognal Trust
The Galanthus Trust
The Gannochy Trust
The Samuel Gardner Memorial Trust
The Garnett Charitable Trust
Garrick Charitable Trust
The Gatsby Charitable Foundation
Gatwick Airport Community Trust
The Robert Gavron Charitable Trust
Jacqueline and Michael Gee Charitable Trust
J Paul Getty Jr Charitable Trust

The Gibbs Charitable Trust
Simon Gibson Charitable Trust
Lady Gibson's Charitable Trust
The Girdlers' Company Charitable Trust
The Glass-House Trust
The Gloucestershire Historic Churches Trust
Golden Charitable Trust
The Jack Goldhill Charitable Trust
The Goldsmiths' Arts Trust Fund
The Goldsmiths' Company Charity
The Golsoncott Foundation
Golubovich Foundation
Nicholas and Judith Goodison's Charitable Settlement
The Gosling Foundation Limited
A and S Graham Charitable Trust
The Granada Foundation
The Grand Order of Water Rats' Charities Fund
The Grange Farm Centre Trust
The J G Graves Charitable Trust
The Great Britain Sasakawa Foundation
The Wiles Greenworld Charitable Trust
The Greys Charitable Trust
Grimmitt Trust
The Grocers' Charity
The Hadfield Trust
The Hadrian Trust
The Hale Trust
Robert Hall Charity
Paul Hamlyn Foundation
The Helen Hamlyn Trust
The Hampshire and Islands Historic Churches Trust
The W A Handley Charitable Trust
The Harding Trust
William Harding's Charity
The Kenneth Hargreaves Charitable Trust
The Harris Charitable Trust
The Peter Harrison Foundation
Haskel Family Foundation
The Dorothy Hay-Bolton Charitable Trust
The Charles Hayward Foundation
The Headley Trust
The Hellenic Foundation
The Hemby Trust
The Henley Educational Charity
The Herefordshire Historic Churches Trust
The Heritage of London Trust Ltd

The Derek Hill Foundation
Hille Pandana
The Hinrichsen Foundation
The Hintze Family Charitable Foundation
Hobson Charity Limited
Matthew Hodder Charitable Trust
The Holbeck Charitable Trust
The Holst Foundation
The Homestead Charitable Trust
The Horne Foundation
The Reta Lila Howard Foundation
The Geoffrey C Hughes Charitable Trust
Human Relief Foundation
Huntingdon Freemen's Charity
The Idlewild Trust
The Iliffe Family Charitable Trust
The Inland Waterways Association
The Inlight Trust
The Ireland Fund of Great Britain
The Irish Youth Foundation (UK) Ltd (incorporating The Lawlor Foundation)
Jacobs Charitable Trust
The John Jarrold Trust
Jerwood Charitable Foundation
The JMK Charitable Trust
The Joanies Trust
The Johnnie Johnson Trust
The Johnson Wax Ltd Charitable Trust
Jusaca Charitable Trust
The Stanley Kalms Foundation
The Kalou Foundation
The Boris Karloff Charitable Foundation
The Kathleen Trust
The Michael and Ilse Katz Foundation
The Kelly Family Charitable Trust
The Robert Kiln Charitable Trust
The Eric and Margaret Kinder Charitable Trust
The Marina Kleinwort Charitable Trust
The Sir James Knott Trust
The Kobler Trust
The Kohn Foundation
The Neil Kreitman Foundation
The Christopher Laing Foundation
The David Laing Foundation
Lancashire Environmental Fund
The R J Larg Family Charitable Trust
The Lark Trust

Laslett's (Hinton) Charity

The Lawson Beckman
Charitable Trust

The Raymond and Blanche
Lawson Charitable Trust

The Carole and Geoffrey
Lawson Foundation

The David Lean Foundation

The Leathersellers' Company
Charitable Fund

The Leche Trust

Leeds Building Society
Charitable Foundation

Leicestershire Historic
Churches Trust

The Leverhulme Trust

Lord Leverhulme's Charitable
Trust

The Joseph Levy Charitable
Foundation

John Lewis Partnership
General Community Fund

Liberum Foundation

The Limbourne Trust

Limoges Charitable Trust

The Linbury Trust

The Lincolnshire Old Churches
Trust

The Linden Charitable Trust

The Lister Charitable Trust

The George John and Sheilah
Livanos Charitable Trust

The Charles Lloyd Foundation

Lloyds TSB Foundation for
Northern Ireland

The London Marathon
Charitable Trust

The William and Katherine
Longman Trust

The Lord's Taverners

Lady Lumley's Educational
Foundation

The Ruth and Jack Lunzer
Charitable Trust

Lord and Lady Lurgan Trust

John Lyon's Charity

The Sir Jack Lyons Charitable
Trust

The Mackintosh Foundation

The MacRobert Trust

Ian Mactaggart Trust

Mageni Trust

Man Group plc Charitable
Trust

Manchester Airport Community
Trust Fund

The Manifold Charitable Trust

W M Mann Foundation

The Manoukian Charitable
Foundation

Market Harborough and The
Bowdens Charity

Michael Marks Charitable
Trust

The Marks Family Foundation

The Marsh Christian Trust

Marshall's Charity

Sir George Martin Trust

John Martin's Charity

The Nancie Massey Charitable
Trust

The Mayfield Valley Arts Trust

The Mears Foundation

The Anthony and Elizabeth
Mellows Charitable
Settlement

Brian Mercer Charitable Trust

The Mercers' Charitable
Foundation

The Merchant Venturers'
Charity

The Merchants' House of
Glasgow

The Metropolitan Drinking
Fountain and Cattle Trough
Association

Gerald Micklem Charitable
Trust

Miles Trust for the Putney and
Roehampton Community

Millennium Stadium Charitable
Trust

The Miller Foundation

The Millichope Foundation

The Millward Charitable Trust

Milton Keynes Community
Foundation

The Peter Minet Trust

The Esmé Mitchell Trust

The Modiano Charitable Trust

Monmouthshire County Council
Welsh Church Act Fund

The Monument Trust

The Henry Moore Foundation

The Nigel Moores Family
Charitable Trust

The Peter Moores Foundation

The Morel Charitable Trust

Diana and Allan Morgenthau
Charitable Trust

The Stanley Morrison
Charitable Trust

The Mount Everest Foundation

The Mugdock Children's Trust

The John R Murray Charitable
Trust

The Kitty and Daniel Nabarro
Charitable Trust

The Naggar Charitable Trust

The Eleni Nakou Foundation

The National Art Collections
Fund

The National Churches Trust
(formerly the Historic
Churches Preservation
Trust with the Incorporated
Church Building Society)

The National Manuscripts
Conservation Trust

Network for Social Change

Nominet Charitable Foundation

The Normanby Charitable Trust

The Northern Rock Foundation

The Northumbria Historic
Churches Trust

The Northwood Charitable
Trust

The Norton Foundation

The Norwich Church of England
Young Men's Society

The Norwich Historic Churches
Trust Ltd

The Noswad Charity

The Nottinghamshire Historic
Churches Trust

The Oakdale Trust

The Oakley Charitable Trust

The Ofenheim Charitable Trust

Oglesby Charitable Trust

The Old Broad Street Charity
Trust

Old Possum's Practical Trust

The Oldham Foundation

Orrin Charitable Trust

The Ouseley Trust

The Owen Family Trust

The Pallant Charitable Trust

The James Pantyfedwen
Foundation

The Parthenon Trust

Miss M E Swinton Paterson's
Charitable Trust

The Jack Patston Charitable
Trust

The Pedmore Sporting Club
Trust Fund

The Pell Charitable Trust

Peltz Trust

The Performing Right Society
Foundation

The Bernard Piggott Trust

The Pilgrim Trust

The Austin and Hope
Pilkington Trust

The Col W W Pilkington Will
Trusts The General Charity
Fund

Polden-Puckham Charitable
Foundation

The Polonsky Foundation

The John Porter Charitable
Trust

The Porter Foundation

The Premier League Charitable
Fund

The Prince of Wales's
Charitable Foundation

PSA Peugeot Citroen Charity
Trust

The Puri Foundation

Mr and Mrs J A Pye's
Charitable Settlement

Quercus Trust

The R V W Trust

The Radcliffe Trust

The Ragdoll Foundation

The Peggy Ramsay Foundation

The Sigrid Rausing Trust

The Ravensdale Trust
The Rayne Foundation
The Rayne Trust
The Reed Foundation
The Max Reinhardt Charitable
  Trust
The Rhododendron Trust
The Rhondda Cynon Taff
  Welsh Church Acts Fund
The Sir Cliff Richard Charitable
  Trust
The Clive Richards Charity
The Richmond Parish Lands
  Charity
Rix-Thompson-Rothenberg
  Foundation
The Robertson Trust
The Rock Solid Trust
The Roman Research Trust
Mrs L D Rope Third Charitable
  Settlement
The Rose Foundation
The Rothley Trust
The Roughley Charitable Trust
The Rowing Foundation
The Rowlands Trust
The Joseph Rowntree
  Charitable Trust
Royal Docks Trust (London)
The J S and E C Rymer
  Charitable Trust
The Jeremy and John Sacher
  Charitable Trust
The Michael Harry Sacher
  Trust
The Raymond and Beverley
  Sackler 1988 Foundation
The Sackler Trust (formerly Dr
  Mortimer and Theresa
  Sackler Foundation)
The Saddlers' Company
  Charitable Fund
The Alan and Babette
  Sainsbury Charitable Fund
The Saintbury Trust
The Andrew Salvesen
  Charitable Trust
Basil Samuel Charitable Trust
Coral Samuel Charitable Trust
The Peter Samuel Charitable
  Trust
The Scarfe Charitable Trust
Schroder Charity Trust
The Scotshill Trust
The Frieda Scott Charitable
  Trust
The Scottish Arts Council
Scottish Coal Industry Special
  Welfare Fund
The Scottish International
  Education Trust
The Scouloudi Foundation
The Searle Charitable Trust
The Samuel Sebba Charitable
  Trust

The Archie Sherman Charitable
  Trust
The R C Sherriff Trust
The Shetland Charitable Trust
The Shipwrights' Company
  Charitable Fund
The Sickle Foundation
The N Smith Charitable
  Settlement
The Martin Smith Foundation
The Stanley Smith UK
  Horticultural Trust
Friends of Somerset Churches
  and Chapels
The E C Sosnow Charitable
  Trust
Spears-Stutz Charitable Trust
The Spero Foundation
Split Infinitive Trust
St Andrew's Conservation
  Trust
The Steel Charitable Trust
Stevenson Family's Charitable
  Trust
The Stewards' Charitable Trust
Peter Stormonth Darling
  Charitable Trust
The Suffolk Historic Churches
  Trust
The Summerfield Charitable
  Trust
The Surrey Historic Buildings
  Trust Ltd
The Sussex Historic Churches
  Trust
Sutton Coldfield Municipal
  Charities
The Connie and Albert Taylor
  Charitable Trust
A P Taylor Trust
The Thistle Trust
The Thompson Family
  Charitable Trust
The Tinsley Foundation
Miss S M Tutton Charitable
  Trust
Two Ridings Community
  Foundation
The Underwood Trust
Unity Theatre Trust
Vale of Glamorgan – Welsh
  Church Fund
The Vardy Foundation
Veneziana Fund
The Nigel Vinson Charitable
  Trust
Robert and Felicity Waley-
  Cohen Charitable Trust
Sir Siegmund Warburg's
  Voluntary Settlement
The Ward Blenkinsop Trust
The John Warren Foundation
The Waterloo Foundation
The Waterways Trust
The Howard Watson Symington
  Memorial Charity

Welsh Church Fund Dyfed
  area (Carmarthenshire,
  Ceredigion and
  Pembrokeshire)
The Welton Foundation
The Westcroft Trust
The Garfield Weston
  Foundation
The Barbara Whatmore
  Charitable Trust
The Whitaker Charitable Trust
The Colonel W H Whitbread
  Charitable Trust
A H and B C Whiteley
  Charitable Trust
The Williams Charitable Trust
The Harold Hyam Wingate
  Foundation
Anona Winn Charitable Trust
The Winton Charitable
  Foundation
The Wixamtree Trust
The Maurice Wohl Charitable
  Foundation
The Wolfson Foundation
The Woodward Charitable
  Trust
The Worcestershire and
  Dudley Historic Churches
  Trust
The Fred and Della Worms
  Charitable Trust
Miss E B Wrightson's
  Charitable Settlement
The Wyseliot Charitable Trust
The W Wing Yip and Brothers
  Foundation
The York Children's Trust
The Yorkshire Dales
  Millennium Trust
The Yorkshire Historic
  Churches Trust
Youth Music
The Marjorie and Arnold Ziff
  Charitable Foundation
The Zochonis Charitable Trust

Arts and culture

The A B Charitable Trust
The Victor Adda Foundation
Angus Allnatt Charitable
  Foundation
The AMW Charitable Trust
Andor Charitable Trust
The Eric Anker-Petersen
  Charity
The Armourers' and Brasiers'
  Gauntlet Trust
Arts Council England
The Arts Council of Northern
  Ireland
The Arts Council of Wales
The Ashden Trust
The Ashendene Trust

The Ashley Family Foundation
(formerly The Laura Ashley
Foundation)
The Aurelius Charitable Trust
B W Charitable Trust
The Ballinger Charitable Trust
The Baring Foundation
Barrington Family Charitable
Trust
The Hervey Benham Charitable
Trust
Bergqvist Charitable Trust
The Nicholas Boas Charitable
Trust
The Bowerman Charitable
Trust
John and Susan Bowers Fund
The Liz and Terry Bramall
Charitable Trust
British Institute at Ankara
The Britten-Pears Foundation
The Rory and Elizabeth Brooks
Foundation
T B H Brunner's Charitable
Settlement
The Rosemary Bugden
Charitable Trust
The Audrey and Stanley Burton
1960 Charitable Trust
The Derek Butler Trust
C J Cadbury Charitable Trust
Edward Cadbury Charitable
Trust
P H G Cadbury Charitable
Trust
The William A Cadbury
Charitable Trust
The Edward and Dorothy
Cadbury Trust
Calouste Gulbenkian
Foundation
The Carnegie Dunfermline
Trust
Elizabeth Cayzer Charitable
Trust
The Checkatrade Foundation
J A Clark Charitable Trust
The Clore Duffield Foundation
Miss V L Clore's 1967
Charitable Trust
The Francis Coales Charitable
Foundation
The John Coates Charitable
Trust
The Denise Cohen Charitable
Trust
The John S Cohen Foundation
The R and S Cohen
Foundation
Colwinston Charitable Trust
Colyer-Fergusson Charitable
Trust
The Ernest Cook Trust
The Craignish Trust
Creative Scotland
The Crescent Trust

The Cross Trust
The D'Oyly Carte Charitable
Trust
The Daiwa Anglo-Japanese
Foundation
The Gwendoline and Margaret
Davies Charity
Peter De Haan Charitable
Trust
The Leopold De Rothschild
Charitable Trust
The Deakin Charitable Trust
The Delius Trust
The Denton Wilde Sapte
Charitable Trust
Dischma Charitable Trust
The Djanogly Foundation
The Drapers' Charitable Fund
The Duis Charitable Trust
Dunard Fund
Ronald Duncan Literary
Foundation
The Dyers' Company
Charitable Trust
The Earmark Trust
Eden Arts Trust
The Gilbert and Eileen Edgar
Foundation
The Elephant Trust
The John Ellerman Foundation
The Elmgrant Trust
The Elmley Foundation
The Equity Trust Fund
The Eranda Foundation
The Ericson Trust
Esmée Fairbairn Foundation
The Family Rich Charities Trust
The Lord Faringdon Charitable
Trust
The John Feeney Charitable
Trust
Fife Council/Common Good
Funds and Trusts
Gerald Finzi Charitable Trust
The Sir John Fisher Foundation
The Joyce Fletcher Charitable
Trust
The Follett Trust
Ford Britain Trust
The Fort Foundation
The Foyle Foundation
The Gordon Fraser Charitable
Trust
The Hugh Fraser Foundation
The Freshgate Trust
Foundation
The Samuel Gardner Memorial
Trust
The Garnett Charitable Trust
Garrick Charitable Trust
The Gatsby Charitable
Foundation
Gatwick Airport Community
Trust
The Robert Gavron Charitable
Trust

Jacqueline and Michael Gee
Charitable Trust
J Paul Getty Jr Charitable Trust
The Gibbs Charitable Trust
Simon Gibson Charitable Trust
Lady Gibson's Charitable Trust
The Girdlers' Company
Charitable Trust
The Glass-House Trust
Golden Charitable Trust
The Jack Goldhill Charitable
Trust
The Goldsmiths' Arts Trust
Fund
The Goldsmiths' Company
Charity
The Golsoncott Foundation
Golubovich Foundation
Nicholas and Judith
Goodison's Charitable
Settlement
A and S Graham Charitable
Trust
The Granada Foundation
The Grand Order of Water
Rats' Charities Fund
The J G Graves Charitable
Trust
The Great Britain Sasakawa
Foundation
The Greys Charitable Trust
Grimmitt Trust
The Grocers' Charity
The Hadfield Trust
The Hadrian Trust
Paul Hamlyn Foundation
The W A Handley Charitable
Trust
The Harding Trust
The Kenneth Hargreaves
Charitable Trust
The Harris Charitable Trust
Haskel Family Foundation
The Headley Trust
The Hellenic Foundation
The Hemby Trust
The Henley Educational Charity
The Heritage of London Trust
Ltd
The Derek Hill Foundation
The Hinrichsen Foundation
The Hintze Family Charitable
Foundation
Hobson Charity Limited
Matthew Hodder Charitable
Trust
The Holst Foundation
The Homestead Charitable
Trust
The Horne Foundation
The Reta Lila Howard
Foundation
The Geoffrey C Hughes
Charitable Trust
Human Relief Foundation
The Idlewild Trust

The Ireland Fund of Great
Britain
Jacobs Charitable Trust
The John Jarrold Trust
Jerwood Charitable Foundation
The Joanies Trust
The Stanley Kalms Foundation
The Boris Karloff Charitable
Foundation
The Kathleen Trust
The Michael and Ilse Katz
Foundation
The Robert Kiln Charitable
Trust
The Marina Kleinwort
Charitable Trust
The Kobler Trust
The Kohn Foundation
The Christopher Laing
Foundation
The David Laing Foundation
The R J Larg Family Charitable
Trust
The Lark Trust
The Lawson Beckman
Charitable Trust
The Carole and Geoffrey
Lawson Foundation
The Leathersellers' Company
Charitable Fund
The Leche Trust
Leeds Building Society
Charitable Foundation
The Leverhulme Trust
Lord Leverhulme's Charitable
Trust
The Joseph Levy Charitable
Foundation
The Limbourne Trust
The Linbury Trust
The Linden Charitable Trust
The Charles Lloyd Foundation
Lloyds TSB Foundation for
Northern Ireland
The London Marathon
Charitable Trust
The William and Katherine
Longman Trust
The Ruth and Jack Lunzer
Charitable Trust
Lord and Lady Lurgan Trust
John Lyon's Charity
The Sir Jack Lyons Charitable
Trust
The Mackintosh Foundation
The MacRobert Trust
Ian Mactaggart Trust
Mageni Trust
Man Group plc Charitable
Trust
The Manifold Charitable Trust
W M Mann Foundation
Market Harborough and The
Bowdens Charity
Michael Marks Charitable
Trust

The Marsh Christian Trust
Sir George Martin Trust
John Martin's Charity
The Nancie Massey Charitable
Trust
The Mayfield Valley Arts Trust
The Anthony and Elizabeth
Mellows Charitable
Settlement
Brian Mercer Charitable Trust
The Mercers' Charitable
Foundation
The Merchants' House of
Glasgow
Miles Trust for the Putney and
Roehampton Community
Millennium Stadium Charitable
Trust
The Millward Charitable Trust
The Peter Minet Trust
The Esmé Mitchell Trust
The Modiano Charitable Trust
Monmouthshire County Council
Welsh Church Act Fund
The Monument Trust
The Henry Moore Foundation
The Nigel Moores Family
Charitable Trust
The Peter Moores Foundation
The Morel Charitable Trust
Diana and Allan Morgenthau
Charitable Trust
The John R Murray Charitable
Trust
The Eleni Nakou Foundation
The National Art Collections
Fund
The National Manuscripts
Conservation Trust
Network for Social Change
The Normanby Charitable Trust
The Northwood Charitable
Trust
The Noswad Charity
The Oakdale Trust
The Oakley Charitable Trust
The Ofenheim Charitable Trust
Oglesby Charitable Trust
The Old Broad Street Charity
Trust
Old Possum's Practical Trust
The Oldham Foundation
Orrin Charitable Trust
The Ouseley Trust
The Owen Family Trust
The Pallant Charitable Trust
The James Pantyfedwen
Foundation
The Parthenon Trust
The Pell Charitable Trust
Peltz Trust
The Performing Right Society
Foundation
The Bernard Piggott Trust
The Pilgrim Trust

The Austin and Hope
Pilkington Trust
The Col W W Pilkington Will
Trusts The General Charity
Fund
The Polonsky Foundation
The John Porter Charitable
Trust
The Porter Foundation
The Prince of Wales's
Charitable Foundation
Mr and Mrs J A Pye's
Charitable Settlement
Quercus Trust
The R V W Trust
The Radcliffe Trust
The Ragdoll Foundation
The Peggy Ramsay Foundation
The Sigrid Rausing Trust
The Ravensdale Trust
The Rayne Foundation
The Max Reinhardt Charitable
Trust
The Rhododendron Trust
The Rhondda Cynon Taff
Welsh Church Acts Fund
The Clive Richards Charity
Rix-Thompson-Rothenberg
Foundation
The Robertson Trust
The Rose Foundation
The Roughley Charitable Trust
The Rowlands Trust
Royal Docks Trust (London)
The Jeremy and John Sacher
Charitable Trust
The Michael Harry Sacher
Trust
The Raymond and Beverley
Sackler 1988 Foundation
The Sackler Trust (formerly Dr
Mortimer and Theresa
Sackler Foundation)
The Alan and Babette
Sainsbury Charitable Fund
The Andrew Salvesen
Charitable Trust
Basil Samuel Charitable Trust
Coral Samuel Charitable Trust
The Scarfe Charitable Trust
Schroder Charity Trust
The Frieda Scott Charitable
Trust
The Scottish Arts Council
The Scottish International
Education Trust
The Archie Sherman Charitable
Trust
The R C Sherriff Trust
The Shetland Charitable Trust
The Sickle Foundation
The N Smith Charitable
Settlement
The Martin Smith Foundation
The E C Sosnow Charitable
Trust

Spears-Stutz Charitable Trust
Stevenson Family's Charitable
  Trust
The Summerfield Charitable
  Trust
A P Taylor Trust
The Thistle Trust
Miss S M Tutton Charitable
  Trust
Unity Theatre Trust
The Vardy Foundation
Veneziana Fund
Robert and Felicity Waley-
  Cohen Charitable Trust
Sir Siegmund Warburg's
  Voluntary Settlement
The Ward Blenkinsop Trust
The Waterloo Foundation
The Welton Foundation
The Barbara Whatmore
  Charitable Trust
The Whitaker Charitable Trust
A H and B C Whiteley
  Charitable Trust
The Williams Charitable Trust
The Harold Hyam Wingate
  Foundation
Anona Winn Charitable Trust
The Maurice Wohl Charitable
  Foundation
The Wolfson Foundation
The Woodward Charitable
  Trust
The Fred and Della Worms
  Charitable Trust
The Wyseliot Charitable Trust
The York Children's Trust
Youth Music
The Marjorie and Arnold Ziff
  Charitable Foundation
The Zochonis Charitable Trust

Access to the arts

Creative Scotland
The Robert Gavron Charitable
  Trust
Paul Hamlyn Foundation
The Linbury Trust
Lloyds TSB Foundation for
  Northern Ireland
Miles Trust for the Putney and
  Roehampton Community
The Scottish Arts Council

Amateur and community arts

The Ashden Trust
Calouste Gulbenkian
  Foundation
Colyer-Fergusson Charitable
  Trust
Eden Arts Trust
The Ericson Trust

The Joyce Fletcher Charitable
  Trust
The Robert Gavron Charitable
  Trust
The Horne Foundation
The Joanies Trust
The R J Larg Family Charitable
  Trust
The Joseph Levy Charitable
  Foundation
John Martin's Charity
The Monument Trust
The Oakdale Trust
The James Pantyfedwen
  Foundation
The Ragdoll Foundation
The Scottish Arts Council
The Woodward Charitable
  Trust

Community arts

The Ashden Trust
Colyer-Fergusson Charitable
  Trust
Eden Arts Trust
The Ericson Trust
The Monument Trust
The Scottish Arts Council

Eisteddfodau

The Oakdale Trust
The James Pantyfedwen
  Foundation

Participation in the arts

Eden Arts Trust
The Robert Gavron Charitable
  Trust
The Horne Foundation
The Ragdoll Foundation
The Scottish Arts Council
The Woodward Charitable
  Trust

Art and culture of specific countries

The Baring Foundation
Calouste Gulbenkian
  Foundation
Creative Scotland
The Daiwa Anglo-Japanese
  Foundation
The Great Britain Sasakawa
  Foundation
The Hellenic Foundation
Miles Trust for the Putney and
  Roehampton Community

The Eleni Nakou Foundation
The Scottish Arts Council

Greek art and culture

The Hellenic Foundation

Japanese art and culture

The Daiwa Anglo-Japanese
  Foundation
The Great Britain Sasakawa
  Foundation

Portugese art and culture

Calouste Gulbenkian
  Foundation

Scottish and Gaelic art and culture

Creative Scotland
The Scottish Arts Council

Arts management, policy and planning

The Eric Anker-Petersen
  Charity
Creative Scotland
Esmée Fairbairn Foundation
Miles Trust for the Putney and
  Roehampton Community
The Peter Moores Foundation
The Scottish Arts Council

Combined arts

The Earmark Trust
The Elephant Trust
The Joyce Fletcher Charitable
  Trust
Jerwood Charitable Foundation

Crafts

The Ernest Cook Trust
The Girdlers' Company
  Charitable Trust
The Radcliffe Trust
The Scottish Arts Council

Disability arts

The A B Charitable Trust
Creative Scotland
The Robert Gavron Charitable Trust
Lloyds TSB Foundation for Northern Ireland
Rix-Thompson-Rothenberg Foundation

Libraries

The Francis Coales Charitable Foundation
Colwinston Charitable Trust
The J G Graves Charitable Trust
Paul Hamlyn Foundation
The Headley Trust
The Heritage of London Trust Ltd
The Mercers' Charitable Foundation
The John R Murray Charitable Trust
The Pilgrim Trust

Literature

The Elmgrant Trust
The Joyce Fletcher Charitable Trust
The Follett Trust
Garrick Charitable Trust
Matthew Hodder Charitable Trust
The Limbourne Trust
The John R Murray Charitable Trust
The Scottish Arts Council

Museums and galleries

The Victor Adda Foundation
The Armourers' and Brasiers' Gauntlet Trust
The Aurelius Charitable Trust
The Clore Duffield Foundation
The Francis Coales Charitable Foundation
The Crescent Trust
The Djanogly Foundation
The Duis Charitable Trust
The Sir John Fisher Foundation
The Joyce Fletcher Charitable Trust
J Paul Getty Jr Charitable Trust
The Girdlers' Company Charitable Trust
Golden Charitable Trust
The J G Graves Charitable Trust

The W A Handley Charitable Trust
The Headley Trust
The Heritage of London Trust Ltd
The Idlewild Trust
The Leche Trust
The Linbury Trust
The Manifold Charitable Trust
The Marsh Christian Trust
Sir George Martin Trust
The Mercers' Charitable Foundation
The Henry Moore Foundation
The Peter Moores Foundation
The National Art Collections Fund
The National Manuscripts Conservation Trust
Orrin Charitable Trust
The Pilgrim Trust
The Radcliffe Trust
The Sigrid Rausing Trust
The Raymond and Beverley Sackler 1988 Foundation
Spears-Stutz Charitable Trust
The Summerfield Charitable Trust

Performing arts

Angus Allnatt Charitable Foundation
The Eric Anker-Petersen Charity
The Hervey Benham Charitable Trust
The Britten-Pears Foundation
The Rosemary Bugden Charitable Trust
The Derek Butler Trust
C J Cadbury Charitable Trust
Colwinston Charitable Trust
Creative Scotland
The Cross Trust
The Deakin Charitable Trust
The Delius Trust
The Duis Charitable Trust
Dunard Fund
The Equity Trust Fund
Esmée Fairbairn Foundation
The Family Rich Charities Trust
The John Feeney Charitable Trust
Gerald Finzi Charitable Trust
The Sir John Fisher Foundation
The Joyce Fletcher Charitable Trust
The Fort Foundation
The Gordon Fraser Charitable Trust
The Hugh Fraser Foundation
The Freshgate Trust Foundation
Garrick Charitable Trust

The Gatsby Charitable Foundation
The Gibbs Charitable Trust
The Girdlers' Company Charitable Trust
The Grand Order of Water Rats' Charities Fund
The Harding Trust
The Harris Charitable Trust
The Headley Trust
The Henley Educational Charity
The Hinrichsen Foundation
The Holst Foundation
The Geoffrey C Hughes Charitable Trust
The Idlewild Trust
Jerwood Charitable Foundation
The Boris Karloff Charitable Foundation
The Kathleen Trust
The Michael and Ilse Katz Foundation
The Robert Kiln Charitable Trust
The Kohn Foundation
The Leche Trust
The Limbourne Trust
The Linbury Trust
The Charles Lloyd Foundation
The Mackintosh Foundation
The MacRobert Trust
The Manifold Charitable Trust
W M Mann Foundation
Sir George Martin Trust
John Martin's Charity
The Mayfield Valley Arts Trust
The Mercers' Charitable Foundation
The Merchants' House of Glasgow
Miles Trust for the Putney and Roehampton Community
The Millward Charitable Trust
The Peter Moores Foundation
The Morel Charitable Trust
The Northwood Charitable Trust
The Oakdale Trust
The Ouseley Trust
The Pallant Charitable Trust
The Pell Charitable Trust
The Performing Right Society Foundation
The Bernard Piggott Trust
Mr and Mrs J A Pye's Charitable Settlement
The R V W Trust
The Radcliffe Trust
The Rhondda Cynon Taff Welsh Church Acts Fund
The Rowlands Trust
The Scottish Arts Council
Miss S M Tutton Charitable Trust
The Whitaker Charitable Trust

The Williams Charitable Trust
Youth Music

Dance

The Girdlers' Company
    Charitable Trust
The Scottish Arts Council

Music

Angus Allnatt Charitable
    Foundation
The Hervey Benham Charitable
    Trust
The Britten-Pears Foundation
The Rosemary Bugden
    Charitable Trust
The Derek Butler Trust
C J Cadbury Charitable Trust
The Cross Trust
The Deakin Charitable Trust
The Delius Trust
Dunard Fund
Esmée Fairbairn Foundation
The Family Rich Charities Trust
The John Feeney Charitable
    Trust
Gerald Finzi Charitable Trust
The Joyce Fletcher Charitable
    Trust
The Hugh Fraser Foundation
The Freshgate Trust
    Foundation
The Gatsby Charitable
    Foundation
The Harding Trust
The Harris Charitable Trust
The Hinrichsen Foundation
The Holst Foundation
The Kathleen Trust
The Michael and Ilse Katz
    Foundation
The Robert Kiln Charitable
    Trust
The Kohn Foundation
The Leche Trust
The Charles Lloyd Foundation
The Mackintosh Foundation
The MacRobert Trust
The Manifold Charitable Trust
W M Mann Foundation
Sir George Martin Trust
John Martin's Charity
The Mayfield Valley Arts Trust
The Peter Moores Foundation
The Oakdale Trust
The Ouseley Trust
The Pallant Charitable Trust
The Performing Right Society
    Foundation
The R V W Trust
The Radcliffe Trust
The Rhondda Cynon Taff
    Welsh Church Acts Fund

The Rowlands Trust
The Scottish Arts Council
Miss S M Tutton Charitable
    Trust
The Whitaker Charitable Trust
Youth Music

Theatre

The Eric Anker-Petersen
    Charity
The Cross Trust
The Equity Trust Fund
Esmée Fairbairn Foundation
The Gatsby Charitable
    Foundation
The Gibbs Charitable Trust
The Grand Order of Water
    Rats' Charities Fund
The Headley Trust
The Leche Trust
The Mackintosh Foundation
The Peter Moores Foundation
The Morel Charitable Trust
The Bernard Piggott Trust
The Scottish Arts Council
The Williams Charitable Trust

Visual arts

The Ashley Family Foundation
    (formerly The Laura Ashley
    Foundation)
Colwinston Charitable Trust
Creative Scotland
The Duis Charitable Trust
Dunard Fund
The Elephant Trust
The Joyce Fletcher Charitable
    Trust
The Gordon Fraser Charitable
    Trust
Jerwood Charitable Foundation
John Martin's Charity
Brian Mercer Charitable Trust
The Mercers' Charitable
    Foundation
The Henry Moore Foundation
The Peter Moores Foundation
The National Art Collections
    Fund
The Max Reinhardt Charitable
    Trust
The Scottish Arts Council
Robert and Felicity Waley-
    Cohen Charitable Trust

Fine art

The Mercers' Charitable
    Foundation
The Henry Moore Foundation
The Peter Moores Foundation

The National Art Collections
    Fund
The Max Reinhardt Charitable
    Trust
Robert and Felicity Waley-
    Cohen Charitable Trust

Public art/ Sculpture

The Henry Moore Foundation

Heritage and the built environment

The Alice Trust
Allchurches Trust Ltd
The Architectural Heritage
Fund
The Arthur Ronald Dyer
Charitable Trust
The Ove Arup Foundation
A J H Ashby Will Trust
The Association of Friends of
Essex Churches
The Baird Trust
The Barcapel Foundation
The Bedfordshire and
Hertfordshire Historic
Churches Trust
The Bellahouston Bequest
Fund
The Hervey Benham Charitable
Trust
Birmingham International
Airport Community Trust
T B H Brunner's Charitable
Settlement
The Buckinghamshire Historic
Churches Trust
The Arnold Burton 1998
Charitable Trust
The Cambridgeshire Historic
Churches Trust
The Carpenters' Company
Charitable Trust
Stephen Clark 1957
Charitable Trust
The Francis Coales Charitable
Foundation
Colyer-Fergusson Charitable
Trust
Country Houses Foundation
The Helen and Geoffrey De
Freitas Charitable Trust
The Derbyshire Churches and
Chapels Preservation Trust
The Devon Historic Churches
Trust
The Dorset Historic Churches
Trust
The Drapers' Charitable Fund
The Dulverton Trust
The Houghton Dunn Charitable
Trust
The Gilbert and Eileen Edgar
Foundation
The Edinburgh Trust, No 2
Account
The Ellis Campbell Foundation
The Elmgrant Trust
The Essex Heritage Trust
The Alan Evans Memorial Trust
Esmée Fairbairn Foundation
The Fairway Trust
The February Foundation
Fife Council/Common Good
Funds and Trusts

Fisherbeck Charitable Trust
The Fishmongers' Company's
Charitable Trust
Marc Fitch Fund
The Jill Franklin Trust
The Freshgate Trust
Foundation
The Friends of Kent Churches
The Frognal Trust
The Galanthus Trust
The Gannochy Trust
The Samuel Gardner Memorial
Trust
Gatwick Airport Community
Trust
J Paul Getty Jr Charitable Trust
The Girdlers' Company
Charitable Trust
The Glass-House Trust
The Gloucestershire Historic
Churches Trust
The Goldsmiths' Company
Charity
The Golsoncott Foundation
The Gosling Foundation
Limited
The Wiles Greenworld
Charitable Trust
The Greys Charitable Trust
The Grocers' Charity
The Hadrian Trust
The Hampshire and Islands
Historic Churches Trust
The W A Handley Charitable
Trust
The Kenneth Hargreaves
Charitable Trust
The Dorothy Hay-Bolton
Charitable Trust
The Charles Hayward
Foundation
The Headley Trust
The Hemby Trust
The Herefordshire Historic
Churches Trust
The Heritage of London Trust
Ltd
The Holbeck Charitable Trust
The Idlewild Trust
The Iliffe Family Charitable
Trust
The Inland Waterways
Association
The Johnnie Johnson Trust
Laslett's (Hinton) Charity
The Raymond and Blanche
Lawson Charitable Trust
The Leche Trust
Leeds Building Society
Charitable Foundation
Leicestershire Historic
Churches Trust
Limoges Charitable Trust
The Linbury Trust
The Lincolnshire Old Churches
Trust

The Charles Lloyd Foundation
Manchester Airport Community
Trust Fund
The Manifold Charitable Trust
Market Harborough and The
Bowdens Charity
The Marsh Christian Trust
Marshall's Charity
The Mears Foundation
The Anthony and Elizabeth
Mellows Charitable
Settlement
The Mercers' Charitable
Foundation
The Metropolitan Drinking
Fountain and Cattle Trough
Association
Gerald Micklem Charitable
Trust
Miles Trust for the Putney and
Roehampton Community
The Esmé Mitchell Trust
Monmouthshire County Council
Welsh Church Act Fund
The Monument Trust
The Peter Moores Foundation
The National Churches Trust
(formerly the Historic
Churches Preservation
Trust with the Incorporated
Church Building Society)
The Normanby Charitable Trust
The Northern Rock Foundation
The Northumbria Historic
Churches Trust
The Norwich Historic Churches
Trust Ltd
The Nottinghamshire Historic
Churches Trust
The Owen Family Trust
The James Pantyfedwen
Foundation
Miss M E Swinton Paterson's
Charitable Trust
The Jack Patston Charitable
Trust
The Pilgrim Trust
The Prince of Wales's
Charitable Foundation
The Rhondda Cynon Taff
Welsh Church Acts Fund
The Robertson Trust
The Rock Solid Trust
Mrs L D Rope Third Charitable
Settlement
The Roughley Charitable Trust
Royal Docks Trust (London)
The J S and E C Rymer
Charitable Trust
The Peter Samuel Charitable
Trust
Schroder Charity Trust
The Scottish Arts Council
The Shetland Charitable Trust
The Stanley Smith UK
Horticultural Trust

Friends of Somerset Churches
and Chapels
St Andrew's Conservation
Trust
Stevenson Family's Charitable
Trust
Peter Stormonth Darling
Charitable Trust
The Suffolk Historic Churches
Trust
The Surrey Historic Buildings
Trust Ltd
The Sussex Historic Churches
Trust
The Connie and Albert Taylor
Charitable Trust
Vale of Glamorgan – Welsh
Church Fund
Veneziana Fund
The John Warren Foundation
The Waterways Trust
Welsh Church Fund Dyfed
area (Carmarthenshire,
Ceredigion and
Pembrokeshire)
The Colonel W H Whitbread
Charitable Trust
The Wolfson Foundation
The Worcestershire and
Dudley Historic Churches
Trust
The Yorkshire Dales
Millennium Trust
The Yorkshire Historic
Churches Trust
The Marjorie and Arnold Ziff
Charitable Foundation

Arts and the envrionment

The Carpenters' Company
Charitable Trust
The Samuel Gardner Memorial
Trust
J Paul Getty Jr Charitable Trust
The Glass-House Trust
The Headley Trust
The Heritage of London Trust
Ltd
Leeds Building Society
Charitable Foundation
Manchester Airport Community
Trust Fund
The Metropolitan Drinking
Fountain and Cattle Trough
Association
Monmouthshire County Council
Welsh Church Act Fund
The Monument Trust
The Scottish Arts Council
The Shetland Charitable Trust
The Stanley Smith UK
Horticultural Trust

The Marjorie and Arnold Ziff
Charitable Foundation

Architecture

The Glass-House Trust
The Heritage of London Trust
Ltd
Monmouthshire County Council
Welsh Church Act Fund

Landscape

The Samuel Gardner Memorial
Trust
J Paul Getty Jr Charitable Trust
Manchester Airport Community
Trust Fund
The Metropolitan Drinking
Fountain and Cattle Trough
Association
The Stanley Smith UK
Horticultural Trust
The Marjorie and Arnold Ziff
Charitable Foundation

Heritage

The Architectural Heritage
Fund
A J H Ashby Will Trust
The Hervey Benham Charitable
Trust
Birmingham International
Airport Community Trust
T B H Brunner's Charitable
Settlement
The Arnold Burton 1998
Charitable Trust
The Carpenters' Company
Charitable Trust
The Francis Coales Charitable
Foundation
The Helen and Geoffrey De
Freitas Charitable Trust
The Houghton Dunn Charitable
Trust
The Gilbert and Eileen Edgar
Foundation
The Essex Heritage Trust
Esmée Fairbairn Foundation
The Fairway Trust
The Fishmongers' Company's
Charitable Trust
Marc Fitch Fund
The Freshgate Trust
Foundation
The Frognal Trust
The Samuel Gardner Memorial
Trust
J Paul Getty Jr Charitable Trust
The Goldsmiths' Company
Charity

The Gosling Foundation
Limited
The Grocers' Charity
The W A Handley Charitable
Trust
The Headley Trust
The Heritage of London Trust
Ltd
Leeds Building Society
Charitable Foundation
The Linbury Trust
The Manifold Charitable Trust
Market Harborough and The
Bowdens Charity
The Marsh Christian Trust
The Mears Foundation
The Anthony and Elizabeth
Mellows Charitable
Settlement
The Mercers' Charitable
Foundation
Gerald Micklem Charitable
Trust
Miles Trust for the Putney and
Roehampton Community
The Esmé Mitchell Trust
Monmouthshire County Council
Welsh Church Act Fund
The Monument Trust
The Peter Moores Foundation
The Normanby Charitable Trust
The Northern Rock Foundation
The Owen Family Trust
Miss M E Swinton Paterson's
Charitable Trust
The Pilgrim Trust
The Robertson Trust
Mrs L D Rope Third Charitable
Settlement
The Peter Samuel Charitable
Trust
Peter Stormonth Darling
Charitable Trust
The Surrey Historic Buildings
Trust Ltd
The Connie and Albert Taylor
Charitable Trust
Veneziana Fund
The Wolfson Foundation

Maintenance and preservation of buildings

The Alice Trust
Allchurches Trust Ltd
The Architectural Heritage
Fund
The Association of Friends of
Essex Churches
The Baird Trust
The Bedfordshire and
Hertfordshire Historic
Churches Trust

The Bellahouston Bequest
Fund

The Buckinghamshire Historic
Churches Trust

The Cambridgeshire Historic
Churches Trust

The Carpenters' Company
Charitable Trust

Stephen Clark 1957
Charitable Trust

The Francis Coales Charitable
Foundation

Colyer-Fergusson Charitable
Trust

The Derbyshire Churches and
Chapels Preservation Trust

The Devon Historic Churches
Trust

The Dorset Historic Churches
Trust

The Dulverton Trust

The Edinburgh Trust, No 2
Account

The Ellis Campbell Foundation

The Essex Heritage Trust

The Alan Evans Memorial Trust

Esmée Fairbairn Foundation

The Fairway Trust

Fife Council/Common Good
Funds and Trusts

The Fishmongers' Company's
Charitable Trust

The Jill Franklin Trust

The Friends of Kent Churches

The Girdlers' Company
Charitable Trust

The Gloucestershire Historic
Churches Trust

The Greys Charitable Trust

The Grocers' Charity

The Hadrian Trust

The Hampshire and Islands
Historic Churches Trust

The Dorothy Hay-Bolton
Charitable Trust

The Headley Trust

The Hemby Trust

The Herefordshire Historic
Churches Trust

The Heritage of London Trust
Ltd

The Idlewild Trust

Laslett's (Hinton) Charity

The Raymond and Blanche
Lawson Charitable Trust

Leicestershire Historic
Churches Trust

The Lincolnshire Old Churches
Trust

The Charles Lloyd Foundation

Manchester Airport Community
Trust Fund

The Manifold Charitable Trust

Marshall's Charity

Miles Trust for the Putney and
Roehampton Community

Monmouthshire County Council
Welsh Church Act Fund

The Monument Trust

The National Churches Trust
(formerly the Historic
Churches Preservation
Trust with the Incorporated
Church Building Society)

The Northumbria Historic
Churches Trust

The Norwich Historic Churches
Trust Ltd

The Nottinghamshire Historic
Churches Trust

The James Pantyfedwen
Foundation

The Jack Patston Charitable
Trust

The Pilgrim Trust

The Prince of Wales's
Charitable Foundation

The Rhondda Cynon Taff
Welsh Church Acts Fund

The Rock Solid Trust

Royal Docks Trust (London)

Friends of Somerset Churches
and Chapels

The Suffolk Historic Churches
Trust

The Surrey Historic Buildings
Trust Ltd

The Sussex Historic Churches
Trust

The Connie and Albert Taylor
Charitable Trust

Vale of Glamorgan – Welsh
Church Fund

The John Warren Foundation

Welsh Church Fund Dyfed
area (Carmarthenshire,
Ceredigion and
Pembrokeshire)

The Worcestershire and
Dudley Historic Churches
Trust

The Yorkshire Historic
Churches Trust

Religious buildings

Allchurches Trust Ltd

The Architectural Heritage
Fund

The Association of Friends of
Essex Churches

The Bedfordshire and
Hertfordshire Historic
Churches Trust

The Bellahouston Bequest
Fund

The Buckinghamshire Historic
Churches Trust

The Cambridgeshire Historic
Churches Trust

Stephen Clark 1957
Charitable Trust

The Francis Coales Charitable
Foundation

Colyer-Fergusson Charitable
Trust

The Derbyshire Churches and
Chapels Preservation Trust

The Devon Historic Churches
Trust

The Dorset Historic Churches
Trust

The Alan Evans Memorial Trust

The Fishmongers' Company's
Charitable Trust

The Jill Franklin Trust

The Friends of Kent Churches

The Girdlers' Company
Charitable Trust

The Gloucestershire Historic
Churches Trust

The Grocers' Charity

The Hadrian Trust

The Hampshire and Islands
Historic Churches Trust

The Dorothy Hay-Bolton
Charitable Trust

The Headley Trust

The Hemby Trust

The Herefordshire Historic
Churches Trust

The Heritage of London Trust
Ltd

Laslett's (Hinton) Charity

Leicestershire Historic
Churches Trust

The Lincolnshire Old Churches
Trust

The Charles Lloyd Foundation

The Manifold Charitable Trust

Marshall's Charity

Miles Trust for the Putney and
Roehampton Community

Monmouthshire County Council
Welsh Church Act Fund

The Monument Trust

The National Churches Trust
(formerly the Historic
Churches Preservation
Trust with the Incorporated
Church Building Society)

The Northumbria Historic
Churches Trust

The Norwich Historic Churches
Trust Ltd

The Nottinghamshire Historic
Churches Trust

The James Pantyfedwen
Foundation

The Jack Patston Charitable
Trust

The Pilgrim Trust

The Prince of Wales's
Charitable Foundation

The Rhondda Cynon Taff
Welsh Church Acts Fund

The Rock Solid Trust

Friends of Somerset Churches
and Chapels
The Suffolk Historic Churches
Trust
The Sussex Historic Churches
Trust
Vale of Glamorgan – Welsh
Church Fund
The John Warren Foundation
Welsh Church Fund Dyfed
area (Carmarthenshire,
Ceredigion and
Pembrokeshire)
The Worcestershire and
Dudley Historic Churches
Trust
The Yorkshire Historic
Churches Trust

Restoration and maintenance of inland waterways

The Carpenters' Company
Charitable Trust
The Inland Waterways
Association
Leeds Building Society
Charitable Foundation
Gerald Micklem Charitable
Trust
The Waterways Trust

Built environment – education and research

The Ove Arup Foundation
The Carpenters' Company
Charitable Trust
The Gannochy Trust
Leeds Building Society
Charitable Foundation

Humanities

The Aurelius Charitable Trust
British Institute at Ankara
The Barrow Cadbury Trust and
the Barrow Cadbury Fund
Calouste Gulbenkian
Foundation
The Cemlyn-Jones Trust
The Francis Coales Charitable
Foundation
The Denise Cohen Charitable
Trust
The Daiwa Anglo-Japanese
Foundation
The Edinburgh Trust, No 2
Account
The Elmgrant Trust
Marc Fitch Fund
The Golsoncott Foundation
The Great Britain Sasakawa
Foundation
The Inlight Trust
The Robert Kiln Charitable
Trust
The Neil Kreitman Foundation
The Lawson Beckman
Charitable Trust
Leeds Building Society
Charitable Foundation
The Mount Everest Foundation
The Kitty and Daniel Nabarro
Charitable Trust
The Eleni Nakou Foundation
Peltz Trust
Polden-Puckham Charitable
Foundation
The Sir Cliff Richard Charitable
Trust
The Roman Research Trust
Mrs L D Rope Third Charitable
Settlement
The Rothley Trust
The Joseph Rowntree
Charitable Trust
The Scouloudi Foundation
The Tinsley Foundation
The Westcroft Trust
The W Wing Yip and Brothers
Foundation
The York Children's Trust

Archaeology

Marc Fitch Fund
The Robert Kiln Charitable
Trust
The Roman Research Trust

History

The Cemlyn-Jones Trust
The Francis Coales Charitable
Foundation
Marc Fitch Fund

The Neil Kreitman Foundation
The Roman Research Trust
The Scouloudi Foundation

International understanding

The Barrow Cadbury Trust and
the Barrow Cadbury Fund
Calouste Gulbenkian
Foundation
The Daiwa Anglo-Japanese
Foundation
The Edinburgh Trust, No 2
Account
The Great Britain Sasakawa
Foundation
The Mount Everest Foundation
The Kitty and Daniel Nabarro
Charitable Trust
The Eleni Nakou Foundation
The Rothley Trust
The Tinsley Foundation
The Westcroft Trust
The W Wing Yip and Brothers
Foundation
The York Children's Trust

Philosophy and ethics

The Inlight Trust
Polden-Puckham Charitable
Foundation
The Sir Cliff Richard Charitable
Trust
Mrs L D Rope Third Charitable
Settlement
The Joseph Rowntree
Charitable Trust

Media and communications

The Eric Anker-Petersen Charity
The Follett Trust
Paul Hamlyn Foundation
The David Lean Foundation
Leeds Building Society Charitable Foundation
Nominet Charitable Foundation
Unity Theatre Trust

Recreation and sport

Access Sport
Angus Allnatt Charitable Foundation
Arsenal Charitable Trust
A J H Ashby Will Trust
The John Beckwith Charitable Trust
The Bedford Charity (The Harpur Trust)
The Bellahouston Bequest Fund
The Big Lottery Fund
Birmingham International Airport Community Trust
Blackheart Foundation (UK) Limited
BOOST Charitable Trust
The Carnegie Dunfermline Trust
Carter's Educational Foundation
The Chipping Sodbury Town Lands Charity
The Robert Clutterbuck Charitable Trust
The Bernard Coleman Charitable Trust
The Congleton Inclosure Trust
The D J H Currie Memorial Trust
The Hamilton Davies Trust
The Gilbert and Eileen Edgar Foundation
The Vernon N Ely Charitable Trust
The English Schools' Football Association
Samuel William Farmer Trust
The February Foundation
The John Feeney Charitable Trust
Fife Council/Common Good Funds and Trusts
The Football Association National Sports Centre Trust
The Football Association Youth Trust
The Football Foundation
The Joseph Strong Frazer Trust
The Thomas Freke and Lady Norton Charity
Gatwick Airport Community Trust
The Girdlers' Company Charitable Trust
The Granada Foundation
The Grange Farm Centre Trust
The J G Graves Charitable Trust
The Hale Trust
Robert Hall Charity
William Harding's Charity

The Kenneth Hargreaves Charitable Trust
The Peter Harrison Foundation
The Dorothy Hay-Bolton Charitable Trust
The Henley Educational Charity
The Heritage of London Trust Ltd
Huntingdon Freemen's Charity
The Kalou Foundation
The Kelly Family Charitable Trust
Lancashire Environmental Fund
Leeds Building Society Charitable Foundation
The Joseph Levy Charitable Foundation
The Lister Charitable Trust
The George John and Sheilah Livanos Charitable Trust
The London Marathon Charitable Trust
The Lord's Taverners
Lady Lumley's Educational Foundation
John Lyon's Charity
Manchester Airport Community Trust Fund
W M Mann Foundation
The Mears Foundation
The Merchant Venturers' Charity
Gerald Micklem Charitable Trust
Millennium Stadium Charitable Trust
The Peter Minet Trust
Monmouthshire County Council Welsh Church Act Fund
The Morel Charitable Trust
The Stanley Morrison Charitable Trust
The Mugdock Children's Trust
The Northern Rock Foundation
The Norwich Church of England Young Men's Society
The Pedmore Sporting Club Trust Fund
The Premier League Charitable Fund
PSA Peugeot Citroen Charity Trust
The Puri Foundation
Mr and Mrs J A Pye's Charitable Settlement
The Richmond Parish Lands Charity
The Robertson Trust
The Rowing Foundation
Royal Docks Trust (London)
The Saddlers' Company Charitable Fund
Scottish Coal Industry Special Welfare Fund
The Searle Charitable Trust

The Shetland Charitable Trust
The Shipwrights' Company
   Charitable Fund
The Martin Smith Foundation
The Stewards' Charitable Trust
Peter Stormonth Darling
   Charitable Trust
The Connie and Albert Taylor
   Charitable Trust
The Thompson Family
   Charitable Trust
The Howard Watson Symington
   Memorial Charity
The Winton Charitable
   Foundation
Miss E B Wrightson's
   Charitable Settlement
The York Children's Trust

Parks and open spaces

The John Feeney Charitable
   Trust
The J G Graves Charitable
   Trust
The Heritage of London Trust
   Ltd
The Merchant Venturers'
   Charity

Recreation facilities

The Carnegie Dunfermline
   Trust
Carter's Educational
   Foundation
The Chipping Sodbury Town
   Lands Charity
Samuel William Farmer Trust
The Football Association
   National Sports Centre
   Trust
The Thomas Freke and Lady
   Norton Charity
The Granada Foundation
The Hale Trust
William Harding's Charity
The Peter Harrison Foundation
Lancashire Environmental
   Fund
The Joseph Levy Charitable
   Foundation
Lady Lumley's Educational
   Foundation
The Northern Rock Foundation

Sports for people with a disability

BOOST Charitable Trust
The Football Association
   National Sports Centre
   Trust
The Kenneth Hargreaves
   Charitable Trust
The Peter Harrison Foundation
The Dorothy Hay-Bolton
   Charitable Trust
The Henley Educational Charity
The Joseph Levy Charitable
   Foundation
The London Marathon
   Charitable Trust
The Lord's Taverners
Gerald Micklem Charitable
   Trust
Mr and Mrs J A Pye's
   Charitable Settlement
The Rowing Foundation

Sports

Access Sport
Angus Allnatt Charitable
   Foundation
A J H Ashby Will Trust
The John Beckwith Charitable
   Trust
BOOST Charitable Trust
The D J H Currie Memorial
   Trust
The Vernon N Ely Charitable
   Trust
The English Schools' Football
   Association
The Football Association
   National Sports Centre
   Trust
The Football Association Youth
   Trust
The Football Foundation
The Peter Harrison Foundation
The Henley Educational Charity
The Joseph Levy Charitable
   Foundation
The George John and Sheilah
   Livanos Charitable Trust
The London Marathon
   Charitable Trust
The Lord's Taverners
W M Mann Foundation
Millennium Stadium Charitable
   Trust
The Peter Minet Trust
The Richmond Parish Lands
   Charity
The Rowing Foundation
The Saddlers' Company
   Charitable Fund
The Searle Charitable Trust
The Shipwrights' Company
   Charitable Fund

The Martin Smith Foundation
The Stewards' Charitable Trust
Peter Stormonth Darling
   Charitable Trust
The Thompson Family
   Charitable Trust
The York Children's Trust

Development, housing and employment

The ACT Foundation
The AIM Foundation
The Ajahma Charitable Trust
The Ashden Trust
The Ashley Family Foundation (formerly The Laura Ashley Foundation)
The BAA Communities Trust
The Balmore Trust
The Big Lottery Fund
Birmingham International Airport Community Trust
The Boots Charitable Trust
The Oliver Borthwick Memorial Trust
R S Brownless Charitable Trust
The Buckinghamshire Foundation
Henry T and Lucy B Cadbury Charitable Trust
The Cadbury Foundation
The Barrow Cadbury Trust and the Barrow Cadbury Fund
CAFOD (Catholic Agency for Overseas Development)
Calouste Gulbenkian Foundation
Calypso Browning Trust
The Chelsea Building Society Charitable Foundation
The Church and Community Fund
The Church Urban Fund
The Clothworkers' Foundation
The Coalfields Regeneration Trust
The Community Foundation for Northern Ireland
The Consolidated Charities for the Infirm Merchant Taylors' Company
The Cooks Charity
The Cotton Industry War Memorial Trust
Cumbria Community Foundation
Baron Davenport's Charity
The Helen and Geoffrey De Freitas Charitable Trust
The Digbeth Trust
The Drapers' Charitable Fund
The Duis Charitable Trust
The Dulverton Trust
The Dyers' Company Charitable Trust
The Edith Maud Ellis 1985 Charitable Trust
The Emmandjay Charitable Trust
Esmée Fairbairn Foundation

Allan and Nesta Ferguson Charitable Settlement
The Sir John Fisher Foundation
The Football Association National Sports Centre Trust
The Football Foundation
The Oliver Ford Charitable Trust
The Donald Forrester Trust
Sydney E Franklin Deceased's New Second Charity
Friends Provident Charitable Foundation
Worshipful Company of Furniture Makers Charitable Fund
The Gatsby Charitable Foundation
Gatwick Airport Community Trust
Jacqueline and Michael Gee Charitable Trust
J Paul Getty Jr Charitable Trust
The Girdlers' Company Charitable Trust
The Glass-House Trust
Gloucestershire Community Foundation
Grand Charitable Trust of the Order of Women Freemasons
The Grocers' Charity
The Hadfield Trust
Hampton Fuel Allotment Charity
The W A Handley Charitable Trust
The Harbour Foundation
The Haymills Charitable Trust
The Charles Hayward Foundation
The Hemby Trust
Matthew Hodder Charitable Trust
The Horne Trust
The Worshipful Company of Horners' Charitable Trusts
HTA Sheba Foundation UK Humanitarian and Charitable One Trust (HACOT)
The Hyde Charitable Trust – Youth Plus
Impetus Trust
The Irish Youth Foundation (UK) Ltd (incorporating The Lawlor Foundation)
Isle of Dogs Community Foundation
The Johnson Foundation
Jusaca Charitable Trust
The Peter Kershaw Trust
The Mary Kinross Charitable Trust
The Heinz, Anna and Carol Kroch Foundation

LandAid Charitable Trust
The Allen Lane Foundation
Laslett's (Hinton) Charity
The Leathersellers' Company Charitable Fund
Leeds Building Society Charitable Foundation
Liberum Foundation
Lindenleaf Charitable Trust
Liverpool Sailors' Home Trust
Lloyds TSB Foundation for Northern Ireland
The London Community Foundation (formerly Capital Community Foundation)
The Lotus Foundation
C F Lunoe Trust Fund
John Lyon's Charity
Magdalen Hospital Trust
The Charlotte Marshall Charitable Trust
The Mathew Trust
Matliwala Family Charitable Trust
The Mears Foundation
The Merchant Venturers' Charity
The Merchants' House of Glasgow
Community Foundation for Merseyside
Miles Trust for the Putney and Roehampton Community
The Millfield House Foundation
Monmouthshire County Council Welsh Church Act Fund
The Monument Trust
John Moores Foundation
Peter John Murray Trust (PJM Trust)
The Kitty and Daniel Nabarro Charitable Trust
The Nadezhda Charitable Trust
The Nationwide Foundation
The Worshipful Company of Needlemakers' Charitable Fund
The Noon Foundation
The Norda Trust
North West London Community Foundation
The Northern Rock Foundation
The Norton Foundation
The Nottinghamshire Miners' Welfare Trust Fund
Novi Most International
The Oldham Foundation
The Pervez Musharraf Foundation
The Phillips Charitable Trust
The Pilgrim Trust
The Worshipful Company of Plaisterers Charitable Trust
Prairie Trust
The Premier League Charitable Fund

The Puebla Charitable Trust
Mr and Mrs J A Pye's
  Charitable Settlement
Ranworth Trust
The Sigrid Rausing Trust
The Rayne Foundation
The Robertson Trust
Mrs L D Rope Third Charitable
  Settlement
The Joseph Rowntree
  Charitable Trust
Royal Docks Trust (London)
The Saddlers' Company
  Charitable Fund
The Scottish Community
  Foundation
The Scottish International
  Education Trust
The Searle Charitable Trust
The Shanti Charitable Trust
The Sheldon Trust
Dr Richard Solomon's
  Charitable Trust
The Spero Foundation
The Stokenchurch Educational
  Charity
Sutton Coldfield Municipal
  Charities
The Hugh and Ruby Sykes
  Charitable Trust
Ulster Garden Villages Ltd
The Nigel Vinson Charitable
  Trust
The Scurrah Wainwright Charity
Wakeham Trust
Wales Council for Voluntary
  Action
War on Want
The Waterloo Foundation
The Wixamtree Trust
The Wood Family Trust
Woodlands Trust

Community and economic development

The AIM Foundation
The Ashden Trust
The Ashley Family Foundation
  (formerly The Laura Ashley
  Foundation)
The BAA Communities Trust
The Balmore Trust
The Big Lottery Fund
Birmingham International
  Airport Community Trust
The Boots Charitable Trust
The Buckinghamshire
  Foundation
The Cadbury Foundation
The Barrow Cadbury Trust and
  the Barrow Cadbury Fund
Calouste Gulbenkian
  Foundation

The Church and Community
  Fund
The Church Urban Fund
The Coalfields Regeneration
  Trust
The Community Foundation for
  Northern Ireland
Cumbria Community
  Foundation
The Helen and Geoffrey De
  Freitas Charitable Trust
The Digbeth Trust
The Dulverton Trust
The Edith Maud Ellis 1985
  Charitable Trust
Esmée Fairbairn Foundation
Allan and Nesta Ferguson
  Charitable Settlement
The Football Association
  National Sports Centre
  Trust
The Football Foundation
Sydney E Franklin Deceased's
  New Second Charity
Friends Provident Charitable
  Foundation
The Gatsby Charitable
  Foundation
Gatwick Airport Community
  Trust
J Paul Getty Jr Charitable Trust
The Glass-House Trust
Gloucestershire Community
  Foundation
The Grocers' Charity
The Hadfield Trust
The Harbour Foundation
The Haymills Charitable Trust
HTA Sheba Foundation UK
The Hyde Charitable Trust –
  Youth Plus
Isle of Dogs Community
  Foundation
The Johnson Foundation
The Mary Kinross Charitable
  Trust
LandAid Charitable Trust
The Allen Lane Foundation
Leeds Building Society
  Charitable Foundation
Lindenleaf Charitable Trust
The London Community
  Foundation (formerly Capital
  Community Foundation)
The Lotus Foundation
The Mathew Trust
Matliwala Family Charitable
  Trust
The Merchant Venturers'
  Charity
Community Foundation for
  Merseyside
Miles Trust for the Putney and
  Roehampton Community
The Millfield House Foundation

Monmouthshire County Council
  Welsh Church Act Fund
John Moores Foundation
The Kitty and Daniel Nabarro
  Charitable Trust
The Noon Foundation
The Norda Trust
North West London Community
  Foundation
The Northern Rock Foundation
Novi Most International
The Pervez Musharraf
  Foundation
Prairie Trust
The Premier League Charitable
  Fund
The Puebla Charitable Trust
Ranworth Trust
The Sigrid Rausing Trust
The Robertson Trust
The Joseph Rowntree
  Charitable Trust
Royal Docks Trust (London)
The Scottish Community
  Foundation
The Scottish International
  Education Trust
The Shanti Charitable Trust
The Sheldon Trust
Dr Richard Solomon's
  Charitable Trust
The Spero Foundation
The Stokenchurch Educational
  Charity
Sutton Coldfield Municipal
  Charities
The Hugh and Ruby Sykes
  Charitable Trust
The Scurrah Wainwright Charity
Wakeham Trust
Wales Council for Voluntary
  Action
The Wixamtree Trust
Woodlands Trust

Housing

The Oliver Borthwick Memorial
  Trust
Henry T and Lucy B Cadbury
  Charitable Trust
Calypso Browning Trust
The Chelsea Building Society
  Charitable Foundation
The Clothworkers' Foundation
The Consolidated Charities for
  the Infirm Merchant
  Taylors' Company
Baron Davenport's Charity
The Duis Charitable Trust
The Emmandjay Charitable
  Trust
The Oliver Ford Charitable
  Trust
The Girdlers' Company
  Charitable Trust

The Glass-House Trust
Hampton Fuel Allotment
   Charity
The W A Handley Charitable
   Trust
The Charles Hayward
   Foundation
The Hemby Trust
The Horne Trust
The Hyde Charitable Trust –
   Youth Plus
The Irish Youth Foundation
   (UK) Ltd (incorporating The
   Lawlor Foundation)
Jusaca Charitable Trust
The Peter Kershaw Trust
The Heinz, Anna and Carol
   Kroch Foundation
LandAid Charitable Trust
Laslett's (Hinton) Charity
Leeds Building Society
   Charitable Foundation
Lloyds TSB Foundation for
   Northern Ireland
John Lyon's Charity
Magdalen Hospital Trust
The Charlotte Marshall
   Charitable Trust
The Monument Trust
The Nadezhda Charitable Trust
The Nationwide Foundation
The Norton Foundation
The Oldham Foundation
The Pilgrim Trust
Mr and Mrs J A Pye's
   Charitable Settlement
The Rayne Foundation
Mrs L D Rope Third Charitable
   Settlement
Ulster Garden Villages Ltd
Woodlands Trust

Specific industries

The Clothworkers' Foundation
The Cooks Charity
The Cotton Industry War
   Memorial Trust
Cumbria Community
   Foundation
The Drapers' Charitable Fund
The Dyers' Company
   Charitable Trust
The Sir John Fisher Foundation
The Oliver Ford Charitable
   Trust
Worshipful Company of
   Furniture Makers Charitable
   Fund
The W A Handley Charitable
   Trust
Matthew Hodder Charitable
   Trust
The Worshipful Company of
   Horners' Charitable Trusts

The Leathersellers' Company
   Charitable Fund
Liverpool Sailors' Home Trust
C F Lunoe Trust Fund
The Merchants' House of
   Glasgow
The Worshipful Company of
   Needlemakers' Charitable
   Fund
The Phillips Charitable Trust
The Worshipful Company of
   Plaisterers Charitable Trust
The Saddlers' Company
   Charitable Fund
The Searle Charitable Trust

Education and training

The 19
   Trus
The Al
   Tr
The Aberdeenshire
   Trust Scheme
The Acacia Charitable Trust
The Sylvia Adams Charitable
   Trust
AF Trust Company
Aldgate and All Hallows'
   Barking Exhibition
   Foundation
All Saints Educational Trust
The Alliance Family Foundation
Angus Allnatt Charitable
   Foundation
The Pat Allsop Charitable Trust
Almondsbury Charity
The Altajir Trust
The Ammco Trust
Viscount Amory's Charitable
   Trust
The AMW Charitable Trust
Anglo American Group
   Foundation
Anguish's Educational
   Foundation
The Apax Foundation
Ambrose and Ann Appelbe
   Trust
The John Armitage Charitable
   Trust
The Armourers' and Brasiers'
   Gauntlet Trust
The Arts Council of Wales
A J H Ashby Will Trust
The Norman C Ashton
   Foundation
The Association of Colleges
   Charitable Trust
The Astor of Hever Trust
The Lord Austin Trust
The BAA Communities Trust
The Scott Bader
   Commonwealth Ltd
The Baily Thomas Charitable
   Fund
The Roy and Pixie Baker
   Charitable Trust
The Balcombe Charitable Trust
The George Balint Charitable
   Trust
The Bamford Charitable
   Foundation
The Banbury Charities
The Charity of William Barrow
BCH Trust
The Beaufort House Trust
   Limited
The Becketts and Sargeants
   Educational Foundation

...d Charity (The
...ur Trust)
...it Trust
Bellahouston Bequest
Fund
The Ruth Berkowitz Charitable
Trust
The Bestway Foundation
BibleLands
The Big Lottery Fund
Blackheart Foundation (UK)
Limited
The Blanchminster Trust
Blatchington Court Trust
The Nicholas Boas Charitable
Trust
The Boltons Trust
The Booth Charities
The Boots Charitable Trust
The Harry Bottom Charitable
Trust
The Bowland Charitable Trust
The Liz and Terry Bramall
Charitable Trust
The Breadsticks Foundation
The Brendish Family
Foundation
Bridgepoint Inspire
The Bristol Charities
John Bristow and Thomas
Mason Trust
Britannia Foundation
British Record Industry Trust
The J and M Britton Charitable
Trust
The Rory and Elizabeth Brooks
Foundation
The Charles Brotherton Trust
Brown-Mellows Trust
Brushmill Ltd
The Buffini Chao Foundation
The Rosemary Bugden
Charitable Trust
The BUPA Foundation
The Clara E Burgess Charity
The Audrey and Stanley Burton
1960 Charitable Trust
The Arnold Burton 1998
Charitable Trust
The Derek Butler Trust
The James Caan Foundation
Edward Cadbury Charitable
Trust
The William A Cadbury
Charitable Trust
The Cadbury Foundation
The Edward and Dorothy
Cadbury Trust
CAFOD (Catholic Agency for
Overseas Development)
Calouste Gulbenkian
Foundation
The Campden Charities
Trustee
The Carlton House Charitable
Trust

The Richard Carne Trust
The Carnegie Trust for the
Universities of Scotland
The Carpenters' Company
Charitable Trust
The Carr-Gregory Trust
The Carron Charitable
Settlement
Carter's Educational
Foundation
Sir John Cass's Foundation
The Cemlyn-Jones Trust
CfBT Education Trust
The Worshipful Company of
Chartered Accountants
General Charitable Trust
(also known as CALC)
The Cheruby Trust
The Childwick Trust
The Chipping Sodbury Town
Lands Charity
The Chrimes Family Charitable
Trust
Chrysalis Trust
The Church Burgesses
Educational Foundation
Church Burgesses Trust
The City Educational Trust
Fund
J A Clark Charitable Trust
The Clore Duffield Foundation
The Coalfields Regeneration
Trust
Coats Foundation Trust
The Denise Cohen Charitable
Trust
The Vivienne and Samuel
Cohen Charitable Trust
The John S Cohen Foundation
The R and S Cohen
Foundation
The John and Freda Coleman
Charitable Trust
The Coltstaple Trust
The Comino Foundation
The Douglas Compton James
Charitable Trust
The Congleton Inclosure Trust
Gordon Cook Foundation
The Lord Cozens-Hardy Trust
The Craignish Trust
The Harry Crook Foundation
The Cross Trust
The Peter Cruddas Foundation
Cruden Foundation Ltd
The Ronald Cruickshank's
Foundation
Cullum Family Trust
The Cutler Trust (the
Worshipful Company of
Makers of Playing Cards)
The Daiwa Anglo-Japanese
Foundation
The Hamilton Davies Trust
The Deakin Charitable Trust
The Demigryphon Trust

The Devon Educational Trust
David and Rose Diamond Trust
The Dibden Allotments Fund
Dischma Charitable Trust
The Djanogly Foundation
The DM Charitable Trust
The Dorcas Trust
The Dorema Charitable Trust
Double 'O' Charity Ltd
The Drapers' Charitable Fund
Dromintee Trust
The Duis Charitable Trust
The Dyers' Company
Charitable Trust
The James Dyson Foundation
Earls Colne and Halstead
Educational Charity
Eastern Counties Educational
Trust Limited
The Sir John Eastwood
Foundation
The Gilbert and Eileen Edgar
Foundation
The Edinburgh Trust, No 2
Account
Educational Foundation of
Alderman John Norman
Edupoor Limited
The William Edwards
Educational Charity
The Ellinson Foundation Ltd
The Ellis Campbell Foundation
The Elm House Trust
The Elmgrant Trust
EMI Music Sound Foundation
The Emilienne Charitable Trust
The Emmandjay Charitable
Trust
The Worshipful Company of
Engineers Charitable Trust
Fund
The Equilibrium Foundation
The Equitable Charitable Trust
The Eranda Foundation
The Ernest Hecht Charitable
Foundation
The Essex Youth Trust
Euro Charity Trust
The F P Limited Charitable
Trust
Esmée Fairbairn Foundation
The Fairway Trust
Faisaltex Charitable Trust
The Lord Faringdon Charitable
Trust
Samuel William Farmer Trust
Farthing Trust
The February Foundation
The George Fentham
Birmingham Charity
Allan and Nesta Ferguson
Charitable Settlement
Fife Council/Common Good
Funds and Trusts
Fisherbeck Charitable Trust

The Fishmongers' Company's Charitable Trust
The Ian Fleming Charitable Trust
The Joyce Fletcher Charitable Trust
Florence's Charitable Trust
The Flow Foundation
The Follett Trust
The Football Association National Sports Centre Trust
The Football Foundation
Ford Britain Trust
The Donald Forrester Trust
The Fort Foundation
Lord Forte Foundation
Foundation for Management Education
The Foyle Foundation
The Jill Franklin Trust
The Hugh Fraser Foundation
The Joseph Strong Frazer Trust
The Louis and Valerie Freedman Charitable Settlement
The Freemasons' Grand Charity
The Thomas Freke and Lady Norton Charity
The Freshgate Trust Foundation
The Friarsgate Trust
Friends of Muir Group
Mejer and Gertrude Miriam Frydman Foundation
The Angela Gallagher Memorial Fund
The Samuel Gardner Memorial Trust
The Garnett Charitable Trust
The Gatsby Charitable Foundation
Gatwick Airport Community Trust
The Robert Gavron Charitable Trust
Jacqueline and Michael Gee Charitable Trust
The Girdlers' Company Charitable Trust
The Glastonbury Trust Limited
The Golden Bottle Trust
The Goldsmiths' Company Charity
The Golsoncott Foundation
Nicholas and Judith Goodison's Charitable Settlement
The Everard and Mina Goodman Charitable Foundation
The Hemraj Goyal Foundation
A and S Graham Charitable Trust
The Granada Foundation

The J G Graves Charitable Trust
The Great Britain Sasakawa Foundation
The Great Stone Bridge Trust of Edenbridge
Greggs Foundation (formerly Greggs Trust)
Grimmitt Trust
The Grocers' Charity
The Guildry Incorporation of Perth
The H and M Charitable Trust
H C D Memorial Fund
The Hadrian Trust
The Hale Trust
Paul Hamlyn Foundation
The Helen Hamlyn Trust
Sue Hammerson's Charitable Trust
Hampton Fuel Allotment Charity
The Kathleen Hannay Memorial Charity
The Haramead Trust
The Harbour Charitable Trust
The Harbour Foundation
William Harding's Charity
The Harebell Centenary Fund
The Kenneth Hargreaves Charitable Trust
The Harris Charity
Haskel Family Foundation
The Maurice Hatter Foundation
The Dorothy Hay-Bolton Charitable Trust
The Haymills Charitable Trust
The Headley Trust
May Hearnshaw's Charity
The Heathcoat Trust
The Hedley Foundation
The Michael and Morven Heller Charitable Foundation
The Simon Heller Charitable Settlement
The Hemby Trust
The Henley Educational Charity
Philip Henman Trust
The Charles Littlewood Hill Trust
R G Hills Charitable Trust
Hinduja Foundation
The Hintze Family Charitable Foundation
The Hitchin Educational Foundation
Hobson Charity Limited
Hockerill Educational Foundation
Matthew Hodder Charitable Trust
The Sir Julian Hodge Charitable Trust
The Jane Hodge Foundation
The Holbeck Charitable Trust
John Holford's Charity

Hope for Youth (formerly Women Caring Trust)
The Hope Trust
The Horizon Foundation
The Antony Hornby Charitable Trust
The Horne Foundation
The Hornsey Parochial Charities
The Reta Lila Howard Foundation
HTA Sheba Foundation UK
Hulme Trust Estates (Educational)
Human Relief Foundation
Humanitarian and Charitable One Trust (HACOT)
The Humanitarian Trust
The Hunter Foundation
Miss Agnes H Hunter's Trust
The Huntingdon Foundation
The Hyde Charitable Trust – Youth Plus
The Iliffe Family Charitable Trust
The International Bankers Charitable Trust (The Worshipful Company of International Bankers)
The Ireland Fund of Great Britain
The Irish Youth Foundation (UK) Ltd (incorporating The Lawlor Foundation)
Isle of Dogs Community Foundation
J A R Charitable Trust
The J J Charitable Trust
The Jabbs Foundation
The Ruth and Lionel Jacobson Trust (Second Fund) No 2
John James Bristol Foundation
The Marjory Jameson Trust
The Jerusalem Trust
Jerwood Charitable Foundation
The Joanies Trust
The Michael John Trust
The Johnson Foundation
The Johnson Wax Ltd Charitable Trust
The Joron Charitable Trust
The Ian Karten Charitable Trust
The Kass Charitable Trust
The Kaufman Charitable Trust
The Soli and Leah Kelaty Trust Fund
Kelsick's Educational Foundation
The KempWelch Charitable Trust
E and E Kernkraut Charities Limited
The Peter Kershaw Trust
Keswick Hall Trust

The Robert Kiln Charitable
Trust
Robert Kitchin (Saddlers'
Company)
The Sir James Knott Trust
The Kohn Foundation
The KPMG Foundation
The Kreditor Charitable Trust
The Kreitman Foundation
The Neil Kreitman Foundation
John Laing Charitable Trust
Maurice and Hilda Laing
Charitable Trust
The David Laing Foundation
The Lambert Charitable Trust
Duchy of Lancaster Benevolent
Fund
The Allen Lane Foundation
The Lanvern Foundation
The Lawson Beckman
Charitable Trust
The Carole and Geoffrey
Lawson Foundation
The Leathersellers' Company
Charitable Fund
The Leche Trust
The Arnold Lee Charitable
Trust
Leeds Building Society
Charitable Foundation
The Kennedy Leigh Charitable
Trust
The Leigh Trust
The P Leigh-Bramwell Trust 'E'
The Mark Leonard Trust
The Leverhulme Trade
Charities Trust
The Leverhulme Trust
Lord Leverhulme's Charitable
Trust
The Joseph Levy Charitable
Foundation
Lewis Family Charitable Trust
John Lewis Partnership
General Community Fund
The Lewis Ward Trust
Liberum Foundation
Lichfield Conduit Lands
Limoges Charitable Trust
The Linbury Trust
Lloyds TSB Foundation for
Northern Ireland
Llysdinam Charitable Trust
Localtrent Ltd
The Loftus Charitable Trust
The Lord's Taverners
The C L Loyd Charitable Trust
LSA Charitable Trust
The Marie Helen Luen
Charitable Trust
Henry Lumley Charitable Trust
Lady Lumley's Educational
Foundation
The Ruth and Jack Lunzer
Charitable Trust
Lord and Lady Lurgan Trust

John Lyon's Charity
The Sir Jack Lyons Charitable
Trust
The Joy and Malcolm Lyons
Foundation
The Madeline Mabey Trust
The Mackintosh Foundation
The MacRobert Trust
Ian Mactaggart Trust
James Madison Trust
Magdalen Hospital Trust
The Magen Charitable Trust
The Mahavir Trust (also known
as the K S Mehta
Charitable Trust)
Man Group plc Charitable
Trust
The Manifold Charitable Trust
W M Mann Foundation
The Manoukian Charitable
Foundation
Maranatha Christian Trust
The Marianne Foundation
Market Harborough and The
Bowdens Charity
The Hilda and Samuel Marks
Foundation
The Michael Marsh Charitable
Trust
The Marsh Christian Trust
The Charlotte Marshall
Charitable Trust
Marshgate Charitable
Settlement
Sir George Martin Trust
John Martin's Charity
The John Mason Family Trust
The Nancie Massey Charitable
Trust
The Mathew Trust
The Maxell Educational Trust
The McKenna Charitable Trust
The Mears Foundation
The Medlock Charitable Trust
Melow Charitable Trust
The Mercers' Charitable
Foundation
The Merchant Taylors'
Company Charities Fund
The Merchant Venturers'
Charity
The Merchants' House of
Glasgow
T and J Meyer Family
Foundation Limited
Mi Yu Foundation
Gerald Micklem Charitable
Trust
Miles Trust for the Putney and
Roehampton Community
The Miller Foundation
The Millichope Foundation
The Edgar Milward Charity
The Peter Minet Trust
Minge's Gift and the Pooled
Trusts

Minton Charitable Trust
The Mirfield Educational
Charity
The Mitchell Charitable Trust
The Moette Charitable Trust
Monmouthshire County Council
Welsh Church Act Fund
The Colin Montgomerie
Charitable Foundation
The Henry Moore Foundation
John Moores Foundation
The Peter Moores Foundation
The Morel Charitable Trust
The Mr and Mrs J T Morgan
Foundation
Diana and Allan Morgenthau
Charitable Trust
The Morris Charitable Trust
G M Morrison Charitable Trust
The Stanley Morrison
Charitable Trust
Vyoel Moshe Charitable Trust
The Moss Charitable Trust
The Robert and Margaret
Moss Charitable Trust
Moto in the Community Trust
J P Moulton Charitable
Foundation
The MSE Charity
The Music Sales Charitable
Trust
Muslim Hands
The Mutual Trust Group
MW (CL) Foundation
MW (GK) Foundation
MW (HO) Foundation
MW (RH) Foundation
The Kitty and Daniel Nabarro
Charitable Trust
The Eleni Nakou Foundation
The Nchima Trust
The Worshipful Company of
Needlemakers' Charitable
Fund
New Court Charitable Trust
The Newcomen Collett
Foundation
Alderman Newton's
Educational Foundation
Nominet Charitable Foundation
The Noon Foundation
The Normanby Charitable Trust
The North British Hotel Trust
The Northampton Municipal
Church Charities
The Northumberland Village
Homes Trust
The Northwood Charitable
Trust
The Norton Foundation
The Norton Rose Charitable
Foundation
The Norwich Town Close
Estate Charity

The Nottingham Gordon Memorial Trust for Boys and Girls
The Nottinghamshire Miners' Welfare Trust Fund
The Nuffield Foundation
The Father O'Mahoney Memorial Trust
The Oakley Charitable Trust
Oglesby Charitable Trust
Oizer Charitable Trust
The Old Broad Street Charity Trust
Old Possum's Practical Trust
Open Gate
The Owen Family Trust
City of Oxford Charity
Padwa Charitable Foundation
The Palmer Foundation
The James Pantyfedwen Foundation
The Park House Charitable Trust
The Parthenon Trust
Ambika Paul Foundation
The Dowager Countess Eleanor Peel Trust
Peltz Trust
The Performing Right Society Foundation
The Pervez Musharraf Foundation
The Jack Petchey Foundation
Philological Foundation
The Bernard Piggott Trust
The Pilgrim Trust
The Worshipful Company of Plaisterers Charitable Trust
The Pollywally Charitable Trust
The Polonsky Foundation
The Ponton House Trust
The John Porter Charitable Trust
The Porter Foundation
Porticus UK
The David and Elaine Potter Foundation
The Praebendo Charitable Foundation
The Premier League Charitable Fund
The Tom Press Charitable Foundation
The William Price Charitable Trust
The Lucy Price Relief-in-Need Charity
Sir John Priestman Charity Trust
The Prince of Wales's Charitable Foundation
Private Equity Foundation
PSA Peugeot Citroen Charity Trust
The Puri Foundation

Mr and Mrs J A Pye's Charitable Settlement
Quartet Community Foundation (formerly the Greater Bristol Foundation)
The Queen Anne's Gate Foundation
The Queen's Silver Jubilee Trust
Richard Radcliffe Charitable Trust
The Radcliffe Trust
The Peggy Ramsay Foundation
The Rank Foundation
Ranworth Trust
The Rashbass Family Trust
The Ravensdale Trust
The Roger Raymond Charitable Trust
The Rayne Foundation
The Eva Reckitt Trust Fund
The Red Rose Charitable Trust
The Reed Foundation
Richard Reeve's Foundation
Relief Fund for Romania Limited
Reuben Brothers Foundation
The Clive Richards Charity
The Violet M Richards Charity
The Richmond Parish Lands Charity
Ridgesave Limited
Riverside Charitable Trust Limited
Rix-Thompson-Rothenberg Foundation
The Robertson Trust
The Roddick Foundation
The Sir James Roll Charitable Trust
Mrs L D Rope Third Charitable Settlement
The Rose Foundation
The Rothermere Foundation
The Rotherwick Foundation
The Rothley Trust
The Christopher Rowbotham Charitable Trust
The Rowland Family Foundation
The Rowlands Trust
Royal Docks Trust (London)
Royal Masonic Trust for Girls and Boys
Ryklow Charitable Trust 1992 (also known as A B Williamson Charitable Trust)
The J S and E C Rymer Charitable Trust
The Michael Harry Sacher Trust
The Saddlers' Company Charitable Fund
Erach and Roshan Sadri Foundation

Saint Luke's College Foundation
The Saintbury Trust
The Salt Foundation
The Andrew Salvesen Charitable Trust
Basil Samuel Charitable Trust
Coral Samuel Charitable Trust
The Samworth Foundation
Santander UK Foundation Limited
Schroder Charity Trust
The Scott Trust Foundation
The Scottish Arts Council
The Scottish International Education Trust
The Samuel Sebba Charitable Trust
SEM Charitable Trust
The Seneca Trust
The Ayrton Senna Foundation
SFIA Educational Trust Limited
Shaara Ezra – The Moses Foundation
The Jean Shanks Foundation
The Sheepdrove Trust
The Shekinah Legacy
The Archie Sherman Cardiff Foundation
The Archie Sherman Charitable Trust
SHINE (Support and Help in Education)
The Bassil Shippam and Alsford Trust
The Shoe Zone Trust
The Sickle Foundation
Sino-British Fellowship Trust
Sloane Robinson Foundation
The Leslie Smith Foundation
The Martin Smith Foundation
The R C Snelling Charitable Trust
The E C Sosnow Charitable Trust
The South Square Trust
The Stephen R and Philippa H Southall Charitable Trust
The Southdown Trust
R H Southern Trust
The Southover Manor General Education Trust
The Spero Foundation
Split Infinitive Trust
The Spoore, Merry and Rixman Foundation
Rosalyn and Nicholas Springer Charitable Trust
St Christopher's College Educational Trust
St Gabriel's Trust
St James's Place Foundation
Sir Walter St John's Educational Charity
The Stanley Foundation Ltd

Stevenson Family's Charitable
Trust
The Stokenchurch Educational
Charity
The Stone-Mallabar Charitable
Foundation
Peter Storrs Trust
Stratford upon Avon Town
Trust
The W O Street Charitable
Foundation
The Sudborough Foundation
Sueberry Ltd
Summary Limited
The Summerfield Charitable
Trust
Sussex Community Foundation
The Sutasoma Trust
Sutton Coldfield Municipal
Charities
The Sutton Trust
The Hugh and Ruby Sykes
Charitable Trust
Tallow Chandlers Benevolent
Fund
The Mrs A Lacy Tate Trust
Humphrey Richardson Taylor
Charitable Trust
The Connie and Albert Taylor
Charitable Trust
The Cyril Taylor Charitable
Trust
Tesco Charity Trust
The Thompson Family
Charitable Trust
The Thornton Trust
The Thriplow Charitable Trust
Mrs R P Tindall's Charitable
Trust
The Tobacco Pipe Makers and
Tobacco Trade Benevolent
Fund
The Tolkien Trust
The Tory Family Foundation
Tottenham Grammar School
Foundation
The Towry Law Charitable Trust
(also known as the Castle
Educational Trust)
The Triangle Trust (1949) Fund
The Trust for Education
TVML Foundation
Ultach Trust
Uxbridge United Welfare Trust
Vale of Glamorgan – Welsh
Church Fund
The Vardy Foundation
The Variety Club Children's
Charity
Roger Vere Foundation
The William and Ellen Vinten
Trust
The Vintners' Company
Charitable Foundation
Wakeham Trust

Robert and Felicity Waley-
Cohen Charitable Trust
The Walker Trust
The Thomas Wall Trust
The Ward Blenkinsop Trust
The Waterloo Foundation
The Howard Watson Symington
Memorial Charity
John Watson's Trust
Webb Memorial Trust
The James Weir Foundation
The Weldon UK Charitable
Trust
The Westminster Foundation
The Garfield Weston
Foundation
The Whitaker Charitable Trust
The Colonel W H Whitbread
Charitable Trust
The Simon Whitbread
Charitable Trust
The Whittlesey Charity
The Williams Charitable Trust
Williams Serendipity Trust
The Wilson Foundation
The Harold Hyam Wingate
Foundation
The Winton Charitable
Foundation
The Michael and Anna Wix
Charitable Trust
The Wixamtree Trust
The Charles Wolfson
Charitable Trust
The Wolfson Foundation
The Wood Family Trust
Woodroffe Benton Foundation
ME Woolfe Charitable Trust
Worcester Municipal Charities
(incorporating Worcester
Consolidated Municipal
Charity and Worcester
Municipal Exhibitions
Foundation)
The Fred and Della Worms
Charitable Trust
Miss E B Wrightson's
Charitable Settlement
The Yapp Charitable Trust
The W Wing Yip and Brothers
Foundation
The York Children's Trust
Youth Music
Suha Yusuf Charitable Trust
The Marjorie and Arnold Ziff
Charitable Foundation
The Zochonis Charitable Trust

Higher education

AF Trust Company
The Alliance Family Foundation
The Altajir Trust
The Beit Trust
The Harry Bottom Charitable
Trust

The Rory and Elizabeth Brooks
Foundation
The BUPA Foundation
The Carlton House Charitable
Trust
The Carnegie Trust for the
Universities of Scotland
The Elmgrant Trust
The Essex Youth Trust
The Fairway Trust
The February Foundation
The Football Association
National Sports Centre
Trust
The Hugh Fraser Foundation
The Joseph Strong Frazer Trust
The Gatsby Charitable
Foundation
Paul Hamlyn Foundation
The Haymills Charitable Trust
The Henley Educational Charity
Hulme Trust Estates
(Educational)
The Ian Karten Charitable
Trust
Kelsick's Educational
Foundation
Keswick Hall Trust
The Kreitman Foundation
The Leche Trust
The Leverhulme Trade
Charities Trust
The Loftus Charitable Trust
John Lyon's Charity
The Sir Jack Lyons Charitable
Trust
James Madison Trust
Miles Trust for the Putney and
Roehampton Community
Monmouthshire County Council
Welsh Church Act Fund
The Peter Moores Foundation
J P Moulton Charitable
Foundation
The Eleni Nakou Foundation
The Northwood Charitable
Trust
The Polonsky Foundation
Mr and Mrs J A Pye's
Charitable Settlement
The Red Rose Charitable Trust
Richard Reeve's Foundation
The Robertson Trust
Sloane Robinson Foundation
The South Square Trust
Stevenson Family's Charitable
Trust
The Thriplow Charitable Trust
Webb Memorial Trust
The Wilson Foundation
The Winton Charitable
Foundation

Informal, continuing and adult education

The Association of Colleges
  Charitable Trust
The Beit Trust
The Big Lottery Fund
The Boots Charitable Trust
The Cadbury Foundation
The John and Freda Coleman
  Charitable Trust
The Duis Charitable Trust
The Elmgrant Trust
The Essex Youth Trust
The Fairway Trust
The Hugh Fraser Foundation
The Freemasons' Grand
  Charity
The Gatsby Charitable
  Foundation
Gatwick Airport Community
  Trust
The Girdlers' Company
  Charitable Trust
Greggs Foundation (formerly
  Greggs Trust)
Paul Hamlyn Foundation
The Haymills Charitable Trust
Hope for Youth (formerly
  Women Caring Trust)
The Hyde Charitable Trust –
  Youth Plus
Isle of Dogs Community
  Foundation
Jerwood Charitable Foundation
Kelsick's Educational
  Foundation
John Laing Charitable Trust
The Allen Lane Foundation
John Lyon's Charity
Magdalen Hospital Trust
The Mahavir Trust (also known
  as the K S Mehta
  Charitable Trust)
The Mathew Trust
The Merchant Venturers'
  Charity
Miles Trust for the Putney and
  Roehampton Community
The Millichope Foundation
The Peter Minet Trust
Monmouthshire County Council
  Welsh Church Act Fund
John Moores Foundation
The MSE Charity
The Nuffield Foundation
Mr and Mrs J A Pye's
  Charitable Settlement
Richard Reeve's Foundation
The Christopher Rowbotham
  Charitable Trust
Sloane Robinson Foundation
The Trust for Education
The Wilson Foundation
The Yapp Charitable Trust

Vocational education and training

The John and Freda Coleman
  Charitable Trust
The Hugh Fraser Foundation
The Freemasons' Grand
  Charity
The Gatsby Charitable
  Foundation
The Girdlers' Company
  Charitable Trust
The Haymills Charitable Trust
Hope for Youth (formerly
  Women Caring Trust)
The Hyde Charitable Trust –
  Youth Plus
Isle of Dogs Community
  Foundation
Jerwood Charitable Foundation
Kelsick's Educational
  Foundation
The Allen Lane Foundation
John Lyon's Charity
Magdalen Hospital Trust
The Nuffield Foundation
The Christopher Rowbotham
  Charitable Trust

Integrated education

The Beit Trust
The Essex Youth Trust
Hope for Youth (formerly
  Women Caring Trust)
Sloane Robinson Foundation

Management of schools

Calouste Gulbenkian
  Foundation
CfBT Education Trust
The Marjory Jameson Trust
Monmouthshire County Council
  Welsh Church Act Fund
The Kitty and Daniel Nabarro
  Charitable Trust
The Nuffield Foundation
Sloane Robinson Foundation

Particular subjects, curriculum development

All Saints Educational Trust
Angus Allnatt Charitable
  Foundation
The Altajir Trust

The Arts Council of Wales
The Beit Trust
The Big Lottery Fund
British Record Industry Trust
The Derek Butler Trust
Calouste Gulbenkian
  Foundation
The Richard Carne Trust
The Cemlyn-Jones Trust
CfBT Education Trust
Church Burgesses Trust
The Clore Duffield Foundation
Coats Foundation Trust
The Deakin Charitable Trust
The Duis Charitable Trust
The James Dyson Foundation
The Ellis Campbell Foundation
The Elmgrant Trust
EMI Music Sound Foundation
The Worshipful Company of
  Engineers Charitable Trust
  Fund
The Ian Fleming Charitable
  Trust
The Joyce Fletcher Charitable
  Trust
Lord Forte Foundation
Foundation for Management
  Education
The Samuel Gardner Memorial
  Trust
The Gatsby Charitable
  Foundation
The Girdlers' Company
  Charitable Trust
The Glastonbury Trust Limited
The Golsoncott Foundation
Nicholas and Judith
  Goodison's Charitable
  Settlement
The J G Graves Charitable
  Trust
Paul Hamlyn Foundation
The Harbour Foundation
The Headley Trust
The Michael and Morven Heller
  Charitable Foundation
Hockerill Educational
  Foundation
Matthew Hodder Charitable
  Trust
The Hope Trust
The Hyde Charitable Trust –
  Youth Plus
The International Bankers
  Charitable Trust (The
  Worshipful Company of
  International Bankers)
The J J Charitable Trust
The Ruth and Lionel Jacobson
  Trust (Second Fund) No 2
The Jerusalem Trust
The Joanies Trust
Keswick Hall Trust
The Robert Kiln Charitable
  Trust

Maurice and Hilda Laing
  Charitable Trust
The Leverhulme Trust
The Joseph Levy Charitable
  Foundation
The Linbury Trust
Llysdinam Charitable Trust
Magdalen Hospital Trust
The Maxell Educational Trust
Miles Trust for the Putney and
  Roehampton Community
The Henry Moore Foundation
The Peter Moores Foundation
The MSE Charity
The Music Sales Charitable
  Trust
The Kitty and Daniel Nabarro
  Charitable Trust
The Nuffield Foundation
The Old Broad Street Charity
  Trust
Old Possum's Practical Trust
The Performing Right Society
  Foundation
The Pilgrim Trust
Sir John Priestman Charity
  Trust
Richard Radcliffe Charitable
  Trust
The Radcliffe Trust
The Peggy Ramsay Foundation
The Sir James Roll Charitable
  Trust
Mrs L D Rope Third Charitable
  Settlement
Saint Luke's College
  Foundation
The Scottish Arts Council
The Sickle Foundation
Sloane Robinson Foundation
The South Square Trust
Split Infinitive Trust
St Christopher's College
  Educational Trust
St Gabriel's Trust
Humphrey Richardson Taylor
  Charitable Trust
Ultach Trust
The William and Ellen Vinten
  Trust
Miss E B Wrightson's
  Charitable Settlement
Youth Music

Arts education and training

Angus Allnatt Charitable
  Foundation
The Arts Council of Wales
British Record Industry Trust
The Derek Butler Trust
Calouste Gulbenkian
  Foundation
The Richard Carne Trust

The Cemlyn-Jones Trust
The Clore Duffield Foundation
Coats Foundation Trust
The Deakin Charitable Trust
The Duis Charitable Trust
The James Dyson Foundation
The Elmgrant Trust
EMI Music Sound Foundation
The Ian Fleming Charitable
  Trust
The Joyce Fletcher Charitable
  Trust
The Samuel Gardner Memorial
  Trust
The Golsoncott Foundation
Nicholas and Judith
  Goodison's Charitable
  Settlement
Paul Hamlyn Foundation
The Headley Trust
Matthew Hodder Charitable
  Trust
The Joanies Trust
The Robert Kiln Charitable
  Trust
The Linbury Trust
Miles Trust for the Putney and
  Roehampton Community
The Henry Moore Foundation
The Peter Moores Foundation
The Music Sales Charitable
  Trust
The Performing Right Society
  Foundation
The Pilgrim Trust
The Radcliffe Trust
The Peggy Ramsay Foundation
The Scottish Arts Council
The Sickle Foundation
The South Square Trust
Split Infinitive Trust
Humphrey Richardson Taylor
  Charitable Trust
Miss E B Wrightson's
  Charitable Settlement
Youth Music

Business education

The Ellis Campbell Foundation
Foundation for Management
  Education
The Gatsby Charitable
  Foundation
The International Bankers
  Charitable Trust (The
  Worshipful Company of
  International Bankers)
The MSE Charity
The Old Broad Street Charity
  Trust

Citizenship, personal and social education

The Big Lottery Fund
The Elmgrant Trust
The Kitty and Daniel Nabarro
  Charitable Trust

Domestic/ lifeskills education

All Saints Educational Trust
The Duis Charitable Trust
The Girdlers' Company
  Charitable Trust
Miles Trust for the Putney and
  Roehampton Community

Hospitality education

Lord Forte Foundation

Literacy education

CfBT Education Trust
The Duis Charitable Trust
The Elmgrant Trust
The Headley Trust
Matthew Hodder Charitable
  Trust
The Hyde Charitable Trust –
  Youth Plus
The J J Charitable Trust
Miles Trust for the Putney and
  Roehampton Community
The Kitty and Daniel Nabarro
  Charitable Trust
Old Possum's Practical Trust
Ultach Trust

Religious education

All Saints Educational Trust
The Altajir Trust
Church Burgesses Trust
The Girdlers' Company
  Charitable Trust
The Glastonbury Trust Limited
Hockerill Educational
  Foundation
The Hope Trust
The Ruth and Lionel Jacobson
  Trust (Second Fund) No 2
The Jerusalem Trust
Keswick Hall Trust
Maurice and Hilda Laing
  Charitable Trust

The Joseph Levy Charitable
Foundation
Miles Trust for the Putney and
Roehampton Community
Sir John Priestman Charity
Trust
Saint Luke's College
Foundation
St Christopher's College
Educational Trust
St Gabriel's Trust

Science education

The Gatsby Charitable
Foundation
The J G Graves Charitable
Trust
The Michael and Morven Heller
Charitable Foundation
Llysdinam Charitable Trust
The Kitty and Daniel Nabarro
Charitable Trust
The Nuffield Foundation
Mrs L D Rope Third Charitable
Settlement
The William and Ellen Vinten
Trust

Sports education

The Girdlers' Company
Charitable Trust

Technology, engineering and computer education

The James Dyson Foundation
The Worshipful Company of
Engineers Charitable Trust
Fund
The Gatsby Charitable
Foundation
The Harbour Foundation
The Headley Trust
The Michael and Morven Heller
Charitable Foundation
Magdalen Hospital Trust
The Maxell Educational Trust
The Kitty and Daniel Nabarro
Charitable Trust
Richard Radcliffe Charitable
Trust
The Sir James Roll Charitable
Trust
The William and Ellen Vinten
Trust

Pre-school education, nursery schools

Carter's Educational
Foundation
The Elmgrant Trust
Samuel William Farmer Trust
The Football Association
National Sports Centre
Trust
The Thomas Freke and Lady
Norton Charity
The Angela Gallagher Memorial
Fund
Gatwick Airport Community
Trust
The Hale Trust
Hampton Fuel Allotment
Charity
The Hemby Trust
The Henley Educational Charity
John Lyon's Charity
The Madeline Mabey Trust
Miles Trust for the Putney and
Roehampton Community
Monmouthshire County Council
Welsh Church Act Fund
Mr and Mrs J A Pye's
Charitable Settlement
Richard Reeve's Foundation

Primary and secondary school education

The Alliance Family Foundation
The Ammco Trust
A J H Ashby Will Trust
The BAA Communities Trust
The Baily Thomas Charitable
Fund
The Charity of William Barrow
The Harry Bottom Charitable
Trust
The Bristol Charities
The Cadbury Foundation
Calouste Gulbenkian
Foundation
Carter's Educational
Foundation
The Congleton Inclosure Trust
The Daiwa Anglo-Japanese
Foundation
The Hamilton Davies Trust
The Deakin Charitable Trust
The Dibden Allotments Fund
Earls Colne and Halstead
Educational Charity
Eastern Counties Educational
Trust Limited
The William Edwards
Educational Charity
The Ellis Campbell Foundation

The Elmgrant Trust
The Equitable Charitable Trust
The Fairway Trust
Faisaltex Charitable Trust
Samuel William Farmer Trust
The February Foundation
The Joyce Fletcher Charitable
Trust
The Football Association
National Sports Centre
Trust
Ford Britain Trust
The Joseph Strong Frazer Trust
The Thomas Freke and Lady
Norton Charity
Mejer and Gertrude Miriam
Frydman Foundation
The Angela Gallagher Memorial
Fund
The Gatsby Charitable
Foundation
Gatwick Airport Community
Trust
The Robert Gavron Charitable
Trust
The Girdlers' Company
Charitable Trust
The Hale Trust
Paul Hamlyn Foundation
Hampton Fuel Allotment
Charity
The Harris Charity
The Haymills Charitable Trust
The Headley Trust
The Hedley Foundation
The Henley Educational Charity
The Charles Littlewood Hill
Trust
John Holford's Charity
The Horne Foundation
The Hornsey Parochial
Charities
Hulme Trust Estates
(Educational)
The J J Charitable Trust
The Ruth and Lionel Jacobson
Trust (Second Fund) No 2
The Ian Karten Charitable
Trust
Kelsick's Educational
Foundation
The Peter Kershaw Trust
The Leche Trust
Leeds Building Society
Charitable Foundation
The Mark Leonard Trust
The Leverhulme Trust
The Joseph Levy Charitable
Foundation
The Lord's Taverners
John Lyon's Charity
The Joy and Malcolm Lyons
Foundation
The Madeline Mabey Trust
The Charlotte Marshall
Charitable Trust

Sir George Martin Trust
The Maxell Educational Trust
The Medlock Charitable Trust
The Mercers' Charitable
  Foundation
Gerald Micklem Charitable
  Trust
Miles Trust for the Putney and
  Roehampton Community
The Mirfield Educational
  Charity
Monmouthshire County Council
  Welsh Church Act Fund
The Kitty and Daniel Nabarro
  Charitable Trust
The Newcomen Collett
  Foundation
The North British Hotel Trust
The Nuffield Foundation
The Owen Family Trust
City of Oxford Charity
The Jack Petchey Foundation
Philological Foundation
PSA Peugeot Citroen Charity
  Trust
Mr and Mrs J A Pye's
  Charitable Settlement
Richard Reeve's Foundation
Relief Fund for Romania
  Limited
Rix-Thompson-Rothenberg
  Foundation
The Robertson Trust
The Salt Foundation
Sloane Robinson Foundation
The Leslie Smith Foundation
The South Square Trust
St James's Place Foundation
John Watson's Trust
The Colonel W H Whitbread
  Charitable Trust
The Wilson Foundation
The Wixamtree Trust

Faith schools

The Alliance Family Foundation
Faisaltex Charitable Trust
Mejer and Gertrude Miriam
  Frydman Foundation
Miles Trust for the Putney and
  Roehampton Community
The Owen Family Trust

Public and independent schools

The Daiwa Anglo-Japanese
  Foundation
The Elmgrant Trust
The Equitable Charitable Trust
The Fairway Trust
Samuel William Farmer Trust

The Hale Trust
The Headley Trust
The Peter Kershaw Trust
The Leche Trust
The Leverhulme Trust
Sir George Martin Trust
The Mercers' Charitable
  Foundation
The Nuffield Foundation
The Owen Family Trust

Special needs schools

The Ammco Trust
The Baily Thomas Charitable
  Fund
Eastern Counties Educational
  Trust Limited
The Ellis Campbell Foundation
The Elmgrant Trust
The Equitable Charitable Trust
Samuel William Farmer Trust
The Joyce Fletcher Charitable
  Trust
Ford Britain Trust
The Thomas Freke and Lady
  Norton Charity
The Angela Gallagher Memorial
  Fund
The Girdlers' Company
  Charitable Trust
The Hale Trust
The J J Charitable Trust
The Ruth and Lionel Jacobson
  Trust (Second Fund) No 2
The Ian Karten Charitable
  Trust
Kelsick's Educational
  Foundation
Leeds Building Society
  Charitable Foundation
The Joseph Levy Charitable
  Foundation
The Lord's Taverners
Gerald Micklem Charitable
  Trust
Miles Trust for the Putney and
  Roehampton Community
The Kitty and Daniel Nabarro
  Charitable Trust
The North British Hotel Trust
Relief Fund for Romania
  Limited
Rix-Thompson-Rothenberg
  Foundation
St James's Place Foundation
John Watson's Trust

State schools

The Deakin Charitable Trust
The Mark Leonard Trust
Richard Reeve's Foundation

Teacher training

Monmouthshire County Council
  Welsh Church Act Fund
The Nuffield Foundation

Environment and animals

The 1970 Trust
The Aberbrothock Skea Trust
The AIM Foundation
The Alborada Trust
Anglo American Group
    Foundation
The Animal Defence Trust
The Arthur Ronald Dyer
    Charitable Trust
A J H Ashby Will Trust
The Ashden Trust
The Ashendene Trust
The Associated Country
    Women of the World
    (ACWW)
The Astor Foundation
The Astor of Hever Trust
The BAA Communities Trust
Harry Bacon Foundation
The Scott Bader
    Commonwealth Ltd
The C Alma Baker Trust
The Balcombe Charitable Trust
The Balney Charitable Trust
Lord Barnby's Foundation
The Beit Trust
The Bellahouston Bequest
    Fund
The Hervey Benham Charitable
    Trust
The Big Lottery Fund
Birmingham International
    Airport Community Trust
The Blair Foundation
The Body Shop Foundation
The Bothwell Charitable Trust
John and Susan Bowers Fund
Briggs Animal Welfare Trust
The Bromley Trust
Brown-Mellows Trust
C J Cadbury Charitable Trust
Edward Cadbury Charitable
    Trust
The Christopher Cadbury
    Charitable Trust
The G W Cadbury Charitable
    Trust
The William A Cadbury
    Charitable Trust
The Cadbury Foundation
The Edward and Dorothy
    Cadbury Trust
CAFOD (Catholic Agency for
    Overseas Development)
Calouste Gulbenkian
    Foundation
Calypso Browning Trust
M R Cannon 1998 Charitable
    Trust
The Carron Charitable
    Settlement
The Leslie Mary Carter
    Charitable Trust

The Wilfrid and Constance
    Cave Foundation
The Cemlyn-Jones Trust
The Chelsea Square 1994
    Trust
CLA Charitable Trust
J A Clark Charitable Trust
The Cleopatra Trust
The Robert Clutterbuck
    Charitable Trust
The John Coates Charitable
    Trust
The John S Cohen Foundation
Colyer-Fergusson Charitable
    Trust
The Conscience Trust
The Conservation Foundation
The Ernest Cook Trust
The Marjorie Coote Animal
    Charity Trust
The Craignish Trust
The Ronald Cruickshank's
    Foundation
The D J H Currie Memorial
    Trust
The Dennis Curry Charitable
    Trust
The D'Oyly Carte Charitable
    Trust
The Dr and Mrs A Darlington
    Charitable Trust
The Helen and Geoffrey De
    Freitas Charitable Trust
Peter De Haan Charitable
    Trust
William Dean Countryside and
    Educational Trust
The Delves Charitable Trust
Dischma Charitable Trust
The Dorus Trust
The Duis Charitable Trust
The Dulverton Trust
The Dumbreck Charity
Dunard Fund
The Houghton Dunn Charitable
    Trust
The Dunn Family Charitable
    Trust
EAGA Partnership Charitable
    Trust
Audrey Earle Charitable Trust
The EBM Charitable Trust
The Ecology Trust
The Edinburgh Trust, No 2
    Account
The John Ellerman Foundation
The Ellis Campbell Foundation
The Elmgrant Trust
The Ericson Trust
The Alan Evans Memorial Trust
The Beryl Evetts and Robert
    Luff Animal Welfare Trust
The Matthew Eyton Animal
    Welfare Trust
Esmée Fairbairn Foundation
Samuel William Farmer Trust

The Farmers' Company
    Charitable Fund
Fife Council/Common Good
    Funds and Trusts
The Fishmongers' Company's
    Charitable Trust
The Flow Foundation
Ford Britain Trust
The Oliver Ford Charitable
    Trust
The Donald Forrester Trust
The Anna Rosa Forster
    Charitable Trust
Sydney E Franklin Deceased's
    New Second Charity
The Gordon Fraser Charitable
    Trust
The Hugh Fraser Foundation
The Freshfield Foundation
Maurice Fry Charitable Trust
The Fuellers Charitable Trust
    Fund
The G D Charitable Trust
The Galanthus Trust
The Gannochy Trust
The Worshipful Company of
    Gardeners of London
The Garnett Charitable Trust
The Gatsby Charitable
    Foundation
Gatwick Airport Community
    Trust
Generations Charitable Trust
J Paul Getty Jr Charitable Trust
The G C Gibson Charitable
    Trust
The Girdlers' Company
    Charitable Trust
The Glastonbury Trust Limited
The GMW Charitable Trust
The GNC Trust
The Gosling Foundation
    Limited
The Gough Charitable Trust
GrantScape
The Green Room Charitable
    Trust
The Wiles Greenworld
    Charitable Trust
The Gunter Charitable Trust
H C D Memorial Fund
The Hadfield Trust
The Hadrian Trust
The Doris Louise Hailes
    Charitable Trust
The Hamamelis Trust
The Harebell Centenary Fund
The Kenneth Hargreaves
    Charitable Trust
The Edith Lilian Harrison 2000
    Foundation
William Geoffrey Harvey's
    Discretionary Settlement
The Headley Trust
The G D Herbert Charitable
    Trust

The Joanna Herbert-Stepney Charitable Settlement (also known as The Paget Charitable Trust)

The J G Hogg Charitable Trust

The Homestead Charitable Trust

The Cuthbert Horn Trust

The Reta Lila Howard Foundation

The Geoffrey C Hughes Charitable Trust

The Michael and Shirley Hunt Charitable Trust

The Idlewild Trust

The J J Charitable Trust

The Barbara Joyce Jarrald Charitable Trust

The John Jarrold Trust

Rees Jeffreys Road Fund

The Johnson Wax Ltd Charitable Trust

The Jordan Charitable Foundation

The Kennel Club Charitable Trust

The Robert Kiln Charitable Trust

Ernest Kleinwort Charitable Trust

The Kreitman Foundation

John Laing Charitable Trust

The Christopher Laing Foundation

The Martin Laing Foundation

Lancashire Environmental Fund

The Langley Charitable Trust

Mrs F B Laurence Charitable Trust

The Leach Fourteenth Trust

The Leathersellers' Company Charitable Fund

The Mark Leonard Trust

Lord Leverhulme's Charitable Trust

The John Spedan Lewis Foundation

John Lewis Partnership General Community Fund

The Limbourne Trust

Limoges Charitable Trust

The Linbury Trust

Llysdinam Charitable Trust

The William and Katherine Longman Trust

The Lotus Foundation

LSA Charitable Trust

The Lyons Charitable Trust

The R S Macdonald Charitable Trust

The Mackintosh Foundation

The MacRobert Trust

The Mahavir Trust (also known as the K S Mehta Charitable Trust)

Manchester Airport Community Trust Fund

The Manifold Charitable Trust

Marchig Animal Welfare Trust

Market Harborough and The Bowdens Charity

Michael Marks Charitable Trust

Marmot Charitable Trust

The Marsh Christian Trust

Sir George Martin Trust

Martin McLaren Memorial Trust

The Mears Foundation

The Mercers' Charitable Foundation

The Mersey Docks and Harbour Company Charitable Fund

The Metropolitan Drinking Fountain and Cattle Trough Association

T and J Meyer Family Foundation Limited

Millennium Stadium Charitable Trust

The Miller Foundation

The Millichope Foundation

The Millward Charitable Trust

The Peter Minet Trust

The Minos Trust

The D C Moncrieff Charitable Trust

The Montague Thompson Coon Charitable Trust

The Monument Trust

The Morel Charitable Trust

Moto in the Community Trust

The Edith Murphy Foundation

The Kitty and Daniel Nabarro Charitable Trust

The Nchima Trust

Network for Social Change

The NFU Mutual Charitable Trust

Alice Noakes Memorial Charitable Trust

The Nottinghamshire Miners' Welfare Trust Fund

The Sir Peter O'Sullevan Charitable Trust

The Oakdale Trust

The Oakley Charitable Trust

The Ofenheim Charitable Trust

Oglesby Charitable Trust

Old Possum's Practical Trust

The John Oldacre Foundation

The Oldham Foundation

Onaway Trust

Open Gate

Orrin Charitable Trust

The Owen Family Trust

Panton Trust

The Frank Parkinson Agricultural Trust

The Jack Patston Charitable Trust

The Peacock Charitable Trust

The Persula Foundation

The Petplan Charitable Trust

The Phillips Charitable Trust

The Pilgrim Trust

The Cecil Pilkington Charitable Trust

The Elise Pilkington Charitable Trust

The Col W W Pilkington Will Trusts The General Charity Fund

Polden-Puckham Charitable Foundation

The John Porter Charitable Trust

The Porter Foundation

Prairie Trust

The Prince of Wales's Charitable Foundation

The Foundation of Prince William and Prince Harry

Princess Anne's Charities

Mr and Mrs J A Pye's Charitable Settlement

Quartet Community Foundation (formerly the Greater Bristol Foundation)

The Joseph Rank Trust

The Sigrid Rausing Trust

The Rhododendron Trust

The Ripple Effect Foundation

The River Farm Foundation

The Robertson Trust

The Rochester Bridge Trust

The Roddick Foundation

The Rothera Charitable Settlement

The Roughley Charitable Trust

The Rowlands Trust

Royal Docks Trust (London)

The Rufford Foundation

The Rufford Small Grants Foundation

Ryklow Charitable Trust 1992 (also known as A B Williamson Charitable Trust)

The Michael Harry Sacher Trust

The Jean Sainsbury Animal Welfare Trust

The Saintbury Trust

The Saints and Sinners Trust

Salters' Charitable Foundation

The Hon. M J Samuel Charitable Trust

The Peter Samuel Charitable Trust

The Sandra Charitable Trust

The Scarfe Charitable Trust

Schroder Charity Trust

The Scotshill Trust

The Scouloudi Foundation

Seafarers UK (King George's
Fund for Sailors)
The Linley Shaw Foundation
The Sheepdrove Trust
The Sylvia and Colin Shepherd
Charitable Trust
The Shetland Charitable Trust
The Shipwrights' Company
Charitable Fund
The Simpson Education and
Conservation Trust
The John Slater Foundation
Ruth Smart Foundation
The SMB Charitable Trust
The N Smith Charitable
Settlement
The Stanley Smith UK
Horticultural Trust
Philip Smith's Charitable Trust
The R C Snelling Charitable
Trust
The Sobell Foundation
The South Square Trust
The Stephen R and Philippa H
Southall Charitable Trust
The W F Southall Trust
R H Southern Trust
The Spero Foundation
The Stafford Trust
The Staples Trust
The Steel Charitable Trust
The June Stevens Foundation
Stevenson Family's Charitable
Trust
The Sylvanus Charitable Trust
The Mrs A Lacy Tate Trust
The Connie and Albert Taylor
Charitable Trust
Tearfund
The Loke Wan Tho Memorial
Foundation
The Three Guineas Trust
The Underwood Trust
The Valentine Charitable Trust
The William and Patricia
Venton Charitable Trust
Roger Vere Foundation
Wales Council for Voluntary
Action
The Waterloo Foundation
The David Webster Charitable
Trust
The Westminster Foundation
The Garfield Weston
Foundation
The Whitaker Charitable Trust
The Colonel W H Whitbread
Charitable Trust
The Simon Whitbread
Charitable Trust
A H and B C Whiteley
Charitable Trust
The Whitley Animal Protection
Trust
The Richard Wilcox Welfare
Charity

The Will Charitable Trust
The H D H Wills 1965
Charitable Trust
J and J R Wilson Trust
The Wixamtree Trust
Woodlands Trust
Woodroffe Benton Foundation
The Woodward Charitable
Trust
The A and R Woolf Charitable
Trust
ME Woolfe Charitable Trust
The Diana Edgson Wright
Charitable Trust
Yorkshire Agricultural Society
The Yorkshire Dales
Millennium Trust
Zephyr Charitable Trust

Agriculture and fishing

The C Alma Baker Trust
CLA Charitable Trust
The Ecology Trust
The John Ellerman Foundation
Esmée Fairbairn Foundation
The Farmers' Company
Charitable Fund
The Fishmongers' Company's
Charitable Trust
The Oliver Ford Charitable
Trust
The Worshipful Company of
Gardeners of London
The Gatsby Charitable
Foundation
The G C Gibson Charitable
Trust
The Headley Trust
The J J Charitable Trust
The John Spedan Lewis
Foundation
The Limbourne Trust
LSA Charitable Trust
The MacRobert Trust
Manchester Airport Community
Trust Fund
Marchig Animal Welfare Trust
Martin McLaren Memorial
Trust
The Mears Foundation
The NFU Mutual Charitable
Trust
The John Oldacre Foundation
The Frank Parkinson
Agricultural Trust
The Cecil Pilkington Charitable
Trust
Mr and Mrs J A Pye's
Charitable Settlement
Quartet Community Foundation
(formerly the Greater Bristol
Foundation)

The Peter Samuel Charitable
Trust
Seafarers UK (King George's
Fund for Sailors)
The Stanley Smith UK
Horticultural Trust
The Waterloo Foundation
The Garfield Weston
Foundation
Yorkshire Agricultural Society

Farming and food production

CLA Charitable Trust
The Farmers' Company
Charitable Fund
The Gatsby Charitable
Foundation
The J J Charitable Trust
The Limbourne Trust
Mr and Mrs J A Pye's
Charitable Settlement

Fishing and fisheries

The Fishmongers' Company's
Charitable Trust
The John Spedan Lewis
Foundation
Seafarers UK (King George's
Fund for Sailors)

Forestry

CLA Charitable Trust
The Headley Trust
Manchester Airport Community
Trust Fund
Mr and Mrs J A Pye's
Charitable Settlement
The Peter Samuel Charitable
Trust

Horticulture

CLA Charitable Trust
The Oliver Ford Charitable
Trust
The Worshipful Company of
Gardeners of London
The Gatsby Charitable
Foundation
The John Spedan Lewis
Foundation
LSA Charitable Trust
The MacRobert Trust
Martin McLaren Memorial
Trust
The Stanley Smith UK
Horticultural Trust

Animal care

The Alborada Trust
The Animal Defence Trust
The Arthur Ronald Dyer
  Charitable Trust
The Astor Foundation
Harry Bacon Foundation
The Bellahouston Bequest
  Fund
Briggs Animal Welfare Trust
Calypso Browning Trust
The Wilfrid and Constance
  Cave Foundation
The Cemlyn-Jones Trust
The Chelsea Square 1994
  Trust
The Robert Clutterbuck
  Charitable Trust
The Marjorie Coote Animal
  Charity Trust
The Dumbreck Charity
The EBM Charitable Trust
The Beryl Evetts and Robert
  Luff Animal Welfare Trust
The Matthew Eyton Animal
  Welfare Trust
The Anna Rosa Forster
  Charitable Trust
The GMW Charitable Trust
The GNC Trust
The Doris Louise Hailes
  Charitable Trust
The Edith Lilian Harrison 2000
  Foundation
William Geoffrey Harvey's
  Discretionary Settlement
The Joanna Herbert-Stepney
  Charitable Settlement (also
  known as The Paget
  Charitable Trust)
The J G Hogg Charitable Trust
The Homestead Charitable
  Trust
The Michael and Shirley Hunt
  Charitable Trust
The Barbara Joyce Jarrald
  Charitable Trust
The Kennel Club Charitable
  Trust
The William and Katherine
  Longman Trust
The Lyons Charitable Trust
The R S Macdonald Charitable
  Trust
Marchig Animal Welfare Trust
The Millward Charitable Trust
The Edith Murphy Foundation
Alice Noakes Memorial
  Charitable Trust
The Sir Peter O'Sullevan
  Charitable Trust
Old Possum's Practical Trust
The Oldham Foundation
Open Gate
The Persula Foundation
The Petplan Charitable Trust

The Phillips Charitable Trust
The Elise Pilkington Charitable
  Trust
The Joseph Rank Trust
The Jean Sainsbury Animal
  Welfare Trust
The Saints and Sinners Trust
The Sandra Charitable Trust
The Scotshill Trust
The John Slater Foundation
Ruth Smart Foundation
The Sylvanus Charitable Trust
The William and Patricia
  Venton Charitable Trust
The Richard Wilcox Welfare
  Charity
The H D H Wills 1965
  Charitable Trust
J and J R Wilson Trust
The Wixamtree Trust
ME Woolfe Charitable Trust

Animal conservation

A J H Ashby Will Trust
Birmingham International
  Airport Community Trust
The Body Shop Foundation
The Carron Charitable
  Settlement
The Wilfrid and Constance
  Cave Foundation
The Cemlyn-Jones Trust
The Robert Clutterbuck
  Charitable Trust
The Marjorie Coote Animal
  Charity Trust
The Dr and Mrs A Darlington
  Charitable Trust
William Dean Countryside and
  Educational Trust
The Dumbreck Charity
Samuel William Farmer Trust
Sydney E Franklin Deceased's
  New Second Charity
Maurice Fry Charitable Trust
The GMW Charitable Trust
The GNC Trust
William Geoffrey Harvey's
  Discretionary Settlement
The Joanna Herbert-Stepney
  Charitable Settlement (also
  known as The Paget
  Charitable Trust)
The Barbara Joyce Jarrald
  Charitable Trust
The Kreitman Foundation
The John Spedan Lewis
  Foundation
The Lotus Foundation
Marchig Animal Welfare Trust
The Oakdale Trust
Old Possum's Practical Trust
The Owen Family Trust

The Jack Patston Charitable
  Trust
Mr and Mrs J A Pye's
  Charitable Settlement
The Joseph Rank Trust
The Rhododendron Trust
The Rufford Small Grants
  Foundation
Ryklow Charitable Trust 1992
  (also known as A B
  Williamson Charitable Trust)
The Michael Harry Sacher
  Trust
The Jean Sainsbury Animal
  Welfare Trust
The Simpson Education and
  Conservation Trust
The David Webster Charitable
  Trust
The Whitley Animal Protection
  Trust
The H D H Wills 1965
  Charitable Trust
ME Woolfe Charitable Trust
The Diana Edgson Wright
  Charitable Trust

Climate change

The Bromley Trust
The John Ellerman Foundation
Esmée Fairbairn Foundation
The Joseph Rank Trust
The Three Guineas Trust
The Waterloo Foundation

Countryside

The Aberbrothock Skea Trust
The Astor Foundation
The BAA Communities Trust
The Big Lottery Fund
The Blair Foundation
The Bothwell Charitable Trust
The Bromley Trust
The Cadbury Foundation
M R Cannon 1998 Charitable
  Trust
CLA Charitable Trust
Colyer-Fergusson Charitable
  Trust
The Ernest Cook Trust
The D J H Currie Memorial
  Trust
The D'Oyly Carte Charitable
  Trust
The Dr and Mrs A Darlington
  Charitable Trust
The Helen and Geoffrey De
  Freitas Charitable Trust
The Dunn Family Charitable
  Trust
The John Ellerman Foundation
The Ellis Campbell Foundation
The Alan Evans Memorial Trust

Esmée Fairbairn Foundation
Samuel William Farmer Trust
The Freshfield Foundation
Maurice Fry Charitable Trust
The Galanthus Trust
The Gannochy Trust
Gatwick Airport Community
  Trust
J Paul Getty Jr Charitable Trust
The Girdlers' Company
  Charitable Trust
The GNC Trust
The Gough Charitable Trust
The Green Room Charitable
  Trust
The Idlewild Trust
The John Spedan Lewis
  Foundation
Manchester Airport Community
  Trust Fund
Sir George Martin Trust
The Mears Foundation
The Kitty and Daniel Nabarro
  Charitable Trust
The Pilgrim Trust
The Cecil Pilkington Charitable
  Trust
Quartet Community Foundation
  (formerly the Greater Bristol
  Foundation)
The Joseph Rank Trust
The Rufford Small Grants
  Foundation
Ryklow Charitable Trust 1992
  (also known as A B
  Williamson Charitable Trust)
Schroder Charity Trust
The Linley Shaw Foundation
The Connie and Albert Taylor
  Charitable Trust
The Valentine Charitable Trust
The Waterloo Foundation
The David Webster Charitable
  Trust
The Garfield Weston
  Foundation
The Whitaker Charitable Trust
The Colonel W H Whitbread
  Charitable Trust
The Simon Whitbread
  Charitable Trust
The Will Charitable Trust
Woodroffe Benton Foundation
Zephyr Charitable Trust

Environmental education and research

The BAA Communities Trust
The Big Lottery Fund
Birmingham International
  Airport Community Trust
The Body Shop Foundation
The Cadbury Foundation

CLA Charitable Trust
The Ernest Cook Trust
The Helen and Geoffrey De
  Freitas Charitable Trust
William Dean Countryside and
  Educational Trust
The Duis Charitable Trust
The Dulverton Trust
The Dunn Family Charitable
  Trust
EAGA Partnership Charitable
  Trust
The John Ellerman Foundation
Esmée Fairbairn Foundation
Gatwick Airport Community
  Trust
The Green Room Charitable
  Trust
The J J Charitable Trust
The Mark Leonard Trust
The John Spedan Lewis
  Foundation
The Limbourne Trust
Llysdinam Charitable Trust
Manchester Airport Community
  Trust Fund
Marchig Animal Welfare Trust
Marmot Charitable Trust
The Mears Foundation
The Kitty and Daniel Nabarro
  Charitable Trust
Network for Social Change
Oglesby Charitable Trust
The Cecil Pilkington Charitable
  Trust
The Porter Foundation
Quartet Community Foundation
  (formerly the Greater Bristol
  Foundation)
The Joseph Rank Trust
The Rufford Small Grants
  Foundation
The Saintbury Trust
The Stanley Smith UK
  Horticultural Trust
The Sobell Foundation
The Spero Foundation
The Staples Trust
The Waterloo Foundation
The Garfield Weston
  Foundation
The Woodward Charitable
  Trust

Natural environment

A J H Ashby Will Trust
The Ashendene Trust
The BAA Communities Trust
The Balney Charitable Trust
The Blair Foundation
The Bromley Trust
The Christopher Cadbury
  Charitable Trust

The Cadbury Foundation
The Carron Charitable
  Settlement
The Robert Clutterbuck
  Charitable Trust
The Conscience Trust
The Conservation Foundation
The Ernest Cook Trust
The D'Oyly Carte Charitable
  Trust
The Dr and Mrs A Darlington
  Charitable Trust
The Helen and Geoffrey De
  Freitas Charitable Trust
William Dean Countryside and
  Educational Trust
The Dulverton Trust
The Houghton Dunn Charitable
  Trust
The Dunn Family Charitable
  Trust
The John Ellerman Foundation
The Elmgrant Trust
The Ericson Trust
Esmée Fairbairn Foundation
Samuel William Farmer Trust
Maurice Fry Charitable Trust
The Galanthus Trust
The Gannochy Trust
Gatwick Airport Community
  Trust
J Paul Getty Jr Charitable Trust
The Girdlers' Company
  Charitable Trust
The Glastonbury Trust Limited
The Green Room Charitable
  Trust
The Headley Trust
The J J Charitable Trust
The John Spedan Lewis
  Foundation
The Limbourne Trust
Manchester Airport Community
  Trust Fund
Marchig Animal Welfare Trust
The Marsh Christian Trust
The Mears Foundation
The Mercers' Charitable
  Foundation
The Mersey Docks and
  Harbour Company
  Charitable Fund
The Metropolitan Drinking
  Fountain and Cattle Trough
  Association
T and J Meyer Family
  Foundation Limited
Millennium Stadium Charitable
  Trust
The Peter Minet Trust
The Nchima Trust
The Oakdale Trust
The Owen Family Trust
The Jack Patston Charitable
  Trust

The Cecil Pilkington Charitable
Trust
Polden-Puckham Charitable
Foundation
Mr and Mrs J A Pye's
Charitable Settlement
Quartet Community Foundation
(formerly the Greater Bristol
Foundation)
The Joseph Rank Trust
The Sigrid Rausing Trust
The Rhododendron Trust
The Rufford Small Grants
Foundation
Ryklow Charitable Trust 1992
(also known as A B
Williamson Charitable Trust)
The Saintbury Trust
The Hon. M J Samuel
Charitable Trust
The Peter Samuel Charitable
Trust
Schroder Charity Trust
The Simpson Education and
Conservation Trust
The Stanley Smith UK
Horticultural Trust
Stevenson Family's Charitable
Trust
The Valentine Charitable Trust
The Waterloo Foundation
The David Webster Charitable
Trust
The Garfield Weston
Foundation
The Will Charitable Trust
The H D H Wills 1965
Charitable Trust
Woodroffe Benton Foundation
Zephyr Charitable Trust

Flora and fauna

A J H Ashby Will Trust
The Ashendene Trust
The Balney Charitable Trust
The Blair Foundation
The Ernest Cook Trust
The Dulverton Trust
The Houghton Dunn Charitable
Trust
The J J Charitable Trust
Manchester Airport Community
Trust Fund
Marchig Animal Welfare Trust
The Marsh Christian Trust
The Mercers' Charitable
Foundation
The Jack Patston Charitable
Trust
Mr and Mrs J A Pye's
Charitable Settlement
The Peter Samuel Charitable
Trust
The Simpson Education and
Conservation Trust

The Stanley Smith UK
Horticultural Trust
The Valentine Charitable Trust
The Will Charitable Trust
The H D H Wills 1965
Charitable Trust

Water resources

The Headley Trust
The Mersey Docks and
Harbour Company
Charitable Fund
The Metropolitan Drinking
Fountain and Cattle Trough
Association
The Nchima Trust
Mr and Mrs J A Pye's
Charitable Settlement

Wild places, wilderness

The Dulverton Trust
J Paul Getty Jr Charitable Trust
The Girdlers' Company
Charitable Trust

Pollution abatement and control

The John Ellerman Foundation
Esmée Fairbairn Foundation
Gatwick Airport Community
Trust
The Green Room Charitable
Trust
Lancashire Environmental
Fund
The Limbourne Trust
Marmot Charitable Trust
The Mears Foundation
Prairie Trust
Quartet Community Foundation
(formerly the Greater Bristol
Foundation)
The Joseph Rank Trust
The Sigrid Rausing Trust
The Saintbury Trust
The Valentine Charitable Trust
The Waterloo Foundation
The Garfield Weston
Foundation
Woodroffe Benton Foundation
Zephyr Charitable Trust

Sustainable environment

The 1970 Trust
The AIM Foundation

The Associated Country
Women of the World
(ACWW)
The BAA Communities Trust
The Body Shop Foundation
The Bromley Trust
The Cadbury Foundation
Calouste Gulbenkian
Foundation
J A Clark Charitable Trust
The Conscience Trust
The Dunn Family Charitable
Trust
EAGA Partnership Charitable
Trust
The Ecology Trust
The John Ellerman Foundation
Esmée Fairbairn Foundation
The Freshfield Foundation
The Fuellers Charitable Trust
Fund
The Gannochy Trust
Gatwick Airport Community
Trust
Generations Charitable Trust
The Glastonbury Trust Limited
The Green Room Charitable
Trust
The J J Charitable Trust
John Laing Charitable Trust
Lancashire Environmental
Fund
The Mark Leonard Trust
The Limbourne Trust
Manchester Airport Community
Trust Fund
Marmot Charitable Trust
The Mears Foundation
Open Gate
Polden-Puckham Charitable
Foundation
Quartet Community Foundation
(formerly the Greater Bristol
Foundation)
The Joseph Rank Trust
The Sigrid Rausing Trust
The Rufford Small Grants
Foundation
The Saintbury Trust
The Staples Trust
The Waterloo Foundation
The David Webster Charitable
Trust
The Garfield Weston
Foundation
Woodroffe Benton Foundation
Zephyr Charitable Trust

Energy issues

The 1970 Trust
The BAA Communities Trust
EAGA Partnership Charitable
Trust
The Fuellers Charitable Trust
Fund

The Mark Leonard Trust

Loss of environment

The Rufford Small Grants Foundation

Transport

The 1970 Trust
Gatwick Airport Community Trust
The Gosling Foundation Limited
The Green Room Charitable Trust
The J J Charitable Trust
Rees Jeffreys Road Fund
The Mears Foundation
Quartet Community Foundation (formerly the Greater Bristol Foundation)
The Joseph Rank Trust
The Rochester Bridge Trust
Seafarers UK (King George's Fund for Sailors)
The Shipwrights' Company Charitable Fund
The Garfield Weston Foundation

General charitable purposes

The 1989 Willan Charitable Trust
The 29th May 1961 Charitable Trust
The Acacia Charitable Trust
The Adnams Charity
The Green and Lilian F M Ainsworth and Family Benevolent Fund
The Sylvia Aitken Charitable Trust
The Albion Trust
D G Albright Charitable Trust
Allchurches Trust Ltd
The H B Allen Charitable Trust
The Alliance Family Foundation
Almondsbury Charity
AM Charitable Trust
The Amalur Foundation Limited
Sir John and Lady Amory's Charitable Trust
The Ampelos Trust
Andor Charitable Trust
The Henry Angest Foundation
The Annandale Charitable Trust
The Anson Charitable Trust
Ambrose and Ann Appelbe Trust
The John Apthorp Charitable Trust
The Arbib Foundation
The John M Archer Charitable Trust
The Ardeola Charitable Trust
The Ardwick Trust
The Argentarius Foundation
The Armourers' and Brasiers' Gauntlet Trust
The Arnold Foundation
Arsenal Charitable Trust
The Ashendene Trust
The Norman C Ashton Foundation
The Ashworth Charitable Trust
The Ian Askew Charitable Trust
The Astor Foundation
Autonomous Research Charitable Trust
The Avenue Charitable Trust
AW Charitable Trust
Awards for All
The Aylesford Family Charitable Trust
B W Charitable Trust
The BACTA Charitable Trust
The Scott Bader Commonwealth Ltd
The Bagri Foundation
The Andrew Balint Charitable Trust
The George Balint Charitable Trust

The Paul Balint Charitable Trust
The Albert Casanova Ballard Deceased Trust
Balmain Charitable Trust
The Bamford Charitable Foundation
The Banbury Charities
The Band Trust
Peter Barker-Mill Memorial Charity
Lord Barnby's Foundation
The Barnsbury Charitable Trust
The Barnstaple Bridge Trust
The Misses Barrie Charitable Trust
Stephen J Barry Charitable Trust
The Bartlett Taylor Charitable Trust
The Worshipful Company of Basketmakers' Charitable Trust
The Paul Bassham Charitable Trust
The Batchworth Trust
The Bay Tree Charitable Trust
D H and L H Baylin Charitable Trust
The Louis Baylis (Maidenhead Advertiser) Charitable Trust
BC Partners Foundation
BCH Trust
The Bearder Charity
The James Beattie Charitable Trust
The Beaverbrook Foundation
The Beccles Town Lands Charity
The Becker Family Charitable Trust
The Victoria and David Beckham Children's Charity
The Peter Beckwith Charitable Trust
The Bedfordshire and Luton Community Foundation
The David and Ruth Behrend Fund
Bellasis Trust
The Bellinger Donnay Trust
The Benfield Motors Charitable Trust
The Benham Charitable Settlement
Maurice and Jacqueline Bennett Charitable Trust
Michael and Leslie Bennett Charitable Trust
The Gerald Bentall Charitable Trust
The Ruth Berkowitz Charitable Trust
The Berkshire Community Foundation

Thomas Betton's Charity for
Pensions and Relief-in-Need
The Bideford Bridge Trust
The Billmeir Charitable Trust
The Bingham Trust
The Birmingham Community
Foundation
The Lord Mayor of
Birmingham's Charity
Birthday House Trust
The Michael Bishop
Foundation
The Bertie Black Foundation
Blackheart Foundation (UK)
Limited
Isabel Blackman Foundation
The BlackRock (UK) Charitable
Trust
The Blair Foundation
The Sir Victor Blank Charitable
Settlement
The Neville and Elaine Blond
Charitable Trust
The Bluston Charitable
Settlement
The Bonamy Charitable Trust
The John and Celia Bonham
Christie Charitable Trust
The Charlotte Bonham-Carter
Charitable Trust
The Linda and Gordon
Bonnyman Charitable Trust
The Bordon and Liphook
Charity
H E and E L Botteley
Charitable Trust
Community Foundation for
Bournemouth, Dorset and
Poole
The Bower Trust
The William Brake Charitable
Trust
The Liz and Terry Bramall
Charitable Trust
The Bransford Trust
The Brendish Family
Foundation
Bridgepoint Inspire
The Britto Foundation
The J and M Britton Charitable
Trust
The Charles and Edna
Broadhurst Charitable Trust
The Roger Brooke Charitable
Trust
Joseph Brough Charitable
Trust
The Swinfen Broun Charitable
Trust
Mrs E E Brown Charitable
Settlement
Bill Brown's Charitable
Settlement
Brown-Mellows Trust
Brownsword Charitable
Foundation

T B H Brunner's Charitable
Settlement
The Jack Brunton Charitable
Trust
The Bruntwood Charity
The Bryant Trust
The Buckinghamshire Masonic
Centenary Fund
Buckland Charitable Trust
The Buffini Chao Foundation
The Bulldog Trust Limited
The Burden Trust
Burdens Charitable Foundation
The Geoffrey Burton Charitable
Trust
Consolidated Charity of Burton
upon Trent
The Derek Butler Trust
The C Charitable Trust
Edward Cadbury Charitable
Trust
P H G Cadbury Charitable
Trust
The Christopher Cadbury
Charitable Trust
The G W Cadbury Charitable
Trust
The Richard Cadbury
Charitable Trust
The Edward and Dorothy
Cadbury Trust
The George Cadbury Trust
The Cadogan Charity
The Callander Charitable Trust
Calleva Foundation
The Camelia Trust
The Frederick and Phyllis Cann
Trust
The Canning Trust
H and L Cantor Trust
Cardy Beaver Foundation
The Carew Pole Charitable
Trust
The D W T Cargill Fund
The Carlton House Charitable
Trust
The Carpenters' Company
Charitable Trust
The Carrington Charitable
Trust
The Carvill Trust
The Casey Trust
The Castanea Trust
The Caswell Family Charitable
Trust
The Catalyst Charitable Trust
(formerly the Buckle Family
Charitable Trust)
The Joseph and Annie Cattle
Trust
The Thomas Sivewright Catto
Charitable Settlement
The Wilfrid and Constance
Cave Foundation
The Cayo Foundation

The B G S Cayzer Charitable
Trust
The Cazenove Charitable Trust
The CBD Charitable Trust
R E Chadwick Charitable Trust
The Amelia Chadwick Trust
The Pamela Champion
Foundation
The Chapman Charitable Trust
The Charities Advisory Trust
The Charter 600 Charity
The Worshipful Company of
Chartered Accountants
General Charitable Trust
(also known as CALC)
The Cheruby Trust
The Cheshire Provincial Fund
of Benevolence
The Chetwode Foundation
Chevioty Asset Management
Charitable Trust
The Malcolm Chick Charity
Childs Charitable Trust
The Chippenham Borough
Lands Charity
CHK Charities Limited
The Chownes Foundation
Christian Aid
Chrysalis Trust
Church Burgesses Trust
City and County of Swansea
Welsh Church Act Fund
The Hilda and Alice Clark
Charitable Trust
The Roger and Sarah Bancroft
Clark Charitable Trust
The Cleary Foundation
The Cleevely Family Charitable
Trust
Lord Clinton's Charitable Trust
Closehelm Ltd
The Clothworkers' Foundation
Clydpride Ltd
The Coalfields Regeneration
Trust
The John Coates Charitable
Trust
The Cobalt Trust
The Cobtree Charity Trust Ltd
The John S Cohen Foundation
John Coldman Charitable Trust
The Cole Charitable Trust
The Colefax Charitable Trust
The George Henry Collins
Charity
The Sir Jeremiah Colman Gift
Trust
Community Foundation for
Calderdale
The Compton Charitable Trust
The Douglas Compton James
Charitable Trust
The Congleton Inclosure Trust
The Cook and Wolstenholme
Charitable Trust

The Catherine Cookson
Charitable Trust
The Cookson Charitable Trust
Mabel Cooper Charity
The Alice Ellen Cooper Dean
Charitable Foundation
The Helen Jean Cope Trust
The Gershon Coren Charitable
Foundation
Michael Cornish Charitable
Trust
The Evan Cornish Foundation
Cornwall Community
Foundation
The Duke of Cornwall's
Benevolent Fund
The Cornwell Charitable Trust
The Sidney and Elizabeth
Corob Charitable Trust
County Durham Community
Foundation
The Augustine Courtauld Trust
Coutts Charitable Trust
The General Charities of the
City of Coventry
Coventry Building Society
Charitable Foundation
The Sir Tom Cowie Charitable
Trust
Cowley Charitable Foundation
The Lord Cozens-Hardy Trust
The Craignish Trust
The Craps Charitable Trust
The Cray Trust
Cripplegate Foundation
The Croydon Relief in Need
Charities
The Mayor of Croydon's
Charity Fund
Cruden Foundation Ltd
The Ronald Cruickshank's
Foundation
The R D Crusaders Foundation
Cullum Family Trust
The Culra Charitable Trust
The Cumber Family Charitable
Trust
Cumberland Building Society
Charitable Foundation
The Dennis Curry Charitable
Trust
The Raymond Curtis Charitable
Trust
The Manny Cussins
Foundation
The Cutler Trust (the
Worshipful Company of
Makers of Playing Cards)
The Cwmbran Trust
The D G Charitable Settlement
The Daisy Trust
The Alderman Joe Davidson
Memorial Trust
Michael Davies Charitable
Settlement

The Gwendoline and Margaret
Davies Charity
Davis-Rubens Charitable Trust
The De Clermont Charitable
Company Ltd
Peter De Haan Charitable
Trust
The De Laszlo Foundation
The Leopold De Rothschild
Charitable Trust
The Dellal Foundation
The Delves Charitable Trust
The Demigryphon Trust
The Denton Wilde Sapte
Charitable Trust
The Earl of Derby's Charitable
Trust
Derbyshire Community
Foundation
Devon Community Foundation
The Duke of Devonshire's
Charitable Trust
The Sandy Dewhirst Charitable
Trust
The Laduma Dhamecha
Charitable Trust
Alan and Sheila Diamond
Charitable Trust
David and Rose Diamond Trust
The Dibden Allotments Fund
The Gillian Dickinson Trust
The Dickon Trust
Dischma Charitable Trust
The Djanogly Foundation
The DLM Charitable Trust
Louise Dobson Charitable
Trust
The Dollond Charitable Trust
The Dorus Trust
Double 'O' Charity Ltd
The R M Douglas Charitable
Trust
The Drapers' Charitable Fund
Dromintee Trust
The Dulverton Trust
The P B Dumbell Charitable
Trust
The Dumbreck Charity
Ronald Duncan Literary
Foundation
The Dunn Family Charitable
Trust
The Charles Dunstone
Charitable Trust
Mildred Duveen Charitable
Trust
Annette Duvollet Charitable
Trust
The Dwek Family Charitable
Trust
The Dyers' Company
Charitable Trust
The James Dyson Foundation
The Eagle Charity Trust
Audrey Earle Charitable Trust
The Earley Charity

The Earmark Trust
East London Community
Foundation
The Gilbert and Eileen Edgar
Foundation
The Edinburgh Trust, No 2
Account
Edinburgh Voluntary
Organisations' Trust Funds
The George Elias Charitable
Trust
The Wilfred and Elsie Elkes
Charity Fund
The Maud Elkington Charitable
Trust
The Ellerdale Trust
The Edith Maud Ellis 1985
Charitable Trust
The Elm House Trust
The Elmgrant Trust
The Emerton-Christie Charity
Empath UK
The Englefield Charitable Trust
The Epigoni Trust
The Equilibrium Foundation
The Erskine Cunningham Hill
Trust
Essex Community Foundation
The Essex Fairway Charitable
Trust
Essex Provincial Charity Fund
The Estelle Trust
Joseph Ettedgui Charitable
Foundation
The Eventhall Family
Charitable Trust
The Everard Foundation
The Mayor of Exeter's Appeal
Fund
The William and Christine
Eynon Charity
The Faber Charitable Trust
The Fairstead Trust
The Fairway Trust
The Fairwind Trust
The Lord Faringdon Charitable
Trust
The Thomas Farr Charitable
Trust
Walter Farthing (Trust) Limited
Farthing Trust
The Fassnidge Memorial Trust
The Fawcett Charitable Trust
The John Feeney Charitable
Trust
The A M Fenton Trust
The Fidelity UK Foundation
The Bluff Field Charitable Trust
The Doris Field Charitable
Trust
Fife Council/Common Good
Funds and Trusts
The Sir John Fisher Foundation
Fisherbeck Charitable Trust
The Earl Fitzwilliam Charitable
Trust

The Rose Flatau Charitable Trust
Florence's Charitable Trust
The Mrs Yvonne Flux Charitable Trust
The Gerald Fogel Charitable Trust
The Foresters' Charity Stewards UK Trust
Forever Manchester (The Community Foundation for Greater Manchester)
Gwyneth Forrester Trust
The Donald Forrester Trust
The Isaac and Freda Frankel Memorial Charitable Trust
The Elizabeth Frankland Moore and Star Foundation
The Gordon Fraser Charitable Trust
The Hugh Fraser Foundation
The Joseph Strong Frazer Trust
The Louis and Valerie Freedman Charitable Settlement
The Michael and Clara Freeman Charitable Trust
The Freemasons' Grand Charity
The Charles S French Charitable Trust
The Anne French Memorial Trust
The Freshgate Trust Foundation
The Friarsgate Trust
Friends of Wiznitz Limited
The Patrick Frost Foundation
The Fuellers Charitable Trust Fund
Worshipful Company of Furniture Makers Charitable Fund
The Galbraith Trust
The Gale Family Charitable Trust
The Gamlen Charitable Trust
The Gamma Trust
The Ganzoni Charitable Trust
The Gatsby Charitable Foundation
The Robert Gavron Charitable Trust
Simon Gibson Charitable Trust
The G C Gibson Charitable Trust
Lady Gibson's Charitable Trust
The Harvey and Hilary Gilbert Charitable Trust
Global Charities (formerly GCap Charities)
Worshipful Company of Glovers of London Charity Fund
GMC Trust
The GMW Charitable Trust

The GNC Trust
The Golden Bottle Trust
The Goldmark Trust
The Goldsmiths' Company Charity
The Everard and Mina Goodman Charitable Foundation
Mike Gooley Trailfinders Charity
The Gosling Foundation Limited
The Gough Charitable Trust
The Gould Charitable Trust
The Hemraj Goyal Foundation
A B Grace Trust
The Graff Foundation
A and S Graham Charitable Trust
Grampian Police Diced Cap Charitable Fund
Grand Charitable Trust of the Order of Women Freemasons
Grantham Yorke Trust
GrantScape
The J G Graves Charitable Trust
The Gray Trust
The Great Stone Bridge Trust of Edenbridge
The Great Torrington Town Lands Charity
The Constance Green Foundation
The Philip Green Memorial Trust
The Green Room Charitable Trust
Mrs H R Greene Charitable Settlement
Greenham Common Community Trust Limited
Greggs Foundation (formerly Greggs Trust)
The Gretna Charitable Trust
The Grocers' Charity
The GRP Charitable Trust
The Bishop of Guildford's Foundation
The Walter Guinness Charitable Trust
The Gunter Charitable Trust
The H and J Spack Charitable Trust
H and T Clients Charitable Trust
The Edith Winifred Hall Charitable Trust
Robert Hall Charity
Hamilton Wallace Trust
Sue Hammerson's Charitable Trust
The Hammonds Charitable Trust

Hampshire and Isle of Wight Community Foundation
The Hampstead Wells and Campden Trust
Hampton Fuel Allotment Charity
The W A Handley Charitable Trust
The Kathleen Hannay Memorial Charity
The Doughty Hanson Charitable Foundation
Lord Hanson Foundation
The Haramead Trust
The Harbour Charitable Trust
The Harbour Foundation
The Hare of Steep Charitable Trust
The Harebell Centenary Fund
The Hargrave Foundation
The Edith Lilian Harrison 2000 Foundation
The Spencer Hart Charitable Trust
The Hartley Charitable Trust
The Edward Harvist Trust Fund
The Maurice Hatter Foundation
The M A Hawe Settlement
The Hawerby Trust
The Hawthorne Charitable Trust
Headley-Pitt Charitable Trust
Heagerty Charitable Trust
May Hearnshaw's Charity
The Heart of England Community Foundation
The Heathcoat Trust
Heathside Charitable Trust
The Charlotte Heber-Percy Charitable Trust
The Hedera Charitable Trust
Percy Hedley 1990 Charitable Trust
The Hedley Denton Charitable Trust
The Hemby Trust
The Christina Mary Hendrie Trust for Scottish and Canadian Charities
The Tim Henman Charitable Foundation
Esther Hennell Charitable Trust
The Joanna Herbert-Stepney Charitable Settlement (also known as The Paget Charitable Trust)
The Herefordshire Community Foundation
The Hertfordshire Community Foundation
The Rosalind Hicks Charitable Trust
The Higgs Charitable Trust
The Hilden Charitable Fund
The Hill Charitable Trust

Hille Pandana
The Hillingdon Partnership Trust
R G Hills Charitable Trust
Lady Hind Trust
The Henry C Hoare Charitable Trust
The Eleemosynary Charity of William Hobbayne
The Sir Julian Hodge Charitable Trust
The Jane Hodge Foundation
The J G Hogg Charitable Trust
The Hollick Family Charitable Trust
The Holliday Foundation
The Dorothy Holmes Charitable Trust
The Holmes Family Trust (Sheffield)
P H Holt Foundation
Mary Homfray Charitable Trust
The Horizon Foundation
The Antony Hornby Charitable Trust
The Worshipful Company of Horners' Charitable Trusts
The Hornsey Parochial Charities
The Hospital of God at Greatham
The Sir Joseph Hotung Charitable Settlement
The House of Industry Estate
The Daniel Howard Trust
The Clifford Howarth Charity Trust
The Howe Family Foundation
HTA Sheba Foundation UK
The Hudson Foundation
The Huggard Charitable Trust
The Hull and East Riding Charitable Trust
The P Y N and B Hyams Trust
The Iliffe Family Charitable Trust
Impetus Trust
The Ingram Trust
The Inman Charity
The Inverforth Charitable Trust
The Ironmongers' Foundation
The Charles Irving Charitable Trust
Irwin Trust
The ISA Charity
The Isaacs Charitable Trust
The J Isaacs Charitable Trust
The Isle of Anglesey Charitable Trust
Isle of Dogs Community Foundation
The Jabbs Foundation
Elizabeth Jackson Charitable Trust
John James Bristol Foundation
The Nick Jenkins Foundation

The Jenour Foundation
The Jephcott Charitable Trust
The Jonathan Joels Charitable Trust
The Norman Joels Charitable Trust
The Johnson Group Cleaners Charity
The Joicey Trust
The Jones 1986 Charitable Trust
Dezna Robins Jones Charitable Foundation
The Marjorie and Geoffrey Jones Charitable Trust
The Muriel Jones Foundation
The Jordan Charitable Foundation
The Joron Charitable Trust
The Lady Eileen Joseph Foundation
The Josh Charitable Trust
JTH Charitable Trust
The Anton Jurgens Charitable Trust
The Stanley Kalms Foundation
The Kalou Foundation
The Karenza Foundation
The Boris Karloff Charitable Foundation
The Michael and Ilse Katz Foundation
The Kaufman Charitable Trust
The Geoffrey John Kaye Charitable Foundation
The Soli and Leah Kelaty Trust Fund
The Kennedy Charitable Foundation
The Nancy Kenyon Charitable Trust
Keren Association
E and E Kernkraut Charities Limited
The Kessler Foundation
The Ursula Keyes Trust
The Eric and Margaret Kinder Charitable Trust
The King Henry VIII Endowed Trust Warwick
King Sturge Charitable Trust
The King/Cullimore Charitable Trust
Kinsurdy Charitable Trust
The Richard Kirkman Charitable Trust
Robert Kitchin (Saddlers' Company)
Ernest Kleinwort Charitable Trust
The Sir James Knott Trust
The Late Sir Pierce Lacy Charity Trust
John Laing Charitable Trust
The Christopher Laing Foundation

The David Laing Foundation
The Kirby Laing Foundation
The Martin Laing Foundation
Duchy of Lancaster Benevolent Fund
The Jack Lane Charitable Trust
The Langdale Trust
The Langley Charitable Trust
The Langtree Trust
Lauchentilly Charitable Foundation 1988
The Lauffer Family Charitable Foundation
The Kathleen Laurence Trust
The Lawson Beckman Charitable Trust
The Raymond and Blanche Lawson Charitable Trust
The Leach Fourteenth Trust
The Leathersellers' Company Charitable Fund
The Lord Mayor of Leeds Appeal Fund
Leeds Building Society Charitable Foundation
Leicester Charity Link (formerly The Leicester Charity Organisation Society)
The Kennedy Leigh Charitable Trust
Morris Leigh Foundation
Mrs Vera Leigh's Charity
The P Leigh-Bramwell Trust 'E'
The Lennox and Wyfold Foundation
The Erica Leonard Trust
The Mark Leonard Trust
Lord Leverhulme's Charitable Trust
The Sir Edward Lewis Foundation
Liberum Foundation
Lichfield Conduit Lands
The Liebreich Foundation
The Lightbridge Foundation
The Thomas Lilley Memorial Trust
Limoges Charitable Trust
The Linbury Trust
Lincolnshire Community Foundation
The Linden Charitable Trust
Lindenleaf Charitable Trust
The Enid Linder Foundation
The Linmardon Trust
The Ruth and Stuart Lipton Charitable Trust
The Lister Charitable Trust
The Second Joseph Aaron Littman Foundation
The George John and Sheilah Livanos Charitable Trust
Liverpool Charity and Voluntary Services
Jack Livingstone Charitable Trust

The Elaine and Angus Lloyd
Charitable Trust
The Lloyd Fund
Lloyd's Charities Trust
Lloyds TSB Foundation for
Northern Ireland
Lloyds TSB Foundation for the
Channel Islands
The Locker Foundation
The London Community
Foundation (formerly Capital
Community Foundation)
The William and Katherine
Longman Trust
The Loseley and Guildway
Charitable Trust
The Lower Green Foundation
The Lowy Mitchell Foundation
The C L Loyd Charitable Trust
Henry Lumley Charitable Trust
Paul Lunn-Rockliffe Charitable
Trust
The Lynn Foundation
The Lyras Family Charitable
Trust
The M D and S Charitable
Trust
The E M MacAndrew Trust
Macdonald-Buchanan
Charitable Trust
The Macfarlane Walker Trust
The Mackay and Brewer
Charitable Trust
The Mackintosh Foundation
The MacRobert Trust
The Mactaggart Third Fund
Ian Mactaggart Trust
Magdalen Hospital Trust
The Brian Maguire Charitable
Trust
The Mahavir Trust (also known
as the K S Mehta
Charitable Trust)
The Makin Charitable Trust
Malbin Trust
The Mallinckrodt Foundation
Man Group plc Charitable
Trust
The Manchester Guardian
Society Charitable Trust
Lord Mayor of Manchester's
Charity Appeal Trust
Mandeville Trust
The Manifold Charitable Trust
W M Mann Foundation
R W Mann Trust
The Stella and Alexander
Margulies Charitable Trust
Market Harborough and The
Bowdens Charity
The Marks Family Foundation
The Ann and David Marks
Foundation
The Hilda and Samuel Marks
Foundation
J P Marland Charitable Trust

The Marsh Christian Trust
The Charlotte Marshall
Charitable Trust
The Jim Marshall Charitable
Trust
The D G Marshall of
Cambridge Trust
Sir George Martin Trust
John Martin's Charity
The John Mason Family Trust
The Violet Mauray Charitable
Trust
The Maxell Educational Trust
The Maxwell Family Foundation
Evelyn May Trust
Mazars Charitable Trust
The A M McGreevy No 5
Charitable Settlement
The McKenna Charitable Trust
Martin McLaren Memorial
Trust
The Helen Isabella McMorran
Charitable Foundation
The James Frederick and Ethel
Anne Measures Charity
The Medlock Charitable Trust
The Menzies Charity
Foundation
The Mercers' Charitable
Foundation
The Merchant Venturers'
Charity
The Merchants' House of
Glasgow
The Mersey Docks and
Harbour Company
Charitable Fund
Community Foundation for
Merseyside
London Masonic Charitable
Trust
Mi Yu Foundation
Gerald Micklem Charitable
Trust
The Masonic Province of
Middlesex Charitable Trust
Midhurst Pensions Trust
The Hugh and Mary Miller
Bequest Trust
The Miller Foundation
The Millhouses Charitable
Trust
The Millichope Foundation
The Mills Charity
Milton Keynes Community
Foundation
The Edgar Milward Charity
The Keith and Joan
Mindelsohn Charitable
Trust
The Minos Trust
Minton Charitable Trust
The Mirianog Trust
The Laurence Misener
Charitable Trust
The Misselbrook Trust

The Brian Mitchell Charitable
Settlement
The Esmé Mitchell Trust
Keren Mitzvah Trust
The Mizpah Trust
The Mobbs Memorial Trust Ltd
The Modiano Charitable Trust
The Mole Charitable Trust
The Monatrea Charitable Trust
The D C Moncrieff Charitable
Trust
The Colin Montgomerie
Charitable Foundation
The Monument Trust
The Moonpig Foundation
George A Moore Foundation
The Morgan Charitable
Foundation
The Mr and Mrs J T Morgan
Foundation
Diana and Allan Morgenthau
Charitable Trust
The Oliver Morland Charitable
Trust
The Bernard Morris Charitable
Trust
The Willie and Mabel Morris
Charitable Trust
The Peter Morrison Charitable
Foundation
G M Morrison Charitable Trust
The Stanley Morrison
Charitable Trust
Vyoel Moshe Charitable Trust
The Mulberry Trust
The Mushroom Fund
The Kitty and Daniel Nabarro
Charitable Trust
The Naggar Charitable Trust
The Janet Nash Charitable
Settlement
The NDL Foundation
Needham Market and Barking
Welfare Charities
The Worshipful Company of
Needlemakers' Charitable
Fund
The James Neill Trust Fund
Network for Social Change
New Court Charitable Trust
Newpier Charity Ltd
The Night Garden Charity
The Noon Foundation
Norie Charitable Trust
The Norman Family Charitable
Trust
The Duncan Norman Trust
Fund
The Normanby Charitable Trust
The Northwood Charitable
Trust
The Notgrove Trust
Nottinghamshire Community
Foundation
The Nottinghamshire Miners'
Welfare Trust Fund

The Oak Trust
The Oakdale Trust
The Oakmoor Charitable Trust
The Odin Charitable Trust
Oglesby Charitable Trust
The Old Broad Street Charity Trust
Old Possum's Practical Trust
Onaway Trust
The Ormsby Charitable Trust
Orrin Charitable Trust
The Oxfordshire Community Foundation
The P F Charitable Trust
Padwa Charitable Foundation
Panahpur (previously Panahpur Charitable Trust)
The James Pantyfedwen Foundation
The Paphitis Charitable Trust
The Paragon Trust
The Samuel and Freda Parkinson Charitable Trust
Miss M E Swinton Paterson's Charitable Trust
The Patrick Charitable Trust
The Peacock Charitable Trust
The Susanna Peake Charitable Trust
The Dowager Countess Eleanor Peel Trust
Pegasus (Stanley) Trust
The Pell Charitable Trust
The Pennycress Trust
The Pervez Musharraf Foundation
The Pharsalia Charitable Trust
The Philips and Rubens Charitable Trust
The Phillips Family Charitable Trust
The David Pickford Charitable Foundation
The Bernard Piggott Trust
The Cecil Pilkington Charitable Trust
The Sir Harry Pilkington Trust
Miss A M Pilkington's Charitable Trust
The DLA Piper Charitable Trust
The Worshipful Company of Plaisterers Charitable Trust
G S Plaut Charitable Trust Limited
The Poling Charitable Trust
The George and Esme Pollitzer Charitable Settlement
The J S F Pollitzer Charitable Settlement
The Mayor of Poole's Appeal Fund
The Popocatepetl Trust
Edith and Ferdinand Porjes Charitable Trust
The John Porter Charitable Trust

The Porter Foundation
The Portrack Charitable Trust
The David and Elaine Potter Foundation
The W L Pratt Charitable Trust
The Premier League Charitable Fund
Premierquote Ltd
The Primrose Trust
The Foundation of Prince William and Prince Harry
Princess Anne's Charities
Prison Service Charity Fund
The Privy Purse Charitable Trust
The Proven Family Trust
The Provincial Grand Charity of the Province of Derbyshire
PSA Peugeot Citroen Charity Trust
Quartet Community Foundation (formerly the Greater Bristol Foundation)
The Queen's Silver Jubilee Trust
R J M Charitable Trust
The Monica Rabagliati Charitable Trust
Rachel Charitable Trust
The Mr and Mrs Philip Rackham Charitable Trust
The Rainford Trust
The Joseph and Lena Randall Charitable Trust
The Rank Foundation
The Joseph Rank Trust
Ranworth Trust
The Rashbass Family Trust
The Ratcliff Foundation
The Ratcliffe Charitable Trust
The Ravensdale Trust
The John Rayner Charitable Trust
The Sir James Reckitt Charity
The Red Arrows Trust
The Red Rose Charitable Trust
The C A Redfern Charitable Foundation
The Reed Foundation
Relief Fund for Romania Limited
The Rest Harrow Trust
Reuben Brothers Foundation
The Joan K Reynell Charitable Trust
The Nathaniel Reyner Trust Fund
The Rhododendron Trust
The Rhondda Cynon Taff Welsh Church Acts Fund
Daisie Rich Trust
C B Richard Ellis Charitable Trust
The Clive Richards Charity
The Richmond Parish Lands Charity

Ridgesave Limited
The Ripple Effect Foundation
The Sir John Ritblat Family Foundation
The River Farm Foundation
The Rivers Charitable Trust
Riverside Charitable Trust Limited
The Robertson Trust
Robyn Charitable Trust
The Rochester Bridge Trust
The Rofeh Trust
Richard Rogers Charitable Settlement
Rokach Family Charitable Trust
The Helen Roll Charitable Trust
The Sir James Roll Charitable Trust
Romeera Foundation
The Gerald Ronson Foundation
The C A Rookes Charitable Trust
Mrs L D Rope Third Charitable Settlement
The Rose Foundation
The Rothermere Foundation
The Rothley Trust
The Roughley Charitable Trust
The Rowland Family Foundation
The Rowlands Trust
Royal Artillery Charitable Fund
The RRAF Charitable Trust
The Alfred and Frances Rubens Charitable Trust
The Rubin Foundation
William Arthur Rudd Memorial Trust
The Rufford Foundation
The Rugby Group Benevolent Fund Limited
The Russell Trust
The J S and E C Rymer Charitable Trust
The Jeremy and John Sacher Charitable Trust
The Michael Harry Sacher Trust
The Sackler Trust (formerly Dr Mortimer and Theresa Sackler Foundation)
The Saddlers' Company Charitable Fund
The Alan and Babette Sainsbury Charitable Fund
The Saintbury Trust
The Salamander Charitable Trust
The Salt Trust
Salters' Charitable Foundation
The Andrew Salvesen Charitable Trust
The Sammermar Trust
Basil Samuel Charitable Trust
Coral Samuel Charitable Trust

The Samworth Foundation
The Sandhu Charitable
Foundation
The Sands Family Trust
The Sants Charitable Trust
Jimmy Savile Charitable Trust
The Schmidt-Bodner Charitable
Trust
The R H Scholes Charitable
Trust
The Schreib Trust
The Schroder Foundation
The Scotshill Trust
The Frieda Scott Charitable
Trust
The Storrow Scott Will Trust
The Scottish Community
Foundation
The Scouloudi Foundation
The Searchlight Electric
Charitable Trust
The Samuel Sebba Charitable
Trust
SEM Charitable Trust
Shaara Ezra – The Moses
Foundation
The Cyril Shack Trust
The Shanti Charitable Trust
ShareGift (The Orr Mackintosh
Foundation)
The Sheepdrove Trust
The Sheldon Trust
The P and D Shepherd
Charitable Trust
The Sylvia and Colin Shepherd
Charitable Trust
The Archie Sherman Charitable
Trust
The Barnett and Sylvia Shine
No 2 Charitable Trust
The Sickle Foundation
David and Jennifer Sieff
Charitable Trust
The Julius Silman Charitable
Trust
The Leslie Silver Charitable
Trust
The Huntly and Margery
Sinclair Charitable Trust
The Charles Skey Charitable
Trust
Skipton Building Society
Charitable Foundation
The John Slater Foundation
Rita and David Slowe
Charitable Trust
The SMB Charitable Trust
The N Smith Charitable
Settlement
The Amanda Smith Charitable
Trust
The E H Smith Charitable Trust
The Smith Charitable Trust
The Leslie Smith Foundation
Social Business Trust (Scale-
Up)

Solihull Community Foundation
The Solo Charitable
Settlement
Dr Richard Solomon's
Charitable Trust
The South Square Trust
The Stephen R and Philippa H
Southall Charitable Trust
The W F Southall Trust
The Southwold Trust
Spar Charitable Fund
The Spear Charitable Trust
Spears-Stutz Charitable Trust
The Worshipful Company of
Spectacle Makers' Charity
The Jessie Spencer Trust
The Ralph and Irma Sperring
Charity
Rosalyn and Nicholas Springer
Charitable Trust
The Spurrell Charitable Trust
The Geoff and Fiona Squire
Foundation
St James' Trust Settlement
The Late St Patrick White
Charitable Trust
The Stanton Ballard Charitable
Trust
The Star Charitable Trust
The Peter Stebbings Memorial
Charity
The Steel Charitable Trust
The Hugh Stenhouse
Foundation
The Sigmund Sternberg
Charitable Foundation
The Stevenage Community
Trust
The June Stevens Foundation
Stevenson Family's Charitable
Trust
The Steventon Allotments and
Relief-in-Need Charity
The Andy Stewart Charitable
Foundation
The Stewarts Law Foundation
The Leonard Laity Stoate
Charitable Trust
The Edward Stocks-Massey
Bequest Fund
The Stoller Charitable Trust
The M J C Stone Charitable
Trust
The Samuel Storey Family
Charitable Trust
The Strangward Trust
The Strasser Foundation
Stratford upon Avon Town
Trust
Strathclyde Police Benevolent
Fund
The A B Strom and R Strom
Charitable Trust
The Sudborough Foundation
The Suffolk Foundation
The Alan Sugar Foundation

Sugarworld Trust
The Bernard Sunley Charitable
Foundation
Surrey Community Foundation
Sussex Community Foundation
The Adrienne and Leslie
Sussman Charitable Trust
The Sutasoma Trust
Sutton Coldfield Municipal
Charities
The Suva Foundation Limited
Swansea and Brecon Diocesan
Board of Finance Limited
The John Swire (1989)
Charitable Trust
The Swire Charitable Trust
The Hugh and Ruby Sykes
Charitable Trust
The Charles and Elsie Sykes
Trust
The Hugh Symons Charitable
Trust
The Stella Symons Charitable
Trust
The Talbot Village Trust
Tallow Chandlers Benevolent
Fund
The Tangent Charitable Trust
The Lady Tangye Charitable
Trust
The Tanner Trust
The Mrs A Lacy Tate Trust
The Taurus Foundation
The Tay Charitable Trust
C B and H H Taylor 1984 Trust
Rosanna Taylor's 1987 Charity
Trust
The Tedworth Charitable Trust
Tees Valley Community
Foundation
The Templeton Goodwill Trust
The Thames Wharf Charity
The West Charitable Trust
The David Thomas Charitable
Trust
The Arthur and Margaret
Thompson Charitable Trust
The Elspeth J Thompson
Charitable Trust
The Maurice and Vivien
Thompson Charitable Trust
The Thompson Family
Charitable Trust
The Thompson6 Charitable
Trust
The Thornton Foundation
The Tisbury Telegraph Trust
The Tolkien Trust
Tollemache (Buckminster)
Charitable Trust
Toni and Guy Charitable
Foundation Limited
The Tower Hill Trust
The Toy Trust
The Mayor of Trafford's Charity
Fund

Annie Tranmer Charitable Trust
The Constance Travis Charitable Trust
The Treeside Trust
The Tresillian Trust
The Triangle Trust (1949) Fund
The Truemark Trust
Truemart Limited
Trust Sixty Three
The Trusthouse Charitable Foundation
The Tudor Trust
The R D Turner Charitable Trust
The Douglas Turner Trust
The Florence Turner Trust
The TUUT Charitable Trust
TVML Foundation
Community Foundation Serving Tyne and Wear and Northumberland
UKI Charitable Foundation
Ulverston Town Lands Charity
The Underwood Trust
UnLtd (Foundation for Social Entrepreneurs)
The Michael Uren Foundation
The David Uri Memorial Trust
The Vail Foundation
The Valiant Charitable Trust
The Albert Van Den Bergh Charitable Trust
John and Lucille van Geest Foundation
Mrs Maud Van Norden's Charitable Foundation
The Vandervell Foundation
The Vardy Foundation
The Verdon-Smith Family Charitable Settlement
Roger Vere Foundation
Victoria Homes Trust
The Nigel Vinson Charitable Trust
The Viznitz Foundation
Voluntary Action Fund
Wade's Charity
The Wakefield and Tetley Trust
The F J Wallis Charitable Settlement
The Ward Blenkinsop Trust
The George Ward Charitable Trust
G R Waters Charitable Trust 2000
Weatherley Charitable Trust
The William Webster Charitable Trust
The Weinberg Foundation
The Weinstock Fund
The James Weir Foundation
The Joir and Kato Weisz Foundation
The Barbara Welby Trust

Welsh Church Fund Dyfed area (Carmarthenshire, Ceredigion and Pembrokeshire)
The Welton Foundation
The Wessex Youth Trust
The West Derby Wastelands Charity
West London Synagogue Charitable Fund
Mrs S K West's Charitable Trust
The Garfield Weston Foundation
The Melanie White Foundation Limited
White Stuff Foundation
The Whitecourt Charitable Trust
A H and B C Whiteley Charitable Trust
The Whittlesey Charity
The Lionel Wigram Memorial Trust
The Kay Williams Charitable Foundation
The Williams Charitable Trust
Williams Serendipity Trust
The H D H Wills 1965 Charitable Trust
The Dame Violet Wills Will Trust
The Wilmcote Charitrust
Sumner Wilson Charitable Trust
David Wilson Foundation
The Community Foundation for Wiltshire and Swindon
The Harold Hyam Wingate Foundation
Wirral Mayor's Charity
The Witzenfeld Foundation
The Wixamtree Trust
The Woburn 1986 Charitable Trust
The Charles Wolfson Charitable Trust
The Wolseley Charitable Trust
The James Wood Bequest Fund
The Woodcock Charitable Trust
The F Glenister Woodger Trust
The Woodward Charitable Trust
The A and R Woolf Charitable Trust
ME Woolfe Charitable Trust
The Wragge and Co. Charitable Trust
The Diana Edgson Wright Charitable Trust
The Matthews Wrightson Charity Trust
The Joan Wyatt Charitable Trust
Wychville Ltd

The Wyndham Charitable Trust
The Yardley Great Trust
The Dennis Alan Yardy Charitable Trust
Yorkshire Building Society Charitable Foundation
The South Yorkshire Community Foundation
The John Young Charitable Settlement
The William Allen Young Charitable Trust
The Marjorie and Arnold Ziff Charitable Foundation
The Zochonis Charitable Trust
The Zolfo Cooper Foundation
Zurich Community Trust (UK) Limited

Health

The 1970 Trust
The 1989 Willan Charitable Trust
The Aberbrothock Skea Trust
The ACT Foundation
Action Medical Research
The Company of Actuaries' Charitable Trust Fund
The Adamson Trust
The Adint Charitable Trust
Age UK (formerly Help the Aged and Age Concern)
The AIM Foundation
The Green and Lilian F M Ainsworth and Family Benevolent Fund
The Sylvia Aitken Charitable Trust
The Ajahma Charitable Trust
The Alchemy Foundation
The Alliance Family Foundation
The Pat Allsop Charitable Trust
Almondsbury Charity
The Ammco Trust
Andor Charitable Trust
Anglo American Group Foundation
The John Armitage Charitable Trust
The Armourers' and Brasiers' Gauntlet Trust
The Artemis Charitable Trust
Arthritis Research UK
The Arts and Entertainment Charitable Trust
The Norman C Ashton Foundation
Astellas European Foundation
Asthma UK
The Astor Foundation
The Astor of Hever Trust
The Lord Austin Trust
The John Avins Trustees
Harry Bacon Foundation
Veta Bailey Charitable Trust
The Baily Thomas Charitable Fund
The Baker Charitable Trust
The Roy and Pixie Baker Charitable Trust
The Balcombe Charitable Trust
The Albert Casanova Ballard Deceased Trust
The Band Trust
The Barbers' Company General Charities
The Barbour Foundation
The Barcapel Foundation
Barchester Healthcare Foundation
The Barclay Foundation
The Barnwood House Trust
The Misses Barrie Charitable Trust
The Batchworth Trust

B-CH 1971 Charitable Trust
The John Beckwith Charitable Trust
The Peter Beckwith Charitable Trust
The Bellahouston Bequest Fund
The Bellhouse Foundation
Bergqvist Charitable Trust
The Ruth Berkowitz Charitable Trust
The Bestway Foundation
The Mason Bibby 1981 Trust
BibleLands
The Big Lottery Fund
The Billmeir Charitable Trust
The Bintaub Charitable Trust
The Birmingham District Nursing Charitable Trust
The Birmingham Hospital Saturday Fund Medical Charity and Welfare Trust
Sir Alec Black's Charity
Blackheart Foundation (UK) Limited
The Herbert and Peter Blagrave Charitable Trust
The Boltons Trust
The Booth Charities
The Boots Charitable Trust
The Boshier-Hinton Foundation
The Bothwell Charitable Trust
The Harry Bottom Charitable Trust
P G and N J Boulton Trust
Sir Clive Bourne Family Trust
The Bowerman Charitable Trust
The Liz and Terry Bramall Charitable Trust
The Tony Bramall Charitable Trust
The Breadsticks Foundation
The Breast Cancer Research Trust
The Brendish Family Foundation
The Brighton District Nursing Association Trust
The British Council for Prevention of Blindness
The British Dietetic Association General and Education Trust Fund
British Heart Foundation
The David Brooke Charity
The Rory and Elizabeth Brooks Foundation
The Charles Brotherton Trust
Bill Brown's Charitable Settlement
R S Brownless Charitable Trust
Buckland Charitable Trust
The BUPA Foundation
The Burden Trust

The Burdett Trust for Nursing
The Burry Charitable Trust
The Audrey and Stanley Burton 1960 Charitable Trust
The Arnold Burton 1998 Charitable Trust
The Derek Butler Trust
Henry T and Lucy B Cadbury Charitable Trust
P H G Cadbury Charitable Trust
The William A Cadbury Charitable Trust
The Cadbury Foundation
The Edward and Dorothy Cadbury Trust
CAFOD (Catholic Agency for Overseas Development)
M R Cannon 1998 Charitable Trust
The Carr-Gregory Trust
The Carron Charitable Settlement
The Elizabeth Casson Trust
The Castang Foundation
The Wilfrid and Constance Cave Foundation
The Cayo Foundation
Celtic Charity Fund
The Cemlyn-Jones Trust
Champneys Charitable Foundation
The Charities Advisory Trust
The Checkatrade Foundation
Chest, Heart and Stroke Scotland
Child Growth Foundation
Children's Liver Disease Foundation
The Children's Research Fund
The Childwick Trust
The Chrimes Family Charitable Trust
J A Clark Charitable Trust
The Clarke Charitable Settlement
The Cleopatra Trust
Miss V L Clore's 1967 Charitable Trust
The Clothworkers' Foundation
Richard Cloudesley's Charity
The Clover Trust
The Coalfields Regeneration Trust
The John Coates Charitable Trust
The Denise Cohen Charitable Trust
The Vivienne and Samuel Cohen Charitable Trust
The Colchester Catalyst Charity
John Coldman Charitable Trust
The Bernard Coleman Charitable Trust
The Colt Foundation

The Coltstaple Trust
The Congleton Inclosure Trust
The Consolidated Charities for the Infirm Merchant Taylors' Company
Harold and Daphne Cooper Charitable Trust
The J Reginald Corah Foundation Fund
Michael Cornish Charitable Trust
The Cotton Trust
The John Cowan Foundation
The Michael Cowan Foundation
The Sir William Coxen Trust Fund
The Lord Cozens-Hardy Trust
Michael Crawford Children's Charity
The Crescent Trust
Criffel Charitable Trust
The Violet and Milo Cripps Charitable Trust
The Peter Cruddas Foundation
Cruden Foundation Ltd
The Cunningham Trust
The Harry Cureton Charitable Trust
The Manny Cussins Foundation
The D'Oyly Carte Charitable Trust
Roald Dahl's Marvellous Children's Charity
The Dr and Mrs A Darlington Charitable Trust
Baron Davenport's Charity
The Wilfrid Bruce Davis Charitable Trust
The De Clermont Charitable Company Ltd
The Deakin Charitable Trust
The Delves Charitable Trust
The Demigryphon Trust
The Denman Charitable Trust
The Denton Charitable Trust
The Denton Wilde Sapte Charitable Trust
The J N Derbyshire Trust
Diabetes UK
The Dinwoodie Settlement
Disability Aid Fund (The Roger and Jean Jefcoate Trust)
The Djanogly Foundation
The Derek and Eileen Dodgson Foundation
The Dorema Charitable Trust
The Dorus Trust
The Drayson Foundation
Dromintee Trust
The Duis Charitable Trust
The Dumbreck Charity
The Dunhill Medical Trust
The Houghton Dunn Charitable Trust

The Dunn Family Charitable Trust
The W E Dunn Trust
The Dyers' Company Charitable Trust
The James Dyson Foundation
The Earmark Trust
The Sir John Eastwood Foundation
The EBM Charitable Trust
The Gilbert and Eileen Edgar Foundation
Gilbert Edgar Trust
The Edinburgh Trust, No 2 Account
The Gerald Palmer Eling Trust Company
The John Ellerman Foundation
James Ellis Charitable Trust
The Emerton-Christie Charity
The Emmandjay Charitable Trust
The Englefield Charitable Trust
The Epigoni Trust
Epilepsy Research UK
The Equilibrium Foundation
The Eranda Foundation
Essex Provincial Charity Fund
The Patrick Evans Foundation
The Eveson Charitable Trust
The F P Limited Charitable Trust
Faisaltex Charitable Trust
The Family Rich Charities Trust
The Lord Faringdon Charitable Trust
Samuel William Farmer Trust
Joseph Fattorini Charitable Trust 'B' Account
Elizabeth Ferguson Charitable Trust Fund
Fife Council/Common Good Funds and Trusts
Dixie Rose Findlay Charitable Trust
The Sir John Fisher Foundation
The Fishmongers' Company's Charitable Trust
The Fitton Trust
Bud Flanagan Leukaemia Fund
The Ian Fleming Charitable Trust
Florence's Charitable Trust
The Flow Foundation
The Follett Trust
The Lady Forester Trust
The Foresters' Charity Stewards UK Trust
The Donald Forrester Trust
The Anna Rosa Forster Charitable Trust
The Fort Foundation
The Forte Charitable Trust
The Jill Franklin Trust
The Hugh Fraser Foundation
The Joseph Strong Frazer Trust

The Louis and Valerie Freedman Charitable Settlement
The Freemasons' Grand Charity
The Freshfield Foundation
The Freshgate Trust Foundation
The Friarsgate Trust
The Frognal Trust
T F C Frost Charitable Trust
Maurice Fry Charitable Trust
The Fuserna Foundation
The Galanthus Trust
The Ganzoni Charitable Trust
The Garnett Charitable Trust
The Gatsby Charitable Foundation
Gatwick Airport Community Trust
The Robert Gavron Charitable Trust
Jacqueline and Michael Gee Charitable Trust
The General Nursing Council for England and Wales Trust
J Paul Getty Jr Charitable Trust
Simon Gibson Charitable Trust
The G C Gibson Charitable Trust
The Girdlers' Company Charitable Trust
The B and P Glasser Charitable Trust
GMC Trust
The Meir Golda Trust
The Sydney and Phyllis Goldberg Memorial Charitable Trust
The Golden Bottle Trust
Golden Charitable Trust
The Jack Goldhill Charitable Trust
The Goldsmiths' Company Charity
The Everard and Mina Goodman Charitable Foundation
Mike Gooley Trailfinders Charity
The Hemraj Goyal Foundation
Grand Charitable Trust of the Order of Women Freemasons
The Grand Order of Water Rats' Charities Fund
Grantham Yorke Trust
The Great Britain Sasakawa Foundation
The Constance Green Foundation
The Philip Green Memorial Trust
Grimmitt Trust
The Grocers' Charity

The Gunter Charitable Trust
H C D Memorial Fund
The Doris Louise Hailes
   Charitable Trust
E F and M G Hall Charitable
   Trust
Robert Hall Charity
The Hamamelis Trust
Hamilton Wallace Trust
The Helen Hamlyn Trust
Sue Hammerson's Charitable
   Trust
Hampton Fuel Allotment
   Charity
The W A Handley Charitable
   Trust
The Kathleen Hannay
   Memorial Charity
The Haramead Trust
The Harbour Charitable Trust
The Harebell Centenary Fund
The Hargrave Foundation
The Kenneth Hargreaves
   Charitable Trust
The Harris Charitable Trust
The Harris Family Charitable
   Trust
The Edith Lilian Harrison 2000
   Foundation
The John Harrison Charitable
   Trust
The N and P Hartley Memorial
   Trust
The Alfred And Peggy Harvey
   Charitable Trust
Hasluck Charitable Trust
The Maurice Hatter Foundation
The Haymills Charitable Trust
The Charles Hayward
   Foundation
The Headley Trust
The Hedley Foundation
The Michael and Morven Heller
   Charitable Foundation
The Simon Heller Charitable
   Settlement
Help the Hospices
The Hemby Trust
The Christina Mary Hendrie
   Trust for Scottish and
   Canadian Charities
The G D Herbert Charitable
   Trust
The Joanna Herbert-Stepney
   Charitable Settlement (also
   known as The Paget
   Charitable Trust)
The Charles Littlewood Hill
   Trust
Hille Pandana
R G Hills Charitable Trust
Lady Hind Trust
Hinduja Foundation
The Hintze Family Charitable
   Foundation

The Sir Julian Hodge
   Charitable Trust
The Jane Hodge Foundation
The Holbeck Charitable Trust
The Hollands-Warren Fund
The Edward Holt Trust
The Homelands Charitable
   Trust
The Homestead Charitable
   Trust
The Antony Hornby Charitable
   Trust
The Horne Trust
The Hospital Saturday Fund
HTA Sheba Foundation UK
Human Relief Foundation
Humanitarian and Charitable
   One Trust (HACOT)
The Humanitarian Trust
The Humberside Charitable
   Health Trust
The Albert Hunt Trust
Miss Agnes H Hunter's Trust
Huntingdon Freemen's Charity
The Nani Huyu Charitable Trust
The Iliffe Family Charitable
   Trust
International Spinal Research
   Trust
The Isaacs Charitable Trust
The Jabbs Foundation
The Ruth and Lionel Jacobson
   Trust (Second Fund) No 2
John James Bristol Foundation
The Marjory Jameson Trust
The Jarman Charitable Trust
The Barbara Joyce Jarrald
   Charitable Trust
The John Jarrold Trust
The Jeffrey Charitable Trust
The Nicholas Joels Charitable
   Trust
The Elton John Aids
   Foundation
The Michael John Trust
The Lillie Johnson Charitable
   Trust
The Johnson Foundation
The Johnson Wax Ltd
   Charitable Trust
The Jones 1986 Charitable
   Trust
Dezna Robins Jones Charitable
   Foundation
The Joron Charitable Trust
The Judith Trust
The Kalou Foundation
The Ian Karten Charitable
   Trust
The Michael and Ilse Katz
   Foundation
The Emmanuel Kaye
   Foundation
The Caron Keating Foundation
The Kelly Family Charitable
   Trust

The KempWelch Charitable
   Trust
The Kay Kendall Leukaemia
   Fund
The Kennedy Charitable
   Foundation
The Peter Kershaw Trust
The Ursula Keyes Trust
The King's Fund
The Kingsbury Charity
The Mary Kinross Charitable
   Trust
Kirschel Foundation
Ernest Kleinwort Charitable
   Trust
The Kobler Trust
The Kohn Foundation
The KPMG Foundation
The Kreditor Charitable Trust
The Kreitman Foundation
The Heinz, Anna and Carol
   Kroch Foundation
The Kyte Charitable Trust
Maurice and Hilda Laing
   Charitable Trust
The Christopher Laing
   Foundation
The David Laing Foundation
The Beatrice Laing Trust
The Lambert Charitable Trust
The Langdale Trust
The Langley Charitable Trust
The Lanvern Foundation
The R J Larg Family Charitable
   Trust
Laslett's (Hinton) Charity
Mrs F B Laurence Charitable
   Trust
The Kathleen Laurence Trust
The Edgar E Lawley Foundation
The Lawson Beckman
   Charitable Trust
The Raymond and Blanche
   Lawson Charitable Trust
The Mason Le Page Charitable
   Trust
The Leathersellers' Company
   Charitable Fund
The Arnold Lee Charitable
   Trust
The William Leech Charity
Leeds Building Society
   Charitable Foundation
The Leigh Trust
Lesley Lesley and Mutter Trust
Leukaemia and Lymphoma
   Research
The Joseph Levy Charitable
   Foundation
Lewis Family Charitable Trust
John Lewis Partnership
   General Community Fund
The Lewis Ward Trust
Lifeline 4 Kids
Limoges Charitable Trust
The Linbury Trust

The Linden Charitable Trust
The Enid Linder Foundation
The Lister Charitable Trust
Frank Litchfield Charitable Trust
The Andrew and Mary Elizabeth Little Charitable Trust
The George John and Sheilah Livanos Charitable Trust
The Elaine and Angus Lloyd Charitable Trust
Lloyds TSB Foundation for Northern Ireland
Lloyds TSB Foundation for the Channel Islands
The Locker Foundation
The Trust for London (formerly the City Parochial Foundation)
London Catalyst (formerly The Metropolitan Hospital-Sunday Fund)
The London Law Trust
The Lord's Taverners
The Lotus Foundation
The C L Loyd Charitable Trust
The Marie Helen Luen Charitable Trust
Robert Luff Foundation Ltd
Henry Lumley Charitable Trust
Lord and Lady Lurgan Trust
The Lyons Charitable Trust
The Lyras Family Charitable Trust
The Madeline Mabey Trust
The E M MacAndrew Trust
The R S Macdonald Charitable Trust
Macdonald-Buchanan Charitable Trust
The Mackintosh Foundation
The MacRobert Trust
The Mahavir Trust (also known as the K S Mehta Charitable Trust)
Mandeville Trust
R W Mann Trust
The Leslie and Lilian Manning Trust
The Manoukian Charitable Foundation
The Marcela Trust
Market Harborough and The Bowdens Charity
The Marks Family Foundation
The Hilda and Samuel Marks Foundation
The Michael Marsh Charitable Trust
The Marsh Christian Trust
The Charlotte Marshall Charitable Trust
Marshgate Charitable Settlement
Sir George Martin Trust

John Martin's Charity
The Nancie Massey Charitable Trust
The Violet Mauray Charitable Trust
The Maxwell Family Foundation
Evelyn May Trust
The Robert McAlpine Foundation
The McKenna Charitable Trust
D D McPhail Charitable Settlement
The Medlock Charitable Trust
The Anthony and Elizabeth Mellows Charitable Settlement
Meningitis Trust
Brian Mercer Charitable Trust
The Mercers' Charitable Foundation
The Merchant Taylors' Company Charities Fund
Mercury Phoenix Trust
The Tony Metherell Charitable Trust
T and J Meyer Family Foundation Limited
Mi Yu Foundation
Gerald Micklem Charitable Trust
The Migraine Trust
Miles Trust for the Putney and Roehampton Community
The Hugh and Mary Miller Bequest Trust
The Miller Foundation
The Millichope Foundation
The Millward Charitable Trust
The Peter Minet Trust
Minge's Gift and the Pooled Trusts
The Mishcon Family Charitable Trust
The Mitchell Charitable Trust
Monmouthshire County Council Welsh Church Act Fund
The Montague Thompson Coon Charitable Trust
The Monument Trust
The Peter Moores Foundation
The Morel Charitable Trust
The Morgan Charitable Foundation
Diana and Allan Morgenthau Charitable Trust
The Morris Charitable Trust
The Willie and Mabel Morris Charitable Trust
G M Morrison Charitable Trust
Brian and Jill Moss Charitable Trust
The Moss Charitable Trust
The Robert and Margaret Moss Charitable Trust
The Mothercare Charitable Foundation

J P Moulton Charitable Foundation
The Edwina Mountbatten Trust
The Edith Murphy Foundation
Murphy-Neumann Charity Company Limited
Peter John Murray Trust (PJM Trust)
The Naggar Charitable Trust
The Janet Nash Charitable Settlement
The Nchima Trust
The Neighbourly Charitable Trust
Network for Social Change
New Court Charitable Trust
The Frances and Augustus Newman Foundation
The Normanby Charitable Trust
The North British Hotel Trust
The North West Cancer Research Fund
North West London Community Foundation
The Northampton Queen's Institute Relief in Sickness Fund
The Northcott Devon Medical Foundation
The Northwood Charitable Trust
The Norton Foundation
The Norton Rose Charitable Foundation
The Nottingham General Dispensary
The Nottinghamshire Miners' Welfare Trust Fund
The Nuffield Foundation
The Father O'Mahoney Memorial Trust
The Oakdale Trust
The Oakley Charitable Trust
The Ofenheim Charitable Trust
Oglesby Charitable Trust
The Olga Charitable Trust
The O'Sullivan Family Charitable Trust
The Owen Family Trust
The Park Charitable Trust
The Parthenon Trust
Arthur James Paterson Charitable Trust
The Constance Paterson Charitable Trust
Paycare Charity Trust (formerly known as Patients' Aid Association Hospital and Medical Charities Trust)
The Harry Payne Trust
The Peacock Charitable Trust
The Pedmore Sporting Club Trust Fund
The Dowager Countess Eleanor Peel Trust
Peltz Trust

Pendragon Charitable Trust
The Persula Foundation
The Pervez Musharraf
  Foundation
The Pharsalia Charitable Trust
The Bernard Piggott Trust
The Cecil Pilkington Charitable
  Trust
The Pilkington Charities Fund
The Austin and Hope
  Pilkington Trust
The Col W W Pilkington Will
  Trusts The General Charity
  Fund
G S Plaut Charitable Trust
  Limited
The John Porter Charitable
  Trust
The Porter Foundation
The J E Posnansky Charitable
  Trust
The Mary Potter Convent
  Hospital Trust
The Praebendo Charitable
  Foundation
The Premier League Charitable
  Fund
The Tom Press Charitable
  Foundation
The Douglas Prestwich
  Charitable Trust
Sir John Priestman Charity
  Trust
The Prince of Wales's
  Charitable Foundation
The Foundation of Prince
  William and Prince Harry
Princess Anne's Charities
The Priory Foundation
The Richard and Christine
  Purchas Charitable Trust
Mr and Mrs J A Pye's
  Charitable Settlement
The Pyne Charitable Trust
The Queen Anne's Gate
  Foundation
The Monica Rabagliati
  Charitable Trust
The Mr and Mrs Philip
  Rackham Charitable Trust
Richard Radcliffe Charitable
  Trust
The Rank Foundation
The Joseph Rank Trust
The Fanny Rapaport Charitable
  Settlement
The Rashbass Family Trust
The Ravensdale Trust
The Roger Raymond Charitable
  Trust
The Rayne Foundation
The Red Rose Charitable Trust
The C A Redfern Charitable
  Foundation
The Reed Foundation

The Max Reinhardt Charitable
  Trust
Relief Fund for Romania
  Limited
REMEDI
Reuben Brothers Foundation
The Violet M Richards Charity
The Richmond Parish Lands
  Charity
The River Farm Foundation
Riverside Charitable Trust
  Limited
Thomas Roberts Trust
The Robertson Trust
Edwin George Robinson
  Charitable Trust
The Roddick Foundation
The Rosca Trust
The Rose Foundation
Rosetrees Trust
The Rothera Charitable
  Settlement
The Rotherwick Foundation
The Rothley Trust
Mrs Gladys Row Fogo
  Charitable Trust
The Christopher Rowbotham
  Charitable Trust
The Rowlands Trust
The RRAF Charitable Trust
The Rufford Foundation
Ryklow Charitable Trust 1992
  (also known as A B
  Williamson Charitable Trust)
The J S and E C Rymer
  Charitable Trust
The Jeremy and John Sacher
  Charitable Trust
The Michael Harry Sacher
  Trust
The Raymond and Beverley
  Sackler 1988 Foundation
The Sackler Trust (formerly Dr
  Mortimer and Theresa
  Sackler Foundation)
The Alan and Babette
  Sainsbury Charitable Fund
The Saintbury Trust
The Saints and Sinners Trust
Salters' Charitable Foundation
The Andrew Salvesen
  Charitable Trust
Basil Samuel Charitable Trust
The Peter Samuel Charitable
  Trust
The Camilla Samuel Fund
The Sandra Charitable Trust
The Scarfe Charitable Trust
Schroder Charity Trust
The Scotshill Trust
Scott (Eredine) Charitable
  Trust
Sir Samuel Scott of Yews
  Trust
The Sir James and Lady Scott
  Trust

The Scouloudi Foundation
The Helene Sebba Charitable
  Trust
The Samuel Sebba Charitable
  Trust
The Ayrton Senna Foundation
Shaara Ezra – The Moses
  Foundation
The Jean Shanks Foundation
The Sheepdrove Trust
The Sheffield and District
  Hospital Services
  Charitable Fund
The Sylvia and Colin Shepherd
  Charitable Trust
The Archie Sherman Cardiff
  Foundation
The Bassil Shippam and
  Alsford Trust
The Shirley Foundation
The Barbara A Shuttleworth
  Memorial Trust
The Simpson Education and
  Conservation Trust
The Huntly and Margery
  Sinclair Charitable Trust
The John Slater Foundation
The SMB Charitable Trust
The N Smith Charitable
  Settlement
The Henry Smith Charity
The R C Snelling Charitable
  Trust
The Sobell Foundation
The E C Sosnow Charitable
  Trust
The South Square Trust
The Sovereign Health Care
  Charitable Trust
Sparks Charity (Sport Aiding
  Medical Research For Kids)
The Worshipful Company of
  Spectacle Makers' Charity
The Spero Foundation
Rosalyn and Nicholas Springer
  Charitable Trust
Springfields Employees'
  Medical Research and
  Charity Trust Fund
St Francis's Leprosy Guild
St James's Place Foundation
St Michael's and All Saints'
  Charities
St Monica Trust Community
  Fund
The Stanley Foundation Ltd
The Peter Stebbings Memorial
  Charity
The Steel Charitable Trust
The Steinberg Family
  Charitable Trust
Stevenson Family's Charitable
  Trust
The Andy Stewart Charitable
  Foundation
The Sir Halley Stewart Trust

The Stoller Charitable Trust
The Stone-Mallabar Charitable
   Foundation
Peter Stormonth Darling
   Charitable Trust
The Strangward Trust
The Strawberry Charitable
   Trust
The W O Street Charitable
   Foundation
Sueberry Ltd
Sussex Community Foundation
The Hugh and Ruby Sykes
   Charitable Trust
The Charles and Elsie Sykes
   Trust
The Tajtelbaum Charitable
   Trust
The Gay and Keith Talbot Trust
The Talbot Trusts
Tallow Chandlers Benevolent
   Fund
The Connie and Albert Taylor
   Charitable Trust
Thackray Medical Research
   Trust
The Loke Wan Tho Memorial
   Foundation
The Thompson Family
   Charitable Trust
The Len Thomson Charitable
   Trust
The Sue Thomson Foundation
The Sir Jules Thorn Charitable
   Trust
The Three Guineas Trust
TJH Foundation
The Tolkien Trust
The Tompkins Foundation
The Tory Family Foundation
The Towry Law Charitable Trust
   (also known as the Castle
   Educational Trust)
The True Colours Trust
The James Tudor Foundation
UKI Charitable Foundation
The Ulverscroft Foundation
The Underwood Trust
The Valentine Charitable Trust
The Albert Van Den Bergh
   Charitable Trust
John and Lucille van Geest
   Foundation
The Variety Club Children's
   Charity
Roger Vere Foundation
The Vintners' Company
   Charitable Foundation
Vision Charity
The Volant Charitable Trust
The Wakefield and Tetley Trust
Robert and Felicity Waley-
   Cohen Charitable Trust
The Walker Trust
Wallace and Gromit's
   Children's Foundation

The Ward Blenkinsop Trust
The Waterloo Foundation
Blyth Watson Charitable Trust
The Weinstein Foundation
The Wellcome Trust
The Welton Foundation
The Westcroft Trust
The Garfield Weston
   Foundation
The Simon Whitbread
   Charitable Trust
The Richard Wilcox Welfare
   Charity
The Felicity Wilde Charitable
   Trust
The Will Charitable Trust
The Kay Williams Charitable
   Foundation
The Williams Charitable Trust
Williams Serendipity Trust
The Harold Hyam Wingate
   Foundation
Anona Winn Charitable Trust
The Michael and Anna Wix
   Charitable Trust
The Wixamtree Trust
The Maurice Wohl Charitable
   Foundation
The Charles Wolfson
   Charitable Trust
The Wolfson Foundation
The Wood Family Trust
Woodroffe Benton Foundation
The Woodward Charitable
   Trust
The A and R Woolf Charitable
   Trust
ME Woolfe Charitable Trust
The Fred and Della Worms
   Charitable Trust
The Wragge and Co. Charitable
   Trust
Miss E B Wrightson's
   Charitable Settlement
The Wyseliot Charitable Trust
The Xerox (UK) Trust
The York Children's Trust
The William Allen Young
   Charitable Trust
The John K Young Endowment
   Fund
Suha Yusuf Charitable Trust
Zephyr Charitable Trust
The Marjorie and Arnold Ziff
   Charitable Foundation
The Zochonis Charitable Trust
Zurich Community Trust (UK)
   Limited

Alternative, complementary medicine

The AIM Foundation
Disability Aid Fund (The Roger
   and Jean Jefcoate Trust)
The Sir John Fisher Foundation
The Joanna Herbert-Stepney
   Charitable Settlement (also
   known as The Paget
   Charitable Trust)
London Catalyst (formerly The
   Metropolitan Hospital-
   Sunday Fund)
Mr and Mrs J A Pye's
   Charitable Settlement
The Joseph Rank Trust
Rosalyn and Nicholas Springer
   Charitable Trust
The Simon Whitbread
   Charitable Trust

Health care

The 1970 Trust
The Aberbrothock Skea Trust
The ACT Foundation
Almondsbury Charity
The Artemis Charitable Trust
The Norman C Ashton
   Foundation
Veta Bailey Charitable Trust
The Barbers' Company General
   Charities
The Barclay Foundation
The Barnwood House Trust
The Birmingham District
   Nursing Charitable Trust
Sir Alec Black's Charity
The Boshier-Hinton Foundation
The Harry Bottom Charitable
   Trust
The Tony Bramall Charitable
   Trust
The Breadsticks Foundation
The Burdett Trust for Nursing
The William A Cadbury
   Charitable Trust
The Cadbury Foundation
The Carron Charitable
   Settlement
The Elizabeth Casson Trust
Chest, Heart and Stroke
   Scotland
The Clarke Charitable
   Settlement
The Congleton Inclosure Trust
The John Cowan Foundation
The Sir William Coxen Trust
   Fund
The Violet and Milo Cripps
   Charitable Trust
The Manny Cussins
   Foundation

The D'Oyly Carte Charitable
   Trust
Baron Davenport's Charity
The Deakin Charitable Trust
The Denton Wilde Sapte
   Charitable Trust
The Dinwoodie Settlement
Disability Aid Fund (The Roger
   and Jean Jefcoate Trust)
The Duis Charitable Trust
The Dunhill Medical Trust
Gilbert Edgar Trust
James Ellis Charitable Trust
The Emmandjay Charitable
   Trust
The Eranda Foundation
The Eveson Charitable Trust
The Family Rich Charities Trust
Samuel William Farmer Trust
Joseph Fattorini Charitable
   Trust 'B' Account
Elizabeth Ferguson Charitable
   Trust Fund
Fife Council/Common Good
   Funds and Trusts
The Lady Forester Trust
The Forte Charitable Trust
The Hugh Fraser Foundation
The Freemasons' Grand
   Charity
The Freshfield Foundation
The Freshgate Trust
   Foundation
Maurice Fry Charitable Trust
The Ganzoni Charitable Trust
The Gatsby Charitable
   Foundation
Gatwick Airport Community
   Trust
The General Nursing Council
   for England and Wales
   Trust
Simon Gibson Charitable Trust
The Girdlers' Company
   Charitable Trust
GMC Trust
The Goldsmiths' Company
   Charity
The Grand Order of Water
   Rats' Charities Fund
The Constance Green
   Foundation
Robert Hall Charity
Hampton Fuel Allotment
   Charity
The W A Handley Charitable
   Trust
The Kenneth Hargreaves
   Charitable Trust
The Harris Family Charitable
   Trust
The Edith Lilian Harrison 2000
   Foundation
The Haymills Charitable Trust
The Charles Hayward
   Foundation

The Hedley Foundation
The Michael and Morven Heller
   Charitable Foundation
Help the Hospices
The Hemby Trust
The Joanna Herbert-Stepney
   Charitable Settlement (also
   known as The Paget
   Charitable Trust)
The Charles Littlewood Hill
   Trust
The Hintze Family Charitable
   Foundation
The Hollands-Warren Fund
The Homelands Charitable
   Trust
The Horne Trust
The Hospital Saturday Fund
Human Relief Foundation
The Humanitarian Trust
Huntingdon Freemen's Charity
The Ruth and Lionel Jacobson
   Trust (Second Fund) No 2
The Jarman Charitable Trust
The Ian Karten Charitable
   Trust
The Kennedy Charitable
   Foundation
The Peter Kershaw Trust
The King's Fund
Ernest Kleinwort Charitable
   Trust
The Langdale Trust
Laslett's (Hinton) Charity
The Raymond and Blanche
   Lawson Charitable Trust
Leeds Building Society
   Charitable Foundation
Lesley Lesley and Mutter Trust
The Joseph Levy Charitable
   Foundation
John Lewis Partnership
   General Community Fund
Lifeline 4 Kids
The Andrew and Mary
   Elizabeth Little Charitable
   Trust
Lloyds TSB Foundation for
   Northern Ireland
The Trust for London (formerly
   the City Parochial
   Foundation)
London Catalyst (formerly The
   Metropolitan Hospital-
   Sunday Fund)
The Lord's Taverners
Lord and Lady Lurgan Trust
The MacRobert Trust
Market Harborough and The
   Bowdens Charity
The Marsh Christian Trust
Sir George Martin Trust
John Martin's Charity
Evelyn May Trust
The Robert McAlpine
   Foundation

The Medlock Charitable Trust
The Anthony and Elizabeth
   Mellows Charitable
   Settlement
The Tony Metherell Charitable
   Trust
Gerald Micklem Charitable
   Trust
Miles Trust for the Putney and
   Roehampton Community
Monmouthshire County Council
   Welsh Church Act Fund
The Monument Trust
The Morgan Charitable
   Foundation
Brian and Jill Moss Charitable
   Trust
The Edwina Mountbatten Trust
Peter John Murray Trust (PJM
   Trust)
The Frances and Augustus
   Newman Foundation
The North British Hotel Trust
The Northampton Queen's
   Institute Relief in Sickness
   Fund
The Nottingham General
   Dispensary
The Nuffield Foundation
The Owen Family Trust
The Park Charitable Trust
The Constance Paterson
   Charitable Trust
Paycare Charity Trust (formerly
   known as Patients' Aid
   Association Hospital and
   Medical Charities Trust)
The Mary Potter Convent
   Hospital Trust
The Douglas Prestwich
   Charitable Trust
Sir John Priestman Charity
   Trust
The Prince of Wales's
   Charitable Foundation
The Richard and Christine
   Purchas Charitable Trust
Richard Radcliffe Charitable
   Trust
The Joseph Rank Trust
The Rayne Foundation
Relief Fund for Romania
   Limited
Reuben Brothers Foundation
The Violet M Richards Charity
Riverside Charitable Trust
   Limited
Thomas Roberts Trust
The Rose Foundation
The Rotherwick Foundation
The Christopher Rowbotham
   Charitable Trust
The Sackler Trust (formerly Dr
   Mortimer and Theresa
   Sackler Foundation)
The Saintbury Trust

The Sheepdrove Trust
The Sheffield and District
Hospital Services
Charitable Fund
The Sylvia and Colin Shepherd
Charitable Trust
The E C Sosnow Charitable
Trust
The South Square Trust
Rosalyn and Nicholas Springer
Charitable Trust
St James's Place Foundation
Stevenson Family's Charitable
Trust
The Strawberry Charitable
Trust
The Tajtelbaum Charitable
Trust
The Connie and Albert Taylor
Charitable Trust
The True Colours Trust
John and Lucille van Geest
Foundation
The Variety Club Children's
Charity
Wallace and Gromit's
Children's Foundation
Blyth Watson Charitable Trust
The Westcroft Trust
Anona Winn Charitable Trust
The Charles Wolfson
Charitable Trust
The Xerox (UK) Trust

Health training

Veta Bailey Charitable Trust
The Barbers' Company General
Charities
The Dinwoodie Settlement
The Nuffield Foundation

Medical equipment

The Barnwood House Trust
Sir Alec Black's Charity
Samuel William Farmer Trust
The Grand Order of Water
Rats' Charities Fund
The Constance Green
Foundation
The Hedley Foundation
The Ian Karten Charitable
Trust
The Joseph Levy Charitable
Foundation
Lifeline 4 Kids
London Catalyst (formerly The
Metropolitan Hospital-
Sunday Fund)
The Lord's Taverners
The Frances and Augustus
Newman Foundation
The North British Hotel Trust

Paycare Charity Trust (formerly
known as Patients' Aid
Association Hospital and
Medical Charities Trust)
The Sylvia and Colin Shepherd
Charitable Trust
The Variety Club Children's
Charity

Medical institutions

The Aberbrothock Skea Trust
The Barnwood House Trust
The Birmingham District
Nursing Charitable Trust
Sir Alec Black's Charity
The Harry Bottom Charitable
Trust
Chest, Heart and Stroke
Scotland
The Clarke Charitable
Settlement
The John Cowan Foundation
The Sir William Coxen Trust
Fund
The Violet and Milo Cripps
Charitable Trust
Baron Davenport's Charity
The Deakin Charitable Trust
The Duis Charitable Trust
The Dunhill Medical Trust
Gilbert Edgar Trust
The Emmandjay Charitable
Trust
The Eveson Charitable Trust
Samuel William Farmer Trust
Joseph Fattorini Charitable
Trust 'B' Account
Elizabeth Ferguson Charitable
Trust Fund
Fife Council/Common Good
Funds and Trusts
The Hugh Fraser Foundation
The Freemasons' Grand
Charity
The Ganzoni Charitable Trust
Gatwick Airport Community
Trust
The Girdlers' Company
Charitable Trust
The Constance Green
Foundation
Robert Hall Charity
Hampton Fuel Allotment
Charity
The Haymills Charitable Trust
The Charles Hayward
Foundation
The Hedley Foundation
The Michael and Morven Heller
Charitable Foundation
Help the Hospices
The Homelands Charitable
Trust

The Horne Trust
The Hospital Saturday Fund
The Ruth and Lionel Jacobson
Trust (Second Fund) No 2
The Jarman Charitable Trust
The Kennedy Charitable
Foundation
The Peter Kershaw Trust
Ernest Kleinwort Charitable
Trust
The Raymond and Blanche
Lawson Charitable Trust
Leeds Building Society
Charitable Foundation
The Joseph Levy Charitable
Foundation
Lloyds TSB Foundation for
Northern Ireland
Lord and Lady Lurgan Trust
The Marsh Christian Trust
Sir George Martin Trust
Evelyn May Trust
The Robert McAlpine
Foundation
The Medlock Charitable Trust
The Anthony and Elizabeth
Mellows Charitable
Settlement
The Tony Metherell Charitable
Trust
Gerald Micklem Charitable
Trust
Miles Trust for the Putney and
Roehampton Community
Monmouthshire County Council
Welsh Church Act Fund
The Monument Trust
The Morgan Charitable
Foundation
The North British Hotel Trust
The Northampton Queen's
Institute Relief in Sickness
Fund
The Nottingham General
Dispensary
The Owen Family Trust
The Park Charitable Trust
Paycare Charity Trust (formerly
known as Patients' Aid
Association Hospital and
Medical Charities Trust)
The Douglas Prestwich
Charitable Trust
Sir John Priestman Charity
Trust
The Prince of Wales's
Charitable Foundation
Richard Radcliffe Charitable
Trust
The Rayne Foundation
The Rose Foundation
The Sackler Trust (formerly Dr
Mortimer and Theresa
Sackler Foundation)

The Sheffield and District
Hospital Services
Charitable Fund
St James's Place Foundation
The Tajtelbaum Charitable
Trust
The Connie and Albert Taylor
Charitable Trust
Blyth Watson Charitable Trust

Nursing

The Barbers' Company General
Charities
The Birmingham District
Nursing Charitable Trust
The General Nursing Council
for England and Wales
Trust
The Hedley Foundation
The Ruth and Lionel Jacobson
Trust (Second Fund) No 2
The Joseph Levy Charitable
Foundation
The Edwina Mountbatten Trust

Primary health care

The 1970 Trust
The Ruth and Lionel Jacobson
Trust (Second Fund) No 2

Therapy

The Artemis Charitable Trust
The Elizabeth Casson Trust
The Trust for London (formerly
the City Parochial
Foundation)

Health education/ prevention/ development

The AIM Foundation
The Big Lottery Fund
The Tony Bramall Charitable
Trust
The British Dietetic
Association General and
Education Trust Fund
The Derek Butler Trust
Henry T and Lucy B Cadbury
Charitable Trust
Chest, Heart and Stroke
Scotland
The Colt Foundation
The Cotton Trust
Disability Aid Fund (The Roger
and Jean Jefcoate Trust)
Gilbert Edgar Trust

The John Ellerman Foundation
J Paul Getty Jr Charitable Trust
Hampton Fuel Allotment
Charity
The Haramead Trust
The Joanna Herbert-Stepney
Charitable Settlement (also
known as The Paget
Charitable Trust)
Human Relief Foundation
The Kelly Family Charitable
Trust
The King's Fund
Lloyds TSB Foundation for
Northern Ireland
London Catalyst (formerly The
Metropolitan Hospital-
Sunday Fund)
Mercury Phoenix Trust
Monmouthshire County Council
Welsh Church Act Fund
The Robert and Margaret
Moss Charitable Trust
The Richard and Christine
Purchas Charitable Trust
Mr and Mrs J A Pye's
Charitable Settlement
The Joseph Rank Trust
Relief Fund for Romania
Limited
The Violet M Richards Charity
The Rosca Trust
Rosalyn and Nicholas Springer
Charitable Trust
The York Children's Trust

Health promotion

The Big Lottery Fund
The British Dietetic
Association General and
Education Trust Fund
Chest, Heart and Stroke
Scotland
The Robert and Margaret
Moss Charitable Trust

History of medicine

The Joanna Herbert-Stepney
Charitable Settlement (also
known as The Paget
Charitable Trust)
The Joseph Rank Trust
Thackray Medical Research
Trust
The Wellcome Trust

Medical research

The 1989 Willan Charitable
Trust
The Aberbrothock Skea Trust

Action Medical Research
The Company of Actuaries'
Charitable Trust Fund
The Adamson Trust
Age UK (formerly Help the
Aged and Age Concern)
The Green and Lilian F M
Ainsworth and Family
Benevolent Fund
The Sylvia Aitken Charitable
Trust
The Alliance Family Foundation
The Pat Allsop Charitable Trust
Anglo American Group
Foundation
The Armourers' and Brasiers'
Gauntlet Trust
Arthritis Research UK
Astellas European Foundation
Asthma UK
The Astor Foundation
The Astor of Hever Trust
The Baily Thomas Charitable
Fund
The Baker Charitable Trust
The Barbers' Company General
Charities
The Barclay Foundation
The Barnwood House Trust
The John Beckwith Charitable
Trust
The Bellhouse Foundation
Bergqvist Charitable Trust
The Ruth Berkowitz Charitable
Trust
The Herbert and Peter
Blagrave Charitable Trust
P G and N J Boulton Trust
The Breast Cancer Research
Trust
The British Council for
Prevention of Blindness
British Heart Foundation
The Charles Brotherton Trust
Buckland Charitable Trust
The BUPA Foundation
The Burden Trust
The Burry Charitable Trust
The Arnold Burton 1998
Charitable Trust
The Derek Butler Trust
P H G Cadbury Charitable
Trust
The Castang Foundation
The Cayo Foundation
Celtic Charity Fund
The Cemlyn-Jones Trust
The Charities Advisory Trust
The Checkatrade Foundation
Chest, Heart and Stroke
Scotland
Child Growth Foundation
Children's Liver Disease
Foundation
The Children's Research Fund
The Childwick Trust

The Clarke Charitable
  Settlement
The Cleopatra Trust
The Clothworkers' Foundation
The Bernard Coleman
  Charitable Trust
The Colt Foundation
The Cotton Trust
The John Cowan Foundation
The Michael Cowan
  Foundation
The Sir William Coxen Trust
  Fund
Cruden Foundation Ltd
The Cunningham Trust
Roald Dahl's Marvellous
  Children's Charity
The De Clermont Charitable
  Company Ltd
The Denman Charitable Trust
The Denton Charitable Trust
Diabetes UK
The Dinwoodie Settlement
The Dorus Trust
The Dunhill Medical Trust
The Dunn Family Charitable
  Trust
The James Dyson Foundation
The Earmark Trust
The EBM Charitable Trust
The Gilbert and Eileen Edgar
  Foundation
Gilbert Edgar Trust
The John Ellerman Foundation
James Ellis Charitable Trust
The Emmandjay Charitable
  Trust
Epilepsy Research UK
The Eranda Foundation
Essex Provincial Charity Fund
The Eveson Charitable Trust
The Family Rich Charities Trust
Samuel William Farmer Trust
Elizabeth Ferguson Charitable
  Trust Fund
The Sir John Fisher Foundation
The Fishmongers' Company's
  Charitable Trust
Bud Flanagan Leukaemia Fund
The Ian Fleming Charitable
  Trust
The Follett Trust
The Anna Rosa Forster
  Charitable Trust
The Hugh Fraser Foundation
The Joseph Strong Frazer Trust
The Freemasons' Grand
  Charity
The Frognal Trust
T F C Frost Charitable Trust
Maurice Fry Charitable Trust
The Garnett Charitable Trust
The Gatsby Charitable
  Foundation
The Girdlers' Company
  Charitable Trust

GMC Trust
The Sydney and Phyllis
  Goldberg Memorial
  Charitable Trust
Golden Charitable Trust
Mike Gooley Trailfinders
  Charity
The Great Britain Sasakawa
  Foundation
The Philip Green Memorial
  Trust
The Gunter Charitable Trust
The Hamamelis Trust
Hamilton Wallace Trust
The W A Handley Charitable
  Trust
The Harbour Charitable Trust
The Harebell Centenary Fund
The Kenneth Hargreaves
  Charitable Trust
The Harris Charitable Trust
The John Harrison Charitable
  Trust
The N and P Hartley Memorial
  Trust
The Alfred And Peggy Harvey
  Charitable Trust
The Haymills Charitable Trust
The Hedley Foundation
The Michael and Morven Heller
  Charitable Foundation
The Simon Heller Charitable
  Settlement
The Christina Mary Hendrie
  Trust for Scottish and
  Canadian Charities
The Sir Julian Hodge
  Charitable Trust
The Jane Hodge Foundation
The Holbeck Charitable Trust
The Edward Holt Trust
The Homelands Charitable
  Trust
The Homestead Charitable
  Trust
The Antony Hornby Charitable
  Trust
Miss Agnes H Hunter's Trust
International Spinal Research
  Trust
The Jabbs Foundation
The John Jarrold Trust
The Jeffrey Charitable Trust
The Elton John Aids
  Foundation
The Jones 1986 Charitable
  Trust
The Emmanuel Kaye
  Foundation
The Caron Keating Foundation
The KempWelch Charitable
  Trust
The Kay Kendall Leukaemia
  Fund
The Peter Kershaw Trust

The Mary Kinross Charitable
  Trust
Ernest Kleinwort Charitable
  Trust
The Kohn Foundation
The Kyte Charitable Trust
The R J Larg Family Charitable
  Trust
The Kathleen Laurence Trust
The Edgar E Lawley Foundation
The William Leech Charity
The Leigh Trust
Leukaemia and Lymphoma
  Research
The Joseph Levy Charitable
  Foundation
Lewis Family Charitable Trust
The Linbury Trust
Frank Litchfield Charitable
  Trust
The George John and Sheilah
  Livanos Charitable Trust
The London Law Trust
The Lotus Foundation
The Marie Helen Luen
  Charitable Trust
Robert Luff Foundation Ltd
Lord and Lady Lurgan Trust
The Madeline Mabey Trust
The R S Macdonald Charitable
  Trust
Macdonald-Buchanan
  Charitable Trust
The Mackintosh Foundation
Mandeville Trust
The Manoukian Charitable
  Foundation
The Marcela Trust
Marshgate Charitable
  Settlement
The Nancie Massey Charitable
  Trust
Evelyn May Trust
The Robert McAlpine
  Foundation
D D McPhail Charitable
  Settlement
The Medlock Charitable Trust
Meningitis Trust
Brian Mercer Charitable Trust
The Mercers' Charitable
  Foundation
The Tony Metherell Charitable
  Trust
Gerald Micklem Charitable
  Trust
The Migraine Trust
The Millward Charitable Trust
Monmouthshire County Council
  Welsh Church Act Fund
The Montague Thompson
  Coon Charitable Trust
The Monument Trust
The Peter Moores Foundation
The Willie and Mabel Morris
  Charitable Trust

G M Morrison Charitable Trust

The Robert and Margaret
Moss Charitable Trust

The Mothercare Charitable
Foundation

J P Moulton Charitable
Foundation

The Frances and Augustus
Newman Foundation

The North British Hotel Trust

The North West Cancer
Research Fund

The Northcott Devon Medical
Foundation

The Northwood Charitable
Trust

The Nottingham General
Dispensary

The Nuffield Foundation

The Oakdale Trust

Oglesby Charitable Trust

The O'Sullivan Family
Charitable Trust

The Owen Family Trust

The Parthenon Trust

Arthur James Paterson
Charitable Trust

The Constance Paterson
Charitable Trust

Paycare Charity Trust (formerly
known as Patients' Aid
Association Hospital and
Medical Charities Trust)

The Harry Payne Trust

The Dowager Countess
Eleanor Peel Trust

Pendragon Charitable Trust

The Persula Foundation

The Cecil Pilkington Charitable
Trust

The Pilkington Charities Fund

The Col W W Pilkington Will
Trusts The General Charity
Fund

The Richard and Christine
Purchas Charitable Trust

Mr and Mrs J A Pye's
Charitable Settlement

The Monica Rabagliati
Charitable Trust

The Mr and Mrs Philip
Rackham Charitable Trust

The Rank Foundation

The Rayne Foundation

The Max Reinhardt Charitable
Trust

REMEDI

The Violet M Richards Charity

The Robertson Trust

Edwin George Robinson
Charitable Trust

Rosetrees Trust

Mrs Gladys Row Fogo
Charitable Trust

The Rowlands Trust

Ryklow Charitable Trust 1992
(also known as A B
Williamson Charitable Trust)

The Raymond and Beverley
Sackler 1988 Foundation

The Alan and Babette
Sainsbury Charitable Fund

The Andrew Salvesen
Charitable Trust

The Peter Samuel Charitable
Trust

The Camilla Samuel Fund

The Scarfe Charitable Trust

Sir Samuel Scott of Yews
Trust

The Jean Shanks Foundation

The Sheepdrove Trust

The Shirley Foundation

The Simpson Education and
Conservation Trust

The SMB Charitable Trust

The N Smith Charitable
Settlement

The Henry Smith Charity

The South Square Trust

Sparks Charity (Sport Aiding
Medical Research For Kids)

The Worshipful Company of
Spectacle Makers' Charity

Rosalyn and Nicholas Springer
Charitable Trust

St Francis's Leprosy Guild

St James's Place Foundation

The Sir Halley Stewart Trust

Peter Stormonth Darling
Charitable Trust

The Charles and Elsie Sykes
Trust

Tallow Chandlers Benevolent
Fund

The Connie and Albert Taylor
Charitable Trust

The Len Thomson Charitable
Trust

The Sir Jules Thorn Charitable
Trust

The Towry Law Charitable Trust
(also known as the Castle
Educational Trust)

The Ulverscroft Foundation

John and Lucille van Geest
Foundation

Roger Vere Foundation

The Vintners' Company
Charitable Foundation

Vision Charity

The Wellcome Trust

The Welton Foundation

The Felicity Wilde Charitable
Trust

The Will Charitable Trust

The Kay Williams Charitable
Foundation

The Williams Charitable Trust

The Harold Hyam Wingate
Foundation

Anona Winn Charitable Trust

The Charles Wolfson
Charitable Trust

The Wolfson Foundation

Woodroffe Benton Foundation

Miss E B Wrightson's
Charitable Settlement

The Wyseliot Charitable Trust

The John K Young Endowment
Fund

Philanthropy and the voluntary sector

Almondsbury Charity
The Baring Foundation
The Big Lottery Fund
The Edward and Dorothy
   Cadbury Trust
CAF (Charities Aid Foundation)
Calouste Gulbenkian
   Foundation
The Digbeth Trust
Esmée Fairbairn Foundation
Samuel William Farmer Trust
Gatwick Airport Community
   Trust
The Hadrian Trust
Paul Hamlyn Foundation
The Kenneth Hargreaves
   Charitable Trust
The Hemby Trust
Impetus Trust
The Kaufman Charitable Trust
The Eric and Margaret Kinder
   Charitable Trust
The William Leech Charity
The Mark Leonard Trust
Lloyds TSB Foundation for
   Northern Ireland
Lloyds TSB Foundation for the
   Channel Islands
The London Law Trust
The Medlock Charitable Trust
Mi Yu Foundation
The Millfield House Foundation
The Moonpig Foundation
John Moores Foundation
The MSE Charity
The Northern Rock Foundation
Pears Foundation
The Jack Petchey Foundation
The Rashbass Family Trust
Mrs L D Rope Third Charitable
   Settlement
The Joseph Rowntree
   Charitable Trust
Two Ridings Community
   Foundation
UnLtd (Foundation for Social
   Entrepreneurs)
'v'
Voluntary Action Fund
Wakeham Trust
Wales Council for Voluntary
   Action

Voluntarism

The Big Lottery Fund
Calouste Gulbenkian
   Foundation
Esmée Fairbairn Foundation
The Hemby Trust
The William Leech Charity

The Mark Leonard Trust
Lloyds TSB Foundation for
   Northern Ireland
The London Law Trust
The Jack Petchey Foundation
Mrs L D Rope Third Charitable
   Settlement
UnLtd (Foundation for Social
   Entrepreneurs)
'v'
Wakeham Trust
Wales Council for Voluntary
   Action

Community participation

The Big Lottery Fund
Calouste Gulbenkian
   Foundation
The Hemby Trust
The Mark Leonard Trust
The London Law Trust
The Jack Petchey Foundation
UnLtd (Foundation for Social
   Entrepreneurs)
Wakeham Trust

Voluntary sector capacity building

Almondsbury Charity
The Baring Foundation
CAF (Charities Aid Foundation)
The Digbeth Trust
Gatwick Airport Community
   Trust
The Hadrian Trust
Paul Hamlyn Foundation
The MSE Charity
The Northern Rock Foundation
Voluntary Action Fund

Religious activities

4 Charity Foundation
Brian Abrams Charitable Trust
Eric Abrams Charitable Trust
The Acacia Charitable Trust
Achiezer Association Ltd
Achisomoch Aid Company
   Limited
Adenfirst Ltd
Aid to the Church in Need (UK)
The Alabaster Trust
Alba Charitable Trust
The Alexis Trust
All Saints Educational Trust
The Alliance Family Foundation
The Almond Trust
Almondsbury Charity
The Altajir Trust
Altamont Ltd
Alvor Charitable Trust
AM Charitable Trust
Amabrill Limited
Viscount Amory's Charitable
   Trust
The Anchor Foundation
The Andrew Anderson Trust
Andor Charitable Trust
The André Christian Trust
The Archer Trust
The Ardwick Trust
The John Armitage Charitable
   Trust
The Armourers' and Brasiers'
   Gauntlet Trust
The AS Charitable Trust
Ashburnham Thanksgiving
   Trust
The Ashendene Trust
The Astor of Hever Trust
AW Charitable Trust
The Austin Bailey Trust
The Baird Trust
The Baker Charitable Trust
The Andrew Balint Charitable
   Trust
The George Balint Charitable
   Trust
The Paul Balint Charitable
   Trust
The Balney Charitable Trust
William P Bancroft (No 2)
   Charitable Trust and
   Jenepher Gillett Trust
The Barclay Foundation
Barleycorn Trust
Bay Charitable Trust
BCH Trust
The Beacon Trust
Bear Mordechai Ltd
The Beaufort House Trust
   Limited
Beauland Ltd
The Becker Family Charitable
   Trust

The Bellahouston Bequest
Fund
Belljoe Tzedoko Ltd
Maurice and Jacqueline
Bennett Charitable Trust
Michael and Leslie Bennett
Charitable Trust
The Ruth Berkowitz Charitable
Trust
BHST
The Bintaub Charitable Trust
The Bisgood Charitable Trust
(registered as Miss Jeanne
Bisgood's Charitable Trust)
The Bishop's Development
Fund
The Sydney Black Charitable
Trust
The Bertie Black Foundation
The Sir Victor Blank Charitable
Settlement
The Neville and Elaine Blond
Charitable Trust
The Blueberry Charitable Trust
The Bluston Charitable
Settlement
The Bonamy Charitable Trust
Salo Bordon Charitable Trust
H E and E L Botteley
Charitable Trust
The Harry Bottom Charitable
Trust
P G and N J Boulton Trust
The A H and E Boulton Trust
Sir Clive Bourne Family Trust
Bourneheights Limited
The Bowerman Charitable
Trust
The Bowland Charitable Trust
The Liz and Terry Bramall
Charitable Trust
Bristol Archdeaconry Charity
Mrs E E Brown Charitable
Settlement
T B H Brunner's Charitable
Settlement
Brushmill Ltd
Buckingham Trust
The Burden Trust
The Audrey and Stanley Burton
1960 Charitable Trust
The Arnold Burton 1998
Charitable Trust
C and F Charitable Trust
Edward Cadbury Charitable
Trust
Henry T and Lucy B Cadbury
Charitable Trust
The William A Cadbury
Charitable Trust
The Cambridgeshire Historic
Churches Trust
H and L Cantor Trust
Carlee Ltd
The Carlton House Charitable
Trust

The Carpenter Charitable Trust
The Carpenters' Company
Charitable Trust
The Catholic Charitable Trust
Catholic Foreign Missions
The Catholic Trust for England
and Wales
The Cemlyn-Jones Trust
The CH (1980) Charitable
Trust
Charitworth Limited
The Chasah Trust
Chasdei Tovim Me'oros
Childs Charitable Trust
The Childwick Trust
The Christabella Charitable
Trust
Christian Response to Eastern
Europe
The Church and Community
Fund
Church Burgesses Trust
Church of Ireland Priorities
Fund
The Church Urban Fund
The Hilda and Alice Clark
Charitable Trust
The Roger and Sarah Bancroft
Clark Charitable Trust
The Clarke Charitable
Settlement
The Clore Duffield Foundation
Miss V L Clore's 1967
Charitable Trust
Closehelm Ltd
Richard Cloudesley's Charity
Clydpride Ltd
The Denise Cohen Charitable
Trust
The Vivienne and Samuel
Cohen Charitable Trust
John Coldman Charitable Trust
The E Alec Colman Charitable
Fund Ltd
Col-Reno Ltd
The Congregational and
General Charitable Trust
Harold and Daphne Cooper
Charitable Trust
The Gershon Coren Charitable
Foundation
The Corinthian Trust
Edwin Cornforth 1983 Charity
Trust
The Cornwall Historic
Churches Trust
The Sidney and Elizabeth
Corob Charitable Trust
The Corona Charitable Trust
The Costa Family Charitable
Trust (formerly the Morgan
Williams Charitable Trust)
The Craps Charitable Trust
Criffel Charitable Trust
The Cuby Charitable Trust

The Manny Cussins
Foundation
Itzchok Meyer Cymerman Trust
Ltd
The Daily Prayer Union
Charitable Trust Ltd
Oizer Dalim Trust
The Davidson Family
Charitable Trust
The Alderman Joe Davidson
Memorial Trust
Davis-Rubens Charitable Trust
The Leopold De Rothschild
Charitable Trust
The Deakin Charitable Trust
The Debmar Benevolent Trust
The Dellal Foundation
Alan and Sheila Diamond
Charitable Trust
David and Rose Diamond Trust
The Djanogly Foundation
The DM Charitable Trust
The Dollond Charitable Trust
Domepride Ltd
The Dorcas Trust
The Dorema Charitable Trust
The Doughty Charity Trust
The Dugdale Charitable Trust
The Duis Charitable Trust
The Dulverton Trust
The Houghton Dunn Charitable
Trust
Dushinsky Trust Ltd
The Dyers' Company
Charitable Trust
The Earmark Trust
The Ebenezer Trust
The Gilbert and Eileen Edgar
Foundation
The George Elias Charitable
Trust
The Gerald Palmer Eling Trust
Company
Ellador Ltd
The Ellinson Foundation Ltd
The Edith Maud Ellis 1985
Charitable Trust
The Elmgrant Trust
Elshore Ltd
The Vernon N Ely Charitable
Trust
The Emmandjay Charitable
Trust
The Englefield Charitable Trust
Entindale Ltd
The Ernest Hecht Charitable
Foundation
The Erskine Cunningham Hill
Trust
The Esfandi Charitable
Foundation
The Exilarch's Foundation
Extonglen Limited
F C Charitable Trust
The F P Limited Charitable
Trust

The Faber Charitable Trust
The Fairway Trust
Famos Foundation Trust
Farthing Trust
Joseph Fattorini Charitable
    Trust 'B' Account
Federation of Jewish Relief
    Organisations
Finnart House School Trust
Firtree Trust
Fisherbeck Charitable Trust
The Rose Flatau Charitable
    Trust
The Flow Foundation
The Gerald Fogel Charitable
    Trust
Fordeve Ltd
The Forest Hill Charitable Trust
The Forte Charitable Trust
The Four Winds Trust
The Isaac and Freda Frankel
    Memorial Charitable Trust
The Hugh Fraser Foundation
The Joseph Strong Frazer Trust
The Thomas Freke and Lady
    Norton Charity
The Anne French Memorial
    Trust
The Friends Hall Farm Street
    Trust
Friends of Biala Ltd
Friends of Boyan Trust
Friends of Wiznitz Limited
Mejer and Gertrude Miriam
    Frydman Foundation
The Fulmer Charitable Trust
Gableholt Limited
The Gale Family Charitable
    Trust
The Angela Gallagher Memorial
    Fund
The Ganzoni Charitable Trust
Garvan Limited
Jacqueline and Michael Gee
    Charitable Trust
The Gibbs Charitable Trust
The Girdlers' Company
    Charitable Trust
The B and P Glasser
    Charitable Trust
Global Care
The GMW Charitable Trust
The Meir Golda Trust
Golden Charitable Trust
The Jack Goldhill Charitable
    Trust
The Everard and Mina
    Goodman Charitable
    Foundation
Leonard Gordon Charitable
    Trust
The Gough Charitable Trust
The Grace Charitable Trust
The Grahame Charitable
    Foundation Limited

The Philip Green Memorial
    Trust
Philip and Judith Green Trust
Naomi and Jeffrey Greenwood
    Charitable Trust
The Greys Charitable Trust
The M and R Gross Charities
    Limited
The Grove Charitable Trust
The GRP Charitable Trust
The Gur Trust
The H and J Spack Charitable
    Trust
The H P Charitable Trust
E F and M G Hall Charitable
    Trust
Sue Hammerson's Charitable
    Trust
The W A Handley Charitable
    Trust
Beatrice Hankey Foundation
    Ltd
The Kathleen Hannay
    Memorial Charity
Harbo Charities Limited
The Harbour Foundation
The Harris Charitable Trust
Haskel Family Foundation
The Hathaway Trust
The Maurice Hatter Foundation
Headley-Pitt Charitable Trust
Heagerty Charitable Trust
May Hearnshaw's Charity
Heathside Charitable Trust
The Helping Foundation
The Joanna Herbert-Stepney
    Charitable Settlement (also
    known as The Paget
    Charitable Trust)
The Hesed Trust
The Bernhard Heuberger
    Charitable Trust
Hexham and Newcastle
    Diocesan Trust (1947)
The P and C Hickinbotham
    Charitable Trust
Highcroft Charitable Trust
Hinchley Charitable Trust
Hinduja Foundation
Stuart Hine Trust
Hockerill Educational
    Foundation
Matthew Hodder Charitable
    Trust
The Sir Julian Hodge
    Charitable Trust
The Jane Hodge Foundation
The Holbeck Charitable Trust
The Holden Charitable Trust
The Holmes Family Trust
    (Sheffield)
The Homelands Charitable
    Trust
The Homestead Charitable
    Trust

Sir Harold Hood's Charitable
    Trust
The Hope Trust
The Daniel Howard Trust
The Humanitarian Trust
The Huntingdon Foundation
Hurdale Charity Limited
The Hutton Foundation
The Huxham Charitable Trust
The P Y N and B Hyams Trust
Infinity Capital Trust
The Inlight Trust
Investream Charitable Trust
Irshad Trust
Irwin Trust
The Isaacs Charitable Trust
J A R Charitable Trust
Jacobs Charitable Trust
The Ruth and Lionel Jacobson
    Trust (Second Fund) No 2
The Susan and Stephen
    James Charitable
    Settlement (also known as
    the Stephen James
    Charitable Trust)
The James Trust
The Marjory Jameson Trust
The Jarman Charitable Trust
Jay Education Trust
JCA Charitable Foundation
The Jerusalem Trust
Jewish Child's Day
The Jewish Youth Fund
The JMK Charitable Trust
The Harold Joels Charitable
    Trust
The Nicholas Joels Charitable
    Trust
The Norman Joels Charitable
    Trust
The Joron Charitable Trust
The J E Joseph Charitable
    Fund
Jusaca Charitable Trust
The Bernard Kahn Charitable
    Trust
The Stanley Kalms Foundation
The Kasner Charitable Trust
The Kass Charitable Trust
The Michael and Ilse Katz
    Foundation
The Katzauer Charitable
    Settlement
The C S Kaufman Charitable
    Trust
The Kaufman Charitable Trust
The Geoffrey John Kaye
    Charitable Foundation
The Emmanuel Kaye
    Foundation
The Soli and Leah Kelaty Trust
    Fund
The KempWelch Charitable
    Trust
The Kennedy Charitable
    Foundation

Keren Association
Kermaville Ltd
E and E Kernkraut Charities Limited
The Kessler Foundation
Keswick Hall Trust
The King Henry VIII Endowed Trust Warwick
Kirschel Foundation
The Kobler Trust
The Kohn Foundation
Kollel and Co. Limited
The Kreditor Charitable Trust
Kupath Gemach Chaim Bechesed Viznitz Trust
The Late Sir Pierce Lacy Charity Trust
The K P Ladd Charitable Trust
Maurice and Hilda Laing Charitable Trust
The Beatrice Laing Trust
The Lambert Charitable Trust
Duchy of Lancaster Benevolent Fund
The Lancaster Foundation
The Langdale Trust
The Langley Charitable Trust
Largsmount Ltd
Laslett's (Hinton) Charity
Laufer Charitable Trust
The Lauffer Family Charitable Foundation
The Lawson Beckman Charitable Trust
The Carole and Geoffrey Lawson Foundation
The Leathersellers' Company Charitable Fund
The Arnold Lee Charitable Trust
The William Leech Charity
The Kennedy Leigh Charitable Trust
Morris Leigh Foundation
The P Leigh-Bramwell Trust 'E'
The Leonard Trust
The Joseph Levy Charitable Foundation
Lewis Family Charitable Trust
The Lind Trust
Lindale Educational Foundation
The Ruth and Stuart Lipton Charitable Trust
Jack Livingstone Charitable Trust
The Elaine and Angus Lloyd Charitable Trust
The Charles Lloyd Foundation
Llysdinam Charitable Trust
Localtrent Ltd
The Locker Foundation
The Loftus Charitable Trust
The Lolev Charitable Trust
The Lowy Mitchell Foundation
The C L Loyd Charitable Trust

Paul Lunn-Rockliffe Charitable Trust
The Ruth and Jack Lunzer Charitable Trust
The Lyndhurst Trust
The Lynwood Trust
The Sir Jack Lyons Charitable Trust
The Joy and Malcolm Lyons Foundation
The Lyras Family Charitable Trust
Sylvanus Lyson's Charity
The M and C Trust
The M D and S Charitable Trust
The M K Charitable Trust
The SV and PE Magee Family Charitable Trust
The Magen Charitable Trust
The Mahavir Trust (also known as the K S Mehta Charitable Trust)
Malbin Trust
Maranatha Christian Trust
Marbeh Torah Trust
The Stella and Alexander Margulies Charitable Trust
Mariapolis Limited
The Ann and David Marks Foundation
The Michael Marsh Charitable Trust
The Marsh Christian Trust
The Charlotte Marshall Charitable Trust
Marshall's Charity
Marshgate Charitable Settlement
Sir George Martin Trust
John Martin's Charity
The John Mason Family Trust
The Mason Porter Charitable Trust
Matliwala Family Charitable Trust
The Matt 6.3 Charitable Trust
The Violet Mauray Charitable Trust
Mayfair Charities Ltd
Mazars Charitable Trust
The Anthony and Elizabeth Mellows Charitable Settlement
Melodor Ltd
Melow Charitable Trust
Menuchar Ltd
Mercaz Torah Vechesed Limited
The Mercers' Charitable Foundation
The Merchant Taylors' Company Charities Fund
Miles Trust for the Putney and Roehampton Community
The Miller Foundation

The Millfield Trust
The Millhouses Charitable Trust
The Edgar Milward Charity
The Minos Trust
The Laurence Misener Charitable Trust
The Mishcon Family Charitable Trust
The Mitchell Charitable Trust
The Mizpah Trust
The Modiano Charitable Trust
The Mole Charitable Trust
Monmouthshire County Council Welsh Church Act Fund
The Colin Montgomerie Charitable Foundation
The Peter Moores Foundation
The Mr and Mrs J T Morgan Foundation
Diana and Allan Morgenthau Charitable Trust
The Oliver Morland Charitable Trust
S C and M E Morland's Charitable Trust
The Peter Morrison Charitable Foundation
Moshal Charitable Trust
The Moshulu Charitable Trust
Brian and Jill Moss Charitable Trust
The Moss Charitable Trust
Moss Family Charitable Trust
Muslim Hands
MW (CL) Foundation
MW (GK) Foundation
MW (HO) Foundation
MW (RH) Foundation
MYA Charitable Trust
MYR Charitable Trust
The Nadezhda Charitable Trust
The Naggar Charitable Trust
Nathan Charitable Trust
Nazareth Trust Fund
The Worshipful Company of Needlemakers' Charitable Fund
Nemoral Ltd
Ner Foundation
Nesswall Ltd
Mr and Mrs F E F Newman Charitable Trust
Newpier Charity Ltd
The Chevras Ezras Nitzrochim Trust
NJD Charitable Trust
Normalyn Charitable Trust
The Northumbria Historic Churches Trust
The Norwich Church of England Young Men's Society
The Norwood and Newton Settlement
The Nottinghamshire Historic Churches Trust

The Ogle Christian Trust
The Oikonomia Trust
Oizer Charitable Trust
The Owen Family Trust
The Doris Pacey Charitable
    Foundation
Padwa Charitable Foundation
The Panacea Society
Panahpur (previously Panahpur
    Charitable Trust)
The James Pantyfedwen
    Foundation
The Park Charitable Trust
The Park House Charitable
    Trust
Miss M E Swinton Paterson's
    Charitable Trust
The Jack Patston Charitable
    Trust
The Payne Charitable Trust
The Harry Payne Trust
The David Pearlman Charitable
    Foundation
Pears Foundation
Peltz Trust
B E Perl Charitable Trust
The Persson Charitable Trust
    (formerly Highmoore Hall
    Charitable Trust)
The Philips and Rubens
    Charitable Trust
The Phillips Family Charitable
    Trust
The David Pickford Charitable
    Foundation
The Bernard Piggott Trust
G S Plaut Charitable Trust
    Limited
The Polehanger Trust
The George and Esme Pollitzer
    Charitable Settlement
The Pollywally Charitable Trust
Edith and Ferdinand Porjes
    Charitable Trust
The John Porter Charitable
    Trust
Porticus UK
The J E Posnansky Charitable
    Trust
The Praebendo Charitable
    Foundation
Premierquote Ltd
Premishlaner Charitable Trust
Sir John Priestman Charity
    Trust
The Pyne Charitable Trust
Quothquan Trust
R J M Charitable Trust
R S Charitable Trust
Rachel Charitable Trust
The Bishop Radford Trust
The Rank Foundation
The Joseph Rank Trust
The Fanny Rapaport Charitable
    Settlement
The Rashbass Family Trust

The Ravensdale Trust
The Rayden Charitable Trust
The Rayne Trust
The Sir James Reckitt Charity
The Rehoboth Trust
The Rest Harrow Trust
The Nathaniel Reyner Trust
    Fund
The Sir Cliff Richard Charitable
    Trust
The Clive Richards Charity
Ridgesave Limited
The Sir John Ritblat Family
    Foundation
The River Trust
The Rock Foundation
The Rock Solid Trust
The Rofeh Trust
Rokach Family Charitable Trust
The Sir James Roll Charitable
    Trust
The Gerald Ronson Foundation
Mrs L D Rope Third Charitable
    Settlement
The Rotherwick Foundation
Rowanville Ltd
The Rowland Family
    Foundation
The Joseph Rowntree
    Charitable Trust
The RRAF Charitable Trust
The Alfred and Frances
    Rubens Charitable Trust
The Rubin Foundation
S F Foundation
S O Charitable Trust
The Jeremy and John Sacher
    Charitable Trust
The Michael Harry Sacher
    Trust
The Ruzin Sadagora Trust
Saint Sarkis Charity Trust
The Salamander Charitable
    Trust
Salters' Charitable Foundation
The Hon. M J Samuel
    Charitable Trust
The Peter Samuel Charitable
    Trust
The Scarfe Charitable Trust
The Schapira Charitable Trust
The Annie Schiff Charitable
    Trust
The Schmidt-Bodner Charitable
    Trust
The Schreib Trust
The Schreiber Charitable Trust
The Helene Sebba Charitable
    Trust
The Samuel Sebba Charitable
    Trust
The Seedfield Trust
Sellata Ltd
SEM Charitable Trust
The Seven Fifty Trust
The Cyril Shack Trust

The Shanti Charitable Trust
The Archie Sherman Cardiff
    Foundation
The Archie Sherman Charitable
    Trust
The Bassil Shippam and
    Alsford Trust
Shlomo Memorial Fund Limited
The J A Shone Memorial Trust
The Julius Silman Charitable
    Trust
The Leslie Silver Charitable
    Trust
The Simpson Foundation
The SMB Charitable Trust
The R C Snelling Charitable
    Trust
The Sobell Foundation
Solev Co Ltd
The Solo Charitable
    Settlement
Songdale Ltd
The Souter Charitable Trust
The W F Southall Trust
Sparquote Limited
Spears-Stutz Charitable Trust
The Moss Spiro Will Charitable
    Foundation
Spring Harvest
Rosalyn and Nicholas Springer
    Charitable Trust
Springrule Ltd
St Teilo's Trust
The Steel Charitable Trust
The Steinberg Family
    Charitable Trust
C E K Stern Charitable Trust
The Sigmund Sternberg
    Charitable Foundation
Stervon Ltd
The Stewards' Company
    Limited (incorporating the J
    W Laing Trust and the J W
    Laing Biblical Scholarship
    Trust)
The Sir Halley Stewart Trust
The Leonard Laity Stoate
    Charitable Trust
The Stobart Newlands
    Charitable Trust
The Strawberry Charitable
    Trust
The A B Strom and R Strom
    Charitable Trust
Sueberry Ltd
The Alan Sugar Foundation
Sugarworld Trust
Summary Limited
The Adrienne and Leslie
    Sussman Charitable Trust
Sutton Coldfield Municipal
    Charities
The Sylvanus Charitable Trust
T and S Trust Fund
The Tabeel Trust
Tadlus Limited

The Tajtelbaum Charitable
Trust
Talteg Ltd
The Tangent Charitable Trust
The Lady Tangye Charitable
Trust
The David Tannen Charitable
Trust
The Lili Tapper Charitable
Foundation
C B and H H Taylor 1984 Trust
Tearfund
Tegham Limited
The West Charitable Trust
The Thornton Trust
Mrs R P Tindall's Charitable
Trust
The Tisbury Telegraph Trust
The Tolkien Trust
Tomchei Torah Charitable
Trust
The Torah Temimah Trust
Toras Chesed (London) Trust
The Tory Family Foundation
Truedene Co. Ltd
Truemart Limited
Trumros Limited
Tudor Rose Ltd
The Tufton Charitable Trust
Trustees of Tzedakah
UKI Charitable Foundation
Ulting Overseas Trust
The Union of Orthodox Hebrew
Congregation
The United Society for the
Propagation of the Gospel
The David Uri Memorial Trust
The Vail Foundation
The Van Neste Foundation
The Vardy Foundation
Roger Vere Foundation
Vivdale Ltd
The Viznitz Foundation
Robert and Felicity Waley-
Cohen Charitable Trust
Wallington Missionary Mart
and Auctions
The Weinstein Foundation
West London Synagogue
Charitable Fund
The Westcroft Trust
The Westminster Foundation
The Whitecourt Charitable
Trust
The Norman Whiteley Trust
The Williams Family Charitable
Trust
Dame Violet Wills Charitable
Trust
The Benjamin Winegarten
Charitable Trust
The Harold Hyam Wingate
Foundation
The Michael and Anna Wix
Charitable Trust
The Wixamtree Trust

The Maurice Wohl Charitable
Foundation
The Charles Wolfson
Charitable Trust
The Wolfson Family Charitable
Trust
Women's World Day of Prayer
(NCWWDPEWNI)
The James Wood Bequest
Fund
Woodlands Foundation Limited
Woodlands Green Ltd
The A and R Woolf Charitable
Trust
The Worcestershire and
Dudley Historic Churches
Trust
The Fred and Della Worms
Charitable Trust
Wychdale Ltd
Wychville Ltd
Yankov Charitable Trust
The Yorkshire Historic
Churches Trust
The Marjorie and Arnold Ziff
Charitable Foundation
Stephen Zimmerman
Charitable Trust

Christianity

Aid to the Church in Need (UK)
The Alabaster Trust
The Alexis Trust
The Almond Trust
Almondsbury Charity
Alvor Charitable Trust
Viscount Amory's Charitable
Trust
The Anchor Foundation
The Andrew Anderson Trust
The André Christian Trust
The Archer Trust
The Armourers' and Brasiers'
Gauntlet Trust
The AS Charitable Trust
Ashburnham Thanksgiving
Trust
The Ashendene Trust
The Baird Trust
The Balney Charitable Trust
William P Bancroft (No 2)
Charitable Trust and
Jenepher Gillett Trust
Barleycorn Trust
The Beacon Trust
The Beaufort House Trust
Limited
The Bisgood Charitable Trust
(registered as Miss Jeanne
Bisgood's Charitable Trust)
The Bishop's Development
Fund
The Sydney Black Charitable
Trust

H E and E L Botteley
Charitable Trust
The Harry Bottom Charitable
Trust
P G and N J Boulton Trust
The A H and E Boulton Trust
The Bowland Charitable Trust
The Liz and Terry Bramall
Charitable Trust
Bristol Archdeaconry Charity
T B H Brunner's Charitable
Settlement
Buckingham Trust
The Burden Trust
Henry T and Lucy B Cadbury
Charitable Trust
The William A Cadbury
Charitable Trust
The Cambridgeshire Historic
Churches Trust
The Carpenter Charitable Trust
The Carpenters' Company
Charitable Trust
The Catholic Charitable Trust
Catholic Foreign Missions
The Catholic Trust for England
and Wales
The Chasah Trust
Childs Charitable Trust
The Christabella Charitable
Trust
Christian Response to Eastern
Europe
The Church and Community
Fund
Church Burgesses Trust
The Church Urban Fund
The Hilda and Alice Clark
Charitable Trust
The Roger and Sarah Bancroft
Clark Charitable Trust
The Clarke Charitable
Settlement
Richard Cloudesley's Charity
John Coldman Charitable Trust
The Congregational and
General Charitable Trust
The Corinthian Trust
Edwin Cornforth 1983 Charity
Trust
The Cornwall Historic
Churches Trust
The Costa Family Charitable
Trust (formerly the Morgan
Williams Charitable Trust)
Criffel Charitable Trust
The Daily Prayer Union
Charitable Trust Ltd
The Dorcas Trust
The Dugdale Charitable Trust
The Dulverton Trust
The Houghton Dunn Charitable
Trust
The Dyers' Company
Charitable Trust
The Earmark Trust

The Ebenezer Trust
The Edith Maud Ellis 1985
    Charitable Trust
The Vernon N Ely Charitable
    Trust
The Emmandjay Charitable
    Trust
The Englefield Charitable Trust
The Erskine Cunningham Hill
    Trust
F C Charitable Trust
The Fairway Trust
Farthing Trust
Joseph Fattorini Charitable
    Trust 'B' Account
Firtree Trust
Fisherbeck Charitable Trust
The Forest Hill Charitable Trust
The Forte Charitable Trust
The Four Winds Trust
The Thomas Freke and Lady
    Norton Charity
The Anne French Memorial
    Trust
The Friends Hall Farm Street
    Trust
The Fulmer Charitable Trust
The Gale Family Charitable
    Trust
The Angela Gallagher Memorial
    Fund
The Ganzoni Charitable Trust
The Gibbs Charitable Trust
The Girdlers' Company
    Charitable Trust
Global Care
Golden Charitable Trust
The Gough Charitable Trust
The Grace Charitable Trust
Philip and Judith Green Trust
The Greys Charitable Trust
E F and M G Hall Charitable
    Trust
The W A Handley Charitable
    Trust
Beatrice Hankey Foundation
    Ltd
The Kathleen Hannay
    Memorial Charity
The Harris Charitable Trust
Headley-Pitt Charitable Trust
Heagerty Charitable Trust
May Hearnshaw's Charity
The Joanna Herbert-Stepney
    Charitable Settlement (also
    known as The Paget
    Charitable Trust)
The Hesed Trust
Hexham and Newcastle
    Diocesan Trust (1947)
The P and C Hickinbotham
    Charitable Trust
Hinchley Charitable Trust
Stuart Hine Trust
Hockerill Educational
    Foundation

Matthew Hodder Charitable
    Trust
The Jane Hodge Foundation
The Holbeck Charitable Trust
The Holmes Family Trust
    (Sheffield)
The Homelands Charitable
    Trust
The Homestead Charitable
    Trust
Sir Harold Hood's Charitable
    Trust
The Hope Trust
The Hutton Foundation
The Huxham Charitable Trust
Irwin Trust
J A R Charitable Trust
The James Trust
The Marjory Jameson Trust
The Jarman Charitable Trust
The Jerusalem Trust
The KempWelch Charitable
    Trust
The Kennedy Charitable
    Foundation
The King Henry VIII Endowed
    Trust Warwick
The Late Sir Pierce Lacy
    Charity Trust
The K P Ladd Charitable Trust
Maurice and Hilda Laing
    Charitable Trust
The Beatrice Laing Trust
Duchy of Lancaster Benevolent
    Fund
The Lancaster Foundation
The Langdale Trust
The Langley Charitable Trust
Laslett's (Hinton) Charity
The Leathersellers' Company
    Charitable Fund
The William Leech Charity
The P Leigh-Bramwell Trust 'E'
The Leonard Trust
The Lind Trust
Lindale Educational
    Foundation
The Elaine and Angus Lloyd
    Charitable Trust
The Charles Lloyd Foundation
Llysdinam Charitable Trust
Paul Lunn-Rockliffe Charitable
    Trust
The Lyndhurst Trust
The Lynwood Trust
Sylvanus Lyson's Charity
Maranatha Christian Trust
Mariapolis Limited
The Marsh Christian Trust
The Charlotte Marshall
    Charitable Trust
Marshall's Charity
Marshgate Charitable
    Settlement
Sir George Martin Trust
John Martin's Charity

The John Mason Family Trust
The Mason Porter Charitable
    Trust
The Matt 6.3 Charitable Trust
Mazars Charitable Trust
The Anthony and Elizabeth
    Mellows Charitable
    Settlement
The Mercers' Charitable
    Foundation
The Merchant Taylors'
    Company Charities Fund
Miles Trust for the Putney and
    Roehampton Community
The Millfield Trust
The Millhouses Charitable
    Trust
The Edgar Milward Charity
The Minos Trust
The Mizpah Trust
Monmouthshire County Council
    Welsh Church Act Fund
The Peter Moores Foundation
The Mr and Mrs J T Morgan
    Foundation
The Oliver Morland Charitable
    Trust
S C and M E Morland's
    Charitable Trust
The Moshulu Charitable Trust
The Moss Charitable Trust
The Nadezhda Charitable Trust
Nathan Charitable Trust
Nazareth Trust Fund
Mr and Mrs F E F Newman
    Charitable Trust
The Northumbria Historic
    Churches Trust
The Norwich Church of England
    Young Men's Society
The Norwood and Newton
    Settlement
The Nottinghamshire Historic
    Churches Trust
The Ogle Christian Trust
The Oikonomia Trust
The Owen Family Trust
The Panacea Society
Panahpur (previously Panahpur
    Charitable Trust)
The James Pantyfedwen
    Foundation
The Park House Charitable
    Trust
Miss M E Swinton Paterson's
    Charitable Trust
The Jack Patston Charitable
    Trust
The Payne Charitable Trust
The Persson Charitable Trust
    (formerly Highmoore Hall
    Charitable Trust)
The David Pickford Charitable
    Foundation
The Bernard Piggott Trust
The Polehanger Trust

The Praebendo Charitable
   Foundation
Sir John Priestman Charity
   Trust
The Pyne Charitable Trust
Quothquan Trust
The Bishop Radford Trust
The Rank Foundation
The Ravensdale Trust
The Sir James Reckitt Charity
The Rehoboth Trust
The Nathaniel Reyner Trust
   Fund
The Sir Cliff Richard Charitable
   Trust
The Clive Richards Charity
The River Trust
The Rock Foundation
The Rock Solid Trust
Mrs L D Rope Third Charitable
   Settlement
The Rotherwick Foundation
The Joseph Rowntree
   Charitable Trust
Saint Sarkis Charity Trust
The Salamander Charitable
   Trust
Salters' Charitable Foundation
The Scarfe Charitable Trust
The Seedfield Trust
The Seven Fifty Trust
The Shanti Charitable Trust
The Bassil Shippam and
   Alsford Trust
The J A Shone Memorial Trust
The Simpson Foundation
The SMB Charitable Trust
The Souter Charitable Trust
The W F Southall Trust
Spring Harvest
St Teilo's Trust
The Stewards' Company
   Limited (incorporating the J
   W Laing Trust and the J W
   Laing Biblical Scholarship
   Trust)
The Sir Halley Stewart Trust
The Leonard Laity Stoate
   Charitable Trust
The Stobart Newlands
   Charitable Trust
Sugarworld Trust
Summary Limited
The Sylvanus Charitable Trust
The Tabeel Trust
The Lady Tangye Charitable
   Trust
C B and H H Taylor 1984 Trust
Tearfund
The Thornton Trust
Mrs R P Tindall's Charitable
   Trust
The Tisbury Telegraph Trust
The Tolkien Trust
The Tory Family Foundation
The Tufton Charitable Trust

Ulting Overseas Trust
The United Society for the
   Propagation of the Gospel
The Van Neste Foundation
The Vardy Foundation
Wallington Missionary Mart
   and Auctions
The Westcroft Trust
The Westminster Foundation
The Whitecourt Charitable
   Trust
The Norman Whiteley Trust
Dame Violet Wills Charitable
   Trust
The Wixamtree Trust
Women's World Day of Prayer
   (NCWWDPEWNI)
The James Wood Bequest
   Fund
The Worcestershire and
   Dudley Historic Churches
   Trust
The Yorkshire Historic
   Churches Trust

Christian causes

The Alexis Trust
The Almond Trust
Alvor Charitable Trust
The Andrew Anderson Trust
The Archer Trust
Ashburnham Thanksgiving
   Trust
The Baird Trust
Barleycorn Trust
H E and E L Botteley
   Charitable Trust
Bristol Archdeaconry Charity
The Carpenter Charitable Trust
The Carpenters' Company
   Charitable Trust
Church Burgesses Trust
The Church Urban Fund
The Englefield Charitable Trust
Farthing Trust
Firtree Trust
The Forest Hill Charitable Trust
The Forte Charitable Trust
The Four Winds Trust
The Anne French Memorial
   Trust
The Friends Hall Farm Street
   Trust
The Angela Gallagher Memorial
   Fund
The Gibbs Charitable Trust
The Girdlers' Company
   Charitable Trust
Global Care
The Joanna Herbert-Stepney
   Charitable Settlement (also
   known as The Paget
   Charitable Trust)
Stuart Hine Trust

Matthew Hodder Charitable
   Trust
The Jerusalem Trust
The KempWelch Charitable
   Trust
Maurice and Hilda Laing
   Charitable Trust
The Langdale Trust
The William Leech Charity
The Marsh Christian Trust
Sir George Martin Trust
Mazars Charitable Trust
The Mercers' Charitable
   Foundation
Miles Trust for the Putney and
   Roehampton Community
Nathan Charitable Trust
Nazareth Trust Fund
The Norwood and Newton
   Settlement
The Owen Family Trust
The Panacea Society
The Park House Charitable
   Trust
The Payne Charitable Trust
Quothquan Trust
The Sir Cliff Richard Charitable
   Trust
The River Trust
The Rock Solid Trust
Mrs L D Rope Third Charitable
   Settlement
The Salamander Charitable
   Trust
Salters' Charitable Foundation
The Seedfield Trust
The Shanti Charitable Trust
The J A Shone Memorial Trust
Spring Harvest
The Stewards' Company
   Limited (incorporating the J
   W Laing Trust and the J W
   Laing Biblical Scholarship
   Trust)
The Stobart Newlands
   Charitable Trust
Tearfund
Mrs R P Tindall's Charitable
   Trust
The Tufton Charitable Trust
The Vardy Foundation
The Whitecourt Charitable
   Trust

Christian churches

Aid to the Church in Need (UK)
Almondsbury Charity
Viscount Amory's Charitable
   Trust
The Ashendene Trust
The Baird Trust
The Balney Charitable Trust
William P Bancroft (No 2)
   Charitable Trust and
   Jenepher Gillett Trust

The Bisgood Charitable Trust
(registered as Miss Jeanne
Bisgood's Charitable Trust)
The Bishop's Development
Fund
The Sydney Black Charitable
Trust
The A H and E Boulton Trust
T B H Brunner's Charitable
Settlement
Henry T and Lucy B Cadbury
Charitable Trust
The William A Cadbury
Charitable Trust
The Cambridgeshire Historic
Churches Trust
The Catholic Charitable Trust
Catholic Foreign Missions
The Catholic Trust for England
and Wales
The Church and Community
Fund
Church Burgesses Trust
The Hilda and Alice Clark
Charitable Trust
The Roger and Sarah Bancroft
Clark Charitable Trust
Richard Cloudesley's Charity
The Congregational and
General Charitable Trust
The Corinthian Trust
Edwin Cornforth 1983 Charity
Trust
The Cornwall Historic
Churches Trust
The Dugdale Charitable Trust
The Houghton Dunn Charitable
Trust
The Ebenezer Trust
The Edith Maud Ellis 1985
Charitable Trust
The Emmandjay Charitable
Trust
The Erskine Cunningham Hill
Trust
Joseph Fattorini Charitable
Trust 'B' Account
The Thomas Freke and Lady
Norton Charity
The Anne French Memorial
Trust
The Friends Hall Farm Street
Trust
The Gale Family Charitable
Trust
The Angela Gallagher Memorial
Fund
The Gibbs Charitable Trust
The Girdlers' Company
Charitable Trust
The Gough Charitable Trust
The Greys Charitable Trust
E F and M G Hall Charitable
Trust
The W A Handley Charitable
Trust

The Harris Charitable Trust
Headley-Pitt Charitable Trust
Heagerty Charitable Trust
Hexham and Newcastle
Diocesan Trust (1947)
The P and C Hickinbotham
Charitable Trust
Stuart Hine Trust
The Jane Hodge Foundation
The Homelands Charitable
Trust
Sir Harold Hood's Charitable
Trust
The Hope Trust
The Huxham Charitable Trust
J A R Charitable Trust
The Jarman Charitable Trust
The Kennedy Charitable
Foundation
The King Henry VIII Endowed
Trust Warwick
Laslett's (Hinton) Charity
The P Leigh-Bramwell Trust 'E'
Lindale Educational
Foundation
The Charles Lloyd Foundation
Sylvanus Lyson's Charity
The Charlotte Marshall
Charitable Trust
Marshall's Charity
The Anthony and Elizabeth
Mellows Charitable
Settlement
Monmouthshire County Council
Welsh Church Act Fund
The Oliver Morland Charitable
Trust
S C and M E Morland's
Charitable Trust
Nazareth Trust Fund
The Northumbria Historic
Churches Trust
The Norwood and Newton
Settlement
The Nottinghamshire Historic
Churches Trust
The Ogle Christian Trust
The Owen Family Trust
Miss M E Swinton Paterson's
Charitable Trust
The Bernard Piggott Trust
Sir John Priestman Charity
Trust
The Bishop Radford Trust
The Sir James Reckitt Charity
The Nathaniel Reyner Trust
Fund
The Clive Richards Charity
Mrs L D Rope Third Charitable
Settlement
The Rotherwick Foundation
The Joseph Rowntree
Charitable Trust
Saint Sarkis Charity Trust
The Simpson Foundation
The W F Southall Trust

St Teilo's Trust
The Leonard Laity Stoate
Charitable Trust
The Sylvanus Charitable Trust
The Lady Tangye Charitable
Trust
C B and H H Taylor 1984 Trust
The Thornton Trust
The Tolkien Trust
The Westcroft Trust
The Westminster Foundation
The Norman Whiteley Trust
The Wixamtree Trust
The James Wood Bequest
Fund
The Worcestershire and
Dudley Historic Churches
Trust
The Yorkshire Historic
Churches Trust

Christian social thought

The Carpenters' Company
Charitable Trust
The Jerusalem Trust
The Sir Halley Stewart Trust

Ecumenicalism

The Carpenters' Company
Charitable Trust
The Gibbs Charitable Trust
Mariapolis Limited
Mrs L D Rope Third Charitable
Settlement

Missionary work, evangelism

The Armourers' and Brasiers'
Gauntlet Trust
Barleycorn Trust
The Beacon Trust
P G and N J Boulton Trust
The A H and E Boulton Trust
The Carpenters' Company
Charitable Trust
The Chasah Trust
The Daily Prayer Union
Charitable Trust Ltd
The Dugdale Charitable Trust
The Fairway Trust
Farthing Trust
Philip and Judith Green Trust
Beatrice Hankey Foundation
Ltd
The Hesed Trust
Stuart Hine Trust
Hockerill Educational
Foundation
The Hope Trust

The Huxham Charitable Trust
The Jerusalem Trust
Maurice and Hilda Laing
  Charitable Trust
The Beatrice Laing Trust
The Lancaster Foundation
The Langley Charitable Trust
Paul Lunn-Rockliffe Charitable
  Trust
The Lyndhurst Trust
Maranatha Christian Trust
The Millhouses Charitable
  Trust
The Moshulu Charitable Trust
Nathan Charitable Trust
Nazareth Trust Fund
The Ogle Christian Trust
The Owen Family Trust
Panahpur (previously Panahpur
  Charitable Trust)
The Payne Charitable Trust
The Persson Charitable Trust
  (formerly Highmoore Hall
  Charitable Trust)
Quothquan Trust
The Rank Foundation
The Sir Cliff Richard Charitable
  Trust
The Rock Foundation
The Seedfield Trust
The J A Shone Memorial Trust
Spring Harvest
St Teilo's Trust
The Stewards' Company
  Limited (incorporating the J
  W Laing Trust and the J W
  Laing Biblical Scholarship
  Trust)
The Tabeel Trust
The Thornton Trust
Ulting Overseas Trust
The United Society for the
  Propagation of the Gospel
Wallington Missionary Mart
  and Auctions
The Norman Whiteley Trust
Dame Violet Wills Charitable
  Trust
Women's World Day of Prayer
  (NCWWDPEWNI)

Hinduism

The Carpenters' Company
  Charitable Trust

Inter-faith activities

The Carpenters' Company
  Charitable Trust
The Duis Charitable Trust
The Edith Maud Ellis 1985
  Charitable Trust
The Elmgrant Trust

The Anne French Memorial
  Trust
Hinduja Foundation
The Joseph Levy Charitable
  Foundation
The Sir James Roll Charitable
  Trust
The Sigmund Sternberg
  Charitable Foundation
The Sir Halley Stewart Trust
West London Synagogue
  Charitable Fund

Islam

The Altajir Trust
The Carpenters' Company
  Charitable Trust
Irshad Trust
Matliwala Family Charitable
  Trust
Muslim Hands

Judaism

4 Charity Foundation
Brian Abrams Charitable Trust
Eric Abrams Charitable Trust
The Acacia Charitable Trust
Achiezer Association Ltd
Achisomoch Aid Company
  Limited
Adenfirst Ltd
Alba Charitable Trust
The Alliance Family Foundation
Altamont Ltd
AM Charitable Trust
Amabrill Limited
Andor Charitable Trust
The Ardwick Trust
AW Charitable Trust
The Baker Charitable Trust
The Andrew Balint Charitable
  Trust
The George Balint Charitable
  Trust
The Paul Balint Charitable
  Trust
Bay Charitable Trust
BCH Trust
Bear Mordechai Ltd
Beauland Ltd
The Becker Family Charitable
  Trust
Belljoe Tzedoko Ltd
Maurice and Jacqueline
  Bennett Charitable Trust
Michael and Leslie Bennett
  Charitable Trust
The Ruth Berkowitz Charitable
  Trust
BHST
The Bintaub Charitable Trust
The Bertie Black Foundation

The Sir Victor Blank Charitable
  Settlement
The Neville and Elaine Blond
  Charitable Trust
The Blueberry Charitable Trust
The Bluston Charitable
  Settlement
The Bonamy Charitable Trust
Salo Bordon Charitable Trust
Sir Clive Bourne Family Trust
Bourneheights Limited
Mrs E E Brown Charitable
  Settlement
Brushmill Ltd
The Audrey and Stanley Burton
  1960 Charitable Trust
The Arnold Burton 1998
  Charitable Trust
C and F Charitable Trust
H and L Cantor Trust
Carlee Ltd
The Carlton House Charitable
  Trust
The Carpenters' Company
  Charitable Trust
The CH (1980) Charitable
  Trust
Charitworth Limited
Chasdei Tovim Me'oros
The Childwick Trust
The Clore Duffield Foundation
Miss V L Clore's 1967
  Charitable Trust
Closehelm Ltd
Clydpride Ltd
The Denise Cohen Charitable
  Trust
The Vivienne and Samuel
  Cohen Charitable Trust
The E Alec Colman Charitable
  Fund Ltd
Col-Reno Ltd
Harold and Daphne Cooper
  Charitable Trust
The Gershon Coren Charitable
  Foundation
The Sidney and Elizabeth
  Corob Charitable Trust
The Corona Charitable Trust
The Craps Charitable Trust
The Cuby Charitable Trust
The Manny Cussins
  Foundation
Itzchok Meyer Cymerman Trust
  Ltd
Oizer Dalim Trust
The Davidson Family
  Charitable Trust
The Alderman Joe Davidson
  Memorial Trust
Davis-Rubens Charitable Trust
The Leopold De Rothschild
  Charitable Trust
The Debmar Benevolent Trust
The Dellal Foundation

Alan and Sheila Diamond
  Charitable Trust
David and Rose Diamond Trust
The Djanogly Foundation
The DM Charitable Trust
The Dollond Charitable Trust
Domepride Ltd
The Doughty Charity Trust
The Duis Charitable Trust
Dushinsky Trust Ltd
The George Elias Charitable
  Trust
Ellador Ltd
The Ellinson Foundation Ltd
Elshore Ltd
Entindale Ltd
The Esfandi Charitable
  Foundation
The Exilarch's Foundation
Extonglen Limited
The Faber Charitable Trust
Famos Foundation Trust
Federation of Jewish Relief
  Organisations
Finnart House School Trust
The Rose Flatau Charitable
  Trust
The Flow Foundation
The Gerald Fogel Charitable
  Trust
Fordeve Ltd
The Isaac and Freda Frankel
  Memorial Charitable Trust
Friends of Biala Ltd
Friends of Boyan Trust
Friends of Wiznitz Limited
Mejer and Gertrude Miriam
  Frydman Foundation
Gableholt Limited
Garvan Limited
Jacqueline and Michael Gee
  Charitable Trust
The B and P Glasser
  Charitable Trust
The Meir Golda Trust
Golden Charitable Trust
The Jack Goldhill Charitable
  Trust
The Everard and Mina
  Goodman Charitable
  Foundation
Leonard Gordon Charitable
  Trust
The Grahame Charitable
  Foundation Limited
The Philip Green Memorial
  Trust
Naomi and Jeffrey Greenwood
  Charitable Trust
The M and R Gross Charities
  Limited
The Grove Charitable Trust
The GRP Charitable Trust
The Gur Trust
The H and J Spack Charitable
  Trust

The H P Charitable Trust
Harbo Charities Limited
The Harbour Foundation
Haskel Family Foundation
The Hathaway Trust
The Maurice Hatter Foundation
Heathside Charitable Trust
The Helping Foundation
The Bernhard Heuberger
  Charitable Trust
Highcroft Charitable Trust
The Holden Charitable Trust
The Daniel Howard Trust
The Humanitarian Trust
The Huntingdon Foundation
Hurdale Charity Limited
The P Y N and B Hyams Trust
Infinity Capital Trust
Investream Charitable Trust
The Isaacs Charitable Trust
Jacobs Charitable Trust
The Ruth and Lionel Jacobson
  Trust (Second Fund) No 2
The Susan and Stephen
  James Charitable
  Settlement (also known as
  the Stephen James
  Charitable Trust)
Jay Education Trust
JCA Charitable Foundation
Jewish Child's Day
The Jewish Youth Fund
The Harold Joels Charitable
  Trust
The Nicholas Joels Charitable
  Trust
The Norman Joels Charitable
  Trust
The Joron Charitable Trust
The J E Joseph Charitable
  Fund
Jusaca Charitable Trust
The Bernard Kahn Charitable
  Trust
The Stanley Kalms Foundation
The Kasner Charitable Trust
The Kass Charitable Trust
The Michael and Ilse Katz
  Foundation
The Katzauer Charitable
  Settlement
The C S Kaufman Charitable
  Trust
The Kaufman Charitable Trust
The Geoffrey John Kaye
  Charitable Foundation
The Emmanuel Kaye
  Foundation
Keren Association
Kermaville Ltd
E and E Kernkraut Charities
  Limited
The Kessler Foundation
Kirschel Foundation
The Kobler Trust
The Kohn Foundation

Kollel and Co. Limited
The Kreditor Charitable Trust
Kupath Gemach Chaim
  Bechesed Viznitz Trust
The Lambert Charitable Trust
Largsmount Ltd
Laufer Charitable Trust
The Lauffer Family Charitable
  Foundation
The Lawson Beckman
  Charitable Trust
The Carole and Geoffrey
  Lawson Foundation
The Arnold Lee Charitable
  Trust
The Kennedy Leigh Charitable
  Trust
Morris Leigh Foundation
The Joseph Levy Charitable
  Foundation
Lewis Family Charitable Trust
The Ruth and Stuart Lipton
  Charitable Trust
Jack Livingstone Charitable
  Trust
Localtrent Ltd
The Locker Foundation
The Loftus Charitable Trust
The Lolev Charitable Trust
The Lowy Mitchell Foundation
The Ruth and Jack Lunzer
  Charitable Trust
The Sir Jack Lyons Charitable
  Trust
The Joy and Malcolm Lyons
  Foundation
The M and C Trust
The M D and S Charitable
  Trust
The M K Charitable Trust
The Magen Charitable Trust
Malbin Trust
Marbeh Torah Trust
The Stella and Alexander
  Margulies Charitable Trust
The Ann and David Marks
  Foundation
The Violet Mauray Charitable
  Trust
Mayfair Charities Ltd
Melodor Ltd
Melow Charitable Trust
Menuchar Ltd
Mercaz Torah Vechesed
  Limited
The Laurence Misener
  Charitable Trust
The Mishcon Family Charitable
  Trust
The Mitchell Charitable Trust
The Modiano Charitable Trust
The Mole Charitable Trust
Diana and Allan Morgenthau
  Charitable Trust
The Peter Morrison Charitable
  Foundation

Moshal Charitable Trust
Brian and Jill Moss Charitable
    Trust
Moss Family Charitable Trust
MW (CL) Foundation
MW (GK) Foundation
MW (HO) Foundation
MW (RH) Foundation
MYA Charitable Trust
MYR Charitable Trust
The Naggar Charitable Trust
Nemoral Ltd
Ner Foundation
Nesswall Ltd
Newpier Charity Ltd
The Chevras Ezras Nitzrochim
    Trust
NJD Charitable Trust
Normalyn Charitable Trust
Oizer Charitable Trust
The Doris Pacey Charitable
    Foundation
The Park Charitable Trust
The David Pearlman Charitable
    Foundation
Pears Foundation
Peltz Trust
B E Perl Charitable Trust
The Philips and Rubens
    Charitable Trust
The Phillips Family Charitable
    Trust
G S Plaut Charitable Trust
    Limited
The George and Esme Pollitzer
    Charitable Settlement
The Pollywally Charitable Trust
Edith and Ferdinand Porjes
    Charitable Trust
The John Porter Charitable
    Trust
The J E Posnansky Charitable
    Trust
Premierquote Ltd
Premishlaner Charitable Trust
R J M Charitable Trust
R S Charitable Trust
Rachel Charitable Trust
The Fanny Rapaport Charitable
    Settlement
The Rayden Charitable Trust
The Rayne Trust
The Rest Harrow Trust
Ridgesave Limited
The Sir John Ritblat Family
    Foundation
Rokach Family Charitable Trust
The Gerald Ronson Foundation
Rowanville Ltd
The Alfred and Frances
    Rubens Charitable Trust
The Rubin Foundation
S F Foundation
S O Charitable Trust
The Ruzin Sadagora Trust

The Hon. M J Samuel
    Charitable Trust
The Peter Samuel Charitable
    Trust
The Schapira Charitable Trust
The Annie Schiff Charitable
    Trust
The Schmidt-Bodner Charitable
    Trust
The Schreib Trust
The Schreiber Charitable Trust
The Helene Sebba Charitable
    Trust
The Samuel Sebba Charitable
    Trust
Sellata Ltd
SEM Charitable Trust
The Cyril Shack Trust
The Archie Sherman Cardiff
    Foundation
The Archie Sherman Charitable
    Trust
Shlomo Memorial Fund Limited
The Julius Silman Charitable
    Trust
The Leslie Silver Charitable
    Trust
The Sobell Foundation
Solev Co Ltd
The Solo Charitable
    Settlement
Songdale Ltd
Sparquote Limited
Spears-Stutz Charitable Trust
The Moss Spiro Will Charitable
    Foundation
Rosalyn and Nicholas Springer
    Charitable Trust
Springrule Ltd
The Steinberg Family
    Charitable Trust
C E K Stern Charitable Trust
The Sigmund Sternberg
    Charitable Foundation
Stervon Ltd
The Strawberry Charitable
    Trust
The A B Strom and R Strom
    Charitable Trust
Sueberry Ltd
The Alan Sugar Foundation
The Adrienne and Leslie
    Sussman Charitable Trust
T and S Trust Fund
Tadlus Limited
The Tajtelbaum Charitable
    Trust
Talteg Ltd
The Tangent Charitable Trust
The David Tannen Charitable
    Trust
The Lili Tapper Charitable
    Foundation
Tegham Limited
Tomchei Torah Charitable
    Trust

The Torah Temimah Trust
Toras Chesed (London) Trust
Truedene Co. Ltd
Truemart Limited
Trumros Limited
Tudor Rose Ltd
Trustees of Tzedakah
The Union of Orthodox Hebrew
    Congregation
The David Uri Memorial Trust
The Vail Foundation
Vivdale Ltd
The Viznitz Foundation
Robert and Felicity Waley-
    Cohen Charitable Trust
The Weinstein Foundation
West London Synagogue
    Charitable Fund
The Williams Family Charitable
    Trust
The Benjamin Winegarten
    Charitable Trust
The Harold Hyam Wingate
    Foundation
The Michael and Anna Wix
    Charitable Trust
The Maurice Wohl Charitable
    Foundation
The Charles Wolfson
    Charitable Trust
The Wolfson Family Charitable
    Trust
Woodlands Foundation Limited
Woodlands Green Ltd
The A and R Woolf Charitable
    Trust
The Fred and Della Worms
    Charitable Trust
Wychdale Ltd
Wychville Ltd
Yankov Charitable Trust
The Marjorie and Arnold Ziff
    Charitable Foundation
Stephen Zimmerman
    Charitable Trust

Jewish causes, work

Altamont Ltd
The Audrey and Stanley Burton
    1960 Charitable Trust
The Arnold Burton 1998
    Charitable Trust
Miss V L Clore's 1967
    Charitable Trust
The Duis Charitable Trust
Ellador Ltd
The Faber Charitable Trust
Leonard Gordon Charitable
    Trust
Naomi and Jeffrey Greenwood
    Charitable Trust
The Hathaway Trust

The Susan and Stephen
James Charitable
Settlement (also known as
the Stephen James
Charitable Trust)
The Lambert Charitable Trust
Malbin Trust
The Modiano Charitable Trust
Moss Family Charitable Trust
Normalyn Charitable Trust
Pears Foundation
Peltz Trust
The Pollywally Charitable Trust
Sellata Ltd
Sparquote Limited
The Moss Spiro Will Charitable
Foundation
Rosalyn and Nicholas Springer
Charitable Trust
The Tangent Charitable Trust
The Wolfson Family Charitable
Trust

Orthodox Judaism

Achisomoch Aid Company
Limited
Amabrill Limited
The Becker Family Charitable
Trust
Belljoe Tzedoko Ltd
Bourneheights Limited
C and F Charitable Trust
The Doughty Charity Trust
Extonglen Limited
Friends of Boyan Trust
The H P Charitable Trust
The Helping Foundation
The Lolev Charitable Trust
Mayfair Charities Ltd
Mercaz Torah Vechesed
Limited
MW (CL) Foundation
MW (HO) Foundation
MW (RH) Foundation
Nemoral Ltd
Newpier Charity Ltd
Rowanville Ltd
C E K Stern Charitable Trust
T and S Trust Fund
Tadlus Limited
Tegham Limited
The Torah Temimah Trust
Vivdale Ltd

Religious understanding

The Carpenters' Company
Charitable Trust
The Doughty Charity Trust
The Gilbert and Eileen Edgar
Foundation
The Elmgrant Trust

The Anne French Memorial
Trust
Keswick Hall Trust
The Kennedy Leigh Charitable
Trust
The Joseph Levy Charitable
Foundation
Quothquan Trust

Rights, law and conflict

The 1970 Trust
The A B Charitable Trust
The Ajahma Charitable Trust
The AS Charitable Trust
The Scott Bader
Commonwealth Ltd
The Jack and Ada Beattie
Foundation
The Body Shop Foundation
John and Susan Bowers Fund
Britannia Foundation
The British Gas (Scottish Gas)
Energy Trust
The Bromley Trust
The William A Cadbury
Charitable Trust
The Barrow Cadbury Trust and
the Barrow Cadbury Fund
CAFOD (Catholic Agency for
Overseas Development)
Calouste Gulbenkian
Foundation
Celtic Charity Fund
The Charities Advisory Trust
The Chelsea Building Society
Charitable Foundation
J A Clark Charitable Trust
The Community Foundation for
Northern Ireland
The Daiwa Anglo-Japanese
Foundation
The Denton Wilde Sapte
Charitable Trust
The Dorus Trust
The Duis Charitable Trust
The Dulverton Trust
EDF Energy Trust (EDFET)
The Edith Maud Ellis 1985
Charitable Trust
The Embleton Trust
The Emmandjay Charitable
Trust
Esmée Fairbairn Foundation
Farthing Trust
Allan and Nesta Ferguson
Charitable Settlement
Ford Britain Trust
Sydney E Franklin Deceased's
New Second Charity
Friends Provident Charitable
Foundation
Maurice Fry Charitable Trust
The G D Charitable Trust
The Gamlen Charitable Trust
J Paul Getty Jr Charitable Trust
Greggs Foundation (formerly
Greggs Trust)
Paul Hamlyn Foundation
The Helen Hamlyn Trust
The Hilden Charitable Fund
Hope for Youth (formerly
Women Caring Trust)

The Ireland Fund of Great
  Britain
The J R S S T Charitable Trust
The Joffe Charitable Trust
The Allen Lane Foundation
The Law Society Charity
The Leigh Trust
The Mark Leonard Trust
The Joseph Levy Charitable
  Foundation
Lloyds TSB Foundation for
  Northern Ireland
The Trust for London (formerly
  the City Parochial
  Foundation)
London Legal Support Trust
Mariapolis Limited
Marmot Charitable Trust
The Millfield House Foundation
John Moores Foundation
The Peter Moores Foundation
S C and M E Morland's
  Charitable Trust
The Kitty and Daniel Nabarro
  Charitable Trust
The Nadezhda Charitable Trust
Network for Social Change
Newby Trust Limited
The Noon Foundation
The Northern Rock Foundation
Novi Most International
The Nuffield Foundation
The Harry Payne Trust
The Persula Foundation
Polden-Puckham Charitable
  Foundation
The David and Elaine Potter
  Foundation
Prairie Trust
The Monica Rabagliati
  Charitable Trust
The Eleanor Rathbone
  Charitable Trust
The Sigrid Rausing Trust
The Roddick Foundation
Rosa – the UK fund for women
  and girls
The Joseph Rowntree
  Charitable Trust
Joseph Rowntree Reform Trust
  Limited
The Alan and Babette
  Sainsbury Charitable Fund
Santander UK Foundation
  Limited
The Severn Trent Water
  Charitable Trust Fund
The W F Southall Trust
The Staples Trust
The Tinsley Foundation
United Utilities Trust Fund
The Scurrah Wainwright Charity
War on Want

Worcester Municipal Charities
  (incorporating Worcester
  Consolidated Municipal
  Charity and Worcester
  Municipal Exhibitions
  Foundation)
The Xerox (UK) Trust
The York Children's Trust

Citizen participation

The Barrow Cadbury Trust and
  the Barrow Cadbury Fund
The Nuffield Foundation
The Joseph Rowntree
  Charitable Trust
Joseph Rowntree Reform Trust
  Limited
The Tinsley Foundation

Conflict resolution

The AS Charitable Trust
The Scott Bader
  Commonwealth Ltd
The William A Cadbury
  Charitable Trust
The Barrow Cadbury Trust and
  the Barrow Cadbury Fund
Calouste Gulbenkian
  Foundation
The Charities Advisory Trust
J A Clark Charitable Trust
The Daiwa Anglo-Japanese
  Foundation
The Dulverton Trust
The Edith Maud Ellis 1985
  Charitable Trust
Esmée Fairbairn Foundation
Allan and Nesta Ferguson
  Charitable Settlement
J Paul Getty Jr Charitable Trust
Hope for Youth (formerly
  Women Caring Trust)
The Ireland Fund of Great
  Britain
The Joffe Charitable Trust
The Allen Lane Foundation
Mariapolis Limited
Marmot Charitable Trust
S C and M E Morland's
  Charitable Trust
The Kitty and Daniel Nabarro
  Charitable Trust
The Noon Foundation
Novi Most International
The Harry Payne Trust
Polden-Puckham Charitable
  Foundation
Prairie Trust
The Joseph Rowntree
  Charitable Trust
The W F Southall Trust

Legal advice and services

Britannia Foundation
The British Gas (Scottish Gas)
  Energy Trust
The Chelsea Building Society
  Charitable Foundation
The Denton Wilde Sapte
  Charitable Trust
EDF Energy Trust (EDFET)
The Embleton Trust
The Emmandjay Charitable
  Trust
Friends Provident Charitable
  Foundation
The Law Society Charity
Lloyds TSB Foundation for
  Northern Ireland
The Trust for London (formerly
  the City Parochial
  Foundation)
London Legal Support Trust
John Moores Foundation
The Northern Rock Foundation
The Nuffield Foundation
Santander UK Foundation
  Limited
The Severn Trent Water
  Charitable Trust Fund
United Utilities Trust Fund
Worcester Municipal Charities
  (incorporating Worcester
  Consolidated Municipal
  Charity and Worcester
  Municipal Exhibitions
  Foundation)

Rights, equality and justice

The 1970 Trust
The A B Charitable Trust
The Ajahma Charitable Trust
The Body Shop Foundation
John and Susan Bowers Fund
The Bromley Trust
The Barrow Cadbury Trust and
  the Barrow Cadbury Fund
Calouste Gulbenkian
  Foundation
Celtic Charity Fund
The Dorus Trust
The Duis Charitable Trust
Farthing Trust
Allan and Nesta Ferguson
  Charitable Settlement
Ford Britain Trust
Sydney E Franklin Deceased's
  New Second Charity
The G D Charitable Trust
Greggs Foundation (formerly
  Greggs Trust)
Paul Hamlyn Foundation
The Helen Hamlyn Trust

The Hilden Charitable Fund
Hope for Youth (formerly
  Women Caring Trust)
The J R S S T Charitable Trust
The Joffe Charitable Trust
The Allen Lane Foundation
The Law Society Charity
The Leigh Trust
The Mark Leonard Trust
The Joseph Levy Charitable
  Foundation
The Trust for London (formerly
  the City Parochial
  Foundation)
The Millfield House Foundation
John Moores Foundation
The Peter Moores Foundation
The Kitty and Daniel Nabarro
  Charitable Trust
The Nadezhda Charitable Trust
Network for Social Change
Newby Trust Limited
The Noon Foundation
The Nuffield Foundation
The Persula Foundation
Polden-Puckham Charitable
  Foundation
The Monica Rabagliati
  Charitable Trust
The Eleanor Rathbone
  Charitable Trust
The Sigrid Rausing Trust
The Roddick Foundation
Rosa – the UK fund for women
  and girls
The Joseph Rowntree
  Charitable Trust
Joseph Rowntree Reform Trust
  Limited
The Alan and Babette
  Sainsbury Charitable Fund
The Staples Trust
The Tinsley Foundation
The Scurrah Wainwright Charity
The Xerox (UK) Trust
The York Children's Trust

Human rights

The 1970 Trust
The A B Charitable Trust
The Ajahma Charitable Trust
The Body Shop Foundation
The Bromley Trust
The Barrow Cadbury Trust and
  the Barrow Cadbury Fund
Farthing Trust
The Helen Hamlyn Trust
The Persula Foundation
Polden-Puckham Charitable
  Foundation
The Monica Rabagliati
  Charitable Trust
The Sigrid Rausing Trust
The Roddick Foundation
The Tinsley Foundation

Civil liberties

The 1970 Trust
The Barrow Cadbury Trust and
  the Barrow Cadbury Fund
The Joseph Rowntree
  Charitable Trust
Joseph Rowntree Reform Trust
  Limited
The Tinsley Foundation

Cultural equity

Calouste Gulbenkian
  Foundation
Greggs Foundation (formerly
  Greggs Trust)
Paul Hamlyn Foundation
The Kitty and Daniel Nabarro
  Charitable Trust

Disability rights

Calouste Gulbenkian
  Foundation
The Dorus Trust
The G D Charitable Trust
John Moores Foundation
Newby Trust Limited
The Xerox (UK) Trust

Economic justice

Allan and Nesta Ferguson
  Charitable Settlement
The Millfield House Foundation
The Sigrid Rausing Trust
The Joseph Rowntree
  Charitable Trust
The Tinsley Foundation

Racial justice

The Barrow Cadbury Trust and
  the Barrow Cadbury Fund
Celtic Charity Fund
The Duis Charitable Trust
Farthing Trust
Ford Britain Trust
The Hilden Charitable Fund
The Leigh Trust
The Joseph Levy Charitable
  Foundation
John Moores Foundation
The Peter Moores Foundation
The Noon Foundation
The Joseph Rowntree
  Charitable Trust
The Tinsley Foundation

Social justice

John and Susan Bowers Fund
The Duis Charitable Trust
Network for Social Change
Joseph Rowntree Reform Trust
  Limited
The Tinsley Foundation
The Scurrah Wainwright Charity
The Xerox (UK) Trust

Women's rights

The Duis Charitable Trust
John Moores Foundation
Polden-Puckham Charitable
  Foundation
The Eleanor Rathbone
  Charitable Trust
The Sigrid Rausing Trust
Rosa – the UK fund for women
  and girls
The Staples Trust

Young people's rights

Calouste Gulbenkian
  Foundation
The Duis Charitable Trust
Hope for Youth (formerly
  Women Caring Trust)
The Mark Leonard Trust
The Nadezhda Charitable Trust
The Nuffield Foundation
The Xerox (UK) Trust
The York Children's Trust

Science and technology

The 1970 Trust
The Armourers' and Brasiers' Gauntlet Trust
Astellas European Foundation
The Big Lottery Fund
British Ornithologists' Union
The Ernest Cook Trust
The Crescent Trust
William Dean Countryside and Educational Trust
The Dunn Family Charitable Trust
The James Dyson Foundation
The Beryl Evetts and Robert Luff Animal Welfare Trust
The Gatsby Charitable Foundation
The Granada Foundation
Paul Hamlyn Foundation
The Simon Heller Charitable Settlement
The Michael John Trust
The Kohn Foundation
The Leathersellers' Company Charitable Fund
The John Spedan Lewis Foundation
The MacRobert Trust
The Miller Foundation
The Mountbatten Memorial Trust
The Kitty and Daniel Nabarro Charitable Trust
The Nuffield Foundation
Open Gate
Pendragon Charitable Trust
The Petplan Charitable Trust
The David and Elaine Potter Foundation
Ranworth Trust
Mrs L D Rope Third Charitable Settlement
The Rowlands Trust
The Jeremy and John Sacher Charitable Trust
The Raymond and Beverley Sackler 1988 Foundation
The Sackler Trust (formerly Dr Mortimer and Theresa Sackler Foundation)
The Alan and Babette Sainsbury Charitable Fund
The Andrew Salvesen Charitable Trust
The Simpson Education and Conservation Trust
The Thompson Family Charitable Trust
The Waterloo Foundation
The Wellcome Trust
The Wilkinson Charitable Foundation
The Wolfson Foundation

The John K Young Endowment Fund

Engineering/ technology

The 1970 Trust
The Armourers' and Brasiers' Gauntlet Trust
The Ernest Cook Trust
The James Dyson Foundation
Paul Hamlyn Foundation
The Mountbatten Memorial Trust
The Kitty and Daniel Nabarro Charitable Trust
Open Gate
Ranworth Trust

Life sciences

The Big Lottery Fund
British Ornithologists' Union
The Ernest Cook Trust
The Crescent Trust
William Dean Countryside and Educational Trust
The Dunn Family Charitable Trust
The Beryl Evetts and Robert Luff Animal Welfare Trust
The Gatsby Charitable Foundation
The John Spedan Lewis Foundation
Pendragon Charitable Trust
The Petplan Charitable Trust
The Andrew Salvesen Charitable Trust
The Simpson Education and Conservation Trust
The Thompson Family Charitable Trust
The Waterloo Foundation
The Wellcome Trust

Physical/earth sciences

The Armourers' and Brasiers' Gauntlet Trust
Mrs L D Rope Third Charitable Settlement
The John K Young Endowment Fund

Social sciences, policy and research

Age UK (formerly Help the Aged and Age Concern)
British Institute at Ankara
CAF (Charities Aid Foundation)
CfBT Education Trust
EAGA Partnership Charitable Trust
The Elmgrant Trust
Esmée Fairbairn Foundation
The Gatsby Charitable Foundation
The Robert Gavron Charitable Trust
The Kenneth Hargreaves Charitable Trust
Haskel Family Foundation
Houblon-Norman/George Fund
The Allen Lane Foundation
The Leverhulme Trust
The Joseph Levy Charitable Foundation
The Trust for London (formerly the City Parochial Foundation)
James Madison Trust
The McDougall Trust
Monmouthshire County Council Welsh Church Act Fund
The Kitty and Daniel Nabarro Charitable Trust
The Eleni Nakou Foundation
The Nuffield Foundation
The Polonsky Foundation
Prairie Trust
The Joseph Rowntree Charitable Trust
The Joseph Rowntree Foundation
The Steel Charitable Trust
The Sir Halley Stewart Trust
The Nigel Vinson Charitable Trust
War on Want
Webb Memorial Trust

Economics

Age UK (formerly Help the Aged and Age Concern)
CAF (Charities Aid Foundation)
Houblon-Norman/George Fund

Political science

Esmée Fairbairn Foundation
The Gatsby Charitable Foundation
The Allen Lane Foundation
James Madison Trust
The McDougall Trust

The Eleni Nakou Foundation
The Joseph Rowntree
    Charitable Trust
The Joseph Rowntree
    Foundation
Webb Memorial Trust

Physical/earth sciences

Age UK (formerly Help the
    Aged and Age Concern)
CfBT Education Trust
The Gatsby Charitable
    Foundation
The Robert Gavron Charitable
    Trust
The Kenneth Hargreaves
    Charitable Trust
Haskel Family Foundation
The Joseph Levy Charitable
    Foundation
The Trust for London (formerly
    the City Parochial
    Foundation)
Monmouthshire County Council
    Welsh Church Act Fund
The Kitty and Daniel Nabarro
    Charitable Trust
Prairie Trust
The Joseph Rowntree
    Foundation
The Sir Halley Stewart Trust
Webb Memorial Trust

Social welfare

The 1970 Trust
The 1989 Willan Charitable
    Trust
The 29th May 1961 Charitable
    Trust
The Acacia Charitable Trust
The ACT Foundation
The Company of Actuaries'
    Charitable Trust Fund
The Sylvia Adams Charitable
    Trust
The Adint Charitable Trust
Age Scotland (Formerly Age
    Concern Scotland and Help
    the Aged)
Age UK (formerly Help the
    Aged and Age Concern)
The Green and Lilian F M
    Ainsworth and Family
    Benevolent Fund
The Sylvia Aitken Charitable
    Trust
The Ajahma Charitable Trust
The Alborada Trust
The Alchemy Foundation
Almondsbury Charity
The Ammco Trust
Viscount Amory's Charitable
    Trust
The AMW Charitable Trust
The Andrew Anderson Trust
The Apax Foundation
The Appletree Trust
Archbishop of Wales' Fund for
    Children
The Archer Trust
The Ardwick Trust
The Argus Appeal
The John Armitage Charitable
    Trust
The Armourers' and Brasiers'
    Gauntlet Trust
The Artemis Charitable Trust
The Arts and Entertainment
    Charitable Trust
The Ashendene Trust
The Ashworth Charitable Trust
The Associated Country
    Women of the World
    (ACWW)
AstonMansfield Charitable
    Trust
The Astor Foundation
The Lord Austin Trust
The Avon and Somerset Police
    Community Trust
Awards for All
The Scott Bader
    Commonwealth Ltd
The Roy and Pixie Baker
    Charitable Trust
The Balcombe Charitable Trust
The Albert Casanova Ballard
    Deceased Trust
The Ballinger Charitable Trust

The Balmore Trust
The Balney Charitable Trust
The Band Trust
The Barbour Foundation
Barchester Healthcare
    Foundation
The Barclay Foundation
Lord Barnby's Foundation
Barnes Workhouse Fund
The Barnwood House Trust
The Charity of William Barrow
The Batchworth Trust
BBC Children in Need
BCH Trust
The Jack and Ada Beattie
    Foundation
The Victoria and David
    Beckham Children's Charity
The John Beckwith Charitable
    Trust
The Peter Beckwith Charitable
    Trust
The Bedford Charity (The
    Harpur Trust)
The Bedfordshire and Luton
    Community Foundation
The Beit Trust
The Bellahouston Bequest
    Fund
Bergqvist Charitable Trust
The Bestway Foundation
The Mason Bibby 1981 Trust
The Big Lottery Fund
The Birmingham District
    Nursing Charitable Trust
The Sydney Black Charitable
    Trust
The Blanchminster Trust
The Blueberry Charitable Trust
The Boltons Trust
The Booth Charities
The Boots Charitable Trust
Salo Bordon Charitable Trust
P G and N J Boulton Trust
The A H and E Boulton Trust
The Anthony Bourne
    Foundation
Community Foundation for
    Bournemouth, Dorset and
    Poole
The Liz and Terry Bramall
    Charitable Trust
The Bristol Charities
John Bristow and Thomas
    Mason Trust
Britannia Foundation
British Humane Association
The Bromley Trust
The David Brooke Charity
The Rory and Elizabeth Brooks
    Foundation
Bill Brown's Charitable
    Settlement
The Bruntwood Charity
Brushmill Ltd
Buckland Charitable Trust

The Burden Trust
The Clara E Burgess Charity
The Audrey and Stanley Burton 1960 Charitable Trust
The Arnold Burton 1998 Charitable Trust
The Burton Breweries Charitable Trust
Butchers' Company General Charities
The Noel Buxton Trust
Ann Byrne Charitable Trust
The James Caan Foundation
Edward Cadbury Charitable Trust
The G W Cadbury Charitable Trust
The William A Cadbury Charitable Trust
The Edward and Dorothy Cadbury Trust
The Barrow Cadbury Trust and the Barrow Cadbury Fund
CAFOD (Catholic Agency for Overseas Development)
Calouste Gulbenkian Foundation
The Calpe Trust
The Cambridgeshire Community Foundation
The Campden Charities Trustee
The Carpenter Charitable Trust
The Carr-Gregory Trust
The Leslie Mary Carter Charitable Trust
Carter's Educational Foundation
The Cattanach Charitable Trust
The Wilfrid and Constance Cave Foundation
The Cayo Foundation
The Chapman Charitable Trust
John William Chapman's Charitable Trust
The Checkatrade Foundation
The Chelsea Square 1994 Trust
The Cheruby Trust
The Chipping Sodbury Town Lands Charity
The Chrimes Family Charitable Trust
Christadelphian Samaritan Fund
Christian Response to Eastern Europe
Chrysalis Trust
The Church and Community Fund
The Church Urban Fund
The City Bridge Trust (formerly known as Bridge House Trust)
The Cleopatra Trust

Miss V L Clore's 1967 Charitable Trust
The Clothworkers' Foundation
Richard Cloudesley's Charity
The Clover Trust
The Robert Clutterbuck Charitable Trust
The Coalfields Regeneration Trust
The Denise Cohen Charitable Trust
The Vivienne and Samuel Cohen Charitable Trust
The R and S Cohen Foundation
The E Alec Colman Charitable Fund Ltd
The Coltstaple Trust
Colyer-Fergusson Charitable Trust
Comic Relief
The Community Foundation for Northern Ireland
The Douglas Compton James Charitable Trust
The Congleton Inclosure Trust
The Consolidated Charities for the Infirm Merchant Taylors' Company
The Cook and Wolstenholme Charitable Trust
The Cooks Charity
The Co-operative Foundation
The J Reginald Corah Foundation Fund
The Gershon Coren Charitable Foundation
Michael Cornish Charitable Trust
Cornwall Community Foundation
County Durham Community Foundation
Coutts Charitable Trust
The John Cowan Foundation
The Lord Cozens-Hardy Trust
Michael Crawford Children's Charity
Criffel Charitable Trust
The Violet and Milo Cripps Charitable Trust
The Croydon Relief in Need Charities
Cruden Foundation Ltd
The Ronald Cruickshank's Foundation
Cullum Family Trust
Cumbria Community Foundation
The D J H Currie Memorial Trust
The Dr and Mrs A Darlington Charitable Trust
Baron Davenport's Charity
The Davidson (Nairn) Charitable Trust

The Hamilton Davies Trust
Peter De Haan Charitable Trust
The Denman Charitable Trust
The Denton Charitable Trust
Derbyshire Community Foundation
The J N Derbyshire Trust
David and Rose Diamond Trust
The Dibden Allotments Fund
Disability Aid Fund (The Roger and Jean Jefcoate Trust)
Dischma Charitable Trust
The Djanogly Foundation
The DM Charitable Trust
The Derek and Eileen Dodgson Foundation
The Dorcas Trust
The Dorema Charitable Trust
The Dorus Trust
Double 'O' Charity Ltd
The R M Douglas Charitable Trust
The Drapers' Charitable Fund
The Dulverton Trust
The Dumbreck Charity
The Houghton Dunn Charitable Trust
The W E Dunn Trust
The Dyers' Company Charitable Trust
The James Dyson Foundation
The Eagle Charity Trust
East London Community Foundation
Eastern Counties Educational Trust Limited
The Sir John Eastwood Foundation
The Ebenezer Trust
The EBM Charitable Trust
Gilbert Edgar Trust
Edinburgh Children's Holiday Fund
The Edinburgh Trust, No 2 Account
Edinburgh Voluntary Organisations' Trust Funds
Edupoor Limited
Dr Edwards Bishop King's Fulham Endowment Fund
The Gerald Palmer Eling Trust Company
The Maud Elkington Charitable Trust
The Ellerdale Trust
The Edith Maud Ellis 1985 Charitable Trust
The Vernon N Ely Charitable Trust
The Emerton-Christie Charity
The Emilienne Charitable Trust
The Emmandjay Charitable Trust
The Englefield Charitable Trust
The Enkalon Foundation

The Epigoni Trust
The Equilibrium Foundation
The Eranda Foundation
The Ericson Trust
The Ernest Hecht Charitable
    Foundation
Essex Community Foundation
Euro Charity Trust
Sir John Evelyn's Charity
The Eveson Charitable Trust
The Execution Charitable Trust
F C Charitable Trust
Esmée Fairbairn Foundation
The Fairway Trust
The Family Rich Charities Trust
The Lord Faringdon Charitable
    Trust
Samuel William Farmer Trust
The Fassnidge Memorial Trust
The Fawcett Charitable Trust
The February Foundation
The John Feeney Charitable
    Trust
The George Fentham
    Birmingham Charity
Elizabeth Ferguson Charitable
    Trust Fund
Fife Council/Common Good
    Funds and Trusts
Dixie Rose Findlay Charitable
    Trust
The Sir John Fisher Foundation
Fisherbeck Charitable Trust
The Fishmongers' Company's
    Charitable Trust
The Fitton Trust
Florence's Charitable Trust
The Flow Foundation
The Football Association
    National Sports Centre
    Trust
The Forces Trust (Working
    Name)
Ford Britain Trust
The Oliver Ford Charitable
    Trust
The Forest Hill Charitable Trust
The Lady Forester Trust
The Foresters' Fund for
    Children
The Foresters' Charity
    Stewards UK Trust
Forever Manchester (The
    Community Foundation for
    Greater Manchester)
The Donald Forrester Trust
The Fort Foundation
Sydney E Franklin Deceased's
    New Second Charity
The Jill Franklin Trust
The Gordon Fraser Charitable
    Trust
The Hugh Fraser Foundation
The Joseph Strong Frazer Trust

The Louis and Valerie
    Freedman Charitable
    Settlement
The Freemasons' Grand
    Charity
The Thomas Freke and Lady
    Norton Charity
The Freshgate Trust
    Foundation
Friends of Muir Group
The Frognal Trust
Maurice Fry Charitable Trust
The Fuserna Foundation
The Angela Gallagher Memorial
    Fund
The Gannochy Trust
The Ganzoni Charitable Trust
The Gatsby Charitable
    Foundation
Gatwick Airport Community
    Trust
The Robert Gavron Charitable
    Trust
J Paul Getty Jr Charitable Trust
The Gibbs Charitable Trust
Simon Gibson Charitable Trust
The Girdlers' Company
    Charitable Trust
The B and P Glasser
    Charitable Trust
The Glass-House Trust
The GMW Charitable Trust
The Sydney and Phyllis
    Goldberg Memorial
    Charitable Trust
The Jack Goldhill Charitable
    Trust
The Goldsmiths' Company
    Charity
The Goodman Foundation
Mike Gooley Trailfinders
    Charity
The Gosling Foundation
    Limited
The Gough Charitable Trust
A and S Graham Charitable
    Trust
Grand Charitable Trust of the
    Order of Women
    Freemasons
Grantham Yorke Trust
The Constance Green
    Foundation
Greggs Foundation (formerly
    Greggs Trust)
Grimmitt Trust
The Bishop of Guildford's
    Foundation
The Guildry Incorporation of
    Perth
The Gunter Charitable Trust
Dr Guthrie's Association
The H and M Charitable Trust
H C D Memorial Fund
The Hackney Parochial
    Charities

The Hadfield Trust
The Hadley Trust
The Hadrian Trust
The Alfred Haines Charitable
    Trust
The Hale Trust
E F and M G Hall Charitable
    Trust
Robert Hall Charity
Sue Hammerson's Charitable
    Trust
Hampshire and Isle of Wight
    Community Foundation
The Hampstead Wells and
    Campden Trust
Hampton Fuel Allotment
    Charity
The W A Handley Charitable
    Trust
The Hanley Trust
The Kathleen Hannay
    Memorial Charity
The Haramead Trust
Miss K M Harbinson's
    Charitable Trust
The Harborne Parish Lands
    Charity
The Harbour Charitable Trust
The Harding Trust
William Harding's Charity
The Hargrave Foundation
The Kenneth Hargreaves
    Charitable Trust
The Harris Charitable Trust
The Harris Charity
The Harrison and Potter Trust
The N and P Hartley Memorial
    Trust
The Alfred And Peggy Harvey
    Charitable Trust
Hasluck Charitable Trust
The Dorothy Hay-Bolton
    Charitable Trust
The Charles Hayward
    Foundation
The Headley Trust
May Hearnshaw's Charity
The Heathcoat Trust
The Hedley Foundation
The H J Heinz Company
    Limited Charitable Trust
The Hemby Trust
The Christina Mary Hendrie
    Trust for Scottish and
    Canadian Charities
The Henley Educational Charity
Philip Henman Trust
The G D Herbert Charitable
    Trust
The Joanna Herbert-Stepney
    Charitable Settlement (also
    known as The Paget
    Charitable Trust)
The Hertfordshire Community
    Foundation

The Hesslewood Children's Trust (Hull Seamen's and General Orphanage)

The P and C Hickinbotham Charitable Trust

The High Sheriff's Police Trust for the County of West Midlands (Building Blocks)

The Hilden Charitable Fund

The Charles Littlewood Hill Trust

Lady Hind Trust

Hinduja Foundation

Hobson Charity Limited

The J G Hogg Charitable Trust

John Holford's Charity

The Edward Holt Trust

The Holywood Trust

The Homelands Charitable Trust

The Homestead Charitable Trust

Hope for Youth (formerly Women Caring Trust)

HopMarket Charity

The Horizon Foundation

The Horne Foundation

The Horne Trust

The Hornsey Parochial Charities

The Reta Lila Howard Foundation

HTA Sheba Foundation UK

Human Relief Foundation

Humanitarian and Charitable One Trust (HACOT)

The Humanitarian Trust

The Michael and Shirley Hunt Charitable Trust

The Albert Hunt Trust

Miss Agnes H Hunter's Trust

Huntingdon Freemen's Charity

John Huntingdon's Charity

The Nani Huyu Charitable Trust

The Hyde Charitable Trust – Youth Plus

Impetus Trust

The Indigo Trust

The Inner London Magistrates Court Poor Box and Feeder Charity

The Ireland Fund of Great Britain

The Irish Youth Foundation (UK) Ltd (incorporating The Lawlor Foundation)

The ITF Seafarers Trust

J A R Charitable Trust

The Ruth and Lionel Jacobson Trust (Second Fund) No 2

Jaffe Family Relief Fund

The Jarman Charitable Trust

The John Jarrold Trust

The Jeffrey Charitable Trust

Jesus Hospital Charity

The Nicholas Joels Charitable Trust

The Lillie Johnson Charitable Trust

The Johnson Foundation

The Johnnie Johnson Trust

The Johnson Wax Ltd Charitable Trust

The Jones 1986 Charitable Trust

The Cyril and Eve Jumbo Charitable Trust

The Anton Jurgens Charitable Trust

The Kalou Foundation

The Kass Charitable Trust

The Emmanuel Kaye Foundation

The Kelly Family Charitable Trust

Kelsick's Educational Foundation

The KempWelch Charitable Trust

William Kendall's Charity (Wax Chandlers' Company)

Kent Community Foundation

The Peter Kershaw Trust

The King's Fund

The Kingsbury Charity

The Mary Kinross Charitable Trust

Kirkley Poor's Lands Estate

Ernest Kleinwort Charitable Trust

The Sir James Knott Trust

The KPMG Foundation

The Kreditor Charitable Trust

The Kreitman Foundation

The Neil Kreitman Foundation

The Heinz, Anna and Carol Kroch Foundation

The Kyte Charitable Trust

John Laing Charitable Trust

The Christopher Laing Foundation

The David Laing Foundation

The Beatrice Laing Trust

The Lambert Charitable Trust

Community Foundation for Lancashire

Lancashire Environmental Fund

Duchy of Lancaster Benevolent Fund

The Allen Lane Foundation

The Langdale Trust

The Langley Charitable Trust

The LankellyChase Foundation

The R J Larg Family Charitable Trust

The Lark Trust

Laslett's (Hinton) Charity

Mrs F B Laurence Charitable Trust

The Kathleen Laurence Trust

The Edgar E Lawley Foundation

The Lawson Beckman Charitable Trust

The Raymond and Blanche Lawson Charitable Trust

The Carole and Geoffrey Lawson Foundation

The Leach Fourteenth Trust

The William Leech Charity

Leeds Building Society Charitable Foundation

The Leeds Community Foundation

The Kennedy Leigh Charitable Trust

The Leigh Trust

The Mark Leonard Trust

The Leverhulme Trade Charities Trust

Lord Leverhulme's Charitable Trust

The Joseph Levy Charitable Foundation

John Lewis Partnership General Community Fund

Liberum Foundation

The Limbourne Trust

The Linbury Trust

Lindenleaf Charitable Trust

The Enid Linder Foundation

The Lister Charitable Trust

The Andrew and Mary Elizabeth Little Charitable Trust

The Elaine and Angus Lloyd Charitable Trust

Lloyds TSB Foundation for England and Wales

Lloyds TSB Foundation for Northern Ireland

Lloyds TSB Foundation for the Channel Islands

Llysdinam Charitable Trust

Localtrent Ltd

The Trust for London (formerly the City Parochial Foundation)

London Catalyst (formerly The Metropolitan Hospital-Sunday Fund)

The London Community Foundation (formerly Capital Community Foundation)

The Lotus Foundation

The C L Loyd Charitable Trust

The Marie Helen Luen Charitable Trust

Henry Lumley Charitable Trust

Lady Lumley's Educational Foundation

Paul Lunn-Rockliffe Charitable Trust

The Lynwood Trust

John Lyon's Charity

The Lyons Charitable Trust

The Joy and Malcolm Lyons
Foundation
The M and C Trust
The R S Macdonald Charitable
Trust
The MacRobert Trust
Ian Mactaggart Trust
The Magdalen and Lasher
Charity
Magdalen Hospital Trust
Mageni Trust
The Mahavir Trust (also known
as the K S Mehta
Charitable Trust)
Man Group plc Charitable
Trust
The Manifold Charitable Trust
R W Mann Trust
The Leslie and Lilian Manning
Trust
The Manoukian Charitable
Foundation
Market Harborough and The
Bowdens Charity
The Hilda and Samuel Marks
Foundation
Marr-Munning Trust
The Michael Marsh Charitable
Trust
The Marsh Christian Trust
The Charlotte Marshall
Charitable Trust
Sir George Martin Trust
John Martin's Charity
The John Mason Family Trust
The Maxwell Family Foundation
The Robert McAlpine
Foundation
The Mears Foundation
The Medlock Charitable Trust
Melow Charitable Trust
Brian Mercer Charitable Trust
The Mercers' Charitable
Foundation
The Merchant Taylors'
Company Charities Fund
The Merchants' House of
Glasgow
Community Foundation for
Merseyside
The Zachary Merton and
George Woofindin
Convalescent Trust
The Tony Metherell Charitable
Trust
Mi Yu Foundation
Mickleham Charitable Trust
Gerald Micklem Charitable
Trust
Miles Trust for the Putney and
Roehampton Community
Millennium Stadium Charitable
Trust
The Miller Foundation
The Mills Charity
The Millward Charitable Trust

Milton Keynes Community
Foundation
The Peter Minet Trust
The Mirfield Educational
Charity
The Mishcon Family Charitable
Trust
The Mitchell Charitable Trust
The Mizpah Trust
The Modiano Charitable Trust
The Moette Charitable Trust
The D C Moncrieff Charitable
Trust
Monmouthshire County Council
Welsh Church Act Fund
The Monument Trust
John Moores Foundation
The Morel Charitable Trust
The Morgan Charitable
Foundation
S C and M E Morland's
Charitable Trust
The Morris Charitable Trust
G M Morrison Charitable Trust
Vyoel Moshe Charitable Trust
The Moss Charitable Trust
The Robert and Margaret
Moss Charitable Trust
Moto in the Community Trust
Mountbatten Festival of Music
The Mugdock Children's Trust
The Edith Murphy Foundation
Murphy-Neumann Charity
Company Limited
Peter John Murray Trust (PJM
Trust)
MW (CL) Foundation
MW (GK) Foundation
MW (HO) Foundation
MW (RH) Foundation
The Kitty and Daniel Nabarro
Charitable Trust
The Nadezhda Charitable Trust
The Nationwide Foundation
The Nchima Trust
The Worshipful Company of
Needlemakers' Charitable
Fund
The New Appeals Organisation
for the City and County of
Nottingham
New Court Charitable Trust
Newby Trust Limited
Mr and Mrs F E F Newman
Charitable Trust
Nominet Charitable Foundation
The Norda Trust
The Normanby Charitable Trust
The North British Hotel Trust
North West London Community
Foundation
The Northampton Municipal
Church Charities
The Northampton Queen's
Institute Relief in Sickness
Fund

The Earl of Northampton's
Charity
The Northcott Devon
Foundation
The Northern Rock Foundation
The Northmoor Trust
The Northumberland Village
Homes Trust
The Norton Foundation
The Norton Rose Charitable
Foundation
The Norwich Town Close
Estate Charity
The Nottingham General
Dispensary
The Nottingham Gordon
Memorial Trust for Boys
and Girls
The Nottinghamshire Miners'
Welfare Trust Fund
The Nuffield Foundation
The Father O'Mahoney
Memorial Trust
The Oakdale Trust
The Oakley Charitable Trust
The Ofenheim Charitable Trust
Ogilvie Charities Deed No.2
(including the Charity of
Mary Catherine Ford Smith)
The Old Enfield Charitable
Trust
The Oldham Foundation
The Olga Charitable Trust
The O'Sullivan Family
Charitable Trust
The Owen Family Trust
Eleanor Palmer Trust
The Panacea Society
The Paphitis Charitable Trust
The Park House Charitable
Trust
The Parthenon Trust
The Constance Paterson
Charitable Trust
Miss M E Swinton Paterson's
Charitable Trust
The Harry Payne Trust
The Peacock Charitable Trust
Pears Foundation
The Pedmore Sporting Club
Trust Fund
Pendragon Charitable Trust
The Persula Foundation
The Pervez Musharraf
Foundation
The Jack Petchey Foundation
The Phillips Family Charitable
Trust
The Bernard Piggott Trust
The Pilgrim Trust
The Elise Pilkington Charitable
Trust
The Pilkington Charities Fund
The Austin and Hope
Pilkington Trust

The Col W W Pilkington Will Trusts The General Charity Fund
G S Plaut Charitable Trust Limited
The Pollywally Charitable Trust
The John Porter Charitable Trust
The Porter Foundation
Porticus UK
The Portishead Nautical Trust
The J E Posnansky Charitable Trust
The Mary Potter Convent Hospital Trust
The Praebendo Charitable Foundation
The Premier League Charitable Fund
The Lucy Price Relief-in-Need Charity
Sir John Priestman Charity Trust
The Foundation of Prince William and Prince Harry
Princess Anne's Charities
The Priory Foundation
Private Equity Foundation
PSA Peugeot Citroen Charity Trust
The Puri Foundation
Quartet Community Foundation (formerly the Greater Bristol Foundation)
Queen Mary's Roehampton Trust
The Queen's Silver Jubilee Trust
R S Charitable Trust
The Monica Rabagliati Charitable Trust
The Rainford Trust
The Rank Foundation
The Joseph Rank Trust
The Fanny Rapaport Charitable Settlement
The Rashbass Family Trust
The Ratcliff Pension Charity
The E L Rathbone Charitable Trust
The Eleanor Rathbone Charitable Trust
The Sigrid Rausing Trust
The Ravensdale Trust
The Rayne Foundation
The Rayne Trust
The Sir James Reckitt Charity
The Eva Reckitt Trust Fund
The C A Redfern Charitable Foundation
The Reed Foundation
Relief Fund for Romania Limited
The Rhododendron Trust
The Rhondda Cynon Taff Welsh Church Acts Fund

The Sir Cliff Richard Charitable Trust
The Richmond Parish Lands Charity
The Ripple Effect Foundation
The River Farm Foundation
Riverside Charitable Trust Limited
Rix-Thompson-Rothenberg Foundation
Thomas Roberts Trust
The Robertson Trust
The Roddick Foundation
The Sir James Roll Charitable Trust
The C A Rookes Charitable Trust
Mrs L D Rope Third Charitable Settlement
The Rosca Trust
Alexandra Rose Charities
The Cecil Rosen Foundation
The Rothera Charitable Settlement
The Rothley Trust
The Christopher Rowbotham Charitable Trust
The Rowland Family Foundation
The Rowlands Trust
The Joseph Rowntree Foundation
Royal British Legion
Royal Docks Trust (London)
Royal Masonic Trust for Girls and Boys
The Royal Scots Benevolent Society
The RRAF Charitable Trust
The Rufford Foundation
Ryklow Charitable Trust 1992 (also known as A B Williamson Charitable Trust)
The Michael Harry Sacher Trust
Erach and Roshan Sadri Foundation
The Saga Charitable Trust
Saint Sarkis Charity Trust
The Saintbury Trust
The Saints and Sinners Trust
Salters' Charitable Foundation
The Andrew Salvesen Charitable Trust
Coral Samuel Charitable Trust
The Peter Samuel Charitable Trust
The Sandra Charitable Trust
Schroder Charity Trust
The Scotshill Trust
Scott (Eredine) Charitable Trust
The Francis C Scott Charitable Trust
The Frieda Scott Charitable Trust

The Sir James and Lady Scott Trust
Scottish Coal Industry Special Welfare Fund
The Scottish Community Foundation
The Scottish International Education Trust
The Scouloudi Foundation
Seafarers UK (King George's Fund for Sailors)
The Searle Charitable Trust
The Samuel Sebba Charitable Trust
Leslie Sell Charitable Trust
Sellata Ltd
The Seneca Trust
The Shanley Charitable Trust
The Sheffield and District Hospital Services Charitable Fund
The Sheldon Trust
The Sylvia and Colin Shepherd Charitable Trust
The Archie Sherman Cardiff Foundation
The Archie Sherman Charitable Trust
The Shetland Charitable Trust
The Shipwrights' Company Charitable Fund
The Shoe Zone Trust
The J A Shone Memorial Trust
The Mary Elizabeth Siebel Charity
The Skelton Bounty
The SMB Charitable Trust
The Mrs Smith and Mount Trust
The N Smith Charitable Settlement
The Henry Smith Charity
The Leslie Smith Foundation
Philip Smith's Charitable Trust
The Snowball Trust
The Sobell Foundation
The E C Sosnow Charitable Trust
The Souter Charitable Trust
The South Square Trust
The W F Southall Trust
Spears-Stutz Charitable Trust
Split Infinitive Trust
Rosalyn and Nicholas Springer Charitable Trust
Springfields Employees' Medical Research and Charity Trust Fund
St James's Place Foundation
St Katharine and Shadwell Trust
St Michael's and All Saints' Charities
St Monica Trust Community Fund
The Stafford Trust

The Stanley Foundation Ltd
The Peter Stebbings Memorial
Charity
The Steel Charitable Trust
Stevenson Family's Charitable
Trust
The Stokenchurch Educational
Charity
The Stone Family Foundation
The Strangward Trust
Stratford upon Avon Town
Trust
The W O Street Charitable
Foundation
Sueberry Ltd
The Suffolk Foundation
Summary Limited
The Summerfield Charitable
Trust
Surrey Community Foundation
Sussex Community Foundation
Sutton Coldfield Municipal
Charities
Swan Mountain Trust
The Gay and Keith Talbot Trust
Talteg Ltd
The Lady Tangye Charitable
Trust
The Tanner Trust
The Connie and Albert Taylor
Charitable Trust
The Taylor Family Foundation
The Tedworth Charitable Trust
Tesco Charity Trust
The Len Thomson Charitable
Trust
The Sue Thomson Foundation
The Sir Jules Thorn Charitable
Trust
The Three Oaks Trust
Mrs R P Tindall's Charitable
Trust
The Tisbury Telegraph Trust
TJH Foundation
The Tolkien Trust
The Tompkins Foundation
The Tory Family Foundation
The Towry Law Charitable Trust
(also known as the Castle
Educational Trust)
The Triangle Trust (1949) Fund
The True Colours Trust
Truemart Limited
Trust Sixty Three
The Tudor Trust
Two Ridings Community
Foundation
Community Foundation Serving
Tyne and Wear and
Northumberland
Trustees of Tzedakah
Ulster Garden Villages Ltd
The Underwood Trust
UnLtd (Foundation for Social
Entrepreneurs)
The Valentine Charitable Trust

The Valiant Charitable Trust
The Albert Van Den Bergh
Charitable Trust
The Van Neste Foundation
The Variety Club Children's
Charity
The William and Patricia
Venton Charitable Trust
Roger Vere Foundation
Vintners' Gifts Charity
The Vodafone (Group)
Foundation
The Volant Charitable Trust
Voluntary Action Fund
Wade's Charity
The Wakefield and Tetley Trust
Wakeham Trust
The Community Foundation in
Wales
Wales Council for Voluntary
Action
The Thomas Wall Trust
Walton on Thames Charity
The Ward Blenkinsop Trust
The Waterloo Foundation
The Wates Foundation
Blyth Watson Charitable Trust
The Howard Watson Symington
Memorial Charity
John Watson's Trust
The Weavers' Company
Benevolent Fund
The Weinstein Foundation
The James Weir Foundation
The Weldon UK Charitable
Trust
The West Yorkshire Police
Community Fund
The Westcroft Trust
The Westminster Foundation
The Garfield Weston
Foundation
The Simon Whitbread
Charitable Trust
White Stuff Foundation
The Whittlesey Charity
Williams Serendipity Trust
The Wilson Foundation
J and J R Wilson Trust
The Community Foundation for
Wiltshire and Swindon
The Francis Winham
Foundation
Anona Winn Charitable Trust
The Michael and Anna Wix
Charitable Trust
The Wixamtree Trust
The Maurice Wohl Charitable
Foundation
The Wolfson Foundation
The Wood Family Trust
Woodlands Trust
Woodroffe Benton Foundation
The Woodward Charitable
Trust

Worcester Municipal Charities
(incorporating Worcester
Consolidated Municipal
Charity and Worcester
Municipal Exhibitions
Foundation)
The Fred and Della Worms
Charitable Trust
The Wragge and Co. Charitable
Trust
The Diana Edgson Wright
Charitable Trust
Miss E B Wrightson's
Charitable Settlement
The Wyseliot Charitable Trust
The York Children's Trust
The Yorkshire Dales
Millennium Trust
The William Allen Young
Charitable Trust
Zephyr Charitable Trust
The Marjorie and Arnold Ziff
Charitable Foundation
The Zochonis Charitable Trust
Zurich Community Trust (UK)
Limited

Community care
services

The 1989 Willan Charitable
Trust
The Company of Actuaries'
Charitable Trust Fund
Age Scotland (Formerly Age
Concern Scotland and Help
the Aged)
Age UK (formerly Help the
Aged and Age Concern)
The Green and Lilian F M
Ainsworth and Family
Benevolent Fund
The Appletree Trust
Archbishop of Wales' Fund for
Children
The Archer Trust
The Artemis Charitable Trust
The Astor Foundation
The Avon and Somerset Police
Community Trust
The Ballinger Charitable Trust
The Barnwood House Trust
The Victoria and David
Beckham Children's Charity
The Big Lottery Fund
The Birmingham District
Nursing Charitable Trust
The Anthony Bourne
Foundation
John Bristow and Thomas
Mason Trust
The David Brooke Charity
The Rory and Elizabeth Brooks
Foundation

The Burton Breweries
Charitable Trust
The Noel Buxton Trust
Calouste Gulbenkian
Foundation
Carter's Educational
Foundation
The Cattanach Charitable Trust
The Clover Trust
The Cook and Wolstenholme
Charitable Trust
The J Reginald Corah
Foundation Fund
The John Cowan Foundation
The D J H Currie Memorial
Trust
Baron Davenport's Charity
The Hamilton Davies Trust
Disability Aid Fund (The Roger
and Jean Jefcoate Trust)
The Dorus Trust
The Dulverton Trust
The Dumbreck Charity
Gilbert Edgar Trust
Edinburgh Children's Holiday
Fund
The Edinburgh Trust, No 2
Account
The Emerton-Christie Charity
The Emmandjay Charitable
Trust
The Eveson Charitable Trust
Esmée Fairbairn Foundation
The Fairway Trust
The Family Rich Charities Trust
Samuel William Farmer Trust
The Fassnidge Memorial Trust
The February Foundation
The John Feeney Charitable
Trust
Elizabeth Ferguson Charitable
Trust Fund
Dixie Rose Findlay Charitable
Trust
Ford Britain Trust
The Oliver Ford Charitable
Trust
The Foresters' Fund for
Children
The Jill Franklin Trust
The Gordon Fraser Charitable
Trust
The Louis and Valerie
Freedman Charitable
Settlement
The Freshgate Trust
Foundation
The Frognal Trust
The Angela Gallagher Memorial
Fund
The Ganzoni Charitable Trust
The Gatsby Charitable
Foundation
Gatwick Airport Community
Trust
J Paul Getty Jr Charitable Trust

The Girdlers' Company
Charitable Trust
The Glass-House Trust
The Gosling Foundation
Limited
The Gough Charitable Trust
Grantham Yorke Trust
The Constance Green
Foundation
Grimmitt Trust
Dr Guthrie's Association
The Hadrian Trust
The Alfred Haines Charitable
Trust
The Hale Trust
Robert Hall Charity
The W A Handley Charitable
Trust
The Haramead Trust
The Harbour Charitable Trust
The Kenneth Hargreaves
Charitable Trust
The Harris Charitable Trust
The Harris Charity
The Alfred And Peggy Harvey
Charitable Trust
The Charles Hayward
Foundation
May Hearnshaw's Charity
The H J Heinz Company
Limited Charitable Trust
The Hemby Trust
The Christina Mary Hendrie
Trust for Scottish and
Canadian Charities
The Henley Educational Charity
Philip Henman Trust
The Joanna Herbert-Stepney
Charitable Settlement (also
known as The Paget
Charitable Trust)
The Hesslewood Children's
Trust (Hull Seamen's and
General Orphanage)
The High Sheriff's Police Trust
for the County of West
Midlands (Building Blocks)
The Hilden Charitable Fund
The Charles Littlewood Hill
Trust
The Holywood Trust
Hope for Youth (formerly
Women Caring Trust)
The Horne Trust
The Reta Lila Howard
Foundation
Miss Agnes H Hunter's Trust
Huntingdon Freemen's Charity
The Hyde Charitable Trust –
Youth Plus
The Irish Youth Foundation
(UK) Ltd (incorporating The
Lawlor Foundation)
The Ruth and Lionel Jacobson
Trust (Second Fund) No 2
The Jarman Charitable, Trust

The Jeffrey Charitable Trust
The Lillie Johnson Charitable
Trust
The Johnnie Johnson Trust
The Jones 1986 Charitable
Trust
The Kelly Family Charitable
Trust
Kelsick's Educational
Foundation
The KempWelch Charitable
Trust
The Peter Kershaw Trust
The King's Fund
The Mary Kinross Charitable
Trust
The KPMG Foundation
John Laing Charitable Trust
The Lambert Charitable Trust
Duchy of Lancaster Benevolent
Fund
The Allen Lane Foundation
The R J Larg Family Charitable
Trust
The Lark Trust
The Edgar E Lawley Foundation
The Raymond and Blanche
Lawson Charitable Trust
The Carole and Geoffrey
Lawson Foundation
The Leach Fourteenth Trust
The William Leech Charity
Leeds Building Society
Charitable Foundation
The Mark Leonard Trust
Lord Leverhulme's Charitable
Trust
The Joseph Levy Charitable
Foundation
Lloyds TSB Foundation for
Northern Ireland
Lloyds TSB Foundation for the
Channel Islands
London Catalyst (formerly The
Metropolitan Hospital-
Sunday Fund)
The Lotus Foundation
Lady Lumley's Educational
Foundation
John Lyon's Charity
The R S Macdonald Charitable
Trust
The MacRobert Trust
Magdalen Hospital Trust
Mageni Trust
Market Harborough and The
Bowdens Charity
Sir George Martin Trust
The Mears Foundation
The Mercers' Charitable
Foundation
The Merchants' House of
Glasgow
The Zachary Merton and
George Woofindin
Convalescent Trust

Gerald Micklem Charitable Trust

Miles Trust for the Putney and Roehampton Community

The Mirfield Educational Charity

Monmouthshire County Council Welsh Church Act Fund

The Monument Trust

John Moores Foundation

The Mugdock Children's Trust

The Kitty and Daniel Nabarro Charitable Trust

The Nadezhda Charitable Trust

The Nationwide Foundation

The Nchima Trust

Newby Trust Limited

The North British Hotel Trust

The Northcott Devon Foundation

The Northern Rock Foundation

The Nottingham General Dispensary

The Nottingham Gordon Memorial Trust for Boys and Girls

The Nuffield Foundation

The Panacea Society

The Paphitis Charitable Trust

The Constance Paterson Charitable Trust

Miss M E Swinton Paterson's Charitable Trust

Pears Foundation

The Persula Foundation

The Jack Petchey Foundation

The Bernard Piggott Trust

The Pilkington Charities Fund

G S Plaut Charitable Trust Limited

The Portishead Nautical Trust

The Mary Potter Convent Hospital Trust

The Lucy Price Relief-in-Need Charity

Sir John Priestman Charity Trust

PSA Peugeot Citroen Charity Trust

The Monica Rabagliati Charitable Trust

The Rank Foundation

The Rayne Foundation

The Reed Foundation

Relief Fund for Romania Limited

The Rhondda Cynon Taff Welsh Church Acts Fund

The Richmond Parish Lands Charity

Rix-Thompson-Rothenberg Foundation

The Robertson Trust

The C A Rookes Charitable Trust

Mrs L D Rope Third Charitable Settlement

The Rothley Trust

The Rowlands Trust

Ryklow Charitable Trust 1992 (also known as A B Williamson Charitable Trust)

The Michael Harry Sacher Trust

The Saintbury Trust

The Andrew Salvesen Charitable Trust

The Sandra Charitable Trust

The Francis C Scott Charitable Trust

Scottish Coal Industry Special Welfare Fund

Seafarers UK (King George's Fund for Sailors)

The Searle Charitable Trust

Leslie Sell Charitable Trust

The Sheldon Trust

The Sylvia and Colin Shepherd Charitable Trust

The Shipwrights' Company Charitable Fund

The Mary Elizabeth Siebel Charity

The Mrs Smith and Mount Trust

The Leslie Smith Foundation

The Snowball Trust

St Monica Trust Community Fund

The Connie and Albert Taylor Charitable Trust

The Taylor Family Foundation

The Tedworth Charitable Trust

The Sue Thomson Foundation

The True Colours Trust

The Albert Van Den Bergh Charitable Trust

The Variety Club Children's Charity

The William and Patricia Venton Charitable Trust

Wade's Charity

Wakeham Trust

John Watson's Trust

The Weavers' Company Benevolent Fund

The Simon Whitbread Charitable Trust

Williams Serendipity Trust

The Wilson Foundation

J and J R Wilson Trust

The Francis Winham Foundation

Woodlands Trust

The Woodward Charitable Trust

The Wragge and Co. Charitable Trust

The York Children's Trust

The Marjorie and Arnold Ziff Charitable Foundation

Services for and about children and young people

The 1989 Willan Charitable Trust

The Company of Actuaries' Charitable Trust Fund

The Green and Lilian F M Ainsworth and Family Benevolent Fund

Archbishop of Wales' Fund for Children

The Artemis Charitable Trust

The Victoria and David Beckham Children's Charity

The Big Lottery Fund

The Anthony Bourne Foundation

The David Brooke Charity

The Burton Breweries Charitable Trust

The Noel Buxton Trust

Calouste Gulbenkian Foundation

Carter's Educational Foundation

The Cattanach Charitable Trust

The Clover Trust

The Cook and Wolstenholme Charitable Trust

The J Reginald Corah Foundation Fund

The John Cowan Foundation

Baron Davenport's Charity

The Dulverton Trust

The Dumbreck Charity

Gilbert Edgar Trust

Edinburgh Children's Holiday Fund

The Edinburgh Trust, No 2 Account

The Emmandjay Charitable Trust

The Eveson Charitable Trust

Esmée Fairbairn Foundation

The Fairway Trust

Samuel William Farmer Trust

The John Feeney Charitable Trust

Elizabeth Ferguson Charitable Trust Fund

Dixie Rose Findlay Charitable Trust

Ford Britain Trust

The Foresters' Fund for Children

The Gordon Fraser Charitable Trust

The Louis and Valerie Freedman Charitable Settlement

The Freshgate Trust Foundation

The Frognal Trust

The Angela Gallagher Memorial
Fund
The Ganzoni Charitable Trust
The Gatsby Charitable
Foundation
Gatwick Airport Community
Trust
J Paul Getty Jr Charitable Trust
The Girdlers' Company
Charitable Trust
The Glass-House Trust
The Gosling Foundation
Limited
The Gough Charitable Trust
Grantham Yorke Trust
The Constance Green
Foundation
Dr Guthrie's Association
The Alfred Haines Charitable
Trust
The Hale Trust
Robert Hall Charity
The W A Handley Charitable
Trust
The Haramead Trust
The Harbour Charitable Trust
The Harris Charitable Trust
The Harris Charity
May Hearnshaw's Charity
The H J Heinz Company
Limited Charitable Trust
The Hemby Trust
The Christina Mary Hendrie
Trust for Scottish and
Canadian Charities
The Henley Educational Charity
Philip Henman Trust
The Joanna Herbert-Stepney
Charitable Settlement (also
known as The Paget
Charitable Trust)
The Hesslewood Children's
Trust (Hull Seamen's and
General Orphanage)
The High Sheriff's Police Trust
for the County of West
Midlands (Building Blocks)
The Hilden Charitable Fund
The Charles Littlewood Hill
Trust
The Holywood Trust
Hope for Youth (formerly
Women Caring Trust)
The Reta Lila Howard
Foundation
Miss Agnes H Hunter's Trust
The Hyde Charitable Trust –
Youth Plus
The Irish Youth Foundation
(UK) Ltd (incorporating The
Lawlor Foundation)
The Ruth and Lionel Jacobson
Trust (Second Fund) No 2
The Jarman Charitable Trust
The Jeffrey Charitable Trust

The Lillie Johnson Charitable
Trust
The Johnnie Johnson Trust
The Kelly Family Charitable
Trust
Kelsick's Educational
Foundation
The KempWelch Charitable
Trust
The Peter Kershaw Trust
The Mary Kinross Charitable
Trust
The KPMG Foundation
John Laing Charitable Trust
Duchy of Lancaster Benevolent
Fund
The R J Larg Family Charitable
Trust
The Edgar E Lawley Foundation
The Carole and Geoffrey
Lawson Foundation
The William Leech Charity
Leeds Building Society
Charitable Foundation
The Mark Leonard Trust
Lord Leverhulme's Charitable
Trust
The Lotus Foundation
Lady Lumley's Educational
Foundation
John Lyon's Charity
The R S Macdonald Charitable
Trust
The MacRobert Trust
Magdalen Hospital Trust
Mageni Trust
The Merchants' House of
Glasgow
Gerald Micklem Charitable
Trust
Miles Trust for the Putney and
Roehampton Community
The Mirfield Educational
Charity
John Moores Foundation
The Mugdock Children's Trust
The Nadezhda Charitable Trust
Newby Trust Limited
The North British Hotel Trust
The Northern Rock Foundation
The Nottingham Gordon
Memorial Trust for Boys
and Girls
The Nuffield Foundation
The Paphitis Charitable Trust
The Constance Paterson
Charitable Trust
Miss M E Swinton Paterson's
Charitable Trust
Pears Foundation
The Persula Foundation
The Jack Petchey Foundation
The Bernard Piggott Trust
The Pilkington Charities Fund
The Portishead Nautical Trust

The Lucy Price Relief-in-Need
Charity
PSA Peugeot Citroen Charity
Trust
The Monica Rabagliati
Charitable Trust
The Rank Foundation
Relief Fund for Romania
Limited
The Rhondda Cynon Taff
Welsh Church Acts Fund
The Richmond Parish Lands
Charity
The Rothley Trust
Ryklow Charitable Trust 1992
(also known as A B
Williamson Charitable Trust)
The Andrew Salvesen
Charitable Trust
The Sandra Charitable Trust
The Francis C Scott Charitable
Trust
Scottish Coal Industry Special
Welfare Fund
Seafarers UK (King George's
Fund for Sailors)
The Searle Charitable Trust
Leslie Sell Charitable Trust
The Sylvia and Colin Shepherd
Charitable Trust
The Shipwrights' Company
Charitable Fund
The Mrs Smith and Mount
Trust
The Leslie Smith Foundation
The Snowball Trust
The Connie and Albert Taylor
Charitable Trust
The Taylor Family Foundation
The Tedworth Charitable Trust
The Variety Club Children's
Charity
Wade's Charity
John Watson's Trust
The Weavers' Company
Benevolent Fund
The Simon Whitbread
Charitable Trust
Williams Serendipity Trust
The Wilson Foundation
The York Children's Trust
The Marjorie and Arnold Ziff
Charitable Foundation

Services for and about older people

The Company of Actuaries'
Charitable Trust Fund
Age Scotland (Formerly Age
Concern Scotland and Help
the Aged)
Age UK (formerly Help the
Aged and Age Concern)
The Barnwood House Trust

The Birmingham District
   Nursing Charitable Trust
The Clover Trust
The Cook and Wolstenholme
   Charitable Trust
The John Cowan Foundation
The D J H Currie Memorial
   Trust
Baron Davenport's Charity
Disability Aid Fund (The Roger
   and Jean Jefcoate Trust)
The Dumbreck Charity
The Eveson Charitable Trust
Samuel William Farmer Trust
The Fassnidge Memorial Trust
Dixie Rose Findlay Charitable
   Trust
Gatwick Airport Community
   Trust
The Girdlers' Company
   Charitable Trust
The Constance Green
   Foundation
The Alfred Haines Charitable
   Trust
The W A Handley Charitable
   Trust
The Charles Hayward
   Foundation
The Hemby Trust
The Christina Mary Hendrie
   Trust for Scottish and
   Canadian Charities
The KempWelch Charitable
   Trust
The Lambert Charitable Trust
The Edgar E Lawley Foundation
The Joseph Levy Charitable
   Foundation
Sir George Martin Trust
The Mercers' Charitable
   Foundation
The Merchants' House of
   Glasgow
The North British Hotel Trust
The Pilkington Charities Fund
G S Plaut Charitable Trust
   Limited
PSA Peugeot Citroen Charity
   Trust
Relief Fund for Romania
   Limited
The C A Rookes Charitable
   Trust
The Rowlands Trust
The Andrew Salvesen
   Charitable Trust
Scottish Coal Industry Special
   Welfare Fund
Seafarers UK (King George's
   Fund for Sailors)
The Sylvia and Colin Shepherd
   Charitable Trust
The Mary Elizabeth Siebel
   Charity

The Connie and Albert Taylor
   Charitable Trust
The William and Patricia
   Venton Charitable Trust
J and J R Wilson Trust
The Francis Winham
   Foundation

Services for and about vulnerable people/people who are ill

The 1989 Willan Charitable
   Trust
The Company of Actuaries'
   Charitable Trust Fund
The Green and Lilian F M
   Ainsworth and Family
   Benevolent Fund
The Appletree Trust
The Archer Trust
The Artemis Charitable Trust
The Birmingham District
   Nursing Charitable Trust
The Dumbreck Charity
The Family Rich Charities Trust
Samuel William Farmer Trust
The John Feeney Charitable
   Trust
Dixie Rose Findlay Charitable
   Trust
Ford Britain Trust
The Oliver Ford Charitable
   Trust
The Jill Franklin Trust
The Freshgate Trust
   Foundation
The Angela Gallagher Memorial
   Fund
Gatwick Airport Community
   Trust
J Paul Getty Jr Charitable Trust
The Girdlers' Company
   Charitable Trust
The Constance Green
   Foundation
The Hadrian Trust
The W A Handley Charitable
   Trust
May Hearnshaw's Charity
The Hemby Trust
The Horne Trust
Huntingdon Freemen's Charity
The Ruth and Lionel Jacobson
   Trust (Second Fund) No 2
The Jeffrey Charitable Trust
The Peter Kershaw Trust
The Allen Lane Foundation
The Lark Trust
Leeds Building Society
   Charitable Foundation
The Joseph Levy Charitable
   Foundation

London Catalyst (formerly The
   Metropolitan Hospital-
   Sunday Fund)
John Lyon's Charity
Magdalen Hospital Trust
Market Harborough and The
   Bowdens Charity
The Zachary Merton and
   George Woofindin
   Convalescent Trust
John Moores Foundation
The Mugdock Children's Trust
The Kitty and Daniel Nabarro
   Charitable Trust
The Nchima Trust
Newby Trust Limited
The North British Hotel Trust
The Northcott Devon
   Foundation
The Nottingham General
   Dispensary
The Panacea Society
The Pilkington Charities Fund
G S Plaut Charitable Trust
   Limited
The Portishead Nautical Trust
The Mary Potter Convent
   Hospital Trust
Sir John Priestman Charity
   Trust
The Rothley Trust
The Rowlands Trust
The Andrew Salvesen
   Charitable Trust
The Sylvia and Colin Shepherd
   Charitable Trust
The Leslie Smith Foundation
The Snowball Trust
The Connie and Albert Taylor
   Charitable Trust
The Sue Thomson Foundation
The True Colours Trust
Woodlands Trust
The Wragge and Co. Charitable
   Trust

Services for carers

The Astor Foundation
The Emerton-Christie Charity
The Eveson Charitable Trust
Dixie Rose Findlay Charitable
   Trust
The Angela Gallagher Memorial
   Fund
Gatwick Airport Community
   Trust
The Girdlers' Company
   Charitable Trust
The Harris Charitable Trust
The Hemby Trust
The Ruth and Lionel Jacobson
   Trust (Second Fund) No 2
The Peter Kershaw Trust
The Joseph Levy Charitable
   Foundation

London Catalyst (formerly The
 Metropolitan Hospital-
 Sunday Fund)
Gerald Micklem Charitable
 Trust
The North British Hotel Trust
The Northern Rock Foundation
Rix-Thompson-Rothenberg
 Foundation

Services for victims of crime

Dixie Rose Findlay Charitable
 Trust
The Girdlers' Company
 Charitable Trust
The Hemby Trust

Services for women

Dixie Rose Findlay Charitable
 Trust
The Lotus Foundation
The Northern Rock Foundation
The Reed Foundation
The Woodward Charitable
 Trust

Community centres and activities

The Ballinger Charitable Trust
The Big Lottery Fund
The A H and E Boulton Trust
John Bristow and Thomas
 Mason Trust
Colyer-Fergusson Charitable
 Trust
The Co-operative Foundation
The John Cowan Foundation
The Hamilton Davies Trust
Disability Aid Fund (The Roger
 and Jean Jefcoate Trust)
Eastern Counties Educational
 Trust Limited
Gilbert Edgar Trust
Dr Edwards Bishop King's
 Fulham Endowment Fund
The Emmandjay Charitable
 Trust
Samuel William Farmer Trust
The George Fentham
 Birmingham Charity
The Sir John Fisher Foundation
The Football Association
 National Sports Centre
 Trust
Ford Britain Trust
The Thomas Freke and Lady
 Norton Charity

The Angela Gallagher Memorial
 Fund
The Gannochy Trust
Gatwick Airport Community
 Trust
Mike Gooley Trailfinders
 Charity
Grantham Yorke Trust
Greggs Foundation (formerly
 Greggs Trust)
Grimmitt Trust
The Alfred Haines Charitable
 Trust
The W A Handley Charitable
 Trust
The Kenneth Hargreaves
 Charitable Trust
The Hedley Foundation
The Hemby Trust
The Horne Foundation
The Hornsey Parochial
 Charities
The Hyde Charitable Trust –
 Youth Plus
The Jones 1986 Charitable
 Trust
Lancashire Environmental
 Fund
Duchy of Lancaster Benevolent
 Fund
Lord Leverhulme's Charitable
 Trust
Lloyds TSB Foundation for
 Northern Ireland
Lloyds TSB Foundation for the
 Channel Islands
John Lyon's Charity
Magdalen Hospital Trust
The Michael Marsh Charitable
 Trust
John Martin's Charity
The Mears Foundation
Gerald Micklem Charitable
 Trust
Monmouthshire County Council
 Welsh Church Act Fund
The Nationwide Foundation
The North British Hotel Trust
The Northern Rock Foundation
Ogilvie Charities Deed No.2
 (including the Charity of
 Mary Catherine Ford Smith)
The Owen Family Trust
The Rhododendron Trust
The Richmond Parish Lands
 Charity
The Ripple Effect Foundation
The Robertson Trust
The Sir James Roll Charitable
 Trust
The Rothley Trust
Royal Docks Trust (London)
The Saga Charitable Trust
The Saintbury Trust
The Frieda Scott Charitable
 Trust

The Scottish Community
 Foundation
The Sheldon Trust
The Sylvia and Colin Shepherd
 Charitable Trust
The Archie Sherman Cardiff
 Foundation
The Stokenchurch Educational
 Charity
The Summerfield Charitable
 Trust
The Len Thomson Charitable
 Trust
Wade's Charity
Wakeham Trust
The Westcroft Trust
The Yorkshire Dales
 Millennium Trust

Community and social centres

The A H and E Boulton Trust
John Bristow and Thomas
 Mason Trust
The Co-operative Foundation
The John Cowan Foundation
Gilbert Edgar Trust
Samuel William Farmer Trust
The Thomas Freke and Lady
 Norton Charity
The Kenneth Hargreaves
 Charitable Trust
The Hedley Foundation
The Horne Foundation
Lancashire Environmental
 Fund
John Lyon's Charity
Magdalen Hospital Trust
Gerald Micklem Charitable
 Trust
Monmouthshire County Council
 Welsh Church Act Fund
The Northern Rock Foundation
The Owen Family Trust
The Rhododendron Trust
The Frieda Scott Charitable
 Trust
The Summerfield Charitable
 Trust
Wakeham Trust

Community organisations

The Big Lottery Fund
John Bristow and Thomas
 Mason Trust
Disability Aid Fund (The Roger
 and Jean Jefcoate Trust)
The Emmandjay Charitable
 Trust
Ford Britain Trust

The Hornsey Parochial
Charities
Duchy of Lancaster Benevolent
Fund
The Rothley Trust
The Saga Charitable Trust
The Scottish Community
Foundation
The Len Thomson Charitable
Trust
Wakeham Trust

Community centres and outings

The Big Lottery Fund
The Angela Gallagher Memorial
Fund
The Alfred Haines Charitable
Trust
Magdalen Hospital Trust
Ogilvie Charities Deed No.2
(including the Charity of
Mary Catherine Ford Smith)
Wakeham Trust

Emergency response

The Balney Charitable Trust
Bergqvist Charitable Trust
P G and N J Boulton Trust
The Calpe Trust
The Carpenter Charitable Trust
Christadelphian Samaritan
Fund
Christian Response to Eastern
Europe
The Robert Clutterbuck
Charitable Trust
The Dulverton Trust
The Dyers' Company
Charitable Trust
The Edinburgh Trust, No 2
Account
The Emmandjay Charitable
Trust
The Family Rich Charities Trust
The Sir John Fisher Foundation
The Forces Trust (Working
Name)
The Forest Hill Charitable Trust
Sydney E Franklin Deceased's
New Second Charity
The Gibbs Charitable Trust
The Gosling Foundation
Limited
The Alfred Haines Charitable
Trust
The W A Handley Charitable
Trust
Miss K M Harbinson's
Charitable Trust

The Kenneth Hargreaves
Charitable Trust
The Charles Littlewood Hill
Trust
The Horne Trust
Lloyds TSB Foundation for
Northern Ireland
The MacRobert Trust
Magdalen Hospital Trust
The Mahavir Trust (also known
as the K S Mehta
Charitable Trust)
Man Group plc Charitable
Trust
Marr-Munning Trust
The Mears Foundation
The Modiano Charitable Trust
Monmouthshire County Council
Welsh Church Act Fund
John Moores Foundation
Mountbatten Festival of Music
The Father O'Mahoney
Memorial Trust
The Parthenon Trust
The Pervez Musharraf
Foundation
The Pilkington Charities Fund
Queen Mary's Roehampton
Trust
The Sigrid Rausing Trust
The Rhododendron Trust
The Robertson Trust
The Sir James Roll Charitable
Trust
The Rothley Trust
The Rowlands Trust
Royal British Legion
The Royal Scots Benevolent
Society
The SMB Charitable Trust
The E C Sosnow Charitable
Trust
Stevenson Family's Charitable
Trust
The Gay and Keith Talbot Trust
The Lady Tangye Charitable
Trust
The Tisbury Telegraph Trust
Trust Sixty Three
Roger Vere Foundation
Woodroffe Benton Foundation
Miss E B Wrightson's
Charitable Settlement

Armed forces

The Balney Charitable Trust
The Robert Clutterbuck
Charitable Trust
The Dyers' Company
Charitable Trust
The Edinburgh Trust, No 2
Account
The Sir John Fisher Foundation
The Forces Trust (Working
Name)

The Gosling Foundation
Limited
The W A Handley Charitable
Trust
The Charles Littlewood Hill
Trust
Mountbatten Festival of Music
Queen Mary's Roehampton
Trust
The Rowlands Trust
Royal British Legion
The Royal Scots Benevolent
Society

Relief assistance

Bergqvist Charitable Trust
P G and N J Boulton Trust
The Calpe Trust
The Carpenter Charitable Trust
Christadelphian Samaritan
Fund
Christian Response to Eastern
Europe
The Dulverton Trust
The Emmandjay Charitable
Trust
The Forest Hill Charitable Trust
Sydney E Franklin Deceased's
New Second Charity
The Gibbs Charitable Trust
The Alfred Haines Charitable
Trust
The W A Handley Charitable
Trust
Miss K M Harbinson's
Charitable Trust
Magdalen Hospital Trust
The Mahavir Trust (also known
as the K S Mehta
Charitable Trust)
Marr-Munning Trust
The Modiano Charitable Trust
John Moores Foundation
The Father O'Mahoney
Memorial Trust
The Parthenon Trust
The Pervez Musharraf
Foundation
The Pilkington Charities Fund
The Sigrid Rausing Trust
The Rhododendron Trust
The Rothley Trust
The SMB Charitable Trust
Stevenson Family's Charitable
Trust
The Gay and Keith Talbot Trust
The Lady Tangye Charitable
Trust
The Tisbury Telegraph Trust
Trust Sixty Three
Roger Vere Foundation

Soically preventative schemes

The 1970 Trust
The Ashendene Trust
The Avon and Somerset Police Community Trust
The Ballinger Charitable Trust
Britannia Foundation
The Bromley Trust
The Noel Buxton Trust
The G W Cadbury Charitable Trust
The Barrow Cadbury Trust and the Barrow Cadbury Fund
The Cayo Foundation
The Violet and Milo Cripps Charitable Trust
The Hamilton Davies Trust
The Emilienne Charitable Trust
The Ericson Trust
Gatwick Airport Community Trust
J Paul Getty Jr Charitable Trust
The Kenneth Hargreaves Charitable Trust
The Charles Hayward Foundation
The Hemby Trust
The High Sheriff's Police Trust for the County of West Midlands (Building Blocks)
The Hilden Charitable Fund
The Hyde Charitable Trust – Youth Plus
The Indigo Trust
The Irish Youth Foundation (UK) Ltd (incorporating The Lawlor Foundation)
The Mary Kinross Charitable Trust
The Leigh Trust
The Joseph Levy Charitable Foundation
The Lister Charitable Trust
Lloyds TSB Foundation for Northern Ireland
The Lotus Foundation
Magdalen Hospital Trust
The Charlotte Marshall Charitable Trust
The Mercers' Charitable Foundation
The Merchant Taylors' Company Charities Fund
The Kitty and Daniel Nabarro Charitable Trust
The Nadezhda Charitable Trust
The Norda Trust
The Nuffield Foundation
The Oakdale Trust
The Persula Foundation
The Pilgrim Trust
The Portishead Nautical Trust
The Ripple Effect Foundation
The Robertson Trust
Saint Sarkis Charity Trust
The Saintbury Trust
Swan Mountain Trust
The Weavers' Company Benevolent Fund
The West Yorkshire Police Community Fund
The Woodward Charitable Trust

Crime prevention

The 1970 Trust
Britannia Foundation
The Barrow Cadbury Trust and the Barrow Cadbury Fund
The Cayo Foundation
Gatwick Airport Community Trust
The Kenneth Hargreaves Charitable Trust
The Hemby Trust
The High Sheriff's Police Trust for the County of West Midlands (Building Blocks)
The Hyde Charitable Trust – Youth Plus
The Joseph Levy Charitable Foundation
Lloyds TSB Foundation for Northern Ireland
Magdalen Hospital Trust

Family justice

The Charles Hayward Foundation
The Nuffield Foundation

Family planning

The G W Cadbury Charitable Trust
The Kitty and Daniel Nabarro Charitable Trust

Prisons and penal reform

The Bromley Trust
The Noel Buxton Trust
The Barrow Cadbury Trust and the Barrow Cadbury Fund
The Violet and Milo Cripps Charitable Trust
The Ericson Trust
J Paul Getty Jr Charitable Trust
The Charles Hayward Foundation
The Hilden Charitable Fund
The Indigo Trust

The Mary Kinross Charitable Trust
The Leigh Trust
The Mercers' Charitable Foundation
The Oakdale Trust
The Persula Foundation
The Pilgrim Trust
Saint Sarkis Charity Trust
Swan Mountain Trust
The Woodward Charitable Trust

Substance abuse education

The Ashendene Trust
The Emilienne Charitable Trust
The Lister Charitable Trust
The Lotus Foundation
The Charlotte Marshall Charitable Trust
The Merchant Taylors' Company Charities Fund
The Portishead Nautical Trust
The Robertson Trust
The Woodward Charitable Trust

Beneficial groups

Age

■ Babies

The 1989 Willan Charitable
Trust
Lord Barnby's Foundation
The Victoria and David
Beckham Children's Charity
Lifeline 4 Kids
The Edwina Mountbatten Trust
The Francis C Scott Charitable
Trust

■ Children (up to 11)

The 1989 Willan Charitable
Trust
The Adamson Trust
The Pat Allsop Charitable Trust
BibleLands
The Clara E Burgess Charity
The Noel Buxton Trust
Cash for Kids Radio Clyde
The Cattanach Charitable Trust
Celtic Charity Fund
The Cleopatra Trust
The John Coates Charitable
Trust
The D J H Currie Memorial
Trust
The Raymond Curtis Charitable
Trust
The Manny Cussins
Foundation
The Demigryphon Trust
The Dorus Trust
The Dumbreck Charity
Edinburgh Children's Holiday
Fund
The Wilfred and Elsie Elkes
Charity Fund
The Maud Elkington Charitable
Trust
The English Schools' Football
Association
The Epigoni Trust
Samuel William Farmer Trust
Elizabeth Ferguson Charitable
Trust Fund
Dixie Rose Findlay Charitable
Trust
The Joyce Fletcher Charitable
Trust
The Frognal Trust
The Angela Gallagher Memorial
Fund
The Girdlers' Company
Charitable Trust
Global Care
The Gosling Foundation
Limited

E F and M G Hall Charitable
Trust
The Haramead Trust
The Harebell Centenary Fund
The Harris Charitable Trust
The Joanna Herbert-Stepney
Charitable Settlement (also
known as The Paget
Charitable Trust)
The Charles Littlewood Hill
Trust
Hope for Youth (formerly
Women Caring Trust)
The Reta Lila Howard
Foundation
The Hunter Foundation
Jewish Child's Day
The Lanvern Foundation
The Edgar E Lawley Foundation
The Carole and Geoffrey
Lawson Foundation
Lifeline 4 Kids
The Lyons Charitable Trust
The Madeline Mabey Trust
The R S Macdonald Charitable
Trust
The Mackintosh Foundation
The Maxell Educational Trust
Evelyn May Trust
The Mugdock Children's Trust
Murphy-Neumann Charity
Company Limited
The Nuffield Foundation
The Constance Paterson
Charitable Trust
The Pilkington Charities Fund
Sir John Priestman Charity
Trust
The Priory Foundation
The Ragdoll Foundation
SFIA Educational Trust Limited
The Sylvia and Colin Shepherd
Charitable Trust
The Bassil Shippam and
Alsford Trust
Stanley Smith General
Charitable Trust
Philip Smith's Charitable Trust
The Stoller Charitable Trust
The Tedworth Charitable Trust
Tesco Charity Trust
The Sue Thomson Foundation
The Toy Trust
The Variety Club Children's
Charity
The Barbara Ward Children's
Foundation
The Wates Foundation
The Wilson Foundation
The Yapp Charitable Trust
The Zochonis Charitable Trust

■ Young people (12 – 25)

The Adamson Trust
The Green and Lilian F M
Ainsworth and Family
Benevolent Fund
Angus Allnatt Charitable
Foundation
The AMW Charitable Trust
The Beit Trust
The Big Lottery Fund
The David Brooke Charity
The Charles Brotherton Trust
The Burton Breweries
Charitable Trust
Cash for Kids Radio Clyde
The Church Burgesses
Educational Foundation
Lord Clinton's Charitable Trust
The Clover Trust
The Coalfields Regeneration
Trust
The Cray Trust
The Cross Trust
The Raymond Curtis Charitable
Trust
Peter De Haan Charitable
Trust
The Djanogly Foundation
The Dulverton Trust
Annette Duvollet Charitable
Trust
The Dyers' Company
Charitable Trust
The Sir John Eastwood
Foundation
Edinburgh Children's Holiday
Fund
The Edinburgh Trust, No 2
Account
The Wilfred and Elsie Elkes
Charity Fund
EMI Music Sound Foundation
The Emmandjay Charitable
Trust
The English Schools' Football
Association
The Essex Youth Trust
Esmée Fairbairn Foundation
The George Fentham
Birmingham Charity
Dixie Rose Findlay Charitable
Trust
Ford Britain Trust
The Fort Foundation
The Hugh Fraser Foundation
The Frognal Trust
The Gannochy Trust
J Paul Getty Jr Charitable Trust
The Girdlers' Company
Charitable Trust
The Glass-House Trust
The Gough Charitable Trust
Grantham Yorke Trust
The Grocers' Charity
The Hadfield Trust

The Hadrian Trust
The Alfred Haines Charitable
   Trust
The Harris Charitable Trust
The Hawthorne Charitable
   Trust
The Haymills Charitable Trust
The Hedley Foundation
The Christina Mary Hendrie
   Trust for Scottish and
   Canadian Charities
The Hilden Charitable Fund
The Charles Littlewood Hill
   Trust
The Holywood Trust
Hope for Youth (formerly
   Women Caring Trust)
The Horne Foundation
The Reta Lila Howard
   Foundation
The Humanitarian Trust
The Hunter Foundation
The James Trust
The Mary Kinross Charitable
   Trust
Ernest Kleinwort Charitable
   Trust
The Lanvern Foundation
The R J Larg Family Charitable
   Trust
The Mark Leonard Trust
Lifeline 4 Kids
The Enid Linder Foundation
The R S Macdonald Charitable
   Trust
The MacRobert Trust
The Marsh Christian Trust
Sir George Martin Trust
The Nancie Massey Charitable
   Trust
The Maxell Educational Trust
The Mercers' Charitable
   Foundation
The Peter Moores Foundation
The Stanley Morrison
   Charitable Trust
The Mugdock Children's Trust
Newby Trust Limited
The Northcott Devon
   Foundation
The Norwich Church of England
   Young Men's Society
The Nuffield Foundation
Miss M E Swinton Paterson's
   Charitable Trust
The Peacock Charitable Trust
The Jack Petchey Foundation
The Ponton House Trust
The Priory Foundation
The Rank Foundation
The Ratcliff Pension Charity
Richard Reeve's Foundation
The Rhondda Cynon Taff
   Welsh Church Acts Fund
The Richmond Parish Lands
   Charity

The Robertson Trust
Mrs L D Rope Third Charitable
   Settlement
The Rotherwick Foundation
The Andrew Salvesen
   Charitable Trust
The Sandra Charitable Trust
The Searle Charitable Trust
SFIA Educational Trust Limited
The Bassil Shippam and
   Alsford Trust
The Shipwrights' Company
   Charitable Fund
The Southdown Trust
The Southover Manor General
   Education Trust
St Hilda's Trust
Sir Walter St John's
   Educational Charity
The W O Street Charitable
   Foundation
The Summerfield Charitable
   Trust
The Len Thomson Charitable
   Trust
The Sue Thomson Foundation
UnLtd (Foundation for Social
   Entrepreneurs)
Victoria Homes Trust
The Vodafone (Group)
   Foundation
The Barbara Ward Children's
   Foundation
The Wates Foundation
The Wilson Foundation
Woodlands Trust
The Xerox (UK) Trust
The Yapp Charitable Trust
The John K Young Endowment
   Fund
The Marjorie and Arnold Ziff
   Charitable Foundation

....

■ Older people

The A B Charitable Trust
The ACT Foundation
The Company of Actuaries'
   Charitable Trust Fund
Age Scotland (formerly Age
   Concern Scotland and Help
   the Aged)
Age UK (formerly Help the
   Aged and Age Concern)
The Green and Lilian F M
   Ainsworth and Family
   Benevolent Fund
Viscount Amory's Charitable
   Trust
The Argus Appeal
The Lord Austin Trust
Autonomous Research
   Charitable Trust
The Baker Charitable Trust
The Ballinger Charitable Trust
The Band Trust

Barchester Healthcare
   Foundation
The Barclay Foundation
The Barnwood House Trust
The Louis Baylis (Maidenhead
   Advertiser) Charitable Trust
The Benfield Motors Charitable
   Trust
The Gerald Bentall Charitable
   Trust
The Mason Bibby 1981 Trust
Percy Bilton Charity
The Bisgood Charitable Trust
   (registered as Miss Jeanne
   Bisgood's Charitable Trust)
The Herbert and Peter
   Blagrave Charitable Trust
The Bothwell Charitable Trust
P G and N J Boulton Trust
The Harold and Alice Bridges
   Charity
The David Brooke Charity
The Charles Brotherton Trust
The William A Cadbury
   Charitable Trust
The Joseph and Annie Cattle
   Trust
The Checkatrade Foundation
The Chelsea Building Society
   Charitable Foundation
Lord Clinton's Charitable Trust
The Clore Duffield Foundation
The Clothworkers' Foundation
The Clover Trust
The Coalfields Regeneration
   Trust
Comic Relief
The Consolidated Charities for
   the Infirm Merchant
   Taylors' Company
The Cook and Wolstenholme
   Charitable Trust
The Marjorie Coote Old
   People's Charity
Cumbria Community
   Foundation
The Raymond Curtis Charitable
   Trust
The Manny Cussins
   Foundation
The Dr and Mrs A Darlington
   Charitable Trust
The Denton Charitable Trust
The Djanogly Foundation
The Derek and Eileen Dodgson
   Foundation
The Drapers' Charitable Fund
The Dulverton Trust
The P B Dumbell Charitable
   Trust
The Dumbreck Charity
The Dunhill Medical Trust
The Sir John Eastwood
   Foundation
The Gilbert and Eileen Edgar
   Foundation

The W G Edwards Charitable Foundation

The Wilfred and Elsie Elkes Charity Fund

The Maud Elkington Charitable Trust

The John Ellerman Foundation

The Equilibrium Foundation

The Ericson Trust

The Erskine Cunningham Hill Trust

The Eveson Charitable Trust

Esmée Fairbairn Foundation

The Fairway Trust

The Fairwind Trust

The Lord Faringdon Charitable Trust

Samuel William Farmer Trust

The Fassnidge Memorial Trust

Joseph Fattorini Charitable Trust 'B' Account

The Margaret Fisher Charitable Trust

The Roy Fletcher Charitable Trust

The Football Association National Sports Centre Trust

The Donald Forrester Trust

The Hugh Fraser Foundation

The Joseph Strong Frazer Trust

The Freemasons' Grand Charity

The Friarsgate Trust

Friends of Muir Group

The Frognal Trust

The Fuserna Foundation

The Girdlers' Company Charitable Trust

The Gosling Foundation Limited

Grand Charitable Trust of the Order of Women Freemasons

The Constance Green Foundation

The Philip Green Memorial Trust

Greggs Foundation (formerly Greggs Trust)

Grimmitt Trust

The Grocers' Charity

The Bishop of Guildford's Foundation

The Guildry Incorporation of Perth

The Hadfield Trust

The Hadrian Trust

The Alfred Haines Charitable Trust

E F and M G Hall Charitable Trust

The Helen Hamlyn Trust

Hampton Fuel Allotment Charity

The W A Handley Charitable Trust

William Harding's Charity

The Harebell Centenary Fund

The Kenneth Hargreaves Charitable Trust

The Harrison and Potter Trust

The N and P Hartley Memorial Trust

The Alfred And Peggy Harvey Charitable Trust

The Dorothy Hay-Bolton Charitable Trust

The Charles Hayward Foundation

The Headley Trust

Headley-Pitt Charitable Trust

The Heart of England Community Foundation

The Hemby Trust

The Christina Mary Hendrie Trust for Scottish and Canadian Charities

The Sir Julian Hodge Charitable Trust

The Edward Holt Trust

The Cuthbert Horn Trust

The Hospital of God at Greatham

The Hudson Foundation

Miss Agnes H Hunter's Trust

Huntingdon Freemen's Charity

The Charles Irving Charitable Trust

The Ruth and Lionel Jacobson Trust (Second Fund) No 2

John James Bristol Foundation

The Jones 1986 Charitable Trust

The Cyril and Eve Jumbo Charitable Trust

The Anton Jurgens Charitable Trust

The Kaufman Charitable Trust

The KempWelch Charitable Trust

Ernest Kleinwort Charitable Trust

The Sir James Knott Trust

The Martin Laing Foundation

The Beatrice Laing Trust

The Lambert Charitable Trust

Duchy of Lancaster Benevolent Fund

The Allen Lane Foundation

The Edgar E Lawley Foundation

The Herd Lawson and Muriel Lawson Charitable Trust

The Joseph Levy Charitable Foundation

The Linbury Trust

Lincolnshire Community Foundation

The Linden Charitable Trust

Jack Livingstone Charitable Trust

Lloyds TSB Foundation for England and Wales

Paul Lunn-Rockliffe Charitable Trust

Lord and Lady Lurgan Trust

The M and C Trust

The E M MacAndrew Trust

Macdonald-Buchanan Charitable Trust

The Macfarlane Walker Trust

Man Group plc Charitable Trust

The Marks Family Foundation

The Ann and David Marks Foundation

The Michael Marsh Charitable Trust

The Marsh Christian Trust

The Charlotte Marshall Charitable Trust

Sir George Martin Trust

The Nancie Massey Charitable Trust

The Violet Mauray Charitable Trust

The Maxwell Family Foundation

Evelyn May Trust

The Robert McAlpine Foundation

D D McPhail Charitable Settlement

The Mercers' Charitable Foundation

The Merchant Taylors' Company Charities Fund

The Merchant Venturers' Charity

The Zachary Merton and George Woofindin Convalescent Trust

The Tony Metherell Charitable Trust

Miles Trust for the Putney and Roehampton Community

Milton Keynes Community Foundation

The Peter Minet Trust

The Mitchell Charitable Trust

Monmouthshire County Council Welsh Church Act Fund

The Peter Moores Foundation

The Morris Charitable Trust

The Peter Morrison Charitable Foundation

The Edith Murphy Foundation

Murphy-Neumann Charity Company Limited

The Nationwide Foundation

Nominet Charitable Foundation

The North British Hotel Trust

The Northampton Queen's Institute Relief in Sickness Fund

The Northern Rock Foundation

The Northwood Charitable Trust

The Nuffield Foundation
The Oakley Charitable Trust
Ogilvie Charities Deed No.2
(including the Charity of
Mary Catherine Ford Smith)
The Oldham Foundation
Arthur James Paterson
Charitable Trust
The Constance Paterson
Charitable Trust
Paycare Charity Trust (formerly
known as Patients' Aid
Association Hospital and
Medical Charities Trust)
The Harry Payne Trust
The Pedmore Sporting Club
Trust Fund
The Dowager Countess
Eleanor Peel Trust
Pendragon Charitable Trust
The Pervez Musharraf
Foundation
The Elise Pilkington Charitable
Trust
The Pilkington Charities Fund
The Austin and Hope
Pilkington Trust
G S Plaut Charitable Trust
Limited
The Ponton House Trust
The Powell Foundation
The Praebendo Charitable
Foundation
The Douglas Prestwich
Charitable Trust
Sir John Priestman Charity
Trust
The Proven Family Trust
The Provincial Grand Charity of
the Province of Derbyshire
PSA Peugeot Citroen Charity
Trust
The Puri Foundation
Mr and Mrs J A Pye's
Charitable Settlement
The Queen's Silver Jubilee
Trust
The Rank Foundation
The Joseph Rank Trust
The Rashbass Family Trust
The Ratcliff Pension Charity
The Ravensdale Trust
The Roger Raymond Charitable
Trust
The Rayne Foundation
The Rayne Trust
The Sir James Reckitt Charity
The Red Rose Charitable Trust
Relief Fund for Romania
Limited
The Violet M Richards Charity
The Richmond Parish Lands
Charity
Riverside Charitable Trust
Limited
The Robertson Trust

The C A Rookes Charitable
Trust
The Rosca Trust
The Cecil Rosen Foundation
Mrs Gladys Row Fogo
Charitable Trust
The Rowlands Trust
The RRAF Charitable Trust
The Andrew Salvesen
Charitable Trust
The Helene Sebba Charitable
Trust
The Sylvia and Colin Shepherd
Charitable Trust
The Bassil Shippam and
Alsford Trust
The Mary Elizabeth Siebel
Charity
The Henry Smith Charity
Stanley Smith General
Charitable Trust
Philip Smith's Charitable Trust
The R C Snelling Charitable
Trust
The Sobell Foundation
The Sovereign Health Care
Charitable Trust
The Spero Foundation
St Monica Trust Community
Fund
The Stafford Trust
The Stanley Foundation Ltd
The Stanton Ballard Charitable
Trust
The June Stevens Foundation
The Summerfield Charitable
Trust
A P Taylor Trust
Tesco Charity Trust
The Tolkien Trust
UnLtd (Foundation for Social
Entrepreneurs)
The Valiant Charitable Trust
The Albert Van Den Bergh
Charitable Trust
John and Lucille van Geest
Foundation
The Van Neste Foundation
The William and Patricia
Venton Charitable Trust
The Viznitz Foundation
The Wakefield and Tetley Trust
J and J R Wilson Trust
The Community Foundation for
Wiltshire and Swindon
The Francis Winham
Foundation
The Michael and Anna Wix
Charitable Trust
The Wixamtree Trust
Woodlands Trust
The Yapp Charitable Trust
Yorkshire Building Society
Charitable Foundation
The Marjorie and Arnold Ziff
Charitable Foundation

Class, group, occupation or former occupation

■ Armed forces

ABF The Soldiers' Charity
(formerly the Army
Benevolent Fund)
The Ammco Trust
The Armourers' and Brasiers'
Gauntlet Trust
The Balney Charitable Trust
The Baltic Charitable Fund
The Robert Clutterbuck
Charitable Trust
The De Clermont Charitable
Company Ltd
The Dulverton Trust
The Edinburgh Trust, No 2
Account
The Erskine Cunningham Hill
Trust
The Donald Forrester Trust
The Girdlers' Company
Charitable Trust
Mike Gooley Trailfinders
Charity
The W A Handley Charitable
Trust
The Charles Littlewood Hill
Trust
The Sir James Knott Trust
The Beatrice Laing Trust
The Raymond and Blanche
Lawson Charitable Trust
The MacRobert Trust
Mountbatten Festival of Music
The Noswad Charity
The Prince of Wales's
Charitable Foundation
The Foundation of Prince
William and Prince Harry
Princess Anne's Charities
Queen Mary's Roehampton
Trust
The Red Arrows Trust
Alexandra Rose Charities
The Rowlands Trust
Royal Artillery Charitable Fund
Royal British Legion
The Royal Scots Benevolent
Society
Salters' Charitable Foundation
Scott (Eredine) Charitable
Trust
Seafarers UK (King George's
Fund for Sailors)
The Leslie Smith Foundation
Philip Smith's Charitable Trust
The Stafford Trust
The Westminster Foundation
Anona Winn Charitable Trust

■ Art, culture sports and recreation

The Arts Council of Wales
The Richard Carne Trust
The Equity Trust Fund
The John Feeney Charitable Trust
The Follett Trust
Maurice Fry Charitable Trust
The Goldsmiths' Company Charity
Paul Hamlyn Foundation
The Derek Hill Foundation
The Hinrichsen Foundation
The Horne Foundation
The Boris Karloff Charitable Foundation
The Kathleen Trust
The Leverhulme Trust
The Anthony and Elizabeth Mellows Charitable Settlement
The R V W Trust
The Peggy Ramsay Foundation
The Rayne Foundation
The Tillett Trust
Miss S M Tutton Charitable Trust
Unity Theatre Trust

■ The environment, agriculture

The C Alma Baker Trust
Samuel William Farmer Trust
The Farmers' Company Charitable Fund
The Fishmongers' Company's Charitable Trust
The Girdlers' Company Charitable Trust
The Joicey Trust
Frank Litchfield Charitable Trust
The NFU Mutual Charitable Trust
Yorkshire Agricultural Society
The Yorkshire Dales Millennium Trust

■ Fishermen

The Fishmongers' Company's Charitable Trust
The Joicey Trust

■ Law, mediation and advice services

The Law Society Charity

■ Manufacturing and service industries

The Arts Council of Wales
The Clothworkers' Foundation
Coats Foundation Trust
The Cotton Industry War Memorial Trust
Florence's Charitable Trust
Worshipful Company of Glovers of London Charity Fund
The Leverhulme Trade Charities Trust
Minge's Gift and the Pooled Trusts
Riverside Charitable Trust Limited

■ Medicine and health

The John Avins Trustees
Veta Bailey Charitable Trust
B-CH 1971 Charitable Trust
The British Dietetic Association General and Education Trust Fund
British Heart Foundation
The Carron Charitable Settlement
The Dinwoodie Settlement
Maurice Fry Charitable Trust
The General Nursing Council for England and Wales Trust
The Kenneth Hargreaves Charitable Trust
The Michael and Morven Heller Charitable Foundation
John Lewis Partnership General Community Fund
Evelyn May Trust
The Northcott Devon Medical Foundation
The Rayne Foundation
The Sandra Charitable Trust

■ Religion

All Saints Educational Trust
Ashburnham Thanksgiving Trust
The Corinthian Trust
The Anne French Memorial Trust
The Hesed Trust
The Hope Trust
The James Trust
The Langley Charitable Trust

The Lyndhurst Trust
Sylvanus Lyson's Charity
Marshall's Charity
The Bishop Radford Trust
The Rehoboth Trust
St Teilo's Trust
Ulting Overseas Trust
Wallington Missionary Mart and Auctions
The James Wood Bequest Fund

■ Science, technology and engineering

The Colt Foundation
Maurice Fry Charitable Trust
The Michael and Morven Heller Charitable Foundation
The Leverhulme Trade Charities Trust
The Leverhulme Trust
The Kitty and Daniel Nabarro Charitable Trust
The Nottinghamshire Miners' Welfare Trust Fund
Scottish Coal Industry Special Welfare Fund

■ Sporting or social clubs (including Masons)

Essex Provincial Charity Fund
The Freemasons' Grand Charity
Grand Charitable Trust of the Order of Women Freemasons
The Provincial Grand Charity of the Province of Derbyshire

■ Textile workers and designers

The Arts Council of Wales
Coats Foundation Trust
The Cotton Industry War Memorial Trust
Minge's Gift and the Pooled Trusts

■ Transport

The Baltic Charitable Fund
The Worshipful Company of Carmen Benevolent Trust
The Erskine Cunningham Hill Trust
Dixie Rose Findlay Charitable Trust
The Donald Forrester Trust

The Gosling Foundation
Limited
The H and M Charitable Trust
The W A Handley Charitable
Trust
P H Holt Foundation
The ITF Seafarers Trust
The Joicey Trust
The George John and Sheilah
Livanos Charitable Trust
The Merchants' House of
Glasgow
The Mersey Docks and
Harbour Company
Charitable Fund
The Phillips Charitable Trust
Seafarers UK (King George's
Fund for Sailors)
Seamen's Hospital Society
The Shipwrights' Company
Charitable Fund

Disability

■ People with a mental impairment

The 1989 Willan Charitable
Trust
The Aberbrothock Skea Trust
The Sylvia Adams Charitable
Trust
The Adamson Trust
The Green and Lilian F M
Ainsworth and Family
Benevolent Fund
The Archer Trust
The Baily Thomas Charitable
Fund
The Herbert and Peter
Blagrave Charitable Trust
The Joseph and Annie Cattle
Trust
The Chelsea Building Society
Charitable Foundation
The J Reginald Corah
Foundation Fund
The Drapers' Charitable Fund
The Dumbreck Charity
The W E Dunn Trust
Eastern Counties Educational
Trust Limited
The EBM Charitable Trust
The John Ellerman Foundation
James Ellis Charitable Trust
The Emmandjay Charitable
Trust
The Eveson Charitable Trust
Esmée Fairbairn Foundation
Samuel William Farmer Trust
The Roy Fletcher Charitable
Trust
The Forbes Charitable
Foundation
Ford Britain Trust

The Oliver Ford Charitable
Trust
The Foyle Foundation
The Jill Franklin Trust
The Hugh Fraser Foundation
The Joseph Strong Frazer Trust
The Freemasons' Grand
Charity
The Gatsby Charitable
Foundation
The Robert Gavron Charitable
Trust
J Paul Getty Jr Charitable Trust
Simon Gibson Charitable Trust
The Girdlers' Company
Charitable Trust
The Good Neighbours Trust
The Gosling Foundation
Limited
The Constance Green
Foundation
Greggs Foundation (formerly
Greggs Trust)
The Grocers' Charity
The Alfred Haines Charitable
Trust
The W A Handley Charitable
Trust
The Hawthorne Charitable
Trust
The Headley Trust
The Hedley Foundation
The Charles Littlewood Hill
Trust
The Hull and East Riding
Charitable Trust
The Iliffe Family Charitable
Trust
The J J Charitable Trust
The Jeffrey Charitable Trust
The Jones 1986 Charitable
Trust
The Judith Trust
The Ian Karten Charitable
Trust
The Sir James Knott Trust
The KPMG Foundation
The Kirby Laing Foundation
The Beatrice Laing Trust
Duchy of Lancaster Benevolent
Fund
The Leach Fourteenth Trust
The Linbury Trust
The Enid Linder Foundation
Lloyds TSB Foundation for
England and Wales
Lloyds TSB Foundation for
Northern Ireland
London Catalyst (formerly The
Metropolitan Hospital-
Sunday Fund)
The Lord's Taverners
The MacRobert Trust
Ian Mactaggart Trust
Magdalen Hospital Trust

The Michael Marsh Charitable
Trust
The Marsh Christian Trust
The Jim Marshall Charitable
Trust
The Robert McAlpine
Foundation
The McKenna Charitable Trust
The Tony Metherell Charitable
Trust
Miles Trust for the Putney and
Roehampton Community
The Hugh and Mary Miller
Bequest Trust
The Peter Minet Trust
John Moores Foundation
Murphy-Neumann Charity
Company Limited
The Kitty and Daniel Nabarro
Charitable Trust
The Neighbourly Charitable
Trust
The Northern Rock Foundation
The Noswad Charity
The Nottingham General
Dispensary
The Nuffield Foundation
The Parthenon Trust
The Susanna Peake Charitable
Trust
The Persula Foundation
The Pilkington Charities Fund
The Platinum Trust
The Ponton House Trust
The Douglas Prestwich
Charitable Trust
The Red Rose Charitable Trust
Relief Fund for Romania
Limited
The Clive Richards Charity
The Richmond Parish Lands
Charity
Rix-Thompson-Rothenberg
Foundation
The Robertson Trust
The Cecil Rosen Foundation
The Rowlands Trust
The Saddlers' Company
Charitable Fund
SFIA Educational Trust Limited
The Sylvia and Colin Shepherd
Charitable Trust
The Shirley Foundation
The Mrs Smith and Mount
Trust
David Solomons Charitable
Trust
St James's Place Foundation
The Strangward Trust
The Summerfield Charitable
Trust
The Three Guineas Trust
John and Lucille van Geest
Foundation
Vision Charity
John Watson's Trust

The Will Charitable Trust
Woodlands Trust
The Woodward Charitable
Trust
The Xerox (UK) Trust
The York Children's Trust

■ People with autism

The Girdlers' Company
Charitable Trust
The Headley Trust
Magdalen Hospital Trust
The Shirley Foundation
The Three Guineas Trust

■ People who have suffered brain damage

The Girdlers' Company
Charitable Trust
John and Lucille van Geest
Foundation

■ People with dyslexia

The Joseph and Annie Cattle
Trust
The J J Charitable Trust
The KPMG Foundation
The Linbury Trust
Vision Charity

■ People with learning difficulties

The Aberbrothock Skea Trust
The Sylvia Adams Charitable
Trust
The Green and Lilian F M
Ainsworth and Family
Benevolent Fund
The Baily Thomas Charitable
Fund
The Herbert and Peter
Blagrave Charitable Trust
The Chelsea Building Society
Charitable Foundation
The J Reginald Corah
Foundation Fund
The Drapers' Charitable Fund
The Dumbreck Charity
The W E Dunn Trust
Eastern Counties Educational
Trust Limited
The EBM Charitable Trust
The John Ellerman Foundation
James Ellis Charitable Trust
The Emmandjay Charitable
Trust
The Eveson Charitable Trust
Esmée Fairbairn Foundation

The Roy Fletcher Charitable
Trust
The Forbes Charitable
Foundation
Ford Britain Trust
The Oliver Ford Charitable
Trust
The Foyle Foundation
The Jill Franklin Trust
The Hugh Fraser Foundation
The Joseph Strong Frazer Trust
The Freemasons' Grand
Charity
The Gatsby Charitable
Foundation
The Robert Gavron Charitable
Trust
J Paul Getty Jr Charitable Trust
Simon Gibson Charitable Trust
The Good Neighbours Trust
The Gosling Foundation
Limited
The Constance Green
Foundation
Greggs Foundation (formerly
Greggs Trust)
The Grocers' Charity
The Alfred Haines Charitable
Trust
The W A Handley Charitable
Trust
The Hawthorne Charitable
Trust
The Hedley Foundation
The Charles Littlewood Hill
Trust
The Hull and East Riding
Charitable Trust
The Iliffe Family Charitable
Trust
The Jeffrey Charitable Trust
The Jones 1986 Charitable
Trust
The Judith Trust
The Ian Karten Charitable
Trust
The Sir James Knott Trust
The Kirby Laing Foundation
Duchy of Lancaster Benevolent
Fund
The Leach Fourteenth Trust
The Enid Linder Foundation
Lloyds TSB Foundation for
England and Wales
Lloyds TSB Foundation for
Northern Ireland
London Catalyst (formerly The
Metropolitan Hospital-
Sunday Fund)
The Lord's Taverners
The MacRobert Trust
Ian Mactaggart Trust
Magdalen Hospital Trust
The Michael Marsh Charitable
Trust
The Marsh Christian Trust

The Jim Marshall Charitable
Trust
The Robert McAlpine
Foundation
The Tony Metherell Charitable
Trust
Miles Trust for the Putney and
Roehampton Community
The Hugh and Mary Miller
Bequest Trust
The Peter Minet Trust
John Moores Foundation
Murphy-Neumann Charity
Company Limited
The Kitty and Daniel Nabarro
Charitable Trust
The Neighbourly Charitable
Trust
The Northern Rock Foundation
The Noswad Charity
The Nottingham General
Dispensary
The Nuffield Foundation
The Parthenon Trust
The Susanna Peake Charitable
Trust
The Persula Foundation
The Pilkington Charities Fund
The Platinum Trust
The Ponton House Trust
The Douglas Prestwich
Charitable Trust
Relief Fund for Romania
Limited
The Clive Richards Charity
The Richmond Parish Lands
Charity
Rix-Thompson-Rothenberg
Foundation
The Robertson Trust
The Cecil Rosen Foundation
The Rowlands Trust
The Saddlers' Company
Charitable Fund
SFIA Educational Trust Limited
The Sylvia and Colin Shepherd
Charitable Trust
The Mrs Smith and Mount
Trust
St James's Place Foundation
The Strangward Trust
The Summerfield Charitable
Trust
The Will Charitable Trust
Woodlands Trust
The Woodward Charitable
Trust
The Xerox (UK) Trust
The York Children's Trust

■ People with a physical impairment

The 1989 Willan Charitable
Trust
The Aberbrothock Skea Trust

The Sylvia Adams Charitable Trust
The Adamson Trust
The Green and Lilian F M Ainsworth and Family Benevolent Fund
The Ajahma Charitable Trust
The Cleopatra Trust
The Dibden Allotments Fund
The Dorus Trust
The Drapers' Charitable Fund
The Dumbreck Charity
The W E Dunn Trust
The Sir John Eastwood Foundation
The EBM Charitable Trust
The John Ellerman Foundation
James Ellis Charitable Trust
The Emerton-Christie Charity
The Emmandjay Charitable Trust
The Epigoni Trust
The Eveson Charitable Trust
Esmée Fairbairn Foundation
Samuel William Farmer Trust
The Roy Fletcher Charitable Trust
The Follett Trust
Ford Britain Trust
The Donald Forrester Trust
The Jill Franklin Trust
The Hugh Fraser Foundation
The Freemasons' Grand Charity
The Frognal Trust
The Gatsby Charitable Foundation
The Robert Gavron Charitable Trust
J Paul Getty Jr Charitable Trust
Simon Gibson Charitable Trust
The Girdlers' Company Charitable Trust
The Good Neighbours Trust
The Gosling Foundation Limited
The Constance Green Foundation
Greggs Foundation (formerly Greggs Trust)
The Grocers' Charity
H C D Memorial Fund
The Hadley Trust
The Hadrian Trust
The Alfred Haines Charitable Trust
The W A Handley Charitable Trust
The Peter Harrison Foundation
The N and P Hartley Memorial Trust
The Hawthorne Charitable Trust
The Headley Trust
The Hedley Foundation

The Charles Littlewood Hill Trust
The Hospital Saturday Fund
The Hull and East Riding Charitable Trust
Miss Agnes H Hunter's Trust
The Iliffe Family Charitable Trust
The Jones 1986 Charitable Trust
The Anton Jurgens Charitable Trust
The Ian Karten Charitable Trust
The Sir James Knott Trust
The Kirby Laing Foundation
The Beatrice Laing Trust
Duchy of Lancaster Benevolent Fund
Mrs F B Laurence Charitable Trust
The Leach Fourteenth Trust
Lifeline 4 Kids
The Enid Linder Foundation
Lloyds TSB Foundation for England and Wales
Lloyds TSB Foundation for Northern Ireland
London Catalyst (formerly The Metropolitan Hospital-Sunday Fund)
The Lord's Taverners
The R S Macdonald Charitable Trust
The MacRobert Trust
Ian Mactaggart Trust
The Michael Marsh Charitable Trust
The Marsh Christian Trust
The Jim Marshall Charitable Trust
The McKenna Charitable Trust
The Mercers' Charitable Foundation
The Tony Metherell Charitable Trust
Miles Trust for the Putney and Roehampton Community
The Hugh and Mary Miller Bequest Trust
Milton Keynes Community Foundation
The Peter Minet Trust
John Moores Foundation
Murphy-Neumann Charity Company Limited
The Neighbourly Charitable Trust
Newby Trust Limited
The Northern Rock Foundation
The Noswad Charity
The Nottingham General Dispensary
The Parthenon Trust
The Peacock Charitable Trust

The Susanna Peake Charitable Trust
The Dowager Countess Eleanor Peel Trust
The Persula Foundation
The Pilkington Charities Fund
The Platinum Trust
The Ponton House Trust
The Douglas Prestwich Charitable Trust
Richard Radcliffe Charitable Trust
The Red Rose Charitable Trust
Relief Fund for Romania Limited
The Clive Richards Charity
The Richmond Parish Lands Charity
The Robertson Trust
Mrs L D Rope Third Charitable Settlement
The Cecil Rosen Foundation
The Rowlands Trust
Royal Docks Trust (London)
The Saddlers' Company Charitable Fund
SFIA Educational Trust Limited
The Sylvia and Colin Shepherd Charitable Trust
Stanley Smith General Charitable Trust
St James's Place Foundation
The Strangward Trust
The Summerfield Charitable Trust
The Wixamtree Trust
Woodlands Trust
The Woodward Charitable Trust
The Xerox (UK) Trust
The York Children's Trust

....

■ People with a sensory impairment

Blatchington Court Trust
The British Council for Prevention of Blindness
The Charities Advisory Trust
The John Cowan Foundation
The Wilfred and Elsie Elkes Charity Fund
James Ellis Charitable Trust
The Eveson Charitable Trust
Samuel William Farmer Trust
Dixie Rose Findlay Charitable Trust
The Joseph Strong Frazer Trust
The Frognal Trust
The Girdlers' Company Charitable Trust
The Dorothy Hay-Bolton Charitable Trust
The Anne Herd Memorial Trust
Miss Agnes H Hunter's Trust

The Lillie Johnson Charitable
  Trust
The Anton Jurgens Charitable
  Trust
The Raymond and Blanche
  Lawson Charitable Trust
The John Spedan Lewis
  Foundation
The R S Macdonald Charitable
  Trust
Brian Mercer Charitable Trust
The Tony Metherell Charitable
  Trust
Mickleham Charitable Trust
Gerald Micklem Charitable
  Trust
The Northwood Charitable
  Trust
The Persula Foundation
Richard Radcliffe Charitable
  Trust
The Max Reinhardt Charitable
  Trust
The Worshipful Company of
  Spectacle Makers' Charity
The Ulverscroft Foundation
John and Lucille van Geest
  Foundation
Vision Charity
The Will Charitable Trust
The York Children's Trust

....

■ Hearing loss

The Wilfred and Elsie Elkes
  Charity Fund
The Eveson Charitable Trust
Samuel William Farmer Trust
The Joseph Strong Frazer Trust
The Girdlers' Company
  Charitable Trust
The Northwood Charitable
  Trust
The Persula Foundation
The Max Reinhardt Charitable
  Trust
John and Lucille van Geest
  Foundation

....

■ Sight loss

Blatchington Court Trust
The British Council for
  Prevention of Blindness
The John Cowan Foundation
The Wilfred and Elsie Elkes
  Charity Fund
The Eveson Charitable Trust
Samuel William Farmer Trust
Dixie Rose Findlay Charitable
  Trust
The Joseph Strong Frazer Trust
The Frognal Trust
The Girdlers' Company
  Charitable Trust

The Anne Herd Memorial Trust
Miss Agnes H Hunter's Trust
The Raymond and Blanche
  Lawson Charitable Trust
The R S Macdonald Charitable
  Trust
Brian Mercer Charitable Trust
Mickleham Charitable Trust
The Persula Foundation
The Worshipful Company of
  Spectacle Makers' Charity
The Ulverscroft Foundation
John and Lucille van Geest
  Foundation
Vision Charity
The Will Charitable Trust

Ethnicity

The BACTA Charitable Trust
The Big Lottery Fund
The Bintaub Charitable Trust
The Football Association
  National Sports Centre
  Trust
The Wiles Greenworld
  Charitable Trust
Greggs Foundation (formerly
  Greggs Trust)
The Hadrian Trust
Hampton Fuel Allotment
  Charity
The Hospital of God at
  Greatham
The LankellyChase Foundation
The Joseph Levy Charitable
  Foundation
Lincolnshire Community
  Foundation
Lloyds TSB Foundation for
  England and Wales
The Trust for London (formerly
  the City Parochial
  Foundation)
The Ann and David Marks
  Foundation
John Moores Foundation
The Northern Rock Foundation
The Jack Petchey Foundation
The Popocatepetl Trust
The Rashbass Family Trust
The Sigrid Rausing Trust
The Alan and Babette
  Sainsbury Charitable Fund
Shaara Ezra – The Moses
  Foundation
The Spero Foundation
The Viznitz Foundation

Faith

4 Charity Foundation
Brian Abrams Charitable Trust
Eric Abrams Charitable Trust
The Acacia Charitable Trust

Achisomoch Aid Company
  Limited
Adenfirst Ltd
Aid to the Church in Need (UK)
Alba Charitable Trust
The Alexis Trust
All Saints Educational Trust
The Alliance Family Foundation
The Almond Trust
Alvor Charitable Trust
Amabrill Limited
The AMW Charitable Trust
The Anchor Foundation
The Andrew Anderson Trust
Ashburnham Thanksgiving
  Trust
AW Charitable Trust
The BACTA Charitable Trust
The Baker Charitable Trust
The George Balint Charitable
  Trust
William P Bancroft (No 2)
  Charitable Trust and
  Jenepher Gillett Trust
Bay Charitable Trust
BCH Trust
Beauland Ltd
Belljoe Tzedoko Ltd
The Ruth Berkowitz Charitable
  Trust
The Bintaub Charitable Trust
The Sir Victor Blank Charitable
  Settlement
The Neville and Elaine Blond
  Charitable Trust
The Bonamy Charitable Trust
P G and N J Boulton Trust
Sir Clive Bourne Family Trust
Bristol Archdeaconry Charity
Mrs E E Brown Charitable
  Settlement
Buckingham Trust
The Audrey and Stanley Burton
  1960 Charitable Trust
The Arnold Burton 1998
  Charitable Trust
C and F Charitable Trust
Henry T and Lucy B Cadbury
  Charitable Trust
The William A Cadbury
  Charitable Trust
H and L Cantor Trust
Carlee Ltd
The CH (1980) Charitable
  Trust
Charitworth Limited
Chasdei Tovim Me'oros
Childs Charitable Trust
The Christabella Charitable
  Trust
The Roger and Sarah Bancroft
  Clark Charitable Trust
Closehelm Ltd
The Clover Trust
Clydpride Ltd

The E Alec Colman Charitable Fund Ltd
Col-Reno Ltd
The Gershon Coren Charitable Foundation
Edwin Cornforth 1983 Charity Trust
The Sidney and Elizabeth Corob Charitable Trust
The Corona Charitable Trust
The Costa Family Charitable Trust (formerly the Morgan Williams Charitable Trust)
The Manny Cussins Foundation
Itzchok Meyer Cymerman Trust Ltd
Oizer Dalim Trust
The Davidson Family Charitable Trust
Davis-Rubens Charitable Trust
The Debmar Benevolent Trust
The Dellal Foundation
David and Rose Diamond Trust
The Djanogly Foundation
The DM Charitable Trust
Domepride Ltd
The Doughty Charity Trust
The P B Dumbell Charitable Trust
Dushinsky Trust Ltd
The George Elias Charitable Trust
Ellador Ltd
The Ellinson Foundation Ltd
The Edith Maud Ellis 1985 Charitable Trust
Elshore Ltd
Entindale Ltd
The Esfandi Charitable Foundation
The Exilarch's Foundation
Extonglen Limited
Joseph Fattorini Charitable Trust 'B' Account
Federation of Jewish Relief Organisations
Finnart House School Trust
The Rose Flatau Charitable Trust
The Gerald Fogel Charitable Trust
Fordeve Ltd
The Forte Charitable Trust
The Isaac and Freda Frankel Memorial Charitable Trust
The Thomas Freke and Lady Norton Charity
The Friends Hall Farm Street Trust
Friends of Biala Ltd
Friends of Boyan Trust
Friends of Wiznitz Limited
Mejer and Gertrude Miriam Frydman Foundation

The Angela Gallagher Memorial Fund
Garvan Limited
The B and P Glasser Charitable Trust
Global Care
The Meir Golda Trust
The Grahame Charitable Foundation Limited
The Wiles Greenworld Charitable Trust
The M and R Gross Charities Limited
The Grove Charitable Trust
The Gur Trust
The H P Charitable Trust
Beatrice Hankey Foundation Ltd
Harbo Charities Limited
The Harbour Foundation
Haskel Family Foundation
Heagerty Charitable Trust
The Helping Foundation
Hexham and Newcastle Diocesan Trust (1947)
Highcroft Charitable Trust
Hinchley Charitable Trust
The Holden Charitable Trust
The Hope Trust
The Daniel Howard Trust
The Humanitarian Trust
The Huntingdon Foundation
Hurdale Charity Limited
The P Y N and B Hyams Trust
Infinity Capital Trust
The Isaacs Charitable Trust
Jacobs Charitable Trust
The Susan and Stephen James Charitable Settlement (also known as the Stephen James Charitable Trust)
The James Trust
The Marjory Jameson Trust
Jay Education Trust
JCA Charitable Foundation
The Jerusalem Trust
Jewish Child's Day
The Jewish Youth Fund
The JMK Charitable Trust
The Harold Joels Charitable Trust
The Nicholas Joels Charitable Trust
The Norman Joels Charitable Trust
The J E Joseph Charitable Fund
The Judith Trust
The Bernard Kahn Charitable Trust
The Stanley Kalms Foundation
The Kasner Charitable Trust
The Katzauer Charitable Settlement

The C S Kaufman Charitable Trust
The Kaufman Charitable Trust
The Geoffrey John Kaye Charitable Foundation
The Emmanuel Kaye Foundation
Keren Association
Kermaville Ltd
E and E Kernkraut Charities Limited
The Kessler Foundation
Kirschel Foundation
The Kohn Foundation
Kollel and Co. Limited
Kupath Gemach Chaim Bechesed Viznitz Trust
The Late Sir Pierce Lacy Charity Trust
Laufer Charitable Trust
The Lauffer Family Charitable Foundation
The Herd Lawson and Muriel Lawson Charitable Trust
The Arnold Lee Charitable Trust
Morris Leigh Foundation
Lewis Family Charitable Trust
The Lind Trust
The Second Joseph Aaron Littman Foundation
Jack Livingstone Charitable Trust
The Charles Lloyd Foundation
Localtrent Ltd
The Locker Foundation
The Loftus Charitable Trust
The Lolev Charitable Trust
The Trust for London (formerly the City Parochial Foundation)
The Lowy Mitchell Foundation
The Ruth and Jack Lunzer Charitable Trust
The Sir Jack Lyons Charitable Trust
The Joy and Malcolm Lyons Foundation
Sylvanus Lyson's Charity
The M and C Trust
The M K Charitable Trust
Macdonald-Buchanan Charitable Trust
The Magen Charitable Trust
Malbin Trust
The Mallinckrodt Foundation
Marbeh Torah Trust
The Stella and Alexander Margulies Charitable Trust
The Ann and David Marks Foundation
The Hilda and Samuel Marks Foundation
The Mason Porter Charitable Trust

The Violet Mauray Charitable Trust
Mayfair Charities Ltd
Melodor Ltd
Melow Charitable Trust
Menuchar Ltd
Mercaz Torah Vechesed Limited
Miles Trust for the Putney and Roehampton Community
The Minos Trust
The Mishcon Family Charitable Trust
The Mitchell Charitable Trust
Keren Mitzvah Trust
The Modiano Charitable Trust
The Moette Charitable Trust
The Mole Charitable Trust
The Morgan Charitable Foundation
The Oliver Morland Charitable Trust
S C and M E Morland's Charitable Trust
The Peter Morrison Charitable Foundation
Moshal Charitable Trust
Brian and Jill Moss Charitable Trust
The Mutual Trust Group
MYA Charitable Trust
MYR Charitable Trust
The Nadezhda Charitable Trust
The Naggar Charitable Trust
Nathan Charitable Trust
Nemoral Ltd
Ner Foundation
Nesswall Ltd
NJD Charitable Trust
The Northampton Municipal Church Charities
The Norwood and Newton Settlement
The Ogle Christian Trust
Oizer Charitable Trust
Open Gate
The Owen Family Trust
The Doris Pacey Charitable Foundation
The Payne Charitable Trust
The David Pearlman Charitable Foundation
Pendragon Charitable Trust
The Persson Charitable Trust (formerly Highmoore Hall Charitable Trust)
The Phillips Family Charitable Trust
The David Pickford Charitable Foundation
The Pollywally Charitable Trust
Porticus UK
The J E Posnansky Charitable Trust
Premishlaner Charitable Trust

Sir John Priestman Charity Trust
Quothquan Trust
R J M Charitable Trust
R S Charitable Trust
The Bishop Radford Trust
The Joseph Rank Trust
The Fanny Rapaport Charitable Settlement
The Ravensdale Trust
The Rayden Charitable Trust
The Rayne Trust
The Sir James Reckitt Charity
The Rehoboth Trust
The Rest Harrow Trust
The Rhondda Cynon Taff Welsh Church Acts Fund
The Clive Richards Charity
The Sir John Ritblat Family Foundation
The Rock Solid Trust
The Gerald Ronson Foundation
Rowanville Ltd
S F Foundation
S O Charitable Trust
The Ruzin Sadagora Trust
Saint Luke's College Foundation
The Hon. M J Samuel Charitable Trust
The Annie Schiff Charitable Trust
The Schmidt-Bodner Charitable Trust
The Schreib Trust
The Schreiber Charitable Trust
The Samuel Sebba Charitable Trust
Sellata Ltd
The Cyril Shack Trust
Shlomo Memorial Fund Limited
The Leslie Silver Charitable Trust
The Simpson Foundation
The Moss Spiro Will Charitable Foundation
Springrule Ltd
St Christopher's College Educational Trust
C E K Stern Charitable Trust
The Strawberry Charitable Trust
The A B Strom and R Strom Charitable Trust
T and S Trust Fund
Tadlus Limited
The Tajtelbaum Charitable Trust
The David Tannen Charitable Trust
The Lili Tapper Charitable Foundation
C B and H H Taylor 1984 Trust
The Torah Temimah Trust
Toras Chesed (London) Trust
Truemart Limited

Trustees of Tzedakah
The Union of Orthodox Hebrew Congregation
The Vail Foundation
Vivdale Ltd
The John Warren Foundation
The Weinstein Foundation
The Benjamin Winegarten Charitable Trust
The Maurice Wohl Charitable Foundation
The Wolfson Family Charitable Trust
Woodlands Foundation Limited
Wychville Ltd
Yankov Charitable Trust
The Marjorie and Arnold Ziff Charitable Foundation
Stephen Zimmerman Charitable Trust

....
■ **Christians**
Aid to the Church in Need (UK)
The Alexis Trust
All Saints Educational Trust
The Almond Trust
Alvor Charitable Trust
The AMW Charitable Trust
The Anchor Foundation
The Andrew Anderson Trust
Ashburnham Thanksgiving Trust
William P Bancroft (No 2) Charitable Trust and Jenepher Gillett Trust
P G and N J Boulton Trust
Bristol Archdeaconry Charity
Buckingham Trust
Henry T and Lucy B Cadbury Charitable Trust
The William A Cadbury Charitable Trust
Childs Charitable Trust
The Christabella Charitable Trust
The Roger and Sarah Bancroft Clark Charitable Trust
The Clover Trust
The Costa Family Charitable Trust (formerly the Morgan Williams Charitable Trust)
The P B Dumbell Charitable Trust
The Edith Maud Ellis 1985 Charitable Trust
Joseph Fattorini Charitable Trust 'B' Account
The Forte Charitable Trust
The Thomas Freke and Lady Norton Charity
The Friends Hall Farm Street Trust
The Angela Gallagher Memorial Fund
Global Care

Beatrice Hankey Foundation Ltd

Heagerty Charitable Trust

Hexham and Newcastle Diocesan Trust (1947)

Hinchley Charitable Trust

The Hope Trust

The James Trust

The Marjory Jameson Trust

The Jerusalem Trust

The Late Sir Pierce Lacy Charity Trust

The Herd Lawson and Muriel Lawson Charitable Trust

The Lind Trust

The Charles Lloyd Foundation

Sylvanus Lyson's Charity

Macdonald-Buchanan Charitable Trust

The Mallinckrodt Foundation

The Mason Porter Charitable Trust

Miles Trust for the Putney and Roehampton Community

The Minos Trust

The Oliver Morland Charitable Trust

S C and M E Morland's Charitable Trust

The Nadezhda Charitable Trust

Nathan Charitable Trust

The Norwood and Newton Settlement

The Ogle Christian Trust

Open Gate

The Owen Family Trust

The Payne Charitable Trust

Pendragon Charitable Trust

The Persson Charitable Trust (formerly Highmoore Hall Charitable Trust)

The David Pickford Charitable Foundation

Sir John Priestman Charity Trust

Quothquan Trust

The Bishop Radford Trust

The Joseph Rank Trust

The Ravensdale Trust

The Sir James Reckitt Charity

The Rehoboth Trust

The Rhondda Cynon Taff Welsh Church Acts Fund

The Clive Richards Charity

The Rock Solid Trust

The Simpson Foundation

St Christopher's College Educational Trust

C B and H H Taylor 1984 Trust

The John Warren Foundation

....

■ **People of the Jewish faith**

4 Charity Foundation

Brian Abrams Charitable Trust

Eric Abrams Charitable Trust

The Acacia Charitable Trust

Achisomoch Aid Company Limited

Adenfirst Ltd

Alba Charitable Trust

The Alliance Family Foundation

Amabrill Limited

AW Charitable Trust

The Baker Charitable Trust

The George Balint Charitable Trust

Bay Charitable Trust

BCH Trust

Beauland Ltd

Belljoe Tzedoko Ltd

The Ruth Berkowitz Charitable Trust

The Sir Victor Blank Charitable Settlement

The Neville and Elaine Blond Charitable Trust

The Bonamy Charitable Trust

Sir Clive Bourne Family Trust

Mrs E E Brown Charitable Settlement

The Audrey and Stanley Burton 1960 Charitable Trust

The Arnold Burton 1998 Charitable Trust

C and F Charitable Trust

H and L Cantor Trust

Carlee Ltd

The CH (1980) Charitable Trust

Charitworth Limited

Chasdei Tovim Me'oros

Closehelm Ltd

Clydpride Ltd

The E Alec Colman Charitable Fund Ltd

Col-Reno Ltd

The Gershon Coren Charitable Foundation

The Sidney and Elizabeth Corob Charitable Trust

The Corona Charitable Trust

The Manny Cussins Foundation

Itzchok Meyer Cymerman Trust Ltd

Oizer Dalim Trust

The Davidson Family Charitable Trust

Davis-Rubens Charitable Trust

The Debmar Benevolent Trust

The Dellal Foundation

David and Rose Diamond Trust

The Djanogly Foundation

The DM Charitable Trust

Domepride Ltd

The Doughty Charity Trust

Dushinsky Trust Ltd

The George Elias Charitable Trust

Ellador Ltd

The Ellinson Foundation Ltd

Elshore Ltd

Entindale Ltd

The Esfandi Charitable Foundation

The Exilarch's Foundation

Extonglen Limited

Federation of Jewish Relief Organisations

Finnart House School Trust

The Gerald Fogel Charitable Trust

Fordeve Ltd

The Isaac and Freda Frankel Memorial Charitable Trust

Friends of Biala Ltd

Friends of Boyan Trust

Friends of Wiznitz Limited

Mejer and Gertrude Miriam Frydman Foundation

Garvan Limited

The B and P Glasser Charitable Trust

The Meir Golda Trust

The Grahame Charitable Foundation Limited

The M and R Gross Charities Limited

The Grove Charitable Trust

The Gur Trust

The H P Charitable Trust

Harbo Charities Limited

The Harbour Foundation

Haskel Family Foundation

The Helping Foundation

Highcroft Charitable Trust

The Holden Charitable Trust

The Daniel Howard Trust

The Humanitarian Trust

The Huntingdon Foundation

Hurdale Charity Limited

The P Y N and B Hyams Trust

Infinity Capital Trust

The Isaacs Charitable Trust

Jacobs Charitable Trust

The Susan and Stephen James Charitable Settlement (also known as the Stephen James Charitable Trust)

Jay Education Trust

JCA Charitable Foundation

Jewish Child's Day

The Jewish Youth Fund

The Harold Joels Charitable Trust

The Nicholas Joels Charitable Trust

The Norman Joels Charitable Trust

The J E Joseph Charitable Fund

The Judith Trust

The Bernard Kahn Charitable Trust

The Stanley Kalms Foundation

The Kasner Charitable Trust
The Katzauer Charitable
Settlement
The C S Kaufman Charitable
Trust
The Kaufman Charitable Trust
The Geoffrey John Kaye
Charitable Foundation
The Emmanuel Kaye
Foundation
Keren Association
Kermaville Ltd
E and E Kernkraut Charities
Limited
The Kessler Foundation
Kirschel Foundation
The Kohn Foundation
Kollel and Co. Limited
Kupath Gemach Chaim
Bechesed Viznitz Trust
Laufer Charitable Trust
The Lauffer Family Charitable
Foundation
The Arnold Lee Charitable
Trust
Morris Leigh Foundation
Lewis Family Charitable Trust
The Second Joseph Aaron
Littman Foundation
Jack Livingstone Charitable
Trust
Localtrent Ltd
The Locker Foundation
The Loftus Charitable Trust
The Lolev Charitable Trust
The Lowy Mitchell Foundation
The Ruth and Jack Lunzer
Charitable Trust
The Sir Jack Lyons Charitable
Trust
The Joy and Malcolm Lyons
Foundation
The M and C Trust
The M K Charitable Trust
The Magen Charitable Trust
Malbin Trust
Marbeh Torah Trust
The Stella and Alexander
Margulies Charitable Trust
The Ann and David Marks
Foundation
The Hilda and Samuel Marks
Foundation
The Violet Mauray Charitable
Trust
Mayfair Charities Ltd
Melodor Ltd
Melow Charitable Trust
Menuchar Ltd
Mercaz Torah Vechesed
Limited
The Mishcon Family Charitable
Trust
The Mitchell Charitable Trust
Keren Mitzvah Trust
The Modiano Charitable Trust

The Moette Charitable Trust
The Mole Charitable Trust
The Morgan Charitable
Foundation
The Peter Morrison Charitable
Foundation
Moshal Charitable Trust
Brian and Jill Moss Charitable
Trust
The Mutual Trust Group
MYA Charitable Trust
MYR Charitable Trust
The Naggar Charitable Trust
Nemoral Ltd
Ner Foundation
Nesswall Ltd
NJD Charitable Trust
Oizer Charitable Trust
The Doris Pacey Charitable
Foundation
The David Pearlman Charitable
Foundation
The Phillips Family Charitable
Trust
The Pollywally Charitable Trust
The J E Posnansky Charitable
Trust
Premishlaner Charitable Trust
R J M Charitable Trust
R S Charitable Trust
The Fanny Rapaport Charitable
Settlement
The Rayden Charitable Trust
The Rayne Trust
The Rest Harrow Trust
The Sir John Ritblat Family
Foundation
The Gerald Ronson Foundation
Rowanville Ltd
S F Foundation
S O Charitable Trust
The Ruzin Sadagora Trust
The Hon. M J Samuel
Charitable Trust
The Annie Schiff Charitable
Trust
The Schmidt-Bodner Charitable
Trust
The Schreib Trust
The Schreiber Charitable Trust
The Samuel Sebba Charitable
Trust
Sellata Ltd
The Cyril Shack Trust
Shlomo Memorial Fund Limited
The Leslie Silver Charitable
Trust
The Moss Spiro Will Charitable
Foundation
Springrule Ltd
C E K Stern Charitable Trust
The Strawberry Charitable
Trust
The A B Strom and R Strom
Charitable Trust
T and S Trust Fund

Tadlus Limited
The Tajtelbaum Charitable
Trust
The David Tannen Charitable
Trust
The Lili Tapper Charitable
Foundation
The Torah Temimah Trust
Toras Chesed (London) Trust
Truemart Limited
Trustees of Tzedakah
The Union of Orthodox Hebrew
Congregation
The Vail Foundation
Vivdale Ltd
The Weinstein Foundation
The Benjamin Winegarten
Charitable Trust
The Maurice Wohl Charitable
Foundation
The Wolfson Family Charitable
Trust
Woodlands Foundation Limited
Wychville Ltd
Yankov Charitable Trust
The Marjorie and Arnold Ziff
Charitable Foundation
Stephen Zimmerman
Charitable Trust

Gender and relationships

■ Adopted or fostered children

The Girdlers' Company
Charitable Trust
Hampton Fuel Allotment
Charity
The Hemby Trust
The Hospital of God at
Greatham
The Clifford Howarth Charity
Trust
The Hyde Charitable Trust –
Youth Plus
The Anton Jurgens Charitable
Trust
John Lyon's Charity

■ Bereaved

Baron Davenport's Charity
The Hemby Trust
The Hospital of God at
Greatham
The Clifford Howarth Charity
Trust
Alexandra Rose Charities

■ Carers

The Alchemy Foundation
The Dulverton Trust
Esmée Fairbairn Foundation
The Fishmongers' Company's
  Charitable Trust
The Hugh Fraser Foundation
The Girdlers' Company
  Charitable Trust
The Harris Charitable Trust
The Headley Trust
The Heart of England
  Community Foundation
The Hemby Trust
The Hospital of God at
  Greatham
The Clifford Howarth Charity
  Trust
The Anton Jurgens Charitable
  Trust
The King's Fund
Lloyds TSB Foundation for
  England and Wales
London Catalyst (formerly The
  Metropolitan Hospital-
  Sunday Fund)
John Lyon's Charity
The Zachary Merton and
  George Woofindin
  Convalescent Trust
John Moores Foundation
The Olga Charitable Trust
Mr and Mrs J A Pye's
  Charitable Settlement
Rix-Thompson-Rothenberg
  Foundation
The True Colours Trust

■ Families

The Carlsson Family
  Foundation
Hampton Fuel Allotment
  Charity
The Kelly Family Charitable
  Trust
The Leverhulme Trade
  Charities Trust
The Limbourne Trust
Lloyds TSB Foundation for
  England and Wales
Mariapolis Limited
The Charlotte Marshall
  Charitable Trust
The Nottingham Gordon
  Memorial Trust for Boys
  and Girls
Porticus UK
Quothquan Trust
Relief Fund for Romania
  Limited
Ryklow Charitable Trust 1992
  (also known as A B
  Williamson Charitable Trust)

■ Lesbians and gay men

The Heart of England
  Community Foundation
The Hospital of God at
  Greatham
The King's Fund
The Allen Lane Foundation

■ Orphans

The Girdlers' Company
  Charitable Trust
The Hospital of God at
  Greatham
Muslim Hands
Stanley Smith General
  Charitable Trust

■ Parents

The Carlsson Family
  Foundation
The Girdlers' Company
  Charitable Trust
The Glass-House Trust
Greggs Foundation (formerly
  Greggs Trust)
The Alfred Haines Charitable
  Trust
The Heart of England
  Community Foundation
The Hemby Trust
The Hospital of God at
  Greatham
The Clifford Howarth Charity
  Trust
The Hyde Charitable Trust –
  Youth Plus
Lloyds TSB Foundation for
  England and Wales
Lloyds TSB Foundation for
  Northern Ireland
John Lyon's Charity
The Mothercare Charitable
  Foundation
Quothquan Trust
The Tedworth Charitable Trust

■ Lone parents

The Carlsson Family
  Foundation
The Girdlers' Company
  Charitable Trust
The Alfred Haines Charitable
  Trust
The Heart of England
  Community Foundation
The Hemby Trust
The Hospital of God at
  Greatham
The Clifford Howarth Charity
  Trust

The Hyde Charitable Trust –
  Youth Plus
John Lyon's Charity
Quothquan Trust

■ Women

The 1970 Trust
The A B Charitable Trust
The Ajahma Charitable Trust
The Associated Country
  Women of the World
  (ACWW)
The Balmore Trust
The Freemasons' Grand
  Charity
J Paul Getty Jr Charitable Trust
The Hemraj Goyal Foundation
Greggs Foundation (formerly
  Greggs Trust)
The Hadrian Trust
The Heart of England
  Community Foundation
The Horizon Foundation
The Hospital of God at
  Greatham
The Judith Trust
The Allen Lane Foundation
The Lotus Foundation
R W Mann Trust
John Moores Foundation
The Eleanor Rathbone
  Charitable Trust
The Sigrid Rausing Trust
The Reed Foundation
Rosa – the UK fund for women
  and girls
The Staples Trust
The Tresillian Trust
The Volant Charitable Trust

III health

The A B Charitable Trust
The Aberbrothock Skea Trust
The Sylvia Adams Charitable
  Trust
The AMW Charitable Trust
The Appletree Trust
Arthritis Research UK
The Arthur Ronald Dyer
  Charitable Trust
Asthma UK
The BACTA Charitable Trust
The Baker Charitable Trust
B-CH 1971 Charitable Trust
The Benfield Motors Charitable
  Trust
The Ruth Berkowitz Charitable
  Trust
The Bintaub Charitable Trust
The Herbert and Peter
  Blagrave Charitable Trust
The Tony Bramall Charitable
  Trust

John Bristow and Thomas Mason Trust
British Heart Foundation
The Charles Brotherton Trust
R S Brownless Charitable Trust
Buckingham Trust
The E F Bulmer Benevolent Fund
The BUPA Foundation
The Derek Butler Trust
P H G Cadbury Charitable Trust
Celtic Charity Fund
Champneys Charitable Foundation
The Chelsea Building Society Charitable Foundation
Child Growth Foundation
The Cleopatra Trust
The Consolidated Charities for the Infirm Merchant Taylors' Company
The John Cowan Foundation
Criffel Charitable Trust
The Violet and Milo Cripps Charitable Trust
Roald Dahl's Marvellous Children's Charity
The Denton Charitable Trust
Diabetes UK
The Dorus Trust
Dromintee Trust
The W E Dunn Trust
Eastern Counties Educational Trust Limited
The Sir John Eastwood Foundation
Gilbert Edgar Trust
The Wilfred and Elsie Elkes Charity Fund
The John Ellerman Foundation
The Emmandjay Charitable Trust
The Epigoni Trust
Epilepsy Research UK
The Patrick Evans Foundation
Esmée Fairbairn Foundation
The Family Rich Charities Trust
Samuel William Farmer Trust
The February Foundation
Dixie Rose Findlay Charitable Trust
Bud Flanagan Leukaemia Fund
The Rose Flatau Charitable Trust
Florence's Charitable Trust
The Follett Trust
The Forte Charitable Trust
The Jill Franklin Trust
The Hugh Fraser Foundation
The Fuserna Foundation
The Gatsby Charitable Foundation
Generations Charitable Trust
J Paul Getty Jr Charitable Trust

The Girdlers' Company Charitable Trust
The B and P Glasser Charitable Trust
The Gosling Foundation Limited
The J G Graves Charitable Trust
The Constance Green Foundation
The Wiles Greenworld Charitable Trust
Grimmitt Trust
The Bishop of Guildford's Foundation
The Hadley Trust
The Doris Louise Hailes Charitable Trust
Hampton Fuel Allotment Charity
The W A Handley Charitable Trust
The Harborne Parish Lands Charity
The Kenneth Hargreaves Charitable Trust
The Harris Family Charitable Trust
The Edith Lilian Harrison 2000 Foundation
The John Harrison Charitable Trust
The Peter Harrison Foundation
The N and P Hartley Memorial Trust
May Hearnshaw's Charity
The Heart of England Community Foundation
The Hedley Foundation
The Hemby Trust
The Christina Mary Hendrie Trust for Scottish and Canadian Charities
The High Sheriff's Police Trust for the County of West Midlands (Building Blocks)
R G Hills Charitable Trust
The Hintze Family Charitable Foundation
The Hospital of God at Greatham
The Clifford Howarth Charity Trust
HTA Sheba Foundation UK
The Hull and East Riding Charitable Trust
Human Relief Foundation
The Humanitarian Trust
Miss Agnes H Hunter's Trust
Huntingdon Freemen's Charity
The Iliffe Family Charitable Trust
Impetus Trust
The Charles Irving Charitable Trust

The Ruth and Lionel Jacobson Trust (Second Fund) No 2
The Elton John Aids Foundation
The Jones 1986 Charitable Trust
The Judith Trust
The Anton Jurgens Charitable Trust
The Kalou Foundation
The Ian Karten Charitable Trust
The Caron Keating Foundation
The Mary Kinross Charitable Trust
The Kohn Foundation
The Heinz, Anna and Carol Kroch Foundation
The Kirby Laing Foundation
The Beatrice Laing Trust
The Allen Lane Foundation
The LankellyChase Foundation
The R J Larg Family Charitable Trust
The Kathleen Laurence Trust
The Mason Le Page Charitable Trust
The Leigh Trust
Leukaemia and Lymphoma Research
The Joseph Levy Charitable Foundation
The Lewis Ward Trust
The Linbury Trust
Lincolnshire Community Foundation
The Linden Charitable Trust
Lloyds TSB Foundation for Northern Ireland
The Loftus Charitable Trust
John Lyon's Charity
The Mackintosh Foundation
Ian Mactaggart Trust
Magdalen Hospital Trust
The Marsh Christian Trust
The Charlotte Marshall Charitable Trust
The Maxwell Family Foundation
Brian Mercer Charitable Trust
The Mercers' Charitable Foundation
The Merchants' House of Glasgow
Mercury Phoenix Trust
The Zachary Merton and George Woofindin Convalescent Trust
The Tony Metherell Charitable Trust
Gerald Micklem Charitable Trust
The Miller Foundation
The Montague Thompson Coon Charitable Trust
The Monument Trust
John Moores Foundation

The Peter Morrison Charitable Foundation
The Mugdock Children's Trust
Peter John Murray Trust (PJM Trust)
The Northampton Queen's Institute Relief in Sickness Fund
The Northern Rock Foundation
The Northwood Charitable Trust
The Owen Family Trust
The Panacea Society
The Park Charitable Trust
The Constance Paterson Charitable Trust
Paycare Charity Trust (formerly known as Patients' Aid Association Hospital and Medical Charities Trust)
The Pedmore Sporting Club Trust Fund
The Pilgrim Trust
G S Plaut Charitable Trust Limited
The Pollywally Charitable Trust
The Mary Potter Convent Hospital Trust
Sir John Priestman Charity Trust
The Provincial Grand Charity of the Province of Derbyshire
Mr and Mrs J A Pye's Charitable Settlement
Richard Radcliffe Charitable Trust
The Ravensdale Trust
Relief Fund for Romania Limited
Riverside Charitable Trust Limited
Thomas Roberts Trust
The Robertson Trust
The Christopher Rowbotham Charitable Trust
The Rowlands Trust
The Andrew Salvesen Charitable Trust
The Hon. M J Samuel Charitable Trust
The Seneca Trust
The Snowball Trust
The Sovereign Health Care Charitable Trust
Split Infinitive Trust
St Francis's Leprosy Guild
St James's Place Foundation
Swan Mountain Trust
The Talbot Trusts
The Connie and Albert Taylor Charitable Trust
The Thornton Trust
The True Colours Trust
The James Tudor Foundation
John and Lucille van Geest Foundation

The Vintners' Company Charitable Foundation
The Weinstein Foundation
The Lionel Wigram Memorial Trust
The Will Charitable Trust
Woodlands Trust
The Woodward Charitable Trust
ME Woolfe Charitable Trust
The Xerox (UK) Trust

■ People with cardiovascular disorders

British Heart Foundation
The John Cowan Foundation
The Girdlers' Company Charitable Trust
The Kathleen Laurence Trust
Gerald Micklem Charitable Trust
The Park Charitable Trust
John and Lucille van Geest Foundation

■ People with glandular and endocrine disorders

Child Growth Foundation
The Cleopatra Trust
Diabetes UK
The Dorus Trust
The Epigoni Trust
The Girdlers' Company Charitable Trust

■ People with immune system disorders

The Derek Butler Trust
The Elton John Aids Foundation
Lloyds TSB Foundation for Northern Ireland
The Mackintosh Foundation
Magdalen Hospital Trust
Mercury Phoenix Trust
Gerald Micklem Charitable Trust
The Monument Trust
John Moores Foundation
The True Colours Trust

■ People with a mental impairment

The A B Charitable Trust
The Sylvia Adams Charitable Trust

The Chelsea Building Society Charitable Foundation
The Dorus Trust
Eastern Counties Educational Trust Limited
The Sir John Eastwood Foundation
The John Ellerman Foundation
The Hugh Fraser Foundation
The Fuserna Foundation
The Gatsby Charitable Foundation
J Paul Getty Jr Charitable Trust
The Girdlers' Company Charitable Trust
The Hadley Trust
The Peter Harrison Foundation
Miss Agnes H Hunter's Trust
The Iliffe Family Charitable Trust
The Charles Irving Charitable Trust
The Judith Trust
The Ian Karten Charitable Trust
The Mary Kinross Charitable Trust
The Kohn Foundation
The Kirby Laing Foundation
The Beatrice Laing Trust
The Allen Lane Foundation
The LankellyChase Foundation
John Lyon's Charity
The Mercers' Charitable Foundation
The Northern Rock Foundation
The Pilgrim Trust
Relief Fund for Romania Limited
The Hon. M J Samuel Charitable Trust
Swan Mountain Trust
The Will Charitable Trust
Woodlands Trust

■ People with musculoskeletal disorders

Arthritis Research UK
The John Cowan Foundation
Miss Agnes H Hunter's Trust
The Kathleen Laurence Trust

■ People with neurological disorders

The John Cowan Foundation
Roald Dahl's Marvellous Children's Charity
The Wilfred and Elsie Elkes Charity Fund
Epilepsy Research UK

Dixie Rose Findlay Charitable Trust
The Forte Charitable Trust
The Girdlers' Company Charitable Trust
The John Harrison Charitable Trust
The Hospital of God at Greatham
Gerald Micklem Charitable Trust
The Owen Family Trust

■ People with oncological disorders

P H G Cadbury Charitable Trust
The Cleopatra Trust
The John Cowan Foundation
The Denton Charitable Trust
The Dorus Trust
The Patrick Evans Foundation
Bud Flanagan Leukaemia Fund
The Girdlers' Company Charitable Trust
The Christina Mary Hendrie Trust for Scottish and Canadian Charities
Miss Agnes H Hunter's Trust
The Caron Keating Foundation
The R J Larg Family Charitable Trust
Leukaemia and Lymphoma Research
Brian Mercer Charitable Trust
The Tony Metherell Charitable Trust
The Owen Family Trust
The Park Charitable Trust
John and Lucille van Geest Foundation
The Will Charitable Trust

■ People with respiratory disorders

The Girdlers' Company Charitable Trust
Miss Agnes H Hunter's Trust
Relief Fund for Romania Limited
John and Lucille van Geest Foundation

■ People with skin disorders

The Lewis Ward Trust
St Francis's Leprosy Guild

■ People who are substance misusers

Celtic Charity Fund
The Cleopatra Trust
The Dorus Trust
Gilbert Edgar Trust
The Epigoni Trust
Esmée Fairbairn Foundation
J Paul Getty Jr Charitable Trust
The High Sheriff's Police Trust for the County of West Midlands (Building Blocks)
The Leigh Trust
The Linbury Trust
John Lyon's Charity
The Marsh Christian Trust
The Mercers' Charitable Foundation
John Moores Foundation
The Northern Rock Foundation
The Pilgrim Trust
The Robertson Trust
The Vintners' Company Charitable Foundation
Woodlands Trust
The Woodward Charitable Trust

■ Palliative care

P H G Cadbury Charitable Trust
The John Cowan Foundation
The Emmandjay Charitable Trust
The Girdlers' Company Charitable Trust
The Constance Green Foundation
The Peter Harrison Foundation
The N and P Hartley Memorial Trust
The Hedley Foundation
The Caron Keating Foundation
The Marsh Christian Trust
The Zachary Merton and George Woofindin Convalescent Trust
The Mugdock Children's Trust
Richard Radcliffe Charitable Trust
St James's Place Foundation
The Connie and Albert Taylor Charitable Trust
The True Colours Trust
John and Lucille van Geest Foundation
The Xerox (UK) Trust

Nationality

■ Asian

Matliwala Family Charitable Trust
The W Wing Yip and Brothers Foundation

■ Eastern European

Armenian General Benevolent Union London Trust
The Armenian Relief Society of Great Britain Trust
Golubovich Foundation
The Manoukian Charitable Foundation
Saint Sarkis Charity Trust

■ Southern European

Calouste Gulbenkian Foundation
The Lyras Family Charitable Trust

■ Irish

The Ireland Fund of Great Britain
The Irish Youth Foundation (UK) Ltd (incorporating The Lawlor Foundation)

Social or economic circumstances

The 1970 Trust
The 1989 Willan Charitable Trust
The 29th May 1961 Charitable Trust
The A B Charitable Trust
The ACT Foundation
The Company of Actuaries' Charitable Trust Fund
The Sylvia Adams Charitable Trust
The Green and Lilian F M Ainsworth and Family Benevolent Fund
The Ajahma Charitable Trust
The Alchemy Foundation
The Aldgate Freedom Foundation
The Alliance Family Foundation
The Pat Allsop Charitable Trust
The Appletree Trust
The Archer Trust
The Ashden Trust
The Ashendene Trust
AstonMansfield Charitable Trust

Awards for All (see also the
    Big Lottery Fund)
The BACTA Charitable Trust
The Scott Bader
    Commonwealth Ltd
The George Balint Charitable
    Trust
The Band Trust
The Jack and Ada Beattie
    Foundation
The Bedford Charity (The
    Harpur Trust)
The Beit Trust
The Bellahouston Bequest
    Fund
The Benfield Motors Charitable
    Trust
Bergqvist Charitable Trust
The Big Lottery Fund (see also
    Awards for All)
Percy Bilton Charity
The Bintaub Charitable Trust
The Oliver Borthwick Memorial
    Trust
P G and N J Boulton Trust
The Breadsticks Foundation
John Bristow and Thomas
    Mason Trust
Britannia Foundation
R S Brownless Charitable
    Trust
Buckingham Trust
The E F Bulmer Benevolent
    Fund
Consolidated Charity of Burton
    upon Trent
Butchers' Company General
    Charities
The Noel Buxton Trust
Ann Byrne Charitable Trust
The C Charitable Trust
Henry T and Lucy B Cadbury
    Charitable Trust
The William A Cadbury
    Charitable Trust
The Barrow Cadbury Trust and
    the Barrow Cadbury Fund
CAFOD (Catholic Agency for
    Overseas Development)
The Calpe Trust
Calypso Browning Trust
The Campden Charities
    Trustee
The Charities Advisory Trust
The Chelsea Building Society
    Charitable Foundation
The Chrimes Family Charitable
    Trust
Christadelphian Samaritan
    Fund
Christian Aid
Chrysalis Trust
The Church Urban Fund
CLA Charitable Trust
The Cleopatra Trust
The Clore Duffield Foundation

Closehelm Ltd
Richard Cloudesley's Charity
The Coalfields Regeneration
    Trust
The R and S Cohen
    Foundation
The Coltstaple Trust
Colyer-Fergusson Charitable
    Trust
Comic Relief
The Consolidated Charities for
    the Infirm Merchant
    Taylors' Company
The Cotton Trust
Michael Crawford Children's
    Charity
The Violet and Milo Cripps
    Charitable Trust
Cumbria Community
    Foundation
The Dawe Charitable Trust
The Dorfred Charitable Trust
The Dorus Trust
Double 'O' Charity Ltd
The Doughty Charity Trust
The Drapers' Charitable Fund
Dromintee Trust
The Duis Charitable Trust
The P B Dumbell Charitable
    Trust
The W E Dunn Trust
Eastern Counties Educational
    Trust Limited
The EBM Charitable Trust
Gilbert Edgar Trust
Dr Edwards Bishop King's
    Fulham Endowment Fund
The Wilfred and Elsie Elkes
    Charity Fund
The John Ellerman Foundation
The Ellinson Foundation Ltd
The Edith Maud Ellis 1985
    Charitable Trust
The Ellis Campbell Foundation
The Emmandjay Charitable
    Trust
The Enkalon Foundation
The Epigoni Trust
The Ericson Trust
Euro Charity Trust
The Eveson Charitable Trust
The Execution Charitable Trust
Esmée Fairbairn Foundation
Faisaltex Charitable Trust
The George Fentham
    Birmingham Charity
The Doris Field Charitable
    Trust
The Fifty Fund
Fisherbeck Charitable Trust
The Fishmongers' Company's
    Charitable Trust
The Rose Flatau Charitable
    Trust
The Roy Fletcher Charitable
    Trust

The Follett Trust
The Anna Rosa Forster
    Charitable Trust
Sydney E Franklin Deceased's
    New Second Charity
The Jill Franklin Trust
The Hugh Fraser Foundation
The Freemasons' Grand
    Charity
Friends Provident Charitable
    Foundation
Maurice Fry Charitable Trust
The G D Charitable Trust
The Angela Gallagher Memorial
    Fund
The Gannochy Trust
The Gatsby Charitable
    Foundation
The Robert Gavron Charitable
    Trust
Jacqueline and Michael Gee
    Charitable Trust
Generations Charitable Trust
J Paul Getty Jr Charitable Trust
The Girdlers' Company
    Charitable Trust
Global Care
Global Charities (formerly
    GCap Charities)
The Everard and Mina
    Goodman Charitable
    Foundation
The J G Graves Charitable
    Trust
The Constance Green
    Foundation
The Philip Green Memorial
    Trust
Mrs H R Greene Charitable
    Settlement
The Wiles Greenworld
    Charitable Trust
Greggs Foundation (formerly
    Greggs Trust)
The Grocers' Charity
The David and Marie Grumitt
    Foundation
The Bishop of Guildford's
    Foundation
H C D Memorial Fund
The Hackney Parochial
    Charities
The Hadley Trust
The Alfred Haines Charitable
    Trust
The Hale Trust
Paul Hamlyn Foundation
Hampton Fuel Allotment
    Charity
The Kathleen Hannay
    Memorial Charity
The Haramead Trust
The Harbour Foundation
William Harding's Charity
The Kenneth Hargreaves
    Charitable Trust

The Harrison and Potter Trust
The Peter Harrison Foundation
The Charles Hayward
  Foundation
May Hearnshaw's Charity
The Heart of England
  Community Foundation
Help the Homeless
The Hemby Trust
The Henley Educational Charity
The High Sheriff's Police Trust
  for the County of West
  Midlands (Building Blocks)
Highcroft Charitable Trust
The Hilden Charitable Fund
R G Hills Charitable Trust
Hobson Charity Limited
The Holbeck Charitable Trust
The Horne Foundation
The Horne Trust
The Hornsey Parochial
  Charities
The Hospital of God at
  Greatham
The Clifford Howarth Charity
  Trust
HTA Sheba Foundation UK
Human Relief Foundation
Humanitarian and Charitable
  One Trust (HACOT)
The Humanitarian Trust
The Michael and Shirley Hunt
  Charitable Trust
The Hunter Foundation
Miss Agnes H Hunter's Trust
The Hyde Charitable Trust –
  Youth Plus
Impetus Trust
The Indigo Trust
The Ireland Fund of Great
  Britain
The Irish Youth Foundation
  (UK) Ltd (incorporating The
  Lawlor Foundation)
The Charles Irving Charitable
  Trust
The J J Charitable Trust
The Jephcott Charitable Trust
The Joffe Charitable Trust
The Johnson Foundation
The Jones 1986 Charitable
  Trust
The Lady Eileen Joseph
  Foundation
Jusaca Charitable Trust
The Kalou Foundation
The Kaufman Charitable Trust
The King's Fund
The Mary Kinross Charitable
  Trust
The Kohn Foundation
The KPMG Foundation
The Heinz, Anna and Carol
  Kroch Foundation
The Kyte Charitable Trust
John Laing Charitable Trust

Maurice and Hilda Laing
  Charitable Trust
The Martin Laing Foundation
The Beatrice Laing Trust
LandAid Charitable Trust
The Allen Lane Foundation
The LankellyChase Foundation
Mrs F B Laurence Charitable
  Trust
The Law Society Charity
The Leathersellers' Company
  Charitable Fund
The William Leech Charity
The Leigh Trust
The Leonard Trust
The Mark Leonard Trust
The Joseph Levy Charitable
  Foundation
John Lewis Partnership
  General Community Fund
The Limbourne Trust
The Linbury Trust
Lincolnshire Community
  Foundation
The Enid Linder Foundation
The Andrew and Mary
  Elizabeth Little Charitable
  Trust
The Elaine and Angus Lloyd
  Charitable Trust
Lloyds TSB Foundation for
  England and Wales
Lloyds TSB Foundation for
  Northern Ireland
Localtrent Ltd
The Loftus Charitable Trust
The Trust for London (formerly
  the City Parochial
  Foundation)
The Loseley and Guildway
  Charitable Trust
The Lotus Foundation
The C L Loyd Charitable Trust
LSA Charitable Trust
The Marie Helen Luen
  Charitable Trust
Paul Lunn-Rockliffe Charitable
  Trust
John Lyon's Charity
The Mackintosh Foundation
Ian Mactaggart Trust
Magdalen Hospital Trust
The Mahavir Trust (also known
  as the K S Mehta
  Charitable Trust)
Man Group plc Charitable
  Trust
R W Mann Trust
The Michael Marsh Charitable
  Trust
The Marsh Christian Trust
The Charlotte Marshall
  Charitable Trust
The Mathew Trust
Evelyn May Trust
The McKenna Charitable Trust

The Mears Foundation
The Mercers' Charitable
  Foundation
The Merchant Taylors'
  Company Charities Fund
The Merchant Venturers'
  Charity
Mickleham Charitable Trust
Gerald Micklem Charitable
  Trust
Miles Trust for the Putney and
  Roehampton Community
The Millfield House Foundation
Milton Keynes Community
  Foundation
The Peter Minet Trust
Minge's Gift and the Pooled
  Trusts
Monmouthshire County Council
  Welsh Church Act Fund
The Colin Montgomerie
  Charitable Foundation
The Monument Trust
John Moores Foundation
The Morel Charitable Trust
The Moss Charitable Trust
The Robert and Margaret
  Moss Charitable Trust
The Edith Murphy Foundation
Murphy-Neumann Charity
  Company Limited
Peter John Murray Trust (PJM
  Trust)
Muslim Hands
The Kitty and Daniel Nabarro
  Charitable Trust
The Nationwide Foundation
Network for Social Change
Nominet Charitable Foundation
The Norda Trust
The North British Hotel Trust
North West London Community
  Foundation
The Northcott Devon
  Foundation
The Northern Rock Foundation
The Northmoor Trust
The Norton Foundation
Novi Most International
The Nuffield Foundation
The Odin Charitable Trust
Ogilvie Charities Deed No.2
  (including the Charity of
  Mary Catherine Ford Smith)
Oglesby Charitable Trust
Old Possum's Practical Trust
The Olga Charitable Trust
Onaway Trust
Oxfam (GB)
The Palmer Foundation
The Parthenon Trust
Paycare Charity Trust (formerly
  known as Patients' Aid
  Association Hospital and
  Medical Charities Trust)
The Harry Payne Trust

Pendragon Charitable Trust
The Persula Foundation
The Pilgrim Trust
The Elise Pilkington Charitable
   Trust
The Pilkington Charities Fund
The Pollywally Charitable Trust
The Portishead Nautical Trust
The W L Pratt Charitable Trust
Sir John Priestman Charity
   Trust
The Foundation of Prince
   William and Prince Harry
The Puebla Charitable Trust
The Puri Foundation
Mr and Mrs J A Pye's
   Charitable Settlement
The Queen Anne's Gate
   Foundation
Quothquan Trust
The Ravensdale Trust
The Rayne Foundation
The Rayne Trust
The Sir James Reckitt Charity
The Eva Reckitt Trust Fund
The Reed Foundation
Relief Fund for Romania
   Limited
The Rhondda Cynon Taff
   Welsh Church Acts Fund
The Clive Richards Charity
The Richmond Parish Lands
   Charity
The River Farm Foundation
Riverside Charitable Trust
   Limited
Thomas Roberts Trust
The Robertson Trust
Mrs L D Rope Third Charitable
   Settlement
The Rowland Family
   Foundation
The Rowlands Trust
The Joseph Rowntree
   Charitable Trust
Royal Docks Trust (London)
Ryklow Charitable Trust 1992
   (also known as A B
   Williamson Charitable Trust)
Erach and Roshan Sadri
   Foundation
The Alan and Babette
   Sainsbury Charitable Fund
Saint Sarkis Charity Trust
Salters' Charitable Foundation
The Sandra Charitable Trust
Santander UK Foundation
   Limited
Scottish Coal Industry Special
   Welfare Fund
The Seedfield Trust
The Severn Trent Water
   Charitable Trust Fund
SFIA Educational Trust Limited
The Shanley Charitable Trust
The Shekinah Legacy

The Mrs Smith and Mount
   Trust
The Sobell Foundation
The E C Sosnow Charitable
   Trust
R H Southern Trust
The Sovereign Health Care
   Charitable Trust
Spears-Stutz Charitable Trust
The Spero Foundation
Split Infinitive Trust
The Stone Family Foundation
Summary Limited
The Summerfield Charitable
   Trust
Sutton Coldfield Municipal
   Charities
Swan Mountain Trust
Tegham Limited
The Thornton Trust
The Tinsley Foundation
The Tolkien Trust
The Tresillian Trust
Trust Sixty Three
UKI Charitable Foundation
The United Society for the
   Propagation of the Gospel
Uxbridge United Welfare Trust
The Scurrah Wainwright Charity
The Wakefield and Tetley Trust
Wakeham Trust
The Wates Foundation
John Watson's Trust
The Weavers' Company
   Benevolent Fund
The Barbara Whatmore
   Charitable Trust
White Stuff Foundation
The Community Foundation for
   Wiltshire and Swindon
The Michael and Anna Wix
   Charitable Trust
The Wood Family Trust
Woodlands Trust
Woodroffe Benton Foundation
The Woodward Charitable
   Trust
The Yapp Charitable Trust
Zurich Community Trust (UK)
   Limited

■ People with an alternative lifestyle (inc. travellers)

The Allen Lane Foundation
The Odin Charitable Trust
The Woodward Charitable
   Trust

■ People who are educationally disadvantaged

The Big Lottery Fund (see also
   Awards for All)
Eastern Counties Educational
   Trust Limited
The Ellis Campbell Foundation
The Girdlers' Company
   Charitable Trust
Global Care
H C D Memorial Fund
The Hadley Trust
Human Relief Foundation
Miss Agnes H Hunter's Trust
The KPMG Foundation
John Lyon's Charity
The Michael Marsh Charitable
   Trust
White Stuff Foundation

■ People who are homeless

The 29th May 1961 Charitable
   Trust
The A B Charitable Trust
The Sylvia Adams Charitable
   Trust
The Aldgate Freedom
   Foundation
The Ashden Trust
The Bedford Charity (The
   Harpur Trust)
The Beit Trust
The Oliver Borthwick Memorial
   Trust
Britannia Foundation
Henry T and Lucy B Cadbury
   Charitable Trust
Calypso Browning Trust
The Charities Advisory Trust
The Chelsea Building Society
   Charitable Foundation
Christian Aid
The Cleopatra Trust
The Coltstaple Trust
The Dawe Charitable Trust
The Dorus Trust
The Drapers' Charitable Fund
Gilbert Edgar Trust
The Wilfred and Elsie Elkes
   Charity Fund
The John Ellerman Foundation
The Ellinson Foundation Ltd
The Emmandjay Charitable
   Trust
The Epigoni Trust
The Ericson Trust
The Eveson Charitable Trust
Esmée Fairbairn Foundation
Fisherbeck Charitable Trust
The Fishmongers' Company's
   Charitable Trust
The Hugh Fraser Foundation

The Freemasons' Grand
Charity
The G D Charitable Trust
J Paul Getty Jr Charitable Trust
The Girdlers' Company
Charitable Trust
Global Care
The Constance Green
Foundation
Greggs Foundation (formerly
Greggs Trust)
The David and Marie Grumitt
Foundation
The Bishop of Guildford's
Foundation
The Alfred Haines Charitable
Trust
Hampton Fuel Allotment
Charity
The Harbour Foundation
The Kenneth Hargreaves
Charitable Trust
The Harrison and Potter Trust
The Peter Harrison Foundation
Help the Homeless
The Hemby Trust
The Hilden Charitable Fund
The Horne Foundation
The Horne Trust
The Hospital of God at
Greatham
Miss Agnes H Hunter's Trust
The Hyde Charitable Trust –
Youth Plus
The Irish Youth Foundation
(UK) Ltd (incorporating The
Lawlor Foundation)
The Charles Irving Charitable
Trust
The King's Fund
John Laing Charitable Trust
Maurice and Hilda Laing
Charitable Trust
The Beatrice Laing Trust
LandAid Charitable Trust
The Joseph Levy Charitable
Foundation
The Marie Helen Luen
Charitable Trust
Paul Lunn-Rockliffe Charitable
Trust
John Lyon's Charity
The Mackintosh Foundation
The Marsh Christian Trust
Miles Trust for the Putney and
Roehampton Community
The Peter Minet Trust
John Moores Foundation
The Kitty and Daniel Nabarro
Charitable Trust
Network for Social Change
The Odin Charitable Trust
The Persula Foundation
The Pilgrim Trust
The Portishead Nautical Trust

Relief Fund for Romania
Limited
The Robertson Trust
Mrs L D Rope Third Charitable
Settlement
Erach and Roshan Sadri
Foundation
The Mrs Smith and Mount
Trust
The Sobell Foundation
The Summerfield Charitable
Trust
Woodlands Trust
The Woodward Charitable
Trust

....

■ People who are housebound

Paycare Charity Trust (formerly
known as Patients' Aid
Association Hospital and
Medical Charities Trust)
The Elise Pilkington Charitable
Trust

....

■ People who are disadvantaged by location

Mrs H R Greene Charitable
Settlement
Relief Fund for Romania
Limited
White Stuff Foundation

....

■ Migrants

The 29th May 1961 Charitable
Trust
The Barrow Cadbury Trust and
the Barrow Cadbury Fund

....

■ Offenders

The 29th May 1961 Charitable
Trust
The A B Charitable Trust
The Alchemy Foundation
The Ashendene Trust
The Big Lottery Fund (see also
Awards for All)
The Noel Buxton Trust
The William A Cadbury
Charitable Trust
The Barrow Cadbury Trust and
the Barrow Cadbury Fund
The Violet and Milo Cripps
Charitable Trust
The Drapers' Charitable Fund
The Emmandjay Charitable
Trust
Esmée Fairbairn Foundation

The Gatsby Charitable
Foundation
The Robert Gavron Charitable
Trust
J Paul Getty Jr Charitable Trust
The Girdlers' Company
Charitable Trust
Mrs H R Greene Charitable
Settlement
Greggs Foundation (formerly
Greggs Trust)
H C D Memorial Fund
The Hadley Trust
Paul Hamlyn Foundation
The Charles Hayward
Foundation
The Hemby Trust
The High Sheriff's Police Trust
for the County of West
Midlands (Building Blocks)
The Hilden Charitable Fund
The Michael and Shirley Hunt
Charitable Trust
The Indigo Trust
The J J Charitable Trust
The Mary Kinross Charitable
Trust
The KPMG Foundation
The Allen Lane Foundation
The LankellyChase Foundation
The Mark Leonard Trust
The Linbury Trust
John Lyon's Charity
The Mercers' Charitable
Foundation
The Monument Trust
The Norda Trust
The Nuffield Foundation
The Odin Charitable Trust
The Pilgrim Trust
The Portishead Nautical Trust
Mr and Mrs J A Pye's
Charitable Settlement
The Rhondda Cynon Taff
Welsh Church Acts Fund
Saint Sarkis Charity Trust
Swan Mountain Trust
The Weavers' Company
Benevolent Fund
Woodlands Trust

....

■ Ex-offenders

The 29th May 1961 Charitable
Trust
The Ashendene Trust
Esmée Fairbairn Foundation
J Paul Getty Jr Charitable Trust
The Girdlers' Company
Charitable Trust
Greggs Foundation (formerly
Greggs Trust)
Paul Hamlyn Foundation
The Hemby Trust
The Michael and Shirley Hunt
Charitable Trust

The J J Charitable Trust
The Allen Lane Foundation
The Linbury Trust
John Lyon's Charity
The Mercers' Charitable
  Foundation
The Norda Trust
The Odin Charitable Trust
Mr and Mrs J A Pye's
  Charitable Settlement
The Weavers' Company
  Benevolent Fund

■ People on probation

The Emmandjay Charitable
  Trust

■ Prisoners and their families

The A B Charitable Trust
The Noel Buxton Trust
The Michael and Shirley Hunt
  Charitable Trust
The Norda Trust
The Odin Charitable Trust
The Weavers' Company
  Benevolent Fund

■ Young people at risk of offending

The Big Lottery Fund (see also
  Awards for All)
The Gatsby Charitable
  Foundation
J Paul Getty Jr Charitable Trust
Mrs H R Greene Charitable
  Settlement
Paul Hamlyn Foundation
The Hemby Trust
The High Sheriff's Police Trust
  for the County of West
  Midlands (Building Blocks)
The J J Charitable Trust
The Mary Kinross Charitable
  Trust
The KPMG Foundation
The Mark Leonard Trust
The Nuffield Foundation
The Portishead Nautical Trust
The Rhondda Cynon Taff
  Welsh Church Acts Fund
The Weavers' Company
  Benevolent Fund
Woodlands Trust

■ People who are poor, on low incomes

The 1989 Willan Charitable
  Trust
The 29th May 1961 Charitable
  Trust
The Sylvia Adams Charitable
  Trust
The Ajahma Charitable Trust
The Aldgate Freedom
  Foundation
The Alliance Family Foundation
The Pat Allsop Charitable Trust
The Appletree Trust
The Archer Trust
AstonMansfield Charitable
  Trust
The George Balint Charitable
  Trust
The Bellahouston Bequest
  Fund
The Benfield Motors Charitable
  Trust
P G and N J Boulton Trust
John Bristow and Thomas
  Mason Trust
Buckingham Trust
The E F Bulmer Benevolent
  Fund
Butchers' Company General
  Charities
CAFOD (Catholic Agency for
  Overseas Development)
The Chrimes Family Charitable
  Trust
Christian Aid
The Church Urban Fund
CLA Charitable Trust
Closehelm Ltd
The R and S Cohen
  Foundation
Michael Crawford Children's
  Charity
Double 'O' Charity Ltd
The Doughty Charity Trust
The Drapers' Charitable Fund
Eastern Counties Educational
  Trust Limited
The EBM Charitable Trust
Euro Charity Trust
The Eveson Charitable Trust
The George Fentham
  Birmingham Charity
The Fifty Fund
The Fishmongers' Company's
  Charitable Trust
Sydney E Franklin Deceased's
  New Second Charity
The Hugh Fraser Foundation
Maurice Fry Charitable Trust
The Angela Gallagher Memorial
  Fund
The Girdlers' Company
  Charitable Trust

Global Care
The Everard and Mina
  Goodman Charitable
  Foundation
The J G Graves Charitable
  Trust
Mrs H R Greene Charitable
  Settlement
Greggs Foundation (formerly
  Greggs Trust)
The Grocers' Charity
The Bishop of Guildford's
  Foundation
H C D Memorial Fund
The Hadley Trust
The Hale Trust
Hampton Fuel Allotment
  Charity
The Haramead Trust
May Hearnshaw's Charity
The Hemby Trust
The Henley Educational Charity
Highcroft Charitable Trust
R G Hills Charitable Trust
The Hornsey Parochial
  Charities
The Hospital of God at
  Greatham
Human Relief Foundation
The Hunter Foundation
The Hyde Charitable Trust –
  Youth Plus
The Ireland Fund of Great
  Britain
The Jephcott Charitable Trust
The Johnson Foundation
The Jones 1986 Charitable
  Trust
The Lady Eileen Joseph
  Foundation
The Kohn Foundation
The Heinz, Anna and Carol
  Kroch Foundation
Maurice and Hilda Laing
  Charitable Trust
The Beatrice Laing Trust
LandAid Charitable Trust
The Leathersellers' Company
  Charitable Fund
John Lewis Partnership
  General Community Fund
The Enid Linder Foundation
The Andrew and Mary
  Elizabeth Little Charitable
  Trust
Localtrent Ltd
LSA Charitable Trust
The Marie Helen Luen
  Charitable Trust
Paul Lunn-Rockliffe Charitable
  Trust
Ian Mactaggart Trust
Magdalen Hospital Trust
The Mahavir Trust (also known
  as the K S Mehta
  Charitable Trust)

The Michael Marsh Charitable
Trust
The McKenna Charitable Trust
Gerald Micklem Charitable
Trust
Miles Trust for the Putney and
Roehampton Community
Monmouthshire County Council
Welsh Church Act Fund
The Colin Montgomerie
Charitable Foundation
The Morel Charitable Trust
The Moss Charitable Trust
The Robert and Margaret
Moss Charitable Trust
The Edith Murphy Foundation
Muslim Hands
The Kitty and Daniel Nabarro
Charitable Trust
The Northmoor Trust
The Odin Charitable Trust
The Olga Charitable Trust
Oxfam (GB)
The Elise Pilkington Charitable
Trust
The Pollywally Charitable Trust
The Portishead Nautical Trust
Sir John Priestman Charity
Trust
The Puebla Charitable Trust
The Puri Foundation
Mr and Mrs J A Pye's
Charitable Settlement
Quothquan Trust
The Rhondda Cynon Taff
Welsh Church Acts Fund
The Clive Richards Charity
The Richmond Parish Lands
Charity
Riverside Charitable Trust
Limited
Mrs L D Rope Third Charitable
Settlement
The Rowland Family
Foundation
The Rowlands Trust
The Joseph Rowntree
Charitable Trust
Royal Docks Trust (London)
The Sandra Charitable Trust
Scottish Coal Industry Special
Welfare Fund
The Seedfield Trust
The Severn Trent Water
Charitable Trust Fund
The Shanley Charitable Trust
The Shekinah Legacy
R H Southern Trust
Spears-Stutz Charitable Trust
The Summerfield Charitable
Trust
Tegham Limited
The Thornton Trust
The Tinsley Foundation
UKI Charitable Foundation
Uxbridge United Welfare Trust

The Barbara Whatmore
Charitable Trust
White Stuff Foundation

....

■ **Prostitutes, sex
workers**

The LankellyChase Foundation

....

■ **Refugees and
asylum seekers**

The 29th May 1961 Charitable
Trust
The A B Charitable Trust
The Barrow Cadbury Trust and
the Barrow Cadbury Fund
The Charities Advisory Trust
The Edith Maud Ellis 1985
Charitable Trust
The Ericson Trust
Maurice Fry Charitable Trust
H C D Memorial Fund
The Harbour Foundation
The Hilden Charitable Fund
The King's Fund
The KPMG Foundation
The Allen Lane Foundation
The LankellyChase Foundation
The Leigh Trust
The Mackintosh Foundation
John Moores Foundation
Network for Social Change
The Norda Trust
The Odin Charitable Trust
The Pilgrim Trust
The Pilkington Charities Fund
Mr and Mrs J A Pye's
Charitable Settlement
The Reed Foundation
The Alan and Babette
Sainsbury Charitable Fund
The Woodward Charitable
Trust

....

■ **Victims, oppressed
people**

The 1970 Trust
The Alchemy Foundation
Bergqvist Charitable Trust
The Barrow Cadbury Trust and
the Barrow Cadbury Fund
CAFOD (Catholic Agency for
Overseas Development)
The Charities Advisory Trust
Christadelphian Samaritan
Fund
Christian Aid
The Coltstaple Trust
The Dorfred Charitable Trust
The Follett Trust
The Anna Rosa Forster
Charitable Trust

Sydney E Franklin Deceased's
New Second Charity
The Jill Franklin Trust
The Freemasons' Grand
Charity
Maurice Fry Charitable Trust
The Angela Gallagher Memorial
Fund
J Paul Getty Jr Charitable Trust
The Girdlers' Company
Charitable Trust
Global Care
Greggs Foundation (formerly
Greggs Trust)
The Charles Hayward
Foundation
The Heart of England
Community Foundation
The Hemby Trust
The Horne Trust
The Hospital of God at
Greatham
Human Relief Foundation
The Hyde Charitable Trust –
Youth Plus
The Charles Irving Charitable
Trust
The Heinz, Anna and Carol
Kroch Foundation
The Allen Lane Foundation
The LankellyChase Foundation
The Law Society Charity
The Leathersellers' Company
Charitable Fund
The William Leech Charity
The Leigh Trust
The Leonard Trust
The Joseph Levy Charitable
Foundation
The Loseley and Guildway
Charitable Trust
The Lotus Foundation
Evelyn May Trust
Monmouthshire County Council
Welsh Church Act Fund
The Morel Charitable Trust
Muslim Hands
The Nationwide Foundation
Network for Social Change
Novi Most International
Oxfam (GB)
The Parthenon Trust
The Pilkington Charities Fund
The Portishead Nautical Trust
The W L Pratt Charitable Trust
Mr and Mrs J A Pye's
Charitable Settlement
The Sir James Reckitt Charity
The Eva Reckitt Trust Fund
The Joseph Rowntree
Charitable Trust
Ryklow Charitable Trust 1992
(also known as A B
Williamson Charitable Trust)
The Tinsley Foundation
The Tresillian Trust

Trust Sixty Three
Woodroffe Benton Foundation
The Woodward Charitable
Trust

■ People who have suffered abuse, violence or torture

The Angela Gallagher Memorial
Fund
J Paul Getty Jr Charitable Trust
The Girdlers' Company
Charitable Trust
Global Care
Greggs Foundation (formerly
Greggs Trust)
The Charles Hayward
Foundation
The Hemby Trust
The Hospital of God at
Greatham
The Hyde Charitable Trust –
Youth Plus
The Charles Irving Charitable
Trust
The Heinz, Anna and Carol
Kroch Foundation
The Allen Lane Foundation
The LankellyChase Foundation
The Lotus Foundation
The Nationwide Foundation
The Portishead Nautical Trust
Mr and Mrs J A Pye's
Charitable Settlement
Ryklow Charitable Trust 1992
(also known as A B
Williamson Charitable Trust)
The Woodward Charitable
Trust

■ Victims of crime

The Girdlers' Company
Charitable Trust
The Hemby Trust
The Charles Irving Charitable
Trust
The Heinz, Anna and Carol
Kroch Foundation
Ryklow Charitable Trust 1992
(also known as A B
Williamson Charitable Trust)

■ Victims of disasters

Bergqvist Charitable Trust
Christadelphian Samaritan
Fund
Christian Aid
The Dorfred Charitable Trust
The Follett Trust
Sydney E Franklin Deceased's
New Second Charity

The Freemasons' Grand
Charity
Maurice Fry Charitable Trust
The Angela Gallagher Memorial
Fund
Human Relief Foundation
The Leathersellers' Company
Charitable Fund
The William Leech Charity
The Leonard Trust
The Loseley and Guildway
Charitable Trust
Evelyn May Trust
Monmouthshire County Council
Welsh Church Act Fund
Muslim Hands
Oxfam (GB)
The Parthenon Trust
The Pilkington Charities Fund
The W L Pratt Charitable Trust
The Sir James Reckitt Charity
Woodroffe Benton Foundation

■ People suffering from famine

The Alchemy Foundation
Bergqvist Charitable Trust
CAFOD (Catholic Agency for
Overseas Development)
Christadelphian Samaritan
Fund
The Coltstaple Trust
The Dorfred Charitable Trust
The Anna Rosa Forster
Charitable Trust
Sydney E Franklin Deceased's
New Second Charity
Maurice Fry Charitable Trust
The Angela Gallagher Memorial
Fund
Global Care
The Leonard Trust
The Joseph Levy Charitable
Foundation
The Morel Charitable Trust
Oxfam (GB)
The Parthenon Trust
Ryklow Charitable Trust 1992
(also known as A B
Williamson Charitable Trust)
Trust Sixty Three

■ People suffering injustice

The Charities Advisory Trust
Sydney E Franklin Deceased's
New Second Charity
Global Care
The Law Society Charity
The Leigh Trust
Network for Social Change
The Joseph Rowntree
Charitable Trust

■ Victims of war or conflict

CAFOD (Catholic Agency for
Overseas Development)
The Dorfred Charitable Trust
Maurice Fry Charitable Trust
Global Care
Human Relief Foundation
The Heinz, Anna and Carol
Kroch Foundation
Muslim Hands
Novi Most International
Oxfam (GB)
The Pilkington Charities Fund
The Eva Reckitt Trust Fund

Trusts by type
of grant

This index contains two separate listings:

List of types of grant: This lists all the headings used in the DGMT to categorise types of grant.

Trusts by type of grant: This lists trusts under the types of grant for which they have expressed a funding preference.

Trusts by type of grants

These pages contain two separate listings

*List of type of grants
This lists all of the headings used in the DGMT to categorise types of grants*

*Trusts by type of grants
This lists trusts under the types of grants for which they have expressed a funding preference*

Type of support

Capital support

■ Building/renovation

The 1970 Trust
The 1989 Willan Charitable Trust
The 29th May 1961 Charitable Trust
The Aberbrothock Skea Trust
The Aberdeen Endowments Trust
The Aberdeenshire Educational Trust Scheme
Achiezer Association Ltd
Achisomoch Aid Company Limited
The ACT Foundation
Action Medical Research
The Sylvia Adams Charitable Trust
The Victor Adda Foundation
The Adint Charitable Trust
The Adnams Charity
Age UK (formerly Help the Aged and Age Concern)
Aid to the Church in Need (UK)
The Sylvia Aitken Charitable Trust
The Aldgate Freedom Foundation
Allchurches Trust Ltd
The H B Allen Charitable Trust
The Alliance Family Foundation
Angus Allnatt Charitable Foundation
The Pat Allsop Charitable Trust
Almondsbury Charity
Altamont Ltd
Alvor Charitable Trust
The Ammco Trust
Viscount Amory's Charitable Trust
The AMW Charitable Trust
The Andrew Anderson Trust
The André Christian Trust
Anguish's Educational Foundation
The Animal Defence Trust
The Eric Anker-Petersen Charity
The Appletree Trust
The John Apthorp Charitable Trust
The Arbib Foundation
The John M Archer Charitable Trust
The Archer Trust
The Architectural Heritage Fund
The Ardwick Trust
The Argus Appeal
The Armenian Relief Society of Great Britain Trust

Arsenal Charitable Trust
The Artemis Charitable Trust
The Arts and Entertainment Charitable Trust
Arts Council England
The Arts Council of Northern Ireland
The Arts Council of Wales
The Ove Arup Foundation
The AS Charitable Trust
The Ashden Trust
The Ashendene Trust
The Norman C Ashton Foundation
The Ashworth Charitable Trust
The Ian Askew Charitable Trust
The Associated Country Women of the World (ACWW)
The Association of Colleges Charitable Trust
The Association of Friends of Essex Churches
Astellas European Foundation
Asthma UK
The Astor Foundation
The Astor of Hever Trust
The Aurelius Charitable Trust
The Avenue Charitable Trust
The John Avins Trustees
AW Charitable Trust
The Aylesford Family Charitable Trust
The BAA Communities Trust
The BACTA Charitable Trust
The Scott Bader Commonwealth Ltd
The Bagri Foundation
Veta Bailey Charitable Trust
The Austin Bailey Trust
The Baily Thomas Charitable Fund
The Baird Trust
The Baker Charitable Trust
The Balcombe Charitable Trust
The Albert Casanova Ballard Deceased Trust
The Ballinger Charitable Trust
The Balmore Trust
The Balney Charitable Trust
The Baltic Charitable Fund
The Bamford Charitable Foundation
The Banbury Charities
William P Bancroft (No 2) Charitable Trust and Jenepher Gillett Trust
The Band Trust
The Barbers' Company General Charities
Barchester Healthcare Foundation
The Barclay Foundation
The Baring Foundation
Peter Barker-Mill Memorial Charity

Barleycorn Trust
Barnes Workhouse Fund
The Barnsbury Charitable Trust
The Barnstaple Bridge Trust
The Misses Barrie Charitable Trust
Barrington Family Charitable Trust
The Charity of William Barrow
Stephen J Barry Charitable Trust
The Bartlett Taylor Charitable Trust
The Paul Bassham Charitable Trust
The Batchworth Trust
The Bay Tree Charitable Trust
D H and L H Baylin Charitable Trust
The Louis Baylis (Maidenhead Advertiser) Charitable Trust
BBC Children in Need
B-CH 1971 Charitable Trust
The Beacon Trust
The Bearder Charity
The James Beattie Charitable Trust
The Beaufort House Trust Limited
The Beaverbrook Foundation
The Beccles Town Lands Charity
The Becker Family Charitable Trust
The Becketts and Sargeants Educational Foundation
The John Beckwith Charitable Trust
The Peter Beckwith Charitable Trust
The Bedford Charity (The Harpur Trust)
The Bedfordshire and Hertfordshire Historic Churches Trust
The David and Ruth Behrend Fund
The Beit Trust
The Bellahouston Bequest Fund
The Bellinger Donnay Trust
Belljoe Tzedoko Ltd
The Benfield Motors Charitable Trust
The Benham Charitable Settlement
The Hervey Benham Charitable Trust
Maurice and Jacqueline Bennett Charitable Trust
The Gerald Bentall Charitable Trust
Bergqvist Charitable Trust
The Berkshire Community Foundation
The Bestway Foundation

Thomas Betton's Charity for
  Pensions and Relief-in-Need
BHST
The Mason Bibby 1981 Trust
BibleLands
The Bideford Bridge Trust
The Big Lottery Fund
The Billmeir Charitable Trust
Percy Bilton Charity
The Bingham Trust
The Bintaub Charitable Trust
The Birmingham District
  Nursing Charitable Trust
The Birmingham Hospital
  Saturday Fund Medical
  Charity and Welfare Trust
Birmingham International
  Airport Community Trust
The Lord Mayor of
  Birmingham's Charity
The Bisgood Charitable Trust
  (registered as Miss Jeanne
  Bisgood's Charitable Trust)
The Michael Bishop
  Foundation
The Bishop's Development
  Fund
The Bertie Black Foundation
Isabel Blackman Foundation
The Herbert and Peter
  Blagrave Charitable Trust
The Blair Foundation
The Blanchminster Trust
The Sir Victor Blank Charitable
  Settlement
The Neville and Elaine Blond
  Charitable Trust
The Bluston Charitable
  Settlement
The Body Shop Foundation
The Boltons Trust
The Bonamy Charitable Trust
The John and Celia Bonham
  Christie Charitable Trust
The Charlotte Bonham-Carter
  Charitable Trust
Bonhomie United Charity
  Society
The Boots Charitable Trust
The Bordon and Liphook
  Charity
The Oliver Borthwick Memorial
  Trust
The Bothwell Charitable Trust
H E and E L Botteley
  Charitable Trust
The Harry Bottom Charitable
  Trust
The Anthony Bourne
  Foundation
The Bower Trust
The Bowerman Charitable
  Trust
John and Susan Bowers Fund
The Bowland Charitable Trust

The William Brake Charitable
  Trust
The Tony Bramall Charitable
  Trust
The Harold and Alice Bridges
  Charity
The Brighton District Nursing
  Association Trust
Bristol Archdeaconry Charity
John Bristow and Thomas
  Mason Trust
Britannia Foundation
The British Council for
  Prevention of Blindness
The British Dietetic
  Association General and
  Education Trust Fund
The British Gas (Scottish Gas)
  Energy Trust
British Heart Foundation
British Humane Association
British Institute at Ankara
British Ornithologists' Union
British Record Industry Trust
The Britto Foundation
The J and M Britton Charitable
  Trust
The Charles and Edna
  Broadhurst Charitable Trust
The Roger Brooke Charitable
  Trust
The David Brooke Charity
The Charles Brotherton Trust
Joseph Brough Charitable
  Trust
The Swinfen Broun Charitable
  Trust
Mrs E E Brown Charitable
  Settlement
Brown-Mellows Trust
The Jack Brunton Charitable
  Trust
The Bryant Trust
The Buckinghamshire
  Foundation
The Buckinghamshire Historic
  Churches Trust
The Buckinghamshire Masonic
  Centenary Fund
The Rosemary Bugden
  Charitable Trust
The Bulldog Trust Limited
The E F Bulmer Benevolent
  Fund
Burdens Charitable Foundation
The Clara E Burgess Charity
The Burry Charitable Trust
The Arnold Burton 1998
  Charitable Trust
The Burton Breweries
  Charitable Trust
The Geoffrey Burton Charitable
  Trust
Consolidated Charity of Burton
  upon Trent

Butchers' Company General
  Charities
The C Charitable Trust
Henry T and Lucy B Cadbury
  Charitable Trust
The Christopher Cadbury
  Charitable Trust
The G W Cadbury Charitable
  Trust
The Richard Cadbury
  Charitable Trust
The Edward and Dorothy
  Cadbury Trust
The George Cadbury Trust
CAFOD (Catholic Agency for
  Overseas Development)
The Callander Charitable Trust
Calleva Foundation
Calypso Browning Trust
The Cambridgeshire Historic
  Churches Trust
The Campden Charities
  Trustee
The Canning Trust
The Carew Pole Charitable
  Trust
The D W T Cargill Fund
Carlee Ltd
The Carlton House Charitable
  Trust
The Worshipful Company of
  Carmen Benevolent Trust
The Carnegie Dunfermline
  Trust
The Carpenter Charitable Trust
The Carpenters' Company
  Charitable Trust
The Carrington Charitable
  Trust
The Carron Charitable
  Settlement
The Leslie Mary Carter
  Charitable Trust
The Carvill Trust
The Casey Trust
Cash for Kids Radio Clyde
The Elizabeth Casson Trust
The Castang Foundation
The Catalyst Charitable Trust
  (formerly the Buckle Family
  Charitable Trust)
The Catholic Charitable Trust
Catholic Foreign Missions
The Catholic Trust for England
  and Wales
The Joseph and Annie Cattle
  Trust
The Thomas Sivewright Catto
  Charitable Settlement
The Wilfrid and Constance
  Cave Foundation
The Cayo Foundation
Elizabeth Cayzer Charitable
  Trust
The B G S Cayzer Charitable
  Trust

The Cazenove Charitable Trust
Celtic Charity Fund
The Cemlyn-Jones Trust
The Pamela Champion
Foundation
The Chapman Charitable Trust
John William Chapman's
Charitable Trust
The Charities Advisory Trust
Charitworth Limited
The Charter 600 Charity
The Worshipful Company of
Chartered Accountants
General Charitable Trust
(also known as CALC)
The Chelsea Square 1994
Trust
The Cheruby Trust
The Cheshire Provincial Fund
of Benevolence
The Chetwode Foundation
Chevioty Asset Management
Charitable Trust
The Malcolm Chick Charity
Childs Charitable Trust
The Childwick Trust
The Chippenham Borough
Lands Charity
The Chipping Sodbury Town
Lands Charity
CHK Charities Limited
The Chownes Foundation
The Chrimes Family Charitable
Trust
Christadelphian Samaritan
Fund
Christian Aid
Christian Response to Eastern
Europe
Chrysalis Trust
The Church and Community
Fund
The Church Burgesses
Educational Foundation
Church Burgesses Trust
City and County of Swansea
Welsh Church Act Fund
The City Bridge Trust (formerly
known as Bridge House
Trust)
The City Educational Trust
Fund
Stephen Clark 1957
Charitable Trust
The Hilda and Alice Clark
Charitable Trust
The Roger and Sarah Bancroft
Clark Charitable Trust
The Clarke Charitable
Settlement
The Cleary Foundation
The Cleopatra Trust
Lord Clinton's Charitable Trust
The Clore Duffield Foundation
Miss V L Clore's 1967
Charitable Trust

Closehelm Ltd
The Clothworkers' Foundation
Richard Cloudesley's Charity
The Clover Trust
The Robert Clutterbuck
Charitable Trust
Clydpride Ltd
The Francis Coales Charitable
Foundation
The Coalfields Regeneration
Trust
The John Coates Charitable
Trust
Coats Foundation Trust
The Cobtree Charity Trust Ltd
The Denise Cohen Charitable
Trust
The Vivienne and Samuel
Cohen Charitable Trust
The John S Cohen Foundation
The R and S Cohen
Foundation
The Colchester Catalyst
Charity
The Cole Charitable Trust
The Colefax Charitable Trust
The John and Freda Coleman
Charitable Trust
The George Henry Collins
Charity
The E Alec Colman Charitable
Fund Ltd
The Sir Jeremiah Colman Gift
Trust
The Colt Foundation
The Coltstaple Trust
Colwinston Charitable Trust
Colyer-Fergusson Charitable
Trust
The Comino Foundation
Community Foundation for
Calderdale
The Community Foundation for
Northern Ireland
The Compton Charitable Trust
The Congleton Inclosure Trust
The Congregational and
General Charitable Trust
The Conservation Foundation
The Consolidated Charities for
the Infirm Merchant
Taylors' Company
The Cooks Charity
The Catherine Cookson
Charitable Trust
Mabel Cooper Charity
The Alice Ellen Cooper Dean
Charitable Foundation
The Co-operative Foundation
The Marjorie Coote Animal
Charity Trust
The Marjorie Coote Old
People's Charity
The Helen Jean Cope Trust
The J Reginald Corah
Foundation Fund

The Gershon Coren Charitable
Foundation
The Corinthian Trust
Edwin Cornforth 1983 Charity
Trust
The Cornwall Historic
Churches Trust
The Duke of Cornwall's
Benevolent Fund
The Cornwell Charitable Trust
The Sidney and Elizabeth
Corob Charitable Trust
The Corona Charitable Trust
The Costa Family Charitable
Trust (formerly the Morgan
Williams Charitable Trust)
The Cotton Industry War
Memorial Trust
Country Houses Foundation
County Durham Community
Foundation
The General Charities of the
City of Coventry
Coventry Building Society
Charitable Foundation
The John Cowan Foundation
The Sir William Coxen Trust
Fund
The Lord Cozens-Hardy Trust
The Craignish Trust
The Craps Charitable Trust
Michael Crawford Children's
Charity
The Cray Trust
The Crescent Trust
Cripplegate Foundation
The Violet and Milo Cripps
Charitable Trust
The Harry Crook Foundation
The Cross Trust
The Croydon Relief in Need
Charities
The Mayor of Croydon's
Charity Fund
Cruden Foundation Ltd
The Ronald Cruickshank's
Foundation
The R D Crusaders Foundation
The Culra Charitable Trust
The Cumber Family Charitable
Trust
Cumberland Building Society
Charitable Foundation
Cumbria Community
Foundation
The D J H Currie Memorial
Trust
The Dennis Curry Charitable
Trust
The Raymond Curtis Charitable
Trust
The Manny Cussins
Foundation
The Cwmbran Trust
Itzchok Meyer Cymerman Trust
Ltd

The D G Charitable Settlement
The D'Oyly Carte Charitable
   Trust
The Daisy Trust
The Daiwa Anglo-Japanese
   Foundation
The Dr and Mrs A Darlington
   Charitable Trust
Baron Davenport's Charity
The Davidson (Nairn)
   Charitable Trust
The Davidson Family
   Charitable Trust
The Alderman Joe Davidson
   Memorial Trust
Michael Davies Charitable
   Settlement
The Gwendoline and Margaret
   Davies Charity
The Wilfrid Bruce Davis
   Charitable Trust
Davis-Rubens Charitable Trust
The Dawe Charitable Trust
The De Clermont Charitable
   Company Ltd
The Leopold De Rothschild
   Charitable Trust
The Deakin Charitable Trust
William Dean Countryside and
   Educational Trust
The Debmar Benevolent Trust
The Dellal Foundation
The Delves Charitable Trust
The Demigryphon Trust
The Denman Charitable Trust
The Denton Charitable Trust
The Denton Wilde Sapte
   Charitable Trust
The Earl of Derby's Charitable
   Trust
The Derbyshire Churches and
   Chapels Preservation Trust
Derbyshire Community
   Foundation
The J N Derbyshire Trust
Devon Community Foundation
The Devon Educational Trust
The Devon Historic Churches
   Trust
The Duke of Devonshire's
   Charitable Trust
The Sandy Dewhirst Charitable
   Trust
The Laduma Dhamecha
   Charitable Trust
The Dibden Allotments Fund
The Dickon Trust
The Digbeth Trust
The Dinwoodie Settlement
Dischma Charitable Trust
The DLM Charitable Trust
Louise Dobson Charitable
   Trust
The Derek and Eileen Dodgson
   Foundation
The Dollond Charitable Trust

Domepride Ltd
The Dorcas Trust
The Dorset Historic Churches
   Trust
The Dorus Trust
The Doughty Charity Trust
The R M Douglas Charitable
   Trust
The Drapers' Charitable Fund
The Dugdale Charitable Trust
The Duis Charitable Trust
The P B Dumbell Charitable
   Trust
The Dumbreck Charity
Dunard Fund
Ronald Duncan Literary
   Foundation
The Houghton Dunn Charitable
   Trust
The Dunn Family Charitable
   Trust
The W E Dunn Trust
Dushinsky Trust Ltd
The Dwek Family Charitable
   Trust
The Dyers' Company
   Charitable Trust
The Eagle Charity Trust
The Earley Charity
Earls Colne and Halstead
   Educational Charity
The Earmark Trust
East Kent Provincial Charities
East London Community
   Foundation
Eastern Counties Educational
   Trust Limited
The Sir John Eastwood
   Foundation
The Ebenezer Trust
The EBM Charitable Trust
Eden Arts Trust
EDF Energy Trust (EDFET)
The Gilbert and Eileen Edgar
   Foundation
Edinburgh Children's Holiday
   Fund
The Edinburgh Trust, No 2
   Account
The W G Edwards Charitable
   Foundation
The William Edwards
   Educational Charity
The Elephant Trust
The George Elias Charitable
   Trust
The Gerald Palmer Eling Trust
   Company
The Wilfred and Elsie Elkes
   Charity Fund
The Maud Elkington Charitable
   Trust
The Ellerdale Trust
The John Ellerman Foundation
The Ellinson Foundation Ltd
The Ellis Campbell Foundation

James Ellis Charitable Trust
The Elmgrant Trust
The Elmley Foundation
The Vernon N Ely Charitable
   Trust
The Embleton Trust
The Emerton-Christie Charity
The Emmandjay Charitable
   Trust
The Worshipful Company of
   Engineers Charitable Trust
   Fund
The Englefield Charitable Trust
The English Schools' Football
   Association
The Enkalon Foundation
Entindale Ltd
The Epigoni Trust
Epilepsy Research UK
The Equitable Charitable Trust
The Equity Trust Fund
The Ericson Trust
The Erskine Cunningham Hill
   Trust
Essex Community Foundation
The Essex Fairway Charitable
   Trust
The Essex Heritage Trust
Essex Provincial Charity Fund
The Essex Youth Trust
Euro Charity Trust
Sir John Evelyn's Charity
The Eventhall Family
   Charitable Trust
The Everard Foundation
The Eveson Charitable Trust
The Beryl Evetts and Robert
   Luff Animal Welfare Trust
The Execution Charitable Trust
The Mayor of Exeter's Appeal
   Fund
The Exilarch's Foundation
F C Charitable Trust
The F P Limited Charitable
   Trust
The Faber Charitable Trust
Esmée Fairbairn Foundation
The Fairway Trust
Faisaltex Charitable Trust
The Family Rich Charities Trust
The Lord Faringdon Charitable
   Trust
Samuel William Farmer Trust
The Farmers' Company
   Charitable Fund
The Thomas Farr Charitable
   Trust
Walter Farthing (Trust) Limited
The Fassnidge Memorial Trust
Joseph Fattorini Charitable
   Trust 'B' Account
The Fawcett Charitable Trust
The February Foundation
Federation of Jewish Relief
   Organisations

The John Feeney Charitable
Trust
The George Fentham
Birmingham Charity
The A M Fenton Trust
Allan and Nesta Ferguson
Charitable Settlement
The Fidelity UK Foundation
The Bluff Field Charitable Trust
The Doris Field Charitable
Trust
Fife Council/Common Good
Funds and Trusts
Firtree Trust
The Fishmongers' Company's
Charitable Trust
The Fitton Trust
The Earl Fitzwilliam Charitable
Trust
Bud Flanagan Leukaemia Fund
The Rose Flatau Charitable
Trust
The Ian Fleming Charitable
Trust
The Joyce Fletcher Charitable
Trust
The Flow Foundation
The Gerald Fogel Charitable
Trust
The Follett Trust
The Football Association
National Sports Centre
Trust
The Football Association Youth
Trust
The Football Foundation
The Forbes Charitable
Foundation
The Forces Trust (Working
Name)
Ford Britain Trust
The Oliver Ford Charitable
Trust
The Forest Hill Charitable Trust
The Foresters' Charity
Stewards UK Trust
Gwyneth Forrester Trust
The Fort Foundation
The Forte Charitable Trust
Foundation for Management
Education
The Four Winds Trust
The Foyle Foundation
The Isaac and Freda Frankel
Memorial Charitable Trust
The Elizabeth Frankland Moore
and Star Foundation
The Gordon Fraser Charitable
Trust
The Hugh Fraser Foundation
The Joseph Strong Frazer Trust
The Louis and Valerie
Freedman Charitable
Settlement
The Thomas Freke and Lady
Norton Charity

The Charles S French
Charitable Trust
The Anne French Memorial
Trust
The Freshfield Foundation
The Freshgate Trust
Foundation
The Friarsgate Trust
The Friends Hall Farm Street
Trust
The Friends of Kent Churches
Friends Provident Charitable
Foundation
The Frognal Trust
The Patrick Frost Foundation
Maurice Fry Charitable Trust
The Fuellers Charitable Trust
Fund
The Fulmer Charitable Trust
Worshipful Company of
Furniture Makers Charitable
Fund
Gableholt Limited
The Galbraith Trust
The Gale Family Charitable
Trust
The Gamlen Charitable Trust
The Gamma Trust
The Gannochy Trust
The Ganzoni Charitable Trust
The Worshipful Company of
Gardeners of London
The Samuel Gardner Memorial
Trust
The Garnett Charitable Trust
Garvan Limited
The Gatsby Charitable
Foundation
Gatwick Airport Community
Trust
The Robert Gavron Charitable
Trust
J Paul Getty Jr Charitable Trust
The Gibbs Charitable Trust
Simon Gibson Charitable Trust
The G C Gibson Charitable
Trust
Lady Gibson's Charitable Trust
The Harvey and Hilary Gilbert
Charitable Trust
The Girdlers' Company
Charitable Trust
The B and P Glasser
Charitable Trust
The Glass-House Trust
Global Care
Global Charities (formerly
GCap Charities)
Gloucestershire Community
Foundation
The Gloucestershire Historic
Churches Trust
Worshipful Company of
Glovers of London Charity
Fund
GMC Trust

The GNC Trust
The Meir Golda Trust
The Sydney and Phyllis
Goldberg Memorial
Charitable Trust
The Golden Bottle Trust
The Jack Goldhill Charitable
Trust
The Goldsmiths' Arts Trust
Fund
The Goldsmiths' Company
Charity
The Golsoncott Foundation
The Everard and Mina
Goodman Charitable
Foundation
Mike Gooley Trailfinders
Charity
The Gosling Foundation
Limited
The Gough Charitable Trust
The Gould Charitable Trust
The Grace Charitable Trust
A B Grace Trust
The Graff Foundation
The Grahame Charitable
Foundation Limited
Grampian Police Diced Cap
Charitable Fund
The Granada Foundation
Grand Charitable Trust of the
Order of Women
Freemasons
The Grand Order of Water
Rats' Charities Fund
The Grange Farm Centre Trust
Grantham Yorke Trust
The J G Graves Charitable
Trust
The Gray Trust
The Great Stone Bridge Trust
of Edenbridge
The Great Torrington Town
Lands Charity
The Constance Green
Foundation
The Philip Green Memorial
Trust
Greenham Common
Community Trust Limited
Naomi and Jeffrey Greenwood
Charitable Trust
Greggs Foundation (formerly
Greggs Trust)
The Gretna Charitable Trust
The Grocers' Charity
The M and R Gross Charities
Limited
The Grove Charitable Trust
The GRP Charitable Trust
The David and Marie Grumitt
Foundation
The Bishop of Guildford's
Foundation
The Guildry Incorporation of
Perth

The Walter Guinness
　Charitable Trust
The Gunter Charitable Trust
The Gur Trust
Dr Guthrie's Association
The H and M Charitable Trust
H C D Memorial Fund
The H P Charitable Trust
The Hackney Parochial
　Charities
The Hadfield Trust
The Hadley Trust
The Hadrian Trust
The Hale Trust
E F and M G Hall Charitable
　Trust
The Edith Winifred Hall
　Charitable Trust
Robert Hall Charity
The Hamamelis Trust
Hamilton Wallace Trust
The Hammonds Charitable
　Trust
The Hampshire and Islands
　Historic Churches Trust
Hampshire and Isle of Wight
　Community Foundation
Hampton Fuel Allotment
　Charity
The W A Handley Charitable
　Trust
Beatrice Hankey Foundation
　Ltd
The Hanley Trust
The Kathleen Hannay
　Memorial Charity
The Doughty Hanson
　Charitable Foundation
Lord Hanson Foundation
The Haramead Trust
Miss K M Harbinson's
　Charitable Trust
The Harborne Parish Lands
　Charity
The Harbour Charitable Trust
The Harbour Foundation
The Harding Trust
William Harding's Charity
The Hare of Steep Charitable
　Trust
The Harebell Centenary Fund
The Kenneth Hargreaves
　Charitable Trust
The Harris Charitable Trust
The Harris Charity
The Harrison and Potter Trust
The John Harrison Charitable
　Trust
The Peter Harrison Foundation
The Spencer Hart Charitable
　Trust
The Hartley Charitable Trust
The N and P Hartley Memorial
　Trust
William Geoffrey Harvey's
　Discretionary Settlement

The Edward Harvist Trust Fund
Haskel Family Foundation
The Hathaway Trust
The Maurice Hatter Foundation
The M A Hawe Settlement
The Hawthorne Charitable
　Trust
The Dorothy Hay-Bolton
　Charitable Trust
The Haymills Charitable Trust
The Headley Trust
Headley-Pitt Charitable Trust
Heagerty Charitable Trust
The Heart of England
　Community Foundation
The Heathcoat Trust
Heathside Charitable Trust
The Charlotte Heber-Percy
　Charitable Trust
The Hedley Denton Charitable
　Trust
The Hedley Foundation
The H J Heinz Company
　Limited Charitable Trust
The Hellenic Foundation
The Michael and Morven Heller
　Charitable Foundation
The Simon Heller Charitable
　Settlement
The Hemby Trust
The Christina Mary Hendrie
　Trust for Scottish and
　Canadian Charities
The Henley Educational Charity
Esther Hennell Charitable
　Trust
The G D Herbert Charitable
　Trust
The Joanna Herbert-Stepney
　Charitable Settlement (also
　known as The Paget
　Charitable Trust)
The Anne Herd Memorial Trust
The Herefordshire Historic
　Churches Trust
The Heritage of London Trust
　Ltd
The Hesed Trust
The Hesslewood Children's
　Trust (Hull Seamen's and
　General Orphanage)
The Bernhard Heuberger
　Charitable Trust
Hexham and Newcastle
　Diocesan Trust (1947)
The P and C Hickinbotham
　Charitable Trust
The Higgs Charitable Trust
Alan Edward Higgs Charity
The High Sheriff's Police Trust
　for the County of West
　Midlands (Building Blocks)
Highcroft Charitable Trust
The Charles Littlewood Hill
　Trust

The Hillingdon Partnership
　Trust
The Hinrichsen Foundation
The Hitchin Educational
　Foundation
The Eleemosynary Charity of
　William Hobbayne
Hobson Charity Limited
Matthew Hodder Charitable
　Trust
The Sir Julian Hodge
　Charitable Trust
The J G Hogg Charitable Trust
The Holden Charitable Trust
John Holford's Charity
The Hollick Family Charitable
　Trust
The Dorothy Holmes Charitable
　Trust
The Edward Holt Trust
The Holywood Trust
The Homelands Charitable
　Trust
The Homestead Charitable
　Trust
Sir Harold Hood's Charitable
　Trust
Hope for Youth (formerly
　Women Caring Trust)
HopMarket Charity
The Cuthbert Horn Trust
The Antony Hornby Charitable
　Trust
The Horne Foundation
The Horne Trust
The Worshipful Company of
　Horners' Charitable Trusts
The Hornsey Parochial
　Charities
The Hospital Saturday Fund
Houblon-Norman/George Fund
The House of Industry Estate
The Reta Lila Howard
　Foundation
The Daniel Howard Trust
The Clifford Howarth Charity
　Trust
The Hudson Foundation
The Geoffrey C Hughes
　Charitable Trust
The Hull and East Riding
　Charitable Trust
Hulme Trust Estates
　(Educational)
Human Relief Foundation
The Humanitarian Trust
The Michael and Shirley Hunt
　Charitable Trust
The Hunter Foundation
Miss Agnes H Hunter's Trust
The Huntingdon Foundation
Huntingdon Freemen's Charity
John Huntingdon's Charity
Hurdale Charity Limited
The Nani Huyu Charitable Trust
The P Y N and B Hyams Trust

The Hyde Charitable Trust –
Youth Plus
The Idlewild Trust
The Iliffe Family Charitable
Trust
The Indigo Trust
The Ingram Trust
The Inland Waterways
Association
The Inman Charity
The Inner London Magistrates
Court Poor Box and Feeder
Charity
The Ireland Fund of Great
Britain
The Irish Youth Foundation
(UK) Ltd (incorporating The
Lawlor Foundation)
The Ironmongers' Foundation
Irshad Trust
The Charles Irving Charitable
Trust
Irwin Trust
The ISA Charity
The Isaacs Charitable Trust
The J Isaacs Charitable Trust
The Isle of Anglesey Charitable
Trust
The ITF Seafarers Trust
The J R S S T Charitable Trust
Elizabeth Jackson Charitable
Trust
The Ruth and Lionel Jacobson
Trust (Second Fund) No 2
Jaffe Family Relief Fund
The Susan and Stephen
James Charitable
Settlement (also known as
the Stephen James
Charitable Trust)
The James Trust
The Marjory Jameson Trust
The John Jarrold Trust
JCA Charitable Foundation
The Jeffrey Charitable Trust
The Jenour Foundation
The Jephcott Charitable Trust
Jesus Hospital Charity
The Jewish Youth Fund
The JMK Charitable Trust
The Joanies Trust
The Harold Joels Charitable
Trust
The Jonathan Joels Charitable
Trust
The Nicholas Joels Charitable
Trust
The Norman Joels Charitable
Trust
The Lillie Johnson Charitable
Trust
The Johnson Foundation
The Johnson Group Cleaners
Charity
The Johnnie Johnson Trust

The Johnson Wax Ltd
Charitable Trust
The Joicey Trust
The Jones 1986 Charitable
Trust
The Marjorie and Geoffrey
Jones Charitable Trust
The Jordan Charitable
Foundation
The J E Joseph Charitable
Fund
The Lady Eileen Joseph
Foundation
JTH Charitable Trust
The Anton Jurgens Charitable
Trust
The Bernard Kahn Charitable
Trust
The Stanley Kalms Foundation
The Karenza Foundation
The Boris Karloff Charitable
Foundation
The Ian Karten Charitable
Trust
The Kasner Charitable Trust
The Kass Charitable Trust
The Kathleen Trust
The Michael and Ilse Katz
Foundation
The Katzauer Charitable
Settlement
The C S Kaufman Charitable
Trust
The Geoffrey John Kaye
Charitable Foundation
The Emmanuel Kaye
Foundation
Kelsick's Educational
Foundation
The KempWelch Charitable
Trust
The Kay Kendall Leukaemia
Fund
The Kennedy Charitable
Foundation
The Nancy Kenyon Charitable
Trust
Keren Association
Kermaville Ltd
The Kessler Foundation
The Ursula Keyes Trust
The King Henry VIII Endowed
Trust Warwick
The King/Cullimore Charitable
Trust
The Kingsbury Charity
The Mary Kinross Charitable
Trust
Kirkley Poor's Lands Estate
The Richard Kirkman
Charitable Trust
Kirschel Foundation
Robert Kitchin (Saddlers'
Company)
Ernest Kleinwort Charitable
Trust

The Marina Kleinwort
Charitable Trust
The Sir James Knott Trust
The Kobler Trust
The Kohn Foundation
The Kreditor Charitable Trust
The Kreitman Foundation
The Neil Kreitman Foundation
The Heinz, Anna and Carol
Kroch Foundation
The Kyte Charitable Trust
The Late Sir Pierce Lacy
Charity Trust
John Laing Charitable Trust
Maurice and Hilda Laing
Charitable Trust
The Christopher Laing
Foundation
The Kirby Laing Foundation
The Martin Laing Foundation
The Beatrice Laing Trust
The Lambert Charitable Trust
Lancashire Environmental
Fund
Duchy of Lancaster Benevolent
Fund
The Lancaster Foundation
The Langdale Trust
The Langley Charitable Trust
The Langtree Trust
The LankellyChase Foundation
The Lanvern Foundation
The R J Larg Family Charitable
Trust
Largsmount Ltd
The Lark Trust
Laslett's (Hinton) Charity
Lauchentilly Charitable
Foundation 1988
The Lauffer Family Charitable
Foundation
The Kathleen Laurence Trust
The Edgar E Lawley Foundation
The Herd Lawson and Muriel
Lawson Charitable Trust
The Lawson Beckman
Charitable Trust
The Raymond and Blanche
Lawson Charitable Trust
The Carole and Geoffrey
Lawson Foundation
The Mason Le Page Charitable
Trust
The Leach Fourteenth Trust
The David Lean Foundation
The Leathersellers' Company
Charitable Fund
The Arnold Lee Charitable
Trust
The William Leech Charity
The Lord Mayor of Leeds
Appeal Fund
Leicester Charity Link (formerly
The Leicester Charity
Organisation Society)

Leicestershire Historic Churches Trust
The Kennedy Leigh Charitable Trust
The Leigh Trust
Mrs Vera Leigh's Charity
The P Leigh-Bramwell Trust 'E'
The Lennox and Wyfold Foundation
The Erica Leonard Trust
The Leonard Trust
The Mark Leonard Trust
Lesley Lesley and Mutter Trust
The Leverhulme Trade Charities Trust
The Leverhulme Trust
Lord Leverhulme's Charitable Trust
The Joseph Levy Charitable Foundation
The Sir Edward Lewis Foundation
John Lewis Partnership General Community Fund
Lichfield Conduit Lands
Lifeline 4 Kids
The Thomas Lilley Memorial Trust
The Linbury Trust
The Lincolnshire Old Churches Trust
The Lind Trust
Lindale Educational Foundation
The Linden Charitable Trust
The Enid Linder Foundation
The Linmardon Trust
The Ruth and Stuart Lipton Charitable Trust
The Lister Charitable Trust
Frank Litchfield Charitable Trust
The Andrew and Mary Elizabeth Little Charitable Trust
The Second Joseph Aaron Littman Foundation
The George John and Sheilah Livanos Charitable Trust
Liverpool Charity and Voluntary Services
Liverpool Sailors' Home Trust
The Elaine and Angus Lloyd Charitable Trust
The Charles Lloyd Foundation
The Lloyd Fund
Lloyd's Charities Trust
Lloyds TSB Foundation for Northern Ireland
Lloyds TSB Foundation for the Channel Islands
The Locker Foundation
The Loftus Charitable Trust
The Lolev Charitable Trust

London Catalyst (formerly The Metropolitan Hospital-Sunday Fund)
The London Community Foundation (formerly Capital Community Foundation)
The London Law Trust
The London Marathon Charitable Trust
The William and Katherine Longman Trust
The Loseley and Guildway Charitable Trust
The Lotus Foundation
The C L Loyd Charitable Trust
The Marie Helen Luen Charitable Trust
Robert Luff Foundation Ltd
Henry Lumley Charitable Trust
Lady Lumley's Educational Foundation
C F Lunoe Trust Fund
The Ruth and Jack Lunzer Charitable Trust
Lord and Lady Lurgan Trust
The Lynn Foundation
The Lynwood Trust
John Lyon's Charity
The Lyons Charitable Trust
The Sir Jack Lyons Charitable Trust
The Lyras Family Charitable Trust
The M and C Trust
The M D and S Charitable Trust
The M K Charitable Trust
The Madeline Mabey Trust
The E M MacAndrew Trust
The R S Macdonald Charitable Trust
Macdonald-Buchanan Charitable Trust
The Macfarlane Walker Trust
The Mackay and Brewer Charitable Trust
The Mackintosh Foundation
The MacRobert Trust
The Magdalen and Lasher Charity
Magdalen Hospital Trust
The Magen Charitable Trust
Man Group plc Charitable Trust
The Manchester Guardian Society Charitable Trust
Lord Mayor of Manchester's Charity Appeal Trust
Mandeville Trust
The Manifold Charitable Trust
W M Mann Foundation
The Leslie and Lilian Manning Trust
Marbeh Torah Trust
Marchig Animal Welfare Trust

The Stella and Alexander Margulies Charitable Trust
Market Harborough and The Bowdens Charity
The Ann and David Marks Foundation
The Hilda and Samuel Marks Foundation
J P Marland Charitable Trust
The Michael Marsh Charitable Trust
The Charlotte Marshall Charitable Trust
The Jim Marshall Charitable Trust
The D G Marshall of Cambridge Trust
Marshall's Charity
Marshgate Charitable Settlement
Sir George Martin Trust
John Martin's Charity
The Mason Porter Charitable Trust
The Nancie Massey Charitable Trust
The Mathew Trust
The Matt 6.3 Charitable Trust
The Violet Mauray Charitable Trust
The Maxell Educational Trust
Evelyn May Trust
Mayfair Charities Ltd
The Mayfield Valley Arts Trust
Mazars Charitable Trust
The Robert McAlpine Foundation
The McDougall Trust
The McKenna Charitable Trust
The Helen Isabella McMorran Charitable Foundation
The James Frederick and Ethel Anne Measures Charity
The Medlock Charitable Trust
The Anthony and Elizabeth Mellows Charitable Settlement
Melow Charitable Trust
The Mercers' Charitable Foundation
The Merchant Taylors' Company Charities Fund
The Merchant Venturers' Charity
The Merchants' House of Glasgow
The Mersey Docks and Harbour Company Charitable Fund
Community Foundation for Merseyside
The Zachary Merton and George Woofindin Convalescent Trust
The Tony Metherell Charitable Trust

The Metropolitan Drinking
    Fountain and Cattle Trough
    Association
Gerald Micklem Charitable
    Trust
Midhurst Pensions Trust
The Migraine Trust
Miles Trust for the Putney and
    Roehampton Community
The Hugh and Mary Miller
    Bequest Trust
The Miller Foundation
The Millfield Trust
The Millhouses Charitable
    Trust
The Millichope Foundation
The Mills Charity
The Millward Charitable Trust
The Clare Milne Trust
Milton Keynes Community
    Foundation
The Edgar Milward Charity
The Keith and Joan
    Mindelsohn Charitable
    Trust
The Peter Minet Trust
The Minos Trust
The Mirfield Educational
    Charity
The Laurence Misener
    Charitable Trust
The Mishcon Family Charitable
    Trust
The Misselbrook Trust
The Mitchell Charitable Trust
The Esmé Mitchell Trust
Keren Mitzvah Trust
The Mizpah Trust
The Mobbs Memorial Trust Ltd
The Modiano Charitable Trust
The Moette Charitable Trust
The Mole Charitable Trust
The D C Moncrieff Charitable
    Trust
Monmouthshire County Council
    Welsh Church Act Fund
The Montague Thompson
    Coon Charitable Trust
The Colin Montgomerie
    Charitable Foundation
The Monument Trust
George A Moore Foundation
The Nigel Moores Family
    Charitable Trust
The Peter Moores Foundation
The Morel Charitable Trust
The Morgan Charitable
    Foundation
The Mr and Mrs J T Morgan
    Foundation
The Oliver Morland Charitable
    Trust
The Bernard Morris Charitable
    Trust
The Morris Charitable Trust

The Willie and Mabel Morris
    Charitable Trust
The Peter Morrison Charitable
    Foundation
The Stanley Morrison
    Charitable Trust
Vyoel Moshe Charitable Trust
The Moss Charitable Trust
The Robert and Margaret
    Moss Charitable Trust
Moss Family Charitable Trust
The Mount Everest Foundation
The Edwina Mountbatten Trust
Mountbatten Festival of Music
The Mountbatten Memorial
    Trust
The Mugdock Children's Trust
The Mulberry Trust
The Edith Murphy Foundation
The Mushroom Fund
The Music Sales Charitable
    Trust
Muslim Hands
The Mutual Trust Group
The Kitty and Daniel Nabarro
    Charitable Trust
The Nadezhda Charitable Trust
The Naggar Charitable Trust
The Eleni Nakou Foundation
The Janet Nash Charitable
    Settlement
Nathan Charitable Trust
The National Manuscripts
    Conservation Trust
The Nchima Trust
Needham Market and Barking
    Welfare Charities
The Worshipful Company of
    Needlemakers' Charitable
    Fund
The Neighbourly Charitable
    Trust
The James Neill Trust Fund
Nemoral Ltd
Network for Social Change
The Newcomen Collett
    Foundation
Alderman Newton's
    Educational Foundation
The Chevras Ezras Nitzrochim
    Trust
The Noon Foundation
The Norda Trust
Norie Charitable Trust
Normalyn Charitable Trust
The Norman Family Charitable
    Trust
The Duncan Norman Trust
    Fund
The Normanby Charitable Trust
The North British Hotel Trust
The Northampton Municipal
    Church Charities
The Northampton Queen's
    Institute Relief in Sickness
    Fund

The Earl of Northampton's
    Charity
The Northcott Devon
    Foundation
The Northcott Devon Medical
    Foundation
The Northmoor Trust
The Northumberland Village
    Homes Trust
The Northumbria Historic
    Churches Trust
The Northwood Charitable
    Trust
The Norton Foundation
The Norwich Church of England
    Young Men's Society
The Norwich Historic Churches
    Trust Ltd
The Norwich Town Close
    Estate Charity
The Norwood and Newton
    Settlement
The Noswad Charity
The Notgrove Trust
The Nottingham General
    Dispensary
The Nottingham Gordon
    Memorial Trust for Boys
    and Girls
Nottinghamshire Community
    Foundation
The Nottinghamshire Historic
    Churches Trust
The Nottinghamshire Miners'
    Welfare Trust Fund
Novi Most International
The Father O'Mahoney
    Memorial Trust
The Sir Peter O'Sullevan
    Charitable Trust
The Oak Trust
The Oakdale Trust
The Oakley Charitable Trust
The Oakmoor Charitable Trust
The Odin Charitable Trust
The Ofenheim Charitable Trust
Ogilvie Charities Deed No.2
    (including the Charity of
    Mary Catherine Ford Smith)
Oglesby Charitable Trust
The Oikonomia Trust
Oizer Charitable Trust
The Old Broad Street Charity
    Trust
The Old Enfield Charitable
    Trust
The John Oldacre Foundation
The Oldham Foundation
Onaway Trust
Open Gate
The Ormsby Charitable Trust
Orrin Charitable Trust
The Owen Family Trust
Oxfam (GB)
The Oxfordshire Community
    Foundation

The P F Charitable Trust
Padwa Charitable Foundation
The Pallant Charitable Trust
The Palmer Foundation
Eleanor Palmer Trust
The Panacea Society
Panton Trust
The James Pantyfedwen
  Foundation
The Paragon Trust
The Park House Charitable
  Trust
The Frank Parkinson
  Agricultural Trust
The Samuel and Freda
  Parkinson Charitable Trust
The Parthenon Trust
The Constance Paterson
  Charitable Trust
The Patrick Charitable Trust
The Jack Patston Charitable
  Trust
Paycare Charity Trust (formerly
  known as Patients' Aid
  Association Hospital and
  Medical Charities Trust)
The Harry Payne Trust
The Susanna Peake Charitable
  Trust
The Pedmore Sporting Club
  Trust Fund
The Dowager Countess
  Eleanor Peel Trust
The Pennycress Trust
The Performing Right Society
  Foundation
The Persson Charitable Trust
  (formerly Highmoore Hall
  Charitable Trust)
The Jack Petchey Foundation
The Petplan Charitable Trust
The Philips and Rubens
  Charitable Trust
The Phillips Charitable Trust
The Phillips Family Charitable
  Trust
Philological Foundation
The Bernard Piggott Trust
The Pilgrim Trust
The Cecil Pilkington Charitable
  Trust
The Pilkington Charities Fund
The Austin and Hope
  Pilkington Trust
The Sir Harry Pilkington Trust
The Col W W Pilkington Will
  Trusts The General Charity
  Fund
The DLA Piper Charitable Trust
The Worshipful Company of
  Plaisterers Charitable Trust
The Platinum Trust
The Poling Charitable Trust
The George and Esme Pollitzer
  Charitable Settlement

The J S F Pollitzer Charitable
  Settlement
The Ponton House Trust
The Mayor of Poole's Appeal
  Fund
Edith and Ferdinand Porjes
  Charitable Trust
The John Porter Charitable
  Trust
The Porter Foundation
The Portishead Nautical Trust
The Portrack Charitable Trust
The J E Posnansky Charitable
  Trust
The Powell Foundation
Premierquote Ltd
Premishlaner Charitable Trust
The William Price Charitable
  Trust
The Lucy Price Relief-in-Need
  Charity
Sir John Priestman Charity
  Trust
The Primrose Trust
The Prince of Wales's
  Charitable Foundation
The Priory Foundation
Prison Service Charity Fund
The Privy Purse Charitable
  Trust
The Proven Family Trust
The Provincial Grand Charity of
  the Province of Derbyshire
PSA Peugeot Citroen Charity
  Trust
The Puebla Charitable Trust
The Richard and Christine
  Purchas Charitable Trust
The Puri Foundation
Mr and Mrs J A Pye's
  Charitable Settlement
Quartet Community Foundation
  (formerly the Greater Bristol
  Foundation)
Queen Mary's Roehampton
  Trust
The Queen's Silver Jubilee
  Trust
R S Charitable Trust
The Monica Rabagliati
  Charitable Trust
Rachel Charitable Trust
The Mr and Mrs Philip
  Rackham Charitable Trust
Richard Radcliffe Charitable
  Trust
The Radcliffe Trust
The Ragdoll Foundation
The Rainford Trust
The Peggy Ramsay Foundation
The Joseph and Lena Randall
  Charitable Trust
The Rank Foundation
The Fanny Rapaport Charitable
  Settlement
The Ratcliff Foundation

The Ratcliff Pension Charity
The Ratcliffe Charitable Trust
The Eleanor Rathbone
  Charitable Trust
The Sigrid Rausing Trust
The Ravensdale Trust
The Rayden Charitable Trust
The Roger Raymond Charitable
  Trust
The Rayne Foundation
The Rayne Trust
The John Rayner Charitable
  Trust
The Sir James Reckitt Charity
The Red Arrows Trust
Red Hill Charitable Trust
The Red Rose Charitable Trust
The C A Redfern Charitable
  Foundation
The Reed Foundation
Richard Reeve's Foundation
The Max Reinhardt Charitable
  Trust
Relief Fund for Romania
  Limited
The Rest Harrow Trust
Reuben Brothers Foundation
The Joan K Reynell Charitable
  Trust
The Nathaniel Reyner Trust
  Fund
The Rhododendron Trust
The Clive Richards Charity
The Richmond Parish Lands
  Charity
Ridgesave Limited
The Ripple Effect Foundation
The Sir John Ritblat Family
  Foundation
Thomas Roberts Trust
The Robertson Trust
The Rochester Bridge Trust
The Rock Foundation
The Rock Solid Trust
The Rofeh Trust
Richard Rogers Charitable
  Settlement
Rokach Family Charitable Trust
The Helen Roll Charitable
  Trust
The Sir James Roll Charitable
  Trust
The Roman Research Trust
Romeera Foundation
The C A Rookes Charitable
  Trust
The Rosca Trust
The Rose Foundation
The Cecil Rosen Foundation
The Rothermere Foundation
The Rotherwick Foundation
The Rothley Trust
The Roughley Charitable Trust
Mrs Gladys Row Fogo
  Charitable Trust
Rowanville Ltd

The Rowing Foundation
The Rowlands Trust
Royal Artillery Charitable Fund
Royal British Legion
Royal Docks Trust (London)
Royal Masonic Trust for Girls
   and Boys
The Royal Scots Benevolent
   Society
The Alfred and Frances
   Rubens Charitable Trust
The Rubin Foundation
William Arthur Rudd Memorial
   Trust
The Russell Trust
The J S and E C Rymer
   Charitable Trust
S O Charitable Trust
The Jeremy and John Sacher
   Charitable Trust
The Michael Harry Sacher
   Trust
The Raymond and Beverley
   Sackler 1988 Foundation
The Sackler Trust (formerly Dr
   Mortimer and Theresa
   Sackler Foundation)
The Ruzin Sadagora Trust
The Saddlers' Company
   Charitable Fund
The Saga Charitable Trust
The Jean Sainsbury Animal
   Welfare Trust
The Alan and Babette
   Sainsbury Charitable Fund
The Sainsbury Family
   Charitable Trusts
The Saintbury Trust
The Saints and Sinners Trust
The Salamander Charitable
   Trust
The Salt Foundation
The Salt Trust
The Sammermar Trust
Basil Samuel Charitable Trust
The Hon. M J Samuel
   Charitable Trust
The Peter Samuel Charitable
   Trust
The Camilla Samuel Fund
The Samworth Foundation
The Sandra Charitable Trust
Jimmy Savile Charitable Trust
The Scarfe Charitable Trust
The Schapira Charitable Trust
The Schmidt-Bodner Charitable
   Trust
The R H Scholes Charitable
   Trust
The Schreib Trust
The Schreiber Charitable Trust
The Francis C Scott Charitable
   Trust
The Frieda Scott Charitable
   Trust

The Sir James and Lady Scott
   Trust
The Scott Trust Foundation
The Storrow Scott Will Trust
The Scottish Arts Council
Scottish Coal Industry Special
   Welfare Fund
The Scottish Community
   Foundation
The Scouloudi Foundation
Seafarers UK (King George's
   Fund for Sailors)
Seamen's Hospital Society
The Searchlight Electric
   Charitable Trust
The Searle Charitable Trust
The Helene Sebba Charitable
   Trust
The Samuel Sebba Charitable
   Trust
The Seedfield Trust
Leslie Sell Charitable Trust
The Ayrton Senna Foundation
The Seven Fifty Trust
The Severn Trent Water
   Charitable Trust Fund
The Cyril Shack Trust
The Shanti Charitable Trust
ShareGift (The Orr Mackintosh
   Foundation)
The Linley Shaw Foundation
The Sheffield and District
   Hospital Services
   Charitable Fund
The P and D Shepherd
   Charitable Trust
The Sylvia and Colin Shepherd
   Charitable Trust
The Archie Sherman Cardiff
   Foundation
The Archie Sherman Charitable
   Trust
The R C Sherriff Trust
The Shetland Charitable Trust
SHINE (Support and Help in
   Education)
The Barnett and Sylvia Shine
   No 2 Charitable Trust
The Bassil Shippam and
   Alsford Trust
The Shipwrights' Company
   Charitable Fund
The Shirley Foundation
Shlomo Memorial Fund Limited
The J A Shone Memorial Trust
The Barbara A Shuttleworth
   Memorial Trust
The Mary Elizabeth Siebel
   Charity
David and Jennifer Sieff
   Charitable Trust
The Julius Silman Charitable
   Trust
The Leslie Silver Charitable
   Trust

The Simpson Education and
   Conservation Trust
The Simpson Foundation
The Huntly and Margery
   Sinclair Charitable Trust
Sino-British Fellowship Trust
The Skelton Bounty
The Charles Skey Charitable
   Trust
The John Slater Foundation
The SMB Charitable Trust
The Mrs Smith and Mount
   Trust
The N Smith Charitable
   Settlement
The Amanda Smith Charitable
   Trust
The E H Smith Charitable Trust
The Smith Charitable Trust
The Henry Smith Charity
The Leslie Smith Foundation
The Martin Smith Foundation
Stanley Smith General
   Charitable Trust
The Stanley Smith UK
   Horticultural Trust
The Snowball Trust
The Sobell Foundation
Solihull Community Foundation
The Solo Charitable
   Settlement
Dr Richard Solomon's
   Charitable Trust
Friends of Somerset Churches
   and Chapels
The E C Sosnow Charitable
   Trust
The South Square Trust
The Stephen R and Philippa H
   Southall Charitable Trust
The W F Southall Trust
The Southover Manor General
   Education Trust
The Southwold Trust
The Sovereign Health Care
   Charitable Trust
Sparquote Limited
The Spear Charitable Trust
The Worshipful Company of
   Spectacle Makers' Charity
The Jessie Spencer Trust
The Ralph and Irma Sperring
   Charity
The Moss Spiro Will Charitable
   Foundation
The Spoore, Merry and Rixman
   Foundation
Spring Harvest
Springrule Ltd
The Spurrell Charitable Trust
The Geoff and Fiona Squire
   Foundation
St Andrew's Conservation
   Trust
St Francis's Leprosy Guild
St Gabriel's Trust

St James' Trust Settlement
St James's Place Foundation
St Michael's and All Saints' Charities
The Late St Patrick White Charitable Trust
St Teilo's Trust
The Stanley Foundation Ltd
The Stanton Ballard Charitable Trust
The Staples Trust
The Star Charitable Trust
The Steel Charitable Trust
The Steinberg Family Charitable Trust
The Hugh Stenhouse Foundation
The Sigmund Sternberg Charitable Foundation
Stervon Ltd
The Stevenage Community Trust
The June Stevens Foundation
The Steventon Allotments and Relief-in-Need Charity
The Stewards' Company Limited (incorporating the J W Laing Trust and the J W Laing Biblical Scholarship Trust)
The Leonard Laity Stoate Charitable Trust
The Stobart Newlands Charitable Trust
The Edward Stocks-Massey Bequest Fund
The Stokenchurch Educational Charity
The Stoller Charitable Trust
The M J C Stone Charitable Trust
The Stone-Mallabar Charitable Foundation
The Samuel Storey Family Charitable Trust
Peter Stormonth Darling Charitable Trust
The Strangward Trust
The Strasser Foundation
Stratford upon Avon Town Trust
Strathclyde Police Benevolent Fund
The W O Street Charitable Foundation
The Sudborough Foundation
The Suffolk Historic Churches Trust
The Summerfield Charitable Trust
The Bernard Sunley Charitable Foundation
The Surrey Historic Buildings Trust Ltd
The Sussex Historic Churches Trust

The Sutasoma Trust
Sutton Coldfield Municipal Charities
Swansea and Brecon Diocesan Board of Finance Limited
The John Swire (1989) Charitable Trust
The Swire Charitable Trust
The Hugh and Ruby Sykes Charitable Trust
The Charles and Elsie Sykes Trust
The Sylvanus Charitable Trust
The Stella Symons Charitable Trust
The Tabeel Trust
The Tajtelbaum Charitable Trust
The Talbot Trusts
The Talbot Village Trust
Tallow Chandlers Benevolent Fund
The Tangent Charitable Trust
The Lady Tangye Charitable Trust
The David Tannen Charitable Trust
The Tanner Trust
The Lili Tapper Charitable Foundation
The Mrs A Lacy Tate Trust
The Tay Charitable Trust
Humphrey Richardson Taylor Charitable Trust
The Connie and Albert Taylor Charitable Trust
The Cyril Taylor Charitable Trust
A P Taylor Trust
Tearfund
The Tedworth Charitable Trust
Tees Valley Community Foundation
The Templeton Goodwill Trust
Tesco Charity Trust
The Thames Wharf Charity
The Thistle Trust
The Loke Wan Tho Memorial Foundation
The Arthur and Margaret Thompson Charitable Trust
The Thompson Family Charitable Trust
The Len Thomson Charitable Trust
The Sue Thomson Foundation
The Sir Jules Thorn Charitable Trust
The Thornton Foundation
The Thornton Trust
The Three Guineas Trust
The Three Oaks Trust
The Thriplow Charitable Trust
Mrs R P Tindall's Charitable Trust
The Tinsley Foundation

The Tisbury Telegraph Trust
TJH Foundation
The Tobacco Pipe Makers and Tobacco Trade Benevolent Fund
The Tolkien Trust
Tollemache (Buckminster) Charitable Trust
Tomchei Torah Charitable Trust
The Tompkins Foundation
The Tory Family Foundation
Tottenham Grammar School Foundation
The Tower Hill Trust
The Towry Law Charitable Trust (also known as the Castle Educational Trust)
The Toy Trust
The Mayor of Trafford's Charity Fund
The Constance Travis Charitable Trust
The Treeside Trust
The Triangle Trust (1949) Fund
The True Colours Trust
Truedene Co. Ltd
The Truemark Trust
Truemart Limited
Trumros Limited
Trust Sixty Three
The Trusthouse Charitable Foundation
Tudor Rose Ltd
The Tudor Trust
The Tufton Charitable Trust
The R D Turner Charitable Trust
The Douglas Turner Trust
The Florence Turner Trust
Miss S M Tutton Charitable Trust
The TUUT Charitable Trust
Community Foundation Serving Tyne and Wear and Northumberland
Trustees of Tzedakah
Ulster Garden Villages Ltd
Ultach Trust
Ulting Overseas Trust
The Ulverscroft Foundation
Ulverston Town Lands Charity
The Underwood Trust
The Union of Orthodox Hebrew Congregation
The United Society for the Propagation of the Gospel
The David Uri Memorial Trust
Uxbridge United Welfare Trust
Vale of Glamorgan – Welsh Church Fund
The Valentine Charitable Trust
John and Lucille van Geest Foundation
The Van Neste Foundation

Mrs Maud Van Norden's Charitable Foundation

The Vandervell Foundation

The Vardy Foundation

The Variety Club Children's Charity

Veneziana Fund

The Verdon-Smith Family Charitable Settlement

Victoria Homes Trust

The Nigel Vinson Charitable Trust

The William and Ellen Vinten Trust

The Vintners' Company Charitable Foundation

Vintners' Gifts Charity

Vision Charity

Vivdale Ltd

The Viznitz Foundation

Voluntary Action Fund

Wade's Charity

The Community Foundation in Wales

Wales Council for Voluntary Action

Robert and Felicity Waley-Cohen Charitable Trust

The F J Wallis Charitable Settlement

War on Want

The Ward Blenkinsop Trust

The George Ward Charitable Trust

The Barbara Ward Children's Foundation

The John Warren Foundation

G R Waters Charitable Trust 2000

The Waterways Trust

John Watson's Trust

Weatherley Charitable Trust

The Weavers' Company Benevolent Fund

The William Webster Charitable Trust

The Weinberg Foundation

The Weinstein Foundation

The Weinstock Fund

The James Weir Foundation

The Barbara Welby Trust

The Weldon UK Charitable Trust

The Wellcome Trust

Welsh Church Fund Dyfed area (Carmarthenshire, Ceredigion and Pembrokeshire)

The Welton Foundation

The Wessex Youth Trust

The West Derby Wastelands Charity

West London Synagogue Charitable Fund

The West Yorkshire Police Community Fund

The Westminster Foundation

The Garfield Weston Foundation

The Colonel W H Whitbread Charitable Trust

The Simon Whitbread Charitable Trust

The Whitecourt Charitable Trust

The Norman Whiteley Trust

The Whitley Animal Protection Trust

The Whittlesey Charity

The Lionel Wigram Memorial Trust

The Felicity Wilde Charitable Trust

The Wilkinson Charitable Foundation

The Kay Williams Charitable Foundation

The Williams Family Charitable Trust

The H D H Wills 1965 Charitable Trust

The Dame Violet Wills Will Trust

The Wilmcote Charitrust

David Wilson Foundation

The Wilson Foundation

J and J R Wilson Trust

The Community Foundation for Wiltshire and Swindon

The Benjamin Winegarten Charitable Trust

The Francis Winham Foundation

Wirral Mayor's Charity

The Michael and Anna Wix Charitable Trust

The Wixamtree Trust

The Woburn 1986 Charitable Trust

The Maurice Wohl Charitable Foundation

The Charles Wolfson Charitable Trust

The Wolfson Family Charitable Trust

The Wolfson Foundation

The James Wood Bequest Fund

Woodlands Green Ltd

Woodlands Trust

The Woodward Charitable Trust

Worcester Municipal Charities (incorporating Worcester Consolidated Municipal Charity and Worcester Municipal Exhibitions Foundation)

The Worcestershire and Dudley Historic Churches Trust

The Fred and Della Worms Charitable Trust

The Wragge and Co. Charitable Trust

The Diana Edgson Wright Charitable Trust

The Matthews Wrightson Charity Trust

Miss E B Wrightson's Charitable Settlement

Wychdale Ltd

Wychville Ltd

The Wyndham Charitable Trust

The Wyseliot Charitable Trust

The Xerox (UK) Trust

The Yardley Great Trust

The Dennis Alan Yardy Charitable Trust

The W Wing Yip and Brothers Foundation

The York Children's Trust

Yorkshire Agricultural Society

Yorkshire Building Society Charitable Foundation

The South Yorkshire Community Foundation

The Yorkshire Dales Millennium Trust

The Yorkshire Historic Churches Trust

The John Young Charitable Settlement

The William Allen Young Charitable Trust

The John K Young Endowment Fund

Youth Music

Zephyr Charitable Trust

The Marjorie and Arnold Ziff Charitable Foundation

Stephen Zimmerman Charitable Trust

The Zochonis Charitable Trust

Zurich Community Trust (UK) Limited

....

■ Collections and aquisitions

The 1970 Trust

The 1989 Willan Charitable Trust

The 29th May 1961 Charitable Trust

The Aberbrothock Skea Trust

The Aberdeen Endowments Trust

Achiezer Association Ltd

Achisomoch Aid Company Limited

The ACT Foundation

Action Medical Research

The Company of Actuaries' Charitable Trust Fund

The Sylvia Adams Charitable Trust

The Victor Adda Foundation
The Adint Charitable Trust
Aid to the Church in Need (UK)
The Sylvia Aitken Charitable
   Trust
The Ajahma Charitable Trust
Aldgate and All Hallows'
   Barking Exhibition
   Foundation
The Aldgate Freedom
   Foundation
Allchurches Trust Ltd
The H B Allen Charitable Trust
The Alliance Family Foundation
The Pat Allsop Charitable Trust
Almondsbury Charity
Altamont Ltd
Alvor Charitable Trust
The Ammco Trust
Viscount Amory's Charitable
   Trust
The AMW Charitable Trust
The André Christian Trust
Anguish's Educational
   Foundation
The Animal Defence Trust
The Eric Anker-Petersen
   Charity
Ambrose and Ann Appelbe
   Trust
The Appletree Trust
The John Apthorp Charitable
   Trust
The Arbib Foundation
The John M Archer Charitable
   Trust
The Archer Trust
The Ardwick Trust
The Argus Appeal
The Armenian Relief Society of
   Great Britain Trust
The Armourers' and Brasiers'
   Gauntlet Trust
Arsenal Charitable Trust
The Arts and Entertainment
   Charitable Trust
Arts Council England
The Arts Council of Northern
   Ireland
The Arts Council of Wales
The Ove Arup Foundation
The AS Charitable Trust
The Ashden Trust
The Ashendene Trust
The Ashley Family Foundation
   (formerly The Laura Ashley
   Foundation)
The Norman C Ashton
   Foundation
The Ashworth Charitable Trust
The Ian Askew Charitable Trust
The Associated Country
   Women of the World
   (ACWW)
The Association of Colleges
   Charitable Trust

Astellas European Foundation
Asthma UK
The Astor Foundation
The Astor of Hever Trust
The Aurelius Charitable Trust
The Avenue Charitable Trust
The John Avins Trustees
The Avon and Somerset Police
   Community Trust
AW Charitable Trust
The Aylesford Family
   Charitable Trust
The BAA Communities Trust
The BACTA Charitable Trust
The Bagri Foundation
Veta Bailey Charitable Trust
The Austin Bailey Trust
The Baird Trust
The Baker Charitable Trust
The Balcombe Charitable Trust
The Albert Casanova Ballard
   Deceased Trust
The Ballinger Charitable Trust
The Balmore Trust
The Balney Charitable Trust
The Baltic Charitable Fund
The Bamford Charitable
   Foundation
The Banbury Charities
William P Bancroft (No 2)
   Charitable Trust and
   Jenepher Gillett Trust
The Band Trust
The Barbers' Company General
   Charities
The Barbour Foundation
Barchester Healthcare
   Foundation
The Barclay Foundation
Peter Barker-Mill Memorial
   Charity
Barleycorn Trust
Barnes Workhouse Fund
The Barnsbury Charitable Trust
The Barnstaple Bridge Trust
The Misses Barrie Charitable
   Trust
Barrington Family Charitable
   Trust
The Charity of William Barrow
Stephen J Barry Charitable
   Trust
The Bartlett Taylor Charitable
   Trust
The Paul Bassham Charitable
   Trust
The Batchworth Trust
The Bay Tree Charitable Trust
D H and L H Baylin Charitable
   Trust
The Louis Baylis (Maidenhead
   Advertiser) Charitable Trust
B-CH 1971 Charitable Trust
The Beacon Trust
The Bearder Charity

The James Beattie Charitable
   Trust
The Beaufort House Trust
   Limited
The Beaverbrook Foundation
The Beccles Town Lands
   Charity
The Becker Family Charitable
   Trust
The Becketts and Sargeants
   Educational Foundation
The Peter Beckwith Charitable
   Trust
The David and Ruth Behrend
   Fund
The Beit Trust
The Bellahouston Bequest
   Fund
The Bellinger Donnay Trust
Belljoe Tzedoko Ltd
The Benfield Motors Charitable
   Trust
The Benham Charitable
   Settlement
Maurice and Jacqueline
   Bennett Charitable Trust
The Gerald Bentall Charitable
   Trust
Bergqvist Charitable Trust
The Berkshire Community
   Foundation
The Bestway Foundation
Thomas Betton's Charity for
   Pensions and Relief-in-Need
BHST
The Mason Bibby 1981 Trust
BibleLands
The Bideford Bridge Trust
The Big Lottery Fund
The Billmeir Charitable Trust
The Bingham Trust
The Bintaub Charitable Trust
The Birmingham District
   Nursing Charitable Trust
The Birmingham Hospital
   Saturday Fund Medical
   Charity and Welfare Trust
Birmingham International
   Airport Community Trust
The Lord Mayor of
   Birmingham's Charity
The Bisgood Charitable Trust
   (registered as Miss Jeanne
   Bisgood's Charitable Trust)
The Michael Bishop
   Foundation
The Bishop's Development
   Fund
The Bertie Black Foundation
Isabel Blackman Foundation
The Herbert and Peter
   Blagrave Charitable Trust
The Blair Foundation
The Blanchminster Trust
The Sir Victor Blank Charitable
   Settlement

The Neville and Elaine Blond
Charitable Trust
The Bluston Charitable
Settlement
The Body Shop Foundation
The Bonamy Charitable Trust
The John and Celia Bonham
Christie Charitable Trust
The Charlotte Bonham-Carter
Charitable Trust
Bonhomie United Charity
Society
The Boots Charitable Trust
The Bordon and Liphook
Charity
The Oliver Borthwick Memorial
Trust
The Bothwell Charitable Trust
H E and E L Botteley
Charitable Trust
The Harry Bottom Charitable
Trust
The Anthony Bourne
Foundation
The Bower Trust
The Bowerman Charitable
Trust
John and Susan Bowers Fund
The Bowland Charitable Trust
The William Brake Charitable
Trust
The Tony Bramall Charitable
Trust
The Harold and Alice Bridges
Charity
The Brighton District Nursing
Association Trust
Bristol Archdeaconry Charity
John Bristow and Thomas
Mason Trust
Britannia Foundation
The British Council for
Prevention of Blindness
The British Dietetic
Association General and
Education Trust Fund
The British Gas (Scottish Gas)
Energy Trust
British Heart Foundation
British Humane Association
British Institute at Ankara
British Ornithologists' Union
British Record Industry Trust
The Britto Foundation
The J and M Britton Charitable
Trust
The Charles and Edna
Broadhurst Charitable Trust
The Roger Brooke Charitable
Trust
The David Brooke Charity
The Charles Brotherton Trust
Joseph Brough Charitable
Trust
The Swinfen Broun Charitable
Trust

Mrs E E Brown Charitable
Settlement
The Jack Brunton Charitable
Trust
The Bryant Trust
The Buckinghamshire
Foundation
The Buckinghamshire Masonic
Centenary Fund
The Rosemary Bugden
Charitable Trust
The Bulldog Trust Limited
The E F Bulmer Benevolent
Fund
Burdens Charitable Foundation
The Clara E Burgess Charity
The Burry Charitable Trust
The Arnold Burton 1998
Charitable Trust
The Burton Breweries
Charitable Trust
The Geoffrey Burton Charitable
Trust
Consolidated Charity of Burton
upon Trent
Butchers' Company General
Charities
The Noel Buxton Trust
Henry T and Lucy B Cadbury
Charitable Trust
The Christopher Cadbury
Charitable Trust
The G W Cadbury Charitable
Trust
The Richard Cadbury
Charitable Trust
The Edward and Dorothy
Cadbury Trust
The George Cadbury Trust
CAFOD (Catholic Agency for
Overseas Development)
The Callander Charitable Trust
Calypso Browning Trust
The Canning Trust
The Carew Pole Charitable
Trust
The D W T Cargill Fund
Carlee Ltd
The Carlton House Charitable
Trust
The Worshipful Company of
Carmen Benevolent Trust
The Carnegie Dunfermline
Trust
The Carpenter Charitable Trust
The Carpenters' Company
Charitable Trust
The Carrington Charitable
Trust
The Carron Charitable
Settlement
The Leslie Mary Carter
Charitable Trust
The Carvill Trust
The Casey Trust
The Elizabeth Casson Trust

The Castang Foundation
The Catalyst Charitable Trust
(formerly the Buckle Family
Charitable Trust)
The Catholic Charitable Trust
Catholic Foreign Missions
The Catholic Trust for England
and Wales
The Joseph and Annie Cattle
Trust
The Thomas Sivewright Catto
Charitable Settlement
The Wilfrid and Constance
Cave Foundation
The Cayo Foundation
Elizabeth Cayzer Charitable
Trust
The B G S Cayzer Charitable
Trust
The Cazenove Charitable Trust
Celtic Charity Fund
The Cemlyn-Jones Trust
The Pamela Champion
Foundation
The Chapman Charitable Trust
John William Chapman's
Charitable Trust
The Charities Advisory Trust
Charitworth Limited
The Charter 600 Charity
The Worshipful Company of
Chartered Accountants
General Charitable Trust
(also known as CALC)
The Chasah Trust
The Chelsea Building Society
Charitable Foundation
The Chelsea Square 1994
Trust
The Cheruby Trust
The Cheshire Provincial Fund
of Benevolence
The Chetwode Foundation
Chevioty Asset Management
Charitable Trust
The Malcolm Chick Charity
Childs Charitable Trust
The Childwick Trust
The Chippenham Borough
Lands Charity
The Chipping Sodbury Town
Lands Charity
CHK Charities Limited
The Chownes Foundation
The Chrimes Family Charitable
Trust
The Christabella Charitable
Trust
Christadelphian Samaritan
Fund
Christian Aid
Christian Response to Eastern
Europe
The Church and Community
Fund

The Church Burgesses
Educational Foundation
Church Burgesses Trust
City and County of Swansea
Welsh Church Act Fund
The City Educational Trust
Fund
Stephen Clark 1957
Charitable Trust
J A Clark Charitable Trust
The Hilda and Alice Clark
Charitable Trust
The Roger and Sarah Bancroft
Clark Charitable Trust
The Clarke Charitable
Settlement
The Cleary Foundation
The Cleopatra Trust
Lord Clinton's Charitable Trust
The Clore Duffield Foundation
Miss V L Clore's 1967
Charitable Trust
Closehelm Ltd
The Clothworkers' Foundation
The Clover Trust
The Robert Clutterbuck
Charitable Trust
Clydpride Ltd
The John Coates Charitable
Trust
Coats Foundation Trust
The Cobtree Charity Trust Ltd
The Denise Cohen Charitable
Trust
The Vivienne and Samuel
Cohen Charitable Trust
The John S Cohen Foundation
The R and S Cohen
Foundation
The Colchester Catalyst
Charity
The Cole Charitable Trust
The Colefax Charitable Trust
The John and Freda Coleman
Charitable Trust
The George Henry Collins
Charity
The E Alec Colman Charitable
Fund Ltd
The Sir Jeremiah Colman Gift
Trust
The Colt Foundation
The Coltstaple Trust
Colwinston Charitable Trust
Colyer-Fergusson Charitable
Trust
The Comino Foundation
Community Foundation for
Calderdale
The Compton Charitable Trust
The Congleton Inclosure Trust
The Conservation Foundation
The Consolidated Charities for
the Infirm Merchant
Taylors' Company
The Cooks Charity

The Catherine Cookson
Charitable Trust
Mabel Cooper Charity
The Alice Ellen Cooper Dean
Charitable Foundation
The Co-operative Foundation
The Marjorie Coote Animal
Charity Trust
The Marjorie Coote Old
People's Charity
The Helen Jean Cope Trust
The J Reginald Corah
Foundation Fund
The Gershon Coren Charitable
Foundation
The Corinthian Trust
Edwin Cornforth 1983 Charity
Trust
The Duke of Cornwall's
Benevolent Fund
The Cornwell Charitable Trust
The Sidney and Elizabeth
Corob Charitable Trust
The Corona Charitable Trust
The Costa Family Charitable
Trust (formerly the Morgan
Williams Charitable Trust)
The Cotton Industry War
Memorial Trust
The Cotton Trust
County Durham Community
Foundation
The Augustine Courtauld Trust
The General Charities of the
City of Coventry
Coventry Building Society
Charitable Foundation
The John Cowan Foundation
The Sir William Coxen Trust
Fund
The Lord Cozens-Hardy Trust
The Craignish Trust
The Craps Charitable Trust
Michael Crawford Children's
Charity
The Cray Trust
Creative Scotland
The Crescent Trust
The Violet and Milo Cripps
Charitable Trust
The Harry Crook Foundation
The Cross Trust
The Croydon Relief in Need
Charities
The Mayor of Croydon's
Charity Fund
Cruden Foundation Ltd
The Ronald Cruickshank's
Foundation
The R D Crusaders Foundation
The Culra Charitable Trust
The Cumber Family Charitable
Trust
Cumberland Building Society
Charitable Foundation

Cumbria Community
Foundation
The D J H Currie Memorial
Trust
The Dennis Curry Charitable
Trust
The Raymond Curtis Charitable
Trust
The Manny Cussins
Foundation
The Cwmbran Trust
Itzchok Meyer Cymerman Trust
Ltd
The D G Charitable Settlement
The D'Oyly Carte Charitable
Trust
The Daily Prayer Union
Charitable Trust Ltd
The Daisy Trust
The Daiwa Anglo-Japanese
Foundation
The Dr and Mrs A Darlington
Charitable Trust
The Davidson (Nairn)
Charitable Trust
The Davidson Family
Charitable Trust
The Alderman Joe Davidson
Memorial Trust
Michael Davies Charitable
Settlement
The Gwendoline and Margaret
Davies Charity
The Wilfrid Bruce Davis
Charitable Trust
Davis-Rubens Charitable Trust
The Dawe Charitable Trust
The De Clermont Charitable
Company Ltd
The Leopold De Rothschild
Charitable Trust
The Deakin Charitable Trust
William Dean Countryside and
Educational Trust
The Debmar Benevolent Trust
The Delius Trust
The Dellal Foundation
The Delves Charitable Trust
The Demigryphon Trust
The Denman Charitable Trust
The Denton Charitable Trust
The Denton Wilde Sapte
Charitable Trust
The Earl of Derby's Charitable
Trust
Derbyshire Community
Foundation
The J N Derbyshire Trust
Devon Community Foundation
The Devon Educational Trust
The Duke of Devonshire's
Charitable Trust
The Sandy Dewhirst Charitable
Trust
The Laduma Dhamecha
Charitable Trust

The Dibden Allotments Fund
The Dickon Trust
The Digbeth Trust
The Dinwoodie Settlement
Dischma Charitable Trust
The DLM Charitable Trust
Louise Dobson Charitable
    Trust
The Derek and Eileen Dodgson
    Foundation
The Dollond Charitable Trust
Domepride Ltd
The Dorcas Trust
The Dorus Trust
The Doughty Charity Trust
The R M Douglas Charitable
    Trust
The Drapers' Charitable Fund
The Dugdale Charitable Trust
The Duis Charitable Trust
The P B Dumbell Charitable
    Trust
The Dumbreck Charity
Dunard Fund
Ronald Duncan Literary
    Foundation
The Houghton Dunn Charitable
    Trust
The Dunn Family Charitable
    Trust
The W E Dunn Trust
Dushinsky Trust Ltd
The Dwek Family Charitable
    Trust
The Dyers' Company
    Charitable Trust
The Eagle Charity Trust
The Earley Charity
Earls Colne and Halstead
    Educational Charity
The Earmark Trust
East Kent Provincial Charities
East London Community
    Foundation
Eastern Counties Educational
    Trust Limited
The Ebenezer Trust
The EBM Charitable Trust
Eden Arts Trust
EDF Energy Trust (EDFET)
The Gilbert and Eileen Edgar
    Foundation
Edinburgh Children's Holiday
    Fund
The Edinburgh Trust, No 2
    Account
Edinburgh Voluntary
    Organisations' Trust Funds
The W G Edwards Charitable
    Foundation
The William Edwards
    Educational Charity
The Elephant Trust
The George Elias Charitable
    Trust

The Gerald Palmer Eling Trust
    Company
The Wilfred and Elsie Elkes
    Charity Fund
The Ellerdale Trust
The John Ellerman Foundation
The Ellinson Foundation Ltd
The Ellis Campbell Foundation
James Ellis Charitable Trust
The Elmgrant Trust
The Elmley Foundation
The Vernon N Ely Charitable
    Trust
The Embleton Trust
The Emerton-Christie Charity
EMI Music Sound Foundation
The Emmandjay Charitable
    Trust
The Worshipful Company of
    Engineers Charitable Trust
    Fund
The Englefield Charitable Trust
The English Schools' Football
    Association
The Enkalon Foundation
Entindale Ltd
The Epigoni Trust
Epilepsy Research UK
The Equity Trust Fund
The Ericson Trust
The Erskine Cunningham Hill
    Trust
Essex Community Foundation
The Essex Fairway Charitable
    Trust
The Essex Heritage Trust
Essex Provincial Charity Fund
The Essex Youth Trust
Euro Charity Trust
Sir John Evelyn's Charity
The Eventhall Family
    Charitable Trust
The Everard Foundation
The Beryl Evetts and Robert
    Luff Animal Welfare Trust
The Execution Charitable Trust
The Mayor of Exeter's Appeal
    Fund
The Exilarch's Foundation
F C Charitable Trust
The F P Limited Charitable
    Trust
The Faber Charitable Trust
The Fairway Trust
Faisaltex Charitable Trust
The Family Rich Charities Trust
The Lord Faringdon Charitable
    Trust
Samuel William Farmer Trust
The Farmers' Company
    Charitable Fund
The Thomas Farr Charitable
    Trust
Walter Farthing (Trust) Limited
The Fassnidge Memorial Trust

Joseph Fattorini Charitable
    Trust 'B' Account
The Fawcett Charitable Trust
Federation of Jewish Relief
    Organisations
The John Feeney Charitable
    Trust
The George Fentham
    Birmingham Charity
The A M Fenton Trust
Allan and Nesta Ferguson
    Charitable Settlement
The Fidelity UK Foundation
The Bluff Field Charitable Trust
The Doris Field Charitable
    Trust
Fife Council/Common Good
    Funds and Trusts
Firtree Trust
The Fitton Trust
The Earl Fitzwilliam Charitable
    Trust
Bud Flanagan Leukaemia Fund
The Rose Flatau Charitable
    Trust
The Ian Fleming Charitable
    Trust
The Joyce Fletcher Charitable
    Trust
The Roy Fletcher Charitable
    Trust
The Flow Foundation
The Gerald Fogel Charitable
    Trust
The Follett Trust
The Football Association
    National Sports Centre
    Trust
The Football Foundation
The Forbes Charitable
    Foundation
The Forces Trust (Working
    Name)
The Oliver Ford Charitable
    Trust
The Forest Hill Charitable Trust
The Foresters' Charity
    Stewards UK Trust
Forever Manchester (The
    Community Foundation for
    Greater Manchester)
Gwyneth Forrester Trust
The Fort Foundation
The Forte Charitable Trust
Foundation for Management
    Education
The Four Winds Trust
The Foyle Foundation
The Isaac and Freda Frankel
    Memorial Charitable Trust
The Elizabeth Frankland Moore
    and Star Foundation
The Jill Franklin Trust
The Gordon Fraser Charitable
    Trust
The Hugh Fraser Foundation

The Joseph Strong Frazer Trust

The Louis and Valerie Freedman Charitable Settlement

The Thomas Freke and Lady Norton Charity

The Charles S French Charitable Trust

The Anne French Memorial Trust

The Freshfield Foundation

The Freshgate Trust Foundation

The Friarsgate Trust

The Friends Hall Farm Street Trust

Friends Provident Charitable Foundation

The Frognal Trust

The Patrick Frost Foundation

Maurice Fry Charitable Trust

The Fuellers Charitable Trust Fund

The Fulmer Charitable Trust

Worshipful Company of Furniture Makers Charitable Fund

Gablehot Limited

The Galbraith Trust

The Gale Family Charitable Trust

The Angela Gallagher Memorial Fund

The Gamlen Charitable Trust

The Gamma Trust

The Gannochy Trust

The Ganzoni Charitable Trust

The Worshipful Company of Gardeners of London

The Samuel Gardner Memorial Trust

The Garnett Charitable Trust

Garvan Limited

The Gatsby Charitable Foundation

Gatwick Airport Community Trust

The Robert Gavron Charitable Trust

The Gibbs Charitable Trust

Simon Gibson Charitable Trust

The G C Gibson Charitable Trust

Lady Gibson's Charitable Trust

The Harvey and Hilary Gilbert Charitable Trust

The Girdlers' Company Charitable Trust

The B and P Glasser Charitable Trust

The Glass-House Trust

Global Care

Global Charities (formerly GCap Charities)

Gloucestershire Community Foundation

Worshipful Company of Glovers of London Charity Fund

The GNC Trust

The Meir Golda Trust

The Sydney and Phyllis Goldberg Memorial Charitable Trust

The Golden Bottle Trust

The Jack Goldhill Charitable Trust

The Goldsmiths' Arts Trust Fund

The Goldsmiths' Company Charity

The Good Neighbours Trust

The Everard and Mina Goodman Charitable Foundation

Mike Gooley Trailfinders Charity

The Gosling Foundation Limited

The Gough Charitable Trust

The Gould Charitable Trust

The Grace Charitable Trust

A B Grace Trust

The Graff Foundation

The Grahame Charitable Foundation Limited

Grampian Police Diced Cap Charitable Fund

The Granada Foundation

Grand Charitable Trust of the Order of Women Freemasons

The Grand Order of Water Rats' Charities Fund

The Grange Farm Centre Trust

Grantham Yorke Trust

The Gray Trust

The Great Stone Bridge Trust of Edenbridge

The Great Torrington Town Lands Charity

The Philip Green Memorial Trust

Greenham Common Community Trust Limited

Naomi and Jeffrey Greenwood Charitable Trust

The Gretna Charitable Trust

The Grocers' Charity

The M and R Gross Charities Limited

The Grove Charitable Trust

The GRP Charitable Trust

The David and Marie Grumitt Foundation

The Bishop of Guildford's Foundation

The Guildry Incorporation of Perth

The Walter Guinness Charitable Trust

The Gunter Charitable Trust

The Gur Trust

Dr Guthrie's Association

The H and M Charitable Trust

H C D Memorial Fund

The H P Charitable Trust

The Hackney Parochial Charities

The Hadfield Trust

The Hadrian Trust

The Alfred Haines Charitable Trust

The Hale Trust

E F and M G Hall Charitable Trust

The Edith Winifred Hall Charitable Trust

Robert Hall Charity

The Hamamelis Trust

Hamilton Wallace Trust

Paul Hamlyn Foundation

The Hammonds Charitable Trust

The Hampshire and Islands Historic Churches Trust

The W A Handley Charitable Trust

Beatrice Hankey Foundation Ltd

The Hanley Trust

The Kathleen Hannay Memorial Charity

The Doughty Hanson Charitable Foundation

Lord Hanson Foundation

The Haramead Trust

Miss K M Harbinson's Charitable Trust

The Harborne Parish Lands Charity

The Harbour Charitable Trust

The Harbour Foundation

The Harding Trust

William Harding's Charity

The Hare of Steep Charitable Trust

The Harebell Centenary Fund

The Kenneth Hargreaves Charitable Trust

The Harris Charitable Trust

The Harris Charity

The Harrison and Potter Trust

The John Harrison Charitable Trust

The Spencer Hart Charitable Trust

The Hartley Charitable Trust

The N and P Hartley Memorial Trust

William Geoffrey Harvey's Discretionary Settlement

The Edward Harvist Trust Fund

Haskel Family Foundation

The Hathaway Trust

The M A Hawe Settlement

The Hawthorne Charitable Trust

The Dorothy Hay-Bolton
Charitable Trust
The Haymills Charitable Trust
The Headley Trust
Headley-Pitt Charitable Trust
Heagerty Charitable Trust
The Heart of England
Community Foundation
The Heathcoat Trust
Heathside Charitable Trust
The Charlotte Heber-Percy
Charitable Trust
The Hedley Denton Charitable
Trust
The Hedley Foundation
The H J Heinz Company
Limited Charitable Trust
The Hellenic Foundation
The Michael and Morven Heller
Charitable Foundation
The Simon Heller Charitable
Settlement
The Hemby Trust
The Christina Mary Hendrie
Trust for Scottish and
Canadian Charities
The Henley Educational Charity
Esther Hennell Charitable
Trust
The G D Herbert Charitable
Trust
The Joanna Herbert-Stepney
Charitable Settlement (also
known as The Paget
Charitable Trust)
The Anne Herd Memorial Trust
The Herefordshire Historic
Churches Trust
The Heritage of London Trust
Ltd
The Hesed Trust
The Hesslewood Children's
Trust (Hull Seamen's and
General Orphanage)
The Bernhard Heuberger
Charitable Trust
Hexham and Newcastle
Diocesan Trust (1947)
The P and C Hickinbotham
Charitable Trust
The Higgs Charitable Trust
The High Sheriff's Police Trust
for the County of West
Midlands (Building Blocks)
Highcroft Charitable Trust
The Charles Littlewood Hill
Trust
The Hillingdon Partnership
Trust
The Hinrichsen Foundation
The Hitchin Educational
Foundation
The Eleemosynary Charity of
William Hobbayne
Hobson Charity Limited

Matthew Hodder Charitable
Trust
The Sir Julian Hodge
Charitable Trust
The J G Hogg Charitable Trust
The Holden Charitable Trust
John Holford's Charity
The Hollick Family Charitable
Trust
The Dorothy Holmes Charitable
Trust
The Edward Holt Trust
The Holywood Trust
The Homelands Charitable
Trust
The Homestead Charitable
Trust
Sir Harold Hood's Charitable
Trust
Hope for Youth (formerly
Women Caring Trust)
The Hope Trust
HopMarket Charity
The Cuthbert Horn Trust
The Antony Hornby Charitable
Trust
The Horne Trust
The Worshipful Company of
Horners' Charitable Trusts
The Hornsey Parochial
Charities
The Hospital of God at
Greatham
The Hospital Saturday Fund
Houblon-Norman/George Fund
The House of Industry Estate
The Reta Lila Howard
Foundation
The Daniel Howard Trust
The Hudson Foundation
The Geoffrey C Hughes
Charitable Trust
The Hull and East Riding
Charitable Trust
Hulme Trust Estates
(Educational)
Human Relief Foundation
The Humanitarian Trust
The Michael and Shirley Hunt
Charitable Trust
The Hunter Foundation
Miss Agnes H Hunter's Trust
The Huntingdon Foundation
Huntingdon Freemen's Charity
John Huntingdon's Charity
Hurdale Charity Limited
The Nani Huyu Charitable Trust
The P Y N and B Hyams Trust
The Hyde Charitable Trust –
Youth Plus
The Idlewild Trust
The Iliffe Family Charitable
Trust
The Indigo Trust
The Ingram Trust

The Inland Waterways
Association
The Inlight Trust
The Inman Charity
The Inner London Magistrates
Court Poor Box and Feeder
Charity
The Ireland Fund of Great
Britain
The Irish Youth Foundation
(UK) Ltd (incorporating The
Lawlor Foundation)
The Ironmongers' Foundation
Irshad Trust
The Charles Irving Charitable
Trust
Irwin Trust
The ISA Charity
The Isaacs Charitable Trust
The J Isaacs Charitable Trust
The ITF Seafarers Trust
The J R S S T Charitable Trust
Elizabeth Jackson Charitable
Trust
The Ruth and Lionel Jacobson
Trust (Second Fund) No 2
Jaffe Family Relief Fund
The Susan and Stephen
James Charitable
Settlement (also known as
the Stephen James
Charitable Trust)
The James Trust
The Jarman Charitable Trust
The John Jarrold Trust
JCA Charitable Foundation
The Jeffrey Charitable Trust
The Jenour Foundation
The Jephcott Charitable Trust
Jesus Hospital Charity
Jewish Child's Day
The Jewish Youth Fund
The JMK Charitable Trust
The Joanies Trust
The Harold Joels Charitable
Trust
The Jonathan Joels Charitable
Trust
The Nicholas Joels Charitable
Trust
The Norman Joels Charitable
Trust
The Lillie Johnson Charitable
Trust
The Johnson Foundation
The Johnson Group Cleaners
Charity
The Johnnie Johnson Trust
The Johnson Wax Ltd
Charitable Trust
The Joicey Trust
The Jones 1986 Charitable
Trust
The Marjorie and Geoffrey
Jones Charitable Trust

The Jordan Charitable Foundation

The J E Joseph Charitable Fund

The Lady Eileen Joseph Foundation

JTH Charitable Trust

The Anton Jurgens Charitable Trust

The Bernard Kahn Charitable Trust

The Stanley Kalms Foundation

The Karenza Foundation

The Boris Karloff Charitable Foundation

The Kasner Charitable Trust

The Kass Charitable Trust

The Kathleen Trust

The Michael and Ilse Katz Foundation

The Katzauer Charitable Settlement

The C S Kaufman Charitable Trust

The Geoffrey John Kaye Charitable Foundation

The Emmanuel Kaye Foundation

Kelsick's Educational Foundation

The KempWelch Charitable Trust

William Kendall's Charity (Wax Chandlers' Company)

The Kennel Club Charitable Trust

The Nancy Kenyon Charitable Trust

Keren Association

Kermaville Ltd

The Peter Kershaw Trust

The Kessler Foundation

Keswick Hall Trust

The Ursula Keyes Trust

The Robert Kiln Charitable Trust

The King Henry VIII Endowed Trust Warwick

The King/Cullimore Charitable Trust

The Kingsbury Charity

Kirkley Poor's Lands Estate

The Richard Kirkman Charitable Trust

Kirschel Foundation

Robert Kitchin (Saddlers' Company)

Ernest Kleinwort Charitable Trust

The Marina Kleinwort Charitable Trust

The Kobler Trust

The Kohn Foundation

The Kreditor Charitable Trust

The Kreitman Foundation

The Neil Kreitman Foundation

The Heinz, Anna and Carol Kroch Foundation

The Kyte Charitable Trust

The Late Sir Pierce Lacy Charity Trust

The Christopher Laing Foundation

The Martin Laing Foundation

The Lambert Charitable Trust

Lancashire Environmental Fund

Duchy of Lancaster Benevolent Fund

The Langdale Trust

The Langley Charitable Trust

The Langtree Trust

The LankellyChase Foundation

The Lanvern Foundation

The R J Larg Family Charitable Trust

Largsmount Ltd

The Lark Trust

Laslett's (Hinton) Charity

Lauchentilly Charitable Foundation 1988

The Lauffer Family Charitable Foundation

The Kathleen Laurence Trust

The Edgar E Lawley Foundation

The Herd Lawson and Muriel Lawson Charitable Trust

The Lawson Beckman Charitable Trust

The Raymond and Blanche Lawson Charitable Trust

The Carole and Geoffrey Lawson Foundation

The Mason Le Page Charitable Trust

The Leach Fourteenth Trust

The David Lean Foundation

The Arnold Lee Charitable Trust

The Lord Mayor of Leeds Appeal Fund

Leeds Building Society Charitable Foundation

Leicester Charity Link (formerly The Leicester Charity Organisation Society)

The Kennedy Leigh Charitable Trust

The Leigh Trust

Mrs Vera Leigh's Charity

The P Leigh-Bramwell Trust 'E'

The Lennox and Wyfold Foundation

The Erica Leonard Trust

The Leonard Trust

The Mark Leonard Trust

Lesley Lesley and Mutter Trust

The Leverhulme Trust

The Joseph Levy Charitable Foundation

The John Spedan Lewis Foundation

The Sir Edward Lewis Foundation

John Lewis Partnership General Community Fund

Lichfield Conduit Lands

Lifeline 4 Kids

The Thomas Lilley Memorial Trust

The Linbury Trust

The Lind Trust

Lindale Educational Foundation

The Linden Charitable Trust

The Linmardon Trust

The Ruth and Stuart Lipton Charitable Trust

The Lister Charitable Trust

Frank Litchfield Charitable Trust

The Andrew and Mary Elizabeth Little Charitable Trust

The Second Joseph Aaron Littman Foundation

Liverpool Charity and Voluntary Services

Liverpool Sailors' Home Trust

The Elaine and Angus Lloyd Charitable Trust

The Charles Lloyd Foundation

The Lloyd Fund

Lloyd's Charities Trust

Lloyds TSB Foundation for the Channel Islands

The Locker Foundation

The Loftus Charitable Trust

The Lolev Charitable Trust

The Trust for London (formerly the City Parochial Foundation)

London Catalyst (formerly The Metropolitan Hospital-Sunday Fund)

The London Community Foundation (formerly Capital Community Foundation)

The London Law Trust

The William and Katherine Longman Trust

The Loseley and Guildway Charitable Trust

The Lotus Foundation

The C L Loyd Charitable Trust

The Marie Helen Luen Charitable Trust

Robert Luff Foundation Ltd

Henry Lumley Charitable Trust

Lady Lumley's Educational Foundation

C F Lunoe Trust Fund

The Ruth and Jack Lunzer Charitable Trust

Lord and Lady Lurgan Trust

The Lyndhurst Trust

The Lynn Foundation

The Lynwood Trust

John Lyon's Charity
The Lyons Charitable Trust
The Sir Jack Lyons Charitable
   Trust
The Lyras Family Charitable
   Trust
Sylvanus Lyson's Charity
The M and C Trust
The M D and S Charitable
   Trust
The M K Charitable Trust
The Madeline Mabey Trust
The E M MacAndrew Trust
The R S Macdonald Charitable
   Trust
Macdonald-Buchanan
   Charitable Trust
The Macfarlane Walker Trust
The Mackay and Brewer
   Charitable Trust
The Mackintosh Foundation
The MacRobert Trust
The Magdalen and Lasher
   Charity
Magdalen Hospital Trust
The Magen Charitable Trust
Man Group plc Charitable
   Trust
The Manchester Guardian
   Society Charitable Trust
Lord Mayor of Manchester's
   Charity Appeal Trust
Mandeville Trust
The Manifold Charitable Trust
W M Mann Foundation
The Leslie and Lilian Manning
   Trust
Marbeh Torah Trust
Marchig Animal Welfare Trust
The Stella and Alexander
   Margulies Charitable Trust
Market Harborough and The
   Bowdens Charity
The Ann and David Marks
   Foundation
The Hilda and Samuel Marks
   Foundation
J P Marland Charitable Trust
The Michael Marsh Charitable
   Trust
The Marsh Christian Trust
The Charlotte Marshall
   Charitable Trust
The Jim Marshall Charitable
   Trust
The D G Marshall of
   Cambridge Trust
Marshall's Charity
Marshgate Charitable
   Settlement
Sir George Martin Trust
The Mason Porter Charitable
   Trust
The Nancie Massey Charitable
   Trust
The Mathew Trust

The Matt 6.3 Charitable Trust
The Violet Mauray Charitable
   Trust
The Maxell Educational Trust
The Maxwell Family Foundation
Evelyn May Trust
The Mayfield Valley Arts Trust
Mazars Charitable Trust
The Robert McAlpine
   Foundation
The McDougall Trust
The McKenna Charitable Trust
The Helen Isabella McMorran
   Charitable Foundation
The James Frederick and Ethel
   Anne Measures Charity
The Anthony and Elizabeth
   Mellows Charitable
   Settlement
Melow Charitable Trust
The Mercers' Charitable
   Foundation
The Merchant Taylors'
   Company Charities Fund
The Merchant Venturers'
   Charity
The Merchants' House of
   Glasgow
The Mersey Docks and
   Harbour Company
   Charitable Fund
Community Foundation for
   Merseyside
The Zachary Merton and
   George Woofindin
   Convalescent Trust
The Tony Metherell Charitable
   Trust
The Metropolitan Drinking
   Fountain and Cattle Trough
   Association
Gerald Micklem Charitable
   Trust
Midhurst Pensions Trust
The Migraine Trust
Miles Trust for the Putney and
   Roehampton Community
The Hugh and Mary Miller
   Bequest Trust
The Miller Foundation
The Millfield Trust
The Millhouses Charitable
   Trust
The Millichope Foundation
The Mills Charity
The Millward Charitable Trust
The Clare Milne Trust
Milton Keynes Community
   Foundation
The Edgar Milward Charity
The Keith and Joan
   Mindelsohn Charitable
   Trust
The Peter Minet Trust
The Minos Trust

The Mirfield Educational
   Charity
The Laurence Misener
   Charitable Trust
The Mishcon Family Charitable
   Trust
The Misselbrook Trust
The Mitchell Charitable Trust
The Esmé Mitchell Trust
Keren Mitzvah Trust
The Mizpah Trust
The Mobbs Memorial Trust Ltd
The Modiano Charitable Trust
The Moette Charitable Trust
The Mole Charitable Trust
The D C Moncrieff Charitable
   Trust
Monmouthshire County Council
   Welsh Church Act Fund
The Montague Thompson
   Coon Charitable Trust
The Colin Montgomerie
   Charitable Foundation
The Monument Trust
The Henry Moore Foundation
The Nigel Moores Family
   Charitable Trust
The Peter Moores Foundation
The Morel Charitable Trust
The Morgan Charitable
   Foundation
The Mr and Mrs J T Morgan
   Foundation
The Oliver Morland Charitable
   Trust
The Bernard Morris Charitable
   Trust
The Morris Charitable Trust
The Willie and Mabel Morris
   Charitable Trust
The Peter Morrison Charitable
   Foundation
The Stanley Morrison
   Charitable Trust
Vyoel Moshe Charitable Trust
The Moss Charitable Trust
The Robert and Margaret
   Moss Charitable Trust
Moss Family Charitable Trust
The Mount Everest Foundation
The Edwina Mountbatten Trust
Mountbatten Festival of Music
The Mountbatten Memorial
   Trust
The Mugdock Children's Trust
The Mulberry Trust
The Edith Murphy Foundation
The Mushroom Fund
The Music Sales Charitable
   Trust
Muslim Hands
The Mutual Trust Group
The Kitty and Daniel Nabarro
   Charitable Trust
The Nadezhda Charitable Trust
The Naggar Charitable Trust

The Eleni Nakou Foundation
The Janet Nash Charitable
   Settlement
Nathan Charitable Trust
The National Art Collections
   Fund
The National Churches Trust
   (formerly the Historic
   Churches Preservation
   Trust with the Incorporated
   Church Building Society)
The National Manuscripts
   Conservation Trust
The Nchima Trust
Needham Market and Barking
   Welfare Charities
The Worshipful Company of
   Needlemakers' Charitable
   Fund
The Neighbourly Charitable
   Trust
The James Neill Trust Fund
Nemoral Ltd
Network for Social Change
The New Appeals Organisation
   for the City and County of
   Nottingham
New Court Charitable Trust
The Newcomen Collett
   Foundation
Alderman Newton's
   Educational Foundation
The Chevras Ezras Nitzrochim
   Trust
The Noon Foundation
The Norda Trust
Norie Charitable Trust
Normalyn Charitable Trust
The Norman Family Charitable
   Trust
The Duncan Norman Trust
   Fund
The Normanby Charitable Trust
The North West Cancer
   Research Fund
The Northampton Municipal
   Church Charities
The Northampton Queen's
   Institute Relief in Sickness
   Fund
The Earl of Northampton's
   Charity
The Northcott Devon
   Foundation
The Northcott Devon Medical
   Foundation
The Northmoor Trust
The Northumberland Village
   Homes Trust
The Northumbria Historic
   Churches Trust
The Northwood Charitable
   Trust
The Norton Foundation
The Norwich Church of England
   Young Men's Society

The Norwich Historic Churches
   Trust Ltd
The Norwich Town Close
   Estate Charity
The Norwood and Newton
   Settlement
The Noswad Charity
The Notgrove Trust
The Nottingham General
   Dispensary
The Nottingham Gordon
   Memorial Trust for Boys
   and Girls
Nottinghamshire Community
   Foundation
The Nottinghamshire Historic
   Churches Trust
The Nottinghamshire Miners'
   Welfare Trust Fund
Novi Most International
The Father O'Mahoney
   Memorial Trust
The Sir Peter O'Sullevan
   Charitable Trust
The Oak Trust
The Oakdale Trust
The Oakley Charitable Trust
The Oakmoor Charitable Trust
The Odin Charitable Trust
The Ofenheim Charitable Trust
Ogilvie Charities Deed No.2
   (including the Charity of
   Mary Catherine Ford Smith)
The Ogle Christian Trust
The Oikonomia Trust
Oizer Charitable Trust
The Old Broad Street Charity
   Trust
The Old Enfield Charitable
   Trust
The John Oldacre Foundation
The Oldham Foundation
Onaway Trust
Open Gate
The Ormsby Charitable Trust
Orrin Charitable Trust
The Ouseley Trust
The Owen Family Trust
Oxfam (GB)
The Oxfordshire Community
   Foundation
The P F Charitable Trust
Padwa Charitable Foundation
The Pallant Charitable Trust
The Palmer Foundation
Eleanor Palmer Trust
The Panacea Society
Panton Trust
The James Pantyfedwen
   Foundation
The Paragon Trust
The Park House Charitable
   Trust
The Frank Parkinson
   Agricultural Trust

The Samuel and Freda
   Parkinson Charitable Trust
The Parthenon Trust
The Constance Paterson
   Charitable Trust
The Patrick Charitable Trust
The Jack Patston Charitable
   Trust
Paycare Charity Trust (formerly
   known as Patients' Aid
   Association Hospital and
   Medical Charities Trust)
The Payne Charitable Trust
The Harry Payne Trust
The Susanna Peake Charitable
   Trust
The Pedmore Sporting Club
   Trust Fund
The Pennycress Trust
The Performing Right Society
   Foundation
The Persson Charitable Trust
   (formerly Highmoore Hall
   Charitable Trust)
The Persula Foundation
The Jack Petchey Foundation
The Petplan Charitable Trust
The Philips and Rubens
   Charitable Trust
The Phillips Charitable Trust
The Phillips Family Charitable
   Trust
Philological Foundation
The David Pickford Charitable
   Foundation
The Bernard Piggott Trust
The Pilgrim Trust
The Cecil Pilkington Charitable
   Trust
The Austin and Hope
   Pilkington Trust
The Sir Harry Pilkington Trust
The Col W W Pilkington Will
   Trusts The General Charity
   Fund
The DLA Piper Charitable Trust
The Worshipful Company of
   Plaisterers Charitable Trust
The Platinum Trust
The Poling Charitable Trust
The George and Esme Pollitzer
   Charitable Settlement
The J S F Pollitzer Charitable
   Settlement
The Ponton House Trust
The Mayor of Poole's Appeal
   Fund
Edith and Ferdinand Porjes
   Charitable Trust
The John Porter Charitable
   Trust
The Porter Foundation
The Portishead Nautical Trust
The Portrack Charitable Trust
The J E Posnansky Charitable
   Trust

The Powell Foundation
The W L Pratt Charitable Trust
Premierquote Ltd
Premishlaner Charitable Trust
The William Price Charitable
   Trust
The Lucy Price Relief-in-Need
   Charity
Sir John Priestman Charity
   Trust
The Primrose Trust
The Prince of Wales's
   Charitable Foundation
The Priory Foundation
Prison Service Charity Fund
The Privy Purse Charitable
   Trust
The Proven Family Trust
The Provincial Grand Charity of
   the Province of Derbyshire
PSA Peugeot Citroen Charity
   Trust
The Puebla Charitable Trust
The Richard and Christine
   Purchas Charitable Trust
The Puri Foundation
The Queen's Silver Jubilee
   Trust
R S Charitable Trust
The R V W Trust
The Monica Rabagliati
   Charitable Trust
Rachel Charitable Trust
The Mr and Mrs Philip
   Rackham Charitable Trust
Richard Radcliffe Charitable
   Trust
The Radcliffe Trust
The Ragdoll Foundation
The Rainford Trust
The Peggy Ramsay Foundation
The Joseph and Lena Randall
   Charitable Trust
The Fanny Rapaport Charitable
   Settlement
The Ratcliff Foundation
The Ratcliff Pension Charity
The Ratcliffe Charitable Trust
The Eleanor Rathbone
   Charitable Trust
The Sigrid Rausing Trust
The Ravensdale Trust
The Rayden Charitable Trust
The Roger Raymond Charitable
   Trust
The Rayne Foundation
The Rayne Trust
The John Rayner Charitable
   Trust
The Sir James Reckitt Charity
Red Hill Charitable Trust
The Red Rose Charitable Trust
The C A Redfern Charitable
   Foundation
The Reed Foundation

Richard Reeve's Foundation
The Max Reinhardt Charitable
   Trust
Relief Fund for Romania
   Limited
The Rest Harrow Trust
Reuben Brothers Foundation
The Joan K Reynell Charitable
   Trust
The Nathaniel Reyner Trust
   Fund
The Rhododendron Trust
The Rhondda Cynon Taff
   Welsh Church Acts Fund
The Clive Richards Charity
The Richmond Parish Lands
   Charity
Ridgesave Limited
The Ripple Effect Foundation
The Sir John Ritblat Family
   Foundation
The River Trust
Thomas Roberts Trust
The Robertson Trust
The Rochester Bridge Trust
The Rock Foundation
The Rock Solid Trust
The Rofeh Trust
Richard Rogers Charitable
   Settlement
Rokach Family Charitable Trust
The Helen Roll Charitable
   Trust
The Sir James Roll Charitable
   Trust
The Roman Research Trust
Romeera Foundation
The C A Rookes Charitable
   Trust
The Rosca Trust
The Cecil Rosen Foundation
The Rothermere Foundation
The Rotherwick Foundation
The Rothley Trust
The Roughley Charitable Trust
Mrs Gladys Row Fogo
   Charitable Trust
Rowanville Ltd
The Christopher Rowbotham
   Charitable Trust
The Rowing Foundation
The Rowlands Trust
Royal Artillery Charitable Fund
Royal British Legion
Royal Docks Trust (London)
Royal Masonic Trust for Girls
   and Boys
The Royal Scots Benevolent
   Society
The Alfred and Frances
   Rubens Charitable Trust
The Rubin Foundation
William Arthur Rudd Memorial
   Trust
The Russell Trust

The J S and E C Rymer
   Charitable Trust
S O Charitable Trust
The Jeremy and John Sacher
   Charitable Trust
The Michael Harry Sacher
   Trust
The Raymond and Beverley
   Sackler 1988 Foundation
The Sackler Trust (Formerly Dr
   Mortimer and Theresa
   Sackler Foundation)
The Ruzin Sadagora Trust
The Saddlers' Company
   Charitable Fund
The Saga Charitable Trust
The Jean Sainsbury Animal
   Welfare Trust
The Alan and Babette
   Sainsbury Charitable Fund
The Sainsbury Family
   Charitable Trusts
The Saintbury Trust
The Saints and Sinners Trust
The Salamander Charitable
   Trust
The Salt Foundation
The Salt Trust
The Sammermar Trust
Basil Samuel Charitable Trust
The Hon. M J Samuel
   Charitable Trust
The Peter Samuel Charitable
   Trust
The Camilla Samuel Fund
The Samworth Foundation
The Sandra Charitable Trust
Jimmy Savile Charitable Trust
The Scarfe Charitable Trust
The Schapira Charitable Trust
The Schmidt-Bodner Charitable
   Trust
The R H Scholes Charitable
   Trust
The Schreib Trust
The Schreiber Charitable Trust
The Francis C Scott Charitable
   Trust
The Frieda Scott Charitable
   Trust
The Sir James and Lady Scott
   Trust
The Scott Trust Foundation
The Storrow Scott Will Trust
The Scottish Arts Council
Scottish Coal Industry Special
   Welfare Fund
The Scottish Community
   Foundation
The Scouloudi Foundation
Seamen's Hospital Society
The Searchlight Electric
   Charitable Trust
The Searle Charitable Trust
The Helene Sebba Charitable
   Trust

The Samuel Sebba Charitable
Trust
The Seedfield Trust
Leslie Sell Charitable Trust
The Ayrton Senna Foundation
The Seven Fifty Trust
The Severn Trent Water
Charitable Trust Fund
The Cyril Shack Trust
The Shanti Charitable Trust
ShareGift (The Orr Mackintosh
Foundation)
The Linley Shaw Foundation
The Sheepdrove Trust
The Sheffield and District
Hospital Services
Charitable Fund
The Sheldon Trust
The P and D Shepherd
Charitable Trust
The Sylvia and Colin Shepherd
Charitable Trust
The Archie Sherman Cardiff
Foundation
The Archie Sherman Charitable
Trust
The R C Sherriff Trust
The Shetland Charitable Trust
SHINE (Support and Help in
Education)
The Barnett and Sylvia Shine
No 2 Charitable Trust
The Bassil Shippam and
Alsford Trust
The Shipwrights' Company
Charitable Fund
The Shirley Foundation
Shlomo Memorial Fund Limited
The J A Shone Memorial Trust
The Barbara A Shuttleworth
Memorial Trust
David and Jennifer Sieff
Charitable Trust
The Julius Silman Charitable
Trust
The Leslie Silver Charitable
Trust
The Simpson Education and
Conservation Trust
The Simpson Foundation
The Huntly and Margery
Sinclair Charitable Trust
Sino-British Fellowship Trust
The Skelton Bounty
The Charles Skey Charitable
Trust
Skipton Building Society
Charitable Foundation
The John Slater Foundation
The SMB Charitable Trust
The Mrs Smith and Mount
Trust
The N Smith Charitable
Settlement
The Amanda Smith Charitable
Trust

The E H Smith Charitable Trust
The Smith Charitable Trust
The Leslie Smith Foundation
The Martin Smith Foundation
Stanley Smith General
Charitable Trust
The Stanley Smith UK
Horticultural Trust
The Snowball Trust
Solihull Community Foundation
The Solo Charitable
Settlement
Dr Richard Solomon's
Charitable Trust
The E C Sosnow Charitable
Trust
The Souter Charitable Trust
The South Square Trust
The Stephen R and Philippa H
Southall Charitable Trust
The W F Southall Trust
The Southwold Trust
The Sovereign Health Care
Charitable Trust
Sparquote Limited
The Spear Charitable Trust
The Worshipful Company of
Spectacle Makers' Charity
The Jessie Spencer Trust
The Ralph and Irma Sperring
Charity
The Moss Spiro Will Charitable
Foundation
The Spoore, Merry and Rixman
Foundation
Springfields Employees'
Medical Research and
Charity Trust Fund
Springrule Ltd
The Spurrell Charitable Trust
The Geoff and Fiona Squire
Foundation
St Francis's Leprosy Guild
St Gabriel's Trust
St James' Trust Settlement
St James's Place Foundation
Sir Walter St John's
Educational Charity
St Katharine and Shadwell
Trust
St Michael's and All Saints'
Charities
The Late St Patrick White
Charitable Trust
St Teilo's Trust
The Stanley Foundation Ltd
The Stanton Ballard Charitable
Trust
The Star Charitable Trust
The Peter Stebbings Memorial
Charity
The Steel Charitable Trust
The Steinberg Family
Charitable Trust
The Hugh Stenhouse
Foundation

The Sigmund Sternberg
Charitable Foundation
Stervon Ltd
The Stevenage Community
Trust
The June Stevens Foundation
The Steventon Allotments and
Relief-in-Need Charity
The Leonard Laity Stoate
Charitable Trust
The Edward Stocks-Massey
Bequest Fund
The Stokenchurch Educational
Charity
The Stoller Charitable Trust
The M J C Stone Charitable
Trust
The Stone-Mallabar Charitable
Foundation
The Samuel Storey Family
Charitable Trust
Peter Stormonth Darling
Charitable Trust
The Strangward Trust
The Strasser Foundation
Strathclyde Police Benevolent
Fund
The Sudborough Foundation
The Suffolk Historic Churches
Trust
The Summerfield Charitable
Trust
The Bernard Sunley Charitable
Foundation
The Surrey Historic Buildings
Trust Ltd
The Sussex Historic Churches
Trust
The Sutasoma Trust
Swansea and Brecon Diocesan
Board of Finance Limited
The John Swire (1989)
Charitable Trust
The Swire Charitable Trust
The Hugh and Ruby Sykes
Charitable Trust
The Charles and Elsie Sykes
Trust
The Sylvanus Charitable Trust
The Stella Symons Charitable
Trust
The Tabeel Trust
The Tajtelbaum Charitable
Trust
The Talbot Trusts
The Talbot Village Trust
Tallow Chandlers Benevolent
Fund
The Tangent Charitable Trust
The Lady Tangye Charitable
Trust
The David Tannen Charitable
Trust
The Tanner Trust
The Lili Tapper Charitable
Foundation

The Mrs A Lacy Tate Trust
The Tay Charitable Trust
Humphrey Richardson Taylor
Charitable Trust
The Connie and Albert Taylor
Charitable Trust
The Cyril Taylor Charitable
Trust
A P Taylor Trust
Tearfund
The Tedworth Charitable Trust
The Templeton Goodwill Trust
Tesco Charity Trust
The Thames Wharf Charity
The Thistle Trust
The Loke Wan Tho Memorial
Foundation
The Arthur and Margaret
Thompson Charitable Trust
The Thompson Family
Charitable Trust
The Len Thomson Charitable
Trust
The Sue Thomson Foundation
The Thornton Foundation
The Thornton Trust
The Three Guineas Trust
The Three Oaks Trust
The Thriplow Charitable Trust
The Tinsley Foundation
The Tisbury Telegraph Trust
TJH Foundation
The Tobacco Pipe Makers and
Tobacco Trade Benevolent
Fund
The Tolkien Trust
Tollemache (Buckminster)
Charitable Trust
Tomchei Torah Charitable
Trust
The Tompkins Foundation
The Tory Family Foundation
Tottenham Grammar School
Foundation
The Tower Hill Trust
The Towry Law Charitable Trust
(also known as the Castle
Educational Trust)
The Toy Trust
The Mayor of Trafford's Charity
Fund
The Constance Travis
Charitable Trust
The Treeside Trust
The True Colours Trust
Truedene Co. Ltd
The Truemark Trust
Truemart Limited
Trumros Limited
Trust Sixty Three
Tudor Rose Ltd
The Tudor Trust
The Tufton Charitable Trust
The R D Turner Charitable
Trust
The Douglas Turner Trust

The Florence Turner Trust
Miss S M Tutton Charitable
Trust
The TUUT Charitable Trust
Trustees of Tzedakah
Ulster Garden Villages Ltd
Ultach Trust
Ulting Overseas Trust
The Ulverscroft Foundation
Ulverston Town Lands Charity
The Underwood Trust
The Union of Orthodox Hebrew
Congregation
The United Society for the
Propagation of the Gospel
The David Uri Memorial Trust
Uxbridge United Welfare Trust
Vale of Glamorgan – Welsh
Church Fund
The Valentine Charitable Trust
The Van Neste Foundation
Mrs Maud Van Norden's
Charitable Foundation
The Vandervell Foundation
The Vardy Foundation
Veneziana Fund
The Verdon-Smith Family
Charitable Settlement
Victoria Homes Trust
The Nigel Vinson Charitable
Trust
The William and Ellen Vinten
Trust
The Vintners' Company
Charitable Foundation
Vintners' Gifts Charity
Vision Charity
Vivdale Ltd
The Viznitz Foundation
Wade's Charity
The Scurrah Wainwright Charity
Wakeham Trust
The Community Foundation in
Wales
Wales Council for Voluntary
Action
Robert and Felicity Waley-
Cohen Charitable Trust
The Thomas Wall Trust
The F J Wallis Charitable
Settlement
War on Want
The Ward Blenkinsop Trust
The George Ward Charitable
Trust
The Barbara Ward Children's
Foundation
The John Warren Foundation
G R Waters Charitable Trust
2000
The Waterways Trust
The Howard Watson Symington
Memorial Charity
John Watson's Trust
Weatherley Charitable Trust

The Weavers' Company
Benevolent Fund
The William Webster
Charitable Trust
The Weinberg Foundation
The Weinstein Foundation
The Weinstock Fund
The James Weir Foundation
The Barbara Welby Trust
The Weldon UK Charitable
Trust
Welsh Church Fund Dyfed
area (Carmarthenshire,
Ceredigion and
Pembrokeshire)
The Welton Foundation
The Wessex Youth Trust
The West Derby Wastelands
Charity
West London Synagogue
Charitable Fund
The West Yorkshire Police
Community Fund
The Westminster Foundation
The Garfield Weston
Foundation
The Whitaker Charitable Trust
The Colonel W H Whitbread
Charitable Trust
The Simon Whitbread
Charitable Trust
The Whitecourt Charitable
Trust
The Norman Whiteley Trust
The Whitley Animal Protection
Trust
The Whittlesey Charity
The Lionel Wigram Memorial
Trust
The Felicity Wilde Charitable
Trust
The Wilkinson Charitable
Foundation
The Kay Williams Charitable
Foundation
The Williams Family Charitable
Trust
The H D H Wills 1965
Charitable Trust
The Dame Violet Wills Will
Trust
The Wilmcote Charitrust
David Wilson Foundation
The Wilson Foundation
J and J R Wilson Trust
The Community Foundation for
Wiltshire and Swindon
The Benjamin Winegarten
Charitable Trust
The Francis Winham
Foundation
Wirral Mayor's Charity
The Michael and Anna Wix
Charitable Trust
The Wixamtree Trust

The Woburn 1986 Charitable
Trust
The Maurice Wohl Charitable
Foundation
The Charles Wolfson
Charitable Trust
The Wolfson Family Charitable
Trust
The Wolfson Foundation
Women's World Day of Prayer
(NCWWDPEWNI)
The James Wood Bequest
Fund
Woodlands Green Ltd
Woodlands Trust
The Woodward Charitable
Trust
Worcester Municipal Charities
(incorporating Worcester
Consolidated Municipal
Charity and Worcester
Municipal Exhibitions
Foundation)
The Worcestershire and
Dudley Historic Churches
Trust
The Fred and Della Worms
Charitable Trust
The Wragge and Co. Charitable
Trust
The Diana Edgson Wright
Charitable Trust
The Matthews Wrightson
Charity Trust
Miss E B Wrightson's
Charitable Settlement
Wychdale Ltd
Wychville Ltd
The Wyndham Charitable Trust
The Wyseliot Charitable Trust
The Xerox (UK) Trust
The Yardley Great Trust
The Dennis Alan Yardy
Charitable Trust
The W Wing Yip and Brothers
Foundation
The York Children's Trust
Yorkshire Agricultural Society
Yorkshire Building Society
Charitable Foundation
The Yorkshire Dales
Millennium Trust
The John Young Charitable
Settlement
The William Allen Young
Charitable Trust
The John K Young Endowment
Fund
Youth Music
Zephyr Charitable Trust
The Marjorie and Arnold Ziff
Charitable Foundation
Stephen Zimmerman
Charitable Trust
The Zochonis Charitable Trust

Zurich Community Trust (UK)
Limited

....

■ Computer systems and equipment

The 1970 Trust
The 1989 Willan Charitable
Trust
The 29th May 1961 Charitable
Trust
The Aberbrothock Skea Trust
The Aberdeen Endowments
Trust
The Aberdeenshire Educational
Trust Scheme
Achiezer Association Ltd
Achisomoch Aid Company
Limited
The ACT Foundation
Action Medical Research
The Company of Actuaries'
Charitable Trust Fund
The Sylvia Adams Charitable
Trust
The Victor Adda Foundation
The Adint Charitable Trust
Age Scotland (Formerly Age
Concern Scotland and Help
the Aged)
Age UK (formerly Help the
Aged and Age Concern)
Aid to the Church in Need (UK)
The Sylvia Aitken Charitable
Trust
The Ajahma Charitable Trust
Aldgate and All Hallows'
Barking Exhibition
Foundation
The Aldgate Freedom
Foundation
Allchurches Trust Ltd
The H B Allen Charitable Trust
The Alliance Family Foundation
Angus Allnatt Charitable
Foundation
The Pat Allsop Charitable Trust
Almondsbury Charity
Altamont Ltd
Alvor Charitable Trust
The Ammco Trust
Viscount Amory's Charitable
Trust
The AMW Charitable Trust
The André Christian Trust
Anguish's Educational
Foundation
The Animal Defence Trust
The Eric Anker-Petersen
Charity
Ambrose and Ann Appelbe
Trust
The Appletree Trust
The John Apthorp Charitable
Trust
The Arbib Foundation

The John M Archer Charitable
Trust
The Archer Trust
The Ardwick Trust
The Argus Appeal
The Armenian Relief Society of
Great Britain Trust
The Armourers' and Brasiers'
Gauntlet Trust
Arsenal Charitable Trust
The Artemis Charitable Trust
The Arts and Entertainment
Charitable Trust
Arts Council England
The Arts Council of Northern
Ireland
The Arts Council of Wales
The Ove Arup Foundation
The AS Charitable Trust
The Ashden Trust
The Ashendene Trust
The Ashley Family Foundation
(formerly The Laura Ashley
Foundation)
The Norman C Ashton
Foundation
The Ashworth Charitable Trust
The Ian Askew Charitable Trust
The Associated Country
Women of the World
(ACWW)
The Association of Colleges
Charitable Trust
Astellas European Foundation
Asthma UK
The Astor Foundation
The Astor of Hever Trust
The Aurelius Charitable Trust
The Avenue Charitable Trust
The John Avins Trustees
The Avon and Somerset Police
Community Trust
AW Charitable Trust
The Aylesford Family
Charitable Trust
The BAA Communities Trust
The BACTA Charitable Trust
The Scott Bader
Commonwealth Ltd
The Bagri Foundation
Veta Bailey Charitable Trust
The Austin Bailey Trust
The Baily Thomas Charitable
Fund
The Baird Trust
The Baker Charitable Trust
The Balcombe Charitable Trust
The Albert Casanova Ballard
Deceased Trust
The Ballinger Charitable Trust
The Balmore Trust
The Balney Charitable Trust
The Baltic Charitable Fund
The Bamford Charitable
Foundation
The Banbury Charities

William P Bancroft (No 2)
Charitable Trust and
Jenepher Gillett Trust
The Band Trust
The Barbers' Company General
Charities
The Barbour Foundation
Barchester Healthcare
Foundation
The Barclay Foundation
The Baring Foundation
Peter Barker-Mill Memorial
Charity
Barleycorn Trust
Barnes Workhouse Fund
The Barnsbury Charitable Trust
The Barnstaple Bridge Trust
The Barnwood House Trust
The Misses Barrie Charitable
Trust
Barrington Family Charitable
Trust
The Charity of William Barrow
Stephen J Barry Charitable
Trust
The Bartlett Taylor Charitable
Trust
The Paul Bassham Charitable
Trust
The Batchworth Trust
The Bay Tree Charitable Trust
D H and L H Baylin Charitable
Trust
The Louis Baylis (Maidenhead
Advertiser) Charitable Trust
BBC Children in Need
B-CH 1971 Charitable Trust
The Beacon Trust
The Bearder Charity
The James Beattie Charitable
Trust
The Beaufort House Trust
Limited
The Beaverbrook Foundation
The Beccles Town Lands
Charity
The Becker Family Charitable
Trust
The Becketts and Sargeants
Educational Foundation
The John Beckwith Charitable
Trust
The Peter Beckwith Charitable
Trust
The Bedford Charity (The
Harpur Trust)
The David and Ruth Behrend
Fund
The Beit Trust
The Bellahouston Bequest
Fund
The Bellinger Donnay Trust
Belljoe Tzedoko Ltd
The Benfield Motors Charitable
Trust

The Benham Charitable
Settlement
The Hervey Benham Charitable
Trust
Maurice and Jacqueline
Bennett Charitable Trust
The Gerald Bentall Charitable
Trust
Bergqvist Charitable Trust
The Berkshire Community
Foundation
The Bestway Foundation
Thomas Betton's Charity for
Pensions and Relief-in-Need
BHST
The Mason Bibby 1981 Trust
BibleLands
The Bideford Bridge Trust
The Big Lottery Fund
The Billmeir Charitable Trust
Percy Bilton Charity
The Bingham Trust
The Bintaub Charitable Trust
The Birmingham District
Nursing Charitable Trust
The Birmingham Hospital
Saturday Fund Medical
Charity and Welfare Trust
Birmingham International
Airport Community Trust
The Lord Mayor of
Birmingham's Charity
The Bisgood Charitable Trust
(registered as Miss Jeanne
Bisgood's Charitable Trust)
The Michael Bishop
Foundation
The Bishop's Development
Fund
The Bertie Black Foundation
Isabel Blackman Foundation
The Herbert and Peter
Blagrave Charitable Trust
The Blair Foundation
The Blanchminster Trust
The Sir Victor Blank Charitable
Settlement
The Neville and Elaine Blond
Charitable Trust
The Bluston Charitable
Settlement
The Body Shop Foundation
The Boltons Trust
The Bonamy Charitable Trust
The John and Celia Bonham
Christie Charitable Trust
The Charlotte Bonham-Carter
Charitable Trust
Bonhomie United Charity
Society
The Boots Charitable Trust
The Bordon and Liphook
Charity
The Oliver Borthwick Memorial
Trust
The Bothwell Charitable Trust

H E and E L Botteley
Charitable Trust
The Harry Bottom Charitable
Trust
The Anthony Bourne
Foundation
The Bower Trust
The Bowerman Charitable
Trust
John and Susan Bowers Fund
The Bowland Charitable Trust
The William Brake Charitable
Trust
The Tony Bramall Charitable
Trust
The Harold and Alice Bridges
Charity
The Brighton District Nursing
Association Trust
Bristol Archdeaconry Charity
John Bristow and Thomas
Mason Trust
Britannia Foundation
The British Council for
Prevention of Blindness
The British Dietetic
Association General and
Education Trust Fund
The British Gas (Scottish Gas)
Energy Trust
British Heart Foundation
British Humane Association
British Institute at Ankara
British Ornithologists' Union
British Record Industry Trust
The Britto Foundation
The J and M Britton Charitable
Trust
The Charles and Edna
Broadhurst Charitable Trust
The Roger Brooke Charitable
Trust
The David Brooke Charity
The Charles Brotherton Trust
Joseph Brough Charitable
Trust
The Swinfen Broun Charitable
Trust
Mrs E E Brown Charitable
Settlement
The Jack Brunton Charitable
Trust
The Bryant Trust
The Buckinghamshire
Foundation
The Buckinghamshire Masonic
Centenary Fund
The Rosemary Bugden
Charitable Trust
The Bulldog Trust Limited
The E F Bulmer Benevolent
Fund
Burdens Charitable Foundation
The Clara E Burgess Charity
The Burry Charitable Trust

The Arnold Burton 1998 Charitable Trust

The Burton Breweries Charitable Trust

The Geoffrey Burton Charitable Trust

Consolidated Charity of Burton upon Trent

Butchers' Company General Charities

The Noel Buxton Trust

Henry T and Lucy B Cadbury Charitable Trust

The Christopher Cadbury Charitable Trust

The G W Cadbury Charitable Trust

The Richard Cadbury Charitable Trust

The Edward and Dorothy Cadbury Trust

The George Cadbury Trust

CAF (Charities Aid Foundation)

CAFOD (Catholic Agency for Overseas Development)

The Callander Charitable Trust

Calleva Foundation

Calypso Browning Trust

The Campden Charities Trustee

The Canning Trust

The Carew Pole Charitable Trust

The D W T Cargill Fund

Carlee Ltd

The Carlton House Charitable Trust

The Worshipful Company of Carmen Benevolent Trust

The Carnegie Dunfermline Trust

The Carpenter Charitable Trust

The Carpenters' Company Charitable Trust

The Carrington Charitable Trust

The Carron Charitable Settlement

The Leslie Mary Carter Charitable Trust

The Carvill Trust

The Casey Trust

Sir John Cass's Foundation

The Elizabeth Casson Trust

The Castang Foundation

The Catalyst Charitable Trust (formerly the Buckle Family Charitable Trust)

The Catholic Charitable Trust

Catholic Foreign Missions

The Catholic Trust for England and Wales

The Joseph and Annie Cattle Trust

The Thomas Sivewright Catto Charitable Settlement

The Wilfrid and Constance Cave Foundation

The Cayo Foundation

The B G S Cayzer Charitable Trust

The Cazenove Charitable Trust

Celtic Charity Fund

The Cemlyn-Jones Trust

The Pamela Champion Foundation

The Chapman Charitable Trust

John William Chapman's Charitable Trust

The Charities Advisory Trust

Charitworth Limited

The Charter 600 Charity

The Worshipful Company of Chartered Accountants General Charitable Trust (also known as CALC)

The Chasah Trust

The Chelsea Building Society Charitable Foundation

The Chelsea Square 1994 Trust

The Cheruby Trust

The Cheshire Provincial Fund of Benevolence

The Chetwode Foundation

Chevioty Asset Management Charitable Trust

The Malcolm Chick Charity

Childs Charitable Trust

The Childwick Trust

The Chippenham Borough Lands Charity

The Chipping Sodbury Town Lands Charity

CHK Charities Limited

The Chownes Foundation

The Chrimes Family Charitable Trust

The Christabella Charitable Trust

Christadelphian Samaritan Fund

Christian Aid

Christian Response to Eastern Europe

The Church and Community Fund

The Church Burgesses Educational Foundation

Church Burgesses Trust

The Church Urban Fund

City and County of Swansea Welsh Church Act Fund

The City Bridge Trust (formerly known as Bridge House Trust)

The City Educational Trust Fund

Stephen Clark 1957 Charitable Trust

J A Clark Charitable Trust

The Hilda and Alice Clark Charitable Trust

The Roger and Sarah Bancroft Clark Charitable Trust

The Clarke Charitable Settlement

The Cleary Foundation

The Cleopatra Trust

Lord Clinton's Charitable Trust

The Clore Duffield Foundation

Miss V L Clore's 1967 Charitable Trust

Closehelm Ltd

The Clothworkers' Foundation

Richard Cloudesley's Charity

The Clover Trust

The Robert Clutterbuck Charitable Trust

Clydpride Ltd

The Coalfields Regeneration Trust

The John Coates Charitable Trust

Coats Foundation Trust

The Cobtree Charity Trust Ltd

The Denise Cohen Charitable Trust

The Vivienne and Samuel Cohen Charitable Trust

The John S Cohen Foundation

The R and S Cohen Foundation

The Colchester Catalyst Charity

The Cole Charitable Trust

The Colefax Charitable Trust

The John and Freda Coleman Charitable Trust

The George Henry Collins Charity

The E Alec Colman Charitable Fund Ltd

The Sir Jeremiah Colman Gift Trust

The Colt Foundation

The Coltstaple Trust

Colwinston Charitable Trust

Colyer-Fergusson Charitable Trust

Comic Relief

The Comino Foundation

Community Foundation for Calderdale

The Community Foundation for Northern Ireland

The Compton Charitable Trust

The Congleton Inclosure Trust

The Conservation Foundation

The Consolidated Charities for the Infirm Merchant Taylors' Company

The Ernest Cook Trust

The Cooks Charity

The Catherine Cookson Charitable Trust

Mabel Cooper Charity

The Alice Ellen Cooper Dean Charitable Foundation

The Co-operative Foundation

The Marjorie Coote Animal Charity Trust

The Marjorie Coote Old People's Charity

The Helen Jean Cope Trust

The J Reginald Corah Foundation Fund

The Gershon Coren Charitable Foundation

The Corinthian Trust

Edwin Cornforth 1983 Charity Trust

The Duke of Cornwall's Benevolent Fund

The Cornwell Charitable Trust

The Sidney and Elizabeth Corob Charitable Trust

The Corona Charitable Trust

The Costa Family Charitable Trust (formerly the Morgan Williams Charitable Trust)

The Cotton Industry War Memorial Trust

The Augustine Courtauld Trust

The General Charities of the City of Coventry

Coventry Building Society Charitable Foundation

The John Cowan Foundation

The Sir William Coxen Trust Fund

The Lord Cozens-Hardy Trust

The Craignish Trust

The Craps Charitable Trust

Michael Crawford Children's Charity

The Cray Trust

Creative Scotland

The Crescent Trust

Cripplegate Foundation

The Violet and Milo Cripps Charitable Trust

The Harry Crook Foundation

The Cross Trust

The Croydon Relief in Need Charities

The Mayor of Croydon's Charity Fund

Cruden Foundation Ltd

The Ronald Cruickshank's Foundation

The R D Crusaders Foundation

The Culra Charitable Trust

The Cumber Family Charitable Trust

Cumberland Building Society Charitable Foundation

Cumbria Community Foundation

The D J H Currie Memorial Trust

The Dennis Curry Charitable Trust

The Raymond Curtis Charitable Trust

The Manny Cussins Foundation

The Cwmbran Trust

Itzchok Meyer Cymerman Trust Ltd

The D G Charitable Settlement

The D'Oyly Carte Charitable Trust

The Daily Prayer Union Charitable Trust Ltd

The Daisy Trust

The Daiwa Anglo-Japanese Foundation

The Dr and Mrs A Darlington Charitable Trust

Baron Davenport's Charity

The Davidson (Nairn) Charitable Trust

The Davidson Family Charitable Trust

The Alderman Joe Davidson Memorial Trust

Michael Davies Charitable Settlement

The Gwendoline and Margaret Davies Charity

The Wilfrid Bruce Davis Charitable Trust

Davis-Rubens Charitable Trust

The Dawe Charitable Trust

The De Clermont Charitable Company Ltd

The Leopold De Rothschild Charitable Trust

The Deakin Charitable Trust

William Dean Countryside and Educational Trust

The Debmar Benevolent Trust

The Dellal Foundation

The Delves Charitable Trust

The Demigryphon Trust

The Denman Charitable Trust

The Denton Charitable Trust

The Denton Wilde Sapte Charitable Trust

The Earl of Derby's Charitable Trust

Derbyshire Community Foundation

The J N Derbyshire Trust

Devon Community Foundation

The Devon Educational Trust

The Duke of Devonshire's Charitable Trust

The Sandy Dewhirst Charitable Trust

The Laduma Dhamecha Charitable Trust

Diabetes UK

The Dibden Allotments Fund

The Dickon Trust

The Digbeth Trust

The Dinwoodie Settlement

Dischma Charitable Trust

The DLM Charitable Trust

Louise Dobson Charitable Trust

The Derek and Eileen Dodgson Foundation

The Dollond Charitable Trust

Domepride Ltd

The Dorcas Trust

The Dorus Trust

The Doughty Charity Trust

The R M Douglas Charitable Trust

The Drapers' Charitable Fund

The Dugdale Charitable Trust

The Duis Charitable Trust

The Dulverton Trust

The P B Dumbell Charitable Trust

The Dumbreck Charity

Ronald Duncan Literary Foundation

The Houghton Dunn Charitable Trust

The Dunn Family Charitable Trust

The W E Dunn Trust

Dushinsky Trust Ltd

The Dwek Family Charitable Trust

The Dyers' Company Charitable Trust

The Eagle Charity Trust

The Earley Charity

Earls Colne and Halstead Educational Charity

The Earmark Trust

East Kent Provincial Charities

East London Community Foundation

Eastern Counties Educational Trust Limited

The Sir John Eastwood Foundation

The Ebenezer Trust

The EBM Charitable Trust

Eden Arts Trust

EDF Energy Trust (EDFET)

The Gilbert and Eileen Edgar Foundation

Edinburgh Children's Holiday Fund

The Edinburgh Trust, No 2 Account

Edinburgh Voluntary Organisations' Trust Funds

The W G Edwards Charitable Foundation

The William Edwards Educational Charity

The Elephant Trust

The George Elias Charitable Trust

The Gerald Palmer Eling Trust Company

The Wilfred and Elsie Elkes Charity Fund

The Maud Elkington Charitable Trust
The Ellerdale Trust
The John Ellerman Foundation
The Ellinson Foundation Ltd
The Ellis Campbell Foundation
James Ellis Charitable Trust
The Elmgrant Trust
The Elmley Foundation
The Vernon N Ely Charitable Trust
The Embleton Trust
The Emerton-Christie Charity
EMI Music Sound Foundation
The Emmandjay Charitable Trust
The Worshipful Company of Engineers Charitable Trust Fund
The Englefield Charitable Trust
The English Schools' Football Association
The Enkalon Foundation
Entindale Ltd
The Epigoni Trust
Epilepsy Research UK
The Equitable Charitable Trust
The Equity Trust Fund
The Ericson Trust
The Erskine Cunningham Hill Trust
Essex Community Foundation
The Essex Fairway Charitable Trust
The Essex Heritage Trust
Essex Provincial Charity Fund
The Essex Youth Trust
Euro Charity Trust
Sir John Evelyn's Charity
The Eventhall Family Charitable Trust
The Everard Foundation
The Eveson Charitable Trust
The Beryl Evetts and Robert Luff Animal Welfare Trust
The Execution Charitable Trust
The Mayor of Exeter's Appeal Fund
The Exilarch's Foundation
F C Charitable Trust
The F P Limited Charitable Trust
The Faber Charitable Trust
Esmée Fairbairn Foundation
The Fairway Trust
Faisaltex Charitable Trust
The Family Rich Charities Trust
The Lord Faringdon Charitable Trust
Samuel William Farmer Trust
The Farmers' Company Charitable Fund
The Thomas Farr Charitable Trust
Walter Farthing (Trust) Limited
The Fassnidge Memorial Trust

Joseph Fattorini Charitable Trust 'B' Account
The Fawcett Charitable Trust
Federation of Jewish Relief Organisations
The John Feeney Charitable Trust
The George Fentham Birmingham Charity
The A M Fenton Trust
Allan and Nesta Ferguson Charitable Settlement
The Fidelity UK Foundation
The Bluff Field Charitable Trust
The Doris Field Charitable Trust
Fife Council/Common Good Funds and Trusts
Firtree Trust
The Fishmongers' Company's Charitable Trust
The Fitton Trust
The Earl Fitzwilliam Charitable Trust
Bud Flanagan Leukaemia Fund
The Rose Flatau Charitable Trust
The Ian Fleming Charitable Trust
The Joyce Fletcher Charitable Trust
The Roy Fletcher Charitable Trust
The Flow Foundation
The Gerald Fogel Charitable Trust
The Follett Trust
The Football Association National Sports Centre Trust
The Forbes Charitable Foundation
The Forces Trust (Working Name)
The Oliver Ford Charitable Trust
The Forest Hill Charitable Trust
The Foresters' Charity Stewards UK Trust
Forever Manchester (The Community Foundation for Greater Manchester)
Gwyneth Forrester Trust
The Fort Foundation
The Forte Charitable Trust
Foundation for Management Education
The Four Winds Trust
The Isaac and Freda Frankel Memorial Charitable Trust
The Elizabeth Frankland Moore and Star Foundation
The Jill Franklin Trust
The Gordon Fraser Charitable Trust
The Hugh Fraser Foundation

The Joseph Strong Frazer Trust
The Louis and Valerie Freedman Charitable Settlement
The Thomas Freke and Lady Norton Charity
The Charles S French Charitable Trust
The Anne French Memorial Trust
The Freshfield Foundation
The Freshgate Trust Foundation
The Friarsgate Trust
The Friends Hall Farm Street Trust
Friends Provident Charitable Foundation
The Frognal Trust
The Patrick Frost Foundation
Maurice Fry Charitable Trust
The Fuellers Charitable Trust Fund
The Fulmer Charitable Trust
Worshipful Company of Furniture Makers Charitable Fund
Gableholt Limited
The Galbraith Trust
The Gale Family Charitable Trust
The Angela Gallagher Memorial Fund
The Gamlen Charitable Trust
The Gamma Trust
The Gannochy Trust
The Ganzoni Charitable Trust
The Worshipful Company of Gardeners of London
The Samuel Gardner Memorial Trust
The Garnett Charitable Trust
Garvan Limited
The Gatsby Charitable Foundation
Gatwick Airport Community Trust
The Robert Gavron Charitable Trust
J Paul Getty Jr Charitable Trust
The Gibbs Charitable Trust
Simon Gibson Charitable Trust
The G C Gibson Charitable Trust
Lady Gibson's Charitable Trust
The Harvey and Hilary Gilbert Charitable Trust
The Girdlers' Company Charitable Trust
The B and P Glasser Charitable Trust
The Glass-House Trust
Global Care
Global Charities (formerly GCap Charities)

Gloucestershire Community
Foundation
Worshipful Company of
Glovers of London Charity
Fund
The GNC Trust
The Meir Golda Trust
The Sydney and Phyllis
Goldberg Memorial
Charitable Trust
The Golden Bottle Trust
The Jack Goldhill Charitable
Trust
The Goldsmiths' Arts Trust
Fund
The Goldsmiths' Company
Charity
The Golsoncott Foundation
The Good Neighbours Trust
The Everard and Mina
Goodman Charitable
Foundation
Mike Gooley Trailfinders
Charity
The Gosling Foundation
Limited
The Gough Charitable Trust
The Gould Charitable Trust
The Grace Charitable Trust
A B Grace Trust
The Graff Foundation
The Grahame Charitable
Foundation Limited
Grampian Police Diced Cap
Charitable Fund
The Granada Foundation
Grand Charitable Trust of the
Order of Women
Freemasons
The Grand Order of Water
Rats' Charities Fund
The Grange Farm Centre Trust
Grantham Yorke Trust
The J G Graves Charitable
Trust
The Gray Trust
The Great Stone Bridge Trust
of Edenbridge
The Great Torrington Town
Lands Charity
The Constance Green
Foundation
The Philip Green Memorial
Trust
Greenham Common
Community Trust Limited
Naomi and Jeffrey Greenwood
Charitable Trust
Greggs Foundation (formerly
Greggs Trust)
The Gretna Charitable Trust
The Grocers' Charity
The M and R Gross Charities
Limited
The Grove Charitable Trust
The GRP Charitable Trust

The David and Marie Grumitt
Foundation
The Bishop of Guildford's
Foundation
The Guildry Incorporation of
Perth
The Walter Guinness
Charitable Trust
The Gunter Charitable Trust
The Gur Trust
Dr Guthrie's Association
The H and M Charitable Trust
H C D Memorial Fund
The H P Charitable Trust
The Hackney Parochial
Charities
The Hadfield Trust
The Hadley Trust
The Hadrian Trust
The Alfred Haines Charitable
Trust
The Hale Trust
E F and M G Hall Charitable
Trust
The Edith Winifred Hall
Charitable Trust
Robert Hall Charity
The Hamamelis Trust
Hamilton Wallace Trust
Paul Hamlyn Foundation
The Hammonds Charitable
Trust
The Hampshire and Islands
Historic Churches Trust
Hampton Fuel Allotment
Charity
The W A Handley Charitable
Trust
Beatrice Hankey Foundation
Ltd
The Hanley Trust
The Kathleen Hannay
Memorial Charity
The Doughty Hanson
Charitable Foundation
Lord Hanson Foundation
The Haramead Trust
Miss K M Harbinson's
Charitable Trust
The Harborne Parish Lands
Charity
The Harbour Charitable Trust
The Harbour Foundation
The Harding Trust
William Harding's Charity
The Hare of Steep Charitable
Trust
The Harebell Centenary Fund
The Kenneth Hargreaves
Charitable Trust
The Harris Charitable Trust
The Harris Charity
The Harrison and Potter Trust
The John Harrison Charitable
Trust

The Spencer Hart Charitable
Trust
The Hartley Charitable Trust
The N and P Hartley Memorial
Trust
William Geoffrey Harvey's
Discretionary Settlement
The Edward Harvist Trust Fund
Haskel Family Foundation
The Hathaway Trust
The M A Hawe Settlement
The Hawthorne Charitable
Trust
The Dorothy Hay-Bolton
Charitable Trust
The Haymills Charitable Trust
The Headley Trust
Headley-Pitt Charitable Trust
Heagerty Charitable Trust
The Heart of England
Community Foundation
The Heathcoat Trust
Heathside Charitable Trust
The Charlotte Heber-Percy
Charitable Trust
The Hedley Denton Charitable
Trust
The Hedley Foundation
The H J Heinz Company
Limited Charitable Trust
The Hellenic Foundation
The Michael and Morven Heller
Charitable Foundation
The Simon Heller Charitable
Settlement
The Hemby Trust
The Christina Mary Hendrie
Trust for Scottish and
Canadian Charities
The Henley Educational Charity
Esther Hennell Charitable
Trust
The G D Herbert Charitable
Trust
The Joanna Herbert-Stepney
Charitable Settlement (also
known as The Paget
Charitable Trust)
The Anne Herd Memorial Trust
The Herefordshire Historic
Churches Trust
The Heritage of London Trust
Ltd
The Hesed Trust
The Hesslewood Children's
Trust (Hull Seamen's and
General Orphanage)
The Bernhard Heuberger
Charitable Trust
Hexham and Newcastle
Diocesan Trust (1947)
The P and C Hickinbotham
Charitable Trust
The Higgs Charitable Trust
Alan Edward Higgs Charity

The High Sheriff's Police Trust for the County of West Midlands (Building Blocks)

Highcroft Charitable Trust

The Charles Littlewood Hill Trust

The Hillingdon Partnership Trust

The Hinrichsen Foundation

The Hitchin Educational Foundation

The Eleemosynary Charity of William Hobbayne

Hobson Charity Limited

Matthew Hodder Charitable Trust

The Sir Julian Hodge Charitable Trust

The J G Hogg Charitable Trust

The Holden Charitable Trust

John Holford's Charity

The Hollick Family Charitable Trust

The Dorothy Holmes Charitable Trust

The Edward Holt Trust

The Holywood Trust

The Homelands Charitable Trust

The Homestead Charitable Trust

Sir Harold Hood's Charitable Trust

Hope for Youth (formerly Women Caring Trust)

The Hope Trust

HopMarket Charity

The Cuthbert Horn Trust

The Antony Hornby Charitable Trust

The Horne Foundation

The Horne Trust

The Worshipful Company of Horners' Charitable Trusts

The Hornsey Parochial Charities

The Hospital of God at Greatham

The Hospital Saturday Fund

Houblon-Norman/George Fund

The House of Industry Estate

The Reta Lila Howard Foundation

The Daniel Howard Trust

The Clifford Howarth Charity Trust

The Hudson Foundation

The Geoffrey C Hughes Charitable Trust

The Hull and East Riding Charitable Trust

Hulme Trust Estates (Educational)

Human Relief Foundation

The Humanitarian Trust

The Michael and Shirley Hunt Charitable Trust

The Hunter Foundation

Miss Agnes H Hunter's Trust

The Huntingdon Foundation

Huntingdon Freemen's Charity

John Huntingdon's Charity

Hurdale Charity Limited

The Nani Huyu Charitable Trust

The P Y N and B Hyams Trust

The Hyde Charitable Trust – Youth Plus

The Idlewild Trust

The Iliffe Family Charitable Trust

The Indigo Trust

The Ingram Trust

The Inland Waterways Association

The Inlight Trust

The Inman Charity

The Inner London Magistrates Court Poor Box and Feeder Charity

The Ireland Fund of Great Britain

The Irish Youth Foundation (UK) Ltd (incorporating The Lawlor Foundation)

The Ironmongers' Foundation

Irshad Trust

Irwin Trust

The ISA Charity

The Isaacs Charitable Trust

The J Isaacs Charitable Trust

The Isle of Anglesey Charitable Trust

The ITF Seafarers Trust

The J R S S T Charitable Trust

Elizabeth Jackson Charitable Trust

The Ruth and Lionel Jacobson Trust (Second Fund) No 2

Jaffe Family Relief Fund

The Susan and Stephen James Charitable Settlement (also known as the Stephen James Charitable Trust)

The James Trust

The Jarman Charitable Trust

The John Jarrold Trust

JCA Charitable Foundation

The Jeffrey Charitable Trust

The Jenour Foundation

The Jephcott Charitable Trust

Jesus Hospital Charity

Jewish Child's Day

The Jewish Youth Fund

The JMK Charitable Trust

The Joanies Trust

The Harold Joels Charitable Trust

The Jonathan Joels Charitable Trust

The Nicholas Joels Charitable Trust

The Norman Joels Charitable Trust

The Lillie Johnson Charitable Trust

The Johnson Foundation

The Johnson Group Cleaners Charity

The Johnnie Johnson Trust

The Johnson Wax Ltd Charitable Trust

The Joicey Trust

The Jones 1986 Charitable Trust

The Marjorie and Geoffrey Jones Charitable Trust

The Jordan Charitable Foundation

The J E Joseph Charitable Fund

The Lady Eileen Joseph Foundation

JTH Charitable Trust

The Anton Jurgens Charitable Trust

The Bernard Kahn Charitable Trust

The Stanley Kalms Foundation

The Karenza Foundation

The Boris Karloff Charitable Foundation

The Ian Karten Charitable Trust

The Kasner Charitable Trust

The Kass Charitable Trust

The Kathleen Trust

The Michael and Ilse Katz Foundation

The Katzauer Charitable Settlement

The C S Kaufman Charitable Trust

The Geoffrey John Kaye Charitable Foundation

The Emmanuel Kaye Foundation

Kelsick's Educational Foundation

The KempWelch Charitable Trust

The Kay Kendall Leukaemia Fund

William Kendall's Charity (Wax Chandlers' Company)

The Kennedy Charitable Foundation

The Kennel Club Charitable Trust

The Nancy Kenyon Charitable Trust

Keren Association

Kermaville Ltd

The Peter Kershaw Trust

The Kessler Foundation

Keswick Hall Trust

The Ursula Keyes Trust
The Robert Kiln Charitable
    Trust
The King Henry VIII Endowed
    Trust Warwick
The King/Cullimore Charitable
    Trust
The Kingsbury Charity
The Mary Kinross Charitable
    Trust
Kirkley Poor's Lands Estate
The Richard Kirkman
    Charitable Trust
Kirschel Foundation
Robert Kitchin (Saddlers'
    Company)
Ernest Kleinwort Charitable
    Trust
The Marina Kleinwort
    Charitable Trust
The Sir James Knott Trust
The Kobler Trust
The Kohn Foundation
The Kreditor Charitable Trust
The Kreitman Foundation
The Neil Kreitman Foundation
The Heinz, Anna and Carol
    Kroch Foundation
The Kyte Charitable Trust
The Late Sir Pierce Lacy
    Charity Trust
John Laing Charitable Trust
Maurice and Hilda Laing
    Charitable Trust
The Christopher Laing
    Foundation
The Kirby Laing Foundation
The Martin Laing Foundation
The Beatrice Laing Trust
The Lambert Charitable Trust
Lancashire Environmental
    Fund
Duchy of Lancaster Benevolent
    Fund
The Lancaster Foundation
The Langdale Trust
The Langley Charitable Trust
The Langtree Trust
The LankellyChase Foundation
The Lanvern Foundation
The R J Larg Family Charitable
    Trust
Largsmount Ltd
The Lark Trust
Laslett's (Hinton) Charity
Lauchentilly Charitable
    Foundation 1988
The Lauffer Family Charitable
    Foundation
The Kathleen Laurence Trust
The Edgar E Lawley Foundation
The Herd Lawson and Muriel
    Lawson Charitable Trust
The Lawson Beckman
    Charitable Trust

The Raymond and Blanche
    Lawson Charitable Trust
The Carole and Geoffrey
    Lawson Foundation
The Mason Le Page Charitable
    Trust
The Leach Fourteenth Trust
The David Lean Foundation
The Leathersellers' Company
    Charitable Fund
The Arnold Lee Charitable
    Trust
The William Leech Charity
The Lord Mayor of Leeds
    Appeal Fund
Leeds Building Society
    Charitable Foundation
Leicester Charity Link (formerly
    The Leicester Charity
    Organisation Society)
The Kennedy Leigh Charitable
    Trust
The Leigh Trust
Mrs Vera Leigh's Charity
The P Leigh-Bramwell Trust 'E'
The Lennox and Wyfold
    Foundation
The Erica Leonard Trust
The Leonard Trust
The Mark Leonard Trust
Lesley Lesley and Mutter Trust
Leukaemia and Lymphoma
    Research
The Leverhulme Trade
    Charities Trust
Lord Leverhulme's Charitable
    Trust
The Joseph Levy Charitable
    Foundation
The John Spedan Lewis
    Foundation
The Sir Edward Lewis
    Foundation
John Lewis Partnership
    General Community Fund
Lichfield Conduit Lands
Lifeline 4 Kids
The Thomas Lilley Memorial
    Trust
The Linbury Trust
The Lind Trust
Lindale Educational
    Foundation
The Linden Charitable Trust
The Enid Linder Foundation
The Linmardon Trust
The Ruth and Stuart Lipton
    Charitable Trust
The Lister Charitable Trust
Frank Litchfield Charitable
    Trust
The Andrew and Mary
    Elizabeth Little Charitable
    Trust
The Second Joseph Aaron
    Littman Foundation

The George John and Sheilah
    Livanos Charitable Trust
Liverpool Charity and Voluntary
    Services
Liverpool Sailors' Home Trust
The Elaine and Angus Lloyd
    Charitable Trust
The Charles Lloyd Foundation
The Lloyd Fund
Lloyd's Charities Trust
Lloyds TSB Foundation for
    England and Wales
Lloyds TSB Foundation for
    Northern Ireland
Lloyds TSB Foundation for the
    Channel Islands
The Locker Foundation
The Loftus Charitable Trust
The Lolev Charitable Trust
The Trust for London (formerly
    the City Parochial
    Foundation)
London Catalyst (formerly The
    Metropolitan Hospital-
    Sunday Fund)
The London Community
    Foundation (formerly Capital
    Community Foundation)
The London Law Trust
The William and Katherine
    Longman Trust
The Lord's Taverners
The Loseley and Guildway
    Charitable Trust
The Lotus Foundation
The C L Loyd Charitable Trust
The Marie Helen Luen
    Charitable Trust
Robert Luff Foundation Ltd
Henry Lumley Charitable Trust
Lady Lumley's Educational
    Foundation
C F Lunoe Trust Fund
The Ruth and Jack Lunzer
    Charitable Trust
Lord and Lady Lurgan Trust
The Lyndhurst Trust
The Lynn Foundation
The Lynwood Trust
The Lyons Charitable Trust
The Sir Jack Lyons Charitable
    Trust
The Lyras Family Charitable
    Trust
Sylvanus Lyson's Charity
The M and C Trust
The M D and S Charitable
    Trust
The M K Charitable Trust
The Madeline Mabey Trust
The E M MacAndrew Trust
The R S Macdonald Charitable
    Trust
Macdonald-Buchanan
    Charitable Trust
The Macfarlane Walker Trust

The Mackay and Brewer
Charitable Trust
The Mackintosh Foundation
The MacRobert Trust
The Magdalen and Lasher
Charity
Magdalen Hospital Trust
The Magen Charitable Trust
Man Group plc Charitable
Trust
Manchester Airport Community
Trust Fund
The Manchester Guardian
Society Charitable Trust
Lord Mayor of Manchester's
Charity Appeal Trust
Mandeville Trust
The Manifold Charitable Trust
W M Mann Foundation
The Leslie and Lilian Manning
Trust
Marbeh Torah Trust
Marchig Animal Welfare Trust
The Stella and Alexander
Margulies Charitable Trust
Market Harborough and The
Bowdens Charity
The Ann and David Marks
Foundation
The Hilda and Samuel Marks
Foundation
J P Marland Charitable Trust
The Michael Marsh Charitable
Trust
The Marsh Christian Trust
The Charlotte Marshall
Charitable Trust
The Jim Marshall Charitable
Trust
The D G Marshall of
Cambridge Trust
Marshgate Charitable
Settlement
Sir George Martin Trust
John Martin's Charity
The Mason Porter Charitable
Trust
The Nancie Massey Charitable
Trust
The Mathew Trust
The Matt 6.3 Charitable Trust
The Violet Mauray Charitable
Trust
The Maxell Educational Trust
The Maxwell Family Foundation
Evelyn May Trust
Mayfair Charities Ltd
The Mayfield Valley Arts Trust
Mazars Charitable Trust
The Robert McAlpine
Foundation
The McDougall Trust
The McKenna Charitable Trust
The Helen Isabella McMorran
Charitable Foundation

The James Frederick and Ethel
Anne Measures Charity
The Medlock Charitable Trust
The Anthony and Elizabeth
Mellows Charitable
Settlement
Melow Charitable Trust
The Mercers' Charitable
Foundation
The Merchant Taylors'
Company Charities Fund
The Merchant Venturers'
Charity
The Merchants' House of
Glasgow
The Mersey Docks and
Harbour Company
Charitable Fund
Community Foundation for
Merseyside
The Zachary Merton and
George Woofindin
Convalescent Trust
The Tony Metherell Charitable
Trust
The Metropolitan Drinking
Fountain and Cattle Trough
Association
Gerald Micklem Charitable
Trust
Midhurst Pensions Trust
The Migraine Trust
Miles Trust for the Putney and
Roehampton Community
The Hugh and Mary Miller
Bequest Trust
The Miller Foundation
The Millfield Trust
The Millhouses Charitable
Trust
The Millichope Foundation
The Mills Charity
The Millward Charitable Trust
The Clare Milne Trust
Milton Keynes Community
Foundation
The Edgar Milward Charity
The Keith and Joan
Mindelsohn Charitable
Trust
The Peter Minet Trust
The Minos Trust
The Mirfield Educational
Charity
The Laurence Misener
Charitable Trust
The Mishcon Family Charitable
Trust
The Misselbrook Trust
The Mitchell Charitable Trust
The Esmé Mitchell Trust
Keren Mitzvah Trust
The Mizpah Trust
The Mobbs Memorial Trust Ltd
The Modiano Charitable Trust
The Moette Charitable Trust

The Mole Charitable Trust
The D C Moncrieff Charitable
Trust
Monmouthshire County Council
Welsh Church Act Fund
The Montague Thompson
Coon Charitable Trust
The Colin Montgomerie
Charitable Foundation
The Monument Trust
The Nigel Moores Family
Charitable Trust
John Moores Foundation
The Peter Moores Foundation
The Morel Charitable Trust
The Morgan Charitable
Foundation
The Mr and Mrs J T Morgan
Foundation
The Oliver Morland Charitable
Trust
The Bernard Morris Charitable
Trust
The Morris Charitable Trust
The Willie and Mabel Morris
Charitable Trust
The Peter Morrison Charitable
Foundation
The Stanley Morrison
Charitable Trust
Vyoel Moshe Charitable Trust
The Moss Charitable Trust
The Robert and Margaret
Moss Charitable Trust
Moss Family Charitable Trust
The Mount Everest Foundation
The Edwina Mountbatten Trust
Mountbatten Festival of Music
The Mountbatten Memorial
Trust
The Mugdock Children's Trust
The Mulberry Trust
The Edith Murphy Foundation
The Mushroom Fund
The Music Sales Charitable
Trust
Muslim Hands
The Mutual Trust Group
The Kitty and Daniel Nabarro
Charitable Trust
The Nadezhda Charitable Trust
The Naggar Charitable Trust
The Eleni Nakou Foundation
The Janet Nash Charitable
Settlement
Nathan Charitable Trust
The National Churches Trust
(formerly the Historic
Churches Preservation
Trust with the Incorporated
Church Building Society)
The National Manuscripts
Conservation Trust
The Nchima Trust
Needham Market and Barking
Welfare Charities

The Worshipful Company of
Needlemakers' Charitable
Fund
The Neighbourly Charitable
Trust
The James Neill Trust Fund
Nemoral Ltd
Network for Social Change
The New Appeals Organisation
for the City and County of
Nottingham
New Court Charitable Trust
The Newcomen Collett
Foundation
Alderman Newton's
Educational Foundation
The Chevras Ezras Nitzrochim
Trust
Nominet Charitable Foundation
The Noon Foundation
The Norda Trust
Norie Charitable Trust
Normalyn Charitable Trust
The Norman Family Charitable
Trust
The Duncan Norman Trust
Fund
The Normanby Charitable Trust
The North British Hotel Trust
The North West Cancer
Research Fund
The Northampton Municipal
Church Charities
The Northampton Queen's
Institute Relief in Sickness
Fund
The Earl of Northampton's
Charity
The Northcott Devon
Foundation
The Northcott Devon Medical
Foundation
The Northmoor Trust
The Northumberland Village
Homes Trust
The Northwood Charitable
Trust
The Norton Foundation
The Norwich Church of England
Young Men's Society
The Norwich Historic Churches
Trust Ltd
The Norwich Town Close
Estate Charity
The Norwood and Newton
Settlement
The Noswad Charity
The Notgrove Trust
The Nottingham General
Dispensary
The Nottingham Gordon
Memorial Trust for Boys
and Girls
Nottinghamshire Community
Foundation

The Nottinghamshire Historic
Churches Trust
The Nottinghamshire Miners'
Welfare Trust Fund
Novi Most International
The Father O'Mahoney
Memorial Trust
The Sir Peter O'Sullevan
Charitable Trust
The Oak Trust
The Oakdale Trust
The Oakley Charitable Trust
The Oakmoor Charitable Trust
The Odin Charitable Trust
The Ofenheim Charitable Trust
Ogilvie Charities Deed No.2
(including the Charity of
Mary Catherine Ford Smith)
The Ogle Christian Trust
The Oikonomia Trust
Oizer Charitable Trust
The Old Broad Street Charity
Trust
The Old Enfield Charitable
Trust
The John Oldacre Foundation
The Oldham Foundation
Onaway Trust
Open Gate
The Ormsby Charitable Trust
Orrin Charitable Trust
The Ouseley Trust
The Owen Family Trust
Oxfam (GB)
The Oxfordshire Community
Foundation
The P F Charitable Trust
Padwa Charitable Foundation
The Pallant Charitable Trust
The Palmer Foundation
Eleanor Palmer Trust
The Panacea Society
Panton Trust
The James Pantyfedwen
Foundation
The Paragon Trust
The Park House Charitable
Trust
The Frank Parkinson
Agricultural Trust
The Samuel and Freda
Parkinson Charitable Trust
The Parthenon Trust
The Constance Paterson
Charitable Trust
The Patrick Charitable Trust
The Jack Patston Charitable
Trust
Paycare Charity Trust (formerly
known as Patients' Aid
Association Hospital and
Medical Charities Trust)
The Payne Charitable Trust
The Harry Payne Trust
The Susanna Peake Charitable
Trust

The Pedmore Sporting Club
Trust Fund
The Dowager Countess
Eleanor Peel Trust
The Pennycress Trust
The Performing Right Society
Foundation
The Persson Charitable Trust
(formerly Highmoore Hall
Charitable Trust)
The Persula Foundation
The Jack Petchey Foundation
The Petplan Charitable Trust
The Philips and Rubens
Charitable Trust
The Phillips Charitable Trust
The Phillips Family Charitable
Trust
Philological Foundation
The David Pickford Charitable
Foundation
The Bernard Piggott Trust
The Cecil Pilkington Charitable
Trust
The Pilkington Charities Fund
The Austin and Hope
Pilkington Trust
The Sir Harry Pilkington Trust
The Col W W Pilkington Will
Trusts The General Charity
Fund
The DLA Piper Charitable Trust
The Worshipful Company of
Plaisterers Charitable Trust
The Platinum Trust
The Poling Charitable Trust
The George and Esme Pollitzer
Charitable Settlement
The J S F Pollitzer Charitable
Settlement
The Ponton House Trust
The Mayor of Poole's Appeal
Fund
Edith and Ferdinand Porjes
Charitable Trust
The John Porter Charitable
Trust
The Porter Foundation
The Portishead Nautical Trust
The Portrack Charitable Trust
The J E Posnansky Charitable
Trust
The Powell Foundation
The W L Pratt Charitable Trust
Premierquote Ltd
Premishlaner Charitable Trust
The William Price Charitable
Trust
The Lucy Price Relief-in-Need
Charity
Sir John Priestman Charity
Trust
The Primrose Trust
The Prince of Wales's
Charitable Foundation
The Priory Foundation

Prison Service Charity Fund

The Privy Purse Charitable Trust

The Proven Family Trust

The Provincial Grand Charity of the Province of Derbyshire

PSA Peugeot Citroen Charity Trust

The Puebla Charitable Trust

The Richard and Christine Purchas Charitable Trust

The Puri Foundation

Mr and Mrs J A Pye's Charitable Settlement

Quartet Community Foundation (formerly the Greater Bristol Foundation)

Queen Mary's Roehampton Trust

The Queen's Silver Jubilee Trust

R S Charitable Trust

The R V W Trust

The Monica Rabagliati Charitable Trust

Rachel Charitable Trust

The Mr and Mrs Philip Rackham Charitable Trust

Richard Radcliffe Charitable Trust

The Radcliffe Trust

The Ragdoll Foundation

The Rainford Trust

The Peggy Ramsay Foundation

The Joseph and Lena Randall Charitable Trust

The Rank Foundation

The Fanny Rapaport Charitable Settlement

The Ratcliff Foundation

The Ratcliff Pension Charity

The Ratcliffe Charitable Trust

The Eleanor Rathbone Charitable Trust

The Sigrid Rausing Trust

The Ravensdale Trust

The Rayden Charitable Trust

The Roger Raymond Charitable Trust

The Rayne Foundation

The Rayne Trust

The John Rayner Charitable Trust

The Sir James Reckitt Charity

The Red Arrows Trust

Red Hill Charitable Trust

The Red Rose Charitable Trust

The C A Redfern Charitable Foundation

The Reed Foundation

Richard Reeve's Foundation

The Max Reinhardt Charitable Trust

Relief Fund for Romania Limited

REMEDI

The Rest Harrow Trust

Reuben Brothers Foundation

The Joan K Reynell Charitable Trust

The Nathaniel Reyner Trust Fund

The Rhododendron Trust

The Rhondda Cynon Taff Welsh Church Acts Fund

The Clive Richards Charity

The Richmond Parish Lands Charity

Ridgesave Limited

The Ripple Effect Foundation

The Sir John Ritblat Family Foundation

The River Trust

Thomas Roberts Trust

The Robertson Trust

The Rochester Bridge Trust

The Rock Foundation

The Rock Solid Trust

The Rofeh Trust

Richard Rogers Charitable Settlement

Rokach Family Charitable Trust

The Helen Roll Charitable Trust

The Sir James Roll Charitable Trust

The Roman Research Trust

Romeera Foundation

The C A Rookes Charitable Trust

The Rosca Trust

The Cecil Rosen Foundation

The Rothermere Foundation

The Rotherwick Foundation

The Rothley Trust

The Roughley Charitable Trust

Mrs Gladys Row Fogo Charitable Trust

Rowanville Ltd

The Christopher Rowbotham Charitable Trust

The Rowing Foundation

The Rowlands Trust

The Joseph Rowntree Charitable Trust

Royal Artillery Charitable Fund

Royal British Legion

Royal Docks Trust (London)

Royal Masonic Trust for Girls and Boys

The Royal Scots Benevolent Society

The Alfred and Frances Rubens Charitable Trust

The Rubin Foundation

William Arthur Rudd Memorial Trust

The Rufford Foundation

The Russell Trust

The J S and E C Rymer Charitable Trust

S O Charitable Trust

The Jeremy and John Sacher Charitable Trust

The Michael Harry Sacher Trust

The Raymond and Beverley Sackler 1988 Foundation

The Sackler Trust (formerly Dr Mortimer and Theresa Sackler Foundation)

The Ruzin Sadagora Trust

The Saddlers' Company Charitable Fund

The Saga Charitable Trust

The Jean Sainsbury Animal Welfare Trust

The Alan and Babette Sainsbury Charitable Fund

The Sainsbury Family Charitable Trusts

The Saintbury Trust

The Saints and Sinners Trust

The Salamander Charitable Trust

The Salt Foundation

The Salt Trust

The Sammermar Trust

Basil Samuel Charitable Trust

The Hon. M J Samuel Charitable Trust

The Peter Samuel Charitable Trust

The Camilla Samuel Fund

The Samworth Foundation

The Sandra Charitable Trust

Santander UK Foundation Limited

Jimmy Savile Charitable Trust

The Scarfe Charitable Trust

The Schapira Charitable Trust

The Schmidt-Bodner Charitable Trust

The R H Scholes Charitable Trust

The Schreib Trust

The Schreiber Charitable Trust

The Francis C Scott Charitable Trust

The Frieda Scott Charitable Trust

Sir Samuel Scott of Yews Trust

The Sir James and Lady Scott Trust

The Scott Trust Foundation

The Storrow Scott Will Trust

The Scottish Arts Council

Scottish Coal Industry Special Welfare Fund

The Scottish Community Foundation

The Scouloudi Foundation

Seafarers UK (King George's Fund for Sailors)

Seamen's Hospital Society

The Searchlight Electric Charitable Trust

The Searle Charitable Trust

The Helene Sebba Charitable Trust

The Samuel Sebba Charitable Trust

The Seedfield Trust

Leslie Sell Charitable Trust

The Ayrton Senna Foundation

The Seven Fifty Trust

The Severn Trent Water Charitable Trust Fund

SFIA Educational Trust Limited

The Cyril Shack Trust

The Shanti Charitable Trust

ShareGift (The Orr Mackintosh Foundation)

The Linley Shaw Foundation

The Sheepdrove Trust

The Sheffield and District Hospital Services Charitable Fund

The Sheldon Trust

The P and D Shepherd Charitable Trust

The Sylvia and Colin Shepherd Charitable Trust

The Archie Sherman Cardiff Foundation

The Archie Sherman Charitable Trust

The R C Sherriff Trust

The Shetland Charitable Trust

SHINE (Support and Help in Education)

The Barnett and Sylvia Shine No 2 Charitable Trust

The Bassil Shippam and Alsford Trust

The Shipwrights' Company Charitable Fund

The Shirley Foundation

Shlomo Memorial Fund Limited

The J A Shone Memorial Trust

The Barbara A Shuttleworth Memorial Trust

The Mary Elizabeth Siebel Charity

David and Jennifer Sieff Charitable Trust

The Julius Silman Charitable Trust

The Leslie Silver Charitable Trust

The Simpson Education and Conservation Trust

The Simpson Foundation

The Huntly and Margery Sinclair Charitable Trust

Sino-British Fellowship Trust

The Skelton Bounty

The Charles Skey Charitable Trust

Skipton Building Society Charitable Foundation

The John Slater Foundation

The SMB Charitable Trust

The Mrs Smith and Mount Trust

The N Smith Charitable Settlement

The Amanda Smith Charitable Trust

The E H Smith Charitable Trust

The Smith Charitable Trust

The Henry Smith Charity

The Leslie Smith Foundation

The Martin Smith Foundation

Stanley Smith General Charitable Trust

The Stanley Smith UK Horticultural Trust

The Snowball Trust

The Sobell Foundation

Solihull Community Foundation

The Solo Charitable Settlement

Dr Richard Solomon's Charitable Trust

The E C Sosnow Charitable Trust

The Souter Charitable Trust

The South Square Trust

The Stephen R and Philippa H Southall Charitable Trust

The W F Southall Trust

The Southover Manor General Education Trust

The Southwold Trust

The Sovereign Health Care Charitable Trust

Sparquote Limited

The Spear Charitable Trust

The Worshipful Company of Spectacle Makers' Charity

The Jessie Spencer Trust

The Ralph and Irma Sperring Charity

The Moss Spiro Will Charitable Foundation

The Spoore, Merry and Rixman Foundation

Spring Harvest

Springfields Employees' Medical Research and Charity Trust Fund

Springrule Ltd

The Spurrell Charitable Trust

The Geoff and Fiona Squire Foundation

St Francis's Leprosy Guild

St Gabriel's Trust

St James' Trust Settlement

St James's Place Foundation

Sir Walter St John's Educational Charity

St Katharine and Shadwell Trust

St Michael's and All Saints' Charities

The Late St Patrick White Charitable Trust

St Teilo's Trust

The Stanley Foundation Ltd

The Stanton Ballard Charitable Trust

The Staples Trust

The Star Charitable Trust

The Peter Stebbings Memorial Charity

The Steel Charitable Trust

The Steinberg Family Charitable Trust

The Hugh Stenhouse Foundation

The Sigmund Sternberg Charitable Foundation

Stervon Ltd

The Stevenage Community Trust

The June Stevens Foundation

The Steventon Allotments and Relief-in-Need Charity

The Stewards' Company Limited (incorporating the J W Laing Trust and the J W Laing Biblical Scholarship Trust)

The Leonard Laity Stoate Charitable Trust

The Stobart Newlands Charitable Trust

The Edward Stocks-Massey Bequest Fund

The Stokenchurch Educational Charity

The Stoller Charitable Trust

The M J C Stone Charitable Trust

The Stone-Mallabar Charitable Foundation

The Samuel Storey Family Charitable Trust

Peter Stormonth Darling Charitable Trust

The Strangward Trust

The Strasser Foundation

Stratford upon Avon Town Trust

Strathclyde Police Benevolent Fund

The W O Street Charitable Foundation

The Sudborough Foundation

The Suffolk Historic Churches Trust

The Summerfield Charitable Trust

The Bernard Sunley Charitable Foundation

The Surrey Historic Buildings Trust Ltd

The Sussex Historic Churches Trust

The Sutasoma Trust

Sutton Coldfield Municipal Charities

Swansea and Brecon Diocesan Board of Finance Limited

The John Swire (1989)
  Charitable Trust
The Swire Charitable Trust
The Hugh and Ruby Sykes
  Charitable Trust
The Charles and Elsie Sykes
  Trust
The Sylvanus Charitable Trust
The Stella Symons Charitable
  Trust
The Tabeel Trust
The Tajtelbaum Charitable
  Trust
The Talbot Trusts
The Talbot Village Trust
Tallow Chandlers Benevolent
  Fund
The Tangent Charitable Trust
The Lady Tangye Charitable
  Trust
The David Tannen Charitable
  Trust
The Tanner Trust
The Lili Tapper Charitable
  Foundation
The Mrs A Lacy Tate Trust
The Tay Charitable Trust
Humphrey Richardson Taylor
  Charitable Trust
The Connie and Albert Taylor
  Charitable Trust
The Cyril Taylor Charitable
  Trust
A P Taylor Trust
Tearfund
The Tedworth Charitable Trust
Tees Valley Community
  Foundation
The Templeton Goodwill Trust
Tesco Charity Trust
The Thames Wharf Charity
The Thistle Trust
The Loke Wan Tho Memorial
  Foundation
The Arthur and Margaret
  Thompson Charitable Trust
The Thompson Family
  Charitable Trust
The Len Thomson Charitable
  Trust
The Sue Thomson Foundation
The Sir Jules Thorn Charitable
  Trust
The Thornton Foundation
The Thornton Trust
The Three Guineas Trust
The Three Oaks Trust
The Thriplow Charitable Trust
The Tinsley Foundation
The Tisbury Telegraph Trust
TJH Foundation
The Tobacco Pipe Makers and
  Tobacco Trade Benevolent
  Fund
The Tolkien Trust

Tollemache (Buckminster)
  Charitable Trust
Tomchei Torah Charitable
  Trust
The Tompkins Foundation
The Tory Family Foundation
Tottenham Grammar School
  Foundation
The Tower Hill Trust
The Towry Law Charitable Trust
  (also known as the Castle
  Educational Trust)
The Toy Trust
The Mayor of Trafford's Charity
  Fund
The Constance Travis
  Charitable Trust
The Treeside Trust
The Triangle Trust (1949) Fund
The True Colours Trust
Truedene Co. Ltd
The Truemark Trust
Truemart Limited
Trumros Limited
Trust Sixty Three
Tudor Rose Ltd
The Tudor Trust
The Tufton Charitable Trust
The R D Turner Charitable
  Trust
The Douglas Turner Trust
The Florence Turner Trust
Miss S M Tutton Charitable
  Trust
The TUUT Charitable Trust
Community Foundation Serving
  Tyne and Wear and
  Northumberland
Trustees of Tzedakah
Ulster Garden Villages Ltd
Ultach Trust
Ulting Overseas Trust
The Ulverscroft Foundation
Ulverston Town Lands Charity
The Underwood Trust
The Union of Orthodox Hebrew
  Congregation
The United Society for the
  Propagation of the Gospel
The David Uri Memorial Trust
Uxbridge United Welfare Trust
Vale of Glamorgan – Welsh
  Church Fund
The Valentine Charitable Trust
John and Lucille van Geest
  Foundation
The Van Neste Foundation
Mrs Maud Van Norden's
  Charitable Foundation
The Vandervell Foundation
The Vardy Foundation
The Variety Club Children's
  Charity
Veneziana Fund
The Verdon-Smith Family
  Charitable Settlement

Victoria Homes Trust
The Nigel Vinson Charitable
  Trust
The William and Ellen Vinten
  Trust
The Vintners' Company
  Charitable Foundation
Vintners' Gifts Charity
Vision Charity
Vivdale Ltd
The Viznitz Foundation
Wade's Charity
The Scurrah Wainwright Charity
Wakeham Trust
The Community Foundation in
  Wales
Wales Council for Voluntary
  Action
Robert and Felicity Waley-
  Cohen Charitable Trust
The Thomas Wall Trust
The F J Wallis Charitable
  Settlement
Walton on Thames Charity
War on Want
The Ward Blenkinsop Trust
The George Ward Charitable
  Trust
The Barbara Ward Children's
  Foundation
The John Warren Foundation
G R Waters Charitable Trust
  2000
The Waterways Trust
The Howard Watson Symington
  Memorial Charity
John Watson's Trust
Weatherley Charitable Trust
The Weavers' Company
  Benevolent Fund
The William Webster
  Charitable Trust
The Weinberg Foundation
The Weinstein Foundation
The Weinstock Fund
The James Weir Foundation
The Barbara Welby Trust
The Weldon UK Charitable
  Trust
The Wellcome Trust
Welsh Church Fund Dyfed
  area (Carmarthenshire,
  Ceredigion and
  Pembrokeshire)
The Welton Foundation
The Wessex Youth Trust
The West Derby Wastelands
  Charity
West London Synagogue
  Charitable Fund
The West Yorkshire Police
  Community Fund
The Westminster Foundation
The Garfield Weston
  Foundation
The Whitaker Charitable Trust

The Colonel W H Whitbread
 Charitable Trust
The Simon Whitbread
 Charitable Trust
The Whitecourt Charitable
 Trust
The Norman Whiteley Trust
The Whitley Animal Protection
 Trust
The Whittlesey Charity
The Lionel Wigram Memorial
 Trust
The Felicity Wilde Charitable
 Trust
The Wilkinson Charitable
 Foundation
The Kay Williams Charitable
 Foundation
The Williams Family Charitable
 Trust
The H D H Wills 1965
 Charitable Trust
The Dame Violet Wills Will
 Trust
The Wilmcote Charitrust
David Wilson Foundation
The Wilson Foundation
J and J R Wilson Trust
The Community Foundation for
 Wiltshire and Swindon
The Benjamin Winegarten
 Charitable Trust
The Francis Winham
 Foundation
Wirral Mayor's Charity
The Michael and Anna Wix
 Charitable Trust
The Wixamtree Trust
The Woburn 1986 Charitable
 Trust
The Maurice Wohl Charitable
 Foundation
The Charles Wolfson
 Charitable Trust
The Wolfson Family Charitable
 Trust
The Wolfson Foundation
The James Wood Bequest
 Fund
Woodlands Green Ltd
Woodlands Trust
The Woodward Charitable
 Trust
Worcester Municipal Charities
 (incorporating Worcester
 Consolidated Municipal
 Charity and Worcester
 Municipal Exhibitions
 Foundation)
The Worcestershire and
 Dudley Historic Churches
 Trust
The Fred and Della Worms
 Charitable Trust
The Wragge and Co. Charitable
 Trust

The Diana Edgson Wright
 Charitable Trust
The Matthews Wrightson
 Charity Trust
Miss E B Wrightson's
 Charitable Settlement
Wychdale Ltd
Wychville Ltd
The Wyndham Charitable Trust
The Wyseliot Charitable Trust
The Xerox (UK) Trust
The Yardley Great Trust
The Dennis Alan Yardy
 Charitable Trust
The W Wing Yip and Brothers
 Foundation
The York Children's Trust
Yorkshire Agricultural Society
Yorkshire Building Society
 Charitable Foundation
The South Yorkshire
 Community Foundation
The Yorkshire Dales
 Millennium Trust
The John Young Charitable
 Settlement
The William Allen Young
 Charitable Trust
The John K Young Endowment
 Fund
Youth Music
Zephyr Charitable Trust
The Marjorie and Arnold Ziff
 Charitable Foundation
Stephen Zimmerman
 Charitable Trust
The Zochonis Charitable Trust
Zurich Community Trust (UK)
 Limited

....

■ Equipment

The 1970 Trust
The 1989 Willan Charitable
 Trust
The 29th May 1961 Charitable
 Trust
The Aberbrothock Skea Trust
The Aberdeen Endowments
 Trust
The Aberdeenshire Educational
 Trust Scheme
Access Sport
Achiezer Association Ltd
Achisomoch Aid Company
 Limited
The ACT Foundation
Action Medical Research
The Company of Actuaries'
 Charitable Trust Fund
The Sylvia Adams Charitable
 Trust
The Victor Adda Foundation
The Adint Charitable Trust
The Adnams Charity

Age Scotland (Formerly Age
 Concern Scotland and Help
 the Aged)
Age UK (formerly Help the
 Aged and Age Concern)
Aid to the Church in Need (UK)
The Sylvia Aitken Charitable
 Trust
Aldgate and All Hallows'
 Barking Exhibition
 Foundation
The Aldgate Freedom
 Foundation
Allchurches Trust Ltd
The H B Allen Charitable Trust
The Alliance Family Foundation
Angus Allnatt Charitable
 Foundation
The Pat Allsop Charitable Trust
Almondsbury Charity
Altamont Ltd
Alvor Charitable Trust
The Ammco Trust
Viscount Amory's Charitable
 Trust
The AMW Charitable Trust
The Andrew Anderson Trust
The André Christian Trust
Anguish's Educational
 Foundation
The Animal Defence Trust
The Eric Anker-Petersen
 Charity
Ambrose and Ann Appelbe
 Trust
The Appletree Trust
The John Apthorp Charitable
 Trust
The Arbib Foundation
The John M Archer Charitable
 Trust
The Archer Trust
The Ardwick Trust
The Argus Appeal
The Armenian Relief Society of
 Great Britain Trust
The Armourers' and Brasiers'
 Gauntlet Trust
Arsenal Charitable Trust
The Artemis Charitable Trust
The Arts and Entertainment
 Charitable Trust
Arts Council England
The Arts Council of Northern
 Ireland
The Arts Council of Wales
The Ove Arup Foundation
The AS Charitable Trust
The Ashden Trust
The Ashendene Trust
The Ashley Family Foundation
 (formerly The Laura Ashley
 Foundation)
The Norman C Ashton
 Foundation
The Ashworth Charitable Trust

The Ian Askew Charitable Trust
The Associated Country
  Women of the World
  (ACWW)
The Association of Colleges
  Charitable Trust
Astellas European Foundation
Asthma UK
The Astor Foundation
The Astor of Hever Trust
The Aurelius Charitable Trust
The Avenue Charitable Trust
The John Avins Trustees
The Avon and Somerset Police
  Community Trust
AW Charitable Trust
The Aylesford Family
  Charitable Trust
The BAA Communities Trust
The BACTA Charitable Trust
The Scott Bader
  Commonwealth Ltd
The Bagri Foundation
Veta Bailey Charitable Trust
The Austin Bailey Trust
The Baily Thomas Charitable
  Fund
The Baird Trust
The Baker Charitable Trust
The Balcombe Charitable Trust
The Albert Casanova Ballard
  Deceased Trust
The Ballinger Charitable Trust
The Balmore Trust
The Balney Charitable Trust
The Baltic Charitable Fund
The Bamford Charitable
  Foundation
The Banbury Charities
William P Bancroft (No 2)
  Charitable Trust and
  Jenepher Gillett Trust
The Band Trust
The Barbers' Company General
  Charities
The Barbour Foundation
Barchester Healthcare
  Foundation
The Barclay Foundation
The Baring Foundation
Peter Barker-Mill Memorial
  Charity
Barleycorn Trust
Barnes Workhouse Fund
The Barnsbury Charitable Trust
The Barnstaple Bridge Trust
The Barnwood House Trust
The Misses Barrie Charitable
  Trust
Barrington Family Charitable
  Trust
The Charity of William Barrow
Stephen J Barry Charitable
  Trust
The Bartlett Taylor Charitable
  Trust

The Paul Bassham Charitable
  Trust
The Batchworth Trust
The Bay Tree Charitable Trust
D H and L H Baylin Charitable
  Trust
The Louis Baylis (Maidenhead
  Advertiser) Charitable Trust
BBC Children in Need
B-CH 1971 Charitable Trust
The Beacon Trust
The Bearder Charity
The James Beattie Charitable
  Trust
The Beaufort House Trust
  Limited
The Beaverbrook Foundation
The Beccles Town Lands
  Charity
The Becker Family Charitable
  Trust
The Becketts and Sargeants
  Educational Foundation
The John Beckwith Charitable
  Trust
The Peter Beckwith Charitable
  Trust
The Bedford Charity (The
  Harpur Trust)
The David and Ruth Behrend
  Fund
The Beit Trust
The Bellahouston Bequest
  Fund
The Bellinger Donnay Trust
Belljoe Tzedoko Ltd
The Benfield Motors Charitable
  Trust
The Benham Charitable
  Settlement
The Hervey Benham Charitable
  Trust
Maurice and Jacqueline
  Bennett Charitable Trust
The Gerald Bentall Charitable
  Trust
Bergqvist Charitable Trust
The Berkshire Community
  Foundation
The Bestway Foundation
Thomas Betton's Charity for
  Pensions and Relief-in-Need
BHST
The Mason Bibby 1981 Trust
BibleLands
The Bideford Bridge Trust
The Big Lottery Fund
The Billmeir Charitable Trust
Percy Bilton Charity
The Bingham Trust
The Bintaub Charitable Trust
The Birmingham District
  Nursing Charitable Trust
The Birmingham Hospital
  Saturday Fund Medical
  Charity and Welfare Trust

Birmingham International
  Airport Community Trust
The Lord Mayor of
  Birmingham's Charity
The Bisgood Charitable Trust
  (registered as Miss Jeanne
  Bisgood's Charitable Trust)
The Michael Bishop
  Foundation
The Bishop's Development
  Fund
The Bertie Black Foundation
Sir Alec Black's Charity
Isabel Blackman Foundation
The Herbert and Peter
  Blagrave Charitable Trust
The Blair Foundation
The Blanchminster Trust
The Sir Victor Blank Charitable
  Settlement
The Neville and Elaine Blond
  Charitable Trust
The Bluston Charitable
  Settlement
The Body Shop Foundation
The Boltons Trust
The Bonamy Charitable Trust
The John and Celia Bonham
  Christie Charitable Trust
The Charlotte Bonham-Carter
  Charitable Trust
Bonhomie United Charity
  Society
The Boots Charitable Trust
The Bordon and Liphook
  Charity
The Oliver Borthwick Memorial
  Trust
The Bothwell Charitable Trust
H E and E L Botteley
  Charitable Trust
The Harry Bottom Charitable
  Trust
The Anthony Bourne
  Foundation
The Bower Trust
The Bowerman Charitable
  Trust
John and Susan Bowers Fund
The Bowland Charitable Trust
The William Brake Charitable
  Trust
The Tony Bramall Charitable
  Trust
The Harold and Alice Bridges
  Charity
The Brighton District Nursing
  Association Trust
Bristol Archdeaconry Charity
John Bristow and Thomas
  Mason Trust
Britannia Foundation
The British Council for
  Prevention of Blindness

The British Dietetic Association General and Education Trust Fund
The British Gas (Scottish Gas) Energy Trust
British Heart Foundation
British Humane Association
British Institute at Ankara
British Ornithologists' Union
British Record Industry Trust
The Britto Foundation
The J and M Britton Charitable Trust
The Charles and Edna Broadhurst Charitable Trust
The Roger Brooke Charitable Trust
The David Brooke Charity
The Charles Brotherton Trust
Joseph Brough Charitable Trust
The Swinfen Broun Charitable Trust
Mrs E E Brown Charitable Settlement
The Jack Brunton Charitable Trust
The Bryant Trust
The Buckinghamshire Foundation
The Buckinghamshire Masonic Centenary Fund
The Rosemary Bugden Charitable Trust
The Bulldog Trust Limited
The E F Bulmer Benevolent Fund
The BUPA Foundation
Burdens Charitable Foundation
The Clara E Burgess Charity
The Burry Charitable Trust
The Arnold Burton 1998 Charitable Trust
The Burton Breweries Charitable Trust
The Geoffrey Burton Charitable Trust
Consolidated Charity of Burton upon Trent
Butchers' Company General Charities
The Noel Buxton Trust
The C Charitable Trust
Henry T and Lucy B Cadbury Charitable Trust
The Christopher Cadbury Charitable Trust
The G W Cadbury Charitable Trust
The Richard Cadbury Charitable Trust
The Edward and Dorothy Cadbury Trust
The George Cadbury Trust
The Barrow Cadbury Trust and the Barrow Cadbury Fund

CAFOD (Catholic Agency for Overseas Development)
The Callander Charitable Trust
Calleva Foundation
Calypso Browning Trust
The Campden Charities Trustee
The Canning Trust
The Carew Pole Charitable Trust
The D W T Cargill Fund
Carlee Ltd
The Carlton House Charitable Trust
The Worshipful Company of Carmen Benevolent Trust
The Carnegie Dunfermline Trust
The Carpenter Charitable Trust
The Carpenters' Company Charitable Trust
The Carrington Charitable Trust
The Carron Charitable Settlement
The Leslie Mary Carter Charitable Trust
The Carvill Trust
The Casey Trust
Sir John Cass's Foundation
The Elizabeth Casson Trust
The Castang Foundation
The Catalyst Charitable Trust (formerly the Buckle Family Charitable Trust)
The Catholic Charitable Trust
Catholic Foreign Missions
The Catholic Trust for England and Wales
The Joseph and Annie Cattle Trust
The Thomas Sivewright Catto Charitable Settlement
The Wilfrid and Constance Cave Foundation
The Cayo Foundation
Elizabeth Cayzer Charitable Trust
The B G S Cayzer Charitable Trust
The Cazenove Charitable Trust
Celtic Charity Fund
The Cemlyn-Jones Trust
The Pamela Champion Foundation
Champneys Charitable Foundation
The Chapman Charitable Trust
John William Chapman's Charitable Trust
The Charities Advisory Trust
Charitworth Limited
The Charter 600 Charity

The Worshipful Company of Chartered Accountants General Charitable Trust (also known as CALC)
The Chasah Trust
The Chelsea Building Society Charitable Foundation
The Chelsea Square 1994 Trust
The Cheruby Trust
The Cheshire Provincial Fund of Benevolence
The Chetwode Foundation
Chevioty Asset Management Charitable Trust
The Malcolm Chick Charity
Children's Liver Disease Foundation
Childs Charitable Trust
The Childwick Trust
The Chippenham Borough Lands Charity
The Chipping Sodbury Town Lands Charity
CHK Charities Limited
The Chownes Foundation
The Chrimes Family Charitable Trust
The Christabella Charitable Trust
Christadelphian Samaritan Fund
Christian Aid
Christian Response to Eastern Europe
Chrysalis Trust
The Church and Community Fund
The Church Burgesses Educational Foundation
Church Burgesses Trust
The Church Urban Fund
City and County of Swansea Welsh Church Act Fund
The City Bridge Trust (formerly known as Bridge House Trust)
The City Educational Trust Fund
Stephen Clark 1957 Charitable Trust
J A Clark Charitable Trust
The Hilda and Alice Clark Charitable Trust
The Roger and Sarah Bancroft Clark Charitable Trust
The Clarke Charitable Settlement
The Cleary Foundation
The Cleopatra Trust
Lord Clinton's Charitable Trust
The Clore Duffield Foundation
Miss V L Clore's 1967 Charitable Trust
Closehelm Ltd
The Clothworkers' Foundation

Richard Cloudesley's Charity

The Clover Trust

The Robert Clutterbuck Charitable Trust

Clydpride Ltd

The Coalfields Regeneration Trust

The John Coates Charitable Trust

Coats Foundation Trust

The Cobtree Charity Trust Ltd

The Denise Cohen Charitable Trust

The Vivienne and Samuel Cohen Charitable Trust

The John S Cohen Foundation

The R and S Cohen Foundation

The Colchester Catalyst Charity

The Cole Charitable Trust

The Colefax Charitable Trust

The John and Freda Coleman Charitable Trust

The George Henry Collins Charity

The E Alec Colman Charitable Fund Ltd

The Sir Jeremiah Colman Gift Trust

The Colt Foundation

The Coltstaple Trust

Colwinston Charitable Trust

Colyer-Fergusson Charitable Trust

The Comino Foundation

Community Foundation for Calderdale

The Community Foundation for Northern Ireland

The Compton Charitable Trust

The Congleton Inclosure Trust

The Conservation Foundation

The Consolidated Charities for the Infirm Merchant Taylors' Company

The Ernest Cook Trust

The Cooks Charity

The Catherine Cookson Charitable Trust

Mabel Cooper Charity

The Alice Ellen Cooper Dean Charitable Foundation

The Co-operative Foundation

The Marjorie Coote Animal Charity Trust

The Marjorie Coote Old People's Charity

The Helen Jean Cope Trust

The J Reginald Corah Foundation Fund

The Gershon Coren Charitable Foundation

The Corinthian Trust

Edwin Cornforth 1983 Charity Trust

The Duke of Cornwall's Benevolent Fund

The Cornwell Charitable Trust

The Sidney and Elizabeth Corob Charitable Trust

The Corona Charitable Trust

The Costa Family Charitable Trust (formerly the Morgan Williams Charitable Trust)

The Cotton Industry War Memorial Trust

The Cotton Trust

County Durham Community Foundation

The General Charities of the City of Coventry

Coventry Building Society Charitable Foundation

The John Cowan Foundation

The Sir William Coxen Trust Fund

The Lord Cozens-Hardy Trust

The Craignish Trust

The Craps Charitable Trust

Michael Crawford Children's Charity

The Cray Trust

Creative Scotland

The Crescent Trust

Cripplegate Foundation

The Violet and Milo Cripps Charitable Trust

The Harry Crook Foundation

The Cross Trust

The Croydon Relief in Need Charities

The Mayor of Croydon's Charity Fund

Cruden Foundation Ltd

The Ronald Cruickshank's Foundation

The R D Crusaders Foundation

The Culra Charitable Trust

The Cumber Family Charitable Trust

Cumberland Building Society Charitable Foundation

Cumbria Community Foundation

The D J H Currie Memorial Trust

The Dennis Curry Charitable Trust

The Raymond Curtis Charitable Trust

The Manny Cussins Foundation

The Cwmbran Trust

Itzchok Meyer Cymerman Trust Ltd

The D G Charitable Settlement

The D'Oyly Carte Charitable Trust

The Daily Prayer Union Charitable Trust Ltd

The Daisy Trust

The Daiwa Anglo-Japanese Foundation

The Dr and Mrs A Darlington Charitable Trust

Baron Davenport's Charity

The Davidson (Nairn) Charitable Trust

The Davidson Family Charitable Trust

The Alderman Joe Davidson Memorial Trust

Michael Davies Charitable Settlement

The Gwendoline and Margaret Davies Charity

The Wilfrid Bruce Davis Charitable Trust

Davis-Rubens Charitable Trust

The Dawe Charitable Trust

The De Clermont Charitable Company Ltd

The Leopold De Rothschild Charitable Trust

The Deakin Charitable Trust

William Dean Countryside and Educational Trust

The Debmar Benevolent Trust

The Dellal Foundation

The Delves Charitable Trust

The Demigryphon Trust

The Denman Charitable Trust

The Denton Charitable Trust

The Denton Wilde Sapte Charitable Trust

The Earl of Derby's Charitable Trust

The Derbyshire Churches and Chapels Preservation Trust

Derbyshire Community Foundation

The J N Derbyshire Trust

Devon Community Foundation

The Devon Educational Trust

The Devon Historic Churches Trust

The Duke of Devonshire's Charitable Trust

The Sandy Dewhirst Charitable Trust

The Laduma Dhamecha Charitable Trust

Diabetes UK

The Dibden Allotments Fund

The Dickon Trust

The Digbeth Trust

The Dinwoodie Settlement

Disability Aid Fund (The Roger and Jean Jefcoate Trust)

Dischma Charitable Trust

The DLM Charitable Trust

Louise Dobson Charitable Trust

The Derek and Eileen Dodgson Foundation

The Dollond Charitable Trust

Domepride Ltd

The Dorcas Trust
The Dorset Historic Churches
    Trust
The Dorus Trust
The Doughty Charity Trust
The R M Douglas Charitable
    Trust
The Drapers' Charitable Fund
The Dugdale Charitable Trust
The Duis Charitable Trust
The Dulverton Trust
The P B Dumbell Charitable
    Trust
The Dumbreck Charity
Dunard Fund
Ronald Duncan Literary
    Foundation
The Houghton Dunn Charitable
    Trust
The Dunn Family Charitable
    Trust
The W E Dunn Trust
Dushinsky Trust Ltd
The Dwek Family Charitable
    Trust
The Dyers' Company
    Charitable Trust
The Eagle Charity Trust
The Earley Charity
Earls Colne and Halstead
    Educational Charity
The Earmark Trust
East Kent Provincial Charities
East London Community
    Foundation
Eastern Counties Educational
    Trust Limited
The Sir John Eastwood
    Foundation
The Ebenezer Trust
The EBM Charitable Trust
Eden Arts Trust
EDF Energy Trust (EDFET)
The Gilbert and Eileen Edgar
    Foundation
Edinburgh Children's Holiday
    Fund
The Edinburgh Trust, No 2
    Account
Edinburgh Voluntary
    Organisations' Trust Funds
The W G Edwards Charitable
    Foundation
The William Edwards
    Educational Charity
The Elephant Trust
The George Elias Charitable
    Trust
The Gerald Palmer Eling Trust
    Company
The Wilfred and Elsie Elkes
    Charity Fund
The Maud Elkington Charitable
    Trust
The Ellerdale Trust
The John Ellerman Foundation

The Ellinson Foundation Ltd
The Ellis Campbell Foundation
James Ellis Charitable Trust
The Elmgrant Trust
The Elmley Foundation
The Vernon N Ely Charitable
    Trust
The Embleton Trust
The Emerton-Christie Charity
EMI Music Sound Foundation
The Emmandjay Charitable
    Trust
The Worshipful Company of
    Engineers Charitable Trust
    Fund
The Englefield Charitable Trust
The English Schools' Football
    Association
The Enkalon Foundation
Entindale Ltd
The Epigoni Trust
Epilepsy Research UK
The Equitable Charitable Trust
The Equity Trust Fund
The Ericson Trust
The Erskine Cunningham Hill
    Trust
Essex Community Foundation
The Essex Fairway Charitable
    Trust
The Essex Heritage Trust
Essex Provincial Charity Fund
The Essex Youth Trust
Euro Charity Trust
Sir John Evelyn's Charity
The Eventhall Family
    Charitable Trust
The Everard Foundation
The Eveson Charitable Trust
The Beryl Evetts and Robert
    Luff Animal Welfare Trust
The Execution Charitable Trust
The Mayor of Exeter's Appeal
    Fund
The Exilarch's Foundation
F C Charitable Trust
The F P Limited Charitable
    Trust
The Faber Charitable Trust
Esmée Fairbairn Foundation
The Fairway Trust
Faisaltex Charitable Trust
The Family Rich Charities Trust
The Lord Faringdon Charitable
    Trust
Samuel William Farmer Trust
The Farmers' Company
    Charitable Fund
The Thomas Farr Charitable
    Trust
Walter Farthing (Trust) Limited
The Fassnidge Memorial Trust
Joseph Fattorini Charitable
    Trust 'B' Account
The Fawcett Charitable Trust

Federation of Jewish Relief
    Organisations
The John Feeney Charitable
    Trust
The George Fentham
    Birmingham Charity
The A M Fenton Trust
Allan and Nesta Ferguson
    Charitable Settlement
The Fidelity UK Foundation
The Bluff Field Charitable Trust
The Doris Field Charitable
    Trust
Fife Council/Common Good
    Funds and Trusts
Firtree Trust
The Fishmongers' Company's
    Charitable Trust
The Fitton Trust
The Earl Fitzwilliam Charitable
    Trust
Bud Flanagan Leukaemia Fund
The Rose Flatau Charitable
    Trust
The Ian Fleming Charitable
    Trust
The Joyce Fletcher Charitable
    Trust
The Roy Fletcher Charitable
    Trust
The Flow Foundation
The Gerald Fogel Charitable
    Trust
The Follett Trust
The Football Association
    National Sports Centre
    Trust
The Football Association Youth
    Trust
The Football Foundation
The Forbes Charitable
    Foundation
The Forces Trust (Working
    Name)
Ford Britain Trust
The Oliver Ford Charitable
    Trust
The Forest Hill Charitable Trust
The Foresters' Charity
    Stewards UK Trust
Forever Manchester (The
    Community Foundation for
    Greater Manchester)
Gwyneth Forrester Trust
The Fort Foundation
The Forte Charitable Trust
Foundation for Management
    Education
The Four Winds Trust
The Foyle Foundation
The Isaac and Freda Frankel
    Memorial Charitable Trust
The Elizabeth Frankland Moore
    and Star Foundation
The Jill Franklin Trust

The Gordon Fraser Charitable Trust
The Hugh Fraser Foundation
The Joseph Strong Frazer Trust
The Louis and Valerie Freedman Charitable Settlement
The Thomas Freke and Lady Norton Charity
The Charles S French Charitable Trust
The Anne French Memorial Trust
The Freshfield Foundation
The Freshgate Trust Foundation
The Friarsgate Trust
The Friends Hall Farm Street Trust
Friends Provident Charitable Foundation
The Frognal Trust
The Patrick Frost Foundation
Maurice Fry Charitable Trust
The Fuellers Charitable Trust Fund
The Fulmer Charitable Trust
Worshipful Company of Furniture Makers Charitable Fund
Gablehoult Limited
The Galbraith Trust
The Gale Family Charitable Trust
The Gamlen Charitable Trust
The Gamma Trust
The Gannochy Trust
The Ganzoni Charitable Trust
The Worshipful Company of Gardeners of London
The Samuel Gardner Memorial Trust
The Garnett Charitable Trust
Garvan Limited
The Gatsby Charitable Foundation
Gatwick Airport Community Trust
The Robert Gavron Charitable Trust
J Paul Getty Jr Charitable Trust
The Gibbs Charitable Trust
Simon Gibson Charitable Trust
The G C Gibson Charitable Trust
Lady Gibson's Charitable Trust
The Harvey and Hilary Gilbert Charitable Trust
The Girdlers' Company Charitable Trust
The B and P Glasser Charitable Trust
The Glass-House Trust
Global Care
Global Charities (formerly GCap Charities)

Gloucestershire Community Foundation
Worshipful Company of Glovers of London Charity Fund
GMC Trust
The GNC Trust
The Meir Golda Trust
The Sydney and Phyllis Goldberg Memorial Charitable Trust
The Golden Bottle Trust
The Jack Goldhill Charitable Trust
The Goldsmiths' Arts Trust Fund
The Goldsmiths' Company Charity
The Golsoncott Foundation
The Good Neighbours Trust
The Everard and Mina Goodman Charitable Foundation
Mike Gooley Trailfinders Charity
The Gosling Foundation Limited
The Gough Charitable Trust
The Gould Charitable Trust
The Grace Charitable Trust
A B Grace Trust
The Graff Foundation
The Grahame Charitable Foundation Limited
Grampian Police Diced Cap Charitable Fund
The Granada Foundation
Grand Charitable Trust of the Order of Women Freemasons
The Grand Order of Water Rats' Charities Fund
The Grange Farm Centre Trust
Grantham Yorke Trust
The J G Graves Charitable Trust
The Gray Trust
The Great Stone Bridge Trust of Edenbridge
The Great Torrington Town Lands Charity
The Constance Green Foundation
The Philip Green Memorial Trust
Greenham Common Community Trust Limited
Naomi and Jeffrey Greenwood Charitable Trust
Greggs Foundation (formerly Greggs Trust)
The Gretna Charitable Trust
The Grocers' Charity
The M and R Gross Charities Limited
The Grove Charitable Trust

The GRP Charitable Trust
The David and Marie Grumitt Foundation
The Bishop of Guildford's Foundation
The Guildry Incorporation of Perth
The Walter Guinness Charitable Trust
The Gunter Charitable Trust
The Gur Trust
Dr Guthrie's Association
The H and M Charitable Trust
H C D Memorial Fund
The H P Charitable Trust
The Hackney Parochial Charities
The Hadfield Trust
The Hadley Trust
The Hadrian Trust
The Alfred Haines Charitable Trust
The Hale Trust
E F and M G Hall Charitable Trust
The Edith Winifred Hall Charitable Trust
Robert Hall Charity
The Hamamelis Trust
Hamilton Wallace Trust
The Hammonds Charitable Trust
The Hampshire and Islands Historic Churches Trust
Hampshire and Isle of Wight Community Foundation
Hampton Fuel Allotment Charity
The W A Handley Charitable Trust
Beatrice Hankey Foundation Ltd
The Hanley Trust
The Kathleen Hannay Memorial Charity
The Doughty Hanson Charitable Foundation
Lord Hanson Foundation
The Haramead Trust
Miss K M Harbinson's Charitable Trust
The Harborne Parish Lands Charity
The Harbour Charitable Trust
The Harbour Foundation
The Harding Trust
William Harding's Charity
The Hare of Steep Charitable Trust
The Harebell Centenary Fund
The Kenneth Hargreaves Charitable Trust
The Harris Charitable Trust
The Harris Charity
The Harrison and Potter Trust

The John Harrison Charitable Trust
The Peter Harrison Foundation
The Spencer Hart Charitable Trust
The Hartley Charitable Trust
The N and P Hartley Memorial Trust
William Geoffrey Harvey's Discretionary Settlement
The Edward Harvist Trust Fund
Haskel Family Foundation
The Hathaway Trust
The M A Hawe Settlement
The Hawthorne Charitable Trust
The Dorothy Hay-Bolton Charitable Trust
The Haymills Charitable Trust
The Headley Trust
Headley-Pitt Charitable Trust
Heagerty Charitable Trust
The Heart of England Community Foundation
The Heathcoat Trust
Heathside Charitable Trust
The Charlotte Heber-Percy Charitable Trust
The Hedley Denton Charitable Trust
The Hedley Foundation
The H J Heinz Company Limited Charitable Trust
The Hellenic Foundation
The Michael and Morven Heller Charitable Foundation
The Simon Heller Charitable Settlement
The Hemby Trust
The Christina Mary Hendrie Trust for Scottish and Canadian Charities
The Henley Educational Charity
Philip Henman Trust
Esther Hennell Charitable Trust
The G D Herbert Charitable Trust
The Joanna Herbert-Stepney Charitable Settlement (also known as The Paget Charitable Trust)
The Anne Herd Memorial Trust
The Herefordshire Historic Churches Trust
The Heritage of London Trust Ltd
The Hesed Trust
The Hesslewood Children's Trust (Hull Seamen's and General Orphanage)
The Bernhard Heuberger Charitable Trust
Hexham and Newcastle Diocesan Trust (1947)

The P and C Hickinbotham Charitable Trust
The Higgs Charitable Trust
Alan Edward Higgs Charity
The High Sheriff's Police Trust for the County of West Midlands (Building Blocks)
Highcroft Charitable Trust
The Charles Littlewood Hill Trust
The Hillingdon Partnership Trust
The Hinrichsen Foundation
The Hitchin Educational Foundation
The Eleemosynary Charity of William Hobbayne
Hobson Charity Limited
Matthew Hodder Charitable Trust
The Sir Julian Hodge Charitable Trust
The J G Hogg Charitable Trust
The Holden Charitable Trust
John Holford's Charity
The Hollick Family Charitable Trust
The Dorothy Holmes Charitable Trust
The Edward Holt Trust
The Holywood Trust
The Homelands Charitable Trust
The Homestead Charitable Trust
Sir Harold Hood's Charitable Trust
Hope for Youth (formerly Women Caring Trust)
The Hope Trust
HopMarket Charity
The Cuthbert Horn Trust
The Antony Hornby Charitable Trust
The Horne Foundation
The Horne Trust
The Worshipful Company of Horners' Charitable Trusts
The Hornsey Parochial Charities
The Hospital of God at Greatham
The Hospital Saturday Fund
Houblon-Norman/George Fund
The House of Industry Estate
The Reta Lila Howard Foundation
The Daniel Howard Trust
The Clifford Howarth Charity Trust
The Hudson Foundation
The Geoffrey C Hughes Charitable Trust
The Hull and East Riding Charitable Trust

Hulme Trust Estates (Educational)
Human Relief Foundation
The Humanitarian Trust
The Michael and Shirley Hunt Charitable Trust
The Hunter Foundation
Miss Agnes H Hunter's Trust
The Huntingdon Foundation
Huntingdon Freemen's Charity
John Huntingdon's Charity
Hurdale Charity Limited
The Nani Huyu Charitable Trust
The P Y N and B Hyams Trust
The Hyde Charitable Trust – Youth Plus
The Idlewild Trust
The Iliffe Family Charitable Trust
The Indigo Trust
The Ingram Trust
The Inland Waterways Association
The Inlight Trust
The Inman Charity
The Inner London Magistrates Court Poor Box and Feeder Charity
The Ireland Fund of Great Britain
The Irish Youth Foundation (UK) Ltd (incorporating The Lawlor Foundation)
The Ironmongers' Foundation
Irshad Trust
Irwin Trust
The ISA Charity
The Isaacs Charitable Trust
The J Isaacs Charitable Trust
The Isle of Anglesey Charitable Trust
The ITF Seafarers Trust
The J R S S T Charitable Trust
Elizabeth Jackson Charitable Trust
The Ruth and Lionel Jacobson Trust (Second Fund) No 2
Jaffe Family Relief Fund
The Susan and Stephen James Charitable Settlement (also known as the Stephen James Charitable Trust)
The James Trust
The Marjory Jameson Trust
The Jarman Charitable Trust
The John Jarrold Trust
JCA Charitable Foundation
The Jeffrey Charitable Trust
Rees Jeffreys Road Fund
The Jenour Foundation
The Jephcott Charitable Trust
Jesus Hospital Charity
The Jewish Youth Fund
The JMK Charitable Trust
The Joanies Trust

The Harold Joels Charitable
Trust
The Jonathan Joels Charitable
Trust
The Nicholas Joels Charitable
Trust
The Norman Joels Charitable
Trust
The Lillie Johnson Charitable
Trust
The Johnson Foundation
The Johnson Group Cleaners
Charity
The Johnnie Johnson Trust
The Johnson Wax Ltd
Charitable Trust
The Joicey Trust
The Jones 1986 Charitable
Trust
The Marjorie and Geoffrey
Jones Charitable Trust
The Jordan Charitable
Foundation
The J E Joseph Charitable
Fund
The Lady Eileen Joseph
Foundation
JTH Charitable Trust
The Anton Jurgens Charitable
Trust
The Bernard Kahn Charitable
Trust
The Stanley Kalms Foundation
The Karenza Foundation
The Boris Karloff Charitable
Foundation
The Ian Karten Charitable
Trust
The Kasner Charitable Trust
The Kass Charitable Trust
The Kathleen Trust
The Michael and Ilse Katz
Foundation
The Katzauer Charitable
Settlement
The C S Kaufman Charitable
Trust
The Geoffrey John Kaye
Charitable Foundation
The Emmanuel Kaye
Foundation
Kelsick's Educational
Foundation
The KempWelch Charitable
Trust
The Kay Kendall Leukaemia
Fund
William Kendall's Charity (Wax
Chandlers' Company)
The Kennedy Charitable
Foundation
The Kennel Club Charitable
Trust
The Nancy Kenyon Charitable
Trust
Keren Association

Kermaville Ltd
The Peter Kershaw Trust
The Kessler Foundation
Keswick Hall Trust
The Ursula Keyes Trust
The Robert Kiln Charitable
Trust
The King Henry VIII Endowed
Trust Warwick
The King/Cullimore Charitable
Trust
The Kingsbury Charity
The Mary Kinross Charitable
Trust
Kirkley Poor's Lands Estate
The Richard Kirkman
Charitable Trust
Kirschel Foundation
Robert Kitchin (Saddlers'
Company)
Ernest Kleinwort Charitable
Trust
The Marina Kleinwort
Charitable Trust
The Sir James Knott Trust
The Kobler Trust
The Kohn Foundation
The Kreditor Charitable Trust
The Kreitman Foundation
The Neil Kreitman Foundation
The Heinz, Anna and Carol
Kroch Foundation
The Kyte Charitable Trust
The Late Sir Pierce Lacy
Charity Trust
John Laing Charitable Trust
Maurice and Hilda Laing
Charitable Trust
The Christopher Laing
Foundation
The Kirby Laing Foundation
The Martin Laing Foundation
The Beatrice Laing Trust
The Lambert Charitable Trust
Lancashire Environmental
Fund
Duchy of Lancaster Benevolent
Fund
The Lancaster Foundation
The Langdale Trust
The Langley Charitable Trust
The Langtree Trust
The LankellyChase Foundation
The Lanvern Foundation
The R J Larg Family Charitable
Trust
Largsmount Ltd
The Lark Trust
Laslett's (Hinton) Charity
Lauchentilly Charitable
Foundation 1988
The Lauffer Family Charitable
Foundation
The Kathleen Laurence Trust
The Edgar E Lawley Foundation

The Herd Lawson and Muriel
Lawson Charitable Trust
The Lawson Beckman
Charitable Trust
The Raymond and Blanche
Lawson Charitable Trust
The Carole and Geoffrey
Lawson Foundation
The Mason Le Page Charitable
Trust
The Leach Fourteenth Trust
The David Lean Foundation
The Leathersellers' Company
Charitable Fund
The Arnold Lee Charitable
Trust
The William Leech Charity
The Lord Mayor of Leeds
Appeal Fund
Leeds Building Society
Charitable Foundation
Leicester Charity Link (formerly
The Leicester Charity
Organisation Society)
The Kennedy Leigh Charitable
Trust
The Leigh Trust
Mrs Vera Leigh's Charity
The P Leigh-Bramwell Trust 'E'
The Lennox and Wyfold
Foundation
The Erica Leonard Trust
The Leonard Trust
The Mark Leonard Trust
Lesley Lesley and Mutter Trust
Leukaemia and Lymphoma
Research
The Leverhulme Trade
Charities Trust
Lord Leverhulme's Charitable
Trust
The Joseph Levy Charitable
Foundation
The John Spedan Lewis
Foundation
The Sir Edward Lewis
Foundation
John Lewis Partnership
General Community Fund
Lichfield Conduit Lands
Lifeline 4 Kids
The Thomas Lilley Memorial
Trust
The Linbury Trust
The Lind Trust
Lindale Educational
Foundation
The Linden Charitable Trust
The Enid Linder Foundation
The Linmardon Trust
The Ruth and Stuart Lipton
Charitable Trust
The Lister Charitable Trust
Frank Litchfield Charitable
Trust

The Andrew and Mary Elizabeth Little Charitable Trust

The Second Joseph Aaron Littman Foundation

The George John and Sheilah Livanos Charitable Trust

Liverpool Charity and Voluntary Services

Liverpool Sailors' Home Trust

The Elaine and Angus Lloyd Charitable Trust

The Charles Lloyd Foundation

The Lloyd Fund

Lloyd's Charities Trust

Lloyds TSB Foundation for England and Wales

Lloyds TSB Foundation for Northern Ireland

Lloyds TSB Foundation for the Channel Islands

The Locker Foundation

The Loftus Charitable Trust

The Lolev Charitable Trust

London Catalyst (formerly The Metropolitan Hospital-Sunday Fund)

The London Community Foundation (formerly Capital Community Foundation)

The London Law Trust

The London Marathon Charitable Trust

The William and Katherine Longman Trust

The Lord's Taverners

The Loseley and Guildway Charitable Trust

The Lotus Foundation

The C L Loyd Charitable Trust

The Marie Helen Luen Charitable Trust

Robert Luff Foundation Ltd

Henry Lumley Charitable Trust

Lady Lumley's Educational Foundation

C F Lunoe Trust Fund

The Ruth and Jack Lunzer Charitable Trust

Lord and Lady Lurgan Trust

The Lyndhurst Trust

The Lynn Foundation

The Lynwood Trust

John Lyon's Charity

The Lyons Charitable Trust

The Sir Jack Lyons Charitable Trust

The Lyras Family Charitable Trust

Sylvanus Lyson's Charity

The M and C Trust

The M D and S Charitable Trust

The M K Charitable Trust

The Madeline Mabey Trust

The E M MacAndrew Trust

The R S Macdonald Charitable Trust

Macdonald-Buchanan Charitable Trust

The Macfarlane Walker Trust

The Mackay and Brewer Charitable Trust

The Mackintosh Foundation

The MacRobert Trust

The Magdalen and Lasher Charity

Magdalen Hospital Trust

The Magen Charitable Trust

Man Group plc Charitable Trust

The Manchester Guardian Society Charitable Trust

Lord Mayor of Manchester's Charity Appeal Trust

Mandeville Trust

The Manifold Charitable Trust

W M Mann Foundation

The Leslie and Lilian Manning Trust

Marbeh Torah Trust

Marchig Animal Welfare Trust

The Stella and Alexander Margulies Charitable Trust

Market Harborough and The Bowdens Charity

The Ann and David Marks Foundation

The Hilda and Samuel Marks Foundation

J P Marland Charitable Trust

The Michael Marsh Charitable Trust

The Marsh Christian Trust

The Charlotte Marshall Charitable Trust

The Jim Marshall Charitable Trust

The D G Marshall of Cambridge Trust

Marshall's Charity

Marshgate Charitable Settlement

Sir George Martin Trust

John Martin's Charity

The Mason Porter Charitable Trust

The Nancie Massey Charitable Trust

The Mathew Trust

The Matt 6.3 Charitable Trust

The Violet Mauray Charitable Trust

The Maxell Educational Trust

The Maxwell Family Foundation

Evelyn May Trust

Mayfair Charities Ltd

The Mayfield Valley Arts Trust

Mazars Charitable Trust

The Robert McAlpine Foundation

The McDougall Trust

The McKenna Charitable Trust

The Helen Isabella McMorran Charitable Foundation

The James Frederick and Ethel Anne Measures Charity

The Medlock Charitable Trust

The Anthony and Elizabeth Mellows Charitable Settlement

Melow Charitable Trust

The Mercers' Charitable Foundation

The Merchant Taylors' Company Charities Fund

The Merchant Venturers' Charity

The Merchants' House of Glasgow

The Mersey Docks and Harbour Company Charitable Fund

Community Foundation for Merseyside

The Zachary Merton and George Woofindin Convalescent Trust

The Tony Metherell Charitable Trust

The Metropolitan Drinking Fountain and Cattle Trough Association

Gerald Micklem Charitable Trust

Midhurst Pensions Trust

The Migraine Trust

Miles Trust for the Putney and Roehampton Community

The Hugh and Mary Miller Bequest Trust

The Miller Foundation

The Millfield Trust

The Millhouses Charitable Trust

The Millichope Foundation

The Mills Charity

The Millward Charitable Trust

The Clare Milne Trust

Milton Keynes Community Foundation

The Edgar Milward Charity

The Keith and Joan Mindelsohn Charitable Trust

The Peter Minet Trust

The Minos Trust

The Mirfield Educational Charity

The Laurence Misener Charitable Trust

The Mishcon Family Charitable Trust

The Misselbrook Trust

The Mitchell Charitable Trust

The Esmé Mitchell Trust

Keren Mitzvah Trust

The Mizpah Trust

The Mobbs Memorial Trust Ltd
The Modiano Charitable Trust
The Moette Charitable Trust
The Mole Charitable Trust
The D C Moncrieff Charitable Trust
Monmouthshire County Council Welsh Church Act Fund
The Montague Thompson Coon Charitable Trust
The Colin Montgomerie Charitable Foundation
The Monument Trust
George A Moore Foundation
The Nigel Moores Family Charitable Trust
John Moores Foundation
The Peter Moores Foundation
The Morel Charitable Trust
The Morgan Charitable Foundation
The Mr and Mrs J T Morgan Foundation
The Oliver Morland Charitable Trust
The Bernard Morris Charitable Trust
The Morris Charitable Trust
The Willie and Mabel Morris Charitable Trust
The Peter Morrison Charitable Foundation
The Stanley Morrison Charitable Trust
Vyoel Moshe Charitable Trust
The Moss Charitable Trust
The Robert and Margaret Moss Charitable Trust
Moss Family Charitable Trust
The Mount Everest Foundation
The Edwina Mountbatten Trust
Mountbatten Festival of Music
The Mountbatten Memorial Trust
The Mugdock Children's Trust
The Mulberry Trust
The Edith Murphy Foundation
The Mushroom Fund
The Music Sales Charitable Trust
Muslim Hands
The Mutual Trust Group
The Kitty and Daniel Nabarro Charitable Trust
The Nadezhda Charitable Trust
The Naggar Charitable Trust
The Eleni Nakou Foundation
The Janet Nash Charitable Settlement
Nathan Charitable Trust
The National Manuscripts Conservation Trust
The Nchima Trust
Needham Market and Barking Welfare Charities

The Worshipful Company of Needlemakers' Charitable Fund
The Neighbourly Charitable Trust
The James Neill Trust Fund
Nemoral Ltd
Network for Social Change
The New Appeals Organisation for the City and County of Nottingham
New Court Charitable Trust
The Newcomen Collett Foundation
The Frances and Augustus Newman Foundation
Alderman Newton's Educational Foundation
The Chevras Ezras Nitzrochim Trust
The Noon Foundation
The Norda Trust
Norie Charitable Trust
Normalyn Charitable Trust
The Norman Family Charitable Trust
The Duncan Norman Trust Fund
The Normanby Charitable Trust
The North British Hotel Trust
The North West Cancer Research Fund
The Northampton Municipal Church Charities
The Northampton Queen's Institute Relief in Sickness Fund
The Earl of Northampton's Charity
The Northcott Devon Foundation
The Northcott Devon Medical Foundation
The Northmoor Trust
The Northumberland Village Homes Trust
The Northumbria Historic Churches Trust
The Northwood Charitable Trust
The Norton Foundation
The Norwich Church of England Young Men's Society
The Norwich Historic Churches Trust Ltd
The Norwich Town Close Estate Charity
The Norwood and Newton Settlement
The Noswad Charity
The Notgrove Trust
The Nottingham General Dispensary
The Nottingham Gordon Memorial Trust for Boys and Girls

Nottinghamshire Community Foundation
The Nottinghamshire Historic Churches Trust
The Nottinghamshire Miners' Welfare Trust Fund
Novi Most International
The Father O'Mahoney Memorial Trust
The Sir Peter O'Sullevan Charitable Trust
The Oak Trust
The Oakdale Trust
The Oakley Charitable Trust
The Oakmoor Charitable Trust
The Odin Charitable Trust
The Ofenheim Charitable Trust
Ogilvie Charities Deed No.2 (including the Charity of Mary Catherine Ford Smith)
The Ogle Christian Trust
The Oikonomia Trust
Oizer Charitable Trust
The Old Broad Street Charity Trust
The Old Enfield Charitable Trust
The John Oldacre Foundation
The Oldham Foundation
Onaway Trust
Open Gate
The Ormsby Charitable Trust
Orrin Charitable Trust
The Owen Family Trust
Oxfam (GB)
The Oxfordshire Community Foundation
The P F Charitable Trust
Padwa Charitable Foundation
The Pallant Charitable Trust
The Palmer Foundation
Eleanor Palmer Trust
The Panacea Society
Panton Trust
The James Pantyfedwen Foundation
The Paragon Trust
The Park House Charitable Trust
The Frank Parkinson Agricultural Trust
The Samuel and Freda Parkinson Charitable Trust
The Parthenon Trust
The Constance Paterson Charitable Trust
The Patrick Charitable Trust
The Jack Patston Charitable Trust
Paycare Charity Trust (previously known as Patients' Aid Association Hospital and Medical Charities Trust)
The Payne Charitable Trust
The Harry Payne Trust

The Susanna Peake Charitable Trust
The Pedmore Sporting Club Trust Fund
The Dowager Countess Eleanor Peel Trust
The Pennycress Trust
The Performing Right Society Foundation
The Persson Charitable Trust (formerly Highmoore Hall Charitable Trust)
The Persula Foundation
The Jack Petchey Foundation
The Petplan Charitable Trust
The Philips and Rubens Charitable Trust
The Phillips Charitable Trust
The Phillips Family Charitable Trust
Philological Foundation
The David Pickford Charitable Foundation
The Bernard Piggott Trust
The Cecil Pilkington Charitable Trust
The Pilkington Charities Fund
The Austin and Hope Pilkington Trust
The Sir Harry Pilkington Trust
The Col W W Pilkington Will Trusts The General Charity Fund
The DLA Piper Charitable Trust
The Worshipful Company of Plaisterers Charitable Trust
The Platinum Trust
The Poling Charitable Trust
The George and Esme Pollitzer Charitable Settlement
The J S F Pollitzer Charitable Settlement
The Ponton House Trust
The Mayor of Poole's Appeal Fund
Edith and Ferdinand Porjes Charitable Trust
The John Porter Charitable Trust
The Porter Foundation
The Portishead Nautical Trust
The Portrack Charitable Trust
The J E Posnansky Charitable Trust
The Powell Foundation
The W L Pratt Charitable Trust
Premierquote Ltd
Premishlaner Charitable Trust
The William Price Charitable Trust
The Lucy Price Relief-in-Need Charity
Sir John Priestman Charity Trust
The Primrose Trust

The Prince of Wales's Charitable Foundation
The Priory Foundation
Prison Service Charity Fund
The Privy Purse Charitable Trust
The Proven Family Trust
The Provincial Grand Charity of the Province of Derbyshire
PSA Peugeot Citroen Charity Trust
The Puebla Charitable Trust
The Richard and Christine Purchas Charitable Trust
The Puri Foundation
Mr and Mrs J A Pye's Charitable Settlement
Quartet Community Foundation (formerly the Greater Bristol Foundation)
Queen Mary's Roehampton Trust
The Queen's Silver Jubilee Trust
R S Charitable Trust
The R V W Trust
The Monica Rabagliati Charitable Trust
Rachel Charitable Trust
The Mr and Mrs Philip Rackham Charitable Trust
Richard Radcliffe Charitable Trust
The Radcliffe Trust
The Ragdoll Foundation
The Rainford Trust
The Peggy Ramsay Foundation
The Joseph and Lena Randall Charitable Trust
The Rank Foundation
The Fanny Rapaport Charitable Settlement
The Ratcliff Foundation
The Ratcliff Pension Charity
The Ratcliffe Charitable Trust
The Eleanor Rathbone Charitable Trust
The Sigrid Rausing Trust
The Ravensdale Trust
The Rayden Charitable Trust
The Roger Raymond Charitable Trust
The Rayne Foundation
The Rayne Trust
The John Rayner Charitable Trust
The Sir James Reckitt Charity
The Red Arrows Trust
Red Hill Charitable Trust
The Red Rose Charitable Trust
The C A Redfern Charitable Foundation
The Reed Foundation
Richard Reeve's Foundation
The Max Reinhardt Charitable Trust

Relief Fund for Romania Limited
REMEDI
The Rest Harrow Trust
Reuben Brothers Foundation
The Joan K Reynell Charitable Trust
The Nathaniel Reyner Trust Fund
The Rhododendron Trust
The Rhondda Cynon Taff Welsh Church Acts Fund
The Clive Richards Charity
The Richmond Parish Lands Charity
Ridgesave Limited
The Ripple Effect Foundation
The Sir John Ritblat Family Foundation
The River Trust
Thomas Roberts Trust
The Robertson Trust
The Rochester Bridge Trust
The Rock Foundation
The Rock Solid Trust
The Rofeh Trust
Richard Rogers Charitable Settlement
Rokach Family Charitable Trust
The Helen Roll Charitable Trust
The Sir James Roll Charitable Trust
The Roman Research Trust
Romeera Foundation
The C A Rookes Charitable Trust
Mrs L D Rope Third Charitable Settlement
The Rosca Trust
The Cecil Rosen Foundation
The Rothermere Foundation
The Rotherwick Foundation
The Rothley Trust
The Roughley Charitable Trust
Mrs Gladys Row Fogo Charitable Trust
Rowanville Ltd
The Christopher Rowbotham Charitable Trust
The Rowing Foundation
The Rowlands Trust
The Joseph Rowntree Charitable Trust
Royal Artillery Charitable Fund
Royal British Legion
Royal Docks Trust (London)
Royal Masonic Trust for Girls and Boys
The Royal Scots Benevolent Society
The Alfred and Frances Rubens Charitable Trust
The Rubin Foundation
William Arthur Rudd Memorial Trust

The Rufford Foundation
The Russell Trust
The J S and E C Rymer
  Charitable Trust
S O Charitable Trust
The Jeremy and John Sacher
  Charitable Trust
The Michael Harry Sacher
  Trust
The Raymond and Beverley
  Sackler 1988 Foundation
The Sackler Trust (Formerly Dr
  Mortimer and Theresa
  Sackler Foundation)
The Ruzin Sadagora Trust
The Saddlers' Company
  Charitable Fund
The Saga Charitable Trust
The Jean Sainsbury Animal
  Welfare Trust
The Alan and Babette
  Sainsbury Charitable Fund
The Sainsbury Family
  Charitable Trusts
The Saintbury Trust
The Saints and Sinners Trust
The Salamander Charitable
  Trust
The Salt Foundation
The Salt Trust
The Sammermar Trust
Basil Samuel Charitable Trust
The Hon. M J Samuel
  Charitable Trust
The Peter Samuel Charitable
  Trust
The Camilla Samuel Fund
The Samworth Foundation
The Sandra Charitable Trust
Santander UK Foundation
  Limited
Jimmy Savile Charitable Trust
The Scarfe Charitable Trust
The Schapira Charitable Trust
The Schmidt-Bodner Charitable
  Trust
The Schreib Trust
The Schreiber Charitable Trust
The Francis C Scott Charitable
  Trust
The Frieda Scott Charitable
  Trust
The Sir James and Lady Scott
  Trust
The Scott Trust Foundation
The Storrow Scott Will Trust
The Scottish Arts Council
Scottish Coal Industry Special
  Welfare Fund
The Scottish Community
  Foundation
The Scouloudi Foundation
Seafarers UK (King George's
  Fund for Sailors)
Seamen's Hospital Society

The Searchlight Electric
  Charitable Trust
The Searle Charitable Trust
The Helene Sebba Charitable
  Trust
The Samuel Sebba Charitable
  Trust
The Seedfield Trust
Leslie Sell Charitable Trust
The Ayrton Senna Foundation
The Seven Fifty Trust
The Severn Trent Water
  Charitable Trust Fund
SFIA Educational Trust Limited
The Cyril Shack Trust
The Shanti Charitable Trust
ShareGift (The Orr Mackintosh
  Foundation)
The Linley Shaw Foundation
The Sheepdrove Trust
The Sheffield and District
  Hospital Services
  Charitable Fund
The Sheldon Trust
The P and D Shepherd
  Charitable Trust
The Sylvia and Colin Shepherd
  Charitable Trust
The Archie Sherman Cardiff
  Foundation
The Archie Sherman Charitable
  Trust
The R C Sherriff Trust
The Shetland Charitable Trust
SHINE (Support and Help in
  Education)
The Barnett and Sylvia Shine
  No 2 Charitable Trust
The Bassil Shippam and
  Alsford Trust
The Shipwrights' Company
  Charitable Fund
The Shirley Foundation
Shlomo Memorial Fund Limited
The J A Shone Memorial Trust
The Barbara A Shuttleworth
  Memorial Trust
The Mary Elizabeth Siebel
  Charity
David and Jennifer Sieff
  Charitable Trust
The Julius Silman Charitable
  Trust
The Leslie Silver Charitable
  Trust
The Simpson Education and
  Conservation Trust
The Simpson Foundation
The Huntly and Margery
  Sinclair Charitable Trust
Sino-British Fellowship Trust
The Skelton Bounty
The Charles Skey Charitable
  Trust
Skipton Building Society
  Charitable Foundation

The John Slater Foundation
The SMB Charitable Trust
The Mrs Smith and Mount
  Trust
The N Smith Charitable
  Settlement
The Amanda Smith Charitable
  Trust
The E H Smith Charitable Trust
The Smith Charitable Trust
The Henry Smith Charity
The Leslie Smith Foundation
The Martin Smith Foundation
Stanley Smith General
  Charitable Trust
The Stanley Smith UK
  Horticultural Trust
The Snowball Trust
The Sobell Foundation
Solihull Community Foundation
The Solo Charitable
  Settlement
Dr Richard Solomon's
  Charitable Trust
The E C Sosnow Charitable
  Trust
The Souter Charitable Trust
The South Square Trust
The Stephen R and Philippa H
  Southall Charitable Trust
The W F Southall Trust
The Southover Manor General
  Education Trust
The Southwold Trust
The Sovereign Health Care
  Charitable Trust
Sparks Charity (Sport Aiding
  Medical Research For Kids)
Sparquote Limited
The Spear Charitable Trust
The Worshipful Company of
  Spectacle Makers' Charity
The Jessie Spencer Trust
The Ralph and Irma Sperring
  Charity
The Moss Spiro Will Charitable
  Foundation
The Spoore, Merry and Rixman
  Foundation
Spring Harvest
Springfields Employees'
  Medical Research and
  Charity Trust Fund
Springrule Ltd
The Spurrell Charitable Trust
The Geoff and Fiona Squire
  Foundation
St Francis's Leprosy Guild
St Gabriel's Trust
St James' Trust Settlement
St James's Place Foundation
Sir Walter St John's
  Educational Charity
St Katharine and Shadwell
  Trust

St Michael's and All Saints'
Charities
The Late St Patrick White
Charitable Trust
St Teilo's Trust
The Stanley Foundation Ltd
The Stanton Ballard Charitable
Trust
The Staples Trust
The Star Charitable Trust
The Peter Stebbings Memorial
Charity
The Steel Charitable Trust
The Steinberg Family
Charitable Trust
The Hugh Stenhouse
Foundation
The Sigmund Sternberg
Charitable Foundation
Stervon Ltd
The Stevenage Community
Trust
The June Stevens Foundation
The Steventon Allotments and
Relief-in-Need Charity
The Stewards' Company
Limited (incorporating the J
W Laing Trust and the J W
Laing Biblical Scholarship
Trust)
The Leonard Laity Stoate
Charitable Trust
The Stobart Newlands
Charitable Trust
The Edward Stocks-Massey
Bequest Fund
The Stokenchurch Educational
Charity
The Stoller Charitable Trust
The M J C Stone Charitable
Trust
The Stone-Mallabar Charitable
Foundation
The Samuel Storey Family
Charitable Trust
Peter Stormonth Darling
Charitable Trust
The Strangward Trust
The Strasser Foundation
Stratford upon Avon Town
Trust
Strathclyde Police Benevolent
Fund
The W O Street Charitable
Foundation
The Sudborough Foundation
The Suffolk Historic Churches
Trust
The Summerfield Charitable
Trust
The Bernard Sunley Charitable
Foundation
The Surrey Historic Buildings
Trust Ltd
The Sussex Historic Churches
Trust

The Sutasoma Trust
Sutton Coldfield Municipal
Charities
Swansea and Brecon Diocesan
Board of Finance Limited
The John Swire (1989)
Charitable Trust
The Swire Charitable Trust
The Hugh and Ruby Sykes
Charitable Trust
The Charles and Elsie Sykes
Trust
The Sylvanus Charitable Trust
The Stella Symons Charitable
Trust
The Tabeel Trust
The Tajtelbaum Charitable
Trust
The Talbot Trusts
The Talbot Village Trust
Tallow Chandlers Benevolent
Fund
The Tangent Charitable Trust
The Lady Tangye Charitable
Trust
The David Tannen Charitable
Trust
The Tanner Trust
The Lili Tapper Charitable
Foundation
The Mrs A Lacy Tate Trust
The Tay Charitable Trust
Humphrey Richardson Taylor
Charitable Trust
The Connie and Albert Taylor
Charitable Trust
The Cyril Taylor Charitable
Trust
A P Taylor Trust
Tearfund
The Tedworth Charitable Trust
Tees Valley Community
Foundation
The Templeton Goodwill Trust
Tesco Charity Trust
Thackray Medical Research
Trust
The Thames Wharf Charity
The Thistle Trust
The Loke Wan Tho Memorial
Foundation
The Arthur and Margaret
Thompson Charitable Trust
The Thompson Family
Charitable Trust
The Len Thomson Charitable
Trust
The Sue Thomson Foundation
The Sir Jules Thorn Charitable
Trust
The Thornton Foundation
The Thornton Trust
The Three Guineas Trust
The Three Oaks Trust
The Thriplow Charitable Trust

Mrs R P Tindall's Charitable
Trust
The Tinsley Foundation
The Tisbury Telegraph Trust
TJH Foundation
The Tobacco Pipe Makers and
Tobacco Trade Benevolent
Fund
The Tolkien Trust
Tollemache (Buckminster)
Charitable Trust
Tomchei Torah Charitable
Trust
The Tompkins Foundation
The Tory Family Foundation
Tottenham Grammar School
Foundation
The Tower Hill Trust
The Towry Law Charitable Trust
(also known as the Castle
Educational Trust)
The Toy Trust
The Mayor of Trafford's Charity
Fund
The Constance Travis
Charitable Trust
The Treeside Trust
The Triangle Trust (1949) Fund
The True Colours Trust
Truedene Co. Ltd
The Truemark Trust
Truemart Limited
Trumros Limited
Trust Sixty Three
The Trusthouse Charitable
Foundation
Tudor Rose Ltd
The Tudor Trust
The Tufton Charitable Trust
The R D Turner Charitable
Trust
The Douglas Turner Trust
The Florence Turner Trust
Miss S M Tutton Charitable
Trust
The TUUT Charitable Trust
Community Foundation Serving
Tyne and Wear and
Northumberland
Trustees of Tzedakah
Ulster Garden Villages Ltd
Ultach Trust
Ulting Overseas Trust
The Ulverscroft Foundation
Ulverston Town Lands Charity
The Underwood Trust
The Union of Orthodox Hebrew
Congregation
The United Society for the
Propagation of the Gospel
The David Uri Memorial Trust
Uxbridge United Welfare Trust
Vale of Glamorgan – Welsh
Church Fund
The Valentine Charitable Trust

John and Lucille van Geest
Foundation
The Van Neste Foundation
Mrs Maud Van Norden's
Charitable Foundation
The Vandervell Foundation
The Vardy Foundation
The Variety Club Children's
Charity
Veneziana Fund
The Verdon-Smith Family
Charitable Settlement
Victoria Homes Trust
The Nigel Vinson Charitable
Trust
The William and Ellen Vinten
Trust
The Vintners' Company
Charitable Foundation
Vintners' Gifts Charity
Vision Charity
Vivdale Ltd
The Viznitz Foundation
Voluntary Action Fund
Wade's Charity
The Scurrah Wainwright Charity
Wakeham Trust
The Community Foundation in
Wales
Wales Council for Voluntary
Action
Robert and Felicity Waley-
Cohen Charitable Trust
The Thomas Wall Trust
The F J Wallis Charitable
Settlement
Walton on Thames Charity
War on Want
The Ward Blenkinsop Trust
The George Ward Charitable
Trust
The Barbara Ward Children's
Foundation
The John Warren Foundation
G R Waters Charitable Trust
2000
The Waterways Trust
The Howard Watson Symington
Memorial Charity
John Watson's Trust
Weatherley Charitable Trust
The Weavers' Company
Benevolent Fund
The William Webster
Charitable Trust
The Weinberg Foundation
The Weinstein Foundation
The Weinstock Fund
The James Weir Foundation
The Barbara Welby Trust
The Weldon UK Charitable
Trust
The Wellcome Trust

Welsh Church Fund Dyfed
area (Carmarthenshire,
Ceredigion and
Pembrokeshire)
The Welton Foundation
The Wessex Youth Trust
The West Derby Wastelands
Charity
West London Synagogue
Charitable Fund
The West Yorkshire Police
Community Fund
The Westminster Foundation
The Garfield Weston
Foundation
The Whitaker Charitable Trust
The Colonel W H Whitbread
Charitable Trust
The Simon Whitbread
Charitable Trust
The Whitecourt Charitable
Trust
The Norman Whiteley Trust
The Whitley Animal Protection
Trust
The Whittlesey Charity
The Lionel Wigram Memorial
Trust
The Felicity Wilde Charitable
Trust
The Wilkinson Charitable
Foundation
The Kay Williams Charitable
Foundation
The Williams Family Charitable
Trust
The H D H Wills 1965
Charitable Trust
The Dame Violet Wills Will
Trust
The Wilmcote Charitrust
David Wilson Foundation
The Wilson Foundation
J and J R Wilson Trust
The Community Foundation for
Wiltshire and Swindon
The Benjamin Winegarten
Charitable Trust
The Francis Winham
Foundation
Wirral Mayor's Charity
The Michael and Anna Wix
Charitable Trust
The Wixamtree Trust
The Woburn 1986 Charitable
Trust
The Maurice Wohl Charitable
Foundation
The Charles Wolfson
Charitable Trust
The Wolfson Family Charitable
Trust
The Wolfson Foundation
The James Wood Bequest
Fund
Woodlands Green Ltd

Woodlands Trust
The Woodward Charitable
Trust
Worcester Municipal Charities
(incorporating Worcester
Consolidated Municipal
Charity and Worcester
Municipal Exhibitions
Foundation)
The Worcestershire and
Dudley Historic Churches
Trust
The Fred and Della Worms
Charitable Trust
The Wragge and Co. Charitable
Trust
The Diana Edgson Wright
Charitable Trust
The Matthews Wrightson
Charity Trust
Miss E B Wrightson's
Charitable Settlement
Wychdale Ltd
Wychville Ltd
The Wyndham Charitable Trust
The Wyseliot Charitable Trust
The Xerox (UK) Trust
The Yardley Great Trust
The Dennis Alan Yardy
Charitable Trust
The W Wing Yip and Brothers
Foundation
The York Children's Trust
Yorkshire Agricultural Society
Yorkshire Building Society
Charitable Foundation
The South Yorkshire
Community Foundation
The Yorkshire Dales
Millennium Trust
The John Young Charitable
Settlement
The William Allen Young
Charitable Trust
The John K Young Endowment
Fund
Zephyr Charitable Trust
The Marjorie and Arnold Ziff
Charitable Foundation
Stephen Zimmerman
Charitable Trust
The Zochonis Charitable Trust
Zurich Community Trust (UK)
Limited

....

■ Vehicles

The 1970 Trust
The 1989 Willan Charitable
Trust
The 29th May 1961 Charitable
Trust
The Aberbrothock Skea Trust
The Aberdeen Endowments
Trust

The Aberdeenshire Educational
    Trust Scheme
Achiezer Association Ltd
Achisomoch Aid Company
    Limited
The ACT Foundation
Action Medical Research
The Company of Actuaries'
    Charitable Trust Fund
The Sylvia Adams Charitable
    Trust
The Victor Adda Foundation
The Adint Charitable Trust
Age UK (formerly Help the
    Aged and Age Concern)
Aid to the Church in Need (UK)
The Sylvia Aitken Charitable
    Trust
The Ajahma Charitable Trust
Aldgate and All Hallows'
    Barking Exhibition
    Foundation
The Aldgate Freedom
    Foundation
Allchurches Trust Ltd
The H B Allen Charitable Trust
The Alliance Family Foundation
Angus Allnatt Charitable
    Foundation
The Pat Allsop Charitable Trust
Almondsbury Charity
Altamont Ltd
Alvor Charitable Trust
The Ammco Trust
Viscount Amory's Charitable
    Trust
The AMW Charitable Trust
The André Christian Trust
Anguish's Educational
    Foundation
The Animal Defence Trust
The Eric Anker-Petersen
    Charity
Ambrose and Ann Appelbe
    Trust
The Appletree Trust
The John Apthorp Charitable
    Trust
The Arbib Foundation
The John M Archer Charitable
    Trust
The Archer Trust
The Ardwick Trust
The Argus Appeal
The Armenian Relief Society of
    Great Britain Trust
The Armourers' and Brasiers'
    Gauntlet Trust
Arsenal Charitable Trust
The Artemis Charitable Trust
The Arts and Entertainment
    Charitable Trust
Arts Council England
The Arts Council of Northern
    Ireland
The Arts Council of Wales

The Ove Arup Foundation
The AS Charitable Trust
The Ashden Trust
The Ashendene Trust
The Ashley Family Foundation
    (formerly The Laura Ashley
    Foundation)
The Norman C Ashton
    Foundation
The Ashworth Charitable Trust
The Ian Askew Charitable Trust
The Associated Country
    Women of the World
    (ACWW)
The Association of Colleges
    Charitable Trust
Astellas European Foundation
Asthma UK
The Astor Foundation
The Astor of Hever Trust
The Aurelius Charitable Trust
The Avenue Charitable Trust
The John Avins Trustees
The Avon and Somerset Police
    Community Trust
AW Charitable Trust
The Aylesford Family
    Charitable Trust
The BAA Communities Trust
The BACTA Charitable Trust
The Scott Bader
    Commonwealth Ltd
The Bagri Foundation
Veta Bailey Charitable Trust
The Austin Bailey Trust
The Baily Thomas Charitable
    Fund
The Baird Trust
The Baker Charitable Trust
The Balcombe Charitable Trust
The Albert Casanova Ballard
    Deceased Trust
The Ballinger Charitable Trust
The Balmore Trust
The Balney Charitable Trust
The Baltic Charitable Fund
The Bamford Charitable
    Foundation
The Banbury Charities
William P Bancroft (No 2)
    Charitable Trust and
    Jenepher Gillett Trust
The Band Trust
The Barbers' Company General
    Charities
The Barbour Foundation
Barchester Healthcare
    Foundation
The Barclay Foundation
The Baring Foundation
Peter Barker-Mill Memorial
    Charity
Barleycorn Trust
Barnes Workhouse Fund
The Barnsbury Charitable Trust
The Barnstaple Bridge Trust

The Barnwood House Trust
The Misses Barrie Charitable
    Trust
Barrington Family Charitable
    Trust
The Charity of William Barrow
Stephen J Barry Charitable
    Trust
The Bartlett Taylor Charitable
    Trust
The Paul Bassham Charitable
    Trust
The Batchworth Trust
The Bay Tree Charitable Trust
D H and L H Baylin Charitable
    Trust
The Louis Baylis (Maidenhead
    Advertiser) Charitable Trust
BBC Children in Need
B-CH 1971 Charitable Trust
The Beacon Trust
The Bearder Charity
The James Beattie Charitable
    Trust
The Beaufort House Trust
    Limited
The Beaverbrook Foundation
The Beccles Town Lands
    Charity
The Becker Family Charitable
    Trust
The Becketts and Sargeants
    Educational Foundation
The John Beckwith Charitable
    Trust
The Peter Beckwith Charitable
    Trust
The Bedford Charity (The
    Harpur Trust)
The David and Ruth Behrend
    Fund
The Beit Trust
The Bellahouston Bequest
    Fund
The Bellinger Donnay Trust
Belljoe Tzedoko Ltd
The Benfield Motors Charitable
    Trust
The Benham Charitable
    Settlement
The Hervey Benham Charitable
    Trust
Maurice and Jacqueline
    Bennett Charitable Trust
The Gerald Bentall Charitable
    Trust
Bergqvist Charitable Trust
The Berkshire Community
    Foundation
The Bestway Foundation
Thomas Betton's Charity for
    Pensions and Relief-in-Need
BHST
The Mason Bibby 1981 Trust
BibleLands
The Bideford Bridge Trust

The Big Lottery Fund
The Billmeir Charitable Trust
Percy Bilton Charity
The Bingham Trust
The Bintaub Charitable Trust
The Birmingham District
    Nursing Charitable Trust
Birmingham International
    Airport Community Trust
The Lord Mayor of
    Birmingham's Charity
The Bisgood Charitable Trust
    (registered as Miss Jeanne
    Bisgood's Charitable Trust)
The Michael Bishop
    Foundation
The Bishop's Development
    Fund
The Bertie Black Foundation
Isabel Blackman Foundation
The Herbert and Peter
    Blagrave Charitable Trust
The Blair Foundation
The Blanchminster Trust
The Sir Victor Blank Charitable
    Settlement
The Neville and Elaine Blond
    Charitable Trust
The Bluston Charitable
    Settlement
The Body Shop Foundation
The Boltons Trust
The Bonamy Charitable Trust
The John and Celia Bonham
    Christie Charitable Trust
The Charlotte Bonham-Carter
    Charitable Trust
Bonhomie United Charity
    Society
The Boots Charitable Trust
The Bordon and Liphook
    Charity
The Oliver Borthwick Memorial
    Trust
The Bothwell Charitable Trust
H E and E L Botteley
    Charitable Trust
The Harry Bottom Charitable
    Trust
The Anthony Bourne
    Foundation
The Bower Trust
The Bowerman Charitable
    Trust
John and Susan Bowers Fund
The Bowland Charitable Trust
The William Brake Charitable
    Trust
The Tony Bramall Charitable
    Trust
The Harold and Alice Bridges
    Charity
The Brighton District Nursing
    Association Trust
Bristol Archdeaconry Charity

John Bristow and Thomas
    Mason Trust
Britannia Foundation
The British Council for
    Prevention of Blindness
The British Dietetic
    Association General and
    Education Trust Fund
The British Gas (Scottish Gas)
    Energy Trust
British Heart Foundation
British Humane Association
British Institute at Ankara
British Ornithologists' Union
British Record Industry Trust
The Britto Foundation
The J and M Britton Charitable
    Trust
The Charles and Edna
    Broadhurst Charitable Trust
The Roger Brooke Charitable
    Trust
The David Brooke Charity
The Charles Brotherton Trust
Joseph Brough Charitable
    Trust
The Swinfen Broun Charitable
    Trust
Mrs E E Brown Charitable
    Settlement
The Jack Brunton Charitable
    Trust
The Bryant Trust
The Buckinghamshire
    Foundation
The Buckinghamshire Masonic
    Centenary Fund
The Rosemary Bugden
    Charitable Trust
The Bulldog Trust Limited
The E F Bulmer Benevolent
    Fund
Burdens Charitable Foundation
The Clara E Burgess Charity
The Burry Charitable Trust
The Arnold Burton 1998
    Charitable Trust
The Burton Breweries
    Charitable Trust
The Geoffrey Burton Charitable
    Trust
Consolidated Charity of Burton
    upon Trent
Butchers' Company General
    Charities
The Noel Buxton Trust
Henry T and Lucy B Cadbury
    Charitable Trust
The Christopher Cadbury
    Charitable Trust
The G W Cadbury Charitable
    Trust
The Richard Cadbury
    Charitable Trust
The Edward and Dorothy
    Cadbury Trust

The George Cadbury Trust
CAFOD (Catholic Agency for
    Overseas Development)
The Callander Charitable Trust
Calleva Foundation
Calypso Browning Trust
The Campden Charities
    Trustee
The Canning Trust
The Carew Pole Charitable
    Trust
The D W T Cargill Fund
Carlee Ltd
The Carlton House Charitable
    Trust
The Worshipful Company of
    Carmen Benevolent Trust
The Carnegie Dunfermline
    Trust
The Carpenter Charitable Trust
The Carpenters' Company
    Charitable Trust
The Carrington Charitable
    Trust
The Carron Charitable
    Settlement
The Leslie Mary Carter
    Charitable Trust
The Carvill Trust
The Casey Trust
The Elizabeth Casson Trust
The Castang Foundation
The Catalyst Charitable Trust
    (formerly the Buckle Family
    Charitable Trust)
The Catholic Charitable Trust
Catholic Foreign Missions
The Catholic Trust for England
    and Wales
The Joseph and Annie Cattle
    Trust
The Thomas Sivewright Catto
    Charitable Settlement
The Wilfrid and Constance
    Cave Foundation
The Cayo Foundation
The B G S Cayzer Charitable
    Trust
The Cazenove Charitable Trust
Celtic Charity Fund
The Cemlyn-Jones Trust
The Pamela Champion
    Foundation
The Chapman Charitable Trust
John William Chapman's
    Charitable Trust
The Charities Advisory Trust
Charitworth Limited
The Charter 600 Charity
The Worshipful Company of
    Chartered Accountants
    General Charitable Trust
    (also known as CALC)
The Chasah Trust
The Chelsea Square 1994
    Trust

The Cheruby Trust
The Cheshire Provincial Fund
    of Benevolence
The Chetwode Foundation
Chevioty Asset Management
    Charitable Trust
The Malcolm Chick Charity
Childs Charitable Trust
The Childwick Trust
The Chippenham Borough
    Lands Charity
The Chipping Sodbury Town
    Lands Charity
CHK Charities Limited
The Chownes Foundation
The Chrimes Family Charitable
    Trust
The Christabella Charitable
    Trust
Christadelphian Samaritan
    Fund
Christian Aid
Christian Response to Eastern
    Europe
The Church and Community
    Fund
The Church Burgesses
    Educational Foundation
Church Burgesses Trust
The Church Urban Fund
City and County of Swansea
    Welsh Church Act Fund
The City Educational Trust
    Fund
Stephen Clark 1957
    Charitable Trust
J A Clark Charitable Trust
The Hilda and Alice Clark
    Charitable Trust
The Roger and Sarah Bancroft
    Clark Charitable Trust
The Clarke Charitable
    Settlement
The Cleary Foundation
The Cleopatra Trust
Lord Clinton's Charitable Trust
The Clore Duffield Foundation
Miss V L Clore's 1967
    Charitable Trust
Closehelm Ltd
The Clothworkers' Foundation
Richard Cloudesley's Charity
The Clover Trust
The Robert Clutterbuck
    Charitable Trust
Clydpride Ltd
The Coalfields Regeneration
    Trust
The John Coates Charitable
    Trust
Coats Foundation Trust
The Cobtree Charity Trust Ltd
The Denise Cohen Charitable
    Trust
The Vivienne and Samuel
    Cohen Charitable Trust

The John S Cohen Foundation
The R and S Cohen
    Foundation
The Colchester Catalyst
    Charity
The Cole Charitable Trust
The Colefax Charitable Trust
The John and Freda Coleman
    Charitable Trust
The George Henry Collins
    Charity
The E Alec Colman Charitable
    Fund Ltd
The Sir Jeremiah Colman Gift
    Trust
The Colt Foundation
The Coltstaple Trust
Colwinston Charitable Trust
The Comino Foundation
Community Foundation for
    Calderdale
The Compton Charitable Trust
The Congleton Inclosure Trust
The Conservation Foundation
The Consolidated Charities for
    the Infirm Merchant
    Taylors' Company
The Ernest Cook Trust
The Cooks Charity
The Catherine Cookson
    Charitable Trust
Mabel Cooper Charity
The Alice Ellen Cooper Dean
    Charitable Foundation
The Co-operative Foundation
The Marjorie Coote Animal
    Charity Trust
The Marjorie Coote Old
    People's Charity
The Helen Jean Cope Trust
The J Reginald Corah
    Foundation Fund
The Gershon Coren Charitable
    Foundation
The Corinthian Trust
Edwin Cornforth 1983 Charity
    Trust
The Duke of Cornwall's
    Benevolent Fund
The Cornwell Charitable Trust
The Sidney and Elizabeth
    Corob Charitable Trust
The Corona Charitable Trust
The Costa Family Charitable
    Trust (formerly the Morgan
    Williams Charitable Trust)
The Cotton Industry War
    Memorial Trust
The Cotton Trust
The Augustine Courtauld Trust
The General Charities of the
    City of Coventry
Coventry Building Society
    Charitable Foundation
The John Cowan Foundation

The Sir William Coxen Trust
    Fund
The Lord Cozens-Hardy Trust
The Craignish Trust
The Craps Charitable Trust
Michael Crawford Children's
    Charity
The Cray Trust
Creative Scotland
The Crescent Trust
Cripplegate Foundation
The Violet and Milo Cripps
    Charitable Trust
The Harry Crook Foundation
The Cross Trust
The Croydon Relief in Need
    Charities
The Mayor of Croydon's
    Charity Fund
Cruden Foundation Ltd
The Ronald Cruickshank's
    Foundation
The R D Crusaders Foundation
The Culra Charitable Trust
The Cumber Family Charitable
    Trust
Cumberland Building Society
    Charitable Foundation
Cumbria Community
    Foundation
The D J H Currie Memorial
    Trust
The Dennis Curry Charitable
    Trust
The Raymond Curtis Charitable
    Trust
The Manny Cussins
    Foundation
The Cwmbran Trust
Itzchok Meyer Cymerman Trust
    Ltd
The D G Charitable Settlement
The D'Oyly Carte Charitable
    Trust
The Daily Prayer Union
    Charitable Trust Ltd
The Daisy Trust
The Daiwa Anglo-Japanese
    Foundation
The Dr and Mrs A Darlington
    Charitable Trust
Baron Davenport's Charity
The Davidson (Nairn)
    Charitable Trust
The Davidson Family
    Charitable Trust
The Alderman Joe Davidson
    Memorial Trust
Michael Davies Charitable
    Settlement
The Gwendoline and Margaret
    Davies Charity
The Wilfrid Bruce Davis
    Charitable Trust
Davis-Rubens Charitable Trust
The Dawe Charitable Trust

The De Clermont Charitable
Company Ltd
The Leopold De Rothschild
Charitable Trust
The Deakin Charitable Trust
William Dean Countryside and
Educational Trust
The Debmar Benevolent Trust
The Dellal Foundation
The Delves Charitable Trust
The Demigryphon Trust
The Denman Charitable Trust
The Denton Charitable Trust
The Denton Wilde Sapte
Charitable Trust
The Earl of Derby's Charitable
Trust
Derbyshire Community
Foundation
The J N Derbyshire Trust
The Devon Educational Trust
The Duke of Devonshire's
Charitable Trust
The Sandy Dewhirst Charitable
Trust
The Laduma Dhamecha
Charitable Trust
The Dibden Allotments Fund
The Dickon Trust
The Digbeth Trust
The Dinwoodie Settlement
Dischma Charitable Trust
The DLM Charitable Trust
Louise Dobson Charitable
Trust
The Derek and Eileen Dodgson
Foundation
The Dollond Charitable Trust
Domepride Ltd
The Dorcas Trust
The Dorus Trust
The Doughty Charity Trust
The R M Douglas Charitable
Trust
The Drapers' Charitable Fund
The Dugdale Charitable Trust
The Duis Charitable Trust
The Dulverton Trust
The P B Dumbell Charitable
Trust
The Dumbreck Charity
Dunard Fund
Ronald Duncan Literary
Foundation
The Houghton Dunn Charitable
Trust
The Dunn Family Charitable
Trust
The W E Dunn Trust
Dushinsky Trust Ltd
The Dwek Family Charitable
Trust
The Dyers' Company
Charitable Trust
The Eagle Charity Trust
The Earley Charity

Earls Colne and Halstead
Educational Charity
The Earmark Trust
East Kent Provincial Charities
East London Community
Foundation
Eastern Counties Educational
Trust Limited
The Sir John Eastwood
Foundation
The Ebenezer Trust
The EBM Charitable Trust
Eden Arts Trust
EDF Energy Trust (EDFET)
The Gilbert and Eileen Edgar
Foundation
Edinburgh Children's Holiday
Fund
The Edinburgh Trust, No 2
Account
Edinburgh Voluntary
Organisations' Trust Funds
The W G Edwards Charitable
Foundation
The William Edwards
Educational Charity
The Elephant Trust
The George Elias Charitable
Trust
The Gerald Palmer Eling Trust
Company
The Wilfred and Elsie Elkes
Charity Fund
The Maud Elkington Charitable
Trust
The Ellerdale Trust
The Ellinson Foundation Ltd
The Ellis Campbell Foundation
James Ellis Charitable Trust
The Elmgrant Trust
The Elmley Foundation
The Vernon N Ely Charitable
Trust
The Embleton Trust
The Emerton-Christie Charity
The Emmandjay Charitable
Trust
The Worshipful Company of
Engineers Charitable Trust
Fund
The Englefield Charitable Trust
The English Schools' Football
Association
The Enkalon Foundation
Entindale Ltd
The Epigoni Trust
Epilepsy Research UK
The Equitable Charitable Trust
The Equity Trust Fund
The Ericson Trust
The Erskine Cunningham Hill
Trust
Essex Community Foundation
The Essex Fairway Charitable
Trust
The Essex Heritage Trust

Essex Provincial Charity Fund
The Essex Youth Trust
Euro Charity Trust
Sir John Evelyn's Charity
The Eventhall Family
Charitable Trust
The Everard Foundation
The Eveson Charitable Trust
The Beryl Evetts and Robert
Luff Animal Welfare Trust
The Execution Charitable Trust
The Mayor of Exeter's Appeal
Fund
The Exilarch's Foundation
F C Charitable Trust
The F P Limited Charitable
Trust
The Faber Charitable Trust
Esmée Fairbairn Foundation
The Fairway Trust
Faisaltex Charitable Trust
The Family Rich Charities Trust
The Lord Faringdon Charitable
Trust
Samuel William Farmer Trust
The Farmers' Company
Charitable Fund
The Thomas Farr Charitable
Trust
Walter Farthing (Trust) Limited
The Fassnidge Memorial Trust
Joseph Fattorini Charitable
Trust 'B' Account
The Fawcett Charitable Trust
Federation of Jewish Relief
Organisations
The John Feeney Charitable
Trust
The George Fentham
Birmingham Charity
The A M Fenton Trust
Allan and Nesta Ferguson
Charitable Settlement
The Fidelity UK Foundation
The Bluff Field Charitable Trust
The Doris Field Charitable
Trust
Fife Council/Common Good
Funds and Trusts
Firtree Trust
The Fishmongers' Company's
Charitable Trust
The Fitton Trust
The Earl Fitzwilliam Charitable
Trust
Bud Flanagan Leukaemia Fund
The Rose Flatau Charitable
Trust
The Ian Fleming Charitable
Trust
The Joyce Fletcher Charitable
Trust
The Roy Fletcher Charitable
Trust
The Flow Foundation

The Gerald Fogel Charitable
  Trust
The Follett Trust
The Football Association
  National Sports Centre
  Trust
The Football Association Youth
  Trust
The Forbes Charitable
  Foundation
The Forces Trust (Working
  Name)
Ford Britain Trust
The Oliver Ford Charitable
  Trust
The Forest Hill Charitable Trust
The Foresters' Charity
  Stewards UK Trust
Forever Manchester (The
  Community Foundation for
  Greater Manchester)
Gwyneth Forrester Trust
The Fort Foundation
The Forte Charitable Trust
Foundation for Management
  Education
The Four Winds Trust
The Isaac and Freda Frankel
  Memorial Charitable Trust
The Elizabeth Frankland Moore
  and Star Foundation
The Jill Franklin Trust
The Gordon Fraser Charitable
  Trust
The Hugh Fraser Foundation
The Joseph Strong Frazer Trust
The Louis and Valerie
  Freedman Charitable
  Settlement
The Thomas Freke and Lady
  Norton Charity
The Charles S French
  Charitable Trust
The Anne French Memorial
  Trust
The Freshfield Foundation
The Freshgate Trust
  Foundation
The Friarsgate Trust
The Friends Hall Farm Street
  Trust
Friends Provident Charitable
  Foundation
The Frognal Trust
The Patrick Frost Foundation
Maurice Fry Charitable Trust
The Fuellers Charitable Trust
  Fund
The Fulmer Charitable Trust
Worshipful Company of
  Furniture Makers Charitable
  Fund
Gableholt Limited
The Galbraith Trust
The Gale Family Charitable
  Trust

The Angela Gallagher Memorial
  Fund
The Gamlen Charitable Trust
The Gamma Trust
The Gannochy Trust
The Ganzoni Charitable Trust
The Worshipful Company of
  Gardeners of London
The Samuel Gardner Memorial
  Trust
The Garnett Charitable Trust
Garvan Limited
The Gatsby Charitable
  Foundation
Gatwick Airport Community
  Trust
The Robert Gavron Charitable
  Trust
J Paul Getty Jr Charitable Trust
The Gibbs Charitable Trust
Simon Gibson Charitable Trust
The G C Gibson Charitable
  Trust
Lady Gibson's Charitable Trust
The Harvey and Hilary Gilbert
  Charitable Trust
The Girdlers' Company
  Charitable Trust
The B and P Glasser
  Charitable Trust
The Glass-House Trust
Global Care
Gloucestershire Community
  Foundation
Worshipful Company of
  Glovers of London Charity
  Fund
The GNC Trust
The Meir Golda Trust
The Sydney and Phyllis
  Goldberg Memorial
  Charitable Trust
The Golden Bottle Trust
The Jack Goldhill Charitable
  Trust
The Goldsmiths' Arts Trust
  Fund
The Goldsmiths' Company
  Charity
The Golsoncott Foundation
The Good Neighbours Trust
The Everard and Mina
  Goodman Charitable
  Foundation
Mike Gooley Trailfinders
  Charity
The Gosling Foundation
  Limited
The Gough Charitable Trust
The Gould Charitable Trust
The Grace Charitable Trust
A B Grace Trust
The Graff Foundation
The Grahame Charitable
  Foundation Limited

Grampian Police Diced Cap
  Charitable Fund
The Granada Foundation
Grand Charitable Trust of the
  Order of Women
  Freemasons
The Grand Order of Water
  Rats' Charities Fund
The Grange Farm Centre Trust
Grantham Yorke Trust
The J G Graves Charitable
  Trust
The Gray Trust
The Great Stone Bridge Trust
  of Edenbridge
The Great Torrington Town
  Lands Charity
The Constance Green
  Foundation
The Philip Green Memorial
  Trust
Greenham Common
  Community Trust Limited
Naomi and Jeffrey Greenwood
  Charitable Trust
Greggs Foundation (formerly
  Greggs Trust)
The Gretna Charitable Trust
The Grocers' Charity
The M and R Gross Charities
  Limited
The Grove Charitable Trust
The GRP Charitable Trust
The David and Marie Grumitt
  Foundation
The Bishop of Guildford's
  Foundation
The Guildry Incorporation of
  Perth
The Walter Guinness
  Charitable Trust
The Gunter Charitable Trust
The Gur Trust
Dr Guthrie's Association
The H and M Charitable Trust
H C D Memorial Fund
The H P Charitable Trust
The Hackney Parochial
  Charities
The Hadfield Trust
The Hadley Trust
The Hadrian Trust
The Alfred Haines Charitable
  Trust
The Hale Trust
E F and M G Hall Charitable
  Trust
The Edith Winifred Hall
  Charitable Trust
Robert Hall Charity
The Hamamelis Trust
Hamilton Wallace Trust
Paul Hamlyn Foundation
The Hammonds Charitable
  Trust

The Hampshire and Islands
Historic Churches Trust
Hampton Fuel Allotment
Charity
The W A Handley Charitable
Trust
Beatrice Hankey Foundation
Ltd
The Hanley Trust
The Kathleen Hannay
Memorial Charity
The Doughty Hanson
Charitable Foundation
Lord Hanson Foundation
The Haramead Trust
Miss K M Harbinson's
Charitable Trust
The Harborne Parish Lands
Charity
The Harbour Charitable Trust
The Harbour Foundation
The Harding Trust
William Harding's Charity
The Hare of Steep Charitable
Trust
The Harebell Centenary Fund
The Kenneth Hargreaves
Charitable Trust
The Harris Charitable Trust
The Harris Charity
The Harrison and Potter Trust
The John Harrison Charitable
Trust
The Spencer Hart Charitable
Trust
The Hartley Charitable Trust
The N and P Hartley Memorial
Trust
William Geoffrey Harvey's
Discretionary Settlement
The Edward Harvist Trust Fund
Haskel Family Foundation
The Hathaway Trust
The M A Hawe Settlement
The Hawthorne Charitable
Trust
The Dorothy Hay-Bolton
Charitable Trust
The Haymills Charitable Trust
The Headley Trust
Headley-Pitt Charitable Trust
Heagerty Charitable Trust
The Heart of England
Community Foundation
The Heathcoat Trust
Heathside Charitable Trust
The Charlotte Heber-Percy
Charitable Trust
The Hedley Denton Charitable
Trust
The Hedley Foundation
The H J Heinz Company
Limited Charitable Trust
The Hellenic Foundation
The Michael and Morven Heller
Charitable Foundation

The Simon Heller Charitable
Settlement
The Hemby Trust
The Christina Mary Hendrie
Trust for Scottish and
Canadian Charities
The Henley Educational Charity
Esther Hennell Charitable
Trust
The G D Herbert Charitable
Trust
The Joanna Herbert-Stepney
Charitable Settlement (also
known as The Paget
Charitable Trust)
The Anne Herd Memorial Trust
The Herefordshire Historic
Churches Trust
The Heritage of London Trust
Ltd
The Hesed Trust
The Hesslewood Children's
Trust (Hull Seamen's and
General Orphanage)
The Bernhard Heuberger
Charitable Trust
Hexham and Newcastle
Diocesan Trust (1947)
The P and C Hickinbotham
Charitable Trust
The Higgs Charitable Trust
Alan Edward Higgs Charity
The High Sheriff's Police Trust
for the County of West
Midlands (Building Blocks)
Highcroft Charitable Trust
The Charles Littlewood Hill
Trust
The Hillingdon Partnership
Trust
The Hinrichsen Foundation
The Hitchin Educational
Foundation
The Eleemosynary Charity of
William Hobbayne
Hobson Charity Limited
Matthew Hodder Charitable
Trust
The Sir Julian Hodge
Charitable Trust
The J G Hogg Charitable Trust
The Holden Charitable Trust
John Holford's Charity
The Hollick Family Charitable
Trust
The Dorothy Holmes Charitable
Trust
The Edward Holt Trust
The Holywood Trust
The Homelands Charitable
Trust
The Homestead Charitable
Trust
Sir Harold Hood's Charitable
Trust

Hope for Youth (formerly
Women Caring Trust)
The Hope Trust
HopMarket Charity
The Cuthbert Horn Trust
The Antony Hornby Charitable
Trust
The Horne Foundation
The Horne Trust
The Worshipful Company of
Horners' Charitable Trusts
The Hornsey Parochial
Charities
The Hospital of God at
Greatham
The Hospital Saturday Fund
Houblon-Norman/George Fund
The House of Industry Estate
The Reta Lila Howard
Foundation
The Daniel Howard Trust
The Clifford Howarth Charity
Trust
The Hudson Foundation
The Geoffrey C Hughes
Charitable Trust
The Hull and East Riding
Charitable Trust
Hulme Trust Estates
(Educational)
Human Relief Foundation
The Humanitarian Trust
The Michael and Shirley Hunt
Charitable Trust
The Hunter Foundation
Miss Agnes H Hunter's Trust
Huntingdon Freemen's Charity
John Huntingdon's Charity
Hurdale Charity Limited
The Nani Huyu Charitable Trust
The P Y N and B Hyams Trust
The Hyde Charitable Trust –
Youth Plus
The Idlewild Trust
The Iliffe Family Charitable
Trust
The Indigo Trust
The Ingram Trust
The Inland Waterways
Association
The Inlight Trust
The Inman Charity
The Inner London Magistrates
Court Poor Box and Feeder
Charity
The Ireland Fund of Great
Britain
The Irish Youth Foundation
(UK) Ltd (incorporating The
Lawlor Foundation)
The Ironmongers' Foundation
Irshad Trust
The Charles Irving Charitable
Trust
Irwin Trust
The ISA Charity

The Isaacs Charitable Trust
The J Isaacs Charitable Trust
The Isle of Anglesey Charitable Trust
The ITF Seafarers Trust
The J R S S T Charitable Trust
Elizabeth Jackson Charitable Trust
The Ruth and Lionel Jacobson Trust (Second Fund) No 2
Jaffe Family Relief Fund
The Susan and Stephen James Charitable Settlement (also known as the Stephen James Charitable Trust)
The James Trust
The Jarman Charitable Trust
The John Jarrold Trust
JCA Charitable Foundation
The Jeffrey Charitable Trust
The Jenour Foundation
The Jephcott Charitable Trust
Jesus Hospital Charity
Jewish Child's Day
The Jewish Youth Fund
The JMK Charitable Trust
The Joanies Trust
The Harold Joels Charitable Trust
The Jonathan Joels Charitable Trust
The Nicholas Joels Charitable Trust
The Norman Joels Charitable Trust
The Lillie Johnson Charitable Trust
The Johnson Foundation
The Johnson Group Cleaners Charity
The Johnnie Johnson Trust
The Johnson Wax Ltd Charitable Trust
The Joicey Trust
The Jones 1986 Charitable Trust
The Marjorie and Geoffrey Jones Charitable Trust
The Jordan Charitable Foundation
The J E Joseph Charitable Fund
The Lady Eileen Joseph Foundation
JTH Charitable Trust
The Anton Jurgens Charitable Trust
The Bernard Kahn Charitable Trust
The Stanley Kalms Foundation
The Karenza Foundation
The Boris Karloff Charitable Foundation
The Ian Karten Charitable Trust

The Kasner Charitable Trust
The Kass Charitable Trust
The Kathleen Trust
The Michael and Ilse Katz Foundation
The Katzauer Charitable Settlement
The C S Kaufman Charitable Trust
The Geoffrey John Kaye Charitable Foundation
The Emmanuel Kaye Foundation
Kelsick's Educational Foundation
The KempWelch Charitable Trust
The Kay Kendall Leukaemia Fund
William Kendall's Charity (Wax Chandlers' Company)
The Kennedy Charitable Foundation
The Kennel Club Charitable Trust
The Nancy Kenyon Charitable Trust
Keren Association
Kermaville Ltd
The Peter Kershaw Trust
The Kessler Foundation
Keswick Hall Trust
The Ursula Keyes Trust
The Robert Kiln Charitable Trust
The King Henry VIII Endowed Trust Warwick
The King/Cullimore Charitable Trust
The Kingsbury Charity
The Mary Kinross Charitable Trust
Kirkley Poor's Lands Estate
The Richard Kirkman Charitable Trust
Kirschel Foundation
Robert Kitchin (Saddlers' Company)
Ernest Kleinwort Charitable Trust
The Marina Kleinwort Charitable Trust
The Sir James Knott Trust
The Kobler Trust
The Kohn Foundation
The Kreditor Charitable Trust
The Kreitman Foundation
The Neil Kreitman Foundation
The Heinz, Anna and Carol Kroch Foundation
The Kyte Charitable Trust
The Late Sir Pierce Lacy Charity Trust
John Laing Charitable Trust
Maurice and Hilda Laing Charitable Trust

The Christopher Laing Foundation
The Kirby Laing Foundation
The Martin Laing Foundation
The Beatrice Laing Trust
The Lambert Charitable Trust
Lancashire Environmental Fund
Duchy of Lancaster Benevolent Fund
The Lancaster Foundation
The Langdale Trust
The Langley Charitable Trust
The Langtree Trust
The LankellyChase Foundation
The Lanvern Foundation
The R J Larg Family Charitable Trust
Largsmount Ltd
The Lark Trust
Laslett's (Hinton) Charity
Lauchentilly Charitable Foundation 1988
The Lauffer Family Charitable Foundation
The Kathleen Laurence Trust
The Edgar E Lawley Foundation
The Herd Lawson and Muriel Lawson Charitable Trust
The Lawson Beckman Charitable Trust
The Raymond and Blanche Lawson Charitable Trust
The Carole and Geoffrey Lawson Foundation
The Mason Le Page Charitable Trust
The Leach Fourteenth Trust
The David Lean Foundation
The Leathersellers' Company Charitable Fund
The Arnold Lee Charitable Trust
The William Leech Charity
The Lord Mayor of Leeds Appeal Fund
Leeds Building Society Charitable Foundation
Leicester Charity Link (formerly The Leicester Charity Organisation Society)
The Kennedy Leigh Charitable Trust
The Leigh Trust
Mrs Vera Leigh's Charity
The P Leigh-Bramwell Trust 'E'
The Lennox and Wyfold Foundation
The Erica Leonard Trust
The Leonard Trust
The Mark Leonard Trust
Lesley Lesley and Mutter Trust
The Leverhulme Trade Charities Trust
Lord Leverhulme's Charitable Trust

The Joseph Levy Charitable
    Foundation
The John Spedan Lewis
    Foundation
The Sir Edward Lewis
    Foundation
John Lewis Partnership
    General Community Fund
Lichfield Conduit Lands
Lifeline 4 Kids
The Thomas Lilley Memorial
    Trust
The Linbury Trust
The Lind Trust
Lindale Educational
    Foundation
The Linden Charitable Trust
The Enid Linder Foundation
The Linmardon Trust
The Ruth and Stuart Lipton
    Charitable Trust
The Lister Charitable Trust
Frank Litchfield Charitable
    Trust
The Andrew and Mary
    Elizabeth Little Charitable
    Trust
The Second Joseph Aaron
    Littman Foundation
The George John and Sheilah
    Livanos Charitable Trust
Liverpool Charity and Voluntary
    Services
Liverpool Sailors' Home Trust
The Elaine and Angus Lloyd
    Charitable Trust
The Charles Lloyd Foundation
The Lloyd Fund
Lloyd's Charities Trust
Lloyds TSB Foundation for
    England and Wales
Lloyds TSB Foundation for
    Northern Ireland
Lloyds TSB Foundation for the
    Channel Islands
The Locker Foundation
The Loftus Charitable Trust
The Lolev Charitable Trust
The Trust for London (formerly
    the City Parochial
    Foundation)
London Catalyst (formerly The
    Metropolitan Hospital-
    Sunday Fund)
The London Community
    Foundation (formerly Capital
    Community Foundation)
The London Law Trust
The William and Katherine
    Longman Trust
The Lord's Taverners
The Loseley and Guildway
    Charitable Trust
The Lotus Foundation
The C L Loyd Charitable Trust

The Marie Helen Luen
    Charitable Trust
Robert Luff Foundation Ltd
Henry Lumley Charitable Trust
Lady Lumley's Educational
    Foundation
C F Lunoe Trust Fund
The Ruth and Jack Lunzer
    Charitable Trust
Lord and Lady Lurgan Trust
The Lyndhurst Trust
The Lynn Foundation
The Lynwood Trust
John Lyon's Charity
The Lyons Charitable Trust
The Sir Jack Lyons Charitable
    Trust
The Lyras Family Charitable
    Trust
Sylvanus Lyson's Charity
The M and C Trust
The M D and S Charitable
    Trust
The M K Charitable Trust
The Madeline Mabey Trust
The E M MacAndrew Trust
The R S Macdonald Charitable
    Trust
Macdonald-Buchanan
    Charitable Trust
The Macfarlane Walker Trust
The Mackay and Brewer
    Charitable Trust
The Mackintosh Foundation
The MacRobert Trust
The Magdalen and Lasher
    Charity
Magdalen Hospital Trust
The Magen Charitable Trust
Man Group plc Charitable
    Trust
The Manchester Guardian
    Society Charitable Trust
Lord Mayor of Manchester's
    Charity Appeal Trust
Mandeville Trust
The Manifold Charitable Trust
The Leslie and Lilian Manning
    Trust
Marbeh Torah Trust
Marchig Animal Welfare Trust
The Stella and Alexander
    Margulies Charitable Trust
Market Harborough and The
    Bowdens Charity
The Ann and David Marks
    Foundation
The Hilda and Samuel Marks
    Foundation
J P Marland Charitable Trust
The Michael Marsh Charitable
    Trust
The Marsh Christian Trust
The Charlotte Marshall
    Charitable Trust

The Jim Marshall Charitable
    Trust
The D G Marshall of
    Cambridge Trust
Marshgate Charitable
    Settlement
Sir George Martin Trust
John Martin's Charity
The Mason Porter Charitable
    Trust
The Nancie Massey Charitable
    Trust
The Mathew Trust
The Matt 6.3 Charitable Trust
The Violet Mauray Charitable
    Trust
The Maxell Educational Trust
Evelyn May Trust
Mayfair Charities Ltd
The Mayfield Valley Arts Trust
Mazars Charitable Trust
The Robert McAlpine
    Foundation
The McDougall Trust
The McKenna Charitable Trust
The Helen Isabella McMorran
    Charitable Foundation
The James Frederick and Ethel
    Anne Measures Charity
The Medlock Charitable Trust
The Anthony and Elizabeth
    Mellows Charitable
    Settlement
Melow Charitable Trust
The Mercers' Charitable
    Foundation
The Merchant Taylors'
    Company Charities Fund
The Merchant Venturers'
    Charity
The Merchants' House of
    Glasgow
The Mersey Docks and
    Harbour Company
    Charitable Fund
Community Foundation for
    Merseyside
The Zachary Merton and
    George Woofindin
    Convalescent Trust
The Tony Metherell Charitable
    Trust
The Metropolitan Drinking
    Fountain and Cattle Trough
    Association
Gerald Micklem Charitable
    Trust
Midhurst Pensions Trust
The Migraine Trust
Miles Trust for the Putney and
    Roehampton Community
The Hugh and Mary Miller
    Bequest Trust
The Miller Foundation
The Millfield Trust

The Millhouses Charitable
Trust
The Millichope Foundation
The Mills Charity
The Millward Charitable Trust
The Clare Milne Trust
Milton Keynes Community
Foundation
The Edgar Milward Charity
The Keith and Joan
Mindelsohn Charitable
Trust
The Peter Minet Trust
The Minos Trust
The Mirfield Educational
Charity
The Laurence Misener
Charitable Trust
The Mishcon Family Charitable
Trust
The Misselbrook Trust
The Mitchell Charitable Trust
The Esmé Mitchell Trust
Keren Mitzvah Trust
The Mizpah Trust
The Mobbs Memorial Trust Ltd
The Modiano Charitable Trust
The Moette Charitable Trust
The Mole Charitable Trust
The D C Moncrieff Charitable
Trust
Monmouthshire County Council
Welsh Church Act Fund
The Montague Thompson
Coon Charitable Trust
The Colin Montgomerie
Charitable Foundation
The Monument Trust
The Nigel Moores Family
Charitable Trust
The Peter Moores Foundation
The Morel Charitable Trust
The Morgan Charitable
Foundation
The Mr and Mrs J T Morgan
Foundation
The Oliver Morland Charitable
Trust
The Bernard Morris Charitable
Trust
The Morris Charitable Trust
The Willie and Mabel Morris
Charitable Trust
The Peter Morrison Charitable
Foundation
The Stanley Morrison
Charitable Trust
Vyoel Moshe Charitable Trust
The Moss Charitable Trust
The Robert and Margaret
Moss Charitable Trust
Moss Family Charitable Trust
The Mount Everest Foundation
The Edwina Mountbatten Trust
Mountbatten Festival of Music

The Mountbatten Memorial
Trust
The Mugdock Children's Trust
The Mulberry Trust
The Edith Murphy Foundation
The Mushroom Fund
The Music Sales Charitable
Trust
Muslim Hands
The Mutual Trust Group
The Kitty and Daniel Nabarro
Charitable Trust
The Nadezhda Charitable Trust
The Naggar Charitable Trust
The Eleni Nakou Foundation
The Janet Nash Charitable
Settlement
Nathan Charitable Trust
The National Churches Trust
(formerly the Historic
Churches Preservation
Trust with the Incorporated
Church Building Society)
The National Manuscripts
Conservation Trust
The Nchima Trust
Needham Market and Barking
Welfare Charities
The Worshipful Company of
Needlemakers' Charitable
Fund
The Neighbourly Charitable
Trust
The James Neill Trust Fund
Nemoral Ltd
Network for Social Change
The New Appeals Organisation
for the City and County of
Nottingham
New Court Charitable Trust
The Newcomen Collett
Foundation
Alderman Newton's
Educational Foundation
The Chevras Ezras Nitzrochim
Trust
The Noon Foundation
The Norda Trust
Norie Charitable Trust
Normalyn Charitable Trust
The Norman Family Charitable
Trust
The Duncan Norman Trust
Fund
The Normanby Charitable Trust
The North British Hotel Trust
The North West Cancer
Research Fund
The Northampton Municipal
Church Charities
The Northampton Queen's
Institute Relief in Sickness
Fund
The Earl of Northampton's
Charity

The Northcott Devon
Foundation
The Northcott Devon Medical
Foundation
The Northmoor Trust
The Northumberland Village
Homes Trust
The Northwood Charitable
Trust
The Norton Foundation
The Norwich Church of England
Young Men's Society
The Norwich Historic Churches
Trust Ltd
The Norwich Town Close
Estate Charity
The Noswad Charity
The Notgrove Trust
The Nottingham General
Dispensary
The Nottingham Gordon
Memorial Trust for Boys
and Girls
Nottinghamshire Community
Foundation
The Nottinghamshire Historic
Churches Trust
The Nottinghamshire Miners'
Welfare Trust Fund
Novi Most International
The Father O'Mahoney
Memorial Trust
The Sir Peter O'Sullevan
Charitable Trust
The Oak Trust
The Oakdale Trust
The Oakley Charitable Trust
The Oakmoor Charitable Trust
The Odin Charitable Trust
The Ofenheim Charitable Trust
Ogilvie Charities Deed No.2
(including the Charity of
Mary Catherine Ford Smith)
The Ogle Christian Trust
The Oikonomia Trust
Oizer Charitable Trust
The Old Broad Street Charity
Trust
The Old Enfield Charitable
Trust
The John Oldacre Foundation
The Oldham Foundation
Onaway Trust
Open Gate
The Ormsby Charitable Trust
Orrin Charitable Trust
The Ouseley Trust
The Owen Family Trust
Oxfam (GB)
The Oxfordshire Community
Foundation
The P F Charitable Trust
Padwa Charitable Foundation
The Pallant Charitable Trust
The Palmer Foundation
Eleanor Palmer Trust

The Panacea Society
Panton Trust
The James Pantyfedwen
    Foundation
The Paragon Trust
The Park House Charitable
    Trust
The Frank Parkinson
    Agricultural Trust
The Samuel and Freda
    Parkinson Charitable Trust
The Parthenon Trust
The Constance Paterson
    Charitable Trust
The Patrick Charitable Trust
The Jack Patston Charitable
    Trust
The Payne Charitable Trust
The Harry Payne Trust
The Susanna Peake Charitable
    Trust
The Pedmore Sporting Club
    Trust Fund
The Dowager Countess
    Eleanor Peel Trust
The Pennycress Trust
The Performing Right Society
    Foundation
The Persson Charitable Trust
    (formerly Highmoore Hall
    Charitable Trust)
The Persula Foundation
The Jack Petchey Foundation
The Petplan Charitable Trust
The Philips and Rubens
    Charitable Trust
The Phillips Charitable Trust
The Phillips Family Charitable
    Trust
Philological Foundation
The David Pickford Charitable
    Foundation
The Bernard Piggott Trust
The Cecil Pilkington Charitable
    Trust
The Pilkington Charities Fund
The Austin and Hope
    Pilkington Trust
The Sir Harry Pilkington Trust
The Col W W Pilkington Will
    Trusts The General Charity
    Fund
The DLA Piper Charitable Trust
The Worshipful Company of
    Plaisterers Charitable Trust
The Platinum Trust
The Poling Charitable Trust
The George and Esme Pollitzer
    Charitable Settlement
The J S F Pollitzer Charitable
    Settlement
The Ponton House Trust
The Mayor of Poole's Appeal
    Fund
Edith and Ferdinand Porjes
    Charitable Trust

The John Porter Charitable
    Trust
The Porter Foundation
The Portishead Nautical Trust
The Portrack Charitable Trust
The J E Posnansky Charitable
    Trust
The Powell Foundation
The W L Pratt Charitable Trust
Premierquote Ltd
Premishlaner Charitable Trust
The William Price Charitable
    Trust
The Lucy Price Relief-in-Need
    Charity
Sir John Priestman Charity
    Trust
The Primrose Trust
The Prince of Wales's
    Charitable Foundation
The Priory Foundation
Prison Service Charity Fund
The Privy Purse Charitable
    Trust
The Proven Family Trust
The Provincial Grand Charity of
    the Province of Derbyshire
PSA Peugeot Citroen Charity
    Trust
The Puebla Charitable Trust
The Richard and Christine
    Purchas Charitable Trust
The Puri Foundation
Mr and Mrs J A Pye's
    Charitable Settlement
Queen Mary's Roehampton
    Trust
The Queen's Silver Jubilee
    Trust
R S Charitable Trust
The R V W Trust
The Monica Rabagliati
    Charitable Trust
Rachel Charitable Trust
The Mr and Mrs Philip
    Rackham Charitable Trust
Richard Radcliffe Charitable
    Trust
The Radcliffe Trust
The Rainford Trust
The Peggy Ramsay Foundation
The Joseph and Lena Randall
    Charitable Trust
The Rank Foundation
The Fanny Rapaport Charitable
    Settlement
The Ratcliff Foundation
The Ratcliff Pension Charity
The Ratcliffe Charitable Trust
The Eleanor Rathbone
    Charitable Trust
The Sigrid Rausing Trust
The Ravensdale Trust
The Rayden Charitable Trust
The Roger Raymond Charitable
    Trust

The Rayne Foundation
The Rayne Trust
The John Rayner Charitable
    Trust
The Sir James Reckitt Charity
The Red Arrows Trust
Red Hill Charitable Trust
The Red Rose Charitable Trust
The C A Redfern Charitable
    Foundation
The Reed Foundation
Richard Reeve's Foundation
The Max Reinhardt Charitable
    Trust
Relief Fund for Romania
    Limited
The Rest Harrow Trust
Reuben Brothers Foundation
The Joan K Reynell Charitable
    Trust
The Nathaniel Reyner Trust
    Fund
The Rhododendron Trust
The Rhondda Cynon Taff
    Welsh Church Acts Fund
The Clive Richards Charity
The Richmond Parish Lands
    Charity
Ridgesave Limited
The Ripple Effect Foundation
The Sir John Ritblat Family
    Foundation
The River Trust
Thomas Roberts Trust
The Robertson Trust
The Rochester Bridge Trust
The Rock Foundation
The Rock Solid Trust
The Rofeh Trust
Richard Rogers Charitable
    Settlement
Rokach Family Charitable Trust
The Helen Roll Charitable
    Trust
The Sir James Roll Charitable
    Trust
The Roman Research Trust
Romeera Foundation
The C A Rookes Charitable
    Trust
Mrs L D Rope Third Charitable
    Settlement
The Rosca Trust
The Cecil Rosen Foundation
The Rothermere Foundation
The Rotherwick Foundation
The Rothley Trust
The Roughley Charitable Trust
Mrs Gladys Row Fogo
    Charitable Trust
Rowanville Ltd
The Christopher Rowbotham
    Charitable Trust
The Rowing Foundation
The Rowlands Trust
Royal Artillery Charitable Fund

Royal British Legion
Royal Docks Trust (London)
Royal Masonic Trust for Girls
and Boys
The Royal Scots Benevolent
Society
The Alfred and Frances
Rubens Charitable Trust
The Rubin Foundation
William Arthur Rudd Memorial
Trust
The Rufford Foundation
The Russell Trust
The J S and E C Rymer
Charitable Trust
S O Charitable Trust
The Jeremy and John Sacher
Charitable Trust
The Michael Harry Sacher
Trust
The Sackler Trust (Formerly Dr
Mortimer and Theresa
Sackler Foundation)
The Ruzin Sadagora Trust
The Saddlers' Company
Charitable Fund
The Saga Charitable Trust
The Jean Sainsbury Animal
Welfare Trust
The Alan and Babette
Sainsbury Charitable Fund
The Sainsbury Family
Charitable Trusts
The Saintbury Trust
The Saints and Sinners Trust
The Salamander Charitable
Trust
The Salt Foundation
The Salt Trust
The Sammermar Trust
Basil Samuel Charitable Trust
The Hon. M J Samuel
Charitable Trust
The Peter Samuel Charitable
Trust
The Camilla Samuel Fund
The Samworth Foundation
The Sandra Charitable Trust
Santander UK Foundation
Limited
Jimmy Savile Charitable Trust
The Scarfe Charitable Trust
The Schapira Charitable Trust
The Schmidt-Bodner Charitable
Trust
The R H Scholes Charitable
Trust
The Schreib Trust
The Schreiber Charitable Trust
The Francis C Scott Charitable
Trust
The Frieda Scott Charitable
Trust
The Sir James and Lady Scott
Trust
The Scott Trust Foundation

The Scottish Arts Council
Scottish Coal Industry Special
Welfare Fund
The Scottish Community
Foundation
The Scouloudi Foundation
Seafarers UK (King George's
Fund for Sailors)
Seamen's Hospital Society
The Searchlight Electric
Charitable Trust
The Searle Charitable Trust
The Helene Sebba Charitable
Trust
The Samuel Sebba Charitable
Trust
The Seedfield Trust
Leslie Sell Charitable Trust
The Ayrton Senna Foundation
The Seven Fifty Trust
The Severn Trent Water
Charitable Trust Fund
SFIA Educational Trust Limited
The Cyril Shack Trust
The Shanti Charitable Trust
ShareGift (The Orr Mackintosh
Foundation)
The Linley Shaw Foundation
The Sheepdrove Trust
The Sheffield and District
Hospital Services
Charitable Fund
The Sheldon Trust
The P and D Shepherd
Charitable Trust
The Sylvia and Colin Shepherd
Charitable Trust
The Archie Sherman Cardiff
Foundation
The Archie Sherman Charitable
Trust
The R C Sherriff Trust
The Shetland Charitable Trust
SHINE (Support and Help in
Education)
The Barnett and Sylvia Shine
No 2 Charitable Trust
The Bassil Shippam and
Alsford Trust
The Shipwrights' Company
Charitable Fund
The Shirley Foundation
Shlomo Memorial Fund Limited
The J A Shone Memorial Trust
The Barbara A Shuttleworth
Memorial Trust
David and Jennifer Sieff
Charitable Trust
The Julius Silman Charitable
Trust
The Leslie Silver Charitable
Trust
The Simpson Education and
Conservation Trust
The Simpson Foundation

The Huntly and Margery
Sinclair Charitable Trust
Sino-British Fellowship Trust
The Skelton Bounty
The Charles Skey Charitable
Trust
Skipton Building Society
Charitable Foundation
The John Slater Foundation
The SMB Charitable Trust
The Mrs Smith and Mount
Trust
The N Smith Charitable
Settlement
The Amanda Smith Charitable
Trust
The E H Smith Charitable Trust
The Smith Charitable Trust
The Henry Smith Charity
The Leslie Smith Foundation
The Martin Smith Foundation
Stanley Smith General
Charitable Trust
The Stanley Smith UK
Horticultural Trust
The Snowball Trust
The Sobell Foundation
Solihull Community Foundation
The Solo Charitable
Settlement
Dr Richard Solomon's
Charitable Trust
The E C Sosnow Charitable
Trust
The Souter Charitable Trust
The South Square Trust
The Stephen R and Philippa H
Southall Charitable Trust
The W F Southall Trust
The Southover Manor General
Education Trust
The Southwold Trust
The Sovereign Health Care
Charitable Trust
Sparquote Limited
The Spear Charitable Trust
The Worshipful Company of
Spectacle Makers' Charity
The Jessie Spencer Trust
The Ralph and Irma Sperring
Charity
The Moss Spiro Will Charitable
Foundation
The Spoore, Merry and Rixman
Foundation
Spring Harvest
Springfields Employees'
Medical Research and
Charity Trust Fund
Springrule Ltd
The Spurrell Charitable Trust
The Geoff and Fiona Squire
Foundation
St Francis's Leprosy Guild
St Gabriel's Trust
St James' Trust Settlement

St James's Place Foundation

Sir Walter St John's Educational Charity

St Michael's and All Saints' Charities

The Late St Patrick White Charitable Trust

St Teilo's Trust

The Stanley Foundation Ltd

The Stanton Ballard Charitable Trust

The Staples Trust

The Star Charitable Trust

The Peter Stebbings Memorial Charity

The Steel Charitable Trust

The Steinberg Family Charitable Trust

The Hugh Stenhouse Foundation

The Sigmund Sternberg Charitable Foundation

Stervon Ltd

The Stevenage Community Trust

The June Stevens Foundation

The Steventon Allotments and Relief-in-Need Charity

The Stewards' Company Limited (incorporating the J W Laing Trust and the J W Laing Biblical Scholarship Trust)

The Leonard Laity Stoate Charitable Trust

The Stobart Newlands Charitable Trust

The Edward Stocks-Massey Bequest Fund

The Stokenchurch Educational Charity

The Stoller Charitable Trust

The M J C Stone Charitable Trust

The Stone-Mallabar Charitable Foundation

The Samuel Storey Family Charitable Trust

Peter Stormonth Darling Charitable Trust

The Strangward Trust

The Strasser Foundation

Stratford upon Avon Town Trust

Strathclyde Police Benevolent Fund

The W O Street Charitable Foundation

The Sudborough Foundation

The Suffolk Historic Churches Trust

The Summerfield Charitable Trust

The Bernard Sunley Charitable Foundation

The Surrey Historic Buildings Trust Ltd

The Sussex Historic Churches Trust

The Sutasoma Trust

Sutton Coldfield Municipal Charities

Swansea and Brecon Diocesan Board of Finance Limited

The John Swire (1989) Charitable Trust

The Swire Charitable Trust

The Hugh and Ruby Sykes Charitable Trust

The Charles and Elsie Sykes Trust

The Sylvanus Charitable Trust

The Stella Symons Charitable Trust

The Tabeel Trust

The Tajtelbaum Charitable Trust

The Talbot Trusts

The Talbot Village Trust

Tallow Chandlers Benevolent Fund

The Tangent Charitable Trust

The Lady Tangye Charitable Trust

The David Tannen Charitable Trust

The Tanner Trust

The Lili Tapper Charitable Foundation

The Mrs A Lacy Tate Trust

The Tay Charitable Trust

Humphrey Richardson Taylor Charitable Trust

The Connie and Albert Taylor Charitable Trust

The Cyril Taylor Charitable Trust

A P Taylor Trust

Tearfund

The Tedworth Charitable Trust

Tees Valley Community Foundation

The Templeton Goodwill Trust

Tesco Charity Trust

The Thistle Trust

The Loke Wan Tho Memorial Foundation

The Arthur and Margaret Thompson Charitable Trust

The Thompson Family Charitable Trust

The Len Thomson Charitable Trust

The Sue Thomson Foundation

The Sir Jules Thorn Charitable Trust

The Thornton Foundation

The Thornton Trust

The Three Guineas Trust

The Three Oaks Trust

The Thriplow Charitable Trust

The Tinsley Foundation

The Tisbury Telegraph Trust

TJH Foundation

The Tobacco Pipe Makers and Tobacco Trade Benevolent Fund

The Tolkien Trust

Tollemache (Buckminster) Charitable Trust

Tomchei Torah Charitable Trust

The Tompkins Foundation

The Tory Family Foundation

Tottenham Grammar School Foundation

The Tower Hill Trust

The Towry Law Charitable Trust (also known as the Castle Educational Trust)

The Mayor of Trafford's Charity Fund

The Constance Travis Charitable Trust

The Treeside Trust

The Triangle Trust (1949) Fund

The True Colours Trust

Truedene Co. Ltd

The Truemark Trust

Truemart Limited

Trumros Limited

Trust Sixty Three

The Trusthouse Charitable Foundation

Tudor Rose Ltd

The Tudor Trust

The Tufton Charitable Trust

The R D Turner Charitable Trust

The Douglas Turner Trust

The Florence Turner Trust

Miss S M Tutton Charitable Trust

The TUUT Charitable Trust

Community Foundation Serving Tyne and Wear and Northumberland

Trustees of Tzedakah

Ulster Garden Villages Ltd

Ultach Trust

Ulting Overseas Trust

The Ulverscroft Foundation

Ulverston Town Lands Charity

The Union of Orthodox Hebrew Congregation

The United Society for the Propagation of the Gospel

The David Uri Memorial Trust

Uxbridge United Welfare Trust

Vale of Glamorgan – Welsh Church Fund

The Valentine Charitable Trust

John and Lucille van Geest Foundation

The Van Neste Foundation

Mrs Maud Van Norden's Charitable Foundation

The Vandervell Foundation
The Vardy Foundation
The Variety Club Children's
   Charity
Veneziana Fund
The Verdon-Smith Family
   Charitable Settlement
Victoria Homes Trust
The Nigel Vinson Charitable
   Trust
The William and Ellen Vinten
   Trust
The Vintners' Company
   Charitable Foundation
Vintners' Gifts Charity
Vision Charity
Vivdale Ltd
The Viznitz Foundation
Wade's Charity
The Scurrah Wainwright Charity
The Community Foundation in
   Wales
Wales Council for Voluntary
   Action
Robert and Felicity Waley-
   Cohen Charitable Trust
The Thomas Wall Trust
The F J Wallis Charitable
   Settlement
Walton on Thames Charity
War on Want
The Ward Blenkinsop Trust
The George Ward Charitable
   Trust
The Barbara Ward Children's
   Foundation
G R Waters Charitable Trust
   2000
The Waterways Trust
The Howard Watson Symington
   Memorial Charity
John Watson's Trust
Weatherley Charitable Trust
The Weavers' Company
   Benevolent Fund
The William Webster
   Charitable Trust
The Weinberg Foundation
The Weinstein Foundation
The Weinstock Fund
The James Weir Foundation
The Barbara Welby Trust
The Weldon UK Charitable
   Trust
Welsh Church Fund Dyfed
   area (Carmarthenshire,
   Ceredigion and
   Pembrokeshire)
The Welton Foundation
The Wessex Youth Trust
The West Derby Wastelands
   Charity
West London Synagogue
   Charitable Fund
The West Yorkshire Police
   Community Fund

The Westminster Foundation
The Garfield Weston
   Foundation
The Whitaker Charitable Trust
The Colonel W H Whitbread
   Charitable Trust
The Simon Whitbread
   Charitable Trust
The Whitecourt Charitable
   Trust
The Norman Whiteley Trust
The Whitley Animal Protection
   Trust
The Whittlesey Charity
The Lionel Wigram Memorial
   Trust
The Felicity Wilde Charitable
   Trust
The Kay Williams Charitable
   Foundation
The Williams Family Charitable
   Trust
The H D H Wills 1965
   Charitable Trust
The Dame Violet Wills Will
   Trust
The Wilmcote Charitrust
David Wilson Foundation
The Wilson Foundation
J and J R Wilson Trust
The Community Foundation for
   Wiltshire and Swindon
The Benjamin Winegarten
   Charitable Trust
The Francis Winham
   Foundation
Wirral Mayor's Charity
The Michael and Anna Wix
   Charitable Trust
The Wixamtree Trust
The Woburn 1986 Charitable
   Trust
The Maurice Wohl Charitable
   Foundation
The Charles Wolfson
   Charitable Trust
The Wolfson Family Charitable
   Trust
The Wolfson Foundation
The James Wood Bequest
   Fund
Woodlands Green Ltd
Woodlands Trust
The Woodward Charitable
   Trust
Worcester Municipal Charities
   (incorporating Worcester
   Consolidated Municipal
   Charity and Worcester
   Municipal Exhibitions
   Foundation)
The Worcestershire and
   Dudley Historic Churches
   Trust
The Fred and Della Worms
   Charitable Trust

The Wragge and Co. Charitable
   Trust
The Diana Edgson Wright
   Charitable Trust
The Matthews Wrightson
   Charity Trust
Miss E B Wrightson's
   Charitable Settlement
Wychdale Ltd
Wychville Ltd
The Wyndham Charitable Trust
The Wyseliot Charitable Trust
The Xerox (UK) Trust
The Yardley Great Trust
The Dennis Alan Yardy
   Charitable Trust
The W Wing Yip and Brothers
   Foundation
The York Children's Trust
Yorkshire Agricultural Society
Yorkshire Building Society
   Charitable Foundation
The South Yorkshire
   Community Foundation
The Yorkshire Dales
   Millennium Trust
The John Young Charitable
   Settlement
The William Allen Young
   Charitable Trust
The John K Young Endowment
   Fund
Youth Music
Zephyr Charitable Trust
The Marjorie and Arnold Ziff
   Charitable Foundation
Stephen Zimmerman
   Charitable Trust
The Zochonis Charitable Trust
Zurich Community Trust (UK)
   Limited

Core support

■ Core costs

The 29th May 1961 Charitable
   Trust
The Sylvia Adams Charitable
   Trust
The Adint Charitable Trust
The Ajahma Charitable Trust
The Aldgate Freedom
   Foundation
All Saints Educational Trust
The H B Allen Charitable Trust
The Ammco Trust
The Andrew Anderson Trust
The Ardwick Trust
The Armourers' and Brasiers'
   Gauntlet Trust
The Ian Askew Charitable Trust
The Astor Foundation
The Lord Austin Trust

The Aylesford Family
  Charitable Trust
The Baker Charitable Trust
The Barbour Foundation
Barnes Workhouse Fund
The Charity of William Barrow
BBC Children in Need
The Beaverbrook Foundation
The Bedfordshire and Luton
  Community Foundation
The Bellahouston Bequest
  Fund
The Bellhouse Foundation
The Berkshire Community
  Foundation
BibleLands
The Bingham Trust
The Bisgood Charitable Trust
  (registered as Miss Jeanne
  Bisgood's Charitable Trust)
The Sydney Black Charitable
  Trust
Sir Alec Black's Charity
The Body Shop Foundation
The Booth Charities
The Harry Bottom Charitable
  Trust
Community Foundation for
  Bournemouth, Dorset and
  Poole
John and Susan Bowers Fund
British Institute at Ankara
British Record Industry Trust
The J and M Britton Charitable
  Trust
The Bromley Trust
The Charles Brotherton Trust
The Swinfen Broun Charitable
  Trust
Brown-Mellows Trust
The Bryant Trust
The E F Bulmer Benevolent
  Fund
The BUPA Foundation
The Geoffrey Burton Charitable
  Trust
Butchers' Company General
  Charities
The Cadbury Foundation
Community Foundation for
  Calderdale
Calleva Foundation
The Calpe Trust
The Cambridgeshire
  Community Foundation
The Campden Charities
  Trustee
The Carew Pole Charitable
  Trust
The Carnegie Trust for the
  Universities of Scotland
The Casey Trust
The Chapman Charitable Trust
The Charter 600 Charity
The Malcolm Chick Charity
The Childwick Trust

Chrysalis Trust
The City Bridge Trust (formerly
  known as Bridge House
  Trust)
Stephen Clark 1957
  Charitable Trust
J A Clark Charitable Trust
Miss V L Clore's 1967
  Charitable Trust
The Clothworkers' Foundation
The Robert Clutterbuck
  Charitable Trust
Coats Foundation Trust
The Cole Charitable Trust
The John and Freda Coleman
  Charitable Trust
The Colt Foundation
Colwinston Charitable Trust
Comic Relief
The Congleton Inclosure Trust
Gordon Cook Foundation
The Alice Ellen Cooper Dean
  Charitable Foundation
The J Reginald Corah
  Foundation Fund
Michael Cornish Charitable
  Trust
County Durham Community
  Foundation
The Augustine Courtauld Trust
Cripplegate Foundation
Cullum Family Trust
The Cumber Family Charitable
  Trust
The Cwmbran Trust
The D'Oyly Carte Charitable
  Trust
William Dean Countryside and
  Educational Trust
The J N Derbyshire Trust
Devon Community Foundation
Disability Aid Fund (The Roger
  and Jean Jefcoate Trust)
The Drapers' Charitable Fund
The Dulverton Trust
The W E Dunn Trust
The Eagle Charity Trust
East London Community
  Foundation
The Ebenezer Trust
Dr Edwards Bishop King's
  Fulham Endowment Fund
The Ellerdale Trust
The Elmley Foundation
The Englefield Charitable Trust
Epilepsy Research UK
The Essex Fairway Charitable
  Trust
The Essex Youth Trust
The Eveson Charitable Trust
Esmée Fairbairn Foundation
Samuel William Farmer Trust
The John Feeney Charitable
  Trust
Gerald Finzi Charitable Trust

The Fishmongers' Company's
  Charitable Trust
The Foresters' Charity
  Stewards UK Trust
The Donald Forrester Trust
The Forte Charitable Trust
Sydney E Franklin Deceased's
  New Second Charity
The Jill Franklin Trust
The Freemasons' Grand
  Charity
The Freshgate Trust
  Foundation
The Patrick Frost Foundation
The Galanthus Trust
The Gamlen Charitable Trust
The Ganzoni Charitable Trust
The Gibbs Charitable Trust
Simon Gibson Charitable Trust
The G C Gibson Charitable
  Trust
The Girdlers' Company
  Charitable Trust
The Glastonbury Trust Limited
The Goldsmiths' Company
  Charity
The Golsoncott Foundation
The Great Britain Sasakawa
  Foundation
The Gretna Charitable Trust
Dr Guthrie's Association
H C D Memorial Fund
The Hadrian Trust
The Hamamelis Trust
Paul Hamlyn Foundation
Hampshire and Isle of Wight
  Community Foundation
The Kathleen Hannay
  Memorial Charity
The Harborne Parish Lands
  Charity
William Harding's Charity
The Harebell Centenary Fund
The Peter Harrison Foundation
Hasluck Charitable Trust
Headley-Pitt Charitable Trust
The Joanna Herbert-Stepney
  Charitable Settlement (also
  known as The Paget
  Charitable Trust)
The Hertfordshire Community
  Foundation
Hexham and Newcastle
  Diocesan Trust (1947)
The P and C Hickinbotham
  Charitable Trust
Alan Edward Higgs Charity
The High Sheriff's Police Trust
  for the County of West
  Midlands (Building Blocks)
The Hill Charitable Trust
The Charles Littlewood Hill
  Trust
Lady Hind Trust
Matthew Hodder Charitable
  Trust

The Holbeck Charitable Trust
The Holywood Trust
The Homelands Charitable
Trust
Mary Homfray Charitable Trust
Sir Harold Hood's Charitable
Trust
The Huggard Charitable Trust
The Hull and East Riding
Charitable Trust
Miss Agnes H Hunter's Trust
The Innocent Foundation
The Inverforth Charitable Trust
The Irish Youth Foundation
(UK) Ltd (incorporating The
Lawlor Foundation)
The Charles Irving Charitable
Trust
The ITF Seafarers Trust
John James Bristol Foundation
The James Trust
The Jephcott Charitable Trust
The Joanies Trust
The Joicey Trust
The Jordan Charitable
Foundation
Jusaca Charitable Trust
The Kelly Family Charitable
Trust
Kent Community Foundation
The Peter Kershaw Trust
Keswick Hall Trust
The Robert Kiln Charitable
Trust
The Mary Kinross Charitable
Trust
The Sir James Knott Trust
The Jack Lane Charitable Trust
The Allen Lane Foundation
The Leathersellers' Company
Charitable Fund
The William Leech Charity
The Kennedy Leigh Charitable
Trust
The Lennox and Wyfold
Foundation
The Erica Leonard Trust
Lincolnshire Community
Foundation
The Second Joseph Aaron
Littman Foundation
Lloyds TSB Foundation for
England and Wales
Lloyds TSB Foundation for
Northern Ireland
Llysdinam Charitable Trust
The Lynwood Trust
John Lyon's Charity
The R S Macdonald Charitable
Trust
The MacRobert Trust
Magdalen Hospital Trust
Man Group plc Charitable
Trust
W M Mann Foundation
R W Mann Trust

The Ann and David Marks
Foundation
The Marsh Christian Trust
The Jim Marshall Charitable
Trust
The Nancie Massey Charitable
Trust
Mayfair Charities Ltd
The Mears Foundation
Meningitis Trust
The Mercers' Charitable
Foundation
The Tony Metherell Charitable
Trust
Gerald Micklem Charitable
Trust
Miles Trust for the Putney and
Roehampton Community
The Millichope Foundation
The Clare Milne Trust
The Mitchell Charitable Trust
The Mobbs Memorial Trust Ltd
George A Moore Foundation
John Moores Foundation
G M Morrison Charitable Trust
The Moss Charitable Trust
The Mothercare Charitable
Foundation
The Mugdock Children's Trust
The Mulberry Trust
Murphy-Neumann Charity
Company Limited
The Kitty and Daniel Nabarro
Charitable Trust
The Nationwide Foundation
Nazareth Trust Fund
The Nchima Trust
The Neighbourly Charitable
Trust
The Frances and Augustus
Newman Foundation
Alice Noakes Memorial
Charitable Trust
The Northampton Municipal
Church Charities
The Notgrove Trust
The Oak Trust
The Oakdale Trust
The Oakley Charitable Trust
The Odin Charitable Trust
The Old Broad Street Charity
Trust
Open Gate
The Owen Family Trust
The P F Charitable Trust
Eleanor Palmer Trust
The Frank Parkinson
Agricultural Trust
The Dowager Countess
Eleanor Peel Trust
The Jack Petchey Foundation
Polden-Puckham Charitable
Foundation
The Ponton House Trust
The Mary Potter Convent
Hospital Trust

The Powell Foundation
Prairie Trust
The Provincial Grand Charity of
the Province of Derbyshire
Mr and Mrs J A Pye's
Charitable Settlement
The Rainford Trust
The Ratcliff Foundation
The Rayne Foundation
The Rayne Trust
The John Rayner Charitable
Trust
The Sir James Reckitt Charity
Relief Fund for Romania
Limited
REMEDI
The Rhododendron Trust
The Clive Richards Charity
The Ripple Effect Foundation
Rix-Thompson-Rothenberg
Foundation
The Rosca Trust
Mrs Gladys Row Fogo
Charitable Trust
The Christopher Rowbotham
Charitable Trust
The Joseph Rowntree
Charitable Trust
Royal British Legion
The Alfred and Frances
Rubens Charitable Trust
The Rufford Foundation
The Saintbury Trust
Santander UK Foundation
Limited
The Scarfe Charitable Trust
The R H Scholes Charitable
Trust
The Francis C Scott Charitable
Trust
The Frieda Scott Charitable
Trust
The Sir James and Lady Scott
Trust
The Scottish Community
Foundation
Seafarers UK (King George's
Fund for Sailors)
The Seedfield Trust
SFIA Educational Trust Limited
The Sheldon Trust
SHINE (Support and Help in
Education)
The Simpson Education and
Conservation Trust
The Charles Skey Charitable
Trust
Rita and David Slowe
Charitable Trust
The Mrs Smith and Mount
Trust
The Souter Charitable Trust
R H Southern Trust
The Sovereign Health Care
Charitable Trust
The Jessie Spencer Trust

The Spurrell Charitable Trust
St Christopher's College
　Educational Trust
St Hilda's Trust
Sir Walter St John's
　Educational Charity
The St Laurence Relief In
　Need Trust
St Teilo's Trust
The Steel Charitable Trust
The Stobart Newlands
　Charitable Trust
The Edward Stocks-Massey
　Bequest Fund
The Samuel Storey Family
　Charitable Trust
The Summerfield Charitable
　Trust
Sussex Community Foundation
The Talbot Trusts
The Sir Jules Thorn Charitable
　Trust
The Thriplow Charitable Trust
Mrs R P Tindall's Charitable
　Trust
The Tisbury Telegraph Trust
The Towry Law Charitable Trust
　(also known as the Castle
　Educational Trust)
The Constance Travis
　Charitable Trust
The Treeside Trust
The Trusthouse Charitable
　Foundation
The James Tudor Foundation
The Tudor Trust
The R D Turner Charitable
　Trust
The Douglas Turner Trust
Two Ridings Community
　Foundation
John and Lucille van Geest
　Foundation
The Vandervell Foundation
Victoria Homes Trust
Voluntary Action Fund
The Scurrah Wainwright Charity
Wallington Missionary Mart
　and Auctions
The Wates Foundation
Webb Memorial Trust
The James Weir Foundation
The Barbara Welby Trust
The Garfield Weston
　Foundation
The Whitaker Charitable Trust
The Simon Whitbread
　Charitable Trust
White Stuff Foundation
The Norman Whiteley Trust
The Whittlesey Charity
The Wilkinson Charitable
　Foundation
The Dame Violet Wills Will
　Trust

The Harold Hyam Wingate
　Foundation
The Wixamtree Trust
The Wood Family Trust
Woodlands Trust
The Wragge and Co. Charitable
　Trust
The Wyndham Charitable Trust
The Yapp Charitable Trust
The Yardley Great Trust
The South Yorkshire
　Community Foundation
The John K Young Endowment
　Fund
Stephen Zimmerman
　Charitable Trust
Zurich Community Trust (UK)
　Limited

....

■ Development
funding

The 1970 Trust
The 1989 Willan Charitable
　Trust
The 29th May 1961 Charitable
　Trust
The A B Charitable Trust
The Aberbrothock Skea Trust
ABF The Soldiers' Charity
　(formerly the Army
　Benevolent Fund)
Brian Abrams Charitable Trust
Eric Abrams Charitable Trust
The Acacia Charitable Trust
Achiezer Association Ltd
Achisomoch Aid Company
　Limited
The ACT Foundation
Action Medical Research
The Company of Actuaries'
　Charitable Trust Fund
The Sylvia Adams Charitable
　Trust
The Adamson Trust
The Victor Adda Foundation
Adenfirst Ltd
The Adint Charitable Trust
The Adnams Charity
AF Trust Company
Age Scotland (Formerly Age
　Concern Scotland and Help
　the Aged)
Age UK (formerly Help the
　Aged and Age Concern)
Aid to the Church in Need (UK)
The Green and Lilian F M
　Ainsworth and Family
　Benevolent Fund
The Sylvia Aitken Charitable
　Trust
The Ajahma Charitable Trust
The Alabaster Trust
Alba Charitable Trust
The Albion Trust
The Alborada Trust

D G Albright Charitable Trust
The Alchemy Foundation
Aldgate and All Hallows'
　Barking Exhibition
　Foundation
The Aldgate Freedom
　Foundation
The Alexis Trust
All Saints Educational Trust
Allchurches Trust Ltd
The H B Allen Charitable Trust
The Alliance Family Foundation
Angus Allnatt Charitable
　Foundation
The Pat Allsop Charitable Trust
The Almond Trust
Almondsbury Charity
The Altajir Trust
Altamont Ltd
Alvor Charitable Trust
AM Charitable Trust
The Ammco Trust
Viscount Amory's Charitable
　Trust
The Ampelos Trust
The AMW Charitable Trust
The Anchor Foundation
The Andrew Anderson Trust
Andor Charitable Trust
The André Christian Trust
Anglo American Group
　Foundation
Anguish's Educational
　Foundation
The Animal Defence Trust
The Eric Anker-Petersen
　Charity
The Annandale Charitable
　Trust
The Anson Charitable Trust
The Apax Foundation
Ambrose and Ann Appelbe
　Trust
The Appletree Trust
The John Apthorp Charitable
　Trust
The Arbib Foundation
Archbishop of Wales' Fund for
　Children
The John M Archer Charitable
　Trust
The Archer Trust
The Architectural Heritage
　Fund
The Ardeola Charitable Trust
The Argentarius Foundation
The Argus Appeal
Armenian General Benevolent
　Union London Trust
The Armenian Relief Society of
　Great Britain Trust
The Armourers' and Brasiers'
　Gauntlet Trust
The Arnold Foundation
Arsenal Charitable Trust
The Artemis Charitable Trust

The Arts and Entertainment
Charitable Trust
Arts Council England
The Arts Council of Northern
Ireland
The Arts Council of Wales
The Ove Arup Foundation
The AS Charitable Trust
Ashburnham Thanksgiving
Trust
A J H Ashby Will Trust
The Ashden Trust
The Ashendene Trust
The Ashley Family Foundation
(formerly The Laura Ashley
Foundation)
The Norman C Ashton
Foundation
The Ian Askew Charitable Trust
The Associated Country
Women of the World
(ACWW)
The Association of Colleges
Charitable Trust
Astellas European Foundation
Asthma UK
AstonMansfield Charitable
Trust
The Astor Foundation
The Astor of Hever Trust
The Aurelius Charitable Trust
The Avenue Charitable Trust
The Avon and Somerset Police
Community Trust
AW Charitable Trust
The BAA Communities Trust
Harry Bacon Foundation
The BACTA Charitable Trust
The Scott Bader
Commonwealth Ltd
The Bagri Foundation
Veta Bailey Charitable Trust
The Austin Bailey Trust
The Baily Thomas Charitable
Fund
The Baird Trust
The Baker Charitable Trust
The Roy and Pixie Baker
Charitable Trust
The Balcombe Charitable Trust
The Albert Casanova Ballard
Deceased Trust
The Ballinger Charitable Trust
Balmain Charitable Trust
The Balmore Trust
The Balney Charitable Trust
The Baltic Charitable Fund
The Bamford Charitable
Foundation
The Banbury Charities
William P Bancroft (No 2)
Charitable Trust and
Jenepher Gillett Trust
The Band Trust
The Barbers' Company General
Charities

The Barbour Foundation
The Barcapel Foundation
Barchester Healthcare
Foundation
The Barclay Foundation
The Baring Foundation
Peter Barker-Mill Memorial
Charity
Barleycorn Trust
Lord Barnby's Foundation
Barnes Workhouse Fund
The Barnsbury Charitable Trust
The Barnwood House Trust
The Misses Barrie Charitable
Trust
Barrington Family Charitable
Trust
Stephen J Barry Charitable
Trust
The Bartlett Taylor Charitable
Trust
The Paul Bassham Charitable
Trust
The Batchworth Trust
Bay Charitable Trust
The Bay Tree Charitable Trust
D H and L H Baylin Charitable
Trust
The Louis Baylis (Maidenhead
Advertiser) Charitable Trust
BC Partners Foundation
B-CH 1971 Charitable Trust
BCH Trust
The Beacon Trust
Bear Mordechai Ltd
The Bearder Charity
The James Beattie Charitable
Trust
The Jack and Ada Beattie
Foundation
The Beaufort House Trust
Limited
Beauland Ltd
The Beaverbrook Foundation
The Beccles Town Lands
Charity
The Becker Family Charitable
Trust
The Becketts and Sargeants
Educational Foundation
The John Beckwith Charitable
Trust
The Peter Beckwith Charitable
Trust
The Bedford Charity (The
Harpur Trust)
The Bedfordshire and Luton
Community Foundation
The David and Ruth Behrend
Fund
The Beit Trust
The Bellahouston Bequest
Fund
Bellasis Trust
The Bellhouse Foundation
The Bellinger Donnay Trust

Belljoe Tzedoko Ltd
The Benfield Motors Charitable
Trust
The Benham Charitable
Settlement
Maurice and Jacqueline
Bennett Charitable Trust
Michael and Leslie Bennett
Charitable Trust
The Ruth Berkowitz Charitable
Trust
The Berkshire Community
Foundation
The Bestway Foundation
Thomas Betton's Charity for
Pensions and Relief-in-Need
BHST
The Mason Bibby 1981 Trust
BibleLands
The Bideford Bridge Trust
The Big Lottery Fund
The Billmeir Charitable Trust
The Bingham Trust
The Bintaub Charitable Trust
The Birmingham Community
Foundation
The Birmingham District
Nursing Charitable Trust
The Birmingham Hospital
Saturday Fund Medical
Charity and Welfare Trust
Birmingham International
Airport Community Trust
The Lord Mayor of
Birmingham's Charity
Birthday House Trust
The Michael Bishop
Foundation
The Bishop's Development
Fund
The Bertie Black Foundation
Blackheart Foundation (UK)
Limited
Isabel Blackman Foundation
The BlackRock (UK) Charitable
Trust
The Herbert and Peter
Blagrave Charitable Trust
The Blair Foundation
The Blanchminster Trust
The Sir Victor Blank Charitable
Settlement
The Neville and Elaine Blond
Charitable Trust
The Blueberry Charitable Trust
The Bluston Charitable
Settlement
The Nicholas Boas Charitable
Trust
The Body Shop Foundation
The Boltons Trust
The Bonamy Charitable Trust
The John and Celia Bonham
Christie Charitable Trust
The Charlotte Bonham-Carter
Charitable Trust

Bonhomie United Charity
Society
The Linda and Gordon
Bonnyman Charitable Trust
BOOST Charitable Trust
The Booth Charities
The Boots Charitable Trust
The Bordon and Liphook
Charity
Salo Bordon Charitable Trust
The Oliver Borthwick Memorial
Trust
The Boshier-Hinton Foundation
The Bothwell Charitable Trust
H E and E L Botteley
Charitable Trust
The Harry Bottom Charitable
Trust
P G and N J Boulton Trust
The A H and E Boulton Trust
Sir Clive Bourne Family Trust
The Anthony Bourne
Foundation
Bourneheights Limited
Community Foundation for
Bournemouth, Dorset and
Poole
The Bower Trust
The Bowerman Charitable
Trust
John and Susan Bowers Fund
The Bowland Charitable Trust
The William Brake Charitable
Trust
The Liz and Terry Bramall
Charitable Trust
The Tony Bramall Charitable
Trust
The Bransford Trust
The Breadsticks Foundation
The Brendish Family
Foundation
Bridgepoint Inspire
The Harold and Alice Bridges
Charity
Briggs Animal Welfare Trust
The Brighton District Nursing
Association Trust
Bristol Archdeaconry Charity
The Bristol Charities
John Bristow and Thomas
Mason Trust
Britannia Foundation
The British Council for
Prevention of Blindness
The British Dietetic
Association General and
Education Trust Fund
The British Gas (Scottish Gas)
Energy Trust
British Heart Foundation
British Humane Association
British Institute at Ankara
British Ornithologists' Union
British Record Industry Trust
The Britto Foundation

The J and M Britton Charitable
Trust
The Charles and Edna
Broadhurst Charitable Trust
The Bromley Trust
The Roger Brooke Charitable
Trust
The David Brooke Charity
The Rory and Elizabeth Brooks
Foundation
The Charles Brotherton Trust
Joseph Brough Charitable
Trust
The Swinfen Broun Charitable
Trust
Mrs E E Brown Charitable
Settlement
Bill Brown's Charitable
Settlement
R S Brownless Charitable
Trust
Brown-Mellows Trust
Brownsword Charitable
Foundation
T B H Brunner's Charitable
Settlement
The Bruntwood Charity
Brushmill Ltd
The Bryant Trust
Buckingham Trust
The Buckinghamshire
Foundation
The Buckinghamshire Masonic
Centenary Fund
Buckland Charitable Trust
The Rosemary Bugden
Charitable Trust
The Bulldog Trust Limited
The E F Bulmer Benevolent
Fund
The Burden Trust
Burdens Charitable Foundation
The Burdett Trust for Nursing
The Clara E Burgess Charity
The Burry Charitable Trust
The Audrey and Stanley Burton
1960 Charitable Trust
The Arnold Burton 1998
Charitable Trust
The Burton Breweries
Charitable Trust
The Geoffrey Burton Charitable
Trust
Consolidated Charity of Burton
upon Trent
Butchers' Company General
Charities
The Derek Butler Trust
The Noel Buxton Trust
Ann Byrne Charitable Trust
C and F Charitable Trust
The C Charitable Trust
The James Caan Foundation
C J Cadbury Charitable Trust
Edward Cadbury Charitable
Trust

Henry T and Lucy B Cadbury
Charitable Trust
P H G Cadbury Charitable
Trust
The Christopher Cadbury
Charitable Trust
The G W Cadbury Charitable
Trust
The Richard Cadbury
Charitable Trust
The William A Cadbury
Charitable Trust
The Cadbury Foundation
The Edward and Dorothy
Cadbury Trust
The George Cadbury Trust
The Barrow Cadbury Trust and
the Barrow Cadbury Fund
The Cadogan Charity
CAF (Charities Aid Foundation)
CAFOD (Catholic Agency for
Overseas Development)
The Callander Charitable Trust
Calleva Foundation
Calouste Gulbenkian
Foundation
Calypso Browning Trust
The Cambridgeshire
Community Foundation
The Camelia Trust
The Campden Charities
Trustee
The Canning Trust
M R Cannon 1998 Charitable
Trust
H and L Cantor Trust
Cardy Beaver Foundation
The Carew Pole Charitable
Trust
The D W T Cargill Fund
Carlee Ltd
The Carlton House Charitable
Trust
The Worshipful Company of
Carmen Benevolent Trust
The Carnegie Dunfermline
Trust
The Carnegie Trust for the
Universities of Scotland
The Carpenter Charitable Trust
The Carpenters' Company
Charitable Trust
The Carrington Charitable
Trust
The Carron Charitable
Settlement
The Leslie Mary Carter
Charitable Trust
The Carvill Trust
The Casey Trust
Cash for Kids Radio Clyde
Sir John Cass's Foundation
The Elizabeth Casson Trust
The Castanea Trust
The Castang Foundation

The Catalyst Charitable Trust (formerly the Buckle Family Charitable Trust)

The Catholic Charitable Trust

Catholic Foreign Missions

The Catholic Trust for England and Wales

The Cattanach Charitable Trust

The Joseph and Annie Cattle Trust

The Thomas Sivewright Catto Charitable Settlement

The Wilfrid and Constance Cave Foundation

The Cayo Foundation

Elizabeth Cayzer Charitable Trust

The B G S Cayzer Charitable Trust

The Cazenove Charitable Trust

The CBD Charitable Trust

Celtic Charity Fund

The Cemlyn-Jones Trust

CfBT Education Trust

The CH (1980) Charitable Trust

R E Chadwick Charitable Trust

The Amelia Chadwick Trust

The Pamela Champion Foundation

The Chapman Charitable Trust

John William Chapman's Charitable Trust

The Charities Advisory Trust

Charitworth Limited

The Charter 600 Charity

The Worshipful Company of Chartered Accountants General Charitable Trust (also known as CALC)

The Chasah Trust

Chasdei Tovim Me'oros

The Checkatrade Foundation

The Chelsea Building Society Charitable Foundation

The Chelsea Square 1994 Trust

The Cheruby Trust

The Cheshire Provincial Fund of Benevolence

The Chetwode Foundation

Chevioty Asset Management Charitable Trust

The Malcolm Chick Charity

Child Growth Foundation

Childs Charitable Trust

The Childwick Trust

The Chipping Sodbury Town Lands Charity

CHK Charities Limited

The Chownes Foundation

The Chrimes Family Charitable Trust

The Christabella Charitable Trust

Christadelphian Samaritan Fund

Christian Aid

Christian Response to Eastern Europe

Chrysalis Trust

The Church and Community Fund

The Church Burgesses Educational Foundation

Church Burgesses Trust

The Church Urban Fund

City and County of Swansea Welsh Church Act Fund

The City Bridge Trust (formerly known as Bridge House Trust)

The City Educational Trust Fund

CLA Charitable Trust

Stephen Clark 1957 Charitable Trust

J A Clark Charitable Trust

The Hilda and Alice Clark Charitable Trust

The Roger and Sarah Bancroft Clark Charitable Trust

The Clarke Charitable Settlement

The Cleary Foundation

The Cleevely Family Charitable Trust

The Cleopatra Trust

Lord Clinton's Charitable Trust

The Clore Duffield Foundation

Miss V L Clore's 1967 Charitable Trust

Closehelm Ltd

The Clothworkers' Foundation

Richard Cloudesley's Charity

The Clover Trust

The Robert Clutterbuck Charitable Trust

Clydpride Ltd

The Coalfields Regeneration Trust

The John Coates Charitable Trust

Coats Foundation Trust

The Cobalt Trust

The Cobtree Charity Trust Ltd

The Denise Cohen Charitable Trust

The Vivienne and Samuel Cohen Charitable Trust

The John S Cohen Foundation

The R and S Cohen Foundation

The Colchester Catalyst Charity

John Coldman Charitable Trust

The Cole Charitable Trust

The Colefax Charitable Trust

The John and Freda Coleman Charitable Trust

The Bernard Coleman Charitable Trust

The E Alec Colman Charitable Fund Ltd

The Sir Jeremiah Colman Gift Trust

Col-Reno Ltd

The Colt Foundation

The Coltstaple Trust

Colwinston Charitable Trust

Colyer-Fergusson Charitable Trust

Comic Relief

The Comino Foundation

Community Foundation for Calderdale

The Community Foundation for Northern Ireland

The Compton Charitable Trust

The Congleton Inclosure Trust

The Conscience Trust

The Conservation Foundation

The Consolidated Charities for the Infirm Merchant Taylors' Company

The Cook and Wolstenholme Charitable Trust

Gordon Cook Foundation

The Ernest Cook Trust

The Cooks Charity

The Catherine Cookson Charitable Trust

The Cookson Charitable Trust

Harold and Daphne Cooper Charitable Trust

Mabel Cooper Charity

The Alice Ellen Cooper Dean Charitable Foundation

The Co-operative Foundation

The Marjorie Coote Animal Charity Trust

The Marjorie Coote Old People's Charity

The Helen Jean Cope Trust

The J Reginald Corah Foundation Fund

The Gershon Coren Charitable Foundation

The Corinthian Trust

Edwin Cornforth 1983 Charity Trust

The Evan Cornish Foundation

The Duke of Cornwall's Benevolent Fund

The Cornwell Charitable Trust

The Sidney and Elizabeth Corob Charitable Trust

The Corona Charitable Trust

The Costa Family Charitable Trust (formerly the Morgan Williams Charitable Trust)

The Cotton Industry War Memorial Trust

The Cotton Trust

County Durham Community Foundation

The Augustine Courtauld Trust
Coutts Charitable Trust
The General Charities of the
City of Coventry
Coventry Building Society
Charitable Foundation
The John Cowan Foundation
The Michael Cowan
Foundation
Cowley Charitable Foundation
The Sir William Coxen Trust
Fund
The Lord Cozens-Hardy Trust
The Craignish Trust
The Craps Charitable Trust
Michael Crawford Children's
Charity
The Cray Trust
Creative Scotland
The Crescent Trust
Criffel Charitable Trust
Cripplegate Foundation
The Violet and Milo Cripps
Charitable Trust
The Harry Crook Foundation
The Cross Trust
The Croydon Relief in Need
Charities
The Mayor of Croydon's
Charity Fund
The Peter Cruddas Foundation
Cruden Foundation Ltd
The Ronald Cruickshank's
Foundation
The R D Crusaders Foundation
The Cuby Charitable Trust
The Culra Charitable Trust
The Cumber Family Charitable
Trust
Cumberland Building Society
Charitable Foundation
Cumbria Community
Foundation
The D J H Currie Memorial
Trust
The Dennis Curry Charitable
Trust
The Raymond Curtis Charitable
Trust
The Manny Cussins
Foundation
The Cutler Trust (the
Worshipful Company of
Makers of Playing Cards)
The Cwmbran Trust
Itzchok Meyer Cymerman Trust
Ltd
The D G Charitable Settlement
Roald Dahl's Marvellous
Children's Charity
The Daily Prayer Union
Charitable Trust Ltd
The Daisy Trust
The Daiwa Anglo-Japanese
Foundation
Oizer Dalim Trust

The Dr and Mrs A Darlington
Charitable Trust
Baron Davenport's Charity
The Davidson (Nairn)
Charitable Trust
The Davidson Family
Charitable Trust
The Alderman Joe Davidson
Memorial Trust
Michael Davies Charitable
Settlement
The Gwendoline and Margaret
Davies Charity
The Wilfrid Bruce Davis
Charitable Trust
Davis-Rubens Charitable Trust
The Dawe Charitable Trust
The De Clermont Charitable
Company Ltd
Peter De Haan Charitable
Trust
The De Laszlo Foundation
The Leopold De Rothschild
Charitable Trust
The Deakin Charitable Trust
William Dean Countryside and
Educational Trust
The Debmar Benevolent Trust
The Dellal Foundation
The Delves Charitable Trust
The Demigryphon Trust
The Denman Charitable Trust
The Denton Charitable Trust
The Denton Wilde Sapte
Charitable Trust
The Earl of Derby's Charitable
Trust
Derbyshire Community
Foundation
The J N Derbyshire Trust
Devon Community Foundation
The Devon Educational Trust
The Duke of Devonshire's
Charitable Trust
The Sandy Dewhirst Charitable
Trust
The Laduma Dhamecha
Charitable Trust
Diabetes UK
Alan and Sheila Diamond
Charitable Trust
The Dibden Allotments Fund
The Dickon Trust
The Digbeth Trust
The Dinwoodie Settlement
Dischma Charitable Trust
The DLM Charitable Trust
The DM Charitable Trust
Louise Dobson Charitable
Trust
The Derek and Eileen Dodgson
Foundation
The Dollond Charitable Trust
Domepride Ltd
The Dorcas Trust
The Dorema Charitable Trust

The Dorus Trust
Double 'O' Charity Ltd
The Doughty Charity Trust
The R M Douglas Charitable
Trust
The Drapers' Charitable Fund
Dromintee Trust
The Dugdale Charitable Trust
The Duis Charitable Trust
The Dulverton Trust
The P B Dumbell Charitable
Trust
The Dumbreck Charity
Dunard Fund
Ronald Duncan Literary
Foundation
The Dunhill Medical Trust
The Houghton Dunn Charitable
Trust
The Dunn Family Charitable
Trust
The W E Dunn Trust
The Charles Dunstone
Charitable Trust
Dushinsky Trust Ltd
Mildred Duveen Charitable
Trust
Annette Duvollet Charitable
Trust
The Dwek Family Charitable
Trust
The Dyers' Company
Charitable Trust
The James Dyson Foundation
The Eagle Charity Trust
Audrey Earle Charitable Trust
The Earley Charity
Earls Colne and Halstead
Educational Charity
The Earmark Trust
East Kent Provincial Charities
East London Community
Foundation
Eastern Counties Educational
Trust Limited
The Sir John Eastwood
Foundation
The Ebenezer Trust
The EBM Charitable Trust
Eden Arts Trust
EDF Energy Trust (EDFET)
The Gilbert and Eileen Edgar
Foundation
Gilbert Edgar Trust
Edinburgh Children's Holiday
Fund
The Edinburgh Trust, No 2
Account
Edinburgh Voluntary
Organisations' Trust Funds
Educational Foundation of
Alderman John Norman
The W G Edwards Charitable
Foundation
The William Edwards
Educational Charity

The Elephant Trust
The George Elias Charitable
  Trust
The Gerald Palmer Eling Trust
  Company
The Wilfred and Elsie Elkes
  Charity Fund
The Maud Elkington Charitable
  Trust
Ellador Ltd
The Ellerdale Trust
The John Ellerman Foundation
The Ellinson Foundation Ltd
The Ellis Campbell Foundation
James Ellis Charitable Trust
The Elmgrant Trust
The Elmley Foundation
Elshore Ltd
The Vernon N Ely Charitable
  Trust
The Embleton Trust
The Emerton-Christie Charity
The Emilienne Charitable Trust
The Emmandjay Charitable
  Trust
Empath UK
The Worshipful Company of
  Engineers Charitable Trust
  Fund
The Englefield Charitable Trust
The English Schools' Football
  Association
The Enkalon Foundation
Entindale Ltd
The Epigoni Trust
Epilepsy Research UK
The Equitable Charitable Trust
The Equity Trust Fund
The Ericson Trust
The Erskine Cunningham Hill
  Trust
Essex Community Foundation
The Essex Fairway Charitable
  Trust
The Essex Heritage Trust
Essex Provincial Charity Fund
The Essex Youth Trust
Joseph Ettedgui Charitable
  Foundation
Euro Charity Trust
The Alan Evans Memorial Trust
Sir John Evelyn's Charity
The Eventhall Family
  Charitable Trust
The Everard Foundation
The Eveson Charitable Trust
The Beryl Evetts and Robert
  Luff Animal Welfare Trust
The Execution Charitable Trust
The Mayor of Exeter's Appeal
  Fund
The Exilarch's Foundation
The Matthew Eyton Animal
  Welfare Trust
F C Charitable Trust

The F P Limited Charitable
  Trust
The Faber Charitable Trust
Esmée Fairbairn Foundation
The Fairstead Trust
The Fairway Trust
Faisaltex Charitable Trust
The Family Rich Charities Trust
Famos Foundation Trust
The Lord Faringdon Charitable
  Trust
Samuel William Farmer Trust
The Farmers' Company
  Charitable Fund
The Thomas Farr Charitable
  Trust
Walter Farthing (Trust) Limited
Farthing Trust
The Fassnidge Memorial Trust
Joseph Fattorini Charitable
  Trust 'B' Account
The Fawcett Charitable Trust
The February Foundation
Federation of Jewish Relief
  Organisations
The John Feeney Charitable
  Trust
The George Fentham
  Birmingham Charity
The A M Fenton Trust
Allan and Nesta Ferguson
  Charitable Settlement
Elizabeth Ferguson Charitable
  Trust Fund
The Fidelity UK Foundation
The Bluff Field Charitable Trust
The Doris Field Charitable
  Trust
Fife Council/Common Good
  Funds and Trusts
The Fifty Fund
Dixie Rose Findlay Charitable
  Trust
Finnart House School Trust
Gerald Finzi Charitable Trust
Firtree Trust
The Sir John Fisher Foundation
The Fishmongers' Company's
  Charitable Trust
Marc Fitch Fund
The Fitton Trust
The Earl Fitzwilliam Charitable
  Trust
Bud Flanagan Leukaemia Fund
The Rose Flatau Charitable
  Trust
The Ian Fleming Charitable
  Trust
The Joyce Fletcher Charitable
  Trust
The Roy Fletcher Charitable
  Trust
Florence's Charitable Trust
The Flow Foundation
The Gerald Fogel Charitable
  Trust

The Follett Trust
The Football Association
  National Sports Centre
  Trust
The Football Association Youth
  Trust
The Football Foundation
The Forbes Charitable
  Foundation
The Forces Trust (Working
  Name)
Ford Britain Trust
The Oliver Ford Charitable
  Trust
Fordeve Ltd
The Forest Hill Charitable Trust
The Foresters' Charity
  Stewards UK Trust
Forever Manchester (The
  Community Foundation for
  Greater Manchester)
Gwyneth Forrester Trust
The Donald Forrester Trust
The Anna Rosa Forster
  Charitable Trust
The Fort Foundation
The Forte Charitable Trust
Lord Forte Foundation
Foundation for Management
  Education
The Four Winds Trust
The Foyle Foundation
The Isaac and Freda Frankel
  Memorial Charitable Trust
The Elizabeth Frankland Moore
  and Star Foundation
Sydney E Franklin Deceased's
  New Second Charity
The Jill Franklin Trust
The Gordon Fraser Charitable
  Trust
The Hugh Fraser Foundation
The Joseph Strong Frazer Trust
The Louis and Valerie
  Freedman Charitable
  Settlement
The Michael and Clara
  Freeman Charitable Trust
The Freemasons' Grand
  Charity
The Thomas Freke and Lady
  Norton Charity
The Charles S French
  Charitable Trust
The Anne French Memorial
  Trust
The Freshfield Foundation
The Freshgate Trust
  Foundation
The Friarsgate Trust
The Friends Hall Farm Street
  Trust
Friends of Biala Ltd
Friends of Wiznitz Limited
Friends Provident Charitable
  Foundation

The Frognal Trust
T F C Frost Charitable Trust
The Patrick Frost Foundation
Maurice Fry Charitable Trust
Mejer and Gertrude Miriam
 Frydman Foundation
The Fuellers Charitable Trust
 Fund
The Fulmer Charitable Trust
Worshipful Company of
 Furniture Makers Charitable
 Fund
Gableholt Limited
The Galbraith Trust
The Gale Family Charitable
 Trust
The Angela Gallagher Memorial
 Fund
The Gamlen Charitable Trust
The Gamma Trust
The Gannochy Trust
The Ganzoni Charitable Trust
The Worshipful Company of
 Gardeners of London
The Samuel Gardner Memorial
 Trust
The Garnett Charitable Trust
Garrick Charitable Trust
Garvan Limited
The Gatsby Charitable
 Foundation
Gatwick Airport Community
 Trust
The Robert Gavron Charitable
 Trust
Jacqueline and Michael Gee
 Charitable Trust
The General Nursing Council
 for England and Wales
 Trust
Generations Charitable Trust
J Paul Getty Jr Charitable Trust
The Gibbs Charitable Trust
Simon Gibson Charitable Trust
The G C Gibson Charitable
 Trust
Lady Gibson's Charitable Trust
The Harvey and Hilary Gilbert
 Charitable Trust
The Girdlers' Company
 Charitable Trust
The B and P Glasser
 Charitable Trust
The Glass-House Trust
The Glastonbury Trust Limited
Global Care
Global Charities (formerly
 GCap Charities)
Gloucestershire Community
 Foundation
Worshipful Company of
 Glovers of London Charity
 Fund
GMC Trust
The GMW Charitable Trust
The GNC Trust

The Meir Golda Trust
The Sydney and Phyllis
 Goldberg Memorial
 Charitable Trust
The Golden Bottle Trust
Golden Charitable Trust
The Jack Goldhill Charitable
 Trust
The Goldsmiths' Arts Trust
 Fund
The Goldsmiths' Company
 Charity
The Golsoncott Foundation
Golubovich Foundation
The Good Neighbours Trust
Nicholas and Judith
 Goodison's Charitable
 Settlement
The Everard and Mina
 Goodman Charitable
 Foundation
Mike Gooley Trailfinders
 Charity
Leonard Gordon Charitable
 Trust
The Gosling Foundation
 Limited
The Gough Charitable Trust
The Gould Charitable Trust
The Grace Charitable Trust
A B Grace Trust
The Graff Foundation
A and S Graham Charitable
 Trust
The Grahame Charitable
 Foundation Limited
Grampian Police Diced Cap
 Charitable Fund
The Granada Foundation
Grand Charitable Trust of the
 Order of Women
 Freemasons
The Grand Order of Water
 Rats' Charities Fund
The Grange Farm Centre Trust
Grantham Yorke Trust
The Gray Trust
The Great Britain Sasakawa
 Foundation
The Great Stone Bridge Trust
 of Edenbridge
The Great Torrington Town
 Lands Charity
The Constance Green
 Foundation
The Philip Green Memorial
 Trust
The Green Room Charitable
 Trust
Mrs H R Greene Charitable
 Settlement
Greenham Common
 Community Trust Limited
Naomi and Jeffrey Greenwood
 Charitable Trust

Greggs Foundation (formerly
 Greggs Trust)
The Gretna Charitable Trust
The Greys Charitable Trust
Grimmitt Trust
The Grocers' Charity
The M and R Gross Charities
 Limited
The Grove Charitable Trust
The GRP Charitable Trust
The David and Marie Grumitt
 Foundation
The Bishop of Guildford's
 Foundation
The Guildry Incorporation of
 Perth
The Walter Guinness
 Charitable Trust
The Gunter Charitable Trust
The Gur Trust
Dr Guthrie's Association
The H and M Charitable Trust
H C D Memorial Fund
The H P Charitable Trust
The Hackney Parochial
 Charities
The Hadfield Trust
The Hadley Trust
The Hadrian Trust
The Alfred Haines Charitable
 Trust
The Hale Trust
E F and M G Hall Charitable
 Trust
The Edith Winifred Hall
 Charitable Trust
Robert Hall Charity
The Hamamelis Trust
Hamilton Wallace Trust
Paul Hamlyn Foundation
Sue Hammerson's Charitable
 Trust
The Hammonds Charitable
 Trust
The Hampshire and Islands
 Historic Churches Trust
The Hampstead Wells and
 Campden Trust
Hampton Fuel Allotment
 Charity
The W A Handley Charitable
 Trust
Beatrice Hankey Foundation
 Ltd
The Hanley Trust
The Kathleen Hannay
 Memorial Charity
The Doughty Hanson
 Charitable Foundation
Lord Hanson Foundation
The Haramead Trust
Miss K M Harbinson's
 Charitable Trust
Harbo Charities Limited
The Harborne Parish Lands
 Charity

The Harbour Charitable Trust
The Harbour Foundation
The Harding Trust
William Harding's Charity
The Hare of Steep Charitable
Trust
The Harebell Centenary Fund
The Kenneth Hargreaves
Charitable Trust
The Harris Charitable Trust
The Harris Charity
The Harris Family Charitable
Trust
The Edith Lilian Harrison 2000
Foundation
The Harrison and Potter Trust
The John Harrison Charitable
Trust
The Spencer Hart Charitable
Trust
The Hartley Charitable Trust
The N and P Hartley Memorial
Trust
The Alfred And Peggy Harvey
Charitable Trust
William Geoffrey Harvey's
Discretionary Settlement
Haskel Family Foundation
The Hathaway Trust
The Maurice Hatter Foundation
The M A Hawe Settlement
The Hawerby Trust
The Hawthorne Charitable
Trust
The Dorothy Hay-Bolton
Charitable Trust
The Haymills Charitable Trust
The Headley Trust
Headley-Pitt Charitable Trust
Heagerty Charitable Trust
May Hearnshaw's Charity
The Heart of England
Community Foundation
The Heathcoat Trust
Heathside Charitable Trust
The Charlotte Heber-Percy
Charitable Trust
The Hedera Charitable Trust
Percy Hedley 1990 Charitable
Trust
The Hedley Denton Charitable
Trust
The Hedley Foundation
The H J Heinz Company
Limited Charitable Trust
The Hellenic Foundation
The Michael and Morven Heller
Charitable Foundation
The Simon Heller Charitable
Settlement
The Hemby Trust
The Christina Mary Hendrie
Trust for Scottish and
Canadian Charities
The Henley Educational Charity
Philip Henman Trust

Esther Hennell Charitable
Trust
The G D Herbert Charitable
Trust
The Joanna Herbert-Stepney
Charitable Settlement (also
known as The Paget
Charitable Trust)
The Anne Herd Memorial Trust
The Herefordshire Historic
Churches Trust
The Heritage of London Trust
Ltd
The Hertfordshire Community
Foundation
The Hesed Trust
The Hesslewood Children's
Trust (Hull Seamen's and
General Orphanage)
The Bernhard Heuberger
Charitable Trust
Hexham and Newcastle
Diocesan Trust (1947)
The Higgs Charitable Trust
Alan Edward Higgs Charity
The High Sheriff's Police Trust
for the County of West
Midlands (Building Blocks)
Highcroft Charitable Trust
The Hilden Charitable Fund
The Derek Hill Foundation
The Charles Littlewood Hill
Trust
The Hillingdon Partnership
Trust
R G Hills Charitable Trust
Hinchley Charitable Trust
Lady Hind Trust
Hinduja Foundation
Stuart Hine Trust
The Hinrichsen Foundation
The Hitchin Educational
Foundation
The Eleemosynary Charity of
William Hobbayne
Hobson Charity Limited
Hockerill Educational
Foundation
Matthew Hodder Charitable
Trust
The Sir Julian Hodge
Charitable Trust
The Jane Hodge Foundation
The J G Hogg Charitable Trust
The Holbeck Charitable Trust
The Holden Charitable Trust
John Holford's Charity
The Hollick Family Charitable
Trust
The Holliday Foundation
The Dorothy Holmes Charitable
Trust
The Holmes Family Trust
(Sheffield)
The Holst Foundation
P H Holt Foundation

The Edward Holt Trust
The Holywood Trust
The Homelands Charitable
Trust
The Homestead Charitable
Trust
Mary Homfray Charitable Trust
Sir Harold Hood's Charitable
Trust
Hope for Youth (formerly
Women Caring Trust)
The Hope Trust
HopMarket Charity
The Horizon Foundation
The Cuthbert Horn Trust
The Antony Hornby Charitable
Trust
The Horne Foundation
The Horne Trust
The Worshipful Company of
Horners' Charitable Trusts
The Hornsey Parochial
Charities
The Hospital of God at
Greatham
The Hospital Saturday Fund
The Sir Joseph Hotung
Charitable Settlement
Houblon-Norman/George Fund
The House of Industry Estate
The Reta Lila Howard
Foundation
The Daniel Howard Trust
HTA Sheba Foundation UK
The Hudson Foundation
The Huggard Charitable Trust
The Geoffrey C Hughes
Charitable Trust
The Hull and East Riding
Charitable Trust
Hulme Trust Estates
(Educational)
Human Relief Foundation
The Humanitarian Trust
The Michael and Shirley Hunt
Charitable Trust
The Albert Hunt Trust
The Hunter Foundation
Miss Agnes H Hunter's Trust
The Huntingdon Foundation
Huntingdon Freemen's Charity
John Huntingdon's Charity
Hurdale Charity Limited
The Hutton Foundation
The Nani Huyu Charitable Trust
The P Y N and B Hyams Trust
The Hyde Charitable Trust –
Youth Plus
The Idlewild Trust
The Iliffe Family Charitable
Trust
Impetus Trust
The Indigo Trust
Infinity Capital Trust
The Ingram Trust

The Inland Waterways
Association
The Inlight Trust
The Inman Charity
The Inner London Magistrates
Court Poor Box and Feeder
Charity
The Innocent Foundation
The Ireland Fund of Great
Britain
The Irish Youth Foundation
(UK) Ltd (incorporating The
Lawlor Foundation)
The Ironmongers' Foundation
Irshad Trust
The Charles Irving Charitable
Trust
Irwin Trust
The ISA Charity
The Isaacs Charitable Trust
The J Isaacs Charitable Trust
The Isle of Anglesey Charitable
Trust
Isle of Dogs Community
Foundation
The ITF Seafarers Trust
J A R Charitable Trust
The J J Charitable Trust
The J R S S T Charitable Trust
The Jabbs Foundation
Elizabeth Jackson Charitable
Trust
Jacobs Charitable Trust
The Ruth and Lionel Jacobson
Trust (Second Fund) No 2
Jaffe Family Relief Fund
John James Bristol Foundation
The Susan and Stephen
James Charitable
Settlement (also known as
the Stephen James
Charitable Trust)
The James Trust
The Marjory Jameson Trust
The Jarman Charitable Trust
The Barbara Joyce Jarrald
Charitable Trust
Jay Education Trust
JCA Charitable Foundation
The Jeffrey Charitable Trust
Rees Jeffreys Road Fund
The Jenour Foundation
The Jerusalem Trust
Jesus Hospital Charity
Jewish Child's Day
The Jewish Youth Fund
The JMK Charitable Trust
The Joanies Trust
The Harold Joels Charitable
Trust
The Jonathan Joels Charitable
Trust
The Nicholas Joels Charitable
Trust
The Norman Joels Charitable
Trust

The Joffe Charitable Trust
The Elton John Aids
Foundation
The Michael John Trust
The Lillie Johnson Charitable
Trust
The Johnson Foundation
The Johnson Group Cleaners
Charity
The Johnnie Johnson Trust
The Johnson Wax Ltd
Charitable Trust
The Joicey Trust
The Jones 1986 Charitable
Trust
The Marjorie and Geoffrey
Jones Charitable Trust
The Muriel Jones Foundation
The Jordan Charitable
Foundation
The Joron Charitable Trust
The J E Joseph Charitable
Fund
The Lady Eileen Joseph
Foundation
JTH Charitable Trust
The Cyril and Eve Jumbo
Charitable Trust
The Anton Jurgens Charitable
Trust
Jusaca Charitable Trust
The Bernard Kahn Charitable
Trust
The Stanley Kalms Foundation
The Kalou Foundation
The Karenza Foundation
The Boris Karloff Charitable
Foundation
The Ian Karten Charitable
Trust
The Kasner Charitable Trust
The Kass Charitable Trust
The Kathleen Trust
The Michael and Ilse Katz
Foundation
The Katzauer Charitable
Settlement
The C S Kaufman Charitable
Trust
The Geoffrey John Kaye
Charitable Foundation
The Emmanuel Kaye
Foundation
The Kelly Family Charitable
Trust
Kelsick's Educational
Foundation
The KempWelch Charitable
Trust
The Kay Kendall Leukaemia
Fund
The Kennel Club Charitable
Trust
Kent Community Foundation
The Nancy Kenyon Charitable
Trust

Keren Association
Kermaville Ltd
E and E Kernkraut Charities
Limited
The Peter Kershaw Trust
The Kessler Foundation
Keswick Hall Trust
The Ursula Keyes Trust
The Kiawah Charitable Trust
The King/Cullimore Charitable
Trust
The King's Fund
The Kingsbury Charity
The Mary Kinross Charitable
Trust
Kinsurdy Charitable Trust
Kirkley Poor's Lands Estate
The Richard Kirkman
Charitable Trust
Kirschel Foundation
Robert Kitchin (Saddlers'
Company)
Ernest Kleinwort Charitable
Trust
The Marina Kleinwort
Charitable Trust
The Kobler Trust
The Kohn Foundation
Kollel and Co. Limited
The Kreditor Charitable Trust
The Kreitman Foundation
The Neil Kreitman Foundation
The Heinz, Anna and Carol
Kroch Foundation
Kupath Gemach Chaim
Bechesed Viznitz Trust
The Kyte Charitable Trust
The Late Sir Pierce Lacy
Charity Trust
The K P Ladd Charitable Trust
John Laing Charitable Trust
Maurice and Hilda Laing
Charitable Trust
The Christopher Laing
Foundation
The Kirby Laing Foundation
The Martin Laing Foundation
The Beatrice Laing Trust
The Lambert Charitable Trust
Community Foundation for
Lancashire
Duchy of Lancaster Benevolent
Fund
The Lancaster Foundation
The Allen Lane Foundation
The Langdale Trust
The Langley Charitable Trust
The Langtree Trust
The LankellyChase Foundation
The Lanvern Foundation
The R J Larg Family Charitable
Trust
Largsmount Ltd
The Lark Trust
Laslett's (Hinton) Charity

Lauchentilly Charitable
Foundation 1988
Laufer Charitable Trust
The Lauffer Family Charitable
Foundation
Mrs F B Laurence Charitable
Trust
The Kathleen Laurence Trust
The Law Society Charity
The Edgar E Lawley Foundation
The Herd Lawson and Muriel
Lawson Charitable Trust
The Lawson Beckman
Charitable Trust
The Raymond and Blanche
Lawson Charitable Trust
The Carole and Geoffrey
Lawson Foundation
The Mason Le Page Charitable
Trust
The Leach Fourteenth Trust
The David Lean Foundation
The Leathersellers' Company
Charitable Fund
The Arnold Lee Charitable
Trust
The Lord Mayor of Leeds
Appeal Fund
Leeds Building Society
Charitable Foundation
The Leeds Community
Foundation
Leicester Charity Link (formerly
The Leicester Charity
Organisation Society)
The Kennedy Leigh Charitable
Trust
Morris Leigh Foundation
The Leigh Trust
Mrs Vera Leigh's Charity
The P Leigh-Bramwell Trust 'E'
The Lennox and Wyfold
Foundation
The Erica Leonard Trust
The Leonard Trust
The Mark Leonard Trust
Lesley Lesley and Mutter Trust
Leukaemia and Lymphoma
Research
The Leverhulme Trade
Charities Trust
The Leverhulme Trust
The Joseph Levy Charitable
Foundation
Lewis Family Charitable Trust
The John Spedan Lewis
Foundation
The Sir Edward Lewis
Foundation
John Lewis Partnership
General Community Fund
Lichfield Conduit Lands
Lifeline 4 Kids
The Lightbridge Foundation
The Thomas Lilley Memorial
Trust

Limoges Charitable Trust
The Linbury Trust
The Lincolnshire Old Churches
Trust
The Lind Trust
Lindale Educational
Foundation
The Linden Charitable Trust
Lindenleaf Charitable Trust
The Enid Linder Foundation
The Linmarden Trust
The Ruth and Stuart Lipton
Charitable Trust
The Lister Charitable Trust
Frank Litchfield Charitable
Trust
The Andrew and Mary
Elizabeth Little Charitable
Trust
The Second Joseph Aaron
Littman Foundation
The George John and Sheilah
Livanos Charitable Trust
Liverpool Charity and Voluntary
Services
Liverpool Sailors' Home Trust
Jack Livingstone Charitable
Trust
The Elaine and Angus Lloyd
Charitable Trust
The Charles Lloyd Foundation
The Lloyd Fund
Lloyd's Charities Trust
Lloyds TSB Foundation for
England and Wales
Lloyds TSB Foundation for
Northern Ireland
Lloyds TSB Foundation for the
Channel Islands
Llysdinam Charitable Trust
Localtrent Ltd
The Locker Foundation
The Loftus Charitable Trust
The Lolev Charitable Trust
The Trust for London (formerly
the City Parochial
Foundation)
London Catalyst (formerly The
Metropolitan Hospital-
Sunday Fund)
The London Community
Foundation (formerly Capital
Community Foundation)
The London Law Trust
The William and Katherine
Longman Trust
The Loseley and Guildway
Charitable Trust
The Lotus Foundation
The Lowy Mitchell Foundation
The C L Loyd Charitable Trust
LSA Charitable Trust
The Marie Helen Luen
Charitable Trust
Robert Luff Foundation Ltd
Henry Lumley Charitable Trust

Lady Lumley's Educational
Foundation
Paul Lunn-Rockliffe Charitable
Trust
C F Lunoe Trust Fund
The Ruth and Jack Lunzer
Charitable Trust
Lord and Lady Lurgan Trust
The Lyndhurst Trust
The Lynn Foundation
The Lynwood Trust
John Lyon's Charity
The Lyons Charitable Trust
The Sir Jack Lyons Charitable
Trust
The Joy and Malcolm Lyons
Foundation
The Lyras Family Charitable
Trust
Sylvanus Lyson's Charity
The M and C Trust
The M D and S Charitable
Trust
The M K Charitable Trust
The Madeline Mabey Trust
The E M MacAndrew Trust
The R S Macdonald Charitable
Trust
Macdonald-Buchanan
Charitable Trust
The Macfarlane Walker Trust
The Mackay and Brewer
Charitable Trust
The Mackintosh Foundation
The MacRobert Trust
Ian Mactaggart Trust
The Magdalen and Lasher
Charity
Magdalen Hospital Trust
The SV and PE Magee Family
Charitable Trust
The Magen Charitable Trust
Mageni Trust
The Brian Maguire Charitable
Trust
The Mahavir Trust (also known
as the K S Mehta
Charitable Trust)
The Makin Charitable Trust
Man Group plc Charitable
Trust
Manchester Airport Community
Trust Fund
The Manchester Guardian
Society Charitable Trust
Lord Mayor of Manchester's
Charity Appeal Trust
Mandeville Trust
The Manifold Charitable Trust
W M Mann Foundation
The Leslie and Lilian Manning
Trust
Maranatha Christian Trust
Marbeh Torah Trust
Marchig Animal Welfare Trust

The Stella and Alexander Margulies Charitable Trust
The Marianne Foundation
Mariapolis Limited
Market Harborough and The Bowdens Charity
Michael Marks Charitable Trust
The Ann and David Marks Foundation
The Hilda and Samuel Marks Foundation
J P Marland Charitable Trust
Marr-Munning Trust
The Michael Marsh Charitable Trust
The Marsh Christian Trust
The Charlotte Marshall Charitable Trust
The Jim Marshall Charitable Trust
The D G Marshall of Cambridge Trust
Marshgate Charitable Settlement
John Martin's Charity
The John Mason Family Trust
The Mason Porter Charitable Trust
The Nancie Massey Charitable Trust
The Mathew Trust
Matliwala Family Charitable Trust
The Matt 6.3 Charitable Trust
The Violet Mauray Charitable Trust
The Maxell Educational Trust
The Maxwell Family Foundation
Evelyn May Trust
The Mayfield Valley Arts Trust
Mazars Charitable Trust
The McDougall Trust
The A M McGreevy No 5 Charitable Settlement
The McKenna Charitable Trust
Martin McLaren Memorial Trust
The Helen Isabella McMorran Charitable Foundation
D D McPhail Charitable Settlement
The Mears Foundation
The James Frederick and Ethel Anne Measures Charity
The Medlock Charitable Trust
The Anthony and Elizabeth Mellows Charitable Settlement
Melodor Ltd
Melow Charitable Trust
Meningitis Trust
Menuchar Ltd
The Menzies Charity Foundation

The Mercers' Charitable Foundation
The Merchant Taylors' Company Charities Fund
The Merchant Venturers' Charity
The Merchants' House of Glasgow
Mercury Phoenix Trust
The Mersey Docks and Harbour Company Charitable Fund
Community Foundation for Merseyside
The Zachary Merton and George Woofindin Convalescent Trust
The Tony Metherell Charitable Trust
The Metropolitan Drinking Fountain and Cattle Trough Association
London Masonic Charitable Trust
T and J Meyer Family Foundation Limited
Mickleham Charitable Trust
Gerald Micklem Charitable Trust
Midhurst Pensions Trust
The Migraine Trust
Miles Trust for the Putney and Roehampton Community
Millennium Stadium Charitable Trust
The Hugh and Mary Miller Bequest Trust
The Miller Foundation
The Millfield Trust
The Millhouses Charitable Trust
The Millichope Foundation
The Mills Charity
The Millward Charitable Trust
The Clare Milne Trust
Milton Keynes Community Foundation
The Edgar Milward Charity
The Peter Minet Trust
Minge's Gift and the Pooled Trusts
The Minos Trust
Minton Charitable Trust
The Mirfield Educational Charity
The Mirianog Trust
The Laurence Misener Charitable Trust
The Mishcon Family Charitable Trust
The Misselbrook Trust
The Brian Mitchell Charitable Settlement
The Mitchell Charitable Trust
The Esmé Mitchell Trust
Keren Mitzvah Trust

The Mizpah Trust
The Mobbs Memorial Trust Ltd
The Modiano Charitable Trust
The Moette Charitable Trust
The Mole Charitable Trust
The Monatrea Charitable Trust
The D C Moncrieff Charitable Trust
Monmouthshire County Council Welsh Church Act Fund
The Montague Thompson Coon Charitable Trust
The Colin Montgomerie Charitable Foundation
The Monument Trust
George A Moore Foundation
The Henry Moore Foundation
The Nigel Moores Family Charitable Trust
The Peter Moores Foundation
The Morel Charitable Trust
The Morgan Charitable Foundation
The Mr and Mrs J T Morgan Foundation
Diana and Allan Morgenthau Charitable Trust
The Oliver Morland Charitable Trust
S C and M E Morland's Charitable Trust
The Bernard Morris Charitable Trust
The Morris Charitable Trust
The Willie and Mabel Morris Charitable Trust
The Peter Morrison Charitable Foundation
The Stanley Morrison Charitable Trust
Moshal Charitable Trust
Vyoel Moshe Charitable Trust
The Moshulu Charitable Trust
Brian and Jill Moss Charitable Trust
The Moss Charitable Trust
The Robert and Margaret Moss Charitable Trust
Moss Family Charitable Trust
The Mount Everest Foundation
The Edwina Mountbatten Trust
Mountbatten Festival of Music
The Mountbatten Memorial Trust
The Mugdock Children's Trust
The Mulberry Trust
The Edith Murphy Foundation
Murphy-Neumann Charity Company Limited
Peter John Murray Trust (PJM Trust)
The Mushroom Fund
The Music Sales Charitable Trust
Muslim Hands
The Mutual Trust Group

MW (CL) Foundation
MW (GK) Foundation
MW (HO) Foundation
MW (RH) Foundation
MYA Charitable Trust
The Kitty and Daniel Nabarro
Charitable Trust
The Nadezhda Charitable Trust
The Naggar Charitable Trust
The Eleni Nakou Foundation
The Janet Nash Charitable
Settlement
Nathan Charitable Trust
The National Churches Trust
(formerly the Historic
Churches Preservation
Trust with the Incorporated
Church Building Society)
The National Manuscripts
Conservation Trust
Nazareth Trust Fund
The Nchima Trust
Needham Market and Barking
Welfare Charities
The Worshipful Company of
Needlemakers' Charitable
Fund
The Neighbourly Charitable
Trust
The James Neill Trust Fund
Nemoral Ltd
Nesswall Ltd
Network for Social Change
The New Appeals Organisation
for the City and County of
Nottingham
New Court Charitable Trust
Newby Trust Limited
The Newcomen Collett
Foundation
Mr and Mrs F E F Newman
Charitable Trust
Newpier Charity Ltd
Alderman Newton's
Educational Foundation
The Night Garden Charity
The Chevras Ezras Nitzrochim
Trust
NJD Charitable Trust
Alice Noakes Memorial
Charitable Trust
Nominet Charitable Foundation
The Noon Foundation
The Norda Trust
Norie Charitable Trust
Normalyn Charitable Trust
The Norman Family Charitable
Trust
The Duncan Norman Trust
Fund
The Normanby Charitable Trust
The North British Hotel Trust
The North West Cancer
Research Fund
The Northampton Municipal
Church Charities

The Northampton Queen's
Institute Relief in Sickness
Fund
The Earl of Northampton's
Charity
The Northcott Devon Medical
Foundation
The Northern Rock Foundation
The Northmoor Trust
The Northumberland Village
Homes Trust
The Northwood Charitable
Trust
The Norton Foundation
The Norwich Church of England
Young Men's Society
The Norwich Historic Churches
Trust Ltd
The Norwich Town Close
Estate Charity
The Norwood and Newton
Settlement
The Noswad Charity
The Notgrove Trust
The Nottingham General
Dispensary
The Nottingham Gordon
Memorial Trust for Boys
and Girls
Nottinghamshire Community
Foundation
The Nottinghamshire Historic
Churches Trust
The Nottinghamshire Miners'
Welfare Trust Fund
Novi Most International
The Nuffield Foundation
The Father O'Mahoney
Memorial Trust
The Sir Peter O'Sullevan
Charitable Trust
The Oak Trust
The Oakdale Trust
The Oakley Charitable Trust
The Oakmoor Charitable Trust
The Odin Charitable Trust
The Ofenheim Charitable Trust
Ogilvie Charities Deed No.2
(including the Charity of
Mary Catherine Ford Smith)
The Ogle Christian Trust
The Oikonomia Trust
Oizer Charitable Trust
The Old Broad Street Charity
Trust
The Old Enfield Charitable
Trust
Old Possum's Practical Trust
The John Oldacre Foundation
The Oldham Foundation
The Olga Charitable Trust
Onaway Trust
Open Gate
The Ormsby Charitable Trust
Orrin Charitable Trust

The O'Sullivan Family
Charitable Trust
The Ouseley Trust
The Owen Family Trust
Oxfam (GB)
The Oxfordshire Community
Foundation
The P F Charitable Trust
Padwa Charitable Foundation
The Pallant Charitable Trust
The Palmer Foundation
The Panacea Society
Panahpur (previously Panahpur
Charitable Trust)
Panton Trust
The Paphitis Charitable Trust
The Paragon Trust
The Park Charitable Trust
The Park House Charitable
Trust
The Frank Parkinson
Agricultural Trust
The Samuel and Freda
Parkinson Charitable Trust
The Parthenon Trust
Arthur James Paterson
Charitable Trust
The Constance Paterson
Charitable Trust
Miss M E Swinton Paterson's
Charitable Trust
The Patrick Charitable Trust
The Jack Patston Charitable
Trust
Ambika Paul Foundation
Paycare Charity Trust
(previously known as
Patients' Aid Association
Hospital and Medical
Charities Trust)
The Payne Charitable Trust
The Harry Payne Trust
The Peacock Charitable Trust
The Susanna Peake Charitable
Trust
Pears Foundation
The Pedmore Sporting Club
Trust Fund
The Dowager Countess
Eleanor Peel Trust
Pegasus (Stanley) Trust
The Pell Charitable Trust
Peltz Trust
Pendragon Charitable Trust
The Pennycress Trust
The Performing Right Society
Foundation
B E Perl Charitable Trust
The Persson Charitable Trust
(formerly Highmoore Hall
Charitable Trust)
The Persula Foundation
The Jack Petchey Foundation
The Petplan Charitable Trust
The Pharsalia Charitable Trust

The Philips and Rubens
Charitable Trust
The Phillips Charitable Trust
The Phillips Family Charitable
Trust
Philological Foundation
The David Pickford Charitable
Foundation
The Bernard Piggott Trust
The Pilgrim Trust
The Cecil Pilkington Charitable
Trust
The Elise Pilkington Charitable
Trust
The Pilkington Charities Fund
The Austin and Hope
Pilkington Trust
The Sir Harry Pilkington Trust
The Col W W Pilkington Will
Trusts The General Charity
Fund
Miss A M Pilkington's
Charitable Trust
The DLA Piper Charitable Trust
The Worshipful Company of
Plaisterers Charitable Trust
The Platinum Trust
G S Plaut Charitable Trust
Limited
Polden-Puckham Charitable
Foundation
The Polehanger Trust
The Poling Charitable Trust
The George and Esme Pollitzer
Charitable Settlement
The J S F Pollitzer Charitable
Settlement
The Polonsky Foundation
The Ponton House Trust
The Mayor of Poole's Appeal
Fund
Edith and Ferdinand Porjes
Charitable Trust
The John Porter Charitable
Trust
The Porter Foundation
Porticus UK
The Portrack Charitable Trust
The J E Posnansky Charitable
Trust
The Mary Potter Convent
Hospital Trust
The David and Elaine Potter
Foundation
The Powell Foundation
Prairie Trust
The W L Pratt Charitable Trust
Premierquote Ltd
Premishlaner Charitable Trust
The Lucy Price Relief-in-Need
Charity
Sir John Priestman Charity
Trust
The Primrose Trust
The Prince of Wales's
Charitable Foundation

The Foundation of Prince
William and Prince Harry
Princess Anne's Charities
The Priory Foundation
Prison Service Charity Fund
Private Equity Foundation
The Privy Purse Charitable
Trust
The Proven Family Trust
The Provincial Grand Charity of
the Province of Derbyshire
PSA Peugeot Citroen Charity
Trust
The Puebla Charitable Trust
The Richard and Christine
Purchas Charitable Trust
The Puri Foundation
Mr and Mrs J A Pye's
Charitable Settlement
Quartet Community Foundation
(formerly the Greater Bristol
Foundation)
The Queen Anne's Gate
Foundation
The Queen's Silver Jubilee
Trust
Quercus Trust
R J M Charitable Trust
R S Charitable Trust
The R V W Trust
The Monica Rabagliati
Charitable Trust
Rachel Charitable Trust
The Mr and Mrs Philip
Rackham Charitable Trust
Richard Radcliffe Charitable
Trust
The Radcliffe Trust
The Bishop Radford Trust
The Ragdoll Foundation
The Rainford Trust
The Peggy Ramsay Foundation
The Joseph and Lena Randall
Charitable Trust
The Rank Foundation
The Joseph Rank Trust
Ranworth Trust
The Fanny Rapaport Charitable
Settlement
The Ratcliff Foundation
The Ratcliff Pension Charity
The Ratcliffe Charitable Trust
The E L Rathbone Charitable
Trust
The Eleanor Rathbone
Charitable Trust
The Sigrid Rausing Trust
The Ravensdale Trust
The Rayden Charitable Trust
The Roger Raymond Charitable
Trust
The Rayne Foundation
The Rayne Trust
The John Rayner Charitable
Trust
The Sir James Reckitt Charity

The Eva Reckitt Trust Fund
The Red Arrows Trust
The Red Rose Charitable Trust
The C A Redfern Charitable
Foundation
The Reed Foundation
Richard Reeve's Foundation
The Max Reinhardt Charitable
Trust
Relief Fund for Romania
Limited
REMEDI
The Rest Harrow Trust
Reuben Brothers Foundation
The Joan K Reynell Charitable
Trust
The Nathaniel Reyner Trust
Fund
The Rhododendron Trust
Daisie Rich Trust
C B Richard Ellis Charitable
Trust
The Clive Richards Charity
The Richmond Parish Lands
Charity
Ridgesave Limited
The Ripple Effect Foundation
The Sir John Ritblat Family
Foundation
The River Trust
Riverside Charitable Trust
Limited
Thomas Roberts Trust
The Robertson Trust
Edwin George Robinson
Charitable Trust
Robyn Charitable Trust
The Rochester Bridge Trust
The Rock Foundation
The Rock Solid Trust
The Roddick Foundation
The Rofeh Trust
Richard Rogers Charitable
Settlement
Rokach Family Charitable Trust
The Helen Roll Charitable
Trust
The Sir James Roll Charitable
Trust
The Roman Research Trust
Romeera Foundation
The C A Rookes Charitable
Trust
The Rosca Trust
Alexandra Rose Charities
The Cecil Rosen Foundation
Rosetrees Trust
The Rothermere Foundation
The Rotherwick Foundation
The Roughley Charitable Trust
Mrs Gladys Row Fogo
Charitable Trust
Rowanville Ltd
The Christopher Rowbotham
Charitable Trust
The Rowing Foundation

The Rowlands Trust
The Joseph Rowntree
   Charitable Trust
The Joseph Rowntree
   Foundation
Joseph Rowntree Reform Trust
   Limited
Royal Artillery Charitable Fund
Royal British Legion
Royal Docks Trust (London)
Royal Masonic Trust for Girls
   and Boys
The Royal Scots Benevolent
   Society
The Alfred and Frances
   Rubens Charitable Trust
The Rubin Foundation
William Arthur Rudd Memorial
   Trust
The Rufford Foundation
The Russell Trust
Ryklow Charitable Trust 1992
   (also known as A B
   Williamson Charitable Trust)
The J S and E C Rymer
   Charitable Trust
S F Foundation
S O Charitable Trust
The Jeremy and John Sacher
   Charitable Trust
The Michael Harry Sacher
   Trust
The Sackler Trust (Formerly Dr
   Mortimer and Theresa
   Sackler Foundation)
The Ruzin Sadagora Trust
The Saddlers' Company
   Charitable Fund
The Saga Charitable Trust
The Jean Sainsbury Animal
   Welfare Trust
The Alan and Babette
   Sainsbury Charitable Fund
The Sainsbury Family
   Charitable Trusts
Saint Sarkis Charity Trust
The Saintbury Trust
The Saints and Sinners Trust
The Salamander Charitable
   Trust
The Salt Trust
Salters' Charitable Foundation
The Andrew Salvesen
   Charitable Trust
The Sammermar Trust
Basil Samuel Charitable Trust
Coral Samuel Charitable Trust
The Hon. M J Samuel
   Charitable Trust
The Peter Samuel Charitable
   Trust
The Camilla Samuel Fund
The Samworth Foundation
The Sandra Charitable Trust
Santander UK Foundation
   Limited

Jimmy Savile Charitable Trust
The Scarfe Charitable Trust
The Schapira Charitable Trust
The Annie Schiff Charitable
   Trust
The Schmidt-Bodner Charitable
   Trust
The R H Scholes Charitable
   Trust
The Schreib Trust
The Schreiber Charitable Trust
Schroder Charity Trust
Scott (Eredine) Charitable
   Trust
The Francis C Scott Charitable
   Trust
The Frieda Scott Charitable
   Trust
Sir Samuel Scott of Yews
   Trust
The Sir James and Lady Scott
   Trust
The Scott Trust Foundation
The Storrow Scott Will Trust
The Scottish Arts Council
Scottish Coal Industry Special
   Welfare Fund
The Scottish Community
   Foundation
The Scottish International
   Education Trust
The Scouloudi Foundation
Seafarers UK (King George's
   Fund for Sailors)
Seamen's Hospital Society
The Searchlight Electric
   Charitable Trust
The Searle Charitable Trust
The Helene Sebba Charitable
   Trust
The Samuel Sebba Charitable
   Trust
The Seedfield Trust
Sellata Ltd
SEM Charitable Trust
The Seneca Trust
The Ayrton Senna Foundation
The Seven Fifty Trust
The Severn Trent Water
   Charitable Trust Fund
SFIA Educational Trust Limited
The Cyril Shack Trust
The Jean Shanks Foundation
The Shanti Charitable Trust
ShareGift (The Orr Mackintosh
   Foundation)
The Linley Shaw Foundation
The Sheepdrove Trust
The Sheffield and District
   Hospital Services
   Charitable Fund
The Shekinah Legacy
The Sheldon Trust
The P and D Shepherd
   Charitable Trust

The Sylvia and Colin Shepherd
   Charitable Trust
The Archie Sherman Cardiff
   Foundation
The Archie Sherman Charitable
   Trust
The R C Sherriff Trust
The Shetland Charitable Trust
SHINE (Support and Help in
   Education)
The Barnett and Sylvia Shine
   No 2 Charitable Trust
The Bassil Shippam and
   Alsford Trust
The Shipwrights' Company
   Charitable Fund
The Shirley Foundation
Shlomo Memorial Fund Limited
The J A Shone Memorial Trust
The Barbara A Shuttleworth
   Memorial Trust
The Sickle Foundation
The Mary Elizabeth Siebel
   Charity
David and Jennifer Sieff
   Charitable Trust
The Julius Silman Charitable
   Trust
The Leslie Silver Charitable
   Trust
The Simpson Foundation
The Huntly and Margery
   Sinclair Charitable Trust
Sino-British Fellowship Trust
The Skelton Bounty
The Charles Skey Charitable
   Trust
Skipton Building Society
   Charitable Foundation
The John Slater Foundation
Rita and David Slowe
   Charitable Trust
Ruth Smart Foundation
The SMB Charitable Trust
The Mrs Smith and Mount
   Trust
The N Smith Charitable
   Settlement
The Amanda Smith Charitable
   Trust
The E H Smith Charitable Trust
The Smith Charitable Trust
The Henry Smith Charity
The Leslie Smith Foundation
The Martin Smith Foundation
Stanley Smith General
   Charitable Trust
The Stanley Smith UK
   Horticultural Trust
Philip Smith's Charitable Trust
The R C Snelling Charitable
   Trust
The Snowball Trust
The Sobell Foundation
Solev Co Ltd
Solihull Community Foundation

The Solo Charitable
Settlement
Dr Richard Solomon's
Charitable Trust
David Solomons Charitable
Trust
Songdale Ltd
The E C Sosnow Charitable
Trust
The Souter Charitable Trust
The South Square Trust
The Stephen R and Philippa H
Southall Charitable Trust
The W F Southall Trust
R H Southern Trust
The Southover Manor General
Education Trust
The Southwold Trust
The Sovereign Health Care
Charitable Trust
Spar Charitable Fund
Sparks Charity (Sport Aiding
Medical Research For Kids)
Sparquote Limited
The Spear Charitable Trust
Spears-Stutz Charitable Trust
The Jessie Spencer Trust
The Ralph and Irma Sperring
Charity
The Moss Spiro Will Charitable
Foundation
The Spoore, Merry and Rixman
Foundation
Spring Harvest
Rosalyn and Nicholas Springer
Charitable Trust
Springfields Employees'
Medical Research and
Charity Trust Fund
Springrule Ltd
The Spurrell Charitable Trust
The Geoff and Fiona Squire
Foundation
St Francis's Leprosy Guild
St Gabriel's Trust
St Hilda's Trust
St James' Trust Settlement
Sir Walter St John's
Educational Charity
St Katharine and Shadwell
Trust
St Michael's and All Saints'
Charities
The Late St Patrick White
Charitable Trust
St Teilo's Trust
The Stafford Trust
The Stanley Foundation Ltd
The Stanton Ballard Charitable
Trust
The Staples Trust
The Star Charitable Trust
The Peter Stebbings Memorial
Charity
The Steinberg Family
Charitable Trust

The Hugh Stenhouse
Foundation
C E K Stern Charitable Trust
The Sigmund Sternberg
Charitable Foundation
Stervon Ltd
The Stevenage Community
Trust
The June Stevens Foundation
Stevenson Family's Charitable
Trust
The Steventon Allotments and
Relief-in-Need Charity
The Stewards' Charitable Trust
The Stewards' Company
Limited (incorporating the J
W Laing Trust and the J W
Laing Biblical Scholarship
Trust)
The Sir Halley Stewart Trust
The Stobart Newlands
Charitable Trust
The Edward Stocks-Massey
Bequest Fund
The Stokenchurch Educational
Charity
The Stoller Charitable Trust
The M J C Stone Charitable
Trust
The Stone-Mallabar Charitable
Foundation
The Samuel Storey Family
Charitable Trust
Peter Stormonth Darling
Charitable Trust
Peter Storrs Trust
The Strangward Trust
The Strasser Foundation
Stratford upon Avon Town
Trust
Strathclyde Police Benevolent
Fund
The W O Street Charitable
Foundation
The A B Strom and R Strom
Charitable Trust
The Sudborough Foundation
Sueberry Ltd
The Suffolk Foundation
The Suffolk Historic Churches
Trust
The Alan Sugar Foundation
Sugarworld Trust
The Summerfield Charitable
Trust
The Surrey Historic Buildings
Trust Ltd
The Sussex Historic Churches
Trust
The Adrienne and Leslie
Sussman Charitable Trust
The Sutasoma Trust
Sutton Coldfield Municipal
Charities
The Sutton Trust
Swan Mountain Trust

Swansea and Brecon Diocesan
Board of Finance Limited
The John Swire (1989)
Charitable Trust
The Swire Charitable Trust
The Hugh and Ruby Sykes
Charitable Trust
The Charles and Elsie Sykes
Trust
The Sylvanus Charitable Trust
The Stella Symons Charitable
Trust
The Tabeel Trust
Tadlus Limited
The Tajtelbaum Charitable
Trust
The Talbot Trusts
Tallow Chandlers Benevolent
Fund
Talteg Ltd
The Tangent Charitable Trust
The Lady Tangye Charitable
Trust
The David Tannen Charitable
Trust
The Tanner Trust
The Lili Tapper Charitable
Foundation
The Mrs A Lacy Tate Trust
The Taurus Foundation
The Tay Charitable Trust
C B and H H Taylor 1984 Trust
Humphrey Richardson Taylor
Charitable Trust
The Connie and Albert Taylor
Charitable Trust
The Cyril Taylor Charitable
Trust
A P Taylor Trust
Rosanna Taylor's 1987 Charity
Trust
Tearfund
The Tedworth Charitable Trust
Tees Valley Community
Foundation
Tegham Limited
The Templeton Goodwill Trust
Tesco Charity Trust
Thackray Medical Research
Trust
The Thames Wharf Charity
The Thistle Trust
The Loke Wan Tho Memorial
Foundation
The David Thomas Charitable
Trust
The Arthur and Margaret
Thompson Charitable Trust
The Maurice and Vivien
Thompson Charitable Trust
The Thompson Family
Charitable Trust
The Thompson6 Charitable
Trust
The Len Thomson Charitable
Trust

The Sue Thomson Foundation

The Sir Jules Thorn Charitable Trust

The Thornton Foundation

The Thornton Trust

The Three Guineas Trust

The Three Oaks Trust

The Thriplow Charitable Trust

Mrs R P Tindall's Charitable Trust

The Tinsley Foundation

The Tisbury Telegraph Trust

TJH Foundation

The Tobacco Pipe Makers and Tobacco Trade Benevolent Fund

The Tolkien Trust

Tomchei Torah Charitable Trust

The Tompkins Foundation

The Torah Temimah Trust

Toras Chesed (London) Trust

The Tory Family Foundation

Tottenham Grammar School Foundation

The Tower Hill Trust

The Towry Law Charitable Trust (also known as the Castle Educational Trust)

The Mayor of Trafford's Charity Fund

Annie Tranmer Charitable Trust

The Constance Travis Charitable Trust

The Treeside Trust

The Tresillian Trust

The Triangle Trust (1949) Fund

The True Colours Trust

Truedene Co. Ltd

The Truemark Trust

Truemart Limited

Trumros Limited

Trust Sixty Three

The Trusthouse Charitable Foundation

The James Tudor Foundation

Tudor Rose Ltd

The Tudor Trust

The Tufton Charitable Trust

The R D Turner Charitable Trust

The Douglas Turner Trust

The Florence Turner Trust

Miss S M Tutton Charitable Trust

The TUUT Charitable Trust

Two Ridings Community Foundation

Community Foundation Serving Tyne and Wear and Northumberland

Trustees of Tzedakah

UKI Charitable Foundation

Ulster Garden Villages Ltd

Ultach Trust

Ulting Overseas Trust

The Ulverscroft Foundation

Ulverston Town Lands Charity

The Underwood Trust

The Union of Orthodox Hebrew Congregation

The United Society for the Propagation of the Gospel

UnLtd (Foundation for Social Entrepreneurs)

The David Uri Memorial Trust

Uxbridge United Welfare Trust

'v'

Vale of Glamorgan – Welsh Church Fund

The Valentine Charitable Trust

The Valiant Charitable Trust

The Albert Van Den Bergh Charitable Trust

John and Lucille van Geest Foundation

The Van Neste Foundation

Mrs Maud Van Norden's Charitable Foundation

The Vandervell Foundation

The Vardy Foundation

The Variety Club Children's Charity

The Verdon-Smith Family Charitable Settlement

Roger Vere Foundation

Victoria Homes Trust

The Nigel Vinson Charitable Trust

The William and Ellen Vinten Trust

The Vintners' Company Charitable Foundation

Vintners' Gifts Charity

Vision Charity

Vivdale Ltd

The Viznitz Foundation

The Volant Charitable Trust

Wade's Charity

The Scurrah Wainwright Charity

The Wakefield and Tetley Trust

Wakeham Trust

The Community Foundation in Wales

Wales Council for Voluntary Action

Robert and Felicity Waley-Cohen Charitable Trust

The Thomas Wall Trust

Wallace and Gromit's Children's Foundation

The F J Wallis Charitable Settlement

War on Want

Sir Siegmund Warburg's Voluntary Settlement

The Ward Blenkinsop Trust

The George Ward Charitable Trust

The Barbara Ward Children's Foundation

The John Warren Foundation

G R Waters Charitable Trust 2000

The Waterways Trust

The Wates Foundation

Blyth Watson Charitable Trust

The Howard Watson Symington Memorial Charity

John Watson's Trust

Weatherley Charitable Trust

The Weavers' Company Benevolent Fund

The David Webster Charitable Trust

The Weinberg Foundation

The Weinstein Foundation

The Weinstock Fund

The Joir and Kato Weisz Foundation

The Weldon UK Charitable Trust

The Wellcome Trust

Welsh Church Fund Dyfed area (Carmarthenshire, Ceredigion and Pembrokeshire)

The Welton Foundation

The Wessex Youth Trust

The West Derby Wastelands Charity

West London Synagogue Charitable Fund

The West Yorkshire Police Community Fund

Mrs S K West's Charitable Trust

The Westcroft Trust

The Westminster Foundation

The Garfield Weston Foundation

The Barbara Whatmore Charitable Trust

The Whitaker Charitable Trust

The Colonel W H Whitbread Charitable Trust

The Simon Whitbread Charitable Trust

The Melanie White Foundation Limited

White Stuff Foundation

The Whitecourt Charitable Trust

A H and B C Whiteley Charitable Trust

The Norman Whiteley Trust

The Whitley Animal Protection Trust

The Whittlesey Charity

The Lionel Wigram Memorial Trust

The Richard Wilcox Welfare Charity

The Felicity Wilde Charitable Trust

The Wilkinson Charitable Foundation

The Will Charitable Trust

The Kay Williams Charitable
Foundation
The Williams Charitable Trust
The Williams Family Charitable
Trust
Williams Serendipity Trust
The H D H Wills 1965
Charitable Trust
The Dame Violet Wills Will
Trust
The Wilmcote Charitrust
Sumner Wilson Charitable
Trust
David Wilson Foundation
The Wilson Foundation
J and J R Wilson Trust
The Community Foundation for
Wiltshire and Swindon
The Benjamin Winegarten
Charitable Trust
The Harold Hyam Wingate
Foundation
The Francis Winham
Foundation
Anona Winn Charitable Trust
Wirral Mayor's Charity
The Witzenfeld Foundation
The Michael and Anna Wix
Charitable Trust
The Wixamtree Trust
The Woburn 1986 Charitable
Trust
The Maurice Wohl Charitable
Foundation
The Charles Wolfson
Charitable Trust
The James Wood Bequest
Fund
The Wood Family Trust
The Woodcock Charitable Trust
Woodlands Foundation Limited
Woodlands Green Ltd
Woodlands Trust
Woodroffe Benton Foundation
The Woodward Charitable
Trust
The A and R Woolf Charitable
Trust
ME Woolfe Charitable Trust
Worcester Municipal Charities
(incorporating Worcester
Consolidated Municipal
Charity and Worcester
Municipal Exhibitions
Foundation)
The Worcestershire and
Dudley Historic Churches
Trust
The Fred and Della Worms
Charitable Trust
The Wragge and Co. Charitable
Trust
The Diana Edgson Wright
Charitable Trust
The Matthews Wrightson
Charity Trust

Miss E B Wrightson's
Charitable Settlement
The Joan Wyatt Charitable
Trust
Wychdale Ltd
Wychville Ltd
The Wyndham Charitable Trust
The Wyseliot Charitable Trust
The Xerox (UK) Trust
Yankov Charitable Trust
The Yapp Charitable Trust
The Dennis Alan Yardy
Charitable Trust
The W Wing Yip and Brothers
Foundation
The York Children's Trust
Yorkshire Agricultural Society
The South Yorkshire
Community Foundation
The Yorkshire Dales
Millennium Trust
The John Young Charitable
Settlement
The William Allen Young
Charitable Trust
The John K Young Endowment
Fund
Youth Music
Zephyr Charitable Trust
The Marjorie and Arnold Ziff
Charitable Foundation
Stephen Zimmerman
Charitable Trust
The Zochonis Charitable Trust
The Zolfo Cooper Foundation

....

■ Replacement of statutory funding

The 29th May 1961 Charitable
Trust
The Sylvia Adams Charitable
Trust
The Bingham Trust
The Harry Bottom Charitable
Trust
Community Foundation for
Bournemouth, Dorset and
Poole
John and Susan Bowers Fund
The Bryant Trust
The Cadbury Foundation
The Campden Charities
Trustee
The Chownes Foundation
The Alice Ellen Cooper Dean
Charitable Foundation
The Ellerdale Trust
The Englefield Charitable Trust
The Essex Fairway Charitable
Trust
The Essex Heritage Trust
The Girdlers' Company
Charitable Trust
The Goldsmiths' Company
Charity

The Gretna Charitable Trust
The Hamamelis Trust
Hasluck Charitable Trust
The Holbeck Charitable Trust
Sir Harold Hood's Charitable
Trust
The Susan and Stephen
James Charitable
Settlement (also known as
the Stephen James
Charitable Trust)
The Robert Kiln Charitable
Trust
The Mary Kinross Charitable
Trust
The Jack Lane Charitable Trust
The Langtree Trust
The Second Joseph Aaron
Littman Foundation
W M Mann Foundation
The Tony Metherell Charitable
Trust
The Mothercare Charitable
Foundation
The Odin Charitable Trust
The Old Broad Street Charity
Trust
Relief Fund for Romania
Limited
The Rhododendron Trust
Mrs L D Rope Third Charitable
Settlement
The Rosca Trust
The Scottish Community
Foundation
The Sylvia and Colin Shepherd
Charitable Trust
Sino-British Fellowship Trust
The St Laurence Relief In
Need Trust
The Samuel Storey Family
Charitable Trust
Swan Mountain Trust
The Tobacco Pipe Makers and
Tobacco Trade Benevolent
Fund
The Trusthouse Charitable
Foundation
White Stuff Foundation
The Dame Violet Wills Will
Trust
The John K Young Endowment
Fund

....

■ Salaries

The 29th May 1961 Charitable
Trust
The Sylvia Adams Charitable
Trust
The Alborada Trust
All Saints Educational Trust
The Ammco Trust
The Armourers' and Brasiers'
Gauntlet Trust
The Ian Askew Charitable Trust

The Associated Country
Women of the World
(ACWW)
The Aylesford Family
Charitable Trust
Barnes Workhouse Fund
BBC Children in Need
The Bedfordshire and Luton
Community Foundation
The Bellhouse Foundation
The Berkshire Community
Foundation
Thomas Betton's Charity for
Pensions and Relief-in-Need
BibleLands
The Bingham Trust
The Body Shop Foundation
The Booth Charities
The Boshier-Hinton Foundation
The Harry Bottom Charitable
Trust
Community Foundation for
Bournemouth, Dorset and
Poole
John and Susan Bowers Fund
British Record Industry Trust
The J and M Britton Charitable
Trust
The Charles Brotherton Trust
The Bryant Trust
The E F Bulmer Benevolent
Fund
The BUPA Foundation
The Cadbury Foundation
Community Foundation for
Calderdale
The Cambridgeshire
Community Foundation
The Campden Charities
Trustee
The Carew Pole Charitable
Trust
The Charter 600 Charity
The Malcolm Chick Charity
The Chippenham Borough
Lands Charity
The Church Urban Fund
The City Bridge Trust (formerly
known as Bridge House
Trust)
J A Clark Charitable Trust
The Clothworkers' Foundation
The Colt Foundation
Comic Relief
The Alice Ellen Cooper Dean
Charitable Foundation
The J Reginald Corah
Foundation Fund
Michael Cornish Charitable
Trust
County Durham Community
Foundation
The Augustine Courtauld Trust
Cripplegate Foundation
The D'Oyly Carte Charitable
Trust

The J N Derbyshire Trust
Devon Community Foundation
The Drapers' Charitable Fund
East London Community
Foundation
Eastern Counties Educational
Trust Limited
The Ellerdale Trust
Epilepsy Research UK
The Equitable Charitable Trust
The Essex Fairway Charitable
Trust
The Essex Youth Trust
The Eveson Charitable Trust
Esmée Fairbairn Foundation
The John Feeney Charitable
Trust
The Donald Forrester Trust
The Freemasons' Grand
Charity
The Galanthus Trust
The Gibbs Charitable Trust
Simon Gibson Charitable Trust
The Girdlers' Company
Charitable Trust
Gloucestershire Community
Foundation
The Goldsmiths' Company
Charity
The Gretna Charitable Trust
Dr Guthrie's Association
The Hadfield Trust
The Hadrian Trust
The Hamamelis Trust
Paul Hamlyn Foundation
Hampshire and Isle of Wight
Community Foundation
The Harborne Parish Lands
Charity
William Harding's Charity
The Peter Harrison Foundation
Hasluck Charitable Trust
The Joanna Herbert-Stepney
Charitable Settlement (also
known as The Paget
Charitable Trust)
The Anne Herd Memorial Trust
The Hertfordshire Community
Foundation
Hexham and Newcastle
Diocesan Trust (1947)
Alan Edward Higgs Charity
The Holbeck Charitable Trust
The Holywood Trust
Sir Harold Hood's Charitable
Trust
Miss Agnes H Hunter's Trust
The Innocent Foundation
International Spinal Research
Trust
The Irish Youth Foundation
(UK) Ltd (incorporating The
Lawlor Foundation)
The Ironmongers' Foundation
The J R S S T Charitable Trust
Rees Jeffreys Road Fund

The Joanies Trust
The Joicey Trust
The Judith Trust
Jusaca Charitable Trust
The Kelly Family Charitable
Trust
William Kendall's Charity (Wax
Chandlers' Company)
The Peter Kershaw Trust
Keswick Hall Trust
The Mary Kinross Charitable
Trust
The Sir James Knott Trust
The Allen Lane Foundation
The Leathersellers' Company
Charitable Fund
Lincolnshire Community
Foundation
Lloyds TSB Foundation for
England and Wales
Lloyds TSB Foundation for
Northern Ireland
London Catalyst (formerly The
Metropolitan Hospital-
Sunday Fund)
The Lotus Foundation
John Lyon's Charity
The R S Macdonald Charitable
Trust
The MacRobert Trust
Magdalen Hospital Trust
Man Group plc Charitable
Trust
W M Mann Foundation
The Jim Marshall Charitable
Trust
The Nancie Massey Charitable
Trust
The Mathew Trust
The Robert McAlpine
Foundation
Meningitis Trust
The Mercers' Charitable
Foundation
Gerald Micklem Charitable
Trust
The Clare Milne Trust
The Edgar Milward Charity
John Moores Foundation
The Moss Charitable Trust
The Mothercare Charitable
Foundation
The Mugdock Children's Trust
The Mulberry Trust
The Kitty and Daniel Nabarro
Charitable Trust
The Nationwide Foundation
Nazareth Trust Fund
The Frances and Augustus
Newman Foundation
The Northampton Municipal
Church Charities
The Northcott Devon
Foundation
The Nuffield Foundation
The Oak Trust

The Oakdale Trust
The Odin Charitable Trust
The Old Broad Street Charity Trust
The Jack Petchey Foundation
Polden-Puckham Charitable Foundation
The Mary Potter Convent Hospital Trust
The Powell Foundation
Prairie Trust
The Rainford Trust
The Ratcliff Foundation
The Rayne Foundation
The Rayne Trust
Relief Fund for Romania Limited
REMEDI
The Rhododendron Trust
Rix-Thompson-Rothenberg Foundation
The Joseph Rowntree Charitable Trust
Joseph Rowntree Reform Trust Limited
Royal British Legion
The Rufford Foundation
The Saintbury Trust
Santander UK Foundation Limited
The Francis C Scott Charitable Trust
The Frieda Scott Charitable Trust
The Sir James and Lady Scott Trust
The Scottish Community Foundation
Seafarers UK (King George's Fund for Sailors)
The Sheldon Trust
SHINE (Support and Help in Education)
The Simpson Education and Conservation Trust
Rita and David Slowe Charitable Trust
The Mrs Smith and Mount Trust
David Solomons Charitable Trust
St Christopher's College Educational Trust
St Hilda's Trust
St James's Place Foundation
Sir Walter St John's Educational Charity
The St Laurence Relief In Need Trust
St Teilo's Trust
The Steel Charitable Trust
The Sir Halley Stewart Trust
The Samuel Storey Family Charitable Trust
The Summerfield Charitable Trust

Sussex Community Foundation
The Thriplow Charitable Trust
Mrs R P Tindall's Charitable Trust
The Treeside Trust
The Trusthouse Charitable Foundation
The James Tudor Foundation
The Tudor Trust
Two Ridings Community Foundation
John and Lucille van Geest Foundation
The Vandervell Foundation
Victoria Homes Trust
Voluntary Action Fund
The Scurrah Wainwright Charity
The Thomas Wall Trust
The Wates Foundation
The Weavers' Company Benevolent Fund
The Whitaker Charitable Trust
The Simon Whitbread Charitable Trust
White Stuff Foundation
The Norman Whiteley Trust
The Whittlesey Charity
Dame Violet Wills Charitable Trust
The Wixamtree Trust
The Wood Family Trust
Woodlands Trust
The Yardley Great Trust
The South Yorkshire Community Foundation
The John K Young Endowment Fund
Zurich Community Trust (UK) Limited

....

■ Strategic funding

The 1970 Trust
The 1989 Willan Charitable Trust
The 29th May 1961 Charitable Trust
The A B Charitable Trust
The Aberbrothock Skea Trust
ABF The Soldiers' Charity (formerly the Army Benevolent Fund)
Brian Abrams Charitable Trust
Eric Abrams Charitable Trust
The Acacia Charitable Trust
Achiezer Association Ltd
Achisomoch Aid Company Limited
The ACT Foundation
Action Medical Research
The Company of Actuaries' Charitable Trust Fund
The Sylvia Adams Charitable Trust
The Adamson Trust
The Victor Adda Foundation

Adenfirst Ltd
The Adint Charitable Trust
The Adnams Charity
AF Trust Company
Age Scotland (Formerly Age Concern Scotland and Help the Aged)
Age UK (formerly Help the Aged and Age Concern)
Aid to the Church in Need (UK)
The Green and Lilian F M Ainsworth and Family Benevolent Fund
The Sylvia Aitken Charitable Trust
The Ajahma Charitable Trust
The Alabaster Trust
Alba Charitable Trust
The Alborada Trust
D G Albright Charitable Trust
The Alchemy Foundation
Aldgate and All Hallows' Barking Exhibition Foundation
The Aldgate Freedom Foundation
The Alexis Trust
All Saints Educational Trust
Allchurches Trust Ltd
The H B Allen Charitable Trust
The Alliance Family Foundation
Angus Allnatt Charitable Foundation
The Pat Allsop Charitable Trust
The Almond Trust
Almondsbury Charity
The Altajir Trust
Altamont Ltd
Alvor Charitable Trust
AM Charitable Trust
The Ammco Trust
Viscount Amory's Charitable Trust
The Ampelos Trust
The AMW Charitable Trust
The Anchor Foundation
The Andrew Anderson Trust
Andor Charitable Trust
The André Christian Trust
Anglo American Group Foundation
Anguish's Educational Foundation
The Animal Defence Trust
The Eric Anker-Petersen Charity
The Annandale Charitable Trust
The Anson Charitable Trust
The Apax Foundation
Ambrose and Ann Appelbe Trust
The Appletree Trust
The John Apthorp Charitable Trust
The Arbib Foundation

Archbishop of Wales' Fund for
   Children
The John M Archer Charitable
   Trust
The Archer Trust
The Ardwick Trust
The Argentarius Foundation
The Argus Appeal
Armenian General Benevolent
   Union London Trust
The Armenian Relief Society of
   Great Britain Trust
The Armourers' and Brasiers'
   Gauntlet Trust
The Arnold Foundation
Arsenal Charitable Trust
The Artemis Charitable Trust
The Arts and Entertainment
   Charitable Trust
Arts Council England
The Arts Council of Northern
   Ireland
The Arts Council of Wales
The Ove Arup Foundation
The AS Charitable Trust
Ashburnham Thanksgiving
   Trust
A J H Ashby Will Trust
The Ashden Trust
The Ashendene Trust
The Ashley Family Foundation
   (formerly The Laura Ashley
   Foundation)
The Ian Askew Charitable Trust
The Associated Country
   Women of the World
   (ACWW)
The Association of Colleges
   Charitable Trust
Astellas European Foundation
Asthma UK
The Astor Foundation
The Astor of Hever Trust
The Aurelius Charitable Trust
The Avenue Charitable Trust
The Avon and Somerset Police
   Community Trust
AW Charitable Trust
The BAA Communities Trust
Harry Bacon Foundation
The BACTA Charitable Trust
The Scott Bader
   Commonwealth Ltd
The Bagri Foundation
Veta Bailey Charitable Trust
The Austin Bailey Trust
The Baily Thomas Charitable
   Fund
The Baird Trust
The Baker Charitable Trust
The Roy and Pixie Baker
   Charitable Trust
The Balcombe Charitable Trust
The Albert Casanova Ballard
   Deceased Trust
The Ballinger Charitable Trust

Balmain Charitable Trust
The Balmore Trust
The Balney Charitable Trust
The Baltic Charitable Fund
The Bamford Charitable
   Foundation
The Banbury Charities
William P Bancroft (No 2)
   Charitable Trust and
   Jenepher Gillett Trust
The Band Trust
The Barbers' Company General
   Charities
The Barbour Foundation
The Barcapel Foundation
Barchester Healthcare
   Foundation
The Barclay Foundation
The Baring Foundation
Peter Barker-Mill Memorial
   Charity
Barleycorn Trust
Lord Barnby's Foundation
Barnes Workhouse Fund
The Barnsbury Charitable Trust
The Barnwood House Trust
The Misses Barrie Charitable
   Trust
Barrington Family Charitable
   Trust
Stephen J Barry Charitable
   Trust
The Bartlett Taylor Charitable
   Trust
The Paul Bassham Charitable
   Trust
The Batchworth Trust
Bay Charitable Trust
The Bay Tree Charitable Trust
D H and L H Baylin Charitable
   Trust
The Louis Baylis (Maidenhead
   Advertiser) Charitable Trust
BBC Children in Need
BC Partners Foundation
B-CH 1971 Charitable Trust
The Beacon Trust
Bear Mordechai Ltd
The Bearder Charity
The James Beattie Charitable
   Trust
The Jack and Ada Beattie
   Foundation
The Beaufort House Trust
   Limited
Beauland Ltd
The Beaverbrook Foundation
The Beccles Town Lands
   Charity
The Becker Family Charitable
   Trust
The Becketts and Sargeants
   Educational Foundation
The John Beckwith Charitable
   Trust

The Peter Beckwith Charitable
   Trust
The Bedford Charity (The
   Harpur Trust)
The Bedfordshire and Luton
   Community Foundation
The David and Ruth Behrend
   Fund
The Beit Trust
The Bellahouston Bequest
   Fund
Bellasis Trust
The Bellhouse Foundation
The Bellinger Donnay Trust
Belljoe Tzedoko Ltd
The Benfield Motors Charitable
   Trust
The Benham Charitable
   Settlement
Maurice and Jacqueline
   Bennett Charitable Trust
Michael and Leslie Bennett
   Charitable Trust
The Gerald Bentall Charitable
   Trust
Bergqvist Charitable Trust
The Ruth Berkowitz Charitable
   Trust
The Berkshire Community
   Foundation
The Bestway Foundation
Thomas Betton's Charity for
   Pensions and Relief-in-Need
BHST
The Mason Bibby 1981 Trust
BibleLands
The Bideford Bridge Trust
The Big Lottery Fund
The Billmeir Charitable Trust
The Bingham Trust
The Bintaub Charitable Trust
The Birmingham Community
   Foundation
The Birmingham District
   Nursing Charitable Trust
The Birmingham Hospital
   Saturday Fund Medical
   Charity and Welfare Trust
Birmingham International
   Airport Community Trust
The Lord Mayor of
   Birmingham's Charity
Birthday House Trust
The Michael Bishop
   Foundation
The Bishop's Development
   Fund
The Bertie Black Foundation
Blackheart Foundation (UK)
   Limited
Isabel Blackman Foundation
The BlackRock (UK) Charitable
   Trust
The Herbert and Peter
   Blagrave Charitable Trust
The Blair Foundation

The Blanchminster Trust

The Sir Victor Blank Charitable Settlement

The Neville and Elaine Blond Charitable Trust

The Blueberry Charitable Trust

The Bluston Charitable Settlement

The Nicholas Boas Charitable Trust

The Body Shop Foundation

The Boltons Trust

The Bonamy Charitable Trust

The John and Celia Bonham Christie Charitable Trust

The Charlotte Bonham-Carter Charitable Trust

Bonhomie United Charity Society

BOOST Charitable Trust

The Booth Charities

The Boots Charitable Trust

The Bordon and Liphook Charity

Salo Bordon Charitable Trust

The Oliver Borthwick Memorial Trust

The Boshier-Hinton Foundation

The Bothwell Charitable Trust

H E and E L Botteley Charitable Trust

The Harry Bottom Charitable Trust

P G and N J Boulton Trust

The A H and E Boulton Trust

Sir Clive Bourne Family Trust

The Anthony Bourne Foundation

Bourneheights Limited

Community Foundation for Bournemouth, Dorset and Poole

The Bower Trust

The Bowerman Charitable Trust

John and Susan Bowers Fund

The Bowland Charitable Trust

The William Brake Charitable Trust

The Tony Bramall Charitable Trust

The Bransford Trust

The Breadsticks Foundation

Bridgepoint Inspire

The Harold and Alice Bridges Charity

Briggs Animal Welfare Trust

The Brighton District Nursing Association Trust

Bristol Archdeaconry Charity

The Bristol Charities

John Bristow and Thomas Mason Trust

Britannia Foundation

The British Council for Prevention of Blindness

The British Dietetic Association General and Education Trust Fund

The British Gas (Scottish Gas) Energy Trust

British Heart Foundation

British Humane Association

British Institute at Ankara

British Ornithologists' Union

British Record Industry Trust

The Britto Foundation

The J and M Britton Charitable Trust

The Charles and Edna Broadhurst Charitable Trust

The Bromley Trust

The Roger Brooke Charitable Trust

The David Brooke Charity

The Rory and Elizabeth Brooks Foundation

Joseph Brough Charitable Trust

The Swinfen Broun Charitable Trust

Mrs E E Brown Charitable Settlement

Bill Brown's Charitable Settlement

R S Brownless Charitable Trust

Brown-Mellows Trust

Brownsword Charitable Foundation

T B H Brunner's Charitable Settlement

The Bruntwood Charity

Brushmill Ltd

The Bryant Trust

Buckingham Trust

The Buckinghamshire Foundation

The Buckinghamshire Masonic Centenary Fund

The Rosemary Bugden Charitable Trust

The Bulldog Trust Limited

The E F Bulmer Benevolent Fund

The Burden Trust

Burdens Charitable Foundation

The Burdett Trust for Nursing

The Clara E Burgess Charity

The Burry Charitable Trust

The Audrey and Stanley Burton 1960 Charitable Trust

The Arnold Burton 1998 Charitable Trust

The Burton Breweries Charitable Trust

The Geoffrey Burton Charitable Trust

Consolidated Charity of Burton upon Trent

Butchers' Company General Charities

The Derek Butler Trust

The Noel Buxton Trust

Ann Byrne Charitable Trust

C and F Charitable Trust

The C Charitable Trust

C J Cadbury Charitable Trust

Edward Cadbury Charitable Trust

Henry T and Lucy B Cadbury Charitable Trust

P H G Cadbury Charitable Trust

The Christopher Cadbury Charitable Trust

The G W Cadbury Charitable Trust

The Richard Cadbury Charitable Trust

The William A Cadbury Charitable Trust

The Cadbury Foundation

The Edward and Dorothy Cadbury Trust

The George Cadbury Trust

The Barrow Cadbury Trust and the Barrow Cadbury Fund

The Cadogan Charity

CAFOD (Catholic Agency for Overseas Development)

The Callander Charitable Trust

Calleva Foundation

Calouste Gulbenkian Foundation

The Calpe Trust

Calypso Browning Trust

The Cambridgeshire Community Foundation

The Camelia Trust

The Campden Charities Trustee

The Canning Trust

M R Cannon 1998 Charitable Trust

H and L Cantor Trust

Cardy Beaver Foundation

The Carew Pole Charitable Trust

The D W T Cargill Fund

Carlee Ltd

The Carlton House Charitable Trust

The Worshipful Company of Carmen Benevolent Trust

The Carnegie Dunfermline Trust

The Carnegie Trust for the Universities of Scotland

The Carpenter Charitable Trust

The Carpenters' Company Charitable Trust

The Carrington Charitable Trust

The Carron Charitable Settlement

The Leslie Mary Carter Charitable Trust

The Carvill Trust

The Casey Trust

Cash for Kids Radio Clyde

Sir John Cass's Foundation

The Elizabeth Casson Trust

The Castanea Trust

The Castang Foundation

The Catalyst Charitable Trust (formerly the Buckle Family Charitable Trust)

The Catholic Charitable Trust

Catholic Foreign Missions

The Catholic Trust for England and Wales

The Cattanach Charitable Trust

The Joseph and Annie Cattle Trust

The Thomas Sivewright Catto Charitable Settlement

The Wilfrid and Constance Cave Foundation

The Cayo Foundation

Elizabeth Cayzer Charitable Trust

The B G S Cayzer Charitable Trust

The Cazenove Charitable Trust

The CBD Charitable Trust

Celtic Charity Fund

The Cemlyn-Jones Trust

CfBT Education Trust

The CH (1980) Charitable Trust

R E Chadwick Charitable Trust

The Amelia Chadwick Trust

The Pamela Champion Foundation

The Chapman Charitable Trust

John William Chapman's Charitable Trust

The Charities Advisory Trust

Charitworth Limited

The Charter 600 Charity

The Worshipful Company of Chartered Accountants General Charitable Trust (also known as CALC)

The Chasah Trust

Chasdei Tovim Me'oros

The Checkatrade Foundation

The Chelsea Building Society Charitable Foundation

The Chelsea Square 1994 Trust

The Cheruby Trust

The Cheshire Provincial Fund of Benevolence

The Chetwode Foundation

Chevioty Asset Management Charitable Trust

The Malcolm Chick Charity

Childs Charitable Trust

The Childwick Trust

The Chipping Sodbury Town Lands Charity

CHK Charities Limited

The Chownes Foundation

The Chrimes Family Charitable Trust

The Christabella Charitable Trust

Christadelphian Samaritan Fund

Christian Aid

Christian Response to Eastern Europe

Chrysalis Trust

The Church and Community Fund

The Church Burgesses Educational Foundation

Church Burgesses Trust

The Church Urban Fund

City and County of Swansea Welsh Church Act Fund

The City Bridge Trust (formerly known as Bridge House Trust)

The City Educational Trust Fund

CLA Charitable Trust

Stephen Clark 1957 Charitable Trust

J A Clark Charitable Trust

The Hilda and Alice Clark Charitable Trust

The Roger and Sarah Bancroft Clark Charitable Trust

The Clarke Charitable Settlement

The Cleary Foundation

The Cleevely Family Charitable Trust

The Cleopatra Trust

Lord Clinton's Charitable Trust

The Clore Duffield Foundation

Miss V L Clore's 1967 Charitable Trust

Closehelm Ltd

The Clothworkers' Foundation

Richard Cloudesley's Charity

The Clover Trust

The Robert Clutterbuck Charitable Trust

Clydpride Ltd

The Coalfields Regeneration Trust

The John Coates Charitable Trust

Coats Foundation Trust

The Cobalt Trust

The Cobtree Charity Trust Ltd

The Denise Cohen Charitable Trust

The Vivienne and Samuel Cohen Charitable Trust

The John S Cohen Foundation

The R and S Cohen Foundation

The Colchester Catalyst Charity

John Coldman Charitable Trust

The Cole Charitable Trust

The Colefax Charitable Trust

The John and Freda Coleman Charitable Trust

The Bernard Coleman Charitable Trust

The George Henry Collins Charity

The E Alec Colman Charitable Fund Ltd

The Sir Jeremiah Colman Gift Trust

Col-Reno Ltd

The Colt Foundation

The Coltstaple Trust

Colwinston Charitable Trust

Colyer-Fergusson Charitable Trust

Comic Relief

The Comino Foundation

Community Foundation for Calderdale

The Community Foundation for Northern Ireland

The Compton Charitable Trust

The Congleton Inclosure Trust

The Conscience Trust

The Conservation Foundation

The Consolidated Charities for the Infirm Merchant Taylors' Company

The Cook and Wolstenholme Charitable Trust

Gordon Cook Foundation

The Ernest Cook Trust

The Cooks Charity

The Catherine Cookson Charitable Trust

The Cookson Charitable Trust

Harold and Daphne Cooper Charitable Trust

Mabel Cooper Charity

The Alice Ellen Cooper Dean Charitable Foundation

The Co-operative Foundation

The Marjorie Coote Animal Charity Trust

The Marjorie Coote Old People's Charity

The Helen Jean Cope Trust

The J Reginald Corah Foundation Fund

The Gershon Coren Charitable Foundation

The Corinthian Trust

Edwin Cornforth 1983 Charity Trust

The Evan Cornish Foundation

The Cornwell Charitable Trust

The Sidney and Elizabeth Corob Charitable Trust

The Corona Charitable Trust

The Costa Family Charitable Trust (formerly the Morgan Williams Charitable Trust)

The Cotton Industry War
  Memorial Trust
The Cotton Trust
County Durham Community
  Foundation
The Augustine Courtauld Trust
Coutts Charitable Trust
The General Charities of the
  City of Coventry
Coventry Building Society
  Charitable Foundation
The John Cowan Foundation
The Michael Cowan
  Foundation
Cowley Charitable Foundation
The Sir William Coxen Trust
  Fund
The Lord Cozens-Hardy Trust
The Craignish Trust
The Craps Charitable Trust
Michael Crawford Children's
  Charity
The Cray Trust
Creative Scotland
The Crescent Trust
Criffel Charitable Trust
Cripplegate Foundation
The Violet and Milo Cripps
  Charitable Trust
The Harry Crook Foundation
The Cross Trust
The Croydon Relief in Need
  Charities
The Mayor of Croydon's
  Charity Fund
Cruden Foundation Ltd
The Ronald Cruickshank's
  Foundation
The R D Crusaders Foundation
The Cuby Charitable Trust
The Culra Charitable Trust
The Cumber Family Charitable
  Trust
Cumberland Building Society
  Charitable Foundation
Cumbria Community
  Foundation
The D J H Currie Memorial
  Trust
The Dennis Curry Charitable
  Trust
The Raymond Curtis Charitable
  Trust
The Manny Cussins
  Foundation
The Cutler Trust (the
  Worshipful Company of
  Makers of Playing Cards)
The Cwmbran Trust
Itzchok Meyer Cymerman Trust
  Ltd
The D G Charitable Settlement
The D'Oyly Carte Charitable
  Trust
Roald Dahl's Marvellous
  Children's Charity

The Daily Prayer Union
  Charitable Trust Ltd
The Daisy Trust
The Daiwa Anglo-Japanese
  Foundation
Oizer Dalim Trust
The Dr and Mrs A Darlington
  Charitable Trust
Baron Davenport's Charity
The Davidson (Nairn)
  Charitable Trust
The Davidson Family
  Charitable Trust
The Alderman Joe Davidson
  Memorial Trust
Michael Davies Charitable
  Settlement
The Gwendoline and Margaret
  Davies Charity
The Wilfrid Bruce Davis
  Charitable Trust
Davis-Rubens Charitable Trust
The Dawe Charitable Trust
The De Clermont Charitable
  Company Ltd
Peter De Haan Charitable
  Trust
The De Laszlo Foundation
The Leopold De Rothschild
  Charitable Trust
The Deakin Charitable Trust
William Dean Countryside and
  Educational Trust
The Debmar Benevolent Trust
The Dellal Foundation
The Delves Charitable Trust
The Demigryphon Trust
The Denman Charitable Trust
The Denton Charitable Trust
The Denton Wilde Sapte
  Charitable Trust
The Earl of Derby's Charitable
  Trust
Derbyshire Community
  Foundation
The J N Derbyshire Trust
Devon Community Foundation
The Devon Educational Trust
The Duke of Devonshire's
  Charitable Trust
The Sandy Dewhirst Charitable
  Trust
The Laduma Dhamecha
  Charitable Trust
Alan and Sheila Diamond
  Charitable Trust
The Dibden Allotments Fund
The Dickon Trust
The Digbeth Trust
The Dinwoodie Settlement
Dischma Charitable Trust
The DM Charitable Trust
Louise Dobson Charitable
  Trust
The Derek and Eileen Dodgson
  Foundation

The Dollond Charitable Trust
Domepride Ltd
The Dorcas Trust
Double 'O' Charity Ltd
The Doughty Charity Trust
The R M Douglas Charitable
  Trust
The Drapers' Charitable Fund
Dromintee Trust
The Dugdale Charitable Trust
The Duis Charitable Trust
The Dulverton Trust
The P B Dumbell Charitable
  Trust
The Dumbreck Charity
Dunard Fund
Ronald Duncan Literary
  Foundation
The Dunhill Medical Trust
The Houghton Dunn Charitable
  Trust
The Dunn Family Charitable
  Trust
The W E Dunn Trust
The Charles Dunstone
  Charitable Trust
Dushinsky Trust Ltd
Mildred Duveen Charitable
  Trust
Annette Duvollet Charitable
  Trust
The Dwek Family Charitable
  Trust
The Dyers' Company
  Charitable Trust
The James Dyson Foundation
The Eagle Charity Trust
Audrey Earle Charitable Trust
The Earley Charity
Earls Colne and Halstead
  Educational Charity
The Earmark Trust
East Kent Provincial Charities
East London Community
  Foundation
Eastern Counties Educational
  Trust Limited
The Sir John Eastwood
  Foundation
The Ebenezer Trust
The EBM Charitable Trust
Eden Arts Trust
EDF Energy Trust (EDFET)
The Gilbert and Eileen Edgar
  Foundation
Gilbert Edgar Trust
Edinburgh Children's Holiday
  Fund
The Edinburgh Trust, No 2
  Account
Edinburgh Voluntary
  Organisations' Trust Funds
Educational Foundation of
  Alderman John Norman
The W G Edwards Charitable
  Foundation

The William Edwards
    Educational Charity
The Elephant Trust
The George Elias Charitable
    Trust
The Gerald Palmer Eling Trust
    Company
The Wilfred and Elsie Elkes
    Charity Fund
The Maud Elkington Charitable
    Trust
Ellador Ltd
The Ellerdale Trust
The John Ellerman Foundation
The Ellinson Foundation Ltd
The Edith Maud Ellis 1985
    Charitable Trust
The Ellis Campbell Foundation
James Ellis Charitable Trust
The Elmgrant Trust
The Elmley Foundation
Elshore Ltd
The Vernon N Ely Charitable
    Trust
The Embleton Trust
The Emerton-Christie Charity
The Emilienne Charitable Trust
The Emmandjay Charitable
    Trust
Empath UK
The Worshipful Company of
    Engineers Charitable Trust
    Fund
The Englefield Charitable Trust
The English Schools' Football
    Association
The Enkalon Foundation
Entindale Ltd
The Epigoni Trust
Epilepsy Research UK
The Equitable Charitable Trust
The Equity Trust Fund
The Ericson Trust
The Erskine Cunningham Hill
    Trust
Essex Community Foundation
The Essex Fairway Charitable
    Trust
The Essex Heritage Trust
Essex Provincial Charity Fund
The Essex Youth Trust
Joseph Ettedgui Charitable
    Foundation
Euro Charity Trust
The Alan Evans Memorial Trust
Sir John Evelyn's Charity
The Eventhall Family
    Charitable Trust
The Everard Foundation
The Eveson Charitable Trust
The Beryl Evetts and Robert
    Luff Animal Welfare Trust
The Execution Charitable Trust
The Mayor of Exeter's Appeal
    Fund
The Exilarch's Foundation

The Matthew Eyton Animal
    Welfare Trust
F C Charitable Trust
The F P Limited Charitable
    Trust
The Faber Charitable Trust
Esmée Fairbairn Foundation
The Fairstead Trust
The Fairway Trust
Faisaltex Charitable Trust
The Family Rich Charities Trust
Famos Foundation Trust
The Lord Faringdon Charitable
    Trust
Samuel William Farmer Trust
The Farmers' Company
    Charitable Fund
The Thomas Farr Charitable
    Trust
Walter Farthing (Trust) Limited
Farthing Trust
The Fassnidge Memorial Trust
Joseph Fattorini Charitable
    Trust 'B' Account
The Fawcett Charitable Trust
The February Foundation
Federation of Jewish Relief
    Organisations
The John Feeney Charitable
    Trust
The George Fentham
    Birmingham Charity
The A M Fenton Trust
Allan and Nesta Ferguson
    Charitable Settlement
Elizabeth Ferguson Charitable
    Trust Fund
The Fidelity UK Foundation
The Bluff Field Charitable Trust
The Doris Field Charitable
    Trust
Fife Council/Common Good
    Funds and Trusts
Dixie Rose Findlay Charitable
    Trust
Finnart House School Trust
Firtree Trust
The Sir John Fisher Foundation
The Fishmongers' Company's
    Charitable Trust
The Fitton Trust
The Earl Fitzwilliam Charitable
    Trust
Bud Flanagan Leukaemia Fund
The Rose Flatau Charitable
    Trust
The Ian Fleming Charitable
    Trust
The Joyce Fletcher Charitable
    Trust
The Roy Fletcher Charitable
    Trust
Florence's Charitable Trust
The Flow Foundation
The Gerald Fogel Charitable
    Trust

The Follett Trust
The Football Association
    National Sports Centre
    Trust
The Football Foundation
The Forbes Charitable
    Foundation
The Forces Trust (Working
    Name)
Ford Britain Trust
The Oliver Ford Charitable
    Trust
Fordeve Ltd
The Forest Hill Charitable Trust
The Foresters' Charity
    Stewards UK Trust
Forever Manchester (The
    Community Foundation for
    Greater Manchester)
Gwyneth Forrester Trust
The Donald Forrester Trust
The Anna Rosa Forster
    Charitable Trust
The Fort Foundation
The Forte Charitable Trust
Lord Forte Foundation
Foundation for Management
    Education
The Four Winds Trust
The Foyle Foundation
The Isaac and Freda Frankel
    Memorial Charitable Trust
The Elizabeth Frankland Moore
    and Star Foundation
Sydney E Franklin Deceased's
    New Second Charity
The Jill Franklin Trust
The Gordon Fraser Charitable
    Trust
The Hugh Fraser Foundation
The Joseph Strong Frazer Trust
The Louis and Valerie
    Freedman Charitable
    Settlement
The Freemasons' Grand
    Charity
The Thomas Freke and Lady
    Norton Charity
The Charles S French
    Charitable Trust
The Anne French Memorial
    Trust
The Freshfield Foundation
The Freshgate Trust
    Foundation
The Friarsgate Trust
The Friends Hall Farm Street
    Trust
Friends of Biala Ltd
Friends of Wiznitz Limited
Friends Provident Charitable
    Foundation
The Frognal Trust
T F C Frost Charitable Trust
The Patrick Frost Foundation
Maurice Fry Charitable Trust

Mejer and Gertrude Miriam
  Frydman Foundation
The Fuellers Charitable Trust
  Fund
The Fulmer Charitable Trust
Worshipful Company of
  Furniture Makers Charitable
  Fund
Gableholt Limited
The Galbraith Trust
The Gale Family Charitable
  Trust
The Angela Gallagher Memorial
  Fund
The Gamlen Charitable Trust
The Gamma Trust
The Gannochy Trust
The Ganzoni Charitable Trust
The Worshipful Company of
  Gardeners of London
The Samuel Gardner Memorial
  Trust
The Garnett Charitable Trust
Garrick Charitable Trust
Garvan Limited
The Gatsby Charitable
  Foundation
Gatwick Airport Community
  Trust
The Robert Gavron Charitable
  Trust
The General Nursing Council
  for England and Wales
  Trust
Generations Charitable Trust
J Paul Getty Jr Charitable Trust
The Gibbs Charitable Trust
Simon Gibson Charitable Trust
The G C Gibson Charitable
  Trust
Lady Gibson's Charitable Trust
The Harvey and Hilary Gilbert
  Charitable Trust
The Girdlers' Company
  Charitable Trust
The B and P Glasser
  Charitable Trust
The Glass-House Trust
The Glastonbury Trust Limited
Global Care
Global Charities (formerly
  GCap Charities)
Gloucestershire Community
  Foundation
Worshipful Company of
  Glovers of London Charity
  Fund
GMC Trust
The GMW Charitable Trust
The GNC Trust
The Meir Golda Trust
The Sydney and Phyllis
  Goldberg Memorial
  Charitable Trust
The Golden Bottle Trust
Golden Charitable Trust

The Jack Goldhill Charitable
  Trust
The Goldsmiths' Arts Trust
  Fund
The Goldsmiths' Company
  Charity
The Golsoncott Foundation
Golubovich Foundation
The Good Neighbours Trust
Nicholas and Judith
  Goodison's Charitable
  Settlement
The Everard and Mina
  Goodman Charitable
  Foundation
Mike Gooley Trailfinders
  Charity
Leonard Gordon Charitable
  Trust
The Gosling Foundation
  Limited
The Gough Charitable Trust
The Gould Charitable Trust
The Grace Charitable Trust
A B Grace Trust
The Graff Foundation
The Grahame Charitable
  Foundation Limited
Grampian Police Diced Cap
  Charitable Fund
The Granada Foundation
Grand Charitable Trust of the
  Order of Women
  Freemasons
The Grand Order of Water
  Rats' Charities Fund
The Grange Farm Centre Trust
Grantham Yorke Trust
The Gray Trust
The Great Britain Sasakawa
  Foundation
The Great Stone Bridge Trust
  of Edenbridge
The Great Torrington Town
  Lands Charity
The Constance Green
  Foundation
The Philip Green Memorial
  Trust
The Green Room Charitable
  Trust
Mrs H R Greene Charitable
  Settlement
Greenham Common
  Community Trust Limited
Naomi and Jeffrey Greenwood
  Charitable Trust
Greggs Foundation (formerly
  Greggs Trust)
The Gretna Charitable Trust
The Greys Charitable Trust
Grimmitt Trust
The Grocers' Charity
The M and R Gross Charities
  Limited
The Grove Charitable Trust

The GRP Charitable Trust
The David and Marie Grumitt
  Foundation
The Bishop of Guildford's
  Foundation
The Guildry Incorporation of
  Perth
The Walter Guinness
  Charitable Trust
The Gunter Charitable Trust
The Gur Trust
Dr Guthrie's Association
The H and M Charitable Trust
H C D Memorial Fund
The H P Charitable Trust
The Hackney Parochial
  Charities
The Hadfield Trust
The Hadley Trust
The Hadrian Trust
The Alfred Haines Charitable
  Trust
The Hale Trust
E F and M G Hall Charitable
  Trust
The Edith Winifred Hall
  Charitable Trust
Robert Hall Charity
The Hamamelis Trust
Hamilton Wallace Trust
Paul Hamlyn Foundation
Sue Hammerson's Charitable
  Trust
The Hammonds Charitable
  Trust
The Hampshire and Islands
  Historic Churches Trust
The Hampstead Wells and
  Campden Trust
Hampton Fuel Allotment
  Charity
The W A Handley Charitable
  Trust
Beatrice Hankey Foundation
  Ltd
The Hanley Trust
The Kathleen Hannay
  Memorial Charity
The Doughty Hanson
  Charitable Foundation
Lord Hanson Foundation
The Haramead Trust
Miss K M Harbinson's
  Charitable Trust
Harbo Charities Limited
The Harborne Parish Lands
  Charity
The Harbour Charitable Trust
The Harbour Foundation
The Harding Trust
William Harding's Charity
The Hare of Steep Charitable
  Trust
The Harebell Centenary Fund
The Kenneth Hargreaves
  Charitable Trust

The Harris Charitable Trust
The Harris Charity
The Harris Family Charitable
Trust
The Harrison and Potter Trust
The John Harrison Charitable
Trust
The Spencer Hart Charitable
Trust
The Hartley Charitable Trust
The N and P Hartley Memorial
Trust
The Alfred And Peggy Harvey
Charitable Trust
William Geoffrey Harvey's
Discretionary Settlement
Haskel Family Foundation
The Hathaway Trust
The Maurice Hatter Foundation
The M A Hawe Settlement
The Hawerby Trust
The Hawthorne Charitable
Trust
The Dorothy Hay-Bolton
Charitable Trust
The Haymills Charitable Trust
The Headley Trust
Headley-Pitt Charitable Trust
Heagerty Charitable Trust
May Hearnshaw's Charity
The Heart of England
Community Foundation
The Heathcoat Trust
Heathside Charitable Trust
The Charlotte Heber-Percy
Charitable Trust
The Hedera Charitable Trust
Percy Hedley 1990 Charitable
Trust
The Hedley Denton Charitable
Trust
The Hedley Foundation
The H J Heinz Company
Limited Charitable Trust
The Hellenic Foundation
The Michael and Morven Heller
Charitable Foundation
The Simon Heller Charitable
Settlement
The Hemby Trust
The Christina Mary Hendrie
Trust for Scottish and
Canadian Charities
The Henley Educational Charity
Philip Henman Trust
Esther Hennell Charitable
Trust
The G D Herbert Charitable
Trust
The Joanna Herbert-Stepney
Charitable Settlement (also
known as The Paget
Charitable Trust)
The Anne Herd Memorial Trust
The Herefordshire Historic
Churches Trust

The Heritage of London Trust
Ltd
The Hertfordshire Community
Foundation
The Hesed Trust
The Hesslewood Children's
Trust (Hull Seamen's and
General Orphanage)
The Bernhard Heuberger
Charitable Trust
Hexham and Newcastle
Diocesan Trust (1947)
The Higgs Charitable Trust
Alan Edward Higgs Charity
The High Sheriff's Police Trust
for the County of West
Midlands (Building Blocks)
Highcroft Charitable Trust
The Hilden Charitable Fund
The Derek Hill Foundation
The Charles Littlewood Hill
Trust
The Hillingdon Partnership
Trust
R G Hills Charitable Trust
Hinchley Charitable Trust
Lady Hind Trust
Hinduja Foundation
Stuart Hine Trust
The Hinrichsen Foundation
The Hitchin Educational
Foundation
The Eleemosynary Charity of
William Hobbayne
Hobson Charity Limited
Hockerill Educational
Foundation
Matthew Hodder Charitable
Trust
The Sir Julian Hodge
Charitable Trust
The Jane Hodge Foundation
The J G Hogg Charitable Trust
The Holbeck Charitable Trust
The Holden Charitable Trust
John Holford's Charity
The Hollick Family Charitable
Trust
The Holliday Foundation
The Dorothy Holmes Charitable
Trust
The Holmes Family Trust
(Sheffield)
The Holst Foundation
P H Holt Foundation
The Edward Holt Trust
The Holywood Trust
The Homelands Charitable
Trust
The Homestead Charitable
Trust
Mary Homfray Charitable Trust
Sir Harold Hood's Charitable
Trust
Hope for Youth (formerly
Women Caring Trust)

The Hope Trust
HopMarket Charity
The Cuthbert Horn Trust
The Antony Hornby Charitable
Trust
The Horne Foundation
The Horne Trust
The Worshipful Company of
Horners' Charitable Trusts
The Hornsey Parochial
Charities
The Hospital of God at
Greatham
The Hospital Saturday Fund
The Sir Joseph Hotung
Charitable Settlement
Houblon-Norman/George Fund
The House of Industry Estate
The Reta Lila Howard
Foundation
The Daniel Howard Trust
HTA Sheba Foundation UK
The Hudson Foundation
The Huggard Charitable Trust
The Geoffrey C Hughes
Charitable Trust
The Hull and East Riding
Charitable Trust
Hulme Trust Estates
(Educational)
Human Relief Foundation
The Humanitarian Trust
The Michael and Shirley Hunt
Charitable Trust
The Albert Hunt Trust
The Hunter Foundation
Miss Agnes H Hunter's Trust
The Huntingdon Foundation
Huntingdon Freemen's Charity
John Huntingdon's Charity
Hurdale Charity Limited
The Hutton Foundation
The Nani Huyu Charitable Trust
The P Y N and B Hyams Trust
The Hyde Charitable Trust –
Youth Plus
The Idlewild Trust
The Iliffe Family Charitable
Trust
Impetus Trust
The Indigo Trust
Infinity Capital Trust
The Ingram Trust
The Inland Waterways
Association
The Inlight Trust
The Inman Charity
The Inner London Magistrates
Court Poor Box and Feeder
Charity
The Innocent Foundation
The Ireland Fund of Great
Britain
The Irish Youth Foundation
(UK) Ltd (incorporating The
Lawlor Foundation)

The Ironmongers' Foundation
Irshad Trust
The Charles Irving Charitable
Trust
Irwin Trust
The ISA Charity
The Isaacs Charitable Trust
The J Isaacs Charitable Trust
The Isle of Anglesey Charitable
Trust
Isle of Dogs Community
Foundation
The ITF Seafarers Trust
J A R Charitable Trust
The J J Charitable Trust
The J R S S T Charitable Trust
The Jabbs Foundation
Elizabeth Jackson Charitable
Trust
Jacobs Charitable Trust
The Ruth and Lionel Jacobson
Trust (Second Fund) No 2
Jaffe Family Relief Fund
John James Bristol Foundation
The Susan and Stephen
James Charitable
Settlement (also known as
the Stephen James
Charitable Trust)
The James Trust
The Jarman Charitable Trust
The Barbara Joyce Jarrald
Charitable Trust
Jay Education Trust
JCA Charitable Foundation
The Jeffrey Charitable Trust
Rees Jeffreys Road Fund
The Jenour Foundation
The Jerusalem Trust
Jesus Hospital Charity
Jewish Child's Day
The Jewish Youth Fund
The JMK Charitable Trust
The Joanies Trust
The Harold Joels Charitable
Trust
The Jonathan Joels Charitable
Trust
The Nicholas Joels Charitable
Trust
The Norman Joels Charitable
Trust
The Joffe Charitable Trust
The Elton John Aids
Foundation
The Michael John Trust
The Lillie Johnson Charitable
Trust
The Johnson Foundation
The Johnson Group Cleaners
Charity
The Johnnie Johnson Trust
The Johnson Wax Ltd
Charitable Trust
The Joicey Trust

The Jones 1986 Charitable
Trust
The Marjorie and Geoffrey
Jones Charitable Trust
The Muriel Jones Foundation
The Jordan Charitable
Foundation
The J E Joseph Charitable
Fund
The Lady Eileen Joseph
Foundation
JTH Charitable Trust
The Cyril and Eve Jumbo
Charitable Trust
The Anton Jurgens Charitable
Trust
Jusaca Charitable Trust
The Bernard Kahn Charitable
Trust
The Stanley Kalms Foundation
The Kalou Foundation
The Karenza Foundation
The Boris Karloff Charitable
Foundation
The Ian Karten Charitable
Trust
The Kasner Charitable Trust
The Kass Charitable Trust
The Kathleen Trust
The Michael and Ilse Katz
Foundation
The Katzauer Charitable
Settlement
The C S Kaufman Charitable
Trust
The Geoffrey John Kaye
Charitable Foundation
The Emmanuel Kaye
Foundation
The Kelly Family Charitable
Trust
Kelsick's Educational
Foundation
The KempWelch Charitable
Trust
The Kay Kendall Leukaemia
Fund
The Kennedy Charitable
Foundation
The Kennel Club Charitable
Trust
Kent Community Foundation
The Nancy Kenyon Charitable
Trust
Keren Association
Kermaville Ltd
E and E Kernkraut Charities
Limited
The Peter Kershaw Trust
The Kessler Foundation
Keswick Hall Trust
The Ursula Keyes Trust
The Kiawah Charitable Trust
The King/Cullimore Charitable
Trust
The King's Fund

The Kingsbury Charity
The Mary Kinross Charitable
Trust
Kinsurdy Charitable Trust
Kirkley Poor's Lands Estate
The Richard Kirkman
Charitable Trust
Kirschel Foundation
Robert Kitchin (Saddlers'
Company)
Ernest Kleinwort Charitable
Trust
The Marina Kleinwort
Charitable Trust
The Sir James Knott Trust
The Kobler Trust
The Kohn Foundation
Kollel and Co. Limited
The Kreditor Charitable Trust
The Kreitman Foundation
The Neil Kreitman Foundation
The Heinz, Anna and Carol
Kroch Foundation
Kupath Gemach Chaim
Bechesed Viznitz Trust
The Kyte Charitable Trust
The Late Sir Pierce Lacy
Charity Trust
The K P Ladd Charitable Trust
John Laing Charitable Trust
Maurice and Hilda Laing
Charitable Trust
The Christopher Laing
Foundation
The Kirby Laing Foundation
The Martin Laing Foundation
The Beatrice Laing Trust
The Lambert Charitable Trust
Community Foundation for
Lancashire
Duchy of Lancaster Benevolent
Fund
The Lancaster Foundation
The Allen Lane Foundation
The Langdale Trust
The Langley Charitable Trust
The Langtree Trust
The LankellyChase Foundation
The Lanvern Foundation
The R J Larg Family Charitable
Trust
Largsmount Ltd
The Lark Trust
Laslett's (Hinton) Charity
Lauchentilly Charitable
Foundation 1988
Laufer Charitable Trust
The Lauffer Family Charitable
Foundation
Mrs F B Laurence Charitable
Trust
The Kathleen Laurence Trust
The Law Society Charity
The Edgar E Lawley Foundation
The Herd Lawson and Muriel
Lawson Charitable Trust

The Lawson Beckman
 Charitable Trust
The Raymond and Blanche
 Lawson Charitable Trust
The Carole and Geoffrey
 Lawson Foundation
The Mason Le Page Charitable
 Trust
The Leach Fourteenth Trust
The David Lean Foundation
The Leathersellers' Company
 Charitable Fund
The Arnold Lee Charitable
 Trust
The Lord Mayor of Leeds
 Appeal Fund
Leeds Building Society
 Charitable Foundation
The Leeds Community
 Foundation
Leicester Charity Link (formerly
 The Leicester Charity
 Organisation Society)
The Kennedy Leigh Charitable
 Trust
Morris Leigh Foundation
The Leigh Trust
Mrs Vera Leigh's Charity
The P Leigh-Bramwell Trust 'E'
The Lennox and Wyfold
 Foundation
The Erica Leonard Trust
The Leonard Trust
The Mark Leonard Trust
Lesley Lesley and Mutter Trust
Leukaemia and Lymphoma
 Research
The Leverhulme Trade
 Charities Trust
The Joseph Levy Charitable
 Foundation
Lewis Family Charitable Trust
The John Spedan Lewis
 Foundation
The Sir Edward Lewis
 Foundation
John Lewis Partnership
 General Community Fund
Lichfield Conduit Lands
Lifeline 4 Kids
The Lightbridge Foundation
The Thomas Lilley Memorial
 Trust
Limoges Charitable Trust
The Linbury Trust
The Lincolnshire Old Churches
 Trust
The Lind Trust
Lindale Educational
 Foundation
The Linden Charitable Trust
The Enid Linder Foundation
The Linmardon Trust
The Ruth and Stuart Lipton
 Charitable Trust
The Lister Charitable Trust

Frank Litchfield Charitable
 Trust
The Andrew and Mary
 Elizabeth Little Charitable
 Trust
The Second Joseph Aaron
 Littman Foundation
The George John and Sheilah
 Livanos Charitable Trust
Liverpool Charity and Voluntary
 Services
Liverpool Sailors' Home Trust
Jack Livingstone Charitable
 Trust
The Elaine and Angus Lloyd
 Charitable Trust
The Charles Lloyd Foundation
The Lloyd Fund
Lloyd's Charities Trust
Lloyds TSB Foundation for
 England and Wales
Lloyds TSB Foundation for
 Northern Ireland
Lloyds TSB Foundation for the
 Channel Islands
Llysdinam Charitable Trust
Localtrent Ltd
The Locker Foundation
The Loftus Charitable Trust
The Lolev Charitable Trust
The Trust for London (formerly
 the City Parochial
 Foundation)
London Catalyst (formerly The
 Metropolitan Hospital-
 Sunday Fund)
The London Community
 Foundation (formerly Capital
 Community Foundation)
The London Law Trust
The William and Katherine
 Longman Trust
The Loseley and Guildway
 Charitable Trust
The Lotus Foundation
The Lowy Mitchell Foundation
The C L Loyd Charitable Trust
LSA Charitable Trust
The Marie Helen Luen
 Charitable Trust
Robert Luff Foundation Ltd
Henry Lumley Charitable Trust
Lady Lumley's Educational
 Foundation
Paul Lunn-Rockliffe Charitable
 Trust
C F Lunoe Trust Fund
The Ruth and Jack Lunzer
 Charitable Trust
Lord and Lady Lurgan Trust
The Lyndhurst Trust
The Lynn Foundation
The Lynwood Trust
John Lyon's Charity
The Lyons Charitable Trust

The Sir Jack Lyons Charitable
 Trust
The Joy and Malcolm Lyons
 Foundation
The Lyras Family Charitable
 Trust
Sylvanus Lyson's Charity
The M and C Trust
The M D and S Charitable
 Trust
The M K Charitable Trust
The Madeline Mabey Trust
The E M MacAndrew Trust
The R S Macdonald Charitable
 Trust
Macdonald-Buchanan
 Charitable Trust
The Macfarlane Walker Trust
The Mackay and Brewer
 Charitable Trust
The Mackintosh Foundation
The MacRobert Trust
Ian Mactaggart Trust
The Magdalen and Lasher
 Charity
Magdalen Hospital Trust
The SV and PE Magee Family
 Charitable Trust
The Magen Charitable Trust
Mageni Trust
The Brian Maguire Charitable
 Trust
The Mahavir Trust (also known
 as the K S Mehta
 Charitable Trust)
The Makin Charitable Trust
Man Group plc Charitable
 Trust
Manchester Airport Community
 Trust Fund
The Manchester Guardian
 Society Charitable Trust
Lord Mayor of Manchester's
 Charity Appeal Trust
Mandeville Trust
The Manifold Charitable Trust
W M Mann Foundation
The Leslie and Lilian Manning
 Trust
Maranatha Christian Trust
Marbeh Torah Trust
Marchig Animal Welfare Trust
Mariapolis Limited
Market Harborough and The
 Bowdens Charity
Michael Marks Charitable
 Trust
The Ann and David Marks
 Foundation
The Hilda and Samuel Marks
 Foundation
J P Marland Charitable Trust
Marr-Munning Trust
The Michael Marsh Charitable
 Trust
The Marsh Christian Trust

The Charlotte Marshall
  Charitable Trust
The Jim Marshall Charitable
  Trust
The D G Marshall of
  Cambridge Trust
Marshgate Charitable
  Settlement
John Martin's Charity
The John Mason Family Trust
The Mason Porter Charitable
  Trust
The Nancie Massey Charitable
  Trust
The Mathew Trust
Matliwala Family Charitable
  Trust
The Matt 6.3 Charitable Trust
The Violet Mauray Charitable
  Trust
The Maxell Educational Trust
The Maxwell Family Foundation
Evelyn May Trust
The Mayfield Valley Arts Trust
Mazars Charitable Trust
The Robert McAlpine
  Foundation
The McDougall Trust
The A M McGreevy No 5
  Charitable Settlement
The McKenna Charitable Trust
Martin McLaren Memorial
  Trust
The Helen Isabella McMorran
  Charitable Foundation
D D McPhail Charitable
  Settlement
The Mears Foundation
The James Frederick and Ethel
  Anne Measures Charity
The Medlock Charitable Trust
The Anthony and Elizabeth
  Mellows Charitable
  Settlement
Melodor Ltd
Melow Charitable Trust
Meningitis Trust
Menuchar Ltd
The Menzies Charity
  Foundation
The Mercers' Charitable
  Foundation
The Merchant Taylors'
  Company Charities Fund
The Merchant Venturers'
  Charity
The Merchants' House of
  Glasgow
Mercury Phoenix Trust
The Mersey Docks and
  Harbour Company
  Charitable Fund
Community Foundation for
  Merseyside

The Zachary Merton and
  George Woofindin
  Convalescent Trust
The Tony Metherell Charitable
  Trust
The Metropolitan Drinking
  Fountain and Cattle Trough
  Association
London Masonic Charitable
  Trust
T and J Meyer Family
  Foundation Limited
Mickleham Charitable Trust
Gerald Micklem Charitable
  Trust
Midhurst Pensions Trust
The Migraine Trust
Miles Trust for the Putney and
  Roehampton Community
Millennium Stadium Charitable
  Trust
The Hugh and Mary Miller
  Bequest Trust
The Miller Foundation
The Millfield Trust
The Millhouses Charitable
  Trust
The Millichope Foundation
The Mills Charity
The Millward Charitable Trust
The Clare Milne Trust
Milton Keynes Community
  Foundation
The Edgar Milward Charity
The Peter Minet Trust
Minge's Gift and the Pooled
  Trusts
The Minos Trust
Minton Charitable Trust
The Mirfield Educational
  Charity
The Mirianog Trust
The Laurence Misener
  Charitable Trust
The Mishcon Family Charitable
  Trust
The Misselbrook Trust
The Mitchell Charitable Trust
The Esmé Mitchell Trust
Keren Mitzvah Trust
The Mizpah Trust
The Mobbs Memorial Trust Ltd
The Modiano Charitable Trust
The Moette Charitable Trust
The Mole Charitable Trust
The Monatrea Charitable Trust
The D C Moncrieff Charitable
  Trust
Monmouthshire County Council
  Welsh Church Act Fund
The Montague Thompson
  Coon Charitable Trust
The Colin Montgomerie
  Charitable Foundation
The Monument Trust
George A Moore Foundation

The Nigel Moores Family
  Charitable Trust
The Peter Moores Foundation
The Morel Charitable Trust
The Morgan Charitable
  Foundation
The Mr and Mrs J T Morgan
  Foundation
Diana and Allan Morgenthau
  Charitable Trust
The Oliver Morland Charitable
  Trust
S C and M E Morland's
  Charitable Trust
The Bernard Morris Charitable
  Trust
The Morris Charitable Trust
The Willie and Mabel Morris
  Charitable Trust
The Peter Morrison Charitable
  Foundation
The Stanley Morrison
  Charitable Trust
Moshal Charitable Trust
Vyoel Moshe Charitable Trust
The Moshulu Charitable Trust
Brian and Jill Moss Charitable
  Trust
The Moss Charitable Trust
The Robert and Margaret
  Moss Charitable Trust
Moss Family Charitable Trust
The Mount Everest Foundation
The Edwina Mountbatten Trust
Mountbatten Festival of Music
The Mountbatten Memorial
  Trust
The Mugdock Children's Trust
The Mulberry Trust
The Edith Murphy Foundation
Murphy-Neumann Charity
  Company Limited
Peter John Murray Trust (PJM
  Trust)
The Mushroom Fund
The Music Sales Charitable
  Trust
Muslim Hands
The Mutual Trust Group
MW (CL) Foundation
MW (GK) Foundation
MW (HO) Foundation
MW (RH) Foundation
MYA Charitable Trust
The Kitty and Daniel Nabarro
  Charitable Trust
The Nadezhda Charitable Trust
The Naggar Charitable Trust
The Eleni Nakou Foundation
The Janet Nash Charitable
  Settlement
Nathan Charitable Trust

The National Churches Trust
(formerly the Historic
Churches Preservation
Trust with the Incorporated
Church Building Society)
The National Manuscripts
Conservation Trust
Nazareth Trust Fund
The Nchima Trust
Needham Market and Barking
Welfare Charities
The Worshipful Company of
Needlemakers' Charitable
Fund
The Neighbourly Charitable
Trust
The James Neill Trust Fund
Nemoral Ltd
Nesswall Ltd
Network for Social Change
The New Appeals Organisation
for the City and County of
Nottingham
New Court Charitable Trust
Newby Trust Limited
The Newcomen Collett
Foundation
Mr and Mrs F E F Newman
Charitable Trust
Newpier Charity Ltd
Alderman Newton's
Educational Foundation
The Night Garden Charity
The Chevras Ezras Nitzrochim
Trust
NJD Charitable Trust
Alice Noakes Memorial
Charitable Trust
The Noon Foundation
The Norda Trust
Norie Charitable Trust
Normalyn Charitable Trust
The Norman Family Charitable
Trust
The Duncan Norman Trust
Fund
The Normanby Charitable Trust
The North British Hotel Trust
The North West Cancer
Research Fund
The Northampton Municipal
Church Charities
The Northampton Queen's
Institute Relief in Sickness
Fund
The Earl of Northampton's
Charity
The Northcott Devon Medical
Foundation
The Northern Rock Foundation
The Northmoor Trust
The Northumberland Village
Homes Trust
The Northwood Charitable
Trust
The Norton Foundation

The Norwich Church of England
Young Men's Society
The Norwich Historic Churches
Trust Ltd
The Norwich Town Close
Estate Charity
The Norwood and Newton
Settlement
The Noswad Charity
The Notgrove Trust
The Nottingham General
Dispensary
The Nottingham Gordon
Memorial Trust for Boys
and Girls
Nottinghamshire Community
Foundation
The Nottinghamshire Historic
Churches Trust
The Nottinghamshire Miners'
Welfare Trust Fund
Novi Most International
The Father O'Mahoney
Memorial Trust
The Sir Peter O'Sullevan
Charitable Trust
The Oak Trust
The Oakdale Trust
The Oakley Charitable Trust
The Oakmoor Charitable Trust
The Odin Charitable Trust
The Ofenheim Charitable Trust
Ogilvie Charities Deed No.2
(including the Charity of
Mary Catherine Ford Smith)
The Ogle Christian Trust
The Oikonomia Trust
Oizer Charitable Trust
The Old Broad Street Charity
Trust
The Old Enfield Charitable
Trust
Old Possum's Practical Trust
The John Oldacre Foundation
The Oldham Foundation
The Olga Charitable Trust
Onaway Trust
Open Gate
The Ormsby Charitable Trust
Orrin Charitable Trust
The Ouseley Trust
The Owen Family Trust
Oxfam (GB)
The Oxfordshire Community
Foundation
The P F Charitable Trust
Padwa Charitable Foundation
The Pallant Charitable Trust
The Palmer Foundation
The Panacea Society
Panahpur (previously Panahpur
Charitable Trust)
Panton Trust
The Paphitis Charitable Trust
The Paragon Trust
The Park Charitable Trust

The Park House Charitable
Trust
The Frank Parkinson
Agricultural Trust
The Samuel and Freda
Parkinson Charitable Trust
The Parthenon Trust
Arthur James Paterson
Charitable Trust
The Constance Paterson
Charitable Trust
Miss M E Swinton Paterson's
Charitable Trust
The Patrick Charitable Trust
The Jack Patston Charitable
Trust
Ambika Paul Foundation
Paycare Charity Trust
(previously known as
Patients' Aid Association
Hospital and Medical
Charities Trust)
The Payne Charitable Trust
The Harry Payne Trust
The Susanna Peake Charitable
Trust
Pears Foundation
The Pedmore Sporting Club
Trust Fund
The Dowager Countess
Eleanor Peel Trust
Pegasus (Stanley) Trust
The Pell Charitable Trust
Peltz Trust
The Pennycress Trust
The Performing Right Society
Foundation
B E Perl Charitable Trust
The Persson Charitable Trust
(formerly Highmoore Hall
Charitable Trust)
The Persula Foundation
The Jack Petchey Foundation
The Petplan Charitable Trust
The Pharsalia Charitable Trust
The Philips and Rubens
Charitable Trust
The Phillips Charitable Trust
The Phillips Family Charitable
Trust
Philological Foundation
The David Pickford Charitable
Foundation
The Bernard Piggott Trust
The Pilgrim Trust
The Cecil Pilkington Charitable
Trust
The Elise Pilkington Charitable
Trust
The Pilkington Charities Fund
The Austin and Hope
Pilkington Trust
The Sir Harry Pilkington Trust
The Col W W Pilkington Will
Trusts The General Charity
Fund

Miss A M Pilkington's
Charitable Trust
The DLA Piper Charitable Trust
The Worshipful Company of
Plaisterers Charitable Trust
The Platinum Trust
G S Plaut Charitable Trust
Limited
Polden-Puckham Charitable
Foundation
The Polehanger Trust
The Poling Charitable Trust
The George and Esme Pollitzer
Charitable Settlement
The J S F Pollitzer Charitable
Settlement
The Polonsky Foundation
The Ponton House Trust
The Mayor of Poole's Appeal
Fund
Edith and Ferdinand Porjes
Charitable Trust
The John Porter Charitable
Trust
The Porter Foundation
Porticus UK
The Portrack Charitable Trust
The J E Posnansky Charitable
Trust
The Mary Potter Convent
Hospital Trust
The David and Elaine Potter
Foundation
The Powell Foundation
Prairie Trust
The W L Pratt Charitable Trust
Premierquote Ltd
Premishlaner Charitable Trust
The Lucy Price Relief-in-Need
Charity
Sir John Priestman Charity
Trust
The Primrose Trust
The Prince of Wales's
Charitable Foundation
Princess Anne's Charities
The Priory Foundation
Prison Service Charity Fund
Private Equity Foundation
The Privy Purse Charitable
Trust
The Proven Family Trust
PSA Peugeot Citroen Charity
Trust
The Puebla Charitable Trust
The Richard and Christine
Purchas Charitable Trust
The Puri Foundation
Mr and Mrs J A Pye's
Charitable Settlement
Quartet Community Foundation
(formerly the Greater Bristol
Foundation)
The Queen Anne's Gate
Foundation

Queen Mary's Roehampton
Trust
The Queen's Silver Jubilee
Trust
Quercus Trust
R J M Charitable Trust
R S Charitable Trust
The R V W Trust
The Monica Rabagliati
Charitable Trust
Rachel Charitable Trust
The Mr and Mrs Philip
Rackham Charitable Trust
Richard Radcliffe Charitable
Trust
The Radcliffe Trust
The Bishop Radford Trust
The Ragdoll Foundation
The Rainford Trust
The Peggy Ramsay Foundation
The Joseph and Lena Randall
Charitable Trust
The Rank Foundation
The Joseph Rank Trust
Ranworth Trust
The Fanny Rapaport Charitable
Settlement
The Ratcliff Foundation
The Ratcliff Pension Charity
The Ratcliffe Charitable Trust
The Eleanor Rathbone
Charitable Trust
The Sigrid Rausing Trust
The Ravensdale Trust
The Rayden Charitable Trust
The Roger Raymond Charitable
Trust
The Rayne Foundation
The Rayne Trust
The John Rayner Charitable
Trust
The Sir James Reckitt Charity
The Eva Reckitt Trust Fund
The Red Arrows Trust
The Red Rose Charitable Trust
The C A Redfern Charitable
Foundation
The Reed Foundation
Richard Reeve's Foundation
The Max Reinhardt Charitable
Trust
Relief Fund for Romania
Limited
REMEDI
The Rest Harrow Trust
Reuben Brothers Foundation
The Joan K Reynell Charitable
Trust
The Nathaniel Reyner Trust
Fund
The Rhododendron Trust
Daisie Rich Trust
The Sir Cliff Richard Charitable
Trust
C B Richard Ellis Charitable
Trust

The Clive Richards Charity
The Richmond Parish Lands
Charity
Ridgesave Limited
The Ripple Effect Foundation
The Sir John Ritblat Family
Foundation
The River Trust
Riverside Charitable Trust
Limited
Thomas Roberts Trust
The Robertson Trust
Edwin George Robinson
Charitable Trust
Robyn Charitable Trust
The Rochester Bridge Trust
The Rock Foundation
The Rock Solid Trust
The Roddick Foundation
The Rofeh Trust
Richard Rogers Charitable
Settlement
Rokach Family Charitable Trust
The Helen Roll Charitable
Trust
The Sir James Roll Charitable
Trust
The Roman Research Trust
Romeera Foundation
The C A Rookes Charitable
Trust
The Rosca Trust
Alexandra Rose Charities
The Cecil Rosen Foundation
Rosetrees Trust
The Rothermere Foundation
The Rotherwick Foundation
The Roughley Charitable Trust
Mrs Gladys Row Fogo
Charitable Trust
Rowanville Ltd
The Christopher Rowbotham
Charitable Trust
The Rowing Foundation
The Rowlands Trust
The Joseph Rowntree
Charitable Trust
Joseph Rowntree Reform Trust
Limited
Royal Artillery Charitable Fund
Royal British Legion
Royal Docks Trust (London)
Royal Masonic Trust for Girls
and Boys
The Royal Scots Benevolent
Society
The Alfred and Frances
Rubens Charitable Trust
The Rubin Foundation
William Arthur Rudd Memorial
Trust
The Rufford Foundation
The Russell Trust
Ryklow Charitable Trust 1992
(also known as A B
Williamson Charitable Trust)

The J S and E C Rymer
Charitable Trust
S F Foundation
S O Charitable Trust
The Jeremy and John Sacher
Charitable Trust
The Michael Harry Sacher
Trust
The Sackler Trust (Formerly Dr
Mortimer and Theresa
Sackler Foundation)
The Ruzin Sadagora Trust
The Saddlers' Company
Charitable Fund
The Saga Charitable Trust
The Jean Sainsbury Animal
Welfare Trust
The Alan and Babette
Sainsbury Charitable Fund
The Sainsbury Family
Charitable Trusts
Saint Sarkis Charity Trust
The Saintbury Trust
The Saints and Sinners Trust
The Salamander Charitable
Trust
The Salt Trust
Salters' Charitable Foundation
The Andrew Salvesen
Charitable Trust
The Sammermar Trust
Basil Samuel Charitable Trust
Coral Samuel Charitable Trust
The Hon. M J Samuel
Charitable Trust
The Peter Samuel Charitable
Trust
The Camilla Samuel Fund
The Samworth Foundation
The Sandra Charitable Trust
Santander UK Foundation
Limited
Jimmy Savile Charitable Trust
The Scarfe Charitable Trust
The Schapira Charitable Trust
The Annie Schiff Charitable
Trust
The Schmidt-Bodner Charitable
Trust
The R H Scholes Charitable
Trust
The Schreib Trust
The Schreiber Charitable Trust
Schroder Charity Trust
Scott (Eredine) Charitable
Trust
The Francis C Scott Charitable
Trust
The Sir James and Lady Scott
Trust
The Scott Trust Foundation
The Storrow Scott Will Trust
The Scottish Arts Council
Scottish Coal Industry Special
Welfare Fund

The Scottish Community
Foundation
The Scottish International
Education Trust
The Scouloudi Foundation
Seafarers UK (King George's
Fund for Sailors)
Seamen's Hospital Society
The Searchlight Electric
Charitable Trust
The Searle Charitable Trust
The Helene Sebba Charitable
Trust
The Samuel Sebba Charitable
Trust
The Seedfield Trust
Sellata Ltd
SEM Charitable Trust
The Seneca Trust
The Ayrton Senna Foundation
The Seven Fifty Trust
The Severn Trent Water
Charitable Trust Fund
SFIA Educational Trust Limited
The Cyril Shack Trust
The Jean Shanks Foundation
The Shanti Charitable Trust
ShareGift (The Orr Mackintosh
Foundation)
The Linley Shaw Foundation
The Sheepdrove Trust
The Sheffield and District
Hospital Services
Charitable Fund
The Shekinah Legacy
The Sheldon Trust
The P and D Shepherd
Charitable Trust
The Sylvia and Colin Shepherd
Charitable Trust
The Archie Sherman Cardiff
Foundation
The Archie Sherman Charitable
Trust
The R C Sherriff Trust
The Shetland Charitable Trust
SHINE (Support and Help in
Education)
The Barnett and Sylvia Shine
No 2 Charitable Trust
The Bassil Shippam and
Alsford Trust
The Shipwrights' Company
Charitable Fund
The Shirley Foundation
Shlomo Memorial Fund Limited
The J A Shone Memorial Trust
The Barbara A Shuttleworth
Memorial Trust
The Sickle Foundation
The Mary Elizabeth Siebel
Charity
David and Jennifer Sieff
Charitable Trust
The Julius Silman Charitable
Trust

The Leslie Silver Charitable
Trust
The Simpson Education and
Conservation Trust
The Simpson Foundation
The Huntly and Margery
Sinclair Charitable Trust
Sino-British Fellowship Trust
The Skelton Bounty
The Charles Skey Charitable
Trust
Skipton Building Society
Charitable Foundation
The John Slater Foundation
Rita and David Slowe
Charitable Trust
Ruth Smart Foundation
The SMB Charitable Trust
The Mrs Smith and Mount
Trust
The N Smith Charitable
Settlement
The Amanda Smith Charitable
Trust
The E H Smith Charitable Trust
The Smith Charitable Trust
The Henry Smith Charity
The Leslie Smith Foundation
The Martin Smith Foundation
Stanley Smith General
Charitable Trust
The Stanley Smith UK
Horticultural Trust
Philip Smith's Charitable Trust
The R C Snelling Charitable
Trust
The Snowball Trust
The Sobell Foundation
Solev Co Ltd
Solihull Community Foundation
The Solo Charitable
Settlement
Dr Richard Solomon's
Charitable Trust
David Solomons Charitable
Trust
Songdale Ltd
The E C Sosnow Charitable
Trust
The Souter Charitable Trust
The South Square Trust
The Stephen R and Philippa H
Southall Charitable Trust
The W F Southall Trust
R H Southern Trust
The Southover Manor General
Education Trust
The Southwold Trust
Spar Charitable Fund
Sparquote Limited
The Spear Charitable Trust
Spears-Stutz Charitable Trust
The Jessie Spencer Trust
The Ralph and Irma Sperring
Charity

The Moss Spiro Will Charitable
Foundation
The Spoore, Merry and Rixman
Foundation
Spring Harvest
Rosalyn and Nicholas Springer
Charitable Trust
Springfields Employees'
Medical Research and
Charity Trust Fund
Springrule Ltd
The Spurrell Charitable Trust
The Geoff and Fiona Squire
Foundation
St Francis's Leprosy Guild
St Gabriel's Trust
St Hilda's Trust
St James' Trust Settlement
Sir Walter St John's
Educational Charity
St Katharine and Shadwell
Trust
St Michael's and All Saints'
Charities
The Late St Patrick White
Charitable Trust
St Teilo's Trust
The Stafford Trust
The Stanley Foundation Ltd
The Stanton Ballard Charitable
Trust
The Staples Trust
The Star Charitable Trust
The Peter Stebbings Memorial
Charity
The Steinberg Family
Charitable Trust
The Hugh Stenhouse
Foundation
C E K Stern Charitable Trust
The Sigmund Sternberg
Charitable Foundation
Stervon Ltd
The Stevenage Community
Trust
The June Stevens Foundation
Stevenson Family's Charitable
Trust
The Steventon Allotments and
Relief-in-Need Charity
The Stewards' Charitable Trust
The Stewards' Company
Limited (incorporating the J
W Laing Trust and the J W
Laing Biblical Scholarship
Trust)
The Stobart Newlands
Charitable Trust
The Edward Stocks-Massey
Bequest Fund
The Stokenchurch Educational
Charity
The Stoller Charitable Trust
The M J C Stone Charitable
Trust

The Stone-Mallabar Charitable
Foundation
The Samuel Storey Family
Charitable Trust
Peter Stormonth Darling
Charitable Trust
Peter Storrs Trust
The Strangward Trust
The Strasser Foundation
Stratford upon Avon Town
Trust
Strathclyde Police Benevolent
Fund
The W O Street Charitable
Foundation
The A B Strom and R Strom
Charitable Trust
The Sudborough Foundation
Sueberry Ltd
The Suffolk Historic Churches
Trust
The Alan Sugar Foundation
Sugarworld Trust
The Summerfield Charitable
Trust
The Surrey Historic Buildings
Trust Ltd
The Sussex Historic Churches
Trust
The Adrienne and Leslie
Sussman Charitable Trust
The Sutasoma Trust
Sutton Coldfield Municipal
Charities
Swan Mountain Trust
Swansea and Brecon Diocesan
Board of Finance Limited
The John Swire (1989)
Charitable Trust
The Swire Charitable Trust
The Hugh and Ruby Sykes
Charitable Trust
The Charles and Elsie Sykes
Trust
The Sylvanus Charitable Trust
The Stella Symons Charitable
Trust
The Tabeel Trust
Tadlus Limited
The Tajtelbaum Charitable
Trust
Tallow Chandlers Benevolent
Fund
Talteg Ltd
The Tangent Charitable Trust
The Lady Tangye Charitable
Trust
The David Tannen Charitable
Trust
The Tanner Trust
The Lili Tapper Charitable
Foundation
The Mrs A Lacy Tate Trust
The Taurus Foundation
The Tay Charitable Trust
C B and H H Taylor 1984 Trust

Humphrey Richardson Taylor
Charitable Trust
The Connie and Albert Taylor
Charitable Trust
The Cyril Taylor Charitable
Trust
A P Taylor Trust
Rosanna Taylor's 1987 Charity
Trust
Tearfund
The Tedworth Charitable Trust
Tees Valley Community
Foundation
Tegham Limited
The Templeton Goodwill Trust
Tesco Charity Trust
Thackray Medical Research
Trust
The Thames Wharf Charity
The Thistle Trust
The Loke Wan Tho Memorial
Foundation
The David Thomas Charitable
Trust
The Arthur and Margaret
Thompson Charitable Trust
The Elspeth J Thompson
Charitable Trust
The Maurice and Vivien
Thompson Charitable Trust
The Thompson Family
Charitable Trust
The Thompson6 Charitable
Trust
The Len Thomson Charitable
Trust
The Sue Thomson Foundation
The Sir Jules Thorn Charitable
Trust
The Thornton Foundation
The Thornton Trust
The Three Oaks Trust
The Thriplow Charitable Trust
Mrs R P Tindall's Charitable
Trust
The Tinsley Foundation
The Tisbury Telegraph Trust
TJH Foundation
The Tobacco Pipe Makers and
Tobacco Trade Benevolent
Fund
The Tolkien Trust
Tomchei Torah Charitable
Trust
The Tompkins Foundation
The Torah Temimah Trust
Toras Chesed (London) Trust
The Tory Family Foundation
Tottenham Grammar School
Foundation
The Tower Hill Trust
The Towry Law Charitable Trust
(also known as the Castle
Educational Trust)
The Mayor of Trafford's Charity
Fund

Annie Tranmer Charitable Trust
The Constance Travis
    Charitable Trust
The Treeside Trust
The Tresillian Trust
The Triangle Trust (1949) Fund
The True Colours Trust
Truedene Co. Ltd
The Truemark Trust
Truemart Limited
Trumros Limited
Trust Sixty Three
The Trusthouse Charitable
    Foundation
Tudor Rose Ltd
The Tudor Trust
The Tufton Charitable Trust
The R D Turner Charitable
    Trust
The Douglas Turner Trust
The Florence Turner Trust
Miss S M Tutton Charitable
    Trust
The TUUT Charitable Trust
Two Ridings Community
    Foundation
Community Foundation Serving
    Tyne and Wear and
    Northumberland
Trustees of Tzedakah
UKI Charitable Foundation
Ulster Garden Villages Ltd
Ultach Trust
Ulting Overseas Trust
The Ulverscroft Foundation
Ulverston Town Lands Charity
The Underwood Trust
The Union of Orthodox Hebrew
    Congregation
The United Society for the
    Propagation of the Gospel
The David Uri Memorial Trust
Uxbridge United Welfare Trust
'v'
Vale of Glamorgan – Welsh
    Church Fund
The Valentine Charitable Trust
The Valiant Charitable Trust
The Albert Van Den Bergh
    Charitable Trust
John and Lucille van Geest
    Foundation
The Van Neste Foundation
Mrs Maud Van Norden's
    Charitable Foundation
The Vandervell Foundation
The Vardy Foundation
The Variety Club Children's
    Charity
Veneziana Fund
The Verdon-Smith Family
    Charitable Settlement
Roger Vere Foundation
Victoria Homes Trust
The Nigel Vinson Charitable
    Trust

The William and Ellen Vinten
    Trust
The Vintners' Company
    Charitable Foundation
Vintners' Gifts Charity
Vision Charity
Vivdale Ltd
The Viznitz Foundation
Wade's Charity
The Scurrah Wainwright Charity
Wakeham Trust
The Community Foundation in
    Wales
Wales Council for Voluntary
    Action
Robert and Felicity Waley-
    Cohen Charitable Trust
The Thomas Wall Trust
Wallace and Gromit's
    Children's Foundation
The F J Wallis Charitable
    Settlement
War on Want
Sir Siegmund Warburg's
    Voluntary Settlement
The Ward Blenkinsop Trust
The George Ward Charitable
    Trust
The Barbara Ward Children's
    Foundation
G R Waters Charitable Trust
    2000
The Waterways Trust
The Wates Foundation
Blyth Watson Charitable Trust
The Howard Watson Symington
    Memorial Charity
John Watson's Trust
Weatherley Charitable Trust
The Weavers' Company
    Benevolent Fund
The David Webster Charitable
    Trust
The Weinberg Foundation
The Weinstein Foundation
The Weinstock Fund
The James Weir Foundation
The Joir and Kato Weisz
    Foundation
The Weldon UK Charitable
    Trust
The Wellcome Trust
Welsh Church Fund Dyfed
    area (Carmarthenshire,
    Ceredigion and
    Pembrokeshire)
The Welton Foundation
The Wessex Youth Trust
The West Derby Wastelands
    Charity
West London Synagogue
    Charitable Fund
The West Yorkshire Police
    Community Fund
Mrs S K West's Charitable
    Trust

The Westcroft Trust
The Westminster Foundation
The Garfield Weston
    Foundation
The Barbara Whatmore
    Charitable Trust
The Whitaker Charitable Trust
The Colonel W H Whitbread
    Charitable Trust
The Simon Whitbread
    Charitable Trust
The Melanie White Foundation
    Limited
White Stuff Foundation
The Whitecourt Charitable
    Trust
A H and B C Whiteley
    Charitable Trust
The Norman Whiteley Trust
The Whitley Animal Protection
    Trust
The Whittlesey Charity
The Lionel Wigram Memorial
    Trust
The Richard Wilcox Welfare
    Charity
The Felicity Wilde Charitable
    Trust
The Wilkinson Charitable
    Foundation
The Kay Williams Charitable
    Foundation
The Williams Charitable Trust
The Williams Family Charitable
    Trust
Williams Serendipity Trust
The H D H Wills 1965
    Charitable Trust
The Dame Violet Wills Will
    Trust
The Wilmcote Charitrust
Sumner Wilson Charitable
    Trust
David Wilson Foundation
The Wilson Foundation
J and J R Wilson Trust
The Community Foundation for
    Wiltshire and Swindon
The Benjamin Winegarten
    Charitable Trust
The Harold Hyam Wingate
    Foundation
The Francis Winham
    Foundation
Anona Winn Charitable Trust
Wirral Mayor's Charity
The Witzenfeld Foundation
The Michael and Anna Wix
    Charitable Trust
The Wixamtree Trust
The Woburn 1986 Charitable
    Trust
The Maurice Wohl Charitable
    Foundation
The Charles Wolfson
    Charitable Trust

The James Wood Bequest
    Fund
The Wood Family Trust
The Woodcock Charitable Trust
Woodlands Foundation Limited
Woodlands Green Ltd
Woodlands Trust
Woodroffe Benton Foundation
The Woodward Charitable
    Trust
The A and R Woolf Charitable
    Trust
ME Woolfe Charitable Trust
Worcester Municipal Charities
    (incorporating Worcester
    Consolidated Municipal
    Charity and Worcester
    Municipal Exhibitions
    Foundation)
The Worcestershire and
    Dudley Historic Churches
    Trust
The Fred and Della Worms
    Charitable Trust
The Wragge and Co. Charitable
    Trust
The Diana Edgson Wright
    Charitable Trust
The Matthews Wrightson
    Charity Trust
Miss E B Wrightson's
    Charitable Settlement
The Joan Wyatt Charitable
    Trust
Wychdale Ltd
Wychville Ltd
The Wyndham Charitable Trust
The Wyseliot Charitable Trust
The Xerox (UK) Trust
Yankov Charitable Trust
The Yapp Charitable Trust
The Dennis Alan Yardy
    Charitable Trust
The W Wing Yip and Brothers
    Foundation
The York Children's Trust
Yorkshire Agricultural Society
The South Yorkshire
    Community Foundation
The Yorkshire Dales
    Millennium Trust
The John Young Charitable
    Settlement
The William Allen Young
    Charitable Trust
The John K Young Endowment
    Fund
Youth Music
Zephyr Charitable Trust
The Marjorie and Arnold Ziff
    Charitable Foundation
Stephen Zimmerman
    Charitable Trust
The Zochonis Charitable Trust
The Zolfo Cooper Foundation

Project support

■ Full project funding

The 1970 Trust
The 1989 Willan Charitable
    Trust
The 29th May 1961 Charitable
    Trust
The Aberbrothock Skea Trust
The Aberdeen Endowments
    Trust
ABF The Soldiers' Charity
    (formerly the Army
    Benevolent Fund)
Achiezer Association Ltd
Achisomoch Aid Company
    Limited
The ACT Foundation
Action Medical Research
The Sylvia Adams Charitable
    Trust
The Victor Adda Foundation
The Adint Charitable Trust
Age UK (formerly Help the
    Aged and Age Concern)
Aid to the Church in Need (UK)
The Sylvia Aitken Charitable
    Trust
The Ajahma Charitable Trust
Aldgate and All Hallows'
    Barking Exhibition
    Foundation
The Aldgate Freedom
    Foundation
All Saints Educational Trust
Allchurches Trust Ltd
The H B Allen Charitable Trust
The Alliance Family Foundation
Angus Allnatt Charitable
    Foundation
The Pat Allsop Charitable Trust
Almondsbury Charity
Altamont Ltd
Alvor Charitable Trust
The Ammco Trust
Viscount Amory's Charitable
    Trust
The AMW Charitable Trust
The André Christian Trust
Anguish's Educational
    Foundation
The Animal Defence Trust
The Eric Anker-Petersen
    Charity
Ambrose and Ann Appelbe
    Trust
The Appletree Trust
The John Apthorp Charitable
    Trust
The Arbib Foundation
The John M Archer Charitable
    Trust
The Archer Trust
The Architectural Heritage
    Fund

The Argus Appeal
The Armenian Relief Society of
    Great Britain Trust
The Armourers' and Brasiers'
    Gauntlet Trust
Arsenal Charitable Trust
The Artemis Charitable Trust
Arthritis Research UK
The Arts and Entertainment
    Charitable Trust
Arts Council England
The Arts Council of Northern
    Ireland
The Arts Council of Wales
The Ove Arup Foundation
The AS Charitable Trust
The Ashden Trust
The Ashendene Trust
The Ashley Family Foundation
    (formerly The Laura Ashley
    Foundation)
The Norman C Ashton
    Foundation
The Ashworth Charitable Trust
The Ian Askew Charitable Trust
The Associated Country
    Women of the World
    (ACWW)
The Association of Colleges
    Charitable Trust
Astellas European Foundation
Asthma UK
AstonMansfield Charitable
    Trust
The Astor Foundation
The Astor of Hever Trust
The Aurelius Charitable Trust
The Avenue Charitable Trust
AW Charitable Trust
The BAA Communities Trust
The BACTA Charitable Trust
The Scott Bader
    Commonwealth Ltd
The Bagri Foundation
Veta Bailey Charitable Trust
The Austin Bailey Trust
The Baily Thomas Charitable
    Fund
The Baird Trust
The Baker Charitable Trust
The Balcombe Charitable Trust
The Andrew Balint Charitable
    Trust
The Albert Casanova Ballard
    Deceased Trust
The Ballinger Charitable Trust
The Balmore Trust
The Balney Charitable Trust
The Baltic Charitable Fund
The Bamford Charitable
    Foundation
The Banbury Charities
William P Bancroft (No 2)
    Charitable Trust and
    Jenepher Gillett Trust
The Band Trust

The Barbers' Company General
Charities
The Barbour Foundation
Barchester Healthcare
Foundation
The Barclay Foundation
The Baring Foundation
Peter Barker-Mill Memorial
Charity
Barleycorn Trust
Barnes Workhouse Fund
The Barnsbury Charitable Trust
The Barnwood House Trust
The Misses Barrie Charitable
Trust
Barrington Family Charitable
Trust
Stephen J Barry Charitable
Trust
The Bartlett Taylor Charitable
Trust
The Paul Bassham Charitable
Trust
The Batchworth Trust
The Bay Tree Charitable Trust
D H and L H Baylin Charitable
Trust
The Louis Baylis (Maidenhead
Advertiser) Charitable Trust
BBC Children in Need
B-CH 1971 Charitable Trust
The Beacon Trust
The Bearder Charity
The James Beattie Charitable
Trust
The Beaufort House Trust
Limited
The Beaverbrook Foundation
The Beccles Town Lands
Charity
The Becker Family Charitable
Trust
The Becketts and Sargeants
Educational Foundation
The John Beckwith Charitable
Trust
The Peter Beckwith Charitable
Trust
The Bedford Charity (The
Harpur Trust)
The David and Ruth Behrend
Fund
The Beit Trust
The Bellahouston Bequest
Fund
The Bellinger Donnay Trust
Belljoe Tzedoko Ltd
The Benfield Motors Charitable
Trust
The Benham Charitable
Settlement
Maurice and Jacqueline
Bennett Charitable Trust
The Berkshire Community
Foundation
The Bestway Foundation

Thomas Betton's Charity for
Pensions and Relief-in-Need
BHST
The Mason Bibby 1981 Trust
BibleLands
The Bideford Bridge Trust
The Big Lottery Fund
The Billmeir Charitable Trust
The Bingham Trust
The Bintaub Charitable Trust
The Birmingham District
Nursing Charitable Trust
The Birmingham Hospital
Saturday Fund Medical
Charity and Welfare Trust
Birmingham International
Airport Community Trust
The Lord Mayor of
Birmingham's Charity
The Michael Bishop
Foundation
The Bishop's Development
Fund
The Bertie Black Foundation
Isabel Blackman Foundation
The Herbert and Peter
Blagrave Charitable Trust
The Blair Foundation
The Blanchminster Trust
The Sir Victor Blank Charitable
Settlement
The Neville and Elaine Blond
Charitable Trust
The Bluston Charitable
Settlement
The Body Shop Foundation
The Boltons Trust
The Bonamy Charitable Trust
The John and Celia Bonham
Christie Charitable Trust
The Charlotte Bonham-Carter
Charitable Trust
Bonhomie United Charity
Society
The Boots Charitable Trust
The Bordon and Liphook
Charity
The Oliver Borthwick Memorial
Trust
The Boshier-Hinton Foundation
The Bothwell Charitable Trust
H E and E L Botteley
Charitable Trust
The Harry Bottom Charitable
Trust
The Anthony Bourne
Foundation
The Bower Trust
The Bowerman Charitable
Trust
John and Susan Bowers Fund
The Bowland Charitable Trust
The William Brake Charitable
Trust
The Tony Bramall Charitable
Trust

The Harold and Alice Bridges
Charity
The Brighton District Nursing
Association Trust
Bristol Archdeaconry Charity
John Bristow and Thomas
Mason Trust
Britannia Foundation
The British Council for
Prevention of Blindness
The British Dietetic
Association General and
Education Trust Fund
The British Gas (Scottish Gas)
Energy Trust
British Heart Foundation
British Humane Association
British Institute at Ankara
British Ornithologists' Union
The Britten-Pears Foundation
The Britto Foundation
The J and M Britton Charitable
Trust
The Charles and Edna
Broadhurst Charitable Trust
The Bromley Trust
The Roger Brooke Charitable
Trust
The David Brooke Charity
The Charles Brotherton Trust
Joseph Brough Charitable
Trust
The Swinfen Broun Charitable
Trust
Mrs E E Brown Charitable
Settlement
The Bryant Trust
The Buckinghamshire
Foundation
The Buckinghamshire Masonic
Centenary Fund
The Rosemary Bugden
Charitable Trust
The Bulldog Trust Limited
The E F Bulmer Benevolent
Fund
The BUPA Foundation
Burdens Charitable Foundation
The Clara E Burgess Charity
The Burry Charitable Trust
The Arnold Burton 1998
Charitable Trust
The Burton Breweries
Charitable Trust
The Geoffrey Burton Charitable
Trust
Consolidated Charity of Burton
upon Trent
Butchers' Company General
Charities
The Noel Buxton Trust
Henry T and Lucy B Cadbury
Charitable Trust
The Christopher Cadbury
Charitable Trust

Full project funding

The G W Cadbury Charitable
Trust
The Richard Cadbury
Charitable Trust
The Edward and Dorothy
Cadbury Trust
CAF (Charities Aid Foundation)
CAFOD (Catholic Agency for
Overseas Development)
The Callander Charitable Trust
Calleva Foundation
Calouste Gulbenkian
Foundation
The Calpe Trust
Calypso Browning Trust
The Cambridgeshire
Community Foundation
The Campden Charities
Trustee
The Canning Trust
The Carew Pole Charitable
Trust
The D W T Cargill Fund
Carlee Ltd
The Carlton House Charitable
Trust
The Worshipful Company of
Carmen Benevolent Trust
The Carnegie Dunfermline
Trust
The Carpenter Charitable Trust
The Carpenters' Company
Charitable Trust
The Carrington Charitable
Trust
The Carron Charitable
Settlement
The Leslie Mary Carter
Charitable Trust
The Carvill Trust
The Casey Trust
Cash for Kids Radio Clyde
Sir John Cass's Foundation
The Elizabeth Casson Trust
The Castang Foundation
The Catalyst Charitable Trust
(formerly the Buckle Family
Charitable Trust)
The Catholic Charitable Trust
Catholic Foreign Missions
The Catholic Trust for England
and Wales
The Cattanach Charitable Trust
The Joseph and Annie Cattle
Trust
The Thomas Sivewright Catto
Charitable Settlement
The Wilfrid and Constance
Cave Foundation
The Cayo Foundation
The B G S Cayzer Charitable
Trust
The Cazenove Charitable Trust
Celtic Charity Fund
The Cemlyn-Jones Trust
CfBT Education Trust

The Pamela Champion
Foundation
The Chapman Charitable Trust
John William Chapman's
Charitable Trust
The Charities Advisory Trust
Charitworth Limited
The Charter 600 Charity
The Worshipful Company of
Chartered Accountants
General Charitable Trust
(also known as CALC)
The Chasah Trust
The Chelsea Building Society
Charitable Foundation
The Chelsea Square 1994
Trust
The Cheruby Trust
The Cheshire Provincial Fund
of Benevolence
The Chetwode Foundation
Chevioty Asset Management
Charitable Trust
The Malcolm Chick Charity
Childs Charitable Trust
The Childwick Trust
The Chipping Sodbury Town
Lands Charity
CHK Charities Limited
The Chownes Foundation
The Chrimes Family Charitable
Trust
The Christabella Charitable
Trust
Christadelphian Samaritan
Fund
Christian Aid
Christian Response to Eastern
Europe
The Church and Community
Fund
The Church Burgesses
Educational Foundation
Church Burgesses Trust
Church of Ireland Priorities
Fund
The Church Urban Fund
City and County of Swansea
Welsh Church Act Fund
The City Bridge Trust (formerly
known as Bridge House
Trust)
The City Educational Trust
Fund
Stephen Clark 1957
Charitable Trust
J A Clark Charitable Trust
The Hilda and Alice Clark
Charitable Trust
The Roger and Sarah Bancroft
Clark Charitable Trust
The Clarke Charitable
Settlement
The Cleary Foundation
The Cleopatra Trust
Lord Clinton's Charitable Trust

The Clore Duffield Foundation
Miss V L Clore's 1967
Charitable Trust
Closehelm Ltd
Richard Cloudesley's Charity
The Clover Trust
The Robert Clutterbuck
Charitable Trust
Clydpride Ltd
The Coalfields Regeneration
Trust
The John Coates Charitable
Trust
Coats Foundation Trust
The Cobtree Charity Trust Ltd
The Denise Cohen Charitable
Trust
The Vivienne and Samuel
Cohen Charitable Trust
The John S Cohen Foundation
The R and S Cohen
Foundation
The Colchester Catalyst
Charity
The Cole Charitable Trust
The Colefax Charitable Trust
The John and Freda Coleman
Charitable Trust
The George Henry Collins
Charity
The E Alec Colman Charitable
Fund Ltd
The Sir Jeremiah Colman Gift
Trust
The Coltstaple Trust
Colwinston Charitable Trust
Colyer-Fergusson Charitable
Trust
Comic Relief
The Comino Foundation
Community Foundation for
Calderdale
The Community Foundation for
Northern Ireland
The Compton Charitable Trust
The Congleton Inclosure Trust
The Conservation Foundation
The Consolidated Charities for
the Infirm Merchant
Taylors' Company
Gordon Cook Foundation
The Ernest Cook Trust
The Cooks Charity
The Catherine Cookson
Charitable Trust
Mabel Cooper Charity
The Alice Ellen Cooper Dean
Charitable Foundation
The Co-operative Foundation
The Marjorie Coote Animal
Charity Trust
The Marjorie Coote Old
People's Charity
The Helen Jean Cope Trust
The J Reginald Corah
Foundation Fund

The Gershon Coren Charitable Foundation
The Corinthian Trust
Edwin Cornforth 1983 Charity Trust
The Cornwell Charitable Trust
The Sidney and Elizabeth Corob Charitable Trust
The Corona Charitable Trust
The Costa Family Charitable Trust (formerly the Morgan Williams Charitable Trust)
The Cotton Industry War Memorial Trust
The Cotton Trust
County Durham Community Foundation
The Augustine Courtauld Trust
The General Charities of the City of Coventry
Coventry Building Society Charitable Foundation
The John Cowan Foundation
The Sir William Coxen Trust Fund
The Lord Cozens-Hardy Trust
The Craignish Trust
The Craps Charitable Trust
Michael Crawford Children's Charity
The Cray Trust
Creative Scotland
The Crescent Trust
Cripplegate Foundation
The Violet and Milo Cripps Charitable Trust
The Harry Crook Foundation
The Cross Trust
The Croydon Relief in Need Charities
The Mayor of Croydon's Charity Fund
Cruden Foundation Ltd
The Ronald Cruickshank's Foundation
The R D Crusaders Foundation
Cullum Family Trust
The Culra Charitable Trust
Cumberland Building Society Charitable Foundation
Cumbria Community Foundation
The Cunningham Trust
The D J H Currie Memorial Trust
The Dennis Curry Charitable Trust
The Raymond Curtis Charitable Trust
The Manny Cussins Foundation
The Cwmbran Trust
Itzchok Meyer Cymerman Trust Ltd
The D G Charitable Settlement

The D'Oyly Carte Charitable Trust
Roald Dahl's Marvellous Children's Charity
The Daily Prayer Union Charitable Trust Ltd
The Daisy Trust
The Daiwa Anglo-Japanese Foundation
The Dr and Mrs A Darlington Charitable Trust
Baron Davenport's Charity
The Davidson (Nairn) Charitable Trust
The Davidson Family Charitable Trust
The Alderman Joe Davidson Memorial Trust
Michael Davies Charitable Settlement
The Gwendoline and Margaret Davies Charity
The Wilfrid Bruce Davis Charitable Trust
Davis-Rubens Charitable Trust
The Dawe Charitable Trust
The De Clermont Charitable Company Ltd
Peter De Haan Charitable Trust
The Leopold De Rothschild Charitable Trust
The Deakin Charitable Trust
William Dean Countryside and Educational Trust
The Debmar Benevolent Trust
The Delius Trust
The Dellal Foundation
The Delves Charitable Trust
The Demigryphon Trust
The Denman Charitable Trust
The Denton Charitable Trust
The Denton Wilde Sapte Charitable Trust
The Earl of Derby's Charitable Trust
Derbyshire Community Foundation
The J N Derbyshire Trust
Devon Community Foundation
The Devon Educational Trust
The Duke of Devonshire's Charitable Trust
The Sandy Dewhirst Charitable Trust
The Laduma Dhamecha Charitable Trust
Diabetes UK
The Dibden Allotments Fund
The Dickon Trust
The Digbeth Trust
The Dinwoodie Settlement
Dischma Charitable Trust
The DLM Charitable Trust
Louise Dobson Charitable Trust

The Derek and Eileen Dodgson Foundation
The Dollond Charitable Trust
Domepride Ltd
The Dorcas Trust
The Dorus Trust
The Doughty Charity Trust
The R M Douglas Charitable Trust
The Drapers' Charitable Fund
The Dugdale Charitable Trust
The Dulverton Trust
The P B Dumbell Charitable Trust
The Dumbreck Charity
Dunard Fund
Ronald Duncan Literary Foundation
The Houghton Dunn Charitable Trust
The Dunn Family Charitable Trust
The W E Dunn Trust
Dushinsky Trust Ltd
The Dwek Family Charitable Trust
The Dyers' Company Charitable Trust
EAGA Partnership Charitable Trust
The Eagle Charity Trust
The Earley Charity
Earls Colne and Halstead Educational Charity
The Earmark Trust
East Kent Provincial Charities
East London Community Foundation
Eastern Counties Educational Trust Limited
The Sir John Eastwood Foundation
The Ebenezer Trust
The EBM Charitable Trust
Eden Arts Trust
EDF Energy Trust (EDFET)
The Gilbert and Eileen Edgar Foundation
Edinburgh Children's Holiday Fund
The Edinburgh Trust, No 2 Account
Edinburgh Voluntary Organisations' Trust Funds
The W G Edwards Charitable Foundation
The William Edwards Educational Charity
The Elephant Trust
The George Elias Charitable Trust
The Gerald Palmer Eling Trust Company
The Wilfred and Elsie Elkes Charity Fund

The Maud Elkington Charitable Trust

The Ellerdale Trust

The John Ellerman Foundation

The Ellinson Foundation Ltd

James Ellis Charitable Trust

The Elmgrant Trust

The Elmley Foundation

The Vernon N Ely Charitable Trust

The Embleton Trust

The Emerton-Christie Charity

The Emmandjay Charitable Trust

The Worshipful Company of Engineers Charitable Trust Fund

The Englefield Charitable Trust

The English Schools' Football Association

The Enkalon Foundation

Entindale Ltd

The Epigoni Trust

Epilepsy Research UK

The Equitable Charitable Trust

The Equity Trust Fund

The Ericson Trust

The Erskine Cunningham Hill Trust

Essex Community Foundation

The Essex Fairway Charitable Trust

The Essex Heritage Trust

Essex Provincial Charity Fund

The Essex Youth Trust

Euro Charity Trust

Sir John Evelyn's Charity

The Eventhall Family Charitable Trust

The Everard Foundation

The Eveson Charitable Trust

The Beryl Evetts and Robert Luff Animal Welfare Trust

The Execution Charitable Trust

The Mayor of Exeter's Appeal Fund

The Exilarch's Foundation

F C Charitable Trust

The F P Limited Charitable Trust

The Faber Charitable Trust

Esmée Fairbairn Foundation

The Fairway Trust

Faisaltex Charitable Trust

The Family Rich Charities Trust

The Lord Faringdon Charitable Trust

Samuel William Farmer Trust

The Farmers' Company Charitable Fund

The Thomas Farr Charitable Trust

Walter Farthing (Trust) Limited

The Fassnidge Memorial Trust

Joseph Fattorini Charitable Trust 'B' Account

The Fawcett Charitable Trust

Federation of Jewish Relief Organisations

The John Feeney Charitable Trust

The George Fentham Birmingham Charity

The A M Fenton Trust

Allan and Nesta Ferguson Charitable Settlement

The Bluff Field Charitable Trust

The Doris Field Charitable Trust

The Fifty Fund

Firtree Trust

The Fishmongers' Company's Charitable Trust

The Fitton Trust

The Earl Fitzwilliam Charitable Trust

Bud Flanagan Leukaemia Fund

The Rose Flatau Charitable Trust

The Ian Fleming Charitable Trust

The Joyce Fletcher Charitable Trust

The Roy Fletcher Charitable Trust

The Flow Foundation

The Gerald Fogel Charitable Trust

The Follett Trust

The Football Association National Sports Centre Trust

The Football Association Youth Trust

The Football Foundation

The Forbes Charitable Foundation

The Forces Trust (Working Name)

The Oliver Ford Charitable Trust

The Forest Hill Charitable Trust

Forever Manchester (The Community Foundation for Greater Manchester)

Gwyneth Forrester Trust

The Fort Foundation

The Forte Charitable Trust

Foundation for Management Education

The Four Winds Trust

The Foyle Foundation

The Isaac and Freda Frankel Memorial Charitable Trust

The Elizabeth Frankland Moore and Star Foundation

The Jill Franklin Trust

The Gordon Fraser Charitable Trust

The Hugh Fraser Foundation

The Joseph Strong Frazer Trust

The Louis and Valerie Freedman Charitable Settlement

The Freemasons' Grand Charity

The Thomas Freke and Lady Norton Charity

The Charles S French Charitable Trust

The Anne French Memorial Trust

The Freshfield Foundation

The Freshgate Trust Foundation

The Friarsgate Trust

The Friends Hall Farm Street Trust

Friends Provident Charitable Foundation

The Frognal Trust

Maurice Fry Charitable Trust

The Fuellers Charitable Trust Fund

The Fulmer Charitable Trust

Worshipful Company of Furniture Makers Charitable Fund

Gableholt Limited

The Galbraith Trust

The Gale Family Charitable Trust

The Angela Gallagher Memorial Fund

The Gamlen Charitable Trust

The Gamma Trust

The Gannochy Trust

The Ganzoni Charitable Trust

The Worshipful Company of Gardeners of London

The Samuel Gardner Memorial Trust

The Garnett Charitable Trust

Garvan Limited

The Gatsby Charitable Foundation

The Robert Gavron Charitable Trust

The General Nursing Council for England and Wales Trust

J Paul Getty Jr Charitable Trust

The Gibbs Charitable Trust

Simon Gibson Charitable Trust

The G C Gibson Charitable Trust

Lady Gibson's Charitable Trust

The Harvey and Hilary Gilbert Charitable Trust

The Girdlers' Company Charitable Trust

The B and P Glasser Charitable Trust

The Glass-House Trust

Global Care

Global Charities (formerly GCap Charities)

Gloucestershire Community
    Foundation
Worshipful Company of
    Glovers of London Charity
    Fund
The GNC Trust
The Meir Golda Trust
The Sydney and Phyllis
    Goldberg Memorial
    Charitable Trust
The Golden Bottle Trust
The Jack Goldhill Charitable
    Trust
The Goldsmiths' Arts Trust
    Fund
The Goldsmiths' Company
    Charity
The Golsoncott Foundation
The Good Neighbours Trust
The Everard and Mina
    Goodman Charitable
    Foundation
Mike Gooley Trailfinders
    Charity
The Gosling Foundation
    Limited
The Gough Charitable Trust
The Gould Charitable Trust
The Grace Charitable Trust
A B Grace Trust
The Graff Foundation
The Grahame Charitable
    Foundation Limited
Grampian Police Diced Cap
    Charitable Fund
The Granada Foundation
Grand Charitable Trust of the
    Order of Women
    Freemasons
The Grand Order of Water
    Rats' Charities Fund
The Grange Farm Centre Trust
Grantham Yorke Trust
The Gray Trust
The Great Stone Bridge Trust
    of Edenbridge
The Great Torrington Town
    Lands Charity
The Constance Green
    Foundation
The Philip Green Memorial
    Trust
Greenham Common
    Community Trust Limited
Naomi and Jeffrey Greenwood
    Charitable Trust
Greggs Foundation (formerly
    Greggs Trust)
The Gretna Charitable Trust
The Grocers' Charity
The M and R Gross Charities
    Limited
The Grove Charitable Trust
The GRP Charitable Trust
The David and Marie Grumitt
    Foundation

The Bishop of Guildford's
    Foundation
The Guildry Incorporation of
    Perth
The Walter Guinness
    Charitable Trust
The Gunter Charitable Trust
The Gur Trust
Dr Guthrie's Association
The H and M Charitable Trust
H C D Memorial Fund
The H P Charitable Trust
The Hackney Parochial
    Charities
The Hadfield Trust
The Hadley Trust
The Hadrian Trust
The Alfred Haines Charitable
    Trust
The Hale Trust
E F and M G Hall Charitable
    Trust
The Edith Winifred Hall
    Charitable Trust
Robert Hall Charity
The Hamamelis Trust
Hamilton Wallace Trust
Paul Hamlyn Foundation
The Hammonds Charitable
    Trust
The Hampshire and Islands
    Historic Churches Trust
Hampshire and Isle of Wight
    Community Foundation
Hampton Fuel Allotment
    Charity
The W A Handley Charitable
    Trust
Beatrice Hankey Foundation
    Ltd
The Hanley Trust
The Kathleen Hannay
    Memorial Charity
The Doughty Hanson
    Charitable Foundation
Lord Hanson Foundation
The Haramead Trust
Miss K M Harbinson's
    Charitable Trust
The Harborne Parish Lands
    Charity
The Harbour Charitable Trust
The Harbour Foundation
The Harding Trust
William Harding's Charity
The Hare of Steep Charitable
    Trust
The Harebell Centenary Fund
The Kenneth Hargreaves
    Charitable Trust
The Harris Charitable Trust
The Harris Charity
The Harrison and Potter Trust
The John Harrison Charitable
    Trust
The Peter Harrison Foundation

The Spencer Hart Charitable
    Trust
The Hartley Charitable Trust
The N and P Hartley Memorial
    Trust
William Geoffrey Harvey's
    Discretionary Settlement
Haskel Family Foundation
The Hathaway Trust
The Maurice Hatter Foundation
The M A Hawe Settlement
The Hawthorne Charitable
    Trust
The Dorothy Hay-Bolton
    Charitable Trust
The Haymills Charitable Trust
The Headley Trust
Headley-Pitt Charitable Trust
Heagerty Charitable Trust
The Heart of England
    Community Foundation
The Heathcoat Trust
Heathside Charitable Trust
The Charlotte Heber-Percy
    Charitable Trust
The Hedley Denton Charitable
    Trust
The Hedley Foundation
The H J Heinz Company
    Limited Charitable Trust
The Hellenic Foundation
The Michael and Morven Heller
    Charitable Foundation
The Simon Heller Charitable
    Settlement
The Hemby Trust
The Christina Mary Hendrie
    Trust for Scottish and
    Canadian Charities
The Henley Educational Charity
Esther Hennell Charitable
    Trust
The G D Herbert Charitable
    Trust
The Joanna Herbert-Stepney
    Charitable Settlement (also
    known as The Paget
    Charitable Trust)
The Anne Herd Memorial Trust
The Herefordshire Historic
    Churches Trust
The Heritage of London Trust
    Ltd
The Hesed Trust
The Hesslewood Children's
    Trust (Hull Seamen's and
    General Orphanage)
The Bernhard Heuberger
    Charitable Trust
Hexham and Newcastle
    Diocesan Trust (1947)
The Higgs Charitable Trust
Alan Edward Higgs Charity
The High Sheriff's Police Trust
    for the County of West
    Midlands (Building Blocks)

Highcroft Charitable Trust
The Charles Littlewood Hill
Trust
The Hillingdon Partnership
Trust
Lady Hind Trust
The Hinrichsen Foundation
The Hitchin Educational
Foundation
The Eleemosynary Charity of
William Hobbayne
Hobson Charity Limited
Matthew Hodder Charitable
Trust
The Sir Julian Hodge
Charitable Trust
The J G Hogg Charitable Trust
The Holden Charitable Trust
John Holford's Charity
The Hollick Family Charitable
Trust
The Dorothy Holmes Charitable
Trust
The Holst Foundation
The Edward Holt Trust
The Holywood Trust
The Homelands Charitable
Trust
The Homestead Charitable
Trust
Mary Homfray Charitable Trust
Sir Harold Hood's Charitable
Trust
Hope for Youth (formerly
Women Caring Trust)
The Hope Trust
HopMarket Charity
The Cuthbert Horn Trust
The Antony Hornby Charitable
Trust
The Horne Foundation
The Horne Trust
The Worshipful Company of
Horners' Charitable Trusts
The Hornsey Parochial
Charities
The Hospital of God at
Greatham
The Hospital Saturday Fund
Houblon-Norman/George Fund
The House of Industry Estate
The Reta Lila Howard
Foundation
The Daniel Howard Trust
The Hudson Foundation
The Huggard Charitable Trust
The Geoffrey C Hughes
Charitable Trust
The Hull and East Riding
Charitable Trust
Hulme Trust Estates
(Educational)
Human Relief Foundation
The Humanitarian Trust
The Michael and Shirley Hunt
Charitable Trust

The Hunter Foundation
Miss Agnes H Hunter's Trust
The Huntingdon Foundation
Huntingdon Freemen's Charity
John Huntingdon's Charity
Hurdale Charity Limited
The Huxham Charitable Trust
The Nani Huyu Charitable Trust
The P Y N and B Hyams Trust
The Hyde Charitable Trust –
Youth Plus
The Idlewild Trust
The Iliffe Family Charitable
Trust
Impetus Trust
The Indigo Trust
The Ingram Trust
The Inland Waterways
Association
The Inlight Trust
The Inman Charity
The Inner London Magistrates
Court Poor Box and Feeder
Charity
The International Bankers
Charitable Trust (The
Worshipful Company of
International Bankers)
International Spinal Research
Trust
The Ireland Fund of Great
Britain
The Irish Youth Foundation
(UK) Ltd (incorporating The
Lawlor Foundation)
The Ironmongers' Foundation
Irshad Trust
The Charles Irving Charitable
Trust
Irwin Trust
The ISA Charity
The Isaacs Charitable Trust
The J Isaacs Charitable Trust
The ITF Seafarers Trust
The J R S S T Charitable Trust
Elizabeth Jackson Charitable
Trust
The Ruth and Lionel Jacobson
Trust (Second Fund) No 2
Jaffe Family Relief Fund
John James Bristol Foundation
The Susan and Stephen
James Charitable
Settlement (also known as
the Stephen James
Charitable Trust)
The James Trust
The Jarman Charitable Trust
JCA Charitable Foundation
The Jeffrey Charitable Trust
Rees Jeffreys Road Fund
The Jenour Foundation
The Jephcott Charitable Trust
Jerwood Charitable Foundation
Jesus Hospital Charity
Jewish Child's Day

The Jewish Youth Fund
The JMK Charitable Trust
The Joanies Trust
The Harold Joels Charitable
Trust
The Jonathan Joels Charitable
Trust
The Nicholas Joels Charitable
Trust
The Norman Joels Charitable
Trust
The Elton John Aids
Foundation
The Lillie Johnson Charitable
Trust
The Johnson Foundation
The Johnson Group Cleaners
Charity
The Johnnie Johnson Trust
The Johnson Wax Ltd
Charitable Trust
The Joicey Trust
The Jones 1986 Charitable
Trust
The Marjorie and Geoffrey
Jones Charitable Trust
The Jordan Charitable
Foundation
The J E Joseph Charitable
Fund
The Lady Eileen Joseph
Foundation
JTH Charitable Trust
The Judith Trust
The Anton Jurgens Charitable
Trust
The Bernard Kahn Charitable
Trust
The Stanley Kalms Foundation
The Karenza Foundation
The Boris Karloff Charitable
Foundation
The Ian Karten Charitable
Trust
The Kasner Charitable Trust
The Kass Charitable Trust
The Kathleen Trust
The Michael and Ilse Katz
Foundation
The Katzauer Charitable
Settlement
The C S Kaufman Charitable
Trust
The Geoffrey John Kaye
Charitable Foundation
The Emmanuel Kaye
Foundation
Kelsick's Educational
Foundation
The KempWelch Charitable
Trust
The Kay Kendall Leukaemia
Fund
The Kennedy Charitable
Foundation

The Kennel Club Charitable
Trust
The Nancy Kenyon Charitable
Trust
Keren Association
Kermaville Ltd
The Peter Kershaw Trust
The Kessler Foundation
Keswick Hall Trust
The Ursula Keyes Trust
The Robert Kiln Charitable
Trust
The King Henry VIII Endowed
Trust Warwick
The King/Cullimore Charitable
Trust
The King's Fund
The Kingsbury Charity
The Mary Kinross Charitable
Trust
Kirkley Poor's Lands Estate
The Richard Kirkman
Charitable Trust
Kirschel Foundation
Robert Kitchin (Saddlers'
Company)
Ernest Kleinwort Charitable
Trust
The Marina Kleinwort
Charitable Trust
The Kobler Trust
The Kohn Foundation
The Kreditor Charitable Trust
The Kreitman Foundation
The Neil Kreitman Foundation
The Kyte Charitable Trust
The Late Sir Pierce Lacy
Charity Trust
John Laing Charitable Trust
Maurice and Hilda Laing
Charitable Trust
The Christopher Laing
Foundation
The Kirby Laing Foundation
The Martin Laing Foundation
The Beatrice Laing Trust
The Lambert Charitable Trust
Duchy of Lancaster Benevolent
Fund
The Lancaster Foundation
The Allen Lane Foundation
The Langdale Trust
The Langley Charitable Trust
The LankellyChase Foundation
The Lanvern Foundation
The R J Larg Family Charitable
Trust
Largsmount Ltd
The Lark Trust
Laslett's (Hinton) Charity
Lauchentilly Charitable
Foundation 1988
The Lauffer Family Charitable
Foundation
The Kathleen Laurence Trust
The Law Society Charity

The Edgar E Lawley Foundation
The Herd Lawson and Muriel
Lawson Charitable Trust
The Lawson Beckman
Charitable Trust
The Raymond and Blanche
Lawson Charitable Trust
The Carole and Geoffrey
Lawson Foundation
The Mason Le Page Charitable
Trust
The Leach Fourteenth Trust
The David Lean Foundation
The Leathersellers' Company
Charitable Fund
The Leche Trust
The Arnold Lee Charitable
Trust
The Lord Mayor of Leeds
Appeal Fund
Leeds Building Society
Charitable Foundation
Leicester Charity Link (formerly
The Leicester Charity
Organisation Society)
The Kennedy Leigh Charitable
Trust
The Leigh Trust
Mrs Vera Leigh's Charity
The P Leigh-Bramwell Trust 'E'
The Lennox and Wyfold
Foundation
The Erica Leonard Trust
The Leonard Trust
The Mark Leonard Trust
Lesley Lesley and Mutter Trust
Leukaemia and Lymphoma
Research
The Leverhulme Trade
Charities Trust
The Joseph Levy Charitable
Foundation
The John Spedan Lewis
Foundation
The Sir Edward Lewis
Foundation
John Lewis Partnership
General Community Fund
Lichfield Conduit Lands
Lifeline 4 Kids
The Thomas Lilley Memorial
Trust
The Linbury Trust
Lincolnshire Community
Foundation
The Lind Trust
Lindale Educational
Foundation
The Linden Charitable Trust
The Enid Linder Foundation
The Linmardon Trust
The Ruth and Stuart Lipton
Charitable Trust
The Lister Charitable Trust
Frank Litchfield Charitable
Trust

The Andrew and Mary
Elizabeth Little Charitable
Trust
The Second Joseph Aaron
Littman Foundation
The George John and Sheilah
Livanos Charitable Trust
Liverpool Charity and Voluntary
Services
Liverpool Sailors' Home Trust
The Elaine and Angus Lloyd
Charitable Trust
The Charles Lloyd Foundation
The Lloyd Fund
Lloyd's Charities Trust
Lloyds TSB Foundation for
England and Wales
Lloyds TSB Foundation for
Northern Ireland
Lloyds TSB Foundation for the
Channel Islands
The Locker Foundation
The Loftus Charitable Trust
The Lolev Charitable Trust
The Trust for London (formerly
the City Parochial
Foundation)
London Catalyst (formerly The
Metropolitan Hospital-
Sunday Fund)
The London Community
Foundation (formerly Capital
Community Foundation)
The London Law Trust
The William and Katherine
Longman Trust
The Loseley and Guildway
Charitable Trust
The Lotus Foundation
The Lowy Mitchell Foundation
The C L Loyd Charitable Trust
LSA Charitable Trust
The Marie Helen Luen
Charitable Trust
Robert Luff Foundation Ltd
Henry Lumley Charitable Trust
Lady Lumley's Educational
Foundation
C F Lunoe Trust Fund
The Ruth and Jack Lunzer
Charitable Trust
Lord and Lady Lurgan Trust
The Lyndhurst Trust
The Lynn Foundation
The Lynwood Trust
John Lyon's Charity
The Lyons Charitable Trust
The Sir Jack Lyons Charitable
Trust
The Lyras Family Charitable
Trust
Sylvanus Lyson's Charity
The M and C Trust
The M D and S Charitable
Trust
The M K Charitable Trust

The Madeline Mabey Trust
The E M MacAndrew Trust
Macdonald-Buchanan
  Charitable Trust
The Macfarlane Walker Trust
The Mackay and Brewer
  Charitable Trust
The Mackintosh Foundation
The MacRobert Trust
James Madison Trust
The Magdalen and Lasher
  Charity
The Magen Charitable Trust
Man Group plc Charitable
  Trust
Manchester Airport Community
  Trust Fund
The Manchester Guardian
  Society Charitable Trust
Lord Mayor of Manchester's
  Charity Appeal Trust
Mandeville Trust
The Manifold Charitable Trust
W M Mann Foundation
The Leslie and Lilian Manning
  Trust
Marbeh Torah Trust
Marchig Animal Welfare Trust
The Stella and Alexander
  Margulies Charitable Trust
Market Harborough and The
  Bowdens Charity
The Ann and David Marks
  Foundation
The Hilda and Samuel Marks
  Foundation
J P Marland Charitable Trust
The Michael Marsh Charitable
  Trust
The Marsh Christian Trust
The Charlotte Marshall
  Charitable Trust
The Jim Marshall Charitable
  Trust
The D G Marshall of
  Cambridge Trust
Marshall's Charity
Marshgate Charitable
  Settlement
The Mason Porter Charitable
  Trust
The Nancie Massey Charitable
  Trust
The Mathew Trust
The Matt 6.3 Charitable Trust
The Violet Mauray Charitable
  Trust
The Maxell Educational Trust
The Maxwell Family Foundation
Evelyn May Trust
The Mayfield Valley Arts Trust
Mazars Charitable Trust
The McDougall Trust
The McKenna Charitable Trust
The Helen Isabella McMorran
  Charitable Foundation

The James Frederick and Ethel
  Anne Measures Charity
The Medlock Charitable Trust
The Anthony and Elizabeth
  Mellows Charitable
  Settlement
Melow Charitable Trust
The Mercers' Charitable
  Foundation
The Merchant Taylors'
  Company Charities Fund
The Merchant Venturers'
  Charity
The Merchants' House of
  Glasgow
The Mersey Docks and
  Harbour Company
  Charitable Fund
Community Foundation for
  Merseyside
The Zachary Merton and
  George Woofindin
  Convalescent Trust
The Tony Metherell Charitable
  Trust
The Metropolitan Drinking
  Fountain and Cattle Trough
  Association
Gerald Micklem Charitable
  Trust
The Masonic Province of
  Middlesex Charitable Trust
Midhurst Pensions Trust
The Migraine Trust
Miles Trust for the Putney and
  Roehampton Community
Millennium Stadium Charitable
  Trust
The Hugh and Mary Miller
  Bequest Trust
The Miller Foundation
The Millfield House Foundation
The Millfield Trust
The Millhouses Charitable
  Trust
The Millichope Foundation
The Mills Charity
The Millward Charitable Trust
The Clare Milne Trust
Milton Keynes Community
  Foundation
The Edgar Milward Charity
The Peter Minet Trust
The Minos Trust
The Mirfield Educational
  Charity
The Laurence Misener
  Charitable Trust
The Mishcon Family Charitable
  Trust
The Misselbrook Trust
The Brian Mitchell Charitable
  Settlement
The Esmé Mitchell Trust
Keren Mitzvah Trust
The Mizpah Trust

The Mobbs Memorial Trust Ltd
The Modiano Charitable Trust
The Moette Charitable Trust
The Mole Charitable Trust
The D C Moncrieff Charitable
  Trust
Monmouthshire County Council
  Welsh Church Act Fund
The Montague Thompson
  Coon Charitable Trust
The Colin Montgomerie
  Charitable Foundation
The Monument Trust
The Nigel Moores Family
  Charitable Trust
John Moores Foundation
The Peter Moores Foundation
The Morel Charitable Trust
The Morgan Charitable
  Foundation
The Mr and Mrs J T Morgan
  Foundation
The Oliver Morland Charitable
  Trust
The Bernard Morris Charitable
  Trust
The Morris Charitable Trust
The Willie and Mabel Morris
  Charitable Trust
The Peter Morrison Charitable
  Foundation
The Stanley Morrison
  Charitable Trust
Vyoel Moshe Charitable Trust
The Moss Charitable Trust
The Robert and Margaret
  Moss Charitable Trust
Moss Family Charitable Trust
The Mount Everest Foundation
The Edwina Mountbatten Trust
Mountbatten Festival of Music
The Mountbatten Memorial
  Trust
The Mugdock Children's Trust
The Mulberry Trust
The Edith Murphy Foundation
The Mushroom Fund
The Music Sales Charitable
  Trust
Muslim Hands
The Mutual Trust Group
The Kitty and Daniel Nabarro
  Charitable Trust
The Nadezhda Charitable Trust
The Naggar Charitable Trust
The Eleni Nakou Foundation
The Janet Nash Charitable
  Settlement
Nathan Charitable Trust
The National Churches Trust
  (formerly the Historic
  Churches Preservation
  Trust with the Incorporated
  Church Building Society)
The National Manuscripts
  Conservation Trust

The Nchima Trust
Needham Market and Barking Welfare Charities
The Worshipful Company of Needlemakers' Charitable Fund
The Neighbourly Charitable Trust
The James Neill Trust Fund
Nemoral Ltd
Network for Social Change
The New Appeals Organisation for the City and County of Nottingham
New Court Charitable Trust
The Newcomen Collett Foundation
The Frances and Augustus Newman Foundation
Alderman Newton's Educational Foundation
The Chevras Ezras Nitzrochim Trust
The Noon Foundation
The Norda Trust
Norie Charitable Trust
Normalyn Charitable Trust
The Norman Family Charitable Trust
The Duncan Norman Trust Fund
The Normanby Charitable Trust
The North British Hotel Trust
The North West Cancer Research Fund
The Northampton Municipal Church Charities
The Northampton Queen's Institute Relief in Sickness Fund
The Earl of Northampton's Charity
The Northcott Devon Foundation
The Northcott Devon Medical Foundation
The Northern Rock Foundation
The Northmoor Trust
The Northumberland Village Homes Trust
The Northwood Charitable Trust
The Norton Foundation
The Norwich Church of England Young Men's Society
The Norwich Historic Churches Trust Ltd
The Norwich Town Close Estate Charity
The Noswad Charity
The Notgrove Trust
The Nottingham General Dispensary
The Nottingham Gordon Memorial Trust for Boys and Girls

Nottinghamshire Community Foundation
The Nottinghamshire Historic Churches Trust
The Nottinghamshire Miners' Welfare Trust Fund
Novi Most International
The Nuffield Foundation
The Father O'Mahoney Memorial Trust
The Sir Peter O'Sullevan Charitable Trust
The Oak Trust
The Oakdale Trust
The Oakley Charitable Trust
The Oakmoor Charitable Trust
The Odin Charitable Trust
The Ofenheim Charitable Trust
Ogilvie Charities Deed No.2 (including the Charity of Mary Catherine Ford Smith)
The Ogle Christian Trust
Oglesby Charitable Trust
Oizer Charitable Trust
The Old Broad Street Charity Trust
The Old Enfield Charitable Trust
The John Oldacre Foundation
The Oldham Foundation
The Olga Charitable Trust
Onaway Trust
Open Gate
The Ormsby Charitable Trust
Orrin Charitable Trust
The Ouseley Trust
The Owen Family Trust
Oxfam (GB)
City of Oxford Charity
The Oxfordshire Community Foundation
The P F Charitable Trust
Padwa Charitable Foundation
The Pallant Charitable Trust
The Palmer Foundation
The Panacea Society
Panton Trust
The Paragon Trust
The Park House Charitable Trust
The Frank Parkinson Agricultural Trust
The Samuel and Freda Parkinson Charitable Trust
The Parthenon Trust
The Constance Paterson Charitable Trust
The Patrick Charitable Trust
The Jack Patston Charitable Trust
Paycare Charity Trust (previously known as Patients' Aid Association Hospital and Medical Charities Trust)
The Payne Charitable Trust

The Harry Payne Trust
The Susanna Peake Charitable Trust
The Pedmore Sporting Club Trust Fund
The Dowager Countess Eleanor Peel Trust
The Pennycress Trust
The Performing Right Society Foundation
The Persson Charitable Trust (formerly Highmoore Hall Charitable Trust)
The Persula Foundation
The Jack Petchey Foundation
The Petplan Charitable Trust
The Philips and Rubens Charitable Trust
The Phillips Charitable Trust
The Phillips Family Charitable Trust
Philological Foundation
The David Pickford Charitable Foundation
The Pilgrim Trust
The Cecil Pilkington Charitable Trust
The Pilkington Charities Fund
The Austin and Hope Pilkington Trust
The Sir Harry Pilkington Trust
The Col W W Pilkington Will Trusts The General Charity Fund
The DLA Piper Charitable Trust
The Worshipful Company of Plaisterers Charitable Trust
The Platinum Trust
Polden-Puckham Charitable Foundation
The Poling Charitable Trust
The George and Esme Pollitzer Charitable Settlement
The J S F Pollitzer Charitable Settlement
The Ponton House Trust
The Mayor of Poole's Appeal Fund
Edith and Ferdinand Porjes Charitable Trust
The John Porter Charitable Trust
The Porter Foundation
The Portrack Charitable Trust
The J E Posnansky Charitable Trust
The Mary Potter Convent Hospital Trust
The David and Elaine Potter Foundation
The Powell Foundation
The W L Pratt Charitable Trust
Premierquote Ltd
Premishlaner Charitable Trust
The Lucy Price Relief-in-Need Charity

Full project funding

Sir John Priestman Charity Trust

The Primrose Trust

The Prince of Wales's Charitable Foundation

The Priory Foundation

Prison Service Charity Fund

The Privy Purse Charitable Trust

The Proven Family Trust

The Provincial Grand Charity of the Province of Derbyshire

PSA Peugeot Citroen Charity Trust

The Puebla Charitable Trust

The Richard and Christine Purchas Charitable Trust

The Puri Foundation

Mr and Mrs J A Pye's Charitable Settlement

Quartet Community Foundation (formerly the Greater Bristol Foundation)

Queen Mary's Roehampton Trust

The Queen's Silver Jubilee Trust

R S Charitable Trust

The R V W Trust

The Monica Rabagliati Charitable Trust

Rachel Charitable Trust

The Mr and Mrs Philip Rackham Charitable Trust

Richard Radcliffe Charitable Trust

The Radcliffe Trust

The Ragdoll Foundation

The Rainford Trust

The Peggy Ramsay Foundation

The Joseph and Lena Randall Charitable Trust

The Rank Foundation

The Fanny Rapaport Charitable Settlement

The Ratcliff Foundation

The Ratcliff Pension Charity

The Ratcliffe Charitable Trust

The Eleanor Rathbone Charitable Trust

The Sigrid Rausing Trust

The Ravensdale Trust

The Rayden Charitable Trust

The Roger Raymond Charitable Trust

The Rayne Foundation

The Rayne Trust

The John Rayner Charitable Trust

The Sir James Reckitt Charity

The Red Arrows Trust

Red Hill Charitable Trust

The Red Rose Charitable Trust

The C A Redfern Charitable Foundation

The Reed Foundation

Richard Reeve's Foundation

The Max Reinhardt Charitable Trust

Relief Fund for Romania Limited

The Rest Harrow Trust

Reuben Brothers Foundation

The Joan K Reynell Charitable Trust

The Nathaniel Reyner Trust Fund

The Rhododendron Trust

The Sir Cliff Richard Charitable Trust

The Clive Richards Charity

The Violet M Richards Charity

The Richmond Parish Lands Charity

Ridgesave Limited

The Ripple Effect Foundation

The Sir John Ritblat Family Foundation

The River Trust

Thomas Roberts Trust

The Robertson Trust

The Rochester Bridge Trust

The Rock Foundation

The Rock Solid Trust

The Rofeh Trust

Richard Rogers Charitable Settlement

Rokach Family Charitable Trust

The Helen Roll Charitable Trust

The Sir James Roll Charitable Trust

The Roman Research Trust

Romeera Foundation

The C A Rookes Charitable Trust

Mrs L D Rope Third Charitable Settlement

The Rosca Trust

The Rose Foundation

The Cecil Rosen Foundation

Rosetrees Trust

The Rothermere Foundation

The Rotherwick Foundation

The Roughley Charitable Trust

Mrs Gladys Row Fogo Charitable Trust

Rowanville Ltd

The Christopher Rowbotham Charitable Trust

The Rowing Foundation

The Rowlands Trust

The Joseph Rowntree Charitable Trust

The Joseph Rowntree Foundation

Joseph Rowntree Reform Trust Limited

Royal Artillery Charitable Fund

Royal Docks Trust (London)

Royal Masonic Trust for Girls and Boys

The Royal Scots Benevolent Society

The Alfred and Frances Rubens Charitable Trust

The Rubin Foundation

William Arthur Rudd Memorial Trust

The Rufford Foundation

The Russell Trust

The J S and E C Rymer Charitable Trust

S O Charitable Trust

The Jeremy and John Sacher Charitable Trust

The Michael Harry Sacher Trust

The Raymond and Beverley Sackler 1988 Foundation

The Sackler Trust (Formerly Dr Mortimer and Theresa Sackler Foundation)

The Ruzin Sadagora Trust

The Saddlers' Company Charitable Fund

Erach and Roshan Sadri Foundation

The Saga Charitable Trust

The Jean Sainsbury Animal Welfare Trust

The Alan and Babette Sainsbury Charitable Fund

The Sainsbury Family Charitable Trusts

The Saintbury Trust

The Saints and Sinners Trust

The Salamander Charitable Trust

The Salt Foundation

The Salt Trust

The Sammermar Trust

Basil Samuel Charitable Trust

The Hon. M J Samuel Charitable Trust

The Peter Samuel Charitable Trust

The Camilla Samuel Fund

The Samworth Foundation

The Sandra Charitable Trust

Santander UK Foundation Limited

Jimmy Savile Charitable Trust

The Scarfe Charitable Trust

The Schapira Charitable Trust

The Schmidt-Bodner Charitable Trust

The Schreib Trust

The Schreiber Charitable Trust

The Francis C Scott Charitable Trust

The Sir James and Lady Scott Trust

The Scott Trust Foundation

The Storrow Scott Will Trust

The Scottish Arts Council

Scottish Coal Industry Special Welfare Fund

The Scottish Community
Foundation
The Scottish International
Education Trust
The Scouloudi Foundation
Seafarers UK (King George's
Fund for Sailors)
Seamen's Hospital Society
The Searchlight Electric
Charitable Trust
The Searle Charitable Trust
The Helene Sebba Charitable
Trust
The Samuel Sebba Charitable
Trust
The Seedfield Trust
The Ayrton Senna Foundation
The Seven Fifty Trust
The Severn Trent Water
Charitable Trust Fund
The Cyril Shack Trust
The Jean Shanks Foundation
The Shanti Charitable Trust
ShareGift (The Orr Mackintosh
Foundation)
The Linley Shaw Foundation
The Sheepdrove Trust
The Sheffield and District
Hospital Services
Charitable Fund
The Sheldon Trust
The P and D Shepherd
Charitable Trust
The Sylvia and Colin Shepherd
Charitable Trust
The Archie Sherman Cardiff
Foundation
The Archie Sherman Charitable
Trust
The R C Sherriff Trust
The Shetland Charitable Trust
SHINE (Support and Help in
Education)
The Barnett and Sylvia Shine
No 2 Charitable Trust
The Bassil Shippam and
Alsford Trust
The Shipwrights' Company
Charitable Fund
The Shirley Foundation
Shlomo Memorial Fund Limited
The J A Shone Memorial Trust
The Barbara A Shuttleworth
Memorial Trust
The Mary Elizabeth Siebel
Charity
David and Jennifer Sieff
Charitable Trust
The Julius Silman Charitable
Trust
The Leslie Silver Charitable
Trust
The Simpson Education and
Conservation Trust
The Simpson Foundation

The Huntly and Margery
Sinclair Charitable Trust
Sino-British Fellowship Trust
The Skelton Bounty
The Charles Skey Charitable
Trust
Skipton Building Society
Charitable Foundation
The John Slater Foundation
The SMB Charitable Trust
The Mrs Smith and Mount
Trust
The N Smith Charitable
Settlement
The Amanda Smith Charitable
Trust
The E H Smith Charitable Trust
The Smith Charitable Trust
The Henry Smith Charity
The Leslie Smith Foundation
The Martin Smith Foundation
Stanley Smith General
Charitable Trust
The Stanley Smith UK
Horticultural Trust
The Snowball Trust
The Sobell Foundation
Solihull Community Foundation
The Solo Charitable
Settlement
Dr Richard Solomon's
Charitable Trust
The E C Sosnow Charitable
Trust
The Souter Charitable Trust
The South Square Trust
The Stephen R and Philippa H
Southall Charitable Trust
The W F Southall Trust
The Southover Manor General
Education Trust
The Southwold Trust
The Sovereign Health Care
Charitable Trust
Sparks Charity (Sport Aiding
Medical Research For Kids)
Sparquote Limited
The Spear Charitable Trust
The Worshipful Company of
Spectacle Makers' Charity
The Jessie Spencer Trust
The Ralph and Irma Sperring
Charity
The Moss Spiro Will Charitable
Foundation
The Spoore, Merry and Rixman
Foundation
Spring Harvest
Springfields Employees'
Medical Research and
Charity Trust Fund
Springrule Ltd
The Spurrell Charitable Trust
The Geoff and Fiona Squire
Foundation

St Christopher's College
Educational Trust
St Francis's Leprosy Guild
St Gabriel's Trust
St James' Trust Settlement
St James's Place Foundation
Sir Walter St John's
Educational Charity
St Katharine and Shadwell
Trust
St Michael's and All Saints'
Charities
The Late St Patrick White
Charitable Trust
St Teilo's Trust
The Stanley Foundation Ltd
The Stanton Ballard Charitable
Trust
The Staples Trust
The Star Charitable Trust
The Peter Stebbings Memorial
Charity
The Steinberg Family
Charitable Trust
The Hugh Stenhouse
Foundation
The Sigmund Sternberg
Charitable Foundation
Stervon Ltd
The Stevenage Community
Trust
The June Stevens Foundation
The Steventon Allotments and
Relief-in-Need Charity
The Stewards' Charitable Trust
The Stewards' Company
Limited (incorporating the J
W Laing Trust and the J W
Laing Biblical Scholarship
Trust)
The Sir Halley Stewart Trust
The Stobart Newlands
Charitable Trust
The Edward Stocks-Massey
Bequest Fund
The Stokenchurch Educational
Charity
The Stoller Charitable Trust
The M J C Stone Charitable
Trust
The Stone-Mallabar Charitable
Foundation
The Samuel Storey Family
Charitable Trust
Peter Stormonth Darling
Charitable Trust
The Strangward Trust
The Strasser Foundation
Strathclyde Police Benevolent
Fund
The W O Street Charitable
Foundation
The Sudborough Foundation
The Suffolk Foundation
The Suffolk Historic Churches
Trust

The Summerfield Charitable
Trust
The Surrey Historic Buildings
Trust Ltd
The Sussex Historic Churches
Trust
The Sutasoma Trust
Sutton Coldfield Municipal
Charities
Swansea and Brecon Diocesan
Board of Finance Limited
The John Swire (1989)
Charitable Trust
The Swire Charitable Trust
The Hugh and Ruby Sykes
Charitable Trust
The Charles and Elsie Sykes
Trust
The Sylvanus Charitable Trust
The Stella Symons Charitable
Trust
The Tabeel Trust
The Tajtelbaum Charitable
Trust
Tallow Chandlers Benevolent
Fund
The Tangent Charitable Trust
The Lady Tangye Charitable
Trust
The David Tannen Charitable
Trust
The Tanner Trust
The Lili Tapper Charitable
Foundation
The Mrs A Lacy Tate Trust
The Tay Charitable Trust
Humphrey Richardson Taylor
Charitable Trust
The Connie and Albert Taylor
Charitable Trust
The Cyril Taylor Charitable
Trust
A P Taylor Trust
Tearfund
The Tedworth Charitable Trust
Tees Valley Community
Foundation
The Templeton Goodwill Trust
Tesco Charity Trust
The Thames Wharf Charity
The Thistle Trust
The Loke Wan Tho Memorial
Foundation
The Arthur and Margaret
Thompson Charitable Trust
The Thompson Family
Charitable Trust
The Len Thomson Charitable
Trust
The Sue Thomson Foundation
The Sir Jules Thorn Charitable
Trust
The Thornton Foundation
The Thornton Trust
The Three Guineas Trust
The Three Oaks Trust

The Thriplow Charitable Trust
The Tinsley Foundation
The Tisbury Telegraph Trust
TJH Foundation
The Tobacco Pipe Makers and
Tobacco Trade Benevolent
Fund
The Tolkien Trust
Tollemache (Buckminster)
Charitable Trust
Tomchei Torah Charitable
Trust
The Tompkins Foundation
The Tory Family Foundation
Tottenham Grammar School
Foundation
The Tower Hill Trust
The Towry Law Charitable Trust
(also known as the Castle
Educational Trust)
The Toy Trust
The Mayor of Trafford's Charity
Fund
The Constance Travis
Charitable Trust
The Treeside Trust
The Triangle Trust (1949) Fund
The True Colours Trust
Truedene Co. Ltd
The Truemark Trust
Truemart Limited
Trumros Limited
Trust Sixty Three
The Trusthouse Charitable
Foundation
Tudor Rose Ltd
The Tudor Trust
The Tufton Charitable Trust
The R D Turner Charitable
Trust
The Douglas Turner Trust
The Florence Turner Trust
Miss S M Tutton Charitable
Trust
The TUUT Charitable Trust
Community Foundation Serving
Tyne and Wear and
Northumberland
Trustees of Tzedakah
Ulster Garden Villages Ltd
Ultach Trust
Ulting Overseas Trust
The Ulverscroft Foundation
Ulverston Town Lands Charity
The Underwood Trust
The Union of Orthodox Hebrew
Congregation
The United Society for the
Propagation of the Gospel
Unity Theatre Trust
The David Uri Memorial Trust
Uxbridge United Welfare Trust
Vale of Glamorgan – Welsh
Church Fund
The Valentine Charitable Trust
The Van Neste Foundation

Mrs Maud Van Norden's
Charitable Foundation
The Vandervell Foundation
The Vardy Foundation
The Variety Club Children's
Charity
Veneziana Fund
The Verdon-Smith Family
Charitable Settlement
Victoria Homes Trust
The Nigel Vinson Charitable
Trust
The William and Ellen Vinten
Trust
The Vintners' Company
Charitable Foundation
Vintners' Gifts Charity
Vision Charity
Vivdale Ltd
The Viznitz Foundation
Voluntary Action Fund
Wade's Charity
The Scurrah Wainwright Charity
The Community Foundation in
Wales
Wales Council for Voluntary
Action
Robert and Felicity Waley-
Cohen Charitable Trust
The Thomas Wall Trust
The F J Wallis Charitable
Settlement
War on Want
The Ward Blenkinsop Trust
The George Ward Charitable
Trust
The Barbara Ward Children's
Foundation
The John Warren Foundation
G R Waters Charitable Trust
2000
The Waterways Trust
The Wates Foundation
The Howard Watson Symington
Memorial Charity
John Watson's Trust
Weatherley Charitable Trust
The Weavers' Company
Benevolent Fund
Webb Memorial Trust
The Weinberg Foundation
The Weinstein Foundation
The Weinstock Fund
The Weldon UK Charitable
Trust
The Wellcome Trust
Welsh Church Fund Dyfed
area (Carmarthenshire,
Ceredigion and
Pembrokeshire)
The Welton Foundation
The Wessex Youth Trust
The West Derby Wastelands
Charity
West London Synagogue
Charitable Fund

The West Yorkshire Police
Community Fund
The Westminster Foundation
The Garfield Weston
Foundation
The Whitaker Charitable Trust
The Colonel W H Whitbread
Charitable Trust
The Simon Whitbread
Charitable Trust
The Whitecourt Charitable
Trust
The Norman Whiteley Trust
The Whitley Animal Protection
Trust
The Whittlesey Charity
The Lionel Wigram Memorial
Trust
The Felicity Wilde Charitable
Trust
The Will Charitable Trust
The Kay Williams Charitable
Foundation
The Williams Family Charitable
Trust
The H D H Wills 1965
Charitable Trust
The Dame Violet Wills Will
Trust
The Wilmcote Charitrust
David Wilson Foundation
The Wilson Foundation
J and J R Wilson Trust
The Community Foundation for
Wiltshire and Swindon
The Benjamin Winegarten
Charitable Trust
The Francis Winham
Foundation
Wirral Mayor's Charity
The Michael and Anna Wix
Charitable Trust
The Wixamtree Trust
The Woburn 1986 Charitable
Trust
The Maurice Wohl Charitable
Foundation
The Charles Wolfson
Charitable Trust
Women's World Day of Prayer
(NCWWDPEWNI)
The James Wood Bequest
Fund
Woodlands Green Ltd
Woodlands Trust
The Woodward Charitable
Trust
Worcester Municipal Charities
(incorporating Worcester
Consolidated Municipal
Charity and Worcester
Municipal Exhibitions
Foundation)
The Worcestershire and
Dudley Historic Churches
Trust

The Fred and Della Worms
Charitable Trust
The Wragge and Co. Charitable
Trust
The Diana Edgson Wright
Charitable Trust
The Matthews Wrightson
Charity Trust
Miss E B Wrightson's
Charitable Settlement
Wychdale Ltd
Wychville Ltd
The Wyndham Charitable Trust
The Wyseliot Charitable Trust
The Xerox (UK) Trust
The Yapp Charitable Trust
The Dennis Alan Yardy
Charitable Trust
The W Wing Yip and Brothers
Foundation
The York Children's Trust
Yorkshire Agricultural Society
The South Yorkshire
Community Foundation
The Yorkshire Dales
Millennium Trust
The John Young Charitable
Settlement
The William Allen Young
Charitable Trust
The John K Young Endowment
Fund
Zephyr Charitable Trust
The Marjorie and Arnold Ziff
Charitable Foundation
Stephen Zimmerman
Charitable Trust
The Zochonis Charitable Trust
Zurich Community Trust (UK)
Limited

....

■ Project Funding
(excluding
overheads)

The 1970 Trust
The 1989 Willan Charitable
Trust
The 29th May 1961 Charitable
Trust
The Aberbrothock Skea Trust
The Aberdeenshire Educational
Trust Scheme
ABF The Soldiers' Charity
(formerly the Army
Benevolent Fund)
Achiezer Association Ltd
Achisomoch Aid Company
Limited
The ACT Foundation
Action Medical Research
The Company of Actuaries'
Charitable Trust Fund
The Sylvia Adams Charitable
Trust
The Victor Adda Foundation

The Adint Charitable Trust
Age Scotland (Formerly Age
Concern Scotland and Help
the Aged)
Age UK (formerly Help the
Aged and Age Concern)
Aid to the Church in Need (UK)
The Sylvia Aitken Charitable
Trust
The Ajahma Charitable Trust
Aldgate and All Hallows'
Barking Exhibition
Foundation
The Aldgate Freedom
Foundation
All Saints Educational Trust
Allchurches Trust Ltd
The H B Allen Charitable Trust
The Alliance Family Foundation
Angus Allnatt Charitable
Foundation
The Pat Allsop Charitable Trust
Almondsbury Charity
Altamont Ltd
Alvor Charitable Trust
The Ammco Trust
Viscount Amory's Charitable
Trust
The AMW Charitable Trust
The André Christian Trust
Anguish's Educational
Foundation
The Animal Defence Trust
The Eric Anker-Petersen
Charity
Ambrose and Ann Appelbe
Trust
The Appletree Trust
The John Apthorp Charitable
Trust
The Arbib Foundation
The John M Archer Charitable
Trust
The Archer Trust
The Argus Appeal
The Armenian Relief Society of
Great Britain Trust
The Armourers' and Brasiers'
Gauntlet Trust
Arsenal Charitable Trust
The Artemis Charitable Trust
The Arts and Entertainment
Charitable Trust
Arts Council England
The Arts Council of Northern
Ireland
The Arts Council of Wales
The Ove Arup Foundation
The AS Charitable Trust
The Ashden Trust
The Ashendene Trust
The Ashley Family Foundation
(formerly The Laura Ashley
Foundation)
The Ian Askew Charitable Trust

The Associated Country Women of the World (ACWW)

The Association of Colleges Charitable Trust

Astellas European Foundation

Asthma UK

AstonMansfield Charitable Trust

The Astor Foundation

The Astor of Hever Trust

The Aurelius Charitable Trust

The Avenue Charitable Trust

AW Charitable Trust

The BAA Communities Trust

The BACTA Charitable Trust

The Scott Bader Commonwealth Ltd

The Bagri Foundation

Veta Bailey Charitable Trust

The Austin Bailey Trust

The Baily Thomas Charitable Fund

The Baird Trust

The Baker Charitable Trust

The Balcombe Charitable Trust

The Albert Casanova Ballard Deceased Trust

The Ballinger Charitable Trust

The Balmore Trust

The Balney Charitable Trust

The Baltic Charitable Fund

The Bamford Charitable Foundation

The Banbury Charities

William P Bancroft (No 2) Charitable Trust and Jenepher Gillett Trust

The Band Trust

The Barbers' Company General Charities

The Barbour Foundation

Barchester Healthcare Foundation

The Barclay Foundation

The Baring Foundation

Peter Barker-Mill Memorial Charity

Barleycorn Trust

Barnes Workhouse Fund

The Barnsbury Charitable Trust

The Barnwood House Trust

The Misses Barrie Charitable Trust

Barrington Family Charitable Trust

Stephen J Barry Charitable Trust

The Bartlett Taylor Charitable Trust

The Paul Bassham Charitable Trust

The Batchworth Trust

The Bay Tree Charitable Trust

D H and L H Baylin Charitable Trust

The Louis Baylis (Maidenhead Advertiser) Charitable Trust

BBC Children in Need

B-CH 1971 Charitable Trust

The Beacon Trust

The Bearder Charity

The James Beattie Charitable Trust

The Beaufort House Trust Limited

The Beaverbrook Foundation

The Beccles Town Lands Charity

The Becker Family Charitable Trust

The Becketts and Sargeants Educational Foundation

The John Beckwith Charitable Trust

The Peter Beckwith Charitable Trust

The Bedford Charity (The Harpur Trust)

The David and Ruth Behrend Fund

The Beit Trust

The Bellahouston Bequest Fund

The Bellinger Donnay Trust

Belljoe Tzedoko Ltd

The Benfield Motors Charitable Trust

The Benham Charitable Settlement

Maurice and Jacqueline Bennett Charitable Trust

The Berkshire Community Foundation

The Bestway Foundation

Thomas Betton's Charity for Pensions and Relief-in-Need

BHST

The Mason Bibby 1981 Trust

BibleLands

The Bideford Bridge Trust

The Big Lottery Fund

The Billmeir Charitable Trust

The Bingham Trust

The Bintaub Charitable Trust

The Birmingham District Nursing Charitable Trust

The Birmingham Hospital Saturday Fund Medical Charity and Welfare Trust

Birmingham International Airport Community Trust

The Lord Mayor of Birmingham's Charity

The Michael Bishop Foundation

The Bishop's Development Fund

The Bertie Black Foundation

Isabel Blackman Foundation

The Herbert and Peter Blagrave Charitable Trust

The Blair Foundation

The Blanchminster Trust

The Sir Victor Blank Charitable Settlement

The Neville and Elaine Blond Charitable Trust

The Bluston Charitable Settlement

The Nicholas Boas Charitable Trust

The Body Shop Foundation

The Boltons Trust

The Bonamy Charitable Trust

The John and Celia Bonham Christie Charitable Trust

The Charlotte Bonham-Carter Charitable Trust

Bonhomie United Charity Society

The Boots Charitable Trust

The Bordon and Liphook Charity

The Oliver Borthwick Memorial Trust

The Bothwell Charitable Trust

H E and E L Botteley Charitable Trust

The Harry Bottom Charitable Trust

The Anthony Bourne Foundation

The Bower Trust

The Bowerman Charitable Trust

John and Susan Bowers Fund

The Bowland Charitable Trust

The William Brake Charitable Trust

The Liz and Terry Bramall Charitable Trust

The Tony Bramall Charitable Trust

The Harold and Alice Bridges Charity

The Brighton District Nursing Association Trust

Bristol Archdeaconry Charity

John Bristow and Thomas Mason Trust

Britannia Foundation

The British Council for Prevention of Blindness

The British Dietetic Association General and Education Trust Fund

The British Gas (Scottish Gas) Energy Trust

British Heart Foundation

British Humane Association

British Institute at Ankara

British Ornithologists' Union

British Record Industry Trust

The Britten-Pears Foundation

The Britto Foundation

The J and M Britton Charitable Trust

The Charles and Edna Broadhurst Charitable Trust
The Bromley Trust
The Roger Brooke Charitable Trust
The David Brooke Charity
The Charles Brotherton Trust
Joseph Brough Charitable Trust
The Swinfen Broun Charitable Trust
Mrs E E Brown Charitable Settlement
The Bryant Trust
The Buckinghamshire Foundation
The Buckinghamshire Masonic Centenary Fund
Buckland Charitable Trust
The Rosemary Bugden Charitable Trust
The Bulldog Trust Limited
The E F Bulmer Benevolent Fund
Burdens Charitable Foundation
The Clara E Burgess Charity
The Burry Charitable Trust
The Arnold Burton 1998 Charitable Trust
The Burton Breweries Charitable Trust
The Geoffrey Burton Charitable Trust
Consolidated Charity of Burton upon Trent
Butchers' Company General Charities
The Noel Buxton Trust
Henry T and Lucy B Cadbury Charitable Trust
The Christopher Cadbury Charitable Trust
The G W Cadbury Charitable Trust
The Richard Cadbury Charitable Trust
The Edward and Dorothy Cadbury Trust
The George Cadbury Trust
CAF (Charities Aid Foundation)
CAFOD (Catholic Agency for Overseas Development)
The Callander Charitable Trust
Calleva Foundation
Calouste Gulbenkian Foundation
The Calpe Trust
Calypso Browning Trust
The Campden Charities Trustee
The Canning Trust
The Carew Pole Charitable Trust
The D W T Cargill Fund
Carlee Ltd

The Carlton House Charitable Trust
The Worshipful Company of Carmen Benevolent Trust
The Carnegie Dunfermline Trust
The Carpenter Charitable Trust
The Carpenters' Company Charitable Trust
The Carrington Charitable Trust
The Carron Charitable Settlement
The Leslie Mary Carter Charitable Trust
The Carvill Trust
The Casey Trust
Cash for Kids Radio Clyde
Sir John Cass's Foundation
The Elizabeth Casson Trust
The Castang Foundation
The Catalyst Charitable Trust (formerly the Buckle Family Charitable Trust)
The Catholic Charitable Trust
Catholic Foreign Missions
The Catholic Trust for England and Wales
The Cattanach Charitable Trust
The Joseph and Annie Cattle Trust
The Thomas Sivewright Catto Charitable Settlement
The Wilfrid and Constance Cave Foundation
The Cayo Foundation
The B G S Cayzer Charitable Trust
The Cazenove Charitable Trust
Celtic Charity Fund
The Cemlyn-Jones Trust
CfBT Education Trust
The Pamela Champion Foundation
The Chapman Charitable Trust
John William Chapman's Charitable Trust
The Charities Advisory Trust
Charitworth Limited
The Charter 600 Charity
The Worshipful Company of Chartered Accountants General Charitable Trust (also known as CALC)
The Chasah Trust
The Chelsea Building Society Charitable Foundation
The Chelsea Square 1994 Trust
The Cheruby Trust
The Cheshire Provincial Fund of Benevolence
The Chetwode Foundation
Chevioty Asset Management Charitable Trust
The Malcolm Chick Charity

Childs Charitable Trust
The Childwick Trust
The Chipping Sodbury Town Lands Charity
CHK Charities Limited
The Chownes Foundation
The Chrimes Family Charitable Trust
The Christabella Charitable Trust
Christadelphian Samaritan Fund
Christian Aid
Christian Response to Eastern Europe
The Church and Community Fund
The Church Burgesses Educational Foundation
Church Burgesses Trust
Church of Ireland Priorities Fund
The Church Urban Fund
City and County of Swansea Welsh Church Act Fund
The City Bridge Trust (formerly known as Bridge House Trust)
The City Educational Trust Fund
CLA Charitable Trust
Stephen Clark 1957 Charitable Trust
J A Clark Charitable Trust
The Hilda and Alice Clark Charitable Trust
The Roger and Sarah Bancroft Clark Charitable Trust
The Clarke Charitable Settlement
The Cleary Foundation
The Cleopatra Trust
Lord Clinton's Charitable Trust
The Clore Duffield Foundation
Miss V L Clore's 1967 Charitable Trust
Closehelm Ltd
Richard Cloudesley's Charity
The Clover Trust
The Robert Clutterbuck Charitable Trust
Clydpride Ltd
The Coalfields Regeneration Trust
The John Coates Charitable Trust
Coats Foundation Trust
The Cobtree Charity Trust Ltd
The Denise Cohen Charitable Trust
The Vivienne and Samuel Cohen Charitable Trust
The John S Cohen Foundation
The R and S Cohen Foundation

The Colchester Catalyst Charity
The Cole Charitable Trust
The Colefax Charitable Trust
The John and Freda Coleman Charitable Trust
The George Henry Collins Charity
The E Alec Colman Charitable Fund Ltd
The Sir Jeremiah Colman Gift Trust
The Colt Foundation
The Coltstaple Trust
Colwinston Charitable Trust
Colyer-Fergusson Charitable Trust
Comic Relief
The Comino Foundation
Community Foundation for Calderdale
The Community Foundation for Northern Ireland
The Compton Charitable Trust
The Congleton Inclosure Trust
The Conservation Foundation
The Consolidated Charities for the Infirm Merchant Taylors' Company
The Ernest Cook Trust
The Cooks Charity
The Catherine Cookson Charitable Trust
Mabel Cooper Charity
The Alice Ellen Cooper Dean Charitable Foundation
The Co-operative Foundation
The Marjorie Coote Animal Charity Trust
The Marjorie Coote Old People's Charity
The Helen Jean Cope Trust
The J Reginald Corah Foundation Fund
The Gershon Coren Charitable Foundation
The Corinthian Trust
Edwin Cornforth 1983 Charity Trust
The Cornwell Charitable Trust
The Sidney and Elizabeth Corob Charitable Trust
The Corona Charitable Trust
The Costa Family Charitable Trust (formerly the Morgan Williams Charitable Trust)
The Cotton Industry War Memorial Trust
The Cotton Trust
County Durham Community Foundation
The Augustine Courtauld Trust
The General Charities of the City of Coventry
Coventry Building Society Charitable Foundation

The John Cowan Foundation
The Sir William Coxen Trust Fund
The Lord Cozens-Hardy Trust
The Craignish Trust
The Craps Charitable Trust
Michael Crawford Children's Charity
The Cray Trust
The Crescent Trust
Cripplegate Foundation
The Violet and Milo Cripps Charitable Trust
The Harry Crook Foundation
The Cross Trust
The Croydon Relief in Need Charities
The Mayor of Croydon's Charity Fund
Cruden Foundation Ltd
The Ronald Cruickshank's Foundation
The R D Crusaders Foundation
The Culra Charitable Trust
Cumberland Building Society Charitable Foundation
Cumbria Community Foundation
The Cunningham Trust
The D J H Currie Memorial Trust
The Dennis Curry Charitable Trust
The Raymond Curtis Charitable Trust
The Manny Cussins Foundation
The Cwmbran Trust
Itzchok Meyer Cymerman Trust Ltd
The D G Charitable Settlement
Roald Dahl's Marvellous Children's Charity
The Daily Prayer Union Charitable Trust Ltd
The Daisy Trust
The Daiwa Anglo-Japanese Foundation
The Dr and Mrs A Darlington Charitable Trust
Baron Davenport's Charity
The Davidson (Nairn) Charitable Trust
The Davidson Family Charitable Trust
The Alderman Joe Davidson Memorial Trust
Michael Davies Charitable Settlement
The Gwendoline and Margaret Davies Charity
The Wilfrid Bruce Davis Charitable Trust
Davis-Rubens Charitable Trust
The Dawe Charitable Trust

The De Clermont Charitable Company Ltd
Peter De Haan Charitable Trust
The Leopold De Rothschild Charitable Trust
The Deakin Charitable Trust
William Dean Countryside and Educational Trust
The Debmar Benevolent Trust
The Dellal Foundation
The Delves Charitable Trust
The Demigryphon Trust
The Denman Charitable Trust
The Denton Charitable Trust
The Denton Wilde Sapte Charitable Trust
The Earl of Derby's Charitable Trust
Derbyshire Community Foundation
The J N Derbyshire Trust
Devon Community Foundation
The Devon Educational Trust
The Duke of Devonshire's Charitable Trust
The Sandy Dewhirst Charitable Trust
The Laduma Dhamecha Charitable Trust
Diabetes UK
The Dibden Allotments Fund
The Dickon Trust
The Digbeth Trust
The Dinwoodie Settlement
Dischma Charitable Trust
The DLM Charitable Trust
Louise Dobson Charitable Trust
The Derek and Eileen Dodgson Foundation
The Dollond Charitable Trust
Domepride Ltd
The Dorcas Trust
The Dorus Trust
The Doughty Charity Trust
The R M Douglas Charitable Trust
The Drapers' Charitable Fund
The Dugdale Charitable Trust
The Duis Charitable Trust
The Dulverton Trust
The P B Dumbell Charitable Trust
The Dumbreck Charity
Dunard Fund
Ronald Duncan Literary Foundation
The Houghton Dunn Charitable Trust
The Dunn Family Charitable Trust
The W E Dunn Trust
Dushinsky Trust Ltd
The Dwek Family Charitable Trust

The Dyers' Company
Charitable Trust
The Eagle Charity Trust
The Earley Charity
Earls Colne and Halstead
Educational Charity
The Earmark Trust
East Kent Provincial Charities
East London Community
Foundation
Eastern Counties Educational
Trust Limited
The Sir John Eastwood
Foundation
The Ebenezer Trust
The EBM Charitable Trust
Eden Arts Trust
EDF Energy Trust (EDFET)
The Gilbert and Eileen Edgar
Foundation
Edinburgh Children's Holiday
Fund
The Edinburgh Trust, No 2
Account
Edinburgh Voluntary
Organisations' Trust Funds
The W G Edwards Charitable
Foundation
The William Edwards
Educational Charity
The Elephant Trust
The George Elias Charitable
Trust
The Gerald Palmer Eling Trust
Company
The Wilfred and Elsie Elkes
Charity Fund
The Maud Elkington Charitable
Trust
The Ellerdale Trust
The John Ellerman Foundation
The Ellinson Foundation Ltd
James Ellis Charitable Trust
The Elmgrant Trust
The Elmley Foundation
The Vernon N Ely Charitable
Trust
The Embleton Trust
The Emerton-Christie Charity
The Emmandjay Charitable
Trust
The Worshipful Company of
Engineers Charitable Trust
Fund
The Englefield Charitable Trust
The English Schools' Football
Association
The Enkalon Foundation
Entindale Ltd
The Epigoni Trust
Epilepsy Research UK
The Equitable Charitable Trust
The Equity Trust Fund
The Ericson Trust
The Erskine Cunningham Hill
Trust

Essex Community Foundation
The Essex Fairway Charitable
Trust
The Essex Heritage Trust
Essex Provincial Charity Fund
The Essex Youth Trust
Euro Charity Trust
Sir John Evelyn's Charity
The Eventhall Family
Charitable Trust
The Everard Foundation
The Eveson Charitable Trust
The Beryl Evetts and Robert
Luff Animal Welfare Trust
The Execution Charitable Trust
The Mayor of Exeter's Appeal
Fund
The Exilarch's Foundation
F C Charitable Trust
The F P Limited Charitable
Trust
The Faber Charitable Trust
Esmée Fairbairn Foundation
The Fairway Trust
Faisaltex Charitable Trust
The Family Rich Charities Trust
The Lord Faringdon Charitable
Trust
Samuel William Farmer Trust
The Farmers' Company
Charitable Fund
The Thomas Farr Charitable
Trust
Walter Farthing (Trust) Limited
The Fassnidge Memorial Trust
Joseph Fattorini Charitable
Trust 'B' Account
The Fawcett Charitable Trust
Federation of Jewish Relief
Organisations
The John Feeney Charitable
Trust
The George Fentham
Birmingham Charity
The A M Fenton Trust
Allan and Nesta Ferguson
Charitable Settlement
The Fidelity UK Foundation
The Bluff Field Charitable Trust
The Doris Field Charitable
Trust
The Fifty Fund
Firtree Trust
The Fishmongers' Company's
Charitable Trust
The Fitton Trust
The Earl Fitzwilliam Charitable
Trust
Bud Flanagan Leukaemia Fund
The Rose Flatau Charitable
Trust
The Ian Fleming Charitable
Trust
The Joyce Fletcher Charitable
Trust

The Roy Fletcher Charitable
Trust
The Flow Foundation
The Gerald Fogel Charitable
Trust
The Follett Trust
The Football Association
National Sports Centre
Trust
The Football Association Youth
Trust
The Football Foundation
The Forbes Charitable
Foundation
The Forces Trust (Working
Name)
The Oliver Ford Charitable
Trust
The Forest Hill Charitable Trust
Forever Manchester (The
Community Foundation for
Greater Manchester)
Gwyneth Forrester Trust
The Fort Foundation
The Forte Charitable Trust
Foundation for Management
Education
The Four Winds Trust
The Foyle Foundation
The Isaac and Freda Frankel
Memorial Charitable Trust
The Elizabeth Frankland Moore
and Star Foundation
The Jill Franklin Trust
The Gordon Fraser Charitable
Trust
The Hugh Fraser Foundation
The Joseph Strong Frazer Trust
The Louis and Valerie
Freedman Charitable
Settlement
The Freemasons' Grand
Charity
The Thomas Freke and Lady
Norton Charity
The Charles S French
Charitable Trust
The Anne French Memorial
Trust
The Freshfield Foundation
The Freshgate Trust
Foundation
The Friarsgate Trust
The Friends Hall Farm Street
Trust
Friends Provident Charitable
Foundation
The Frognal Trust
Maurice Fry Charitable Trust
The Fuellers Charitable Trust
Fund
The Fulmer Charitable Trust
Worshipful Company of
Furniture Makers Charitable
Fund
Gableholt Limited

The Galbraith Trust

The Gale Family Charitable Trust

The Angela Gallagher Memorial Fund

The Gamlen Charitable Trust

The Gamma Trust

The Gannochy Trust

The Ganzoni Charitable Trust

The Worshipful Company of Gardeners of London

The Samuel Gardner Memorial Trust

Garvan Limited

The Gatsby Charitable Foundation

Gatwick Airport Community Trust

The Robert Gavron Charitable Trust

Jacqueline and Michael Gee Charitable Trust

The General Nursing Council for England and Wales Trust

J Paul Getty Jr Charitable Trust

The Gibbs Charitable Trust

Simon Gibson Charitable Trust

The G C Gibson Charitable Trust

Lady Gibson's Charitable Trust

The Harvey and Hilary Gilbert Charitable Trust

The Girdlers' Company Charitable Trust

The B and P Glasser Charitable Trust

The Glass-House Trust

Global Care

Global Charities (formerly GCap Charities)

Gloucestershire Community Foundation

Worshipful Company of Glovers of London Charity Fund

The GNC Trust

The Meir Golda Trust

The Sydney and Phyllis Goldberg Memorial Charitable Trust

The Golden Bottle Trust

The Jack Goldhill Charitable Trust

The Goldsmiths' Arts Trust Fund

The Goldsmiths' Company Charity

The Golsoncott Foundation

The Good Neighbours Trust

The Everard and Mina Goodman Charitable Foundation

Mike Gooley Trailfinders Charity

Leonard Gordon Charitable Trust

The Gosling Foundation Limited

The Gough Charitable Trust

The Gould Charitable Trust

The Grace Charitable Trust

A B Grace Trust

The Graff Foundation

The Grahame Charitable Foundation Limited

Grampian Police Diced Cap Charitable Fund

The Granada Foundation

Grand Charitable Trust of the Order of Women Freemasons

The Grand Order of Water Rats' Charities Fund

The Grange Farm Centre Trust

Grantham Yorke Trust

The Gray Trust

The Great Britain Sasakawa Foundation

The Great Stone Bridge Trust of Edenbridge

The Great Torrington Town Lands Charity

The Constance Green Foundation

The Philip Green Memorial Trust

Greenham Common Community Trust Limited

Naomi and Jeffrey Greenwood Charitable Trust

Greggs Foundation (formerly Greggs Trust)

The Gretna Charitable Trust

The Grocers' Charity

The M and R Gross Charities Limited

The Grove Charitable Trust

The GRP Charitable Trust

The David and Marie Grumitt Foundation

The Bishop of Guildford's Foundation

The Guildry Incorporation of Perth

The Walter Guinness Charitable Trust

The Gunter Charitable Trust

The Gur Trust

Dr Guthrie's Association

The H and M Charitable Trust

H C D Memorial Fund

The H P Charitable Trust

The Hackney Parochial Charities

The Hadfield Trust

The Hadley Trust

The Hadrian Trust

The Alfred Haines Charitable Trust

The Hale Trust

E F and M G Hall Charitable Trust

Robert Hall Charity

The Hamamelis Trust

Hamilton Wallace Trust

Paul Hamlyn Foundation

The Hammonds Charitable Trust

The Hampshire and Islands Historic Churches Trust

Hampton Fuel Allotment Charity

The W A Handley Charitable Trust

Beatrice Hankey Foundation Ltd

The Hanley Trust

The Kathleen Hannay Memorial Charity

The Doughty Hanson Charitable Foundation

Lord Hanson Foundation

The Haramead Trust

Miss K M Harbinson's Charitable Trust

The Harborne Parish Lands Charity

The Harbour Charitable Trust

The Harbour Foundation

The Harding Trust

William Harding's Charity

The Hare of Steep Charitable Trust

The Harebell Centenary Fund

The Kenneth Hargreaves Charitable Trust

The Harris Charitable Trust

The Harris Charity

The Harrison and Potter Trust

The John Harrison Charitable Trust

The Peter Harrison Foundation

The Spencer Hart Charitable Trust

The Hartley Charitable Trust

The N and P Hartley Memorial Trust

William Geoffrey Harvey's Discretionary Settlement

Haskel Family Foundation

The Hathaway Trust

The Maurice Hatter Foundation

The M A Hawe Settlement

The Hawthorne Charitable Trust

The Dorothy Hay-Bolton Charitable Trust

The Haymills Charitable Trust

The Charles Hayward Foundation

The Headley Trust

Headley-Pitt Charitable Trust

Heagerty Charitable Trust

The Heart of England Community Foundation

The Heathcoat Trust

Heathside Charitable Trust
The Charlotte Heber-Percy Charitable Trust
The Hedley Denton Charitable Trust
The Hedley Foundation
The H J Heinz Company Limited Charitable Trust
The Hellenic Foundation
The Michael and Morven Heller Charitable Foundation
The Simon Heller Charitable Settlement
The Hemby Trust
The Christina Mary Hendrie Trust for Scottish and Canadian Charities
The Henley Educational Charity
Philip Henman Trust
Esther Hennell Charitable Trust
The G D Herbert Charitable Trust
The Joanna Herbert-Stepney Charitable Settlement (also known as The Paget Charitable Trust)
The Anne Herd Memorial Trust
The Herefordshire Historic Churches Trust
The Heritage of London Trust Ltd
The Hesed Trust
The Hesslewood Children's Trust (Hull Seamen's and General Orphanage)
The Bernhard Heuberger Charitable Trust
Hexham and Newcastle Diocesan Trust (1947)
The Higgs Charitable Trust
Alan Edward Higgs Charity
The High Sheriff's Police Trust for the County of West Midlands (Building Blocks)
Highcroft Charitable Trust
The Charles Littlewood Hill Trust
The Hillingdon Partnership Trust
Lady Hind Trust
The Hinrichsen Foundation
The Hitchin Educational Foundation
The Eleemosynary Charity of William Hobbayne
Hobson Charity Limited
Matthew Hodder Charitable Trust
The Sir Julian Hodge Charitable Trust
The J G Hogg Charitable Trust
The Holden Charitable Trust
John Holford's Charity
The Hollick Family Charitable Trust

The Dorothy Holmes Charitable Trust
The Holst Foundation
The Edward Holt Trust
The Holywood Trust
The Homelands Charitable Trust
The Homestead Charitable Trust
Sir Harold Hood's Charitable Trust
Hope for Youth (formerly Women Caring Trust)
The Hope Trust
HopMarket Charity
The Cuthbert Horn Trust
The Antony Hornby Charitable Trust
The Horne Foundation
The Horne Trust
The Worshipful Company of Horners' Charitable Trusts
The Hornsey Parochial Charities
The Hospital of God at Greatham
The Hospital Saturday Fund
Houblon-Norman/George Fund
The House of Industry Estate
The Reta Lila Howard Foundation
The Daniel Howard Trust
The Hudson Foundation
The Huggard Charitable Trust
The Geoffrey C Hughes Charitable Trust
The Hull and East Riding Charitable Trust
Hulme Trust Estates (Educational)
Human Relief Foundation
The Humanitarian Trust
The Michael and Shirley Hunt Charitable Trust
The Hunter Foundation
Miss Agnes H Hunter's Trust
The Huntingdon Foundation
Huntingdon Freemen's Charity
John Huntingdon's Charity
Hurdale Charity Limited
The Nani Huyu Charitable Trust
The P Y N and B Hyams Trust
The Hyde Charitable Trust – Youth Plus
The Idlewild Trust
The Iliffe Family Charitable Trust
The Indigo Trust
The Ingram Trust
The Inland Waterways Association
The Inlight Trust
The Inman Charity
The Inner London Magistrates Court Poor Box and Feeder Charity

The International Bankers Charitable Trust (The Worshipful Company of International Bankers)
The Ireland Fund of Great Britain
The Irish Youth Foundation (UK) Ltd (incorporating The Lawlor Foundation)
The Ironmongers' Foundation
Irshad Trust
The Charles Irving Charitable Trust
Irwin Trust
The ISA Charity
The Isaacs Charitable Trust
The J Isaacs Charitable Trust
The Isle of Anglesey Charitable Trust
The ITF Seafarers Trust
The J R S S T Charitable Trust
Elizabeth Jackson Charitable Trust
The Ruth and Lionel Jacobson Trust (Second Fund) No 2
Jaffe Family Relief Fund
John James Bristol Foundation
The Susan and Stephen James Charitable Settlement (also known as the Stephen James Charitable Trust)
The James Trust
The Marjory Jameson Trust
The Jarman Charitable Trust
JCA Charitable Foundation
The Jeffrey Charitable Trust
The Jenour Foundation
The Jephcott Charitable Trust
Jerwood Charitable Foundation
Jesus Hospital Charity
Jewish Child's Day
The Jewish Youth Fund
The JMK Charitable Trust
The Joanies Trust
The Harold Joels Charitable Trust
The Jonathan Joels Charitable Trust
The Nicholas Joels Charitable Trust
The Norman Joels Charitable Trust
The Elton John Aids Foundation
The Lillie Johnson Charitable Trust
The Johnson Foundation
The Johnson Group Cleaners Charity
The Johnson Wax Ltd Charitable Trust
The Joicey Trust
The Jones 1986 Charitable Trust

The Marjorie and Geoffrey Jones Charitable Trust

The Jordan Charitable Foundation

The J E Joseph Charitable Fund

The Lady Eileen Joseph Foundation

JTH Charitable Trust

The Judith Trust

The Anton Jurgens Charitable Trust

The Bernard Kahn Charitable Trust

The Stanley Kalms Foundation

The Karenza Foundation

The Boris Karloff Charitable Foundation

The Ian Karten Charitable Trust

The Kasner Charitable Trust

The Kass Charitable Trust

The Kathleen Trust

The Michael and Ilse Katz Foundation

The Katzauer Charitable Settlement

The C S Kaufman Charitable Trust

The Geoffrey John Kaye Charitable Foundation

The Emmanuel Kaye Foundation

Kelsick's Educational Foundation

The KempWelch Charitable Trust

The Kay Kendall Leukaemia Fund

The Kennedy Charitable Foundation

The Nancy Kenyon Charitable Trust

Keren Association

Kermaville Ltd

The Peter Kershaw Trust

The Kessler Foundation

Keswick Hall Trust

The Ursula Keyes Trust

The Robert Kiln Charitable Trust

The King/Cullimore Charitable Trust

The King's Fund

The Kingsbury Charity

The Mary Kinross Charitable Trust

Kirkley Poor's Lands Estate

The Richard Kirkman Charitable Trust

Kirschel Foundation

Robert Kitchin (Saddlers' Company)

Ernest Kleinwort Charitable Trust

The Marina Kleinwort Charitable Trust

The Kobler Trust

The Kohn Foundation

The Kreditor Charitable Trust

The Kreitman Foundation

The Neil Kreitman Foundation

The Kyte Charitable Trust

The Late Sir Pierce Lacy Charity Trust

John Laing Charitable Trust

Maurice and Hilda Laing Charitable Trust

The Christopher Laing Foundation

The Kirby Laing Foundation

The Martin Laing Foundation

The Beatrice Laing Trust

The Lambert Charitable Trust

Duchy of Lancaster Benevolent Fund

The Lancaster Foundation

The Allen Lane Foundation

The Langdale Trust

The Langley Charitable Trust

The Langtree Trust

The LankellyChase Foundation

The Lanvern Foundation

The R J Larg Family Charitable Trust

Largsmount Ltd

The Lark Trust

Laslett's (Hinton) Charity

Lauchentilly Charitable Foundation 1988

The Lauffer Family Charitable Foundation

The Kathleen Laurence Trust

The Law Society Charity

The Edgar E Lawley Foundation

The Herd Lawson and Muriel Lawson Charitable Trust

The Lawson Beckman Charitable Trust

The Raymond and Blanche Lawson Charitable Trust

The Carole and Geoffrey Lawson Foundation

The Mason Le Page Charitable Trust

The Leach Fourteenth Trust

The David Lean Foundation

The Leathersellers' Company Charitable Fund

The Leche Trust

The Arnold Lee Charitable Trust

The Lord Mayor of Leeds Appeal Fund

Leeds Building Society Charitable Foundation

Leicester Charity Link (formerly The Leicester Charity Organisation Society)

The Kennedy Leigh Charitable Trust

The Leigh Trust

Mrs Vera Leigh's Charity

The P Leigh-Bramwell Trust 'E'

The Lennox and Wyfold Foundation

The Erica Leonard Trust

The Leonard Trust

The Mark Leonard Trust

Lesley Lesley and Mutter Trust

Leukaemia and Lymphoma Research

The Leverhulme Trade Charities Trust

The Leverhulme Trust

The Joseph Levy Charitable Foundation

The John Spedan Lewis Foundation

The Sir Edward Lewis Foundation

John Lewis Partnership General Community Fund

Lichfield Conduit Lands

Lifeline 4 Kids

The Thomas Lilley Memorial Trust

The Linbury Trust

The Lind Trust

Lindale Educational Foundation

The Linden Charitable Trust

The Enid Linder Foundation

The Linmardon Trust

The Ruth and Stuart Lipton Charitable Trust

The Lister Charitable Trust

Frank Litchfield Charitable Trust

The Andrew and Mary Elizabeth Little Charitable Trust

The Second Joseph Aaron Littman Foundation

The George John and Sheilah Livanos Charitable Trust

Liverpool Sailors' Home Trust

The Elaine and Angus Lloyd Charitable Trust

The Charles Lloyd Foundation

The Lloyd Fund

Lloyd's Charities Trust

Lloyds TSB Foundation for England and Wales

Lloyds TSB Foundation for Northern Ireland

Lloyds TSB Foundation for the Channel Islands

The Locker Foundation

The Loftus Charitable Trust

The Lolev Charitable Trust

The Trust for London (formerly the City Parochial Foundation)

London Catalyst (formerly The Metropolitan Hospital-Sunday Fund)

The London Community
  Foundation (formerly Capital
  Community Foundation)
The London Law Trust
The William and Katherine
  Longman Trust
The Loseley and Guildway
  Charitable Trust
The Lotus Foundation
The C L Loyd Charitable Trust
LSA Charitable Trust
The Marie Helen Luen
  Charitable Trust
Robert Luff Foundation Ltd
Henry Lumley Charitable Trust
Lady Lumley's Educational
  Foundation
C F Lunoe Trust Fund
The Ruth and Jack Lunzer
  Charitable Trust
Lord and Lady Lurgan Trust
The Lyndhurst Trust
The Lynn Foundation
The Lynwood Trust
John Lyon's Charity
The Lyons Charitable Trust
The Sir Jack Lyons Charitable
  Trust
The Lyras Family Charitable
  Trust
Sylvanus Lyson's Charity
The M and C Trust
The M D and S Charitable
  Trust
The M K Charitable Trust
The Madeline Mabey Trust
The E M MacAndrew Trust
Macdonald-Buchanan
  Charitable Trust
The Macfarlane Walker Trust
The Mackay and Brewer
  Charitable Trust
The Mackintosh Foundation
The MacRobert Trust
James Madison Trust
The Magdalen and Lasher
  Charity
The Magen Charitable Trust
Man Group plc Charitable
  Trust
Manchester Airport Community
  Trust Fund
The Manchester Guardian
  Society Charitable Trust
Lord Mayor of Manchester's
  Charity Appeal Trust
Mandeville Trust
The Manifold Charitable Trust
W M Mann Foundation
The Leslie and Lilian Manning
  Trust
Marbeh Torah Trust
Marchig Animal Welfare Trust
The Stella and Alexander
  Margulies Charitable Trust

Market Harborough and The
  Bowdens Charity
The Ann and David Marks
  Foundation
The Hilda and Samuel Marks
  Foundation
J P Marland Charitable Trust
The Michael Marsh Charitable
  Trust
The Marsh Christian Trust
The Charlotte Marshall
  Charitable Trust
The Jim Marshall Charitable
  Trust
The D G Marshall of
  Cambridge Trust
Marshgate Charitable
  Settlement
Sir George Martin Trust
The Mason Porter Charitable
  Trust
The Nancie Massey Charitable
  Trust
The Mathew Trust
The Matt 6.3 Charitable Trust
The Violet Mauray Charitable
  Trust
The Maxell Educational Trust
The Maxwell Family Foundation
Evelyn May Trust
The Mayfield Valley Arts Trust
Mazars Charitable Trust
The McDougall Trust
The McKenna Charitable Trust
The Helen Isabella McMorran
  Charitable Foundation
The James Frederick and Ethel
  Anne Measures Charity
The Medlock Charitable Trust
The Anthony and Elizabeth
  Mellows Charitable
  Settlement
Melow Charitable Trust
The Mercers' Charitable
  Foundation
The Merchant Taylors'
  Company Charities Fund
The Merchant Venturers'
  Charity
The Merchants' House of
  Glasgow
The Mersey Docks and
  Harbour Company
  Charitable Fund
Community Foundation for
  Merseyside
The Zachary Merton and
  George Woofindin
  Convalescent Trust
The Tony Metherell Charitable
  Trust
The Metropolitan Drinking
  Fountain and Cattle Trough
  Association
Gerald Micklem Charitable
  Trust

Midhurst Pensions Trust
The Migraine Trust
Miles Trust for the Putney and
  Roehampton Community
Millennium Stadium Charitable
  Trust
The Hugh and Mary Miller
  Bequest Trust
The Miller Foundation
The Millfield Trust
The Millhouses Charitable
  Trust
The Millichope Foundation
The Mills Charity
The Millward Charitable Trust
The Clare Milne Trust
Milton Keynes Community
  Foundation
The Edgar Milward Charity
The Peter Minet Trust
The Minos Trust
The Mirfield Educational
  Charity
The Laurence Misener
  Charitable Trust
The Mishcon Family Charitable
  Trust
The Misselbrook Trust
The Esmé Mitchell Trust
Keren Mitzvah Trust
The Mizpah Trust
The Mobbs Memorial Trust Ltd
The Modiano Charitable Trust
The Moette Charitable Trust
The Mole Charitable Trust
The D C Moncrieff Charitable
  Trust
Monmouthshire County Council
  Welsh Church Act Fund
The Montague Thompson
  Coon Charitable Trust
The Colin Montgomerie
  Charitable Foundation
The Monument Trust
The Henry Moore Foundation
The Nigel Moores Family
  Charitable Trust
John Moores Foundation
The Peter Moores Foundation
The Morel Charitable Trust
The Morgan Charitable
  Foundation
The Mr and Mrs J T Morgan
  Foundation
The Oliver Morland Charitable
  Trust
The Bernard Morris Charitable
  Trust
The Morris Charitable Trust
The Willie and Mabel Morris
  Charitable Trust
The Peter Morrison Charitable
  Foundation
The Stanley Morrison
  Charitable Trust
Vyoel Moshe Charitable Trust

The Moss Charitable Trust
The Robert and Margaret
  Moss Charitable Trust
Moss Family Charitable Trust
The Mount Everest Foundation
The Edwina Mountbatten Trust
Mountbatten Festival of Music
The Mountbatten Memorial
  Trust
The Mugdock Children's Trust
The Mulberry Trust
The Edith Murphy Foundation
The Mushroom Fund
The Music Sales Charitable
  Trust
Muslim Hands
The Mutual Trust Group
The Kitty and Daniel Nabarro
  Charitable Trust
The Nadezhda Charitable Trust
The Naggar Charitable Trust
The Eleni Nakou Foundation
The Janet Nash Charitable
  Settlement
Nathan Charitable Trust
The National Churches Trust
  (formerly the Historic
  Churches Preservation
  Trust with the Incorporated
  Church Building Society)
The National Manuscripts
  Conservation Trust
The Nchima Trust
Needham Market and Barking
  Welfare Charities
The Worshipful Company of
  Needlemakers' Charitable
  Fund
The Neighbourly Charitable
  Trust
The James Neill Trust Fund
Nemoral Ltd
Network for Social Change
The New Appeals Organisation
  for the City and County of
  Nottingham
New Court Charitable Trust
The Newcomen Collett
  Foundation
The Frances and Augustus
  Newman Foundation
Alderman Newton's
  Educational Foundation
The Chevras Ezras Nitzrochim
  Trust
The Noon Foundation
The Norda Trust
Norie Charitable Trust
Normalyn Charitable Trust
The Norman Family Charitable
  Trust
The Duncan Norman Trust
  Fund
The Normanby Charitable Trust
The North British Hotel Trust

The North West Cancer
  Research Fund
The Northampton Municipal
  Church Charities
The Northampton Queen's
  Institute Relief in Sickness
  Fund
The Earl of Northampton's
  Charity
The Northcott Devon Medical
  Foundation
The Northern Rock Foundation
The Northmoor Trust
The Northumberland Village
  Homes Trust
The Northwood Charitable
  Trust
The Norton Foundation
The Norwich Church of England
  Young Men's Society
The Norwich Historic Churches
  Trust Ltd
The Norwich Town Close
  Estate Charity
The Norwood and Newton
  Settlement
The Noswad Charity
The Notgrove Trust
The Nottingham General
  Dispensary
The Nottingham Gordon
  Memorial Trust for Boys
  and Girls
Nottinghamshire Community
  Foundation
The Nottinghamshire Historic
  Churches Trust
The Nottinghamshire Miners'
  Welfare Trust Fund
Novi Most International
The Father O'Mahoney
  Memorial Trust
The Sir Peter O'Sullevan
  Charitable Trust
The Oak Trust
The Oakdale Trust
The Oakley Charitable Trust
The Oakmoor Charitable Trust
The Odin Charitable Trust
The Ofenheim Charitable Trust
Ogilvie Charities Deed No.2
  (including the Charity of
  Mary Catherine Ford Smith)
The Ogle Christian Trust
Oglesby Charitable Trust
Oizer Charitable Trust
The Old Broad Street Charity
  Trust
The Old Enfield Charitable
  Trust
The John Oldacre Foundation
The Oldham Foundation
The Olga Charitable Trust
Onaway Trust
Open Gate
The Ormsby Charitable Trust

Orrin Charitable Trust
The Ouseley Trust
The Owen Family Trust
Oxfam (GB)
The Oxfordshire Community
  Foundation
The P F Charitable Trust
Padwa Charitable Foundation
The Pallant Charitable Trust
The Palmer Foundation
Eleanor Palmer Trust
The Panacea Society
Panton Trust
The Paragon Trust
The Park House Charitable
  Trust
The Frank Parkinson
  Agricultural Trust
The Samuel and Freda
  Parkinson Charitable Trust
The Parthenon Trust
The Constance Paterson
  Charitable Trust
The Patrick Charitable Trust
The Jack Patston Charitable
  Trust
Paycare Charity Trust
  (previously known as
  Patients' Aid Association
  Hospital and Medical
  Charities Trust)
The Payne Charitable Trust
The Harry Payne Trust
The Susanna Peake Charitable
  Trust
The Pedmore Sporting Club
  Trust Fund
The Dowager Countess
  Eleanor Peel Trust
The Pennycress Trust
The Performing Right Society
  Foundation
The Persson Charitable Trust
  (formerly Highmoore Hall
  Charitable Trust)
The Persula Foundation
The Jack Petchey Foundation
The Petplan Charitable Trust
The Philips and Rubens
  Charitable Trust
The Phillips Charitable Trust
The Phillips Family Charitable
  Trust
Philological Foundation
The David Pickford Charitable
  Foundation
The Pilgrim Trust
The Cecil Pilkington Charitable
  Trust
The Pilkington Charities Fund
The Austin and Hope
  Pilkington Trust
The Sir Harry Pilkington Trust
The Col W W Pilkington Will
  Trusts The General Charity
  Fund

The DLA Piper Charitable Trust
The Worshipful Company of
   Plaisterers Charitable Trust
The Platinum Trust
Polden-Puckham Charitable
   Foundation
The Poling Charitable Trust
The George and Esme Pollitzer
   Charitable Settlement
The J S F Pollitzer Charitable
   Settlement
The Ponton House Trust
The Mayor of Poole's Appeal
   Fund
Edith and Ferdinand Porjes
   Charitable Trust
The John Porter Charitable
   Trust
The Porter Foundation
The Portrack Charitable Trust
The J E Posnansky Charitable
   Trust
The Mary Potter Convent
   Hospital Trust
The David and Elaine Potter
   Foundation
The Powell Foundation
The W L Pratt Charitable Trust
Premierquote Ltd
Premishlaner Charitable Trust
The Lucy Price Relief-in-Need
   Charity
Sir John Priestman Charity
   Trust
The Primrose Trust
The Prince of Wales's
   Charitable Foundation
The Priory Foundation
Prison Service Charity Fund
The Privy Purse Charitable
   Trust
The Proven Family Trust
The Provincial Grand Charity of
   the Province of Derbyshire
PSA Peugeot Citroen Charity
   Trust
The Puebla Charitable Trust
The Richard and Christine
   Purchas Charitable Trust
The Puri Foundation
Mr and Mrs J A Pye's
   Charitable Settlement
Quartet Community Foundation
   (formerly the Greater Bristol
   Foundation)
Queen Mary's Roehampton
   Trust
The Queen's Silver Jubilee
   Trust
R S Charitable Trust
The R V W Trust
The Monica Rabagliati
   Charitable Trust
Rachel Charitable Trust
The Mr and Mrs Philip
   Rackham Charitable Trust

Richard Radcliffe Charitable
   Trust
The Radcliffe Trust
The Ragdoll Foundation
The Rainford Trust
The Peggy Ramsay Foundation
The Joseph and Lena Randall
   Charitable Trust
The Rank Foundation
The Fanny Rapaport Charitable
   Settlement
The Ratcliff Foundation
The Ratcliff Pension Charity
The Ratcliffe Charitable Trust
The Eleanor Rathbone
   Charitable Trust
The Sigrid Rausing Trust
The Ravensdale Trust
The Rayden Charitable Trust
The Roger Raymond Charitable
   Trust
The Rayne Foundation
The Rayne Trust
The John Rayner Charitable
   Trust
The Sir James Reckitt Charity
The Red Arrows Trust
The Red Rose Charitable Trust
The C A Redfern Charitable
   Foundation
The Reed Foundation
Richard Reeve's Foundation
The Max Reinhardt Charitable
   Trust
Relief Fund for Romania
   Limited
The Rest Harrow Trust
Reuben Brothers Foundation
The Joan K Reynell Charitable
   Trust
The Nathaniel Reyner Trust
   Fund
The Rhododendron Trust
The Sir Cliff Richard Charitable
   Trust
The Clive Richards Charity
The Violet M Richards Charity
The Richmond Parish Lands
   Charity
Ridgesave Limited
The Ripple Effect Foundation
The Sir John Ritblat Family
   Foundation
The River Trust
Thomas Roberts Trust
The Robertson Trust
The Rochester Bridge Trust
The Rock Foundation
The Rock Solid Trust
The Rofeh Trust
Richard Rogers Charitable
   Settlement
Rokach Family Charitable Trust
The Helen Roll Charitable
   Trust

The Sir James Roll Charitable
   Trust
The Roman Research Trust
Romeera Foundation
The C A Rookes Charitable
   Trust
The Rosca Trust
The Rose Foundation
The Cecil Rosen Foundation
Rosetrees Trust
The Rothermere Foundation
The Rotherwick Foundation
The Roughley Charitable Trust
Mrs Gladys Row Fogo
   Charitable Trust
Rowanville Ltd
The Christopher Rowbotham
   Charitable Trust
The Rowing Foundation
The Rowlands Trust
The Joseph Rowntree
   Charitable Trust
The Joseph Rowntree
   Foundation
Joseph Rowntree Reform Trust
   Limited
Royal Artillery Charitable Fund
Royal British Legion
Royal Docks Trust (London)
Royal Masonic Trust for Girls
   and Boys
The Royal Scots Benevolent
   Society
The Alfred and Frances
   Rubens Charitable Trust
The Rubin Foundation
William Arthur Rudd Memorial
   Trust
The Rufford Foundation
The Rufford Small Grants
   Foundation
The Russell Trust
The J S and E C Rymer
   Charitable Trust
S O Charitable Trust
The Jeremy and John Sacher
   Charitable Trust
The Michael Harry Sacher
   Trust
The Sackler Trust (Formerly Dr
   Mortimer and Theresa
   Sackler Foundation)
The Ruzin Sadagora Trust
The Saddlers' Company
   Charitable Fund
The Saga Charitable Trust
The Jean Sainsbury Animal
   Welfare Trust
The Alan and Babette
   Sainsbury Charitable Fund
The Sainsbury Family
   Charitable Trusts
Saint Sarkis Charity Trust
The Saintbury Trust
The Saints and Sinners Trust

The Salamander Charitable Trust

The Salt Trust

The Sammermar Trust

Basil Samuel Charitable Trust

The Hon. M J Samuel Charitable Trust

The Peter Samuel Charitable Trust

The Camilla Samuel Fund

The Samworth Foundation

The Sandra Charitable Trust

Santander UK Foundation Limited

Jimmy Savile Charitable Trust

The Scarfe Charitable Trust

The Schapira Charitable Trust

The Schmidt-Bodner Charitable Trust

The R H Scholes Charitable Trust

The Schreib Trust

The Schreiber Charitable Trust

The Francis C Scott Charitable Trust

The Sir James and Lady Scott Trust

The Scott Trust Foundation

The Storrow Scott Will Trust

The Scottish Arts Council

Scottish Coal Industry Special Welfare Fund

The Scottish Community Foundation

The Scottish International Education Trust

The Scouloudi Foundation

Seafarers UK (King George's Fund for Sailors)

Seamen's Hospital Society

The Searchlight Electric Charitable Trust

The Searle Charitable Trust

The Helene Sebba Charitable Trust

The Samuel Sebba Charitable Trust

The Seedfield Trust

The Ayrton Senna Foundation

The Seven Fifty Trust

The Severn Trent Water Charitable Trust Fund

The Cyril Shack Trust

The Jean Shanks Foundation

The Shanti Charitable Trust

ShareGift (The Orr Mackintosh Foundation)

The Linley Shaw Foundation

The Sheepdrove Trust

The Sheffield and District Hospital Services Charitable Fund

The Sheldon Trust

The P and D Shepherd Charitable Trust

The Sylvia and Colin Shepherd Charitable Trust

The Archie Sherman Cardiff Foundation

The Archie Sherman Charitable Trust

The R C Sherriff Trust

The Shetland Charitable Trust

SHINE (Support and Help in Education)

The Barnett and Sylvia Shine No 2 Charitable Trust

The Bassil Shippam and Alsford Trust

The Shipwrights' Company Charitable Fund

The Shirley Foundation

Shlomo Memorial Fund Limited

The J A Shone Memorial Trust

The Barbara A Shuttleworth Memorial Trust

The Mary Elizabeth Siebel Charity

David and Jennifer Sieff Charitable Trust

The Julius Silman Charitable Trust

The Leslie Silver Charitable Trust

The Simpson Education and Conservation Trust

The Simpson Foundation

The Huntly and Margery Sinclair Charitable Trust

Sino-British Fellowship Trust

The Skelton Bounty

The Charles Skey Charitable Trust

Skipton Building Society Charitable Foundation

The John Slater Foundation

The SMB Charitable Trust

The Mrs Smith and Mount Trust

The N Smith Charitable Settlement

The Amanda Smith Charitable Trust

The E H Smith Charitable Trust

The Smith Charitable Trust

The Henry Smith Charity

The Leslie Smith Foundation

The Martin Smith Foundation

Stanley Smith General Charitable Trust

The Stanley Smith UK Horticultural Trust

The Snowball Trust

The Sobell Foundation

Solihull Community Foundation

The Solo Charitable Settlement

Dr Richard Solomon's Charitable Trust

The E C Sosnow Charitable Trust

The Souter Charitable Trust

The South Square Trust

The Stephen R and Philippa H Southall Charitable Trust

The W F Southall Trust

The Southover Manor General Education Trust

The Southwold Trust

The Sovereign Health Care Charitable Trust

Sparks Charity (Sport Aiding Medical Research For Kids)

Sparquote Limited

The Spear Charitable Trust

The Jessie Spencer Trust

The Ralph and Irma Sperring Charity

The Moss Spiro Will Charitable Foundation

The Spoore, Merry and Rixman Foundation

Spring Harvest

Springrule Ltd

The Spurrell Charitable Trust

The Geoff and Fiona Squire Foundation

St Andrew's Conservation Trust

St Francis's Leprosy Guild

St Gabriel's Trust

St Hilda's Trust

St James' Trust Settlement

St James's Place Foundation

Sir Walter St John's Educational Charity

St Katharine and Shadwell Trust

St Michael's and All Saints' Charities

The Late St Patrick White Charitable Trust

St Teilo's Trust

The Stanley Foundation Ltd

The Stanton Ballard Charitable Trust

The Staples Trust

The Star Charitable Trust

The Peter Stebbings Memorial Charity

The Steinberg Family Charitable Trust

The Hugh Stenhouse Foundation

The Sigmund Sternberg Charitable Foundation

Stervon Ltd

The Stevenage Community Trust

The June Stevens Foundation

The Steventon Allotments and Relief-in-Need Charity

The Stewards' Charitable Trust

The Stewards' Company Limited (incorporating the J W Laing Trust and the J W Laing Biblical Scholarship Trust)

The Sir Halley Stewart Trust

The Leonard Laity Stoate Charitable Trust

The Stobart Newlands Charitable Trust

The Edward Stocks-Massey Bequest Fund

The Stokenchurch Educational Charity

The Stoller Charitable Trust

The M J C Stone Charitable Trust

The Stone-Mallabar Charitable Foundation

The Samuel Storey Family Charitable Trust

Peter Stormonth Darling Charitable Trust

The Strangward Trust

The Strasser Foundation

Stratford upon Avon Town Trust

Strathclyde Police Benevolent Fund

The W O Street Charitable Foundation

The Sudborough Foundation

The Suffolk Historic Churches Trust

The Summerfield Charitable Trust

The Surrey Historic Buildings Trust Ltd

The Sussex Historic Churches Trust

The Sutasoma Trust

Sutton Coldfield Municipal Charities

The Sutton Trust

Swansea and Brecon Diocesan Board of Finance Limited

The John Swire (1989) Charitable Trust

The Swire Charitable Trust

The Hugh and Ruby Sykes Charitable Trust

The Charles and Elsie Sykes Trust

The Sylvanus Charitable Trust

The Stella Symons Charitable Trust

The Tabeel Trust

The Tajtelbaum Charitable Trust

Tallow Chandlers Benevolent Fund

The Tangent Charitable Trust

The Lady Tangye Charitable Trust

The David Tannen Charitable Trust

The Tanner Trust

The Lili Tapper Charitable Foundation

The Mrs A Lacy Tate Trust

The Tay Charitable Trust

Humphrey Richardson Taylor Charitable Trust

The Connie and Albert Taylor Charitable Trust

The Cyril Taylor Charitable Trust

A P Taylor Trust

Tearfund

The Tedworth Charitable Trust

Tees Valley Community Foundation

The Templeton Goodwill Trust

Tesco Charity Trust

The Thames Wharf Charity

The Thistle Trust

The Loke Wan Tho Memorial Foundation

The Arthur and Margaret Thompson Charitable Trust

The Thompson Family Charitable Trust

The Len Thomson Charitable Trust

The Sue Thomson Foundation

The Sir Jules Thorn Charitable Trust

The Thornton Foundation

The Thornton Trust

The Three Guineas Trust

The Three Oaks Trust

The Thriplow Charitable Trust

The Tinsley Foundation

The Tisbury Telegraph Trust

TJH Foundation

The Tobacco Pipe Makers and Tobacco Trade Benevolent Fund

The Tolkien Trust

Tollemache (Buckminster) Charitable Trust

Tomchei Torah Charitable Trust

The Tompkins Foundation

The Tory Family Foundation

Tottenham Grammar School Foundation

The Tower Hill Trust

The Towry Law Charitable Trust (also known as the Castle Educational Trust)

The Toy Trust

The Mayor of Trafford's Charity Fund

The Constance Travis Charitable Trust

The Treeside Trust

The Triangle Trust (1949) Fund

The True Colours Trust

Truedene Co. Ltd

The Truemark Trust

Truemart Limited

Trumros Limited

Trust Sixty Three

The Trusthouse Charitable Foundation

Tudor Rose Ltd

The Tudor Trust

The Tufton Charitable Trust

The R D Turner Charitable Trust

The Douglas Turner Trust

The Florence Turner Trust

Miss S M Tutton Charitable Trust

The TUUT Charitable Trust

Community Foundation Serving Tyne and Wear and Northumberland

Trustees of Tzedakah

Ulster Garden Villages Ltd

Ultach Trust

Ulting Overseas Trust

The Ulverscroft Foundation

Ulverston Town Lands Charity

The Underwood Trust

The Union of Orthodox Hebrew Congregation

The United Society for the Propagation of the Gospel

The David Uri Memorial Trust

Uxbridge United Welfare Trust

Vale of Glamorgan – Welsh Church Fund

The Valentine Charitable Trust

John and Lucille van Geest Foundation

The Van Neste Foundation

Mrs Maud Van Norden's Charitable Foundation

The Vandervell Foundation

The Vardy Foundation

The Variety Club Children's Charity

Veneziana Fund

The Verdon-Smith Family Charitable Settlement

Victoria Homes Trust

The Nigel Vinson Charitable Trust

The William and Ellen Vinten Trust

The Vintners' Company Charitable Foundation

Vintners' Gifts Charity

Vision Charity

Vivdale Ltd

The Viznitz Foundation

Wade's Charity

The Scurrah Wainwright Charity

Wakeham Trust

The Community Foundation in Wales

Wales Council for Voluntary Action

Robert and Felicity Waley-Cohen Charitable Trust

The Thomas Wall Trust

The F J Wallis Charitable
Settlement
War on Want
The Ward Blenkinsop Trust
The George Ward Charitable
Trust
The Barbara Ward Children's
Foundation
The John Warren Foundation
G R Waters Charitable Trust
2000
The Waterways Trust
The Wates Foundation
The Howard Watson Symington
Memorial Charity
John Watson's Trust
Weatherley Charitable Trust
The Weavers' Company
Benevolent Fund
The Weinberg Foundation
The Weinstein Foundation
The Weinstock Fund
The Weldon UK Charitable
Trust
The Wellcome Trust
Welsh Church Fund Dyfed
area (Carmarthenshire,
Ceredigion and
Pembrokeshire)
The Welton Foundation
The Wessex Youth Trust
The West Derby Wastelands
Charity
West London Synagogue
Charitable Fund
The West Yorkshire Police
Community Fund
The Westminster Foundation
The Garfield Weston
Foundation
The Whitaker Charitable Trust
The Colonel W H Whitbread
Charitable Trust
The Simon Whitbread
Charitable Trust
The Whitecourt Charitable
Trust
The Norman Whiteley Trust
The Whitley Animal Protection
Trust
The Whittlesey Charity
The Lionel Wigram Memorial
Trust
The Felicity Wilde Charitable
Trust
The Will Charitable Trust
The Kay Williams Charitable
Foundation
The Williams Family Charitable
Trust
The H D H Wills 1965
Charitable Trust
The Dame Violet Wills Will
Trust
The Wilmcote Charitrust
David Wilson Foundation

The Wilson Foundation
J and J R Wilson Trust
The Community Foundation for
Wiltshire and Swindon
The Benjamin Winegarten
Charitable Trust
The Harold Hyam Wingate
Foundation
The Francis Winham
Foundation
Wirral Mayor's Charity
The Michael and Anna Wix
Charitable Trust
The Wixamtree Trust
The Woburn 1986 Charitable
Trust
The Maurice Wohl Charitable
Foundation
The Charles Wolfson
Charitable Trust
The James Wood Bequest
Fund
Woodlands Green Ltd
Woodlands Trust
The Woodward Charitable
Trust
Worcester Municipal Charities
(incorporating Worcester
Consolidated Municipal
Charity and Worcester
Municipal Exhibitions
Foundation)
The Worcestershire and
Dudley Historic Churches
Trust
The Fred and Della Worms
Charitable Trust
The Wragge and Co. Charitable
Trust
The Diana Edgson Wright
Charitable Trust
The Matthews Wrightson
Charity Trust
Miss E B Wrightson's
Charitable Settlement
Wychdale Ltd
Wychville Ltd
The Wyndham Charitable Trust
The Wyseliot Charitable Trust
The Xerox (UK) Trust
The Yapp Charitable Trust
The Dennis Alan Yardy
Charitable Trust
The W Wing Yip and Brothers
Foundation
The York Children's Trust
Yorkshire Agricultural Society
The South Yorkshire
Community Foundation
The Yorkshire Dales
Millennium Trust
The John Young Charitable
Settlement
The William Allen Young
Charitable Trust

The John K Young Endowment
Fund
Youth Music
Zephyr Charitable Trust
The Marjorie and Arnold Ziff
Charitable Foundation
Stephen Zimmerman
Charitable Trust
The Zochonis Charitable Trust
Zurich Community Trust (UK)
Limited

....

■ Seed Funding

The 1970 Trust
The 1989 Willan Charitable
Trust
The 29th May 1961 Charitable
Trust
The Aberbrothock Skea Trust
The Aberdeen Endowments
Trust
The Aberdeenshire Educational
Trust Scheme
ABF The Soldiers' Charity
(formerly the Army
Benevolent Fund)
Achiezer Association Ltd
Achisomoch Aid Company
Limited
Action Medical Research
The Sylvia Adams Charitable
Trust
The Victor Adda Foundation
The Adint Charitable Trust
Age Scotland (Formerly Age
Concern Scotland and Help
the Aged)
Age UK (formerly Help the
Aged and Age Concern)
Aid to the Church in Need (UK)
The Sylvia Aitken Charitable
Trust
The Ajahma Charitable Trust
Aldgate and All Hallows'
Barking Exhibition
Foundation
The Aldgate Freedom
Foundation
All Saints Educational Trust
Allchurches Trust Ltd
The H B Allen Charitable Trust
The Alliance Family Foundation
Angus Allnatt Charitable
Foundation
The Pat Allsop Charitable Trust
Almondsbury Charity
Altamont Ltd
Alvor Charitable Trust
The Ammco Trust
Viscount Amory's Charitable
Trust
The AMW Charitable Trust
The André Christian Trust
Anguish's Educational
Foundation

The Animal Defence Trust

The Eric Anker-Petersen Charity

Ambrose and Ann Appelbe Trust

The Appletree Trust

The John Apthorp Charitable Trust

The Arbib Foundation

The John M Archer Charitable Trust

The Archer Trust

The Ardwick Trust

The Argus Appeal

The Armenian Relief Society of Great Britain Trust

The Armourers' and Brasiers' Gauntlet Trust

Arsenal Charitable Trust

The Artemis Charitable Trust

The Arts and Entertainment Charitable Trust

Arts Council England

The Arts Council of Northern Ireland

The Arts Council of Wales

The Ove Arup Foundation

The AS Charitable Trust

The Ashden Trust

The Ashendene Trust

The Ashley Family Foundation (formerly The Laura Ashley Foundation)

The Norman C Ashton Foundation

The Ashworth Charitable Trust

The Ian Askew Charitable Trust

The Associated Country Women of the World (ACWW)

The Association of Colleges Charitable Trust

Astellas European Foundation

Asthma UK

AstonMansfield Charitable Trust

The Astor Foundation

The Astor of Hever Trust

The Aurelius Charitable Trust

The Avenue Charitable Trust

AW Charitable Trust

The BAA Communities Trust

The BACTA Charitable Trust

The Scott Bader Commonwealth Ltd

The Bagri Foundation

Veta Bailey Charitable Trust

The Austin Bailey Trust

The Baily Thomas Charitable Fund

The Baird Trust

The Baker Charitable Trust

The Balcombe Charitable Trust

The Albert Casanova Ballard Deceased Trust

The Ballinger Charitable Trust

The Balmore Trust

The Balney Charitable Trust

The Baltic Charitable Fund

The Bamford Charitable Foundation

The Banbury Charities

William P Bancroft (No 2) Charitable Trust and Jenepher Gillett Trust

The Band Trust

The Barbers' Company General Charities

The Barbour Foundation

Barchester Healthcare Foundation

The Barclay Foundation

The Baring Foundation

Peter Barker-Mill Memorial Charity

Barleycorn Trust

Barnes Workhouse Fund

The Barnsbury Charitable Trust

The Barnwood House Trust

The Misses Barrie Charitable Trust

Barrington Family Charitable Trust

Stephen J Barry Charitable Trust

The Bartlett Taylor Charitable Trust

The Paul Bassham Charitable Trust

The Batchworth Trust

The Bay Tree Charitable Trust

D H and L H Baylin Charitable Trust

The Louis Baylis (Maidenhead Advertiser) Charitable Trust

BBC Children in Need

B-CH 1971 Charitable Trust

The Beacon Trust

The Bearder Charity

The James Beattie Charitable Trust

The Beaufort House Trust Limited

The Beaverbrook Foundation

The Beccles Town Lands Charity

The Becker Family Charitable Trust

The Becketts and Sargeants Educational Foundation

The John Beckwith Charitable Trust

The Peter Beckwith Charitable Trust

The Bedford Charity (The Harpur Trust)

The David and Ruth Behrend Fund

The Beit Trust

The Bellahouston Bequest Fund

The Bellinger Donnay Trust

Belljoe Tzedoko Ltd

The Benfield Motors Charitable Trust

The Benham Charitable Settlement

Maurice and Jacqueline Bennett Charitable Trust

The Berkshire Community Foundation

The Bestway Foundation

Thomas Betton's Charity for Pensions and Relief-in-Need

BHST

The Mason Bibby 1981 Trust

BibleLands

The Bideford Bridge Trust

The Big Lottery Fund

The Billmeir Charitable Trust

The Bingham Trust

The Bintaub Charitable Trust

The Birmingham District Nursing Charitable Trust

The Birmingham Hospital Saturday Fund Medical Charity and Welfare Trust

Birmingham International Airport Community Trust

The Lord Mayor of Birmingham's Charity

The Michael Bishop Foundation

The Bishop's Development Fund

The Bertie Black Foundation

Isabel Blackman Foundation

The Herbert and Peter Blagrave Charitable Trust

The Blair Foundation

The Blanchminster Trust

The Sir Victor Blank Charitable Settlement

The Neville and Elaine Blond Charitable Trust

The Bluston Charitable Settlement

The Nicholas Boas Charitable Trust

The Body Shop Foundation

The Boltons Trust

The Bonamy Charitable Trust

The John and Celia Bonham Christie Charitable Trust

The Charlotte Bonham-Carter Charitable Trust

Bonhomie United Charity Society

The Boots Charitable Trust

The Bordon and Liphook Charity

The Oliver Borthwick Memorial Trust

The Bothwell Charitable Trust

H E and E L Botteley Charitable Trust

The Harry Bottom Charitable Trust

The Anthony Bourne
   Foundation
The Bower Trust
The Bowerman Charitable
   Trust
John and Susan Bowers Fund
The Bowland Charitable Trust
The William Brake Charitable
   Trust
The Liz and Terry Bramall
   Charitable Trust
The Tony Bramall Charitable
   Trust
The Harold and Alice Bridges
   Charity
The Brighton District Nursing
   Association Trust
Bristol Archdeaconry Charity
John Bristow and Thomas
   Mason Trust
Britannia Foundation
The British Council for
   Prevention of Blindness
The British Dietetic
   Association General and
   Education Trust Fund
The British Gas (Scottish Gas)
   Energy Trust
British Heart Foundation
British Humane Association
British Institute at Ankara
British Ornithologists' Union
British Record Industry Trust
The Britto Foundation
The J and M Britton Charitable
   Trust
The Charles and Edna
   Broadhurst Charitable Trust
The Bromley Trust
The Roger Brooke Charitable
   Trust
The David Brooke Charity
The Charles Brotherton Trust
Joseph Brough Charitable
   Trust
The Swinfen Broun Charitable
   Trust
Mrs E E Brown Charitable
   Settlement
The Bryant Trust
The Buckinghamshire
   Foundation
The Buckinghamshire Masonic
   Centenary Fund
The Rosemary Bugden
   Charitable Trust
The Bulldog Trust Limited
The E F Bulmer Benevolent
   Fund
Burdens Charitable Foundation
The Clara E Burgess Charity
The Burry Charitable Trust
The Arnold Burton 1998
   Charitable Trust
The Burton Breweries
   Charitable Trust

The Geoffrey Burton Charitable
   Trust
Consolidated Charity of Burton
   upon Trent
Butchers' Company General
   Charities
The Noel Buxton Trust
Henry T and Lucy B Cadbury
   Charitable Trust
The Christopher Cadbury
   Charitable Trust
The G W Cadbury Charitable
   Trust
The Richard Cadbury
   Charitable Trust
The Edward and Dorothy
   Cadbury Trust
The George Cadbury Trust
CAF (Charities Aid Foundation)
CAFOD (Catholic Agency for
   Overseas Development)
The Callander Charitable Trust
Calleva Foundation
Calouste Gulbenkian
   Foundation
The Calpe Trust
Calypso Browning Trust
The Campden Charities
   Trustee
The Canning Trust
The Carew Pole Charitable
   Trust
The D W T Cargill Fund
Carlee Ltd
The Carlton House Charitable
   Trust
The Worshipful Company of
   Carmen Benevolent Trust
The Carnegie Dunfermline
   Trust
The Carpenter Charitable Trust
The Carpenters' Company
   Charitable Trust
The Carrington Charitable
   Trust
The Carron Charitable
   Settlement
The Leslie Mary Carter
   Charitable Trust
The Carvill Trust
The Casey Trust
Cash for Kids Radio Clyde
Sir John Cass's Foundation
The Elizabeth Casson Trust
The Castang Foundation
The Catalyst Charitable Trust
   (formerly the Buckle Family
   Charitable Trust)
The Catholic Charitable Trust
Catholic Foreign Missions
The Catholic Trust for England
   and Wales
The Cattanach Charitable Trust
The Joseph and Annie Cattle
   Trust

The Thomas Sivewright Catto
   Charitable Settlement
The Wilfrid and Constance
   Cave Foundation
The Cayo Foundation
The B G S Cayzer Charitable
   Trust
The Cazenove Charitable Trust
Celtic Charity Fund
The Cemlyn-Jones Trust
CfBT Education Trust
The Pamela Champion
   Foundation
The Chapman Charitable Trust
John William Chapman's
   Charitable Trust
The Charities Advisory Trust
Charitworth Limited
The Charter 600 Charity
The Worshipful Company of
   Chartered Accountants
   General Charitable Trust
   (also known as CALC)
The Chasah Trust
The Chelsea Building Society
   Charitable Foundation
The Chelsea Square 1994
   Trust
The Cheruby Trust
The Cheshire Provincial Fund
   of Benevolence
The Chetwode Foundation
Chevioty Asset Management
   Charitable Trust
The Malcolm Chick Charity
Childs Charitable Trust
The Childwick Trust
The Chipping Sodbury Town
   Lands Charity
CHK Charities Limited
The Chownes Foundation
The Chrimes Family Charitable
   Trust
The Christabella Charitable
   Trust
Christadelphian Samaritan
   Fund
Christian Aid
Christian Response to Eastern
   Europe
The Church and Community
   Fund
The Church Burgesses
   Educational Foundation
Church Burgesses Trust
Church of Ireland Priorities
   Fund
The Church Urban Fund
City and County of Swansea
   Welsh Church Act Fund
The City Bridge Trust (formerly
   known as Bridge House
   Trust)
The City Educational Trust
   Fund

Stephen Clark 1957
Charitable Trust
J A Clark Charitable Trust
The Hilda and Alice Clark
Charitable Trust
The Roger and Sarah Bancroft
Clark Charitable Trust
The Clarke Charitable
Settlement
The Cleary Foundation
The Cleopatra Trust
Lord Clinton's Charitable Trust
The Clore Duffield Foundation
Miss V L Clore's 1967
Charitable Trust
Closehelm Ltd
Richard Cloudesley's Charity
The Clover Trust
The Robert Clutterbuck
Charitable Trust
Clydpride Ltd
The Coalfields Regeneration
Trust
The John Coates Charitable
Trust
Coats Foundation Trust
The Cobtree Charity Trust Ltd
The Denise Cohen Charitable
Trust
The Vivienne and Samuel
Cohen Charitable Trust
The John S Cohen Foundation
The R and S Cohen
Foundation
The Colchester Catalyst
Charity
The Cole Charitable Trust
The Colefax Charitable Trust
The John and Freda Coleman
Charitable Trust
The George Henry Collins
Charity
The E Alec Colman Charitable
Fund Ltd
The Sir Jeremiah Colman Gift
Trust
The Colt Foundation
The Coltstaple Trust
Colwinston Charitable Trust
Colyer-Fergusson Charitable
Trust
Comic Relief
The Comino Foundation
Community Foundation for
Calderdale
The Community Foundation for
Northern Ireland
The Compton Charitable Trust
The Congleton Inclosure Trust
The Conservation Foundation
The Consolidated Charities for
the Infirm Merchant
Taylors' Company
The Ernest Cook Trust
The Cooks Charity

The Catherine Cookson
Charitable Trust
Mabel Cooper Charity
The Alice Ellen Cooper Dean
Charitable Foundation
The Co-operative Foundation
The Marjorie Coote Animal
Charity Trust
The Marjorie Coote Old
People's Charity
The Helen Jean Cope Trust
The J Reginald Corah
Foundation Fund
The Gershon Coren Charitable
Foundation
The Corinthian Trust
Edwin Cornforth 1983 Charity
Trust
The Cornwell Charitable Trust
The Sidney and Elizabeth
Corob Charitable Trust
The Corona Charitable Trust
The Costa Family Charitable
Trust (formerly the Morgan
Williams Charitable Trust)
The Cotton Industry War
Memorial Trust
County Durham Community
Foundation
The Augustine Courtauld Trust
The General Charities of the
City of Coventry
Coventry Building Society
Charitable Foundation
The John Cowan Foundation
The Sir William Coxen Trust
Fund
The Lord Cozens-Hardy Trust
The Craignish Trust
The Craps Charitable Trust
Michael Crawford Children's
Charity
The Cray Trust
Creative Scotland
The Crescent Trust
Cripplegate Foundation
The Violet and Milo Cripps
Charitable Trust
The Harry Crook Foundation
The Cross Trust
The Croydon Relief in Need
Charities
The Mayor of Croydon's
Charity Fund
Cruden Foundation Ltd
The Ronald Cruickshank's
Foundation
The R D Crusaders Foundation
The Culra Charitable Trust
Cumberland Building Society
Charitable Foundation
Cumbria Community
Foundation
The Cunningham Trust
The D J H Currie Memorial
Trust

The Dennis Curry Charitable
Trust
The Raymond Curtis Charitable
Trust
The Manny Cussins
Foundation
The Cwmbran Trust
Itzchok Meyer Cymerman Trust
Ltd
The D G Charitable Settlement
The D'Oyly Carte Charitable
Trust
Roald Dahl's Marvellous
Children's Charity
The Daily Prayer Union
Charitable Trust Ltd
The Daisy Trust
The Daiwa Anglo-Japanese
Foundation
The Dr and Mrs A Darlington
Charitable Trust
Baron Davenport's Charity
The Davidson (Nairn)
Charitable Trust
The Davidson Family
Charitable Trust
The Alderman Joe Davidson
Memorial Trust
Michael Davies Charitable
Settlement
The Gwendoline and Margaret
Davies Charity
The Wilfrid Bruce Davis
Charitable Trust
Davis-Rubens Charitable Trust
The Dawe Charitable Trust
The De Clermont Charitable
Company Ltd
The Leopold De Rothschild
Charitable Trust
The Deakin Charitable Trust
William Dean Countryside and
Educational Trust
The Debmar Benevolent Trust
The Dellal Foundation
The Delves Charitable Trust
The Demigryphon Trust
The Denman Charitable Trust
The Denton Charitable Trust
The Denton Wilde Sapte
Charitable Trust
The Earl of Derby's Charitable
Trust
Derbyshire Community
Foundation
The J N Derbyshire Trust
Devon Community Foundation
The Devon Educational Trust
The Duke of Devonshire's
Charitable Trust
The Sandy Dewhirst Charitable
Trust
The Laduma Dhamecha
Charitable Trust
Diabetes UK
The Dibden Allotments Fund

The Dickon Trust
The Digbeth Trust
Dischma Charitable Trust
The Djanogly Foundation
The DLM Charitable Trust
Louise Dobson Charitable
Trust
The Derek and Eileen Dodgson
Foundation
The Dollond Charitable Trust
Domepride Ltd
The Dorcas Trust
The Dorus Trust
The Doughty Charity Trust
The R M Douglas Charitable
Trust
The Drapers' Charitable Fund
The Dugdale Charitable Trust
The Duis Charitable Trust
The Dulverton Trust
The P B Dumbell Charitable
Trust
The Dumbreck Charity
Dunard Fund
Ronald Duncan Literary
Foundation
The Houghton Dunn Charitable
Trust
The Dunn Family Charitable
Trust
The W E Dunn Trust
Dushinsky Trust Ltd
The Dwek Family Charitable
Trust
The Dyers' Company
Charitable Trust
The Eagle Charity Trust
The Earley Charity
Earls Colne and Halstead
Educational Charity
The Earmark Trust
East Kent Provincial Charities
East London Community
Foundation
Eastern Counties Educational
Trust Limited
The Sir John Eastwood
Foundation
The Ebenezer Trust
The EBM Charitable Trust
Eden Arts Trust
EDF Energy Trust (EDFET)
The Gilbert and Eileen Edgar
Foundation
Edinburgh Children's Holiday
Fund
The Edinburgh Trust, No 2
Account
Edinburgh Voluntary
Organisations' Trust Funds
The W G Edwards Charitable
Foundation
The William Edwards
Educational Charity
The Elephant Trust

The George Elias Charitable
Trust
The Gerald Palmer Eling Trust
Company
The Wilfred and Elsie Elkes
Charity Fund
The Maud Elkington Charitable
Trust
The Ellerdale Trust
The John Ellerman Foundation
The Ellinson Foundation Ltd
The Edith Maud Ellis 1985
Charitable Trust
James Ellis Charitable Trust
The Elmgrant Trust
The Elmley Foundation
The Vernon N Ely Charitable
Trust
The Embleton Trust
The Emerton-Christie Charity
The Emmandjay Charitable
Trust
The Worshipful Company of
Engineers Charitable Trust
Fund
The Englefield Charitable Trust
The English Schools' Football
Association
The Enkalon Foundation
Entindale Ltd
The Epigoni Trust
Epilepsy Research UK
The Equitable Charitable Trust
The Equity Trust Fund
The Ericson Trust
The Erskine Cunningham Hill
Trust
Essex Community Foundation
The Essex Fairway Charitable
Trust
The Essex Heritage Trust
Essex Provincial Charity Fund
The Essex Youth Trust
Euro Charity Trust
Sir John Evelyn's Charity
The Eventhall Family
Charitable Trust
The Everard Foundation
The Eveson Charitable Trust
The Beryl Evetts and Robert
Luff Animal Welfare Trust
The Execution Charitable Trust
The Mayor of Exeter's Appeal
Fund
The Exilarch's Foundation
F C Charitable Trust
The F P Limited Charitable
Trust
The Faber Charitable Trust
Esmée Fairbairn Foundation
The Fairway Trust
Faisaltex Charitable Trust
The Family Rich Charities Trust
The Lord Faringdon Charitable
Trust
Samuel William Farmer Trust

The Farmers' Company
Charitable Fund
The Thomas Farr Charitable
Trust
Walter Farthing (Trust) Limited
The Fassnidge Memorial Trust
Joseph Fattorini Charitable
Trust 'B' Account
The Fawcett Charitable Trust
Federation of Jewish Relief
Organisations
The John Feeney Charitable
Trust
The George Fentham
Birmingham Charity
The A M Fenton Trust
Allan and Nesta Ferguson
Charitable Settlement
The Bluff Field Charitable Trust
The Doris Field Charitable
Trust
The Fifty Fund
Firtree Trust
The Fishmongers' Company's
Charitable Trust
The Fitton Trust
The Earl Fitzwilliam Charitable
Trust
Bud Flanagan Leukaemia Fund
The Rose Flatau Charitable
Trust
The Ian Fleming Charitable
Trust
The Joyce Fletcher Charitable
Trust
The Roy Fletcher Charitable
Trust
The Flow Foundation
The Gerald Fogel Charitable
Trust
The Follett Trust
The Football Association
National Sports Centre
Trust
The Football Foundation
The Forbes Charitable
Foundation
The Forces Trust (Working
Name)
The Oliver Ford Charitable
Trust
The Forest Hill Charitable Trust
The Foresters' Charity
Stewards UK Trust
Forever Manchester (The
Community Foundation for
Greater Manchester)
Gwyneth Forrester Trust
The Fort Foundation
The Forte Charitable Trust
Foundation for Management
Education
The Four Winds Trust
The Foyle Foundation
The Isaac and Freda Frankel
Memorial Charitable Trust

The Elizabeth Frankland Moore and Star Foundation
The Jill Franklin Trust
The Gordon Fraser Charitable Trust
The Hugh Fraser Foundation
The Joseph Strong Frazer Trust
The Louis and Valerie Freedman Charitable Settlement
The Freemasons' Grand Charity
The Thomas Freke and Lady Norton Charity
The Charles S French Charitable Trust
The Anne French Memorial Trust
The Freshfield Foundation
The Freshgate Trust Foundation
The Friarsgate Trust
The Friends Hall Farm Street Trust
Friends Provident Charitable Foundation
The Frognal Trust
Maurice Fry Charitable Trust
The Fuellers Charitable Trust Fund
The Fulmer Charitable Trust
Worshipful Company of Furniture Makers Charitable Fund
Gableholt Limited
The Galbraith Trust
The Gale Family Charitable Trust
The Angela Gallagher Memorial Fund
The Gamlen Charitable Trust
The Gamma Trust
The Gannochy Trust
The Ganzoni Charitable Trust
The Worshipful Company of Gardeners of London
The Samuel Gardner Memorial Trust
The Garnett Charitable Trust
Garvan Limited
The Gatsby Charitable Foundation
Gatwick Airport Community Trust
The Robert Gavron Charitable Trust
The General Nursing Council for England and Wales Trust
J Paul Getty Jr Charitable Trust
The Gibbs Charitable Trust
Simon Gibson Charitable Trust
The G C Gibson Charitable Trust
Lady Gibson's Charitable Trust

The Harvey and Hilary Gilbert Charitable Trust
The Girdlers' Company Charitable Trust
The B and P Glasser Charitable Trust
The Glass-House Trust
Global Care
Global Charities (formerly GCap Charities)
Gloucestershire Community Foundation
Worshipful Company of Glovers of London Charity Fund
The GNC Trust
The Meir Golda Trust
The Sydney and Phyllis Goldberg Memorial Charitable Trust
The Golden Bottle Trust
The Jack Goldhill Charitable Trust
The Goldsmiths' Arts Trust Fund
The Goldsmiths' Company Charity
The Good Neighbours Trust
The Everard and Mina Goodman Charitable Foundation
Mike Gooley Trailfinders Charity
The Gosling Foundation Limited
The Gough Charitable Trust
The Gould Charitable Trust
The Grace Charitable Trust
A B Grace Trust
The Graff Foundation
The Grahame Charitable Foundation Limited
Grampian Police Diced Cap Charitable Fund
The Granada Foundation
Grand Charitable Trust of the Order of Women Freemasons
The Grand Order of Water Rats' Charities Fund
The Grange Farm Centre Trust
Grantham Yorke Trust
The Gray Trust
The Great Stone Bridge Trust of Edenbridge
The Great Torrington Town Lands Charity
The Constance Green Foundation
The Philip Green Memorial Trust
Greenham Common Community Trust Limited
Naomi and Jeffrey Greenwood Charitable Trust

Greggs Foundation (formerly Greggs Trust)
The Gretna Charitable Trust
The Grocers' Charity
The M and R Gross Charities Limited
The Grove Charitable Trust
The GRP Charitable Trust
The David and Marie Grumitt Foundation
The Bishop of Guildford's Foundation
The Guildry Incorporation of Perth
The Walter Guinness Charitable Trust
The Gunter Charitable Trust
The Gur Trust
Dr Guthrie's Association
The H and M Charitable Trust
H C D Memorial Fund
The H P Charitable Trust
The Hackney Parochial Charities
The Hadfield Trust
The Hadley Trust
The Hadrian Trust
The Alfred Haines Charitable Trust
The Hale Trust
E F and M G Hall Charitable Trust
The Edith Winifred Hall Charitable Trust
Robert Hall Charity
The Hamamelis Trust
Hamilton Wallace Trust
Paul Hamlyn Foundation
The Hammonds Charitable Trust
The Hampshire and Islands Historic Churches Trust
Hampton Fuel Allotment Charity
The W A Handley Charitable Trust
Beatrice Hankey Foundation Ltd
The Hanley Trust
The Kathleen Hannay Memorial Charity
The Doughty Hanson Charitable Foundation
Lord Hanson Foundation
The Haramead Trust
Miss K M Harbinson's Charitable Trust
The Harborne Parish Lands Charity
The Harbour Charitable Trust
The Harbour Foundation
The Harding Trust
William Harding's Charity
The Hare of Steep Charitable Trust
The Harebell Centenary Fund

The Kenneth Hargreaves
  Charitable Trust
The Harris Charitable Trust
The Harris Charity
The Harrison and Potter Trust
The John Harrison Charitable
  Trust
The Peter Harrison Foundation
The Spencer Hart Charitable
  Trust
The Hartley Charitable Trust
The N and P Hartley Memorial
  Trust
William Geoffrey Harvey's
  Discretionary Settlement
Haskel Family Foundation
The Hathaway Trust
The Maurice Hatter Foundation
The M A Hawe Settlement
The Hawthorne Charitable
  Trust
The Dorothy Hay-Bolton
  Charitable Trust
The Haymills Charitable Trust
The Headley Trust
Headley-Pitt Charitable Trust
Heagerty Charitable Trust
The Heart of England
  Community Foundation
The Heathcoat Trust
Heathside Charitable Trust
The Charlotte Heber-Percy
  Charitable Trust
The Hedley Denton Charitable
  Trust
The Hedley Foundation
The H J Heinz Company
  Limited Charitable Trust
The Hellenic Foundation
The Michael and Morven Heller
  Charitable Foundation
The Simon Heller Charitable
  Settlement
The Hemby Trust
The Christina Mary Hendrie
  Trust for Scottish and
  Canadian Charities
The Henley Educational Charity
Esther Hennell Charitable
  Trust
The G D Herbert Charitable
  Trust
The Joanna Herbert-Stepney
  Charitable Settlement (also
  known as The Paget
  Charitable Trust)
The Anne Herd Memorial Trust
The Herefordshire Historic
  Churches Trust
The Heritage of London Trust
  Ltd
The Hesed Trust
The Hesslewood Children's
  Trust (Hull Seamen's and
  General Orphanage)

The Bernhard Heuberger
  Charitable Trust
Hexham and Newcastle
  Diocesan Trust (1947)
The Higgs Charitable Trust
Alan Edward Higgs Charity
The High Sheriff's Police Trust
  for the County of West
  Midlands (Building Blocks)
Highcroft Charitable Trust
The Charles Littlewood Hill
  Trust
The Hillingdon Partnership
  Trust
Lady Hind Trust
The Hinrichsen Foundation
The Hitchin Educational
  Foundation
The Eleemosynary Charity of
  William Hobbayne
Hobson Charity Limited
Matthew Hodder Charitable
  Trust
The Sir Julian Hodge
  Charitable Trust
The J G Hogg Charitable Trust
The Holden Charitable Trust
John Holford's Charity
The Hollick Family Charitable
  Trust
The Dorothy Holmes Charitable
  Trust
The Holst Foundation
The Edward Holt Trust
The Holywood Trust
The Homelands Charitable
  Trust
The Homestead Charitable
  Trust
Sir Harold Hood's Charitable
  Trust
Hope for Youth (formerly
  Women Caring Trust)
The Hope Trust
HopMarket Charity
The Cuthbert Horn Trust
The Antony Hornby Charitable
  Trust
The Horne Foundation
The Horne Trust
The Worshipful Company of
  Horners' Charitable Trusts
The Hornsey Parochial
  Charities
The Hospital of God at
  Greatham
The Hospital Saturday Fund
Houblon-Norman/George Fund
The House of Industry Estate
The Reta Lila Howard
  Foundation
The Daniel Howard Trust
The Hudson Foundation
The Huggard Charitable Trust
The Geoffrey C Hughes
  Charitable Trust

The Hull and East Riding
  Charitable Trust
Hulme Trust Estates
  (Educational)
Human Relief Foundation
The Humanitarian Trust
The Michael and Shirley Hunt
  Charitable Trust
The Hunter Foundation
Miss Agnes H Hunter's Trust
The Huntingdon Foundation
Huntingdon Freemen's Charity
John Huntingdon's Charity
Hurdale Charity Limited
The Nani Huyu Charitable Trust
The P Y N and B Hyams Trust
The Hyde Charitable Trust –
  Youth Plus
The Idlewild Trust
The Iliffe Family Charitable
  Trust
The Indigo Trust
The Ingram Trust
The Inland Waterways
  Association
The Inlight Trust
The Inman Charity
The Inner London Magistrates
  Court Poor Box and Feeder
  Charity
The Ireland Fund of Great
  Britain
The Irish Youth Foundation
  (UK) Ltd (incorporating The
  Lawlor Foundation)
The Ironmongers' Foundation
Irshad Trust
The Charles Irving Charitable
  Trust
Irwin Trust
The ISA Charity
The Isaacs Charitable Trust
The J Isaacs Charitable Trust
The Isle of Anglesey Charitable
  Trust
The ITF Seafarers Trust
The J R S S T Charitable Trust
Elizabeth Jackson Charitable
  Trust
The Ruth and Lionel Jacobson
  Trust (Second Fund) No 2
Jaffe Family Relief Fund
John James Bristol Foundation
The Susan and Stephen
  James Charitable
  Settlement (also known as
  the Stephen James
  Charitable Trust)
The James Trust
The Jarman Charitable Trust
JCA Charitable Foundation
The Jeffrey Charitable Trust
The Jenour Foundation
Jesus Hospital Charity
Jewish Child's Day
The Jewish Youth Fund

The JMK Charitable Trust
The Joanies Trust
The Harold Joels Charitable Trust
The Jonathan Joels Charitable Trust
The Nicholas Joels Charitable Trust
The Norman Joels Charitable Trust
The Elton John Aids Foundation
The Lillie Johnson Charitable Trust
The Johnson Foundation
The Johnson Group Cleaners Charity
The Johnson Wax Ltd Charitable Trust
The Joicey Trust
The Jones 1986 Charitable Trust
The Marjorie and Geoffrey Jones Charitable Trust
The Jordan Charitable Foundation
The J E Joseph Charitable Fund
The Lady Eileen Joseph Foundation
JTH Charitable Trust
The Anton Jurgens Charitable Trust
The Bernard Kahn Charitable Trust
The Stanley Kalms Foundation
The Karenza Foundation
The Boris Karloff Charitable Foundation
The Ian Karten Charitable Trust
The Kasner Charitable Trust
The Kass Charitable Trust
The Kathleen Trust
The Michael and Ilse Katz Foundation
The Katzauer Charitable Settlement
The C S Kaufman Charitable Trust
The Geoffrey John Kaye Charitable Foundation
The Emmanuel Kaye Foundation
Kelsick's Educational Foundation
The KempWelch Charitable Trust
The Kay Kendall Leukaemia Fund
The Kennedy Charitable Foundation
The Nancy Kenyon Charitable Trust
Keren Association
Kermaville Ltd

The Peter Kershaw Trust
The Kessler Foundation
Keswick Hall Trust
The Ursula Keyes Trust
The Robert Kiln Charitable Trust
The King/Cullimore Charitable Trust
The King's Fund
The Kingsbury Charity
The Mary Kinross Charitable Trust
Kirkley Poor's Lands Estate
The Richard Kirkman Charitable Trust
Kirschel Foundation
Robert Kitchin (Saddlers' Company)
Ernest Kleinwort Charitable Trust
The Marina Kleinwort Charitable Trust
The Kobler Trust
The Kohn Foundation
The Kreditor Charitable Trust
The Kreitman Foundation
The Neil Kreitman Foundation
The Kyte Charitable Trust
The Late Sir Pierce Lacy Charity Trust
John Laing Charitable Trust
Maurice and Hilda Laing Charitable Trust
The Christopher Laing Foundation
The Kirby Laing Foundation
The Martin Laing Foundation
The Beatrice Laing Trust
The Lambert Charitable Trust
Duchy of Lancaster Benevolent Fund
The Lancaster Foundation
The Allen Lane Foundation
The Langdale Trust
The Langley Charitable Trust
The Langtree Trust
The LankellyChase Foundation
The Lanvern Foundation
The R J Larg Family Charitable Trust
Largsmount Ltd
The Lark Trust
Laslett's (Hinton) Charity
Lauchentilly Charitable Foundation 1988
The Lauffer Family Charitable Foundation
The Kathleen Laurence Trust
The Law Society Charity
The Edgar E Lawley Foundation
The Herd Lawson and Muriel Lawson Charitable Trust
The Lawson Beckman Charitable Trust
The Raymond and Blanche Lawson Charitable Trust

The Carole and Geoffrey Lawson Foundation
The Mason Le Page Charitable Trust
The Leach Fourteenth Trust
The David Lean Foundation
The Leathersellers' Company Charitable Fund
The Arnold Lee Charitable Trust
The William Leech Charity
The Lord Mayor of Leeds Appeal Fund
Leeds Building Society Charitable Foundation
Leicester Charity Link (formerly The Leicester Charity Organisation Society)
The Kennedy Leigh Charitable Trust
The Leigh Trust
Mrs Vera Leigh's Charity
The P Leigh-Bramwell Trust 'E'
The Lennox and Wyfold Foundation
The Erica Leonard Trust
The Leonard Trust
The Mark Leonard Trust
Lesley Lesley and Mutter Trust
The Leverhulme Trade Charities Trust
Lord Leverhulme's Charitable Trust
The Joseph Levy Charitable Foundation
The John Spedan Lewis Foundation
The Sir Edward Lewis Foundation
John Lewis Partnership General Community Fund
Lichfield Conduit Lands
Lifeline 4 Kids
The Thomas Lilley Memorial Trust
The Linbury Trust
The Lincolnshire Old Churches Trust
The Lind Trust
Lindale Educational Foundation
The Linden Charitable Trust
The Enid Linder Foundation
The Linmardon Trust
The Ruth and Stuart Lipton Charitable Trust
The Lister Charitable Trust
Frank Litchfield Charitable Trust
The Andrew and Mary Elizabeth Little Charitable Trust
The Second Joseph Aaron Littman Foundation
The George John and Sheilah Livanos Charitable Trust

Liverpool Charity and Voluntary Services
Liverpool Sailors' Home Trust
The Elaine and Angus Lloyd Charitable Trust
The Charles Lloyd Foundation
The Lloyd Fund
Lloyd's Charities Trust
Lloyds TSB Foundation for England and Wales
Lloyds TSB Foundation for Northern Ireland
Lloyds TSB Foundation for the Channel Islands
The Locker Foundation
The Loftus Charitable Trust
The Lolev Charitable Trust
The Trust for London (formerly the City Parochial Foundation)
London Catalyst (formerly The Metropolitan Hospital-Sunday Fund)
The London Community Foundation (formerly Capital Community Foundation)
The London Law Trust
The William and Katherine Longman Trust
The Loseley and Guildway Charitable Trust
The Lotus Foundation
The C L Loyd Charitable Trust
LSA Charitable Trust
The Marie Helen Luen Charitable Trust
Robert Luff Foundation Ltd
Henry Lumley Charitable Trust
Lady Lumley's Educational Foundation
C F Lunoe Trust Fund
The Ruth and Jack Lunzer Charitable Trust
Lord and Lady Lurgan Trust
The Lyndhurst Trust
The Lynn Foundation
The Lynwood Trust
John Lyon's Charity
The Lyons Charitable Trust
The Sir Jack Lyons Charitable Trust
The Lyras Family Charitable Trust
Sylvanus Lyson's Charity
The M and C Trust
The M D and S Charitable Trust
The M K Charitable Trust
The Madeline Mabey Trust
The E M MacAndrew Trust
The R S Macdonald Charitable Trust
Macdonald-Buchanan Charitable Trust
The Macfarlane Walker Trust

The Mackay and Brewer Charitable Trust
The Mackintosh Foundation
The MacRobert Trust
The Magdalen and Lasher Charity
The Magen Charitable Trust
Man Group plc Charitable Trust
Manchester Airport Community Trust Fund
The Manchester Guardian Society Charitable Trust
Lord Mayor of Manchester's Charity Appeal Trust
Mandeville Trust
The Manifold Charitable Trust
W M Mann Foundation
The Leslie and Lilian Manning Trust
Marbeh Torah Trust
Marchig Animal Welfare Trust
The Stella and Alexander Margulies Charitable Trust
Market Harborough and The Bowdens Charity
The Ann and David Marks Foundation
The Hilda and Samuel Marks Foundation
J P Marland Charitable Trust
The Michael Marsh Charitable Trust
The Marsh Christian Trust
The Charlotte Marshall Charitable Trust
The Jim Marshall Charitable Trust
The D G Marshall of Cambridge Trust
Marshgate Charitable Settlement
Sir George Martin Trust
The Mason Porter Charitable Trust
The Nancie Massey Charitable Trust
The Mathew Trust
The Matt 6.3 Charitable Trust
The Violet Mauray Charitable Trust
The Maxell Educational Trust
The Maxwell Family Foundation
Evelyn May Trust
The Mayfield Valley Arts Trust
Mazars Charitable Trust
The McDougall Trust
The McKenna Charitable Trust
The Helen Isabella McMorran Charitable Foundation
The James Frederick and Ethel Anne Measures Charity
The Medlock Charitable Trust
The Anthony and Elizabeth Mellows Charitable Settlement

Melow Charitable Trust
The Mercers' Charitable Foundation
The Merchant Taylors' Company Charities Fund
The Merchant Venturers' Charity
The Merchants' House of Glasgow
The Mersey Docks and Harbour Company Charitable Fund
Community Foundation for Merseyside
The Zachary Merton and George Woofindin Convalescent Trust
The Tony Metherell Charitable Trust
The Metropolitan Drinking Fountain and Cattle Trough Association
Gerald Micklem Charitable Trust
Midhurst Pensions Trust
The Migraine Trust
Miles Trust for the Putney and Roehampton Community
Millennium Stadium Charitable Trust
The Hugh and Mary Miller Bequest Trust
The Miller Foundation
The Millfield Trust
The Millhouses Charitable Trust
The Millichope Foundation
The Mills Charity
The Millward Charitable Trust
The Clare Milne Trust
Milton Keynes Community Foundation
The Edgar Milward Charity
The Peter Minet Trust
The Minos Trust
The Mirfield Educational Charity
The Laurence Misener Charitable Trust
The Mishcon Family Charitable Trust
The Misselbrook Trust
The Esmé Mitchell Trust
Keren Mitzvah Trust
The Mizpah Trust
The Mobbs Memorial Trust Ltd
The Modiano Charitable Trust
The Moette Charitable Trust
The Mole Charitable Trust
The D C Moncrieff Charitable Trust
Monmouthshire County Council Welsh Church Act Fund
The Montague Thompson Coon Charitable Trust

The Colin Montgomerie
Charitable Foundation
The Monument Trust
The Nigel Moores Family
Charitable Trust
The Peter Moores Foundation
The Morel Charitable Trust
The Morgan Charitable
Foundation
The Mr and Mrs J T Morgan
Foundation
The Oliver Morland Charitable
Trust
The Bernard Morris Charitable
Trust
The Morris Charitable Trust
The Willie and Mabel Morris
Charitable Trust
The Peter Morrison Charitable
Foundation
The Stanley Morrison
Charitable Trust
Vyoel Moshe Charitable Trust
The Moss Charitable Trust
The Robert and Margaret
Moss Charitable Trust
Moss Family Charitable Trust
The Mount Everest Foundation
The Edwina Mountbatten Trust
Mountbatten Festival of Music
The Mountbatten Memorial
Trust
The Mugdock Children's Trust
The Mulberry Trust
The Edith Murphy Foundation
The Mushroom Fund
The Music Sales Charitable
Trust
Muslim Hands
The Mutual Trust Group
The Kitty and Daniel Nabarro
Charitable Trust
The Nadezhda Charitable Trust
The Naggar Charitable Trust
The Eleni Nakou Foundation
The Janet Nash Charitable
Settlement
Nathan Charitable Trust
The National Churches Trust
(formerly the Historic
Churches Preservation
Trust with the Incorporated
Church Building Society)
The National Manuscripts
Conservation Trust
The Nchima Trust
Needham Market and Barking
Welfare Charities
The Worshipful Company of
Needlemakers' Charitable
Fund
The Neighbourly Charitable
Trust
The James Neill Trust Fund
Nemoral Ltd
Network for Social Change

The New Appeals Organisation
for the City and County of
Nottingham
New Court Charitable Trust
The Newcomen Collett
Foundation
Alderman Newton's
Educational Foundation
The Chevras Ezras Nitzrochim
Trust
The Noon Foundation
The Norda Trust
Norie Charitable Trust
Normalyn Charitable Trust
The Norman Family Charitable
Trust
The Duncan Norman Trust
Fund
The Normanby Charitable Trust
The North British Hotel Trust
The North West Cancer
Research Fund
The Northampton Municipal
Church Charities
The Northampton Queen's
Institute Relief in Sickness
Fund
The Earl of Northampton's
Charity
The Northcott Devon Medical
Foundation
The Northern Rock Foundation
The Northmoor Trust
The Northumberland Village
Homes Trust
The Northwood Charitable
Trust
The Norton Foundation
The Norwich Church of England
Young Men's Society
The Norwich Historic Churches
Trust Ltd
The Norwich Town Close
Estate Charity
The Norwood and Newton
Settlement
The Noswad Charity
The Notgrove Trust
The Nottingham General
Dispensary
The Nottingham Gordon
Memorial Trust for Boys
and Girls
Nottinghamshire Community
Foundation
The Nottinghamshire Historic
Churches Trust
The Nottinghamshire Miners'
Welfare Trust Fund
Novi Most International
The Father O'Mahoney
Memorial Trust
The Sir Peter O'Sullevan
Charitable Trust
The Oak Trust
The Oakdale Trust

The Oakley Charitable Trust
The Oakmoor Charitable Trust
The Odin Charitable Trust
The Ofenheim Charitable Trust
Ogilvie Charities Deed No.2
(including the Charity of
Mary Catherine Ford Smith)
The Ogle Christian Trust
Oglesby Charitable Trust
The Oikonomia Trust
Oizer Charitable Trust
The Old Broad Street Charity
Trust
The Old Enfield Charitable
Trust
The John Oldacre Foundation
The Oldham Foundation
The Olga Charitable Trust
Onaway Trust
Open Gate
The Ormsby Charitable Trust
Orrin Charitable Trust
The Ouseley Trust
The Owen Family Trust
Oxfam (GB)
The Oxfordshire Community
Foundation
The P F Charitable Trust
Padwa Charitable Foundation
The Pallant Charitable Trust
The Palmer Foundation
The Panacea Society
Panton Trust
The Paragon Trust
The Park House Charitable
Trust
The Frank Parkinson
Agricultural Trust
The Samuel and Freda
Parkinson Charitable Trust
The Parthenon Trust
The Constance Paterson
Charitable Trust
The Patrick Charitable Trust
The Jack Patston Charitable
Trust
Paycare Charity Trust
(previously known as
Patients' Aid Association
Hospital and Medical
Charities Trust)
The Payne Charitable Trust
The Harry Payne Trust
The Susanna Peake Charitable
Trust
The Pedmore Sporting Club
Trust Fund
The Dowager Countess
Eleanor Peel Trust
The Pennycress Trust
The Performing Right Society
Foundation
The Persson Charitable Trust
(formerly Highmoore Hall
Charitable Trust)
The Persula Foundation

The Jack Petchey Foundation
The Petplan Charitable Trust
The Philips and Rubens
 Charitable Trust
The Phillips Charitable Trust
The Phillips Family Charitable
 Trust
Philological Foundation
The David Pickford Charitable
 Foundation
The Bernard Piggott Trust
The Pilgrim Trust
The Cecil Pilkington Charitable
 Trust
The Pilkington Charities Fund
The Austin and Hope
 Pilkington Trust
The Sir Harry Pilkington Trust
The Col W W Pilkington Will
 Trusts The General Charity
 Fund
The DLA Piper Charitable Trust
The Worshipful Company of
 Plaisterers Charitable Trust
The Platinum Trust
Polden-Puckham Charitable
 Foundation
The Poling Charitable Trust
The George and Esme Pollitzer
 Charitable Settlement
The J S F Pollitzer Charitable
 Settlement
The Ponton House Trust
The Mayor of Poole's Appeal
 Fund
Edith and Ferdinand Porjes
 Charitable Trust
The John Porter Charitable
 Trust
The Porter Foundation
The Portrack Charitable Trust
The J E Posnansky Charitable
 Trust
The Mary Potter Convent
 Hospital Trust
The David and Elaine Potter
 Foundation
The Powell Foundation
The W L Pratt Charitable Trust
Premierquote Ltd
Premishlaner Charitable Trust
The Lucy Price Relief-in-Need
 Charity
Sir John Priestman Charity
 Trust
The Primrose Trust
The Prince of Wales's
 Charitable Foundation
The Priory Foundation
Prison Service Charity Fund
The Privy Purse Charitable
 Trust
The Proven Family Trust
The Provincial Grand Charity of
 the Province of Derbyshire

PSA Peugeot Citroen Charity
 Trust
The Puebla Charitable Trust
The Richard and Christine
 Purchas Charitable Trust
The Puri Foundation
Mr and Mrs J A Pye's
 Charitable Settlement
Quartet Community Foundation
 (formerly the Greater Bristol
 Foundation)
Queen Mary's Roehampton
 Trust
The Queen's Silver Jubilee
 Trust
R S Charitable Trust
The R V W Trust
The Monica Rabagliati
 Charitable Trust
Rachel Charitable Trust
The Mr and Mrs Philip
 Rackham Charitable Trust
Richard Radcliffe Charitable
 Trust
The Radcliffe Trust
The Ragdoll Foundation
The Rainford Trust
The Peggy Ramsay Foundation
The Joseph and Lena Randall
 Charitable Trust
The Rank Foundation
The Fanny Rapaport Charitable
 Settlement
The Ratcliff Foundation
The Ratcliff Pension Charity
The Ratcliffe Charitable Trust
The Eleanor Rathbone
 Charitable Trust
The Sigrid Rausing Trust
The Ravensdale Trust
The Rayden Charitable Trust
The Roger Raymond Charitable
 Trust
The Rayne Foundation
The Rayne Trust
The John Rayner Charitable
 Trust
The Sir James Reckitt Charity
The Red Arrows Trust
The Red Rose Charitable Trust
The C A Redfern Charitable
 Foundation
The Reed Foundation
Richard Reeve's Foundation
The Max Reinhardt Charitable
 Trust
Relief Fund for Romania
 Limited
The Rest Harrow Trust
Reuben Brothers Foundation
The Joan K Reynell Charitable
 Trust
The Nathaniel Reyner Trust
 Fund
The Rhododendron Trust

The Sir Cliff Richard Charitable
 Trust
The Clive Richards Charity
The Violet M Richards Charity
The Richmond Parish Lands
 Charity
Ridgesave Limited
The Ripple Effect Foundation
The Sir John Ritblat Family
 Foundation
The River Trust
Thomas Roberts Trust
The Robertson Trust
The Rochester Bridge Trust
The Rock Foundation
The Rock Solid Trust
The Rofeh Trust
Richard Rogers Charitable
 Settlement
Rokach Family Charitable Trust
The Helen Roll Charitable
 Trust
The Sir James Roll Charitable
 Trust
The Roman Research Trust
Romeera Foundation
The C A Rookes Charitable
 Trust
The Rosca Trust
The Cecil Rosen Foundation
Rosetrees Trust
The Rothermere Foundation
The Rotherwick Foundation
The Roughley Charitable Trust
Mrs Gladys Row Fogo
 Charitable Trust
Rowanville Ltd
The Christopher Rowbotham
 Charitable Trust
The Rowing Foundation
The Rowlands Trust
The Joseph Rowntree
 Charitable Trust
The Joseph Rowntree
 Foundation
Joseph Rowntree Reform Trust
 Limited
Royal Artillery Charitable Fund
Royal Docks Trust (London)
Royal Masonic Trust for Girls
 and Boys
The Royal Scots Benevolent
 Society
The Alfred and Frances
 Rubens Charitable Trust
The Rubin Foundation
William Arthur Rudd Memorial
 Trust
The Rufford Foundation
The Russell Trust
The J S and E C Rymer
 Charitable Trust
S O Charitable Trust
The Jeremy and John Sacher
 Charitable Trust

The Michael Harry Sacher Trust

The Sackler Trust (Formerly Dr Mortimer and Theresa Sackler Foundation)

The Ruzin Sadagora Trust

The Saddlers' Company Charitable Fund

The Saga Charitable Trust

The Jean Sainsbury Animal Welfare Trust

The Alan and Babette Sainsbury Charitable Fund

The Sainsbury Family Charitable Trusts

The Saintbury Trust

The Saints and Sinners Trust

The Salamander Charitable Trust

The Salt Foundation

The Salt Trust

The Sammermar Trust

Basil Samuel Charitable Trust

The Hon. M J Samuel Charitable Trust

The Peter Samuel Charitable Trust

The Camilla Samuel Fund

The Samworth Foundation

The Sandra Charitable Trust

Santander UK Foundation Limited

Jimmy Savile Charitable Trust

The Scarfe Charitable Trust

The Schapira Charitable Trust

The Schmidt-Bodner Charitable Trust

The R H Scholes Charitable Trust

The Schreib Trust

The Schreiber Charitable Trust

The Francis C Scott Charitable Trust

The Frieda Scott Charitable Trust

The Sir James and Lady Scott Trust

The Scott Trust Foundation

The Storrow Scott Will Trust

The Scottish Arts Council

Scottish Coal Industry Special Welfare Fund

The Scottish Community Foundation

The Scottish International Education Trust

The Scouloudi Foundation

Seafarers UK (King George's Fund for Sailors)

Seamen's Hospital Society

The Searchlight Electric Charitable Trust

The Searle Charitable Trust

The Helene Sebba Charitable Trust

The Samuel Sebba Charitable Trust

The Seedfield Trust

The Ayrton Senna Foundation

The Seven Fifty Trust

The Cyril Shack Trust

The Jean Shanks Foundation

The Shanti Charitable Trust

ShareGift (The Orr Mackintosh Foundation)

The Linley Shaw Foundation

The Sheepdrove Trust

The Sheffield and District Hospital Services Charitable Fund

The Sheldon Trust

The P and D Shepherd Charitable Trust

The Sylvia and Colin Shepherd Charitable Trust

The Archie Sherman Cardiff Foundation

The Archie Sherman Charitable Trust

The R C Sherriff Trust

The Shetland Charitable Trust

SHINE (Support and Help in Education)

The Barnett and Sylvia Shine No 2 Charitable Trust

The Bassil Shippam and Alsford Trust

The Shipwrights' Company Charitable Fund

The Shirley Foundation

Shlomo Memorial Fund Limited

The J A Shone Memorial Trust

The Barbara A Shuttleworth Memorial Trust

The Mary Elizabeth Siebel Charity

David and Jennifer Sieff Charitable Trust

The Julius Silman Charitable Trust

The Leslie Silver Charitable Trust

The Simpson Education and Conservation Trust

The Simpson Foundation

The Huntly and Margery Sinclair Charitable Trust

Sino-British Fellowship Trust

The Skelton Bounty

The Charles Skey Charitable Trust

Skipton Building Society Charitable Foundation

The John Slater Foundation

The SMB Charitable Trust

The Mrs Smith and Mount Trust

The N Smith Charitable Settlement

The Amanda Smith Charitable Trust

The E H Smith Charitable Trust

The Smith Charitable Trust

The Henry Smith Charity

The Leslie Smith Foundation

The Martin Smith Foundation

Stanley Smith General Charitable Trust

The Stanley Smith UK Horticultural Trust

The Snowball Trust

The Sobell Foundation

Solihull Community Foundation

The Solo Charitable Settlement

Dr Richard Solomon's Charitable Trust

The E C Sosnow Charitable Trust

The Souter Charitable Trust

The South Square Trust

The Stephen R and Philippa H Southall Charitable Trust

The W F Southall Trust

The Southover Manor General Education Trust

The Southwold Trust

The Sovereign Health Care Charitable Trust

Sparquote Limited

The Spear Charitable Trust

The Jessie Spencer Trust

The Ralph and Irma Sperring Charity

The Moss Spiro Will Charitable Foundation

The Spoore, Merry and Rixman Foundation

Spring Harvest

Springfields Employees' Medical Research and Charity Trust Fund

Springrule Ltd

The Spurrell Charitable Trust

The Geoff and Fiona Squire Foundation

St Francis's Leprosy Guild

St Gabriel's Trust

St Hilda's Trust

St James' Trust Settlement

Sir Walter St John's Educational Charity

St Katharine and Shadwell Trust

St Michael's and All Saints' Charities

The Late St Patrick White Charitable Trust

St Teilo's Trust

The Stanley Foundation Ltd

The Stanton Ballard Charitable Trust

The Staples Trust

The Star Charitable Trust

The Peter Stebbings Memorial Charity

The Steinberg Family
Charitable Trust
The Hugh Stenhouse
Foundation
The Sigmund Sternberg
Charitable Foundation
Stervon Ltd
The Stevenage Community
Trust
The June Stevens Foundation
The Steventon Allotments and
Relief-in-Need Charity
The Stewards' Charitable Trust
The Stewards' Company
Limited (incorporating the J
W Laing Trust and the J W
Laing Biblical Scholarship
Trust)
The Sir Halley Stewart Trust
The Stobart Newlands
Charitable Trust
The Edward Stocks-Massey
Bequest Fund
The Stokenchurch Educational
Charity
The Stoller Charitable Trust
The M J C Stone Charitable
Trust
The Stone-Mallabar Charitable
Foundation
The Samuel Storey Family
Charitable Trust
Peter Stormonth Darling
Charitable Trust
The Strangward Trust
The Strasser Foundation
Stratford upon Avon Town
Trust
Strathclyde Police Benevolent
Fund
The W O Street Charitable
Foundation
The Sudborough Foundation
The Suffolk Historic Churches
Trust
The Summerfield Charitable
Trust
The Surrey Historic Buildings
Trust Ltd
The Sussex Historic Churches
Trust
The Sutasoma Trust
Sutton Coldfield Municipal
Charities
Swansea and Brecon Diocesan
Board of Finance Limited
The John Swire (1989)
Charitable Trust
The Swire Charitable Trust
The Hugh and Ruby Sykes
Charitable Trust
The Charles and Elsie Sykes
Trust
The Sylvanus Charitable Trust
The Stella Symons Charitable
Trust

The Tabeel Trust
The Tajtelbaum Charitable
Trust
Tallow Chandlers Benevolent
Fund
The Tangent Charitable Trust
The Lady Tangye Charitable
Trust
The David Tannen Charitable
Trust
The Tanner Trust
The Lili Tapper Charitable
Foundation
The Mrs A Lacy Tate Trust
The Tay Charitable Trust
Humphrey Richardson Taylor
Charitable Trust
The Connie and Albert Taylor
Charitable Trust
The Cyril Taylor Charitable
Trust
A P Taylor Trust
Tearfund
The Tedworth Charitable Trust
Tees Valley Community
Foundation
The Templeton Goodwill Trust
Tesco Charity Trust
The Thames Wharf Charity
The Thistle Trust
The Loke Wan Tho Memorial
Foundation
The Arthur and Margaret
Thompson Charitable Trust
The Thompson Family
Charitable Trust
The Len Thomson Charitable
Trust
The Sue Thomson Foundation
The Sir Jules Thorn Charitable
Trust
The Thornton Foundation
The Thornton Trust
The Three Guineas Trust
The Three Oaks Trust
The Thriplow Charitable Trust
The Tinsley Foundation
The Tisbury Telegraph Trust
TJH Foundation
The Tobacco Pipe Makers and
Tobacco Trade Benevolent
Fund
The Tolkien Trust
Tollemache (Buckminster)
Charitable Trust
Tomchei Torah Charitable
Trust
The Tompkins Foundation
The Tory Family Foundation
Tottenham Grammar School
Foundation
The Tower Hill Trust
The Towry Law Charitable Trust
(also known as the Castle
Educational Trust)

The Mayor of Trafford's Charity
Fund
The Constance Travis
Charitable Trust
The Treeside Trust
The Triangle Trust (1949) Fund
The True Colours Trust
Truedene Co. Ltd
The Truemark Trust
Truemart Limited
Trumros Limited
Trust Sixty Three
Tudor Rose Ltd
The Tudor Trust
The Tufton Charitable Trust
The R D Turner Charitable
Trust
The Douglas Turner Trust
The Florence Turner Trust
Miss S M Tutton Charitable
Trust
The TUUT Charitable Trust
Community Foundation Serving
Tyne and Wear and
Northumberland
Trustees of Tzedakah
Ulster Garden Villages Ltd
Ultach Trust
Ulting Overseas Trust
The Ulverscroft Foundation
Ulverston Town Lands Charity
The Underwood Trust
The Union of Orthodox Hebrew
Congregation
The United Society for the
Propagation of the Gospel
UnLtd (Foundation for Social
Entrepreneurs)
The David Uri Memorial Trust
Uxbridge United Welfare Trust
Vale of Glamorgan – Welsh
Church Fund
The Valentine Charitable Trust
John and Lucille van Geest
Foundation
The Van Neste Foundation
Mrs Maud Van Norden's
Charitable Foundation
The Vandervell Foundation
The Vardy Foundation
The Variety Club Children's
Charity
Veneziana Fund
The Verdon-Smith Family
Charitable Settlement
Victoria Homes Trust
The Nigel Vinson Charitable
Trust
The William and Ellen Vinten
Trust
The Vintners' Company
Charitable Foundation
Vintners' Gifts Charity
Vision Charity
Vivdale Ltd
The Viznitz Foundation

Wade's Charity
The Scurrah Wainwright Charity
Wakeham Trust
The Community Foundation in
Wales
Wales Council for Voluntary
Action
Robert and Felicity Waley-
Cohen Charitable Trust
The Thomas Wall Trust
The F J Wallis Charitable
Settlement
War on Want
The Ward Blenkinsop Trust
The George Ward Charitable
Trust
The Barbara Ward Children's
Foundation
G R Waters Charitable Trust
2000
The Waterways Trust
The Wates Foundation
The Howard Watson Symington
Memorial Charity
John Watson's Trust
Weatherley Charitable Trust
The Weavers' Company
Benevolent Fund
The Weinberg Foundation
The Weinstein Foundation
The Weinstock Fund
The Weldon UK Charitable
Trust
The Wellcome Trust
Welsh Church Fund Dyfed
area (Carmarthenshire,
Ceredigion and
Pembrokeshire)
The Welton Foundation
The Wessex Youth Trust
The West Derby Wastelands
Charity
West London Synagogue
Charitable Fund
The West Yorkshire Police
Community Fund
The Westminster Foundation
The Garfield Weston
Foundation
The Whitaker Charitable Trust
The Colonel W H Whitbread
Charitable Trust
The Simon Whitbread
Charitable Trust
The Whitecourt Charitable
Trust
The Norman Whiteley Trust
The Whitley Animal Protection
Trust
The Whittlesey Charity
The Lionel Wigram Memorial
Trust
The Felicity Wilde Charitable
Trust
The Will Charitable Trust

The Kay Williams Charitable
Foundation
The Williams Family Charitable
Trust
The H D H Wills 1965
Charitable Trust
The Dame Violet Wills Will
Trust
The Wilmcote Charitrust
David Wilson Foundation
The Wilson Foundation
J and J R Wilson Trust
The Community Foundation for
Wiltshire and Swindon
The Benjamin Winegarten
Charitable Trust
The Harold Hyam Wingate
Foundation
The Francis Winham
Foundation
Wirral Mayor's Charity
The Michael and Anna Wix
Charitable Trust
The Wixamtree Trust
The Woburn 1986 Charitable
Trust
The Maurice Wohl Charitable
Foundation
The Charles Wolfson
Charitable Trust
The James Wood Bequest
Fund
Woodlands Green Ltd
Woodlands Trust
Woodroffe Benton Foundation
The Woodward Charitable
Trust
Worcester Municipal Charities
(incorporating Worcester
Consolidated Municipal
Charity and Worcester
Municipal Exhibitions
Foundation)
The Worcestershire and
Dudley Historic Churches
Trust
The Fred and Della Worms
Charitable Trust
The Wragge and Co. Charitable
Trust
The Diana Edgson Wright
Charitable Trust
The Matthews Wrightson
Charity Trust
Miss E B Wrightson's
Charitable Settlement
Wychdale Ltd
Wychville Ltd
The Wyndham Charitable Trust
The Wyseliot Charitable Trust
The Xerox (UK) Trust
The Yapp Charitable Trust
The Dennis Alan Yardy
Charitable Trust
The W Wing Yip and Brothers
Foundation

The York Children's Trust
Yorkshire Agricultural Society
Yorkshire Building Society
Charitable Foundation
The South Yorkshire
Community Foundation
The Yorkshire Dales
Millennium Trust
The John Young Charitable
Settlement
The William Allen Young
Charitable Trust
The John K Young Endowment
Fund
Youth Music
Zephyr Charitable Trust
The Marjorie and Arnold Ziff
Charitable Foundation
Stephen Zimmerman
Charitable Trust
The Zochonis Charitable Trust
Zurich Community Trust (UK)
Limited

Campaigning

The A B Charitable Trust
The Adint Charitable Trust
The Ajahma Charitable Trust
The Alchemy Foundation
The Animal Defence Trust
The Ove Arup Foundation
AstonMansfield Charitable
Trust
The Bedford Charity (The
Harpur Trust)
The Bedfordshire and Luton
Community Foundation
The Bisgood Charitable Trust
(registered as Miss Jeanne
Bisgood's Charitable Trust)
The Body Shop Foundation
The Anthony Bourne
Foundation
The Charles and Edna
Broadhurst Charitable Trust
The Bromley Trust
The Noel Buxton Trust
Christian Aid
The City Bridge Trust (formerly
known as Bridge House
Trust)
The Clover Trust
The Cobalt Trust
The Sir Jeremiah Colman Gift
Trust
Cornwall Community
Foundation
The Cotton Trust
Cripplegate Foundation
Cumbria Community
Foundation
EAGA Partnership Charitable
Trust
The W G Edwards Charitable
Foundation

Essex Community Foundation
The Matthew Eyton Animal
    Welfare Trust
Esmée Fairbairn Foundation
The Fishmongers' Company's
    Charitable Trust
Ford Britain Trust
The Jill Franklin Trust
The Hugh Fraser Foundation
Friends Provident Charitable
    Foundation
The General Nursing Council
    for England and Wales
    Trust
J Paul Getty Jr Charitable Trust
The Goldmark Trust
The Gould Charitable Trust
H C D Memorial Fund
The Hadley Trust
Hampshire and Isle of Wight
    Community Foundation
The Kathleen Hannay
    Memorial Charity
Miss K M Harbinson's
    Charitable Trust
The Harebell Centenary Fund
Haskel Family Foundation
The Hertfordshire Community
    Foundation
The Hospital Saturday Fund
The J R S S T Charitable Trust
The Judith Trust
Jusaca Charitable Trust
The LankellyChase Foundation
The Edgar E Lawley Foundation
The Leeds Community
    Foundation
The Lennox and Wyfold
    Foundation
The Joseph Levy Charitable
    Foundation
The Lloyd Fund
The Trust for London (formerly
    the City Parochial
    Foundation)
London Catalyst (formerly The
    Metropolitan Hospital-
    Sunday Fund)
J P Marland Charitable Trust
The Mercers' Charitable
    Foundation
Community Foundation for
    Merseyside
The Millfield House Foundation
The Millfield Trust
The Mitchell Charitable Trust
The Moss Charitable Trust
Moss Family Charitable Trust
The National Churches Trust
    (formerly the Historic
    Churches Preservation
    Trust with the Incorporated
    Church Building Society)
Newby Trust Limited
The Northcott Devon
    Foundation

The Northern Rock Foundation
Open Gate
G S Plaut Charitable Trust
    Limited
The David and Elaine Potter
    Foundation
Prairie Trust
The Queen's Silver Jubilee
    Trust
The Sigrid Rausing Trust
The Rest Harrow Trust
Rosa – the UK fund for women
    and girls
The Roughley Charitable Trust
The Joseph Rowntree
    Charitable Trust
The Joseph Rowntree
    Foundation
The Samuel Sebba Charitable
    Trust
The Shirley Foundation
Surrey Community Foundation
The Taylor Family Foundation
The David Thomas Charitable
    Trust
The Douglas Turner Trust
The Vardy Foundation
The Wates Foundation
Webb Memorial Trust
The Westcroft Trust
The Community Foundation for
    Wiltshire and Swindon
The Michael and Anna Wix
    Charitable Trust
Woodroffe Benton Foundation
The Wyndham Charitable Trust
The Yapp Charitable Trust
Zurich Community Trust (UK)
    Limited

Loan Finance

The ACT Foundation
The Architectural Heritage
    Fund
The Burton Breweries
    Charitable Trust
The Coalfields Regeneration
    Trust
The Edith Maud Ellis 1985
    Charitable Trust
The Execution Charitable Trust
The February Foundation
Impetus Trust
The Christopher Laing
    Foundation
The Lincolnshire Old Churches
    Trust
The Edward Stocks-Massey
    Bequest Fund
Ulster Garden Villages Ltd

Duration of grant

Trusts listed here have
    expressly stated on a
    questionniare used as part
    of the research for this
    book that they give grants
    for the specified time
    period. Other trusts in this
    book which did not respond
    to the questionnaire may
    also give grants as stated
    below.

....

■ One-off grants

The Sylvia Adams Charitable
    Trust
The Adamson Trust
The Adnams Charity
The Aldgate Freedom
    Foundation
All Saints Educational Trust
The H B Allen Charitable Trust
The Ammco Trust
Sir John and Lady Amory's
    Charitable Trust
The AMW Charitable Trust
The Andrew Anderson Trust
The André Christian Trust
The Animal Defence Trust
The John Apthorp Charitable
    Trust
The Ardwick Trust
The Armourers' and Brasiers'
    Gauntlet Trust
The Associated Country
    Women of the World
    (ACWW)
The Association of Colleges
    Charitable Trust
AstonMansfield Charitable
    Trust
The Astor of Hever Trust
The Aurelius Charitable Trust
The Lord Austin Trust
The John Avins Trustees
The Aylesford Family
    Charitable Trust
The Baird Trust
The Baker Charitable Trust
The Balmore Trust
The Barbour Foundation
Barchester Healthcare
    Foundation
The Barnstaple Bridge Trust
The Misses Barrie Charitable
    Trust
The James Beattie Charitable
    Trust
The Beaverbrook Foundation
The Bellahouston Bequest
    Fund
The Bellhouse Foundation
Bergqvist Charitable Trust

The Berkshire Community
    Foundation
Thomas Betton's Charity for
    Pensions and Relief-in-Need
BibleLands
Percy Bilton Charity
The Bingham Trust
The Sydney Black Charitable
    Trust
Sir Alec Black's Charity
Isabel Blackman Foundation
The Body Shop Foundation
The Booth Charities
The Boshier-Hinton Foundation
The Harry Bottom Charitable
    Trust
John and Susan Bowers Fund
British Institute at Ankara
The J and M Britton Charitable
    Trust
The Charles and Edna
    Broadhurst Charitable Trust
The Charles Brotherton Trust
Brown-Mellows Trust
The Jack Brunton Charitable
    Trust
The Bryant Trust
The Buckinghamshire Historic
    Churches Trust
The E F Bulmer Benevolent
    Fund
C J Cadbury Charitable Trust
P H G Cadbury Charitable
    Trust
The Richard Cadbury
    Charitable Trust
The Cadbury Foundation
The Cambridgeshire
    Community Foundation
The Campden Charities
    Trustee
H and L Cantor Trust
The Carew Pole Charitable
    Trust
The Carnegie Trust for the
    Universities of Scotland
The Leslie Mary Carter
    Charitable Trust
The Chapman Charitable Trust
The Charter 600 Charity
The Malcolm Chick Charity
Children's Liver Disease
    Foundation
The Childwick Trust
The Chippenham Borough
    Lands Charity
The Chrimes Family Charitable
    Trust
The Christabella Charitable
    Trust
Chrysalis Trust
The City Bridge Trust (formerly
    known as Bridge House
    Trust)
CLA Charitable Trust
J A Clark Charitable Trust

The Clothworkers' Foundation
The Robert Clutterbuck
    Charitable Trust
Coats Foundation Trust
The John S Cohen Foundation
The Cole Charitable Trust
The George Henry Collins
    Charity
Comic Relief
Community Foundation for
    Calderdale
The Congleton Inclosure Trust
The Alice Ellen Cooper Dean
    Charitable Foundation
The J Reginald Corah
    Foundation Fund
Michael Cornish Charitable
    Trust
The Cotton Industry War
    Memorial Trust
Country Houses Foundation
County Durham Community
    Foundation
The Augustine Courtauld Trust
The Cray Trust
Criffel Charitable Trust
Cripplegate Foundation
The Mayor of Croydon's
    Charity Fund
Cullum Family Trust
The Culra Charitable Trust
The Cwmbran Trust
The D'Oyly Carte Charitable
    Trust
The Gwendoline and Margaret
    Davies Charity
William Dean Countryside and
    Educational Trust
The Delius Trust
The Derbyshire Churches and
    Chapels Preservation Trust
The J N Derbyshire Trust
The Devon Educational Trust
The Duke of Devonshire's
    Charitable Trust
The Dibden Allotments Fund
The Gillian Dickinson Trust
Disability Aid Fund (The Roger
    and Jean Jefcoate Trust)
The Derek and Eileen Dodgson
    Foundation
The Dorset Historic Churches
    Trust
The Drapers' Charitable Fund
The W E Dunn Trust
The Dwek Family Charitable
    Trust
The Eagle Charity Trust
The Earley Charity
The Earmark Trust
East London Community
    Foundation
The Ebenezer Trust
Dr Edwards Bishop King's
    Fulham Endowment Fund

The W G Edwards Charitable
    Foundation
The Elephant Trust
The Ellerdale Trust
James Ellis Charitable Trust
The Elmley Foundation
The Englefield Charitable Trust
The Equitable Charitable Trust
The Erskine Cunningham Hill
    Trust
The Essex Fairway Charitable
    Trust
The Essex Heritage Trust
The Essex Youth Trust
The Eveson Charitable Trust
Esmée Fairbairn Foundation
Joseph Fattorini Charitable
    Trust 'B' Account
The John Feeney Charitable
    Trust
The Fidelity UK Foundation
The Doris Field Charitable
    Trust
Fife Council/Common Good
    Funds and Trusts
Gerald Finzi Charitable Trust
Firtree Trust
The Fishmongers' Company's
    Charitable Trust
The Joyce Fletcher Charitable
    Trust
Florence's Charitable Trust
The Foresters' Charity
    Stewards UK Trust
The Donald Forrester Trust
The Jill Franklin Trust
The Freemasons' Grand
    Charity
The Thomas Freke and Lady
    Norton Charity
The Freshgate Trust
    Foundation
The Patrick Frost Foundation
The Galanthus Trust
The Angela Gallagher Memorial
    Fund
The Gamma Trust
The Ganzoni Charitable Trust
Generations Charitable Trust
The Gibbs Charitable Trust
The G C Gibson Charitable
    Trust
The Girdlers' Company
    Charitable Trust
Gloucestershire Community
    Foundation
The Gloucestershire Historic
    Churches Trust
The Goldsmiths' Company
    Charity
The Golsoncott Foundation
The Good Neighbours Trust
The J G Graves Charitable
    Trust
The Gretna Charitable Trust
H C D Memorial Fund

The Hadrian Trust
The Hale Trust
The Hamamelis Trust
Paul Hamlyn Foundation
The Kathleen Hannay
  Memorial Charity
William Harding's Charity
The Harebell Centenary Fund
The Peter Harrison Foundation
The N and P Hartley Memorial
  Trust
The Edward Harvist Trust Fund
Hasluck Charitable Trust
The Dorothy Hay-Bolton
  Charitable Trust
The Charles Hayward
  Foundation
Headley-Pitt Charitable Trust
Percy Hedley 1990 Charitable
  Trust
The Anne Herd Memorial Trust
The Herefordshire Historic
  Churches Trust
The Hertfordshire Community
  Foundation
The Hesslewood Children's
  Trust (Hull Seamen's and
  General Orphanage)
The P and C Hickinbotham
  Charitable Trust
The Rosalind Hicks Charitable
  Trust
Alan Edward Higgs Charity
The Hill Charitable Trust
The Charles Littlewood Hill
  Trust
Lady Hind Trust
Stuart Hine Trust
The Eleemosynary Charity of
  William Hobbayne
Matthew Hodder Charitable
  Trust
The Sir Julian Hodge
  Charitable Trust
The Jane Hodge Foundation
The Holbeck Charitable Trust
The Holst Foundation
The Holywood Trust
Mary Homfray Charitable Trust
Sir Harold Hood's Charitable
  Trust
The Cuthbert Horn Trust
The Clifford Howarth Charity
  Trust
The Hull and East Riding
  Charitable Trust
The Ironmongers' Foundation
The Isaacs Charitable Trust
The ITF Seafarers Trust
The J R S S T Charitable Trust
John James Bristol Foundation
The John Jarrold Trust
The Jephcott Charitable Trust
Jewish Child's Day
The Jewish Youth Fund
The Johnson Foundation

The Johnnie Johnson Trust
The Joicey Trust
The Marjorie and Geoffrey
  Jones Charitable Trust
The Jordan Charitable
  Foundation
The Lady Eileen Joseph
  Foundation
Jusaca Charitable Trust
Kelsick's Educational
  Foundation
William Kendall's Charity (Wax
  Chandlers' Company)
The King's Fund
The Sir James Knott Trust
The Heinz, Anna and Carol
  Kroch Foundation
The David Laing Foundation
The Jack Lane Charitable Trust
The Allen Lane Foundation
The Langtree Trust
The Edgar E Lawley Foundation
The David Lean Foundation
The Leathersellers' Company
  Charitable Fund
The Leche Trust
Leicester Charity Link (formerly
  The Leicester Charity
  Organisation Society)
The Kennedy Leigh Charitable
  Trust
The Erica Leonard Trust
The John Spedan Lewis
  Foundation
Lincolnshire Community
  Foundation
The Second Joseph Aaron
  Littman Foundation
The London Marathon
  Charitable Trust
The Lotus Foundation
LSA Charitable Trust
Henry Lumley Charitable Trust
The Lynn Foundation
The Lynwood Trust
The Joy and Malcolm Lyons
  Foundation
The Mackintosh Foundation
The MacRobert Trust
Magdalen Hospital Trust
The Mahavir Trust (also known
  as the K S Mehta
  Charitable Trust)
Man Group plc Charitable
  Trust
W M Mann Foundation
R W Mann Trust
The Marks Family Foundation
The Ann and David Marks
  Foundation
The Jim Marshall Charitable
  Trust
Sir George Martin Trust
The Nancie Massey Charitable
  Trust
The Mathew Trust

Mayfair Charities Ltd
The Robert McAlpine
  Foundation
The Mears Foundation
Meningitis Trust
The Mercers' Charitable
  Foundation
The Merchant Venturers'
  Charity
The Tony Metherell Charitable
  Trust
Miles Trust for the Putney and
  Roehampton Community
The Millichope Foundation
The Clare Milne Trust
The Edgar Milward Charity
The Keith and Joan
  Mindelsohn Charitable
  Trust
Minge's Gift and the Pooled
  Trusts
The Mishcon Family Charitable
  Trust
The Mitchell Charitable Trust
The Mobbs Memorial Trust Ltd
George A Moore Foundation
The Morgan Charitable
  Foundation
The Oliver Morland Charitable
  Trust
S C and M E Morland's
  Charitable Trust
The Mothercare Charitable
  Foundation
The Mugdock Children's Trust
The Mulberry Trust
Murphy-Neumann Charity
  Company Limited
The Nationwide Foundation
The Nchima Trust
The Frances and Augustus
  Newman Foundation
Alderman Newton's
  Educational Foundation
Alice Noakes Memorial
  Charitable Trust
Nominet Charitable Foundation
Norie Charitable Trust
Normalyn Charitable Trust
The Northampton Municipal
  Church Charities
The Earl of Northampton's
  Charity
The Northcott Devon
  Foundation
The Northumbria Historic
  Churches Trust
The Norton Foundation
The Norwich Church of England
  Young Men's Society
The Norwood and Newton
  Settlement
The Notgrove Trust
The Nottingham General
  Dispensary

The Nottingham Gordon
   Memorial Trust for Boys
   and Girls
The Oak Trust
The Oakdale Trust
The Oakley Charitable Trust
The Odin Charitable Trust
Ogilvie Charities Deed No.2
   (including the Charity of
   Mary Catherine Ford Smith)
The Old Broad Street Charity
   Trust
Open Gate
Orrin Charitable Trust
The Ouseley Trust
The Owen Family Trust
City of Oxford Charity
The P F Charitable Trust
Eleanor Palmer Trust
The James Pantyfedwen
   Foundation
Ambika Paul Foundation
The Payne Charitable Trust
The Dowager Countess
   Eleanor Peel Trust
The Jack Petchey Foundation
The Petplan Charitable Trust
The Phillips Charitable Trust
The Bernard Piggott Trust
The Elise Pilkington Charitable
   Trust
The Sir Harry Pilkington Trust
The Poling Charitable Trust
The Ponton House Trust
The Mary Potter Convent
   Hospital Trust
The W L Pratt Charitable Trust
The William Price Charitable
   Trust
The Provincial Grand Charity of
   the Province of Derbyshire
The R V W Trust
The Rainford Trust
The Peggy Ramsay Foundation
The Ratcliff Foundation
The Rayne Foundation
The Rayne Trust
The John Rayner Charitable
   Trust
The Sir James Reckitt Charity
Relief Fund for Romania
   Limited
REMEDI
The Rhondda Cynon Taff
   Welsh Church Acts Fund
The Sir Cliff Richard Charitable
   Trust
The Clive Richards Charity
The Violet M Richards Charity
The Ripple Effect Foundation
Rix-Thompson-Rothenberg
   Foundation
The Rochester Bridge Trust
The Helen Roll Charitable
   Trust

Mrs L D Rope Third Charitable
   Settlement
The Rosca Trust
The Rothley Trust
Mrs Gladys Row Fogo
   Charitable Trust
The Christopher Rowbotham
   Charitable Trust
The Rowing Foundation
Joseph Rowntree Reform Trust
   Limited
Royal British Legion
The Alfred and Frances
   Rubens Charitable Trust
The Russell Trust
Erach and Roshan Sadri
   Foundation
The Saga Charitable Trust
Saint Sarkis Charity Trust
The Saintbury Trust
The Salt Foundation
Santander UK Foundation
   Limited
The Frieda Scott Charitable
   Trust
The Scottish International
   Education Trust
Seafarers UK (King George's
   Fund for Sailors)
The Seedfield Trust
sfgroup Charitable Fund for
   Disabled People
SFIA Educational Trust Limited
The Sheldon Trust
The Sylvia and Colin Shepherd
   Charitable Trust
The Bassil Shippam and
   Alsford Trust
The Shipwrights' Company
   Charitable Fund
The Simpson Education and
   Conservation Trust
Sino-British Fellowship Trust
The Skelton Bounty
The Charles Skey Charitable
   Trust
The Stanley Smith UK
   Horticultural Trust
Friends of Somerset Churches
   and Chapels
The Souter Charitable Trust
The Sovereign Health Care
   Charitable Trust
The Worshipful Company of
   Spectacle Makers' Charity
The Jessie Spencer Trust
The Ralph and Irma Sperring
   Charity
Springfields Employees'
   Medical Research and
   Charity Trust Fund
The Spurrell Charitable Trust
St James's Place Foundation
Sir Walter St John's
   Educational Charity

The St Laurence Relief In
   Need Trust
St Teilo's Trust
The Steel Charitable Trust
Stevenson Family's Charitable
   Trust
The Sir Halley Stewart Trust
The Leonard Laity Stoate
   Charitable Trust
The M J C Stone Charitable
   Trust
Peter Storrs Trust
The Summerfield Charitable
   Trust
The Bernard Sunley Charitable
   Foundation
Swan Mountain Trust
The Gay and Keith Talbot Trust
The Talbot Trusts
The Talbot Village Trust
The Tay Charitable Trust
A P Taylor Trust
Tees Valley Community
   Foundation
The Templeton Goodwill Trust
The David Thomas Charitable
   Trust
The Sir Jules Thorn Charitable
   Trust
The Thriplow Charitable Trust
The Tillett Trust
Mrs R P Tindall's Charitable
   Trust
The Tinsley Foundation
The Tisbury Telegraph Trust
The Tobacco Pipe Makers and
   Tobacco Trade Benevolent
   Fund
Tollemache (Buckminster)
   Charitable Trust
The Toy Trust
The Treeside Trust
The Trusthouse Charitable
   Foundation
The Tudor Trust
The TUUT Charitable Trust
The Ulverscroft Foundation
The Vandervell Foundation
Veneziana Fund
Victoria Homes Trust
Voluntary Action Fund
The Scurrah Wainwright Charity
Wakeham Trust
The Walker Trust
Wallington Missionary Mart
   and Auctions
The Barbara Ward Children's
   Foundation
The John Warren Foundation
The Wates Foundation
Blyth Watson Charitable Trust
John Watson's Trust
Webb Memorial Trust
The William Webster
   Charitable Trust
The James Weir Foundation

The Barbara Welby Trust
White Stuff Foundation
The Whittlesey Charity
The Wilkinson Charitable
   Foundation
Dame Violet Wills Charitable
   Trust
The Harold Hyam Wingate
   Foundation
Women's World Day of Prayer
   (NCWWDPEWNI)
The James Wood Bequest
   Fund
The F Glenister Woodger Trust
Woodlands Trust
Worcester Municipal Charities
   (incorporating Worcester
   Consolidated Municipal
   Charity and Worcester
   Municipal Exhibitions
   Foundation)
The Wragge and Co. Charitable
   Trust
Miss E B Wrightson's
   Charitable Settlement
The Wyndham Charitable Trust
The Yardley Great Trust
Yorkshire Building Society
   Charitable Foundation
The South Yorkshire
   Community Foundation
The John K Young Endowment
   Fund

....

■ Two years

The Sylvia Adams Charitable
   Trust
The Ajahma Charitable Trust
All Saints Educational Trust
The Astor of Hever Trust
The James Beattie Charitable
   Trust
BibleLands
The Body Shop Foundation
The Booth Charities
The Harry Bottom Charitable
   Trust
John and Susan Bowers Fund
British Institute at Ankara
The Swinfen Broun Charitable
   Trust
The BUPA Foundation
The Geoffrey Burton Charitable
   Trust
The Cadbury Foundation
CfBT Education Trust
The Malcolm Chick Charity
Children's Liver Disease
   Foundation
The City Bridge Trust (formerly
   known as Bridge House
   Trust)
The Clothworkers' Foundation
The John and Freda Coleman
   Charitable Trust

Colwinston Charitable Trust
Comic Relief
Cripplegate Foundation
Cullum Family Trust
The Gillian Dickinson Trust
The Dyers' Company
   Charitable Trust
East London Community
   Foundation
The Ellerdale Trust
The Elmley Foundation
Epilepsy Research UK
The Equitable Charitable Trust
The Essex Fairway Charitable
   Trust
The Eveson Charitable Trust
Esmée Fairbairn Foundation
The John Feeney Charitable
   Trust
The Doris Field Charitable
   Trust
Fife Council/Common Good
   Funds and Trusts
The Foresters' Fund for
   Children
The Donald Forrester Trust
Foundation for Management
   Education
The Jill Franklin Trust
The Freshgate Trust
   Foundation
The Galanthus Trust
Generations Charitable Trust
The Gretna Charitable Trust
Paul Hamlyn Foundation
Hampshire and Isle of Wight
   Community Foundation
The Peter Harrison Foundation
The Charles Hayward
   Foundation
The Anne Herd Memorial Trust
The Hertfordshire Community
   Foundation
The Hesslewood Children's
   Trust (Hull Seamen's and
   General Orphanage)
Hexham and Newcastle
   Diocesan Trust (1947)
The Holywood Trust
The Hull and East Riding
   Charitable Trust
International Spinal Research
   Trust
The Irish Youth Foundation
   (UK) Ltd (incorporating The
   Lawlor Foundation)
The ITF Seafarers Trust
The Joanies Trust
The Johnson Foundation
The Johnnie Johnson Trust
The Jordan Charitable
   Foundation
The Allen Lane Foundation
The David Lean Foundation
The Leathersellers' Company
   Charitable Fund

The Erica Leonard Trust
Lincolnshire Community
   Foundation
Lloyds TSB Foundation for
   England and Wales
The MacRobert Trust
Man Group plc Charitable
   Trust
The Ann and David Marks
   Foundation
The Jim Marshall Charitable
   Trust
The Nancie Massey Charitable
   Trust
The Mercers' Charitable
   Foundation
Miles Trust for the Putney and
   Roehampton Community
The Clare Milne Trust
Minge's Gift and the Pooled
   Trusts
Murphy-Neumann Charity
   Company Limited
The Nchima Trust
Nominet Charitable Foundation
The Nuffield Foundation
The Odin Charitable Trust
Open Gate
The Ouseley Trust
The Owen Family Trust
The P F Charitable Trust
The Dowager Countess
   Eleanor Peel Trust
The Petplan Charitable Trust
The Rayne Foundation
The Rayne Trust
The Sir James Reckitt Charity
REMEDI
The Clive Richards Charity
The Violet M Richards Charity
Mrs L D Rope Third Charitable
   Settlement
The Christopher Rowbotham
   Charitable Trust
Joseph Rowntree Reform Trust
   Limited
Royal British Legion
The Saga Charitable Trust
The Scarfe Charitable Trust
The Scottish International
   Education Trust
The Sheldon Trust
The Sickle Foundation
The Simpson Education and
   Conservation Trust
Sino-British Fellowship Trust
The Charles Skey Charitable
   Trust
Sir Walter St John's
   Educational Charity
The St Laurence Relief In
   Need Trust
St Teilo's Trust
The Sir Halley Stewart Trust
The Suffolk Historic Churches
   Trust

Mrs R P Tindall's Charitable
   Trust
The Tinsley Foundation
The Trusthouse Charitable
   Foundation
The Tudor Trust
The TUUT Charitable Trust
The Ulverscroft Foundation
Voluntary Action Fund
The Barbara Ward Children's
   Foundation
The Wates Foundation
White Stuff Foundation
The Whittlesey Charity
The Harold Hyam Wingate
   Foundation
Woodlands Trust
The South Yorkshire
   Community Foundation

....

■ Three years

The 29th May 1961 Charitable
   Trust
The Sylvia Adams Charitable
   Trust
The Ajahma Charitable Trust
All Saints Educational Trust
The H B Allen Charitable Trust
The Astor of Hever Trust
BBC Children in Need
The James Beattie Charitable
   Trust
The Berkshire Community
   Foundation
BibleLands
The Herbert and Peter
   Blagrave Charitable Trust
The Body Shop Foundation
The Booth Charities
The Harry Bottom Charitable
   Trust
John and Susan Bowers Fund
British Institute at Ankara
The BUPA Foundation
Butchers' Company General
   Charities
The Cadbury Foundation
Calleva Foundation
The Calpe Trust
The Carnegie Trust for the
   Universities of Scotland
The Malcolm Chick Charity
Children's Liver Disease
   Foundation
The Chownes Foundation
The City Bridge Trust (formerly
   known as Bridge House
   Trust)
J A Clark Charitable Trust
The Clothworkers' Foundation
The Francis Coales Charitable
   Foundation
Comic Relief
Cripplegate Foundation

The Cumber Family Charitable
   Trust
The D'Oyly Carte Charitable
   Trust
The Gillian Dickinson Trust
The Dulverton Trust
The Ellerdale Trust
The Elmley Foundation
Epilepsy Research UK
The Equitable Charitable Trust
Esmée Fairbairn Foundation
Samuel William Farmer Trust
The John Feeney Charitable
   Trust
The Doris Field Charitable
   Trust
Fife Council/Common Good
   Funds and Trusts
The Donald Forrester Trust
The Forte Charitable Trust
Lord Forte Foundation
The Jill Franklin Trust
The Freshgate Trust
   Foundation
The Galanthus Trust
Generations Charitable Trust
Simon Gibson Charitable Trust
The Glastonbury Trust Limited
The Great Britain Sasakawa
   Foundation
The Gretna Charitable Trust
H C D Memorial Fund
Paul Hamlyn Foundation
The Peter Harrison Foundation
The Charles Hayward
   Foundation
The Anne Herd Memorial Trust
The Hertfordshire Community
   Foundation
The Hope Trust
The Hull and East Riding
   Charitable Trust
The Innocent Foundation
International Spinal Research
   Trust
The Charles Irving Charitable
   Trust
The ITF Seafarers Trust
The James Trust
Rees Jeffreys Road Fund
The Johnnie Johnson Trust
The Jordan Charitable
   Foundation
The Judith Trust
William Kendall's Charity (Wax
   Chandlers' Company)
The Peter Kershaw Trust
The Robert Kiln Charitable
   Trust
The Allen Lane Foundation
The Leathersellers' Company
   Charitable Fund
The William Leech Charity
The Erica Leonard Trust
The Lloyd Fund

Lloyds TSB Foundation for
   England and Wales
The Lotus Foundation
The R S Macdonald Charitable
   Trust
The MacRobert Trust
Man Group plc Charitable
   Trust
The Jim Marshall Charitable
   Trust
The Nancie Massey Charitable
   Trust
The Mercers' Charitable
   Foundation
The Merchant Venturers'
   Charity
Gerald Micklem Charitable
   Trust
Miles Trust for the Putney and
   Roehampton Community
The Millfield House Foundation
The Clare Milne Trust
The Edgar Milward Charity
Minge's Gift and the Pooled
   Trusts
Minton Charitable Trust
John Moores Foundation
The Mulberry Trust
The Nchima Trust
Nominet Charitable Foundation
The Odin Charitable Trust
Open Gate
The Owen Family Trust
The P F Charitable Trust
The James Pantyfedwen
   Foundation
The Frank Parkinson
   Agricultural Trust
The Dowager Countess
   Eleanor Peel Trust
The Jack Petchey Foundation
The Petplan Charitable Trust
Polden-Puckham Charitable
   Foundation
Prairie Trust
Mr and Mrs J A Pye's
   Charitable Settlement
The Rayne Foundation
The Rayne Trust
The Sir James Reckitt Charity
REMEDI
The Violet M Richards Charity
Mrs L D Rope Third Charitable
   Settlement
The Christopher Rowbotham
   Charitable Trust
The Joseph Rowntree
   Charitable Trust
Royal British Legion
The Saga Charitable Trust
The Seedfield Trust
The Sheldon Trust
SHINE (Support and Help in
   Education)
The Bassil Shippam and
   Alsford Trust

The Simpson Education and Conservation Trust
Sino-British Fellowship Trust
The Charles Skey Charitable Trust
Rita and David Slowe Charitable Trust
David Solomons Charitable Trust
The Southdown Trust
Split Infinitive Trust
St Christopher's College Educational Trust
St James's Place Foundation
Sir Walter St John's Educational Charity
The St Laurence Relief In Need Trust
The Sir Halley Stewart Trust
The Bernard Sunley Charitable Foundation
The Sue Thomson Foundation
Mrs R P Tindall's Charitable Trust
The Trust for Education
The Trusthouse Charitable Foundation
The James Tudor Foundation
The Tudor Trust
The TUUT Charitable Trust
The Ulverscroft Foundation
Voluntary Action Fund
The Barbara Ward Children's Foundation
The Wates Foundation
The Weavers' Company Benevolent Fund
The Whitaker Charitable Trust
White Stuff Foundation
The Whittlesey Charity
The Harold Hyam Wingate Foundation
Miss E B Wrightson's Charitable Settlement
The Yapp Charitable Trust
The South Yorkshire Community Foundation
Stephen Zimmerman Charitable Trust
Zurich Community Trust (UK) Limited

....

■ **Longer than three years**

The Adint Charitable Trust
The Alborada Trust
All Saints Educational Trust
The Lord Austin Trust
The John Avins Trustees
Barnes Workhouse Fund
The Charity of William Barrow
The James Beattie Charitable Trust
The Herbert and Peter Blagrave Charitable Trust

The Harry Bottom Charitable Trust
Community Foundation for Bournemouth, Dorset and Poole
British Record Industry Trust
C J Cadbury Charitable Trust
Stephen Clark 1957 Charitable Trust
The Clothworkers' Foundation
Coats Foundation Trust
The George Henry Collins Charity
The Sir Jeremiah Colman Gift Trust
The Colt Foundation
Comic Relief
Gordon Cook Foundation
Criffel Charitable Trust
Cripplegate Foundation
The D G Charitable Settlement
The Denman Charitable Trust
The Ellerdale Trust
Esmée Fairbairn Foundation
The John Feeney Charitable Trust
The Doris Field Charitable Trust
Fife Council/Common Good Funds and Trusts
Firtree Trust
The Forest Hill Charitable Trust
Sydney E Franklin Deceased's New Second Charity
The Freemasons' Grand Charity
The Galanthus Trust
The Gamlen Charitable Trust
Generations Charitable Trust
The Gretna Charitable Trust
H C D Memorial Fund
Paul Hamlyn Foundation
The Harris Charitable Trust
The Joanna Herbert-Stepney Charitable Settlement (also known as The Paget Charitable Trust)
The Hitchin Educational Foundation
Matthew Hodder Charitable Trust
The Homelands Charitable Trust
Mary Homfray Charitable Trust
The Huggard Charitable Trust
The Hunter Foundation
Impetus Trust
International Spinal Research Trust
The Inverforth Charitable Trust
The Ironmongers' Foundation
The ITF Seafarers Trust
Jaffe Family Relief Fund
The Kelly Family Charitable Trust

Kelsick's Educational Foundation
Keswick Hall Trust
The Mary Kinross Charitable Trust
The Leathersellers' Company Charitable Fund
The Erica Leonard Trust
Henry Lumley Charitable Trust
The Lynwood Trust
John Lyon's Charity
Man Group plc Charitable Trust
The Jim Marshall Charitable Trust
Miles Trust for the Putney and Roehampton Community
The Hugh and Mary Miller Bequest Trust
The Millfield House Foundation
The Millichope Foundation
Minge's Gift and the Pooled Trusts
The Modiano Charitable Trust
G M Morrison Charitable Trust
The Moss Charitable Trust
The Mulberry Trust
Murphy-Neumann Charity Company Limited
Alice Noakes Memorial Charitable Trust
The Owen Family Trust
The Dowager Countess Eleanor Peel Trust
The Jack Petchey Foundation
The Joseph and Lena Randall Charitable Trust
The Rayne Foundation
The Rayne Trust
The Sir James Reckitt Charity
REMEDI
The Rufford Foundation
The R H Scholes Charitable Trust
The Francis C Scott Charitable Trust
The Seven Fifty Trust
Sino-British Fellowship Trust
The Charles Skey Charitable Trust
Rita and David Slowe Charitable Trust
R H Southern Trust
The Stobart Newlands Charitable Trust
The Samuel Storey Family Charitable Trust
The Sir Jules Thorn Charitable Trust
Mrs R P Tindall's Charitable Trust
The Tobacco Pipe Makers and Tobacco Trade Benevolent Fund
The Tudor Trust
The TUUT Charitable Trust

The Ulverscroft Foundation
John and Lucille van Geest
Foundation
The Barbara Ward Children's
Foundation
The Barbara Welby Trust
The Westcroft Trust
The Whittlesey Charity
The Harold Hyam Wingate
Foundation
The Wood Family Trust

Average time to pay grant

■ Less than one month

The 29th May 1961 Charitable
Trust
The Adamson Trust
The Ajahma Charitable Trust
Sir John and Lady Amory's
Charitable Trust
The AMW Charitable Trust
The André Christian Trust
The Animal Defence Trust
The Albert Casanova Ballard
Deceased Trust
Barnes Workhouse Fund
The Charity of William Barrow
The James Beattie Charitable
Trust
The Bellhouse Foundation
The Body Shop Foundation
The Booth Charities
The Boshier-Hinton Foundation
The J and M Britton Charitable
Trust
Brown-Mellows Trust
The Geoffrey Burton Charitable
Trust
C J Cadbury Charitable Trust
P H G Cadbury Charitable
Trust
The Richard Cadbury
Charitable Trust
The Cadbury Foundation
The Campden Charities
Trustee
The Casey Trust
The Chapman Charitable Trust
The Chrimes Family Charitable
Trust
The Christabella Charitable
Trust
Chrysalis Trust
The Church Urban Fund
The Congleton Inclosure Trust
The Alice Ellen Cooper Dean
Charitable Foundation
The Cotton Industry War
Memorial Trust
County Durham Community
Foundation
The Augustine Courtauld Trust
The Cray Trust
The J N Derbyshire Trust
Devon Community Foundation
The Devon Educational Trust
The Dibden Allotments Fund
The Drapers' Charitable Fund
The W E Dunn Trust
The Earley Charity
The Ebenezer Trust
The Edinburgh Trust, No 2
Account
The Elephant Trust

James Ellis Charitable Trust
The Essex Fairway Charitable
Trust
The Eveson Charitable Trust
Joseph Fattorini Charitable
Trust 'B' Account
The John Feeney Charitable
Trust
The Fidelity UK Foundation
The Fishmongers' Company's
Charitable Trust
The Foresters' Fund for
Children
The Patrick Frost Foundation
The Gamma Trust
The Ganzoni Charitable Trust
The Gibbs Charitable Trust
The Girdlers' Company
Charitable Trust
Gloucestershire Community
Foundation
The Gloucestershire Historic
Churches Trust
The Goldsmiths' Company
Charity
The Golsoncott Foundation
The J G Graves Charitable
Trust
The Gretna Charitable Trust
Dr Guthrie's Association
H C D Memorial Fund
William Harding's Charity
Headley-Pitt Charitable Trust
The Hesslewood Children's
Trust (Hull Seamen's and
General Orphanage)
The Hill Charitable Trust
The Charles Littlewood Hill
Trust
Lady Hind Trust
Stuart Hine Trust
The Hitchin Educational
Foundation
The Eleemosynary Charity of
William Hobbayne
The Holst Foundation
The Clifford Howarth Charity
Trust
The Hull and East Riding
Charitable Trust
Miss Agnes H Hunter's Trust
The J R S S T Charitable Trust
John James Bristol Foundation
The Susan and Stephen
James Charitable
Settlement (also known as
the Stephen James
Charitable Trust)
The James Trust
The John Jarrold Trust
Jewish Child's Day
The Johnnie Johnson Trust
The Kelly Family Charitable
Trust
Kelsick's Educational
Foundation

Kent Community Foundation
The Sir James Knott Trust
The Heinz, Anna and Carol
   Kroch Foundation
The Langtree Trust
The David Lean Foundation
The Second Joseph Aaron
   Littman Foundation
Lloyds TSB Foundation for
   England and Wales
LSA Charitable Trust
Robert Luff Foundation Ltd
The Lynn Foundation
The Mackintosh Foundation
W M Mann Foundation
R W Mann Trust
The Nancie Massey Charitable
   Trust
The Tony Metherell Charitable
   Trust
Miles Trust for the Putney and
   Roehampton Community
Minge's Gift and the Pooled
   Trusts
The Modiano Charitable Trust
John Moores Foundation
The Oliver Morland Charitable
   Trust
The Moss Charitable Trust
The Mugdock Children's Trust
The Mulberry Trust
Nazareth Trust Fund
The Northcott Devon
   Foundation
The Norwich Church of England
   Young Men's Society
The Notgrove Trust
The Nottingham Gordon
   Memorial Trust for Boys
   and Girls
The Oak Trust
The Oakdale Trust
The Odin Charitable Trust
The Old Broad Street Charity
   Trust
The Frank Parkinson
   Agricultural Trust
The Persula Foundation
Philological Foundation
The Bernard Piggott Trust
The Elise Pilkington Charitable
   Trust
The Poling Charitable Trust
The Powell Foundation
The W L Pratt Charitable Trust
The Rainford Trust
The John Rayner Charitable
   Trust
Relief Fund for Romania
   Limited
The Helen Roll Charitable
   Trust
Mrs L D Rope Third Charitable
   Settlement
The Rosca Trust

Joseph Rowntree Reform Trust
   Limited
The Alfred and Frances
   Rubens Charitable Trust
The Russell Trust
The Saintbury Trust
The Salt Foundation
The Scarfe Charitable Trust
The Francis C Scott Charitable
   Trust
The Sir James and Lady Scott
   Trust
The Seedfield Trust
The Sheldon Trust
The Bassil Shippam and
   Alsford Trust
The Skelton Bounty
The Mrs Smith and Mount
   Trust
The Souter Charitable Trust
The Jessie Spencer Trust
Split Infinitive Trust
Springfields Employees'
   Medical Research and
   Charity Trust Fund
The Spurrell Charitable Trust
St Hilda's Trust
The M J C Stone Charitable
   Trust
Peter Storrs Trust
The Summerfield Charitable
   Trust
The Gay and Keith Talbot Trust
The Talbot Trusts
The Sir Jules Thorn Charitable
   Trust
The Thriplow Charitable Trust
The Toy Trust
The Constance Travis
   Charitable Trust
John and Lucille van Geest
   Foundation
The Walker Trust
Wallington Missionary Mart
   and Auctions
The Barbara Ward Children's
   Foundation
Blyth Watson Charitable Trust
John Watson's Trust
The William Webster
   Charitable Trust
The James Weir Foundation
The Simon Whitbread
   Charitable Trust
The Norman Whiteley Trust
The Whittlesey Charity
Women's World Day of Prayer
   (NCWWDPEWNI)
The James Wood Bequest
   Fund
Woodlands Trust
Miss E B Wrightson's
   Charitable Settlement
Yorkshire Building Society
   Charitable Foundation

Stephen Zimmerman
   Charitable Trust

....

■ Two months

The Ardwick Trust
The Aylesford Family
   Charitable Trust
Barchester Healthcare
   Foundation
Barnes Workhouse Fund
The Bedfordshire and Luton
   Community Foundation
The Berkshire Community
   Foundation
The Bisgood Charitable Trust
   (registered as Miss Jeanne
   Bisgood's Charitable Trust)
The Sydney Black Charitable
   Trust
Isabel Blackman Foundation
British Institute at Ankara
The Jack Brunton Charitable
   Trust
The Bryant Trust
The Cambridgeshire
   Community Foundation
H and L Cantor Trust
The Chrimes Family Charitable
   Trust
Miss V L Clore's 1967
   Charitable Trust
The John and Freda Coleman
   Charitable Trust
Community Foundation for
   Calderdale
Gordon Cook Foundation
The J Reginald Corah
   Foundation Fund
The Culra Charitable Trust
The D'Oyly Carte Charitable
   Trust
The Dulverton Trust
The Dwek Family Charitable
   Trust
The Eagle Charity Trust
The Earmark Trust
The W G Edwards Charitable
   Foundation
The Elmley Foundation
Fife Council/Common Good
   Funds and Trusts
The Forest Hill Charitable Trust
The Thomas Freke and Lady
   Norton Charity
The Great Britain Sasakawa
   Foundation
The Gretna Charitable Trust
Hampshire and Isle of Wight
   Community Foundation
The Harebell Centenary Fund
Hasluck Charitable Trust
Percy Hedley 1990 Charitable
   Trust
Help the Hospices

Hexham and Newcastle
  Diocesan Trust (1947)
The P and C Hickinbotham
  Charitable Trust
Alan Edward Higgs Charity
The Sir Julian Hodge
  Charitable Trust
The Holywood Trust
The Hunter Foundation
The Johnson Foundation
The Kass Charitable Trust
William Kendall's Charity (Wax
  Chandlers' Company)
The Peter Kershaw Trust
The Robert Kiln Charitable
  Trust
The David Laing Foundation
The William Leech Charity
Leicester Charity Link (formerly
  The Leicester Charity
  Organisation Society)
Lincolnshire Community
  Foundation
The Lloyd Fund
Llysdinam Charitable Trust
Meningitis Trust
The Nationwide Foundation
Alderman Newton's
  Educational Foundation
Nominet Charitable Foundation
The Norda Trust
Norie Charitable Trust
The Northampton Municipal
  Church Charities
The Norton Foundation
The Nottingham General
  Dispensary
The Nuffield Foundation
Ogilvie Charities Deed No.2
  (including the Charity of
  Mary Catherine Ford Smith)
Orrin Charitable Trust
City of Oxford Charity
The P F Charitable Trust
Eleanor Palmer Trust
The Sir Harry Pilkington Trust
Polden-Puckham Charitable
  Foundation
Prairie Trust
The Peggy Ramsay Foundation
The Ratcliff Foundation
The Rhododendron Trust
Mrs L D Rope Third Charitable
  Settlement
The Rufford Foundation
Santander UK Foundation
  Limited
The R H Scholes Charitable
  Trust
The Sylvia and Colin Shepherd
  Charitable Trust
The Charles Skey Charitable
  Trust
David Solomons Charitable
  Trust
Sussex Community Foundation

Swan Mountain Trust
The Tobacco Pipe Makers and
  Tobacco Trade Benevolent
  Fund
The Treeside Trust
The James Tudor Foundation
The R D Turner Charitable
  Trust
The Douglas Turner Trust
The Vandervell Foundation
Veneziana Fund
The Scurrah Wainwright Charity
The Barbara Welby Trust
The Westcroft Trust
The Wilkinson Charitable
  Foundation
The Dame Violet Wills Will
  Trust
The Wixamtree Trust
Worcester Municipal Charities
  (incorporating Worcester
  Consolidated Municipal
  Charity and Worcester
  Municipal Exhibitions
  Foundation)
The Wragge and Co. Charitable
  Trust
The Wyndham Charitable Trust
The Yardley Great Trust
The South Yorkshire
  Community Foundation
The John K Young Endowment
  Fund
Zurich Community Trust (UK)
  Limited

....

■ Three months

The Adnams Charity
The Aldgate Freedom
  Foundation
The Ammco Trust
The Andrew Anderson Trust
The Armourers' and Brasiers'
  Gauntlet Trust
The Ian Askew Charitable Trust
AstonMansfield Charitable
  Trust
The Baker Charitable Trust
The Barbour Foundation
The Barnstaple Bridge Trust
BBC Children in Need
The Bellahouston Bequest
  Fund
Bergqvist Charitable Trust
Thomas Betton's Charity for
  Pensions and Relief-in-Need
The Bingham Trust
Sir Alec Black's Charity
The Herbert and Peter
  Blagrave Charitable Trust
Community Foundation for
  Bournemouth, Dorset and
  Poole
British Record Industry Trust

The Swinfen Broun Charitable
  Trust
The E F Bulmer Benevolent
  Fund
Butchers' Company General
  Charities
The Carew Pole Charitable
  Trust
The Carnegie Trust for the
  Universities of Scotland
The Chippenham Borough
  Lands Charity
The Chownes Foundation
The Chrimes Family Charitable
  Trust
Stephen Clark 1957
  Charitable Trust
J A Clark Charitable Trust
The Robert Clutterbuck
  Charitable Trust
Coats Foundation Trust
The John S Cohen Foundation
Michael Cornish Charitable
  Trust
Country Houses Foundation
Cripplegate Foundation
The Cumber Family Charitable
  Trust
The Cwmbran Trust
The Gwendoline and Margaret
  Davies Charity
William Dean Countryside and
  Educational Trust
The Denman Charitable Trust
The Gillian Dickinson Trust
Disability Aid Fund (The Roger
  and Jean Jefcoate Trust)
Dr Edwards Bishop King's
  Fulham Endowment Fund
Epilepsy Research UK
The Essex Youth Trust
Gerald Finzi Charitable Trust
The Foresters' Charity
  Stewards UK Trust
Foundation for Management
  Education
The Friarsgate Trust
The Gamlen Charitable Trust
Generations Charitable Trust
The Glastonbury Trust Limited
GMC Trust
The Good Neighbours Trust
The Gretna Charitable Trust
The Hadrian Trust
The Hale Trust
The Harris Charity
The Edward Harvist Trust Fund
The Joanna Herbert-Stepney
  Charitable Settlement (also
  known as The Paget
  Charitable Trust)
The Anne Herd Memorial Trust
The Herefordshire Historic
  Churches Trust
The Hertfordshire Community
  Foundation

Matthew Hodder Charitable
Trust
The Edward Holt Trust
The Holywood Trust
The Hope Trust
International Spinal Research
Trust
The Ironmongers' Foundation
The Charles Irving Charitable
Trust
Rees Jeffreys Road Fund
Jerwood Charitable Foundation
The Jewish Youth Fund
The Johnson Foundation
Keswick Hall Trust
The King Henry VIII Endowed
Trust Warwick
The Jack Lane Charitable Trust
The Edgar E Lawley Foundation
The Kennedy Leigh Charitable
Trust
The Erica Leonard Trust
Lloyds TSB Foundation for
Northern Ireland
London Catalyst (formerly The
Metropolitan Hospital-
Sunday Fund)
The R S Macdonald Charitable
Trust
The Mahavir Trust (also known
as the K S Mehta
Charitable Trust)
Man Group plc Charitable
Trust
The Marsh Christian Trust
The Jim Marshall Charitable
Trust
The Mears Foundation
The Merchant Venturers'
Charity
The Millichope Foundation
The Keith and Joan
Mindelsohn Charitable
Trust
Minton Charitable Trust
The Mishcon Family Charitable
Trust
The Mobbs Memorial Trust Ltd
George A Moore Foundation
The Frances and Augustus
Newman Foundation
Alice Noakes Memorial
Charitable Trust
The Owen Family Trust
The James Pantyfedwen
Foundation
The Performing Right Society
Foundation
The Jack Petchey Foundation
The Petplan Charitable Trust
The Ponton House Trust
The Mary Potter Convent
Hospital Trust
The R V W Trust
The Joseph and Lena Randall
Charitable Trust

The Rayne Trust
The Rhondda Cynon Taff
Welsh Church Acts Fund
The Clive Richards Charity
Rix-Thompson-Rothenberg
Foundation
The Rothley Trust
The Joseph Rowntree
Charitable Trust
Royal British Legion
Erach and Roshan Sadri
Foundation
The Saga Charitable Trust
sfgroup Charitable Fund for
Disabled People
SFIA Educational Trust Limited
The Simpson Education and
Conservation Trust
Sino-British Fellowship Trust
The Sovereign Health Care
Charitable Trust
The St Laurence Relief In
Need Trust
St Teilo's Trust
The Stobart Newlands
Charitable Trust
The Suffolk Historic Churches
Trust
Tees Valley Community
Foundation
Mrs R P Tindall's Charitable
Trust
The Tinsley Foundation
Tollemache (Buckminster)
Charitable Trust
The Trusthouse Charitable
Foundation
Two Ridings Community
Foundation
Voluntary Action Fund
Wakeham Trust
The Thomas Wall Trust
Webb Memorial Trust
The Garfield Weston
Foundation
White Stuff Foundation

....

■ Four months

The Sylvia Adams Charitable
Trust
The Adint Charitable Trust
The Associated Country
Women of the World
(ACWW)
The Association of Colleges
Charitable Trust
The Astor Foundation
The Misses Barrie Charitable
Trust
BBC Children in Need
BibleLands
The Harry Bottom Charitable
Trust
The Bromley Trust
The BUPA Foundation

CfBT Education Trust
The Charter 600 Charity
The Malcolm Chick Charity
The Chrimes Family Charitable
Trust
The City Bridge Trust (formerly
known as Bridge House
Trust)
The Cole Charitable Trust
The George Henry Collins
Charity
Cullum Family Trust
The Daiwa Anglo-Japanese
Foundation
The Derbyshire Churches and
Chapels Preservation Trust
The Englefield Charitable Trust
Firtree Trust
The Freemasons' Grand
Charity
The Gretna Charitable Trust
The Hadfield Trust
Paul Hamlyn Foundation
The Harborne Parish Lands
Charity
The Holbeck Charitable Trust
The ITF Seafarers' Trust
The Allen Lane Foundation
Sir George Martin Trust
Mayfair Charities Ltd
The Mercers' Charitable
Foundation
The Clare Milne Trust
The Edgar Milward Charity
The Morgan Charitable
Foundation
The Mothercare Charitable
Foundation
The Neighbourly Charitable
Trust
The Oakley Charitable Trust
Open Gate
The Ouseley Trust
The Dowager Countess
Eleanor Peel Trust
The Petplan Charitable Trust
The Phillips Charitable Trust
The Provincial Grand Charity of
the Province of Derbyshire
Mr and Mrs J A Pye's
Charitable Settlement
The Rayne Foundation
The Sir James Reckitt Charity
The Rowing Foundation
Saint Sarkis Charity Trust
The Scottish Community
Foundation
Leslie Sell Charitable Trust
The Shipwrights' Company
Charitable Fund
The Southdown Trust
The Edward Stocks-Massey
Bequest Fund
The Bernard Sunley Charitable
Foundation
The Trust for Education

The Tudor Trust
The TUUT Charitable Trust
The Weavers' Company
 Benevolent Fund
The Whitaker Charitable Trust
The F Glenister Woodger Trust
The Yapp Charitable Trust

....

■ Five months

All Saints Educational Trust
The H B Allen Charitable Trust
The Astor of Hever Trust
The Aurelius Charitable Trust
Comic Relief
Esmée Fairbairn Foundation
The Donald Forrester Trust
The Jill Franklin Trust
The Freshgate Trust
 Foundation
The Gretna Charitable Trust
The Peter Harrison Foundation
The Irish Youth Foundation
 (UK) Ltd (incorporating The
 Lawlor Foundation)
The Jephcott Charitable Trust
The Leathersellers' Company
 Charitable Fund
The John Spedan Lewis
 Foundation
Murphy-Neumann Charity
 Company Limited
The Petplan Charitable Trust
The Sir Cliff Richard Charitable
 Trust
Seafarers UK (King George's
 Fund for Sailors)
St Christopher's College
 Educational Trust
The Steel Charitable Trust
The Sir Halley Stewart Trust
The Samuel Storey Family
 Charitable Trust
The Sue Thomson Foundation

....

■ Six months or more

The Alborada Trust
The John Apthorp Charitable
 Trust
The Lord Austin Trust
The John Avins Trustees
The Baird Trust
Percy Bilton Charity
John and Susan Bowers Fund
The Charles and Edna
 Broadhurst Charitable Trust
The Charles Brotherton Trust
The Calpe Trust
The Leslie Mary Carter
 Charitable Trust
The Childwick Trust
The Clothworkers' Foundation
The Francis Coales Charitable
 Foundation

The George Henry Collins
 Charity
The Sir Jeremiah Colman Gift
 Trust
Colwinston Charitable Trust
Criffel Charitable Trust
The Ellerdale Trust
The Essex Heritage Trust
Samuel William Farmer Trust
The Joyce Fletcher Charitable
 Trust
Florence's Charitable Trust
Sydney E Franklin Deceased's
 New Second Charity
The Angela Gallagher Memorial
 Fund
Simon Gibson Charitable Trust
The Gretna Charitable Trust
The Hamamelis Trust
The Kathleen Hannay
 Memorial Charity
The N and P Hartley Memorial
 Trust
The Dorothy Hay-Bolton
 Charitable Trust
The Charles Hayward
 Foundation
The Rosalind Hicks Charitable
 Trust
The High Sheriff's Police Trust
 for the County of West
 Midlands (Building Blocks)
The Homelands Charitable
 Trust
Sir Harold Hood's Charitable
 Trust
The Cuthbert Horn Trust
Impetus Trust
The Inverforth Charitable Trust
Jaffe Family Relief Fund
The Marjorie and Geoffrey
 Jones Charitable Trust
The Jordan Charitable
 Foundation
The Lady Eileen Joseph
 Foundation
Jusaca Charitable Trust
The King's Fund
Lancashire Environmental
 Fund
The Leche Trust
The Lennox and Wyfold
 Foundation
The London Marathon
 Charitable Trust
The Lotus Foundation
John Lyon's Charity
The MacRobert Trust
Magdalen Hospital Trust
The Mathew Trust
The Robert McAlpine
 Foundation
Gerald Micklem Charitable
 Trust
The Hugh and Mary Miller
 Bequest Trust

The Mitchell Charitable Trust
S C and M E Morland's
 Charitable Trust
G M Morrison Charitable Trust
Murphy-Neumann Charity
 Company Limited
The Northumbria Historic
 Churches Trust
The Norwood and Newton
 Settlement
Ambika Paul Foundation
The Payne Charitable Trust
REMEDI
The Violet M Richards Charity
The Rochester Bridge Trust
Mrs Gladys Row Fogo
 Charitable Trust
The Christopher Rowbotham
 Charitable Trust
The Scottish International
 Education Trust
SHINE (Support and Help in
 Education)
Rita and David Slowe
 Charitable Trust
The Stanley Smith UK
 Horticultural Trust
The Worshipful Company of
 Spectacle Makers' Charity
St James's Place Foundation
Sir Walter St John's
 Educational Charity
The Leonard Laity Stoate
 Charitable Trust
The Talbot Village Trust
The Tay Charitable Trust
The Templeton Goodwill Trust
The David Thomas Charitable
 Trust
The Tillett Trust
Victoria Homes Trust
The Wolfson Foundation
The Wood Family Trust

Percentage of grants to new applicants

■ Less than 10 %

The Alborada Trust
The Aldgate Freedom Foundation
The Andrew Anderson Trust
The André Christian Trust
The Ardwick Trust
The Baker Charitable Trust
The Balmore Trust
The Barbour Foundation
Barnes Workhouse Fund
The Bellhouse Foundation
BibleLands
The Bisgood Charitable Trust (registered as Miss Jeanne Bisgood's Charitable Trust)
The Sydney Black Charitable Trust
Sir Alec Black's Charity
The Harry Bottom Charitable Trust
British Record Industry Trust
The Charles Brotherton Trust
The Swinfen Broun Charitable Trust
The Buckinghamshire Historic Churches Trust
C J Cadbury Charitable Trust
The Cadbury Foundation
The Calpe Trust
The Chippenham Borough Lands Charity
The Christabella Charitable Trust
The John and Freda Coleman Charitable Trust
Gordon Cook Foundation
The Cotton Industry War Memorial Trust
Cullum Family Trust
The Culra Charitable Trust
The Dwek Family Charitable Trust
The Dyers' Company Charitable Trust
The Eagle Charity Trust
The Earmark Trust
The Ebenezer Trust
The Edinburgh Trust, No 2 Account
The Essex Fairway Charitable Trust
The Eveson Charitable Trust
Florence's Charitable Trust
The Forest Hill Charitable Trust
The Donald Forrester Trust
The Thomas Freke and Lady Norton Charity
The Patrick Frost Foundation
The Gamlen Charitable Trust

The Gamma Trust
The G C Gibson Charitable Trust
The Girdlers' Company Charitable Trust
The Gloucestershire Historic Churches Trust
GMC Trust
The Kathleen Hannay Memorial Charity
The Harborne Parish Lands Charity
The Harebell Centenary Fund
The Harris Charitable Trust
The Dorothy Hay-Bolton Charitable Trust
Help the Hospices
The Joanna Herbert-Stepney Charitable Settlement (also known as The Paget Charitable Trust)
The Hill Charitable Trust
Stuart Hine Trust
The Holst Foundation
The Homelands Charitable Trust
Mary Homfray Charitable Trust
The Hope Trust
The Clifford Howarth Charity Trust
The Huggard Charitable Trust
The Innocent Foundation
The Inverforth Charitable Trust
The Charles Irving Charitable Trust
John James Bristol Foundation
The Susan and Stephen James Charitable Settlement (also known as the Stephen James Charitable Trust)
The James Trust
Jewish Child's Day
The Jewish Youth Fund
The Jordan Charitable Foundation
Jusaca Charitable Trust
The Kass Charitable Trust
Kelsick's Educational Foundation
The Peter Kershaw Trust
Keswick Hall Trust
The Mary Kinross Charitable Trust
The Lennox and Wyfold Foundation
The Erica Leonard Trust
Llysdinam Charitable Trust
The Lotus Foundation
Robert Luff Foundation Ltd
Henry Lumley Charitable Trust
The Lynwood Trust
The Ann and David Marks Foundation
The Marsh Christian Trust

The Jim Marshall Charitable Trust
Mayfair Charities Ltd
The Robert McAlpine Foundation
Miles Trust for the Putney and Roehampton Community
The Millfield Trust
The Millichope Foundation
Minge's Gift and the Pooled Trusts
Minton Charitable Trust
The Mishcon Family Charitable Trust
The Mitchell Charitable Trust
The Oliver Morland Charitable Trust
S C and M E Morland's Charitable Trust
G M Morrison Charitable Trust
The Moss Charitable Trust
The Mulberry Trust
Murphy-Neumann Charity Company Limited
The Kitty and Daniel Nabarro Charitable Trust
Nazareth Trust Fund
The Nchima Trust
Alice Noakes Memorial Charitable Trust
Norie Charitable Trust
Orrin Charitable Trust
The Frank Parkinson Agricultural Trust
Ambika Paul Foundation
The Jack Petchey Foundation
The Poling Charitable Trust
Prairie Trust
Princess Anne's Charities
Mr and Mrs J A Pye's Charitable Settlement
The Violet M Richards Charity
The Ripple Effect Foundation
The Christopher Rowbotham Charitable Trust
The Alfred and Frances Rubens Charitable Trust
The Rufford Foundation
The Saga Charitable Trust
The R H Scholes Charitable Trust
Seafarers UK (King George's Fund for Sailors)
Sino-British Fellowship Trust
The Charles Skey Charitable Trust
Rita and David Slowe Charitable Trust
The Worshipful Company of Spectacle Makers' Charity
The June Stevens Foundation
The Stobart Newlands Charitable Trust
The Edward Stocks-Massey Bequest Fund

The M J C Stone Charitable Trust

The Gay and Keith Talbot Trust

The Talbot Trusts

A P Taylor Trust

The Templeton Goodwill Trust

The David Thomas Charitable Trust

The Sue Thomson Foundation

The Tillett Trust

Mrs R P Tindall's Charitable Trust

The Tisbury Telegraph Trust

The Tobacco Pipe Makers and Tobacco Trade Benevolent Fund

The Tompkins Foundation

The Towry Law Charitable Trust (also known as the Castle Educational Trust)

The Treeside Trust

John and Lucille van Geest Foundation

Webb Memorial Trust

The Westcroft Trust

The Whittlesey Charity

Dame Violet Wills Charitable Trust

Worcester Municipal Charities (incorporating Worcester Consolidated Municipal Charity and Worcester Municipal Exhibitions Foundation)

The Wyndham Charitable Trust

....

■ 10–20 %

The Adint Charitable Trust

The H B Allen Charitable Trust

The Animal Defence Trust

The Ian Askew Charitable Trust

The Associated Country Women of the World (ACWW)

AstonMansfield Charitable Trust

The Lord Austin Trust

The John Avins Trustees

The Aylesford Family Charitable Trust

The Albert Casanova Ballard Deceased Trust

The Barnstaple Bridge Trust

The Misses Barrie Charitable Trust

The Berkshire Community Foundation

The Booth Charities

John and Susan Bowers Fund

The Charles and Edna Broadhurst Charitable Trust

The Bromley Trust

The Jack Brunton Charitable Trust

The E F Bulmer Benevolent Fund

The Geoffrey Burton Charitable Trust

Butchers' Company General Charities

P H G Cadbury Charitable Trust

The Richard Cadbury Charitable Trust

H and L Cantor Trust

The Leslie Mary Carter Charitable Trust

The Chownes Foundation

The Chrimes Family Charitable Trust

The John S Cohen Foundation

The George Henry Collins Charity

The J Reginald Corah Foundation Fund

County Durham Community Foundation

The Augustine Courtauld Trust

The Cumber Family Charitable Trust

William Dean Countryside and Educational Trust

The Dibden Allotments Fund

The Derek and Eileen Dodgson Foundation

Dr Edwards Bishop King's Fulham Endowment Fund

James Ellis Charitable Trust

The Elmley Foundation

Firtree Trust

The Joyce Fletcher Charitable Trust

Sydney E Franklin Deceased's New Second Charity

The Galanthus Trust

The Glastonbury Trust Limited

Gloucestershire Community Foundation

The Good Neighbours Trust

The Hadrian Trust

The Harris Charity

The Charles Littlewood Hill Trust

Lady Hind Trust

The Cuthbert Horn Trust

The Hull and East Riding Charitable Trust

Miss Agnes H Hunter's Trust

The Irish Youth Foundation (UK) Ltd (incorporating The Lawlor Foundation)

The ITF Seafarers Trust

The John Jarrold Trust

The Johnson Foundation

The Lady Eileen Joseph Foundation

William Kendall's Charity (Wax Chandlers' Company)

The Second Joseph Aaron Littman Foundation

Lloyds TSB Foundation for Northern Ireland

The MacRobert Trust

The Mahavir Trust (also known as the K S Mehta Charitable Trust)

Sir George Martin Trust

The Merchant Venturers' Charity

The Millfield House Foundation

The Edgar Milward Charity

The Mobbs Memorial Trust Ltd

The Modiano Charitable Trust

The Morgan Charitable Foundation

The Nationwide Foundation

The Northcott Devon Foundation

The Norton Foundation

The Oak Trust

The Oakley Charitable Trust

The Odin Charitable Trust

Open Gate

The Sir Harry Pilkington Trust

The Provincial Grand Charity of the Province of Derbyshire

The Rayne Trust

The Sir James Reckitt Charity

The Rhododendron Trust

The Rhondda Cynon Taff Welsh Church Acts Fund

Mrs L D Rope Third Charitable Settlement

Mrs Gladys Row Fogo Charitable Trust

Erach and Roshan Sadri Foundation

The Saintbury Trust

The Scarfe Charitable Trust

The Frieda Scott Charitable Trust

The Sir James and Lady Scott Trust

SFIA Educational Trust Limited

The Simpson Education and Conservation Trust

David Solomons Charitable Trust

The Sovereign Health Care Charitable Trust

The Jessie Spencer Trust

Springfields Employees' Medical Research and Charity Trust Fund

St Teilo's Trust

Peter Storrs Trust

The Thriplow Charitable Trust

The Tinsley Foundation

Tollemache (Buckminster) Charitable Trust

The Constance Travis Charitable Trust

The TUUT Charitable Trust

Two Ridings Community Foundation

The James Weir Foundation

The Dame Violet Wills Will Trust

The Harold Hyam Wingate Foundation

The Wixamtree Trust

The James Wood Bequest Fund

The John K Young Endowment Fund

Stephen Zimmerman Charitable Trust

■ **20–30 %**

The 29th May 1961 Charitable Trust

The Ammco Trust

The Association of Colleges Charitable Trust

The Charity of William Barrow

The Bellahouston Bequest Fund

Bergqvist Charitable Trust

Community Foundation for Bournemouth, Dorset and Poole

The Bryant Trust

The Casey Trust

CfBT Education Trust

The Childwick Trust

The Church Urban Fund

The Francis Coales Charitable Foundation

The Sir Jeremiah Colman Gift Trust

The Congleton Inclosure Trust

The Alice Ellen Cooper Dean Charitable Foundation

The Cray Trust

Cripplegate Foundation

The Delius Trust

The Denman Charitable Trust

The Gillian Dickinson Trust

The W E Dunn Trust

East London Community Foundation

The W G Edwards Charitable Foundation

The Erskine Cunningham Hill Trust

The Essex Youth Trust

Joseph Fattorini Charitable Trust 'B' Account

The John Feeney Charitable Trust

The Freshgate Trust Foundation

The Angela Gallagher Memorial Fund

Simon Gibson Charitable Trust

The Goldsmiths' Company Charity

H C D Memorial Fund

Hampshire and Isle of Wight Community Foundation

The N and P Hartley Memorial Trust

The Edward Harvist Trust Fund

Alan Edward Higgs Charity

Matthew Hodder Charitable Trust

The Langtree Trust

The William Leech Charity

Leicester Charity Link (formerly The Leicester Charity Organisation Society)

The Kennedy Leigh Charitable Trust

Lincolnshire Community Foundation

The London Marathon Charitable Trust

The Lynn Foundation

John Lyon's Charity

The Mackintosh Foundation

W M Mann Foundation

The Nancie Massey Charitable Trust

Gerald Micklem Charitable Trust

The Keith and Joan Mindelsohn Charitable Trust

George A Moore Foundation

The Neighbourly Charitable Trust

The Norwich Church of England Young Men's Society

The Nuffield Foundation

The Oakdale Trust

The Old Broad Street Charity Trust

The Owen Family Trust

The Bernard Piggott Trust

The Elise Pilkington Charitable Trust

Polden-Puckham Charitable Foundation

The Ponton House Trust

The Mary Potter Convent Hospital Trust

The Powell Foundation

The John Rayner Charitable Trust

The Rothley Trust

The Russell Trust

The Seedfield Trust

Leslie Sell Charitable Trust

The Souter Charitable Trust

St Hilda's Trust

Sir Walter St John's Educational Charity

The Suffolk Historic Churches Trust

The James Tudor Foundation

The Vandervell Foundation

Wallington Missionary Mart and Auctions

The Barbara Ward Children's Foundation

The Barbara Welby Trust

The Whitaker Charitable Trust

The Wilkinson Charitable Foundation

The Wolfson Foundation

The Wragge and Co. Charitable Trust

■ **30–40 %**

The Baird Trust

The Bedfordshire and Luton Community Foundation

British Institute at Ankara

The J and M Britton Charitable Trust

The Cambridgeshire Community Foundation

The Chapman Charitable Trust

The City Bridge Trust (formerly known as Bridge House Trust)

The J N Derbyshire Trust

The Dorset Historic Churches Trust

The Drapers' Charitable Fund

The Englefield Charitable Trust

Epilepsy Research UK

Esmée Fairbairn Foundation

Samuel William Farmer Trust

The Fishmongers' Company's Charitable Trust

The J G Graves Charitable Trust

The Hale Trust

The Anne Herd Memorial Trust

The Hesslewood Children's Trust (Hull Seamen's and General Orphanage)

Hexham and Newcastle Diocesan Trust (1947)

The Eleemosynary Charity of William Hobbayne

Sir Harold Hood's Charitable Trust

Impetus Trust

Jerwood Charitable Foundation

The Johnnie Johnson Trust

Kent Community Foundation

The Robert Kiln Charitable Trust

The King Henry VIII Endowed Trust Warwick

Lancashire Environmental Fund

The Jack Lane Charitable Trust

The Edgar E Lawley Foundation

The Leathersellers' Company Charitable Fund

The Leche Trust

Lloyds TSB Foundation for England and Wales

LSA Charitable Trust

R W Mann Trust

The Tony Metherell Charitable Trust

The P F Charitable Trust

The Phillips Charitable Trust
The W L Pratt Charitable Trust
The R V W Trust
The Ratcliff Foundation
The Joseph Rowntree
  Charitable Trust
The Francis C Scott Charitable
  Trust
The Sylvia and Colin Shepherd
  Charitable Trust
The Bernard Sunley Charitable
  Foundation
Wakeham Trust
John Watson's Trust
Women's World Day of Prayer
  (NCWWDPEWNI)
The F Glenister Woodger Trust
Miss E B Wrightson's
  Charitable Settlement
Zurich Community Trust (UK)
  Limited

....

■ **40–50 %**

All Saints Educational Trust
Sir John and Lady Amory's
  Charitable Trust
The John Apthorp Charitable
  Trust
The Armourers' and Brasiers'
  Gauntlet Trust
The Astor of Hever Trust
The Beaverbrook Foundation
The Bingham Trust
The Body Shop Foundation
The Carew Pole Charitable
  Trust
The Carnegie Trust for the
  Universities of Scotland
The Malcolm Chick Charity
CLA Charitable Trust
Stephen Clark 1957
  Charitable Trust
J A Clark Charitable Trust
Miss V L Clore's 1967
  Charitable Trust
The Clothworkers' Foundation
The Robert Clutterbuck
  Charitable Trust
The Cole Charitable Trust
Colwinston Charitable Trust
Michael Cornish Charitable
  Trust
The Cwmbran Trust
The D'Oyly Carte Charitable
  Trust
The Daiwa Anglo-Japanese
  Foundation
The Gwendoline and Margaret
  Davies Charity
The Devon Educational Trust
The Ellerdale Trust
The Essex Heritage Trust
Gerald Finzi Charitable Trust
The Foresters' Charity
  Stewards UK Trust

The Forte Charitable Trust
Lord Forte Foundation
The Jill Franklin Trust
The Freemasons' Grand
  Charity
The Ganzoni Charitable Trust
Generations Charitable Trust
The Great Britain Sasakawa
  Foundation
Dr Guthrie's Association
The Hadfield Trust
The Hamamelis Trust
The Peter Harrison Foundation
Hasluck Charitable Trust
Percy Hedley 1990 Charitable
  Trust
The Herefordshire Historic
  Churches Trust
The Rosalind Hicks Charitable
  Trust
The High Sheriff's Police Trust
  for the County of West
  Midlands (Building Blocks)
The Holbeck Charitable Trust
The Holywood Trust
The J R S S T Charitable Trust
Rees Jeffreys Road Fund
The Jephcott Charitable Trust
The Marjorie and Geoffrey
  Jones Charitable Trust
The David Laing Foundation
The John Spedan Lewis
  Foundation
London Catalyst (formerly The
  Metropolitan Hospital-
  Sunday Fund)
Magdalen Hospital Trust
Man Group plc Charitable
  Trust
The Mercers' Charitable
  Foundation
Alderman Newton's
  Educational Foundation
Ogilvie Charities Deed No.2
  (including the Charity of
  Mary Catherine Ford Smith)
The Ouseley Trust
Eleanor Palmer Trust
The Dowager Countess
  Eleanor Peel Trust
The Rainford Trust
Relief Fund for Romania
  Limited
The Clive Richards Charity
Rix-Thompson-Rothenberg
  Foundation
Joseph Rowntree Reform Trust
  Limited
Royal British Legion
Saint Sarkis Charity Trust
Santander UK Foundation
  Limited
The Scottish Community
  Foundation
The Sheldon Trust

SHINE (Support and Help in
  Education)
The Shipwrights' Company
  Charitable Fund
The Skelton Bounty
The Mrs Smith and Mount
  Trust
The Stanley Smith UK
  Horticultural Trust
Friends of Somerset Churches
  and Chapels
The Southdown Trust
St Christopher's College
  Educational Trust
The Steel Charitable Trust
The Sir Halley Stewart Trust
Swan Mountain Trust
The Talbot Village Trust
The Tay Charitable Trust
The Toy Trust
The Trust for Education
The R D Turner Charitable
  Trust
The Douglas Turner Trust
Victoria Homes Trust
Voluntary Action Fund
The Walker Trust
The John Warren Foundation
The Simon Whitbread
  Charitable Trust
White Stuff Foundation
The Wood Family Trust
Woodlands Trust
The Yapp Charitable Trust
The South Yorkshire
  Community Foundation

....

■ **Over 50 %**

The Sylvia Adams Charitable
  Trust
The Adamson Trust
The Astor Foundation
The Aurelius Charitable Trust
Thomas Betton's Charity for
  Pensions and Relief-in-Need
The Boshier-Hinton Foundation
The BUPA Foundation
The Charter 600 Charity
Chrysalis Trust
Coats Foundation Trust
Country Houses Foundation
The Duke of Devonshire's
  Charitable Trust
Disability Aid Fund (The Roger
  and Jean Jefcoate Trust)
The Dulverton Trust
Eastern Counties Educational
  Trust Limited
The Elephant Trust
The Equitable Charitable Trust
The Fidelity UK Foundation
The Foresters' Fund for
  Children
The Charles Hayward
  Foundation

Headley-Pitt Charitable Trust
The Hertfordshire Community
    Foundation
The P and C Hickinbotham
    Charitable Trust
The Ironmongers' Foundation
The Kelly Family Charitable
    Trust
The Allen Lane Foundation
The R S Macdonald Charitable
    Trust
The Mathew Trust
The Mears Foundation
Meningitis Trust
The Clare Milne Trust
Nominet Charitable Foundation
The Northumbria Historic
    Churches Trust
The Norwood and Newton
    Settlement
The Nottingham General
    Dispensary
The Nottingham Gordon
    Memorial Trust for Boys
    and Girls
City of Oxford Charity
The James Pantyfedwen
    Foundation
The Peggy Ramsay Foundation
REMEDI
The Rochester Bridge Trust
The Rowing Foundation
The Scottish International
    Education Trust
sfgroup Charitable Fund for
    Disabled People
Split Infinitive Trust
St Andrew's Conservation
    Trust
St James's Place Foundation
The Leonard Laity Stoate
    Charitable Trust
Sussex Community Foundation
The Trusthouse Charitable
    Foundation
Veneziana Fund
The Scurrah Wainwright Charity
The Thomas Wall Trust
The Wates Foundation
The Weavers' Company
    Benevolent Fund
The William Webster
    Charitable Trust
The Yardley Great Trust

The alphabetical register of grant-making trusts

This section lists the individual entries for the grant-making trusts.

■ The 1970 Trust

SC NO SC008788 **ESTABLISHED** 1970
WHERE FUNDING CAN BE GIVEN UK.
WHO CAN BENEFIT Charities which support disadvantaged minorities.
WHAT IS FUNDED The trust states it supports small UK charities 'doing innovative, educational, or experimental work' in the following fields: civil liberties (e.g. freedom of information; constitutional reform; humanising work; children's welfare); the public interest in the face of vested interest groups (such as the advertising, alcohol, road, war, pharmaceuticals, and tobacco industries); disadvantaged minorities, multiracial work, prison reform; new economics ('as if people mattered' – Schumacher) and intermediate technology; public transport, pedestrians, bicycling, road crash prevention, traffic-calming, low-energy lifestyles; and preventative health.
WHAT IS NOT FUNDED No support for larger charities, those with religious connections, or individuals (except in rare cases – and then only through registered charities or educational bodies). No support to central or local government agencies.
TYPE OF GRANT Usually one to three years; sometimes longer.
RANGE OF GRANTS £1,000–£4,000.
SAMPLE GRANTS Previous beneficiaries include: Scarman Trust; Roadpeace; Public Interest Research Centre; Earth Resourses; Parents for Children; Parent to Parent; Slower Speeds Trust; Prisoners' Wives; Pesticles; Blackcare; and Shelter Winter Night.
FINANCES Year 2010–11 Income £29,586 Grants £29,000
TRUSTEE David Rennie.
HOW TO APPLY In writing to the correspondent. Proposals should be summarised on one page with one or two more pages of supporting information. The trust states that it regrettably only has time to reply to the very few applications it is able to fund.
WHO TO APPLY TO David Rennie, Trustee, c/o C W Pagan, Messrs Pagan Osborne, 12 St Catherine Street, Cupar, Fife KY15 4HN Tel 01334 653777 Fax 01334 655063 email enquiries@pagan.co.uk

■ The 1989 Willan Charitable Trust

CC NO 802749 **ESTABLISHED** 1989
WHERE FUNDING CAN BE GIVEN Worldwide, but in practice mainly the north east of England.
WHO CAN BENEFIT Registered charities for the benefit of children; disabled people; carers; volunteers; refugees; and offenders.
WHAT IS FUNDED Grants are given to: advance the education of children and help children in need; benefit people with physical or mental disabilities and alleviate hardship and distress either generally or individually; and further medical research.
WHAT IS NOT FUNDED Grants are not given directly to individuals. Grants for gap year students may be considered if the individual will be working for a charity (in this case the grant would be paid to the charity).
RANGE OF GRANTS £500–£10,000.
SAMPLE GRANTS Previous beneficiaries include: SAFC Foundation and Cancer Connexions (£10,000 each); Amble Multi Agency Crime Prevention Initiative (£6,000); Durham City Centre Youth Project, The Children's Society and the Calvert Trust (£5,000 each); Chester le Street Youth Centre (£4,000); Different Strokes North East,

Northern Roots and People and Drugs (£3,000 each); Leukaemia Research and Coast Video Club (£2,000 each); Northumberland Mountain Rescue and the Association of British Poles (£1,000 each); and Healthwise and Newcastle Gang Show (£500).
FINANCES Year 2009–10 Income £355,641 Grants £497,720 Assets £15,672,128
TRUSTEES Francis A Chapman; Alex Ohlsson; Willan Trustee Ltd.
HOW TO APPLY In writing to the correspondent at the Community Foundation Serving Tyne & Wear. Applications are processed, collated and shortlisted by the Community Foundation on a quarterly basis. The shortlist is then circulated to each of the trustees for consideration and approval.
WHO TO APPLY TO Mark Pierce, Head of Policy, Projects and Programmes, Community Foundation Tyne & Wear and Northumberland, 9th Floor, Cale Cross, 156 Pilgrim Street, Newcastle upon Tyne NE1 6SU Tel 0191 222 0945 Fax 0191 230 0689 email mp@communityfoundation.org.uk

■ The 29th May 1961 Charitable Trust

CC NO 200198 **ESTABLISHED** 1961
WHERE FUNDING CAN BE GIVEN UK, with a special interest in the Warwickshire/Birmingham/Coventry area.
WHO CAN BENEFIT Charitable organisations in the UK. People who are socially disadvantaged may be favoured.
WHAT IS FUNDED General charitable purposes across a broad spectrum, including: art, leisure and youth; health; social welfare; education and training; homelessness and housing; offenders; and conservation and protection.
WHAT IS NOT FUNDED Grants only to registered charities. No grants to individuals.
TYPE OF GRANT One-off, recurring and some spread over two to three years. Grants are given for capital and revenue purposes.
RANGE OF GRANTS £500–£250,000, but the great majority are less than £10,000.
SAMPLE GRANTS University of Warwick (£251,000 in total), toward the running costs of the arts centre and sponsorship of the Coull Quartet; Hereward College (£125,000), towards the costs of improving various aspects of the college for disabled students in Coventry; Coventry & Warwickshire Awards Trust (£100,000), towards the running costs of a sports centre providing facilities for underpriviledged communities in Coventry; RNIB (£100,000), towards the costs of building a new vision school and children's home in Coventry; Shelter (£85,000), towards the costs of a project to prevent ex-offenders becoming homeless upon release; The Prince's Trust (£75,000), towards the general costs of the trust's work in the West Midlands; Macmillan Cancer Support (£50,000), towards the core funding for the national cancer counselling telephone line; Saddlers Wells Trust (£40,000), toward the costs of subsidised tickets for underpriviledged people; NACRO (£30,000), towards the core costs; Historic Royal Palaces (£25,000), towards the cost of conserving the White Tower at the Tower of London; Royal Geographical Society (£10,000), towards the conservation costs of Lowther Lodge in London; Sir Oswald Stoll Foundation (£10,000), towards the costs of building 18 homes for homeless ex-

service people in Chiswick; Wellchild Trust
(£10,000), towards the costs of nurses
providing cover to sick children; New Bridge
(£5,000), towards the costs of assistance to
prisoners both in prison and following their
release; Justice First (£5,000), towards the
costs of an organisation in Teeside supporting
asylum seekers; and the National Council for
One Parent Families (£3,000), towards core
costs.

FINANCES *Year* 2009–10 *Income* £3,090,535
Grants £3,691,983 *Assets* £99,215,577

TRUSTEES Vanni Emanuele Treves; Andrew C Jones;
Anthony J Mead; Paul Varney.

HOW TO APPLY To the secretary in writing, enclosing
in triplicate the most recent annual report and
accounts. Trustees normally meet in February,
May, August and November. Due to the large
number of applications received, they cannot be
acknowledged.

WHO TO APPLY TO The Secretary, Ryder Court,
14 Ryder Street, London SW1 Y 6QB *Tel* 020
7024 9034 *email* enquiries@
29may1961charity.org.uk

....

■ 4 Charity Foundation

CC NO 1077143   **ESTABLISHED** 1999
WHERE FUNDING CAN BE GIVEN UK and Israel.
WHO CAN BENEFIT Jewish charities and causes.
WHAT IS FUNDED Religious activities and education.
SAMPLE GRANTS Previous grants include those to:
the American Jewish Joint Distribution
Committee (£78,000); the Millennium Trust
(£66,000); Keren Yehoshua V'Yisroel
(£43,000); Project Seed (£35,000); World
Jewish Relief (£29,000); Menorah Grammar
School (£27,000); British Friends of Jaffa
Institute (£23,000); Friends of Mir (£19,000);
Heichal Hatorah Foundation (£15,000); Chai
Life Line Cancer Care (£12,000); Jewish Care
(£11,000); and British Friends of Ezer Mizion
(£10,000).

FINANCES *Year* 2009–10 *Income* £6,875,521
Grants £786,345 *Assets* £11,232,293

TRUSTEES Jacob Schimmel; Marc Schimmel;
D Rabson; Mrs A Schimmel.

HOW TO APPLY This trust does not respond to
unsolicited applications.

WHO TO APPLY TO Jacob Schimmel, Trustee, UK I Ltd,
54–56 Euston Street, London NW1 2ES
Tel 020 7387 0155

■ The A B Charitable Trust

cc no 1000147   **established** 1990

where funding can be given Mainly UK.

who can benefit Charities registered in the UK; usually to those working in the UK, though a few are awarded to charities working internationally. The trust favours those charities with an annual income between £150,000 and £1.5 million, which do not have substantial investments or surpluses.

what is funded Charities working where human dignity is imperilled and where there are opportunities for human dignity to be affirmed. Priority is given to charities working to support: refugees and victims of torture; prisoners; older people; people with mental health problems. In relation to these areas, the following cross-cutting themes are of interest to the trustees: women; homelessness; therapeutic art.

what is not funded No grants are made to organisations principally concerned with: animals; children; environment; formal education; medicine; religion; and research. Capital appeals are not normally supported, nor are charities with large national or international links, or areas which should reasonably be funded by government.

type of grant The trust has a small-grants programme (up to £5,000) which responds to appeals on a one-off basis. It seeks to identify charities working on its priorities for larger grants, which could be awarded on a regular basis subject to annual reports and an agreed exit strategy. It is happy to provide funding for core costs.

range of grants £2,500–£50,000.

sample grants Demos and UK Drugs Policy Commission (£50,000 each); Prison Reform Trust (£30,000); Inquest and FPWP Hibiscus (£10,000 each); Women's Therapy Centre and Asylum Support Appeals Project (£7,500 each); Yarl's Wood Befrienders, Action on Elder Abuse, Harrogate Homeless Project, Living Options – Devon, Caxton House and Lakelands Hospice (£5,000 each); Interact Reading Service (£3,500); and Fahamu (£2,500).

finances *Year* 2009–10 *Income* £184,152 *Grants* £406,000 *Assets* £132,842

trustees Claire Bonavero; Olivier Bonavero; Philippe Bonavero; Anne Bonavero; Yves Bonavero; Athol Harley; Alison Swan Parente; Peter Day.

how to apply Applications can be completed online at the trust's website. As well as administrative and financial details, the online application form will ask for a two page summary of the organisation's work, including: background; aims and objectives; activities; achievements. After filling in the online application form you will be sent a reference number. Please send the director the following documents in hard copy quoting the reference number: the two page overview of the organisation's work; a signed copy of the latest certified accounts/statements, with a reporting date that is no more than 12 months prior to the application deadline chosen (the trustees meet four times a year, in January, April, July and October – please see the website for exact deadline dates); up to two items of publicity material that illustrate the work of the organisation, such as annual reviews or leaflets.

who to apply to Sara Harrity, Director, Monmouth House, 87–93 Westbourne Grove, London W2 4UL *Tel* 020 7313 8070 *Fax* 020 7313 9607 *email* mail@abcharitabletrust.org.uk *Website* www.abcharitabletrust.org.uk

■ The Aberbrothock Skea Trust (formerly known as Aberbrothock Charitable Trust)

sc no SC039202   **established** 2008

where funding can be given East of Scotland, north of the Firth of Tay.

who can benefit Organisations benefiting the community with charitable status.

what is funded Children/young people; disability; environment/conservation; hospitals/hospices; and medical research are all considered.

what is not funded The geographical restriction is strictly adhered to. Applications from outside the area, and/or from individuals, will not be considered.

type of grant One-off, including project, research, capital and core costs.

range of grants Up to £2,500.

sample grants Previous beneficiaries have included Red Cross, Colon Cancer Care, Princess Royal Trust, International League of Horses, Kids Out and Dundee Heritage Trust.

finances *Year* 2010–11 *Income* £102,961

trustees G McNicol; Mrs A T L Grant; G G M D Dunlop; E Steven; I Townsend; Lady F Fraser.

other information Although the income remains around the same, the grant total changes every year.

how to apply In writing to the correspondent. Trustees meet to consider grants in March, July and December.

who to apply to The Trustees, Thorntons Law LLP, Brothockbank House, Arbroath, Angus DD11 1NE

■ The Aberdeen Endowments Trust

sc no SC010507   **established** 1909

where funding can be given The former City and Royal Burgh of Aberdeen (i.e. pre-1975).

who can benefit Persons of organisations which belong to the former City and Royal Burgh of Aberdeen.

what is funded Education and the arts. The main purpose of the trust is to give financial assistance to individuals for educational purposes.

what is not funded No grants to people or organisations from outside the former City and Royal Burgh of Aberdeen.

finances *Year* 2010 *Income* £935,234 *Grants* £600,000

trustees Three persons elected by Aberdeen City Council; one by the Senatus Academicus of the University of Aberdeen; two by the governors of Robert Gordon's College, Aberdeen; two by the Church of Scotland Presbytery of Aberdeen; one by the churches of Aberdeen other than the Church of Scotland; one by the Society of Advocates in Aberdeen; one by the Convener Court of the Seven Incorporated Trades of Aberdeen; one by the trade unions having branches in Aberdeen; one by the Aberdeen Local Association of the Educational Institute of

Scotland; plus not less than two and not more than four co-optees.

OTHER INFORMATION The trust awards a number of free places to Robert Gordon's Secondary College, also school bursaries, post-graduate scholarships, travel scholarships, grants for special equipment, sports facilities, promoting education in the arts and adult education

HOW TO APPLY Application forms are available from the correspondent. The Benefactions Committee of the trust, which makes financial awards, normally meets nine or ten times a year.

WHO TO APPLY TO W Russell, Clerk, 19 Albert Street, Aberdeen AB9 1QF *Tel* 01224 640194

■ The Aberdeenshire Educational Trust Scheme

SC NO SC028382 **ESTABLISHED** 1999

WHERE FUNDING CAN BE GIVEN The former county of Aberdeen.

WHO CAN BENEFIT Individuals in education, schools and further education centres, as well as to clubs and other organisations.

WHAT IS FUNDED Providing and maintaining playing fields and other sports facilities including equipment; schools and further education centres to assist in providing special equipment; clubs, societies and organisations which include amongst their activities work of an educational nature; schools and organisations to assist education in art, music and drama; individuals and bodies to undertake educational experiments and research which will be for the benefit of people belonging to Aberdeen County. Help may also be given towards 'regional and national enterprises of an educational nature'.

FINANCES *Year* 2010–11 *Income* £63,077 *Grants* £50,000

HOW TO APPLY On a form available from the correspondent. Full guidelines are also available upon request.

WHO TO APPLY TO The Administrator, Finance Section, Aberdeenshire Council, St Leonard's, Sandyhill Road, Banff, Aberdeenshire

---

■ ABF The Soldiers' Charity (formerly the Army Benevolent Fund)

CC NO 211645 **ESTABLISHED** 1944

WHERE FUNDING CAN BE GIVEN Worldwide.

WHO CAN BENEFIT National headquarters of charities and charitable funds of Corps and Regimental Associations benefiting service and former service people, and their dependants.

WHAT IS FUNDED Support and benefit of people serving, or who have served, in the British Army, or their families/dependants. The work of the charity/service concerned must be of direct benefit to a number of soldiers, former soldiers or their dependants. Not only should this number be considerable but it must also comprise an appreciable portion of the numbers of people who benefit from the work or service of the charity.

TYPE OF GRANT One-off grants.

SAMPLE GRANTS Previous beneficiaries included: Army Families Federation, Royal Commonwealth Ex-Services League, Officers' Association, Portland Training College, Royal Star and Garter Home, Thistle Foundation, Queen Alexandra Hospital Home, Wilton Memorial Trust and the Royal Hospital – Chelsea.

FINANCES *Year* 2009–10 *Income* £12,144,648 *Grants* £5,128,525 *Assets* £42,813,040

TRUSTEES Gen. the Lord Walker; Guy Davies; Peter Sheppard; S M Andrews; P J Carr; S Clark; A W Freemantle; Mrs A M Gallico; A R Gregroy; M B Hockney; A I G Kennedy; Sir Michael Parker; D J M Roberts.

OTHER INFORMATION £2,434,121 went to other charities; £2,694,284 was awarded for the benefit of individuals.

HOW TO APPLY Individual cases should be referred initially to the appropriate Corps or Regimental Association. Charities should apply in writing and enclose the latest annual report and accounts.

WHO TO APPLY TO Col. Paul Cummings, Director of Grants and Welfare, Mountbarrow House, 6–20 Elizabeth Street, London SW1W 9RB *Tel* 0845 241 4820 *Fax* 0845 241 4821 *email* pcummings@soldierscharity.org *Website* www.soldierscharity.org

---

■ Brian Abrams Charitable Trust

CC NO 275941 **ESTABLISHED** 1978

WHERE FUNDING CAN BE GIVEN UK.

WHO CAN BENEFIT Jewish organisations.

WHAT IS FUNDED Jewish causes.

WHAT IS NOT FUNDED No grants to individuals.

SAMPLE GRANTS Previous beneficiaries have included Centre for Torah Education Trust, Friends of Ohr Akiva Institution, Halacha Lemoshe Trust, Hale Adult Hebrew Education Trust, the Heathlands Village, Manchester Jewish Federation, Rabbi Nachman of Breslov Charitable Foundation, Rainsough Charitable Trust, UK Friends of Magen David Adom and United Jewish Israel Appeal.

FINANCES *Year* 2009–10 *Income* £36,328 *Grants* £27,415 *Assets* £633,145

TRUSTEES Betty Abrams; Brian Abrams; Eric Abrams; Gail Gabbie.

HOW TO APPLY The trust has stated that its funds are fully committed and applications are not invited.

WHO TO APPLY TO The Trustees, c/o Lyon Griffiths Limited, Unit 17, Alvaston Business Park, Middlewich Road, Nantwich, Cheshire CW5 6PF

■ Eric Abrams Charitable Trust

CC NO 275939 **ESTABLISHED** 1968

WHERE FUNDING CAN BE GIVEN UK.

WHO CAN BENEFIT Jewish organisations.

WHAT IS FUNDED Jewish causes.

WHAT IS NOT FUNDED No grants to individuals.

SAMPLE GRANTS Previous beneficiaries have included: Friends of Ohr Akiva Institution, Centre for Torah Education Trust, Halacha Lemoshe Trust, Hale Adult Hebrew Education Trust, the Heathlands Village, Manchester Jewish Federation, Rabbi Nachman of Breslov Charitable Foundation, UK Friends of Magen David Adom and United Jewish Israel Appeal.

FINANCES *Year* 2009–10 *Income* £37,069 *Grants* £27,635 *Assets* £653,702

TRUSTEES Brian Abrams; Eric Abrams; Marcia Anne Jacobs; Susan Melanie Abrams.

HOW TO APPLY 'The trustees do not invite appeals, as the trust is fully committed until further notice.'

WHO TO APPLY TO The Trustees, c/o Lyon Griffiths Limited, Unit 17, Alvaston Business Park, Middlewich Road, Nantwich, Cheshire CW5 6PF *Tel* 01270 624445

■ The Acacia Charitable Trust

CC NO 274275   **ESTABLISHED** 1977
WHERE FUNDING CAN BE GIVEN UK and Israel.
WHO CAN BENEFIT Registered charities.
WHAT IS FUNDED Educational and medical charities in the UK. Jewish charities, both in the UK and Israel.
WHAT IS NOT FUNDED No grants to individuals.
TYPE OF GRANT Core and project costs will be considered.
RANGE OF GRANTS Up to £30,000, although most for under £5,000.
SAMPLE GRANTS The Jewish Museum (£41,000); Community Security Trust (£5,000); Norwood and Yad Vashem (£1,000 each); Royal National Theatre (£500); Nightingale House (£250); and Shelter, Jewish Council for Racial Equality and Riding for the Disabled (£100 each).
FINANCES *Year* 2009–10 *Income* £66,850 *Grants* £62,848 *Assets* £1,756,798
TRUSTEES K D Rubens; Angela Gillian Rubens; S A Rubens; P H Rubens.
HOW TO APPLY In writing to the correspondent.
WHO TO APPLY TO The Secretary, c/o H W Fisher & Co, Acre House, 11–15 William Road, London NW1 3ER *Tel* 020 7486 1884 *email* acacia@dircon.co.uk

■ Access Sport

CC NO 1104687   **ESTABLISHED** 2004
WHERE FUNDING CAN BE GIVEN UK.
WHO CAN BENEFIT Grass roots sports clubs working with children, particularly in disadvantaged areas.
WHAT IS FUNDED The development of 'quality sporting programmes which promote fitness and fun'.
TYPE OF GRANT Grants may cover the cost of: club promotion; participant recruitment and subsidies; coach development and education; sports equipment.
FINANCES *Year* 2009–10 *Income* £321,000 *Grants* £68,000 *Assets* £32,000
TRUSTEES J Cracknell; C Beauchamp; J Glover; N Pinkham; J Roper; Q Boyes; F Hardie; C Harley-Martin.
OTHER INFORMATION 'Access Sport is a dynamic charity whose mission is to give more children, particularly in disadvantaged areas, access to a wide range of quality local sport. We empower the inspirational community volunteers who set up and run local sports clubs with cash, expert advice and networking.'
HOW TO APPLY To nominate a club for selection, or to discuss the possibility further, please contact Access Sport by phone or email.
WHO TO APPLY TO The Secretary, Oakhurst, Lustleigh, Devon TQ13 9TG *Tel* 020 8811 4555 *email* club@accesssport.co.uk *Website* www.accesssport.co.uk

■ Achiezer Association Ltd

CC NO 255031   **ESTABLISHED** 1965
WHERE FUNDING CAN BE GIVEN Worldwide.
WHO CAN BENEFIT Charitable organisations. In practice mainly Jewish causes.
WHAT IS FUNDED The relief of elderly people and people in need; advancement of education; advancement of religion; and general charitable purposes.
WHAT IS NOT FUNDED No grants to individuals.
TYPE OF GRANT One-off and recurring.

SAMPLE GRANTS The accounts for the year do not list the individual beneficiaries of the grants made. In the past, the trust has mainly supported Jewish charities with a few small grants being given to medical and welfare charities.
FINANCES *Year* 2008–09 *Income* £965,133 *Grants* £691,308 *Assets* £1,188,374
TRUSTEES David Chontow; Sydney S Chontow; Michael M Chontow.
PUBLICATIONS According to the trust, a list of grant beneficiaries is 'detailed in a separate publication which is available from the Registered Office'. A copy has been requested but is yet to be received.
OTHER INFORMATION In January 2012 the charity's 2009–10 accounts had not be submitted to the Charity Commission and were almost 1 year overdue.
HOW TO APPLY In writing to the correspondent.
WHO TO APPLY TO David Chontow, Trustee, 130–134 Granville Road, London NW2 2LD *Tel* 020 8209 3880 *email* genoffice@dasim.co.uk

■ Achisomoch Aid Company Limited

CC NO 278387   **ESTABLISHED** 1979
WHERE FUNDING CAN BE GIVEN UK and worldwide.
WHO CAN BENEFIT Jewish religious charities.
WHAT IS FUNDED The advancement of religion in accordance with the Jewish faith.
SAMPLE GRANTS Previous beneficiaries have included: the Ah Trust, Beis Malka Trust, Chevras Maoz Ladol, Comet Charities Ltd, Davis Elias Charitable Trust, Havenpoint Ltd, Heritage Retreats, Jewish Educational Trust, Lolev Charitable Trust, Menorah Primary School, Michlala Jerusalem College, SOFT, Tomchei Cholim Trust and Yad Eliezer – Israel.
FINANCES *Year* 2009–10 *Income* £6,385,775 *Grants* £6,633,405 *Assets* £2,042,238
TRUSTEES Isaac M Katz; David Chontow; Jack Emanuel.
OTHER INFORMATION The following information about how the trust operates is given on the its website: 'Achisomoch is a charity voucher agency – it is like a bank. You open an account with us and then pay money into the account. You are given a cheque (voucher) book and can then make (charitable) payments by using these vouchers. As a charity in its own right, we can reclaim the tax rebate under Gift Aid to increase the money in your account and available for distribution to charities. Donations, via vouchers can be made only to registered charities. You get regular statements and can arrange to speak to client services for any help or special instructions.'
HOW TO APPLY In writing to the correspondent.
WHO TO APPLY TO Isaac Mark Katz, Secretary, 35 Templars Avenue, London NW11 ONU *Tel* 020 8731 8988 *email* admin@achisomoch.org *Website* www.achisomoch.org

■ The ACT Foundation

CC NO 1068617   **ESTABLISHED** 1998
WHERE FUNDING CAN BE GIVEN UK and overseas.
WHO CAN BENEFIT Health, welfare and housing.
WHAT IS FUNDED Grants generally fall into the following areas: building – funding modifications to homes, schools, hospices etc.; equipment – provision of specialised wheelchairs, other mobility aids and equipment including medical

equipment to assist independent living; financial assistance – towards the cost of short-term respite breaks at a registered respite centre. Projects that intend to be a platform for continuing services will be expected to demonstrate sustainability. ACT would be concerned to be a sole funder of projects that require ongoing support.

WHAT IS NOT FUNDED The foundation will not make grants: to replace statutory funding; to pay for work that has already commenced or equipment already purchased or on order; towards the operating costs of other charities except in connection with setting up new services; to charities that have not been registered for at least three years; for projects which promote a particular religion or faith; to community centres and youth clubs except where those served are in special need of help (e.g. the elderly or persons with special needs); to Local Authorities; to umbrella or grant-making organisations except where they undertake special assessments not readily available from the foundation's own resources; to universities and colleges, and grant-maintained, private or local education authority schools or their Parent Teacher Associations, except if those schools are for students with special needs; for costs associated with political or publicity campaigns; towards deposits for motobility vehicles.

SAMPLE GRANTS The Dani Taylor Memorial Fund (£21,300); Thames Hospicecare and the Theatre Royal Stratford East (£20,000 each); Lifeworks (£17,000); Wherever the Need – India (£15,000); Barrs Court School, Hampshire Riding Therapy Centre, Seeability and Wessex Autistic Society (£10,000 each); Rainbow Centre for Conductive Education (£8,200); Searchlight Workshops (£6,700); Noah's Ark Trust (£5,000); Lunch on the Run (£2,500); Voice of Carers Across Lothian (£1,500); and Ferring Country Centres (£500).

FINANCES *Year* 2009–10 *Income* £15,746,842 *Grants* £778,884 *Assets* £38,200,554

TRUSTEES Paul Nield; John J O'Sullivan; Michael Street; David Hyde; Robert F White; Denis Taylor.

OTHER INFORMATION The grant total includes £393,798 to 385 individuals.

HOW TO APPLY 'Application by registered charities and overseas charitable organisations has to be by way of letter on the organisation's headed paper and should: give a brief description of your organisation including any statutory or voluntary registration; provide a summary of the work you plan to undertake with the grant, together with a cost breakdown, plans and/or specification if available and a summary of the key milestones for the work; provide information on why you need to do this work and what would happen if you were unable to do it; give details of any other UK-based support received or pledged for your project; specify what you expect the results of the work to be and the number of beneficiaries helped; tell us how you plan to evaluate whether the work achieved its goals; tell us if the work will require capital and/or ongoing operational funding and if so how you plan to meet these costs. In addition you need to attach the following financial information to the letter: a cashflow projection of income and expenditure budget for the work; details of any income already raised for the work and income outstanding and where you plan to raise it from; your latest annual report and accounts. You can apply for a grant at any time. Trustees meet four times a year, but you do not need to time your application to coincide with these meetings. Procedures exist to give approvals between meeting dates, where necessary. We do not publish the dates of Trustees' meetings. We will send you an acknowledgement letter within one week of receiving your application. If your proposal is either in an unacceptable form, or ineligible, or a low priority, we will tell you in this letter. We will assess all acceptable applications and we may contact you for further information and/or make a personal visit. In the case of charitable bodies we may also ask for a presentation. We aim to make decisions on grants of up to £50,000 within one month of receiving your application. Decisions on grants over £50,000 can take up to three months. If the application is for an emergency you may request a faster timescale and we will do our best to assist.'

WHO TO APPLY TO The Grants Officer, 61 Thames Street, Windsor, Berkshire SL4 1QW *Tel* 01753 753900 *Fax* 01753 753901 *email* info@theactfoundation.co.uk *Website* www.theactfoundation.co.uk

....

■ Action Medical Research

CC NO 208701   **ESTABLISHED** 1952

WHERE FUNDING CAN BE GIVEN UK.

WHO CAN BENEFIT University departments, hospitals and research institutes for specific research projects.

WHAT IS FUNDED Child health, including problems affecting pregnancy, childbirth, babies, children and young people. 'We support a broad spectrum of research with the objective of: preventing disease and disability; and alleviating physical disability. Please note that our emphasis is on clinical research or research at the interface between clinical and basic science. We pride ourselves that our research is both innovative and of a high standard as judged by rigorous peer review. Within the above criteria, we also support research and development of equipment and techniques to improve diagnosis, therapy and assistive technology (including orthoses, prostheses and aids to daily living) and we encourage applications in the field of medical engineering.'

WHAT IS NOT FUNDED The charity does not provide: grants towards service provision or audit studies; grants purely for higher education, e.g. BSc/MSc/PhD course fees and subsistence costs; grants for medical or dental electives; grants specifically for PhD studentships (although researchers may independently register for a higher degree); grants for work undertaken outside the UK; any indirect costs such as administrative or other overheads imposed by the university or other institution; costs associated with advertising and recruitment; 'top up' funding for work supported by other funding bodies; costs to attend conferences and meetings (current Action Medical Research grantholders may apply separately); grants to MRC Units, other than RTF awards where the training/facilities cannot be offered elsewhere; grants to other charities; grants for research into complementary/alternative medicine.

TYPE OF GRANT Research comprising: project grants and Research Training Fellowship scheme.

RANGE OF GRANTS The average award is about £80,000. It is unusual to fund projects over £150,000 in their entirety.

SAMPLE GRANTS King's College London (£195,000); University of Nottingham and University of Edinburgh (£193,000); University College

Think carefully about every application. Is it justified?

....

325

London and University of Leicester (£159,000); St Mary's Hospital – University of Manchester (£125,000); Queen's University Belfast (£113,0000); University of Southampton (£83,000); and University of Leeds (£64,000).

FINANCES *Year* 2010 *Income* £7,156,839 *Grants* £3,016,526 *Assets* £7,381,813

TRUSTEES Ms Valerie Hammond; Mrs Karen Jankel; Charles Jackson; Diana Marsland; Prof. Andrew George; Richard Price; Ann Paul; Sir John Wickerson; David Gibbs; Mark Gardiner; Colin Hunsley.

PUBLICATIONS Newsletter; medical conditions leaflets.

HOW TO APPLY 'Outline proposal: all applicants should complete a two page outline proposal form [available from the charity's website] summarising the research and giving an estimation of costs, and email it to the Research Department. The details on the outline form should include the potential clinical application of the work, how it fits the remit of the charity and a description of the work proposed. The purpose of the outline proposal is to establish that your proposed work clearly falls within the charity's remit and priorities. If your work is considered peripheral to our aims, or clearly falls within the remit of another funding organisation, and in cases where demand on our funds is high, we may be unable to pursue an application from you. **Full application:** if the outline proposal is acceptable, you will be invited to complete a full application form online and you will be advised of the timetable. Applications are assessed by peer review, first by independent external referees and then by our scientific advisory panel. The decision to approve a grant is made by the council on the recommendations of the panel. Closing dates for proposals and applications are available on the charity's website.'

WHO TO APPLY TO Martin Richardson, Vincent House, 31 North Parade, Horsham, West Sussex RH12 2DP *Tel* 01403 210406 *Fax* 01403 210541 *email* info@action.org.uk *Website* www.action.org.uk

■ The Company of Actuaries' Charitable Trust Fund

CC NO 280702   **ESTABLISHED** 1980

WHERE FUNDING CAN BE GIVEN UK and overseas, with a preference for the City of London.

WHO CAN BENEFIT Charitable organisations and individuals involved in, or training for, a career in actuary.

WHAT IS FUNDED Support for people who are elderly or disabled; charities helping children and young people; those involved in treating medical conditions or funding medical research; other worthy charities, such as those working with people who are in need.

WHAT IS NOT FUNDED No grants for the propagation of religious or political beliefs, the maintenance of historic buildings or for conservation. The trustees do not usually support an organisation which has received a grant from the fund in the previous 24 months.

RANGE OF GRANTS £500–£2,000, with larger amounts given where liverymen have a significant connection.

SAMPLE GRANTS City University (£7,000); Herriot Watt University (£4,000); Cure Parkinson's Trust (£3,500); Duke of Edinburgh's Award Scheme (£2,500); Lord Mayor's Appeal (£2,000); the

Soldier's Charity (£1,000); and Mansion House Scholarship Appeal (£500).

FINANCES *Year* 2009–10 *Income* £107,728 *Grants* £113,000 *Assets* £245,226

TRUSTEES John A Jolliffe; Nick Dumbreck; Jeff Medlock; Fiona J Morrison; Michael Turner; David Barford.

HOW TO APPLY On a form which can be downloaded from the fund's website. Further information about the Trust can be obtained from the correspondent.

WHO TO APPLY TO Lyndon Jones, Honorary Almoner, 55 Station Road, Beaconsfield, Bucks HP9 1QL *email* charity@companyofactuaries.co.uk *Website* www.actuariescompany.co.uk

■ The Sylvia Adams Charitable Trust

CC NO 1050678   **ESTABLISHED** 1995

WHERE FUNDING CAN BE GIVEN Hertfordshire; work in the UK which has a national impact; and overseas (mainly Africa).

WHO CAN BENEFIT All grants are made through UK registered charities.

WHAT IS FUNDED Projects benefiting people with disabilities, people living in poverty, children and young people. It is particularly interested in helping people to become self-supporting and self-help projects.

WHAT IS NOT FUNDED The trust does not give grants to: individuals; projects in the Middle East or Eastern Europe or the countries of the ex-Soviet Union; work that solely benefits elderly people; or organisations helping animals, medical research or environmental causes.

TYPE OF GRANT One off and recurring for up to 3 years. Project and core costs.

RANGE OF GRANTS Up to £30,000.

SAMPLE GRANTS A capital grant of £250,000 was awarded to Basic Needs UK Trust for its transition into a 'social franchise'. UK beneficiaries included: Motor Neurone Disease Association (£30,000), towards the development of Year of Pathway; Volunteer Reading Help (£25,000), for the post of Head of Volunteering and Best Practice; Friends United Network (£23,000), part-funding the post of clinical manager to expand the befriending service into new boroughs; Tacade (£20,000), for health education resources for visually impaired young people; Volunteer Centre Dacorum (£10,000), for research into supported volunteering; Youth at Risk (£5,000), to cover some core costs of their work with young people; Chrysalis School for Autism (£2,000), for the provision of additional specialist software; and The Activate Forum (£2,000), towards supporting people with physical disabilities into sport and leisure.

FINANCES *Year* 2009–10 *Income* £270,929 *Grants* £802,200 *Assets* £10,022,367

TRUSTEES Richard J Golland; Mark Heasman; Timothy Lawler.

OTHER INFORMATION Grants included: £361,000 overseas; £181,500 UK. It should also be noted that the trustees intend to spend out and close the trust after the 2012–13 financial year.

HOW TO APPLY There is a two stage application process: Stage 1 can **only** be made through the trust's website; Applicants who successfully get through this stage will be asked to submit a fuller Stage 2 application. Telephone queries about the guidelines and application process are welcome in advance of applications being made

■ The Adamson Trust

SC NO SC016517   **ESTABLISHED** 1946
WHERE FUNDING CAN BE GIVEN UK, but preference will be given to requests on behalf of Scottish children.
WHO CAN BENEFIT Children under 18 with a physical or mental disability, both groups and individuals.
WHAT IS FUNDED Assistance with holidays – grants may be given to the parent(s) of children or as block grants; for example, to the special needs unit of a school.
TYPE OF GRANT Usually one-off.
SAMPLE GRANTS Previous beneficiaries have included Barnardo's Dundee Family Support Team, Children's Hospice Association Scotland, Lady Hoare Trust for Physically Disabled Children, Hopscotch Holidays, Over the Wall Gang Group, Peak Holidays, React, Scotland Yard Adventure Centre, Sense Scotland, Special Needs Adventure Play Ground and Scottish Spina Bifida Association.
FINANCES *Year* 2009–10 *Income* £65,417
TRUSTEES R C Farrell; J W H Allen; Dr H Kirkwood; Dr M MacDonald Simpson; Mrs A Cowan.
OTHER INFORMATION Around £75,000 is given in grants each year, mostly to individuals.
HOW TO APPLY In writing to the correspondent. A copy of the latest audited accounts should be included together with details of the organisation, the number of children who would benefit and the proposed holiday.
WHO TO APPLY TO Edward Elworthy, Administrator, PO Box 26334, Crieff, Perthshire PH7 9AB *email* edward@elworthy.net

■ The Victor Adda Foundation

CC NO 291456   **ESTABLISHED** 1984
WHERE FUNDING CAN BE GIVEN UK, but in practice Greenwich.
WHO CAN BENEFIT Charitable organisations.
WHAT IS FUNDED This trust mainly supports the Fan Museum in Greenwich.
SAMPLE GRANTS Fan Museum Trust (£42,000).
FINANCES *Year* 2009–10 *Income* £45,885
          Grants £42,000 *Assets* £1,380,963
TRUSTEES Helene Alexander; Roy Gluckstein; Ann Mosseri.
HOW TO APPLY In writing to the correspondent. Only successful applications are notified of a decision.
WHO TO APPLY TO The Trustees, c/o Kleinwort Benson Trustees Ltd, PO Box 57005, 30 Gresham Street, London EC2V 7PG *Tel* 020 3207 7091

■ Adenfirst Ltd

CC NO 291647   **ESTABLISHED** 1984
WHERE FUNDING CAN BE GIVEN Worldwide.
WHO CAN BENEFIT Jewish organisations only.
WHAT IS FUNDED Jewish causes related to education, medical care, relief of poverty and the advancement of religion.
RANGE OF GRANTS Up to £35,000.
SAMPLE GRANTS Beis Aaron Trust (£30,000); Ezer Vehatzolo and Kahal Chassidim Wiznitz (£20,000 each); and Beth Hamedrash Gur,

Kehal Yisroel D'Chassidei Gur, Lolev Charitable Trust, Mercaz Hatorah Belz Machnovke and Yad Vochesed (£10,000 each).
FINANCES *Year* 2010 *Income* £141,018
          Grants £132,730 *Assets* £1,503,859
TRUSTEES Leonard Bondi; Mrs H F Bondi; Mrs R Cymerman; Sylvia Cymerman; Ian Heitner; Michael Cymerman; Sarah Heitner.
HOW TO APPLY In writing to the correspondent.
WHO TO APPLY TO I M Cymerman, Governor, 479 Holloway Road, London N7 6LE

■ The Adint Charitable Trust

CC NO 265290   **ESTABLISHED** 1973
WHERE FUNDING CAN BE GIVEN Worldwide, in practice UK.
WHO CAN BENEFIT Registered charities.
WHAT IS FUNDED Health and social welfare.
WHAT IS NOT FUNDED Individuals.
TYPE OF GRANT One-off grants and recurrent grants for more than three years are considered, for capital costs (including buildings) and core costs.
RANGE OF GRANTS £50–£15,000. Grants are usually for £10,000 and £5,000.
SAMPLE GRANTS CLIC Sargent, Fight for Sight Eye Research, Mental Health Foundation and Shelter (£10,000 each); Army Benevolent Fund, British Lung Foundation and the Westminster Pastoral Foundation (£5,000 each); and the Anne Frank Trust UK and Headway London (£1,000 each).
FINANCES *Year* 2009–10 *Income* £324,333
          Grants £276,000 *Assets* £6,136,085
TRUSTEES Anthony J Edwards; Mrs Margaret Edwards; Douglas R Oram; Brian Pate.
HOW TO APPLY In writing to the correspondent. Each applicant should make its own case in the way it considers best, but the application should include full details of the applicant charity. The trust notes that it cannot enter into correspondence and unsuccessful applicants will not be notified.
WHO TO APPLY TO Douglas R Oram, Trustee, Suite 42, 571 Finchley Road, London NW3 7BN *email* adintct@gmail.com

■ The Adnams Charity

CC NO 1000203   **ESTABLISHED** 1990
WHERE FUNDING CAN BE GIVEN Within a 25-mile radius of St Edmund's Church, Southwold.
WHO CAN BENEFIT Small local projects.
WHAT IS FUNDED General charitable purposes. The charity gives support to a wide variety of organisations including those involved with health and social welfare, education, recreation, the arts, environment and conservation and historic buildings.
WHAT IS NOT FUNDED The charity does not normally make grants to religious organisations or private clubs unless they can demonstrate that the purpose of the grant is for something of clear public benefit, accessible to all. It does not provide raffle prizes or sponsorship of any kind. No grants are made to individuals. However, public bodies and charities may apply on behalf of individuals. Grants are not made in successive years.
TYPE OF GRANT The trustees prefer applications for specific items. Grants are generally of a one-off nature. The trustees are reluctant to give grants to cover ongoing running costs, although in very exceptional circumstances they may do so.
RANGE OF GRANTS Normally £100–£2,500.

SAMPLE GRANTS Westleton Village Hall and Deben Rowing Club (£2,500 each); St Edmund's Primary School – Hoxne (£2,400); Waveney Crossroads (£2,200); Blofield Primary School PTA (£2,000); North Suffolk and Great Yarmouth Cruse Bereavement Care (£1,800); Credit Action (£1,300); 1st Halesworth Scout Group (£1,000); Harleston Allotments Association (£920); Victim Support (£820); Open Space Theatre Company (£660); IDC Diamonds (£450); St James Village Orchard Project (£350); and Laxfield Village Hall (£200).

FINANCES *Year* 2009–10 *Income* £63,046 *Grants* £78,669 *Assets* £23,137

TRUSTEES Jonathan Adnams, Chair; Rob Chase; Lizzy Cantwell; Guy Heald; Emma Hibbert; Melvyn Horn; Sadie Lofthouse; Simon Loftus; Andy Wood.

HOW TO APPLY Application forms are available on request to the Charity Administrator. Grants are considered at quarterly meetings, in January, April, July and October. Application deadlines usually fall in the previous month and are listed on the charity's website.

WHO TO APPLY TO Rebecca Abrahall, Charity Administrator, Sole Bay Brewery, Southwold, Suffolk IP18 6JW *Tel* 01502 727200 *email* rebecca.abrahall@adnams.co.uk *Website* www.adnams.co.uk/charity

■ AF Trust Company

CC NO 1060319   **ESTABLISHED** 1996
WHERE FUNDING CAN BE GIVEN England.
WHO CAN BENEFIT Higher education institutions.
WHAT IS FUNDED Charitable purposes connected with the provision of higher education.
WHAT IS NOT FUNDED No grants to individuals.
RANGE OF GRANTS Up to £18,000.
SAMPLE GRANTS University of Nottingham (£17,500); University of Reading (£14,250); Imperial College (£13,250); University of Canterbury Christ Church (£7,750); Royal Holloway (£3,000); University of Exeter (£2,250); and Royal Academy of Music and University of Central Lancashire (£1,000 each).
FINANCES *Year* 2009–10 *Income* £3,023,840 *Grants* £60,000 *Assets* £353,035
TRUSTEES Martin Wynne-Jones; David Charles Savage; Jeremy Lindley; Andrew Murphy; David Leah.
OTHER INFORMATION The income figure also relates to funds used to lease buildings from educational establishments and then enter into lease-back arrangements rather than indicating the size of funds available.
HOW TO APPLY In writing to the correspondent. However, unsolicited applications are only accepted from higher education institutions within England.
WHO TO APPLY TO Paul Welch, Secretary, 34 Chapel Street, Thatcham, Reading, Berkshire RG18 4QL *Tel* 01635 867222

■ Age Scotland

SC NO SC010100   **ESTABLISHED** 2009
WHERE FUNDING CAN BE GIVEN Scotland.
WHO CAN BENEFIT Groups for the benefit and welfare of older people.
WHAT IS FUNDED Organising special outings or event, purchasing equipment, producing and distributing information, attending/running and event which will benefit older people, start-up costs for new groups, training costs, developing a substantial new project.

WHAT IS NOT FUNDED No grants to statutory authorities, commercial organisations and individuals.
TYPE OF GRANT Capital; one-off; running costs; salaries; and start-up costs.
RANGE OF GRANTS £40,500 was given in grants less than £1,000. Grants then ranged from £1,000–£10,000.
SAMPLE GRANTS Lightburn Elderly Action Project (LEAP) (£10,000); Deaf Vision and Food Train (£8,000 each); British Red Cross (£6,500); Cowal Elderly Befriending Scheme (£5,000); Grampion 50+ Network (£3,000); Borders Community Care Forum (£2,250); Age Concern Eastwood (£2,000); Crail Street Sheltered Housing (£1,800); Airidhantium Young at Heart Club (£1,500); Forget Me Not Club (£1,250); and Alive and Kicking (£1,000).
FINANCES *Year* 2009–10 *Income* £3,108,033 *Grants* £154,278 *Assets* £1,405,468
TRUSTEES James Wright; Marjory D'Arcy; Primrose Scott; Sir Charles Gray; Jean Campbell; Hamilton Smillie; James Fry; Ian Purvis; Paul Adams; Prof. John Williams; William Martin.
PUBLICATIONS A wide range of fact sheets are available on *money matters, health and wellbeing, travel and lifestyle, home and care and, work and learning*. Research reports are also published on a number of topics. Please see the website for full details.
HOW TO APPLY Local development workers can be contacted to discuss proposals. For an application form contact the resource worker for the local area (List of local resource workers available on website).
WHO TO APPLY TO Judy Cromarty, Causewayside House, 160 Causewayside, Edinburgh EH9 1PR *Tel* 0845 833 0200 *Website* www.ageuk.org.uk/scotland

■ Age UK (formerly Help the Aged and Age Concern)

CC NO 1128267   **ESTABLISHED** 1977
WHERE FUNDING CAN BE GIVEN UK and overseas.
WHO CAN BENEFIT Independently constituted, not-for-profit organisations that are accessible to all people in later life. Research organisations.
WHAT IS FUNDED The trust administers a variety of grant programmes aimed at organisations working to make life better for older people by addressing people's immediate needs or tackling the root causes of problems they are experiencing. Research grants, designed to increase understanding of the aging process, of what it means to grow old and the implications for society and the economy, are also made.
WHAT IS NOT FUNDED No grants to individuals.
TYPE OF GRANT Capital; one-off; running costs; salaries; and start-up costs. Funding is available for up to three years.
RANGE OF GRANTS About £200–£50,000.
FINANCES *Year* 2009–10 *Income* £160,665,000 *Grants* £15,502,000 *Assets* £34,197,000
TRUSTEES Dianne Jeffrey, Chair; Patrick Cusack; Dr Bernadette Fuge; Jeremy Greenhalgh; Timothy Hammond; Chris Hughes; Glyn Kyle; Prof. Brendan McCormack; Jane Newell; Michael Vincent; Pauline Walsh; Jane Wesson; Prof. John Williams; Hilary Wiseman; Prof. James Wright.
PUBLICATIONS A wide range of fact sheets are available on *money matters, health and wellbeing, travel and lifestyle, home and care and, work and learning*. Research reports are

also published on a number of topics. Please see the website for full details.

OTHER INFORMATION A significant proportion of the grant total is given to local Age Concern and Age UK branches.

HOW TO APPLY For further information on general grant programmes currently open to applications, please contact the Grants Team. Applicants interested in research funding should contact the Research Department at Tavis House, 1–6 Tavistock Square, London WC1H 9NA or email research@ageuk.org.uk.

WHO TO APPLY TO Grants Unit, York House, 207–221 Pentonville Road, London N1 9UZ *Tel* 0800 169 8787 *email* contact@ageuk.org. uk *Website* www.ageuk.org.uk

····································

■ Aid to the Church in Need (UK)

CC NO 1097984   **ESTABLISHED** 1947
WHERE FUNDING CAN BE GIVEN Eastern Europe, Africa, Russia, Asia and South America.
WHO CAN BENEFIT Persecuted and suffering Christians, especially Roman Catholics, Russian Orthodox and refugees.
WHAT IS FUNDED Religion and pastoral projects.
WHAT IS NOT FUNDED Private individuals with schooling, medical or living expenses.
TYPE OF GRANT Buildings, capital, core costs, endowment, one-off, project, running costs, salaries and start-up costs.
FINANCES *Year* 2010 *Income* £6,710,383 *Grants* £4,539,317 *Assets* £2,135,530
TRUSTEES Peter Sefton-Williams, Chair; Joanna Bogle; Fr Ronald Creighton-Jobe; Philipp Habsburg-Lothringen; Graham Hutton; Piers Paul Read; Lisa Sanchez-Corea Simpson; Julian Chadwick; Father Paul Morton.
OTHER INFORMATION Please note: the focus of this charity is the church overseas and that individuals without the backing as required may not apply for funding.
HOW TO APPLY The trust has an informative website where the criteria, guidelines and application process are posted. All applications by individuals must have the backing of a Catholic Bishop or religious superior.
WHO TO APPLY TO Neville Kyrke-Smith, National Director, 12–14 Benhill Avenue, Sutton, Surrey SM1 4DA *Tel* 020 8642 8668 *email* acn@ acnuk.org *Website* www.acnuk.org

····································

■ The AIM Foundation

CC NO 263294   **ESTABLISHED** 1971
WHERE FUNDING CAN BE GIVEN Worldwide, in practice UK.
WHO CAN BENEFIT Charitable organisations.
WHAT IS FUNDED Healthcare, community development, youth, environmental matters and other charitable activities particularly related to influencing long-term social change.
WHAT IS NOT FUNDED No grants to individuals.
TYPE OF GRANT Revenue grants: core costs and salaries.
RANGE OF GRANTS Up to £100,000.
SAMPLE GRANTS Variety Club Children's Charity, the College for Integrated Health and the New Economics Foundation (£100,000 each); Essex Community Foundation (£52,000); Kids Company (£30,000); Community Foundation Network (£25,000); Worshipful Company Carmen Benevolent Fund (£20,000); The Soil Association (£15,000); Action for Child and Friends of the Earth (£10,000 each); Wells for
(

India (£5,000); Farm Africa (£4,000); and Westminster Befriend a Family (£3,000).
FINANCES *Year* 2009–10 *Income* £1,058,644 *Grants* £683,328 *Assets* £9,508,924
TRUSTEES Ian Roy Marks; Mrs Angela D Marks; Nicolas Marks; Joanna Pritchard-Barrett; Caroline Marks; Phillipa Bailey.
HOW TO APPLY It cannot be stressed enough that this foundation 'is proactive in its approach' and does not wish to receive applications. Unsolicited requests for assistance will not be responded to under any circumstance.
WHO TO APPLY TO Miss Louisa Tippett, Whittle and Co, 15 High Street, West Mersea, Colchester, Essex CO5 8QA *Tel* 01206 385049 *email* louisa@whittles.co.uk

····································

■ The Green and Lilian F M Ainsworth and Family Benevolent Fund

CC NO 267577   **ESTABLISHED** 1974
WHERE FUNDING CAN BE GIVEN UK, with some preference for Northwest England.
WHO CAN BENEFIT Charities benefiting young, elderly and disabled people.
WHAT IS FUNDED The trustees have a comprehensive list of national charities from which they select each year, requesting the money is spent in the North West. Smaller grants are given to local charities.
WHAT IS NOT FUNDED No grants to individuals or non-registered charities.
TYPE OF GRANT Prefers specific projects.
RANGE OF GRANTS Up to £1,000.
SAMPLE GRANTS Avon riding Centre, Lost Chord, Young People Taking Action, Wirral Inroads and InterAct Reading Service (£500 each); and Frishta Children's Village, the Migraine Trust, Dogs for the Disabled, Red Squirrel Survival Trust and River and Sea Sence (£350 each).
FINANCES *Year* 2009–10 *Income* £29,000 *Grants* £20,850
TRUSTEES The Royal Bank of Scotland plc.
HOW TO APPLY In writing to the trustees, there is no application form.
WHO TO APPLY TO The Trust Section Manager, RBS Trust Services, Eden, Lakeside, Chester Business Park, Wrexham Road, Chester CH4 9QT

····································

■ The Sylvia Aitken Charitable Trust

SC NO SC010556   **ESTABLISHED** 1985
WHERE FUNDING CAN BE GIVEN UK, with a preference for Scotland.
WHO CAN BENEFIT Registered medical research and welfare charities, and any small local groups – particularly in Scotland.
WHAT IS FUNDED General charitable purposes, with a preference for medical and welfare organisations.
WHAT IS NOT FUNDED No grants to individuals: the trust can only support UK registered charities.
SAMPLE GRANTS Previous grant beneficiaries have included: Association for International Cancer Research, Barn Owl Trust, British Lung Foundation, British Stammering Association, the Roy Castle Lung Cancer Foundation, Disabled Living Foundation, Epilepsy Research Trust, Friends of the Lake District, Motor Neurone Disease Association, Network for Surviving Stalking, Royal Scots Dragoon Guards Museum Trust, Sense Scotland, Scottish Child

Psychotherapy Trust, Tall Ships Youth Trust, Tenovus Scotland, Wood Green Animal Shelters and Young Minds.

FINANCES *Year* 2009–10 *Income* £119,645 *Grants* £120,000

TRUSTEES Mrs S M Aitken; Mrs M Harkis; J Ferguson.

HOW TO APPLY In writing to the correspondent. Applicants should outline the charity's objectives and current projects for which funding may be required. The trustees meet at least twice a year, usually in March/April and September/October.

WHO TO APPLY TO The Administrator, Fergusons Chartered Accountants, 24 Woodside, Houston, Renfrewshire PA6 7DD *Tel* 01505 610412

■ The Ajahma Charitable Trust

CC NO 273823   **ESTABLISHED** 1977

WHERE FUNDING CAN BE GIVEN UK and overseas.

WHO CAN BENEFIT Registered charities.

WHAT IS FUNDED Development, health, disability, poverty, women's issues, family planning, human rights and social need.

WHAT IS NOT FUNDED Large organisations with a turnover above £4 million will not normally be considered, nor will applications with any sort of religious bias or those which support animal rights/welfare, arts, medical research, buildings, equipment, local groups or overseas projects where the charity income is less than £500,000 a year. Applications for grants or sponsorship for individuals will not be supported.

TYPE OF GRANT Core and running costs, projects and salaries. Funding is available for up to three years.

SAMPLE GRANTS CAMFED, Global Witness and Womankind Worldwide (£50,000 each); and Blue Sky, Straight Talking and Switchback (£4,500 each).

FINANCES *Year* 2009–10 *Income* £95,222 *Grants* £286,225 *Assets* £2,923,535

TRUSTEES Jennifer Sheridan; Elizabeth Simpson; James Sinclair Taylor; Carole Pound; Roger Paffard.

OTHER INFORMATION In addition to the total grants figure, Headway groups have received awards totalling £50,000 (9 grants).

HOW TO APPLY The trust has reviewed their grant-making criteria and will now pro-actively seek and select organisations to which they wish to award grants. They will no longer consider unsolicited applications.

WHO TO APPLY TO Suzanne Hunt, Administrator, 275 Dover House Road, London SW15 5BP *Tel* 020 8788 5388

■ The Alabaster Trust

CC NO 1050568   **ESTABLISHED** 1995

WHERE FUNDING CAN BE GIVEN UK and overseas.

WHO CAN BENEFIT Organisations benefiting evangelical Christian organisations.

WHAT IS FUNDED General charitable purposes, particularly the advancement of the Christian faith.

WHAT IS NOT FUNDED No grants to individuals.

FINANCES *Year* 2009–10 *Income* £56,036 *Grants* £38,445 *Assets* £53,808

TRUSTEES Jill Kendrick; Graham Kendrick; Abigail Sheldrake; Amy Waterman.

HOW TO APPLY In writing to the correspondent. The trustees meet to consider grants quarterly, usually in March, June, September and December.

WHO TO APPLY TO John Caladine, Trust Administrator, 1 The Avenue, Eastbourne, East Sussex BN21 3YA *Tel* 01323 644579 *email* john@caladine.co.uk

■ Alba Charitable Trust

CC NO 276391   **ESTABLISHED** 1978

WHERE FUNDING CAN BE GIVEN UK and overseas.

WHO CAN BENEFIT Educational institutions.

WHAT IS FUNDED Predominantly Jewish organisations.

RANGE OF GRANTS Up to £20,000.

SAMPLE GRANTS Chasdei Cohen (£5,500); HAYE (£1,500); Jewish Care (£4,000); Lolev Charitable Trust (£20,000).

FINANCES *Year* 2007–08 *Income* £60,583 *Grants* £31,635 *Assets* £286,236

TRUSTEES Leslie Glatt, Chair; Mrs R Glatt; Mrs D Kestel.

OTHER INFORMATION In January 2012 the latest accounts available were from 2007/08, with the trust consistently failing to submit the required information with the Charity Commission.

HOW TO APPLY In writing to the correspondent.

WHO TO APPLY TO Leslie Glatt, Trustee, 3 Goodyers Gardens, Hendon, London NW4 2HD *Tel* 020 7434 3494

■ The Albion Trust

CC NO 1117812   **ESTABLISHED** 2007

WHERE FUNDING CAN BE GIVEN UK.

WHO CAN BENEFIT Registered charities.

WHAT IS FUNDED General charitable purposes.

SAMPLE GRANTS Nordoff-Robbins Music Therapy; Enterprise Education Trust; Downside Fisher Youth Club; ECHO; Lawrence's Roundabout Well Appeal; Stonebridge City Farm; CLIC Sargent; Skill Force Development; Rainbow Trust; Groundwork Black Country; Second Chance; The Honeypot Charity; YMCA Winchester; and Ellen McArthur Trust.

FINANCES *Year* 2009–10 *Income* £21,956 *Grants* £170,384 *Assets* £300,530

TRUSTEES Peter Savage; Diane Savage; Philip Savage; Philip Clancey; Helen Stringer; Coutts & Co.

OTHER INFORMATION Individual grants amounts are not listed.

HOW TO APPLY In writing to the correspondent.

WHO TO APPLY TO Helen Porter, Administrator, Coutts & Co, 440 The Strand, London WC2R 0QS *Tel* 020 7663 6838

■ The Alborada Trust

CC NO 1091660   **ESTABLISHED** 2001

WHERE FUNDING CAN BE GIVEN Worldwide.

WHO CAN BENEFIT Charitable organisations.

WHAT IS FUNDED Veterinary causes in the United Kingdom and Ireland with activities primarily devoted to the welfare of animals and/or in their associated research. Projects throughout the world associated with the relief of poverty, human suffering, sickness or ill health.

RANGE OF GRANTS £20,000–£245,000.

SAMPLE GRANTS Previous beneficiaries: Animal Health Trust (£35,000); and Wildlife Vets International (£22,000).

FINANCES *Year* 2010 *Income* £126,589 *Grants* £50,000

TRUSTEES Miss E K E Rausing; D J Way; R Lerner; Capt. J Nicholson.

HOW TO APPLY Funds are fully committed. The trust does not accept unsolicited applications.

330

Does the trust you have chosen match your needs? Haphazard applications waste postage and time

■ D G Albright Charitable Trust

CC NO 277367   **ESTABLISHED** 1978
WHERE FUNDING CAN BE GIVEN UK, with a preference for Gloucestershire.
WHO CAN BENEFIT Registered charities.
WHAT IS FUNDED General charitable purposes.
WHAT IS NOT FUNDED Grants are not usually made to individuals.
TYPE OF GRANT One-off and recurrent.
RANGE OF GRANTS £300–£4,000.
SAMPLE GRANTS Bromesberrow Parochial Church Council (£4,000); Gloucestershire Macmillan Cancer Relief, National Star College, the Countryside Foundation for Education and the Family Haven – Gloucester (£2,000 each); Hands Around the World, Butterfly Conservation, Fields in Trust and the Calvert Trust (£1,000 each); Dulverton Patient Group and HOPE Family Centre (£500 each); and Bibles for Children (£300).
FINANCES *Year* 2009–10 *Income* £42,380 *Grants* £32,800 *Assets* £1,116,915
TRUSTEES Hon. Dr Gilbert Greenall; Richard Wood.
HOW TO APPLY In writing to the correspondent.
WHO TO APPLY TO Richard Wood, Trustee, Old Church School, Hollow Street, Great Somerford, Chippenham, Wiltshire SN15 5JD *Tel* 01249 720760

■ The Alchemy Foundation

CC NO 292500   **ESTABLISHED** 1985
WHERE FUNDING CAN BE GIVEN UK and overseas.
WHO CAN BENEFIT Community projects, voluntary organisations and registered charities.
WHAT IS FUNDED The foundation's 2009–10 accounts state that its objects are, 'particularly focused on the Orpheus Centre, water projects in the developing world, disability (particularly mobility, access, helplines and communications), social welfare (inner city community projects, disaffected youth, family mediation, homelessness), personal reform, penal reform (work with prisoners, especially young prisoners, and their families), medical research and aid (especially in areas of blindness and disfigurement), individual enterprise (by helping Raleigh International and similar organisations to give opportunities to young people according to need) and respite for carers.'
WHAT IS NOT FUNDED No grants for organisations exclusive to one faith or political belief.
TYPE OF GRANT Capital; revenue; one-off; salaries.
FINANCES *Year* 2009–10 *Income* £297,636 *Grants* £279,719 *Assets* £2,293,128
TRUSTEES Dr Jemima Stilgoe; Holly Stilgoe; Jack Stilgoe; Rufus Stilgoe; Richard Stilgoe; Alex Armitage; Andrew Murison; Annabel Stilgoe; Esther Rantzen; Joseph Stilgoe; Tony Elias.
HOW TO APPLY In writing to the correspondent.
WHO TO APPLY TO Richard Stilgoe, Trustee, Trevereux Manor, Limpsfield Chart, Oxted, Surrey RH8 0TL *Tel* 01883 730600

■ Aldgate and All Hallows' Barking Exhibition Foundation

CC NO 312500   **ESTABLISHED** 1893
WHERE FUNDING CAN BE GIVEN City of London and the London borough of Tower Hamlets.
WHO CAN BENEFIT Children or young people under the age of 25.
WHAT IS FUNDED The foundation is particularly keen to encourage and support: (i) projects initiated by schools that enhance the National Curriculum; (ii) projects aimed at improving literacy and numeracy; (iii) projects aimed at promoting the study of science, mathematics and the arts. Priority will be given to projects that are not yet part of a school's or organisation's regular activities; to developments that are strategic, such as practical initiatives seeking to address the root causes of problems, and those that have the potential to influence policy and practice more widely. The foundation may also from time to time initiate new projects that do not fall into the priority areas for grant making to enable governors to explore ground-breaking or emergent fields of educational practice. .
WHAT IS NOT FUNDED Please note that the foundation does not give grants for: equipment or teachers' salaries that are the responsibility of education authorities; youth groups or community projects; supplementary schools or mother tongue teaching; the purchase, repair or furnishing of buildings; conferences or seminars; university or medical research; trips abroad; stage, film, publication or video production costs; performances, exhibitions or festivals; retrospective requests (i.e. any activity that has already taken place); requests to substitute for the withdrawal or reduction of statutory funding; general fund-raising campaigns or appeals.
FINANCES *Year* 2010 *Income* £79,794 *Grants* £258,651 *Assets* £6,788,600
TRUSTEES J Hall; H W Whitbread; G Forbes; W J Hamilton-Hinds; R Hazlewood; Cllr S Islam; P James; Mrs D Jones; Mrs S Knowles; D Mash; D J Ross; K Everett; Revd B. Olivier; Revd Laura Burgess.
OTHER INFORMATION The 2010 grant total included £21,000 given in grants to individuals.
HOW TO APPLY Initial enquiries should be sent to the foundation. These must include the following information: (i) Information about your school or organisation; including an outline of its current activities, its legal status, aims, brief history, details of staffing levels, management structure and composition of the management committee. (ii) An outline description of, and timetable for, the project for which funding is being sought, including information about who will be involved in and/or benefit from the project. (iii) Details of the aims and outcomes for the project, including information about how you will monitor and evaluate the project. (iv) A detailed budget for the project. (v) Information about any other sources of income and partnership funding for the project.
WHO TO APPLY TO Richard Foley, Clerk to the Governors, 31 Jewry Street, London EC3N 2EY *Tel* 020 7488 2518 *Fax* 020 7488 2519 *email* aldgateandallhallows@sirjohncass.org *Website* www.aldgateallhallows.org.uk

■ The Aldgate Freedom Foundation

CC NO 207046   **ESTABLISHED** 1962

WHERE FUNDING CAN BE GIVEN Freedom part of the parish of St Botolph-without-Aldgate.

WHO CAN BENEFIT Organisations benefiting older people and people who are homeless or otherwise in need.

WHAT IS FUNDED Hospitals and voluntary organisations.

RANGE OF GRANTS Up to £3,500.

SAMPLE GRANTS Portsoken Ward Club for the Three Score Club and Wingate Golden Oldies (£3,500 each); Middlesex Estate Resident's Association (£1,000); and St Botolph's Rectors Discretionary Fund (£300).

FINANCES *Year* 2010 *Income* £58,761 *Grants* £16,250 *Assets* £1,405,609

TRUSTEES Revd L Burgess; M D Bear; S J Borton; G Caughey; H L M Jones; M Peak; I Priest; C Jones; C Knowles.

HOW TO APPLY In writing to the correspondent.

WHO TO APPLY TO M Pierce, Clerk to the Trustees, St Botolph's Church, St Botolph-without-Aldgate, Aldgate, London EC3N 1AB

■ The Alexis Trust

CC NO 262861   **ESTABLISHED** 1971

WHERE FUNDING CAN BE GIVEN UK and overseas.

WHO CAN BENEFIT Individuals and organisations.

WHAT IS FUNDED Support for a variety of causes, principally Christian missionary projects.

WHAT IS NOT FUNDED No grants for building appeals, or to individuals for education.

TYPE OF GRANT One-off, project and some recurring costs will be considered.

SAMPLE GRANTS Nationwide Christian Trust (£10,000); Counties Workers Essex and Tearfund (£2,000 each); UCCF and Barnabas Fund (£1,200 each); and Epping Forest Youth for Christ and SGM Lifewords (£1,000 each).

FINANCES *Year* 2009–10 *Income* £50,465 *Grants* £46,730 *Assets* £434,174

TRUSTEES Prof. Duncan Vere; Chris Harwood; Elisabeth Harwood; Vera Vere.

HOW TO APPLY In writing to the correspondent, although the trust states that most of the funds are regularly committed.

WHO TO APPLY TO Prof. Duncan Vere, Trustee, 14 Broadfield Way, Buckhurst Hill, Essex IG9 5AG

■ The Alice Trust

CC NO 290859   **ESTABLISHED** 1984

WHERE FUNDING CAN BE GIVEN UK, in practice, Buckinghamshire.

WHO CAN BENEFIT The trust's giving is focused on its principal beneficiary, Waddesdon Manor, but very occasionally grants are made to other organisations.

WHAT IS FUNDED The preservation, protection, maintenance and improvement of Waddesdon Manor, its lands and its contents, for the benefit of the public generally, together with the advancement of education in matters of historic, artistic, architectural or aesthetic interest.

SAMPLE GRANTS £3 million for Waddesdon Manor running costs, repair and refurbishment and £125,000 to the Prince's Charities Foundation.

FINANCES *Year* 2009–10 *Income* £40,388,407 *Grants* £3,125,000 *Assets* £119,691,559

TRUSTEES Lord Rothschild; Lady Rothschild; Sir Edward Cazalet; Hon. Beth Rothschild; Lord Cholmondeley; SJP Trustee Company Limited.

OTHER INFORMATION At the end of 2010 the trust received further substantial assets totalling around £47 million following the dissolution of the Rothschild Foundation (CC no. 230159), a connected charity which shared two trustees. Further details are expected in the trust's 2010–11 accounts.

HOW TO APPLY Applications can be made for the advancement of education in matters of historic, artistic, architectural or aesthetic interest, but in view of the commitment of the trust to its principal beneficiary, Waddesdon Manor, it is unlikely that many applications will be successful. The trust states that the trustees meet twice a year to consider grant applications and that grants are occasionally made to other charitable organisations. However, in reality very few grants are made. We would suggest that an informal enquiry is made to the trust before undertaking the preparation of any grant application. The trust acknowledges postal enquiries.

WHO TO APPLY TO Fiona Sinclair, The Dairy, Queen Street, Waddesdon, Aylesbury, Buckinghamshire HP18 0JW *Tel* 01296 653235

■ All Saints Educational Trust

CC NO 312934   **ESTABLISHED** 1978

WHERE FUNDING CAN BE GIVEN UK and overseas.

WHO CAN BENEFIT Ultimately, persons who are or intend to become engaged as teachers or in other capacities connected with education, in particular home economics and religious subjects, and those who teach or intend to teach in multicultural areas.

WHAT IS FUNDED Primarily, the training of Christian teachers. Its main purposes is to: help increase the number of new teachers with Qualified Teacher Status; improve the skills and qualifications of experienced teachers; encourage research that can assist teachers in their work; support specifically the teaching of religious studies and home economics and related areas – such as the promotion of public health and nutrition, both at home and in the Commonwealth.

WHAT IS NOT FUNDED Please note that the trust will not support: general or core funds of any organisation; public appeals; school buildings, equipment or supplies (except library resources); the establishment of new departments in universities and colleges; general bursary funds of other organisations.

TYPE OF GRANT One-off, project or annual grants for a limited period. Funding may be given for more than three years. Preference will be given to 'pump-priming' projects.

SAMPLE GRANTS Previous beneficiaries of corporate awards include: National Association of Teachers in Home Economics, Southwark Cathedral Education Centre, British Nutrition Foundation, Design and Technology Association, Sheffield Hallam University, Wulugu – Ghana, Scripture Union, Christian Education Movement and the Soil Association.

FINANCES *Year* 2009–10 *Income* £379,972 *Grants* £202,355 *Assets* £8,977,311

TRUSTEES Diane McCrea; Revd Canon Peter Hartley; Revd Dr Keith Riglin; David J Trillo; Clive Wright; Barbara E Harvey; Dr Augur Pearce; Prof. Anthony R Leeds; Ven. Stephan J Welch; Stephanie Valentine; Joanna Moriarty; Dr Robert

L Gwynne; Frances M Smith; Anna E Cumbers; Michael C Jacob; Stephen Brooker.

OTHER INFORMATION 1n 2009–10 grants to organisations (Corporate Awards) totalled £39,000, with £159,000 going to individuals in scholarships and bursaries and £4,900 given for the All Saxton Fellowship.

HOW TO APPLY For applications from organisations (not individuals): applicants are invited to discuss their ideas informally with the clerk before making an application. In some cases, a 'link trustee' is appointed to assist the organisation in preparing the application and who will act in a liaison role with the trust. Completed applications are put before the awards committee in April/May, with final decisions made in June. Application forms are available on the trust's website, either in interactive or printable form.

WHO TO APPLY TO The Clerk, Suite 8C, First Floor, VSC Charity Centre, Royal London House, 22–25 Finsbury Square, London EC2A 1DX *Tel* 020 7920 6465 *email* aset@aset.org.uk *Website* www.aset.org.uk

....

■ Allchurches Trust Ltd

CC NO 263960   **ESTABLISHED** 1972

WHERE FUNDING CAN BE GIVEN UK.

WHO CAN BENEFIT Churches and charitable institutions benefiting Christians.

WHAT IS FUNDED Promotion of the Christian religion and contributions to the funds of other charitable institutions.

WHAT IS NOT FUNDED The trust is unable to support: charities with political associations; national charities; individuals; appeals for running costs and salaries. Applications cannot be considered from the same recipient twice in one year or in two consecutive years.

TYPE OF GRANT Primarily one-off.

RANGE OF GRANTS Usually £100–£5,000.

SAMPLE GRANTS Alton Methodist Church, Hampshire; Saint Peter's Catholic Church, Hinckley, Leicestershire; Memorial Community Church (Baptist), Plaistow, London; Faith 4 Families, Auckland; The Anglican Church of Canada, Diocese of Niagara; St. Andrew's Church, Fulham Fields, London; Selby Abbey, North Yorkshire; Community of the Holy Cross, Rempstone, Leicestershire; The Anglican Church of Canada (Indigenous Ministries), Toronto, Ontario; Prison Fellowship, New Zealand; Sheringham Baptist Church, Norfolk.

FINANCES *Year* 2010 *Income* £19,954,000 *Grants* £8,356,000 *Assets* £383,360,000

TRUSTEES Michael Chamberlain; Rt Revd Nigel Stock; Fraser Hart; Bill Yates; Nick J E Sealy; The Ven. Annette Cooper; William Samuel.

HOW TO APPLY Applications should be submitted in writing using the form available on the website.

WHO TO APPLY TO Rachael Hall, Company Secretary, Beaufort House, Brunswick Road, Gloucester GL1 1JZ *Tel* 01452 873189 *Fax* 01452 423557 *email* atl@ecclesiastical.com *Website* www.allchurches.co.uk

....

■ The H B Allen Charitable Trust

CC NO 802306   **ESTABLISHED** 1985

WHERE FUNDING CAN BE GIVEN Worldwide.

WHO CAN BENEFIT Registered charities in the UK.

WHAT IS FUNDED General charitable purposes including, children and young people, general community, medical research, disability, environment and overseas aid.

WHAT IS NOT FUNDED No grants to individuals, organisations which are not UK-registered charities or gap-year students (even if payable to a registered charity).

TYPE OF GRANT One-off and recurrent up to three years, revenue and capital including core costs.

RANGE OF GRANTS Mainly £5,000–£25,000.

SAMPLE GRANTS Exeter Cathedral – Libraries & Archives (£250,000); Wildlife Conservation Research Unit (£40,000); Deafness Research UK (£35,000); Brain Research Trust (£20,000); the Prince's Trust (£15,000); Fauna & Flora International, Woodlands Hospice and the Inspire Foundation (£10,000 each); Dogs for the Disabled, RSPB, Missing People, St Mungo's and Prospect Burma (£5,000 each); and the Rural Youth Trust (£3,000).

FINANCES *Year* 2010 *Income* £1,105,324 *Grants* £1,048,000 *Assets* £29,651,991

TRUSTEES Helen Ratcliffe; Peter Shone.

HOW TO APPLY In writing to the correspondent: including a copy of the organisation's latest annual report and accounts. Applications should be submitted by post, not email, although enquiries prior to any application can be made by email. Please note the following comments from the trust. 'Applicants should note that, at their main annual meeting (usually in January or February), the trustees consider applications received up to 31 December each year but do not carry them forward. Having regard for the time of year when this meeting takes place, it makes sense for applications to be made as late as possible in the calendar year so that the information they contain is most up to date when the trustees meet. It would be preferable, from all points of view, if applications were made only in the last quarter of the calendar year. Although, preferably not in December. The trustees receive a very substantial number of appeals each year. It is not their practice to acknowledge appeals, and they prefer not to enter into correspondence with applicants other than those to whom grants are being made or from whom further information is required. Only successful applicants are notified of the outcome of their application.'

WHO TO APPLY TO Peter Shone, Homefield, Chidden Holt, Hambledon, Waterlooville, Hampshire PO7 4TG *Tel* 023 9263 2406 *email* mail@hballenct.org.uk *Website* www.hballenct.org.uk

....

■ The Alliance Family Foundation

CC NO 258721   **ESTABLISHED** 1968

WHERE FUNDING CAN BE GIVEN Unrestricted, but mainly UK, with some preference for the Manchester area.

WHO CAN BENEFIT Organisations, particularly Jewish causes, benefiting young people and people disadvantaged by poverty.

WHAT IS FUNDED The relief of poverty and advancement of religion, education and medical knowledge.

RANGE OF GRANTS Up to £50,000.

SAMPLE GRANTS Centre for Special Studies – Israel (£63,500); Jewish Community Secondary School Trust and LR Jiao Research Fund Hammersmith Hospital (£50,000 each); Imperial College Trust and the Centre for the Study of Jewish-Muslim Relations (£25,000 each); and Norwood Ravenswood (£22,000).

FINANCES *Year* 2009–10 *Income* £562,833 *Grants* £515,480 *Assets* £12,902,011

TRUSTEES Lord David Alliance; Hon. Graham Alliance; Hon. Sara Esterkin; Hon. Joshua Alliance.

OTHER INFORMATION £126,000 of the grant total went to individuals.

HOW TO APPLY The trust has previously stated that unsolicited applications will not be responded to.

WHO TO APPLY TO Miss J M Ridgway, Secretary, 12th Floor, Bank House, Charlotte Street, Manchester M1 4ET *Tel* 0161 236 8193 *Fax* 0161 236 4814 *email* jridgway@bluebolt. com

■ Angus Allnatt Charitable Foundation

CC NO 1019793   **ESTABLISHED** 1993
WHERE FUNDING CAN BE GIVEN UK.
WHO CAN BENEFIT Young people.
WHAT IS FUNDED This trust makes grants to organisations which offer opportunities for young musicians aged 13 to 25 or which provide water-based activities for those up to the age of 20.
WHAT IS NOT FUNDED No grants to individuals, and none to organisations which use music primarily for therapeutic or social purposes.
TYPE OF GRANT One-off for specific needs or start-up costs. Funding is available for up to one year.
RANGE OF GRANTS £250–£1,000 with a maximum of £2,000.
FINANCES *Year* 2009–10 *Income* £18,006 *Grants* £37,882
TRUSTEES David Briggs; Rodney Dartnall; Marian Durban; Calton Younger; Andrew Hutchison; Leigh Roll.
HOW TO APPLY In writing to the correspondent. Trustees meet three times a year to consider applications. The trust has no staff and no telephone. Appeals falling outside the guidelines will not be considered.
WHO TO APPLY TO Marian Durban, Trustee, 1 The Court, High Street, Harwell, Oxfordshire OX11 0EY *Tel* 01235 820044

■ The Pat Allsop Charitable Trust

CC NO 1030950   **ESTABLISHED** 1973
WHERE FUNDING CAN BE GIVEN UK.
WHO CAN BENEFIT UK organisations benefiting: children; people in property management; people disadvantaged by poverty; people living in urban areas; refugees; and the victims of famine.
WHAT IS FUNDED Medicine and health; welfare; and education. Particularly concerned with: almshouses; housing associations; hospices; medical studies and research; schools and colleges; special needs education; and emergency care for refugees and people affected by famine. The founder of the trust was a partner in Allsop and Co. Chartered Surveyors, Auctioneers and Property Managers, therefore the trust favours supporting those educational projects and charities which have connections with surveying and property management professions.
WHAT IS NOT FUNDED No grants to individuals.
TYPE OF GRANT One-off, project, research and recurring costs.
RANGE OF GRANTS £100–£5,000. The trustees have a policy of making a small number of major donations (over £2,500) and a larger number of smaller donations.
SAMPLE GRANTS Previously: Duke of Edinburgh's Award, Jewish Care – Minerva Business Lunch (£5,000 each); the Story of Christmas (£3,800);

Cambridge International Land Institute, Geoff Marsh Scholarship Fund and Reading Real Estate Foundation (£2,500 each); Crisis, the Honeypot Charity and the Willow Foundation (£1,000 each); Maggie's Cancer Caring Centre and Scottish Community Charity (£500 each); Race for Life (£250); and Variety Club Children's Charity (£100).
FINANCES *Year* 2009–10 *Income* £24,819 *Grants* £62,931
TRUSTEES J P G Randel; P W E Kerr; W J K Taylor; N W M MacKilligin.
HOW TO APPLY The trust does not accept unsolicited applications.
WHO TO APPLY TO J P G Randel, Trustee, 1 The Sanctuary, London SW1P 3JT *Tel* 020 7222 5381 *email* jrandel@lbmw.com

■ The Almond Trust

CC NO 328583   **ESTABLISHED** 1990
WHERE FUNDING CAN BE GIVEN UK and worldwide.
WHO CAN BENEFIT Mostly individuals or organisations of which the trustees have personal knowledge, particularly those benefiting Christians and evangelists.
WHAT IS FUNDED Support of evangelical Christian projects, Christian evangelism, and advancement of Scripture.
TYPE OF GRANT Largely recurrent.
RANGE OF GRANTS Up to £12,000. The average grant in 2009–10 was £4,586.
SAMPLE GRANTS Lawyers' Christian Fellowship (£12,000 in two grants); St Mary's Warbleton PCC (£10,000); Agape, Haggai Institute, Jews for Jesus and Titus Trust (£5,000 each); Friends International (£3,000); and CVM (£1,500).
FINANCES *Year* 2009–10 *Income* £62,909 *Grants* £105,480 *Assets* £93,621
TRUSTEES Sir Jeremy Cooke; Jonathan Cooke; Lady Cooke.
OTHER INFORMATION The grant total includes five payments totalling £8,800, which were given to individuals.
HOW TO APPLY In writing to the correspondent, but please note that the trust states it rarely responds to uninvited applications.
WHO TO APPLY TO Sir Jeremy Cooke, Trustee, 19 West Square, London SE11 4SN

■ Almondsbury Charity

CC NO 202263   **ESTABLISHED** 1963
WHERE FUNDING CAN BE GIVEN The parish of Almondsbury as it existed in 1892, i.e. Almondsbury, Patchway, Easter Compton and parts of Pilning and Bradley Stoke North.
WHO CAN BENEFIT Church of England; residents and organisations in the beneficial area.
WHAT IS FUNDED Grants are made to maintain and repair churches, to further the religious and charitable work of the Church of England and to support educational requirements and sick and needy residents and organisations within the old parish of Almondsbury.
RANGE OF GRANTS Up to £15,000; grants generally given between £1,000 and £3,500.
SAMPLE GRANTS St Chads Church (£15,000); All Saints Church (£5,800); Patchway Community College (£1,800); Wheatfield Primary School (£1,600); Stoke Lodge Primary School (£1,300); St Peters Hospice (£1,200); Almondsbury C E School (£1,100); and Patchway Festival (£500).
FINANCES *Year* 2010 *Income* £53,208 *Grants* £43,013 *Assets* £1,916,105

TRUSTEES A B Gaydon; I Humphries; K J Beard; L Gray; J A Bamforth; Mrs D Wilson; Revd D Byrne; Revd B Topalian; M C D Kirby; Mrs S M Futon; Mrs J Jones.

OTHER INFORMATION The grant total for 2010 includes the total of £7,200 which was distributed in grants to 20 individuals.

HOW TO APPLY On a form available from the correspondent.

WHO TO APPLY TO A B Gaydon, Secretary, Highbank, 7A The Scop, Almondsbury, Bristol BS32 4DU *Tel* 01454 613424 *email* highbankabg@tiscali.co.uk

---

■ The Altajir Trust

CC NO 284116   **ESTABLISHED** 1982

WHERE FUNDING CAN BE GIVEN UK and Arab or Islamic states.

WHO CAN BENEFIT Individuals and organisations.

WHAT IS FUNDED Support for exhibitions, publications, educational activities and other programmes related to Islamic culture and Muslim-Christian relations. The trust provides scholarships for undergraduates and graduates, mainly from the Arab world, to undertake further studies at approved colleges of higher education within the United Kingdom. Funding may also be given towards the cost of conservation of Islamic artefacts and manuscripts in the United Kingdom, assisting conservation in Muslim countries, and to charitable and academic institutions assisting in rebuilding societies in the Islamic world after conflict.

RANGE OF GRANTS Up to £46,000.

SAMPLE GRANTS University of York – Lectureship (£46,000); British Council – Chevening Scholarships (£38,000); British Museum – Curatorial Summer School (£20,000); St John of Jerusalem Eye Hospital (£12,000); Offscreen Education Programme (£7,500); Council for British Research in the Levant (£5,100); University of Sterling – Scholarships (£2,500); and SOAS (£1,500).

FINANCES *Year* 2010 *Income* £718,635 *Grants* £133,420 *Assets* £398,431

TRUSTEES Prof. Alan Jones, Chair; Prof. Roger Williams; Dr Charles Tripp; Dr Noel Brehony.

OTHER INFORMATION The trust also gave a further £247,422 in student support and £9,084 in support for events and publications.

HOW TO APPLY On a form available from the trust's website. The trustees meet about four times a year. Applications can be submitted at any time but may have to await the next trustees' meeting for a decision. However, they will all be acknowledged when received and an indication of the time frame for a decision will be given. Please note: applications should be printed and signed before being sent to the trust.

WHO TO APPLY TO The Trustees, 11 Elvaston Place, London SW7 5QG *Tel* 020 7581 3522 *Fax* 020 7584 1977 *email* awitrust@tiscali.co.uk *Website* www.altajirtrust.org.uk

---

■ Altamont Ltd

CC NO 273971   **ESTABLISHED** 1977

WHERE FUNDING CAN BE GIVEN Worldwide.

WHO CAN BENEFIT Organisations benefiting Jewish people.

WHAT IS FUNDED Jewish charitable purposes.

FINANCES *Year* 2009–10 *Income* £1,779 *Grants* £60,229

TRUSTEES D Last; H Last; Mrs H Kon; Mrs S Adler; Mrs G Wiesenfeld.

HOW TO APPLY In writing to the correspondent.

WHO TO APPLY TO David Last, Trustee, 18 Green Walk, London NW4 2AJ

■ Alvor Charitable Trust

CC NO 1093890   **ESTABLISHED** 2002

WHERE FUNDING CAN BE GIVEN UK, with a preference for Sussex, Norfolk and north east Scotland.

WHO CAN BENEFIT Charitable organisations.

WHAT IS FUNDED Christian social change and general charitable purposes on a local basis.

WHAT IS NOT FUNDED The trust does not look to support animal charities or medical charities outside of the geographic areas mentioned above.

TYPE OF GRANT The trust tends to support smaller projects where the grant will meet a specific need.

RANGE OF GRANTS £500 upwards. The trust typically makes a few larger donations each year and a number of smaller grants.

SAMPLE GRANTS Previously: Kenward Trust (£50,000 in two grants); Salt Sussex Trading Ltd (£40,000 in four grants); Anne Marie School, Ghana (£35,000); Urban Saints (£33,000); Hymns Ancient and Modern (£30,000 in two grants); Romance Academy (£25,000) World In Need (£20,000); Trussell Trust (£15,000); Release International (£10,000); Brighton FareShare (£5,000 each); Chestnut Tree House (£2,000); and Impact Initiatives (£500).

FINANCES *Year* 2009–10 *Income* £14,734 *Grants* £470,000

TRUSTEES C Wills; Shaena Wills; M Atherton; Fiona Atherton; I Wilkins; Julie Wilkins.

HOW TO APPLY In writing to the correspondent.

WHO TO APPLY TO I Wilkins, Chair, Monks Wood, Tompsets Bank, Forest Row, East Sussex RH18 5LW

■ AM Charitable Trust

CC NO 256283   **ESTABLISHED** 1968

WHERE FUNDING CAN BE GIVEN UK and overseas.

WHO CAN BENEFIT Registered charities; Jewish organisations.

WHAT IS FUNDED General charitable purposes, including medical, welfare, arts and conservation causes.

WHAT IS NOT FUNDED No grants to individuals.

TYPE OF GRANT Certain charities are supported for more than one year, although no commitment is usually given to the recipients.

RANGE OF GRANTS £100–£15,000. Mainly smaller amounts under £500 each to non-Jewish organisations.

SAMPLE GRANTS World Jewish Relief and Youth Aliyah – Child Rescue (£15,000 each); British Technion Society (£12,000); Jerusalem Foundation (£10,000); Friends of Boys Town Jerusalem (£5,000); Cancer Research Campaign (£3,000); British Heart Foundation (£2,000); Blond McIndoe Research Foundation (£1,500); New Marlowe Theatre Development Trust (£1,000); NSPCC (£500); Kent Air Ambulance and Oxford and St George's Jewish Youth (£200 each); and Centrepoint (£100).

FINANCES *Year* 2009–10 *Income* £72,332 *Grants* £95,600 *Assets* £1,828,081

TRUSTEES Kleinwort Benson Trustees Ltd.

HOW TO APPLY 'Donations are decided periodically by the Trustee having regard to the wishes of the Settlor, and unsolicited appeals are considered as well as causes which have already been supported. Only successful applicants are notified of the trustee's decision.'

WHO TO APPLY TO The Administrator, Kleinwort Benson Trustees Ltd, 30 Gresham Street, London EC2V 7PG *Tel* 020 3207 7091

■ Amabrill Limited

CC NO 1078968   **ESTABLISHED** 2000

WHERE FUNDING CAN BE GIVEN UK with a preference for north west London.

WHO CAN BENEFIT Jewish charities.

WHAT IS FUNDED The advancement of education and religious practice in accordance with the teachings of the Orthodox Jewish faith.

SAMPLE GRANTS Previous beneficiaries include: Kahal Chassidim Bobov; YMER; BFON Trust; Beth Hamedrash Elyon Golders Green Ltd; Friends of Shekel Hakodesh Ltd; Friends of Mir and Parsha Ltd; Cosmon Bels Ltd; United Talmudical Academy; British Friends of Mosdos Tchernobel; Mayfair Charities Ltd; Friends of Toldos Avrohom Yitzchok; Achisomoch Aid Company; the Gertner Charitable Trust; and Higher Talmudical Education Ltd.

FINANCES *Year* 2009–10 *Income* £2,174,031 *Grants* £2,336,121 *Assets* £3,760,993

TRUSTEES Charles Lerner; Frances R Lerner; Salamon Noe; Israel Grossnass.

HOW TO APPLY Appeal letters are received from, and personal visits made by representatives of Jewish charitable, religious and educational institutions. These requests are then considered by the trustees and grants are made in accordance with the trustees decisions.

WHO TO APPLY TO Charles Lerner, Trustee, 1 Golder's Manor Drive, London NW11 9HU *Tel* 020 8455 6785

■ The Amalur Foundation Limited

CC NO 1090476   **ESTABLISHED** 2002

WHERE FUNDING CAN BE GIVEN Worldwide.

WHO CAN BENEFIT Charitable organisations.

WHAT IS FUNDED General charitable purposes.

SAMPLE GRANTS Previously: Absolute Return for Kids (£110,000); St Patrick's Catholic Church (£50,000); Prostate Research Campaign UK (£10,000); Brain Tumour Research Campaign (£5,500); Breakthrough Breast Cancer (£3,000); and the Extra Care Charitable Trust (£2,000).

FINANCES *Year* 2009–10 *Income* £0 *Grants* £189,262

TRUSTEES Claudia Garuti; David Way; Michael Giedroyc; Helen Mellor.

HOW TO APPLY We are informed (September 2011) by the correspondent that the charity's income is diminishing and that it does not have a long-term future. While the trustees have funds available, they are pleased to consider applications, though this will not be for a great deal longer. Applications should be made to the correspondent in writing please.

WHO TO APPLY TO David Way, Trustee, Fladgate LLP, 16 Great Queen Street, London WC2B 5DG

■ The Ammco Trust

CC NO 327962   **ESTABLISHED** 1988

WHERE FUNDING CAN BE GIVEN Oxfordshire and adjoining counties.

WHO CAN BENEFIT Small local charities and charitable projects based in the area of benefit.

WHAT IS FUNDED Disability, health, medical, special needs education, ex-services, sport and arts/ heritage.

WHAT IS NOT FUNDED No grants to individuals, students or for research.

TYPE OF GRANT One-off.

RANGE OF GRANTS Usually up to £2,000, except in exceptional circumstances.

SAMPLE GRANTS Previous beneficiaries have included BEWSA, Contact a Family Oxford, DebRA Berkshire, Dorothy House Hospice Care Wiltshire, Live Music Now!, Oxford Children's Hospital Campaign, Pathway Workshop Oxford, Riding for the Disabled Association Abingdon Group and Wellbeing of Women.

FINANCES *Year* 2009–10 *Income* £51,081 *Grants* £83,277

TRUSTEES Esther Lewis; Rowena Vickers; Nicholas Cobbold.

HOW TO APPLY In writing to the correspondent; there are no application forms. Applications are considered at any time. An sae is appreciated.

WHO TO APPLY TO Esther Lewis, Glebe Farm, Hinton Waldrist, Faringdon, Oxfordshire SN7 8RX *Tel* 01865 820269

■ Sir John and Lady Amory's Charitable Trust

CC NO 203970   **ESTABLISHED** 1961

WHERE FUNDING CAN BE GIVEN UK, with a preference for Devon and the South West.

WHO CAN BENEFIT Local organisations, plus a few UK-wide charities.

WHAT IS FUNDED General charitable purposes, including education, health and welfare.

TYPE OF GRANT One-off grants for core or running costs.

RANGE OF GRANTS Up to £8,500. Generally for smaller amounts.

SAMPLE GRANTS National Trust (£8,500); and Exeter Cathedral Third Millennium Campaign (£5,000).

FINANCES *Year* 2009–10 *Income* £394,594 *Grants* £83,506 *Assets* £1,948,765

TRUSTEES Sir Ian Heathcoat Amory; Lady Heathcoat Amory; William Heathcoat Amory.

OTHER INFORMATION The sale and purchase of investments during 2009–10 showed an increase in income (£323,122) and expenditure (£312,262).

HOW TO APPLY In writing to the correspondent.

WHO TO APPLY TO Lady Heathcoat Amory, Trustee, The Island, Lowman Green, Tiverton, Devon EX16 4LA *Tel* 01884 254899

■ Viscount Amory's Charitable Trust

CC NO 204958   **ESTABLISHED** 1962

WHERE FUNDING CAN BE GIVEN UK, primarily in Devon.

WHO CAN BENEFIT Particular favour is given to young adults and older people. Charities benefiting people from different family situations, clergy, ex-service and service people, people with disabilities, people disadvantaged by poverty, homeless people and people living in rural areas are also considered.

WHAT IS FUNDED The income is employed mostly in the field of youth service and elderly people particularly to help a number of charitable objects with which the trust has been associated for a number of years, mostly within the county of Devon, including education and training for children and young people.

Conservation and heritage causes are also considered.

WHAT IS NOT FUNDED No grants to individuals from outside South West England.

TYPE OF GRANT Usually one-off including capital (including building) costs. Grants for up to three years will be considered.

RANGE OF GRANTS £1,000–£80,000; typically for £5,000 or less.

SAMPLE GRANTS Exeter Cathedral School (£15,000); Devon Historic Churches Trust (£5,000) Rona Sailing Trust (£74,000); and The National Trust (£8,000).

FINANCES *Year* 2009–10 *Income* £424,003 *Grants* £309,339 *Assets* £11,895,421

TRUSTEES Sir Ian Heathcoat Amory; Catherine Cavender.

HOW TO APPLY In writing to the correspondent, giving general background information, total costs involved, amount raised so far and details of applications to other organisations.

WHO TO APPLY TO The Trust Secretary, The Island, Lowman Green, Tiverton, Devon EX16 4LA *Tel* 01884 254899

■ The Ampelos Trust

CC NO 1048778   **ESTABLISHED** 1995
WHERE FUNDING CAN BE GIVEN UK.
WHO CAN BENEFIT Registered charities.
WHAT IS FUNDED General charitable purposes.
TYPE OF GRANT Usually one-off.
SAMPLE GRANTS Previous beneficiaries have included: Kids for Kids, Handel House Trust, Chester Zoo, Medical Foundation for the Care of Victims of Torture, Shelter, Stroke Association, Princess Royal Trust for Carers and the Seeing Ear.
FINANCES *Year* 2009–10 *Income* £3,774
TRUSTEES Baroness of Babergh Ruth Rendell; Ann Marie Witt; MMH Trustees Limited.
OTHER INFORMATION The income figure for 2009–10 was unusually low (£192,000 in 2008–09). Grants made during the year totalled around £70,000.
HOW TO APPLY In writing to the correspondent.
WHO TO APPLY TO Ms R A Lomer, Secretary, Menzies LLP, 3rd Floor, Kings House, 12–42 Wood Street, Kingston upon Thames, Surrey KT1 1TG *Tel* 020 8974 7500 *email* kingston@menzies.co.uk

■ The AMW Charitable Trust

SC NO SC006959   **ESTABLISHED** 1974
WHERE FUNDING CAN BE GIVEN Scotland only, with a priority for the West of Scotland.
WHO CAN BENEFIT Charitable organisations.
WHAT IS FUNDED A broad range of activity is supported including those connected with religion, education, culture, poverty, sickness, disability, social welfare and young adults.
WHAT IS NOT FUNDED No grants for individuals, or to organisations outside Scotland.
SAMPLE GRANTS Previous beneficiaries have included the Dixon Community, Girl Guiding School, Kelvingrove Refurb Appeal, Lifeboats of the Cycle Appeal, Friends of Glasgow Humane Society, MND Scotland, Maryhill Parish Church, Aberlour Child Care Trust, Dystonia Society, Glasgow School of Arts, Momentum, Hansel Foundation and Muscular Dystrophy Campaign.
FINANCES *Year* 2010–11 *Income* £121,543 *Grants* £50,000
TRUSTEES Joy Travers; Campbell Denholm; Prof. R B Jack.

HOW TO APPLY In writing to the correspondent. Appeals are not acknowledged and the trust only advises successful applicants.

WHO TO APPLY TO The Trustees, c/o KPMG, 191 West George Street, Glasgow G2 2LJ

■ The Anchor Foundation

CC NO 1082485   **ESTABLISHED** 2000
WHERE FUNDING CAN BE GIVEN UK and occasionally overseas.
WHO CAN BENEFIT Christian charities.
WHAT IS FUNDED Social inclusion, particularly through ministries of healing and the arts. Organisations with a number of projects operating are advised to choose a single project for their application.
WHAT IS NOT FUNDED No grants to individuals.
TYPE OF GRANT Applications for capital and revenue funding are considered. Only in very exceptional circumstances will grants be given for building work. It is not the normal practice of the charity to support the same project for more than three years (projects which have had three years funding may apply again two years from the payment of the last grant).
RANGE OF GRANTS Up to £10,000. Mostly for £5,000 or less.
SAMPLE GRANTS Breakout (£8,000); Greenbank Christian Centre (£7,500); NGM Trust (£7,000); the Bethseda Project – Burundi (£6,400); Good News Family Care (£6,000); Heart to Heart and Malt Cross Trust (£5,000 each); Perth YMCA (£4,500); Unlock – Sheffield, Scripture Union and Scottish Love in Action (£4,000 each); and Disha Asha – India (£2,500).
FINANCES *Year* 2009–10 *Income* £142,896 *Grants* £201,209 *Assets* £5,353,932
TRUSTEES Prudence Thimbleby; Revd Michael Mitton; Revd Robin Anker-Petersen; Nina Anker-Petersen.
HOW TO APPLY An initial application form can be completed online at the Anchor Foundation website. Full guidelines for applicants are also available online. Applications are considered at twice yearly trustee meetings in April and November and need to be received by 31 January and 31 July each year. The foundation regrets that applications cannot be acknowledged. Successful applicants will be notified as soon as possible after trustees' meetings – usually before the end of May or the end of November. Unsuccessful applicants may reapply after twelve months.
WHO TO APPLY TO The Secretary, PO Box 21107, Alloa FK12 5WA *email* secretary@theanchorfoundation.org.uk *Website* www.theanchorfoundation.org.uk

■ The Andrew Anderson Trust

CC NO 212170   **ESTABLISHED** 1954
WHERE FUNDING CAN BE GIVEN UK and overseas.
WHO CAN BENEFIT Organisations benefiting: Christians and evangelists; at risk groups; carers; people with disabilities; people disadvantaged by poverty; socially isolated people; and victims of abuse, crime and domestic violence.
WHAT IS FUNDED Grants to evangelical organisations and churches, small grants to health, disability and social welfare causes.
WHAT IS NOT FUNDED Individuals should not apply for travel or education.
SAMPLE GRANTS Previous beneficiaries have included: Aycliffe Evangelical Church, Christian Medical Fellowship, Concern Worldwide,

Emmanuel Baptist Church – Sidmouth, Fellowship of Independent Evangelical Churches, Good Shepherd Mission, Kenward Trust, Latin Link, Proclamation Trust, Rehoboth Christian Centre – Blackpool, Scientific Exploration Society, St Ebbe's PCC – Oxford, St Helen's Church – Bishopsgate, TNT Ministries, Trinity Baptist Church – Gloucester, Whitefield Christian Trust, Weald Trust and Worldshare.

FINANCES *Year* 2009–10 *Income* £277,945 *Grants* £283,970 *Assets* £9,933,921

TRUSTEES Revd Andrew Robertson Anderson, Chair; Anne Alexander Anderson; Margaret Lillian Anderson.

OTHER INFORMATION The grant total includes £226,060 given to organisations and £57,910 to individuals.

HOW TO APPLY The trust has previously stated that 'we prefer to honour existing commitments and initiate new ones through our own contacts rather than respond to applications'.

WHO TO APPLY TO Revd Andrew Robertson Anderson, Trustee, 1 Cote House Lane, Bristol BS9 3UW *Tel* 0117 962 1588

■ Andor Charitable Trust

CC NO 1083572   **ESTABLISHED** 2000

WHERE FUNDING CAN BE GIVEN UK and overseas.

WHO CAN BENEFIT Charitable organisations.

WHAT IS FUNDED Health, arts, Jewish and general charitable purposes.

RANGE OF GRANTS Mostly £2,000–£5,000.

SAMPLE GRANTS National Hospital for Neurology and Neurosurgery (£10,000); the Chicken Shed Theatre Trust (£7,500 in two grants); Macmillan Cancer Support and Médecins Sans Frontières – UK (£5,000 each); Rix Thompson Rothenberg Foundation (£4,000); Cystic Fibrosis Trust and Live Music Now Limited (£3,000 each); and Young Music Makers, Shape London, Riders for Health and Council for Music in Hospitals (£2,000 each).

FINANCES *Year* 2009–10 *Income* £87,775 *Grants* £90,500 *Assets* £3,180,598

TRUSTEES David Rothenberg; Nicholas Lederer; Dr Donald Dean; Jeanne Szego.

HOW TO APPLY In writing to the correspondent.

WHO TO APPLY TO David Rothenberg, Trustee, c/o Blick Rothenberg, 12 York Gate, Regent's Park, London NW1 4QS *Tel* 020 7486 0111

■ The André Christian Trust

CC NO 248466   **ESTABLISHED** 1950

WHERE FUNDING CAN BE GIVEN UK.

WHO CAN BENEFIT Christian organisations.

WHAT IS FUNDED Charities specified in the trust deed; advancement of the Christian religion.

SAMPLE GRANTS Open Air Campaigners (West Country) (£11,000); Exeter Community Family Trust (£8,000); Care for the Family and SIFT (£5,000 each); and Bible Society, Karis Kids, Life Words and Open Doors Exmouth (£1,000 each).

FINANCES *Year* 2010 *Income* £49,252 *Grants* £54,600 *Assets* £1,169,556

TRUSTEES Andrew K Mowll; Stephen Daykin.

HOW TO APPLY In writing to the correspondent. However, the trust states: 'Applications are discouraged since grants are principally made to those organisations which are listed in the trust deed.' Funds are therefore fully committed and unsolicited requests cannot be supported.

WHO TO APPLY TO Andrew K Mowll, Trustee, 2 Clevedon Close, Exeter EX4 6HQ *Tel* 01392 258681

■ The Henry Angest Foundation

CC NO 1114761   **ESTABLISHED** 2006

WHERE FUNDING CAN BE GIVEN UK and overseas.

WHO CAN BENEFIT Charitable organisations.

WHAT IS FUNDED General charitable purposes.

SAMPLE GRANTS Previously: Perth College Development Trust (£80,000); World Pheasant Association (£6,000); Bowel and Cancer Research, British Olympic Association, the R D Crusaders Foundation and East Midlands Zoological Society (£5,000 each); Cancer Research UK (£2,000); the Salvation Army (£1,000); and Botanic Foundation, PACT, Scottish Ballet and Wycombe Abbey School Foundation (£500).

FINANCES *Year* 2010 *Income* £0 *Grants* £13,039

TRUSTEES H Angest; D Angest.

OTHER INFORMATION The charity had no income in the accounting year 2010, however, so far it remains on the Central Register of Charities and its income may increase in the future.

HOW TO APPLY In writing to the correspondent.

WHO TO APPLY TO The Trustees, Arbuthnot House, 20 Ropemaker Street, London EC2Y 9AR *Tel* 020 7012 2400

■ Anglo American Group Foundation

CC NO 1111719   **ESTABLISHED** 2005

WHERE FUNDING CAN BE GIVEN Worldwide.

WHO CAN BENEFIT Charitable organisations.

WHAT IS FUNDED Education, international development, health/HIV, environment and London-based community development.

WHAT IS NOT FUNDED Organisations which are not registered charities.

RANGE OF GRANTS £20,000–£103,000 plus £80,000 in grants under £20,000.

SAMPLE GRANTS Science for Humanity (£50,000); Plan International (£103,352); Engineers without borders (£50,000); Canning House (£21,000); The Terrence Higgins Trust (£26,397); Dyslexia Action (£35,000); Leonard Cheshire Disability (£88,500); Children of the Andes (£50,000); The Prince's Trust (£23,015); British Council (Chevening Scholars) (£50,000).

FINANCES *Year* 2010 *Income* £905,675 *Grants* £953,079 *Assets* £140,544

TRUSTEES Nick Jordan; Chris Corrin; Angela Bromfield; Ian Botha; Duncan Wanblad; Jonathan Samuel; David Weston.

OTHER INFORMATION Established by Anglo American plc who make donations to the foundation from its annual pre-tax profits.

HOW TO APPLY Beneficiary groups, who are registered charities, are requested to complete a rigorous application and frequently present to the board in order to gain funding for their organisation. Charities should contact the trust directly to discuss an application. Trustees meet quarterly to consider applications for funding from bona fide charities whose objectives match those of the foundation. A working party, made up of two members of Anglo American plc staff, consider the applications and puts forward proposals to the trustees.

WHO TO APPLY TO Catherine Mason, 20 Carlton House Terrace, London SW1Y 5AN *Tel* 020 7968 8627 *email* aagf@cht20.co.uk *Website* www.angloamericangroupfoundation.org

■ Anguish's Educational Foundation

CC NO 311288   **ESTABLISHED** 1605

WHERE FUNDING CAN BE GIVEN Norwich and the parishes of Costessey, Hellesdon, Catton, Sprowston, Thorpe St Andrews and Corpusty.

WHO CAN BENEFIT Residents of the area of benefit under the age of 25.

WHAT IS FUNDED School clothing, school trips, books/equipment, sports and musical training, grants for fees/maintenance at university/ tertiary education.

SAMPLE GRANTS The Hamlet Centre Trust (£15,000); Clover Hill Infant and Nursery School (£12,000); CAST Education (£10,000); Asperger East Anglia (£7,500); Africa Health Organisation (£1,700); Norfolk and Norwich Music Club and Catton Grove Primary School (£1,000 each) and Cherman Trust (£800).

FINANCES *Year* 2010–11 *Income* £646,340 *Grants* £371,785 *Assets* £17,716,317

TRUSTEES Brenda Arthur; Roy Blower; Philip Blanchflower; Iain Brooksby; David Fullman; Heather Tyrrell; Geoffrey Loades; Pamela Scutter; Jeanne Southgate; Brenda Ferris; Jeffrey Hooke; Amy Stammers.

OTHER INFORMATION In 2010–11, grants were given mainly to individuals (£322,000). A total of £50,000 was given to organisations.

HOW TO APPLY In writing to the correspondent. Applications from other charities are considered at two meetings in a year. Applications from individuals are considered at seven meetings throughout the year. Individuals are usually invited to the office for an informal interview.

WHO TO APPLY TO David Walker, Clerk to the Trustees, 1 Woolgate Court, St Benedicts Street, Norwich NR2 4AP *Tel* 01603 621023 *email* david.walker@norwichcharitabletrusts.org. uk

■ The Animal Defence Trust

CC NO 263095   **ESTABLISHED** 1971

WHERE FUNDING CAN BE GIVEN UK.

WHO CAN BENEFIT UK organisations benefiting animals.

WHAT IS FUNDED Capital projects for animal welfare/ protection.

WHAT IS NOT FUNDED No grants to individuals.

TYPE OF GRANT Usually one-off payments.

SAMPLE GRANTS Brooke Hospital, Care4Cats, Ferne Animal Sanctuary and Worldwide Veterinary Service (£3,000 each); Animals in Distress, Barn Owl Trust, Bedfordshire Wildlife Rescue, Berwick Animal Rescue, The Cat and Rabbit Centre, Cat Register and Rescue, Compassion in World Farming, Haworth Cat Rescue, International Otter Survival Fund, Plantation Dog Rescue, Tia Greyhound and Lurcher Rescue and Yorkshire Swan and Wildlife Rescue (£1,500 each); and Lagos Animal Protection (£1,000).

FINANCES *Year* 2009–10 *Income* £44,369 *Grants* £78,885 *Assets* £1,367,241

TRUSTEES Marion Saunders; Carole Bowles; Richard J Vines; Jenny Wheadon.

HOW TO APPLY On a form which can be downloaded from the trust's website. Application must be returned by post to: PO Box 44, Plymouth, PL7 5YW.

WHO TO APPLY TO Alan A Meyer, Secretary, Horsey Lightly Fynn, Devon House, 12–15 Dartmouth Street, Queen Anne's Gate, London SW1H 9BL *Tel* 020 7222 8844 *email* ameyer@ horseylightly.com *Website* www. animaldefencetrust.org

■ The Eric Anker-Petersen Charity

CC NO 1061428   **ESTABLISHED** 1997

WHERE FUNDING CAN BE GIVEN UK.

WHO CAN BENEFIT Charitable causes in the fields of screen and stage.

WHAT IS FUNDED Grants are made towards the conservation of classic films.

WHAT IS NOT FUNDED No grants to individuals or for non-charitable purposes.

SAMPLE GRANTS Previous grants were made to Theatrical Ladies Guild, and Imperial War Museum for the following films: *The British Atomic Trials at Maralinga*, *Everybody's Business*, *The Women's Portion* and for the book: *This Film is Dangerous*.

FINANCES *Year* 2009–10 *Income* £15,373

TRUSTEES George Lindsay Duncan; Shan Warnock-Smith; David Eric Long.

HOW TO APPLY In writing to the correspondent. The trust has previously wished to emphasise that it is always looking for projects to support which meet its criteria, outlined above.

WHO TO APPLY TO D E Long, Trustee, 8–10 New Fetter Lane, London EC4A 1RS *Tel* 020 2703 5096

■ The Annandale Charitable Trust

CC NO 1049193   **ESTABLISHED** 1995

WHERE FUNDING CAN BE GIVEN UK.

WHO CAN BENEFIT Major charities.

WHAT IS FUNDED General charitable purposes.

SAMPLE GRANTS Mayhaw Animal Home, Seeability, Rushmoor Healthy Living, Chestnut Tree House Children's Hospice and Brain and Spine Foundation (£5,000 each); British Red Cross, Headway, NSPCC, Redwings Horse Sanctuary and Victim Support (£4,300 each); and Unicef Gaza Children's Appeal, Unicef Sri Lanka Children's Appeal and Unicef Sudan Children's Appeal (£3,000 each).

FINANCES *Year* 2009–10 *Income* £253,717 *Grants* £234,600 *Assets* £10,503,063

TRUSTEES Carole Duggan; HSBC Trust Company (UK) Ltd.

HOW TO APPLY In writing to the correspondent. The trust has previously stated that it has an ongoing programme of funding for specific charities and all its funds are fully committed.

WHO TO APPLY TO The Trust Manager, HSBC Trust Services, 10th Floor, Norwich House, Nelson Gate, Commercial Road, Southampton SO15 1GX *Tel* 02380 722248

■ The Anson Charitable Trust

CC NO 1111010   **ESTABLISHED** 2005

WHERE FUNDING CAN BE GIVEN UK.

WHO CAN BENEFIT Charitable organisations and individuals.

WHAT IS FUNDED General charitable purposes, there is a preference for work with children and older people. Health and medical research causes are also widely supported.

RANGE OF GRANTS £200–£16,000.

SAMPLE GRANTS Prostate Cancer (£16,000); Norfolk Hospice (£10,000); Royal Opera House (£9,500); Southbank (£8,000); ABF The Soldiers' Charity (£6,000); Buckinghamshire Agricultural Association, British Red Cross and Children in Need (£5,000 each); Living Paintings (£3,600); Oundle School Foundation (£3,500); Alzheimer's Trust, Mission to Seafarers and Anthony Nolan Trust (£3,000 each); Prince's Trust (£2,500); Starlight Children and Braille Chess Association (£2,000 each); Build Africa and Watts Gallery (£1,000 each); Water Aid (£600); and Capellania Anglica (£200).

FINANCES *Year* 2009–10 *Income* £335,385 *Grants* £308,084 *Assets* £26,824

TRUSTEES George Anson; Kirsty Anson; Peter Nichols.

HOW TO APPLY In writing to the correspondent.

WHO TO APPLY TO George Anson, Trustee, The Lilies, High Street, Weedon, Aylesbury, Buckinghamshire HP22 4NS *email* lilies@btinternet.com

---

■ The Apax Foundation

CC NO 1112845   **ESTABLISHED** 2006

WHERE FUNDING CAN BE GIVEN UK and overseas.

WHO CAN BENEFIT Charitable organisations.

WHAT IS FUNDED Relief in need and education.

RANGE OF GRANTS Up to £300,000. In 2009–10, donations of £10,000 or less totalled £124,000.

SAMPLE GRANTS Grameen America (£289,000); Private Equity Foundation (£181,000); Business in Community (£127,000); Enterprise Education Trust (£50,000); Leader Quest Foundation (£30,000); Shivia Microfinance (£20,000); Crisis UK (£13,000); and National Gallery Trust (£12,000).

FINANCES *Year* 2009–10 *Income* £3,355,521 *Grants* £922,417 *Assets* £12,226,670

TRUSTEES Sir Ronald Cohen, Chair; Peter Englander; Martin Halusa; Khawar Mann; David Marks; John Megrue; Michael Phillips; Richard Wilson.

OTHER INFORMATION 'The Apax Foundation is the formal channel for Apax Partners' charitable giving and receives a percentage of the firm's profits and carried interest.'

HOW TO APPLY 'Organisations which the trustees identify as potentially suitable recipients of grants are invited to submit funding proposals, which are reviewed by the trustees.' The trustees meet quarterly to review donations and grants.

WHO TO APPLY TO David Marks, Trustee, 33 Jermyn Street, London SW1Y 6DN *Tel* 020 7872 6300 *email* foundation@apax.com

---

■ Ambrose and Ann Appelbe Trust

CC NO 208658   **ESTABLISHED** 1944

WHERE FUNDING CAN BE GIVEN UK.

WHO CAN BENEFIT Organisations benefiting students and research workers and individuals.

WHAT IS FUNDED Education and training, especially postgraduate education (bursaries and fees), literacy, professional or specialist training; general charitable purposes.

WHAT IS NOT FUNDED Buildings are not funded. No funding to for sponsorship with Operation Raleigh, the Project Trust or similar establishments, for medical electives, for school children or for theatrical training.

RANGE OF GRANTS Up to £3,000.

SAMPLE GRANTS Previous beneficiaries have included: Anatomical Donors Association

(£7,000); the Firbank Charitable Trust (£5,500); Orchestra of the Age of Enlightenment (£3,000); Godshill Trust (£2,800); Soil Association (£2,500); WPF (£1,500); National Youth Orchestra, Peterhouse Development Fund, St Gabriel's School Foundation, Tommy's and Zanzibar Aid Project (£1,000 each); Camphill St Albans, the Project Trust and RNLI (£500 each); Southbank Sinfonia (£500 each); and Wesdnesday's Child (£250).

FINANCES *Year* 2010–11 *Income* £28,602 *Grants* £27,050 *Assets* £808,160

TRUSTEES Valentine Thomas; Felix Appelbe; Lucy Hobby; Alexander Appelbe.

HOW TO APPLY In writing to the correspondent, enclosing an sae. Individuals should apply through their college/university.

WHO TO APPLY TO Felix Appelbe, Trustee, Ambrose Appelbe Solicitors, Lincoln's Inn, 7 New Square, London WC2A 3RA

■ The Appletree Trust

SC NO SC004851   **ESTABLISHED** 1982

WHERE FUNDING CAN BE GIVEN UK and overseas, with a preference for Scotland and the north east Fife district.

WHO CAN BENEFIT Charitable organisations.

WHAT IS FUNDED Disability, sickness and poverty causes.

WHAT IS NOT FUNDED No grants to individuals.

TYPE OF GRANT Capital, buildings, project, research. Grants can be for up to two years.

SAMPLE GRANTS Previous grant beneficiaries included: 1st St Andrews Boys' Brigade, Alzheimer Scotland, Arthritis Care In Scotland, the Broomhouse Centre, Children's Hospice Association, Discovery Camps Trust, Home Start East Fife, Marie Curie Cancer Care, PDSA, Prince and Princess of Wales Hospice, RNID, the Salvation Army, Scottish Motor Neurone Disease Association and Scottish Spina Bifida Association.

FINANCES *Year* 2009–10 *Income* £26,716

TRUSTEES The Royal Bank of Scotland plc; Revd W McKane; Revd Dr J D Martin; Revd L R Brown.

HOW TO APPLY In writing to the correspondent. Trustees meet to consider grants in April.

WHO TO APPLY TO Administrator, The Royal Bank of Scotland plc, Trust and Estate Services, Eden Lakeside, Chester Business Park, Wrexham Road, Chester, CH4 9QT

■ The John Apthorp Charitable Trust

CC NO 289713   **ESTABLISHED** 1983

WHERE FUNDING CAN BE GIVEN UK, with a preference for Radlett.

WHO CAN BENEFIT Charitable organisations.

WHAT IS FUNDED General charitable purposes.

RANGE OF GRANTS Typically up to £5,000.

SAMPLE GRANTS Tay Ghillies Association (£55,000); Radlett Choral Society (£7,000); RAFT (£6,000); Radlett Cricket Club, St Mary's Church Trefriw Organ Fund and Battersby Junction Residents (£5,000 each) and The Radlett Society and Green Belt Association (£1,000).

FINANCES *Year* 2009–10 *Income* £64 *Grants* £57,691

TRUSTEES John Apthorp; Justin Apthorp.

HOW TO APPLY Unsolicited appeals are not welcome and will not be answered. The trustees carry out their own research into prospective grant areas.

WHO TO APPLY TO Paul Shaw, c/o Myers Clark, Iveco House, Station Road, Watford WD17 1DL

■ The Arbib Foundation

CC NO 296358   ESTABLISHED 1987
WHERE FUNDING CAN BE GIVEN Unrestricted.
WHO CAN BENEFIT Registered charities and local organisations with charitable purposes.
WHAT IS FUNDED In particular to establish and maintain a River and Rowing Museum in the Thames Valley for the education of the general public in the history, geography and ecology of the Thames Valley and the River Thames, with some donations for general purposes.
WHAT IS NOT FUNDED No grants to individuals.
TYPE OF GRANT Recurrent and single donations.
RANGE OF GRANTS £100–£125,000.
SAMPLE GRANTS Sheffield Institute Foundation for MND (£125,000); Institute of Cancer Research and the River and Rowing Museum Foundation (£100,000 each); and Barbados Community Foundation and Ramsbury Recreational Centre (£50,000 each); Black Watch Museum (£20,000); Royal Opera House Trust (£11,400 in total); Henley Festival and the Royal Horticultural Society (£5,000 each); Wiltshire Wildlife Trust (£3,000); and Tavistock Trust for Aphasia and Henley and District Agricultural Association (£1,000 each).
FINANCES *Year* 2009–10 *Income* £500,185 *Grants* £495,009 *Assets* £98,994
TRUSTEES Sir Martyn Arbib; Lady Arbib; Mrs A Nicoll.
HOW TO APPLY Please note: the trust has previously stated that unsolicited applications are not being considered as funds are fully committed for the 'foreseeable future'.
WHO TO APPLY TO Carol O'Neill, The Old Rectory, 17 Thameside, Henley-on-Thames, Oxfordshire RG9 1BH *Tel* 01491 848890

■ Archbishop of Wales' Fund for Children

CC NO 1102236   ESTABLISHED 2004
WHERE FUNDING CAN BE GIVEN Wales.
WHO CAN BENEFIT Children in need and their families and local communities.
WHAT IS FUNDED The work of organisations in this order of priority: (1) those in the Dioceses of the Church in Wales; (2) those associated with other Christian bodies which are members of Cytun – Churches Together in Wales; (3) other organisations working with children in Wales.
SAMPLE GRANTS Previous beneficiaries have included: the Bridge Mentoring Plus Scheme; Cardiff People First; Family Awareness Drug and Support; MENFA; Pontllanfraith, Brecon, Aberdare and Merthyr Tydfil Contact Centres; and Valley Kids. A number of church-based projects were also supported.
FINANCES *Year* 2009 *Income* £53,844 *Grants* £40,595 *Assets* £99,925
TRUSTEES Revd J Michael Williams, Chair; Cheryl Beach; Ruth Forrester; Caroline Owen; James Tovey.
OTHER INFORMATION Accounts were available from the Charity Commission but without a list of grants.
HOW TO APPLY Application forms are available from the correspondent.
WHO TO APPLY TO Karen Phillips, Administrator, Church in Wales, 39 Cathedral Road, Cardiff CF11 9WH *Tel* 029 2034 8234 *email* awfc@churchinwales.org.uk

■ The John M Archer Charitable Trust

SC NO SC010583   ESTABLISHED 1969
WHERE FUNDING CAN BE GIVEN UK and overseas.
WHO CAN BENEFIT Registered charities.
WHAT IS FUNDED General charitable purposes, including: the prevention or relief of individuals in need; welfare of people who are sick or distressed; alleviation of need; advancement of education; advancement of religious or missionary work; advancement of scientific research and discovery; and preservation of Scottish heritage and the advancement of associated cultural activities.
SAMPLE GRANTS Previous beneficiaries have included Cambodian Hospital Siem Reap for Children, the Canonmills Baptist Church, Castlebrae School Tutoring Programme, Erskine Stewarts Melville College – Arts Centre, Mercy Corps Scotland, the Bobby Moore Fund, Red Cross – Aberdeen Guest House and Royal Liverpool University Hospital – Macular Degeneration Research.
FINANCES *Year* 2009–10 *Income* £49,000 *Grants* £90,000
TRUSTEES Gilbert B Archer; Mrs A Morgan; Mrs W Grant; Mrs C Fraser; Mrs I C Smith.
OTHER INFORMATION The grant total is an approximate yearly figure.
HOW TO APPLY In writing to the correspondent.
WHO TO APPLY TO Mrs W Grant, Secretary, 10 Broughton Place, Edinburgh EH1 3RS

■ The Archer Trust

CC NO 1033534   ESTABLISHED 1994
WHERE FUNDING CAN BE GIVEN Worldwide.
WHO CAN BENEFIT Voluntary organisations, especially those which make good use of volunteers or are located in areas of high unemployment or disadvantage. Preference is given to smaller organisations. Support is given to projects both in the UK and overseas, but for overseas projects only via UK charities.
WHAT IS FUNDED Provision of aid and support to a defined group of needy or deserving people, such as people with mental disabilities or people who are otherwise disadvantaged; Christian causes.
WHAT IS NOT FUNDED No grants are made to individuals (including for gap years), conservation or heritage projects, environmental causes, disability access or animal charities.
RANGE OF GRANTS Usually £250–£3,000.
SAMPLE GRANTS Hertford Regional College (£4,000); International Refugee Trust, Lilias Graham Trust and Sycamore Project (£3,000 each); Paul D'Auria Cancer Resource Centre, the Simon Paul Foundation and Slough Homeless Our Concern (£2,000 each); Christians Against Poverty and Willowfield Parish Community Association (£1,500 each); Archway Project, the Barnabus Trust and Merseyside Youth Challenge Trust (£1,000 each); and Nightstop Teesside, Supporting Dalit Children and Living Hope (£500 each).
FINANCES *Year* 2009–10 *Income* £236,486 *Grants* £61,405 *Assets* £1,528,498
TRUSTEES Mrs C M Archer; M F Baker; J N Archer; F D R MacDougall.
HOW TO APPLY In writing to the correspondent. Unsuccessful applicants will not receive a response, even if an sae is enclosed. Applications are considered twice a year, usually in March and September.

Think carefully about every application. Is it justified?

341

WHO TO APPLY TO The Secretary, Bourne House, Wadesmill, Ware, Hertfordshire SG12 0TT *Website* www.archertrust.org.uk

■ The Architectural Heritage Fund

CC NO 266780　　　　ESTABLISHED 1973

WHERE FUNDING CAN BE GIVEN UK (excluding the Channel Islands and the Isle of Man).

WHO CAN BENEFIT Registered charities only.

WHAT IS FUNDED Support is given in the form of grants, loans, advice and information for the preservation and sustainable re-use of historic buildings.

WHAT IS NOT FUNDED Applications from private individuals and non-charitable organisations. Applications for projects not involving a change of ownership or of use, or for a building not on a statutory list or in a conservation area.

TYPE OF GRANT Loans; feasibility study grants; project administration grants; project organiser grants; refundable project development grants.

RANGE OF GRANTS Grants up to £20,000; loans up to £500,000 (more in exceptional circumstances).

SAMPLE GRANTS Projects supported included those initiated by: Highland Buildings Preservation Trust; Glasgow Building Preservation Trust; Heritage of London Operations Limited; Heritage Trust for the North West; Manchester Historic Buildings Trust; The Vivat Trust; West Midlands Historic Buildings Trust; Cadwgan Building Preservation Trust; and The Strawberry Hill Trust.

FINANCES *Year* 2009–10　*Income* £776,277　*Grants* £572,608　*Assets* £13,086,172

TRUSTEES Colin Amery; Malcolm Crowder; Roy Dantzic; Fionnuala Jay-O'Boyle; George McNeill; John Pavitt; Merlin Waterson; Thomas Lloyd; Liz Davidson; John Townsend; Michael Hoare; John Duggan.

OTHER INFORMATION In addition to the amount given in grants, £25,000 was given in loans.

HOW TO APPLY Detailed notes for applicants for loans and feasibility studies are supplied with the application forms, all of which are available from the fund's website. The trustees meet in March, June, September and December; applications must be received six weeks before meetings.

WHO TO APPLY TO Barbara Wright, Loans and Grants Manager, Alhambra House, 27–31 Charing Cross Road, London WC2H 0AU　*Tel* 020 7925 0199　*Fax* 020 7930 0295　*email* ahf@ahfund. org.uk　*Website* www.ahfund.org.uk

■ The Ardeola Charitable Trust

CC NO 1124380　　　　ESTABLISHED 2008

WHERE FUNDING CAN BE GIVEN Worldwide.

WHO CAN BENEFIT Registered charities.

WHAT IS FUNDED General charitable purposes, although the main beneficiary each year is Target Ovarian Cancer.

SAMPLE GRANTS Target Ovarian Cancer (£595,000); Non-Profit Enterprise and Self-Sustainability Team (NESST Inc) (£54,500); and RedR UK (£3,000).

FINANCES *Year* 2009–10　*Income* £1,927,400　*Grants* £652,464　*Assets* £3,089,140

TRUSTEES Graham Barker; Joanna Barker; Coutts & Co.

HOW TO APPLY In writing to the correspondent.

WHO TO APPLY TO The Trustees, Coutts & Co, Trustee Dept., 440 Strand, London WC2R 0QS　*Tel* 020 7753 1000

■ The Ardwick Trust

CC NO 266981　　　　ESTABLISHED 1975

WHERE FUNDING CAN BE GIVEN UK, Israel and the developing world.

WHO CAN BENEFIT Institutions and registered charities (mainly UK charities) benefiting people of all ages, students and Jews.

WHAT IS FUNDED To support Jewish welfare, along with a wide range of non-Jewish causes to include social welfare, health, education (especially special schools), elderly people, conservation and the environment, child welfare, disability and medical research. In general most of the largest grants go to Jewish organisations, with most of the smaller grants to non-Jewish organisations.

WHAT IS NOT FUNDED No grants to individuals.

TYPE OF GRANT One-off or recurrent grants up to two years. Capital, including buildings, research and start-up costs.

RANGE OF GRANTS Mostly for £500, £200 or £100 each.

SAMPLE GRANTS British Friends of the Hebrew University – Jerusalem, British Technion Society, Jewish Care, UJIA, Weizmann UK and World Jewish Relief (£1,000 each); Cheltenham Ladies' College – bursaries fund, Community Security Trust, Council of Christians and Jews, Headway, Magen David Adorn UK and Shaare Zedek UK (£500); Book Aid International, Food Lifeline, Help the Aged and WellChild (£200 each); and Allergy UK, Mind and Shelter (£100 each).

FINANCES *Year* 2009–10　*Income* £565,605　*Grants* £51,093　*Assets* £2,063,735

TRUSTEES Janet Bloch; Dominic Flynn; Miss Judith Portrait.

HOW TO APPLY In writing to the correspondent.

WHO TO APPLY TO Janet Bloch, Trustee, c/o Knox Cropper, 24 Petworth Road, Haslemere, Surrey GU27 2HR　*Tel* 01428 652788

■ The Argentarius Foundation

CC NO 1079980　　　　ESTABLISHED 2000

WHERE FUNDING CAN BE GIVEN UK.

WHO CAN BENEFIT Charitable organisations.

WHAT IS FUNDED General charitable purposes.

FINANCES *Year* 2009–10　*Income* £20,053　*Grants* £109,194

TRUSTEES Emma Marbach; Judy Jackson; Anna Josse.

OTHER INFORMATION Basic information taken from the Charity Commission website.

HOW TO APPLY In writing to the correspondent.

WHO TO APPLY TO Philip Goodman, Goodman & Co, 14 Basing Hill, London NW11 8TH　*Tel* 020 8458 0955　*email* philip@goodmanandco.com

■ The Argus Appeal

CC NO 1013647　　　　ESTABLISHED 1990

WHERE FUNDING CAN BE GIVEN Sussex.

WHO CAN BENEFIT Local organisations.

WHAT IS FUNDED General charitable purposes.

SAMPLE GRANTS Off the Fence – to help the homeless and The Martletts Hospice (£5,000 each). £33,000 was shared between 33 smaller charities and community organisations.

FINANCES *Year* 2009　*Income* £296,177　*Grants* £76,460　*Assets* £220,805

TRUSTEES Ian Hunter; Sue Meheux; Lee Gibbs; Elsa Gillio; David Goldin; Roger French; Julien Boast; Michael Beard; Sue Addis.

OTHER INFORMATION The grant total in 2009 included £33,000 distributed to individuals.

HOW TO APPLY In writing to the correspondent.

WHO TO APPLY TO Elsa Gillio, Trustee, Argus House, Crowhurst Road, Hollingbury, Brighton BN1 8AR *Tel* 01273 544465 *email* elsa.gillio@theargus.co.uk

■ Armenian General Benevolent Union London Trust

CC NO 282070   **ESTABLISHED** 1981

WHERE FUNDING CAN BE GIVEN UK and overseas.

WHO CAN BENEFIT Armenian individuals and organisations.

WHAT IS FUNDED The purpose of the trust is to advance education among Armenians, particularly those in the UK, and to promote the study of Armenian history, literature, language, culture and religion.

WHAT IS NOT FUNDED No support for projects of a commercial nature.

SAMPLE GRANTS Armenian General Benevolent Union – London Branch (£10,000); Royal Geographical Society of Armenia (£2,300); the Armenian Community and Church Council of Great Britain (£500).

FINANCES *Year* 2009 *Income* £218,541 *Grants* £60,985 *Assets* £3,487,530

TRUSTEES Dr Berge Azadian; Berge Setrakian; Hampar Chakardjian; Aris Atamian; Mrs Annie Kouyoumdjian; Mrs Noushig Yakoubian Setrakian; Assadour Guzelian; Mrs Anahid Manoukian; Mrs Arline Medazoumian; Haig Messerlian; Ms Armine Afrikian.

OTHER INFORMATION The grant total in 2009 included £46,000 given in 21 student loans and grants.

HOW TO APPLY In writing to the correspondent. Applications are considered all year round.

WHO TO APPLY TO The Chair of the Trustees, 51c Parkside, Wimbledon Common, London SW19 5NE

■ The Armenian Relief Society of Great Britain Trust

CC NO 327389   **ESTABLISHED** 1987

WHERE FUNDING CAN BE GIVEN Worldwide.

WHO CAN BENEFIT Individuals and organisations.

WHAT IS FUNDED Welfare of Armenians.

SAMPLE GRANTS Navasardian Charity Trust (£20,000); Armenian Relief Society Inc USA (£19,000); Armenian Scouting Association and Hamazkayin (£2,700 each); Aid Kashatagh (£750); Armenian National Committee (£500); Armenian Community Church Council (£450); Armenian Language Studies (£200); and Armenian Medical Association and British Red Cross (£100 each).

FINANCES *Year* 2009–10 *Income* £58,376 *Grants* £47,504 *Assets* £60,899

TRUSTEES Matilda Megerdichian; Arshalouys Babayan; Sonig Jogaghayan; Rubina Boghosian; Silva Beshirian; Mariette Nazloomian; Heghine Bedrossian.

HOW TO APPLY In writing to the correspondent.

WHO TO APPLY TO Matilda Megerdichian, Trustee, 180 Great West Road, Hounslow TW5 9AR

■ The John Armitage Charitable Trust

CC NO 1079688   **ESTABLISHED** 2000

WHERE FUNDING CAN BE GIVEN England and Wales.

WHO CAN BENEFIT Institutions and registered charities.

WHAT IS FUNDED Medical, relief-in-need, education, religion.

SAMPLE GRANTS Royal Marsden Cancer Campaign and the Wallace Collection (£100,000 each); Marie Curie Cancer Care (£72,000); Hop Skip Jump and the Russian Revival Project (£60,000 each); Bibury Community Trust, Farmor's School, Hartlepool & District Hospice and the Youth Sport Trust (£36,000 each); Amos Trust (£30,000); Bilbury School (£27,000); Juvenile Diabetes Research Foundation (£20,000); Westmonasterium Trust (£15,000); and the Foundation of Prince William & Prince Harry (£6,000).

FINANCES *Year* 2009–10 *Income* £4,059 *Grants* £1,203,667 *Assets* £37,647,768

TRUSTEES John C Armitage; Catherine Armitage; William Francklin.

HOW TO APPLY Applications received by the trust are 'reviewed by the trustees and grants awarded at their discretion'.

WHO TO APPLY TO The Trustees, c/o Sampson West, 34 Ely Place, London EC1N 6TD *Tel* 020 7404 5040 *Fax* 020 7831 1098 *email* finance@sampsonwest.co.uk

■ The Armourers' and Brasiers' Gauntlet Trust

CC NO 279204   **ESTABLISHED** 1979

WHERE FUNDING CAN BE GIVEN UK, with some preference for London.

WHO CAN BENEFIT Charitable organisations.

WHAT IS FUNDED The objectives of the trust are: support for education and research in materials science and technology and for basic science in schools; encouragement of the understanding and preservation of historic armour; encouragement of the armourers' trade in the armed services; encouragement of professional excellence in the training of young officers in the Royal Armoured Corps. It also considers appeals in the following overall categories: (i) community, social care and armed forces; (ii) children, youth and general education; medical and health; (iii) art, arms and armour; and (iv) Christian mission.

WHAT IS NOT FUNDED In general grants are not made to: organisations or groups which are not registered charities; individuals (including sponsorship); organisations or groups whose main object is to fund or support other charitable bodies; organisations or groups which are in direct relief of any reduction of financial support from public funds; charities with a turnover of over £1 million; charities which spend over 10% of their income on fundraising activities; political or commercial appeals; charities whose accounts disclose substantial financial reserves. Nor towards general maintenance, repair or restoration of buildings, including ecclesiastical buildings, unless there is a long standing connection with the Armourers' and Brasiers' Company or unless of outstanding importance to the national heritage.

TYPE OF GRANT 'Regular annual grants are not a policy of the trust at present, but charities can still apply for grants on an annual basis.'

RANGE OF GRANTS 'The trust funds are relatively modest; therefore applications for large sums should be avoided.'

SAMPLE GRANTS Dream Connection, Greenwich Toy & Leisure Library Association, Let's Face It, Morning Star Trust, Students Exploring Marriage Trust and Welch Ally UK Limited (£1,000 each); ALD Life, Baby Lifeline Limited, Batten Disease Family Association, Bowel & Cancer Research, Childhood Eye Cancer Trust, Kids N' Action, Global Bengali Mohila Sharnity, Globetown Community Association, Holiday Endeavour for Lone Parents, Root Development Agency, The F N Charrington Tower Hamlets Mission, The Pavement, The Sequal Trust, The Seventy4 Foundation, The Thomas Morley Trust, Tower Hamlets Friends & Neighbours, Parents for the Early Intervention of Autism in Children, React, Special Toys Educational Postal Service, St Francis' Children's Society, Straight Talking Peer Education, The Child Accident Prevention Trust, The Child Care Action Trust, The Seeing Ear Limited, The Special Yoga Centre and The Trinity Sailing Trust (£500 each).

FINANCES *Year* 2009–10 *Income* £340,761 *Grants* £248,102 *Assets* £5,827,918

TRUSTEES S G B Martin, Chair; Prof. William Bonfield; Sir Timothy Edwards Rugglesbrise; Prof. Sir C J Humphreys; Ven. C J H Wagstaff; Lord Lifford.

OTHER INFORMATION Grants of £45,552 were made to 63 individuals and grants of £202,550 were made to institutions.

HOW TO APPLY In writing to the correspondent, with a copy of the latest annual report and audited accounts. Applications are considered quarterly.

WHO TO APPLY TO The Secretary, Armourers' Hall, 81 Coleman Street, London EC2R 5BJ *Tel* 020 7374 4000 *Fax* 020 7606 7481 *email* info@armourersandbrasiers.co.uk *Website* www.armourersandbrasiers.co.uk

■ The Arnold Foundation

CC NO 1109746   **ESTABLISHED** 2005
WHERE FUNDING CAN BE GIVEN UK.
WHO CAN BENEFIT Charitable organisations.
WHAT IS FUNDED General charitable purposes.
SAMPLE GRANTS Architecture foundation (£15,000); Design Museum (£200,000); Guide Dogs for the Blind Association (£1,000); Marie Curie Cancer Care (£1,000).
FINANCES *Year* 2010–11 *Income* £174 *Grants* £160,000
TRUSTEES Luqman Arnold; Chumsri Arnold; John Guy Rhodes.
HOW TO APPLY In writing to the correspondent.
WHO TO APPLY TO The Trustees, c/o Macfarlanes, 10 Norwich Street, London EC4A 1BD *Tel* 020 7831 9222

■ Arsenal Charitable Trust

CC NO 1008024   **ESTABLISHED** 1992
WHERE FUNDING CAN BE GIVEN Mainly Greater London.
WHO CAN BENEFIT Organisations and individuals.
WHAT IS FUNDED Youth projects and the provision of recreational facilities for the use of people living in the Greater London boroughs; any charitable purpose for the inhabitants of Islington and Hackney. Victims of disaster, victims of sport related injury or death.
RANGE OF GRANTS Up to £40,000.
SAMPLE GRANTS CAVLAS (Sri Lanka Boys' Orphanage) (£40,000); United Jewish Israel Appeal and William Tyndale Charitable Trust

(£10,000 each); London Playing Fields (£5,000); and Headley Court Rehabilitation Centre (£1,000).

FINANCES *Year* 2009–10 *Income* £75,347 *Grants* £72,216 *Assets* £1,029,641

TRUSTEES K J Friar; D Miles; A Sefton.

OTHER INFORMATION In 2009–10, other grants to institutions of less than £1,000 each totalled £6,000.

HOW TO APPLY In writing to the correspondent.

WHO TO APPLY TO The Trustees, Highbury House, 75 Drayton Park, London N5 1BU *Tel* 020 7704 4000

■ The Artemis Charitable Trust

CC NO 291328   **ESTABLISHED** 1985
WHERE FUNDING CAN BE GIVEN UK.
WHO CAN BENEFIT Registered charities benefiting parents, counsellors and psychotherapists.
WHAT IS FUNDED Counselling, psychotherapy, parenting, and human relationship training.
WHAT IS NOT FUNDED 'We cannot entertain applications either from individuals or from organisations which are not registered charities.'
TYPE OF GRANT Recurring.
SAMPLE GRANTS Voluntary Sector Mental Health Providers Forum (£49,000); Relate (£7,000); Royal African Society (£4,000); and Core System Trust (£560).
FINANCES *Year* 2010 *Income* £47,774 *Grants* £61,453 *Assets* £1,543,487
TRUSTEES R W Evans; D S Bergin; W A Evans; D J Evans; M W Evans.
HOW TO APPLY 'Applicants should [. . .] be aware that most of the trust's funds are committed to a number of major ongoing projects and that spare funds available to meet new applications are very limited.'
WHO TO APPLY TO Richard Evans, Trustee, Brook House, Quay Meadow, Bosham, West Sussex PO18 8LY *Tel* 01243 573475

■ Arthritis Research UK

CC NO 207711   **ESTABLISHED** 1936
WHERE FUNDING CAN BE GIVEN Mainly UK.
WHO CAN BENEFIT Mostly universities.
WHAT IS FUNDED Research into the cause and cure of arthritis and related musculoskeletal diseases.
WHAT IS NOT FUNDED Applications for welfare and social matters will not be considered.
TYPE OF GRANT One-off, project, recurring, running costs, and salaries. Programme support is for five years; project grants are usually for three years.
FINANCES *Year* 2009–10 *Income* £39,000,000 *Grants* £29,000,000 *Assets* £100,000,000
TRUSTEES Charles Maisey, Chair; Lord Lewis of Newnham; Prof. Patrick Sissons; Sue Arnott; Jonathan Baker; Graham Brown; Prof. Andrew Carr; Prof. Kevin Davies; Dr Ian Griffiths; Peter Henderson; Tom McGrath; Richard Raworth; Prof. Mike Pringle; Chris Cowpe.
HOW TO APPLY Application forms and guidelines are available from the Arthritis Research UK website.
WHO TO APPLY TO Michael Patrick, Copeman House, St Mary's Court, St Mary's Gate, Chesterfield, Derbyshire S41 7TD *Tel* 01246 558033 *Website* www.arthritisresearchuk.org

■ The Arthur Ronald Dyer Charitable Trust

CC NO 1134181   **ESTABLISHED** 2010
WHERE FUNDING CAN BE GIVEN Undefined, in practice the UK.
WHO CAN BENEFIT Registered charities.
WHAT IS FUNDED Supports other charitable organisations in the following areas: the advancement of health or saving of lives; disability; animals; environment/conservation/heritage.
TRUSTEES NatWest Trust Services.
HOW TO APPLY In writing to the correspondent.
WHO TO APPLY TO NatWest Trust Services, 5th Floor, Trinity Quay 2, Avon Street, Bristol BS2 0PT *Tel* 0117 940 3283

■ The Arts and Entertainment Charitable Trust

CC NO 1031027   **ESTABLISHED** 1994
WHERE FUNDING CAN BE GIVEN UK.
WHO CAN BENEFIT Charitable organisations.
WHAT IS FUNDED Welfare, medical, disability, including those causes relating to children.
SAMPLE GRANTS Previous beneficiaries have included Cancer Treatment and Research, the Children's Leukaemia Ward, ChildLine, the Metropolitan Police Peel Ski Club, the Phoenix Garden Charity, the Royal Grammar School and SOS Children Tsunami Disaster.
FINANCES *Year* 2009–10 *Income* £7,745
TRUSTEES D A Graham; P D C Collins; C N Parsons; Sir W Blackburn; P Madoc; Hon S Nicholls; D R King; I Stokes.
OTHER INFORMATION The trust distributes funds raised by The Heritage Foundation.
HOW TO APPLY In writing to the correspondent. Trustees meet every three months.
WHO TO APPLY TO David A Graham, Administrator, Greenacres, 3 Birchwood Chase, Great Kings Hill, Buckinghamshire HP15 6EH *Tel* 01494 714388 *email* ian.stokes@theheritagefoundation.co.uk *Website* www.theheritagefoundation.co.uk

■ Arts Council England

CC NO 1036733   **ESTABLISHED** 1994
WHERE FUNDING CAN BE GIVEN England.
WHO CAN BENEFIT Organisations and individuals.
WHAT IS FUNDED Developing, sustaining and promoting the arts. The majority of funding is provided to organisations that are regularly funded by the Arts Council.
WHAT IS NOT FUNDED Grants below £1,000.
FINANCES *Year* 2009–10 *Income* £604,204,000 *Grants* £541,600,000 *Assets* £126,424,000
TRUSTEES Members of the Arts Council of England: Alice Rawsthorn; Alistair Spalding; Anil Ruia; Diran Adebayo; Dorothy Wilson; Dr Tom Shakespeare; Ekow Eshun; Francois Matarasso; Janet Barnes; Keith Khan; Lady Sue Woodford Hollick; Prof. Jon Cook; Rosemary Squire; Sir Chris Clarke; Sir Nicholas Kenyon; Liz Forgan; Sheila Healy; Elsie Owusu; Peter Phillips; Kentake Chinyelu-Hope; Caroline collier; Ajay Chowdhury; Veronica Wadley.
PUBLICATIONS The Council produces various publications and information sheets concerning the arts. These are available on the Arts Council website.
HOW TO APPLY Applications can be made either using the online or paper 'Grants for the Arts'

application form. The application pack contains the form, guidance on how to apply and further information about other sources of funding. This is dowloadable from the website or by contacting the enquires team by phone. There is also a useful 'eligibility wizard' on the website.
WHO TO APPLY TO Enquiries Team, 14 Great Peter Street, London SW1P 3NQ *Tel* 0845 300 6200 *Website* www.artscouncil.org.uk

■ Arts Council of Northern Ireland

ESTABLISHED 1995
WHERE FUNDING CAN BE GIVEN UK and Ireland (but projects must benefit people of Northern Ireland).
WHO CAN BENEFIT Artists and arts organisations.
WHAT IS FUNDED 'The Arts Council is the lead development agency for the arts in Northern Ireland. We are the main support for artists and arts organisations, offering a broad range of funding opportunities through our Exchequer and National Lottery funds.'
SAMPLE GRANTS BEAM Creative Network (£31,000); Ulster Orchestra Society (£15,000); Waterside Theatre Company Ltd (£12,000); Arts Care (£10,000); Play Resource Warehouse (£8,000) and In Your Space (NI) Ltd (£4,000).
FINANCES *Year* 2010–11 *Grants* £26,581,834
TRUSTEES Council Members: Ms Rosemary Kelly, Chair; Damien Coyle; Eithne Benson; Kate Bond; William Montgomery; Raymond Fullerton; David Irvine; Anthony Kennedy; Prof. Ian Montgomery; Sharon O'Connor; Joseph Rice; Prof. Paul Seawright; Janine Walker; Peter Spratt; Brian Sore.
HOW TO APPLY Guidelines and full details of how to apply can be found at the Arts Council of Northern Ireland website.
WHO TO APPLY TO The Arts Development Department, MacNeice House, 77 Malone Road, Belfast BT9 6AQ *Tel* 028 9038 5200 *Fax* 028 9066 1715 *email* info@artscouncil-ni.org *Website* www.artscouncil-ni.org

■ The Arts Council of Wales

CC NO 1034245   **ESTABLISHED** 1994
WHERE FUNDING CAN BE GIVEN Wales.
WHO CAN BENEFIT Arts organisations and individuals.
WHAT IS FUNDED Arts activities in Wales.
WHAT IS NOT FUNDED Individual schemes may stipulate restrictions on the origin of beneficiary organisations or individuals. Applications for funding for projects that have already started will not be considered.
SAMPLE GRANTS Welsh National Opera (£4.5 million); Theatr Genedlaethol (£1 million); BBC National Orchestra of Wales (£850,000); Chapter (£600,000); Clwyd Theatr Cymru TYP (£220,000); Wales Literature Exchange (£99,000); Cwmni Mega (£45,000); Hay Festival of Literature and the Arts Ltd (£3,000); Glynn Vivian Art Gallery (£1,250).
FINANCES *Year* 2010 *Income* £33,156,000 *Grants* £27,046,141 *Assets* £1,868,000
TRUSTEES Prof. Dai Smith; Dr Ian Rees; Norah Campbell; Emma Evans; John Geraint; Maggie Hampton; Margaret Jervis; Robin Morrison; Osi Rhys Osmond; Richard Turner; Alan Watkin; Debbie Wilcox; Prof. Gerwyn Wiliams; John Williams; Kate Woodward.
HOW TO APPLY Applicants are asked to contact the relevant local office for details of individual grants schemes.

WHO TO APPLY TO The Arts Funding Unit, Bute Place, Cardiff CF10 5AL *Tel* 0845 8734 900 *Fax* 029 2044 1400 *Minicom* 029 2045 1023 *email* info@artswales.org.uk *Website* www.artswales.org.uk

■ The Ove Arup Foundation

CC NO 328138   **ESTABLISHED** 1989
WHERE FUNDING CAN BE GIVEN Unrestricted.
WHO CAN BENEFIT Organisations benefiting research workers and designers.
WHAT IS FUNDED Education and research in matters related to the built environment, particularly if related to multi-disciplinary design, through educational institutions and charities.
WHAT IS NOT FUNDED No grants to individuals, including students.
TYPE OF GRANT Research and project, including start-up and feasibility costs. They can be one-off or recurrent.
RANGE OF GRANTS Up to £50,000.
SAMPLE GRANTS London School of Economics (£45,000); Royal Academy of Engineering and the University of Edinburgh (£40,000 each); Royal College of Art (£12,000); Institute of Civil Engineers (£10,500); University of South Wales (£10,000); Constructionarium (£8,000); Midlands Architecture and the Design Environment (£7,000); College of Estate Management (£5,000); and University of Warwick Student Union (£500).
FINANCES *Year* 2009–10 *Income* £238,647 *Grants* £184,457 *Assets* £2,764,855
TRUSTEES R B Haryott, Chair; A Chan; F Cousins; M Glover; J Kennedy; M Shears; D Michael; R T M Hill; C Cole; R Hough; P Dilley.
HOW TO APPLY In writing to the correspondent, with brief supporting financial information. Trustees meet quarterly to consider applications (March, June, September and December).
WHO TO APPLY TO Peter Klyhn, c/o Ove Arup & Partners, 13 Fitzroy Street, London W1T 4BQ *Tel* 020 7755 3184 *Website* www.theovearupfoundation.com

■ The AS Charitable Trust

CC NO 242190   **ESTABLISHED** 1965
WHERE FUNDING CAN BE GIVEN UK and developing countries.
WHO CAN BENEFIT Preference for charities in which the trust has special interest, knowledge of or association with. Christian organisations will benefit. Support may go to victims of famine, man-made or natural disasters, and war.
WHAT IS FUNDED The trust is sympathetic to projects which combine the advancement of the Christian religion with Christian lay leadership, third world development, peacemaking and reconciliation, or other areas of social concern.
WHAT IS NOT FUNDED Grants to individuals or large charities are very rare. Such applications are discouraged.
RANGE OF GRANTS £1,000–£16,000, often in multiple gifts to the one charity.
SAMPLE GRANTS GRACE (£16,000 in 11 gifts); Christian International Peace Service (£12,000 in 13 gifts); Epic Arts and Eton College (£1,000 each).
FINANCES *Year* 2008–09 *Income* £266,348 *Grants* £30,894 *Assets* £6,029,125
TRUSTEES Roy Calvocoressi; Mrs Caroline Eady; George Calvocoressi; Simon Sampson.
HOW TO APPLY In writing to the correspondent.

WHO TO APPLY TO Roy Calvocoressi, Bix Bottom Farm, Henley-on-Thames, Oxfordshire RG9 6BH

■ Ashburnham Thanksgiving Trust

CC NO 249109   **ESTABLISHED** 1965
WHERE FUNDING CAN BE GIVEN UK and worldwide.
WHO CAN BENEFIT Individuals and organisations benefiting Christians and evangelists.
WHAT IS FUNDED Only Christian work already known to the trustees is supported, particularly evangelical overseas missionary work.
WHAT IS NOT FUNDED No grants for buildings.
RANGE OF GRANTS Under £5,000.
SAMPLE GRANTS New Destiny Trust (£5,100); Genesis Arts Trust (£4,000); Open Doors (£3,000); Prison Fellowship (£2,800); Ashburnham Christian Trust (£2,600); Interserve (£2,000); Calvary Chapel – Hastings (£1,900); Micah Trust (£1,300); RZIM Zacharias Trust (£1,000); St Luke's Hospital for Clergy (£800); Advantage Africa (£725); London City Mission (£600); SGM Lifewords (£500); Grace Publishing (£324); Cutting Edge Ministries (£200); Arts Centre Group (£180); and Crusade for World Revival (£104).
FINANCES *Year* 2009–10 *Income* £173,571 *Grants* £120,863 *Assets* £5,600,075
TRUSTEES Mrs M Bickersteth; E R Bickersteth; R D Bickersteth; Mrs R F Dowdy.
OTHER INFORMATION A total of £89,000 was distributed in grants to 129 organisations. Further monies were given in restricted grants and grants to individuals.
HOW TO APPLY The trust has stated that its funds are fully committed to current beneficiaries. Unfortunately, it receives far more applications than it is able to deal with.
WHO TO APPLY TO The Charity Secretary, Agmerhurst House, Ashburnham, Battle, East Sussex TN33 9NB

■ A J H Ashby Will Trust

CC NO 803291   **ESTABLISHED** 1990
WHERE FUNDING CAN BE GIVEN UK, especially Lea Valley area of Hertfordshire.
WHO CAN BENEFIT Charitable organisations, sports clubs and schools.
WHAT IS FUNDED Wildlife, particularly birds; heritage; education projects; and children.
WHAT IS NOT FUNDED No grants to individuals or students.
TYPE OF GRANT One-off and recurrent.
SAMPLE GRANTS RSPB (£70,000 in five grants); Wormley Cricket Club (£3,000); West Lea School (£2,500); and Barking Boxing Club (£2,800).
FINANCES *Year* 2009–10 *Income* £853,942 *Grants* £78,310 *Assets* £1,230,111
TRUSTEES HSBC Trust Company (UK) Ltd.
HOW TO APPLY In writing to the correspondent.
WHO TO APPLY TO Sandra Hill, Trust Manager, HSBC Trust Company (UK) Ltd, Trust Services, Norwich House, Nelson Gate, Commercial Road, Southampton SO15 1GX *Tel* 023 8072 2243

■ The Ashden Trust

CC NO 802623   **ESTABLISHED** 1989
WHERE FUNDING CAN BE GIVEN UK and overseas.
WHO CAN BENEFIT Registered charities.
WHAT IS FUNDED Programme areas: Sustainable Development – International and UK; Sustainable Regeneration; People at Risk; Arts

and Sustainability; Social Investment Fund; Low Carbon Fund.

WHAT IS NOT FUNDED The trustees generally do not make grants in response to unsolicited applications. However, How to Apply.

TYPE OF GRANT Primarily project.

SAMPLE GRANTS Ashden Awards for Sustainable Energy (£406,000); BioRegional Development Group (£60,000); 10:10 UK (£50,000); Green Alliance (£40,000); BioFuels Watch (£30,000); Organic Research Centre (£20,000); Campaign Against Living Miserably (£15,000); Forward Thinking (£10,000); and Green Budgets Europe (£4,500).

FINANCES *Year* 2009–10 *Income* £1,807,758 *Grants* £1,077,347 *Assets* £26,728,330

TRUSTEES Sarah Butler-Sloss; Robert Butler-Sloss; Miss Judith Portrait.

OTHER INFORMATION The trust is one of the Sainsbury Family Charitable Trusts which share a common administration. An application to one is taken as an application to all.

HOW TO APPLY 'The Ashden Trust is one of the Sainsbury Family Charitable Trusts. Before applying to one of the trusts, please read these guidelines: The trust does not normally fund individuals for projects, educational fees or to join expeditions. If you apply for a grant in one of these categories, we are afraid the trustees are unable to help. If you are a registered charity or institution with charitable status applying for a grant we must warn you that only an extremely small number of unsolicited applications are successful. Do not apply to more than one of the Sainsbury Family Charitable Trusts. Each application will be considered by each trust which may have an interest in this field. All of the Sainsbury Family Charitable Trusts have pro-active grant-making policies and have chosen to concentrate their support in a limited number of activities. If you have read through the Ashden Trust's website and feel your project fits into the trust's priorities we would be very interested to hear from you by post. The trustees generally do not make grants in response to unsolicited applications. If you would like to apply to the trust you should send a brief description of the proposed project, by post only, to the director. The proposed project needs to cover: why the project is needed; how, where, when the project will be delivered; who will benefit and in what way; income and expenditure budget; details of funding – secured, applied for; description of the organisation. Please do not send any more than 2–4 sides of A4 when applying to the trust, at this point additional material is unnecessary.'

WHO TO APPLY TO Alan Bookbinder, Director, Allington House, 1st Floor, 150 Victoria Street, London SW1E 5AE *Tel* 020 7410 0330 *Fax* 020 7410 0332 *email* ashdentrust@sfct.org.uk *Website* www.ashdentrust.org.uk

■ The Ashendene Trust

CC NO 270749   **ESTABLISHED** 1975

WHERE FUNDING CAN BE GIVEN Unrestricted, in practice mainly London, Oxfordshire and Berkshire.

WHO CAN BENEFIT Registered charities.

WHAT IS FUNDED Small organisations including those assisting ex-offenders, people who are socially deprived, horticulture, the arts and churches. This is a small trust that gives to organisations where the grant will really make an impact.

WHAT IS NOT FUNDED No support for large organisations, education or health. No scholarships or individual grants.

TYPE OF GRANT Capital, core costs and project. Funding available for up to three years.

RANGE OF GRANTS Up to £6,250.

SAMPLE GRANTS Chiswick House and Gardens Trust (£6,250); Wantage Town Land Governers (£5,000); Grasslands Trust, Stepping Stones Trust and Hope UK (£2,500 each); and Terrence Higgins Trust and Switchback (£1,000 each).

FINANCES *Year* 2009–10 *Income* £39,628 *Grants* £41,775 *Assets* £1,009,784

TRUSTEES Camilla Pugh; Sir Edward Cazalet; A D Loehnis; Nicholas Hornby.

HOW TO APPLY In writing to the correspondent. Replies are only made to those who enclose an sae.

WHO TO APPLY TO Sir Simon Hornby, The Ham, Wantage, Oxfordshire OX12 9JA *Tel* 01235 770222

■ The Ashley Family Foundation

CC NO 288099   **ESTABLISHED** 1985

WHERE FUNDING CAN BE GIVEN Mostly Wales, other areas considered.

WHO CAN BENEFIT Charitable organisations. In recent years focus has been on the advancement of education particularly in fine and applied arts and projects supporting communities in Wales, particularly Mid-Wales.

WHAT IS FUNDED The foundation has a strong commitment to art and design and also to Wales, particularly Powys, where the Ashley business was first established. The trustees plan to widen the geographical area within Wales and this is not to the exclusion of English projects which fall within the foundation's criteria for grant-making.

WHAT IS NOT FUNDED The foundation does not fund individuals, business ventures, overseas projects, projects falling within the field of religion or retrospective work.

TYPE OF GRANT One-off up to a period of three years.

RANGE OF GRANTS £500–£25,000.

FINANCES *Year* 2009–10 *Income* £301,740 *Grants* £383,098 *Assets* £10,756,388

TRUSTEES Jane Ashley, Chair; Prof. Susan Golombok; Martyn C Gowar; Emma Shuckburgh; Oriana Baddeley; Sue Timney; Mike Hodgson.

HOW TO APPLY The Ashley Family Foundation (formerly The Laura Ashley Foundation) will consider requests from charities, unincorporated organisations and community groups with a constitution or terms of reference and a charitable purpose. It will consider requests for: core funding, including salaries and overheads. Requests that are below £10,000 are favoured. 'Decisions are based upon benefit and value and each project is considered on its own merit. Final decisions are at the discretion of the trustees.' Potential applicants are encouraged to check the foundation's website before submitting an application. The website states: 'Due to the economic downturn we are receiving an unprecedented increase in requests. We are therefore changing our long held policy of replying to all requests. If you have submitted a stage one proposal and have not heard within eight weeks please assume you have been unsuccessful.'

WHO TO APPLY TO Jane Ashley, Trustee, Ladywell House, Park Street, Newtown SY16 1JB *Tel* 01686 610648 *email* lafwales@tiscali.co.uk *Website* www.ashleyfamilyfoundation.org.uk

■ The Norman C Ashton Foundation

CC NO 260036 **ESTABLISHED** 1969

WHERE FUNDING CAN BE GIVEN Preference for the Leeds area.

WHO CAN BENEFIT Charitable organisations.

WHAT IS FUNDED Educational, healthcare and homelessness.

TYPE OF GRANT One-off.

SAMPLE GRANTS Genesis (£3,000); Action for Sick Children, Child Care Action Group, New Hope and Rothwell Baptist Church (£2,000 each); and Tall Ships Youth Trust (£1,000).

FINANCES *Year* 2009–10 *Income* £28,700 *Grants* £15,000 *Assets* £762,829

TRUSTEES Susan Sharp, Chair; Catherine Ashton; Georgina Stevens.

HOW TO APPLY The foundation does not accept unsolicited applications.

WHO TO APPLY TO Mrs Susan Sharp, Ivy House Barn, School Lane, Walton, Wetherby, West Yorkshire LS23 7DW *Tel* 01937 849608

■ The Ashworth Charitable Trust

CC NO 1045492 **ESTABLISHED** 1995

WHERE FUNDING CAN BE GIVEN UK and worldwide, with some preference for certain specific needs in Honiton, Ottery St Mary, Sidmouth and Wonford Green surgery, Exeter.

WHO CAN BENEFIT Individuals (living in the areas covered by the medical practices in Ottery St Mary, Honiton and Sidmouth only) and organisations.

WHAT IS FUNDED General charitable purposes. Particular emphasis is given to support for the Ironbridge Gorge Museum Trust and to humanitarian projects.

WHAT IS NOT FUNDED No grants for research-based charities; animal charities; 'heritage charities' such as National Trust or other organisations whose aim is the preservation of a building, museum, library and so on (with the exception of the Ironbridge Gorge Museum); 'faith-based' charities, unless the project is for primarily humanitarian purposes and is neither exclusive to those of that particular faith or evangelical in its purpose. Grants to individuals are strictly limited to the geographical area and purpose specified in the general section.

RANGE OF GRANTS £500–£10,000.

SAMPLE GRANTS Hospiscare and Ironbridge Gorge Museum Trust (£10,000 each); Age UK, World in Need and West Suffolk Voluntary Association for the Blind (£3,000 each); Freedom Social Projects, Esther Benjamins Trust and Sunseed Tanzania Trust (£2,500 each); Acid Survivors Trust International and Home Start Exeter (£2,000 each); Community, Equality, Disability Action (£1,500); Widows' Rights International and Aberdare Children's Contact Centre (£1,000 each); and Living Water Satisfies (£750).

FINANCES *Year* 2010–11 *Income* £127,095 *Grants* £113,010 *Assets* £3,720,417

TRUSTEES Mr C F Bennett, Chair; Mrs K A Gray; Mrs H Rouhipour; Mrs S Rouhipour.

OTHER INFORMATION Of the grants total £3,000 was given to 17 individuals from the Doctors' and Social Services Fund.

HOW TO APPLY In writing to the correspondent.

WHO TO APPLY TO Mrs G Towner, Foot Anstey, Senate Court, Southernhay Gardens, Exeter EX1 1NT *Tel* 01392 411221 *Fax* 01392 685220 *email* ashworthtrust@btinternet.com *Website* www.ashworthtrust.org

■ The Ian Askew Charitable Trust

CC NO 264515 **ESTABLISHED** 1972

WHERE FUNDING CAN BE GIVEN UK, with a preference for Sussex, and overseas.

WHO CAN BENEFIT Mainly headquarters organisations.

WHAT IS FUNDED General charitable purposes; education; health research; particularly mental health; preservation of ancient buildings; maintenance and conservation of woodlands.

RANGE OF GRANTS Most grants for £500 or less.

SAMPLE GRANTS Save and Prosper (£1,000); Sussex Historic Churches Association (£750); Action for Kids Street Bruie, Brook Hospital for Animals, Church Urban Fund, Harambee Schools Kenya, National Kidney Federation and Ringmer District Youth Association (£500 each); and National Trust Scotland and the Royal Academy Trust (£25).

FINANCES *Year* 2009–10 *Income* £341,957 *Grants* £73,205 *Assets* £13,987,398

TRUSTEES J R Hecks, Chair; Mrs C Pengelley; R A R Askew; J B Rank; R P G Lewis.

OTHER INFORMATION The trust also maintains the woodlands at Plashett Estate, East Sussex, the main part of which is designated as a site of special and scientific interest. The woodlands are used principally for educational purposes.

HOW TO APPLY In writing to the correspondent. Applications are considered every other month.

WHO TO APPLY TO The Trustees, c/o Baker Tilly, 18 Mount Ephraim Road, Tunbridge Wells, Kent TN1 1ED

■ The Associated Country Women of the World (ACWW)

CC NO 290367 **ESTABLISHED** 1933

WHERE FUNDING CAN BE GIVEN Overseas.

WHO CAN BENEFIT Small local projects and established organisations benefiting children, young adults and rural communities in particular. Projects must have a female emphasis.

WHAT IS FUNDED Education, environmental resources and projects in connection with: literacy, agriculture and income generating schemes.

WHAT IS NOT FUNDED No grants to individuals or students unless they are a member of an ACWW society.

TYPE OF GRANT One-off.

SAMPLE GRANTS Capacity building and skills development programme in India (£9,500); Pig and poultry farming project in Cameroon (£5,000); Mushroom planting project in China (£8,000); Literacy project in Romania (£600); Domestic violence workshop in Tuvalu (£13,000).

FINANCES *Year* 2010 *Income* £636,585 *Grants* £219,795 *Assets* £2,102,277

TRUSTEES Jo Almond; Alison Bumett; May Kidd; Anphia Grobler.

PUBLICATIONS *Working with Women Worldwide.*(Please visit the trust's website for a full list of publications.)

HOW TO APPLY Application forms are available on the trust's website. Applications are considered first by central office staff and then at the next level by the projects committee which meets twice a year.

WHO TO APPLY TO The General Secretary, Mary Sumner House, 24 Tufton Street, London SW1P 3RB *Tel* 020 7799 3875 *Fax* 020 7340 9950 *email* info@acww.org.uk *Website* www. acww.org.uk

■ The Association of Colleges Charitable Trust

CC NO 1040631 **ESTABLISHED** 1994

WHERE FUNDING CAN BE GIVEN UK.

WHO CAN BENEFIT Further education establishments.

WHAT IS FUNDED Further education. The charitable trust is responsible for administering two programmes. The largest of these is the Beacon Awards, which provide monetary grants to award-winning initiatives within further education colleges. The other scheme is the AoC Gold Awards for Further Education Alumni, which reward former members of further education colleges who have since excelled in their chosen field or profession.

WHAT IS NOT FUNDED Grants are not made to individuals.

FINANCES *Year* 2009–10 *Income* £318,337 *Grants* £252,631 *Assets* £150,405

TRUSTEES Alice Thiagaraj; Peter Brophy; Sue Dutton; David Forrester; John Bingham.

OTHER INFORMATION The charitable trust is responsible for administering two programmes. The largest of these is the Beacon Awards, which provide monetary grants to award-winning initiatives within further education colleges. The other scheme is the AoC Gold Awards for Further Education Alumni, which reward former members of further education colleges who have since excelled in their chosen field or profession.

HOW TO APPLY See the trust's website for further information.

WHO TO APPLY TO The Trust Manager, 2–6 Stedman Place, London WC1A 1HU *Website* www.aoc.co. uk

■ The Association of Friends of Essex Churches

CC NO 236033 **ESTABLISHED** 1952

WHERE FUNDING CAN BE GIVEN Essex and the boroughs of Waltham Forest, Redbridge, Newham, Barking and Dagenham and Havering.

WHO CAN BENEFIT Any Christian church.

WHAT IS FUNDED Churches, irrespective of denomination, where the repairs necessary are beyond parish resources.

WHAT IS NOT FUNDED Grants are not given for new work or annual maintenance, for example gutter clearance, or redecoration. No grants towards heating systems.

TYPE OF GRANT One-off (but may apply again in subsequent years) and buildings.

RANGE OF GRANTS £200–£20,000.

FINANCES *Year* 2010 *Income* £136,307 *Grants* £116,322 *Assets* £398,469

TRUSTEES Mrs J Abel Smith, Chair; Mrs C Cottrell; K Gardner; D Lodge; Dr J Bettley; D Woracker; Mrs F Nelmes; R Meloy; Mrs M Blaxall; Mr P A Smith.

OTHER INFORMATION During 2010 grants were offered to a total of 22 churches and ranged in amount from £1,500 to £15,000; a small drop in size from the previous year's grant range of £200 to £20,000.

HOW TO APPLY On a form available from the correspondent. The Grants Committee meets quarterly.

WHO TO APPLY TO Mr K Gardner, Grants Hon. Secretary, Pink Cottage, Curtis Mill Gree, Stapleford Tawney, Essex RM4 1RT *Tel* 01708 745273 *email* john.bloomfield@btinternet.com *Website* www.foect.org.uk

■ Astellas European Foundation

CC NO 1036344 **ESTABLISHED** 1993

WHERE FUNDING CAN BE GIVEN Worldwide.

WHO CAN BENEFIT Scientific research institutes, universities, research workers and medical professionals.

WHAT IS FUNDED The objects of the foundation are: committing long-term support to basic medical and related scientific programmes through organisations such as the Société Internationale D'Urologie; supporting selected short, medium and long-term projects, aimed at integrating basic science and clinical research through interdisciplinary projects; providing facilities, promoting or sponsoring the exchange of ideas and views through lectures and discussions of an educational or cultural nature; promoting, assisting or otherwise supporting charitable institutions aimed at serving good causes.

FINANCES *Year* 2009–10 *Income* £43,000 *Grants* £30,000 *Assets* £7,800,000

TRUSTEES Dr Toichi Takenaka; Yasho Ishii; Ken Jones; Masafumi Nogimori; Masao Yoshida; Yoshirou Miyokawa; Dr Ayad Abdul-Ahad; Yukio Matsui.

HOW TO APPLY In writing to the correspondent.

WHO TO APPLY TO The Trustees, Lovett House, Causeway Corporate Centre, Staines, Middlesex TW18 3AZ *Tel* 01784 419615

■ Asthma UK

CC NO 802364 **ESTABLISHED** 1990

WHERE FUNDING CAN BE GIVEN UK.

WHO CAN BENEFIT Organisations benefiting scientists, clinicians, general practitioners, research workers and people with asthma.

WHAT IS FUNDED Research into and the provision of information and education on asthma and allied respiratory disorders.

WHAT IS NOT FUNDED 'Researchers work across a variety of disciplines within hospitals, universities, GP surgeries and clinics throughout the UK. Asthma UK is therefore able to fund researchers who work directly with people with asthma as well as those who are undertaking basic science research in the laboratory.'

TYPE OF GRANT Project grants and fellowships.

FINANCES *Year* 2009–10 *Income* £8,371,000 *Grants* £6,429,000 *Assets* £3,574,000

TRUSTEES Eric Wiles; Prof. John Griffiths; Jane Tozer; June Vanessa Coppel; Barbara Mary Hope Herts; David William Howitt Steeds; John Lelliott; Dr Anne Thomson; Dr Iain Small; Helen Ralston; John Oliver Stanley Belgrave; Dr Robert Wilson; Sarah Walter; Prof. Jurgen Schwarze.

HOW TO APPLY 'Each year Asthma UK invites proposals for research projects through its website and through the research professional press. All applications for funding are assessed for scientific quality and relevance to asthma by our research committee, which is comprised of an independent panel of scientists, clinicians and lay representatives. Research proposals are also subjected to further scrutiny by international experts through our external review process, who have experience closely related to the subject area. Asthma UK's Council of Trustees then decides how many of the recommended research proposals can be funded, based on the projected income of the charity.'

WHO TO APPLY TO Kessington Ijegbai, Summit House, 70 Wilson Street, London EC2A 2DB *Tel* 020 7786 4900 *Fax* 020 7256 6075 *email* info@ asthma.org.uk *Website* www.asthma.org.uk

■ Aston–Mansfield Charitable Trust

CC NO 208155   **ESTABLISHED** 1930
WHERE FUNDING CAN BE GIVEN The borough of Newham.
WHO CAN BENEFIT Organisations.
WHAT IS FUNDED 'The objects of the charity are to develop the community wealth of East London and promote a diverse and inclusive society in which all are free to participate. Aston-Mansfield's Seed Grants, a small funding programme aimed at newly formed or completely unfunded groups, is a new initiative launched in April 2011. Groups can apply for up to a maximum of £400.'
WHAT IS NOT FUNDED Revenue funding for salaries and maintenance is unlikely to be given. No national appeals and no grants to individuals.
TYPE OF GRANT Capital (including buildings), feasibility studies, one-off, project and research. Funding of one year or less will be considered.
FINANCES *Year* 2010–11 *Income* £429,079 *Grants* £667,185 *Assets* £13,618,177
TRUSTEES Christopher C Keen, Chair; Alan J Shelley; Catherine M Brett; Rt Revd John Gladwin; Dharam B Lall; Andrew F West.
HOW TO APPLY For Seed Grants applicants should see the trust's website where all information is posted. Applicants for all other grants should apply in writing to the correspondent.
WHO TO APPLY TO Geoffrey Wheeler, Company Secretary, Durning Hall, Earlham Grove, Forest Gate, London E7 9AB *Tel* 020 8536 3812 *email* geoffrey.wheeler@aston-mansfield.org.uk *Website* www.aston-mansfield.org.uk

■ The Astor Foundation

CC NO 225708   **ESTABLISHED** 1963
WHERE FUNDING CAN BE GIVEN UK.
WHO CAN BENEFIT Medical research organisations. Children and youth groups, people who are disabled, the countryside, the arts, sport, carers groups and animal welfare.
WHAT IS FUNDED Medical research in its widest sense, favouring research on a broad front rather than in specialised fields. In addition to its medical connection, historically the foundation has also supported initiatives for children and youth groups, people who are disabled, the countryside, the arts, sport, carers groups and animal welfare.
WHAT IS NOT FUNDED No grants to individuals or towards salaries. Grants are given to registered charities only.
TYPE OF GRANT Preference for assistance with the launching and initial stages of new projects and filling in gaps/shortfalls.
RANGE OF GRANTS £500–£45,000; generally £250–£1,500.
SAMPLE GRANTS Friends of UCLH (£5,000); Independence at Home (£4,500); Help the Hospices (£4,000); RNLI (£3,000); UCL Medical School (£2,000); Samantha Dickson Brain Tumour Trust (£1,500); the Ulysses Trust (£1,000); Working Families (£500); and Red Squirrel Survival Trust (£250).
FINANCES *Year* 2009–10 *Income* £104,813 *Grants* £81,250 *Assets* £3,263,784
TRUSTEES R H Astor, Chair; the Hon. Tania Astor; Lord Latymer; C Astor; Dr H Swanton; Prof. J Cunningham.
HOW TO APPLY There are no deadline dates or application forms. Applications should be in writing to the correspondent and must include accounts and an annual report if available. The trustees meet twice yearly, usually in October and April. If the appeal arrives too late for one meeting it will automatically be carried over for consideration at the following meeting. An acknowledgement will be sent on receipt of an appeal. No further communication will be entered into unless the trustees raise any queries regarding the appeal, or unless the appeal is subsequently successful.
WHO TO APPLY TO Lisa Rothwell-Orr, Secretary, PO Box 3096, Marlborough, Wiltshire SN8 3WP *email* astor.foundation@virgin.net

■ The Astor of Hever Trust

CC NO 264134   **ESTABLISHED** 1955
WHERE FUNDING CAN BE GIVEN UK and worldwide, with a preference for Kent and the Grampian region of Scotland.
WHO CAN BENEFIT Both headquarters and local branches of charities, mainly established organisations with particular emphasis on Kent.
WHAT IS FUNDED Charitable bodies in the fields of the arts, medicine, religion, education, conservation, youth and sport.
WHAT IS NOT FUNDED No grants to individuals.
TYPE OF GRANT Unrestricted.
RANGE OF GRANTS £20–£1,000.
FINANCES *Year* 2009–10 *Income* £37,206 *Grants* £27,320 *Assets* £1,009,553
TRUSTEES John Jacob, Third Baron Astor of Hever; Hon. Philip D P Astor; Hon Camilla Astor.
HOW TO APPLY In writing to the correspondent. Trustees meet twice each year. Unsuccessful applications are not acknowledged.
WHO TO APPLY TO Gill Willis, Administrator, Frenchstreet House, Westerham, Kent TN16 1PW *Tel* 01959 565070

■ The Aurelius Charitable Trust

CC NO 271333   **ESTABLISHED** 1975
WHERE FUNDING CAN BE GIVEN UK.
WHO CAN BENEFIT Registered charities, historic societies, museums/galleries and academic bodies.
WHAT IS FUNDED Conservation/preservation of culture inherited from the past; the dissemination of knowledge, particularly in the humanities field; research or publications.
WHAT IS NOT FUNDED No grants to individuals.
TYPE OF GRANT Seed-corn or completion funding not otherwise available, usually one-off.
RANGE OF GRANTS Generally £500–£3,000.
SAMPLE GRANTS Old Royal Naval College, Royal Botanic Gardens, Kew and the British Academy (£5,000 each); the Carpet Museum Trust and English National Opera (£3,000); Friends of the Moot Hall, Maldon (£2,000); Friends of Herefordshire Museums and Arts (£1,500); the Quaker Tapestry at Kendal Ltd (£1,000); and St Margaret' of Antioch (£600).
FINANCES *Year* 2009–10 *Income* £70,239 *Grants* £73,562 *Assets* £2,061,857
TRUSTEES W J Wallis; P E Haynes.
HOW TO APPLY In writing to the correspondent. Donations are generally made on the recommendation of the trust's board of advisors. Unsolicited applications will only be responded to if an sae is included. Trustees meet twice a year.
WHO TO APPLY TO P E Haynes, Trustee, Briarsmead, Old Road, Buckland, Betchworth, Surrey RH3 7DU *Tel* 01737 842186 *email* philip. haynes@tiscali.co.uk

■ The Lord Austin Trust

CC NO 208394   ESTABLISHED 1937

WHERE FUNDING CAN BE GIVEN Birmingham and its immediate area.

WHO CAN BENEFIT Charitable institutions or projects in England, restricted to: local charities based in Birmingham and West Midlands; and national organisations (but not their provincial branches).

WHAT IS FUNDED Emphasis on the welfare of children, the care of older people, medical institutions and research.

WHAT IS NOT FUNDED No support for appeals from, or on behalf of, individual applicants.

TYPE OF GRANT One-off.

RANGE OF GRANTS Up to £10,000.

SAMPLE GRANTS Black Country Living Museum (£10,000); City of Birmingham Symphony Orchestra (£7,000); Birmingham Boys' and Girls' Union (£4,000); Multiple Births Foundations (£3,500); Birmingham Sr Mary's Hospice (£3,000); Foundation for Conductive Education (£2,500); the Prince's Trust (£2,000); Tall Ships Youth Trust (£1,500); and South Birmingham Young Homeless Project (£,1000).

FINANCES Year 2009–10 Income £95,799 Grants £131,500 Assets £3,484,147

TRUSTEES J M G Fea; R S Kettel; A N Andrews.

HOW TO APPLY In writing to the correspondent, including a set of recent accounts. Trustees meet twice a year in or around May and November to consider grants. The trustees stress that new awards are now severely limited.

WHO TO APPLY TO Ms Chrissy Norgrove, c/o Martineau Johnson, 1 Colmore Square, Birmingham B4 6AA Tel 0870 763 2000 email christine.norgrove@martineau-uk.com

■ Autonomous Research Charitable Trust

CC NO 1137503   ESTABLISHED 2010

WHERE FUNDING CAN BE GIVEN UK, mainly London, and Africa.

WHAT IS FUNDED 'To help disadvantaged people get a step up in life. Our focus is therefore upon people rather than wildlife conservation or ecology; to empower people to improve the quality of their lives. We are therefore naturally drawn to projects based around education opportunities or helping with start-up business ventures; to focus our resources upon a small number of key partner charities – both in London and abroad – where we feel we can make a difference and establish long-term relationships; our involvement is not simply about giving money. The partners of Autonomous will also be active in mentoring, providing business and career advice and in a variety of other hands-on roles.'

WHAT IS NOT FUNDED Wildlife or environmental causes are unlikely to be supported.

SAMPLE GRANTS The trust currently has a partnership with three charities: the Tusk Trust, working in Kenya; Plan UK, in Uganda; and One Degree, in London.

TRUSTEES Graham Stuart; Britta Schmidt; Nathalie Garner; Neeta Atkar.

OTHER INFORMATION The correspondent states that the trust's policies and guidelines will develop in due course, but at the moment all applications are simply forwarded to the trustees for consideration.

HOW TO APPLY In writing to the correspondent.

WHO TO APPLY TO Keith Lawrence, Secretary, Moore Stephens, 150 Aldersgate Street, London EC1A 4AB Tel 020 7334 9191 email keith. lawrence@moorestephens.com

■ The Avenue Charitable Trust

CC NO 264804   ESTABLISHED 1972

WHERE FUNDING CAN BE GIVEN Worldwide.

WHO CAN BENEFIT Registered charities and individuals.

WHAT IS FUNDED General charitable purposes.

TYPE OF GRANT One-off and recurrent.

RANGE OF GRANTS Generally £25–£50,000, although occasionally larger grants are given.

SAMPLE GRANTS Delta Trust (£225,000); Neuro-Psychoanalysis Fund (£65,000); David Astor Journalism Award Trust (£50,000); Adonis Mosat Project (£25,000); Living Landscape Project (£10,000); Adam von Trott Memorial Appeal (£5,000); Amnesty International, Cheek By Jowl and Koestler Trust (£1,000 each); and Prisoners Abroad (£500).

FINANCES Year 2009–10 Income £152,528 Grants £383,500 Assets £45,501

TRUSTEES R D L Astor; Hon. Mrs B A Astor; G W B Todd.

HOW TO APPLY The trust has previously stated that all available income is now committed to existing beneficiaries.

WHO TO APPLY TO Susan Simmons, Sayers Butterworth, 18 Bentinck Street, London W1M 5RL Tel 020 7935 8504

■ The John Avins Trustees

CC NO 217301   ESTABLISHED 1931

WHERE FUNDING CAN BE GIVEN Birmingham and district.

WHO CAN BENEFIT Medical charities. Support may be given to medical professionals and research workers.

WHAT IS FUNDED Medical charities in Birmingham and neighbourhood, and the following charities mentioned in the will of John Avins: Birmingham Blue Coat School; Birmingham Royal Institution for the Blind; and Middlemore Homes, Birmingham.

WHAT IS NOT FUNDED No grants to individuals, non-medical charities or for purposes outside the beneficial area.

TYPE OF GRANT One-off.

RANGE OF GRANTS Up to £5,000.

SAMPLE GRANTS Sir John Middlemore Charitable Trust (£5,000); Multiple Births Foundation (£4,000); Theodora Children's Trust and Focus Birmingham, (£2,500 each); Motor Neurone Disease Association and Macmillan Cancer Support (£2,000 each); and Strongbones Children's Trust and Interact Reading Service (£1,000 each).

FINANCES Year 2009–10 Income £44,349 Grants £41,250 Assets £1,230,437

TRUSTEES Hon Alderman I McArdle, Chair; C F Smith; C J Timbrell; V C Sharma; Prof. D Cox; F Collins.

OTHER INFORMATION In 2009–10 a further £2,000 was given in scholarships.

HOW TO APPLY On a form available from the correspondent. Trustees meet in April and November.

WHO TO APPLY TO H M B Carslake, Joint Secretary, 1 Colmore Square, Birmingham B4 6AA Tel 0870 763 2000

■ The Avon and Somerset Police Community Trust

CC NO 1076770   **ESTABLISHED** 1999
WHERE FUNDING CAN BE GIVEN The Avon and Somerset Constabulary area.
WHO CAN BENEFIT Organisations.
WHAT IS FUNDED The trustees favour projects that: promote safety and quality of life in the Avon and Somerset Constabulary area; through the prevention of crime and disorder, protect young people, people who are vulnerable and older people from criminal acts; advance education, including that related to alcohol, drugs, solvent abuse, community relations and responsible citizenship.
WHAT IS NOT FUNDED The trust does not support: individuals, including students; expeditions; bursaries or scholarships; replacement of statutory funding; building works; projects that fall outside the constabulary's geographical area.
RANGE OF GRANTS £450–£2,250.
SAMPLE GRANTS Lodge Causeway Gating Scheme (£1,200); Wessex Counselling Service Project (£500); Bath District First Aid and Knife Initiative (£700); Kinergy (£1,000); Falmouth Road Alley Gating (£450); Battle of the Bands (£1,000); Cotham Park (£950); Childsafe International (£750); Clevedon School Peer educators (£742); Wiveliscombe and area youth work team (£500).
FINANCES *Year* 2009–10 *Income* £39,313 *Grants* £472,516 *Assets* £479,700
TRUSTEES Dr Moira Hamlin; Colin Port; Mary Prior; Henry Elwes; Lady Gass; Ian Hoddell; Roger James; Paul Upham; Paul Hooper; Beatrice Selter.
OTHER INFORMATION The grant total includes funds used to run the trust's own projects and initiatives.
HOW TO APPLY For further information about the trust or advice on obtaining or completing the trust's application form please contact the Trust Manager. The trustees meet quarterly to consider the business of the trust and approve grants in accordance with the trust's aims and objectives. Grants in support of major projects are routinely reviewed and awarded by the trustees at the commencement of each financial year at their April meeting. All other grants are considered on their merit, having met the criteria for a grant as set out in the trust's aims and objectives.
WHO TO APPLY TO Tracey Clegg, Trust Manager, PO Box 37, Valley Road, Portishead, Bristol BS20 8QJ *Tel* 01275 816240 *Fax* 01275 816129 *email* tracey.clegg@avonandsomerset. police.uik *Website* www.avonandsomerset. police.uk

■ AW Charitable Trust

CC NO 283322   **ESTABLISHED** 1961
WHERE FUNDING CAN BE GIVEN Unrestricted.
WHO CAN BENEFIT Jewish educational and religious organisations; registered charities.
WHAT IS FUNDED General charitable purposes.
SAMPLE GRANTS Previous beneficiaries include: TET; Asser Bishvil Foundation; Chevras Oneg Shabbos-Yomtov; Friends of Mir; CML; Toimchei Shabbos Manchester; British Friends of Kupat Hair; Purim Fund; Beenstock Home; and Zoreya Tzedokos.
FINANCES *Year* 2009–10 *Income* £7,282,053 *Grants* £3,917,330 *Assets* £73,311,805
TRUSTEES Rabbi Aubrey Weis; Mrs R Weis.

HOW TO APPLY In writing to the correspondent. The trust considers 'all justified applications for support of educational establishments, places of worship and other charitable actives.'
WHO TO APPLY TO Rabbi Aubrey Weis, Trustee, 1 Allandale Court, Waterpark Road, Manchester M7 4JL *Tel* 0161 740 0116

■ Awards for All (see also the Big Lottery Fund)

WHERE FUNDING CAN BE GIVEN UK.
WHO CAN BENEFIT Community groups/clubs/ societies; registered charity or exempt or excepted charities registered with the Inland Revenue in England; parish or town councils; schools; health bodies; companies limited by guarantee.
WHAT IS NOT FUNDED Generally, organisations with an income more than £20,000 a year (though there are exceptions to this, particularly for projects coming through schools and similar bodies). Also: costs related to existing projects, activities or resources currently provided by your group, for example, ongoing staff costs and utility bills, regular rent payments, maintenance (including maintenance equipment) and annual events; items which only benefit an individual, for example, scholarships or bursaries; activities promoting religious beliefs; activities that are part of statutory obligations or replace statutory funding, including curricular activity in schools; endowments; loan payments; second hand road vehicles; projects with high ongoing maintenance costs – unless your group can show that you have the funds/skills to maintain them once your Awards for All grant runs out.
TYPE OF GRANT Here are some of the things that a grant could be spent on: publicity materials; venue hire; computers; research costs; transport costs; volunteers' expenses; updating equipment for health and safety reasons; refurbishment; training; sessional staff; fees to hire equipment; educational toys and games.
RANGE OF GRANTS £300–£10,000.
FINANCES *Year* 2011–12 *Grants* £61,550,000
OTHER INFORMATION £61.55 million available in 2011–12 (England: £45 million; Northern Ireland: £3.5 million; Scotland: £10.15 million; Wales: £2.9 million)
HOW TO APPLY All information is in the application pack available from the number below. The application form is simple, but the applicant organisation must be organised to the extent of having a constitution, a bank account and a set of accounts (unless a new organisation). If you have a general enquiry or want an application form to be sent to you, please contact Awards for All on one of the following: Tel: 0845 600 20 40; Textphone: 0845 755 66 56; Email: general.enquiries@awardsforall.org.uk. The application form and guidance notes may also be downloaded from the Awards for All website. For projects where the beneficiaries are based in the Eastern, North East, North West, South East or Yorkshire and the Humber regions: Awards for All, 2 St James' Gate, Newcastle Upon Tyne, NE1 4BE; Tel: 0191 376 1600; Fax: 0191 376 1661; Textphone: 0191 376 1776. For projects where the beneficiaries are based in the East Midlands, West Midlands, London or South West regions: Big Lottery Fund, Apex House, 3 Embassy Drive, Calthorpe Road, Edgbaston, Birmingham, B15 1TR; Tel: 0121 345 7700; Fax: 0121 345 8888; Minicom:

0121 345 7666. Awards for All – Wales: for information about Awards for All Wales contact: Tel: 0845 410 2030; Fax: 01686 622458; Textphone: 0845 602 1659; Email: enquiries.wales@biglotteryfund.org.uk. Awards for All – Scotland: 4th Floor, 1 Atlantic Quay, 1 Robertson Street, Glasgow, G2 8JB; Tel: 0141 242 1400; Fax: 0141 242 1401; Textphone: 0141 242 1500; Email: scotland@awardsforall.org.uk. Awards for All – Northern Ireland: 1 Cromac Quay, Cromac Wood, Ormeau Road, Belfast, BT7 2JD; Tel: 028 9055 1455; Fax: 028 9055 1444; Textphone: 028 9055 1431; Email: enquiries.ni@awardsforall.org.uk.

WHO TO APPLY TO (See General section) *Tel* 0845 600 2040 *Website* www.awardsforall.org.uk

....

■ The Aylesford Family Charitable Trust

CC NO 328299   **ESTABLISHED** 1989

WHERE FUNDING CAN BE GIVEN West Midlands and Warwickshire.

WHO CAN BENEFIT Registered charities.

WHAT IS FUNDED General charitable purposes.

WHAT IS NOT FUNDED Grants are not normally given to individuals.

RANGE OF GRANTS £50–£35,000; in practice, £100–£1,500.

SAMPLE GRANTS St James Great Packington Trust (£35,000); Spinal Research, Army Benevolent Fund and Gamekeeper Welfare (£1,500 each); DEC Haiti Quake Appeal, British Consultancy Charity Trust, Armonco Council and Help for Heroes (£1,000 each); SSAFA Forum (£500); and Teenage Cancer Trust, Stroke Association and Rainbow Trust (£250 each).

FINANCES *Year* 2009–10 *Income* £50,992 *Grants* £50,650 *Assets* £1,672,574

TRUSTEES Lord Guernsey; Lady Guernsey.

HOW TO APPLY In writing to the correspondent at any time.

WHO TO APPLY TO The Trustees, Packington Hall, Meriden, Warwickshire CV7 7HF

Think carefully about every application. Is it justified?

....
353

The B-CH Charitable Trust

CC NO 263241   ESTABLISHED 1971
WHERE FUNDING CAN BE GIVEN UK, with preference for Cornwall and Devon.
WHO CAN BENEFIT Registered charities only, benefiting children and sick people. Support may be given to medical professionals and research workers.
WHAT IS FUNDED Children's and medical charities.
WHAT IS NOT FUNDED No grants to individuals.
RANGE OF GRANTS Up to £1,000.
SAMPLE GRANTS DEC (Pakistan Floods), Macmillan Cancer Support, British Red Cross Disaster Fund and ShelterBox (£1,000 each); Spinal Injuries Association, The Dystonia Society, Deafblind UK, Force Cancer Charity, Juvenile Diabetes Research Foundation, Cornwall Hospice Care, Compassion in Dying and Canine Partners (£500 each).
FINANCES Year 2010–11 Income £78,121 Grants £26,000 Assets £928,686
TRUSTEES Miss J Holman; E N Reed.
HOW TO APPLY In writing to the correspondent. The trustees meet twice a year to consider applications.
WHO TO APPLY TO Edward N Reed, c/o Macfarlanes, 20 Cursitor Street, London EC4A 1LT Tel 020 7831 9222

B W Charitable Trust

CC NO 1134407   ESTABLISHED 2010
WHERE FUNDING CAN BE GIVEN Undefined, in practice local.
WHO CAN BENEFIT Registered charities.
WHAT IS FUNDED General charitable purposes, but may possibly have a preference for cultural and arts related organisations.
TRUSTEES David Breuer-Weil; Mrs Samantha Breuer-Weil.
HOW TO APPLY In writing to the correspondent.
WHO TO APPLY TO Pinnick Lewis Chartered Accountants, Handel House, 95 High Street, Edgware HA8 7DB

The BAA Communities Trust

CC NO 1058617   ESTABLISHED 1996
WHERE FUNDING CAN BE GIVEN Local communities around the following BAA run airports: Heathrow, Gatwick, Stansted, Southampton, Edinburgh, Glasgow and Aberdeen. Limited help is available for projects in the area immediately surrounding BAA's HQ in Victoria, London.
WHO CAN BENEFIT National/international charities, delivering projects in or involving people from the communities local to BAA's airports, locally-based charitable organisations, schools and local authorities delivering community projects, grassroots community groups and organisations, local grant makers, national/international charities in support of staff fundraising activity.
WHAT IS FUNDED The trust was established to help communities, primarily those around BAA Limited airports, meet the challenges of the 21st Century. Through their grants they aim to create learning opportunities for young people and so raise their aspirations, break down barriers to employment through skills development, help protect the environment and support airport staff active in the community.
WHAT IS NOT FUNDED Applications which benefit individuals only, whether or not they meet the other criteria, will fail. No support for religious or political projects. Grants will not be made to nationally based organisations unless the direct benefit will be felt locally and the other criteria are satisfied. The trust does not support general running costs or staff costs.
RANGE OF GRANTS £1,000–£40,000 plus £83,000 in 186 grants less than £1,000.
SAMPLE GRANTS Green Corridor Volunteer and Training Scheme (£40,000) Act Daft (£3,200); Bedfont Sports Club (£34,000); Send-it (£5,000); Ware in Bloom (£2,350); December Haiti Earthquake (£20,000); Green Light Trust (£4,000); V-inspired (£8,000); Heathrow Community and Environment awards (£30,000); Ware Skate Park Scheme (£5,000); Carrick Knowe Primary School; Wildlife Trust BCN (£2,350).
FINANCES Year 2010 Income £711,637 Grants £537,413 Assets £1,084,086
TRUSTEES Helen Murley, Chair; Brendan Gold; Alastair McDermid; David McMillan; Alan Coates; Matthew Gorman; Clare Harbord; Punam Kharbanda; Steve Ronald.
HOW TO APPLY The trustees meet 3 times a year to assess applications over £5,000. Each local panel meets three times a year to consider applications under £5,000. Applications can be made via the application form on the trust's website or by contacting the trust's director. The website also has a short guide for grant makers and a list of local contacts.
WHO TO APPLY TO Caroline Nicholls, Director, The Compass Centre, Nelson Road, Hounslow, Middlesex TW6 2GW Tel 07836 342495 email caroline_nicholls@baa.com Website www.baa.com/communitiestrust

Harry Bacon Foundation

CC NO 1056500   ESTABLISHED 1996
WHERE FUNDING CAN BE GIVEN UK.
WHO CAN BENEFIT Registered charities.
WHAT IS FUNDED Particularly medical charities and animal welfare.
RANGE OF GRANTS All grants £6,600.
SAMPLE GRANTS RNLI, Imperial Cancer Research, British Heart Foundation, PDSA, Parkinson's Disease Society, the Arthritis and Rheumatism Council for Research, Donkey Sanctuary and World Horse Welfare.
FINANCES Year 2009–10 Income £44,173 Grants £52,800 Assets £192,171
TRUSTEES NatWest Bank Plc.
HOW TO APPLY In writing to the correspondent. The trustees meet regularly to consider applications.
WHO TO APPLY TO The Trust Manager, NatWest Bank Plc, Trustee Department, 5th Floor, Trinity Quay 2, Avon Street, Bristol BS2 0PT Tel 0117 940 3283

The BACTA Charitable Trust

CC NO 328668   ESTABLISHED 1991
WHERE FUNDING CAN BE GIVEN UK.
WHO CAN BENEFIT UK registered charities.
WHAT IS FUNDED Generally to support causes recommended to it by members of the British Amusement Catering Trade Association (BACTA).

WHAT IS NOT FUNDED No grants for overseas charities or religious purposes.

TYPE OF GRANT Long-term support (usually 2–3 years) to a specific project or charity and one-off donations.

RANGE OF GRANTS £1,000 upwards.

SAMPLE GRANTS Macmillan (£38,000); Rainbow Children's Hospice and Motor Neurone Disease Association (£2,000 each); Birmingham Sands and Child Bereavement Charity (£1,000 each).

FINANCES *Year* 2009–10 *Income* £49,282 *Grants* £43,974 *Assets* £80,962

TRUSTEES J Stergides; M Horwood; J Thomas; S Hawkins; J Oversby-Powell; A Boulton; P Weir; J Godden; D Petrie; G Stergides.

HOW TO APPLY In writing to the correspondent via a BACTA member.

WHO TO APPLY TO The Clerk to the Trustees, Alders House, 133 Aldersgate Street, London EC1A 4JA *Tel* 020 7726 9826 *email* info@bacta.org.uk *Website* www.bacta.org.uk

---

■ The Scott Bader Commonwealth Ltd

CC NO 206391   **ESTABLISHED** 1951

WHERE FUNDING CAN BE GIVEN UK, France, South Africa, Croatia, Dubai, USA, Czech Republic, Sweden, Spain.

WHO CAN BENEFIT Projects, activities or charities which: find difficulty raising funds; are innovative, imaginative and pioneering; or are initiated and/or supported by local people. Each year there is a particular area of focus, so applicants should check current focus before applying.

WHAT IS FUNDED Assistance of distressed and needy people of all nationalities. The commonwealth looks for projects, activities or charities which respond to the needs of those who are most underprivileged, disadvantaged, poor or excluded e.g. poor, homeless, vulnerable children, women and minority communities and people affected by poverty, hunger and disease. Also those who encourage the careful use and protection of the earth's resources (those which assist poor rural people to become self-reliant are particularly encouraged); or promote peace-building and democratic participation. The commonwealth also supports the research, development and advancement of education and advancement of education in industrial participation of a nature beneficial to the community.

WHAT IS NOT FUNDED No support for charities concerned with the well-being of animals, individuals in need or organisations sending volunteers abroad. It does not respond to general appeals or support the larger well-established national charities. It does not provide grants for medical research. It does not make up deficits already incurred, or support the arts, museums, travel/adventure, sports clubs or the construction, renovation or maintenance of buildings.

TYPE OF GRANT One-off and funding over a period (3–5 years).

RANGE OF GRANTS Local Fund: £1,000–£5,000. Central Fund: Up to £25,000.

SAMPLE GRANTS Grants were given in two categories. Local funds – UK – donations ranging from £1,000–£6,000 were made in support of the following six charities: Kids Out; Plunket Foundation; The Kings Arms Project; June & Brian Cox Educational Trust, Volunteer Reading Help and Ro Ro Sailing Project. France –

donations ranging from £900–£2,500 were made to St Joseph De Cluny (in Haiti; Kuborroto; Zinder and Momambique) and Ecole FG de Hem. Croatia – donations ranging from £1,200–£1,500 were made to SOS Children's Village Croatia; Croatian Association for the Blind; PUZ; SNAGA and Firefly. Sweden – Handikappidrott Falkenberg who provide sport programmes for the disabled. Czech Republic – School of Hearing for Handicapped Children in Liberec. Spain – the decision was made in 2010 to use their allocation in support of the Haiti disaster. South Africa – donations ranging from £1,500–£1,800 SOS Children's Village; Embocraft; Fulton School for the Deaf; Feed the Babies Fund and 100 Hills Community Helpers. USA – donations of £200 each were made to support the work of Urban Community School; Providence House; GWRC Boy Scouts of America; The Flying House Farms and KIVA. Dubai – donations ranging from £2,000–£4,500 were made to support the work of four charities – Empacs; St Gregorios Balagram; Yusuf Meherally Centre and Rashi Paediatric Therapy Centre. Central Funds – Currently this fund is to support two large community based environmental/educational projects to the value of £25,000 each. In 2010, LHC Foundation Trust I Care – South Africa and Concern Worldwide – Pakistan received the grants from this fund.

FINANCES *Year* 2010 *Income* £175,045 *Grants* £142,000 *Assets* £45,645,000

TRUSTEES The Board of Management: Heather Puddephatt; Richard Stillwell; Richard Stillwell; Jacquie Findlay; Syed Omar Hayat; Anne Atkinson-Clark; Mary Hilary Pinder; Julie Rodgers; John Wojakowsk and Charles Scott.

OTHER INFORMATION There are two categories of grants as follows: Local Funds and Central Funds. Currently the Central Fund supports two large community based environmental/educational projects to the value of £25,000 each.

HOW TO APPLY In writing or by email to the correspondent. Trustees meet quarterly in February, May, September and November.

WHO TO APPLY TO Sue Carter, Secretary, Wollaston Hall, Wellingborough, Northamptonshire NN29 7RL *Tel* 01933 666755 *Fax* 01933 666608 *email* commonwealth_office@scottbader.com *Website* www.scottbader.com

---

■ The Bagri Foundation

CC NO 1000219   **ESTABLISHED** 1990

WHERE FUNDING CAN BE GIVEN Worldwide.

WHO CAN BENEFIT Organisations and individuals.

WHAT IS FUNDED General charitable purposes.

FINANCES *Year* 2009–10 *Income* £61,446 *Grants* £39,389 *Assets* £2,132,575

TRUSTEES Lord Bagri; Hon. A Bagri; Lady Bagri.

HOW TO APPLY In writing to the correspondent.

WHO TO APPLY TO M C Thompson, Secretary, 80 Cannon Street, London EC4N 6EJ *Tel* 020 7280 0089

■ Veta Bailey Charitable Trust

CC NO 1007411   **ESTABLISHED** 1981

WHERE FUNDING CAN BE GIVEN Developing countries (generally those with GNP less than US$1,000 a head), or UK for work in developing countries.

WHO CAN BENEFIT Organisations (UK or overseas based) training medical personnel in developing countries.

WHAT IS FUNDED Training of doctors and other medical personnel and the development of good healthcare practices in third world and developing countries.

WHAT IS NOT FUNDED No grants to individuals.

TYPE OF GRANT One-off grants.

RANGE OF GRANTS Up to £10,000.

SAMPLE GRANTS Previous beneficiaries have included: Orbis (£6,000); International Centre for Eye Health (£5,000); Sightsavers (£4,000); and Gurkha Welfare Trust (£2,800).

FINANCES *Year* 2009–10 *Income* £20,063 *Grants* £25,000

TRUSTEES Brian Worth; John Humphreys; Sue Yates; Dr Madura Gupta; David Trim.

HOW TO APPLY In writing to the correspondent by June, for consideration at a trustees' meeting in August.

WHO TO APPLY TO Brian Worth, Trustee, The Cottage, Tiltups End, Horsley, Stroud, Gloucestershire GL6 0QE *Tel* 01453 833399

■ The Austin Bailey Trust

CC NO 514912   **ESTABLISHED** 1984

WHERE FUNDING CAN BE GIVEN Swansea and worldwide.

WHO CAN BENEFIT Churches, overseas aid organisations and local organisations.

WHAT IS FUNDED The foundation was set up to give approximately 25% of its income towards the advancement of religion by supporting the activities of local churches, 25% to relief agencies in poorer nations and 50% to local charities or branches of national charities to help people who are disabled, infirm or aged.

RANGE OF GRANTS Up to £10,000.

SAMPLE GRANTS Y-Care India – HIV/AIDS programme (£10,000); Mandimba Alliances in Mozambique (£3,000); the Family Centre – Bonymaen (£2,000); St. Teilo's Church, Caereithin (£1,000); Blaen Wern Farm Trust (£600); CORD – education for children in Gaga (Darfur) refugee camp, All Saints Alive Festival and St Gabriel's Church, Swansea (£500 each); Breast Cancer Care and Shelter Cymru (£400 each); and Waterfront Community Church (£250). .

FINANCES *Year* 2009–10 *Income* £63,530 *Grants* £48,479 *Assets* £514,284

TRUSTEES Clive Vernon Austin Bailey, Chair; Mrs Sandra Morton; Archdeacon Robert Williams; Penelope Ryan; Revd Jonathan Davies.

HOW TO APPLY In writing to the correspondent. Applications are considered in May, September and December.

WHO TO APPLY TO Clive Vernon Austin Bailey, Chair, 64 Bosworth Road, New Barnet, Hertfordshire EN5 5LP *Tel* 020 8449 4327

■ The Baily Thomas Charitable Fund

CC NO 262334   **ESTABLISHED** 1970

WHERE FUNDING CAN BE GIVEN UK.

WHO CAN BENEFIT Community groups, support groups and organisations benefiting people affected by learning disability.

WHAT IS FUNDED The trustees restrict their remit to learning disability. This can include residential facilities; respite; sheltered accommodation; crafts and music; support to volunteers; special schools and special needs education; care in the community; day centres; holidays and outings; play schemes; and research.

WHAT IS NOT FUNDED Grants are not normally awarded to individuals. The following areas are unlikely to receive funding: hospices; minibuses except those for residential and/or day care services for the learning disabled; advocacy projects; arts and theatre projects; physical disabilities unless accompanied by significant learning disabilities.

TYPE OF GRANT Capital and revenue. Loans may be made in certain circumstances. Grants are usually one-off.

RANGE OF GRANTS £250 to £130,000.

SAMPLE GRANTS The Development Trust (£200,000 in 2 grants); University of Cardiff (£115,500); Exmoor Calvert Trust (£100,000); King's College London (£80,000); Hansel Foundation (£75,000); Rix-Thompson-Rothenberg Foundation (£70,000); Mental Health Foundation, the National Society for Epilepsy and St George's Association (£50,000 each).

FINANCES *Year* 2009–10 *Income* £3,689,613 *Grants* £4,446,416 *Assets* £75,725,611

TRUSTEES Prof. William I Fraser; Prof. Anne Farmer; Toby N J Nangle; Suzanne Jane Marriott; Kenneth Young.

OTHER INFORMATION Beneficiaries receiving £50,000 or more were listed in the accounts. There were 348 grants made in total.

HOW TO APPLY 'Meetings of the Trustees are usually held in June and early December each year and applications should therefore be submitted no later than 1 May or 1 October for consideration at the next relevant meeting. Late applications will not be considered. If your application is considered under the Small Grants procedure then this will be reviewed by the Trustees ahead of the usual meetings in June and December. Following the meeting all applicants are contacted formally to advise on the status of their application. Please feel free to submit your application whenever you are ready, rather than waiting for the deadline. Applications can be made online via the trust's website.

General applications: funding is normally considered for capital and revenue costs and for both specific projects and for general running/ core costs. Grants are awarded for amounts from £250 and depend on a number of factors including the purpose, the total funding requirement and the potential sources of other funds including, in some cases, matching funding. Normally one-off grants are awarded but exceptionally a new project may be funded over two or three years, subject to satisfactory reports of progress. Grants should normally be taken up within one year of the issue of the grant offer letter which will include conditions relating to the release of the grant. The following areas of work normally fall within the Fund's policy: capital building/renovation/refurbishment works for residential, nursing and respite care, and schools; employment schemes including woodwork, crafts, printing and horticulture; play schemes and play therapy schemes; day and social activities centres including building costs and running costs; support for families, including respite schemes; independent living schemes; support in the community schemes; swimming and hydro-therapy pools and snoezelen rooms.

Research applications: we consider under learning disability the conditions generally referred to as severe learning difficulties, together with autism. In this area, we consider projects concerning children or adults. Learning disability, thus defined, is our priority for funding. We do not give grants for research into or care of those with mental illness or dyslexia. We generally direct our limited funds towards the initiation of research so that it can progress to the point at which there is sufficient data to support an application to one of the major funding bodies. Applications will only be considered from established research workers and will be subject to normal professional peer review procedures. Applications, limited to 5 pages with the type no smaller than Times New Roman 12, should be in the form of a scientific summary with a research plan to include a brief background and a short account of the design of the study and number of subjects, the methods of assessment and analysis, timetable, main outcomes and some indication of other opportunities arising from the support of such research. A detailed budget of costs should be submitted together with a justification for the support requested. Details should be included of any other applications for funding which have been made to other funders and their outcomes, if known. We do not expect to contribute towards university overheads. A one page Curriculum Vitae will be required for each of the personnel actually carrying out the study and for their supervisor together with a note of the total number of their peer reviewed publications and details of the 10 most significant publications. Evidence may be submitted of the approval of the Ethics Committee of the applicant to the study and approval of the University for the application to the Fund. An 80 word lay summary should also be submitted with the scientific summary. Any papers submitted in excess of those stipulated above will not be passed to the Research Committee for consideration. Before submitting a full application, researchers may submit a one page summary of the proposed study so that the Trustees may indicate whether they are prepared to consider a full application.'

WHO TO APPLY TO Ann Cooper, Secretary to the Trustees, c/o TMF Management (UK) Ltd, 400 Capability Green, Luton LU1 3AE *Tel* 01582 439225 *Fax* 01582 439206 *email* info@bailythomas.org.uk *Website* www.bailythomas.org.uk

■ The Baird Trust

SC NO SC016549   **ESTABLISHED** 1873
WHERE FUNDING CAN BE GIVEN Scotland.
WHO CAN BENEFIT Generally, the Church of Scotland.
WHAT IS FUNDED The trust is chiefly concerned with supporting the repair and refurbishment of the churches and halls belonging to the Church of Scotland. It also endows parishes and gives help to the Church of Scotland in its work.
TYPE OF GRANT One-off for capital and revenue.
SAMPLE GRANTS Previous beneficiaries have included Airth Parish Church, Bellshill West Parish Church, Canisbay Church of Scotland, Church of Scotland Board Ministry, Coltness Memorial Church – Newmains, Kinross Parish Church, Kinnaird Church – Dundee, Lodging House Mission, London Road Church – Edinburgh, Newmachar Parish Church, St Andrew's Erskine Parish Church, St Michael's Parish Church – Edinburgh, Scottish Churches House and South Parish Church – East Kilbride.
FINANCES *Year* 2010 *Income* £276,778 *Grants* £160,000 *Assets* £60,000,000
TRUSTEES Marianne Baird; Hon. Mary Coltman; Maj. J Erskine; Revd Dr Johnston McKay; Alan Borthwick; Dr Alison Elliot; Luke Borwick; Walter Barbour.
HOW TO APPLY The application form can be completed online or by paper copy and submitted to the secretary.

WHO TO APPLY TO Ian Mowat, Secretary, 182 Bath Street, Glasgow G2 4HG *Tel* 0141 332 0476 *Fax* 1413310874 *email* info@bairdtrust.org.uk *Website* www.bairdtrust.org.uk

■ The Baker Charitable Trust

CC NO 273629   **ESTABLISHED** 1977
WHERE FUNDING CAN BE GIVEN UK and overseas.
WHO CAN BENEFIT Mainly headquarters organisations.
WHAT IS FUNDED Priority is given to charities concerned with the welfare of Jewish, elderly and disabled people; neurological research; and people with diabetes and epilepsy. Preference is given to charities in which the trust has special interest, knowledge or association.
WHAT IS NOT FUNDED No grants to individuals or non-registered charities.
TYPE OF GRANT Core costs.
RANGE OF GRANTS £250–£10,000; typical grant £500–£3,000.
SAMPLE GRANTS Previous beneficiaries have included British Council Shaare Zedek Medical Centre, Chai Cancer Care, Community Security Trust, Disabled Living Foundation, Friends of Magen David Adom in Great Britain, Hillel Foundation, Institute of Jewish Policy Research, Jewish Women's Aid, Marie Curie Cancer Care, National Society for Epilepsy, Norwood Ltd, United Jewish Israel Appeal, St John's Hospice, United Synagogue, Winged Fellowship and World Jewish Relief.
FINANCES *Year* 2009–10 *Income* £43,925 *Grants* £43,860 *Assets* £1,152,878
TRUSTEES Dr Harvey Baker; Dr Adrienne Baker.
HOW TO APPLY In writing to the correspondent. The trustees meet to consider applications in January, April, July and October.
WHO TO APPLY TO Dr Harvey Baker, Trustee, 16 Sheldon Avenue, Highgate, London N6 4JT *Tel* 020 8340 5970

■ The Roy and Pixie Baker Charitable Trust

CC NO 1101988   **ESTABLISHED** 1995
WHERE FUNDING CAN BE GIVEN North East of England.
WHO CAN BENEFIT Charitable organisations.
WHAT IS FUNDED Medical research, education, heritage, relief-in-need.
TYPE OF GRANT One-off and recurrent.
RANGE OF GRANTS Up to £4,000.
SAMPLE GRANTS St Clare's Hospice and Marie Curie Cancer Care (£4,000 each); Digital Voice – Young Travellers Multimedia Project and Dementia Care Partnership (£2,500 each); Macmillan Cancer Support and Cathedral Church of St. Nicholas (£2,000 each); National Rheumatoid Arthritis Society and the Wheels Project (£1,000 each); and React (£500).
FINANCES *Year* 2009–10 *Income* £58,421 *Grants* £57,500 *Assets* £2,821,803
TRUSTEES A E Glenton; G W Straker; L A Caisley; D T Irvin; W J Dryden.
HOW TO APPLY In writing to the correspondent, providing full back up information. Trustees' meetings are held half yearly. The trustees require a receipt from the donee in respect of each grant.
WHO TO APPLY TO The Trustees, Ryecroft Glenton, 32 Portland Terrace, Newcastle upon Tyne NE2 1QP *Tel* 0191 281 1292 *email* bakercharitabletrust@ryecroft-glenton.co.uk

The C Alma Baker Trust

CC NO 1113864   **ESTABLISHED** 1981

WHERE FUNDING CAN BE GIVEN UK and overseas, particularly New Zealand.

WHO CAN BENEFIT Individuals or scientific research institutions benefiting young adults, farmers, academics, research workers and students.

WHAT IS FUNDED Agriculture and education with an agricultural connection, particularly in New Zealand and UK. (a) Agricultural research particularly New Zealand. (b) Massey University, New Zealand – Wye College, UK, Undergraduate Scheme. (c) UK YFC Scheme for young farmers to experience New Zealand farming on the trust's property in New Zealand. (d) Annual Travel Fellowship New Zealand–UK, UK–New Zealand. (e) Maori Language Education Scholarship, Wailato University, New Zealand. (f) Postgraduate study grants for agriculture-related subjects in New Zealand. (g) Small grants to other environmental charitable organisations.

WHAT IS NOT FUNDED No general education grants.

TYPE OF GRANT Range of grants, though normally one-off annual grants.

SAMPLE GRANTS Malaysian Palm Oil Association (£400); Books in Homes Programme (£300); and ZANE – Zimbabwe a National Emergency Appeal (£200).

FINANCES *Year* 2009–10 *Income* £90,119 *Grants* £78,039 *Assets* £9,428,192

TRUSTEES C R Boyes, Chair; R Moore; S F B Taylor.

PUBLICATIONS Limestone Downs Annual Report in New Zealand.

OTHER INFORMATION The trust's main asset is Limestone Downs, a sheep and beef property in the North Island, New Zealand utilised for new ideas and development in agriculture to be explored and debated in a working farm environment.

HOW TO APPLY In writing to the correspondent.

WHO TO APPLY TO The Clerk to the Trustees, 20 Hartford Road, Huntingdon, Cambridgeshire PE29 3QH *Tel* 01480 411331 *Website* www.calmabakertrust.co.uk

The Balcombe Charitable Trust

CC NO 267172   **ESTABLISHED** 1975

WHERE FUNDING CAN BE GIVEN UK and overseas.

WHO CAN BENEFIT Registered charities benefiting children and young adults, students, at risk groups, disabled people, people disadvantaged by poverty, socially isolated people, and people who are sick.

WHAT IS FUNDED Education; the environment; health and welfare.

WHAT IS NOT FUNDED No grants to individuals or non-registered charities.

TYPE OF GRANT One-off and recurrent grants.

RANGE OF GRANTS £1,000–£86,500.

SAMPLE GRANTS Durrell Wildlife Conservation Trust (£86,500); Oxfam (£50,000); Action Aid (£41,000); the United Kingdom Committee for UNICEF (£36,000); Princess Royal Trust for Carers (£30,000); NSPCC and the Samaritans (£25,000 each); Money for Madagascar (£23,000); Amnesty International (£20,000); the Esther Benjamin's Trust (£17,000); the Andrew Lees Trust (£15,000); Emmaus UK (£12,000); Young People in Focus Limited, Breast Cancer Care and Mind (£10,000 each); Living Coasts (£9,000); Thai Children's Trust (£7,000); the Theatre Royal Bath Limited and Brook Advisory Centres Limited (£5,000 each);

Volunteer Reading Help (£2,000); and Age Exchange Reminiscence (£1,000).

FINANCES *Year* 2009–10 *Income* £678,219 *Grants* £664,101 *Assets* £27,829,055

TRUSTEES R A Kreitman; Patricia M Kreitman; Nicholas Brown.

HOW TO APPLY In writing to the correspondent.

WHO TO APPLY TO Jonathan W Prevezer, c/o Citroen Wells Chartered Accountants, Devonshire House, 1 Devonshire Street, London W1W 5DR *Tel* 020 7304 2000 *email* jonathan.prevezer@citroenwells.co.uk

The Andrew Balint Charitable Trust

CC NO 273691   **ESTABLISHED** 1961

WHERE FUNDING CAN BE GIVEN UK; Israel; Hungary.

WHO CAN BENEFIT Charitable organisations; Jewish organisations.

WHAT IS FUNDED General charitable causes; health, elderly, ex-service people, Jewish faith, and disability organisations.

TYPE OF GRANT One off and recurring.

RANGE OF GRANTS £50–£20,000.

SAMPLE GRANTS Nightingale House (£20,000); Hungarian Senior Citizens (£7,700); Former Employee Trust (£6,500); Toth – Gabor (£5,400); American Jewish Joint Distribution Committee (£5,000); United Jewish Israel Appeal (£2,600); and Goldschein Joseph (£1,000). A further 36 grants of less than £1,000 were also made.

FINANCES *Year* 2010–11 *Income* £51,843 *Grants* £55,712 *Assets* £1,671,906

TRUSTEES Dr Gabriel Balint-Kurti; Mrs Angela Balint; Mr Roy Balint-Kurti; Mr Daniel Balint-Kurti.

OTHER INFORMATION The Andrew Balint Charitable Trust, The George Balint Charitable Trust, The Paul Charitable Trust and the Trust for Former Employees of Balint Companies are jointly administered. They have some trustees in common and are independent in other matters.

HOW TO APPLY In writing to the correspondent.

WHO TO APPLY TO Carter Backer Winter, Enterprise House, 21 Buckle Street, London E1 8NN *Tel* 020 7309 3800

The George Balint Charitable Trust

CC NO 267482   **ESTABLISHED** 1961

WHERE FUNDING CAN BE GIVEN UK; Israel; Hungary.

WHO CAN BENEFIT Charitable organisations; individuals.

WHAT IS FUNDED General; education; medical care and research; Jewish.

RANGE OF GRANTS £150–£15,000.

SAMPLE GRANTS United Jewish Israel Appeal (£15,000); Hungarian Senior Citizens (£10,200); Former Employees Trust (£8,500); Neviot Olam Institution and British Friends of Bar Ilan University (£2,000 each); Imperial College London (£1,000); Norwood: Children and Families First (£750); and Marie Curie Cancer Care (£200).

FINANCES *Year* 2010–11 *Income* £18,618 *Grants* £48,000

TRUSTEES Dr Andrew Balint; Mr George Rothschild; Mrs Marion Balint-Farkas.

OTHER INFORMATION 'The George Balint Charitable Trust, the Paul Balint Charitable Trust and The Charitable Trust for Former Employees of Balint Companies operate from the same premises and are jointly administered. They have some trustees in common and are independent in all other matters.'

HOW TO APPLY In writing to the correspondent.

WHO TO APPLY TO Mr David Kramer, Carter Backer Winter, Enterprise House, 21 Buckle Street, London E1 8NN *Tel* 020 7309 3800

■ The Paul Balint Charitable Trust

CC NO 273690   **ESTABLISHED** 1977

WHERE FUNDING CAN BE GIVEN UK; Hungary; Israel.

WHO CAN BENEFIT Charitable organisations.

WHAT IS FUNDED General charitable purposes; medical research; education; elderly assistance; relief of poverty.

FINANCES *Year* 2010–11 *Income* £3,540 *Grants* £48,000

TRUSTEES Dr Andrew Balint; Dr Gabriel Balint-Kurti; Dr Marc Balint; Mr Paul Balint.

OTHER INFORMATION The Andrew Balint Charitable Trust, The George Balint Charitable Trust, The Paul Balint Charitable Trust and the Trust for Former Employees of Balint Companies are jointly administered. They have some trustees in common and are independent in other matters.

HOW TO APPLY In writing to the correspondent.

WHO TO APPLY TO Dr Andrew Balint, Administrator, 15 Portland Court, 101 Hendon Lane, London N3 3SH *Tel* 020 8346 1266

■ The Albert Casanova Ballard Deceased Trust

CC NO 201759   **ESTABLISHED** 1962

WHERE FUNDING CAN BE GIVEN Within a 7-mile radius of Plymouth.

WHO CAN BENEFIT Local charities, local branches of national organisations and individuals.

WHAT IS FUNDED General charitable purposes, health, welfare and young people. Grants are made to schoolchildren towards uniforms and other costs.

WHAT IS NOT FUNDED The trust cannot fund anyone or any charity organisation outside of Plymouth (a seven-mile radius from the city centre, within the city of Plymouth boundary, is the trust's limit).

RANGE OF GRANTS Charities: £150–£2,500. Individuals: £100–£200.

SAMPLE GRANTS YMCA (£2,750); Ford Youth and Community Centre (£1,750); Macmillan Cancer Support (£1,500); St Luke's Hospice (£1,250); and PLIMS (£1,200); Mutley Baptist Youth and YWCA (£900 each); Marjon Basketball (£800); Highbury Trust (£600); Parkinson's Disease Society (£500); Lifeline Resources (£400); and Pregnancy Crisis Centre (£300).

FINANCES *Year* 2009–10 *Income* £48,630 *Grants* £48,650 *Assets* £893,929

TRUSTEES Kenneth Banfield, Chair; Audrey Houston; Margaret Pengelly; Joy Rendle; Nigel Norris; Frances Norris; Lynn Smith.

OTHER INFORMATION The 2009–10 grant total included the sum of £22,000 donated to 169 individuals.

HOW TO APPLY In writing to the correspondent. Applications from local charities are considered in November and notices appear in the Evening Herald and The Plymouth Extra around that time. There are no application forms available. Grants for individuals are made once a year in June. Grants will NOT be entertained outside these periods.

WHO TO APPLY TO The Trustees, 6 Victory Street, Keyham, Plymouth PL2 2BY

■ The Ballinger Charitable Trust

CC NO 1121739   **ESTABLISHED** 1994

WHERE FUNDING CAN BE GIVEN North east England, Tyne and Wear.

WHO CAN BENEFIT Registered charities only.

WHAT IS FUNDED 'The focus of the Ballinger Charitable Trust is currently to support projects in the North East of England, principally by providing funds that: support the health, development and well being of young people; support the elderly; improve the quality of life for people and communities; promote cultural/ arts projects based in the North East of England.'

WHAT IS NOT FUNDED No grants to individuals or sponsorships.

SAMPLE GRANTS Previous beneficiaries have included: Bath Institute of Medical Engineering Limited, Durham Association of Clubs for Young People, the Lady Hoare Trust and St Mary's Cathedral.

TRUSTEES Diana Ballinger; John Flynn; Andrew Ballinger; Nicola Crowther.

HOW TO APPLY An online application form can be completed in the first instance at the trust's website. The trust may then make contact at a later date for additional documentation. Alternatively, the application form can be downloaded with the completed application retuned by post. For amounts up to £5,000, the trust is happy to receive a written request in the form of a letter. There is no annual deadline. The larger the fund applied for, the greater the amount of detail will be required in the application form. A decision may take up to six months depending on the size of fund applied for.

WHO TO APPLY TO M S A Ballinger, Trustee, P O Box 245, Morpeth, Northumberland NE61 3DA *Tel* 0191 488 0520 *email* info@ ballingercharitabletrust.org.uk *Website* www. ballingercharitabletrust.org.uk

■ Balmain Charitable Trust

CC NO 1079972   **ESTABLISHED** 1998

WHERE FUNDING CAN BE GIVEN UK.

WHO CAN BENEFIT Charitable organisations.

WHAT IS FUNDED General charitable purposes.

RANGE OF GRANTS Mostly £1,000–£2,000.

SAMPLE GRANTS British Red Cross and Oxfam (£8,000 each); Great Bustard Group (£6,000); Second Chance (£5,200); Royal Opera House Foundation (£5,000); Great Ormond Street Hospital (£4,000); Wiltshire Wildlife Trust and the National Art Collections Fund (£3,000 each); Crisis, Help for Heroes and the National Trust (£2,000); Age Concern, Cerebra, Foxglove Covert and Soil Association (£1,000 each); and the Royal Academy (£190).

FINANCES *Year* 2009–10 *Income* £104,044 *Grants* £109,390 *Assets* £2,427,222

TRUSTEES Paul G Eaton; Andrew B Tappin; Donald S Balmain; Iain D Balmain; Leonora D Balmain; Charles A G Wells.

OTHER INFORMATION Many of the beneficiaries are supported year after year.

HOW TO APPLY In writing to the correspondent.

WHO TO APPLY TO Trust Administrator, c/o Rutter and Alhusen, 2 Longmead, Shaftesbury, Dorset SP7 8PL

■ The Balmore Trust

SC NO SC008930   **ESTABLISHED** 1980

WHERE FUNDING CAN BE GIVEN Developing countries and UK, with a preference for Strathclyde.

WHO CAN BENEFIT Organisations.

WHAT IS FUNDED Two-thirds of grants are given to overseas projects and the remainder to local projects in the UK, working in the areas of education, health, alleviation of poverty and community development. Grant giving in the UK is concentrated mainly in the Glasgow area and favours families, teenagers, and women's aid groups. Overseas, the trust has close connections with community development programmes in India (Kolkata, Rajasthan and Kerala), Burma and Africa (Kenya, South Africa, Swaziland, Lesotho and Namibia).

WHAT IS NOT FUNDED No grants to individuals.

RANGE OF GRANTS £50–£7,000.

SAMPLE GRANTS Previous beneficiaries have included Church House – Bridgeton, Daynes Education Fund – South Africa, East Dunbartonshire Women's Aid, Family Action in Rogerfield and Easterhouse, Friends of CINI – India, Glasgow Children's Holiday Scheme, Humura Child Care Family – Uganda, Inverclyde Youth for Christ Reality at Work, Mission Aviation Fellowship, the Village Storytelling Centre – Pollok and Wells for India – Rajasthan.

FINANCES *Year* 2010–11 *Income* £33,940 *Grants* £25,000

TRUSTEES J Riches; G Burns; J Eldridge; B Holman; Ms R Jarvis; Ms R Riches.

PUBLICATIONS Newsletter available on website

OTHER INFORMATION The Balmore Trust distributes the profits of the Coach House charity craft shop as well as other donations. The trust's policy in grant making is increasingly to build on partnerships already established.

HOW TO APPLY The trust is run entirely voluntarily and the trust states that it is unlikely that money will be available for new applicants, unless they have a personal link with the trust or its shop, the Coach House charity craft shop.

WHO TO APPLY TO The Secretary, Viewfield, Balmore, Torrance, Glasgow G64 4AE *Tel* 01360 620742 *email* mailto:balmoretrust.org.uk *Website* www.balmoretrust.org.uk

■ The Balney Charitable Trust

CC NO 288575   **ESTABLISHED** 1983

WHERE FUNDING CAN BE GIVEN UK, with a preference for north Buckinghamshire and north Bedfordshire.

WHO CAN BENEFIT Individuals and registered charities.

WHAT IS FUNDED The furtherance of any religious and charitable purposes in connection with the parishes of Chicheley, North Crawley and the SCAN Group i.e. Sherington, Astwood, Hardmead and churches with a Chester family connection; the provision of housing for persons in needy circumstances; agriculture, forestry and armed service charities; care of older people and people who are sick and disabled.

WHAT IS NOT FUNDED Local community organisations and individuals outside north Buckinghamshire and north Bedfordshire.

TYPE OF GRANT Start-up costs, capital grants (including contributions to building projects, e.g. local churches) and research. Funding for up to three years will be considered.

RANGE OF GRANTS £25–£5,000.

SAMPLE GRANTS Previously: St Lawrence Church – Chicheley (£7,500); National Trust – Montecute

House (£7,000 in two grants); Queen Alexandra Hospital Home (£5,000); CHIT, Combat Stress, Motor Neurone Disease Association and St Luke's Hospital for the Clergy (£2,000 each); Emmaus Village – Carlton, Help for Heroes, MS Therapy Centre and Tree Aid – Ghana Village Tree Enterprise (£1,000 each); and Fun 4 Young People (£500).

FINANCES *Year* 2009–10 *Income* £90,544 *Grants* £78,441 *Assets* £800,374

TRUSTEES Maj. J G B Chester; R Ruck-Keene.

HOW TO APPLY In writing to the correspondent. Applications are acknowledged if an sae is enclosed, otherwise if the charity has not received a reply within six weeks the application has not been successful.

WHO TO APPLY TO Miss Helen Chapman, The Chicheley Estate, Bartlemas Office, Paveham, Bedford MK43 7PF *Tel* 01234 823663

■ The Baltic Charitable Fund

CC NO 279194   **ESTABLISHED** 1979

WHERE FUNDING CAN BE GIVEN UK, with a preference for the City of London.

WHO CAN BENEFIT Registered charities benefiting residents of the City of London, seafarers, fishermen, and ex-service and service people.

WHAT IS FUNDED Registered charities only which must be connected with the City of London, shipping or the military forces.

WHAT IS NOT FUNDED No support for advertising or charity dinners, and so on.

TYPE OF GRANT One-off.

RANGE OF GRANTS £300–£36,000.

SAMPLE GRANTS City of London School for Girls (£36,000); Lord Mayor's Appeal (£7,500); Marine Society and Sea Cadets, Sailors Society and UCL Development Fund (£5,000 each); the Mission to Seafarers (£3,600); Trinity Sailing Trust (£3,000); Falkland Islands Chapel (£2,000); Jubilee Sailing Trust (£2,500); Medway Seaman's Trust (£1,000); Royal British Legion Poppy Appeal (£500); and Merchant Navy Medal Award (£300).

FINANCES *Year* 2009–10 *Income* £40,439 *Grants* £22,450 *Assets* £1,762,582

TRUSTEES The directors of the Baltic Exchange Limited.

HOW TO APPLY Unsolicited applications are not considered.

WHO TO APPLY TO The Company Secretary, The Baltic Exchange, 38 St Mary Axe, London EC3A 8BH

■ The Bamford Charitable Foundation

CC NO 279848   **ESTABLISHED** 1979

WHERE FUNDING CAN BE GIVEN Within a 40-mile radius of Rocester.

WHO CAN BENEFIT Mainly local organisations.

WHAT IS FUNDED General charitable purposes.

TYPE OF GRANT One-off.

RANGE OF GRANTS Typically up to £15,000, with larger grants occasionally considered.

SAMPLE GRANTS Denstone Foundation (£60,000); Heart of Mary Villa (£15,000); Racing Welfare (£5,000); Morecambe Victim Trust Fund (£3,000); ChildLine, Dyslexia Action and Venetian Heritage Onlus (£2,500 each); and Kate's Home Nursing (£1,000).

FINANCES *Year* 2009–10 *Income* £50,518 *Grants* £93,250 *Assets* £1,377,943

TRUSTEES Sir A P Bamford; Lady C Bamford.

OTHER INFORMATION In 2009–10, four further small grants were made totalling £750.

HOW TO APPLY In writing to the correspondent. 'Successful applicants are required to demonstrate to the trustees that the receipt of the grant is wholly necessary to enable them to fulfil their own objectives.'

WHO TO APPLY TO S E R Owens, Administrator, J C Bamford Excavators Ltd, Lakeside Works, Rocester, Uttoxeter, Staffordshire ST14 5JP

■ The Banbury Charities

CC NO 201418   **ESTABLISHED** 1961

WHERE FUNDING CAN BE GIVEN Banbury or its immediate environs.

WHO CAN BENEFIT Individuals and groups.

WHAT IS FUNDED General charitable purposes.

WHAT IS NOT FUNDED No grants for debts or ongoing expenses.

TYPE OF GRANT One-off grants.

RANGE OF GRANTS Up to £35,000.

SAMPLE GRANTS Banbury Welfare Trust (£35,000); Lady Arran (£28,000); Katherine House Hospice (£10,000); The Glebe Recreational Charity (£9,000); Marlborough Road Methodist Church (£8,000); Balscote Village Hall and Samaritans (£5,000 each); Life Education Centres (£4,000); Azad Football Club (£2,000) and Focus Counselling Service Banbury and Rotary Club of Banbury (£1,000 each).

FINANCES Year 2010 Income £373,913 Grants £321,453 Assets £4,345,180

TRUSTEES C F Blackwell; C A Brodey; H Madeiros; J P Friswell; Mrs J W May; Mrs J M Colegrave; K P Mallon; M A Humphris; N J Morris; A M Heritage; J Briggs; J Justice; C Clarke.

OTHER INFORMATION The Banbury Charities are The Bridge Estate, Lady Arran's Charity, Banbury Arts and Educational Charity, Banbury Sick Poor Fund, Banbury Almshouse Charity, and the Banbury Welfare Trust. The grant total in 2010 included £119,000 given to 428 individuals.

HOW TO APPLY In writing to the correspondent.

WHO TO APPLY TO Anthony Scott Andrews, Clerk to the Trustees, 36 West Bar, Banbury, Oxfordshire OX16 9RU Tel 01295 251234

■ William P Bancroft (No 2) Charitable Trust and Jenepher Gillett Trust

CC NO 288968   **ESTABLISHED** 1984

WHERE FUNDING CAN BE GIVEN UK and overseas.

WHO CAN BENEFIT Mainly charities benefiting Quakers.

WHAT IS FUNDED Mainly Quaker charities or projects including education; peace & reconciliation work; homeless charities.

WHAT IS NOT FUNDED No appeals unconnected with Quakers. No support for individual or student grant applications.

TYPE OF GRANT Buildings, core costs, endowment, one-off and start-up costs. Funding of up to three years will be considered.

RANGE OF GRANTS £500–£5,000.

SAMPLE GRANTS Charney Manor Quake Course (£14,000); BYM (£5,000); Woodbrooke College (£4,000); Quaker Social Action (£2,500); Quaker Peace Centre – Capetown, Fellowship of Reconciliation and Street Talk (£1,000 each); West Midland Quaker Peace Education, Scholarships for Street Kids and Oxford Homeless Medical Fund (£500 each).

FINANCES Year 2010 Income £42,575 Grants £47,500 Assets £787,187

TRUSTEES Dr Godfrey Gillett; Martin B Gillett; Dr D S Gillett; Mrs Jenepher Moseley; Dr C Bancroft Wolff; Mrs M McNaughton.

HOW TO APPLY In writing to the correspondent. Trustees meet in May, applications must be received no later than April.

WHO TO APPLY TO Dr D S Gillett, Trustee, 13 Woodbury Park Road, Tunbridge Wells, Kent TN4 9NQ Tel 01892 528 150

■ The Band Trust

CC NO 279802   **ESTABLISHED** 1976

WHERE FUNDING CAN BE GIVEN Worldwide in practice UK.

WHO CAN BENEFIT Registered UK charities.

WHAT IS FUNDED People with disabilities, children and young people, scholarships, hospices and hospitals, education, older people and people who are disadvantaged.

WHAT IS NOT FUNDED No grants are made to individuals.

TYPE OF GRANT One-off and recurring.

RANGE OF GRANTS Up to £50,000.

SAMPLE GRANTS CLIC Sargent (£45,000); Explore (£30,000); Community Service Volunteers (£15,000); Livability (£10,000); Pakenham Water Mill Appeal (£7,500); West London Action for Children (£5,000); Barristers' Benevolent Fund (£2,000); and the NSPCC (£1,500). Scholarship funds were awarded to the Florence Nightingale Foundation (£28,000) and the Honourable Society of Gray's Inn (£25,000).

FINANCES Year 2009–10 Income £738,301 Grants £655,035 Assets £22,279,625

TRUSTEES The Hon. Lavinia Wallop; The Hon. Nicholas Wallop; Richard J S Mason; Bruce G Streather.

HOW TO APPLY The trust's accounts state that 'the trustees do not wish to receive unsolicited applications for grants'. The trustees identify potential recipients themselves, although their method of doing this is not known. One would assume that they need to be made aware of organisations that fit in with their objectives. The trustees' meetings are held three times a year.

WHO TO APPLY TO Richard J S Mason, Trustee, Moore Stephens, 150 Aldersgate Street, London EC1A 4AB Tel 020 7334 9191 Fax 020 7248 3408 email richard.mason@moorestephens.com

■ The Barbers' Company General Charities

CC NO 265579   **ESTABLISHED** 1973

WHERE FUNDING CAN BE GIVEN UK.

WHO CAN BENEFIT Organisations and individuals.

WHAT IS FUNDED General charitable purposes, including medical education and nursing.

WHAT IS NOT FUNDED No grants to unsolicited applications.

RANGE OF GRANTS £1,000–£50,000.

SAMPLE GRANTS Kings College London (£50,000); Royal College of Surgeons (£40,000); Phyliss Tuckwell Hospice (£22,000); The Guildhall School Trust (£6,400); Reeds School (£5,000); City of London Freeman's School (£2,600) and ABF – The Big Curry, Treloars and The Lord Mayor's Appeal (£1,000 each).

FINANCES Year 2009–10 Income £208,636 Grants £182,821 Assets £1,306,946

TRUSTEES The Barbers Company.

OTHER INFORMATION The trust no longer has direct contact with the hairdressing fraternity. However, a small amount is given each year to satisfy its historical links.

HOW TO APPLY The charities do not welcome unsolicited applications.

WHO TO APPLY TO The Clerk, Barber-Surgeons' Hall, Monkwell Square, Wood Street, London EC2Y 5BL

■ The Barbour Foundation

CC NO 328081   **ESTABLISHED** 1988

WHERE FUNDING CAN BE GIVEN Mainly Tyne and Wear, Northumberland and South Tyneside.

WHO CAN BENEFIT The trust likes to support local activities, and also supports local branches of national charities.

WHAT IS FUNDED Relief of patients suffering from any form of illness or disease, promotion of research into causes of such illnesses; furtherance of education; preservation of buildings and countryside of environmental, historical or architectural interest; relief of people in need. Charities working in the fields of infrastructure development, religious umbrella bodies and animal welfare will also be considered.

WHAT IS NOT FUNDED No support for: requests from outside the geographical area; requests from educational establishments; individual applications, unless backed by a particular charitable organisation; capital grants for building projects.

TYPE OF GRANT Capital, core costs, one-off, project, research, running costs, recurring costs, salaries, and start-up costs. Funding for up to one year will be considered.

RANGE OF GRANTS Small grants £50–£500. Main grants £500 upwards.

SAMPLE GRANTS Previously Northumbria Youth Action Limited (£30,000); Alzheimer's Trust (£13,000); Action Medical Research (£10,000); Derwentside Domestic Abuse Centre, Genesis Appeal and Shelter (£5,000 each); Fairbridge Tyne and Wear (£3,000); Wellbeing of Women (£2,000); Listening Books and Rainbow Trust (£1,500 each); and Butterwick Hospice Care, Save the Children, Someone Cares, Textile Benevolent Association and Whizz-Kids (£1,000 each).

FINANCES *Year* 2009–10 *Income* £12,493 *Grants* £924,871

TRUSTEES Dame Margaret Barbour, Chair; Henry Jacob Tavroges; Helen Humphrey.

OTHER INFORMATION This figure for 2009–10 is an unusually low income for this charity.

HOW TO APPLY On an application form available from PO Box 21, Guisborough, Cleveland, TS14 8YH. The applications should include full back-up information, a statement of accounts and the official charity number of the applicant. A main grants meeting is held every three to four months to consider grants of £500 plus. Applications are processed and researched by the administrator and secretary and further information may be requested. A small grants meeting is held monthly to consider grants up to £500. The trust always receives more applications than it can support. Even if a project fits its policy priority areas, it may not be possible to make a grant.

WHO TO APPLY TO Harold Tavroges, J Barbour & Sons Ltd, PO BOX 37, Jarrow, Tyne & Wear NE32 3YT *Tel* 0191 455 4444 *Website* www.barbour.com

---

■ The Barcapel Foundation

SC NO SC009211   **ESTABLISHED** 1964

WHERE FUNDING CAN BE GIVEN Scotland and other parts of the UK.

WHO CAN BENEFIT Charitable organisations.

WHAT IS FUNDED The three priority areas of interest for funding are health, heritage and youth. (1) Health: 'The foundation supports all aspects of health, a wide ranging remit acknowledging that health is a state of complete physical, mental and social well-being and not merely the absence of disease or infirmity.' (2) Heritage: 'The original financiers of the foundation had a keen interest in our heritage, specifying that one of the foundations aims was *the preservation and beautification of historic properties.* The foundation continues to support the built environment and will support our literary and artistic heritage as well as architectural. (3) Youth: 'The *development of people* is one of the principal objectives of the Foundation. Whilst charitable giving can be used to alleviate problems it can also be used to empower people and this is particularly true of the young.'

WHAT IS NOT FUNDED No support for: individual applications for travel or similar; organisations or individuals engaged in promoting religious or political beliefs; applications for funding costs of feasibility studies or similar. Support is unlikely to be given for local charities whose work takes place outside the British Isles.

RANGE OF GRANTS Up to £50,000.

SAMPLE GRANTS The Royal Museum Project, Riverside Museum Appeal, Fairbridge and National Galleries of Scotland (£50,000 each); University of Westminster, The Cancer Thermal Ablation Fund and Castlemilk Youth Project (£25,000 each).

FINANCES *Year* 2009–10 *Income* £216,937

TRUSTEES Robert Wilson, Chair; James Wilson; Andrew Wilson; Jed Wilson; Clement Wilson; Niall Scott.

HOW TO APPLY A preliminary application form can be downloaded from the foundation's website. Please ensure that interests, aims and objectives are compatible with those of the foundation. Applications are not accepted by email.

WHO TO APPLY TO Moira Givens, The Mews, Skelmorlie Castle, Skelmorlie, Ayrshire PA17 5EY *Tel* 01475 521616 *email* admin@barcapelfoundation.org *Website* www.barcapelfoundation.org

---

■ Barchester Healthcare Foundation

CC NO 1083272   **ESTABLISHED** 2000

WHERE FUNDING CAN BE GIVEN England, Scotland and Wales.

WHO CAN BENEFIT Individuals and organisations.

WHAT IS FUNDED Older people and other adults (18 plus) with a physical or mental disability whose health and/or social care needs cannot be met by the statutory public sector or by the individual. 'Our mission is to make a difference to the lives of older people and other adults with a physical or mental disability, supporting practical solutions that lead to increased personal independence, self-sufficiency and dignity.'

WHAT IS NOT FUNDED Funds will not normally be given to: provide services for which the health and social care authorities have a statutory responsibility; services normally offered in a care home operated by Barchester Healthcare

or by any other company; indirect services such as help lines, newsletters, leaflets or research; core/ running costs or salaries or give financial support to general projects; major building projects; provide continuing year on year support for a project following an initial grant. Any further applications in respect of the same beneficiary will be considered after a period of three years from the initial grant.
The trustees reserve the right to put a cap on grants to a single charity (including all its branches) in any one year.

RANGE OF GRANTS Up to £5,000.

SAMPLE GRANTS The Care Management Group (£2,000); NMBVA (£1,500); Cookley Playing Field and Village Hall Association, Integrated Neurological Services, Manordeillo & District Senior Citizens Association and the Sunnybank Trust (£1,000 each).

FINANCES *Year* 2010 *Income* £311,000 *Grants* £109,000 *Assets* £162,000

TRUSTEES Prof. Malcolm Johnson; Elizabeth Mills; Lesley Flory; Christopher Vellenoweth; Michael D Parsons; Janice Robinson; Nick Oulton.

OTHER INFORMATION The Barchester Healthcare Foundation was established by Barchester Healthcare to reinvest into the communities it serves.

HOW TO APPLY Application can be made via the foundation's website. A decision usually takes approximately ten weeks from the date of application. All applications supported by Barchester Healthcare staff will be given priority.

WHO TO APPLY TO The Administrator, Suite 201, The Chambers, Chelsea Harbour, London SW10 0XF *Tel* 0800 328 3328 *email* info@bhcfoundation. org.uk *Website* www.bhcfoundation.org.uk

---

■ The Barclay Foundation

CC NO 803696   **ESTABLISHED** 1990

WHERE FUNDING CAN BE GIVEN Not defined, in practice, the UK.

WHO CAN BENEFIT Registered charities or organisations undertaking charitable activities.

WHAT IS FUNDED Medical research; young people; the elderly; advancement of religion; people with disabilities; the sick; and the disadvantaged.

TYPE OF GRANT Projects and one-off grants.

RANGE OF GRANTS £1,000–£1.2 million.

SAMPLE GRANTS Great Ormond Street Hospital and Alder Hey Imagine Appeal (£1 million each); The Prince's Foundation (£275,000); University of Oxford (£160,000); The Healing Foundation (£100,000); The Prince's Trust (£60,000); CFS Research Foundation (£50,000); Wellbeing for Women (£20,000); Make-A-Wish Foundation (£18,000); Autism Treatment Centre of America (£12,000); Dorset Orthopaedic Limited (£11,000); Barts and the London Charity (£10,000); Muscular Dystrophy Campaign; Evelina Children's Hospital (£5,000 each); and the Asda Foundation (£1,000).

FINANCES *Year* 2010 *Income* £3,300,751 *Grants* £3,302,305 *Assets* £50,069,000

TRUSTEES Sir David Barclay; Sir Frederick Barclay; Lord Alistair McAlpine of West Green; Aidan Barclay; Howard Barclay.

OTHER INFORMATION Two individuals received grants totalling £12,000

HOW TO APPLY Applications should be in writing, clearly outlining the details of the proposed project, (for medical research, as far as possible in lay terms). The total cost and duration should be stated, also the amount, if any, which has already been raised. Following an initial screening, applications are selected

according to their merits, suitability and funds available. Visits are usually made to projects where substantial funds are involved. The foundation welcomes reports as to progress and requires these on completion of a project.

WHO TO APPLY TO Michael Seal, 3rd Floor, 20 St James's Street, London SW1A 1ES *Tel* 020 7915 0915 *email* mseal@ellerman.co.uk

---

■ The Baring Foundation

CC NO 258583   **ESTABLISHED** 1969

WHERE FUNDING CAN BE GIVEN England and Wales, with a special interest in London, Merseyside, Cornwall and Devon; also UK charities working with NGO partners in developing countries.

WHO CAN BENEFIT Varies from programme to programme; please refer to the foundation's guidelines.

WHAT IS FUNDED Strengthening the voluntary sector, arts and international development.

WHAT IS NOT FUNDED See guidelines for specific programmes. More generally: appeals or charities set up to support statutory organisations; animal welfare charities; grant maintained, private, or local education authority schools or their parent teachers associations; individuals.

SAMPLE GRANTS Children in Crisis (£165,500 over 3 years), to train teachers in South Kivu, Democratic Republic of Congo and develop the capacity of Eben Ezer Ministries; Law Centres Federation (£149,500 over 2 years), to develop a new business model for third sector agencies delivering specialist legal advice; Advice UK (£135,000 over 2 years), to secure evidence of effectiveness and economic value of the BOLD intervention, develop a sustainable method for it and secure support of central and local government; Art in Hospital – Scotland (£75,000 over 3 years), core funding, to enable the employment of an artist co-ordinator, and develop support documentation, evaluation and publication on website as an accessible resource for others and professional development for artists; Green Candle Dance Company (£45,000 over 3 years), core funding, towards core staff costs to underpin the projects that benefit a wide range of London based elders and many existing and emerging practitioners across the country; Legal Aid Practitioners Group (£20,000 over 2 years), to encourage parliamentary involvement and scrutiny of Legal Aid reform by supporting the development of the All Party Parliamentary Group on Legal Aid and developing a team of Legal Aid Champions; DG Legal (£10,000), to carry out feasibility and planning work on a range of activities associated with the rescue and recovery of South West London Law Centres. Part funded with four other trust and foundations: City Bridge Trust, City Parochial Foundation, Esmée Fairbairn Foundation and Lankelly Chase Foundation; and British Association of Settlements & Social Action Centres (£2,000), to support the design and publication of the Shared Energy toolkit, reflecting lessons generated by the Climate Change Special Initiative.

FINANCES *Year* 2010 *Income* £1,318,345 *Grants* £3,301,182 *Assets* £62,302,637

TRUSTEES Amanda Jordan, Chair; Mark Baring; Geoffrey Barnett; Prof. Ann Buchanan; David Elliott; Katherine Garrett-Cox; Janet Morrison; Andrew Hind; Ranjit Sondhi; Dr Danny Sriskandarajah; Christopher Steane; Prof. Myles Wickstead.

PUBLICATIONS Various reports connected with its work are available from the foundation's website.

HOW TO APPLY On application forms available via the foundation's website. Potential applicants should check the foundation's website for current guidelines and application deadlines.

WHO TO APPLY TO David Cutler, Director, 60 London Wall, London EC2M 5TQ *Tel* 020 7767 1348 *Fax* 020 7767 7121 *email* baring.foundation@uk.ing.com *Website* www.baringfoundation.org.uk

■ Peter Barker-Mill Memorial Charity

CC NO 1045479   **ESTABLISHED** 1995

WHERE FUNDING CAN BE GIVEN UK, with a preference for Hampshire, including Southampton.

WHO CAN BENEFIT Charitable organisations.

WHAT IS FUNDED General charitable purposes, arts and culture, community facilities and conservation.

WHAT IS NOT FUNDED No grants to individuals.

RANGE OF GRANTS Usually £250–£20,000.

SAMPLE GRANTS Solent Centre for Architecture and Design (£28,000); Hampshire and Isle of Wight Wildlife Trust (£15,000); Students Exploring Marriage Trust (£12,000); Sussex House School (£10,000); The Rose Road Association (£7,000); Christ Church Colbury and Wessex Medical Research (£5,000 each); Computer Aid International and Music of Life (£3,000 each); Dream Holidays, Headway and The Soldiers, Sailors, Airmen and Families Association (£2,000 each); Music Alive and Berkshire Multiple Sclerosis Therapy Centre (£1,000 each); and The Smile Train UK (£500).

FINANCES *Year* 2009–10 *Income* £67,454 *Grants* £233,853 *Assets* £3,929,760

TRUSTEES C Gwyn-Evans; T Jobling; R M Moyse.

HOW TO APPLY In writing to the correspondent.

WHO TO APPLY TO Christopher Gwyn-Evans, Administrator, c/o Longdown Management Ltd, The Estate Office, Longdown, Marchwood, Southampton SO40 4UH *Tel* 02380 292107 *Fax* 02380 293376

■ Barleycorn Trust

CC NO 296386   **ESTABLISHED** 1987

WHERE FUNDING CAN BE GIVEN Worldwide.

WHO CAN BENEFIT Christian.

WHAT IS FUNDED The advancement of the Christian faith, furtherance of religious or secular education, the encouragement of missionary activity, relief-in-need and welfare.

SAMPLE GRANTS Deaf Church Hove (£5,000); Romanian Aid Fund and Scripture Union International (£3,000); Kids for Kids, Kidz Klub Leeds, Langley House Trust, Magdalene Trust and Stepping Stones (£1,000); and Village Water (£500).

FINANCES *Year* 2010 *Income* £128,875 *Grants* £38,700 *Assets* £1,135,175

TRUSTEES Mrs H M Hazelwood; Mrs S A Beckwith.

HOW TO APPLY In writing to the correspondent.

WHO TO APPLY TO The Trustees, 32 Arundel Road, Sutton, Surrey SM2 6EU

■ Lord Barnby's Foundation

CC NO 251016   **ESTABLISHED** 1966

WHERE FUNDING CAN BE GIVEN UK.

WHO CAN BENEFIT Registered charities.

WHAT IS FUNDED The preservation of the environment; heritage; the countryside and ancient buildings, particularly the 'great Anglican cathedrals' ex-service and service people; Polish people and refugees; welfare of horses and those who look after them; youth and other local organisations in Ashtead – Surrey, Blyth – Nottinghamshire and Bradford – Yorkshire.

WHAT IS NOT FUNDED No grants to individuals.

TYPE OF GRANT One-off, capital (including buildings), project, research. Funding is up to two years.

RANGE OF GRANTS Grants range from £500–£10,000; but are generally for £1,000–£2,000.

SAMPLE GRANTS Help for Heroes, Marie Curie Cancer Care and Countryside Foundation for Education (£10,000 each); European Squirrel Initiative (£7,500); Merlin (£6,000); Zane, Queen Alexandra Hospital Home and Independent Age (£5,000 each); Bradford Amateur Rowing Club (£3,000); Alzheimer's Research Trust (£2,000); Exeter Cathedral, Kids Company and Talking Space (£1,000 each); Scott Polar Research Institute (£500); and Yorkshire Air Ambulance (£250).

FINANCES *Year* 2009–10 *Income* £215,777 *Grants* £241,300 *Assets* £4,109,010

TRUSTEES Hon. George Lopes; Countess Peel; Sir Michael Farquhar; Algy Smith-Maxwell; Laura Greenall.

OTHER INFORMATION The foundation also has an 'appointed fund' under which certain investments have been set aside for the benefit of the textile industry. During the year £13,000 was given through this fund.

HOW TO APPLY Applications will only be considered if received in writing accompanied by a set of the latest accounts. Applicants do not need to send an sae. Appeals are considered three times a year, in February, June and November.

WHO TO APPLY TO Jane Lethbridge, Secretary, PO Box 71, Plymstock, Plymouth PL8 2YP

■ Barnes Workhouse Fund

CC NO 200103   **ESTABLISHED** 1970

WHERE FUNDING CAN BE GIVEN Ancient parish of Barnes only (SW13 postal district in London).

WHO CAN BENEFIT Charitable organisations and individuals.

WHAT IS FUNDED The fund makes grants to organisations who can demonstrate that their activities will benefit some of the inhabitants of its area of benefit.

TYPE OF GRANT Capital (including buildings), core costs, feasibility studies, one-off, project, research, running costs, recurring costs, salaries and start-up costs.

SAMPLE GRANTS Richmond Citizens Advice Bureaux and Castelnau Centre Project (£35,000 each); Mortlake Community Association and Age Concern (£10,000 each); Barnes, East Sheen and Mortlake FISH (£8,000); Lowther Primary School (£7,500); Ethnic Minorities Advocacy Group and Homestart – Richmond upon Thames (£3,000 each); Barnes Music Society and INS Neuro Support for Life (£1,000 each) and Library Summer Outreach Project (£600).

FINANCES *Year* 2010 *Income* £601,933 *Grants* £192,578 *Assets* £7,906,631

TRUSTEES C Reilly; Mr N Phillips; Mrs W V Kyrle-Pope; P B Conrath; J Brocklebank; Mrs

K Pengelley; Prof. T Besley; Mrs L A Hine; Mr P Hodgins.

OTHER INFORMATION The grant total in 2010 includes £27,000 given to individuals.

HOW TO APPLY In writing to the Clerk to the Trustees. Application forms and guidelines are available from the clerk or downloaded from the website. Applications must state clearly the extent to which any project will benefit residents of Barnes (postal district SW13) and include details of other sources of funding. Trustees meet to consider grants every two months in January, March, May, July, September and November each year. For consideration at a meeting, applications must be received by the 13th of the preceding month.

WHO TO APPLY TO The Clerk to the Trustees, PO Box 665, Richmond, London TW10 6YL *Tel* 020 8241 3994 *email* mibbetson@ barnesworkhousefund.org.uk *Website* www. barnesworkhousefund.org.uk

■ The Barnsbury Charitable Trust

CC NO 241383   **ESTABLISHED** 1964
WHERE FUNDING CAN BE GIVEN UK, but no local charities outside Oxfordshire.
WHO CAN BENEFIT Charitable organisations.
WHAT IS FUNDED General charitable purposes.
WHAT IS NOT FUNDED No grants to individuals.
RANGE OF GRANTS £15–£10,000.
SAMPLE GRANTS Oxfordshire Chamber Music Festival (£10,000); Archway Foundation (£6,000); Blackfriars Priory and Pegasus Theatre (£5,000 each); Oxfordshire Family Mediation and the George Mackay Brown Fellowship (£2,500 each); PCC of Letcombe Bassett (£2,000); Charities Aid Foundation (£1,000); Oxfordshire Rural Community Council and Oxford District Mencap (£500 each); St Adhelm's RC Church (£300); Friends of Wychwood and Oxfordshire Museum (£100 each); PCC of St Giles (£50); and the Royal Society of St George (£25).
FINANCES *Year* 2009–10 *Income* £82,082 *Grants* £83,599 *Assets* £2,765,141
TRUSTEES H L J Brunner; M R Brunner; T E Yates.
HOW TO APPLY In writing to the correspondent.
WHO TO APPLY TO H L J Brunner, Trustee, 26 Norham Road, Oxford OX2 6SF

■ The Barnstaple Bridge Trust

CC NO 201288   **ESTABLISHED** 1961
WHERE FUNDING CAN BE GIVEN Barnstaple and immediate neighbourhood.
WHO CAN BENEFIT Local organisations.
WHAT IS FUNDED General, grants are made to a wide range of causes, including welfare, older people and young people, health and medical, schools and sport.
WHAT IS NOT FUNDED No grants to individuals, other than on referral through a caring agency.
TYPE OF GRANT Capital including buildings, core costs, one-off, project, research, running costs, recurring costs and start-up costs will be considered. Funding may be given for up to one year.
RANGE OF GRANTS Up to £20,000.
SAMPLE GRANTS Previous beneficiaries include: Bishops Tawton Almshouses (£20,000); ND Hospice Care (£10,000); Barnstaple Skate Board Track, Children's Hospice and St Peter's – Fremington (£5,000 each); Barnstaple-in-Bloom, Barnstaple Poverty Action Group, Freedom Social Projects, Pilton House and Vivien Moon Foundation (£3,000 each); Bishops

Tawton PCC (£2,500); Holy Trinity Church Barnstaple (£2,000); Cruse Bereavement Care (£1,750); Relate (£1,500); and Abbey Gateway Club, Christians Against Poverty, Friendship House, Home Start and Pilton (£1,000 each).
FINANCES *Year* 2009–10 *Income* £355,921 *Grants* £128,007 *Assets* £4,614,803
TRUSTEES J W Waldron; D C Burgess; R W Forward; A J Bradbury; S Harvey; J Lynch; Cllr J Bartlett; I Scott; Mrs S Haywood; D Trueman; A Isaac.
HOW TO APPLY In writing to the correspondent. The trustees meet quarterly on the first Tuesday of March, June, September and December.
WHO TO APPLY TO C J Bartlett, Clerk, 7 Bridge Chambers, The Strand, Barnstaple, Devon EX31 1HB *Tel* 01271 343995

■ The Barnwood House Trust

CC NO 218401   **ESTABLISHED** 1972
WHERE FUNDING CAN BE GIVEN Gloucestershire.
WHO CAN BENEFIT Gloucestershire-based charitable and voluntary organisations whose services seek to improve the quality of life of local people with long-term disabilities. Individuals who are sick, convalescent, disabled, infirm or in need, hardship or distress.
WHAT IS FUNDED The relief of sickness, poverty and distress affecting people with mental or nervous disorders or with serious physical infirmity or disability. The relief of persons in need by providing housing or other accommodation, care nursing and attention.
WHAT IS NOT FUNDED Grants are not normally made in the following circumstances: people or organisations outside Gloucestershire; people with problems relating to drugs or alcohol, unless they also have physical disabilities or a diagnosed mental illness; To pay for funeral costs; medical equipment; private healthcare; counselling or psychotherapy; top-up nursing home fees; council tax; court fines; house purchase or rent; regular income supplements; needs of non-disabled dependants or carers. Grants will not be awarded retrospectively.
TYPE OF GRANT Small grants and grants to individuals.
RANGE OF GRANTS up to £750.
SAMPLE GRANTS Consortium of Mental Health Day Support Providers (£305,000); Crossroads Care – Cheltenham & Tewkesbury, Independence Trust and People & Places in Gloucestershire (£30,000 each); Whitefriars Sailing Club (£27,500); Stroke Association (£25,000); Forest of Dean Citizen's Advice Bureau and Hop, Skip & Jump (Cotswold) (£18,000 each); Art Shape LTD, Barnwood Residents Association and Watershed Riding for the Disabled (£10,000 each).
FINANCES *Year* 2010 *Income* £2,209,395 *Grants* £1,079,314 *Assets* £69,281,871
TRUSTEES John Colquhoun; James Davidson; Anne Cadbury; Richard Ashenden; Simon Fisher; David A Acland; Clare de Haan; Sara Shipway; Roger Ker; Annabella Scott; Jonathan Carr; Revd John Horan.
PUBLICATIONS *Strategic Framework 2011–2021; ten-year investment plan; five work programmes* is available on the trust's website or request them by post.
OTHER INFORMATION The trust has recently undergone a strategic review which means they will be phasing out any services that they currently provide and have terminated the grants over £750 scheme. Instead the trust is running the community animation programme which aims to work in partnership with people living

with disabilities and mental health problems, the voluntary and community and public sectors, and employers to strengthen capacity.

HOW TO APPLY 'As part of the development of Unlocking Opportunities, our ten year investment plan, we have reviewed the way we make grants and allocate funding to organisations. As from [early] 2011 we no longer award open application grants for sums over £750. For the foreseeable future, the trust will be making funding available to communities across Gloucestershire on a proactive, not a reactive basis. This means that the trust will be seeking to fund specific types of activity, not responding to requests from organisations.'

WHO TO APPLY TO Gail Rodway, Grants Manager, 162 Barnwood Road, Gloucester GL4 7JX *Tel* 01452 611292 *Fax* 01452 372594 *email* gail.rodway@barnwoodtrust.org *Website* www.barnwoodtrust.org

■ The Misses Barrie Charitable Trust

CC NO 279459   **ESTABLISHED** 1979
WHERE FUNDING CAN BE GIVEN UK.
WHO CAN BENEFIT Registered charities.
WHAT IS FUNDED General charitable purposes.
WHAT IS NOT FUNDED No grants to individuals.
TYPE OF GRANT Mainly one-off.
RANGE OF GRANTS Mostly £1,000–£3,000.
SAMPLE GRANTS Scottish Chamber Orchestra and University of Oxford (£10,000 each); Canine Partners and East Neuk Festival (£5,000 each); All England Netball Association, ARC Addington, Down's Syndrome, Hearts and Minds, Listening Books, Scooniehill Group Riding for the Disabled and Surrey Cricket Board (£3,000 each); Headstart 4 Babies, Helen Ley Respite Care Centre, Holidays for Heroes Jersey, Institute of Cancer Research, Integrated Neurological Services, Jumbulance Trust, Life Care (Edinburgh), Lifelites, Lord Cobham, Worcestershire Youth Cricket Trust, Maggie's Cancer Caring Centres, Marie Curie Cancer Care and Youth Link Dundee (£2,000 each); Answer, Braille Chess Association, British Forces Foundation, Broadway Youth Activities, Gurkha Welfare Trust, Highlanders Museum, Spadework, The Albrighton Trust, Tree Club, Virtually Impaired Association Bristol, WRVS Archive and Young Virtuosi Festival (£1,000 each).
FINANCES *Year* 2009–10 *Income* £208,729 *Grants* £187,400 *Assets* £5,314,539
TRUSTEES J A Carter; R S Ogg; Mrs R Fraser.
HOW TO APPLY In writing to the correspondent accompanied by up to date accounts or financial information. Trustees meet three times a year, in April, August and December. 'The trustees regret that due to the large number of unsolicited applications for grants received each week they are not able to notify those which are unsuccessful.'
WHO TO APPLY TO The Trustees, Raymond Carter and Co, 1b Haling Road, South Croydon CR2 6HS *Tel* 020 8686 1686

■ Barrington Family Charitable Trust

CC NO 1078702   **ESTABLISHED** 1999
WHERE FUNDING CAN BE GIVEN UK.
WHO CAN BENEFIT Registered charities.
WHAT IS FUNDED Mainly arts and culture.

FINANCES *Year* 2009–10 *Income* £27,001 *Grants* £29,400
TRUSTEES Jessica Watkins; Jill Barrington; Michael Barrington; Saul Barrington; Amanda Thompson.
HOW TO APPLY In writing to the correspondent.
WHO TO APPLY TO Michael Barrington, Trustee, Fourth Floor, 87 Wimpole Street, London W1G 9RL *Tel* 020 7486 0266

■ The Charity of William Barrow

CC NO 307574   **ESTABLISHED** 1965
WHERE FUNDING CAN BE GIVEN The ancient parish of Borden.
WHO CAN BENEFIT Individuals and schools.
WHAT IS FUNDED The charity distributes its income equally between the Barrows Eleemosynary Charity and Barrows Educational Foundation. The latter supports local schools, one of which is supported each year in accordance with the trust deed. No other organisations were supported.
WHAT IS NOT FUNDED No grants outside the parish of Borden.
FINANCES *Year* 2010 *Income* £201,910 *Grants* £40,221 *Assets* £5,800,435
TRUSTEES P J Mair, Chair; W G Best; J Burton; Mrs E P Cole; E G Doubleday; D A Jarrett; J J Jefferiss; D Jordan; Fr Lewis; Mrs A P Ramage; S C Batt; Mrs C Ford.
HOW TO APPLY In writing to the correspondent for consideration at quarterly meetings of the trustees.
WHO TO APPLY TO The Clerk, c/o George Webb Finn, 43 Park Road, Sittingbourne, Kent ME10 1DX

■ Stephen J Barry Charitable Trust

CC NO 265056   **ESTABLISHED** 1973
WHERE FUNDING CAN BE GIVEN UK.
WHO CAN BENEFIT Charitable organisations.
WHAT IS FUNDED General charitable purposes.
RANGE OF GRANTS Up to £7,000.
SAMPLE GRANTS Previous beneficiaries have included: I Rescue (£7,000); Alzheimer's Research Trust (£5,000); National Gallery (£2,000); Hampstead Synagogue (31,500); and Royal Academy of Arts (£1,250); Jewish Care, Macmillan Cancer Support and Tate Foundation (£1,000 each); Ear Foundation, National Youth Orchestra and Tropical Health Foundation Trust (£500 each); Docklands Settlement and NSPCC (3300 each); Blind Art (£200); and Action Aid (£100).
TRUSTEES Nicholas Barry; Oliver Barry; Stephen Barry; Linda Barry.
HOW TO APPLY In writing to the correspondent.
WHO TO APPLY TO Stephen Barry, Trustee, 19 Newman Street, London W1T 1PF *Tel* 020 7580 6696 *email* sjb@limecourt.com

■ The Bartlett Taylor Charitable Trust

CC NO 285249   **ESTABLISHED** 1982
WHERE FUNDING CAN BE GIVEN Preference for Oxfordshire.
WHO CAN BENEFIT Registered charities.
WHAT IS FUNDED General charitable purposes, with grants given in the following categories: (a) international charities; (b) UK national charities – medical; UK national charities – educational; (c) local organisations – community projects; local organisations – medical; local

organisations – other; (d) individuals – educational; individuals – relief.

RANGE OF GRANTS £100–£1,000.

FINANCES *Year* 2009–10 *Income* £70,847 *Grants* £64,451 *Assets* £1,695,771

TRUSTEES Richard Bartlett; Gareth Alty; Katherine Bradley; Brenda Cook; James W Dingle; Rosemary Warner; Mrs S Boyd.

OTHER INFORMATION 58 grants totalling £11,500 were made to individuals.

HOW TO APPLY In writing to the correspondent. Trustees meet bi-monthly.

WHO TO APPLY TO Katherine Robertson, 24 Church Green, Witney, Oxfordshire OX28 4AT *Tel* 01993 703941 *email* krobertson@ johnwelchandstammers.co.uk

■ The Worshipful Company of Basketmakers' Charitable Trust

CC NO 286901   **ESTABLISHED** 1982

WHERE FUNDING CAN BE GIVEN UK with a preference for inner London.

WHO CAN BENEFIT Support small charities who have innovative solutions to problems.

WHAT IS FUNDED Grants go to a 'variety of causes, for example addiction rehabilitation centres where the person who persists with the treatment is carried through to a job and a home, charities training the disabled for employment and similar small charities where our size of contribution can make a real impact.'

SAMPLE GRANTS Grants were made in the following areas: £3,400 to social care; £2,300 to education; £5,000 to disability; £7,000 to hospices; £4,500 to illness; £3,000 to St Margaret Pattens and £2,500 to blind causes.

FINANCES *Year* 2009–10 *Income* £50,639 *Grants* £27,352 *Assets* £1,062,116

TRUSTEES Peter Costain; John Robinson; George Alford; William Daniels; Jeremy Sorrel; Carol Hawes; Neil Radcliffe.

OTHER INFORMATION The charity supports training in the craft, the Lord Mayor's Appeal and St Margaret Pattens on an ongoing basis. In 2009–10 the sum of £3,500 went to individuals.

HOW TO APPLY In writing to the correspondent. 'Grants payable are determined by the trustees at their two regular meetings in early October and March.'

WHO TO APPLY TO John Robinson, Trustee, Tythe Cottage, Duke Street, Hintlesham, Ipswich IP8 3QP

■ The Paul Bassham Charitable Trust

CC NO 266842   **ESTABLISHED** 1973

WHERE FUNDING CAN BE GIVEN UK, mainly Norfolk.

WHO CAN BENEFIT UK registered charities.

WHAT IS FUNDED General charitable purposes. Preference given to Norfolk charitable causes; if funds permit, other charities with national coverage will be considered.

WHAT IS NOT FUNDED Grants are not made directly to individuals, nor to unregistered organisations.

RANGE OF GRANTS £1,000–£20,000.

SAMPLE GRANTS East Anglia Children's Hospice Quidenham and Norfolk Heart Trust (£25,000 each); and Norfolk Wildlife Trust and YMCA Norwich (£20,000 each); RNLI Norfolk and St Catherine's PCC (£5,000 each); Great Yarmouth Samaritans, Norfolk Brass, Norwich Theatre Royal and Norwich Preservation Trust (£2,000

each); and Brainwave, British Lung Foundation, Dream Holidays, Jubilee Family Centre, Skill Force and Buckingham Emergency Flood Appeal (£1,000 each).

FINANCES *Year* 2009–10 *Income* £350,936 *Grants* £191,800 *Assets* £10,617,650

TRUSTEES A G Munro; R Lovett.

OTHER INFORMATION Richard Lovett is also a trustee of Brigadier D V and Mrs H R Phelps Charitable Settlement (Charity Commission no. 249047).

HOW TO APPLY Only in writing to the correspondent – no formal application forms issued. Telephone enquiries are not invited because of administrative costs. The trustees meet quarterly to consider general applications.

WHO TO APPLY TO R Lovett, Trustee, c/o Howes Percival, The Guildyard, 51 Colegate, Norwich NR3 1DD *Tel* 01603 762103

■ The Batchworth Trust

CC NO 245061   **ESTABLISHED** 1965

WHERE FUNDING CAN BE GIVEN Worldwide.

WHO CAN BENEFIT Major UK and international charities.

WHAT IS FUNDED General charitable purposes, medical, humanitarian aid, social welfare. 'The trustees have a policy of mainly distributing to nationally recognised charities but consider other charities where it felt a grant would be of significant benefit when matched with other funds to launch a new enterprise or initiative.'

WHAT IS NOT FUNDED No grants to individuals.

RANGE OF GRANTS £1,000–£25,000.

SAMPLE GRANTS University of Bristol – research post (£50,000); Cecily's Fund, Cure Parkinson's, the Halo Trust and the Sandpiper Trust (£10,000 each); African Medical Mission, Living Paintings, Mary's Meals and Smile (£5,000 each); Stewartry Trust (£3,000); Fet Lor Youth Club (£2,000); and Dumfries and Galloway Arts Festival (£1,000).

FINANCES *Year* 2009–10 *Income* £280,086 *Grants* £316,000 *Assets* £9,001,117

TRUSTEES Lockwell Trustees Ltd.

HOW TO APPLY In writing to the correspondent. An sae should be included if a reply is required.

WHO TO APPLY TO M R Neve, Administrative Executive, CLB Gatwick LLP, Imperial Buildings, 68 Victoria Road, Horley, Surrey RH6 7PZ *Tel* 01293 776411 *email* mrn@clbgatwick.co.uk

■ Bay Charitable Trust

CC NO 1060537   **ESTABLISHED** 1997

WHERE FUNDING CAN BE GIVEN UK and overseas.

WHO CAN BENEFIT Jewish organisations.

WHAT IS FUNDED 'The objectives of the charity are to give charity for the relief of poverty and the advancement of traditions of the Orthodox Jewish Religion and the study of Torah.'

FINANCES *Year* 2010 *Income* £359,730 *Grants* £469,958 *Assets* £122,122

TRUSTEES I M Kreditor; M Lisser.

HOW TO APPLY In writing to the correspondent.

WHO TO APPLY TO I M Kreditor, Trustee, Hermolis House, Abbeydale Road, Wembley, Middlesex HA0 1AY

■ The Bay Tree Charitable Trust

CC NO 1044091   **ESTABLISHED** 1994

WHERE FUNDING CAN BE GIVEN UK and overseas.

WHO CAN BENEFIT Charitable organisations.

WHAT IS FUNDED Development work.

WHAT IS NOT FUNDED No grants to individuals.
RANGE OF GRANTS Up to £30,000.
SAMPLE GRANTS DEC Haiti Earthquake Appeal
(£25,000); DEC Pakistan Floods Appeal
(£20,000); Age Concern East Cheshire, British
Red Cross – Chilean Earthquake Appeal,
Combat Stress and FareShare (£10,000 each);
and Children of the Andes, Friends of the Earth,
Hop Skip & Jump (Swindon), Integrated
Neurological Services and the Samaritans
(£5,000 each).
FINANCES *Year* 2010 *Income* £136,499
Grants £110,000 *Assets* £3,442,538
TRUSTEES I M P Benton; Miss E L Benton;
P H Benton.
HOW TO APPLY 'All appeals should be by letter
containing the following: aims and objectives of
the charity; nature of appeal; total target if for a
specific project; contributions received against
target; registered charity number; any other
relevant factors. Letters should be accompanied
by a set of the charitable organisation's latest
report and full accounts.'
WHO TO APPLY TO The Trustees, PO Box 53983,
London SW15 1VT

■ D H and L H Baylin Charitable Trust

CC NO 298708   **ESTABLISHED** 1988
WHERE FUNDING CAN BE GIVEN UK.
WHO CAN BENEFIT Charitable organisations.
WHAT IS FUNDED General charitable purposes.
FINANCES *Year* 2009–10 *Income* £10,332
Grants £9,000
TRUSTEES D M Baylin; Mrs L H Baylin.
HOW TO APPLY In writing to the correspondent.
WHO TO APPLY TO Dennis Baylin, Trustee,
28 Manchester Street, London W1U 7LF

■ The Louis Baylis (Maidenhead Advertiser) Charitable Trust

CC NO 210533   **ESTABLISHED** 1962
WHERE FUNDING CAN BE GIVEN Berkshire,
Buckinghamshire and Oxfordshire with a
preference for Maidenhead.
WHO CAN BENEFIT General charitable purposes.
WHAT IS FUNDED The trust states that it was
'established to safeguard the newspaper, The
Maidenhead Advertiser, from all outside
influence and provide for the newspaper's
continuance as part of the civic and social life
of the community it serves'. Grants can be given
towards any charitable purpose, and from the
grants list it appears that all the organisations
supported were within the area covered by the
newspaper.
WHAT IS NOT FUNDED No grants to individuals.
RANGE OF GRANTS £500–£25,000.
SAMPLE GRANTS Beneficiaries included: Maidenhead
Citizens Advice Bureau (£25,000); People to
Places (£17,000); Maidenhead Christmas Lights
Appeal (£7,500); Maidenhead Town Partnership
(£5,000); Boyne Hill Cricket Club (£3,000);
Target Ovarian Cancer (£2,000); and
Parkinson's Disease Society (£500).
FINANCES *Year* 2009–10 *Income* £4,599,610
Grants £213,910 *Assets* £12,477,197
TRUSTEES Tony Stoughton-Harris; P J Sands; Peter
Murcott.
OTHER INFORMATION Of the total grants made,
£14,000 was distributed to 12 national
charities, £13,000 to 10 regional charities, and

a total of £187,000 was donated to local
charities and organisations.
HOW TO APPLY In writing to the correspondent. The
trustees meet twice a year.
WHO TO APPLY TO Andrew Chitty, 78 Queen Street,
Maidenhead, Berkshire SL6 I HY
email lbctrust@baylismedia.co.uk *Website* www.
baylis-trust.org.uk.

■ BBC Children in Need

CC NO 802052   **ESTABLISHED** 1989
WHERE FUNDING CAN BE GIVEN UK.
WHO CAN BENEFIT Non-profit making groups and
organisations benefiting children in the UK aged
18 and under.
WHAT IS FUNDED Practical and lasting support for
children disadvantaged by poverty, disability,
illness, abuse and neglect.
WHAT IS NOT FUNDED Grants will not be given for:
relief of statutory responsibility; applications
from local government or NHS bodies; building
projects which are applying to us for more than
£20,000; the promotion of religion; trips or
projects abroad; medical treatment/research;
projects for pregnancy testing or advice,
information or counselling on pregnancy
choices; general awareness-raising work;
bursaries, sponsored places, fees or equivalent;
individuals (unless an eligible organisation is
applying on their behalf); distribution to
another/other organisation/s, for example, PTAs
applying on behalf of schools; general appeals
or endowment funds; deficit funding or
repayment of loans; retrospective funding
(projects taking place before the grant award
date); projects unable to start within 12 months
of the grant award date; unspecified
expenditure.
TYPE OF GRANT Capital, revenue and recurring for up
to three years.
RANGE OF GRANTS Main Grants over £10,000 per
year for up to three years; Small Grants of
£10,000 or less per year for up to three years.
SAMPLE GRANTS There were 1,275 grants made
during the year – comprehensive details of
funded organisations can be downloaded from
the charity's website.
FINANCES *Year* 2009–10 *Income* £44,204,000
Grants £41,700,000 *Assets* £31,391,000
TRUSTEES Stevie Spring, Chair; Tim Davie; Beverley
Tew; Sir Terry Wogan; Susan Elizabeth; Peter
McBride; Nicholas Eldred; Phil Hodkinson; Bob
Shennan; Danny Cohen.
HOW TO APPLY Straightforward and excellent
application forms and guidelines are available
from the charity's website or from the following
national BBC Children in Need offices:
England (and general helpline): PO Box 1000,
London W12 7WJ. Telephone Number: 020 8576
7788.
Northern Ireland: Broadcasting House, Ormeau
Avenue, Belfast BT2 8HQ. Telephone Number:
028 9033 8221.
Scotland: BBC Scotland, G10, 40 Pacific Drive,
Glasgow, G51 1DA. Telephone Number: 0141
422 6111.
Wales: Broadcasting House, Llandaff, Cardiff CF5
2YQ. Telephone Number: 029 2032 2383.
There are four closing dates for applications – 15
January, 15 April, 15 July and 15 October.
Applicants should allow up to three months after
each closing date for notification of a decision
Application forms must be completed online.
Note: Incomplete or late application forms will not
be assessed.

The charity has recently expressed an interest in receiving more eligible applications from North West England. The charity is particularly interested in hearing from organisations that have not had funding from Children in Need in the past. Contact Philip Jeffery, Regional Officer on 0161 244 3442 or by email atphilip.jeffery@bbc.co.uk.

WHO TO APPLY TO David Ramsden, Chief Executive, PO Box 1000, London W12 7WJ *Tel* 020 8576 7788 *Fax* 020 8576 8887 *email* pudsey@bbc.co.uk *Website* bbc.co.uk/pudsey

■ BC Partners Foundation

CC NO 1136956 **ESTABLISHED** 2010
WHERE FUNDING CAN BE GIVEN UK.
WHAT IS FUNDED General charitable purposes.
TRUSTEES Nikos Stathopolous; Mike Twinning; Joseph Cronley.
OTHER INFORMATION Unfortunately, few details are known about how this new trust will operate.
HOW TO APPLY In writing to the correspondent.
WHO TO APPLY TO The Trustees, BC Partners Limited, 40 Portman Square, London W1H 6DA *Tel* 020 7009 4800 *email* bcpfoundation@bcpartners.com

■ BCH Trust

CC NO 1138652 **ESTABLISHED** 2010
WHERE FUNDING CAN BE GIVEN UK.
WHO CAN BENEFIT Jewish organisations.
WHAT IS FUNDED General charitable purposes with a stated interest in education, social welfare, the Jewish faith and disability.
TRUSTEES Benny Stone; Charles Bernstein; Moshe Rabi.
HOW TO APPLY In writing to the correspondent.
WHO TO APPLY TO Benny Stone, Trustee, 59 Kings Road, Prestwich, Manchester M25 0LQ *email* mail@bchtrust.org

■ The Beacon Trust

CC NO 230087 **ESTABLISHED** 1963
WHERE FUNDING CAN BE GIVEN Mainly UK, but also some overseas (usually in the British Commonwealth) and Spain and Portugal.
WHO CAN BENEFIT Organisations benefiting evangelical Protestants, including Baptists, Anglican and Methodists. Funding is usually given to headquarters organisations.
WHAT IS FUNDED The emphasis of the trust's support is on Christian work overseas, particularly amongst students, although the trust does not support individuals.
WHAT IS NOT FUNDED Applications from individuals are not considered.
TYPE OF GRANT One-off grants for development funding. Longer-term grants may be considered.
SAMPLE GRANTS Latin Link (£9,500); L'Abri (£5,000); and Missionary Aviation, CARE, and Torch Trust for the Blind (£2,000 each).
FINANCES *Year* 2010–11 *Income* £44,870 *Grants* £28,655 *Assets* £2,401,061
TRUSTEES Miss J Benson; Miss J M Spink; M Spink.
OTHER INFORMATION This grant total figure includes £8,000 to individuals.
HOW TO APPLY The trust does not respond to unsolicited applications.
WHO TO APPLY TO Grahame Scofield, Unit 3, Newhouse Farm, Old Crawley Road, Horsham, West Sussex RH12 4RU *Tel* 01293 851715

■ Bear Mordechai Ltd

CC NO 286806 **ESTABLISHED** 1982
WHERE FUNDING CAN BE GIVEN Worldwide.
WHO CAN BENEFIT Individuals, small local projects and national organisations benefiting Jewish people.
WHAT IS FUNDED Jewish charities.
TYPE OF GRANT One-off and recurrent costs.
SAMPLE GRANTS Previous beneficiaries have included: Agudat Yad Yemin Jerusalem, Almat, Chevras Mo'oz Ladol, Craven Walk Charities Trust, Havenpoint, Keren Tzedaka Vachesed, Lolev, UTA and Yetev Lev Yerusholaim.
FINANCES *Year* 2009–10 *Income* £196,764 *Grants* £69,500 *Assets* £1,756,758
TRUSTEES Chaim Benedikt; Eliezer Benedikt; Yechiel Benedikt.
HOW TO APPLY In writing to the correspondent.
WHO TO APPLY TO The Secretary, 40 Fountayne Road, London N16 7DT

■ The Bearder Charity

CC NO 1010529 **ESTABLISHED** 1992
WHERE FUNDING CAN BE GIVEN Calderdale.
WHO CAN BENEFIT Registered charities and individuals.
WHAT IS FUNDED General charitable purposes, particularly the arts, infrastructure support and development, education and training and community facilities and services.
RANGE OF GRANTS Up to £5,000.
SAMPLE GRANTS Beneficiaries included: Sure Start (£5,000); Maurice Jagger Centre (£4,000); Calderdale College (£3,500); Cornholme Social Centre (£3,000); Whizz Kidz (£2,000); Halifax Junior Cricket League (£1,500); Calderdale Educational Welfare Team, Overgate Hospice Choir and Square Chapel Arts (£1,000 each); and The Workshop (£750).
FINANCES *Year* 2009–10 *Income* £107,904 *Grants* £99,544 *Assets* £3,170,308
TRUSTEES R D Smithies, Chair; P W Townend; T Simpson; D Sharpe; L Smith; B Mowforth.
OTHER INFORMATION In 2009–10, a further £61,000 was given in grants to individuals for education and general charitable purposes.
HOW TO APPLY In writing to the correspondent, detailing requirements and costings. Trustee board meetings are held six times a year.
WHO TO APPLY TO R D Smithies, Trustee, 5 King St, Brighouse, West Yorkshire HD6 1NX *email* bearders@btinternet.com *Website* www.bearder-charity.org.uk

■ The James Beattie Charitable Trust

CC NO 265654 **ESTABLISHED** 1961
WHERE FUNDING CAN BE GIVEN Wolverhampton area.
WHO CAN BENEFIT Local projects and organisations benefiting the people of Wolverhampton.
WHAT IS FUNDED General charitable purposes including accommodation and housing; community development, support to voluntary and community organisations; and social care professional bodies. Also health; conservation and the environment; education; community facilities and services; dance groups and orchestras; volunteer bureaux; Christian education and churches; schools; and youth projects such as scouts and air training corps may be considered.
WHAT IS NOT FUNDED No grants to individuals, organisations outside the West Midlands, or

exclusive organisations (e.g. all-white or all-Asian groups).

TYPE OF GRANT Grants awarded for capital including buildings, core costs, project research, running costs, salaries and start-up costs. Grants may be one-off or recurring and funding for a single project may be available for less than one year to more than three.

SAMPLE GRANTS Previous beneficiaries have included Barnardo's, James Beattie House, Cottage Homes, Marie Curie Cancer Care, St Chad's – Pattingham, St Martin's School, Whizz Kidz, Wolverhampton Grammar School and YMCA.

FINANCES *Year* 2009–10 *Income* £50,759 *Grants* £172,805 *Assets* £3,348,979

TRUSTEES Mrs Jane Victoria Redshaw; Michael Walter Redshaw; Kenneth Charles Dolman; Mrs Susannah Jane Norbury.

OTHER INFORMATION In 2009–10, grants were made to 98 organisations totalling £173,000. Donations made ranged between £250 and £12,500 and were made largely to local charities or local branches of national charities.

HOW TO APPLY In writing to the correspondent, including accounts.

WHO TO APPLY TO The Trustees, PO Box 12, Bridgnorth, Shropshire WV15 5LQ *Tel* 01746 716207

■ The Jack and Ada Beattie Foundation

CC NO 1142892   **ESTABLISHED** 2011

WHERE FUNDING CAN BE GIVEN The Midlands and London.

WHO CAN BENEFIT Registered charities and individuals.

WHAT IS FUNDED Social welfare, injustice and equality. The foundation's initial funding priorities are: dignity; freedom; and sanctuary.

TYPE OF GRANT One-off project grants.

RANGE OF GRANTS £500–£2,000.

TRUSTEES Trevor Beattie; Peter Beattie; Paul Beattie.

OTHER INFORMATION The foundation was established in July 2011 by Trevor Beattie, the marketing executive whose advertising company, Beattie McGuinness Bungay, was responsible for high-profile campaigns for French Connection and Playtex amongst others. 'I set up The Jack and Ada Beattie Foundation in honour and memory of my parents. It will adhere to their life-long held principles of fair play, care for the vulnerable and getting the job done. It will fight against inequality in all its forms (when you come from a family of ten, you soon learn the importance of equality. . .) and it will probably bear the Beattie family trait of defiance in the face of adversity.' It is likely that the foundation will have around £175,000 in total available each year for grants.

HOW TO APPLY Initial proposals should be emailed to the foundation. Eligible applicants will then be notified if the foundation is interested in receiving a full application, which is made using a form available on the foundation's website. The foundation gives the following guidance on completing the application form:
'Please complete all sections of the application form and mark 'not appropriate' if that applies. Contact Details: please give all contact details as requested. This will enable the Jack and Ada Beattie Foundation to keep accurate records of your organisation and help speed up the application process should we need to contact you by telephone or email. The contact details

requested are of a member of the management committee and/or trustee. This again will help make the application process more efficient should we need to contact you. Organisation Details: in this section you will help us understand the structure and purpose of your organisation. You can tell us what you do and who is involved. Project Details: please describe the project you are requiring support for, with time-scales attached. Please describe how this project furthers the aims and objectives of your organisation if applicable and the tangible results to be achieved. Statement of Need: please describe how you have identified a need for the project requiring support. Who will be involved in the delivery of this project and who are to be the beneficiaries? Coherence of Values and Objectives: please outline how the values and objectives of your organisation and project align to those of the foundation. Organisation Finance: this information will provide us with an idea as to how your organisation is run; what funders are attached and how effectively you operate. Cost of Your Project: if you are applying for a Grant, please outline the amount of money you need for your project and where the funds are coming from (if you have applied to multiple funders). Please give a thorough breakdown of costs with timescales if appropriate. The foundation offers grants in the region of £500–£2,000. We reserve the right to partially fund a project if we feel this is appropriate. Project Outcomes and Outputs: please outline what you hope to tangibly achieve from this project and how support from the foundation can assist you in doing so. If your application is successful you will be required to monitor and evaluate the project and report back to the foundation. Details will be sent with the grant. Application forms will only be accepted by email unless there are exceptional circumstances. Contact the Foundation Director if you have any queries. The foundation endeavours to acknowledge each stage of the application process. Decisions will be reached within two months of each stage.'

WHO TO APPLY TO Alexandra Taliadoros, Director, 203 Larna House, 116 Commercial Street, London E1 6NF *Tel* 020 3287 8427 *email* info@beattiefoundation.com *Website* www.beattiefoundation.com

■ The Beaufort House Trust Limited

CC NO 286606   **ESTABLISHED** 1983

WHERE FUNDING CAN BE GIVEN UK.

WHO CAN BENEFIT Organisations benefiting Christians, children and young adults.

WHAT IS FUNDED To support schools, colleges, universities or other charitable bodies engaged in the advancement, promotion and furtherance of education, religion or any other charitable purposes.

WHAT IS NOT FUNDED No grants are made to organisations with political associations, UK wide charities or individuals.

TYPE OF GRANT Some recurring, majority one-off.

SAMPLE GRANTS The grant total was broken down as follows: schools (82%); colleges (11%); other educational establishments (7%). Beneficiaries included: Catholic Blind Institute – Liverpool, towards furnishing of the residential unit at the school; Brampton Abbotts Church of England Primary School – Herefordshire, towards building and security costs; Mater Dei School – Dublin, towards staff, equipment, training, equipment and transport costs; and Weston All Saints Church of England Primary School – Somerset, towards the installation of a bio-pool and natural pool to help pupils learn to swim.

FINANCES *Year* 2010 *Income* £90,575 *Grants* £32,100 *Assets* £99,351

TRUSTEES M Chamberlain; W Yates; Revd Nigel Stock; F Hart; Sir P Mawer; C Smith; N Sealy; The Ven. A Cooper; S Meredith; D P Wilson.

OTHER INFORMATION In most years the trust receives donations from Ecclesiastical Insurance Office plc and school fee annuities from Ecclesiastical Life Limited. Ecclesiastical Life Limited and Ecclesiastical Insurance Office plc are subsidiaries of Allchurches Trust Limited. Beaufort House Trust Limited and Allchurches Trust Limited are companies that are controlled by a common board of trustees.

HOW TO APPLY On an application form. The following details will be required: the objectives of the charity; the appeal target; how the funds are to be utilised; funds raised to date; and previous support received from the trust.

WHO TO APPLY TO Mrs R J Hall, Secretary, Beaufort House, Brunswick Road, Gloucester GL1 1JZ

■ Beauland Ltd

CC NO 511374   **ESTABLISHED** 1981

WHERE FUNDING CAN BE GIVEN Worldwide, with some preference for the Manchester area.

WHO CAN BENEFIT To benefit Jewish people and those in need.

WHAT IS FUNDED Educational institutions (including adult education) and institutions for the relief of poverty.

SAMPLE GRANTS Previous beneficiaries have included Asos Chesed, Cosmon Belz, Famos Charity Trust, Radford Education Trust, Sunderland Yeshiva and Yetev Lev.

FINANCES *Year* 2009–10 *Income* £184,049 *Grants* £231,450 *Assets* £2,819,491

TRUSTEES F Neumann; H Neumann; M Friedlander; H Rosemann; J Bleier; R Delange; M Neumann; P Neumann; E Neumann; E Henry.

HOW TO APPLY In writing to the correspondent.

WHO TO APPLY TO M Neumann, Trustee, 32 Stanley Road, Salford M7 4ES

■ The Beaverbrook Foundation

CC NO 310003   **ESTABLISHED** 1954

WHERE FUNDING CAN BE GIVEN UK and Canada.

WHO CAN BENEFIT Registered charities, mainly headquarters organisations or national charities.

WHAT IS FUNDED 'The object of this foundation include: (i) the erection or improvement of the fabric of any church building; (ii) the purchase of books, papers, manuscripts or works of art; (iii) care of the aged or infirm in the UK. One of the areas that the foundation has concentrated on over the past twenty years has been supporting small charitable projects. We recognise that it is often more difficult to raise a few thousand to refurbish a church hall than it is to raise millions for a major public building. In the past twenty years, the foundation has donated to more than 400 charities.'

WHAT IS NOT FUNDED Only registered charities are supported.

TYPE OF GRANT One-off capital grants.

RANGE OF GRANTS Up to £10,000.

SAMPLE GRANTS Grant beneficiaries include: Battle of Britain Memorial Trust (£5,000); Aids Ark and Calvert Trust (£2,000 each) and a number of

other grants for under £2,000 each totalling £6,250.

Previous beneficiaries have included: Alzheimer's Society, Book Aid International, Bob Champion Trust, Down's Syndrome Organisation, London Lighthouse, NSPCC, Royal Academy of Dramatic Art, the Samaritans, St Teresa's Home for the Elderly, Surrey County Scouts Council, Victim Support, West of England School and College and Whizz Kids.

FINANCES *Year* 2010 *Income* £196,996 *Grants* £15,250 *Assets* £13,056,268

TRUSTEES Lord Beaverbrook, Chair; Lady Beaverbrook; Lady Aitken; Hon. Laura Levi; J E A Kidd; Hon. M F Aitken.

OTHER INFORMATION The major project of the last decade has been the renovation of Beaverbrook's country house and gardens at Cherkley Court, near Leatherhead, Surrey. Now that this project is complete, the trustees plan to return their focus to charitable giving and grant making.

HOW TO APPLY There is an online application form at the foundation's website.

WHO TO APPLY TO The Secretary, Ms Ford, Third Floor, 11/12 Dover Street, London W1S 4LJ *Tel* 020 7042 9435 *email* jane@ beaverbrookfoundation.org *Website* www. beaverbrookfoundation.org

■ The Beccles Town Lands Charity

CC NO 210714   **ESTABLISHED** 1963

WHERE FUNDING CAN BE GIVEN Beccles only.

WHO CAN BENEFIT Organisations and individuals in Beccles.

WHAT IS FUNDED General charitable purposes.

WHAT IS NOT FUNDED Applications from outside of, or not to the benefit of, Beccles and its inhabitants will not be considered.

FINANCES *Year* 2009–10 *Income* £124,692 *Grants* £86,634 *Assets* £4,177,736

TRUSTEES James Hartley; Dennis Hipperson; Montagu Pitkin; Kenneth Leggett; Gillian Campbell; Gordon Hickman; Jennifer Langeskov; Keith Gregory; Jane Seppings.

HOW TO APPLY In writing to the correspondent.

WHO TO APPLY TO R W Peck, Secretary, Leman House, Ballygate, Beccles, Suffolk NR34 9ND

■ The Becker Family Charitable Trust

CC NO 1047968   **ESTABLISHED** 1995

WHERE FUNDING CAN BE GIVEN UK and overseas.

WHO CAN BENEFIT Registered charities.

WHAT IS FUNDED General charitable purposes, particularly Orthodox Jewish organisations.

SAMPLE GRANTS Previous beneficiaries have included Keren Shabbas, Lolev CT, Menora Grammar School, Torah Temima and WST.

FINANCES *Year* 2010–11 *Income* £156,915 *Grants* £35,176 *Assets* £339,202

TRUSTEES A Becker; Ms R Becker; Ms D Fried.

HOW TO APPLY In writing to the correspondent. However, please note that the trust has previously stated that its funds were fully committed.

WHO TO APPLY TO A Becker, Trustee, 33 Sinclair Grove, London, NW11 9JH

■ The Becketts and Sargeants Educational Foundation

CC NO 309766   ESTABLISHED 1986

WHERE FUNDING CAN BE GIVEN The borough of Northampton.

WHO CAN BENEFIT Church schools, and individuals under 25 years of age and in need of financial assistance, and either a resident in the borough or attending schools or full-time courses of education at any further education establishment in the borough, or a former pupil of All Saints' Middle School for at least two years.

WHAT IS FUNDED Education.

WHAT IS NOT FUNDED No grants are given for part-time courses.

RANGE OF GRANTS Up to £40,000.

SAMPLE GRANTS All Saints CEVA Primary School (£40,000); Weston Favell School and St. Andrews CEVA Primary School (£1,000 each).

FINANCES Year 2010 Income £218,257 Grants £112,301 Assets £3,024,019

TRUSTEES Philip Richard Saunderson; Richard Pestell; Eileen Beeby; Linda Ann Mayne; Ven. Christine Allsopp; David Smith; Hilary Spenceley; Margaret Pickard; Andrew Cowling; Christopher Davidge.

OTHER INFORMATION The 2010 grant total includes £57,000 given to individuals.

HOW TO APPLY On a form available from the correspondent. Applications are considered four times a year, usually in February/March, May, September and December.

WHO TO APPLY TO Mrs Gill R Evans, Grants Sub-committee Clerk, Hewitsons LLP, 7 Spencer Parade, Northampton NN1 5AB *Tel* 01604 233233 *email* gillevans@hewitsons.com

■ The Victoria and David Beckham Children's Charity

CC NO 1091838   ESTABLISHED 2002

WHERE FUNDING CAN BE GIVEN UK and overseas.

WHO CAN BENEFIT Organisations and individuals.

WHAT IS FUNDED Work benefiting children and general charitable purposes.

SAMPLE GRANTS Previous beneficiaries include UNICEF, Action for Kids, Motability, Demand, Theraplay, Wheelchair Centre, St Joseph's in the Park Parent Fellowship, Gerald Symonds Healthcare Limited and Helping Hand Company.

FINANCES Year 2009–10 Income £13,777

TRUSTEES Victoria Beckham; David Beckham; Jacqueline Adams.

OTHER INFORMATION The charity's basic accounts provide no information on its achievements during the year or who its beneficiaries were.

HOW TO APPLY In writing to the correspondent; however, a letter requesting information from the charity received a standard reply stating that the charity has 'limited funds', and that our request was 'outside the objectives and criteria set and therefore we are unable to help you'. This indicates that correspondence to the charity are not read.

WHO TO APPLY TO Charles Bradbrook, Administrator, Deloitte LLP, 2 New Street Square, London EC4A 3BZ *Tel* 020 7007 6023 *email* cbradbrook@deloitte.co.uk

■ The John Beckwith Charitable Trust

CC NO 800276   ESTABLISHED 1987

WHERE FUNDING CAN BE GIVEN UK and overseas.

WHO CAN BENEFIT Registered charities.

WHAT IS FUNDED General charitable purposes with a preference for: sports programmes for young people; education; children's charities; medical research; the arts; and charities involved with overseas aid.

TYPE OF GRANT Capital, one-off and recurring.

SAMPLE GRANTS Royal Opera House Trust (£100,000); Harrow Development Trust (£90,000); Wycome Abbey School (£21,000); Families of the Fallen (£17,000); Breast Cancer Care (£15,000); RNIB (£9,700); Special Boat Service Association, UNICEF and Sightsavers (£5,000 each); Alzheimer's Society and Ghana Youth Sport Development Programme (£2,000 each); KIDS and Whizz Kids (£1,000 each); and The Mayor's Fund for London (£800).

FINANCES Year 2009–10 Income £657,562 Grants £334,441 Assets £3,176,769

TRUSTEES J L Beckwith; H M Beckwith; C M Meech.

HOW TO APPLY In writing to the correspondent.

WHO TO APPLY TO Ms Sally Holder, Administrator, 124 Sloane Street, London SW1X 9BW

■ The Peter Beckwith Charitable Trust

CC NO 802113   ESTABLISHED 1989

WHERE FUNDING CAN BE GIVEN UK.

WHO CAN BENEFIT Institutions and registered charities benefiting at risk groups, people disadvantaged by poverty and socially isolated people.

WHAT IS FUNDED A broad range of medical and welfare charities. General charitable purposes.

SAMPLE GRANTS Beneficiaries included: Wimbledon and Putney Common Conservators (£10,000); Richmond Theatre (£5,000); Imperial War Museum (£2,000); and BAAF, ORCHID and Starlight Children's Foundation (£1,000 each).

FINANCES Year 2009–10 Income £42,310 Grants £41,406 Assets £11,542

TRUSTEES P M Beckwith; Mrs P G Beckwith; Mrs C T Van Dam; Tamara Veroni.

OTHER INFORMATION 51 grants were made to organisations and 1 grant to an individual.

HOW TO APPLY In writing to the correspondent.

WHO TO APPLY TO The Trustees, Hill Place House, 55a High Street, Wimbledon Village, London SW19 5BA *Tel* 020 8944 1288

■ The Bedford Charity (The Harpur Trust)

CC NO 204817   ESTABLISHED 1566

WHERE FUNDING CAN BE GIVEN Borough of Bedford and surrounding area.

WHO CAN BENEFIT Community groups, schools, individuals (under education object), and organisations. Particularly children and young adults, people with additional support needs, older people, and people disadvantaged by poverty.

WHAT IS FUNDED The promotion of education; the relief of people who are sick or in need, hardship or distress; homelessness; child and adolescent mental health; the provision in the interest of social welfare of facilities for recreation and other leisure-time occupations. The charity's four programmes are: The

Education Challenge Fund; Transitions; Resilience or Psychological Fitness; and Isolation.

WHAT IS NOT FUNDED Grants are not made in support of commercial ventures; for any project that relates primarily to the promotion of any religion; in support of projects that do not benefit the residents of the borough of Bedford; to cover costs already incurred, although exceptions are considered and this should be discussed with the trust prior to an application being submitted; for services which are the responsibility of the local authority, for example, a school applying for a grant to cover the cost of employing a teacher is unlikely to be successful. However, the trust could consider an application from a school for a creative arts project that involved paying a voluntary organisation to deliver lunch time or after school workshops.

TYPE OF GRANT Capital, revenue, salaries, running costs. The very great majority of grant giving is targeted at organisations.

SAMPLE GRANTS All Saints Parish Church (£75,000); CAN – Drugs, Alcohol and Homelessness (£69,000); Home-Start Bedford Borough (£60,000); Bedford Race Equality Council (£38,000); Music in Detention (£21,500); Bedford Creative Arts (£20,000); John Bunyan Museum (£15,000); Methodist Homes for the Aged (£10,000); Philharmonia Orchestra (£9,000); Bedfordshire and Northamptonshire Multiple Sclerosis Therapy Centre (£5,000); Sharnbrook Village Hall Management Committee (£2,500); All Saints PCC Renhold (£1,500).

FINANCES *Year* 2009–10 *Income* £52,397,000 *Grants* £903,733 *Assets* £102,269,000

TRUSTEES Sally Peck, Chair; David Palfreyman; David W Doran; Sue Clark; Ian McEwen; Judith Bray; Rae Levene; Rosemary Wallace; Tony Wildman; John K S Mingay; Colleen Atkins; Jean McCardle; Tina Beddoes; Phillip Wallace; Prof. Stephen Mayson; Murray Stewart; Justin Phillimore; David Meghan; Elizabeth Fordham; Michael Womack; Deirdre Anderson; Gail Dennis; David Dixon; Vina Mayor; Peter Budeck.

OTHER INFORMATION Grants to organisations: £814,000. Grants to individuals: £90,000. The charity also made a donation of £1 million to the endowment fund of the Bedford Academy.

HOW TO APPLY The charity clearly sets out its application procedure as follows: 'Step 1 – Check: First, read our guidance notes to make sure your project is eligible. [These are available on the charity's website upon completion of a short eligibility questionnaire.]; Step 2 – Call: If you think your project is eligible for a grant, call us. It's always better if you do this before you fill in a preliminary proposal form. Remember, some grant applications won't be successful so before you spend time filling in forms, please contact our Grants Manager, Lucy Bardner or our Grants Officer, Peta Frost on 01234 369500 to discuss your project in more detail. It's really important for organisations based outside of the Borough of Bedford who run projects in the Borough to call us before applying; Step 3 – Preliminary proposal form: The fastest and simplest way to apply is to complete and submit our online application form. This form asks you to create a password. Once you've submitted the form it goes straight to our grants database. Alternatively you can download and fill in a PDF version of Preliminary Proposal Form and email or post it back to us or request a hardcopy of the form and notes. Call or email Lucy on 01234 369500 or lbardner@harpur-trust.org.uk Make sure your application form reaches us by the deadline. This is the first stage of your application process. It will enable our grants team and our trustees to give you some initial guidance; Step 4 – Feedback: We'll read and discuss your preliminary proposal and give you feedback. If you've been successful, we'll ask you to fill in a full application form; Step 5 – Full application form: Please don't fill in a full application form unless we've asked you to. We'll do this in step four, above. If you used our online application process to send us your preliminary proposal, you can also use the online system to complete and submit your final application. If you sent us your preliminary proposal as a PDF or hard copy, you can either download the PDF version of the Full Application Form and email or post it back to us or request a hardcopy of the form and notes. Call or email Lucy on 01234 369500 or lbardner@harpur-trust.org.uk. Make sure your application form reaches us by the deadline and that you attach all of the relevant documents we've asked you for on the form. Step 6 – Acknowledgement; Our grants team will usually contact you by phone to let you know that we've received your full application. We may ask you to visit us to discuss your application in more detail; Step 7 – Decision: We'll discuss your proposal at the next meeting of our grants committee. If your application is successful, we'll write to you and let you know. We usually do this within seven working days of the meeting.'

WHO TO APPLY TO Lucy Bardner, Grants Manager, Princeton Court, Pilgrim Centre, Brickhill Drive, Bedford MK41 7PZ *Tel* 01234 369500 *Fax* 01234 369505 *email* grants@harpur-trust. org.uk *Website* www.bedfordcharity.org.uk

....

■ The Bedfordshire and Hertfordshire Historic Churches Trust

CC NO 1005697   **ESTABLISHED** 1991

WHERE FUNDING CAN BE GIVEN Bedfordshire, Hertfordshire and that part of Barnet within the Diocese of St Albans.

WHO CAN BENEFIT Those entrusted with the upkeep of places of active Christian worship.

WHAT IS FUNDED Work to ensure that places of active Christian worship are maintained in a structurally sound and weatherproof condition.

WHAT IS NOT FUNDED No grants to individuals.

TYPE OF GRANT One-off and buildings. Funding may be given for one year or less.

RANGE OF GRANTS £1,000–£5,000.

SAMPLE GRANTS St Mary – Baldock, for tower repairs; All Saints, Odell – towards kitchen and toilets; Methodist Church – Clapham, for fabric repairs; St Andrew – Watford, towards stonework and repairs; All Saints – Houghton Conquest, wall repair; and Baptist – Markyate, roof repairs.

FINANCES *Year* 2009–10 *Income* £221,882 *Grants* £221,500 *Assets* £222,508

TRUSTEES R C H Genochio, Chair; C P Green; A A I Jenkins; P F D Lepper; P A Lomax; S A Russell; T Warburton; W Marsterson; P N Griffiths.

OTHER INFORMATION Annual income comes from member subscription and from the annual 'Bike 'n Hike' event. The trust also acts as a distributive agent for church grants made by the Wixamtree Trust and Waste Recycling Environmental Ltd.

HOW TO APPLY Initial enquiries should be made to the Grants Secretary. Applications can only be made by members of the trust.

Think carefully about every application. Is it justified?

....

373

WHO TO APPLY TO Archie Russell, Grants Secretary, Wychbrook, 31 Ivel Gardens, Biggleswade, Bedfordshire SG18 0AN *Tel* 01767 312966 *email* wychbrook@yahoo.co.uk *Website* www.bedshertshct.org.uk

■ The Bedfordshire and Luton Community Foundation

CC NO 1086516   ESTABLISHED 2001
WHERE FUNDING CAN BE GIVEN The county of Bedfordshire and the borough of Luton.
WHO CAN BENEFIT 'The grant schemes aim to assist community voluntary organisations and groups in Bedfordshire and Luton in new or exciting projects that can help make a positive difference in the local community.'
WHAT IS FUNDED 'The foundation is dedicated to improving the quality of community life of those in Bedfordshire and Luton and in particular those in special need by reason of disability, age, financial or other disadvantage.'
WHAT IS NOT FUNDED No grants are made: to profit-making organisations; for the furtherance of any one religion; to fund political activities; to private business (other than social enterprises); to projects that would otherwise be funded from statutory sources.
FINANCES *Year* 2009–10 *Income* £626,578 *Grants* £475,847 *Assets* £265,542
TRUSTEES Malcolm Newman, Chair; Mark West; Richard Combes; Veta Hudson Rae; Janet Ridge; Peter Chilton; Judy Oliver; Clifton Ibbett; Dr Wendi Momen; Geoff Lambert; John Worboys; Andy Rayment; Keith Rawlings.
HOW TO APPLY Further information and application forms are available from the foundation. Please consult the foundation's website for details of up-to-date schemes.
WHO TO APPLY TO Mark West, Chief Executive, The Smithy, The Village, Old Warden, Bedfordshire SG18 9HQ *Tel* 01767 626459 *email* mark.west@blcf.org.uk *Website* www.blcf.org.uk

■ The David and Ruth Behrend Fund

CC NO 261567   ESTABLISHED 1969
WHERE FUNDING CAN BE GIVEN UK, with a preference for Merseyside.
WHO CAN BENEFIT Registered charities.
WHAT IS FUNDED General charitable purposes. The fund only gives funding to charities known to the settlors.
WHAT IS NOT FUNDED Anyone not known to the settlors.
TYPE OF GRANT Up to £8,000.
SAMPLE GRANTS Merseyside Development Foundation (£8,000); Birkenhead Youth Club (£6,000); Amelia Chadwick Trust (£5,000); Liverpool Central Citizens Advice (£2,500); Liverpool Roots Trust and Liverpool International Nordic Community (£2,000 each); European Play – Work Association and KIND (£1,500 each); and Support for Asylum Seekers and Merseyside Holiday Service (£1,000 each).
FINANCES *Year* 2009–10 *Income* £73,090 *Grants* £74,874 *Assets* £1,372,904
TRUSTEES Liverpool Charity and Voluntary Services.
HOW TO APPLY This fund states that it does not respond to unsolicited applications. 'The charity only makes grants to charities already known to the settlors as this is a personal charitable trust.'

WHO TO APPLY TO The Secretary, 151 Dale Street, Liverpool L2 2AH

■ The Beit Trust

CC NO 232478   ESTABLISHED 1906
WHERE FUNDING CAN BE GIVEN Zimbabwe, Zambia and Malawi.
WHO CAN BENEFIT Individuals and charities benefiting young adults, students, teachers and academics, at-risk groups, people disadvantaged by poverty, and homeless and socially isolated people.
WHAT IS FUNDED Post-primary education; health and welfare. Most grants are for buildings and infrastructure, with occasional grants made for environmental projects.
WHAT IS NOT FUNDED Grants are only given to charities in the areas above and the trust is reluctant to give grants to other grant-making charities. The trust stated in 2004 that it does not provide support for gap year students, undergraduates, individual schoolchildren or vehicles.
TYPE OF GRANT Recurring, one-off, capital, bursaries, postgraduate fellowships.
RANGE OF GRANTS Not normally in excess of £30,000.
FINANCES *Year* 2010 *Income* £2,277,910 *Grants* £1,799,334 *Assets* £75,242,642
TRUSTEES R A C Byatt; C J Driver; Prof. C B D Lavy; R P Lander; Sir K Prendergast.
HOW TO APPLY Contact the trust by telephone or in writing for an application form. Grants are approved by trustees at their six-monthly meetings.
WHO TO APPLY TO Major General A I Ramsey, Secretary, Beit House, Grove Road, Woking, Surrey GU21 5JB *Tel* 01483 772575 *Fax* 01483 725833 *email* enquiries@beittrust.org *Website* www.beittrust.org.uk

■ The Bellahouston Bequest Fund

SC NO SC011781   ESTABLISHED 1888
WHERE FUNDING CAN BE GIVEN Glasgow and district, but not more than five miles beyond the Glasgow city boundary (churches only).
WHO CAN BENEFIT Churches and registered charities in Glasgow or within five miles especially those benefiting Protestant evangelical denominations and clergy of such churches, as well as people disadvantaged by poverty.
WHAT IS FUNDED The trust supports a wide variety of causes. Its main priority is to help build, expand and repair Protestant evangelical churches or places of religious worship, as well as supporting the clergy of these churches. It further states that it is set up to give grants to charities for the relief of poverty or disease and to organisations concerned with promotion of the Protestant religion, education, and conservation of places of historical and artistic significance. It will consider social welfare causes generally and also animal welfare and sport and recreation.
WHAT IS NOT FUNDED No grants to organisations or churches whose work does not fall within the geographical remit of the fund. Overseas projects and political appeals are not supported.
RANGE OF GRANTS Usually between £1,000 and £5,000.
SAMPLE GRANTS Previous beneficiaries have included 119th Glasgow Boys' Brigade, Airborne Initiative, Ballieston Community Care, Bellahouston Academy, Calvay Social Action

Group, Citizens' Theatre, Church of Scotland, Colquhoun Trust, Crosshill Evangelical Church, Dalmarnock After School Care, Erskine Hospital, Girlguiding Scotland, Glasgow School of Art, Glasgow Old People's Welfare Association, Glasgow YMCA, Govanhill Youth Project, House for an Art Lover, Kelvingrove Refurbishment Appeal, Maryhill Parish Church, William McCunn's Trust, Northwest Women's Centre, Pearce Institute, Prince and Princess of Wales Hospice, Shawlands United Reformed Church, St Paul's Parish Council, Strathclyde Youth Club Association, University of Strathclyde and Williamwood Parish Church.

FINANCES *Year* 2009–10 *Income* £148,183

TRUSTEES Peter C Paisley; Peter L Fairley; Andrew Primrose; Donald Blair; Graeme Kidd.

HOW TO APPLY On a form available from the trust for church applications only. Other charitable organisations can apply in writing to the correspondent. The trustees meet to consider grants in March, July, October and December.

WHO TO APPLY TO Edward Barry, Mitchells Roberton Solicitors, George House, 36 North Hanover Street, Glasgow G1 2AD *email* eddie@mitchells-roberton.co.uk

■ Bellasis Trust

CC NO 1085972   **ESTABLISHED** 2000

WHERE FUNDING CAN BE GIVEN UK.

WHO CAN BENEFIT Mainly local charities.

WHAT IS FUNDED General charitable purposes.

RANGE OF GRANTS Up to £10,000.

SAMPLE GRANTS Royal Horticultural Society (£10,000); Mickleham PCC (£2,000); Surrey Community Development, MJC Stone Charitable Trust and Pancreatic Cancer UK (£1,000 each); and Facing Africa – Noma (£750).

FINANCES *Year* 2009–10 *Income* £33,421 *Grants* £21,975 *Assets* £821,360

TRUSTEES Paul Wates; Annette Wates; Annabelle Elliott; Joseph Lulham.

HOW TO APPLY 'The trustees research and consider applicants for grants.'

WHO TO APPLY TO Paul Wates, Trustee, 4th Floor, 65 Kingsway, London WC2B 6TD

■ The Bellhouse Foundation

CC NO 1076698   **ESTABLISHED** 1999

WHERE FUNDING CAN BE GIVEN UK.

WHO CAN BENEFIT Organisations working in the fields of engineering and pharmacology.

WHAT IS FUNDED The advancement of education through the promotion of medical research in the field of engineering and pharmacology.

SAMPLE GRANTS Previous beneficiaries have included: Oxford University Development Trust (£400,000); Magdalen College Development Trust (£150,000); Medical Foundation (£10,000); and the Woodland Trust (£1,000).

FINANCES *Year* 2009–10 *Income* £3,899

TRUSTEES Prof. Brian Bellhouse; Elisabeth Bellhouse; Clare Maurice.

OTHER INFORMATION The foundation's income and total expenditure have reduced significantly in recent years.

HOW TO APPLY In writing to the correspondent.

WHO TO APPLY TO The Trustees, The Lodge, North Street, Islip, Oxfordshire OX5 2QS

■ The Bellinger Donnay Trust

CC NO 289462   **ESTABLISHED** 1984

WHERE FUNDING CAN BE GIVEN Unrestricted, in practice, London, Wiltshire and the south east of England.

WHO CAN BENEFIT Small, independent charities.

WHAT IS FUNDED General charitable causes, in particular, those concerned with youth, older people, people with disabilities and the relief of poverty and deprivation.

WHAT IS NOT FUNDED No grants towards: animal organisations; travel overseas for individuals; medical research; or building projects.

RANGE OF GRANTS Usually up to £1,000; occasionally up to £5,000 or higher.

SAMPLE GRANTS Beneficiaries included: the Broderers Charity Trust and European Youth Orchestra (£5,000 each); Richmond Theatre and Haiti Earthquake Appeal (£2,500 each); Kew Foundation and Polka Theatre (£1,500 each); Age Concern, Macmillan Cancer Care and Centrepoint (£1,000 each); UK Sailing Academy and Combat Stress (£500 each); the Backup Trust and Action for Children (£250 each); George Bailey Trust and Motor Neurone Disease (£100 each); and Council for Assisting Academic Refugees (£50).

FINANCES *Year* 2009–10 *Income* £47,567 *Grants* £36,985 *Assets* £2,153,133

TRUSTEES Lady C M L Bellinger; Mrs L E Spackman; I A Bellinger.

HOW TO APPLY In writing to the correspondent, on no more than two sides of A4 plus the latest audited accounts. Applicants should provide: brief details of the charitable aims of the organisation and of how those aims are being achieved; the organisation's current financial position (income, expenditure, balances and reserves); funding already received/ anticipated from other sources; the proportion of income which is spent on administration, including staff salaries, and raising funds; the amount requested and the purpose for which the grant is to be used. If your application is urgent and requires immediate consideration, please say so when applying. Applications should be submitted by 31 January at the latest. Telephone calls are not accepted, although email queries are welcomed. Applications will not be acknowledged. Applicants from Wiltshire, or for projects in the county, should apply to: Mrs L E Spackman, Callas Hill Farm, High Street, Wanborough, Wiltshire SN4 0AE. All other applications should please be made in writing to: I A Bellinger, Byways, Coombe Hill Road, Kingston upon Thames, Surrey KT2 7DY.

WHO TO APPLY TO I A Bellinger, Byways, Coombe Hill Road, Kingston upon Thames, Surrey KT2 7DY *email* bdct@ianbellinger.co.uk *Website* www.bellingerdonnay.ik.com

■ Belljoe Tzedoko Ltd

CC NO 282726   **ESTABLISHED** 1981

WHERE FUNDING CAN BE GIVEN UK.

WHO CAN BENEFIT Registered charities and institutions.

WHAT IS FUNDED Advancement of religion in accordance with the orthodox Jewish faith and the relief of poverty.

SAMPLE GRANTS Previous beneficiaries have included: Adath Yisroel Synagogue, the B and G Charitable Trust, Beer Miriam, CWC, Kupat Hair, Marbe Torah, Shomre Hachomos, Yeshivo Horomo and Yesodey Hatora.

FINANCES *Year* 2010 *Income* £3,263,067
Grants £65,287 *Assets* £3,297,609

TRUSTEES H J Lobenstein; D Lobenstein;
M Lobenstein.

HOW TO APPLY In writing to the correspondent.

WHO TO APPLY TO H J Lobenstein, Trustee,
27 Fairholt Road, London N16 5EW

■ The Benfield Motors Charitable Trust

CC NO 328149   **ESTABLISHED** 1989

WHERE FUNDING CAN BE GIVEN Worldwide with
preferences for north east England, Leeds and
Edinburgh.

WHO CAN BENEFIT Neighbourhood-based community
projects and national schemes.

WHAT IS FUNDED Grants are given in the areas of
social welfare; community development; work
which supports children, young people and the
elderly, local hospitals and hospices; Christian
activities and the arts.

WHAT IS NOT FUNDED Expeditions, scholarships and
animal charities are not funded.

TYPE OF GRANT One-off.

RANGE OF GRANTS Mostly under £1,000, with some
larger grants reaching between £5,000 and
£40,000.

SAMPLE GRANTS Cathedral Church of St. Nicholas
(£100,000); Cry in the Dark (£40,000);
Community Foundation (£20,000); Traidcraft
(£10,000); DEC – Haiti Earthquake Appeal and
Bible Reading Fellowship (£5,000 each); The
Queen's Nursing Institute and Pendower Good
Neighbour Project (£1,500 each); and New Hope
Leeds and Whizz Kidz (£1,250 each).

FINANCES *Year* 2009–10 *Income* £338,060
Grants £206,350 *Assets* £151,826

TRUSTEES John Squires, Chair; Malcolm Squires;
Stephen Squires.

OTHER INFORMATION In 2009–10, grants were made
to 41 organisations totalling £206,000, 27 of
which were made for £600 or less.

HOW TO APPLY In writing to the correspondent. The
trustees' meet twice a year, this is usually in
May and November with applications needing to
be received by the beginning of April or October
respectively.

WHO TO APPLY TO Mrs Lynn Squires, Hon. Secretary,
c/o Benfield Motor Group, Asama Court,
Newcastle Business Park, Newcastle upon Tyne
NE4 7YD *Tel* 0191 226 1700
email charitabletrust@benfieldmotorgroup.com

■ The Benham Charitable Settlement

CC NO 239371   **ESTABLISHED** 1964

WHERE FUNDING CAN BE GIVEN UK, with very strong
emphasis on Northamptonshire.

WHO CAN BENEFIT Registered charities.

WHAT IS FUNDED The trust's policy is to make a large
number of relatively small grants to groups
working in many charitable fields, including
charities involved in medical research, disability,
elderly people, children and young people,
disadvantaged people, overseas aid, missions
to seamen, the welfare of ex-servicemen,
wildlife, the environment, and the arts. The trust
also supports the Church of England, and the
work of Christian mission throughout the world.
Special emphasis is placed upon those
churches and charitable organisations within the
county of Northamptonshire [especially as far as
new applicants are concerned].

WHAT IS NOT FUNDED No grants to individuals.

TYPE OF GRANT One-off and recurring grants will be
considered.

RANGE OF GRANTS Mostly between £200–£700, with
some larger grants up to £26,000.

SAMPLE GRANTS Northamptonshire Association of
Youth Clubs (£26,000); William Wilberforce
Trust (£8,000); Christ Church – Peckham
(£3,000); ZANE (Zimbabwe A National
Emergency) (£2,000); Camphill Village Trust
(£600); Deafblind UK and Friends of the Elderly
(£500 each); and Myasthenia Gravis Association
(£400).

FINANCES *Year* 2010–11 *Income* £162,929
Grants £120,400 *Assets* £5,305,563

TRUSTEES Mrs M M Tittle; Lady Hutton; E N Langley;
D A H Tittle; Revd. J A Nickols.

HOW TO APPLY In recent years the trust has not
been considering new applications.

WHO TO APPLY TO The Secretary, Hurstbourne,
Portnall Drive, Virginia Water, Surrey GU25 4NR

■ The Hervey Benham Charitable Trust

CC NO 277578   **ESTABLISHED** 1978

WHERE FUNDING CAN BE GIVEN Colchester and North
East Essex.

WHO CAN BENEFIT Individuals or self-help
organisations from Colchester and North East
Essex.

WHAT IS FUNDED Artistic (particularly musical)
activities which benefit the people of Colchester
and district and which would benefit from pump-
priming by the trust and/or a contribution which
enables self-help to function more effectively;
individuals with potential artistic (especially
musical) talent who are held back by physical,
environmental or financial disability;
preservation of Colchester and district's
heritage with particular emphasis on industrial
heritage and the maritime traditions of the
Essex/Suffolk coast; local history and
conservation affecting the heritage and
environment of the area.

WHAT IS NOT FUNDED Capital including buildings,
feasibility studies, interest-free loans, one-off,
and pump-priming costs. Funding is available for
up to three years. Tuition fees are normally paid
direct to educational institutions.

TYPE OF GRANT Capital including buildings, feasibility
studies, interest-free loans, one-off, and pump-
priming costs. Funding is available for up to
three years. Tuition fees are normally paid direct
to educational institutions.

RANGE OF GRANTS Up to £20,000.

SAMPLE GRANTS Kingsway Hall Arts and Community
Trust (£20,000); Cuckoo Farm Studios
(£3,500); Greenstead Community Centre
(£3,000); ACE Youth Musical Theatre (£1,700);
the Mad About Theatre Company, Brightlingsea
Free Music Festival, Hamilton Lodge Trust and
Colchester Scout Gang Show (£1,000 each);
Hervey Benham Young Soloists Concert (£500);
and Slackspace, Colchester (£300).

FINANCES *Year* 2009–10 *Income* £29,499
Grants £43,995 *Assets* £1,154,540

TRUSTEES M Ellis, Chair; A B Phillips; M R Carr;
K E Mirams.

OTHER INFORMATION The 2009–10 grant total
included £11,000 distributed to individuals

HOW TO APPLY In writing to the correspondent by the
normal quarterly dates.

WHO TO APPLY TO J Woodman, Clerk to the Trustees, 18 Wren Close, Stanway, Colchester, Essex CO3 8ZB *Tel* 07795 252929 *email* admin@herveybenhamtrust.org.uk

■ Maurice and Jacqueline Bennett Charitable Trust

CC NO 1047566   ESTABLISHED 1995
WHERE FUNDING CAN BE GIVEN UK and overseas.
WHO CAN BENEFIT Charitable organisations; Jewish charities.
WHAT IS FUNDED General charitable purposes; support of Jewish charitable organisations.
RANGE OF GRANTS Up to £26,000. Usually between £100 and £300.
SAMPLE GRANTS Distributions were: Iron Fell Consult (£26,000); Starlight Child (£3,000); Jewish Care and KOL Nidie (£2,000 each); and Global Enduro (£1,000).
FINANCES *Year* 2009–10 *Income* £39,105 *Grants* £37,310 *Assets* £10,454
TRUSTEES Maurice Bennett; M Jacqueline Bennett.
OTHER INFORMATION In 2009–10, 15 small donations were made totalling £3,100.
HOW TO APPLY In writing to the correspondent.
WHO TO APPLY TO Maurice Bennett, 9 Ingram Avenue, London NW11 6TG

■ Michael and Leslie Bennett Charitable Trust

CC NO 1047611   ESTABLISHED 1995
WHERE FUNDING CAN BE GIVEN UK.
WHO CAN BENEFIT Mostly Jewish organisations.
WHAT IS FUNDED The trust supports a range of causes, but the largest donations were to Jewish organisations.
RANGE OF GRANTS Up to £18,000.
SAMPLE GRANTS World Jewish Relief (£18,000); Norwood Ravenswood (£5,100); Chai Cancer Care (£3,800); United Jewish Israel Appeal and Nightingale (£3,000 each); LJCC (£1,000); and Macmillan Cancer Care (£750).
FINANCES *Year* 2009–10 *Income* £35,837 *Grants* £39,694 *Assets* £296,519
TRUSTEES Michael Bennett; Lesley V Bennett.
HOW TO APPLY In writing to the correspondent.
WHO TO APPLY TO Michael Bennett, Trustee, Bedegars Lea, Kenwood Close, London NW3 7JL

■ The Gerald Bentall Charitable Trust

CC NO 271993   ESTABLISHED 1976
WHERE FUNDING CAN BE GIVEN Mainly southern England including London.
WHO CAN BENEFIT The elderly, people with disability, youth.
WHAT IS FUNDED Hospitals, churches, youth organisations, education.
RANGE OF GRANTS £100–£10,000.
SAMPLE GRANTS Beneficiaries included: Steadfast Sea Cadets (£1,000); Help for Heroes (£600); Old Bentallions Association (£500); Phyllis Tuckwell Hospice (£300); Alzheimer's Research Trust (£250); and Back to Africa (£200); Royal London Society for the Blind, Spinal Injuries Association, Treloar Trust and Wellbeing of Women (£175 each).
FINANCES *Year* 2009–10 *Income* £533,656 *Grants* £19,510 *Assets* £1,089,147

TRUSTEES A J D Anstee; Mrs C L Thorp; Mrs E C Purcell; Mrs C E Jackson.
OTHER INFORMATION In 2009–10 donations ranged between £67 and £500, with the most common being £175.
HOW TO APPLY In writing to the correspondent.
WHO TO APPLY TO Mrs Z Peters, 24 Stoudes Close, Worcester Park, Surrey KT4 7RB *Tel* 020 8330 4586

■ Bergqvist Charitable Trust

CC NO 1015707   ESTABLISHED 1992
WHERE FUNDING CAN BE GIVEN Buckinghamshire and neighbouring counties.
WHO CAN BENEFIT Registered charities and community organisations.
WHAT IS FUNDED Education; medical health; environment; and disaster and famine relief.
WHAT IS NOT FUNDED Grants are not made to individuals, non-registered charities or for animal causes.
TYPE OF GRANT One-off and recurrent grants.
SAMPLE GRANTS Previous beneficiaries have included Generation Trust for medical research, Abracadabra – Royal Surrey Hospital Paediatric Unit, Stoke Mandeville Hospital for MRI scanner appeal, British Epilepsy Association for general purposes, Cancer Care and Haematology at Stoke Mandeville Hospital, PACE school for children with cerebral palsy, British Heart Foundation for research, Church Urban Fund for diocese expenses and Sight Savers International for eyesight research.
FINANCES *Year* 2010 *Income* £66,002 *Grants* £67,521 *Assets* £1,602,592
TRUSTEES Mrs P A Bergqvist, Chair; Philip Bergqvist; Sophia Bergqvist.
HOW TO APPLY In writing to the correspondent.
WHO TO APPLY TO Mrs P A Bergqvist, Trustee, Moat Farm, Water Lane, Ford, Aylesbury, Buckinghamshire HP17 8XD *Tel* 01296 748560

■ The Ruth Berkowitz Charitable Trust

CC NO 1111673   ESTABLISHED 2005
WHERE FUNDING CAN BE GIVEN UK and overseas.
WHO CAN BENEFIT Charitable organisations.
WHAT IS FUNDED Youth; medical research; education; Jewish causes, including education and community.
RANGE OF GRANTS £2,500–£50,000.
SAMPLE GRANTS National Jewish Chaplaincy Board (£47,500); World Jewish Relief (£42,500); Community Security Trust (£40,000); Magen David Adom UK and North West London Jewish Day School (£25,000 each); Lord Ashdown Charitable Settlement (£21,500); Norwood Ravenswood (£20,000); Cancer Research UK and Marie Curie Cancer Care (£15,000 each); London Philharmonic Orchestra Limited (£10,000); British Friends Ohel Sarah and The Z.S.V. Trust (£7,500 each); and Camp Simcha (£4,000).
FINANCES *Year* 2009–10 *Income* £91,197 *Grants* £464,250 *Assets* £4,052,568
TRUSTEES Philip Beckman; Brian Beckman.
HOW TO APPLY In writing to the correspondent.
WHO TO APPLY TO The Trustees, 39 Farm Avenue, London NW2 2BJ *Tel* 020 7388 3577

■ The Berkshire Community Foundation

CC NO 294220 **ESTABLISHED** 1985

WHERE FUNDING CAN BE GIVEN Berkshire, i.e. the unitary authorities of Bracknell, Reading, Slough, Windsor and Maidenhead, West Berkshire and Wokingham.

WHO CAN BENEFIT Voluntary organisations or groups established for charitable purposes and individual children. Grants are directed to: older people; children and young people; people with a long-term illness or disability and their carers; people with mental health needs; minority ethnic communities; those suffering from addiction.

WHAT IS FUNDED Grants are made through various funds to support groups addressing need in the county. Up-to-date details can be found at the foundation's website.

WHAT IS NOT FUNDED 'We do not fund medical research or equipment, sponsored events, animal welfare, overseas travel/expeditions, promotion of religious or political causes, statutory work (in educational institutions or replacing statutory obligation/public funding) or groups with more than one year's unrestricted reserves... Grants are not intended to support major capital appeals and cannot be made retrospectively.'

FINANCES *Year* 2009–10 *Income* £1,247,380 *Grants* £670,167 *Assets* £5,676,625

TRUSTEES Chris Barrett; Ramesh Kukar; Sue Ormiston; Richard Rand; Gordon West; Dick Taylor; Susie Tremlett; Emma van Zeller; Revd Allen Walker; Christine Weston; Richard Griffiths-Jones; Peter Mason; Ray Tapken; David Seward; Catherine Stephenson; Jane Wates; Anthony Wood.

OTHER INFORMATION 'Donations from individuals, companies and charitable trusts are pooled in the foundation's Community Capital Fund from which the foundation draws income to make its grants.'

HOW TO APPLY Full details of how to apply to the various funding streams can be found at the foundation's website.

WHO TO APPLY TO The Grants Team, Arlington Business Park, Theale, Reading, Berkshire RG7 4SA *Tel* 0118 930 3021 *Fax* 0118 930 4933 *email* info@berkshirecf.org *Website* www. berkshirecf.org

■ The Bestway Foundation

CC NO 297178 **ESTABLISHED** 1987

WHERE FUNDING CAN BE GIVEN UK and overseas.

WHO CAN BENEFIT Individuals, UK registered charities, non-registered charities and overseas charities.

WHAT IS FUNDED Advancement of education by grants to schoolchildren and students who are of Indian, Pakistani, Bangladeshi or Sri Lankan origin; relief of sickness, and preservation and protection of health in the UK and overseas, especially in India, Pakistan, Bangladesh and Sri Lanka.

WHAT IS NOT FUNDED No grants for trips/travel abroad.

RANGE OF GRANTS £1,000–£200,000.

SAMPLE GRANTS Bestway Foundation Pakistan (£200,000); Northern University (£50,000); British EduTrust Foundation (£36,000); Duke of Edinburgh Awards (£16,000); Silver Star Appeal (£15,000); Leonard Cheshire Disability (£10,000); SSAT – Southampton City Council for Bellemoor School (£5,500); Concern for Mental Health, GLMW Scout County Development Fund and National Grocers' Benevolent Fund (£2,000 each); Wines and Spirits Trades Benevolent Society (£1,000); and Fleetwood Tigers (£500).

FINANCES *Year* 2009–10 *Income* £886,334 *Grants* £500,722 *Assets* £5,481,632

TRUSTEES A K Bhatti; A K Chaudhary; M Y Sheikh; Z M Choudrey; M A Pervez.

OTHER INFORMATION All trustees of this foundation are directors and shareholders of Bestway (Holdings) Limited, the parent company of Bestway Cash and Carry Limited.

HOW TO APPLY In writing to the correspondent, enclosing an sae. Applications are considered in March/April. Telephone calls are not welcome.

WHO TO APPLY TO M Y Sheikh, Trustee, Bestway Cash and Carry Ltd, Abbey Road, Park Royal, London NW10 7BW *Tel* 020 8453 1234 *email* zulfikaur.wajid-hasan@bestway.co.uk *Website* www.bestwaygroup.co.uk/page/bestway-foundation

■ Thomas Betton's Charity for Pensions and Relief-in-Need

CC NO 280143 **ESTABLISHED** 1973

WHERE FUNDING CAN BE GIVEN UK.

WHO CAN BENEFIT Registered charities only.

WHAT IS FUNDED This charity makes grants for educational activities for children and young people up to the age of 25 from disadvantaged backgrounds. It also gives to specific charitable organisations with which the trustee has an ongoing relationship (a block grant is made to Housing the Homeless which allocates grants to individuals).

WHAT IS NOT FUNDED Applications for grants to individuals are accepted only from registered social workers or other agencies, not directly from individuals.

RANGE OF GRANTS £1,000–£10,000.

SAMPLE GRANTS Housing the Homeless Central Fund (£10,000); Royal Academy for Dramatic Arts (£6,500); Autism initiatives UK (£6,000); Pascal Theatre Company (£5,000); Sheriff's and Recorder's Fund (£2,000); Chad Varah Appeal for Samaritans (£500); and the City of London Police Widows and Orphans Fund (£200).

FINANCES *Year* 2009–10 *Income* £42,567 *Grants* £32,023 *Assets* £949,921

TRUSTEES The Worshipful Company of Ironmongers.

HOW TO APPLY In writing to the correspondent.

WHO TO APPLY TO The Charities Administrator, Ironmongers' Hall, Barbican, London EC2Y 8AA *Tel* 020 7776 2311 *email* helen@ironhall.co.uk *Website* www.ironhall.co.uk

■ BHST

CC NO 1004327 **ESTABLISHED** 1991

WHERE FUNDING CAN BE GIVEN UK and Israel.

WHO CAN BENEFIT Jewish organisations.

WHAT IS FUNDED Jewish charitable purposes.

RANGE OF GRANTS Usually £300–£7,400.

SAMPLE GRANTS Previous beneficiaries include: Adath Yisroel Burial Society (£64,000); Easy Chasnea (£7,000); Shulum Berger Association (£3,000); United Talmudical Association (£2,500); and Beis Rochel (£1,600).

FINANCES *Year* 2009–10 *Income* £409,182 *Grants* £215,233 *Assets* £745,954

TRUSTEES Solomon Laufer; Pinchas Ostreicher; Joshua Sternlicht.

OTHER INFORMATION A total of £124,000 was given in student grants.

HOW TO APPLY In writing to the correspondent.

WHO TO APPLY TO Solomon Laufer, Secretary, Cohen Arnold and Co., New Burlington House, 1075 Finchley Road, London NW11 0PU *Tel* 020 8731 0777 *Fax* 020 8731 0778 *email* mail@cohenarnold.com

■ The Mason Bibby 1981 Trust

CC NO 283231   **ESTABLISHED** 1981

WHERE FUNDING CAN BE GIVEN Merseyside and other areas where the company has or had a presence.

WHO CAN BENEFIT Priority to elderly people and employees and ex-employees of J Bibby and Sons Plc (since renamed Barloworld PLC).

WHAT IS FUNDED Main area of interest is elderly people but applications are considered from other groups, particularly from areas in which the company has a presence.

WHAT IS NOT FUNDED Apart from employees and ex-employees of J Bibby and Sons Plc, applications are considered from registered charities only.

RANGE OF GRANTS £250–£3,500.

SAMPLE GRANTS Liverpool Personal Service Society (£3,300); Age Concern Liverpool (£2,800); Liverpool Charity and Voluntary Services (£1,600); Macmillan Cancer Support (£1,400); Royal School for the Blind, Liverpool (£1,200); The Shakespeare Hospice, Hoylake Cottage Hospital and Hospice of the Good Shepherd (£1,000 each); Talking Newspapers for the Blind and West Lancashire Community Hospice Association (£500 each).

FINANCES *Year* 2009–10 *Income* £81,425 *Grants* £72,290 *Assets* £2,057,722

TRUSTEES J B Bibby, Chair; J P Wood; Mrs D M Fairclough; S W Bowman; J McPheat; A S Gresty; P A Blocksidge; Mrs L F Stead.

OTHER INFORMATION In 2009–10 donations to 35 employees and ex-employees totalled £20,000.

HOW TO APPLY In writing to the correspondent. Trustees meet half yearly. Applications are only acknowledged if a grant is agreed.

WHO TO APPLY TO Mrs D M Fairclough, Trustee, c/o Rathbone Brothers and Co. Ltd, Port of Liverpool Building, Pier head, Liverpool L3 1NW

■ BibleLands

CC NO 1076329   **ESTABLISHED** 1854

WHERE FUNDING CAN BE GIVEN Lands of the Bible, especially Lebanon, the Holy Land and Egypt.

WHO CAN BENEFIT Local organisations working in the beneficial area that benefits people of all ages, faiths and nationalities in the region especially those who are marginalised or vulnerable. Support is given to areas including education, special needs, vocational training, care and support of refugees, medical, social care.

WHAT IS FUNDED BibleLands exists to support and encourage local Christians in the lands of the Bible, who are dedicated to fulfilling the compassionate ministry of Christ.

WHAT IS NOT FUNDED Individuals and UK bodies are not eligible. Grants are confined to Christian-led work, but beneficiaries are helped regardless of faith or nationality.

TYPE OF GRANT Capital including buildings, recurring, core costs, one-off, running costs and start-up costs. Funding is for up to or more than three years. Child sponsorship schemes and ongoing grants to specific projects are also in place.

RANGE OF GRANTS £1,000–£200,000.

SAMPLE GRANTS Nazareth School for Nursing (£152,000); Habitat for Humanity (£112,000); Arab Evangelical School, Hebron (£65,000); Hope School, Belt Jala (£49,000); Armenian Evangelical School, Anjar (£32,500); Birds Nest Orphanage, Byblos (£24,000); Princess Basma Centre (£21,000); Joint Christian Committee for Social Service (£10,000); African Hope Learning Centre (£2,500); Sheepfold (£1,700).

FINANCES *Year* 2010 *Income* £3,586,000 *Grants* £2,626,000 *Assets* £5,162,000

TRUSTEES Mrs J Robertson; Dr C Young; Revd D Burton; Mr D Callander; Miss J Hackney; Mrs V Smith; Revd B Jolly; Mr H Bradley; Dr B McGucken; Mrs L Toner; Mrs K Lewis.

PUBLICATIONS *The Star in the East*, quarterly magazine.

HOW TO APPLY Apply in writing for an application form, giving brief outline of the support being sought.

WHO TO APPLY TO Jeremy Moodey, PO Box 50, High Wycombe, Buckinghamshire HP15 7QU *Tel* 01494 897950 *Fax* 01494 897951 *email* info@biblelands.org.uk *Website* www.biblelands.org.uk

■ The Bideford Bridge Trust

CC NO 204536   **ESTABLISHED** 1973

WHERE FUNDING CAN BE GIVEN Bideford, Devon and its neighbourhood.

WHO CAN BENEFIT Charities and individuals.

WHAT IS FUNDED Grants are dictated by the scheme of the trust, which maintains that the following grants should be made: (i) to encourage education; (ii) to encourage poor people to become more self-sufficient by assisting them in business start-up schemes (iii); to individual applications for charitable assistance (such as on the grounds of poverty or ill health); (iv) to clubs, organisations and charities (v); to assist people with disabilities living in the Parish of Bideford.

WHAT IS NOT FUNDED Computer purchases for individuals. Political donations.

TYPE OF GRANT Core and recurring costs.

RANGE OF GRANTS Generally £500–£50,000.

SAMPLE GRANTS Previous beneficiaries included: Torridge Training Service – Business Start-Ups (£27,000); Bideford Rugby Football Club (£26,000); East-the-Water Community Primary School (£16,000); Bideford Blues and Appledore Junior Football Club (£10,000); Torridge and Bude Citizens Advice Bureau and Torridge Volunteer Centre (£5,000 each); Bideford Folk Festival 2,500 and Macmillan Cancer Relief – Bideford (£2,500); Appledore Book Festival and North Devon Down Syndrome Association (£1,500 each); and Sure Start Bideford Children's Centre (£300).

FINANCES *Year* 2010 *Income* £755,689

TRUSTEES P Christie; W G Isaac; Mrs E Junkison; E Hubber; J Baker; O Chope; A Harper; T J Johns; B J Lacey; D J D Frics.

HOW TO APPLY In writing to the correspondent.

WHO TO APPLY TO P R Sims, Steward, 24 Bridgeland Street, Bideford, Devon EX39 2QB

■ The Big Lottery Fund (see also Awards for All)

ESTABLISHED 2004

WHERE FUNDING CAN BE GIVEN UK.

WHO CAN BENEFIT Charities, statutory bodies.

WHAT IS FUNDED BIG runs many different programmes, some UK-wide and others specific to England, Northern Ireland, Scotland and

Wales. New programmes are introduced from time to time, and others close. Potential applicants are advised to check the fund's website for up-to-date information on current and upcoming programmes.

FINANCES *Year* 2010–11 *Income* £793,793,000 *Grants* £374,000,000 *Assets* £555,886,000

TRUSTEES Peter Ainsworth, Chair; Anna Southall; Nat Sloane; Frank Hewitt; Janet Reed; Alison Magee; Diana Whitworth; Judith Donovan; Roland Doven; John Gartside; Albert Tucker; Rajay Naik.

OTHER INFORMATION There are a number of regional offices. Call 0845 410 2030 for details.

HOW TO APPLY All application forms and guidance are available via the website or by calling 0845 410 2030.

WHO TO APPLY TO (See below) *Tel* 0845 410 2030 *email* enquiries@biglotteryfund.org.uk *Website* www.biglotteryfund.org.uk

■ The Billmeir Charitable Trust

CC NO 208561   **ESTABLISHED** 1956

WHERE FUNDING CAN BE GIVEN UK, with a preference for the Surrey area, specifically Elstead, Tilford, Farnham and Frensham.

WHO CAN BENEFIT Charitable organisations.

WHAT IS FUNDED General charitable purposes. About a quarter of the grants are for health and medical causes.

RANGE OF GRANTS £2,000–£10,000.

FINANCES *Year* 2009–10 *Income* £162,656 *Grants* £120,000 *Assets* £3,799,359

TRUSTEES B C Whitaker; M Whitaker; S Marriott; J Whitaker.

HOW TO APPLY The trust states that it does not request applications and that its funds are fully committed.

WHO TO APPLY TO Keith Lawrence, Secretary, Moore Stephens, 150 Aldersgate Street, London EC1A 4AB *Tel* 020 7334 9191

■ Percy Bilton Charity

CC NO 1094720   **ESTABLISHED** 1962

WHERE FUNDING CAN BE GIVEN UK.

WHO CAN BENEFIT Large grants are only available to registered charities. Unregistered organisations can apply for a small grant but a reference from another charity, Council for Voluntary Service or the local authority youth service will be required.

WHAT IS FUNDED Projects working with disadvantaged and underprivileged young people (under 25), people with disabilities (physical or learning disabilities or mental health problems) and/or older people (aged over 60).

WHAT IS NOT FUNDED The charity will not consider the following (the list is not exhaustive): running expenses for the organisation or individual projects; salaries, training costs or office equipment/furniture; projects for general community use e.g. community centre and church halls; disabled access to community buildings; publication costs e.g. printing/ distributing promotional and information leaflets; projects that have been completed; items that have already been purchased; provision of disabled facilities in schemes mainly for the able-bodied; general funding/circularised appeals; pre-schools or playgroups (other than predominantly for disabled children); play schemes/summer schemes; holidays or expeditions for individuals or groups; trips, activities or events; community sports/play area facilities; consumables (e.g. stationery, arts and

crafts materials); refurbishment or repair of places of worship/church halls; research projects; mainstream pre-schools, schools, colleges and universities (other than special schools); welfare funds for individuals; hospital/ medical equipment; and works to premises not used primarily by the eligible groups.

TYPE OF GRANT One-off.

RANGE OF GRANTS Grants to individuals: up to £200; small grants to organisations: up to £500 towards furnishing and equipment for small projects; main funding single grants for capital expenditure: in excess of £2,000.

SAMPLE GRANTS *Larger grants*: Independent Options (Stockport) Limited (£12,000), to replace the central heating system at the Pines which is a centre providing services for children and adults with disabilities and mental health needs; Family Support Brightlingsea – Essex (£10,000), for the purchase of a minibus to provide door to door transport for older people (average age of over 80) attending their lunch clubs; Quest School – Kent (£8,000), towards the purchase of computer equipment, an interactive whiteboard and desks for the school for young people with autism and learning disabilities; Caldecott Foundation – Kent (£7,000), to purchase 'tough furniture' for residential accommodation for young people who have experienced neglect and abuse; Wirral Society of the Blind and Partially Sighted (£5,000), for the construction of a two room extension to their premises to provide facilities for computer courses and art sessions for people with a visual impairment; Martha Trust – East Sussex (£4,000), to construct a hydrotherapy pool at Mary House, a residential home for young people with profound physical and learning disabilities; Age Concern – Exeter (£3,000), for the refurbishment of kitchen and dining facilities at their cafe which provides hot cooked meals for older people; and CHICKS – Devon (£1,700), to install external lighting for the play barn at Moorland Retreat providing respite holidays for disadvantaged children from inner city areas across the UK.

Small grants: ENABLE NI – County Down and M13 Youth Project – Manchester (£500 each); Shopmobility – Sheffield (£475); KEEN – Oxford (£450); Body and Soul – London (£390); Thalia Theatre Company – Norwich (£350); Edenbridge Mencap – Kent (£330); Different Strokes – Newcastle (£270); Dipton Out of School Hours Club – County Durham (£250); and SeeSaw – Oxford (£75).

FINANCES *Year* 2009–10 *Income* £696,138 *Grants* £583,931 *Assets* £18,591,899

TRUSTEES Miles A Bilton, Chair; James R Lee; Stefan J Paciorek; Kim Lansdown; Hayley Bilton.

OTHER INFORMATION Assistance is also given on a one-off basis to individuals and families who fall within the following categories: older people on a low income and people with physical or learning disabilities or mental health problems. All applications for individuals to be sent in by the relevant social worker on local or health authority headed notepaper. A total of £115,000 was awarded to individuals during 2009–10.

HOW TO APPLY The charity's website gives the following guidance on making an application: '*Large grants (£2,000 and over)* – Please apply on your organisation's headed notepaper giving or attaching the following information. 1–6 must be provided in all cases and 7 as applicable to your appeal: 1. A brief history of your charity, its objectives and work. 2. Description of the project and what you intend to achieve. 3. A copy of your most recent annual report and audited accounts. 4. Details of funds already raised and other sources that you have approached. 5. Proposals to monitor and evaluate the project. 6. Any other relevant information that will help to explain your application. 7. The following additional information that applies to your appeal. *Building/Refurbishment appeals* – Please include: a statement of all costs involved – please itemise major items and professional fees; confirmation that the project has on-going revenue funding; confirmation that all planning and other consents and building regulations approvals have been obtained; details of ownership of the premises and if leased, the length of the unexpired term; timetable of construction/refurbishment and anticipated date of completion. *Equipment appeals* – An itemised list of all equipment with estimate of costs. Please obtain at least 2 competitive estimates except where this is not practicable e.g. specialised equipment. When you plan to purchase the equipment. *Contribution towards purchase of minibuses* – Please note that minibuses can only be considered if used to transport older and disabled people with mobility problems. Please give details of provision made for insurance, tax and maintenance etc. We require confirmation that your organisation can meet future running costs. *Small grants (up to £500)* – Please apply on your organisation's headed notepaper with the following information: brief details about your organisation and its work; a copy of your most recent annual accounts; outline of the project and its principal aims; breakdown of the cost of item/s required; if your organisation is not a registered charity, please supply a reference from a registered charity with whom you work or from the Voluntary Service Council.'

WHO TO APPLY TO Wendy Fuller, Charity Administrator, Bilton House, 7 Culmington Road, Ealing, London W13 9NB *Tel* 020 8579 2829 *Fax* 020 8579 3650 *Website* www. percybiltoncharity.org.uk

■ The Bingham Trust

CC NO 287636   **ESTABLISHED** 1977
WHERE FUNDING CAN BE GIVEN Buxton and district.
WHO CAN BENEFIT Organisations and individuals.
WHAT IS FUNDED Community needs, churches, arts and arthritis research.
WHAT IS NOT FUNDED Generally, limited to the town of Buxton and district.
TYPE OF GRANT One-off, capital including buildings, project, running costs, salaries and start-up costs. Funding is for up to three years.
RANGE OF GRANTS Up to £5,000.
SAMPLE GRANTS High Peak Theatre Trust re Pavilion Arts Centre (£5,000); the Milnthorp Homes and Buxton Festival (£3,000 each); Derbyshire Leicestershire & Rutland Air Ambulance (£2,000); Buxton Methodists Church Youth (£1,600); Group Macmillan Cancer Support and RNIB (£1,000 each); PDSA PetAid (£750); High Peak Community Housing Summer Activities (£500); and Tideswell Community Arts Festival (£200).
FINANCES *Year* 2009–10 *Income* £91,205 *Grants* £82,420 *Assets* £2,216,466
TRUSTEES Dr R G B Willis, Chair; R A Horne; Mrs J H Lawton; Revd P J Meek; Mrs A M Hurst.
OTHER INFORMATION In 2009–10 the trust distributed around 80 grants to individuals and organisations. Grants to organisations totalled

£70,000, while approximately £12,000 was distributed to individuals.
HOW TO APPLY In writing to the correspondent on no more than two pages of A4, stating the total cost of the project and sources of other funding. Applications should arrive before the end of February, June, September and December each year.
WHO TO APPLY TO R Horne, Trustee, Blinder House, Flagg, Buxton, Derbyshire SK17 9QG *email* binghamtrust@aol.com *Website* www. binghamtrust.org.uk

■ The Bintaub Charitable Trust

CC NO 1003915   **ESTABLISHED** 1991
WHERE FUNDING CAN BE GIVEN Greater London, worldwide.
WHO CAN BENEFIT Jewish, health, education, children.
WHAT IS FUNDED Mainly London organisations, towards 'the advancement of education in and the religion of the orthodox Jewish faith'. Grants are also given for other charitable causes, mainly towards medical and children's work.
SAMPLE GRANTS Gateshead Jewish Academy (£6,400); Yeshiva Be'er Hatorah (£6,000); Gateshead Jewish Primary School (£3,000); JTTC (£2,900); Menorah Foundation School (£2,600); Kupat Ha'ir (£2,500); Friends of Yeshivat Lomdei Torah, Friends of Mir and Va'ad Harabbanim L'inyanei Tzedaka (£2,000 each); and Sunderland Kollel (£700).
FINANCES *Year* 2009–10 *Income* £51,500 *Grants* £49,310
TRUSTEES James Frohwein; Tania Frohwein; Daniel Frohwein; Rabbi E Stefansky.
HOW TO APPLY The trust has previously stated that new applications are not being accepted.
WHO TO APPLY TO Mrs Dahlia Rosenberg, Trustee, 125 Wolmer Gardens, Edgware HA8 8QF

■ The Birmingham Community Foundation

CC NO 1048162   **ESTABLISHED** 1995
WHERE FUNDING CAN BE GIVEN Greater Birmingham.
WHO CAN BENEFIT Small community-based groups and organisations involved in activities that regenerate and rebuild communities.
WHAT IS FUNDED Small grants are generally given to community based groups involved in activities that regenerate and build communities, however priority is given to those projects which: encourage community responsibility; develop community capacity; are unable to access other forms of funding; and do not duplicate other work being done within the area.
WHAT IS NOT FUNDED No funding is available for projects operating outside the Greater Birmingham area; general appeals or large national charities (except for local branches working specifically for local people); individuals, for whatever purpose; organisations and individuals in the promotion of political or religious ideology.
RANGE OF GRANTS Mostly under £2,000.
SAMPLE GRANTS Previous beneficiaries include: Great Bridge Community Forum, Netherton Cricket Club, Families for Peace, Talking with Hands, Aston Link, City of Birmingham Special Olympics, Deep Impact Theatre Company, Friends of Hawkesley and Warwickshire Air Ambulance.

FINANCES *Year* 2009–10 *Income* £4,974,913 *Grants* £4,143,753 *Assets* £1,992,306

TRUSTEES David Bucknall, Chair; John Andrews; Kay Cadman; Angela Henry; Shamiela Ahmed; David Scard; Richard Harris; Peter Grace; John Matthews.

HOW TO APPLY Please refer to the foundation's website for full details of how to apply to the various programmes currently being administered.

WHO TO APPLY TO Karen Argyle, Grants Officer, Nechells Baths, Nechells Park Road, Nechells, Birmingham B7 5PD *Tel* 0121 322 5560 *Fax* 0121 322 5579 *email* team@bbccf.org.uk *Website* www.bhamfoundation.co.uk

■ The Birmingham District Nursing Charitable Trust

CC NO 215652   ESTABLISHED 1960

WHERE FUNDING CAN BE GIVEN Within a 20-mile radius of the Council House in Birmingham.

WHO CAN BENEFIT Local organisations benefiting medical professionals. Grants may be made to local branches of national organisations.

WHAT IS FUNDED Medical or nursing organisations; convalescent homes; convalescent homes or rest homes for nurses or other medical or nursing institution; amenities for patients or nursing staff of Birmingham Domiciliary Nursing Service; amenities for patients or nursing staff of any state hospital.

WHAT IS NOT FUNDED No grants are given to individuals.

TYPE OF GRANT One-off and recurrent.

RANGE OF GRANTS Up to £6,000.

SAMPLE GRANTS Birmingham and Three Counties Trust for Nurses and Birmingham St Marys Hospice (£6,000 each); Mary Stevens Hospice, Vitalise and Medical Foundation for Victims of Torture (£5,000 each); Samaritans and Edwards Trust (£3,000 each); Friends of Home Nursing Birmingham (£2,500); Primrose Hospice Cancer Help and Shakespeare Hospice (£2,000 each); Age Concern (£2,100); Norman Laud Association (£1,600); and the Stroke Association (£500).

FINANCES *Year* 2009–10 *Income* £55,364 *Grants* £69,800 *Assets* £1,535,242

TRUSTEES H W Tuckey; Prof. J R Mann; Mrs T Cull; Prof. C M Clifford; Dr P Mayer; S Reynolds; A H Jones.

HOW TO APPLY In writing to the correspondent with a copy of the latest accounts. Applications should be sent in August/September. Trustees meet to consider grants in the first week of November.

WHO TO APPLY TO Anthony Jones, c/o Shakespeare Putsman, Somerset House, Temple Street, Birmingham B2 5DJ

■ The Birmingham Hospital Saturday Fund Medical Charity and Welfare Trust

CC NO 502428   ESTABLISHED 1972

WHERE FUNDING CAN BE GIVEN UK, but mostly centred around the West Midlands and Birmingham area.

WHO CAN BENEFIT Hospitals and other medical and welfare organisations and charities.

WHAT IS FUNDED To improve the quality of life for those disadvantaged in society; provide comforts and amenities for patients in hospital and medical charities, assist medical research, education and science, and support charitable organisations concerned with people who are sick. The trust will consider funding: health; speech therapy; scholarships; building services; information technology and computers; publishing and printing; and health professional bodies.

WHAT IS NOT FUNDED The trust will not generally fund: direct appeals from individuals or students; administration expenditure including salaries; bank loans/deficits/mortgages; items or services which should normally be publicly funded; large general appeals; vehicle operating costs; or motor vehicles for infrequent use and where subsidised vehicle share schemes are available to charitable organisations.

TYPE OF GRANT One-off grants, capital, project and research, all funded for up to one year.

RANGE OF GRANTS Usually up to £2,000.

SAMPLE GRANTS Friends of Victoria School – Northfield (£3,800); NHS West Midlands (£3,400); Birmingham Centre for Arts Therapies and Starlight Children's Foundation (£2,500 each); Vascular Department, Selly Oak Hospital (£2,000); Dream Holidays, Isle of Wight (£1,900); the Mary Stevens Hospice, Stourbridge, West Midlands (£1,600); Institute of Ageing and Health, Birmingham (£1,500); Contact the Elderly, Birmingham (£1,200); Christian Lewis Trust – Cardiff (£1,100); Action Medical Research – Horsham, Children's Heart Foundation and REACT Surrey (£1,000); Katherine House – Stafford (£900); St Martin's Centre for Health and Healing (£750); Deep Impact Theatre Company and Birmingham Heart Care – Walsall (£500 each); and Acorns Children's Hospice – Birmingham (£315).

FINANCES *Year* 2009–10 *Income* £4,000 *Grants* £40,000

TRUSTEES Dr R P Kanas; S G Hall; E S Hickman; M Malone; D J Read; J Salmons.

HOW TO APPLY On a form available from the correspondent. The form requires basic information and should be submitted with financial details. Evidence should be provided that the project has been adequately considered through the provision of quotes or supporting documents, although the trust dislikes applications which provide too much general information or have long-winded descriptions of projects. Applicants should take great care to read the guidance notes on the application form. The trustees' meet four times a year and deadlines are given when application forms are sent out.

WHO TO APPLY TO The Secretary, Gamgee House, 2 Darnley Road, Birmingham B16 8TE *Tel* 0121 454 3601 *email* charitabletrust@bhsf.co.uk

■ Birmingham International Airport Community Trust

CC NO 1071176   ESTABLISHED 1998

WHERE FUNDING CAN BE GIVEN The areas affected by the airport's operation (East Birmingham, Solihull and parts of north Warwickshire).

WHO CAN BENEFIT Established local charities.

WHAT IS FUNDED Areas of work the trust supports are: environment improvement and heritage conservation; bringing the community closer together through facilities for sport, recreation and other leisure-time activities; improving awareness of environmental issues or environmental education and training activities; encouraging and protecting wildlife. It describes the types of projects it wishes to support as including community centres, community groups, sports, playgroups, schools, youth clubs, scouts, gardens/parks, environment, music and churches. Work should benefit a substantial section of the community rather than less inclusive groups, although work with older people or people with special needs is positively encouraged.

WHAT IS NOT FUNDED The following are not eligible for grants: individuals; projects which have already been carried out or paid for; organisations which have statutory responsibilities e.g. hospitals, surgeries, clinics, schools etc. unless the project is clearly not a statutory responsibility. Grants are not normally recurrent, or given towards the purchase of land or buildings.

TYPE OF GRANT Grants may be for capital or revenue projects, although the trust will not commit to recurrent or running costs, such as salaries.

RANGE OF GRANTS Generally up to £3,000.

SAMPLE GRANTS Previous beneficiaries have included: 298th Birmingham Brownies/Rangers Pack, Age Concern – Castle Bromwich, Blakenhale Infant School, Chelmsley Town Football Club, Coleshill Bell Ringers, Coleshill Town Football Club, George Fentham Endowed School, Hatchford Brook Youth and Community Centre and Land Lane Baptist Free Church.

FINANCES *Year* 2009–10 *Income* £50,604 *Grants* £51,594 *Assets* £4,470

TRUSTEES The trust acts independently of the airport management, with nine representatives of the following bodies making up the trustees: The Airport Consultative Committee (3), Birmingham City Council (2), Birmingham International Airport (2) and Solihull Council (2).

HOW TO APPLY On a form available from the correspondent. Full guidelines can be downloaded from the trust's website.

WHO TO APPLY TO The Administrator, Birmingham International Airport Ltd, Birmingham B26 3QJ *Tel* 0121 767 7448 *email* commtrust@bhx.co. uk *Website* www.bhx.co.uk

■ The Lord Mayor of Birmingham's Charity

CC NO 1036968   **ESTABLISHED** 1994

WHERE FUNDING CAN BE GIVEN Birmingham.

WHO CAN BENEFIT Charities determined by the Lord Mayor at the commencement of term of office.

WHAT IS FUNDED Beneficiaries are determined by the Lord Mayor prior to taking up office. Three or four charities/voluntary organisations are usually selected at the beginning of the year. No other donations are made.

WHAT IS NOT FUNDED Charities working outside the area of Birmingham.

TYPE OF GRANT One-off.

FINANCES *Year* 2009–10 *Income* £88,826 *Grants* £75,272 *Assets* £218,092

TRUSTEES Lord Mayor of Birmingham; Deputy Lord Mayor of Birmingham; Sue Anderson; J Whorwood; J Alden; S Barton.

HOW TO APPLY In writing to the correspondent. Although the beneficiaries are often predetermined, applications can be sent in January/February for the new Lord Mayor to consider.

WHO TO APPLY TO Mrs C Dukes, Civic Affairs Manager, Lord Mayor's Parlour, Council House, Birmingham B1 1BB *Tel* 0121 303 2040 *email* lord.mayor@birmingham.gov.uk *Website* www.birmingham.gov.uk

■ Birthday House Trust

CC NO 248028   **ESTABLISHED** 1966

WHERE FUNDING CAN BE GIVEN England and Wales.

WHO CAN BENEFIT Charitable organisations and individuals.

WHAT IS FUNDED General charitable purposes.

WHAT IS NOT FUNDED No applications will be considered from individuals or non-charitable organisations.

TYPE OF GRANT One-off and recurrent.

RANGE OF GRANTS Mostly up to £10,000.

SAMPLE GRANTS Druk White Loftus School (£50,000); Countryside Alliance (£10,000); Merton Road Scouts (£3,000); Sussex Community Foundation and Ecology Trust (£2,500 each); Chichester Cathedral Trust (£2,000); Fire Services National Benevolent Fund and Eastbourne Scout and Guide Hut Committee (£500 each); Fernhurst Recreation Ground Trust and Organic Research Trust (£250 each); and Murray Downland Trust (£50).

FINANCES *Year* 2009–10 *Income* £238,997 *Grants* £71,550 *Assets* £6,126,053

TRUSTEES The Dickinson Trust Limited and Rathbone Trust Company Limited.

OTHER INFORMATION The main work of this trust is engaged with the running of a residential home for people who are elderly in Midhurst, West Sussex. In 2009–10 a further £65,819 was distributed to pensioners.

HOW TO APPLY In writing to the correspondent, including an sae. No application forms are issued and there is no deadline. Only successful applicants are acknowledged.

WHO TO APPLY TO Laura Gosling, c/o Millbank Financial Services LtdPollen House, 10–12 Cork Street, London W1S 3LW *Tel* 020 7439 9061 *email* charity@mfs.co.uk

■ The Bisgood Charitable Trust (registered as Miss Jeanne Bisgood's Charitable Trust)

CC NO 208714   **ESTABLISHED** 1963

WHERE FUNDING CAN BE GIVEN UK, overseas and locally in Bournemouth and Dorset, especially Poole.

WHO CAN BENEFIT Registered charities.

WHAT IS FUNDED General charitable purposes. Main grants have been and will be concentrated on the following categories: (a) operating under Roman Catholic auspices; (b) operating in Poole, Bournemouth and the county of Dorset; (c) national (not local) charities concerned with older people.

WHAT IS NOT FUNDED Grants are not given to local charities which do not fit categories 1 or 2 above. Individuals and non-registered charities are not supported.

TYPE OF GRANT One-off, capital and recurring.

RANGE OF GRANTS £25–£2,500.

SAMPLE GRANTS Previous beneficiaries have included Apex Trust, ITDG, Horder Centre for Arthritis, Impact, St Barnabas' Society, St Francis Leprosy Guild, Sight Savers International and YMCA.

FINANCES *Year* 2009–10 *Income* £170,853 *Grants* £208,200 *Assets* £5,233,504

TRUSTEES Miss J M Bisgood, Chair; Miss P Schulte; P J K Bisgood.

OTHER INFORMATION The trust operates a sub-fund – the Bertram Fund from which grants are usually made anonymously.

HOW TO APPLY In writing to the correspondent, quoting the UK registration number and registered title of the charity. A copy of the most recent accounts should also be enclosed. Applications should NOT be made directly to the Bertram Fund. Applications for capital projects 'should provide brief details of the main purposes, the total target and the current state of the appeal'. The trustees regret that they are unable to acknowledge appeals. The trustees normally meet in late February/early March and September.

WHO TO APPLY TO J M Bisgood, Trustee, 12 Waters Edge, Brudenell Road, Poole BH13 7NN

■ The Michael Bishop Foundation

CC NO 297627   **ESTABLISHED** 1987
WHERE FUNDING CAN BE GIVEN Worldwide with a preference for Birmingham and the Midlands.
WHO CAN BENEFIT Registered charities.
WHAT IS FUNDED Arts, health, child welfare, education and religion.
RANGE OF GRANTS Up to £82,000.
SAMPLE GRANTS Actors Benevolent Fund, The Human Trafficking Foundation, The Imperial War Museum, the Royal Flying Doctor Service of Australia and Terrence Higgins Trust (£25,000 each); Peter Tatchell Human Rights Fund (£15,000); Nightingale Trust (£10,000); Greyfriars Opera (£10,000); Hospices of Hope and Leicestershire Victoria County History Trust (£5,000 each); Barry & Martin's Trust and Birmingham Early Music Festival (£2,500 each); and Army Benevolent Fund (£500).
FINANCES *Year* 2009–10 *Income* £199,745 *Grants* £219,925 *Assets* £2,378,299
TRUSTEES Sir Michael Bishop, Chair; Grahame N Elliott; John T Wolfe; John S Coulson.
HOW TO APPLY In writing to the correspondent.
WHO TO APPLY TO Grahame Elliot, Trustee, 26 Harrop Road, Hale, Altrincham WA15 9DQ *Tel* 0161 904 8300

■ The Bishop's Development Fund

CC NO 700588   **ESTABLISHED** 1988
WHERE FUNDING CAN BE GIVEN The diocese of Wakefield.
WHO CAN BENEFIT Church of England organisations.
WHAT IS FUNDED The objects of the trust are 'to promote any charitable purposes within the areas of the diocese of Wakefield which are in need of spiritual and material assistance by reason of social or economic changes with a view to reinforcing the work of the Church of England among the people of those areas' and 'to promote and assist the charitable work of the Church Urban Fund'.
WHAT IS NOT FUNDED Any application which does not meet the criteria outlined here.
RANGE OF GRANTS £100–£3,500.
SAMPLE GRANTS Beneficiaries included: Christ Church Woodhouse (£3,500); St Thomas Claremount and All Saints Normanton (£3,000 each); St John's Wakefield and Greetland & West Vale (£2,500 each); St Matthew's Northowram and St Luke's Grimethorpe (£1,500 each); and St George Ovenden and South Pennines Rural Officer (£1,000 each).
FINANCES *Year* 2009–10 *Income* £31,425 *Grants* £24,050 *Assets* £644,324
TRUSTEES Bishop of Wakefield; The Right Revd Anthony Robinson; The Ven. Robert Freeman; Mrs Mary Judkins; David Buckingham; Alison Dean; Christine Haigh; The Ven. Peter Townley.
HOW TO APPLY In writing to the correspondent. Only applications formally approved by the parochial

church councils of Church of England churches in the diocese of Wakefield will be considered. The trustees meet four times a year.
WHO TO APPLY TO The Trustees, Church House, 1 South Parade, Wakefield, West Yorkshire WF1 1LP *Tel* 01924 371802

■ The Sydney Black Charitable Trust

CC NO 219855   **ESTABLISHED** 1949
WHERE FUNDING CAN BE GIVEN UK.
WHO CAN BENEFIT Charitable organisations.
WHAT IS FUNDED Youth organisations, religious, medical and other institutions, such as those helping people who are disadvantaged.
TYPE OF GRANT One-off grants for core support, equipment and vehicles.
RANGE OF GRANTS A substantial grant was made to Endeavour (£20,000); others totalled £88,000 and were of between £125–£250 each. About 700 institutions benefited.
FINANCES *Year* 2009–10 *Income* £18,680 *Grants* £114,748
TRUSTEES Mrs J D Crabtree; Mrs H J Dickenson; S J Crabtree; P M Crabtree.
OTHER INFORMATION In 2001 The Edna Black Charitable Trust and The Cyril Black Charitable Trust were incorporated into this trust.
HOW TO APPLY Applications, made in writing to the correspondent, will be considered by the appropriate trust.
WHO TO APPLY TO The Secretary, 30 Welford Place, London SW19 5AJ

■ The Bertie Black Foundation

CC NO 245207   **ESTABLISHED** 1965
WHERE FUNDING CAN BE GIVEN UK, Israel.
WHO CAN BENEFIT Registered charities.
WHAT IS FUNDED The relief and assistance of people who are in need, the advancement of education and religion, and other charitable purposes.
SAMPLE GRANTS Previously: I Rescue (£50,000); Magen David Adom (£47,000 in three grants); Alyn Hospital (£49,000 in two grants); Emunah (£38,000); Laniardo Hospital and Shaare Zedek (£25,000 each); Friends of Israel Sports Centre for Disabled (£20,000); Child Resettlement Trust (£10,000 in four grants); Norwood (£7,600 in four grants); and Hope (£5,200 in four grants).
FINANCES *Year* 2009–10 *Income* £101,335 *Grants* £68,422 *Assets* £2,932,147
TRUSTEES I B Black; D Black; H S Black; Mrs I R Seddon.
HOW TO APPLY The trust states it 'supports causes known to the trustees' and that they 'do not respond to unsolicited requests'.
WHO TO APPLY TO Harry Black, Trustee, Abbots House, 198 Lower High Street, Watford WD17 2FG

■ Sir Alec Black's Charity

CC NO 220295   **ESTABLISHED** 1942
WHERE FUNDING CAN BE GIVEN UK, with a preference for Grimsby.
WHO CAN BENEFIT Ex-employees of Sir Alec Black, charitable institutions benefiting the sick and infirm including hospices, and poor fishermen and dockworkers of Grimsby.
WHAT IS FUNDED Primarily to benefit former employees of Sir Alec Black and to provide bed

linen and pillows to hospitals. Secondarily to benefit sick poor fishermen and dockworkers of Grimsby.

FINANCES *Year* 2009–10 *Income* £88,151 *Grants* £40,746 *Assets* £1,459,474

TRUSTEES Stewart Wilson; Dr Diana F Wilson; Michael Parker; Philip A Mounfield; John N Harrison.

OTHER INFORMATION In 2009–10 grants to former employees of the settlor totalled £16,000. A further £20,000 went in grants to 15 organisations, with £4,700 given to fishermen and dockworkers.

HOW TO APPLY In writing to the correspondent. Trustees meet in May and November; applications need to be received in March or September.

WHO TO APPLY TO Stewart Wilson, Trustee, Wilson Sharpe and Co., 27 Osborne Street, Grimsby, North East Lincolnshire DN31 1NU *email* sabc@wilsonsharpe.co.uk

■ Blackheart Foundation (UK) Limited

CC NO 1136813   **ESTABLISHED** 2010

WHERE FUNDING CAN BE GIVEN UK.

WHO CAN BENEFIT Individuals and organisations.

WHAT IS FUNDED Primarily the areas of health, education and sport.

TRUSTEES Richard Lewis; Ilina Singh; Claire Heath.

OTHER INFORMATION This is a new trust and at the time of writing (summer 2011), financial accounts were not yet due for submission at the Charity Commission. No other source of financial information was available.
The foundation was established in 2010 by Richard Lewis, chief executive of Tristan Capital Partners. Mr Lewis also serves on the board of several other charitable ventures, including the I I Foundation, Teach First and Eastside Young Leaders Academy.

HOW TO APPLY In writing to the correspondent.

WHO TO APPLY TO Richard Lewis, Trustee, 10 Maresfield Gardens, London NW3 5SU *Tel* 020 7016 4848

■ Isabel Blackman Foundation

CC NO 313577   **ESTABLISHED** 1966

WHERE FUNDING CAN BE GIVEN Hastings and St. Leonards-on-sea.

WHO CAN BENEFIT Organisations benefiting children, young adults, older people, retired people, people with disabilities, Christians and people with sight loss or blindness.

WHAT IS FUNDED People who are elderly, blind or disabled, hospitals, churches, voluntary charitable bodies, youth organisations, education.

WHAT IS NOT FUNDED Please note only applications from Hastings and district are considered.

RANGE OF GRANTS Up to £50,000.

SAMPLE GRANTS St Michaels Hospice (Hastings) Ltd (£50,000); All Saints Junior School (£10,000); TS Hastings Association – Hastings Sea Cadets (£6,000); Little Ridge Community Primary School (£5,000); Marie Curie Cancer Care (£3,500); Sara Lee Trust (£3,000); Sussex Association for Spina Bifida and Hydrocephalus and Surviving Christmas (£2,500); Independent Age and Catch 22 (£2,000); Listening Books and Guide Dogs for the Blind (£1,500 each); Act on It (£700); the Crafters Club and PDSA Hastings (£500 each); and RSPB (£300).

FINANCES *Year* 2009–10 *Income* £278,687 *Grants* £193,400 *Assets* £4,687,933

TRUSTEES D J Jukes; Mrs P H Connolly; Mrs M Haley; J F Lamplugh; K Ashmore; C S Deacon.

HOW TO APPLY In writing to the correspondent. The trustees meet bi-monthly to consider applications.

WHO TO APPLY TO D J Jukes, Secretary, 13 Laton Road, Hastings, East Sussex TN34 2ES

■ The BlackRock (UK) Charitable Trust

CC NO 1065447   **ESTABLISHED** 1999

WHERE FUNDING CAN BE GIVEN UK.

WHO CAN BENEFIT Charitable organisations.

WHAT IS FUNDED General charitable purposes.

SAMPLE GRANTS The Prostate Cancer Charity (£31,000); BlackRock Community Action Team (£26,000); Ovarian Cancer Action and The Burnaby Blue Foundation (£7,000 each); Changing Faces and The Duke of Edinburgh's Award (£6,000 each); Women in Prison (£2,500) and Eating Disorders Association and British Red Cross (£1,000 each).

FINANCES *Year* 2010 *Income* £117,988 *Grants* £183,922 *Assets* £27,985

TRUSTEES Richard Royds; Andrew Johnston; Elizabeth Tracey; Alex Popplewell; Peter Walker; Jo Howley; Alistaire McLuckie; Iain Lawson; BlackRock Group Ltd.

OTHER INFORMATION Grants of less than £1,000 totalled £20,000.

HOW TO APPLY 'The trustees invite staff, clients and business associates of BlackRock Investment Management (UK) Limited to submit applications for grants to a registered charity of their choice.' Other appeals would usually be declined.

WHO TO APPLY TO The Trustees, BlackRock, 33 King William Street, London EC4R 9AS

■ The Herbert and Peter Blagrave Charitable Trust

CC NO 277074   **ESTABLISHED** 1978

WHERE FUNDING CAN BE GIVEN Hampshire, Wiltshire and Berkshire.

WHO CAN BENEFIT Registered charities only working in the geographical areas stated.

WHAT IS FUNDED 'Typical applications include organisations that cater for: projects that work with people aged over 65 years; projects that work with children up to 16 years, or young people aged 16 to 25 years who have physical disabilities and/or learning difficulties; projects that work with injured sports people; projects that cater for people with a chronic or terminal illness who fall within our age ranges (children young people under 25 and the elderly); projects that provide respite for the carers of those that fall within our criteria.'

WHAT IS NOT FUNDED Applications are only considered from registered charities. Individuals, including students, are not eligible for grants. Normally, grants are not made in response to general appeals from large national organisations. No grants may be made where funds from statutory sources can be obtained. 'In the interests of good grant-making practice it is trust policy to place a time limit on further applications from the same organisations. Further applications are only considered after a three-year interval.'

TYPE OF GRANT Usually one-off but can be recurrent.

RANGE OF GRANTS Up to £20,000. Small Grants programmes have been set up with Community Foundations in Berkshire and Wiltshire. They administer a programme of direct grants under £3,000 on behalf of the trust.

SAMPLE GRANTS Hampshire & Isle of Wight Community Foundation (£100,000); the Community Foundation for Wiltshire & Swindon and Berkshire Community Foundation (£50,000 each); Avon Tyrell UK Youth (£12,000); Community First for Youth Action Wiltshire and Living Paintings Trust (£10,000); Deafness Research UK (£8,000); Vitalise (£6,000); St Michael's Church, Tilehurst (£5,000); Wellbeing of Women (£4,000); and Brainwave (£2,000).

FINANCES *Year* 2009–10 *Income* £603,768 *Grants* £481,325 *Assets* £31,218,826

TRUSTEES Julian R Whately; Timothy W A Jackson-Stops; Sir Paul A Neave.

OTHER INFORMATION Small Grants programmes have been set up with Community Foundations in Berkshire and Wiltshire. They administer a programme of direct grants under £3,000 on behalf of the trust.

HOW TO APPLY The trustees meet three times a year in March, July and November. Applications should be made using the trust's application form, which can be requested from the trust's offices. Application forms should be received at least eight weeks before the next trustees' meeting. A copy of the latest signed accounts, annual report, annual income and expenditure budget and a detailed income and expenditure budget for the specific project should be enclosed. Once your application has arrived you will be contacted by the director who may arrange to visit your project or carry out an extensive telephone interview to assess your grant request in more detail. Assessment is based mainly on evidence of need, what the grant will deliver and what other resources are available. Successful applicants will be asked to give a report about how a grant has been used within 12 months of receiving it.

WHO TO APPLY TO The Trustees, c/o Rathbone Trust Company Limited, 159 New Bond Street, London W1S 2UD *Tel* 020 7399 0000 *email* blagravetrust@rathbones.com

■ The Blair Foundation

CC NO 801755   **ESTABLISHED** 1989

WHERE FUNDING CAN BE GIVEN UK, particularly southern England and Scotland; overseas.

WHO CAN BENEFIT Organisations, particularly disability and wildlife groups.

WHAT IS FUNDED General, especially conservation and protection of the environment; improving disabled access to wildlife areas; and medical charities.

WHAT IS NOT FUNDED Charities that have objectives which the trustees consider harmful to the environment are not supported.

RANGE OF GRANTS Up to £12,000.

SAMPLE GRANTS Previously: Ayrshire Wildlife Services (£12,000); King's School – Canterbury and Ayreshire Fiddler Orchestra (£10,000 each); Scottish National Trust (£7,000); Home Farm Trust (£5,000); CHAS (£2,000); Handicapped Children's Action Group and Penny Brohn Cancer Care (£1,500); Ro Ro Sailing Project and Sustrans (£1,000 each).

FINANCES *Year* 2010–11 *Income* £17,685 *Grants* £70,000

TRUSTEES Robert Thornton; Jennifer Thornton; Graham Healy; Alan Thornton.

HOW TO APPLY In writing to the correspondent, for consideration at trustees' meetings held at least once a year. A receipt for donations is requested from all donees.

WHO TO APPLY TO The Trustees, c/o Smith and Williamson Limited, 1 Bishops Wharf, Walnut Tree Close, Guildford, Surrey GU1 4RA *Tel* 01483 407100

■ The Blanchminster Trust

CC NO 202118   **ESTABLISHED** 1421

WHERE FUNDING CAN BE GIVEN The parishes of Bude, Stratton and Poughill (i.e. the former urban district of Bude-Stratton on 31 March 1974).

WHO CAN BENEFIT Organisations or individuals residing in the area of benefit and showing proof of financial need. Organisations benefiting children; young adults; older people; academics; students; actors and entertainment professionals; and musicians may be considered.

WHAT IS FUNDED Charities working in the fields of education, social welfare and community aid.

WHAT IS NOT FUNDED Applications from Bude-Stratton only will be considered, or in respect of educational applications from people who have at least one parent so residing.

TYPE OF GRANT Cash or equipment. Cash may be grant or loan, equipment normally 'permanent loan'. Capital including buildings, core costs, feasibility studies, interest free loans, one-off, project, running costs and start-up costs. Funding will be considered for one year or less.

SAMPLE GRANTS Community Action through Sport and Bude Scout Group (£1,000 each); Stratton United Football Club (£500); Berries Kindergarten and Bude & North Cornwall Golf Club Junior section (£300 each) and Exercising for Mobility and Bude Bats Basketball Club (£200 each).

FINANCES *Year* 2010 *Income* £448,640 *Grants* £202,302 *Assets* £10,343,347

TRUSTEES Miss M H Clowes; C B Cornish; J E Gardiner; W J Keat; Mrs V A Newman; C D Nichols; G C Rogers; B C Rowlands; Mrs J M Shepherd; L M J Tozer; O A May; I J Whitfield; M Worden.

HOW TO APPLY In writing to the correspondent. Applicants may be called for an informal interview by the relevant committee. Following this a recommendation is made to the full board of trustees who make the final decision. Applications are considered at monthly meetings. All applications are acknowledged.

WHO TO APPLY TO The Clerk to the Trustees, Blanchminster Building, 38 Lansdown Road, Bude, Cornwall EX23 8EE *Tel* 01288 352851 *email* office@blanchminster.plus.com *Website* www.blanchminster.org.uk

■ The Sir Victor Blank Charitable Settlement

CC NO 1084187   **ESTABLISHED** 2000

WHERE FUNDING CAN BE GIVEN Worldwide.

WHO CAN BENEFIT Jewish organisations and other registered charities.

WHAT IS FUNDED Jewish causes and general charitable purposes.

SAMPLE GRANTS Jewish Care (£30,000); United Jewish Israel Appeal (£27,000); Norwood Ravenswood (£22,000); Hillel Foundation and

Jewish Community Secondary School (£10,000 each); Alexander Devine Children's Cancer Care Trust and Jewish Deaf Association (£5,000 each); Nightingale Patron Scheme (£3,000); University of Nottingham (£2,500); Wow Give Big Charity Event (£2,000); and Campaign to Protect Rural England and Spanish and Portuguese Jews' Home (£1,000 each).

FINANCES *Year* 2009–10 *Income* £251,053 *Grants* £196,100 *Assets* £1,609,249

TRUSTEES Sir M V Blank; Lady S H Blank; R Gulliver.

OTHER INFORMATION Other grants of less than £1,000 each totalled £14,000.

HOW TO APPLY In writing to the correspondent.

WHO TO APPLY TO R Gulliver, Trustee, c/o Wilkins Kennedy, Bridge House, London Bridge, London SE1 9QR *Tel* 020 7403 1877

■ Blatchington Court Trust

CC NO 306350   **ESTABLISHED** 1966

WHERE FUNDING CAN BE GIVEN UK, preference for Sussex.

WHO CAN BENEFIT Charities and other bodies in the field of education for the under 30 age group who are visually impaired.

WHAT IS FUNDED To provide funding for the education of children and young people under 30 years of age with visual impairment. The trust's capital grants programme awards funding for: (i) the provision of recreational and leisure facilities (or contributions towards such facilities), which enable vision impaired people to develop their physical, mental and moral capacities; (ii) any voluntary or charitable organisation approved by the trustees, the objects of which include the promotion of education, training and/or employment of vision impaired young people and their general well-being in pursuance of all the foregoing.

TYPE OF GRANT One-off capital grants.

FINANCES *Year* 2009–10 *Income* £479,091 *Grants* £130,210 *Assets* £10,269,197

TRUSTEES Richard Martin, Chair; Alison Acason; Daniel Ellman-Brown; Georgina James; Roger Jones; Stephen Pavey; Anna Hunter; Jonathan Wilson.

OTHER INFORMATION The grant total in 2009–10 included £80,210 payable in 261 grants to individuals.

HOW TO APPLY On a form available from the correspondent. Applications can be considered at any time. An application on behalf of a registered charity should include audited accounts and up-to-date information on the charity and its commitments.

WHO TO APPLY TO The Executive Manager, Ridgeland House, 165 Dyke Road, Hove, East Sussex BN3 1TL *Tel* 01273 727222 *Fax* 01273 722244 *email* info@blatchingtoncourt.org.uk *Website* www.blatchingtoncourt.org.uk

---

■ The Neville and Elaine Blond Charitable Trust

CC NO 206319   **ESTABLISHED** 1953

WHERE FUNDING CAN BE GIVEN Worldwide.

WHO CAN BENEFIT Particularly Jewish charities.

WHAT IS FUNDED Jewish causes and general charitable purposes.

WHAT IS NOT FUNDED Only registered charities are supported.

RANGE OF GRANTS Up to £50,000.

SAMPLE GRANTS Beth Shalom Holocaust Memorial Centre (£30,000); United Jewish Israel Appeal (£30,000); and British WIZO and Community Security Trust (£10,000 each); Holocaust Educational Trust (£5,000); Halle Orchestra (£4,000); Nordoff Robbins Music Therapy Centre (£2,000); Chicken Shed Theatre (£1,000); and Walk the Walk (£200).

FINANCES *Year* 2009–10 *Income* £60,502 *Grants* £99,200 *Assets* £1,190,626

TRUSTEES Dame Simone Prendergast; P Blond; Mrs A E Susman; S N Susman; Mrs J Skidmore.

HOW TO APPLY In writing to the correspondent. Applications should arrive by 31 January for consideration in late spring.

WHO TO APPLY TO The Trustees, c/o H W Fisher & Co, Chartered Accountants, Acre House, 11–15 William Road, London NW1 3ER *Tel* 020 7388 7000

■ The Blueberry Charitable Trust

CC NO 1080950   **ESTABLISHED** 2000

WHERE FUNDING CAN BE GIVEN UK.

WHO CAN BENEFIT Jewish community and voluntary organisations.

WHAT IS FUNDED Relief-in-need among people who are Jewish; advancement of the Jewish religion.

SAMPLE GRANTS Community Security Trust (£5,000); Manchester Jewish Federation and Manchester Jewish Youth Trust (£4,000 each); and Lubavitch South Manchester Trust (£2,500).

FINANCES *Year* 2009–10 *Income* £43,345 *Grants* £18,387 *Assets* £693,582

TRUSTEES J H Lyons; I Aspinall; K Pinnell.

OTHER INFORMATION A further amount of £2,500 was given out in grants of less than £1,000.

HOW TO APPLY In writing to the correspondent.

WHO TO APPLY TO I Aspinall, Trustee, Number 14, The Embankment, Vale Road, Heaton Mersey, Stockport, Cheshire

---

■ The Bluston Charitable Settlement

CC NO 256691   **ESTABLISHED** 1968

WHERE FUNDING CAN BE GIVEN Mostly UK.

WHO CAN BENEFIT Registered charities, particularly Jewish organisations.

WHAT IS FUNDED General charitable purposes, particularly education, welfare and medical.

WHAT IS NOT FUNDED No grants to individuals.

RANGE OF GRANTS £5,000 to £100,000.

SAMPLE GRANTS Norwood (£100,000); Ohel Torah Beth David (£90,000); Our Children (£50,000); UK Friends of IDC (£32,000); Prisoners Abroad (£25,000); Cancerkin (£19,000); Holocaust Educational Trust (£15,000); JAMI (£10,000); and Maccabi GB (£5,000).

FINANCES *Year* 2010–11 *Income* £466,093 *Grants* £629,938 *Assets* £8,650,516

TRUSTEES Daniel Dover; Martin J Paisner.

HOW TO APPLY In writing to the correspondent. The trustees meet annually in the spring.

WHO TO APPLY TO Martin D Paisner, c/o Prism Gift Fund, 20 Gloucester Place, London W1U 8HA *Tel* 020 7486 7760

■ The Nicholas Boas Charitable Trust

CC NO 1073359   **ESTABLISHED** 1998

WHERE FUNDING CAN BE GIVEN Worldwide.

WHO CAN BENEFIT Educational institutions, charities and other organisations connected with the arts.

WHAT IS FUNDED Education, performing and visual arts.

TYPE OF GRANT One-off.

SAMPLE GRANTS Beneficiaries included: IMS Prussia Cove, English National Opera, Winchester Chamber Music Festival, Tresanton Festival, Bampton Opera, International Summer Academy Vienna, Manchester Camerata, Dartington Summer School, Co-opera, Ulverston Festival, Tete-a-Tete, London String Quartet Foundation, British Youth Opera, Wye Valley Festival and English Music Festival.

FINANCES *Year* 2009–10 *Income* £52,319 *Grants* £43,686 *Assets* £388,373

TRUSTEES Robert Boas; Christopher Boas; Helena Boas; Elisabeth Boas.

OTHER INFORMATION Grants include travel scholarships for students of architecture

HOW TO APPLY In writing to the correspondent.

WHO TO APPLY TO Robert Boas, Trustee, 22 Mansfield Street, London W1G 9NR *Tel* 020 7436 0344 *email* boas22m@btinternet.com

■ The Body Shop Foundation

CC NO 802757　　　　**ESTABLISHED** 1990

WHERE FUNDING CAN BE GIVEN UK and overseas.

WHO CAN BENEFIT Organisations at the forefront of social and environmental change; groups with little hope of conventional funding; projects working to increase public awareness.

WHAT IS FUNDED Grants are given to innovative, grassroots organisations working in the field of human and civil rights, and environmental and animal protection.

WHAT IS NOT FUNDED As the majority of applications come from projects nominated by staff, the foundation does not ask for public applications or nominations. Nor does it: sponsor individuals; fund sporting activities or the arts; sponsor or support fundraising events, receptions or conferences.

TYPE OF GRANT One-off and recurring grants.

RANGE OF GRANTS £5,000–£157,000.

SAMPLE GRANTS End Child Prostitution and Trafficking (ECPAT (Thailand)), Thailand (£157,000); SolarAid, Malawi (£40,000 over 2 years); National Labor Committee (NLC), India (£30,000 over 2 years); Co-ordinated Action Against Domestic Abuse (CAADA), UK (£20,000 over 2 years); Laboratory of Apiculture and Social Insects (LASI), University of Sussex (£20,000); War Trauma Foundation (WTF), Palestine (£15,000); Sussex Beacon, West Sussex (£10,000); Service by Emergency Rider Volunteers (SERV), West Sussex (£7,000) and The Donkey Sanctuary, Canada (£5,000).

FINANCES *Year* 2010–11 *Income* £1,543,235 *Grants* £894,225 *Assets* £390,359

TRUSTEES Lady Jay of Ewelme; Janice R Buckingham; Paul David Sanderson; Paul McGreevy; Victoria Rayment; Simon Henzell-Thomas; Joana Edwards; Jonathan Staunton; Rita Godfrey.

OTHER INFORMATION 'The Body Shop Foundation is The Body Shop International Plc's charitable trust which supports innovative projects across the world working for social and environmental change.'

HOW TO APPLY The Body Shop Foundation does not accept unsolicited applications. The trustees research projects which meet their funding criteria and only then invite organisations to make an application.

WHO TO APPLY TO The Grants Manager, Watersmead, Littlehampton, West Sussex BN17 6LS *Tel* 01903 844039 *email* bodyshopfoundation@thebodyshop.com *Website* thebodyshopfoundation.org

■ The Boltons Trust

CC NO 257951　　　　**ESTABLISHED** 1967

WHERE FUNDING CAN BE GIVEN Unrestricted.

WHO CAN BENEFIT Charitable organisations.

WHAT IS FUNDED Relief of suffering; Jewish causes; cultural and religious teaching; international rights of the individual; other charitable purposes.

TYPE OF GRANT Generally single grants for core costs, project, recurring costs and running costs. Funding is available for one year or less.

SAMPLE GRANTS Previously beneficiaries have included: Council for Christians and Jews; Dartington International Summer School; Jewish Association of Business Ethics; London Philharmonic Orchestra; Norwood; Trinity College of Music; and World ORT.

FINANCES *Year* 2009–10 *Income* £46,272 *Grants* £0 *Assets* £1,267,514

TRUSTEES Mrs C Albuquerque; R M Baldock; S D Albuquerque.

HOW TO APPLY In writing to the correspondent. The trustees meet on a regular basis to consider applications.

WHO TO APPLY TO The Trustees, 12 York Gare, Regent's Park, London NW1 4QS

■ The Bonamy Charitable Trust

CC NO 326424　　　　**ESTABLISHED** 1983

WHERE FUNDING CAN BE GIVEN UK and overseas, with a preference for Liverpool.

WHO CAN BENEFIT Charitable organisations.

WHAT IS FUNDED Jewish causes and general charitable purposes.

FINANCES *Year* 2010 *Income* £127,235 *Grants* £34,637 *Assets* £367,425

TRUSTEES M Moryoussef; J Moryoussef; R Moryoussef.

HOW TO APPLY In writing to the correspondent.

WHO TO APPLY TO M Moryoussef, Trustees, Flat 2, Forest Hills, South Downs Road, Bowdon, Cheshire WA14 3HD

■ The Charlotte Bonham-Carter Charitable Trust

CC NO 292839　　　　**ESTABLISHED** 1985

WHERE FUNDING CAN BE GIVEN UK, with some emphasis on Hampshire.

WHO CAN BENEFIT Registered charities.

WHAT IS FUNDED General charitable purposes which were of particular concern to Lady Charlotte Bonham-Carter during her lifetime or are within the county of Hampshire. 'The trustees continue to support a core number of charities to whom they have made grants in the past as well as reviewing all applications received and making grants to new charities within their grant-giving criteria.'

WHAT IS NOT FUNDED No grants to individuals or non-registered charities.

RANGE OF GRANTS £500–£10,000.

SAMPLE GRANTS National Trust (£10,000); Florence Nightingale Museum (£5,000); City and London Guilds Bursary Fund (£4,000); British Museum – Friends of the Ancient Near East (£3,500);

British Institute for the Study of Iraq (£3,000); Chelsea Physic Garden (£2,000); British Schools Exploring Society, Enterprise Education Trust and Firefly International (£1,000 each); Fields in Trust, National Council for the Conservation of Plants and Gardens and Sir Joseph Banks Archive Project (£500 each).

FINANCES *Year* 2009–10 *Income* £127,117 *Grants* £136,528 *Assets* £3,865,876

TRUSTEES Sir Matthew Farrer; David Bonham-Carter; Eliza Bonham-Carter; Georgina Nayler.

HOW TO APPLY In writing to the correspondent. There are no application forms. The application should include details of the funds required, funds raised so far and the timescale involved. The trust states that: 'unsolicited general applications are unlikely to be successful and only increase the cost of administration. Trustees meet in January and July; applications need to be received by May or November.'

WHO TO APPLY TO Mrs Jenny Cannon, Administrator, Chelwood, Rectory Road, East Carleton, Norwich NR14 8HT

....

■ The John and Celia Bonham Christie Charitable Trust

CC NO 326296　　**ESTABLISHED** 1983

WHERE FUNDING CAN BE GIVEN UK, with some preference for the former county of Avon.

WHO CAN BENEFIT Local and national organisations.

WHAT IS FUNDED Medical charities and organisations, though smaller grants are made to a wide range of other organisations.

WHAT IS NOT FUNDED No grants to individuals.

TYPE OF GRANT Recurrent, over three to five years.

RANGE OF GRANTS £200–£2,000.

SAMPLE GRANTS Previous beneficiaries have included BIBIC, Butterwick Hospice, Cancer Research Campaign, Derby TOC, Digestive Disorder Foundation, Dorothy House, Elizabeth Finn Trust, Foundation for the Study of Infant Cot Deaths, Frome Festival, Home Start South Wiltshire, Inspire Foundation, Kings Medical Trust, Royal Society for the Blind Winsley, Sea Cadet Association, St John's Ambulance and Ten of Us.

FINANCES *Year* 2009–10 *Income* £42,634 *Grants* £29,000 *Assets* £1,338,254

TRUSTEES Richard Bonham Christie; Robert Bonham Christie; Rosemary Ker.

HOW TO APPLY In writing to the correspondent. Only a small number of new applications are supported each year.

WHO TO APPLY TO The Trustees, PO Box 9081, Taynton, Gloucester GL19 3WX

....

■ Bonhomie United Charity Society

CC NO 247816　　**ESTABLISHED** 1966

WHERE FUNDING CAN BE GIVEN Southampton and district.

WHO CAN BENEFIT Local organisations.

WHAT IS FUNDED Disability causes.

WHAT IS NOT FUNDED Individual applications are not eligible, except those made by voluntary organisations and social services on the individual's behalf.

TYPE OF GRANT One-off for buildings and capital.

SAMPLE GRANTS Previous beneficiaries include Wessex Heart – Cardiac Trust, Salvation Army – Southampton, Southampton Mayor's Appeal, Thorner's Homes Southampton, British Red Cross, Southampton Care Association,

Hampshire and Isle of Wight Outward Bound Association and Hampshire Autistic Society.

FINANCES *Year* 2009–10 *Income* £4,065 *Grants* £35,000

TRUSTEES B J Davies; Mrs S Davies; J Davies; R Davies.

HOW TO APPLY The trust states that funds are fully committed, but will consider all applications from within the Southampton and district area only.

WHO TO APPLY TO B J Davies, Trustee, 48 Lingwood Close, Southampton SO16 7GJ *Tel* 023 8076 9000

....

■ The Linda and Gordon Bonnyman Charitable Trust

CC NO 1123441　　**ESTABLISHED** 2008

WHERE FUNDING CAN BE GIVEN Unrestricted.

WHO CAN BENEFIT Unrestricted.

WHAT IS FUNDED General charitable purposes.

FINANCES *Year* 2009–10 *Income* £14,360 *Grants* £200,000

TRUSTEES James Gordon Bonnyman; Linda Bonnyman; James Wallace Taylor Bonnyman.

HOW TO APPLY In writing to the correspondent.

WHO TO APPLY TO Linda Bonnyman, Trustee, Ely Grange, Bells Yew Green Road, Frant, Tunbridge Wells, East Sussex TN3 9DY

....

■ BOOST Charitable Trust

CC NO 1111961　　**ESTABLISHED** 2005

WHERE FUNDING CAN BE GIVEN UK.

WHO CAN BENEFIT Individuals and groups involved in sport.

WHAT IS FUNDED Activities designed to 'champion the disabled and disadvantaged and to inspire them to overcome their challenges through the power of sport'.

RANGE OF GRANTS Grants are categorised into small awards (£500 or less) and large awards (over £500). The majority (by value) of the awards made are large awards where the charity is involved in longer term initiatives.

SAMPLE GRANTS Loughborough Development Trust (£59,000); CP Sport – Boccia and Windsor and Maidenhead District Sports Association for the Disabled (£15,000 each); Southwark City Tennis Club (£10,000); Disability Snowsport UK (£8,500); Shepshed Dolphin Swimming Group and Amputee Games/Limbpower (£5,000 each) and Great Britain Wheelchair Rugby Association (£3,000). £37,000 was also shared between organisations in Swaziland.

FINANCES *Year* 2009–10 *Income* £158,585 *Grants* £191,314 *Assets* £1,181,629

TRUSTEES Robert Houston, Chair; Gillian Houston; Alurie Dutton; Oliver Bartrum.

OTHER INFORMATION The trust aims to **B**uild **O**n **O**verlooked **S**porting **T**alent. All of its activities, are designed to 'champion the disabled and disadvantaged and to inspire them to overcome their challenges through the power of sport'.

HOW TO APPLY Applications should be emailed or posted to the correspondent. The trustees meet quarterly to consider what grants they will make and to review the existing awards. Nominations for grants are elicited by formal and informal means.

WHO TO APPLY TO Lucy Till, Administrator, 5 St Bride Street, London EC4A 4AS *Tel* 020 7078 1955 *Fax* 020 7767 5600 *email* lucy.till@boostct.org *Website* www.boostct.org

■ The Booth Charities

CC NO 221800   ESTABLISHED 1963
WHERE FUNDING CAN BE GIVEN Salford.
WHO CAN BENEFIT Organisations supporting the inhabitants of the City of Salford, especially those over 60 years of age.
WHAT IS FUNDED Relief of elderly people and people in need, including payments of pensions and provision of almshouses; relief of distress and sickness; provision and support of facilities for recreation and other leisure-time occupation; provision and support of educational facilities; any other charitable purpose.
TYPE OF GRANT Capital and revenue funding; up to three years.
SAMPLE GRANTS The Heritage Learning Centre and Museum (£30,000); William Jones Bursary (£20,000); the Lowry Centre Trust (£10,000); Broughton House (£9,000); the Working Class Movement Library (£6,700); Music in Hospitals (£5,000); the Salfordian Trust Co Ltd (£3,800); Boundary Road Methodist Church (£2,000); PDSA (£1,000); and Rainsough Community Centre (£220).
FINANCES *Year* 2009–10 *Income* £918,000 *Grants* £225,683 *Assets* £28,752,000
TRUSTEES William Whittle, Chair; David Tully; Philip Webb; Richard Kershaw; Edward Tudor Evans; Edward Wilson Hunt; Richard Christmas; Roger Weston; Michael Prior; John Willis; Alan Dewhurst.
OTHER INFORMATION £3,200 was awarded to individuals.
HOW TO APPLY In writing to the correspondent.
WHO TO APPLY TO Jonathan Shelmerdine, Clerk to the Trustees, The William Jones Building, 1 Eccles Old Road, Salford M6 7DE *Tel* 0161 736 2989 *Fax* 01270 764795 *email* enquiries@butcher-barlow.co.uk

■ The Boots Charitable Trust

CC NO 1045927   ESTABLISHED 1971
WHERE FUNDING CAN BE GIVEN Nottinghamshire and Nottingham.
WHO CAN BENEFIT Registered charities benefiting people who live in Nottinghamshire. Also small voluntary organisations whose income and expenditure are both less than £5,000 per year, who are not yet therefore required to register with the Charity Commission.
WHAT IS FUNDED (1) Health: community healthcare such as community healthcare services, home care, after care, relief of people who are disabled or have a medical condition and continuing care; and health education and prevention by promoting knowledge and awareness of specific diseases and medical conditions. (2) Lifelong learning: Helping people of any age to achieve their educational potential, supporting supplementary schools, literacy and numeracy projects, community education, vocational/restart education for the unemployed and alternative education for excluded school pupils. (3) Community development: Helping groups to organise and respond to problems and needs in their communities or networks. This could include groups such as Councils for Voluntary Services and self-help groups. (4) Social care including: personal social services – organisations assisting individuals or families to overcome social deprivation, such as people who are homeless or disabled and their carers, lone parent and childcare groups and other family support groups; social preventive schemes –

activities preventing crime, dropping out and general delinquency and providing other social care outreach work, social health and safety awareness schemes and so on; and community social activity – activities to promote social engagement for vulnerable people, mitigating against isolation and loneliness. 'We are especially interested in projects with the capacity to deliver significant impact and which reach the greatest number of people.'
WHAT IS NOT FUNDED The trust does not provide funding for: projects benefiting people outside Nottinghamshire; individuals; organisations which are not registered charities and which have income or expenditure of more than £5,000 per year; charities seeking funds to redistribute to other charities; projects for which there is a legal statutory obligation or which replace statutory funding.
RANGE OF GRANTS Up to £15,000.
SAMPLE GRANTS Beneficiaries included: Rumbles Catering Project (£15,000); Rural Community Action Nottinghamshire (£10,000); Alcohol Problems Advisory Service (£9,800); Nottingham MS Therapy Centre (£9,600); Bassetlaw Mind (£8,800); Nottingham Counselling Service (£6,700); the Maze and Mansfield Family Life Centre (£6,000 each); and the Zone Youth Project (£5,000).
FINANCES *Year* 2009–10 *Income* £263,660 *Grants* £257,319 *Assets* £12,283
TRUSTEES Kay Alison Croot; John Cohen; Ken Piggott; Sandra Rose; Oonagh Turnbull; Evelyn Dickey; Katherine Jayne Mayled; H Voce.
HOW TO APPLY On a form available, with guidelines, from the website or by post. Completed forms should be sent to the correspondent with the latest annual report and accounts. The trustees meet every two months, although applications under £2,000 are dealt with by more quickly.
WHO TO APPLY TO Rachel McGuire, The Appeals Officer, 1 Thane Road West, Nottingham NG2 3AA *Tel* 0115 949 2185 *email* rachel.mcguire@boots.co.uk *Website* www.boots-csr.com

■ The Bordon and Liphook Charity

CC NO 1032428   ESTABLISHED 1994
WHERE FUNDING CAN BE GIVEN Bordon, Liphook and surrounding areas, Hampshire.
WHO CAN BENEFIT Organisations and Individuals.
WHAT IS FUNDED General charitable purposes.
WHAT IS NOT FUNDED Non-priority loans.
TYPE OF GRANT Cash or loan.
SAMPLE GRANTS Previous beneficiaries have included Bordon Harlequins, Community Mental Health Team, Friends of Meadow School, Furniture Helpline, Highview Surgery, NSPCC and Red Cross Luncheon Club.
FINANCES *Year* 2010 *Income* £72,875 *Grants* £47,204 *Assets* £18,146
TRUSTEES C J Tartum; D N Hay; R Reina; G Alexander; V Webb; Mrs. J A Vernon-Smith.
HOW TO APPLY In writing to the correspondent.
WHO TO APPLY TO C J Tantum, Trustee, Room 32, The Forest Centre, Bordon, Hampshire GU35 OTN *Tel* 01420 477787 *email* info@bordonandliphookcharity.co.uk *Website* www.bordonandliphookcharity.co.uk

■ Salo Bordon Charitable Trust

CC NO 266439　　　　**ESTABLISHED** 1973
WHERE FUNDING CAN BE GIVEN UK and worldwide.
WHO CAN BENEFIT Organisations, primarily Jewish.
WHAT IS FUNDED Religious education and social welfare.
SAMPLE GRANTS Previous beneficiaries have included Agudas Israel Housing Association Ltd, Baer Hatorah, Beth Jacob Grammar School, Brisk Yeshivas, Golders Green Beth Hamedrash Congregation Jaffa Institute, Jewish Learning Exchange, London Academy of Jewish Studies, Society of Friends of Torah and WST Charity.
FINANCES *Year* 2009–10 *Income* £563,162 *Grants* £343,518 *Assets* £7,757,841
TRUSTEES Marcel Bordon; Salo Bordon; Lilly Bordon.
HOW TO APPLY In writing to the correspondent.
WHO TO APPLY TO Marcel Bordon, Trustee, 39 Gresham Gardens, London NW11 8PA

■ The Oliver Borthwick Memorial Trust

CC NO 256206　　　　**ESTABLISHED** 1968
WHERE FUNDING CAN BE GIVEN UK.
WHO CAN BENEFIT Registered charities benefiting homeless people and people disadvantaged by poverty. In particular the trustees welcome applications from small but viable charities in disadvantaged inner-city areas.
WHAT IS FUNDED Currently the main areas of interest are to provide shelter and help for homeless people.
WHAT IS NOT FUNDED No grants to individuals, including people working temporarily overseas for a charity where the request is for living expenses, together with applications relating to health, disability and those from non-registered charitable organisations.
TYPE OF GRANT Mainly one-off.
RANGE OF GRANTS Usually £5,000.
SAMPLE GRANTS Queens Cottages, Single Homeless Accommodation Project Ltd, Rape & Sexual Abuse Support Centre, St George's House Charity and Basement Night Drop-In Centre (£5,000 each).
FINANCES *Year* 2008–09 *Income* £44,857 *Grants* £37,000 *Assets* £1,015,208
TRUSTEES M H R Brethedon; R A Graham; J Macdonald; J R Marriott; Mrs V Wrigley; D Scott.
HOW TO APPLY Letters should be set out on a maximum of two sides of A4, giving full details of the project with costs, who the project will serve and the anticipated outcome of the project. Meetings take place once a year in May. Applications should be received no later than April.
WHO TO APPLY TO Mr James Knight, c/o Donor Grants Department, Charities Aid Foundation, Kings Hill, West Malling, Kent ME19 4TA *Tel* 01732 520107 *email* jknight@cfaonline.org

■ The Boshier-Hinton Foundation

CC NO 1108886　　　　**ESTABLISHED** 2005
WHERE FUNDING CAN BE GIVEN England and Wales.
WHO CAN BENEFIT Charitable organisations.
WHAT IS FUNDED Work with children and adults with special educational or other needs.
TYPE OF GRANT One-off grants.
RANGE OF GRANTS £250–£6,000.
SAMPLE GRANTS Accuro (£6,000); British Paralympic Association (£5,000); Meningitis Trust and Happy Days Children's Charity (£3,000 each);

Arthritis Care, All Ability Sports and Leisure, Birmingham Royal Ballet, Cerebral Palsy Sport, Clothing Solutions, Friends of Penn Hall School, Lakelands Hospice and Sign Health (£2,000 each); Calibre Audio Library, Lunch on the Run, Green Light Trust and UK Voice (£1,500 each); BASIC, Deafness Support Network, Disability North, National Autistic Society and the National Blind Tenpin Bowling Association (£1,000 each); Sheffield Theatres Trust (£750); Camden Arts Centre, Dance Umbrella and Step By Step (£500 each); and Worcester Concert Club (£250).
FINANCES *Year* 2009–10 *Income* £123,452 *Grants* £129,069 *Assets* £885,468
TRUSTEES Thea Boshier, Chair; Dr Peter Boshier; James Tye; Janet Beale.
HOW TO APPLY A copy of the latest grant application form is available on request.
WHO TO APPLY TO Dr Peter Boshier, Trustee, Yeomans, Aythorpe Roding, Great Dunmow, Essex CM6 1PD *Tel* 01245 231032 *email* boshierhinton@yahoo.co.uk

■ The Bothwell Charitable Trust

CC NO 299056　　　　**ESTABLISHED** 1987
WHERE FUNDING CAN BE GIVEN England, particularly the South East.
WHO CAN BENEFIT Registered charities benefiting carers, people with disabilities and people disadvantaged by poverty.
WHAT IS FUNDED Health, disability and research.
WHAT IS NOT FUNDED No grants for animal charities, overseas causes, individuals, or charities not registered with the Charity Commission.
TYPE OF GRANT Core costs, running costs and research grants, for one year or less.
RANGE OF GRANTS £1,000 or £2,000.
SAMPLE GRANTS Arthritis Research UK, Blackthorn Trust, British Heart Foundation, ECHO International Health Services Ltd, Friends of the Elderly, Invalid Children's Aid Nationwide, Leukaemia Research Fund (£2,000 each); and Brain Research Trust, British Trust for Conservation Volunteers, Childlink Adoption Society, Multiple Sclerosis Society and Riding for the Disabled Association (£1,000).
FINANCES *Year* 2009–10 *Income* £41,965 *Grants* £38,000 *Assets* £9,230
TRUSTEES Paul L James, Chair; Crispian M P Howard; Theresa McGregor.
HOW TO APPLY In writing to the correspondent. Distributions are usually made in February or March each year.
WHO TO APPLY TO Mr Paul Leonard James, Chair of Trustees, 25 Ellenbridge Way, South Croydon CR2 0EW *Tel* 020 8657 6884

■ H E and E L Botteley Charitable Trust

CC NO 1036927　　　　**ESTABLISHED** 1994
WHERE FUNDING CAN BE GIVEN England and Wales, with some preference for Birmingham area.
WHO CAN BENEFIT Children, young people, older people, people with disabilities.
WHAT IS FUNDED General, overseas aid, Christian welfare.
SAMPLE GRANTS Previously £7,000 each to REACH for Rwanda and Rema UK; £2,000 to Sutton Coldfield Baptist Church; £1,000 to Agape; £500 to Toy Box Charity; and £250 to Birmingham University Guild of Students.

FINANCES *Year* 2009–10 *Income* £24,113 *Grants* £20,000

TRUSTEES Ms S L Botteley; Mrs R Barney.

HOW TO APPLY In writing to the correspondent. The trustees normally meet biannually to consider applications for funding.

WHO TO APPLY TO Ms S L Botteley, Trustee, c/o 10 Oaklands Road, Sutton Coldfield B74 2TB *Tel* 0121 308 0220

■ The Harry Bottom Charitable Trust

CC NO 204675   ESTABLISHED 1960

WHERE FUNDING CAN BE GIVEN UK, with a preference for Yorkshire and Derbyshire.

WHO CAN BENEFIT Registered charities.

WHAT IS FUNDED The trust states that support is divided roughly equally between religion, education and medical causes. Within these categories grants are given to: religion – small local appeals and cathedral appeals; education – universities and schools; and medical – equipment for hospitals and charities concerned with disability.

WHAT IS NOT FUNDED No grants to individuals.

RANGE OF GRANTS £250–£25,000.

SAMPLE GRANTS Yorkshire Baptist Association (£25,000); St Luke's Hospice (£5,000); Sheffield Association for Cerebral Palsy (£3,500); Sheffield Mencap (£3,000); and Girl Guiding (£2,500).

FINANCES *Year* 2009–10 *Income* £211,771 *Grants* £84,083 *Assets* £4,268,291

TRUSTEES Revd J M Kilner; Prof. T H Lilley; Prof. I G Rennie; Prof. A Rawlinson.

HOW TO APPLY In writing to the correspondent at any time.

WHO TO APPLY TO J S Hinsley, c/o Westons, Chartered Accountants, Queen's Buildings, 55 Queen Street, Sheffield S1 2DX

■ P G and N J Boulton Trust

CC NO 272525   ESTABLISHED 1976

WHERE FUNDING CAN BE GIVEN Worldwide.

WHO CAN BENEFIT Organisations with whom the trustees have existing commitments/special interest.

WHAT IS FUNDED Christian missionary work; disaster and poverty relief; medical research and healthcare; disability relief and care of elderly.

WHAT IS NOT FUNDED No grants for: individuals; environment and conservation; culture and heritage; sport and leisure; animal welfare; church building repairs.

RANGE OF GRANTS Up to £11,000.

SAMPLE GRANTS Vision for China (£11,000); New Life Centre (£10,000); Children Alone (£8,500); Intercessors for Britain (£8,000); Shalom Christian Fellowship (£6,000); Longcroft Christian Trust (£4,500); Just Care (£4,000); Christian Institute and International Mission Project (£2,500 each); Barnabas Fund and Shepherd's Purse Trust (£1,500 each); and Cedars School (£1,000).

FINANCES *Year* 2009–10 *Income* £124,669 *Grants* £66,000 *Assets* £3,594,218

TRUSTEES Andrew L Perry; Shirley Perry; Peter H Stafford; Margaret Jardine-Smith.

HOW TO APPLY Please note the following statement from the trust's website: 'We are currently undergoing a long term review of our policies and this means that in practice, we are currently only making donations to organisations to whom we have an existing commitment. This unfortunately means that any new requests for funding at the present time will almost certainly be unsuccessful.'

WHO TO APPLY TO Andrew L Perry, Trustee, PO Box 72, Wirral, Merseyside CH46 6AA *Website* www.boultontrust.org.uk

■ The A H and E Boulton Trust

CC NO 225328   ESTABLISHED 1935

WHERE FUNDING CAN BE GIVEN Worldwide, with some preference for Merseyside.

WHO CAN BENEFIT Christian charities and individuals.

WHAT IS FUNDED The trust mainly supports the erection and maintenance of buildings to be used for preaching the Christian gospel and for relieving the sick or needy. The trustees can also support other Christian institutions, especially missions in the UK and developing world.

TYPE OF GRANT Mostly recurrent.

SAMPLE GRANTS Liverpool City Mission (£30,000); and the Slavic Gospel Association and Pioneer People Wirral (£15,000 each).

FINANCES *Year* 2009–10 *Income* £52,328 *Grants* £62,728 *Assets* £2,778,563

TRUSTEES Dr Frank Gopsill; Jennifer Gopsill; Michael Gopsill; Peter Gopsill.

OTHER INFORMATION An additional grant of £500 was made to a parishioner and a further £2,200 was given in small grants to ministers.

HOW TO APPLY In writing to the correspondent. The trust tends to support a set list of charities and applications are very unlikely to be successful.

WHO TO APPLY TO The Trustees, c/o Moore Stephens LLP, 110–114 Duke Street, Liverpool L1 5AG *Tel* 0151 703 1080

■ Sir Clive Bourne Family Trust

CC NO 290620   ESTABLISHED 1984

WHERE FUNDING CAN BE GIVEN UK.

WHO CAN BENEFIT Individuals and institutions benefiting Jewish people.

WHAT IS FUNDED The trustees favour Jewish causes. A number of health and medical charities (particularly relating to cancer) have also benefited.

RANGE OF GRANTS Up to £39,000.

SAMPLE GRANTS Prostate Cancer Research Foundation (£39,000); Sydney Gold Trust (£13,000); Norwood Ravenswood (£4,700); WIZO UK (£3,700); World Jewish Relief (£3,000); Drugsline (£2,500); Community Security Trust and Hazon Yeshaya (£2,000 each); Jewish Care (£1,500); Langdon Foundation (£1,000); International Spinal Research Trust (£500); Anne Frank Trust (£260); One to One (£200); Jewish Women's Aid (£150); and Institute of Cancer Research (£100).

FINANCES *Year* 2009–10 *Income* £181,028 *Grants* £79,521 *Assets* £4,334,970

TRUSTEES Lady Joy Bourne; Katie Cohen; Lucy Furman; Claire Lefton; Merryl Flitterman.

HOW TO APPLY In writing to the correspondent.

WHO TO APPLY TO Janet Bater, 134–136 High Street, Epping, Essex CM16 4AG

■ The Anthony Bourne Foundation

CC NO 1015759 **ESTABLISHED** 1992
WHERE FUNDING CAN BE GIVEN Unrestricted, in particular, Warwickshire.
WHO CAN BENEFIT Primarily organisations benefiting children and young people.
WHAT IS FUNDED 'Through supporting a wide range of charitable organisations, the trustees have resolved to give support to charities which seek to promote the wellbeing of young people and to foster their active positive engagement in their local communities.'
WHAT IS NOT FUNDED No grants to individuals.
TYPE OF GRANT One-off grants for capital (including buildings), core costs and start-up costs. Funding of up to three years will be considered.
RANGE OF GRANTS £350–£3,000.
SAMPLE GRANTS Previous beneficiaries included: Kids 'n' Action, Lancaster and District YMCA – YZUP Young Offender Project, Life Church, Maximum Life Youth Project and Tiverton Market Drop-In-Centre (£3,000 each); Living Hope Charity, St Margaret's Hospice Somerset and Straight Talking (£1,000); and Warwickshire Association of Youth Clubs – Dream Catcher Appeal (£350).
FINANCES *Year* 2010–11 *Income* £21,263 *Grants* £20,000
TRUSTEES Mrs V A Bourne; Celia Louise Jeune; Chuka Umunna; M A Hunter-Craig.
OTHER INFORMATION All enquiries should be made through the Foundation's website.
HOW TO APPLY All applicants are directed to the Foundation's website, where criteria, guidelines and application process are posted.
WHO TO APPLY TO PO Box 5334, Rugby CV21 9JY *Website* www.anthonybournefoundation.org

■ Bourneheights Limited

CC NO 298359 **ESTABLISHED** 1984
WHERE FUNDING CAN BE GIVEN UK.
WHO CAN BENEFIT Orthodox Jews.
WHAT IS FUNDED Orthodox Jewish organisations.
SAMPLE GRANTS Previous beneficiaries include: Moreshet Hatorah, Mercaz Torah Vahesed Ltd, BFOT, Belz Synagogue, Telz Academy Trust, Gevurath Ari Academy, UTA, Toreth Emeth, Olam Chesed Yiboneh, Before Trust, Heaven Point, Yeshivas Avas Torah and Lubavitch Mechina.
FINANCES *Year* 2009–10 *Income* £2,080,612 *Grants* £1,189,377 *Assets* £6,547,691
TRUSTEES Chaskel Rand; Esther Rand; Erno Berger; Yechiel Chersky; Schloime Rand.
HOW TO APPLY In writing to the correspondent.
WHO TO APPLY TO Schloime Rand, Trustee, Flat 10, Palm Court, Queen Elizabeth's Walk, London N16 5XA

■ Community Foundation for Bournemouth, Dorset and Poole

CC NO 1122113 **ESTABLISHED** 2007
WHERE FUNDING CAN BE GIVEN The county of Dorset, including the unitary authorities of Bournemouth and Poole.
WHO CAN BENEFIT Local organisations.
WHAT IS FUNDED Community initiatives. Available funding changes on ongoing basis, please see the foundation's website for up-to-date information.
WHAT IS NOT FUNDED Each fund has different criteria, please consult the website for up to date eligibility.
RANGE OF GRANTS £200–£69,000.

SAMPLE GRANTS The Listening Ear (£69,000); Bournemouth Churches Housing Association (£43,000); Action for Children (£38,000); Coastal Credit Union Ltd (£37,000); Dorset Race Equality Council (£25,000); Family Matters (£17,000); AFCB Sports Trust (£14,500); Vita Nova (£10,000); South Coast Tigers (£5,000); Poole Sailability (£3,000); Treewise Co-operative Ltd (£2,500); Pulse (£1,400); and 1st Alderholt Brownies (£1,000).
FINANCES *Year* 2009–10 *Income* £897,633 *Grants* £716,891 *Assets* £778,380
TRUSTEES Gary Bentham; Richard Cossey; Gordon Page; Christopher Morle; Michael Green; Jane Raimes; Gwyn Bates; Richard Dimbleby; Ashley Rowlands; Christopher Beale.
HOW TO APPLY Contact the foundation for details of up-to-date programmes. An online contact form is available on the site.
WHO TO APPLY TO Tina Baker, Abchurch Chambers, 24 St Peter's Road, Bournemouth BH1 2LN *Tel* 01202 292255 *email* grants@dorsetcf.org *Website* www.dorsetcommunityfoundation.org

■ The Bower Trust

CC NO 283025 **ESTABLISHED** 1981
WHERE FUNDING CAN BE GIVEN Wales and developing countries, particularly in Africa.
WHO CAN BENEFIT Generally, registered charities.
WHAT IS FUNDED Charities connected activities in the 'third world', particularly in Africa, and Wales.
WHAT IS NOT FUNDED No personal sponsorships. Generally the trustees are not interested in regional requests from charities.
SAMPLE GRANTS Kanga Tanzania, St John's Zambia and Tenovos (£3,000 each); Llanilltud in Flower, Africa Education Trust, Safe Foundation, Save the Rhino (£2,000 each); Dentaid Uganda, EveryChild and Kids for Kids Sudan (£1,000 each); and Medair and Nature Wildlife Trust (£500 each).
FINANCES *Year* 2009–10 *Income* £30,580 *Grants* £58,950 *Assets* £717,913
TRUSTEES Mrs C V E Benfield; G Benfield; F C Slater.
HOW TO APPLY In writing to the correspondent. Trustees meet quarterly to consider grants.
WHO TO APPLY TO Graham Benfield, Trust Administrator, Old Rosedew House, Colhugh Street, Llantwit Major CF61 1RF

■ The Bowerman Charitable Trust

CC NO 289446 **ESTABLISHED** 1984
WHERE FUNDING CAN BE GIVEN UK, with a preference for West Sussex.
WHO CAN BENEFIT Registered charities.
WHAT IS FUNDED Church activities, the arts, medical charities, youth work and other charitable activities.
TYPE OF GRANT One-off.
RANGE OF GRANTS Usually up to £20,000.
SAMPLE GRANTS St Margaret's Church, Angmering (£216,000); English Chamber Orchestra (£13,000); British Youth Opera and Wigmore Hall Trust (£11,000); and the Titus Trust (£10,000).
FINANCES *Year* 2009–10 *Income* £284,267 *Grants* £348,760 *Assets* £11,379,133
TRUSTEES D W Bowerman; C M Bowerman; J M Taylor; K E Bowerman; A M Downham; J M Capper; M Follis.
HOW TO APPLY In writing to the correspondent. The trustees have previously stated that they are

bombarded with applications and unsolicited applications will not be considered.

WHO TO APPLY TO D W Bowerman, Trustee, Champs Hill, Coldwatham, Pulborough, West Sussex RH20 1LY

■ John and Susan Bowers Fund

CC NO 266616 **ESTABLISHED** 1973
WHERE FUNDING CAN BE GIVEN UK and overseas.
WHO CAN BENEFIT Registered charities.
WHAT IS FUNDED Social justice, health and welfare, arts, environment, religion, emergency appeals and development.
RANGE OF GRANTS Up to £1,000.
SAMPLE GRANTS Previous beneficiaries include: Médecins Sans Frontières (£1,000); Impact Foundation and Peace Direct (£700 each); Appropriate Technology Asia and Responding to Conflict (£600 each); Pesticide Action Network and Disasters Emergency Committee (£500 each); Anti-Slavery International and Jeevika Trust (£400 each); and Heathrow Special Needs Farm and Streetchild Africa (£300 each).
FINANCES *Year* 2010–11 *Income* £33,141 *Grants* £24,280 *Assets* £274,723
TRUSTEES Chris Bowers; John Bowers; Sue Bowers; Louise Gorst; Jenny Johns, Stephen Johns; Jennifer Armistead.
OTHER INFORMATION In 2010–11 a total of 127 grants were received, at a rate of around 10 per month. After excluding those that fall outside the fund's distribution policy, 30 were brought to the November Trustees meeting and grants were ultimately agreed for 7. Grants were also made to a further 46 regular recipients.
HOW TO APPLY In writing to the Fund; most new appeals are acknowledged, generally by email. The charity tends to make recurrent grants – 'our reluctance to drop charities we have supported in the past and spread ourselves more thinly, invariably means that only a very small number of new applications receive a positive response.'
WHO TO APPLY TO Sue Bowers, 5 Greenacres Drive, Ringmer, Lewes, East Sussex BN8 5LZ *Tel* 01273 813722 *email* cbowers@gn.apc.org

■ The Bowland Charitable Trust

CC NO 292027 **ESTABLISHED** 1985
WHERE FUNDING CAN BE GIVEN North west England.
WHO CAN BENEFIT Individuals, institutions, and registered charities benefiting, in general, children and young adults.
WHAT IS FUNDED Young people, education and general charitable purposes.
SAMPLE GRANTS National Maths Case Studies Project (£370,000); General Assembly of Unitarian and Free Christian Churches (£234,000); Eagle Heights Academy (£180,000); Community Foundation for Lancashire (£140,000); Young Foundation (£130,000); Gaskell House Restoration Project (£47,000); Emmaus Burnley (£40,000); Clitheroe Castle Heritage Scheme and Young Offenders Academy (£25,000 each); St Albans Cathedral and School of the Future (£10,000 each); and INNIT Productions (£2,500).
FINANCES *Year* 2009 *Income* £730,747 *Grants* £991,044 *Assets* £9,586,622
TRUSTEES H A Cann; R A Cann; C Fahy; H D Turner.
HOW TO APPLY 'The charity invites applications for funding of projects from individuals, charities and other charitable organisations. The applications are made directly to the trustees, who meet regularly to assess the applications.'

WHO TO APPLY TO Carol Fahy, Trustee, Activhouse, Philips Road, Blackburn, Lancashire BB1 5TH *Tel* 01254 290433

■ The William Brake Charitable Trust

CC NO 1023244 **ESTABLISHED** 1984
WHERE FUNDING CAN BE GIVEN UK, with a preference for Kent.
WHO CAN BENEFIT Registered charities.
WHAT IS FUNDED General charitable purposes.
TYPE OF GRANT £1,000–£50,000.
RANGE OF GRANTS £1,000–£50,000.
SAMPLE GRANTS Previous beneficiaries included: Whitely Fund for Nature; the Royal Masonic Benevolent Institution; NSPCC; the Duke of Edinburgh's Award; the Ecology Trust; Wooden Spoon Society; Aurora Tsunami Orphanage; Mike Collingwood Memorial Fund; League of Remembrance; Friends of St Peter's Hospital Chertsey; Canterbury Cathedral Development; Cancer Research UK; Elimination of Leukaemia Fund; Maidstone Mencap Charitable Trust; RNLI; Alzheimer's Society; Breast Cancer Care; Courtyard – Petersfield; Dorothy Grinstead Memorial Fund; Macmillan Cancer Support; and Portland College.
FINANCES *Year* 2009–10 *Income* £114,161 *Grants* £278,900 *Assets* £9,454,188
TRUSTEES Philip R Wilson; Deborah J Isaac; Penelope A Lang; Michael Trigg.
HOW TO APPLY In writing to the correspondent.
WHO TO APPLY TO The Trustees, c/o Gill Turner and Tucker, Colman House, King Street, Maidstone, Kent ME14 1JE

■ The Liz and Terry Bramall Charitable Trust

CC NO 1121670 **ESTABLISHED** 2007
WHERE FUNDING CAN BE GIVEN UK, in practice mainly Yorkshire.
WHO CAN BENEFIT Churches and charitable organisations.
WHAT IS FUNDED Support for the Christian faith; promotion of urban or rural regeneration, in areas of social and economic deprivation; relief of sickness and the advancement of health; education; and arts and culture.
RANGE OF GRANTS Mostly up to £500,000.
SAMPLE GRANTS University of Birmingham – Music Building (£2 million); Royal Horticultural Society – Harlow Carr (£500,000); Sprotborough PCC (£250,000 in three grants); Yorkshire Air Ambulance (£200,000); PPR Foundation and St Michael's Hospice (£100,000 each); When You Wish Upon a Star – Grimsby (£50,000); Harrogate Theatre (£40,000); Bradford Cathedral (£35,000); Chicken Shed and Artlink East Yorkshire (£20,000 each); St Andrews Roundhay Church (£15,000); British Association for Adoption and Fostering (£10,000); Otley Deanery Youth and Children's Network (£6,000); Enterprise Education Trust (£4,000); and Beyond the Streets and Whizz Kids – London (£1,000 each).
FINANCES *Year* 2009–10 *Income* £1,856,689 *Grants* £4,006,815 *Assets* £108,273,894
TRUSTEES Terry Bramall; Liz Bramall; Suzannah Allard; Rebecca Bletcher.
HOW TO APPLY In writing to the correspondent. The trust also states that 'unsolicited requests from national charities will generally only be

considered if there is some public benefit to the Yorkshire region'.

WHO TO APPLY TO Terry Bramall, Trustee, c/o Gordons LLP, Riverside West, Whitehall Road, Leeds, West Yorkshire LS1 4AW *Tel* 0113 227 0100 *Fax* 0113 227 0113

....

■ The Tony Bramall Charitable Trust

CC NO 1001522   **ESTABLISHED** 1990

WHERE FUNDING CAN BE GIVEN UK, with some preference for Yorkshire.

WHO CAN BENEFIT Local charities within Yorkshire and national medical institutions.

WHAT IS FUNDED Medical research, ill health and social welfare.

RANGE OF GRANTS Usually £1,000–£5,000.

SAMPLE GRANTS St Michael's Hospice (£20,000); Children Heart Surgery Fund (£3,000); Henshaw's Society for Blind People (£2,500); Royal Horticultural Society (£2,000); Brain Tumor UK (£500); and Christie Charity (£200).

FINANCES Year 2009–10 *Income* £98,366 *Grants* £34,000 *Assets* £3,953,164

TRUSTEES D C A Bramall; Mrs K S Bramall Odgen; Mrs M J Foody; G M Tate; Miss A Bramall.

HOW TO APPLY In writing to the correspondent.

WHO TO APPLY TO The Trustees, 12 Cardale Court, Beckwith Head Road, Harrogate, North Yorkshire HG3 1RY *Tel* 01423 535300 *email* johnholroyd64@hotmail.com

....

■ The Bransford Trust

CC NO 1106554   **ESTABLISHED** 2004

WHERE FUNDING CAN BE GIVEN Preference for the West Midlands.

WHO CAN BENEFIT Registered charities.

WHAT IS FUNDED General charitable purposes.

SAMPLE GRANTS the Leys School (£190,000); St Richard Hospice (£100,000); Acorns Children's Trust (£30,000); Noah's Ark Trust and Young Enterprise West Midlands (£15,000 each); Vitalise Trust (£10,000); English Symphony Orchestra (£6,000); Bromsgrove Festival (£5,000); and Choice Radio (£1,000).

FINANCES Year 2009–10 *Income* £1,041,833 *Grants* £484,883 *Assets* £8,015,242

TRUSTEES C A Kinnear; B Kinnear; L E S Freeman; A J C Kinnear; A J Neil.

HOW TO APPLY In writing to the correspondent.

WHO TO APPLY TO Dawn Emma Oliver, 5 Deansway, Worcester, Worcestershire WR1 2JG *Tel* 01905 612001 *email* doliver@harrison-clark.co.uk

....

■ The Breadsticks Foundation

CC NO 1125396   **ESTABLISHED** 2008

WHERE FUNDING CAN BE GIVEN UK, Africa and Asia.

WHO CAN BENEFIT Charities and community groups.

WHAT IS FUNDED Healthcare and education, particularly young people and disadvantaged adults.

TYPE OF GRANT Core funding; project funding.

SAMPLE GRANTS Class Act Educational Services – Johannesburg (£377,500); Hope & Homes for Children (£200,000); The Medical Foundation (£153,000); Action on Disability and Development (£78,000); Kids in Need of Education (£62,500); Lao Basic Needs (£61,500); Zisize Educational Team (£25,500); Lao Disabled Women (£22,500); Christine Revell Children's Home (£17,500); Raphael

Support & Skills Development (£5,000); and Volunteer Reading Help (£1,200).

FINANCES Year 2009–10 *Income* £1,218,520 *Grants* £1,004,298 *Assets* £341,051

TRUSTEES Beatrix Payne, Chair; Dr Yolande Knight; Dr Paul Ballantyne; Beatrice Roberts; Trevor Macy.

HOW TO APPLY 'The foundation invites applications for core funding activities or project grants. Applications are invited through the foundation's website. Applicants submit an initial summary application outlining key activities, existing funding and intended use for the applied funding. Initial applications are reviewed by the Executive Committee [trustees] who then begin a second round of information-gathering interviews including scrutiny of financial reports. Grants are usually [awarded] on an annual basis, with some grants nominally committed for up to five years subject to successful monitoring, evaluation and trustee review. Progress reports are usually requested quarterly, with an additional annual report submission. After renewal, grant progress reports may be adjusted to biannual reporting. Funding agreements are mutually agreed and signed prior to the commencement of the grant.'

WHO TO APPLY TO Beatrix Payne, Trustee, 35 Canonbury Square, London N1 2AN *Tel* 020 7288 0667 *email* info@breadsticksfoundation. org *Website* www.breadsticksfoundation.org

....

■ The Breast Cancer Research Trust

CC NO 272214   **ESTABLISHED** 1961

WHERE FUNDING CAN BE GIVEN UK.

WHO CAN BENEFIT Recognised cancer centres or research institutions.

WHAT IS FUNDED Clinical and translational research into the prevention, early diagnosis and treatment of breast cancer.

WHAT IS NOT FUNDED No grants to students.

TYPE OF GRANT Limited grants available up to a term of three years. Grants reviewed annually.

SAMPLE GRANTS University of Birmingham (£72,000); Mount Vernon Hospital (£60,000); University of Leeds (53,000); Imperial College (£42,000); University College London (£35,000); University of Nottingham (£30,000); Royal Marsden Hospital (£20,000); CBC Research (£10,000); Southampton General Hospital and Cardiff University (£9,000 each); and University of Dundee (£7,000).

FINANCES Year 2009–10 *Income* £265,150 *Grants* £345,426 *Assets* £243,672

TRUSTEES Dame Vera Lynn; Prof. Charles Coombes; Jean-Claude Gazet; Virginia Lewis-Jones; Bob Potter; Prof. Trevor J Powles; R M Rainsbury; Dr Margaret Spittle.

HOW TO APPLY Application forms available only from the trust's website.

WHO TO APPLY TO The Honorary Administrator, 48 Wayneflete Tower Avenue, Esher, Surrey KT10 8QG *Tel* 01372 463235 *email* bcrtoffice@aol.com *Website* www. breastcancerresearchtrust.org.uk

....

■ The Brendish Family Foundation

CC NO 1079065   **ESTABLISHED** 2000

WHERE FUNDING CAN BE GIVEN UK and overseas, with a preference for India.

WHO CAN BENEFIT The trust was established in 2000 for general charitable purposes. The trust's recent accounts state that in the future the trustees would like to support projects including those that involved children, education, health care and access to food and water.

WHAT IS FUNDED General, children, education, health care and access to food and water.

SAMPLE GRANTS The Brendish Foundation (£30,000); Child in Need Institute – India (£10,000); the Children with Special Needs Foundation (£5,000); the Busoga Trust (£3,000); Marie Curie Cancer Care (£2,500); Digital Himalayan Project – Cambridge University (£1,500); and Haiti Earthquake Appeal (£1,000).

FINANCES *Year* 2009–10 *Income* £264,335 *Grants* £53,200 *Assets* £850,893

TRUSTEES Graham Chambers; Susan Brendish; Clayton Brendish; Nathan Brendish; Natalie Brendish.

HOW TO APPLY In writing to the correspondent.

WHO TO APPLY TO Graham Chambers, Trustee, Dixon Wilson Chartered Accountants, 22 Chancery Lane, London WC2A 1LS *Tel* 020 7680 8100

■ Bridgepoint Inspire

CC NO 1134525   **ESTABLISHED** 2010
WHERE FUNDING CAN BE GIVEN UK and overseas.
WHO CAN BENEFIT Registered charities.
WHAT IS FUNDED General charitable purposes.
TRUSTEES Mr M Walton; Mr J Murray; Ms R McIntosh; Mr Gibbons; Mr G William; Mr B Bassi; Mr Lovgren; Mr Gunner; Ms B Pelz; Mr J R Wyatt.
OTHER INFORMATION This trust is linked to the international private equity firm, Bridgepoint.
HOW TO APPLY In writing to the correspondent.
WHO TO APPLY TO Grant Administrator, Bridgepoint, 30 Warwick Street, London W1B 5AL *Tel* 020 7432 3500 *Website* www.bridgepoint.eu

■ The Harold and Alice Bridges Charity

CC NO 236654   **ESTABLISHED** 1963
WHERE FUNDING CAN BE GIVEN South Cumbria and North Lancashire (as far south as Preston).
WHO CAN BENEFIT Particular favour is given to children, young adults, older people and village activities.
WHAT IS FUNDED General charitable purposes, particularly young people, elderly people and supporting village activities.
WHAT IS NOT FUNDED No grants to individuals.
TYPE OF GRANT The trustees prefer mainly capital projects which have an element of self help.
RANGE OF GRANTS Usually £500–£5,000.
FINANCES *Year* 2009–10 *Income* £90,663 *Grants* £83,700 *Assets* £2,374,906
TRUSTEES Richard N Hardy.
HOW TO APPLY In writing to the correspondent, followed by completion of a standard application form. The trustees meet three times a year to discuss and approve grant applications and review finances. Cheques are sent out to those successful applicants within days of each meeting.
WHO TO APPLY TO Richard N Hardy, Trustee, Senior Calveley and Hardy Solicitors, 8 Hastings Place, Lytham FY8 5NA *Tel* 01253 733333 *email* rnh@seniorslaw.co.uk

■ Briggs Animal Welfare Trust

CC NO 276459   **ESTABLISHED** 1978
WHERE FUNDING CAN BE GIVEN UK and overseas.
WHO CAN BENEFIT Charities concerned with animal welfare, particularly animals in distress caused by man including wildlife.
WHAT IS FUNDED Although the original objects of the trust were general, but with particular support for animal welfare, the trust's policy is to support only animal welfare causes.
TYPE OF GRANT Ongoing grants.
RANGE OF GRANTS £1,000–£2,000.
SAMPLE GRANTS There are five named beneficiaries in the trust deed: RSPCA, Reystede Animal Sanctuary Ringmer, Brooke Hospital for Animals Cairo, Care of British Columbia House and the Society for the Protection of Animals in North Africa.
FINANCES *Year* 2009–10 *Income* £2,058 *Grants* £85,000
TRUSTEES Louise Hartnett; Adrian Schouten.
OTHER INFORMATION Accounts were received by the Charity Commission but were not available to view.
HOW TO APPLY In writing to the correspondent.
WHO TO APPLY TO The Trustees, Little Champions Farm, Maplehurst Road, West Grinstead, Horsham, West Sussex RH13 6RN

■ The Brighton District Nursing Association Trust

CC NO 213851   **ESTABLISHED** 1963
WHERE FUNDING CAN BE GIVEN Brighton and Hove.
WHO CAN BENEFIT Individuals, organisations benefiting sick people and carers.
WHAT IS FUNDED Health, the relief of sickness and respite care.
TYPE OF GRANT One-off and funding for one year or less may be considered.
SAMPLE GRANTS Somerset Day Centre (£15,000); Oasis Brighton Project (£4,000); Brighton and Hove Carers Centre (£3,500); Beacon (£3,000); Interact Reading Service (£2,500); Brighton Diabetes Group (£2,000) and Parkinson's Disease Society (£1,000).
FINANCES *Year* 2009 *Income* £48,879 *Grants* £38,105 *Assets* £1,926,274
TRUSTEES P J Field, Chair; A D Paige; A D Druce; J Krolick; A Pannett; D Royce; J Watts.
HOW TO APPLY In writing to the correspondent. Trustees meet on a quarterly basis to consider applications.
WHO TO APPLY TO Anthony Druce, Secretary, c/o Fitzhugh Gates, 3 Pavilion Parade, Brighton BN2 1RY *Tel* 01273 686811 *email* anthonyd@fitzhugh.co.uk

■ Bristol Archdeaconry Charity

CC NO 1058853   **ESTABLISHED** 1996
WHERE FUNDING CAN BE GIVEN Archdeaconry of Bristol.
WHO CAN BENEFIT Charities and individuals for advancement of the Church of England.
WHAT IS FUNDED Religious and other charitable purposes of the Church of England in the area of benefit. Grants should generally be associated with church-based ministry and community projects in UPA parishes and made wherever possible by way of start-up funding'.
TYPE OF GRANT Recurrent.
RANGE OF GRANTS £500–£82,000.
SAMPLE GRANTS Community of Sisters of the Church (£11,000); St Martin's PCC (£10,000); St

Matthew & St Nathanael (£8,000); All Saints Fishponds; East Bristol Partnership; St Peters Church, Lawrence Weston; Crossnet (£1,000 each); Aust District Church (£700); St Michael's PCC Bedminster (£600); St Bartholomew's Church Bishopston & St Andrews; Easton Christian Family Centre (£500 each).

FINANCES *Year* 2010 *Income* £118,983 *Grants* £117,305 *Assets* £3,317,932

TRUSTEES J Tidmarsh; R C Metcalfe; S J Mumford; P E Woolf; H D M Wares; S J Baughen; L E Farrall; Canon T J Higgins; T R Thom; A R E Brown; Ven T E McClure.

HOW TO APPLY In writing to the correspondent. Trustees meet three times a year.

WHO TO APPLY TO Mrs E J Wright, Clerk, All Saints' Church, 1 All Saints Court, Bristol BS1 1JN *Tel* 0117 929 2709

The Bristol Charities

CC NO 1109141   **ESTABLISHED** 1960

WHERE FUNDING CAN BE GIVEN Within a 10-mile radius of Bristol city centre.

WHO CAN BENEFIT Individuals and organisations.

WHAT IS FUNDED Education; relief of sickness; and relief of need.

FINANCES *Year* 2009–10 *Income* £1,546,496 *Grants* £295,040 *Assets* £12,660,330

TRUSTEES Barry England, Chair; Dudley Lewis; James Ackland; Kamala Das; Helen E Moss; Susan Hampton; Andrew Hillman; Nick Hutchen; Alfred Morris; Vanessa Stevenson; Stephen Thomas; David Watts; Laura Claydon; Tony Harris; John Webster.

HOW TO APPLY On an application form available from the correspondent.

WHO TO APPLY TO David Jones, Chief Executive, 17 St Augustine's Parade, Bristol BS1 4UL *Tel* 0117 930 0301 *Fax* 0117 925 3824 *email* info@bristolcharities.org.uk *Website* www. bristolcharities.org.uk

John Bristow and Thomas Mason Trust

CC NO 1075971   **ESTABLISHED** 1999

WHERE FUNDING CAN BE GIVEN Parish of Charlwood (as the boundaries stood in 1926).

WHO CAN BENEFIT Children, people with disabilities and people in need.

WHAT IS FUNDED Churches, community amenities, disability, and education.

WHAT IS NOT FUNDED Any application that will not benefit the residents of the Parish of Charlwood (as the boundaries stood in 1926) will not be considered.

RANGE OF GRANTS Usually up to £3,000.

SAMPLE GRANTS Charlwood Parish Hall (£29,000); 9th Horley (Charlwood) Scouts (£4000); St Catherine's Hospice (£3,300); Charlwood Village Infant School – PTA (£3,100); Charlwood and Hookwood Community Steering Commitee (£2,300); 1st Horley Guides (£1,100); Charlwood Mothers Union (£200); and the Charlwood Mothers Union (£200).

FINANCES *Year* 2010 *Income* £77,890 *Grants* £90,509 *Assets* £2,198,136

TRUSTEES Tim Spinney, Chair; Revd Bill Campen; Martin Cooper; Colin Gates; Feargal Hogan; Martin James; Gavin Purser; Jean Smith; Pat Wilson.

HOW TO APPLY Applications should be made on a form available from the correspondent upon written request, and should include an estimate of the total cost of the project, with three quotations where applicable.

WHO TO APPLY TO Miss M Singleton, Secretary, 3 Grayrigg Road, Maidenbower, Crawley RH10 7AB *Tel* 01293 883950 *email* trust. secretary@jbtmt.org.uk *Website* www.jbtmt.org. uk

Britannia Foundation

CC NO 1069081   **ESTABLISHED** 1998

WHERE FUNDING CAN BE GIVEN 'Within 25 miles of Leek, where the society is based, in the counties of Staffordshire, Cheshire and Derbyshire. This area covers the city of Stoke on Trent, and the towns of Stafford, Stone, Uttoxeter, Ashbourne, Buxton, Macclesfield, Congleton and Crewe and the rural communities between them.'

WHO CAN BENEFIT Organisations benefiting homeless people, people in need of training, especially in financial matters and community safety.

WHAT IS FUNDED Initiatives and projects that will make a difference to local communities. Priorities are: homelessness, including helping people to stay in their homes; educational achievement and aspirations; community safety, including crime prevention schemes; and encouraging prudent money management, by improving financial literacy and money advice services. Infrastructure development is also considered.

WHAT IS NOT FUNDED Applications which have received a grant or donation in the last two years (unless under exceptional circumstances); activities which are mainly statutory funded by local or central government; private companies, hospitals, medical centres, medical treatment, medical research, political or pressure groups; animal welfare organisations; promotion of religion; appeals for places of worship; minibuses or other vehicles; sport, music, drama, arts which do not have a learning objective linked to the foundation's key priorities; whiteboards, desk top PCs; contribution to buildings, maintenance or refurbishment costs; museums, galleries, musical festivals; international aid agencies and running costs including salaries (excluded from the community fund).

TYPE OF GRANT Funding for core costs normally restricted to one-off grants. Capital including buildings, feasibility studies, one-off, project, research all considered. Recurring costs, running costs, salaries and start-up costs are exceptional.

RANGE OF GRANTS Usually up to £25,000.

SAMPLE GRANTS Lancashire Education Business Partnership (£25,000); YWCA England and Wales (£24,000); Kingswood Foundation (£17,000); Young Enterprise East England (£15,000); South Derbyshire CAB and Paddock Community Forum (£10,000 each); London Early Years Foundation and Lifeline (£9,000 each); Kingsdown School (£6,000); Pirton Hill Primary School (£4,000); Pinewood Infant School (£2,500) and Staunton-on-Wye Pre School (£1,200).

FINANCES *Year* 2010 *Income* £500,998 *Grants* £395,494 *Assets* £191,255

TRUSTEES G Leftwich; T Franklin; Lord Lawrence Sawyer of Darlington; N Stephenson; D J N Gray; P H Wilkes.

HOW TO APPLY On a form available from the correspondent. Before making an application a copy of the grants and donations policy should be obtained from the foundation to check eligibility. Initial telephone calls are welcomed. Applications for more than £25,000 will only be considered in exceptional cases. Trustees meet twice a year to approve donations. It may take up to four months before a decision is reached.

WHO TO APPLY TO Katy Arnold, Secretary, Britannia House, Leek, Staffordshire ST13 5RG *Tel* 01538 391806 *Fax* 01538 399261 *email* katy.arnold@co-operative.coop

■ The British Council for Prevention of Blindness

CC NO 270941   **ESTABLISHED** 1976
WHERE FUNDING CAN BE GIVEN Worldwide.
WHO CAN BENEFIT Organisations benefiting people with sight loss, and medical professionals, research workers and scientists in the field.
WHAT IS FUNDED Funding research, including fellowships, which has the potential to make breakthroughs in understanding and treating currently incurable eye diseases; and operational research to determine the best methods of preventing blindness.
WHAT IS NOT FUNDED This trust does not deal with the individual welfare of blind people in the UK.
RANGE OF GRANTS Usually for a maximum of £40,000.
FINANCES *Year* 2009–10 *Income* £664,729 *Grants* £186,900 *Assets* £735,071
TRUSTEES S M Brooker; Ms J Boulter; Dr C Harper; Dr J Jay; Prof. J Morgan; Ms C Walker.
HOW TO APPLY Applications can be made throughout the year.
WHO TO APPLY TO The Trustees, 4 Bloomsbury Square, London WC1A 2RP *Tel* 020 7404 7114 *email* info@bcpb.org *Website* www.bcpb.org

■ The British Dietetic Association General and Education Trust Fund

CC NO 282553   **ESTABLISHED** 1981
WHERE FUNDING CAN BE GIVEN UK.
WHO CAN BENEFIT Individuals and to recognised associations or groups of people engaged in dietetic research and associated activities.
WHAT IS FUNDED Education, research and other purposes related to the science of dietetics.
WHAT IS NOT FUNDED No direct support of dietetic students in training or postgraduate qualifications for individuals, i.e. the trust will not pay postgraduate fees/expenses, or elective/MSc study for doctors.
TYPE OF GRANT Project, one-off, research, recurring costs, salaries, start-up costs, interest-free loans and running costs. Funding can be given for up to three years.
FINANCES *Year* 2009–10 *Income* £50,034 *Grants* £53,752 *Assets* £1,386,478
TRUSTEES P Brindley; E Elliot; W T Seddon; M Mackintosh H Davidson.
HOW TO APPLY Application forms can be downloaded from the trust's website.
WHO TO APPLY TO The Secretary to the Trustees, 5th Floor, Charles House, 148–149 Great Charles Street, Queensway, Birmingham B3 3HT *Tel* 0121 200 8080 *email* info@bda.uk.com *Website* www.bda.uk.com

■ The British Gas (Scottish Gas) Energy Trust

CC NO 1106218   **ESTABLISHED** 2004
WHERE FUNDING CAN BE GIVEN England, Scotland and Wales.
WHO CAN BENEFIT Voluntary sector organisations and current domestic customers of British Gas or Scottish Gas.
WHAT IS FUNDED Relief-in-need; the provision of money and debt prevention advice and education, often with a particular fuel poverty emphasis.
WHAT IS NOT FUNDED No grants for: fines for criminal offences; educational or training needs; debts to central government departments; medical equipment, aids and adaptations; holidays; business debts; catalogues; credit cards; personal loans; deposits for secure accommodation; or overpayment of benefits.
TYPE OF GRANT One-off grants for individuals; one-off and recurrent capital and revenue grants for organisations.
SAMPLE GRANTS No specific information of grants was given but £77,000 was shared between organisations.
FINANCES *Year* 2010 *Income* £3,330,776 *Grants* £2,566,894 *Assets* £389,861
TRUSTEES Stephen Harrap; Helen Mcleod; Tom Wright; Gillian Tishler; Maria Wardrobe.
HOW TO APPLY Grants for organisations: funding rounds are publicised on the trust's website and in its newsletter. Grants for individuals: applications should be made by post using a form available from the trust's website.
WHO TO APPLY TO The Trustees, 3rd Floor, Midgate House, Midgate, Peterborough PE1 1TN *Tel* 01733 421021 *email* bget@charisgrants. com *Website* www.britishgasenergytrust.org.uk

■ British Heart Foundation

CC NO 225971   **ESTABLISHED** 1961
WHERE FUNDING CAN BE GIVEN UK.
WHO CAN BENEFIT Organisations that benefit people of all ages; academics; medical professionals; students; and people with heart disease.
WHAT IS FUNDED Medical research into all aspects of heart disease.
WHAT IS NOT FUNDED Applications are accepted only from appropriately qualified individuals.
TYPE OF GRANT Project, programme and fellowship grants.
RANGE OF GRANTS No limit.
FINANCES *Year* 2010–11 *Income* £233,398,000
TRUSTEES The Council.
HOW TO APPLY Criteria, guidelines, forms and application process are available on the Foundation's website.
WHO TO APPLY TO The Research Funds Manager, Greater London House, 180 Hampstead Road, London NW1 7AW *Tel* 020 7935 0185 *email* research@bhf.org.uk *Website* www.bhf. org.uk

■ British Humane Association

CC NO 207120   **ESTABLISHED** 1922
WHERE FUNDING CAN BE GIVEN UK.
WHO CAN BENEFIT (a) Charities directly involved in humanitarian activities; (b) charities distributing grants to individuals; (c) charities providing relief of poverty or sickness, or benefit to the community.
WHAT IS FUNDED Welfare causes.

TYPE OF GRANT One-off, capital and recurring grants will be considered.

SAMPLE GRANTS Send a Cow (£33,000); St John of Jerusalem Eye Hospital (£12,000); Argyll and Bute Care and Repair Children with Cancer and Leukaemia (£10,000); Phoenix Futures (£5,000); and Sir David Evans Bursary and Penarth Sea Scouts (£2,000 each).

FINANCES *Year* 2010 *Income* £111,774 *Grants* £82,000 *Assets* £3,842,036

TRUSTEES Dr J T Breen; B Campbell-Johnson; C Campbell-Johnston; C J Newbold; J M Huntington; P Gee; D J Eldridge; D A Cantlay; A H Chignell.

HOW TO APPLY Applications are not considered.

WHO TO APPLY TO H R J Grant, Company Secretary, The Cottage, New Road, Cutnall Green, Droitwich WR9 0PQ *Tel* 01299 851588

■ British Institute at Ankara

CC NO 313940   **ESTABLISHED** 1948

WHERE FUNDING CAN BE GIVEN UK, Turkey and the Black Sea region.

WHO CAN BENEFIT British and UK-resident students and academics of archaeology and associated fields.

WHAT IS FUNDED Research focused on Turkey and the Black Sea littoral in all academic disciplines within the arts, humanities and social sciences.

FINANCES *Year* 2009–10 *Income* £587,747 *Grants* £104,271 *Assets* £326,406

TRUSTEES Council of Management.

PUBLICATIONS *Anatolian Studies and Anatolian Archaeology*. Both annual publications.

HOW TO APPLY Initial inquiries regarding potential applications are welcomed. Full details can be found on the institute's website.

WHO TO APPLY TO The Administrator, 10 Carlton House Terrace, London SW1Y 5AH *Tel* 020 7969 5204 *email* biaa@britac.ac.uk *Website* www.biaa.ac.uk

---

■ British Ornithologists' Union

CC NO 249877   **ESTABLISHED** 1966

WHERE FUNDING CAN BE GIVEN Worldwide, with a preference for Eastern Europe and northern Asia.

WHO CAN BENEFIT 'The BOU tries to support as wide a range of research projects as is possible, including applications from both amateurs and professionals.'

WHAT IS FUNDED Financial support for research and expeditions. Applications may be on any aspect of ornithology but the BOU will look especially favourably on areas where there are particular difficulties in funding research from national or local sources.

WHAT IS NOT FUNDED UK-based applicants seeking funding for overseas projects should note that the funds being sought should only be used towards defined project requirements outside the UK.

TYPE OF GRANT To individuals for research.

RANGE OF GRANTS £800–£2,000.

SAMPLE GRANTS Projects supported included: Research into the conservation of the critically endangered Spoon-billed Sandpiper in Bangladesh (£19,000); research into climatic impacts on productivity of Arctic Terns in Iceland (£800); Researching the effectiveness of White-shouldered Ibis nest protection in the UK (£2,000).

FINANCES *Year* 2010 *Income* £193,699 *Grants* £10,000 *Assets* £656,904

TRUSTEES T Birkhead; R Bradbury; J Collinson; A Dawson; P Donaldson; R Fuller; J Gill; I Hartley; G Martin; P Oliver; T Pizzari; G Siriwardena; K Smith; C Spottiswoode; S Wanless.

PUBLICATIONS The BOU's international journal 'Ibis' is published quarterly.

OTHER INFORMATION The trust has also set up a website (www.birdgrants.org) to provide information on grants and awards available for bird conservation and ornithological projects.

HOW TO APPLY Further information and application forms can be obtained from the BOU website. Applications are only accepted via email to the following address: grants@bou.org.uk.The deadline for applications is 30 November.

WHO TO APPLY TO S P Dudley, PO Box 417, Peterborough, PE7 3FX, UK *Tel* 01733 844 820 *email* bou@bou.org.uk *Website* www.bou.org.uk

---

■ British Record Industry Trust

CC NO 1000413   **ESTABLISHED** 1989

WHERE FUNDING CAN BE GIVEN Worldwide, in practice UK.

WHO CAN BENEFIT Registered charities benefiting young people involved in the arts, particularly music.

WHAT IS FUNDED The mission of the British Record Industry Trust (BRIT) is to encourage young people in the exploration and pursuit of educational, cultural or therapeutic benefits emanating from music. The trust has an ongoing commitment to the BRIT School for Performing Arts and Technology and Nordoff-Robbins Music Therapy but will also give to other appropriate good causes.

WHAT IS NOT FUNDED No scholarships or grants to individuals. No capital funding projects are considered. Only registered charities in the UK are supported.

TYPE OF GRANT One-off and recurring grants.

RANGE OF GRANTS £1,000–£350,000.

SAMPLE GRANTS BRIT School for the Performing Arts & Technology (£350,000); Nordoff-Robbins Music Therapy (£300,000); Kickz (£47,000); Drugscope (£25,000); Haiti Earthquake Appeal (£1,700); and the Paul Walter Award (£1,000).

FINANCES *Year* 2010 *Income* £1,335,351 *Grants* £724,700 *Assets* £6,803,608

TRUSTEES John Craig, Chair; Andy Cleary; Derek Green; Paul Burger; David Kassner; Rob Dickins; Tony Wadsworth; Jonathan Morrish; Geoff Taylor; David Bryant; Mervyn Lyn.

HOW TO APPLY The trust considers all applications that meet its criteria within the mission statement 'to encourage young people in the exploration and pursuit of educational, cultural or therapeutic benefits emanating from music'. The trust has a long standing relationship with a number of organisations that receive funding each year and consequently is limited to the amount of resources it can offer. Applicants should visit the trust's website and complete the online application form or contact the correspondent for further information. Please note: the trust states that applications where the organisation or project is known to the UK music industry have an advantage. There is space to include an industry contact on the application form.

WHO TO APPLY TO Aliana Harris, Riverside Building, County Hall, Westminster Bridge Road, London SE1 7JA *email* alaina.harris@bpi.co.uk *Website* www.brittrust.co.uk

■ The Britten-Pears Foundation

CC NO 295595   **ESTABLISHED** 1986

WHERE FUNDING CAN BE GIVEN UK, with a preference for East Anglia and Suffolk in particular.

WHO CAN BENEFIT Registered charities organisations or individuals whose aims and objectives are of charitable intent. UK-based commissioning bodies such as festivals, concert halls or professional performers, ranging from solo instrumentalist to symphony orchestra and/or chorus.

WHAT IS FUNDED The commissioning of new music. The Grants Panel will look more favourably on applications that can demonstrate that the work will receive more than one performance and will be looking to support composers who have demonstrated a real gift for their craft or a recognised potential and for a partnership of composer and performer/s that impresses them as a significant project.

WHAT IS NOT FUNDED The Britten-Pears Foundation does not invite applications for grants of a capital nature (including those for instrumental purchase or restoration), for tuition fees, performance costs, recordings, educational or non-musical projects. The foundation does not consider applications for support for performances or recordings of the works of Benjamin Britten, of whose estate it is the beneficiary. Subsidy for works by Britten which, in the Estate's view, need further promotion can be sought from the Britten Estate Limited.

TYPE OF GRANT One-off, some recurring and project. Funding may be given for one year or less, or more than three years. Partnership funding will be considered, though it will wish to be a major contributor in all cases. Matching funding will not be a condition of grant.

RANGE OF GRANTS Up to a maximum of £10,000 per award.

SAMPLE GRANTS Gloriana – Houston/Covent Garden (£80,000); Billy Budd – Santiago/Buenos Aries (£70,000); Midsummer Night's Dream – Sao Carlos/Sao Paulo (£40,000); Curlew River – Israel (£25,000); The National Theatre – Habit of Art workshops (£5,000); David Matthews, Horn quintet – Nash Ensemble (£2,500) and Colin Riley, Double trio – Piano Circus (£1,500).

FINANCES *Year* 2010 *Income* £1,956,677 *Grants* £873,875 *Assets* £20,811,751

TRUSTEES N Prettejohn; C Banks; E Blakeman; A Fane; R Gaddes; Lady S Irvine; Lady G Kenyon; Dr C Matthews; P Ramsbottom; T Wild and S Zisman.

OTHER INFORMATION The foundation's annual income largely derives from the royalties from the performance worldwide of the works of Benjamin Britten and is channelled to the foundation through its trading subsidiary, the Britten Estate Ltd, by Gift Aid. The grant making of this foundation hopes to reflect the wishes of Benjamin Britten and Peter Pears who, in their lifetimes, did much to support the work of fellow composers.

HOW TO APPLY In the first instance details of the work to be commissioned should be submitted, with details of the composer and of the performer/s involved. Full details of how to apply, along with deadlines for applications can be found on the foundation's website.

WHO TO APPLY TO Amanda Arnold, The Red House, Golf Lane, Aldeburgh, Suffolk IP15 5PZ *Tel* 01728 451700 *email* c.shepherd@ brittenpears.org *Website* www.brittenpears.org

■ The Britto Foundation

CC NO 1010897   **ESTABLISHED** 1992

WHERE FUNDING CAN BE GIVEN UK.

WHO CAN BENEFIT Children and organisations benefiting the people of Israel.

WHAT IS FUNDED The largest grants were to Israeli organisations (The trustees emphasised that these causes were 'Israeli' rather than 'Jewish') with arts, sporting and children's organisations also supported.

RANGE OF GRANTS Up to £25,000.

SAMPLE GRANTS Weizmann UK (£25,000); Spanish & Portuguese Jews' Congregation (£11,000); Pinner Synagogue and British Friends of the Ad Museums of Israel (£10,000 each); Kids Kidney research, International Bible Students and Coldstream Guards (£5,000); Natan Foundation (£3,000); Columbia College (£2,000); and Laniado UK (£1,000).

FINANCES *Year* 2009–10 *Income* £32,985 *Grants* £101,700 *Assets* £400,546

TRUSTEES J C Y P Gommes; C L Corman; H K Lewis; T Gommes.

HOW TO APPLY The trustees stated: 'Applications are not sought at this time – trustees choose causes.'

WHO TO APPLY TO The Trustees, Flat 2, 21 Eaton Place, London SW1X 8PT

■ The J and M Britton Charitable Trust

CC NO 1081979   **ESTABLISHED** 1996

WHERE FUNDING CAN BE GIVEN Mainly Bristol and the former county of Avon.

WHO CAN BENEFIT General, education.

WHAT IS FUNDED Local charities such as hospital appeals and other charities that the trustees are involved in.

WHAT IS NOT FUNDED No grants to individuals or to non-registered charities.

RANGE OF GRANTS Up to £20,000.

SAMPLE GRANTS Beneficiaries included: Cancer Research (£20,000); University of Bristol Centenary Appeal (£10,000); Temple Church Organ Fund (£8,000); St Mary's Church Olveston and Merchants Academy Withywood (£5,000 each); Clifton College (£2,500); and Colston's Girls' School (£1,400).

FINANCES *Year* 2009–10 *Income* £76,556 *Grants* £87,900 *Assets* £2,659,724

TRUSTEES R E J Bernays; R O Bernays; Lady Merrison; Mrs A Bernays.

OTHER INFORMATION In 2009–10, several grants of under £1,000 were made for relief of poverty (£24,000) and for charitable and educational purposes (£12,000).

HOW TO APPLY In writing to the correspondent enclosing an sae. Charities can apply at any time, but the trust makes distributions twice a year, usually in May and November.

WHO TO APPLY TO R E J Bernays, Trustee, Kilcot House, Kilcot, Wotton-Under-Edge, Gloucestershire GL12 7RL *Tel* 01454 238571

■ The Charles and Edna Broadhurst Charitable Trust

CC NO 702543   **ESTABLISHED** 1988

WHERE FUNDING CAN BE GIVEN Southport area.

WHO CAN BENEFIT Academics; research workers; Christians; at risk groups; people disadvantaged by poverty; socially isolated people; people with arthritis/rheumatism or cancer.

WHAT IS FUNDED Grants are mainly given to social welfare organisations, and medical academic research, arts and Christian causes.

WHAT IS NOT FUNDED No grants to individuals.

RANGE OF GRANTS £250–£3,000.

SAMPLE GRANTS Previous beneficiaries have included: St Philip's and St Paul's with Wesley Church (£6,000); Cancer Research UK (£4,000); British Cancer Campaign, CLIC Sargent, Derian House Children's Hospice and Southport Music Festival (£2,000 each); Duke of Edinburgh Award Scheme, Elimination of Leukaemia Trust, Listening Books, Meningitis Trust, Multiple Sclerosis Society and UK Sports Association (£1,000 each); Light for Life (£1,500); ARC and Wildlife Trust (£1,000 each); Southport Junior PHAB Club (£600); ChildLine North West (£500); and Royal British Legion (£250).

FINANCES *Year* 2009–10 *Income* £24,851 *Grants* £30,000

TRUSTEES Mrs J Carver, Chair; Mrs G Edmondson; Mrs K A Griffith; D A T Wood.

HOW TO APPLY In writing to the correspondent. Applications are considered twice a year, usually in July and November.

WHO TO APPLY TO D H Hobley, Administrator, 11 Silverthorne Drive, Southport PR9 9PF

....

■ The Bromley Trust

CC NO 801875   **ESTABLISHED** 1989

WHERE FUNDING CAN BE GIVEN Worldwide.

WHO CAN BENEFIT UK registered charities only.

WHAT IS FUNDED The trust supports charities concerned with human rights, prison reform and conservation and sustainability. This well organised and focused trust also offers other organisations with similar interests and objectives the chance to participate in a network of like-minded groups.

WHAT IS NOT FUNDED Grants are only given to UK registered charities. The following are not supported: individuals; expeditions; scholarships, although in certain cases the trust supports research that falls within its aims (but always through a registered charity); statutory authorities, or charities whose main source of funding is via statutory agencies; overseas development or disaster relief; local conservation projects or charities that work with single species; drug rehabilitation programmes.

TYPE OF GRANT Mainly recurrent, unrestricted grants. One-off grants are occasionally made, but these are infrequent. It is the trust's policy to give larger amounts to fewer charities rather than to spread income over a large number of small grants.

RANGE OF GRANTS Up to £25,000.

SAMPLE GRANTS ECPAT UK, Redress Trust, Prison Reform Trust and Ashden Awards (£25,000 each); Marine Conservation, Cape Farewell, Eden and HMP Dartmoor, and Anti-Slavery International (£20,000 each); London Detainee Support Group, Butler Trust, Deptford Churches Centre and REGUA (£15,000 each); Buglife, Clink, Moor Trees and Womankind Worldwide (£10,000 each); World Land Trust, Corston Independent Funders Coalition and Centre for Applied Human Rights (£5,000 each); and the Sherriff's and Recorder's Fund (£4,500).

FINANCES *Year* 2009–10 *Income* £580,417 *Grants* £824,500 *Assets* £15,696,915

TRUSTEES Anne Elizabeth Lady Prance, Chair; Bryan Blamey; Dr Judith Brett; Peter Alan Edwards; Jean Ritchie; Anthony John Roberts.

HOW TO APPLY New applicants are directed, where possible, to the trust's website where the trust's criteria, guidelines and application process are posted. An application form can be accessed from the website for charities that fit the trust's remit, and should be completed and returned via email to applicant@thebromleytrust.org.uk. There is no strict page limit on completed application forms but the average length is approximately 8–10 pages. Applicants are asked not to return applications which are significantly larger than this. The trust aims to notify applicants within 4–6 weeks as to whether or not they are eligible for the next stage of the process. All charities are visited before a grant is made. The trustees meet twice a year in April and October. Please note: the trust asks that organisations who have previously submitted an application do not submit any further requests for funding. Applicant details are held on the trust's database and if any assistance can be provided in the future, they will make contact.

WHO TO APPLY TO Teresa Elwes, Grants Executive, Studio 7, 2 Pinchin Street, Whitechapel, London E1 1SA *Tel* 020 7481 4899 *email* info@thebromleytrust.org.uk *Website* www.thebromleytrust.org.uk

....

■ The Roger Brooke Charitable Trust

CC NO 1071250   **ESTABLISHED** 1998

WHERE FUNDING CAN BE GIVEN UK, with a preference for Hampshire.

WHO CAN BENEFIT Registered charities.

WHAT IS FUNDED General charitable purposes, especially medical research, support for carers and social action.

WHAT IS NOT FUNDED In general, individuals are not supported.

SAMPLE GRANTS Previous beneficiary: The Southampton University Development Fund (£100,000).

FINANCES *Year* 2009–10 *Income* £23,400 *Grants* £44,619

TRUSTEES J P Arnold; C R E Brooke; Mrs N B Brooke; Ms J R Rousso; S H R Brooke.

HOW TO APPLY In writing to the correspondent. Applications will only be acknowledged if successful.

WHO TO APPLY TO J P Arnold, Trustee, Withers, 16 Old Bailey, London EC4M 7EG *Tel* 020 7597 6123

....

■ The David Brooke Charity

CC NO 283658   **ESTABLISHED** 1961

WHERE FUNDING CAN BE GIVEN UK.

WHO CAN BENEFIT Voluntary and community-based groups, especially those concerned with disadvantaged young people.

WHAT IS FUNDED Preference is given to organisations which provide opportunities for self-help programmes and outdoor activity training. Medical charities are also supported.

TYPE OF GRANT Long-term support.

RANGE OF GRANTS Up to £6,000.

SAMPLE GRANTS Thwaites Theatre (£6,000); Great Ormond Street Hospital (£5,000); ASTO and the British Stammering Association (£4,000 each); the Mission to Seafarers and the Samaritans (£3,500 each); Age Concern (£3,000); SSAFA Forces Help (£2,500); the Living Paintings Trust

Think carefully about every application. Is it justified?

401

and the Sobriety Project (£2,000 each); and the Ramblers Association (£1,000).

FINANCES *Year* 2009–10 *Income* £113,799 *Grants* £116,500 *Assets* £2,064,556

TRUSTEES D J Rusman; P M Hutt; N A Brooke.

HOW TO APPLY The correspondent stated that the trust's annual income is not for general distribution as it is committed to a limited number of charities on a long-term basis.

WHO TO APPLY TO D J Rusman, Trustee, Cook Sutton, Tay Court, Blounts Court Road, Sonning Common, Oxfordshire RG4 9RS

■ The Rory and Elizabeth Brooks Foundation

CC NO 1111587   **ESTABLISHED** 2005

WHERE FUNDING CAN BE GIVEN Worldwide.

WHO CAN BENEFIT Charitable organisations.

WHAT IS FUNDED The main objects of the charity are to promote and advance education, medical research, healthcare, community care and arts and culture.

FINANCES *Year* 2009–10 *Income* £532,676 *Grants* £520,116

TRUSTEES Elizabeth Brooks; Roderick Brooks; David Way.

OTHER INFORMATION A list of grants was unavailable, but the total amount was shared between seventeen organisations.

HOW TO APPLY In writing to the correspondent.

WHO TO APPLY TO Miss Josie Lawrence, Grand Buildings, 1–3 Strand, London WC2N 5HR *Tel* 020 7024 2200

■ The Charles Brotherton Trust

CC NO 227067   **ESTABLISHED** 1940

WHERE FUNDING CAN BE GIVEN The cities of Birmingham, Leeds, Liverpool, Wakefield, York and Bebington in the borough of Wirral.

WHO CAN BENEFIT Charitable organisations.

WHAT IS FUNDED 'The charity is principally directed to encourage young people to improve their own lives by taking advantage of educational opportunities and organised recreational activities. The charity is also empowered to help improve the standard of living of the elderly and disabled people and relieve the suffering caused by illness.'

WHAT IS NOT FUNDED Grants to registered charities and recognised bodies only. No grants to individuals.

RANGE OF GRANTS Mostly £250 or less.

SAMPLE GRANTS Most grants were for £250 or less and the vast majority were recurrent. Beneficiaries included: University of Leeds – Brotherton Library (£6,300); University of Leeds (£3,000); University of Birmingham (£2,200); Brotherton Park – Dibbinsdale Nature Centre and Brotherton Charity Trust (£1,000 each); Marie Curie Cancer Care (£375); Wakefield Girls' High School – Bursary Fund (£300); York Christian Youth Holidays and Wakefield District Sight Aid (£200 each); Wakefield District Diabetes Centre (£150); and Park Lodge Lane Allotments Association (£100).

FINANCES *Year* 2010–11 *Income* £64,138 *Grants* £67,500 *Assets* £1,740,909

TRUSTEES C Brotherton-Ratcliffe; D R Brotherton.

OTHER INFORMATION Grants were broken down geographically as follows: £27,000 to the city of Leeds; £13,500 to the city of Birmingham; £6,750 each to the borough of Bebington, the city of Liverpool, the city of Wakefield and the city of York; and £2,000 in miscellaneous grants.

HOW TO APPLY In writing to the correspondent. The application should clearly show the organisation's activities, geographical area of operations, and for what the funds are required. Applications should be accompanied by the organisation's most recent set of accounts. There is no formal application form and applications are not acknowledged. Grants are considered by the trustees at the start of the trust's accounting year in April, and a single payment made to successful applicants in October. (Scholarships are available to students on scientific courses at the universities of Leeds, Liverpool, Birmingham and York, but applications for these must be made to the university in question, not to the above correspondent.)

WHO TO APPLY TO The Secretary, PO Box 374, Harrogate HG1 4YW *Website* www.charlesbrothertontrust.com

■ Joseph Brough Charitable Trust

CC NO 227332   **ESTABLISHED** 1940

WHERE FUNDING CAN BE GIVEN The historic counties of Northumberland and Tyne and Wear and some areas of Durham.

WHO CAN BENEFIT Small community groups with a special interest in Methodist courses.

WHAT IS FUNDED Social and community work.

WHAT IS NOT FUNDED Major appeals are not supported unless they are very close to their target.

RANGE OF GRANTS Up to £10,000.

SAMPLE GRANTS Greggs Charitable Trust (£10,000); County Durham Foundation and Fruit Salad Media Group (£5,000 each); County Durham Foundation (£3,000); Westerhope Methodist Church and Castle Morpeth Citizens Advice Bureau (£2,500 each); Roker Methodist Church and Aspire – Byker Hill Partnership (£1,500 each); Allenheads Regeneration Company (£1,300); and Roker Methodist Church, Benwell Christian Shop Project and Newcastle Muungano Community Association (£1,000 each).

FINANCES *Year* 2009–10 *Income* £27,505 *Grants* £23,000 *Assets* £1,222,187

TRUSTEES Community Foundation (serving Tyne and Wear and Northumberland).

HOW TO APPLY Applicants from Tyne and Wear and Northumberland should obtain the Community Foundation's guidelines by contacting the correspondent Karen Griffiths and make a written application to the foundation rather than to this trust (see separate entry for further information). Applicants from County Durham should write to: County Durham Foundation, Jordan House, Finchal Road, Durham DH1 5HL (Tel: 0191 383 0055; email: cdf@freenet.co.uk).

WHO TO APPLY TO Karen Griffiths, 9th Floor, Cale Cross, 156 Pilgrim Street, Newcastle upon Tyne NE1 6SU *Tel* 0191 222 0945 *Fax* 0191 230 0689 *email* general@communityfoundation.org.uk *Website* www.communityfoundation.org.uk

■ The Swinfen Broun Charitable Trust

CC NO 503515   **ESTABLISHED** 1973

WHERE FUNDING CAN BE GIVEN City of Lichfield.

WHO CAN BENEFIT City of Lichfield, residents/organisations.

WHAT IS FUNDED Support for public buildings and facilities, and general charitable purposes.

WHAT IS NOT FUNDED No grants for the benefit of ecclesiastical or relief of poverty charities.

RANGE OF GRANTS £300–£4,000.

SAMPLE GRANTS Previously St Mary's Centre (£4,000); 6th Lichfield Scout Group, LDAA – Fuse Festival 2009 and LDC – Proms in the Park (£2,000 each); Erasmus Darwin Foundation (£1,800); Lichfield Festival Ltd (£1,250); Lichfield Singers (£500); and Lichfield Cricket Club and Lichfield RUFC (£300 each).

FINANCES *Year* 2009–10 *Income* £23,899

TRUSTEES J N Wilks, Chair; Mrs D English; A D Thompson; B D Diggle; Cllr T V Finn; Mrs J M Eagland; Mrs J A Allsopp; Cllr Norma Bacon; C Lamb; C J Spruce; D Smedley; B W Derrick.

OTHER INFORMATION Grants to seven individuals totalled £1,775.

HOW TO APPLY Application form available from the correspondent.

WHO TO APPLY TO A G Birch, Clerk, 42 Lincoln Close, Lichfield, Staffordshire WS13 7SW *Tel* 01543 304948 *email* alan.birch@ntlworld.com

■ Mrs E E Brown Charitable Settlement

CC NO 261397   **ESTABLISHED** 1970

WHERE FUNDING CAN BE GIVEN UK and Israel.

WHO CAN BENEFIT Registered charities.

WHAT IS FUNDED General charitable purposes.

WHAT IS NOT FUNDED No grants to individuals or to medical research.

TYPE OF GRANT Recurring and one-off.

RANGE OF GRANTS Up to £2,000.

SAMPLE GRANTS Grants exceeding £1,000 included those made to: Jewish Care, Nightingale House, Victim Support, Jewish Historical Society and Oxfam – Emergency Appeal.

FINANCES *Year* 2009–10 *Income* £28,138 *Grants* £23,400 *Assets* £744,796

TRUSTEES M D Brown; Lord Brown of Eaton-under-Heywood.

HOW TO APPLY In writing to the correspondent. However, the trust states that it is not currently considering appeals for assistance, preferring to concentrate on organisations already supported.

WHO TO APPLY TO J Rowan, Barber Harrison and Platt, Accountants, 2 Rutland Park, Sheffield S10 2PD *Tel* 0114 266 7171 *Fax* 0114 266 9846 *email* info@bhp.co.uk

■ Brown-Mellows Trust

CC NO 1135821   **ESTABLISHED** 2010

WHERE FUNDING CAN BE GIVEN UK.

WHO CAN BENEFIT Registered charities.

WHAT IS FUNDED General charitable purposes, with an apparent preference for education, social welfare, the arts and the environment.

TRUSTEES Janet Newman; Alexander Newman; Hannah Newman; Dan Newman.

HOW TO APPLY In writing to the correspondent.

WHO TO APPLY TO The Trustees, c/o Goodman Jones LLP, 29–30 Fitzroy Square, London W1T 6LQ *Tel* 020 7388 2444 *email* info@goodmanjones.com

■ Bill Brown's Charitable Settlement

CC NO 801756   **ESTABLISHED** 1989

WHERE FUNDING CAN BE GIVEN UK.

WHO CAN BENEFIT Charities registered in the UK.

WHAT IS FUNDED General charitable purposes, particularly health and welfare causes.

WHAT IS NOT FUNDED No grants to individuals.

TYPE OF GRANT Mainly recurrent.

RANGE OF GRANTS Mostly £1,000–£10,000.

SAMPLE GRANTS Charities Aid Foundation Trust (£60,000 in two grants); Bristol Grammar School (£43,000); Macmillan Cancer Support and Salvation Army (£13,000 each); DebRA, Leonard Cheshire Foundation, Princess Alice Hospice and the Scout Council – Greater London and Middlesex West Country (£6,500 each); and NCH Action for Children and Richmond Borough Association for Mental Health (£3,300 each).

FINANCES *Year* 2009–10 *Income* £356,037 *Grants* £210,404 *Assets* £10,448,965

TRUSTEES G S Brown; A J Barnett.

OTHER INFORMATION In 2009–10 future commitments were made to Bristol Grammar School totalling £75,000.

HOW TO APPLY In writing containing the following: aims and objectives of the charity; nature of appeal; total target if for a specific project; contributions received against target; registered charity number; any other relevant factors. Appeals should be accompanied by a set of the organisation's latest report and full accounts.

WHO TO APPLY TO The Trustees, BM BOX 4567, London WC1N 3XX

■ R S Brownless Charitable Trust

CC NO 1000320   **ESTABLISHED** 1990

WHERE FUNDING CAN BE GIVEN Mainly UK and occasionally overseas.

WHO CAN BENEFIT Organisations working with children, young adults and people with disabilities.

WHAT IS FUNDED Accommodation and housing, education, job creation and voluntary work.

WHAT IS NOT FUNDED Grants are rarely given to individuals for educational projects or to education or conservation causes or overseas aid.

TYPE OF GRANT Usually one-off; sometimes annual.

RANGE OF GRANTS Up to £2,000 (occasionally more); usually £100–£500.

SAMPLE GRANTS Previous beneficiaries have included Alzheimer's Society, Camp Mohawk, Casa Allianza UK, Crisis, Foundation for Study of Infant Deaths, Prader-Willi Foundation, St Andrew's Hall, UNICEF, Wargrave PCC and Witham on the Hill PCC.

FINANCES *Year* 2009–10 *Income* £52,590 *Grants* £61,780 *Assets* £1,163,591

TRUSTEES Frances Plummer; Philippa Nicolai.

HOW TO APPLY In writing to the correspondent. The trustees meet twice a year, but in special circumstances will meet at other times. The trust is unable to acknowledge all requests.

WHO TO APPLY TO Philippa Nicolai, Trustee, Hennerton Holt, Hennerton, Wargrave, Reading RG10 8PD *Tel* 0118 940 4029

■ Brownsword Charitable Foundation

CC NO 1012615   **ESTABLISHED** 1992
WHERE FUNDING CAN BE GIVEN The City of Bath, principally but not exclusively.
WHO CAN BENEFIT Charitable organisations.
WHAT IS FUNDED General charitable purposes.
RANGE OF GRANTS Up to £200,000.
SAMPLE GRANTS Holburne Museum of Art (£200,000); RUH charitable funds (£150,000); Exeter Cathedral Third Millennium Campaign (£75,000); Disability Snow Sport UK (£10,000); Iford Arts (£5,000); RNLI (£250) and Fight for Sight (£100).
FINANCES *Year* 2010 *Income* £75,831 *Grants* £441,350 *Assets* £5,801,328
TRUSTEES A D Brownsword; C J Brownsword; G E Goodall; R F Calleja.
HOW TO APPLY In writing to the correspondent.
WHO TO APPLY TO Nicholas Burrows, 4 Queen Square, Bath BA1 2HA

■ The T B H Brunner Charitable Settlement

CC NO 260604   **ESTABLISHED** 1969
WHERE FUNDING CAN BE GIVEN UK with some preference for Oxfordshire.
WHO CAN BENEFIT Registered charities and individuals.
WHAT IS FUNDED Church of England preservation projects and other charities dealing with historical preservation, both local to Oxfordshire and nationally; the arts; music; and general charitable purposes.
RANGE OF GRANTS £100–£4,100.
SAMPLE GRANTS Rotherfield Greys PCC (£4,100 in four grants); Institute of Economic Affairs (£2,500); York Minster Fund (£1,300); King Edward Hospital, National Centre for Early Music, Rugby Portobello Trust, Minority Rights Group, Royal Theatrical Fund and the National Federation of Women's Institutes (£1,000 each); British Suzuki Institute (£750); Lincoln Cathedral (£550 in two grants); London School of Economics and Trinity College – Oxford (£500 each); TZABA (£250); Royal British Legion (£200); Garrick Christmas Fund (£150); and the Society for the Protection of Ancient Buildings (£100).
FINANCES *Year* 2009–10 *Income* £48,021 *Grants* £32,600 *Assets* £1,661,354
TRUSTEES Timothy Brunner; Helen Brunner; Dr Imogen Brunner.
HOW TO APPLY In writing to the correspondent.
WHO TO APPLY TO Timothy Brunner, Trustee, Flat 4, 2 Inverness Gardens, London W8 4RN *Tel* 020 7727 6277

■ The Jack Brunton Charitable Trust

CC NO 518407   **ESTABLISHED** 1986
WHERE FUNDING CAN BE GIVEN Old North Riding area of Yorkshire.
WHO CAN BENEFIT Registered charities for the benefit of the population of the rural villages and towns within the beneficial area.
WHAT IS FUNDED General charitable purposes.
WHAT IS NOT FUNDED 'Grants to individuals or out of area applicants are only made in very rare and exceptional circumstances.'
TYPE OF GRANT One-off for capital costs.
RANGE OF GRANTS Usually up to £5,000.

SAMPLE GRANTS Previous beneficiaries included: York Minster (£80,000); Fylingdales Memorial Playground and James Cook Hospital – Middlesbrough (£5,000 each); Listening Books for North Yorkshire, Whitby Disablement Action Group, KARA Family Project – South Bank and Goathland Parish Hall (£2,000 each); Chopsticks – Northallerton (£1,200); and Cleveland Concert Band, Kirbymoorside Friends Meeting House, Dermatrust and Scarborough Blind & Partially Sighted Society (£1,000 each).
FINANCES *Year* 2009–10 *Income* £115,930
TRUSTEES Mrs A J Brunton; J G Brunton; E Marquis; D W Noble; P Reed; J A Lumb; Dr C Hurst.
HOW TO APPLY In writing to the correspondent including full details of costings if relevant.
WHO TO APPLY TO D A Swallow, Administrator, Commercial House, 10 Bridge Road, Stokesley, North Yorkshire TS9 5AA *Tel* 01642 711407

■ The Bruntwood Charity

CC NO 1135777   **ESTABLISHED** 2010
WHERE FUNDING CAN BE GIVEN UK.
WHO CAN BENEFIT Organisations and individuals.
WHAT IS FUNDED General charitable purposes.
TRUSTEES Katharine Vokes; Andy Allan; Rob Yates; Sally Hill; Kathryn Graham.
OTHER INFORMATION This is the charity of Bruntwood Ltd, a company which owns and manages commercial property and offices space in Birmingham, Leeds, Manchester and Liverpool. As it is a newly registered trust, at the time of writing (summer 2011), financial accounts were not yet due for submission at the Charity Commission. No other source of financial information was available.
HOW TO APPLY In writing to the correspondent.
WHO TO APPLY TO Sally Hill, Trustee, Bruntwood Ltd, City Tower, Piccadilly Plaza, Manchester M1 4BT *Tel* 0161 237 3883

■ Brushmill Ltd

CC NO 285420   **ESTABLISHED** 1982
WHERE FUNDING CAN BE GIVEN Worldwide.
WHO CAN BENEFIT Organisations benefiting Jewish people.
WHAT IS FUNDED Jewish charitable purposes, education and social welfare.
SAMPLE GRANTS Previous beneficiaries have included Bais Rochel, Friends of Yeshivas Shaar Hashomaim and Holmleigh Trust.
FINANCES *Year* 2009–10 *Income* £380,850 *Grants* £374,490 *Assets* £8,585
TRUSTEES C Getter, Chair; J Weinberger; Mrs E Weinberger.
OTHER INFORMATION A list of beneficiaries was not available.
HOW TO APPLY In writing to the correspondent.
WHO TO APPLY TO Mrs C Getter, Trustee, 76 Fairholt Road, London N16 5HN

■ The Bryant Trust

CC NO 501450   **ESTABLISHED** 1972
WHERE FUNDING CAN BE GIVEN The following post codes: B1-B48, B51-B59, B62-B76, B81-B94, AS1-WS5, WS9, WS10.
WHO CAN BENEFIT Registered charities only.
WHAT IS FUNDED The trustees welcome grant applications from registered charities working in any of the following areas: community and neighbourhood projects; community projects based on places of worship; disability and

special needs; education; environmental and heritage projects; health and wellbeing; the arts; 'vulnerable groups including: the homeless, addicts, refugees, asylum seekers, victims of crime, ex-prisoners, the elderly, the bereaved' young people.

WHAT IS NOT FUNDED No grants to non-registered charities, animal welfare or individuals. UK-wide charities, even when based in Birmingham, will not be supported unless there are separate local accounts.

TYPE OF GRANT Capital projects are preferred to core funding. Buildings, project, research, salaries, start-up costs will be considered. Funding is available for up to three years.

RANGE OF GRANTS 70–80% of the trust fund is applied making 'Special Grants' to a small number of registered charities of which one or more of the trustees or the Settlors have a special knowledge. The remainder is spent in 'Small Grants' (between £500 and £3,000 to a wide range of local registered charities whose sphere of activity is within a very few miles of Birmingham city centre.

SAMPLE GRANTS Birmingham Law Centre (£50,000); YMCA Birmingham (£30,000); Birmingham Settlement (£25,000); Rehabilitation for Addicted Prisoners' Trust (RAPt) and Midlands Arts Centre (MAC) (£20,000); Medical Foundation, Martineau Gardens and Missing People (£5,000 each); Ackers Adventure and Adoption Support (£2,000 each); African Caribbean Resource Centre, Bentley Beginnings and Solihull Young Carers (£1,000 each); and Central Africa Refugee Link, Stage 2 Youth Centre, Walsall Bereavement Support Service (£500 each).

FINANCES *Year* 2009–10 *Income* £195,490 *Grants* £233,000 *Assets* £5,067,967

TRUSTEES John Smith; Victoria Houghton; Anne Thomas; Martin Smith; Timothy Cole; Charles Jordan; Ranjit Sondhi; George Cole.

OTHER INFORMATION In 2009–10 most of the funds, £163,000, were given in special grants to 8 organisations. Smaller grants were made to 89 organisations and totalled £73,000.

HOW TO APPLY On a form available from the trust's website. All applicants are reminded to send in a completed application form and the latest accounts with any application. Requests are considered twice a year, in May or June and November or December. All applications are acknowledged, and applicants are notified of the outcome, normally within 6 weeks of the meeting.

WHO TO APPLY TO Mr W M Galliard, Secretary, PO Box 1624, Shirley, Solihull, West Midlands B90 9QZ *email* admin@bryanttrust.org.uk *Website* www.bryanttrust.org.uk

■ Buckingham Trust

CC NO 237350   **ESTABLISHED** 1962

WHERE FUNDING CAN BE GIVEN UK and worldwide.

WHO CAN BENEFIT Charitable organisations and churches.

WHAT IS FUNDED Advancement of religion (including missionary activities); relief of people disadvantaged by poverty and older people or those who are ill.

TYPE OF GRANT One-off and recurrent grants.

RANGE OF GRANTS Up to £18,000.

SAMPLE GRANTS Cure International (£18,000); Grace Church (£10,000); St Andrew's Church – Oxford and Tear Fund (£8,200 each); Sewardstone Church (£6,600); St Mark's – Gillingham (£4,000); Titus Trust (£3,400); OMF

International (£2,500); Barnabas Fund (£2,200); Sheiling Trust (£2,000); Tonbridge Baptist Church (£1,900); World in Need (£1,500); Association of Evangelists (£1,300); and Langham Partnership and All Saints – Lindfield (£1,000 each).

FINANCES *Year* 2009–10 *Income* £181,504 *Grants* £199,970 *Assets* £891,749

TRUSTEES Richard Foot; Tina Clay.

OTHER INFORMATION Preference is given to charities of which the trustees have personal interest, knowledge, or association. The trust acts mainly as an agency charity acting on behalf of other donors.

HOW TO APPLY Unsolicited applicants are not considered. As an agency charity, the trustees allow the donors to choose for the funds which they have donated, which registered charities or churches the funds are given to.

WHO TO APPLY TO The Trustees, Foot Davson, 17 Church Road, Tunbridge Wells, Kent TN1 1LG *Tel* 01892 774774 *Fax* 01892 774775

■ The Buckinghamshire Foundation

CC NO 1073861   **ESTABLISHED** 1998

WHERE FUNDING CAN BE GIVEN Buckinghamshire.

WHO CAN BENEFIT Voluntary and community groups.

WHAT IS FUNDED Community development. Please visit the foundation's website for details of up-to-date schemes.

WHAT IS NOT FUNDED No grants to organisations outside of the beneficial area, to individuals, religious or political organisations, animal welfare or to statutory organisations (with the exception of Parish Councils).

RANGE OF GRANTS £200–£10,000.

SAMPLE GRANTS Wycombe Homeless Connect (£10,000); Holtspur Youth Club, Chiltern Gymnastics and North Marsden Community Shop (£5,000 each); Gerrards Cross Cricket Club (£2,500); Dorney Playground Management (£2,000); Amersham Free Church (£1,000) and MK Aces Wheelchair Basketball (£700).

FINANCES *Year* 2010–11 *Income* £958,522 *Grants* £335,708 *Assets* £2,902,614

TRUSTEES Anita English; Peter Keen; Guy Birkby; Graham Peart; Bill McDonald; Mike Clare; Alexander Shephard; David Sumpter; Roy Collis; Cherry Aston; Simon Deans; Colin Hayfield.

HOW TO APPLY In the first instance, an 'expression of interest' form available from the Foundation's website.

WHO TO APPLY TO The Grants Committee, Foundation House, 119A Bicester Road, Aylesbury, Buckinghamshire HP19 9BA *Tel* 01296 330134 *Fax* 01296 330158 *email* info@buckscf.org.uk *Website* www.buckscf.org.uk

■ The Buckinghamshire Historic Churches Trust

CC NO 206471   **ESTABLISHED** 1957

WHERE FUNDING CAN BE GIVEN The county or archdeaconry of Buckingham.

WHO CAN BENEFIT Parochial church councils or trustees of Christian churches and chapels, including Baptist, Anglican, Methodist and Catholic.

WHAT IS FUNDED The preservation, repair, maintenance and upkeep of the fabric of churches or chapels in Buckinghamshire. Grants

Think carefully about every application. Is it justified?

405

are made to churches and chapels embarking upon restoration.

WHAT IS NOT FUNDED Grants cannot be given for repairs to bells, bell frames, bell chambers, window glass, organs, furnishings and work on heating, lighting, decoration or churchyard maintenance. Churches and chapels not in use for public worship are not supported.

TYPE OF GRANT One-off.

SAMPLE GRANTS Kingsey, St Nicholas (£8,000); Great Missenden, St Peter & St Paul (£6,000); Horsenden, St Michael & All Angels (£4,500); Ickford, St Nicholas (£3,000) and Princes Risborough, St Mary (£1,000).

FINANCES *Year* 2009–10 *Income* £171,586 *Grants* £54,550 *Assets* £707,616

TRUSTEES Sir Henry Aubrey-Fletcher; Mrs C Abel-Smith; Mrs C Aston; Hon Rupert Carington; Revd Canon C H J Cavell-Northam; Mrs A Cutcliffe; R W Evans; Hon Mrs J A Farncombe; Mr A Finn-Kelcey; Mrs J Moss; T Oliver; C F Robinson; Mrs M Villiers; Rt Revd Alan Wilson; Mrs M A L Saunders.

HOW TO APPLY An application form is available from the correspondent.

WHO TO APPLY TO Mrs P Keens, Hon. Secretary, 9 St Paul's Court, Stony Stratford, Milton Keynes MK11 1LJ *Tel* 01908 571232 *email* penny. keens@talktalk.net *Website* www.bucks-historic-churches.org

■ The Buckinghamshire Masonic Centenary Fund

CC NO 1007193   **ESTABLISHED** 1991

WHERE FUNDING CAN BE GIVEN Buckinghamshire.

WHO CAN BENEFIT Registered charities and individuals.

WHAT IS FUNDED The fund will normally only give consideration to: non-Masonic charitable causes within Buckinghamshire; specific projects or facilities, rather than general appeals or requests to fund routine activities; Buckinghamshire charities that deal solely with cases in Buckinghamshire, and Buckinghamshire charities that also have connections in adjacent areas; individual cases within Buckinghamshire, or outside Buckinghamshire if there is a strong Buckinghamshire connection, only if referred through, or supported by, community welfare or health agencies because of the implications for State and other welfare benefit provisions.

WHAT IS NOT FUNDED No grants to individuals for expeditions or for youth work overseas, no sponsorship of events or individuals. No grants to heritage, wildlife or conservation projects. No grants towards routine expenditure and activities, including staff costs.

TYPE OF GRANT The focus is normally on specific projects or facilities, complete in themselves, rather than general appeals or requests to fund activities.

RANGE OF GRANTS Usually £500–£7,500.

SAMPLE GRANTS Buckinghamshire Community Foundation (£75,000); 1st Iver Scout Group (£7,500); Florence Nightingale Hospice and Seer Green Parish Hall (£5,000 each); Carers UK – Slough (£3,000); Thames Hospice Care (£2,000); Slough Homeless Our Concern (£1,400); Burrell Garden Fund (£1,000); the Lantern Club (£600); and Cancer Bio Detection Dogs (£250).

FINANCES *Year* 2009–10 *Income* £40,978 *Grants* £120,090 *Assets* £705,751

TRUSTEES R Reed; P N I Harborne; H N Hall; C T Drake.

HOW TO APPLY In writing to the correspondent, setting out aims and objectives on one page of A4 with a copy of the latest audited annual report and accounts if available. Details should be supplied of the specific facilities or projects for which funding is sought. The trustees meet three or four times a year to consider applications. The trust states that some grants are made after the organisation has been visited by a committee member.

WHO TO APPLY TO A R Watkins, Hon. Secretary, 51 Townside, Haddenham, Aylesbury, Buckinghamshire HP17 8AW *Website* www.buckspgl.org

■ Buckland Charitable Trust

CC NO 273679   **ESTABLISHED** 1977

WHERE FUNDING CAN BE GIVEN UK and overseas.

WHO CAN BENEFIT Charitable organisations.

WHAT IS FUNDED General, health, international development and welfare.

RANGE OF GRANTS Up to £4,000.

SAMPLE GRANTS Médecins Sans Frontières (£4,000); Cumbria Community Foundation and Muslim Aid (£3,000 each); Macmillan Cancer Relief and Cancer Research UK (£2,000 each); Camphill Village Trust, Great North Air Ambulance Service, Bishop Simeon Trust, Children with Leukaemia and Eden Valley Hospice (£1,000 each); Alzheimer's Disease Society, Inspire Foundation, Scope and Mind (£500 each); Moredum Foundation and Water Aid (£200 each); and British Lung Foundation (£100).

FINANCES *Year* 2009–10 *Income* £346,018 *Grants* £30,200 *Assets* £1,490,259

TRUSTEES Paul Bannister; Ali Afsari; Anna Bannister.

HOW TO APPLY In writing to the correspondent.

WHO TO APPLY TO The Trustees, c/o Smith and Williamson Limited, 1 Bishops Wharf, Walnut Tree Close, Guildford, Surrey GU1 4RA *Tel* 01483 407100

■ The Buffini Chao Foundation

CC NO 1111022   **ESTABLISHED** 2005

WHERE FUNDING CAN BE GIVEN UK.

WHO CAN BENEFIT Charitable organisations.

WHAT IS FUNDED General charitable purposes, especially organisations working in the field of education and with children.

RANGE OF GRANTS Up to £20,000.

SAMPLE GRANTS Beneficiaries were: National Youth Orchestra (£17,000); Build Africa (£12,000); the Arnold Foundation (£10,000); and EYLA (£1,250).

FINANCES *Year* 2009–10 *Income* £163,081 *Grants* £39,850 *Assets* £2,583,641

TRUSTEES Ms D Buffini; D M Buffini; Mrs M G Hindmarsh.

HOW TO APPLY In writing to the correspondent.

WHO TO APPLY TO Mrs D Buffini, Trustee, 12 Mount Ephraim Road, Tunbridge Wells, Kent TN1 1EG

■ The Rosemary Bugden Charitable Trust

CC NO 327626   **ESTABLISHED** 1987

WHERE FUNDING CAN BE GIVEN UK, with a preference for the former county of Avon (in practice Bath and North East Somerset, Bristol, North Somerset and South Gloucestershire).

WHO CAN BENEFIT Arts, education, general charitable causes.

WHAT IS FUNDED Local schools for the purchase musical instruments.

SAMPLE GRANTS Previously: £25,000 to 113 state schools; £10,000 to the Royal College of Music.

FINANCES *Year* 2009–10 *Income* £23,548 *Grants* £25,000

TRUSTEES John Wetherherd Sharpe; Mrs Elizabeth Anne Frimston.

HOW TO APPLY In writing to the correspondent. However, the trust states that its funds are fully committed for the foreseeable future. No applications will be considered.

WHO TO APPLY TO J Sharpe, Trustee, c/o Osborne Clarke, 2 Temple Back East, Temple Quay, Bristol BS1 6EG *Tel* 0117 917 3022

■ The Bulldog Trust Limited

CC NO 1123081   **ESTABLISHED** 1983

WHERE FUNDING CAN BE GIVEN Worldwide, with a preference for the South of England.

WHO CAN BENEFIT Charitable organisations.

WHAT IS FUNDED General charitable purposes.

WHAT IS NOT FUNDED No grants are given to individuals or to unsolicited applications.

SAMPLE GRANTS University of Winchester (£23,000); Dance United (£13,000); Public Catalogue Foundation, Covenant House-Homeless Kids Toronto and Holidays 4 Heroes (£10,000 each).

FINANCES *Year* 2009–10 *Income* £609,280 *Grants* £184,264 *Assets* £9,046,352

TRUSTEES Patrick Burgess; Martin Riley; Brian Smouha; Mary Fagan; Charles Hoare; Richard Hoare.

HOW TO APPLY The trust regrets that unsolicited applications cannot be accepted.

WHO TO APPLY TO The Trustees, 2 Temple Place, London WC2R 3BD *Website* www.bulldogtrust.org

---

■ The E F Bulmer Benevolent Fund

CC NO 214831   **ESTABLISHED** 1938

WHERE FUNDING CAN BE GIVEN Herefordshire.

WHO CAN BENEFIT Organisations, employees of H P Bulmer Holdings plc or its subsidiaries and individuals.

WHAT IS FUNDED Organisations benefiting people who are sick or disadvantaged by poverty. Employees of H P Bulmer Holdings plc and individuals who are in need.

WHAT IS NOT FUNDED Large UK charities and those from outside Herefordshire are unlikely to be supported.

TYPE OF GRANT One-off for capital (including buildings), core costs, feasibility studies, project, research, running costs, salaries and start-up costs. Funding may be given for up to three years.

RANGE OF GRANTS Up to £10,000.

SAMPLE GRANTS Marie Curie Cancer Care (£10,000); Herefordshire Headway (£7,500); Yeleni Support Centre For Cancer & Chronic Illness (£4,000); and British Heart Foundation, National Osteoporosis Society, Taste for Adventure and Vitalise (£3,000 each).

FINANCES *Year* 2009–10 *Income* £322,495 *Grants* £230,422 *Assets* £11,041,622

TRUSTEES Nigel Bulmer; Edward Bulmer; Jocelyn Harvey Wood; Andrew Patten; Hannah Lort-Phillips.

OTHER INFORMATION The grant total included £66,000 to pensioners of H P Bulmer Holdings plc or its subsidiaries.

HOW TO APPLY In writing to the correspondent, although a voluntary application form is available and will be sent if requested. Applications should be accompanied by a copy of the latest report and accounts. The administrator is very happy to discuss applications by email or telephone prior to the application being submitted. The trustees usually meet four times a year. Smaller groups who may have difficulty in receiving support from large national trusts are normally given priority.

WHO TO APPLY TO James Greenfield, Administrator, Fred Bulmer Centre, Wall Street, Hereford, Herefordshire HR4 9HP *Tel* 01432 271293 *Fax* 01432 271293 *email* kinnersleykids@aol.com *Website* www.efbulmer.co.uk/pages/index.php

---

■ The BUPA Foundation

CC NO 277598   **ESTABLISHED** 1979

WHERE FUNDING CAN BE GIVEN UK.

WHO CAN BENEFIT Medical research institutions.

WHAT IS FUNDED The foundation currently invites applications for medical research grants that have at least one of the following objectives: Achieving sustained behaviour changes in relation to smoking, diet, physical activity and alcohol consumption; facilitating wellbeing and preventing mental ill health; improve patient decision-making through, for example, shared decision-making interventions and improving the design of community health activities by using new technologies to cost-effectively organise and interpret health outcome data. Each year the foundation runs a specialist themed grants programme to promote focused research in a specific area of medical care. Each year a call for submissions on a specified topic in one of its focus areas is made. In addition, the BUPA Foundation awards recognise and reward researchers' previous work as well as 'seeding' follow-on studies if appropriate, or piloting work in a new direction prompted by the successful project. These are presented in November each year, at the BUPA Foundation awards dinner.

WHAT IS NOT FUNDED No grants are made for applications for general appeals, applications from students for sponsorship through college or applications from other charitable organisations.

FINANCES *Year* 2010 *Income* £2,605,833 *Grants* £2,254,756 *Assets* £3,367,674

TRUSTEES Dr J Evans; C Hasluck; Prof. J M Popay; Dr A J Vallance-Owen; Dr V J Warren; Prof. A R Kendrick; Prof. P J Kumar; Dr D Forsyth; Sir M G Marmot; Prof. H E Montgomery; Mr S A John; Mr B Savla; Prof. D Stott; Prof. M J Watkins; Prof. S W Duffy.

HOW TO APPLY Applicants are directed, where possible, to the foundation's website where the criteria, guidelines and application process are posted.

WHO TO APPLY TO The Administrator, BUPA House, 15–19 Bloomsbury Way, London WC1A 2BA *Website* www.bupafoundation.com

■ The Burden Trust

CC NO 235859   ESTABLISHED 1913

WHERE FUNDING CAN BE GIVEN UK and overseas.

WHO CAN BENEFIT Charitable organisations and institutions; hospitals; retirement homes; schools and training institutions.

WHAT IS FUNDED Medical research, the priority is to support research in neurosciences; education and training; the care of older people, children, people who are sick and people in need. There is an overall adherence to the tenets and principles of the Church of England.

WHAT IS NOT FUNDED No grants to individuals.

TYPE OF GRANT Recurring and one-off. Grants are not automatic and must be applied for annually.

SAMPLE GRANTS Trinity College, Bristol (£20,000); Langham Research Scholarships (£15,000); Easton Families Project; Easton Families Project (£12,000); St Mark's Baptist Church (£10,000); Changing Tunes (£6,000); Alzheimer's Research (£5,000) and the Seed Project (£2,500).

FINANCES *Year* 2009–10 *Income* £144,578 *Grants* £117,000 *Assets* £3,731,961

TRUSTEES A C Miles, Chair; Dr Joanna Bacon; R E J Bernays; Dr M G Barker; Prof. A Halestrap.

HOW TO APPLY In writing to the correspondent. Financial information is required in support of the project for which help is requested. No application is responded to without an sae. Applications are considered at the annual trustees meeting.

WHO TO APPLY TO Patrick O'Conor, Secretary, 51 Downs Park West, Westbury Park, Bristol BS6 7QL *Tel* 0117 962 8611 *email* p.oconor@netgates.co.uk

■ Burdens Charitable Foundation

CC NO 273535   ESTABLISHED 1977

WHERE FUNDING CAN BE GIVEN UK, but mostly overseas, with special interest in Sub-Saharan Africa.

WHO CAN BENEFIT Registered charities only.

WHAT IS FUNDED 'There are no formal restrictions on the charitable activities that can be supported, but the trustees' main activities currently embrace the prevention and relief of acute poverty, substantially through the medium of education and healthcare and most especially in countries such as those of sub-Saharan Africa.'

WHAT IS NOT FUNDED Causes which rarely or never benefit include animal welfare (except in less developed countries), the arts and museums, political activities, most medical research, preservation etc. of historic buildings and monuments, individual educational grants and sport, except sport for people with disabilities. No grants are made to individuals.

TYPE OF GRANT Generally one-off grants, exceptionally more than one-year. Capital, project, research, running and recurring costs, salaries and start-up costs will also be considered. No loans are made.

SAMPLE GRANTS The Message Trust (£20,000); Kings World Trust India (£15,000); Build-it and Self Help Africa (£10,000 each); The Charity Service (£7,000); and Tenovus (£5,000).

FINANCES *Year* 2009–10 *Income* £596,239 *Grants* £245,587 *Assets* £20,598,863

TRUSTEES Arthur James Burden; Godfrey Wilfred Burden; Hilary Margaret Perkins; Sally Anne Schofield; Anthony David Burden.

HOW TO APPLY In writing to the correspondent, accompanied by recent, audited accounts and statutory reports, coupled with at least an outline business plan where relevant. Trustees usually meet in March, June, September and December.

WHO TO APPLY TO Arthur James Burden, Trustee, St George's House, 215–219 Chester Road, Manchester M15 4JE

■ The Burdett Trust for Nursing

CC NO 1089849   ESTABLISHED 2001

WHERE FUNDING CAN BE GIVEN Mostly UK.

WHO CAN BENEFIT Nurses and other healthcare professionals involved in innovative projects.

WHAT IS FUNDED The trust makes grants to support the nursing contribution to health care within three key priority areas: 1. *Building Nursing Research Capacity:* to support clinical nursing research and research addressing policy, leadership development and delivery of nursing care. 2. *Building Nurse Leadership Capacity:* supporting nurses in their professional development to create a cadre of excellent nursing and allied health professionals who will become leaders of the future and foster excellence and capacity-building in advancing the nursing profession. 3. *Supporting Local Nurse-led Initiatives:* to support nurse-led initiatives that make a difference at local level and are focused explicitly on improving care for patients and users of services. Details on the current grant programmes can be found on the trust's website.

WHAT IS NOT FUNDED Please consult the relevant programme guidance for information on the funding criteria.

TYPE OF GRANT Usually one-off, although up to three years will be considered.

RANGE OF GRANTS Up to £200,000.

SAMPLE GRANTS International Council for Nurses, Junius S Morgan Benevolent Fund, Roald Dahl Foundation, and Florence Nightingale Foundation.

FINANCES *Year* 2010 *Income* £1,176,534 *Grants* £958,891 *Assets* £70,573,904

TRUSTEES Alan Gibbs, Chair; Dame Christine Beasley; Jack Gibbs; Bill Gordon; Dr Khim Horton; Andrew Martin-Smith; Lady Henrietta St. George; Eileen Sills; Jo Webber.

OTHER INFORMATION The grant total represents the amount of grants committed during the year and includes £667,000 given to institutions and £292,000 given to individuals.

HOW TO APPLY Please see the trust's website for information on the current grant programmes and details on how to apply.

WHO TO APPLY TO Shirley Baines, Administrator, S G Hambros Bank Limited, Norfolk House, 31 St. James's Square, London SW1Y 4JR *Tel* 020 7597 3000 *Fax* 020 7702 9263 *email* administrator@burdettnursingtrust.org.uk *Website* www.burdettnursingtrust.org.uk

■ The Clara E Burgess Charity

CC NO 1072546   ESTABLISHED 1998

WHERE FUNDING CAN BE GIVEN UK and worldwide.

WHO CAN BENEFIT Registered charities benefiting children.

WHAT IS FUNDED Provision of facilities and assistance to enhance the education, health and physical well-being of children, particularly (but not exclusively) those under the age of 10 who have lost one or both parents.

WHAT IS NOT FUNDED No grants to non-registered charities.

TYPE OF GRANT One-off and recurrent grants (up to three years) for capital costs, core costs, salaries, projects, research, and start-up costs.

RANGE OF GRANTS Mostly up to £15,000.

SAMPLE GRANTS Save the Children Haiti Appeal and St Mary's Hospice (£15,000 each); Children & Families in Grief (£14,000); This Way Up and Grief Encounter Project (£10,000 each); Forget Me Not (£7,500); Nelson's Journey (£6,500); Richard House (£5,000); Norwood Children & Families First (£4,000); Trees for Cities (£3,000); Seesaw, Council for British Archaeology, Church Housing Trust and the International Refugee Trust (£2,000 each); and Human Relief and Donagh Wee Folk Playgroup (£1,000 each).

FINANCES *Year* 2009–10 *Income* £263,466 *Grants* £260,504 *Assets* £10,585,911

TRUSTEES The Royal Bank of Scotland.

HOW TO APPLY In writing to the correspondent. Applications are considered in January and July.

WHO TO APPLY TO The Trust Section Manager, RBS Trust Services, Eden, Lakeside, Chester Business Park, Wrexham Road, Chester CH4 9QT

■ The Burry Charitable Trust

CC NO 281045　　　**ESTABLISHED** 1961

WHERE FUNDING CAN BE GIVEN UK, with a preference for Highcliffe and the surrounding and further areas.

WHO CAN BENEFIT Charities, voluntary groups and other not for profit organisations.

WHAT IS FUNDED Medicine and health.

WHAT IS NOT FUNDED No grants to individuals or students.

SAMPLE GRANTS Oakhaven Hospital Trust (£10,000); Not Forgotten Association and Wessex Cardiac Trust (£5,000 each); Help for Heroes (£2,500); Julia's House Hospice and Wessex Autistic Society (£1,500 each); Meningitis UK (£1,000); and First Opportunities (£250).

FINANCES *Year* 2009–10 *Income* £67,172 *Grants* £46,213 *Assets* £924,164

TRUSTEES R J Burry; Mrs J A Knight; A J Osman: N J Lapage.

HOW TO APPLY This trust states that it does not respond to unsolicited applications.

WHO TO APPLY TO R J Burry, Trustee, 261 Lymington Road, Highcliffe, Christchurch, Dorset BH23 5EE

■ The Audrey and Stanley Burton 1960 Charitable Trust

CC NO 1028430　　　**ESTABLISHED** 1960

WHERE FUNDING CAN BE GIVEN Worldwide. In practice, mainly UK with a preference for Yorkshire.

WHO CAN BENEFIT Charitable organisations.

WHAT IS FUNDED Charities supporting education and the arts; Jewish people/Israel; social welfare; health; and overseas and developing countries.

WHAT IS NOT FUNDED No grants to individuals.

TYPE OF GRANT Preferably one-off donations and project grants, occasionally for more than three years.

RANGE OF GRANTS Up to £500,000, but mostly under £20,000.

SAMPLE GRANTS Leeds Jewish Housing Association (£500,000); Medical Foundation Care Victims of Torture (£160,000 in two grants); Médecins Sans Frontières and Donisthorpe Hall (£150,000 each); Save the Children UK and UNICEF (£100,000 each); Northern Ballet Theatre (£80,000); Harrogate Theatre

(£50,000); Crisis and Anne Frank Trust (£25,000 each); Brain and Spine Foundation (£11,000 in two grants); RHS (£10,000); Diabetes UK (£5,000); Harrogate CAB (£2,000); and Council of Christians and Jews (£1,000).

FINANCES *Year* 2009–10 *Income* £3,190,005 *Grants* £3,453,750 *Assets* £8,040,186

TRUSTEES Amanda Burton; Raymond Burton; Jeremy Burton.

HOW TO APPLY In writing to the correspondent. Unsuccessful applicants may not always receive a reply.

WHO TO APPLY TO Keith Pailing, Trustee Management Ltd, 19 Cookridge Street, Leeds LS2 3AG *Tel* 0113 243 6466 *email* trustee.mgmt@ btconnect.com

■ The Arnold Burton 1998 Charitable Trust

CC NO 1074633　　　**ESTABLISHED** 1998

WHERE FUNDING CAN BE GIVEN Worldwide.

WHO CAN BENEFIT Jewish charities.

WHAT IS FUNDED Medical research, education, social welfare and heritage.

WHAT IS NOT FUNDED No grants to individuals.

SAMPLE GRANTS Lubavitch Foundation (£10,000); Fight for Sight and Leeds Art Collection Fund (£5,000 each); RNIB and William Meritt Disabled Living Centre (£1,000 each); Leeds Jewish Welfare Board and Hope and Homes for Children (£500 each); War Memorials Trust (£250); and Pony Sanctuary and RNLI (£100 each).

FINANCES *Year* 2009–10 *Income* £142,037 *Grants* £136,705 *Assets* £5,038,453

TRUSTEES A J Burton; J J Burton; N A Burton; M T Burton.

HOW TO APPLY In writing to the trust managers. Unsuccessful appeals will not necessarily be acknowledged.

WHO TO APPLY TO The Trust Manager, Trustee Management Limited, 19 Cookridge Street, Leeds LS2 3AG *Tel* 0113 243 6466

■ The Burton Breweries Charitable Trust

CC NO 1068847　　　**ESTABLISHED** 1998

WHERE FUNDING CAN BE GIVEN Burton, East Staffordshire and South Derbyshire district (including a small area of north west Leicestershire).

WHO CAN BENEFIT Young people (11–25 years), education and training for individuals of any age who assist young people and youth/community organisations.

WHAT IS FUNDED Young people and youth organisations. Funding is given in areas such as equipment facilities and services, and extra-curricular education and training.

WHAT IS NOT FUNDED Beneficiaries must be aged between 11 and 25 – other age groups are excluded. Organisations and individuals living, or in full-time education, outside the beneficial area are not supported. No support for education where there is provision by the state.

TYPE OF GRANT Capital including buildings, core costs, one-off, project, recurring costs, running costs and start-up costs. Funding is available for up to two years.

RANGE OF GRANTS Up to £2,500.

SAMPLE GRANTS Grants of £1,000 or more included those to: Barton Under Needwond Parish Council, Burton Bike Club and Burton Performing

Think carefully about every application. Is it justified?

409

Arts Centre (£2,500 each); Extreme Support and Hillon Cricket Club (£2,500 each); and Alrewas Cricket Club, the Able Too Forum, and Winshill Youth Forum (£1,000 each).

FINANCES *Year* 2009–10 *Income* £37,230 *Grants* £39,076 *Assets* £739,637

TRUSTEES Neil Preston; Adrian Wedgwood; Stephen Oliver; Sarah Perrins.

HOW TO APPLY In writing to the correspondent. The trustees meet in February, June and October. A copy of the trust's guidelines is available on request or on its website.

WHO TO APPLY TO Brian E Keates, Secretary to the Trustees, Gretton House, Waterside Court, Third Avenue, Centrum 100, Burton on Trent DE14 2WQ *Tel* 01283 740600 *Fax* 01283 511899 *email* info@burtonbctrust.co.uk *Website* www.burtonbctrust.co.uk

....

■ The Geoffrey Burton Charitable Trust

CC NO 290854   **ESTABLISHED** 1984

WHERE FUNDING CAN BE GIVEN UK, especially Suffolk and the Needham Market area.

WHO CAN BENEFIT Charitable organisations.

WHAT IS FUNDED General charitable purposes; welfare and environment/conservation projects.

WHAT IS NOT FUNDED No grants to individuals.

TYPE OF GRANT Buildings and core costs. Funding for one year or less will be considered.

RANGE OF GRANTS Up to £3,000.

SAMPLE GRANTS Mid-Suffolk Citizens Advice – Benefit Uptake and Income Maximisation Project (£2,900); Bacton United Football Club – contribution towards cost of new facilities, Needham Market Entertainment Company – contribution towards sound facilities, Marie Curie Cancer care – funding for work in Suffolk (£1,000 each); Red Rose Chain – general funding (£750); Optua – Share Fun Arts Day, Suffolk Wildlife Trust – Snape Marshes and Waveney Stardust – contribution towards boat (£500 each); Jubilee Sailing Trust – general funding and British Dyslexics – information pack project (£300 each); and Autism Suffolk – general funding (£250).

FINANCES *Year* 2009–10 *Income* £25,076 *Grants* £19,805 *Assets* £551,472

TRUSTEES Roger Nash; Ted Nash; Eric Maule.

HOW TO APPLY In writing to the correspondent.

WHO TO APPLY TO Eric Maule, Trustee, Salix House, Falkenham, Ipswich, Suffolk IP10 0QY *Tel* 01394 448339 *email* ericmaule@hotmail.com

....

■ Consolidated Charity of Burton upon Trent

CC NO 239072   **ESTABLISHED** 1981

WHERE FUNDING CAN BE GIVEN The former county borough of Burton upon Trent and the parishes of Branston, Stretton and Outwoods.

WHO CAN BENEFIT Individuals, and organisations that benefit people in need, who live in the beneficial area.

WHAT IS FUNDED General charitable purposes.

RANGE OF GRANTS Up to £11,000.

SAMPLE GRANTS SARAC (£11,000); Burton upon Trent & District YMCA (£5,000); Burton Venture Trust (£9,000 between two grants); Queen's Hospital, Mellow Dramatics (£3,000 each); Carers Association Southern Staffordshire, Newlife Foundation for Disabled Children

(£2,000 each); Holy Rosary Catholic Primary School and Winshill Cricket Club (£1,000 each).

FINANCES *Year* 2010 *Income* £425,820 *Grants* £160,567 *Assets* £11,134,310

TRUSTEES Mrs V Burton, Chair; Mrs G M Foster; Mrs P P Hill; T Dawn; Mrs B Toon; Mrs A M Parker; Mr D E Salter; Mr J Mariott Peach; Mrs L Nash; Mr P R Davies; Mrs M A Heather; Cllr Mr D F Fletcher; P Ackroyd; Mr G M Hamilton; Cllr Mrs E J Staples; Mr D Clegg Leese; Revd R Styles; Cllr Mr L G Milner.

OTHER INFORMATION In 2010 £67,000 was awarded to organisations and £94,000 to individuals.

HOW TO APPLY On a form which can be downloaded from the trust's website. Applications for grants from organisations are considered by the main committee which meets three times a year.

WHO TO APPLY TO T J Bramall, Clerk to the Trustees, Talbot and Co, 148 High Street, Burton upon Trent, Staffordshire DE14 1JY *Tel* 01283 564716 *email* clerk@consolidatedcharityburton.org.uk *Website* www.consolidatedcharityburton.org.uk

....

■ Butchers' Company General Charities

CC NO 257928   **ESTABLISHED** 1969

WHERE FUNDING CAN BE GIVEN City of London or its adjacent boroughs.

WHO CAN BENEFIT Organisations benefiting people in need.

WHAT IS FUNDED The charities aim to: provide relief to persons who are in conditions of need, hardship, or distress; further its broad remit of charitable giving through grants to appropriate groups and organisations.

WHAT IS NOT FUNDED The committee does not fund groups which it considers have large financial reserves. No grants to individuals.

RANGE OF GRANTS Typically up to £5,000.

SAMPLE GRANTS Lord Mayor's Appeal (£5,000); Treloar Trust (£1,000); DEC – Haiti Appeal and Chile Appeal (£500 each); St Margaret's House Settlement (£400); Hackney Quest, Islington Carers Centre and Spitalfields City Farm (£350 each); Amani Foundation and Barnet Lone Parent Centre (£300 each); and United Guilds Service (£200).

FINANCES *Year* 2009–10 *Income* £258,479 *Grants* £21,800 *Assets* £1,401,059

TRUSTEES The members of the court of the Worshipful Company of Butchers.

OTHER INFORMATION In 2009–10, the sum of £2,800 was given in grants to individuals.

HOW TO APPLY In writing to the correspondent. The committee meets monthly.

WHO TO APPLY TO The Chairman of the Charities Committee, Butchers Hall, 87 Bartholomew Close, London EC1A 7EB *Tel* 020 7600 4106 *email* clerk@butchershall.com *Website* www.butchershall.com

....

■ The Derek Butler Trust

CC NO 1081995   **ESTABLISHED** 2000

WHERE FUNDING CAN BE GIVEN Worldwide, in practice UK.

WHO CAN BENEFIT Institutions and charitable organisations.

WHAT IS FUNDED Medical research, health, music and music education. The charity is particularly interested in supporting research into the study of oesophageal and related cancers of the digestive tract, projects for public education in

....

410

Does the trust you have chosen match your needs? Haphazard applications waste postage and time

respect of HIV/AIDS and relief of sufferers from HIV/AIDS.

RANGE OF GRANTS Usually up to £10,000.

SAMPLE GRANTS Imperial College (£63,000); Food Chain UK (£20,000); Crusaid (£15,000); Naz Project (£13,000); Westminster Cathedral Choir School Choristers Fund (£12,000); GMFA Charity and National Opera Studio (£10,000 each); British Youth Opera – 2010 (£7,800); Jesuit Refugee Service (£6,000); Royal Brompton and Harefield Charitable Fund (£4,500); Purcell School (£2,000); London Song Festival (£1,500); and Prisoner's Education Trust (£1,000).

FINANCES *Year* 2009–10 *Income* £346,909 *Grants* £278,620 *Assets* £11,789,698

TRUSTEES Bernard W Dawson; Donald F Freeman; Revd Michael Fuller; Hilary A E Guest.

HOW TO APPLY In writing to the correspondent. 'The trustees continue to seek new charities to which they can make suitable donations.'

WHO TO APPLY TO Bernard W Dawson, Trustee, c/o Underwood Solicitors LLP, 40 Welbeck Street, London W1G 8LN *Tel* 020 7526 6000 *email* info@thederekbutlertrust.org.uk *Website* www.thederekbutlertrust.org.uk

··

■ The Noel Buxton Trust

CC NO 220881   **ESTABLISHED** 1919

WHERE FUNDING CAN BE GIVEN UK, eastern and southern Africa.

WHO CAN BENEFIT Registered charities, although grants are not made to large popular national charities or in response to general appeals. Smaller local bodies and less popular causes are preferred, which benefit: children under 12 in disadvantaged families; prisoners and their families and young people at risk of offending; and education and development in eastern and southern Africa.

WHAT IS FUNDED Welfare of children in disadvantaged families and children in care; prevention of crime, especially among young people; the rehabilitation of prisoners and the welfare of their families; education and development in eastern and southern Africa.

WHAT IS NOT FUNDED The trust does not give to: academic research; advice centres; animals; the arts of any kind; buildings; conferences; counselling; development education; drug and alcohol work; the elderly; the environment; expeditions, exchanges, study tours, visits, and so on, or anything else involving fares; housing and homelessness; human rights; anything medical or connected with illness or mental or physical disability; anywhere overseas except eastern and southern Africa; peace and disarmament; race relations; youth (except for the prevention of offending); and unemployment. Grants are not made to individuals for any purpose.

TYPE OF GRANT One-off or recurrent. Not for buildings or salaries.

RANGE OF GRANTS £500–£5,000. Most grants are for £1,000 or less.

SAMPLE GRANTS Family Rights Group (£5,000); Dig Deep (£4,000); Tirrim Development Program (£3,600); International Refugee Trust (£3,300); Vision Africa, TWAM – Tools with a Mission (£3,000 each); YKids, Jubilee Debt Campaign, Zimbabwe Benefit Foundation (£2,500 each); Zanzibar Action Project, Retrak, Voice of the Child, Howard League for Penal Reform, String of Pearls Project (£2,000 each); Rushmoor Healthy Living, Befrienders, Bristol Children's Playhouse, Consequences (£1,500 each);

Edinburgh Global Partnerships (£1,000); and Burley-Téréli Friendship Trust (£500).

FINANCES *Year* 2010 *Income* £109,419 *Grants* £105,073 *Assets* £2,254,045

TRUSTEES Richenda Wallace; Joyce Morton; Simon Buxton; Jon Snow; Jo Tunnard; John Littlewood; Brendan Gormley; Miss Emma Ponsonby; Miss Katie Aston; Katie Buxton.

HOW TO APPLY By letter, setting out the reasons why a grant is being requested. Applications should include the applicant's charity registration number and the name of the organisation to which cheques should be made payable if different from that at the head of the appeal letter. Applications should include: budget for current and following year; details of funding already received, promised or applied for from other sources; latest annual report/accounts in the shortest available form. Applications may be made at any time and are not acknowledged. Successful applicants will normally hear from the trust within six months. The trust will not discuss applications on the telephone or correspond about rejected appeals.

WHO TO APPLY TO PO Box 393, Farnham, Surrey GU9 8WZ *Website* www.noelbuxtontrust.org.uk/index.htm

··

■ Ann Byrne Charitable Trust

CC NO 1048360   **ESTABLISHED** 1995

WHERE FUNDING CAN BE GIVEN Norfolk.

WHO CAN BENEFIT Charitable organisations.

WHAT IS FUNDED The main objects of the charity are to provide relief for people who are disabled (physically and mentally), people in need and people who are homeless.

RANGE OF GRANTS Up to £20,000.

SAMPLE GRANTS Beneficiaries included: Nelsons Journey (£10,000); Poppy Centre Stalham, Prospects and Salvation Army (£5,000); Hebron House (£3,000); Children's Trust, Combat Stress, People First of Norfolk and Hamlet Centre Trust (£2,000 each); and Indigo Dyslexia Centre, Leprosy Mission, Stepping Stones and West Norfolk School for Parents (£1,000 each).

FINANCES *Year* 2009–10 *Income* £61,822 *Grants* £95,000 *Assets* £1,560,765

TRUSTEES P R Norton, Chair; Revd S F Nunney; Mrs J A Richardson.

HOW TO APPLY In writing to the correspondent.

WHO TO APPLY TO P R Norton, Chair, 13 The Close, Norwich NR1 4DS

········

■ C and F Charitable Trust

CC NO 274529   **ESTABLISHED** 1977
WHERE FUNDING CAN BE GIVEN UK and overseas.
WHO CAN BENEFIT Orthodox Jewish charities.
WHAT IS FUNDED Relief of poverty amongst the Jewish Community; the furtherance of the Jewish education and religion.
WHAT IS NOT FUNDED Registered charities only.
SAMPLE GRANTS Previous beneficiaries have included Community Council of Gateshead, Ezras Nitrochim, Gur Trust, Kollel Shaarei Shlomo, SOFT and Yetev Lev Jerusalem Trust.
FINANCES *Year* 2009–10 *Income* £138,338 *Grants* £178,500 *Assets* £1,161,920
TRUSTEES Fradel Kaufman; Simon Kaufman.
PUBLICATIONS An analysis of charitable donations is published separately in *C & F Charitable Trust – Schedule of Charitable Donations.* Copies are available on written request to the correspondent.
HOW TO APPLY In writing to the correspondent.
WHO TO APPLY TO The Trustees, c/o Cohen Arnold, New Burlington House, 1075 Finchley Road, London NW11 0PU *Tel* 020 8731 0777

■ The C Charitable Trust

CC NO 1118899   **ESTABLISHED** 2007
WHERE FUNDING CAN BE GIVEN UK.
WHO CAN BENEFIT The trust was established in 2007 for general charitable purposes.
WHAT IS FUNDED The trustees will consider awarding grants to charities that: 'are for the benefit of persons who are making an effort to improve their lives; are for the benefit of persons who are no longer physically or mentally able to help themselves; have a long term beneficial impact on the future of individuals, groups of individuals or organisations; preserve buildings or works of heritage value; are for the benefit of endangered or mistreated animals; protect the environment; are small or minority charities where a small grant will have a significant impact.'
WHAT IS NOT FUNDED The trust will not consider grants for: Citizens Advice; community centres; environmental projects not directly involving land purchase; heritage and building projects; higher education; housing associations; individuals; medical research; minibuses; non-departmental government bodies; overseas projects; previously unsuccessful applicants; Scouts, Cubs, Guides, Brownies and similar organisations; secondary education; single-faith organisations; sports clubs, unless for the mentally and physically disabled; village halls; or youth centres.
SAMPLE GRANTS Scott Polar Research Institute (£225,000); St John's College, Cambridge University (£155,000); East Anglia's Children's Hospices and Fareshare (£50,000 each); Pace Centre (£12,000); Cancer Counselling Trust, DEMAND, Jessie May Trust and Multiple Sclerosis Society (£10,000 each); James Hopkins Trust (£6,000); Edinburgh Young Carers Project, Normandy Community Therapy and Primrose Hospice (£5,000 each); Viva Chamber Orchestra (£4,000); Independent Age

(£3,000); Vitalise (£2,500); and Marches Family Network (£1,500).
FINANCES *Year* 2009–10 *Income* £547,963 *Grants* £728,769 *Assets* £2,359,625
TRUSTEES Mark Langhorn Coombs; Laura O'Grady; James Hurbert Carleton.
OTHER INFORMATION Other grants of less than £1,000 amounted to £800.
HOW TO APPLY The trust gives the following guidance on making an application: 'Electronic applications are preferred, and should be sent to **admin@ccharitabletrust.org**. Please send details and budget of the proposed project, how many people would benefit, how those benefits might be measured (not just financially), what the estimated cost of raising funds for the project is. It is important to include in your email application full accounts for your most recent completed financial year. If sending a hardcopy application to our correspondence address, please note that hardcopy applications take longer to process. **Please do not send DVDs, CDs, glossy brochures or other additional information.** It normally takes 12 weeks from application to applicants being informed of the trustees' decision. There are no application deadlines as trustees make grant decisions on a monthly basis. Please note that less than 10% of all applications are successful.'
WHO TO APPLY TO Richard Pierce-Saunderson, Administrator, Farrer & Co, 66 Lincoln's Inn Fields, London WC2A 3LH *email* admin@ccharitabletrust.org *Website* www.ccharitabletrust.org

■ The James Caan Foundation

CC NO 1136617   **ESTABLISHED** 2010
WHERE FUNDING CAN BE GIVEN UK and Pakistan.
WHO CAN BENEFIT Organisations and individuals.
WHAT IS FUNDED The objects of the foundation are broadly social welfare and education in the UK and Caan's native Pakistan.
SAMPLE GRANTS The foundation is currently focused on the 'Build a Village Project' – building villages in Pakistan to help those who were affected by the 2010 floods.
TRUSTEES James Caan; Deepak Jalan; Hanah Caan.
OTHER INFORMATION This is the charitable foundation of James Caan, entrepreneur and panellist on the Dragon's Den television programme. As the foundation was only registered in 2010, at the time of writing (summer 2011), financial accounts were not yet due for submission at the Charity Commission. No other source of financial information was available.
HOW TO APPLY Please note the following statement from the foundation's website: 'We are currently not providing funding to other organisations, individuals or projects, as we are concentrating all our efforts and funds on the 'Build a Village Project' in Pakistan. We would therefore ask that you kindly consider this when thinking of sending your enquiry, as we are not in a position to offer financial support to other projects at the moment and are unable to respond to such requests.'
WHO TO APPLY TO Hanah Caan, Trustee, Hamilton Bradshaw, 23 Grosvenor Street, London W1K 4QL *Tel* 020 7399 6700 *email* hanah@thejcf.co.uk *Website* www.thejcf.co.uk

■ C J Cadbury Charitable Trust

CC NO 270609   **ESTABLISHED** 1969
WHERE FUNDING CAN BE GIVEN UK.
WHO CAN BENEFIT Registered charities.
WHAT IS FUNDED General, preference for wildlife conservation and music projects.
TYPE OF GRANT Unrestricted.
SAMPLE GRANTS Island Conservation Society UK (£14,000 in three grants) and Hertfordshire Nature Trust (£3,000).
FINANCES *Year* 2009–10 *Income* £35,000 *Grants* £21,000 *Assets* £668,977
TRUSTEES Hugh Carslake; Joy Cadbury; Thomas Cadbury; Lucy Cadbury.
HOW TO APPLY The trust does not generally support unsolicited applications.
WHO TO APPLY TO The Clerk, Martineau, No. 1 Colmore Square, Birmingham B4 6AA *Tel* 0870 763 2000 *Fax* 0870 763 2001

■ Edward Cadbury Charitable Trust

CC NO 227384   **ESTABLISHED** 1945
WHERE FUNDING CAN BE GIVEN Worldwide, in practice mainly UK with a preference for the Midlands region.
WHO CAN BENEFIT Registered charities only.
WHAT IS FUNDED General, including: conservation and the environment; arts and culture; community projects and integration; compassionate support; ecumenical mission and interfaith relations; education and training; research.
WHAT IS NOT FUNDED No student grants or support for individuals.
TYPE OF GRANT Usually one-off grants for a specific purpose or part of a project.
RANGE OF GRANTS £250–£1 million. Generally £500–£5,000.
SAMPLE GRANTS University of Birmingham – Aston Webb Building (£500,000); Ironbridge Gorge Museum Trust (£250,000); Birmingham Museums and Art Gallery and Sir John Middlemore Charitable Trust – Birmingham (£50,000 each); Responding to Conflict and Cancer Research UK (£25,000 each); St John of Jerusalem Eye Hospital and Trinity Christian Centre – Bournville (£10,000 each); Plantlife, Sunfield Children's Home – Clent, and Love of Christ Ministries – South Africa (£5,000 each); Wolverhampton Interfaith Group and YMCA – Worcester (£2,500 each); and Birmingham Civic Society, No Panic, Prison Fellowship, Castle Bromwich Hall Gardens and Deafness Research (£1,000 each).
FINANCES *Year* 2009–10 *Income* £827,109 *Grants* £1,039,400 *Assets* £29,719,259
TRUSTEES Dr Charles E Gillett, Chair; Andrew Littleboy; Charles R Gillett; Nigel Cadbury; Hugh Marriott; Dr William Southall.
HOW TO APPLY In writing to the correspondent at any time and allowing three months for a response. Appeals should clearly and concisely give relevant information concerning the project and its benefits, an outline budget and how the project is to be funded initially and in the future. The organisation's latest annual report and accounts are also required. Applications that do not come within the trust's policy may not be considered or acknowledged.
WHO TO APPLY TO Sue Anderson, Trust Manager, Rokesley, University of Birmingham, Bristol Road, Selly Oak, Birmingham B29 6QF *Tel* 0121 472 1838 *Fax* 0121 472 7013 *email* ecadburytrust@fsmail.net

■ Henry T and Lucy B Cadbury Charitable Trust

CC NO 280314   **ESTABLISHED** 1924
WHERE FUNDING CAN BE GIVEN Mainly UK, but also the Third World.
WHO CAN BENEFIT Registered charities only.
WHAT IS FUNDED Quaker causes and institutions, health, homelessness and support groups.
WHAT IS NOT FUNDED No grants to non-registered charities.
TYPE OF GRANT One-off.
RANGE OF GRANTS £500–£3,500.
SAMPLE GRANTS Quaker United Nations Office (£5,000); Battle Against Tranquilisers, British Pugwash Trust, the People's Kitchen and Slower Speeds Trust (£2,000 each); Action for ME, Money for Madagascar and Tools for Self Reliance (£1,500 each); and Calcutta Rescue Fund, Quaker Opportunity Playgroup and Youth Education Service Midnapore (£1,000 each).
FINANCES *Year* 2010 *Income* £21,158 *Grants* £28,835
TRUSTEES Candia Carolan; C Ruth Charity; Suzannah Gibson; M Bevis Gillett; Tristram Hambly; Elizabeth Rawlins; Tamsin Yates; Dr Emma Hambly.
HOW TO APPLY The trust's income is committed each year and so unsolicited applications are not normally accepted. The trustees meet in March to consider applications.
WHO TO APPLY TO The Secretary, c/o B C M, Box 2024, London WC1N 3XX

■ P H G Cadbury Charitable Trust

CC NO 327174   **ESTABLISHED** 1986
WHERE FUNDING CAN BE GIVEN UK and overseas.
WHO CAN BENEFIT Registered charities.
WHAT IS FUNDED General charitable purposes, particularly the arts; conservation and cancer-related charities also considered.
RANGE OF GRANTS Up to £2,500.
SAMPLE GRANTS Garsington Opera, Helen and Douglas House and the Royal Academy (£1,500 each); The National Trust (£1,200); English National Ballet, Natural History Museum and The Wallace Collection (£1,000 each).
FINANCES *Year* 2010–11 *Income* £26,413 *Grants* £23,245 *Assets* £553,550
TRUSTEES Derek Larder; Peter Cadbury; Sally Cadbury.
HOW TO APPLY The trust does not usually respond to unsolicited applications.
WHO TO APPLY TO Derek Larder, Trustee, KS Carmichael Accountants, PO Box 4UD, London W1A 4UD *Tel* 020 7258 1577 *email* dlarder@kscarmichael.com

■ The Christopher Cadbury Charitable Trust

CC NO 231859   **ESTABLISHED** 1922
WHERE FUNDING CAN BE GIVEN UK, with a strong preference for the Midlands.
WHO CAN BENEFIT Registered charities.
WHAT IS FUNDED To support approved charities by annual contribution. The trustees have drawn up a schedule of commitments covering charities which they have chosen to support.
WHAT IS NOT FUNDED No support for individuals.
SAMPLE GRANTS Fircroft College and Island Conservation Society UK – Aride and (£11,000 each); Playthings Past Museum Trust (£7,500); Devon Wildlife Trust (£6,000); Norfolk Wildlife

Trust (£5,000); Bower Trust, R V J Cadbury Charitable Trust, R A and V B Reekie Charitable Trust and Sarnia Charitable Trust (£2,000 each); Survival International (£1,000); and Avoncroft Arts Society and Selly Oak Nursery School (£500 each).

FINANCES *Year* 2009–10 *Income* £69,999 *Grants* £59,026 *Assets* £1,819,150

TRUSTEES R V J Cadbury; Dr C James Cadbury; Mrs V B Reekie; Dr T N D Peet; P H G Cadbury; Mrs C V E Benfield.

HOW TO APPLY Unsolicited applications are unlikely to be successful.

WHO TO APPLY TO The Trust Administrator, PKF (UK) LLP, New Guild House, 45 Great Charles Street, Queensway, Birmingham B3 2LX *Tel* 0121 212 2222

■ The G W Cadbury Charitable Trust

CC NO 231861　　**ESTABLISHED** 1922

WHERE FUNDING CAN BE GIVEN Worldwide.

WHO CAN BENEFIT Organisations benefiting at-risk groups, people disadvantaged by poverty, and socially isolated people.

WHAT IS FUNDED General charitable purposes with a bias towards population control and conservation.

WHAT IS NOT FUNDED No grants to individuals or non-registered charities, or for scholarships.

FINANCES *Year* 2009–10 *Income* £228,555 *Grants* £148,035 *Assets* £5,634,981

TRUSTEES Miss J C Boal; Mrs L E Boal; P Cadbury Boal; Miss J Lyndall Woodroffe; Mrs C A Woodroffe; N B Woodroffe.

HOW TO APPLY In writing to the correspondent. However, it should be noted that trustees' current commitments are such that no unsolicited applications can be considered at present.

WHO TO APPLY TO The Trust Administrator, PKF (UK) LLP, New Guild House, 45 Great Charles Street, Queensway, Birmingham B3 2LX *Tel* 0121 212 2222

■ The Richard Cadbury Charitable Trust

CC NO 224348　　**ESTABLISHED** 1948

WHERE FUNDING CAN BE GIVEN UK, but mainly Birmingham, Coventry and Worcester.

WHO CAN BENEFIT Organisations with charitable status.

WHAT IS FUNDED Community centres and village halls; libraries and museums; counselling; crime prevention; play schemes; gay and lesbian rights; racial equality, discrimination and relations; social advocacy; health care; hospices and rehabilitation centres; cancer and prenatal research; health promotion; and health-related volunteer schemes. Grants also for accommodation and housing; infrastructure support and development; conservation and environment; and religion.

WHAT IS NOT FUNDED No grants for running costs or core funding.

TYPE OF GRANT One-off and project costs.

RANGE OF GRANTS £250–£1,000.

SAMPLE GRANTS Previously beneficiaries have included: Barnardo's, Centrepoint, Marie Curie Cancer Centre and RNLI (£1,000 each); Birmingham Settlement, Dodford Children's Holiday Farm and NSPCC (£750 each); LEPRA and VSO (£500 each); ESO (£400); Worcester

Live and Youth at Risk – Nottingham (£300 each); and Sandwell Asian Development Association and St David's Church – Selly Oak (£250 each).

FINANCES *Year* 2009–10 *Income* £24,129 *Grants* £40,000

TRUSTEES R B Cadbury; Chair; Mrs M Eardley; D G Slora; Miss J A Slora.

HOW TO APPLY In writing to the correspondent giving reasons why a grant is needed and including a copy of the latest accounts if possible. Meetings are held in February, June and October. Unsolicited applications are not accepted.

WHO TO APPLY TO Mrs M M Eardley, Trustee, 26 Randall Road, Kenilworth, Warwickshire CV8 1JY

■ The William A Cadbury Charitable Trust

CC NO 213629　　**ESTABLISHED** 1923

WHERE FUNDING CAN BE GIVEN West Midlands, especially Birmingham and to a lesser extent, UK, Ireland and overseas.

WHO CAN BENEFIT Organisations serving Birmingham and the West Midlands; organisations whose work has a national significance; organisations outside the West Midlands where the trust has well-established links; organisations in Northern Ireland, and UK-based charities working overseas.

WHAT IS FUNDED Birmingham and the West Midlands: *community action* – community based and organised schemes (which may be centred on a place of worship) aimed at solving local problems and improving the quality of life of community members; *vulnerable groups* – vulnerable groups include the elderly, children and young people, the disabled, asylum seekers and similar minorities; *advice, mediation and counselling* – applicants must be able to point to the rigorous selection, training and monitoring of front line staff (particularly in the absence of formal qualifications) as well as to the overall need for the service provided; *education and training* – trustees are particularly interested in schemes that help people of working age develop new skills in order to re-enter the jobs market; *environment and conservation* – projects which address the impact of climate change and projects to preserve buildings and installations of historic importance and local interest; *medical and healthcare* – covers hospices, self help groups and some medical research which must be based in and be of potential benefit to the West Midlands; *the arts* – music, drama and the visual arts, museums and art galleries. United Kingdom: *the Religious Society of Friends* – support for groups with a clear Quaker connection and support for the work of the Religious Society of Friends in the UK; *penal affairs* – restorative justice, prison based projects and work with ex offenders aimed at reducing re-offending. Ireland: *peace and reconciliation*. International development: *Africa* – the international development programme is concentrated on West Africa and work to reduce poverty on a sustainable basis in both rural and urban communities – schemes that help children access education are also supported; *Asia and Eastern Europe; South America*. Note: The international development programme is heavily oversubscribed and unsolicited applications are unlikely to be successful.

WHAT IS NOT FUNDED The trust does not fund: individuals (whether for research, expeditions, educational purposes or medical treatment); projects concerned with travel, adventure, sports or recreation; organisations which do not have UK charity registration, except those which are legally exempt. Though, small grants may be made to unregistered groups in the West Midlands (as long as they have a constitution, an elected committee and a bank account controlled by two or more committee members).

TYPE OF GRANT Specific grant applications are favoured. Grants are generally one-off or for projects of one year or less. The trust will consider applications for core costs as well as for development/project funding. Grants are not usually awarded on an annual basis, except to a small number of charities for revenue costs.

RANGE OF GRANTS Small grants up to £2,000; large grants usually range from £10,000–£20,000 with an occasional maximum of £50,000.

SAMPLE GRANTS Concern Universal (£115,000 in two grants); Birmingham Museum and Art Gallery – Staffordshire Appeal (£20,000); St Martin in the Bull Ring, Restore, Worgan Trust and the Centre for Alternative Technology (£15,000 each); Action for ME (£13,000); YWCA – Wolverhampton, Warwick Arts Centre, Herefordshire Primary Trust, Lench's Trust and Bournville Parish Church (£10,000 each); Dhaka Ahsania Mission (£8,300); the Haven – Wolverhampton (£7,000); SACDA Creche (£5,000); and Woodbrooke Quaker Study Centre (£3,000).

FINANCES *Year* 2009–10 *Income* £1,755,098 *Grants* £693,355 *Assets* £24,627,676

TRUSTEES James Taylor; Rupert Cadbury; Katherine van Hagen Cadbury; Margaret Salmon; Sarah Stafford; Adrian Thomas; John Penny; Sophy Blandy; Janine Cobain.

HOW TO APPLY Applications can be submitted via the trust's online application form. Alternatively, they can be made in writing to the correspondent, including the following information: charity registration number; a description of the charity's aims and achievements; the grant programme being applied to; an outline and budget for the project for which funding is sought; details of funds raised and the current shortfall; if the organisation has received funding from the trust before, please provide brief details of the outcome of this project. Applications are considered on a continuing basis throughout the year. Small grants are assessed each month. Large grants are awarded at the trustees' meetings held twice annually, normally in May and November. Applicants whose appeals are to be considered at one of the meetings will be notified in advance.

WHO TO APPLY TO Carolyn Bettis, Trust Administrator, Rokesley, University of Birmingham, Bristol Road, Selly Oak, Birmingham B29 6QF *Tel* 0121 472 1464 *email* info@wa-cadbury.org. uk *Website* www.wa-cadbury.org.uk

....

■ The Cadbury Foundation

CC NO 1050482   **ESTABLISHED** 1994

WHERE FUNDING CAN BE GIVEN UK, particularly in areas where the company has operations.

WHO CAN BENEFIT Registered charities.

WHAT IS FUNDED To be eligible for funding from the Cadbury Foundation projects must fall within one of the five key focus areas: education and enterprise, poverty and homelessness, London 2012, the environment and Africa Aid.

SAMPLE GRANTS Young Enterprise (£100,000); Confectioners' Benevolent Fund (£75,000); British Paralympics Association and Groundwork (£50,000 each); World Wildlife Fund (£30,000); Young People's Environment Trust and Business Action on Homelessness (£20,000 each); The Big Issue Foundation (£10,000); Enhancing Children's HIV Outcome (£5,000) and CEO Award (£2,000).

FINANCES *Year* 2010 *Income* £851,863 *Grants* £703,500 *Assets* £904,030

TRUSTEES Richard Michael Doyle; Lawrence MacDougall; Perry Yeatman; Nicole Robinson; Jonathan Horrell; Ben Wiseman; Neil Makin.

HOW TO APPLY In writing to the correspondent.

WHO TO APPLY TO The Administrator, Kraft Foods, Uxbridge Business Park, 3 Sanderson Road, Uxbridge UB8 1DH

....

■ The Edward and Dorothy Cadbury Trust

CC NO 1107327   **ESTABLISHED** 1928

WHERE FUNDING CAN BE GIVEN Preference for the West Midlands area.

WHO CAN BENEFIT Registered charities and community projects.

WHAT IS FUNDED The trust continues to support, where appropriate, the interests of the founders and the particular charitable interests of the trustees. Grants are grouped under six main headings: arts and culture; community projects and integration; compassionate support; education and training; conservation and environment; and research. 'As a matter of good practice, Trustees undertake a programme of visits to organisations where a grant of high value has been made or the activity is of particular interest to the Trust in terms of future development. This has proved helpful in building up positive relationships with grantees and providing networking opportunities.'

WHAT IS NOT FUNDED No grants to individuals.

TYPE OF GRANT Ongoing funding commitments rarely considered.

RANGE OF GRANTS Usually £500–£2,500, with occasional larger grants made.

SAMPLE GRANTS Worcester Breast Unit Campaign (£15,000); Age Concern – Bromsgrove and District Elmhurst School for Dance – Birmingham (£5,000 each); Bromsgrove Festival (£4,000); Bromsgrove Bereavement Counselling (£1,500); National Playbus Association, St Francis Church – Bournville and the Willow Trust (£1,000 each); Cued Speech Association and Sense (£750 each); Big Brum Theatre in Education, Design and Manufacture for Disability – DEMAND, Ellen MacArthur Trust, Brain Tumour UK and Fight for Sight (£500 each).

FINANCES *Year* 2009–10 *Income* £131,358 *Grants* £100,900 *Assets* £5,306,777

TRUSTEES Mrs P A Gillett, Chair; Dr C M Elliott; Mrs P S Ward; Mrs S E Anfilogoff; Mrs J E Gillett; Mrs J A Cadbury.

HOW TO APPLY In writing to the correspondent, giving clear, relevant information concerning the project's aims and its benefits, an outline budget and how the project is to be funded initially and in the future. Up-to-date accounts and annual reports, where available, should be included. Applications can be submitted at any time but three months should be allowed for a response. Applications that do not come within the policy as stated above may not be considered or acknowledged.

WHO TO APPLY TO Miss S Anderson, Company Secretary/Trust Manager, Rokesley, University of Birmingham Selly Oak, Bristol Road, Selly Oak, Birmingham B29 6QF *Tel* 0121 472 1838

■ The George Cadbury Trust

CC NO 1040999   ESTABLISHED 1924

WHERE FUNDING CAN BE GIVEN Preference for the West Midlands, Hampshire and Gloucestershire.
WHO CAN BENEFIT UK-based charities.
WHAT IS FUNDED General charitable purposes.
WHAT IS NOT FUNDED No support for individuals for projects, courses of study, expeditions or sporting tours. No support for overseas appeals.
RANGE OF GRANTS Mostly for £1,000 or less.
SAMPLE GRANTS St John's of Jerusalem Eye Hospital (£52,000); Performance Birmingham Limited (£25,000); Dean and Chapters Gloucester Cathedral (£20,000); Elmhurst Ballet School Trust and Rift Valley Tree Trust (£10,000 each); Age Concern and Birmingham Opera Company (£5,000 each); West Bromwich and District YMCA (£4,000); Save the Elephants (£3,600); Tourism Concern (£2,500); Combat Stress (£2,000); and Gosford Forest Guide House – Co Armagh, Kings College Cambridge and Dunluce Guide House (£1,000 each).
FINANCES *Year* 2009–10 *Income* £336,257 *Grants* £354,950 *Assets* £9,918,503
TRUSTEES Anne L K Cadbury; Robin N Cadbury; Sir Adrian Cadbury; Roger V J Cadbury; A Janie Cadbury.
HOW TO APPLY In writing to the correspondent to be considered quarterly. Please note that very few new applications are supported due to ongoing and alternative commitments.
WHO TO APPLY TO Sarah Moss, PKF (UK) LLP, New Guild House, 45 Great Charles Street, Queensway, Birmingham B3 2LX *Tel* 0121 212 2222

■ The Barrow Cadbury Trust and the Barrow Cadbury Fund

CC NO 1115476   ESTABLISHED 1920

WHERE FUNDING CAN BE GIVEN Unrestricted, with a preference for Birmingham and the Black Country (Wolverhampton, Dudley, West Bromwich, Smethwick or Sandwell).
WHO CAN BENEFIT Charities and voluntary organisations which benefit causes within the trust's programmes. Organisations working on grassroots, user-led projects are preferred. Groups do not have to be a registered charity but should have a formal structure and governing documents.
WHAT IS FUNDED The trust promotes social justice through grant-making, research, influencing public policy and supporting local communities. There are three main programme areas: criminal justice; migration and Europe; and poverty and inclusion. Detailed guidelines are available on the trust's website.
WHAT IS NOT FUNDED The trust does not fund: activities that central or local government is responsible for; animal welfare; arts and cultural projects; capital costs for building, refurbishment and outfitting; endowment funds; fundraising events or activities; general appeals; general health; individuals; housing; learning disability; medical research or equipment; mental health; children under 16 and older people; physical disability; the promotion of religion or belief systems; schools; sponsorship or marketing appeals; unsolicited international projects. The trust will not consider funding the following areas unless they are part of a broader project: *counselling drug and alcohol services* – will only be considered under the trust's criminal justice programme, and must be part of a broader project that meets the aims of the programme; *environmental projects* – will only be considered under the poverty and inclusion programme, and must be as part of a broader project that meets the aims of the programme; *homelessness and destitution* – will only be considered for those leaving the criminal justice system or in relation to the trust's migration programme; *IT training; sporting activities.* The trust asks that organisations submitting a proposal that includes one of these services should contact the grants team first. Colleges and universities can only apply under the policy and research funding streams.
TYPE OF GRANT Project funding, recurring costs, running costs and start-up costs.
RANGE OF GRANTS Average grassroots grant is £15,000–£50,000 per year. The maximum grant is £50,000 per year for two years (£100,000 in total).
SAMPLE GRANTS Detailed examples of previously funded projects are available on the trust's website.
FINANCES *Year* 2009–10 *Income* £1,436,000 *Grants* £4,481,000 *Assets* £63,468,000
TRUSTEES Ruth Cadbury, Chair; Anna Southall; Anna Hickinbotham; Erica Cadbury; Nicola Cadbury; Tim Compton; Tamsin Rupprechter; Gordon Mitchell; Harry Serle.
PUBLICATIONS A number of publications and reports are published on the trust's website.
HOW TO APPLY The trust asks that potential applicants first contact the grants team, either by calling 020 7632 9068 or completing the online enquiry form available through the trust's website. Note: applicants for policy and research grants under the Criminal Justice and Migration and Europe categories are asked to emailgeneral@barrowcadbury.org.uk with their proposal or call 020 7632 9068. If the trust is not able to support the project, it will notify the applicant within one month. It can take three to six months for proposals that the trust wishes to take forward to be assessed and presented to trustees, but the trust will be in contact during this period. Grants are approved by trustees at quarterly meetings throughout the year.
WHO TO APPLY TO Asma Aroui, Programme Administrator, Kean House, 6 Kean Street, London WC2B 4AS *Tel* 020 7632 9060 *Fax* 020 7632 9061 *Website* www.bctrust.org.uk

■ The Cadogan Charity

CC NO 247773   ESTABLISHED 1966

WHERE FUNDING CAN BE GIVEN Worldwide. In practice UK, with a preference for charities operating or based in London or Scotland.
WHO CAN BENEFIT Registered charities.
WHAT IS FUNDED General, in particular social welfare, medical research, services charities, animal welfare, education and conservation and the environment.
WHAT IS NOT FUNDED No grants to individuals.
TYPE OF GRANT Support is usually given over one to two years, although some one-off grants may be made.
RANGE OF GRANTS Up to £300,000.
SAMPLE GRANTS NSPCC – Full Stop Campaign and Children's Trust – Tadworth (£300,000 each);

St Paul's Cathedral Foundation (£250,000); In-Pensioners Mobility Fund (£100,000); Awareness Foundation (£50,000); Papal Visit (£25,000); London Playing Fields Foundation (£20,000); Rotalec – Life Education Centres (£15,000); Army Benevolent Fund, Animal Health Trust, Oatridge Agricultural College and Kippen Sports Development (£10,000 each); Royal British Legion (£6,000); British Heart Foundation and British Lung Foundation (£5,000 each); Focus – Kensington and Chelsea Foundation (£4,000); and Atlantic Salmon Trust (£1,000).

FINANCES *Year* 2009–10 *Income* £1,394,263 *Grants* £1,274,387 *Assets* £28,432,073

TRUSTEES Earl Cadogan; Countess Cadogan; Viscount Chelsea; Lady Anna Thomson; The Hon. William Cadogan.

HOW TO APPLY In writing to the correspondent. However, please note that we have received information stating that the trust's funds are fully committed until 2016.

WHO TO APPLY TO P M Loutit, Secretary, 18 Cadogan Gardens, London SW3 2RP *Tel* 020 7730 4567 *Fax* 020 7881 2300

■ CAF (Charities Aid Foundation)

CC NO 268369   **ESTABLISHED** 1974
WHERE FUNDING CAN BE GIVEN Worldwide.
WHO CAN BENEFIT Charitable organisations.
WHAT IS FUNDED General funding programmes are run on a periodic basis with each programme having its own theme. Usually, the foundation researches suitable organisations and invites them to apply. Loans and investment support is available through the Venturesome scheme for charitable organisations which need finance but whose requirements may be too risky for a bank loan or outside the criteria of a grantmaker. This support might take the form of underwriting, unsecured loans or equity type investments and it is anticipated that the money loaned will be repaid over time.

TYPE OF GRANT One-off grants, loans and investment support.

RANGE OF GRANTS Loans from £25,000–£250,000.

SAMPLE GRANTS Previous beneficiaries include: London Business School, City Centre for Charity Effectiveness Trust – CASS Business School, Nottingham Law Centre, Kairos in Soho, UK Youth Parliament, People in Action, Northern Ireland Childminding Association, Scottish Adult Learning Partnership and African and Caribbean Voices Association.

FINANCES *Year* 2009–10 *Income* £377,433,000 *Assets* £748,674,000

TRUSTEES Dominic Casserley, Chair; Sue Ashtiany; Robin Creswell; Philip Hardaker; Alison Hutchinson; Kim Lavely; Martyn Lewis; David Locke; Stephen Lovegrove; John Lorimer; Iain Mackinnon; Jenny Watson.

HOW TO APPLY In the first instance, applicants to the Venturesome programme should contact the trust directly to discuss their requirements.

WHO TO APPLY TO Advisory Team, 25 Kings Hill Avenue, Kings Hill, West Malling, Kent ME19 4TA *Tel* 03000 123000 *Fax* 03000 123001 *Website* www.cafonline.org

■ CAFOD (Catholic Agency for Overseas Development)

CC NO 285776   **ESTABLISHED** 1962
WHERE FUNDING CAN BE GIVEN Predominantly overseas, with some funding to partners in England and Wales.
WHO CAN BENEFIT Poorer communities overseas and victims of famine, disasters or war.
WHAT IS FUNDED Long-term development work with some of the world's poorest communities. In almost all cases work overseas is planned and run by local people. Programmes include education and skills training, human rights promotion, healthcare, HIV/AIDS, safe water, agriculture and small businesses. Immediate help for people affected by emergencies such as wars and natural disasters is also funded, as is the analysis of the causes of underdevelopment and campaigns on behalf of the world's poor. All programmes seek to promote gender equality. In England and Wales CAFOD's Development Education Fund makes small grants to local or national groups with young people and adults for projects developing education and action on local/global poverty and injustice issues.

WHAT IS NOT FUNDED CAFOD does not make grants to individuals or to organisations whose aims are primarily political.

TYPE OF GRANT Partnership, programme and project.

FINANCES *Year* 2010–11 *Income* £55,919,000 *Grants* £33,906,000 *Assets* £27,777,000

TRUSTEES Fr James O'Keefe; Fr Timothy Radcliffe; Robert Archer; Rt Revd John Arnold; Margaret Mwaniki; Clare Gardner; Dominic Jermey; Mark McGreevy; Victoria Santer; Fr Frank Turner.

HOW TO APPLY UK applicants are advised to contact the Education Fund Coordinator for further details. Criteria, guidelines and application process for Development Education Fund grants can be found on the CAFOD website.

WHO TO APPLY TO James Steel, Director of Finance and Services Division, Romero House, 55 Westminster Bridge Road, London SE1 7JB *Tel* 020 7733 7900 *Fax* 020 7274 9630 *email* cafod@cafod.org.uk *Website* www.cafod.org.uk

■ Community Foundation for Calderdale

CC NO 1002722   **ESTABLISHED** 1991
WHERE FUNDING CAN BE GIVEN Calderdale, with ability to manage funds outside of this area.
WHO CAN BENEFIT Constituted voluntary, community and faith groups, run for and by local people and registered charities working in Calderdale.
WHAT IS FUNDED General. Each scheme has different criteria but priority tends to be given to projects which: achieve outstanding community impact; help people living in communities identified as being particularly disadvantaged; benefit people from black and minority ethnic communities; help people with special needs; benefit older people; and/or benefit young people under the age of 19.

WHAT IS NOT FUNDED The foundation will not fund any of the following: general appeals; projects which have already taken place or for retrospective funding; projects which would normally be funded from statutory sources, i.e., Calderdale MBC, the local education authority, social services or central government; projects for the advancement of religion; projects where the main beneficiaries are animals; projects that do not directly benefit people living in Calderdale; political activities; applications made up entirely of core and/or running costs (exceptions may be made in extraordinary circumstances).

TYPE OF GRANT Revenue, capital, one-off.

RANGE OF GRANTS £100–£40,000 dependent upon scheme.

SAMPLE GRANTS North Kirklees Mind (£40,000); Calderdale Carers Project (£30,000); Mediation Yorkshire; Noah's Ark Community Cafe and Counselling Centre (£20,000 each); Scope Calderdale Community Outreach Service (£11,000); Women's Active project (£5,000); Huddersfield Taekwondo Club (£5,000); Batley Young Peoples Club (£2,000); Whiteknights Emergency Voluntary Service (£900); Mixenden Parents Resource Centre (£800) and Kirklees Transgender Support Group (£600).

FINANCES *Year* 2009–10 *Income* £2,303,415 *Grants* £1,548,916 *Assets* £6,702,260

TRUSTEES Leigh-Anne Stradeski; Brenda Hodgson; Rod Hodgson; Russell Earnshaw; Juliet Chambers; Jennifer Feather; Roger Moore; Clare Townley; John Mitchell; Stuart Rumney; Kate Moreton-Deakin; Wim Batist; Susannah Hammond; Carol Stevenson.

HOW TO APPLY The foundation's website has details of the grant schemes currently being administered. Application packs for all of the programmes are available to download from the website. Alternatively, contact the foundation directly and they will send a pack in the post. If you wish to discuss your project before applying, the grants team are always happy to answer any queries. The foundation also runs a monthly drop-in, where groups can go for advice and support on their applications.

WHO TO APPLY TO Danni Bailey, Senior Administrator, The 1855 Building (first floor), Discovery Road, Halifax HX1 2NG *Tel* 01422 349700 *Fax* 01422 350 017 *email* enquiries@cffc.co.uk *Website* www.cffc.co.uk

■ The Callander Charitable Trust

SC NO SC016609 **ESTABLISHED** 1972

WHERE FUNDING CAN BE GIVEN Falkirk, other parts of central Scotland and Galloway.

WHO CAN BENEFIT Charitable organisations.

WHAT IS FUNDED General charitable purposes.

WHAT IS NOT FUNDED No grants to individuals and non-registered charities.

FINANCES *Year* 2009–10 *Income* £58,385

HOW TO APPLY In writing to the correspondent.

WHO TO APPLY TO The Secretary, Morrisons, 53 Bothwell Street, Glasgow G2 6TS

■ Calleva Foundation

CC NO 1078808 **ESTABLISHED** 1999

WHERE FUNDING CAN BE GIVEN UK and worldwide.

WHO CAN BENEFIT Charitable organisations.

WHAT IS FUNDED Grants were categorised as follows: social services; children's holidays; overseas/international relief; education; arts and culture; medical research; and animal welfare.

FINANCES *Year* 2009 *Income* £256,470 *Grants* £213,070 *Assets* £84,577

TRUSTEES S C Butt; C Butt.

HOW TO APPLY In writing to the correspondent.

WHO TO APPLY TO The Trustees, 4 Cottesmore Gardens, London W8 5PR

■ Calouste Gulbenkian Foundation

ESTABLISHED 1956

WHERE FUNDING CAN BE GIVEN UK and the Republic of Ireland.

WHO CAN BENEFIT Registered charities or tax exempt organisations concerned with the arts, education, social change or Anglo-Portuguese cultural relations.

WHAT IS FUNDED The foundation is organised around programmes in four areas: cultural understanding; fulfilling potential; environment; innovation. The foundation develops its own work, initiatives and partnerships, and is not generally open to applications, with the exception of its Innovation Fund.

WHAT IS NOT FUNDED Work that does not have a direct benefit in the UK or the Republic of Ireland; Individuals; Curriculum based activities in statutory education; Student grants or scholarships for tuition and maintenance; Vocational training; Teaching or research posts or visiting fellowships; Educational resources and equipment; Gap year activities; Group or individual visits abroad, including to Portugal; Core services and standard provisions; Routine information and advice services; Capital costs for housing or the purchase, construction, repair or furnishing of buildings; Equipment, including vehicles, IT, or musical instruments; Scientific or medical research; Medicine or related therapies such as complementary medicine, hospices, counselling and therapy; Promoting religion or belief system; Publications; Website development; Sports; Holidays of any sort; Animal welfare.

TYPE OF GRANT Generally one-off grants, occasionally recurring for a maximum of three years.

RANGE OF GRANTS Average £5,000, with notional limit of £15,000.

SAMPLE GRANTS The Photographers' Gallery (£100,000); Manchester International Festival (£75,000); Botanic Gardens Conservation International (£60,000); Homeless Link (£55,000); Liverpool Biennial of Contemporary Art (£50,000); Clore Duffield Foundation (£45,000); Your Square Mile (£15,000); Social Innovation Camp (£8,000) Central Belfast CAB and Mead Gallery, Warwick Arts Centre (£5,000 each).

FINANCES *Year* 2010 *Grants* £2,210,500

TRUSTEES The foundation's Board of Administration in Lisbon. UK resident trustee: Martin Essayan.

PUBLICATIONS Advice to Applicants for Grants; publications catalogue. The UK Branch commissions and publishes a number of reports and books connected with its programmes of work in the arts, education and social change.

HOW TO APPLY 'How and when to apply – Innovation Fund only: outline ideas should be submitted by email using the Initial enquiry form which is available from the foundation's website. Initial enquiries can be sent in at any time of the year, but you should allow at least three months between this and the proposed starting date of your research period. Initial enquiries will be assessed in the context of other applications and, if short-listed, fuller information will be requested and applicants invited to discuss their project with us. We will specify the additional information we need and the date we require it by. After completion of this stage, final applications will be considered at one of our three annual trustee meetings. Please email the completed Initial Enquiry Form to: info@gulbenkian.org.uk.'

WHO TO APPLY TO Andrew Barnett, Director – UK Branch, 50 Hoxton Square, London N1 6PB *Tel* 020 7012 1400 *Fax* 020 7739 1961 *email* info@gulbenkian.org.uk *Website* www.gulbenkian.org.uk

■ The Calpe Trust

CC NO 1004193   **ESTABLISHED** 1990
WHERE FUNDING CAN BE GIVEN Worldwide.
WHO CAN BENEFIT Registered charities benefiting people in need including refugees, homeless people, people who are socially disadvantaged, victims of war, victims of disasters and so on.
WHAT IS FUNDED Grants towards human rights, health and welfare, emergencies and so on.
WHAT IS NOT FUNDED No grants towards animal welfare or to individuals.
SAMPLE GRANTS Ecumenical Project for International Cooperation Inc (£9,000); New Israel Fund, OXFAM and Salt of the Earth (£5,000 each); Samaritans (£4,000); the World Children's Fund (£1,000); and TRAX – Oxfordshire Motor Project (£400).
FINANCES *Year* 2009–10 *Income* £30,211 *Grants* £27,730 *Assets* £1,041,647
TRUSTEES R H L R Norton, Chair; B E M Norton; E R H Perks.
HOW TO APPLY In writing to the correspondent. Applicants must contact the trust before making an application.
WHO TO APPLY TO R Norton, Trustee, The Hideaway, Sandy Lane, Hatford Down, Faringdon, Oxfordshire SN7 8JH *Tel* 01367 870665 *email* reggienorton@talktalk.net

■ Calypso Browning Trust

CC NO 281986   **ESTABLISHED** 1979
WHERE FUNDING CAN BE GIVEN UK.
WHO CAN BENEFIT Organisations benefiting homeless people and animals.
WHAT IS FUNDED Regular grants made to some chosen charities but very occasionally to new charities in line with the trust's objects.
WHAT IS NOT FUNDED No grants to individuals.
SAMPLE GRANTS Notting Hill Housing Trust (£6,500); Kensington Housing Trust (£6,000); SHELTER (£4,500); Housing Associations Charitable Trust (£4,000); Brighton Housing Trust (£3,500); SPEAR (£1,600); People's Dispensary for Sick Animals and RSPCA (£1,200); and Dogs Trust and The Donkey Sanctuary (£500 each).
FINANCES *Year* 2009–10 *Income* £32,054 *Grants* £36,750 *Assets* £711,030
TRUSTEES A B S Weir; Ms A Kapp.
HOW TO APPLY In writing to the correspondent. Please note that most of the donations/grants are ongoing, as specified in the trust's deed.
WHO TO APPLY TO Michael Byrne, c/o Veale Wasbrough Vizards, Barnards Inn, 86 Fetter Lane, London EC4A 1AD

■ The Cambridgeshire Community Foundation

CC NO 1103314   **ESTABLISHED** 2003
WHERE FUNDING CAN BE GIVEN Cambridgeshire.
WHO CAN BENEFIT Voluntary and charitable groups.
WHAT IS FUNDED Community projects seeking to tackle a need or disadvantage. The foundation administers a number of funds. For up-to-date details, please see its website.
WHAT IS NOT FUNDED No retrospective grants.

TYPE OF GRANT One-off.
RANGE OF GRANTS The majority of the grants awarded are for small amounts of between £500– £5,000.
FINANCES *Year* 2009–10 *Income* £1,939,062 *Grants* £950,484 *Assets* £1,578,727
TRUSTEES Peter Gutteridge; Allyson Broadhurst; Anthony Clay; John Bridge; Nigel Atkinson; Bill Dastur; Mick Leggett; Richard Barnwell; Valerie Holt; Anne Ridgeon; Sam Weller.
OTHER INFORMATION 'We award grants from the funds that local individuals, companies, and local and national government set up with us. The funds have different criteria (including the amounts they give out) and on receiving your application we will match your request to the most appropriate fund (unfortunately we will not be able to find a match for all requests received).'
HOW TO APPLY Guidelines and application forms can be downloaded from the foundation's website.
WHO TO APPLY TO Jane Darlington, Chief Executive, The Quorum, Barnwell Road, Cambridge CB5 8RE *Tel* 01223 410535 *email* info@cambscf.org.uk *Website* www.cambscf.org.uk

■ The Cambridgeshire Historic Churches Trust

CC NO 287486   **ESTABLISHED** 1983
WHERE FUNDING CAN BE GIVEN Cambridgeshire.
WHO CAN BENEFIT Bodies responsible for the upkeep, repair and maintenance of a church, chapel or other building used for public worship.
WHAT IS FUNDED The preservation, repair, maintenance, improvement, upkeep and reconstruction of churches in the county of Cambridge and the monuments, fittings, fixtures, stained glass, furniture, ornaments and chattels in such churches and the churchyards belonging to any such churches.
WHAT IS NOT FUNDED Grants are not usually available for additional building work, re-ordering, re-decoration or minor programmes of maintenance.
TYPE OF GRANT The grants scheme is funded from an annual payment made by Waste Recycling Environmental and is resourced entirely from Landfill Tax credits assigned by Waste Recycling plc.
RANGE OF GRANTS From £1,000–£7,000 primarily for urgent repairs to fabric or renewal of essential services in churches and chapels.
FINANCES *Year* 2009–10 *Income* £42,825 *Grants* £61,500 *Assets* £640,663
TRUSTEES Richard Halsey; Pamela, Lady Wedgwood; Ven. Richard Sledge; Everard Poole; Julian Limentani; Dr John Maddison; Revd. Canon Christopher Barber; Revd David Thompson.
PUBLICATIONS Newsletter.
HOW TO APPLY For further information on how to apply, please see the trust's website.
WHO TO APPLY TO David Collingswood, Grants Officer, 21 The Pasture, Somersham, Huntingdon PE28 3YX *Tel* 01487 741171 *email* grants@cambshistoricchurchestrust.co.uk *Website* www.cambshistoricchurchestrust.co.uk

■ The Camelia trust

CC NO 1081074   **ESTABLISHED** 2000
WHERE FUNDING CAN BE GIVEN Liverpool City and Manchester City.
WHO CAN BENEFIT Charitable organisations.
WHAT IS FUNDED General charitable purposes.

RANGE OF GRANTS Up to £6,000.

SAMPLE GRANTS Christies (£5,200); Henshaw (£4,000); Mobility (£3,000); Sense (£2,700); Tetten Theatre (£2,600); Harvest Trust (£2,500); the Salvation Army (£2,000); Live At Home (£1,500); and Tall Ships Trust, React, Crimestoppers and Contact a Family (£1,000 each).

FINANCES *Year* 2009–10 *Income* £31,836 *Grants* £38,430

TRUSTEES Jennifer Sykes, Dr Prudence Gillett; David Sykes; Michael Taxman.

HOW TO APPLY In writing to the correspondent.

WHO TO APPLY TO Jennifer Sykes, Trustee, Hillside, 9 Wainwright Road, Altrincham, Cheshire WA1 4 4BW

■ The Campden Charities Trustee

CC NO 1104616   **ESTABLISHED** 1629

WHERE FUNDING CAN BE GIVEN The former parish of Kensington, London; a north-south corridor, roughly from north of the Fulham Road to the north of Ladbroke Grove (a map can be viewed on the website).

WHO CAN BENEFIT Individuals and non-statutory not for profit organisations which refer and support individuals.

WHAT IS FUNDED Supporting outcomes for disadvantaged people, particularly young people and adults who have experienced a long period of unemployment.

WHAT IS NOT FUNDED UK charities or charities outside Kensington, unless they are of significant benefit to Kensington residents; schemes or activities which are generally regarded as the responsibility of the statutory authorities; UK fundraising appeals; environmental projects unless connected with education or social need; medical research or equipment; animal welfare; advancement of religion or religious groups, unless they offer non-religious services to the community; commercial and business activities; endowment appeals; projects of a political nature; retrospective capital grants.

TYPE OF GRANT One-off and recurrent funding for buildings, capital, core costs, feasibility studies and full project costs. Pensions to older people, grants in cash or in kind to relieve need, bursaries and all kinds of grants to Kensington-based organisations.

RANGE OF GRANTS £1,000–£119,000.

SAMPLE GRANTS Westway Community Transport (£112,000); Nucleus Legal Advice Centre (£52,000); My Generation (£42,000); Blenheim Project (£30,000); Earls Court YMCA (£30,000); and NOVA (£5,000); London Cyrenians (£4,000); Bramley Sheltered Scheme and Christian Alliance Housing Association (£2,000 each); and Off the Streets and Into Work Sixty Plus (£1,000 each).

FINANCES *Year* 2009–10 *Income* £2,441,552 *Grants* £397,500 *Assets* £90,266,150

TRUSTEES Revd Gillean Craig, Chair; David Banks; Elisabeth Brockmann; Chris Calman; Dr Kit Davis; Steve Hoier; Susan Lockhart; Tim Martin; Terry Myers; Ben Pilling; Victoria Stark; Richard Walker-Arnott; Ms M Rodkina; C Williams.

OTHER INFORMATION An additional £1.6 million was given in grants to individuals.

HOW TO APPLY 'The charity is trying to target its resources where they can be of the most direct benefit to financially disadvantaged individuals. The charity therefore **does not** receive unsolicited applications for funding from organisations. However the charity's officers are eager to meet with colleagues from other not-for-profit organisations to explore ways in which we can work together to help individuals to end dependency on benefits or improve a low wage. If you have contact with individuals whom you would like to refer, please telephone the correspondent on: 020 7313 3797.'

WHO TO APPLY TO Chris Stannard, Clerk to the Trustees, 27a Pembridge Villas, London W11 3EP *Tel* 020 7243 0551 *Fax* 020 7229 4920 *Website* www.cctrustee.org.uk

■ The Frederick and Phyllis Cann Trust

CC NO 1087863   **ESTABLISHED** 1998

WHERE FUNDING CAN BE GIVEN Northamptonshire.

WHO CAN BENEFIT The Trust Deed names seven charities, but trustees are prepared to consider other charities that fall within the charitable objects of the trust.

WHAT IS FUNDED The main objects of the trust are animal welfare, welfare of children and safety at sea.

RANGE OF GRANTS Up to £10,000.

SAMPLE GRANTS Macmillan Cancer Support (£10,000); Lakeland Day Care Hospice, Northampton Association of Youth Clubs and The Salvation Army (£5,000 each); PETA and Livability (£4,000 each); The Donkey Sanctuary (£3,500); Listening Books and Children's Aid Team (£3,000 each); Asthma Relief (£2,000); MS Therapy Centre (£1,500) and Handicapped Children (£1,000).

FINANCES *Year* 2010–11 *Income* £65,643 *Grants* £56,500 *Assets* £2,031,562

TRUSTEES Michael Percival; David Sharp; Keith Panter; Philip Saunderson; Christopher Toller; Laura Steedman.

HOW TO APPLY In writing to the correspondent.

WHO TO APPLY TO Mrs Gill Evans, c/o Hewitsons, 7 Spencer Parade, Northampton NN1 5AB *Tel* 01604 233233

■ The Canning Trust

CC NO 292675   **ESTABLISHED** 1985

WHERE FUNDING CAN BE GIVEN UK and the developing world.

WHO CAN BENEFIT Small concerns.

WHAT IS FUNDED Only donations proposed internally by staff members.

RANGE OF GRANTS Up to £10,000.

SAMPLE GRANTS Previous beneficiaries included: Village Water (£10,000); Tushar Project – Herbertpur Christian Hospital (£4,000); Dogodogo Centre, Softpower and TESFA (£3,000 each); Alive and Kicking (£2,100); Kafue Fisheries (£2,000); St Mary's National School (£1,600); and Loldia (£1,000).

FINANCES *Year* 2009–10 *Income* £4,355 *Grants* £30,000

TRUSTEES Mrs R R Pooley; Mrs R Griffiths; H Moore; K Mecner.

HOW TO APPLY Unsolicited applications are not considered. The trust states that it generally only makes grants to charities which staff; ex-staff and friends are directly involved with.

WHO TO APPLY TO The Trustees, 593–599 Fulham Road, London SW6 5UA *Tel* 020 7381 7410

■ M R Cannon 1998 Charitable Trust

cc no 1072769   **established** 1998
where funding can be given Preference for North Devon, Dorset, Bristol, North Yorkshire and County Durham.
who can benefit Charities and community groups.
what is funded 'The objectives of the charity are general charitable purposes to the benefit of the general public. The trustees have no specific grant making criteria but are interested in supporting medical/health charities and conservation and countryside related initiatives, as well as small local projects in North Devon, Dorset, Bristol, North Yorkshire and County Durham. The trustees also support young people who wish to carry out vocational training or studies.'
range of grants Up to £5,000.
sample grants Previous beneficiaries have included: Wings South West (£5,000); Portsmouth Cathedral and Second Chance (£2,000); Forget Me Not (£1,500); Countryside Foundation for Education (£1,000); North Devon Hospice (£1,000 in two grants); Appledore Arts and Peters Church – Bratton Fleming (£250); Devon and Somerset Air Ambulance (£200); Alwington PCC, Canine Partners, Children's Hospice South West and Dorset Wildlife Trust (£100 each); and RSPCA (£50).
finances *Year* 2009–10 *Income* £6,845 *Grants* £65,000
trustees M R Cannon; Mrs S A T Cannon; C J Mitchell.
how to apply In writing to the correspondent.
who to apply to The Trustees, 53 Stoke Lane, Westbury On Trym, Bristol BS9 3DW

■ H and L Cantor Trust

cc no 220300   **established** 1959
where funding can be given UK, with some preference for Sheffield.
who can benefit Registered charities, with particular consideration to be given to Jewish charities.
what is funded Jewish causes and general charitable purposes.
range of grants Up to £15,000.
sample grants Previous beneficiaries include: Delamere Forest School Ltd, Sheffield Jewish Congregation & Centre, Sheffield Jewish Welfare Organisation, I Rescue, Jewish Childs Day, Sense, Share Zadek UK, Brain Research Trust, PDSA Sheffield and World Cancer Research.
finances *Year* 2009–10 *Income* £11,575 *Grants* £10,000
trustees Lily Cantor; Nicholas Jeffrey.
other information Due to the trust's low income in 2009–10, only basic financial information was available from the Charity Commission.
how to apply Unsolicited applications are not invited.
who to apply to Lilly Cantor, Trustee, 3 Ivy Park Court, 35 Ivy Park Road, Sheffield S10 3LA

■ Cardy Beaver Foundation

cc no 265763   **established** 1973
where funding can be given UK with preference for Berkshire.
who can benefit National and local registered charities.
what is funded General charitable purposes.
what is not funded Registered charities only.

range of grants Usually under £5,000.
sample grants Cancer Research UK, Watermill Theatre Appeal, Wallingford Museum, NSPCC, Berkshire Blind Society, Adventure Dolphin, St Peter's PCC, Church House Trust, RNLI and Asthma Relief (£5,000 each); Julia's House and Elizabeth Foundation (£2,500 each); Com Exchange – Newbury (£2,000); and Pangbourne Fete 2010 (£500).
finances *Year* 2009–10 *Income* £93,425 *Grants* £177,500 *Assets* £2,298,825
trustees John James; Mary Cardy; Sandra Rice.
how to apply In writing to the correspondent.
who to apply to Sandra Rice, Trustee, Clifton House, 17 Reading Road, Pangbourne, Berkshire RG8 7LU *Tel* 0118 984 4713

■ The Carew Pole Charitable Trust

cc no 255375   **established** 1968
where funding can be given UK, in practice, mainly Cornwall.
who can benefit Donations normally made only to registered charities, but applications will be considered from individuals for non-full-time education purposes.
what is funded General charitable purposes principally in Cornwall. In the case of support to churches and village halls, donations are in practice only made to those in the immediate vicinity to Antony House, Torpoint or to those with connections to the Carew Pole Family.
what is not funded The trustees do not support applications from individuals for full-time education.
range of grants Up to £15,000.
sample grants Antony Parochial Church Council (£15,000); Cornwall Community Foundation, Royal Horticultural Society and Royal Institution of Cornwall (£5,000 each); National Trust (£3,500); Royal Academy, Tate Gallery, and Sand Rose Project (£1,500 each); the Army Benevolent Fund and Young Carers Cornwall (£1,000 each); Cornwall Disability Arts Group, Farming and Wildlife Advisory Group and Happy Days Children's Charity (£500 each); and RNLI (£250).
finances *Year* 2009–10 *Income* £63,403 *Grants* £55,640 *Assets* £1,940,012
trustees T J Carew Pole; J Kitson; J Williams.
other information This charitable trust was founded by Sir John Gawen Carew Pole, whose family has both lived in and been connected with Cornwall for many years.
how to apply In writing to the correspondent. The trustees consider and approve major donations in November each year, while other smaller appeals are considered, and donations made, throughout the year.
who to apply to Paul Cressy, The Antony Estate Office, Antony, Torpoint, Cornwall PL11 3AB

■ The D W T Cargill Fund

sc no SC012703   **established** 1939
where funding can be given UK, with a preference for the West of Scotland.
who can benefit Registered charities.
what is funded General charitable purposes, particularly religious causes, medical charities and help for older people.
what is not funded No grants are made to individuals.
type of grant One-off and recurrent.
sample grants Previous beneficiaries have included: City of Glasgow Society of Social

Think carefully about every application. Is it justified?

421

Service, Colquhoun Bequest Fund for Incurables, Crathie Opportunity Holidays, Glasgow and West of Scotland Society for the Blind, Glasgow City Mission, Greenock Medical Aid Society, North Glasgow Community Forum, Scottish Maritime Museum – Irvine, Scottish Episcopal Church, Scottish Motor Neurone Disease Association, Lead Scotland and Three Towns Blind Bowling/Social Club.

FINANCES *Year* 2008–09 *Income* £223,811 *Grants* £200,000

TRUSTEES A C Fyfe; W G Peacock; N A Fyfe; Mirren Elizabeth Graham.

HOW TO APPLY In writing to the correspondent, supported by up-to-date accounts. Trustees meet quarterly.

WHO TO APPLY TO Norman A Fyfe, Trustee, Miller Beckett and Jackson Solicitors, 190 St Vincent Street, Glasgow G2 5SP

■ Carlee Ltd

CC NO 282873   **ESTABLISHED** 1981

WHERE FUNDING CAN BE GIVEN Worldwide.

WHO CAN BENEFIT Talmudic scholars and Jewish people.

WHAT IS FUNDED The advancement of religion in accordance with the orthodox Jewish faith; the relief of poverty; general charitable purposes.

SAMPLE GRANTS Previous beneficiaries have included Antryvale Ltd, Asos Cheshed, Egerton Road Building Fund, Glasgow Kollel, HTVC, Rav Chesed Trust, Tevini, Union of Hebrew Congregations, YHS and YHTC.

FINANCES *Year* 2008–09 *Income* £181,024 *Grants* £313,495 *Assets* £293,452

TRUSTEES Hershel Grunhut; Mrs P Grunhut; Bernard Dor Stroh; Mrs B Stroh.

OTHER INFORMATION Accounts for the year 2009–10 were overdue at the Charity Commission at the time of writing.

HOW TO APPLY In writing to the correspondent.

WHO TO APPLY TO The Secretary, 32 Pagent Road, London N16 5NQ

■ The Carlsson Family Foundation

CC NO 1072954   **ESTABLISHED** 1998

WHERE FUNDING CAN BE GIVEN UK.

WHO CAN BENEFIT Charitable organisations.

WHAT IS FUNDED The promotion of the health and educational welfare of disadvantaged children and their families. 'Committed to this principle the foundation aims: to assist children in poverty with special reference to those in one parent families; to promote child and family welfare, including physical, emotional and mental well-being; to foster the intellectual and personal development of children to promote and encourage a strong sense of responsibility with an emphasis on co-operation and self-help among families; to relate in creative and innovative ways with other charities and social agencies in the wider field of child poverty; to raise consciousness by building educational and communication networks within financial, political and cultural spheres.'

SAMPLE GRANTS Previous beneficiaries include: Georgetown University (£251,000) and St Mary's School – Ascot (£7,200).

FINANCES *Year* 2009–10 *Income* £365,754 *Grants* £500,000 *Assets* £1,531,046

TRUSTEES Roger Carlsson; Courtney Carlsson; Carina Carlsson; Carrie Hague; Matthew Hunt.

OTHER INFORMATION The only grant beneficiary for the year 2009–10 was London Business School, which received £500,000.

HOW TO APPLY In writing to the correspondent.

WHO TO APPLY TO The Trustees, Binfield Court, Church Lane, Binfield, Berkshire RG42 5PJ *email* info@thecarlssonfamilyfoundation.org.uk

■ The Carlton House Charitable Trust

CC NO 296791   **ESTABLISHED** 1986

WHERE FUNDING CAN BE GIVEN UK and overseas.

WHO CAN BENEFIT Charitable organisations and Jewish organisations.

WHAT IS FUNDED The advancement of education, research work and fellowships. Most funds are committed to various charitable institutions in the UK and abroad; a limited number of bursaries are given, mainly connected with the professional interests of the trustees.

TYPE OF GRANT One-off.

RANGE OF GRANTS £35–£9,000.

SAMPLE GRANTS Western Marble Arch Synagogue (£4,500); Community Security Trust (£2,500); Bnai Brith Hillel Foundation, National Trust and Westminster Advocacy Service (£2,000 each); Royal Academy of Music and Imperial College (£1,000 each); British Technion Society and London Philharmonic Orchestra (£500); Nightingale House (£250) and Magon David Adorn (£150).

FINANCES *Year* 2009–10 *Income* £56,727 *Grants* £31,411 *Assets* £1,035,028

TRUSTEES S Cohen; P G Cohen; F A Stein.

OTHER INFORMATION Grants were made totalling £30,000 ranging from £100–£4,500. Grants for £100 or less were given to 153 organisations.

HOW TO APPLY In writing to the correspondent.

WHO TO APPLY TO Stewart S Cohen, Trustee, Craven House, 121 Kingsway, London WC2B 6PA *Tel* 020 7242 5283

■ The Worshipful Company of Carmen Benevolent Trust

CC NO 1050893   **ESTABLISHED** 1995

WHERE FUNDING CAN BE GIVEN City of London and UK.

WHO CAN BENEFIT People connected with transport.

WHAT IS FUNDED Objects of relieving necessitous past or present Liverymen or Freemen of the Company, its employees and servants, or those connected with transport in the UK. The trust is also allowed to made grants to any charitable fund in the City of London or elsewhere.

RANGE OF GRANTS £100–£6,000.

SAMPLE GRANTS Give Them a Sporting Chance (£13,000); Variety Club Children's Charity (£10,000); King Edwards Witely (£6,000); Prince's Charities Foundation and Friends of Moorfield Eye Hospital (£5,000 each); Treloar Trust (£2,500); City of London Freemans School (£1,800); Dream Holidays (£1,100); Jumbulance, Mencap and St Mungo's (£1,000 each); Mobility Trust, Sussex Cancer and Tower Hamlets Opportunities Group (£500 each).

FINANCES *Year* 2009–10 *Income* £146,969 *Grants* £86,925 *Assets* £1,060,019

TRUSTEES J A T Saywell; M J Power; Brig. M H Turner; M W J Older; Mrs M Bonar; M Simpkin; R H Russett.

HOW TO APPLY In writing to the correspondent.

WHO TO APPLY TO Robin East, The Hon. Secretary, Five Kings House, 1 Queen Street Place, London EC4R 1QS *Tel* 020 7489 8289 *email* bentrust@thecarmen.co.uk *Website* www.thecarmen.co.uk

■ The Richard Carne Trust

CC NO 1115903   ESTABLISHED 2006
WHERE FUNDING CAN BE GIVEN UK.
WHO CAN BENEFIT Young people.
WHAT IS FUNDED The performing arts.
RANGE OF GRANTS Up to £50,000 to organisations.
SAMPLE GRANTS Previous beneficiaries included: Royal College of Music (£50,000); Royal Academy of Dramatic Art (£30,000); London Academy of Music and Drama (£25,000); Royal Welsh College of Music and Drama (£20,000); Classical Opera Company and Trinity College of Music (£10,000 each); South Bank Sinfonia (£7,000); Rakhi Sing/Barbiroili Quartet (£4,000); and ENO Young Singers Programme (£2,500).
FINANCES *Year* 2010 *Income* £20,053 *Grants* £109,000
TRUSTEES Kleinwort Benson Trustees Ltd; Philip Edward Carne; Marjorie Christine Carne.
HOW TO APPLY 'The trustees' current policy is to consider all written appeals received, but only successful applications are notified of the trustees' decision. [...] The trustees review the selected charities, and consider new appeals received at their annual trustee meeting, normally held in June. Only successful applicants are notified of the trustees' decision.'
WHO TO APPLY TO Christopher Gilbert, Administrator, Kleinwort Benson Trustees Ltd, 14 St George Street, London W1S 1FE *Tel* 020 3207 7356

■ The Carnegie Dunfermline Trust

SC NO SC015710   ESTABLISHED 1903
WHERE FUNDING CAN BE GIVEN Dunfermline and Rosyth.
WHO CAN BENEFIT Local communities, clubs and societies.
WHAT IS FUNDED 'Projects, activities and schemes with social, community, educational, cultural, sport and recreational purposes for the benefit of those within the defined geographic area of the operation of the Trust. We look for proposals that are innovative and far reaching together with those that particularly impact on young people. We are also interested in active partnerships where organisations decide to work together and adopt a joint approach. Start-up funding is offered on a one-off basis. Additional guidelines are available for schools.'
WHAT IS NOT FUNDED Individuals; closed groups (with the exception of those catering for specialist needs); political, military or sectarian bodies; activities out of the geographic scope of the trust; medical organisations; routine running or salary costs; costs which are the responsibility of a government body.
TYPE OF GRANT Principally single grants and capital funding. Pump priming and start up funding is offered on a one off basis.
RANGE OF GRANTS Typical grant between £300 and £10,000.
SAMPLE GRANTS Eco City Project (£10,000); Hearts and Minds (£6,000); Headroom (£4,000); Dunfermline Knights Cricket Club and Fordell Firs (£2,000 each) and Dunfermline City Hockey Club (£400).

FINANCES *Year* 2010 *Income* £328,089
TRUSTEES The trust has a board of 20 trustees.
HOW TO APPLY On a form which can be downloaded from the trust's website. 'Trustees meet every two months and applications can be submitted at any time. Application forms are available from the website or from the office and initial discussion with the Grants Officer is encouraged. Where possible applications will be acknowledged and further information may be sought. Once all the necessary background is available the application will be considered by the appropriate assessing trustee in the first instance who will decide if a grant under delegated powers is applicable, if it should go to the board, or if it is not suitable to progress. When a grant is awarded the recipient will be notified in writing with any related terms and conditions which will include the take up of the grant within a twenty four month period. If an application is unsuccessful, the trust is unlikely to consider a further application within twelve months.'
WHO TO APPLY TO Elaine Stewart, Grants Officer, Andrew Carnegie House, Pittencieff Street, Dunfermline KY12 8AW *Tel* 01383 749789 *Fax* 01383 749799 *email* grants@carnegietrust.com *Website* www.andrewcarnegie.co.uk

■ The Carnegie Trust for the Universities of Scotland

SC NO SC015600   ESTABLISHED 1901
WHERE FUNDING CAN BE GIVEN Scotland.
WHO CAN BENEFIT Undergraduates of Scottish birth, Scottish parentage or Scottish schooling; graduates and members of staff of the Scottish universities.
WHAT IS FUNDED Universities in Scotland through the improvement of facilities and support of research. Graduates and members of staff of Scottish universities, and undergraduates of Scottish birth or extraction for fees for first degrees at Scottish universities.
TYPE OF GRANT Capital for projects of value to the Scottish universities, with wide discretion on what is allowable.
FINANCES *Year* 2009–10 *Income* £2,596,234 *Grants* £1,965,873
TRUSTEES 12 nominated trustees and 14 ex-officio trustees.
OTHER INFORMATION All of the trust's schemes are described in detail on its website.
HOW TO APPLY Regulations and application forms can be obtained from the secretary and from the website. Preliminary telephone enquiries are welcome.
WHO TO APPLY TO The Secretary, Andrew Carnegie House, Pittencrieff Street, Dunfermline, Fife KY12 8AW *Tel* 01383 724990 *email* jgray@carnegie-trust.org *Website* www.carnegie-trust.org

■ The Carpenter Charitable Trust

CC NO 280692   ESTABLISHED 1980
WHERE FUNDING CAN BE GIVEN UK and overseas.
WHO CAN BENEFIT Humanitarian and Christian outreach charities are preferred.
WHAT IS FUNDED General charitable objects with a Christian bias. 'The charity is established on wide grant giving terms. The trustees continue to pursue their 'preferred' list approach – a list

of charities with which the trustees have developed a good relationship over the years.'

WHAT IS NOT FUNDED 'The trustees do not consider applications for church repairs (other than in respect of Kimpton Church) nor applications from individuals nor any applications received from abroad unless clearly 'sponsored' by an established charity based in England and Wales.'

TYPE OF GRANT One-off (but some are in practice repeated).

RANGE OF GRANTS £250–£2,500.

SAMPLE GRANTS Previously: Mission Aviation Fellowship Europe (£7,500); ORBIS Charitable Trust (£6,000); Andrew Christian Trust, Barnabas Fund, Help in Suffering UK and Relationships Foundation (£5,000 each); DEC Bangladesh (£2,500); Brooke Hospital for Animals, Crisis UK, Merlin and Salvation Army (£1,000 each); Blue Cross, Fight for Sight, Mercy Ships, Prison Fellowship, RSPB, Send a Cow and Tibet Relief (£500 each); and Cats Protection League (£250).

FINANCES *Year* 2009–10 *Income* £19,013 *Grants* £80,000

TRUSTEES M S E Carpenter; G M L Carpenter.

HOW TO APPLY In writing to the correspondent including sufficient details to enable a decision to be made. However, as about half the donations made are repeat grants, the amount available for unsolicited applications remains small.

WHO TO APPLY TO M S E Carpenter, Trustee, The Old Vicarage, Hitchin Road, Kimpton, Hitchin, Hertfordshire SG4 8EF

■ The Carpenters' Company Charitable Trust

CC NO 276996   **ESTABLISHED** 1978

WHERE FUNDING CAN BE GIVEN UK.

WHO CAN BENEFIT Individuals and schools, colleges, universities and other charitable organisations promoting the craft of carpentry.

WHAT IS FUNDED Charitable causes benefiting from grants include organisations supporting the elderly, disabled, homeless, youth and children, education, medical and museums. Craft causes receive a high priority when awards are considered.

WHAT IS NOT FUNDED Grants are not normally made to individual churches or cathedrals, or to educational establishments having no association to the Carpenters' Company. No grants (except educational grants) are made to individual applicants. Funds are usually only available to charities registered with the charity commission or exempt from registration.

SAMPLE GRANTS The Building Crafts College (£731,000).

FINANCES *Year* 2009–10 *Income* £953,995 *Grants* £1,065,262 *Assets* £18,627,445

TRUSTEES Peter A Luton; Malcolm R Francis; Michael I Montague-Smith; Guy Morton-Smith.

HOW TO APPLY In writing to the correspondent.

WHO TO APPLY TO The Clerk, Carpenters' Hall, 1 Throgmorton Avenue, London EC2N 2JJ *Tel* 020 7588 7001 *email* info@carpentersco. com *Website* www.carpentersco.com/ charitable_ccct.php

■ The Carr-Gregory Trust

CC NO 1085580   **ESTABLISHED** 2001

WHERE FUNDING CAN BE GIVEN UK.

WHO CAN BENEFIT Charitable organisations.

WHAT IS FUNDED Arts, social welfare, health and education.

RANGE OF GRANTS Up to £11,000.

SAMPLE GRANTS Grant beneficiaries included: the Royal National Theatre (£11,000); The Royal Academy of Music (£7,000); University of Bristol (£3,000); Alzheimer's Society (£2,000); Calibre Audio Library, Help the Hospices and Prisoner's Education Trust (£1,000 each); The Salvation Army, St Mungo's and The Stroke Foundation (£500 each).

FINANCES *Year* 2010 *Income* £53,537 *Grants* £51,650 *Assets* £458,950

TRUSTEES Russ Carr; Heather Wheelhouse; Linda Carr; H J Nicholls.

OTHER INFORMATION Grants ranging from £500– £11,000 were made to 29 organisations. A further £2,750 was expended for grants totalling £500 or less each.

HOW TO APPLY In writing to the correspondent.

WHO TO APPLY TO Russ Carr, Trustee, 56 Pembroke Road, Clifton, Bristol BS8 3DT

■ The Carrington Charitable Trust

CC NO 265824   **ESTABLISHED** 1973

WHERE FUNDING CAN BE GIVEN UK with a preference for Buckinghamshire.

WHO CAN BENEFIT Local branches of a wide range of charities, and local charities.

WHAT IS FUNDED General charitable purposes.

WHAT IS NOT FUNDED No grants to individuals.

RANGE OF GRANTS Up to £21,000, mostly for smaller amounts.

SAMPLE GRANTS Grenadier Guards – Colonel's Fund (£16,000); Combat Stress (£15,000); Garsington Opera (£13,000); Hope and Homes for Children (£2,500); Bledlow PCC (Holy Trinity Church) (£1,000); Help for Heroes (£750); Aylesbury Grammar School Foundation, Coombe Hill Monument Appeal and Hospice of St Francis (£500 each); Friends of Kew Gardens (£85); Chiltern Open Air Museum (£50) and Bucks Archaeological Society (£12).

FINANCES *Year* 2010–11 *Income* £84,030 *Grants* £59,772 *Assets* £4,776,748

TRUSTEES Rt Hon. Lord Carrington; J A Cloke; Rt Hon. V Carrington.

HOW TO APPLY In writing to the correspondent.

WHO TO APPLY TO J A Cloke, Trustee, c/o Cloke and Co, 475 Salisbury House, London Wall, London EC2M 5QQ

■ The Carron Charitable Settlement

CC NO 289164   **ESTABLISHED** 1984

WHERE FUNDING CAN BE GIVEN UK and overseas.

WHO CAN BENEFIT Charitable organisations.

WHAT IS FUNDED 'The trust was created for charitable purposes in connection with wildlife, education, medicine, the countryside and the printing and publishing trade.' Ongoing support is given to the St Bride's Church – Fleet Street.

WHAT IS NOT FUNDED No grants to individuals.

TYPE OF GRANT Project, research, running costs and salaries.

SAMPLE GRANTS Previous beneficiaries included: St Bride's Church Appeal (£20,000); INTBAU (£10,000); Academy of Aviation and Space

Medicine (£3,000); and Curwen Print Study Centre (£1,500).

FINANCES *Year* 2009–10 *Income* £6,204 *Grants* £36,437

TRUSTEES P G Fowler; W M Allen; D L Morgan.

OTHER INFORMATION There was a significant drop in income during the year (£6,000 2009/10) compared to previous years (£77,000 2007/08).

HOW TO APPLY The trust does not invite applications from the general public.

WHO TO APPLY TO Ms Carolyn Cox, c/o Rothman Panthall and Co., 10 Romsey Road, Eastleigh, Hampshire SO50 9AL *Tel* 023 8061 4555

■ The Leslie Mary Carter Charitable Trust

CC NO 284782   **ESTABLISHED** 1982

WHERE FUNDING CAN BE GIVEN UK, with a preference for Norfolk, Suffolk and North Essex.

WHO CAN BENEFIT Registered charities.

WHAT IS FUNDED The preferred areas for grant giving are conservation/environment and welfare causes. Other applications will be considered but acknowledgements may not always be sent. Trustees prefer well thought-out applications for larger gifts, than many applications for smaller grants.

WHAT IS NOT FUNDED No grants to individuals.

TYPE OF GRANT Capital including buildings, core costs, one-off, project, research, running costs and recurring costs will be considered.

RANGE OF GRANTS Grants generally range from £500–£5,000, but larger grants are sometimes considered.

SAMPLE GRANTS Norfolk Wildlife Trust and St Elizabeth Hospice (£10,000 each); Campaign to Protect Rural England, Colchester Archaeological Trust and Combat Stress (£5,000 each); Barn Owl Trust and Waveney Stardust (£3,000 each); Bat Conservation Trust and Witham Boys' Brigade (£2,000 each); and RSPB and Suffolk Preservation Society (£1,000 each).

FINANCES *Year* 2010 *Income* £156,208 *Grants* £104,500 *Assets* £3,030,271

TRUSTEES Miss L M Carter; S R M Wilson; Martyn Carr.

HOW TO APPLY In writing to the correspondent. Telephone calls are not welcome. There is no need to enclose an sae unless applicants wish to have materials returned. Applications made outside the preferred areas for grant giving will be considered, but acknowledgements may not always be sent.

WHO TO APPLY TO Sam Wilson, Trustee, c/o Birketts, 24–26 Museum Street, Ipswich IP1 1HZ *Tel* 01473 232300

■ Carter's Educational Foundation

CC NO 528161   **ESTABLISHED** 1888

WHERE FUNDING CAN BE GIVEN The ancient parish of Wilford.

WHO CAN BENEFIT The trust supports the South Wilford Endowed Church of England School. It may also give grants to individuals under 25 living in the ancient parish and organisations for such people, with a broadly educational nature, operating within the beneficial area of the ancient parish of Wilford, Nottingham, including Wilford Village, Silverdale, Compton Acres, part of West Bridgford mainly west of Loughborough Road, and parts of the south of the Meadows.

WHAT IS FUNDED Education.

WHAT IS NOT FUNDED No grants to anyone living outside the ancient parish of Wilford, Nottingham or any organisation based outside of that area.

FINANCES *Year* 2010 *Income* £206,791 *Grants* £103,785 *Assets* £6,031,082

TRUSTEES Paula Hammond; Robert Stanley; P Wicks; Cllr T Spencer; Madeleine Cox; R Nettleship (Chair); R Hutchins; P Hammond; R W Stanley; P Wicks; Cllr T Spencer.

HOW TO APPLY Subject to the availability of funds, grants to voluntary charitable organisations in the ancient parish are normally considered at the same time as educational grants for individuals and awarded on the basis of the school year. Trustees meet four times a year however letters of application should be with the clerk to the foundation before 31 May. Letters should identify the base for the organisation's work, outline the nature of the activities involved and the approximate number of young people participating from the ancient parish. If this is the first application from your organisation, please give full details and include a copy of your latest accounts. Applications must be made in writing.

WHO TO APPLY TO S Morrant, Pennine House, 8 Stanford Street, Nottingham NG1 7BQ *Tel* 0115 958 6262 *Website* www.wilford-carters-education.org.uk

---

■ The Carvill Trust

CC NO 1036420   **ESTABLISHED** 1994

WHERE FUNDING CAN BE GIVEN UK.

WHO CAN BENEFIT Registered charities.

WHAT IS FUNDED General charitable purposes.

SAMPLE GRANTS Previous beneficiaries included: Irish Youth Foundation (£14,000); and Academy Ocean Reef and War Child (£10,000 each).

FINANCES *Year* 2009–10 *Income* £13,471 *Grants* £50,000

TRUSTEES R K Carvill; R E Pooley; K D Tuson.

HOW TO APPLY In writing to the correspondent, although the trust states that it only supports beneficiaries known to or connected with the trustees. Unsolicited applications from individuals will not be supported.

WHO TO APPLY TO K D Tuson, Trustee, 5th Floor, Minories House, 2–5 Minories, London EC3N 1BJ *Tel* 020 7780 6900

■ The Casey Trust

CC NO 1055726   **ESTABLISHED** 1996

WHERE FUNDING CAN BE GIVEN UK and developing countries.

WHO CAN BENEFIT Charities benefiting children.

WHAT IS FUNDED Children and young people in the UK and developing countries by supporting new projects.

WHAT IS NOT FUNDED Grants are not given to 'individual applicants requesting funds to continue studies or travel'.

TYPE OF GRANT £750–£10,000. The average grant was for £1,943.

SAMPLE GRANTS Norwood (£10,000); World Medical Fund (£8,000); World Jewish Relief (£5,000); Kisharon (£4,000); Voces Cantabiles Music (£3,500); FRODO (£3,000); the Movement Centre (£2,500); Anit-Slavery, Action for Kids and Headstart for Babies (£2,000 each); TSYJ Transplant Active, the Children's Adventure Farm Trust, the Cruse Bereavement Centre and Theodora Trust (£1,500 each); Computer Aid International, Hospices of Hope, Philharmonia

Think carefully about every application. Is it justified?

425

Orchestra, Books Abroad and Lennox Children's Cancer Fund (£1,000 each).

FINANCES *Year* 2009–10 *Income* £113,979 *Grants* £117,385 *Assets* £2,673,446

TRUSTEES Kenneth Howard; Edwin Green; Hon. Judge Leonard Krikler.

HOW TO APPLY 'Not being a reactive trust, it is regretted that the trustees will be unable to respond to the majority of requests for assistance. In order to both reduce costs and administration the trustees will respond mainly to those charitable institutions known to them. There is no application form.'

WHO TO APPLY TO Kenneth Howard, Trustee, 27 Arkwright Road, London NW3 6BJ

■ Cash for Kids – Radio Clyde

SC NO SC003334   **ESTABLISHED** 1984

WHERE FUNDING CAN BE GIVEN Radio Clyde transmission area, i.e. Inverclyde, Argyll and Bute, Dumfries and Galloway, East Ayrshire, South Ayrshire, North Ayrshire, East Dumbartonshire, West Dumbartonshire, Renfrewshire, East Renfrewshire, Glasgow City Council, North Lanarkshire and South Lanarkshire.

WHO CAN BENEFIT Children and young adults up to the age of 16 disadvantaged through: illness, distress, abuse or neglect; any kind of disability; behavioural or psychological difficulties; living in poverty or situations of deprivation. Organisations benefiting this group.

WHAT IS FUNDED Christmas presents, food, pantomime trips, clothing and other support is given to children via social work departments and through community and voluntary groups.

WHAT IS NOT FUNDED The trust does not fund: trips or projects abroad; medical treatment/research; unspecified expenditure; deficit funding or repayment of loans; retrospective funding (projects taking place before the grant award date); projects unable to start within 6 months of the grant award date; distribution to another/other organisation/s; general appeals or endowment funds; relief of statutory responsibility; the promotion of religion. No funding for capital expenditure except in very special circumstances that must be made clear at the time of applying. Organisations whose administration costs exceed 15% of total expenditure will not be supported.

FINANCES *Year* 2009–10 *Income* £2,167,869 *Grants* £2,082,230 *Assets* £647,751

TRUSTEES J Brown; Ewan Hunter; Ian Grabiner; Sir Tom Hunter; Ms B Ritchie; Ms T McNellan; G Bryce.

HOW TO APPLY Application forms and guidelines are available from the trust's website.

WHO TO APPLY TO Trust Administrator, Radio Clyde, 3 South Avenue, Clydebank Business Park, Glasgow G81 2RX *Tel* 0141 204 1025 *Fax* 0141 565 2370 *email* cashforkids@radioclyde.com *Website* www.clyde1.com/cashforkids

■ Sir John Cass's Foundation

CC NO 312425   **ESTABLISHED** 1748

WHERE FUNDING CAN BE GIVEN The inner London boroughs – Camden, Greenwich, Hackney, Hammersmith and Fulham, Islington, Kensington and Chelsea, Lambeth, Lewisham, Newham, Southwark, Tower Hamlets, Wandsworth, Westminster and the City of London.

WHO CAN BENEFIT Individuals; schools and organisations. The foundation will only consider proposals from schools and organisations that benefit: children or young people under the age of 25, who are permanent residents of named *inner* London boroughs (Camden, Greenwich, Hackney, Hammersmith and Fulham, Islington, Kensington and Chelsea, Lambeth, Lewisham, Newham, Southwark, Tower Hamlets, Wandsworth, Westminster and the City of London), and from disadvantaged backgrounds or areas of high deprivation.

WHAT IS FUNDED Education, especially of people in financial need. The foundation has four areas of focus for grant giving: widening participation in further and higher education; truancy, exclusion and behaviour management; prisoner education; new initiatives.

WHAT IS NOT FUNDED There are many activities and costs that the foundation will not fund. The following list gives an idea of the type the foundation cannot support: projects that do not meet a foundation priority; conferences, seminars and academic research; holiday projects, school journeys, trips abroad or exchange visits; supplementary schools or mother tongue teaching; independent schools; youth and community groups, or projects taking place in these settings; pre-school and nursery education; general fund-raising campaigns or appeals; costs for equipment or salaries that are the statutory responsibility of education authorities; costs to substitute for the withdrawal or reduction of statutory funding; costs for work or activities that have already taken place prior to the grant application; costs already covered by core funding or other grants; curriculum enhancing projects; capital costs, that are exclusively for the purchase, repair or furnishing of buildings, purchase of vehicles, computers, sports equipment or improvements to school grounds.

TYPE OF GRANT Recurrent for individuals; project, recurrent or one-off support for groups, organisations and schools. Funding may be given for up to three years.

RANGE OF GRANTS Usually £5,000–£65,000.

SAMPLE GRANTS Beneficiaries included: Southwark Diocesan Board of Education – Christ Church Primary School Brixton and University of East London (Sir John Cass School of Education) (£200,000 each); Southwark Diocesan Board of Education – academy programme (£100,000); Sir John Cass's Foundation and Redcoats Church of England Secondary School (£60,000 each); East London Business Alliance (£40,000); Shaftesbury Young People (£25,000); Sir John Cass's Foundation Primary School (Cass Benefits) (£14,000); and Prisoners' Education Trust (£6,000).

FINANCES *Year* 2009–10 *Income* £1,712,947 *Grants* £1,012,690 *Assets* £79,214,364

TRUSTEES Michael Bear; Kevin Everett; Mark Boleat; HH Judge Brian Barker; Revd Christopher Burke; Barbara Lane; Graham Forbes; David Turner; Mervyn Streatfeild; Helen Meixner; Dr Ray Ellis; Revd Nigel Kirkup; Sarah Dalgarno; David Hogben; Prof. Michael Thorne; Inigo Woolf; Revd Laura Burgess.

OTHER INFORMATION A further £41,000 was distributed in 57 grants to individuals.

HOW TO APPLY The foundation operates a two stage application process – an initial enquiry and a full application stage. At stage 1, applicants are required to complete and submit the initial enquiry form which is available from the foundation's website and on request from the correspondent. The form asks for outline information about your proposed project; information about how the project meets the foundation's priorities; a summary of the project that includes the following information: the aims of the project including outputs and outcomes, how the project will be delivered; the duration of the project, including when and where it will take place; and a budget covering project costs. Enquiries will then be considered and applicants informed of the decision taken within three weeks. Successful stage 1 applicants will be invited to proceed to Stage 2 and submit a full application. A copy of the stage 2 guidelines will be sent to you at that time. This form should be completed and submitted with copies of the memorandum and articles of association (or constitution) of your organisation, together with the latest annual report and accounts. On receipt of your application foundation staff may meet with you as part of the assessment process. The grants committee meets in March, June and November each year. It normally takes between two and four months from receipt of a full application until a decision is made. All applicants will be sent formal notification of the outcome of their applications within two weeks of the committee decision. Those who are offered a grant will be sent a formal offer letter and copies of the foundation's standard terms and conditions of grant. Copies of the standard terms and conditions of grant are available on the foundation's website. Additional conditions are sometimes included depending on the nature of the grant. All applications are assessed on merit. If your application is refused you can apply again twelve months after the date you submitted your last application.

who to apply to Richard Foley, Grants Manager, 31 Jewry Street, London EC3N 2EY *Tel* 020 7480 5884 *Fax* 020 7488 2519 *email* contactus@sirjohncass.org *Website* www.sirjohncass.org

■ The Elizabeth Casson Trust

cc no 227166   **established** 1930
where funding can be given Worldwide.
who can benefit Occupational therapy schools/departments and individual occupational therapists.
what is funded The training and development of occupational therapists. Ongoing support is given to Oxford Brookes University.
what is not funded No support for anything other than occupational therapy education and training.
type of grant Research projects and courses/travel bursaries that will benefit the profession as well as the individual.
sample grants Fit to Work project (£30,000); University OT reference library (£975); Oxford Research Group (study day & website) (£400); UK Occupational Therapy Research Foundation (£30,000); Scholarships at Tufts University (£18,100) E.M. Macdonald award (£250). 77 grants to individual occupational therapists were made totalling £33,000 including £10,000 for a Tanzanian student to study in South Africa.
finances *Year* 2009–10 *Income* £210,592 *Grants* £614,000 *Assets* £4,934,884
trustees C Rutland, Chair; S Croft; Dr P L Agulnik; G A Paine; R Hallam; B Davies; S A Townsend.
other information The trust was founded in 1930 as Dorset House School of Occupational Therapy (a registered company). In 1948 the founder Dr Elizabeth Casson, registered this trust and an associated trust, the Casson Trust,

under the same number at the Charity Commission. In 1992 Dorset House site was leased to Oxford Brookes University and in 1993 the company changed its name to the Elizabeth Casson Trust.
how to apply On the trust's application form which can be obtained from the website.
who to apply to C A G Gray, Secretary to the Trustees, Corner House, Cote, Oxfordshire OX18 2EG *Tel* 01993 850716 *email* ec.trust@btinternet.com *Website* www.elizabethcassontrust.org.uk

■ The Castanea Trust

cc no 1136180   **established** 2010
where funding can be given UK.
who can benefit Registered charities.
what is funded General charitable purposes.
trustees Geoffrey Wall; Ian Duncan; Mark Feeny.
other information Unfortunately no further information was available at the time of writing (September 2011) on the likely level of funding available from the trust.
how to apply In writing to the correspondent.
who to apply to Mark Feeny, Trustee, Brabners Chaffe Street, Horton House, Exchange Flags, Liverpool L2 3YL *Tel* 0151 600 3000 *email* mark.feeny@brabnerscs.com

■ The Castang Foundation

cc no 1003867   **established** 1991
where funding can be given UK.
who can benefit Registered charities.
what is funded Research into neurodevelopmental disorders in children.
sample grants In 2009–10 the Foundation was funding three research projects: Nutrition Study (£62,000); Infantile Spasms (including West Syndrome) (£38,500); The European Cerebral Palsy Study (£24,000).
finances *Year* 2009–10 *Income* £96,126 *Grants* £124,544 *Assets* £1,998,678
trustees I A Burman; M B Glynn.
how to apply In writing to the correspondent.
who to apply to Ian Burman, c/o Laytons, Carmelite, 50 Victoria Embankment, Blackfriars, London EC4Y OLS *email* ian.burnham@laytons.com *Website* www.castangfoundation.net

■ The Caswell Family Charitable Trust

cc no 1133588   **established** 2010
where funding can be given Undefined, in practice UK.
who can benefit Registered charities.
what is funded General charitable purposes.
trustees F B Caswell; Mrs J Caswell; Ms H Allanson; Ms A Wilson; J J Swift.
how to apply In writing to the correspondent.
who to apply to Joseph J Swift, Trustee, Cobbetts LLP, 58 Mosley Street, Manchester M2 3HZ *Tel* 0845 404 2404

■ The Catalyst Charitable Trust (formerly the Buckle Family Charitable Trust)

CC NO 1001962   **ESTABLISHED** 1990
WHERE FUNDING CAN BE GIVEN Mainly Suffolk and Essex.
WHO CAN BENEFIT Charitable causes.
WHAT IS FUNDED This trust has an interest in supporting small charities in the Suffolk/Essex area.
SAMPLE GRANTS The Suffolk Foundation (£18,000); Hadleigh High School (£15,000); The Oundle Schools Foundation and The Iceni Project (£10,000 each) and Livability (John Grooms), The Tree House Appeal and Macmillan Cancer Support (£5,000 each).
FINANCES *Year* 2009–10 *Income* £28,684 *Grants* £79,750 *Assets* £23,748
TRUSTEES Gillian Buckle; James Buckle; Louise Somerset; Charles Course.
OTHER INFORMATION In 2009–10 a £4,000 grant went to an individual.
HOW TO APPLY In writing to the correspondent although beneficiaries are normally selected through personal contact.
WHO TO APPLY TO Penny Andrews, Buckle Farms, Dairy Farm Office, Dairy Road, Semer, Ipswich IP7 6RA

■ The Catholic Charitable Trust

CC NO 215553   **ESTABLISHED** 1935
WHERE FUNDING CAN BE GIVEN America and Europe.
WHO CAN BENEFIT Traditional Catholic organisations.
WHAT IS FUNDED The traditional teachings of the Roman Catholic faith. The trust's income is usually fully committed.
WHAT IS NOT FUNDED The trust does not normally support a charity unless it is known to the trustees. Grants are not made to individuals.
RANGE OF GRANTS £1,500–£15,000.
SAMPLE GRANTS Society of Saint Pius X – England (£12,000); Latin Mass Society, Fraternity of St Pius X Switzerland and Little Sisters of the Poor (£4,000 each); Cardinal Hume Centre and St Benets Hall Oxford (£2,000 each); and Holy Cross Parish Fulham (£1,000).
FINANCES *Year* 2009 *Income* £54,547 *Grants* £52,098 *Assets* £1,689,464
TRUSTEES John C Vernor-Miles; W E Vernor-Miles; D P Orr.
OTHER INFORMATION Three grants were made to American organisations: the Carmelite Monastery Carmel California and California Friends of the Society of St Pius X, (US$2,000 each); and Oratory of Monterey California ($1,000).
HOW TO APPLY Applications can only be accepted from registered charities and should be in writing to the correspondent. In order to save administration costs replies are not sent to unsuccessful applicants. For the most part funds are fully committed.
WHO TO APPLY TO John C Vernor-Miles, Trustee, c/o Hunters, 9 New Square, Lincoln's Inn, London WC2A 3QN *Tel* 020 7412 0050

■ Catholic Foreign Missions

CC NO 249252   **ESTABLISHED** 1941
WHERE FUNDING CAN BE GIVEN UK and overseas.
WHO CAN BENEFIT Catholic Foreign Missions.
WHAT IS FUNDED Grants are made in support of Catholic Foreign Missions in any part of the world.
SAMPLE GRANTS Grants were made to the following missions: Province of Paris (£964,000); Province of General Curia – Rome (£194,000); Province of Toulouse (£182,000); Province of Ireland (£41,000) and Prelazia De Cameta (£9,000).
FINANCES *Year* 2009–10 *Income* £562,751 *Grants* £1,389,907 *Assets* £16,803,440
TRUSTEES Desmond Bierne; Jean Marie Lesbats; Abel Maniez; Bernard Meade; Eric Saint-Sevin; Philip Walshe; Phillipe Lamblin; Kieran Magovern.
HOW TO APPLY No external applications are considered. The funds are fully committed.
WHO TO APPLY TO Patrick Herschan, c/o Pothecary Witham Weld Solicitors, 70 St George's Square, London SW1V 3RD

■ The Catholic Trust for England and Wales

CC NO 1097482   **ESTABLISHED** 1968
WHERE FUNDING CAN BE GIVEN England and Wales.
WHO CAN BENEFIT Roman Catholic organisations.
WHAT IS FUNDED The advancement of the Roman Catholic religion in England and Wales.
WHAT IS NOT FUNDED No grants to individuals, local projects or projects not immediately advancing the Roman Catholic religion in England and Wales.
SAMPLE GRANTS CARITAS Social Action Network (£56,000); Churches Legislation Advisory Service (£18,000); National Board of Catholic Women (£13,000); Churches Media Council (£6,000); Churches Committee Hospital Chaplaincy (£4,000); and SIGNIS (£2,000).
FINANCES *Year* 2010 *Income* £15,196,599 *Grants* £154,297 *Assets* £11,032,331
TRUSTEES Rt Revd Malcolm McMahon, Chair; Mgr Michael McKenna; Ben Andradi; Alison Cowdall; John Gibbs; Peter Lomas; Canon Nicholas Rothon; Robin Smith; Dr James Whiston; Richard King; Revd John Nelson; Michael Prior; Elizabeth Walmsley.
OTHER INFORMATION The accounts include those of the trust's subsidiary companies: Colloquium Limited, The Papal Visit Limited and The Papal Visit 2010 Limited and this is why the income and assets do not reflect the amounts paid or payable in grants.
HOW TO APPLY The trust has stated previously that it does not respond to unsolicited applications.
WHO TO APPLY TO Revd Marcus Stock, Secretary, 39 Eccleston Square, London SW1V 1BX *Tel* 020 7901 4810 *email* secretariat@cbcew.org.uk *Website* www.catholicchurch.org.uk

■ The Cattanach Charitable Trust

SC NO SC020902   **ESTABLISHED** 1992
WHERE FUNDING CAN BE GIVEN Scotland.
WHO CAN BENEFIT The trust will fund charities registered either in Scotland or in England for work done exclusively in Scotland. 'Organisations should be registered with the Office of the Scottish Charity Regulator, or, if registered with the Charity Commission, should be in the process of registering with OSCR.'

WHAT IS FUNDED 'The Cattanach Charitable Trust believes that improving the well-being of young children can bring about healthier and happier communities. The Trust will focus on organisations and projects which offer hope of a better life to children, especially those under 10 years of age, and to their families and communities. By targeting its grants in this way, the Trust means to address the needs of young children living in difficult or deprived circumstances, and to help them make the most of their talents and opportunities.'

WHAT IS NOT FUNDED The trust will not fund individuals, hospices and palliative care, appliances for illness or disability, organisations concerned with specific diseases, or animal charities.

TYPE OF GRANT The trust prefers to make grants which contribute substantially to smaller-scale projects.

RANGE OF GRANTS Mostly £3,000–£15,000.

SAMPLE GRANTS Homestart – Aberdeen and The Cottage Family Centre (£10,000 each); The SKY Project – Stuff for Youth and Kids (£8,000) and The Lilias Graham Trust (£5,000).

FINANCES *Year* 2009–10 *Income* £1,054,327

TRUSTEES Malcolm Borthwick; Anne Houston; Euan Davidson; Michael Gotz; Duncan McEachran; Alistaire Wilson; Rachel Lewis; Janet Barr.

HOW TO APPLY On a form which can be completed online or downloaded from the trust's website. 'The trust does not normally accept hand-written applications – please phone if you do not have access to a computer.' The trust no longer has application deadlines, but works on a rolling programme. Trust meetings are listed on the website and you should allow around 10 weeks for your application to reach a meeting.

WHO TO APPLY TO Alison Campbell, 15 Warriston Crescent, Edinburgh EH3 5LA *Tel* 0131 557 2052 *email* info@cattanach.org.uk *Website* www.cattanach.org.uk

---

■ **The Joseph and Annie Cattle Trust**

CC NO 262011   **ESTABLISHED** 1970

WHERE FUNDING CAN BE GIVEN Worldwide, with a preference for Hull and East Yorkshire.

WHO CAN BENEFIT Organisations and individuals. 'The aged, disabled and underprivileged are assisted wherever possible as are children suffering from dyslexia. Financial assistance is provided as far as possible by supporting institutions specialising in these areas.'

WHAT IS FUNDED General charitable purposes.

WHAT IS NOT FUNDED Grants are very rarely given to individuals and are only supported through social services or relevant charitable or welfare organisations.

TYPE OF GRANT One-off, capital, recurring and interest-free loans are considered.

RANGE OF GRANTS Up to £15,000.

SAMPLE GRANTS Hull City Council Social Services (£80,000); Sobriety Project (£15,000); Dyslexia Action (£13,000); Holderness Road Methodist Church and Market Weighton Scout & Guide Head Quarters Project (£5,000 each); Cherry Burton Tennis Club (£3,000); Sutton Methodist Church and Yorkshire Eye Research (£2,000 each); and Andrew Marvell Youth Centre, Beeford Cricket Club, House of Light, Hull Boys' Club, Leven Playing Fields Association, Walkington Pre-School and Wilf Ward Family Trust (£1,000 each).

FINANCES *Year* 2009–10 *Income* £353,417 *Grants* £263,690 *Assets* £7,189,457

TRUSTEES J A Collier; M T Gyte; S C Jowers.

OTHER INFORMATION Grants to 63 individuals totalled £34,000.

HOW TO APPLY In writing to the correspondent. Meetings are usually held on the third Monday of each month.

WHO TO APPLY TO Roger Waudby, Administrator, 389–395 Anlaby Road, Hull HU3 6AB *Tel* 01482 211198

■ **The Thomas Sivewright Catto Charitable Settlement**

CC NO 279549   **ESTABLISHED** 1979

WHERE FUNDING CAN BE GIVEN Unrestricted (for UK-based registered charities).

WHO CAN BENEFIT Registered charities only.

WHAT IS FUNDED General charitable purposes.

WHAT IS NOT FUNDED The trust does not support non-registered charities, expeditions, travel bursaries and so on, or unsolicited applications from churches of any denomination. Grants are unlikely to be considered in the areas of community care, playschemes and drug abuse, or for local branches of national organisations.

RANGE OF GRANTS Up to £14,000.

SAMPLE GRANTS Previously: Royal College of Music (£14,000) Royal Scottish Academy of Music and Drama (£12,000); Bowel Cancer Research and King VII's Hospital for Officers (£10,000 each); Haddo House Choral and Operatic Society and World YWCA (£5,000 each); Aviation for Paraplegics and Tetraplegics Trust (£2,000); NACRO (£1,500); Refugee Council, St Mungo's, Shelter and Charlie Waller Memorial Trust (£1,000 each); Crisis (£750); and Sportability (£500).

FINANCES *Year* 2009–10 *Income* £1,063 *Grants* £46,908

TRUSTEES Lord Catto; Olivia Marchant; Zoe Richmond-Watson.

HOW TO APPLY In writing to the correspondent, including an sae.

WHO TO APPLY TO The Secretary to the Trustees, PO Box 47408, London N21 1YW

■ **The Wilfrid and Constance Cave Foundation**

CC NO 241900   **ESTABLISHED** 1965

WHERE FUNDING CAN BE GIVEN UK, with preference for Berkshire, Cornwall, Devon, Dorset, Hampshire, Oxfordshire, Somerset, Warwickshire and Wiltshire.

WHO CAN BENEFIT Registered charities. Mainly local charities or charities which the trustees have personal knowledge of, interest in, or association with are considered.

WHAT IS FUNDED General charitable purposes including conservation, animal welfare, health and social welfare.

WHAT IS NOT FUNDED No grants to individuals.

TYPE OF GRANT Buildings, core costs, one-off, project, research, and running costs. Grants may be given for up to three years.

RANGE OF GRANTS £500–£50,000.

SAMPLE GRANTS Farmers' Club Pinnacle Award (£7,000); East Berkshire Women's Aid (£6,000); West Country River Trust (£6,000); Fairground Heritage Trust (£5,000); Two Moors Festival (£3,000); and Shooting Star Children's Hospice (£1,000).

Think carefully about every application. Is it justified?

429

Alphabetical register of grant making charitable trusts

FINANCES *Year* 2009–10 *Income* £155,078 *Grants* £151,000 *Assets* £4,143,516

TRUSTEES Mrs T Jones; P Simpson; F H C Jones; Mrs J Archer; Mrs J Pickin; M Pickin; Mrs M Waterworth; Mrs N Thompson; R Walker; G Howells; W Howells; M Beckett.

HOW TO APPLY In writing to the correspondent a month before the trustees' meetings held twice each year, in May and October.

WHO TO APPLY TO The Secretary, New Lodge Farm, Drift Road, Winkfield, Windsor SL4 4QQ *email* tcf@eamo.co.uk

■ The Cayo Foundation

CC NO 1080607   **ESTABLISHED** 1999

WHERE FUNDING CAN BE GIVEN UK.

WHO CAN BENEFIT Charitable organisations.

WHAT IS FUNDED Medical research, the fight against crime, children and youth charities and general charitable purposes.

SAMPLE GRANTS Previous beneficiaries included: NSPCC (£125,000); the Disability Foundation, PACT, the Royal Opera House (£25,000 each); the Prince's Foundation (£20,000); Wessex Youth Trust (£10,000); Christian Blind Mission (£6,000); Wellbeing of Women (£3,000); Institute for Policy Research and Royal Humane Society (£2,500 each); and Sue Ryder Care – St John's Hospice (£1,000).

FINANCES *Year* 2009–10 *Income* £339,068 *Grants* £266,458 *Assets* £371,557

TRUSTEES Angela E McCarville; Stewart A Harris.

HOW TO APPLY In writing to the correspondent.

WHO TO APPLY TO Angela E McCarville, 7 Cowley Street, London SW1P 3NB *Tel* 020 7248 6700

■ Elizabeth Cayzer Charitable Trust

CC NO 1059265   **ESTABLISHED** 1996

WHERE FUNDING CAN BE GIVEN UK.

WHO CAN BENEFIT Museums, galleries and other arts organisations and projects.

WHAT IS FUNDED Funds are used in promoting activities related to art, including education, restoration, research, conservation and conferences and exhibitions.

SAMPLE GRANTS Previous beneficiaries have included Elias Ashmole Trust, Dulwich Picture Gallery, the National Gallery and Sir John Soane's Museum.

FINANCES *Year* 2009–10 *Income* £62,029 *Grants* £58,500 *Assets* £2,365,746

TRUSTEES The Hon. Elizabeth Gilmour; Diana Lloyd; Dominic Gibbs.

OTHER INFORMATION This charity was established by The Honourable Elizabeth Gilmour, who has made significant donations to the charity since 1996. In formulating policy the trustees have taken into account the wishes of the Settlor, which are that the assets of the charity should be used in supporting and promoting activities relating to art.

HOW TO APPLY Please note the following statement taken from the charity's 2009–10 accounts: 'The trustees identify the projects and organisations they wish to support and so do not consider grants to people or organisations who apply speculatively. The trust also has a policy of not responding to any correspondence unless it relates to grants it has agreed to make or to the general management of the trust.'

WHO TO APPLY TO The Hon. Elizabeth Gilmour, Trustee, The Cayzer Trust Company Limited,

Cayzer House, 30 Buckingham Gate, London SW1E 6NN *Tel* 020 7802 8080

■ The B G S Cayzer Charitable Trust

CC NO 286063   **ESTABLISHED** 1982

WHERE FUNDING CAN BE GIVEN UK.

WHO CAN BENEFIT Registered charities.

WHAT IS FUNDED General charitable purposes.

WHAT IS NOT FUNDED No grants to organisations outside the UK.

RANGE OF GRANTS Up to £25,000.

SAMPLE GRANTS Previous beneficiaries have included: Friends of the National Maritime Museum, Hike for Hope, Marie Curie Cancer Care, RAFT, St Paul's Cathedral Foundation, Scottish Countryside Alliance Education Trust and Worshipful Company of Shipwrights Charitable Fund.

FINANCES *Year* 2009–10 *Income* £151,357 *Grants* £75,450 *Assets* £2,828,721

TRUSTEES P R Davies; Mrs M Buckley; Mrs A M Hunter; Mrs R N Leslie.

HOW TO APPLY The trust tends to support only people/projects known to the Cayzer family or the trustees. Unsolicited appeals will not be supported.

WHO TO APPLY TO The Administrator, The Cayzer Trust Company Limited, Cayzer House, 30 Buckingham Gate, London SW1E 6NN

■ The Cazenove Charitable Trust

CC NO 1086899   **ESTABLISHED** 1969

WHERE FUNDING CAN BE GIVEN UK.

WHO CAN BENEFIT Charitable organisations. This trust primarily supports the charitable activities sponsored by current and ex-Cazenove employees.

WHAT IS FUNDED General charitable purposes.

SAMPLE GRANTS Wheelpower (£3,000); Cancer Research, Macmillan Cancer Relief (£2,000 each); Army Benevolent Fund (£1,300); Global Vision International, National Autistic Society mad Wooden Spoon (£1,000 each). £12,500 worth of grants were made in sums of less than £1,000.

FINANCES *Year* 2008 *Income* £43,750 *Grants* £24,838 *Assets* £1,007,763

TRUSTEES Sophia Pryor, Chair; Edward M Harley; Michael Wentworth-Stanley; Michael Power.

OTHER INFORMATION In January 2012 the latest accounts available were from 2008, with the trust consistently failing to submit the required information with the Charity Commission.

HOW TO APPLY This trust does not respond to unsolicited applications.

WHO TO APPLY TO Sophia Pryor, Cazenove, 20 Moorgate, London EC2R 6DA *Tel* 020 7155 6147

■ The CBD Charitable Trust

CC NO 1136702   **ESTABLISHED** 2010

WHERE FUNDING CAN BE GIVEN Worldwide.

WHO CAN BENEFIT Children and young people.

WHAT IS FUNDED General charitable purposes.

FINANCES *Year* 2010–11 *Income* £170,800 *Grants* £150,000

TRUSTEES Coutts & Co; Ingrid Scott.

HOW TO APPLY In writing to the correspondent.

Does the trust you have chosen match your needs? Haphazard applications waste postage and time

WHO TO APPLY TO Coutts & Co, Trustee Dept, 440 Strand, London WC2R 0QS *Tel* 020 7663 6825

....

■ Celtic Charity Fund

SC NO SC024648   ESTABLISHED 1995

WHERE FUNDING CAN BE GIVEN Worldwide but with a preference for Scotland and Ireland.

WHO CAN BENEFIT Charitable organisations.

WHAT IS FUNDED The fund has three main areas of support are as follows: children; drug-related projects; promoting religious and ethnic harmony. It also supports three subsidiary areas which are: homelessness; unemployment; alleviation of suffering caused by illness and famine and to aid innocent families within areas of war.

RANGE OF GRANTS £100–£3,000.

FINANCES *Year* 2010–11 *Income* £545,681

TRUSTEES The Board of Trustees is selected by Celtic Football and Athletic Co Ltd.

OTHER INFORMATION There is approximately £100,000 available on an annual basis.

HOW TO APPLY An application form should be requested in writing.

WHO TO APPLY TO The Community Relations Manager, Celtic Football Club, Celtic Park, Glasgow G40 3RE *Website* www.celticfc.net

....

■ The Cemlyn-Jones Trust

CC NO 1039164   ESTABLISHED 1994

WHERE FUNDING CAN BE GIVEN North Wales and Anglesey.

WHO CAN BENEFIT Small local projects.

WHAT IS FUNDED Conservation and protection of general public amenities, historic or public interests in Wales; medical research; protection and welfare of animals and birds; study and promotion of music; activities and requirements of religious and educational bodies.

WHAT IS NOT FUNDED No grants to individuals or non-charitable organisations.

TYPE OF GRANT One-off.

RANGE OF GRANTS £100 upwards.

SAMPLE GRANTS Bangor University (£33,000 in four grants); Music in Hospitals Wales (£2,000); Beaumaris Festival, All Saints Church – Deganwy and Snowdonia Society (£1,000 each); and Llandudno Youth Music Theatre (£500).

FINANCES *Year* 2009–10 *Income* £36,295 *Grants* £38,730 *Assets* £1,023,471

TRUSTEES P G Brown; Mrs J E Lea; Mrs E G Jones.

OTHER INFORMATION Four grants went to Bangor University towards the following funds, schools and departments: Stewardship (£12,000); C J Fellowship fund (£8,000); Outreach (£6,000); School of Ocean Sciences (£4,000); and Royal Society (£3,000).

HOW TO APPLY In writing to the correspondent.

WHO TO APPLY TO P G Brown, Trustee, 59 Madoc Street, Llandudno LL30 2TW *Tel* 01492 874391 *email* philip.brown@brewin.co.uk

....

■ CfBT Education Trust

CC NO 270901   ESTABLISHED 1965

WHERE FUNDING CAN BE GIVEN Worldwide.

WHO CAN BENEFIT Organisations involved in education, particularly those concerned with the development and management of schools; managing and delivering effective learning and teaching; overcoming barriers to learning; and projects involving communication, language and multi-lingualism.

WHAT IS FUNDED Support from CfBT comes under the Evidence for Education programme where support is given through: commissioned research and development projects; research awards by competition/tender; and funding for projects in response to applications and invitation.

WHAT IS NOT FUNDED The trust will generally not consider funding for: business development; funding an extension or expansion of current service delivery; funding an extension of existing R&D projects which are funded by other sources; projects which are only innovative because they are being carried out at a local rather than a national level; buildings, equipment or capital costs; staff salaries (apart from researcher/consultant fees); day-to-day running costs; general appeals; grants to replace statutory funding; funding for individuals to undertake professional development, including those undertaking Masters degrees or Doctorates; expeditions, travel, adventure/ holiday projects; 'gap year' projects; arts, religion, sports and recreation; conservation, heritage or environmental projects; animal rights or welfare; educational exchanges between institutions.

TYPE OF GRANT One-off and recurring grants.

RANGE OF GRANTS £1,000–£500,000.

SAMPLE GRANTS Grants have previously been used to fund: Education in Conflict, Emergencies, Reconstruction and Fragile States (£302,000); Public Private Partnerships in Basic Education: An International Review (£234,000); Student Integration in the United World College, Bosnia and Herzegovina (£55,000); Designing Educational Technologies for Social Justice (£52,000); How Effective are Bullying Prevention Programmes for Children with Special Educational Needs? (£31,000); English Language Teaching – Bridging Programmes for Further Education (£20,000); Programme scoping: Start-up phase for Gifted and Talented and Learning and Skills Programmes (£16,000); and Adult Skills and Higher Education: Separation or Union? (£12,000).

FINANCES *Year* 2009–10 *Income* £83,300,000 *Grants* £1,327,360 *Assets* £25,700,000

TRUSTEES John Webb; John Harwood; Sara Hodson; Alison Macleod; Marion Headicar; Stuart Laing; Sue Hunt; Tim Walsh; Phillip Wood; Sir Jim Rose; Margaret Platts.

HOW TO APPLY Applicants should first submit an outline proposal to the research manager, Karen Whitby who will advise whether the proposal meets the agreed criteria and also how to proceed. The outline should be no more than three sides of A4 and include the following information: the issue or problem to be addressed; the reasons for addressing it; the expected outcome(s); what happens in the course of the project; the amount of funding required and how long it will be needed. Full applications are considered at the meetings of trustees in March, July, September and December. Further application information and upcoming deadline dates are available on the trust's website and in the 'Guide to Applicants' document.

Please note: The 'Apply for funding' page of the trust's website currently states: 'We are proud to reinvest in research and development projects and we commission, or work with in partnership on, innovative educational research and development projects that promote and complement our operational work.

....

The trust is not accepting open channel research until further notice but going forward is tendering research specifications which when available will be posted on our website. Please contact research@cfbt.com if you have any further queries.'

WHO TO APPLY TO Ade Lawal, Board Secretary, 60 Queens Road, Reading, Berkshire RG1 4BS *Tel* 0118 902 1231 *Fax* 0118 902 1434 *email* alawal@cfbt.com *Website* www.cfbt.com

■ The CH (1980) Charitable Trust

CC NO 279481   **ESTABLISHED** 1980
WHERE FUNDING CAN BE GIVEN UK and Israel.
WHO CAN BENEFIT Jewish organisations.
WHAT IS FUNDED Jewish causes.
SAMPLE GRANTS Oxford Centre for Hebrew and Jewish Studies (£100,000); Traditional Alternatives Foundation (£25,000); Jerusalem Foundation (£18,000); Israel Diaspora Trust and Anglo Israel Foundation (£8,000 each); West London Synagogue Charitable Fund (£3,000); B'nal B'rith Hillel Foundation (£1,000); and British Friends of the Israel Guide Dog Centre for the Blind (£500).
FINANCES *Year* 2009–10 *Income* £36,971 *Grants* £163,800 *Assets* £1,641,382
TRUSTEES Kleinwort Benson Trustees Limited.
HOW TO APPLY In writing to the correspondent.
WHO TO APPLY TO The Administrator, 30 Gresham Street, London EC2V 7PG

■ R E Chadwick Charitable Trust

CC NO 1104805   **ESTABLISHED** 2004
WHERE FUNDING CAN BE GIVEN UK.
WHO CAN BENEFIT Registered charities.
WHAT IS FUNDED General charitable purposes.
SAMPLE GRANTS Previous beneficiaries include: Grammar School at Leeds, British Red Cross, Crisis, Leeds Festival Chorus, Myasthenia Gravis Association, RNIB, UNICEF, Arthritis Research, CAFOD, the Country Trust, Friends of St Winifred's, Gloucester Choral Society, Leeds Parish Church Choral Foundation Appeal, Meanwood Valley Urban Farm, Muslim Hands, NSPCC, the Simon Community, Yorkshire Dales Millennium Trust, Landmark Trust, Mission to Deep Sea Fishermen, Nightstop and Royal Horticultural Society – Harlow Carr.
FINANCES *Year* 2009–10 *Income* £24,601 *Grants* £25,000
TRUSTEES Peter Chadwick; Esme Knowles; Paul Knowles; Ann Chadwick.
OTHER INFORMATION No further financial information was available.
HOW TO APPLY In writing to the correspondent.
WHO TO APPLY TO Peter Chadwick, Trustee, Newlaithes Manor, Newlaithes Road, Horsforth, Leeds LS18 4LG *Tel* 0113 244 6100

■ The Amelia Chadwick Trust

CC NO 213795   **ESTABLISHED** 1960
WHERE FUNDING CAN BE GIVEN UK, especially Merseyside.
WHO CAN BENEFIT Neighbourhood-based community projects, some UK organisations.
WHAT IS FUNDED General charitable purposes including education, health, the arts, social welfare and the environment.
WHAT IS NOT FUNDED No grants to individuals.
TYPE OF GRANT Mostly recurring.
RANGE OF GRANTS £100–£25,000.

SAMPLE GRANTS Merseyside Development Foundation (£25,000); St Helen's and District Women's Aid (£18,000); Liverpool PSS (£12,000); European Play-Work Association (£7,000); Birkenhead Youth Club (£5,000); Merseyside Holiday Service (£3,000); Centrepoint, Kid's Cookery School and Sue Ryder Home (£2,000 each); Sheila Kay Fund (£1,500); Age Concern – Liverpool and Shrewsbury House (£1,000 each); British Red Cross (£750); Fortune Centre (£500); and Wirral Independent Support Forum (£100).
FINANCES *Year* 2009–10 *Income* £111,756 *Grants* £118,347 *Assets* £3,317,286
TRUSTEES John McGibbon; Christopher Bibby.
HOW TO APPLY All donations are made through Liverpool Charity and Voluntary Services. Grants are only made to charities known to the trustees, and unsolicited applications are not considered.
WHO TO APPLY TO John McGibbon, Trustee, Guy Williams Layton, Pacific Chambers, 11–13 Victoria Street, Liverpool L2 5QQ *Tel* 0151 236 7171

■ The Pamela Champion Foundation

CC NO 268819   **ESTABLISHED** 1974
WHERE FUNDING CAN BE GIVEN UK, with a preference for Kent.
WHO CAN BENEFIT Registered charities.
WHAT IS FUNDED General charitable purposes.
WHAT IS NOT FUNDED No grants to non-registered charities.
RANGE OF GRANTS Up to £2,500.
SAMPLE GRANTS Fairbridge in Kent and Salvation Army (£2,000 each); Kent MS Society, Farms for City Children, Kingfisher Medway, Lord Whisky and Combat Stress (£1,000 each); London Centre for Children with Cerebral Palsy (£750 each); Canterbury Oast Trust, Deafblind, Livability and Willow Foundation (£500 each); and Hope Appeal (£250).
FINANCES *Year* 2010 *Income* £30,947 *Grants* £25,250 *Assets* £718,275
TRUSTEES Miss M Stanlake; Mrs C Winser; Mrs E Bell; P M Williams.
OTHER INFORMATION Administration costs were almost £3,000.
HOW TO APPLY In writing to the correspondent.
WHO TO APPLY TO Elizabeth Bell, Trustee, Wiltons, Newnham Lane, Eastling, Faversham, Kent ME13 0AS *Tel* 01795 890233

■ Champneys Charitable Foundation

CC NO 1114429   **ESTABLISHED** 2006
WHERE FUNDING CAN BE GIVEN UK.
WHO CAN BENEFIT Charitable organisations.
WHAT IS FUNDED Health, medical and disability causes.
RANGE OF GRANTS Up to £20,000.
SAMPLE GRANTS Silver Star Appeal (£17,000); Multiple Sclerosis Trust (£3,000); Naomi House (£2,700); Sue Ryder Care (£1,000); and In Car Safety (£900).
FINANCES *Year* 2009–10 *Income* £101,023 *Grants* £28,287 *Assets* £34,906
TRUSTEES Dorothy Purdew; Stephen Purdew; Michael Hawkins.
HOW TO APPLY In writing to the correspondent.
WHO TO APPLY TO Bev Strong, Charity Administrator, Henlow Grange, Henlow, Bedfordshire

SG16 6DB *email* charity@champneys.co.uk
Website www.champneys.com

■ The Chapman Charitable Trust

CC NO 232791   ESTABLISHED 1963

WHERE FUNDING CAN BE GIVEN Eastern and south east England, including London, and Wales.

WHO CAN BENEFIT Any recognised charity, but mainly those charities in which the late settlor had, or the trustees have, a personal interest or concern.

WHAT IS FUNDED General charitable purposes. Main areas supported are social services, culture and recreation, education and research, health, environment and heritage.

WHAT IS NOT FUNDED No grants to or for the benefit of individuals, local branches of UK charities, animal welfare, sports tours or sponsored adventure holidays.

RANGE OF GRANTS £500–£10,000.

SAMPLE GRANTS Hampstead & Westminster Hockey Club (£25,000); Pesticide Action Network UK (£15,000 in two grants); Fragile X Society and Queen Alexandra Hospital Home (£12,000 in two grants each); Cherry Trees – respite care for children (£6,000); Phoenix Cinema Trust (£2,500); CoolTan Arts (£1,500).

FINANCES *Year* 2009–10 *Income* £221,224 *Grants* £234,000 *Assets* £6,001,473

TRUSTEES Roger Chapman; Richard Chapman; Bruce Chapman; Guy Chapman; Bryony Chapman.

OTHER INFORMATION There were 69 grants of £1,000 each and 8 Grants of £500 each made to organisations.

HOW TO APPLY In writing at any time. The trustees currently meet to consider grants twice a year at the end of September and in March. They receive a large number of applications and regret that they cannot acknowledge receipt of them. The absence of any communication for six months would mean that an application must have been unsuccessful.

WHO TO APPLY TO Roger S Chapman, Trustee, Crouch Chapman, 62 Wilson Street, London EC2A 2BU *Tel* 020 7782 0007 *email* cct@crouchchapman.co.uk

■ John William Chapman's Charitable Trust

CC NO 223002   ESTABLISHED 1942

WHERE FUNDING CAN BE GIVEN The borough of Doncaster.

WHO CAN BENEFIT Individuals or other bodies assisting individuals in need.

WHAT IS FUNDED Relief-in-need.

WHAT IS NOT FUNDED The trust funds are to be used for the relief of hardship and distress but will not be given for payments in respect of council tax, income tax or where public funds are available for the relief of that hardship. Grants are not given for large, national appeals.

RANGE OF GRANTS £200–£15,000.

SAMPLE GRANTS Previous beneficiaries included: Age Concern; Barnardo's; British Red Cross; British Legion; Doncaster and District Welfare for the Disabled; Doncaster Housing for Young People; National Schizophrenia Society; William Nuttall Cottage Homes; Winged Fellowship.

FINANCES *Year* 2009–10 *Income* £171,776 *Grants* £29,797 *Assets* £3,677,121

TRUSTEES Lady Neill; Miss V R Ferres; M J Hunter; M Gornall; D Kirk.

HOW TO APPLY In writing to the correspondent.

■ The Charities Advisory Trust

CC NO 1040487   ESTABLISHED 1994

WHERE FUNDING CAN BE GIVEN UK and overseas.

WHO CAN BENEFIT Any charitable purpose is considered, but generally the trust is proactive.

WHAT IS FUNDED General charitable purposes, particularly: income generation projects; homelessness; museums; cancer research and treatment; peace and reconciliation; and refugees.

WHAT IS NOT FUNDED 'Nearly all our grants are made because we have prior knowledge of the project or area of concern. In most cases the idea for the project comes from us; we work with suitable organisations to achieve our objectives. We rarely respond to unsolicited applications for projects of which we know nothing. In such cases where support is given, the amounts are usually £200 or less. We do not consider grants to individuals in need. Neither do we give to individuals going on gap year trips to the developing world. We are unlikely to give to large fund-raising charities. We do not give for missionary work.'

TYPE OF GRANT Buildings, capital, core costs, endowments, interest-free loans; one-off, project, research, running costs, recurring costs, salaries and start-up costs. Funding is available for up to and over three years.

SAMPLE GRANTS Survivors Fund (£274,500); Africa Education Trust (£85,000); Ashwini (£46,000); Sight Savers International (£45,000); IPPF (£38,000); Bamboo Bikes (£33,000); Parivarthana (£30,000); Rainforest Concern (£21,000); Mines Advisory Group (£20,000); War Child (£17,000); and Accord (£16,000).

FINANCES *Year* 2009–10 *Income* £1,949,776 *Grants* £2,125,225 *Assets* £2,587,148

TRUSTEES Dr Cornelia Navari; Dr Carolyne Dennis; Brij Bhasin; Ms Dawn Penso.

HOW TO APPLY The trustees are pro-active in looking for causes to support. They are, however, 'happy for charities to keep us informed of developments, as we do change our support as new solutions to needs emerge. **Unsolicited applications for projects of which the trust know nothing are rarely responded to.** To apply, simply send details of your proposal (no more than two pages in length) in the form of a letter. You might try to include the following information: the aims and objectives of your organisation; the project for which you need money; who benefits from the project and how; breakdown of the costs and total estimated costs; how much money you need from us; other funding secured for the project a summary of your latest annual accounts. If we refuse you it is not because your project is not worthwhile – it is because we do not have sufficient funds, or it is simply outside our current area of interest.'

WHO TO APPLY TO Dame Hilary Blume, Director, Radius Works, Back Lane, London NW3 1HL *Tel* 020 7794 9835 *Fax* 020 7431 3739 *email* people@charitiesadvisorytrust.org.uk *Website* www.charitiesadvisorytrust.org.uk

Think carefully about every application. Is it justified?

433

■ Charitworth Limited

CC NO 286908   **ESTABLISHED** 1983
WHERE FUNDING CAN BE GIVEN Worldwide, mainly UK and Israel.
WHO CAN BENEFIT Charitable organisations.
WHAT IS FUNDED Religious, educational and charitable purposes. In practice, mainly Jewish causes.
TYPE OF GRANT One-off and recurring.
RANGE OF GRANTS Up to around £150,000.
SAMPLE GRANTS Previous beneficiaries include: Zichron Nahum; British Friends of Tchernobil; Cosmon Belz; Chevras Maoz Ladal; Dushinsky Trust; Centre for Torah Education Trust; Finchley Road Synagogue; Friends of Viznitz; Beer Yaakov; and Beis Soroh Schneirer.
FINANCES *Year* 2009–10 *Income* £1,046,361 *Grants* £1,166,170 *Assets* £28,668,328
TRUSTEES David Halpern; Reilly Halpern; Sidney Halpern; Samuel J Halpern.
HOW TO APPLY In writing to the correspondent.
WHO TO APPLY TO David Halpern, Trustee, Cohen Arnold and Co., New Burlington House, 1075 Finchley Road, London NW11 0PU *Tel* 020 8731 0777 *Fax* 020 8731 0778

■ The Charter 600 Charity

CC NO 1051146   **ESTABLISHED** 1994
WHERE FUNDING CAN BE GIVEN UK.
WHO CAN BENEFIT Registered charities. Community-based, grass-roots organisations.
WHAT IS FUNDED General charitable purposes, with particular emphasis on education, social and medical welfare support for young people and communities.
WHAT IS NOT FUNDED Applications for charitable grants will only be accepted when put forward by a member of the Mercers' Company.
RANGE OF GRANTS Up to £2,500.
SAMPLE GRANTS Russian Orphan Opportunity Fund (£2,000); Cornwall Multiple Sclerosis Therapy Centre' Faversham Amateur Boxing Club and Touch of Light (£1,500 each); Bray Senior Citizens Club, Croydon Community Against Trafficking and Shirts for Soldiers (£1,000 each); Cherished Memories Support Group, Fewen Educational Trust, St Barnabas Parish Church and Trustees of King George's Field Whitwell (£750 each); Friends in St Helier, Hereford String Orchestra and Willow Foundation (£500 each); and Federation of Youth Clubs and Westminster House Youth Club (£250 each).
FINANCES *Year* 2009–10 *Income* £70,300 *Grants* £41,651 *Assets* £803,156
TRUSTEES The Mercers Company.
HOW TO APPLY The charity does not consider unsolicited applications.
WHO TO APPLY TO The Clerk, Mercers' Hall, Ironmonger Lane, London EC2V 8HE *Website* www.mercers.co.uk

■ The Worshipful Company of Chartered Accountants General Charitable Trust (also known as CALC)

CC NO 327681   **ESTABLISHED** 1988
WHERE FUNDING CAN BE GIVEN UK.
WHO CAN BENEFIT Registered charities and voluntary organisations.
WHAT IS FUNDED At least one theme directly or indirectly of relevance to the work of the profession (chosen by the master on their appointment in October of each year). Other recommendations and proposals put to the trustees by members of the Livery.
SAMPLE GRANTS The Master's project (£56,000); Institute of Chartered Accountants bursary (£10,000); MANGO (£5,000); and The Lord Mayor's Appeal 2010 (£2,500).
FINANCES *Year* 2009–10 *Income* £145,999 *Grants* £124,591 *Assets* £1,202,397
TRUSTEES Henry Gold; Rachel Adams; Colin Brown; John Cardnell; James Macnamara; David Allvey.
OTHER INFORMATION £24,000 was distributed between 29 Primary Schools to promote numeracy and literacy.
HOW TO APPLY Applications must be sponsored by a liveryman of the company.
WHO TO APPLY TO Peter Lusty, Clerk, Hampton City Services, Hampton House, High Street, East Grinstead, West Sussex RH19 3AW *Tel* 01342 319038 *email* peterlusty@btconnect.com

■ The Chasah Trust

CC NO 294898   **ESTABLISHED** 1986
WHERE FUNDING CAN BE GIVEN Greater London and UK.
WHO CAN BENEFIT Evangelists and Christians.
WHAT IS FUNDED The encouragement of missionary activity as well as the advancement of the evangelical tenets of Christianity.
WHAT IS NOT FUNDED Buildings or general appeals are not funded.
RANGE OF GRANTS Up to £15,000.
FINANCES *Year* 2009–10 *Income* £25,971 *Grants* £21,599
TRUSTEES Karen Collier-Keywood; Richard Collier-Keywood.
OTHER INFORMATION The grant total in 2009–10 includes £10,223 donated to individuals.
HOW TO APPLY In writing to the correspondent.
WHO TO APPLY TO Richard D Collier-Keywood, Glydwish Hall, Fontridge Lane, Etchingham, East Sussex TN19 7DG

■ Chasdei Tovim Me'oros

CC NO 1110623   **ESTABLISHED** 2005
WHERE FUNDING CAN BE GIVEN UK and Israel.
WHO CAN BENEFIT Jewish organisations and individuals.
WHAT IS FUNDED Jewish causes.
SAMPLE GRANTS Previous beneficiaries included: Tovim Meoros – Israel (£17,000); ZBE Trust (£5,000); and Chevars Meoz Ladol (£4,300).
FINANCES *Year* 2009–10 *Income* £27,761 *Grants* £16,438 *Assets* £2,302
TRUSTEES F Spitz; M Salamon; Y Bleier.
HOW TO APPLY In writing to the correspondent.
WHO TO APPLY TO Yoel Bleier, Trustee, 17 Durlston Road, London E5 8RP

■ The Checkatrade Foundation

CC NO 1137878   **ESTABLISHED** 2010
WHERE FUNDING CAN BE GIVEN UK.
WHO CAN BENEFIT Registered charities.
WHAT IS FUNDED Social welfare, the arts, health and disability.
TRUSTEES Kevin Byrne; Richard Spiceley; Nadine Hermon; Claire Hossell; Anna Byrne; Bridget Barnes.
OTHER INFORMATION The foundation's first annual report and accounts had yet to be produced at the time of writing (December 2011).
HOW TO APPLY In writing to the correspondent.

WHO TO APPLY TO Nadine Hermon, Trustee, 5 Sherrington Mews, Ellis Square, Selsey, Chichester, West Sussex PO20 0FJ *Tel* 01243 608803 *email* foundation@checkatrade.com *Website* www.checkatrade.com/Charity

---

■ The Chelsea Building Society Charitable Foundation

CC NO 1079292   **ESTABLISHED** 2000
WHERE FUNDING CAN BE GIVEN Beneficiary organisations must be UK based and within a 10 mile radius of a Chelsea Building Society branch office.
WHO CAN BENEFIT Registered charities only. In particular, the trustees are keen to support community based charities.
WHAT IS FUNDED In particular, the trustees are keen to support community based charities where small donations can make a significant difference to local people's lives. Grants are given in the following categories: homelessness; housing; debt advice – encouraging prudent money management. e.g. money advice services which include giving advice and helping disadvantaged people take control of their money including budgeting skills; mental health and learning difficulties; all forms of disability; children and young people; the elderly. 'Please provide clear information on need, effectiveness, impact and the specific value our grant could have to a particular project.'
WHAT IS NOT FUNDED The trustees will not consider grants relating to the following: non registered charities; charities which have applied to the foundation within the previous 24 months; activities which are mainly/normally the statutory responsibility of central or local government or some other responsible body (except proposals for added support services); schools, universities and colleges (except for projects which will specifically benefit disabled students and are additional to statutory responsibilities); hospitals, medical centres, medical treatment research (except projects extra to statutory responsibilities); collecting funds for later distribution to other charities or to individuals; political or pressure groups; profit distributing organisations; individuals or individual fund-raising efforts, including expeditions or overseas travel; general fund raising events, activities or appeals; general funding for salaries and core costs; fabric appeals for places of worship; the promotion of religion; animal welfare or wildlife; charities which have substantial reserves (in excess of 12 months expenditure) or in serious deficit; charities which have an annual income in excess of £500,000; the purchase of minibuses or other vehicles; the acquisition, renovation and refurbishment of buildings.
RANGE OF GRANTS £250–£5,000.
SAMPLE GRANTS Previous beneficiaries include: Winston's Wish (£5,000); the Heart of Kent Hospice (£2,000); the Rose Road Association (£1,500); Carousel Project, Ealing No. 1 Club, House of St Barnabas-in-Soho, Moulsecoomb Neighbourhood Trust and Waltham Forest Churches Night Shelter (£1,000 each); 870 House (£900); The Great Bridge Community Forum Project, Friends of Colnbrook Special School, Guildford and Waverley Cruse Bereavement Care, Off the Fence Trust and Spinal Injuries Association (£500 each); the St Paul's Centre (£450); and Christians Against Poverty (£250).

FINANCES *Year* 2009–10 *Income* £38,655 *Grants* £53,255 *Assets* £28,895
TRUSTEES Mrs M Corke; Ms N Corner.
HOW TO APPLY Applications can only be considered if made in writing on the foundation's application form. The opening date for applications will be confirmed on its website. Please check its website for up-to-date information.
WHO TO APPLY TO The Secretary, Administrative Headquarters, Thirlestaine Hall, Thirlestaine Road, Cheltenham, Gloucestershire GL53 7AL *Tel* 01242 283605 *Fax* 01242 283551 *email* charitablefoundation@thechelsea.co.uk *Website* www.thechelsea-charity-foundation.co.uk

---

■ The Chelsea Square 1994 Trust

CC NO 1040479   **ESTABLISHED** 1994
WHERE FUNDING CAN BE GIVEN Southern England, and to a limited extent, overseas.
WHO CAN BENEFIT Charitable organisations.
WHAT IS FUNDED Chiefly projects related to animals and people who are older or underprivileged.
WHAT IS NOT FUNDED No grants to individuals.
TYPE OF GRANT One-off grants.
SAMPLE GRANTS Cystic Fibrosis Trust, Kids for Kids, Home Start Elmbridge, the Ripieno Choir, Sussex Choir and Treloar Trust (£2,000 each).
FINANCES *Year* 2009–10 *Income* £29,412 *Grants* £15,000
TRUSTEES Patrick Talbot; Jonathan Woods; John Frederick Woods.
HOW TO APPLY In writing to the correspondent with report and accounts. Unsuccessful applicants will not receive a reply; send an sae if you wish documents to be returned.
WHO TO APPLY TO Paul Shiels, c/o Moon Beaver Solicitors, 24–25 Bloomsbury Square, London WC1A 2PL *Tel* 020 7637 0661 *Fax* 020 7436 4663 *email* psheils@mail.com

---

■ The Cheruby Trust

CC NO 327069   **ESTABLISHED** 1986
WHERE FUNDING CAN BE GIVEN UK and worldwide.
WHO CAN BENEFIT Registered charities.
WHAT IS FUNDED Welfare, education and general charitable purposes.
RANGE OF GRANTS £200–£5,000.
SAMPLE GRANTS Water Aid (£5,000); Breadline Africa and British Humanitarian Aid (£3,000 each); WJR – Indonesia Appeal (£2,500); Indian Rural Health Trust (£2,000); DEC – Haiti Earthquake Appeal (£1,000); and Rainforest Concern (£500).
FINANCES *Year* 2009–10 *Income* £31,768 *Grants* £17,000 *Assets* £31,190
TRUSTEES A L Corob; L E Corob; T A Corob; C J Cook: S A Wechsler.
OTHER INFORMATION Grants in 2007/08 amounted to £105,000, indicating a significant drop in expenditure for 2009–10 (£17,000)
HOW TO APPLY In writing to the correspondent.
WHO TO APPLY TO Mrs S Wechsler, Trustee, 62 Grosvenor Street, London W1K 3JF *Tel* 020 7499 4301

■ The Cheshire Provincial Fund of Benevolence

CC NO 219177   **ESTABLISHED** 1963

WHERE FUNDING CAN BE GIVEN Cheshire and parts of Greater Manchester and Merseyside.

WHO CAN BENEFIT Individuals and organisations benefiting Masons and their families.

WHAT IS FUNDED The relief of Masons and their dependants, Masonic charities and other charities, especially medical.

SAMPLE GRANTS Previous beneficiaries have included Children's Cancer Support Group, Mencap, Wirral Autistic Society, Bollington and Macclesfield Sea Cadets and Cathedral Road Kids Project.

FINANCES *Year* 2009–10 *Income* £356,434 *Grants* £73,486 *Assets* £3,312,757

TRUSTEES A Glazier; J Ellershaw; D Hinde; G Viner; T I Cranston; A P Rigby.

OTHER INFORMATION In previous years the trust has given around £2,000 to non-masonic organisations.

HOW TO APPLY In writing to the correspondent.

WHO TO APPLY TO Peter Carroll, Provincial Grand Secretary, Ashcroft House, 36 Clay Lane, Timperley, Altrincham, Greater Manchester WA15 7AB *Tel* 0161 980 6090 *email* enquiries@cheshiremasons.co.uk

■ Chest, Heart and Stroke Scotland

SC NO SC018761   **ESTABLISHED** 1990

WHERE FUNDING CAN BE GIVEN Scotland.

WHO CAN BENEFIT Academics, research workers and medical professionals living and working in Scotland.

WHAT IS FUNDED Medical research into all aspects of the aetiology, diagnosis, prevention, treatment and social impact of chest, heart and stroke illness. Applications directly relating to improvements in patient care, quality of life and health promotion are particularly welcomed.

WHAT IS NOT FUNDED Research involving animals is not funded. Research grants are restricted to those living and working in Scotland.

TYPE OF GRANT Research fellowships, project grants, travel and equipment grants, career development awards, research secondments, and student electives. Funding may be given for up to three years.

RANGE OF GRANTS Research grants up to £90,000.

FINANCES *Year* 2010–11 *Income* £6,791,301 *Grants* £840,000

HOW TO APPLY Please contact the correspondent for further details of how to apply or visit the website where criteria, guidelines and application process are posted.

WHO TO APPLY TO Research Manager, Third Floor, Roseberry House, 9 Haymarket Terrace, Edinburgh EH12 5EZ *Tel* 0131 225 6963 *email* admin@chss.org.uk *Website* www.chss.org.uk

■ The Chetwode Foundation

CC NO 265950   **ESTABLISHED** 1973

WHERE FUNDING CAN BE GIVEN UK, with a preference for Nottinghamshire, Leicestershire and Derby.

WHO CAN BENEFIT Registered charities only.

WHAT IS FUNDED General charitable purposes.

SAMPLE GRANTS North Notts Independent Domestic Abuse Services – NNIDAS (£26,000); Canaan Trust (£10,000); Hope for the Homeless (£8,000); Belvoir Castle Cricket Trust (£4,000); Tythby and Cropwell Butler PCC (£3,000); Newark and Nottinghamshire Agricultural Society (£2,000); Help for Heroes, NSPCC, Brough Methodist Chapel and Hand in Hand Trust (£1,000 each); Bingham and District Choral Society (£750); British Limbless Ex-Service Men's Association (£500); and Chance to Shine (£250).

FINANCES *Year* 2009–10 *Income* £75,424 *Grants* £59,168 *Assets* £1,527,042

TRUSTEES J G Ellis; R N J S Price; A C Price.

HOW TO APPLY 'The foundation's grant making policy is to support a limited number of causes known to the trustees, particularly those supported by the settlor. Unsolicited applications are not normally considered.'

WHO TO APPLY TO J G Ellis, Trustee, Samworth Brothers (Holdings) Ltd, Chetwode House, 1 Samworth Way, Leicester Road, Melton Mowbray, Leicestershire *Tel* 01664 414500

■ Chevioty Asset Management Charitable Trust

CC NO 265596   **ESTABLISHED** 1973

WHERE FUNDING CAN BE GIVEN UK.

WHO CAN BENEFIT Charitable organisations.

WHAT IS FUNDED General charitable purposes.

RANGE OF GRANTS £100–£4,000.

SAMPLE GRANTS TBA Tour de Racing and Leukaemia Research (£3,000 each); Colonels Fund Grenadier Guards, Interhealth, Nicholls Spinal Injury Foundation and the Prostate Cancer Charity (£2,000 each), The Watermill Theatre (£1,000); and NSPCC (£250).

FINANCES *Year* 2009–10 *Income* £17,014

TRUSTEES R P Tullett; A H Bartlett; M N C Kerr-Dineen; R Leigh Wood.

HOW TO APPLY No unsolicited applications.

WHO TO APPLY TO R P Tullett, Trustee, Robert Philip Tullett, Cheviot Asset Management, 90 Long Acre, London WC2E 9RA *Tel* 020 7438 5666

■ The Malcolm Chick Charity

CC NO 327732   **ESTABLISHED** 1988

WHERE FUNDING CAN BE GIVEN UK.

WHO CAN BENEFIT Registered charities.

WHAT IS FUNDED General charitable purposes, but effectively small grants to organisations the trustees are familiar with in the following areas: youth character building – there is an emphasis on grants towards sailing training; armed service charities – grants are limited to those charities supporting ex-army personnel and to charities providing direct care for ex-army personnel, for example grants to homes and charities providing welfare services for such persons; medical research and care – grants are made towards research into causes and treatment of heart disease and for buying equipment suitable for the treatment and care of people recovering from coronary heart disease.

RANGE OF GRANTS £500–£9,000.

SAMPLE GRANTS AHOY Centre and St Dunstan's (£9,000 each); Children's Heart Foundation (£4,000); Barts and the London Charity, the Daneforth Trust, Hove and the Adur Sea Cadet Unity and Tall Ships Youth Trust (£3,000 each); and Soft Power Education, Ocean Youth Trust South and Project Trust (£500 each).

FINANCES *Year* 2009–10 *Income* £23,060 *Grants* £23,576

TRUSTEES D J L Mobsby; R S Fowler; N D Waldman.

HOW TO APPLY Applicants should first write to ask for a copy of the criteria and application forms. Telephone calls are not welcomed. The trustees meet to consider applications in November and completed forms must be returned by the middle of October. There is a separate application form and guidance notes for individual applicants.

WHO TO APPLY TO Jayne Day, Administrator, c/o Pothecary Witham Weld Solicitors, 25C North Street, Bishop's Stortford, Hertfordshire CM23 2LD *Tel* 01279 506421 *email* charities@pwwsolicitors.co.uk

---

■ Child Growth Foundation

CC NO 274325   **ESTABLISHED** 1977
WHERE FUNDING CAN BE GIVEN UK.
WHO CAN BENEFIT Institutions researching child/adult growth disorders, and people with such diseases.
WHAT IS FUNDED Research into the causes and cure of growth disorders in children within the area of benefit and to publish the results of such research. The conditions covered by the foundation are: Turner syndrome; Russell Silver syndrome/intrauterine growth retardation; bone dysplasia; Sotos syndrome; premature sexual maturity; growth/multiple pituitary hormone deficiency.
TYPE OF GRANT Research.
RANGE OF GRANTS Up to £96,000.
SAMPLE GRANTS Institute of Child Health (£96,000); University of Edinburgh (£46,000); Central Manchester University Hospitals (£35,000); Queen Mary's College (£34,000); King's College (£11,000); and Imperial College (£4,400).
FINANCES *Year* 2009–10 *Income* £302,567 *Grants* £226,882 *Assets* £653,591
TRUSTEES Tam Fry, Chair; Nick Child; Russell Chaplin; Rachel Pidcock; Linda Washington; Mark Coyle; Sue Davies; Nick Fullagar.
HOW TO APPLY In writing to the correspondent.
WHO TO APPLY TO Tam Fry, Hon. Chair, 2 Mayfield Avenue, Chiswick W4 1PY *Tel* 020 8995 0257 *email* info@childgrowthfoundation.org *Website* www.childgrowthfoundation.org

---

■ Children's Liver Disease Foundation

CC NO 1067331   **ESTABLISHED** 1998
WHERE FUNDING CAN BE GIVEN UK.
WHO CAN BENEFIT Organisations benefiting children (up to the age of 18) with liver disease.
WHAT IS FUNDED Clinical and laboratory-based research and social research which looks at topics such as how to improve quality of life.
WHAT IS NOT FUNDED The charity does not accept applications from organisations whose work is not associated with paediatric liver disease. No grants to individuals, whether medical professionals or patients. No grants for travel or personal education. No grants for general appeals.
TYPE OF GRANT Research and project (maximum three years). Occasionally medical equipment.
RANGE OF GRANTS Small grant programme: up to £5,000.
SAMPLE GRANTS Birmingham Children's Hospital, King's College Hospital – London, Institute of Reproductive and Developmental Biology – Imperial College London, St James's University Hospital – Leeds, Liver Research Group – Southampton University, National Heart and Lung Institute – London and Queens Medical Centre – University of Nottingham.
FINANCES *Year* 2009–10 *Income* £669,944 *Grants* £73,163 *Assets* £728,083
TRUSTEES Tom Ross, Chair; Bob Benton; Nick Budd; Jayne Carroll; Kellie Charge; Mairi Everard; Michele Hunter; Ann Mowat; David Tildesley.
PUBLICATIONS Research priorities for 2011–14 are available to download from the website.
HOW TO APPLY Applicants are strongly advised to look at the relevant pages on the Children's Liver Disease Foundation website where further information and application forms are available.
WHO TO APPLY TO Catherine Arkley, Chief Executive, 36 Great Charles Street, Queensway, Birmingham B3 3JY *Tel* 0121 212 3839 *Fax* 0121 212 4300 *email* info@childliverdisease.org *Website* www.childliverdisease.org

---

■ The Children's Research Fund

CC NO 226128   **ESTABLISHED** 1962
WHERE FUNDING CAN BE GIVEN UK.
WHO CAN BENEFIT Institutes of child health and university child health departments.
WHAT IS FUNDED Promoting, encouraging and fostering research into all aspects of diseases in children, child health and prevention of illness in children. Support of research centres and research units by grants to academic institutions, hospitals and other bodies with similar aims and objects to the fund. Support after the first year is dependent on receipt of a satisfactory report.
WHAT IS NOT FUNDED No grants for capital projects.
TYPE OF GRANT Research.
SAMPLE GRANTS British Association of Paediatric Surgeons (£25,000); Liverpool School of Tropical Medicine (£7,000); Dr Saula – Africa (£6,000); War Children Of Kuwait (£3,000); and; KIND (£1,000).
FINANCES *Year* 2009–10 *Income* £42,035 *Grants* £40,500 *Assets* £1,477,517
TRUSTEES Hugh Greenwood, Chair; Gerald Inkin; Hugo Greenwood; Rt Hon. Lord Morris of Manchester; Elizabeth Theobald; David Lloyd.
HOW TO APPLY Applicants from child health research units and university departments are invited to send in an initial outline of their proposal; if it is eligible they will then be sent an application form. Applications are considered in March and November.
WHO TO APPLY TO The Trustees, Head Office, 6 Scarthill Property, New Lane, Aughton, Ormskirk, Lancashire L39 4UD *Tel* 01695 420928 *Website* www.childrensresearchfund.org.uk

---

■ The Childs Charitable Trust

CC NO 234618   **ESTABLISHED** 1962
WHERE FUNDING CAN BE GIVEN Worldwide.
WHO CAN BENEFIT Churches or Christian organisations.
WHAT IS FUNDED Christian activity at home and overseas, especially the furtherance of the Christian Gospel.
TYPE OF GRANT One-off and recurrent. Preference for large-scale project grants.
RANGE OF GRANTS Up to around £60,000.
SAMPLE GRANTS Previous beneficiaries include: Home Evangelism, ICC Mission Reserve, Latin Link, Mission Aviation Fellowship, Counties Evangelistic Work, Echoes of Service and Mustard Seed Relief, Scripture Union, Orphaids,

LAMA Ministries, ELAM Ministries, Hour of Revival and University of Bristol.

FINANCES *Year* 2009–10 *Income* £528,681 *Grants* £414,538 *Assets* £9,924,429

TRUSTEES D N Martin; R H Williams; A B Griffiths; S Puttock.

OTHER INFORMATION No grants list was available from the latest accounts.

HOW TO APPLY In writing to the correspondent. The trust states that 'all applications are considered but, unfortunately, not all charitable causes can be supported'. Funds may also be committed for long-term projects.

WHO TO APPLY TO Melanie Churchyard, 3 Cornfield Terrace, Eastbourne, East Sussex BN21 4NN *email* info@childstrust.org

■ The Childwick Trust

CC NO 326853 **ESTABLISHED** 1985

WHERE FUNDING CAN BE GIVEN UK and South Africa.

WHO CAN BENEFIT Registered charities only.

WHAT IS FUNDED In the UK, health, people with disabilities and older people, welfare and research in connection with the bloodstock industry and Jewish charities; in South Africa, education.

WHAT IS NOT FUNDED No funding for: general appeals; animal welfare charities; support students' individual education or gap year costs; drug or alcohol related causes or HIV/Aids related charities; or organisations outside of the UK, apart from pre-school education in South Africa.

TYPE OF GRANT Mainly one-off, project and capital for research and medical equipment.

RANGE OF GRANTS Up to £150,000. Most grants under £10,000.

SAMPLE GRANTS UK: Racing Welfare – Newmarket (£200,000); Northwick Park Institute for Medical Research (£55,000); Animal Health Trust – Newmarket (£50,000); Kings College Hospital (£33,000); MOVE – London (£30,000); Alkaptonuria Trust – Liverpool, Deafblind UK – Peterborough, EACH Children's Hospice – Cambridgeshire, Great Ormond Street Hospital, Grove House Hospice – Hertfordshire and Hospice of St. Francis – Hertfordshire (£20,000 each); Open Door – Hertfordshire, Spinal Injuries Association – Milton Keynes, St. Nicholas Hospice – Suffolk, University College London Hospitals and Scope – London (£15,000 each); Tommy's, London, Toynbee Hall, London and Women's Counselling Centre – Hertfordshire (£10,000 each); and Africana Library Trust, Sense – London, South East Cancer Help Centre and Starlight Children's Foundation – Berkshire (£5,000 each). South Africa: Ntataise Rural Pre-school Development Trust (£101,000); Sekhukhune Educare Project (£28,000); Thusanang Association (£18,000); and Jim Joel Music Scholarship – the Orchestra Company (£5,000).

FINANCES *Year* 2009–10 *Income* £2,290,723 *Grants* £2,610,384 *Assets* £57,554,325

TRUSTEES John Wood, Chair; Anthony Cane; Peter Glossop; Sarah Frost; Peter Anwyl-Harris.

OTHER INFORMATION Grants of less than £5,000 were made totalling £128,000.

HOW TO APPLY In writing to the correspondent. Please note: the trust welcomes initial enquiries by email or telephone, but asks that formal applications are sent by post. There is no official application form but the trust does provide the following guidelines for potential applicants: applications should be made to Karen Groom (Trust Administrator) on the charity's official headed paper and include the email address of the writer; letters should be no longer than two sides of A4 and describe 'fully, clearly and concisely' the project for which funding is being sought and who the beneficiaries will be; detailed costing or a project budget should be included and, if possible, a copy of the latest annual report (accounts will be viewed via the Charity Commission website); details of other sources of funding and any funding applications currently being made are also helpful to include. The trustees meet in May and December to consider applications. Applications are assessed before each meeting to check that they meet the trust's objectives. Applicants will be informed of the outcome within six weeks following the meeting. N.B. Applications for funding in South Africa should be made to Mrs G. Bland (Fund Director) at jimjoel@iafrica.com.

WHO TO APPLY TO Karen Groom, Trust Secretary, 9 The Green, Childwick Bury, St Albans, Hertfordshire AL3 6JJ *Tel* 01727 844666 *email* karen@childwicktrust.org *Website* www.childwicktrust.org

■ The Chippenham Borough Lands Charity

CC NO 270062 **ESTABLISHED** 1990

WHERE FUNDING CAN BE GIVEN Chippenham parish.

WHO CAN BENEFIT Individuals or community/charitable organisations which benefit the people of the Parish of Chippenham. Individuals must be living within the Parish of Chippenham at the date of application, and for a minimum of 2 years immediately prior to applying.

WHAT IS FUNDED The charity's income can be used by, or for the benefit of, the inhabitants of the Parish of Chippenham for: (i) relief of the aged, sick, disabled or poor; (ii) provision of facilities for recreation or other leisure time occupation; (iii) the advancement of education; (iv) the promotion of any other charitable purpose.

WHAT IS NOT FUNDED No help can be given for the following: individual adult sportsmen/woman; direct subsidy to local authorities; religious organisations (except for projects involving substantial non-denominational use for community benefit); retrospective applications; first degrees.

RANGE OF GRANTS Usually £100–£10,000.

SAMPLE GRANTS Previous beneficiaries included: North Wiltshire CAB (£34,000); Chippenham Town Partnership (£25,000); SPLASH (£10,000); Dorothy House Hospice (£9,200); St Nicholas School (£7,000); Hardenhuish School and Sheldon School (£6,000 each); Ivy Lane School and Young People's Support Service (£3,500 each); Queen's Crescent School (£2,000); Chippenham Light OperaGroup (£1,500); Chippenham Cantata (£1,100); and Chippenham Community Festival Association (£1,000).

FINANCES *Year* 2009–10 *Income* £365,635 *Grants* £211,000

TRUSTEES Chris Dawe; Peter Kemp; Mike Braun; Margaret Harrison; Jack Konynenburg; Peter Hutton; Mark Packard; Desna Allen; Graham Bone; Jenny Budgell; Terry Burke; Mary Pile.

OTHER INFORMATION Accounts for 2009–10 were overdue. The grant total is based on previous research. In the past about £35,000 has been given in grants to individuals.

438

Does the trust you have chosen match your needs? Haphazard applications waste postage and time

HOW TO APPLY On a form available from the correspondent, either via an agency or self referral.

WHO TO APPLY TO Catherine Flynn, Jubilee Building, 32 Market Place, Chippenham, Wiltshire SN15 3HP *Tel* 01249 658180 *Fax* 01249 446048 *email* admin@cblc.org.uk *Website* www.cblc.org.uk

■ The Chipping Sodbury Town Lands Charity

CC NO 236364   **ESTABLISHED** 1977
WHERE FUNDING CAN BE GIVEN The parishes of Chipping Sodbury and Old Sodbury.
WHO CAN BENEFIT Individuals and organisations.
WHAT IS FUNDED The trust gives grants for relief-in-need and educational purposes, and also other purposes within Sodbury, including the provision of leisure facilities.
TYPE OF GRANT Buildings, capital, one-off and recurring costs will be considered.
RANGE OF GRANTS £350–£20,000.
SAMPLE GRANTS Chipping Sodbury Endowed School (£20,000); Chipping Sodbury Scouts (£6,500); St John Baptist Church, Chipping Sodbury Cricket Club (£6,000 each); Chipping Sodbury Festival (£3,000); Chipping Sodbury Golf Club and Woodmans Close Residents Club (£1,000 each).
FINANCES *Year* 2010 *Income* £324,136 *Grants* £81,884 *Assets* £8,170,702
TRUSTEES P J Elsworth, Chair; B Ainsley; C A R Hatfield; B Seymour; D Shipp; R Smith; M Cook; Paul L; P S Robins; W Whittle.
OTHER INFORMATION In 2010 £24,000 was made in grants to individuals; including £10,000 towards educational grants and £9,000 towards winter grants.
HOW TO APPLY In writing to the correspondent. The trustees meet on the third week of each month except August.
WHO TO APPLY TO Nicola Gideon, Clerk, Town Hall, 57–59 Broad Street, Chipping Sodbury, Bristol, South Gloucestershire BS37 6AD *Tel* 01454 852223 *email* nicola.gideon@ chippingsodburytownhall.co.uk

■ CHK Charities Limited

CC NO 1050900   **ESTABLISHED** 1995
WHERE FUNDING CAN BE GIVEN Worldwide, in practice mainly UK with a preference for national and West Midlands charities.
WHO CAN BENEFIT Registered charities.
WHAT IS FUNDED Charities working in countryside matters, drug prevention, education, job creation, population control, culture, conservation, deafness, blindness, and the provision of treatment and care for people with disabilities.
WHAT IS NOT FUNDED The following will not normally be considered for funding: organisations not registered as charities or those that have been registered for less than a year; pre-school groups; out of school play schemes including pre-school and holiday schemes; projects which promote a particular religion; 'bottomless pits' and unfocussed causes; very small and narrowly specialised activities; community centres; appeals for places of worship; local authorities; umbrella or grant-making organisations; universities and colleges and grant maintained private or local education authority schools or their Parent Teachers Associations, except if these schools are for students with special needs; individuals or charities applying on behalf of individuals; general requests for donations; professional associations and training of professionals; projects which are abroad even though the charity is based in the UK; expeditions or overseas travel; 'campaigning organisations' or citizens advice projects providing legal advice; community transport projects; general counselling projects, except those in areas of considerable deprivation and with a clearly defined client group.
TYPE OF GRANT One-off, conditionally renewable and large grants.
RANGE OF GRANTS Mostly £2,000–£5,000. Can be over £100,000.
SAMPLE GRANTS Charities Aid Foundation (£105,000); Thomley Activity Centre (£100,000); Footsteps Foundation (£90,000); Royal Shakespeare Company; Endelienta Appeal; Gloucester Cathedral Trust; Cure Parkinson's Trust; National Playing Fields Association; Global Canopy Programme; Auditory Verbal UK; Canine Partners; Army Benevolent Fund; Coram Life Education; Cotswold School (£50,000 each); Prince's Youth Business Trust (£30,000); County Air Ambulance Trust (£13,000); Deaf Blind UK; Sense; Carers UK; Princess Royal Trust for Carers; Academy of Ancient Music; Interact Worldwide (£10,000); Family Haven; Noah's Ark Children's Venture; Mentor Foundation UK; Shakespeare Hospice Trust; Shelter; Marie Curie Cancer Centre (£5,000 each); Dentaid (£4,000); String of Pearls Project; U Can Do It; Farming and Wildlife Advisory Group (£3,000); Clean Rivers Trust (£2,000); and City University London (£1,600).
FINANCES *Year* 2010–11 *Income* £1,885,167 *Grants* £2,368,000 *Assets* £78,542,778
TRUSTEES David Peake; Charlotte Percy; David Acland; Joanna Prest; Katharine Loyd; Lucy Morris; Rupert Prest; Serena Acland; Susanna Peake.
OTHER INFORMATION This trust has a very useful website that should be referred to when considering making an application.
HOW TO APPLY The trust does not have an application form, but suggests that the following guidelines be used when making an application which should be in writing to the secretary: applications should be no longer than four A4 sides; include a short summary of the organisation and its status, e.g., registered charity; confirm the organisation has a Child Protection Policy and carries out CRB checks, if appropriate; provide a summary of the project and why a grant is needed; explain how it will be monitored and evaluated; state any funds that have already been raised/applied for; explain where on-going funding (if required) will be obtained when the grant has been used; state the amount needed if the request is for revenue funding for a specific item; and enclose a job description if the request is for a salary. Applications should also include the most recent audited accounts. Additional information on the application process can be found on the trust's website. Applications can be submitted at any time during the year. Trustees usually meet every two months. Both successful and unsuccessful applicants are expected to wait at least one year before reapplying.
WHO TO APPLY TO Nick R Kerr-Sheppard, Administrator, c/o Kleinwort Benson Trustees Limited, 14 St George Street, London W1S 1FE *Tel* 020 3207 7338 *Fax* 020 3207 7655 *Website* www.chkcharities.co.uk

■ The Chownes Foundation

cc no 327451   **established** 1987

where funding can be given UK, priority is given to charities based in Sussex, particularly in mid Sussex.

who can benefit Organisations and individuals.

what is funded The advancement of religion, the advancement of education among the young, the amelioration of social problems, and the relief of poverty amongst older people and the former members of Sound Diffusion PLC who lost their pensions when the company went into receivership. Preference will be given to projects where a donation may have some meaningful impact on an identified need rather than simply being absorbed into a larger funding requirement.

type of grant One-off, recurrent, buildings, capital, core costs, research and running costs. Funding is available for up to and over three years.

finances *Year* 2009–10 *Income* £99,967 *Grants* £105,372 *Assets* £1,635,340

trustees Mrs U Hazeel; The Rt Revd S Ortiger; M Woolley.

other information £48,000 of the grant total was given to individuals.

how to apply In writing to the correspondent.

who to apply to Sylvia Spencer, Secretary, The Courtyard, Beeding Court, Shoreham Road, Steyning, West Sussex BN44 3TN *Tel* 01903 816699 *email* chownes@russellnew.com

■ The Chrimes Family Charitable Trust

cc no 210199   **established** 1955

where funding can be given Merseyside, Wirral and North Wales.

who can benefit Registered charities.

what is funded The relief of poverty and distress and in the provision of funds towards projects for community welfare and the improvement of health and education with a preference for the support of community welfare in Merseyside and North Wales.

what is not funded No grants to individuals, arts, or conservation.

range of grants Up to £1,000.

finances *Year* 2009–10 *Income* £26,027 *Grants* £25,401 *Assets* £683,603

trustees Anne Williams; Helen Prosser.

other information In 2009–10, grants were broken down into the following categories:

Community welfare	£20,000
Health	£3,300
Research	£1,400
Animal Welfare	£500

how to apply In writing to the correspondent – there are no deadlines. The trust prefers not to receive contact via telephone.

who to apply to Anne Williams, Trustee, Northfield, Upper Raby Road, Neston, Wirral CH64 7TZ

■ The Christabella Charitable Trust

cc no 800610   **established** 1988

where funding can be given General but mainly Essex and surrounding areas.

who can benefit Registered charities, local organisations and individuals.

what is funded Christian causes are much favoured and there are several local organisations regularly supported including St Francis Church in West Horndon and Viz-a-Viz's evangelical work. The trustees prefer 'seed corn' funding of projects involving volunteers. Normally only one or two additional projects of special interest to the trust are supported each year.

what is not funded No support for UK-wide or international charities. Applications for grants towards general running costs or building refurbishment are very unlikely to be supported.

type of grant The trust prefer 'seed corn' funding of projects involving volunteers.

range of grants Up to £20,000.

sample grants Beneficiaries included: Viz-a-Viz (£25,000); National Garden Scheme (£15,000); Aegis Trust (£10,000); LDF Charitable Trust (£9,000); St Francis Church (£6,600); Tabor Centre (£400).

finances *Year* 2009–10 *Income* £407,930 *Grants* £70,102 *Assets* £4,356,962

trustees E B Munroe; Miss C Turner; R Hiburn; I Elliot; R Folwell.

other information This trust's primary objective is to maintain the charity's property at Barnards Farm in West Horndon as the house of the National Malus Collection, to allow the general public access on various published dates each year and for use by other charitable organisations.

how to apply In writing to the correspondent, from whom an application form is available. Please note the trust's 2007–08 accounts stated that 'the lower investment returns experienced in recent years has meant that very little, if any, income has remained for other projects'.

who to apply to Christina Turner, Administrator, Central Chambers, 98 High Street, Rayleigh, Essex SS6 7BY *Tel* 01268 776200 *Fax* 01268 776 400 *Website* www.barnardsfarm.eu

■ Christadelphian Samaritan Fund

cc no 1004457   **established** 1991

where funding can be given UK and overseas.

who can benefit Registered charities.

what is funded Preference is given to human causes and aid to third world.

what is not funded Individuals and non-registered charities are not eligible for support.

type of grant Single donations.

sample grants DEC – Haiti Earthquake Appeal (£29,000); DEC – Pakistan Floods Appeal (£12,000); UNICEF – Pakistan Floods Appeal (£9,000); Oxfam – Niger Drought Appeal (£3,000); and Save The Children Fund, Action Aid and British Red Cross – Chile Earthquake Appeal (£2,000 each).

finances *Year* 2010 *Income* £124,652 *Grants* £146,258 *Assets* £83,662

trustees K H A Smith; D P Ensell; Mrs C M Howarth; W N Moss; J M Hellawell; J M Buckler; R Miles.

how to apply In writing to the correspondent.

who to apply to K H A Smith, Trustee, Westhaven House, Arleston Way, Shipley, West Midlands B90 4LH

■ Christian Aid

cc no 1105851   **established** 1945

where funding can be given Mainly Third World. Limited assistance for development education projects in the UK.

who can benefit Councils of Churches; other ecumenical bodies, development and relief groups; UN agencies which benefit at risk groups; people disadvantaged by poverty; homeless people; refugees; immigrants; socially isolated people; victims of famine, man-made or natural disasters, and war.

WHAT IS FUNDED Organisations which work with the world's poorest people and communities. Funding is given to partner organisations only.

WHAT IS NOT FUNDED Individuals, political causes or organisations whose aims are primarily political are not eligible for grants.

TYPE OF GRANT Project.

FINANCES *Year* 2009–10 *Income* £104,621,000 *Grants* £41,000,000

TRUSTEES Anne Owers; Revd John Davies; Bob Fyfe; Carolyn Gray; Tom Hinton; Phil Hodkinson; Kumar Jacob; Gillian Kingston; Morag Mylne; Bishop Wilton Powell; Revd Alistair Redfern; Brian Ridsdale; Charlotte Seymour-Smith; Grahme Sparkes; Paul Spray; Bridget Walker; Bishop Trevor Williams.

HOW TO APPLY Initial approaches by potential partner organisations should be made in writing.

WHO TO APPLY TO 35–41 Lower Marsh, London SE1 7RI *Tel* 020 7620 4444 *email* info@christian-aid.org *Website* www.christianaid.org.uk

■ Christian Response to Eastern Europe

CC NO 1062623　　**ESTABLISHED** 1997

WHERE FUNDING CAN BE GIVEN Eastern Europe (in practice Romania and Moldova).

WHO CAN BENEFIT Christian organisations working in Eastern Europe.

WHAT IS FUNDED The objects of the charity are to provide relief to disadvantages and vulnerable people living in Eastern Europe. Help is given by supporting families, churches and medical organisations.

SAMPLE GRANTS Gura Biculu Centre building project (£85,000); Gura Biculu farm project (£20,000); Orhei Church and Soup Kitchen (£6,000); Repairs to road in Gambut Village (£3,000); Street Children's home, Beltsey and Well at Gribova (£2,000 each) and God's Vineyard Foundation (£1,000).

FINANCES *Year* 2010 *Income* £203,724 *Grants* £249,298 *Assets* £69,685

TRUSTEES David Northcote-Passmore, Chair; Timothy Mason; Hugh Scudder.

OTHER INFORMATION The 2010 grant total includes £115,000 given to individuals and families.

HOW TO APPLY In writing to the correspondent.

WHO TO APPLY TO David Northcote-Passmore, Chair, Cherith, 130 Honiton Road, Exeter EX1 3EW *Website* www.cr2ee.org.uk

■ Chrysalis Trust

CC NO 1133525　　**ESTABLISHED** 2010

WHERE FUNDING CAN BE GIVEN North East of England, UK national organisations providing benefit across the UK, overseas.

WHO CAN BENEFIT Charities, community groups and educational projects.

WHAT IS FUNDED General, education, social welfare.

WHAT IS NOT FUNDED Grants are not made for: research – academic or medical; holidays or outings; arts or entertainment activities; animal welfare; general appeals.

TYPE OF GRANT One-off grants to support capital costs and core funding.

RANGE OF GRANTS Up to £20,000.

SAMPLE GRANTS Cry in the Dark (£20,000), towards medical and vehicle running costs for Casa Lumina and Hospice Casa Albert – Romania; Excellent Development (£10,000), capital cost of one sand dam – Kenya; Greggs Foundation (£5,000), towards a hardship fund for making small grants to individuals in extreme financial hardship in the North East of England; Deafway (£4,000), towards bedding for a school for deaf children – Nepal; Circle of Life Rediscovery (£2,000), towards outdoor education for young carers; and British Wireless for the Blind Fund (£1,000), towards audio equipment for seven blind people in Newcastle.

FINANCES *Year* 2010–11 *Income* £1,404,672 *Grants* £62,646

TRUSTEES Mark Price Evans; Sarah Evans; Andrew Playle; Alba Lewis.

HOW TO APPLY The trust provides the following helpful information on its website:

Application Checklist

There is no application form. 'Please outline your project on no more than 4 A4 sides using the following checklist: what is the name of your organisation and what is your charitable registration number if you have one?; what does your organisation do?; who are you helping, how many and how?; how many staff and volunteers do you have?; which statutory and voluntary organisations do you have links with, if any?; how much money do you need? [e.g., a contribution of £X towards a total budget of £Y]. Where will the balance of the funds required come from?; what do you need the money for?; when do you need the money?; have you applied to other sources? If so, give details and outcomes; who is your key contact regarding this application and what are their contact details (including telephone, email and mailing address)?. Please attach: a 250 word summary of your proposal; the contact details of 2 organisations or individuals able to provide a reference on your behalf; a copy of your latest audited annual report and accounts or a copy of your most recent bank statement if you do not have accounts; a budget for the project for which the application is made; a please do not attach any unnecessary documentation. Applications should then be submitted preferably by email; if necessary, applications may be sent by post. **What will happen next?** You will receive an acknowledgement that your application has been received. Applications are considered by the Trustees twice a year – usually in June and December, however, applications for amounts less than £1,001 may be considered sooner. We may contact you by telephone or email to discuss your application or to arrange a visit. We aim to let applicants know whether or not their application has been successful within 2 weeks of the trustees meeting at which the application is being considered. **What are the terms and conditions of a grant?** Successful applicants will be asked to sign a simple grant agreement setting out their obligations in relation to the grant. Grants must be used for the purposes outlined in the application. If the project is unable to go ahead as planned we are happy to consider variations as to how the money is to be spent, however, the money must not be used for any other purposes without our agreement. It must be returned if the project does not go ahead. Recipients of a grant will be required to provide a report on the funded project to the trustees within 6 months of receiving the grant.'

WHO TO APPLY TO Sarah Evans, Trustee, Dickinson Dees, One Trinity Gardens, Broad Chare,

Newcastle upon Tyne NE1 2HF *Tel* 0844 984 1500 *Fax* 0844 984 1501 *email* info@chrysalis-trust.co.uk *Website* www.chrysalis-trust.co.uk

■ The Church and Community Fund

cc no 1074857   **ESTABLISHED** 1915
WHERE FUNDING CAN BE GIVEN England and Wales.
WHO CAN BENEFIT Parish, deanery or diocesan projects.
WHAT IS FUNDED Church and community projects.
WHAT IS NOT FUNDED No funding is given towards: projects that are essentially insular and inward looking; projects which are primarily about maintaining the nation's architectural heritage; projects which are primarily about liturgical reordering; restoration works to bells or organs; research projects or personal grants; the repayment of debts or overdrafts; projects which are not directly connected with the Church of England, ecumenical or other faith; partnerships in which the Church of England element is small and projects which are predominantly secular in nature; anything for which the Church Commissioners' funds or diocesan core funding are normally available, including stipend support; feasibility studies (the fund is able to offer limited support towards the preliminary costs of projects, for example professional fees, but where a grants is awarded at this stage, no further funding will be available for the main body of the work).
TYPE OF GRANT One-off and reoccurring.
RANGE OF GRANTS Usually less than £5,000.
SAMPLE GRANTS Emmanuel, West Gorton (£3,500); At Barnabas, Clarksfield (£3,000); St Barnabas with Christchurch, Worcester (£10,000); St Andrew, Haughton-le-Skerne (£4,500); Changing Attitude Sussex (£2,000) Hope's Place, Bristol (£2,000).
FINANCES *Year* 2010 *Income* £1,268,000 *Grants* £500,000 *Assets* £16,259,000
TRUSTEES The Archbishop's Council.
OTHER INFORMATION This fund is an excepted charity but its trustee, the Archbishop's Council, is registered under the above number.
HOW TO APPLY The fund usually has 4 rounds of funding per year. New guidance notes that will contain specific criteria, examples of what type of projects will be funded and more detail about the new strategy will be available [from the fund]. The fund illustrates the application process in a flow chart available on the website. The first part of the process takes 2 weeks in which applications will either be confirmed or sent back if they are incomplete. The second part of the process from confirmation that the application is complete to notification of the outcome takes on average 3 months. These timescales depend upon the submission date of the application and applicants should check the website to ensure the correct application deadlines. Trustees meet 4 times a year.
WHO TO APPLY TO Andrew Hawkings, Grants Manager, Church House, Great Smith Street, London SW1P 3AZ *Tel* 020 7898 1541 *email* ccf@churchofengland.org *Website* www.centralchurchfund.org.uk

■ The Church Burgesses Educational Foundation

cc no 529357   **ESTABLISHED** 1963
WHERE FUNDING CAN BE GIVEN Sheffield.
WHO CAN BENEFIT Individuals and schools benefiting children and young adults.
WHAT IS FUNDED Church schools, independent schools, junior schools, language schools, primary and secondary schools, special schools, tertiary and higher education, and youth organisations. Also funded are bursaries, fees, scholarships, and the purchase of books.
TYPE OF GRANT Core costs, one-off and running costs. Funding may be given for up to three years.
SAMPLE GRANTS Previous beneficiaries have included Dyslexia Institute, the Flower Estate Community Association, Pitstop, Sheffield County Guide Association, Sheffield YMCA, South Yorkshire and Hallam Clubs for Young People, Whirlow Hall Farm Trust and Wybourn Youth Trust.
FINANCES *Year* 2010 *Income* £321,009 *Grants* £313,257 *Assets* £433,540
TRUSTEES Prof. G D Sims; Revd S A P Hunter; J F W Peters; Dr D Bradshaw; Mrs B R Hickman; Miss H Morris; D Stanley.
OTHER INFORMATION The grants total includes £128,000 that was given to individuals.
HOW TO APPLY In writing to the correspondent. Trustees meet four times a year.
WHO TO APPLY TO G J Smallman, Secretary, Wrigleys Solicitors LLP, Fountain Precinct, Balm Green, Sheffield S1 2JA *Tel* 0114 267 5594 *email* sheffieldchurchburgesses@wrigleys.co.uk *Website* www.sheffieldchurchburgesses.org.uk

■ Church Burgesses Trust

cc no 221284   **ESTABLISHED** 1554
WHERE FUNDING CAN BE GIVEN Sheffield.
WHO CAN BENEFIT Voluntary organisations and registered charities.
WHAT IS FUNDED Ecclesiastical purposes, education, and other charitable purposes.
TYPE OF GRANT One-off and recurring.
RANGE OF GRANTS £40–£12,000.
SAMPLE GRANTS St James Norton – grant for church army officer (£23,000); St Luke's Hospice (£20,000); St John's Chapeltown Youth Worker (£18,000); St Paul Wordsworth Avenue (£12,000); The Ascension Oughtibridge (£9,400); Area Deans support grant (£6,000); Church Army (£5,000); and St Mary's Handsworth – Ordinand in Training (£700); St Luke's Hospice (£10,000); Voluntary Action Sheffield (£7,000); Sheffield Association for People with Cerebral Palsy (£5,000); The Oakes Holiday Centre (£2,500); Shopmobility; Manor Young People's Health; SAGE Greenfingers (£2,000 each); and Star Enterprise Work and Play (£1,000).
FINANCES *Year* 2010 *Income* £2,404,765 *Grants* £1,207,246 *Assets* £38,789,414
TRUSTEES D F Booker; Revd S A P Hunter; Nicholas J A Hutton; Julie Banham; Peter W Lee; J F W Peters; Prof. G D Sims; Ian G Walker; Mike R Woffenden; D Stanley; B R Hickman; Mrs S Bain.
PUBLICATIONS *We of Our Bounty* – a history of the Sheffield Church Burgesses.
OTHER INFORMATION The trust's website is very useful and should be referred to.
HOW TO APPLY In writing to the correspondent. The trustees meet in January, April, July and October and at other times during the year through its various committees. The day to day

administration of the trust, work in connection with its assets, liaison with outside bodies such as the Diocese of Sheffield, the administration of its grant programmes and the processing and handling of applications prior to their consideration by relevant committees is delegated to the Law Clerk and applications should be made to him/her. The trust invites applications from Anglican parishes, from individuals involved in Christian work of a wide variety of types and from charities both national and local, involved in general charitable work within the trust's geographical area of remit. Further information, guidelines for applying and application forms are available on the trust's website.

WHO TO APPLY TO Godfrey J Smallman, Secretary, Wrigleys Solicitors LLP, Fountain Precinct, Balm Green, Sheffield S1 2JA *Tel* 0114 267 5594 *Fax* 0114 276 3176 *email* sheffieldchurchburgesses@wrigleys.co.uk *Website* www.sheffieldchurchburgesses.org.uk

....

■ Church of Ireland Priorities Fund

ESTABLISHED 1980

WHERE FUNDING CAN BE GIVEN Ireland.

WHO CAN BENEFIT Charitable organisations.

WHAT IS FUNDED Church of Ireland projects. Areas currently supported by the fund are: ministry; retirement; education; community; areas of need; outreach initiatives.

WHAT IS NOT FUNDED The committee make the following choices whilst considering applications: people not buildings; new projects rather than recurrent expenditure; mission and outreach rather than maintenance; projects and programmes rather than structure.

RANGE OF GRANTS €500–€25,000.

FINANCES *Year* 2010 *Grants* £554,000

PUBLICATIONS Priorities News – Published each year in May

OTHER INFORMATION All the financial information is in euros.

HOW TO APPLY On a form available from the fund's website. Applications must be made by 31 October each year. Applications are considered in February and approved in March.

WHO TO APPLY TO Mrs Sylvia Simpson, Organiser, Church of Ireland House, Church Avenue, Rathmines, Dublin 6 *Tel* 00353 497 8422 *email* priorities@ireland.anglican.org *Website* www.priorities.ireland.anglican.org

....

■ The Church Urban Fund

CC NO 297483   **ESTABLISHED** 1988

WHERE FUNDING CAN BE GIVEN The most deprived areas of England.

WHO CAN BENEFIT Local faith-based groups and activists working to help individuals, families and communities of people living in deprived neighbourhoods in England.

WHAT IS FUNDED The fund's key objectives are to confront disadvantage and inequality in deprived communities and promote their economic, social and spiritual renewal. In particular the trust will support projects that: tackle major problems in their area, such as poverty, unemployment, disaffected youth, lack of community facilities, loneliness and isolation, or housing and homelessness; equip local communities to address local needs and issues and encourage people to take control of their lives; empower the faith community to take an active role in wider community development,

particularly through interfaith and ecumenical developments; are innovative, will make a practical impact and can develop partnerships with other agencies.

WHAT IS NOT FUNDED Projects outside England; individuals; projects not directly tackling profound poverty or specific issues caused by poverty; organisations with an annual turnover of over £150,000 or with significant reserves; projects without church or faith links; existing salary costs except where there is a significant increase in hours in order to expand an existing project or begin new work; ongoing revenue costs; repeated activities (such as an annual summer camp); retrospective funding or loan repayment; campaigning and fundraising activity; revenue and capital funding for national voluntary/ community organisations and public and private sector organisations; activities only open to church members; evangelistic activity not part of a response to poverty; clergy stipends including Church Army posts; general repairs and refurbishment, internal re-ordering of churches for worship, church maintenance or DDA (Disability Discrimination Act) compliance; general appeals.

TYPE OF GRANT Capital, project and revenue funding for up to three years.

RANGE OF GRANTS £100–£5,000.

SAMPLE GRANTS Project Freedom Trust; Sussex Pathways; Faith Drama Productions; Housing Justice; Community Money Advice; Reading Refugee Support Group; The Bridge Pregnancy Crisis Centre; All Saints Hanley (£5,000 each); (£4,900 each); Church Action on Poverty; Bristol Inter Faith Group Keeping Health in Mind (£4,500) Youth Project @ Apostles and Cuthbert's (£4,200); St Andrews Community Network (£4,000).

FINANCES *Year* 2010 *Income* £2,543,000 *Grants* £1,144,000 *Assets* £2,860,000

TRUSTEES Bishop Peter Broadbent; Patrick Coldstream; Michael Eastwood; Ven Paul Hackwood; Andrew Hunter Johnston; Revd Dennis Poole; Derek Twine; Betty Thayer; Revd David Walker; Brian Carroll.

PUBLICATIONS The trust has produced a detailed and helpful grants policy and procedure manual and applicants are advised to read this before making an application. The manual is available from the trust's website. The trust also publishes excellent reports on a wide range of issues related to poverty and deprivation. These are also available on the website.

HOW TO APPLY The trust offers this overview of the application procedure: 'Review whether your project fits in with our criteria; if yes, contact your local Link Officer. Discuss your proposal, and if appropriate you will be offered an application form; complete the application forma and return it with a budget outline and your latest accounts to your officer; your application will be reviewed locally before being forwarded to Church Urban Fund offices for final assessment. The fund aims to assess applications and communicate a decision within one month of receiving the proposal in the central offices. **The main grants programme is suspended indefinitely.**'

WHO TO APPLY TO Lucy Palfreyman, Director of Finance and Resources, Church House, 27 Great Smith Street, Westminster, London SW1P 3AZ *Tel* 020 7898 1647 *Fax* 2078981601 *email* enquiries@cuf.org.uk *Website* www.cuf.org.uk

■ City and County of Swansea Welsh Church Act Fund

CC NO 1071913   **ESTABLISHED** 1997

WHERE FUNDING CAN BE GIVEN City and County of Swansea.

WHO CAN BENEFIT Registered charities.

WHAT IS FUNDED General charitable purposes.

WHAT IS NOT FUNDED No grants to individuals. 'Applications will not be considered for grants, which would normally be dealt with out of the annual budgets of the council's service departments or by public agencies or that would commit the fund to regular payments for a particular purpose.'

TYPE OF GRANT Revenue projects, up to a maximum of £5,000. For capital costs, only churches are eligible, up to a maximum of £1,000.

RANGE OF GRANTS Up to £5,000.

SAMPLE GRANTS Swansea Community Boat Trust and The Play and Leisure Opportunity Library (£2,500 each); Mumbles Development Trust, Young and Gifted Project and Newton Village Hall (£2,000 each); Swansea Carnival Collection and Vision Impaired West Glamorgan (£1,500); Aids Trust Cymru, Swansea City Mission and Educational Trust and Tidy TV Bonymaen Studio Group (£1,000 each); and Glamorgan Drama League and St. Paul's Church Luncheon Club (£500 each).

FINANCES *Year* 2009–10 *Income* £38,574 *Grants* £37,149 *Assets* £933,774

TRUSTEES City and County of Swansea.

HOW TO APPLY On a form available from the correspondent. Trustees meet twice a year to consider grants. 'Applications should be sent by April or the end of September. Successful applicants cannot re-apply for three years.'

WHO TO APPLY TO The Clerk, Financial Department, City and County of Swansea, County Hall, Oystermouth Road, Swansea SA1 3SN

■ The City Bridge Trust (formerly known as Bridge House Trust)

CC NO 1035628   **ESTABLISHED** 1995

WHERE FUNDING CAN BE GIVEN Greater London.

WHO CAN BENEFIT Third sector organisations, mainly registered charities whose activities benefit the people of Greater London.

WHAT IS FUNDED The trust has seven main grant programmes, each with specific aims and objectives. In all cases priority is given to projects which tackle the greatest deprivation or disadvantage. (1) Accessible London – To reduce disadvantage experienced by disabled people by removing those barriers that prevent full participation in society. Emphasis is given to artistic and sporting activities and improving the accessibility of transport and community buildings. (2) Bridging Communities – to strengthen links between communities by building on commonalities and encouraging groups to come together. (3) London's Environment – to improve the quality of London's environment and its sustainable development. (4) Improving Londoners' Mental Health – supports work which meets a wide range of mental health needs and ensures that services are reaching marginalised communities. (5) Older Londoners – to contribute to a London where people can enjoy active, independent and healthy lives in their old age. (6) Positive Transitions to Independent Living – to improve the range of services for people who are going through difficult

transitions and challenges. (7) Strengthening the Third Sector – To strengthen the Voluntary and Community Sector so that it can deliver effective, efficient and sustainable services helping reduce disadvantage.

WHAT IS NOT FUNDED The trust cannot fund: political parties; political lobbying; non-charitable activities; and work which does not benefit the inhabitants of Greater London. The trust does not fund: individuals; grant-making bodies to make grants on its behalf; schools, PTAs, universities or other educational establishments (except where they are undertaking ancillary charitable activities specifically directed towards one of the agreed priority areas); medical or academic research; churches or other religious bodies where the monies will be used for religious purposes; hospitals; projects which have already taken place or building work which has already been completed; statutory bodies; profit making organisations (except social enterprises); and charities established outside the UK. Grants will not usually be given to: work where there is statutory responsibility to provide funding; organisations seeking funding to replace cuts by statutory authorities, except where that funding was explicitly time-limited and for a discretionary (non-statutory) purpose; organisations seeking funding to top up on under-priced contracts; and work where there is significant public funding available (including funding from sports governing bodies).

TYPE OF GRANT Grants for either running costs or capital costs. Grants for running costs are made for 1 to 3 years. Projects of an exceptional or strategic nature may then make an application for a further two years, a maximum total of five years in all.

RANGE OF GRANTS No minimum amount but applications over £25,000 need to be accompanied by a detailed proposal. Large grants to small organisations are unlikely to be made. Grants over £500,000 need the approval of the City of London Corporation's Court Common Council and are very exceptional.

SAMPLE GRANTS Barbican Centre Trust (£1.5 million); Mind in Camden (£150,000); Positively UK; Greening the Third Sector (£100,000 each); Cricklewood Homeless Concern (£95,000); City Centre for Charity Effectiveness Trust Ltd (£80,000); Good Food Matters (£50,000); Royal Horticultural Society (£49,000); Bromley Autistic Trust (£46,000); Arachane Greek Cypriot Women's Group (£35,000); Rampage Holiday Project (£15,000) and Amici Dance Theatre Company (£9,300).

FINANCES *Year* 2010–11 *Income* £40,000,000 *Grants* £16,830,000 *Assets* £828,200,000

TRUSTEES The Corporation of the City of London.

OTHER INFORMATION The City Bridge Trust is the grant making arm of the Bridge House Estates charity whose prime objective is the provision and maintenance of the four bridges across the Thames into the City of London.

HOW TO APPLY Application forms are available from the trust or downloadable from its website, along with full and up-to-date guidelines. This is also available on disk, on tape and in Braille or large print formats. The application will be assessed by a member of the grants team and then considered by the grants committee, this may include a visit. The application process usually takes 3 months from receipt of the application. Organisations may usually hold only one grant at a time however charities with branches or that are running distinct activities in different parts of London may be able to hold up to 3. Applications for over £25,000 need to be accompanied by a detailed proposal and grants over £500,000 need the approval of the City of London Corporation's Court Common Council and are very exceptional. Please note: the trust will not consider applications sent by fax or conventional email.

WHO TO APPLY TO Clare Thomas, Chief Grants Officer, PO Box 270, Guildhall, London EC2P 2EJ *Tel* 020 7332 3710 *Fax* 020 7332 3127 *Minicom* 020 7332 3151 *email* citybridgetrust@cityoflondon.gov.uk *Website* www.citybridgetrust.org.uk/ CityBridgeTrust

....

■ The City Educational Trust Fund

cc no 290840 **ESTABLISHED** 1967
WHERE FUNDING CAN BE GIVEN Generally Greater London.
WHO CAN BENEFIT Institutions in London benefiting young adults, research workers, students and teachers.
WHAT IS FUNDED A variety of educational groups and institutions to promote study, teaching and training in areas such as science, technology, business management, commerce, biology, ecology and the cultural arts.
WHAT IS NOT FUNDED No grants to individuals.
TYPE OF GRANT One-off, ongoing and fixed period grants.
RANGE OF GRANTS Up to £75,000.
SAMPLE GRANTS City University (£75,000); the Centre of the Cell (£50,000); and the Dickens House Museum (£10,000).
FINANCES *Year* 2009–10 *Income* £108,927 *Grants* £135,000 *Assets* £2,629,797
TRUSTEES The Corporation of London.
HOW TO APPLY In writing to the correspondent. Guidelines are available from the trust.
WHO TO APPLY TO The Town Clerk, Corporation of London, PO Box 270, Guildhall, London EC2P 2EJ

....

■ CLA Charitable Trust

cc no 280264 **ESTABLISHED** 1980
WHERE FUNDING CAN BE GIVEN England and Wales only.
WHO CAN BENEFIT Small local projects, innovative projects and newly established projects, where a grant can make a 'real contribution to the success of the project'.
WHAT IS FUNDED (i) To encourage education about the countryside for those who are disabled or disadvantaged, particularly youngsters from urban areas. (ii) To provide facilities for those with disabilities to have access to recreation in the countryside. (iii) To promote education in agriculture, horticulture and conservation for those who are disabled or disadvantaged.
WHAT IS NOT FUNDED No grants to individuals.
TYPE OF GRANT Specific projects or items rather than for ongoing running costs.
RANGE OF GRANTS Rarely more than £2,000.
SAMPLE GRANTS Harper Adams College (£6,000); Avon Riding Centre for the Disabled (£3,200); Woolverstone Project (£3,000); Elizabeth Fitzroy Support (£2,800); Noah's Ark and Watershed RDA (£2,000 each); Queen Alexandra Hospital Home (£1,700); Clapton Common Boys' Club (£1,500); Menro Lluest (£1,300); and Nancy Oldfield Trust (£1,100).
FINANCES *Year* 2009–10 *Income* £66,743 *Grants* £56,108 *Assets* £315,649

TRUSTEES Sir Henry Aubrey-Fletcher; Gordon Lee Steere; Anthony Duckworth-Chad; Hugh Duberly; Neil Mainwaring.
OTHER INFORMATION The CLA Charitable Trust was founded by CLA members in 1980.
HOW TO APPLY In writing to the correspondent. Trustees meet four times a year.
WHO TO APPLY TO Peter Geldart, Director, Hopbine Farm, Main Street, Ossington, Newark NG23 6LJ *Tel* 01636 823835 *Website* www. cla.org.uk

....

■ Stephen Clark 1957 Charitable Trust

cc no 258690 **ESTABLISHED** 1969
WHERE FUNDING CAN BE GIVEN Some preference for Bath and Somerset.
WHO CAN BENEFIT Registered charities.
WHAT IS FUNDED The trust's priorities are 'to make donations to charities in respect of the preservation, embellishment, maintenance, improvement or development of any monuments, churches or other buildings'. The trust prefers local charities to national ones.
WHAT IS NOT FUNDED No grants to animal charities or to individuals.
SAMPLE GRANTS Bath Industrial Heritage Trust (£25,000); Friends of Holburne Museum (£5,035); Wells Cathedral – The Jesse Window (£5,000); Theatre Royal Bath and Iford ARTS (£2,000); Edinburgh University Development Trust, St. John the Baptist (£1,000 each); Traidcraft Exchange, Ulster Youth Orchestra, The Little Theatre Cinema (£500 each); Zimbabwe: A National Emergency (£400); World Hunger Fund (£300); The Neem Tree Trust (£50).
FINANCES *Year* 2010 *Income* £95,674 *Grants* £93,546 *Assets* £1,938,003
TRUSTEES Dr Marianna Clark; Mrs M P Lovell; Ms A Clark.
HOW TO APPLY In writing to the correspondent. Please note, replies are not usually made to unsuccessful applications.
WHO TO APPLY TO Dr Marianna Clark, Trustee, 16 Lansdown Place East, Bath BA1 5ET

....

■ J A Clark Charitable Trust

cc no 1010520 **ESTABLISHED** 1992
WHERE FUNDING CAN BE GIVEN UK, with a preference for South West England.
WHO CAN BENEFIT Charitable organisations.
WHAT IS FUNDED Health, education, peace, preservation of the earth and the arts.
SAMPLE GRANTS Eucalyptus Charitable Foundation (£73,000); Khwendo Kor-Pakistan (£36,000); SHIN (£22,000); Hope Flowers School, Society for Empowering Human Resource, Rwanda Women's Network, CDA Sudan Women and Conflicts Forum (£20,000 each); Odanadi UK and Arab Women's Solidarity Association (£15,000 each); SKADA (£13,000); Oxford Research Group (£10,000); ABC Trust (£6,000); and Hai Ninh Project (£900).
FINANCES *Year* 2009 *Income* £444,256 *Grants* £432,691 *Assets* £13,682,417
TRUSTEES Tom Clark, Chair; Lance Clark; William Pym; Aidan Pelly.
OTHER INFORMATION £422,000 was made in grants to organisations and a further £10,000 was paid to individuals.
HOW TO APPLY This trust does not respond to unsolicited applications.

Think carefully about every application. Is it justified?

....
445

WHO TO APPLY TO Mrs P Grant, Secretary, PO Box 1704, Glastonbury, Somerset BA16 0YB

■ The Hilda and Alice Clark Charitable Trust

CC NO 290916   **ESTABLISHED** 1953
WHERE FUNDING CAN BE GIVEN Street, Somerset.
WHO CAN BENEFIT There is a preference given to the Society of Friends (Quakers) and to children and young adults.
WHAT IS FUNDED General charitable purposes and Quaker causes.
WHAT IS NOT FUNDED Only registered charities are considered.
SAMPLE GRANTS Green Bank Swimming Pool (£15,000); Hope Flowers School – Bethlehem, Britain Yearly Meeting (£10,000 each); Medical Aid For Palestinians (£4,000); Sightsavers International, Quaker Council for European Affairs (£1,000 each); Pickering Friends Meeting House Appeal (£500).
FINANCES *Year* 2009 *Income* £59,278 *Grants* £62,500 *Assets* £1,650,647
TRUSTEES Richard Clark; Thomas Clark; Martin Lovell; Alice Clark; Susannah Clark.
OTHER INFORMATION Accounts for 2009 were available from the Charity Commission website. Accounts for 2010 were overdue.
HOW TO APPLY In writing to the correspondent by 30 September. Trustees meet in December each year.
WHO TO APPLY TO The Secretary, c/o KPMG, 100 Temple Street, Bristol BS1 1AG *Tel* 0117 905 4000

■ The Roger and Sarah Bancroft Clark Charitable Trust

CC NO 211513   **ESTABLISHED** 1960
WHERE FUNDING CAN BE GIVEN UK and overseas, with preference for Somerset and Scotland.
WHO CAN BENEFIT Society of Friends, registered charities and individuals. Preference is given to local appeals.
WHAT IS FUNDED General charitable purposes with particular reference to: Religious Society of Friends and associated bodies; charities connected with Somerset; education (for individuals).
TYPE OF GRANT Recurrent grants.
RANGE OF GRANTS Mostly £50–£6,000.
SAMPLE GRANTS University of Edinburgh (£2,500).
FINANCES *Year* 2009 *Income* £36,442 *Grants* £9,000 *Assets* £1,274,162
TRUSTEES Mary P Lovell; Sarah C Gould; Roger S Goldby; Alice Clark; Robert B Robertson; Martin Lovell.
HOW TO APPLY In writing to the correspondent. There is no application form and telephone calls are not accepted. Trustees meet about three times a year. Applications will be acknowledged if an sae is enclosed or email address given.
WHO TO APPLY TO The Trustees, c/o KPMG LLP, 100 Temple Street, Bristol BS1 6AG

■ The Clarke Charitable Settlement

CC NO 702980   **ESTABLISHED** 1990
WHERE FUNDING CAN BE GIVEN Staffordshire and Derbyshire.
WHO CAN BENEFIT Funding may be considered for Christians, research workers and medical professionals.
WHAT IS FUNDED The advancement of Christian religion, medical research and hospices.
RANGE OF GRANTS Most grants are for under £5,000, although they can be for much more.
SAMPLE GRANTS Beneficiaries included: N. M. A. Future Foundations Appeal and Queen's Hospital Scanner Appeal (£50,000 each); celebrating Our Ancestors – Friends of Barton Churchyard and Parwich Memorial Hall (£5,000 each); Merseyside Holiday Service (£4,000); Kingstone Church (£2,000); MacMillan Cancer Support (£1,200); Disaster Emergency Committee – Haiti Appeal, Katharine House Hospice and Spinal Injuries Association (£1,000); and Staffordshire Yeomanry Museum, Trenton Parish Church and Youth for Christ (£500 each).
FINANCES *Year* 2009–10 *Income* £125,461 *Grants* £146,667 *Assets* £1,564,259
TRUSTEES Lady Hilda Clarke; Sally Hayward; Mary MacGregor; Jane Gerard-Pearse.
HOW TO APPLY In writing to the correspondent, although the trust has previously stated that support is only given to charities known to the trustees or the Clarke family.
WHO TO APPLY TO Lady H J Clarke, Trustee, The Knoll, Main Street, Barton-under-Needwood, Burton-on-Trent, Staffordshire DE13 8AB *Tel* 01283 712294

■ The Cleary Foundation

CC NO 242675   **ESTABLISHED** 1965
WHERE FUNDING CAN BE GIVEN UK, with a preference for Kent.
WHO CAN BENEFIT Registered charities.
WHAT IS FUNDED Principally to apply the income of the foundation for various selected charities for the relief of pain and hardship, and conservation. These include: civil society development; community development; social care professional bodies; churches; music; visual art; arts activities; dance and ballet; dance groups; theatrical companies and theatre groups; horticulture; special schools; community centres and village halls; and parks.
WHAT IS NOT FUNDED No grants to individuals who require aid with further education.
RANGE OF GRANTS Up to £15,000.
SAMPLE GRANTS Previous beneficiaries included: Ripple Down House Trust (£15,000); Deal Summer Music Festival (£1,500); London Children's Flower Society (£650); British Red Cross (£350); St Martin-in-the-Fields Christmas Appeal (£300); and NSPCC Kent (£150).
FINANCES *Year* 2009–10 *Income* £20,684 *Grants* £7,000
TRUSTEES P M Gould, Chair; A T F Gould; P A Cleary; F A Hutley.
HOW TO APPLY In writing to the correspondent, although the trust would welcome a preliminary telephone call to check whether they are in the position of being able to offer grants to new beneficiaries.
WHO TO APPLY TO The Secretary to the Trustees, South Sands Lodge, Beach Road, St Margaret's Bay, Kent CT15 6DZ

■ The Cleevely Family Charitable Trust

CC NO 1137902 **ESTABLISHED** 2010
WHERE FUNDING CAN BE GIVEN Worldwide.
WHO CAN BENEFIT Registered charities.
WHAT IS FUNDED General, children and young people.
TRUSTEES Dr David Cleevely; Rosalind Cleevely; Olivia Florence.
OTHER INFORMATION As Dr Cleevely and his wife Rosalind are patrons of the Prince's Trust, it is likely that the trust has a preference for organisations working with children and young people. There may also be a preference for education and the Cambridge area. The foundation's first annual report and accounts had yet to be produced at the time of writing (December 2011).
HOW TO APPLY In writing to the correspondent.
WHO TO APPLY TO Coutts & Co, Trustee Dept, 440 Strand, London WC2R 0QS *Tel* 020 7753 1000

■ The Cleopatra Trust

CC NO 1004551 **ESTABLISHED** 1990
WHERE FUNDING CAN BE GIVEN Mainly UK.
WHO CAN BENEFIT Registered charities with a national focus.
WHAT IS FUNDED The trust makes grants in the following areas: mental health; cancer welfare/education – not research; diabetes; physical disability – not research; homelessness; addiction; children who are disadvantaged.
WHAT IS NOT FUNDED No grants to individuals, expeditions, research, scholarships, charities with a local focus, local branches of UK-wide charities or towards running costs.
RANGE OF GRANTS £500–£16,000.
SAMPLE GRANTS Fairbridge, Cystic Fibrosis Trust, Maggie's Keswick Jencks Cancer Caring Centres Trust, Shooting Star Hospice (£10,000 each); Wellington College (£5,000) and West Wittering Flood Defence (£2,000).
FINANCES *Year* 2010 *Income* £112,974 *Grants* £47,975 *Assets* £3,332,581
TRUSTEES Dr C Peacock; B Bond; C H Peacock.
HOW TO APPLY This trust no longer accepts applications.
WHO TO APPLY TO Charles H Peacock, Trustee, c/o Charities Aid Foundation, 25 Kings Hill Avenue, King's Hill, West Malling, Kent ME19 4TA *Tel* 01732 520028

■ Lord Clinton's Charitable Trust

CC NO 268061 **ESTABLISHED** 1974
WHERE FUNDING CAN BE GIVEN North and East Devon.
WHO CAN BENEFIT Registered charities benefiting people of all ages, ex-service and service people, seafarers and fishermen, sportsmen and women, volunteers, parents and children, people with disabilities, victims of man-made or natural disasters, people with cancer, paediatric diseases, or sight loss, and people who are terminally ill.
WHAT IS FUNDED Young people and the encouragement of youth activities, people who have disabilities, support for older people, medical aid and research, maritime charities. Respite and sheltered accommodation; churches; information technology and computers; personnel and human resources; support to voluntary and community organisations and volunteers; professional bodies; community centres; village halls and clubs.
WHAT IS NOT FUNDED No support for animal charities. No grants made in response to general appeals from large UK organisations or to smaller bodies working in areas other than those set out above.
TYPE OF GRANT For projects, recurring costs and start-up costs. Funding is available for one year or less.
RANGE OF GRANTS Up to £10,000.
SAMPLE GRANTS Previous beneficiaries have included: University of Exeter Sponsorship x 2 grants (£4,600 each); Vicar's Christmas Fund (£1,400); Kingfisher Award Scheme (£1,200); North Devon Cancer Care (£1,000); Exmouth Lifeboat Station Appeal and Families for Children (£500 each); Brixington Pre-School and the Countryside Foundation (£200 each); and Charity Golf Day (£50).
FINANCES *Year* 2009–10 *Income* £20,010 *Grants* £20,000
TRUSTEES Hon. Charles Fane Trefusis; John C Varley.
HOW TO APPLY In writing to the correspondent. Applications not falling within the trust's objects and funding priorities will not be considered or acknowledged.
WHO TO APPLY TO John C Varley, Trustee, Rolle Estate Office, East Budleigh, Budleigh Salterton, Devon EX9 7BL *Tel* 01395 443881 *Fax* 01395 446126 *email* mail@clintondevon.co.uk *Website* www.clintondevon.co.uk

■ The Clore Duffield Foundation

CC NO 1084412 **ESTABLISHED** 2000
WHERE FUNDING CAN BE GIVEN UK, the larger grants go to London-based institutions.
WHO CAN BENEFIT Institutions and registered charities, particular emphasis on supporting children, young people and society's more vulnerable individuals.
WHAT IS FUNDED Main grants programme, mainly in the fields of museums, galleries and heritage sites (particularly for learning spaces), the arts, education, health, social care and disability and Jewish charities with interests in any of these areas.
WHAT IS NOT FUNDED Potential applicants should note that their organisation must be a registered charity to be eligible. Unfortunately, the foundation does not fund projects retrospectively and will not support applications from the following: individuals; general appeals and circulars. It should also be noted that the following are funded only very rarely: projects outside the UK; staff posts; local branches of national charities; academic or project research; conference costs.
TYPE OF GRANT Capital.
SAMPLE GRANTS University of Oxford – Institute of Ageing (£1 million); Greenwich Foundation (£150,000); George Piper Dances and Imperial War Museum (£100,000 each); RF Creativity, Culture and Education (£90,000); Norwood (£55,000); Royal Opera House (£53,000); South London Gallery and University of Oxford – Ashmolean Museum (£50,000 each); Prince's Teaching Institute and Royal Shakespeare Company (£25,000 each); The Domnar Warehouse and Hampstead Theatre (£10,000 each); The Paul Hamlyn Foundation (£7,000); and British Library, English Touring Opera, Kneehigh Theatre and National Campaign for the Arts (£5,000 each).

FINANCES *Year* 2010 *Income* £4,450,663 *Grants* £4,327,183 *Assets* £80,701,898

TRUSTEES Dame Vivien Duffield, Chair; Caroline Deltra; David Harrel; Michael Trask; Sir Mark Weinberg.

HOW TO APPLY Please refer to the foundation's guidance leaflet which can be downloaded from its website. You are invited to contact the foundation, before making application if you have any queries regarding criteria set or the process itself.

WHO TO APPLY TO Sally Bacon, Executive Director, Studio 3, Chelsea Manor Studios, Flood Street, London SW3 5SR *Tel* 020 7351 6061 *Fax* 020 7351 5308 *email* info@cloreduffield.org.uk *Website* www.cloreduffield.org.uk

■ Miss V L Clore's 1967 Charitable Trust

CC NO 253660 **ESTABLISHED** 1967
WHERE FUNDING CAN BE GIVEN UK.
WHO CAN BENEFIT Registered charities.
WHAT IS FUNDED General charitable purposes, especially performing arts, education, social welfare, health and disability. Jewish causes are also supported.
WHAT IS NOT FUNDED No grants are given to individuals.
RANGE OF GRANTS Usually £200–£5,000.
SAMPLE GRANTS Previously: Chelsea Physic Gardens, Family Friends and Maccabi GB (£5,000 each); North London Hospice (£4,000); West London Synagogue (£2,500); Friends of Castle of Mey, NSPCC, the Pearl Foundation and UF Elias Ashmole Trust (£1,000 each); and Institute for Polish-Jewish Studies and JTMM Mission (£500 each).
FINANCES *Year* 2009–10 *Income* £43,416 *Grants* £45,054 *Assets* £1,216,557
TRUSTEES Dame V L Duffield; David Harrel; Caroline Deltra.
HOW TO APPLY In writing to the correspondent on one to two sides of A4, enclosing an sae.
WHO TO APPLY TO Sally Bacon, Unit 3, Chelsea Manor Studios, Flood Street, London SW3 5SR *Tel* 020 7351 6061 *email* info@cloreduffield.org.uk *Website* www.cloreduffield.org.uk

■ Closehelm Ltd

CC NO 291296 **ESTABLISHED** 1983
WHERE FUNDING CAN BE GIVEN UK and Israel.
WHO CAN BENEFIT Individuals and institutions benefiting Jewish people and people disadvantaged by poverty.
WHAT IS FUNDED The advancement of religion in accordance with the Jewish faith; the relief of poverty; and general charitable purposes.
FINANCES *Year* 2009–10 *Income* £424,952 *Grants* £506,265 *Assets* £3,636,133
TRUSTEES A Van Praagh; Henrietta W Van Praagh; Hannah R Van Praagh.
OTHER INFORMATION A list of grants was not available.
HOW TO APPLY In writing to the correspondent.
WHO TO APPLY TO Henrietta W Van Praagh, Secretary, 30 Armitage Road, London NW11 8RD *Tel* 020 8201 8688

■ The Clothworkers' Foundation

CC NO 274100 **ESTABLISHED** 1977
WHERE FUNDING CAN BE GIVEN UK.
WHO CAN BENEFIT UK registered charities only.
WHAT IS FUNDED Homelessness, alcohol and substance misuse, domestic and sexual violence, prisoners and ex-offenders, integration of minorities, disadvantaged young people, disability, elderly, visual impairment and textiles.
WHAT IS NOT FUNDED The foundation does not make grants to: non UK-registered charities; organisations with an annual turnover of over £10 million (charities working in textiles with an annual turnover of over £10 million, wishing to make an application, are requested to contact the foundation); non-capital costs i.e. running costs, salary costs; organisations that have received a grant from the foundation in the last five years; heritage projects (other than textiles); environment projects; arts and education projects are unlikely to be funded unless they are predominantly focused on disadvantaged young people, the elderly or the disabled; projects that do not fit in with one of the foundation's programme areas; individuals; general or marketing appeals; educational establishments; grant-makers; overseas work/ projects; medical research or equipment; political, industrial, or commercial appeals; relief of state aid or reduction of support from public funds; events; appeals from any organisation where the money will be used for religious purposes, or projects which promote a particular religion; pay for websites, databases, or other software. The foundation no longer funds IT equipment unless it will be used primarily by service users (and not staff or volunteers).
TYPE OF GRANT Capital; one-off; occasionally recurring for more than three years.
RANGE OF GRANTS Up to £1 million in the main grants programme and up to £10,000 in small grants programme.
SAMPLE GRANTS Victoria & Albert Museum (£1 million); Maths in Education & Industry (£250,000); Manchester Deaf Centre and Oxford Association for the Blind (£50,000 each); Osmani Trust, Sedgefield and District CAB and UCL Medical School (£30,000 each); Newlife Foundation for Disabled Children and St John of Jerusalem Eye Hospital (£25,000 each); Sobriety Project (£20,000); Bradford College Textile Archive and Ley Community Drug Services (£15,000); ConstructionSkills (£13,000); Acceptable Enterprises (Larne) (£12,000); Age Concern Richmond-Upon-Thames (£11,000); Bexley Autism Support and Information Centre (£10,000); and Royal Fusiliers Museum (£5,000).
FINANCES *Year* 2010 *Income* £4,751,709 *Grants* £4,920,480 *Assets* £88,923,087
TRUSTEES John Stoddart-Scott, Chair; Maj Oliver Howard; Michael Jarvis; Richard Jonas; Michael Maylon; Christopher McLean May; Dr Carolyn Boulter; Melville Haggard; Anthony West; Christopher Jonas.
HOW TO APPLY There are separate application forms for the main and small grants programmes available from the foundation's website, which also gives full details of the application process and criteria for funding. Both programmes require the following information: completed application form; full project budget; latest accounts for the organisation as submitted to the Charity Commission; copy of the correspondence confirming Northern Ireland charitable status if registered in NI. Applications are accepted at any time, there are no

deadlines. Decisions normally take eight weeks for the small grants programme and six months for the main grants programme. Applications can be submitted by post or email. Email applications will only be accepted if the entire application (including accounts, budget and any supporting information) is sent electronically. If any part of the application cannot be emailed, the entire application must be posted. Any applicants who have specific queries after reading the foundation's guidelines should contact the grants assistant on 020 7623 7041. The foundation does not however, provide advice on matters which are covered on its website. If your application is not successful, you must wait six months before re-applying. A charity which has received a grant in either programme cannot apply again for at least five years.

WHO TO APPLY TO Mr A C Blessley, Clothworkers' Hall, Dunster Court, Mincing Lane, London EC3R 7AH *Tel* 020 7623 7041 *Fax* 020 7397 0107 *email* foundation@clothworkers.co.uk *Website* www.clothworkers.co.uk

■ Richard Cloudesley's Charity

CC NO 205959   **ESTABLISHED** 1517
WHERE FUNDING CAN BE GIVEN Ancient parish of Islington, London.
WHO CAN BENEFIT Voluntary and charitable organisations. Individuals are assisted through the trust's welfare fund.
WHAT IS FUNDED Church of England churches, medical and welfare.
TYPE OF GRANT One-off grants are preferred; the vast majority of grants are free of restrictions. Grants for capital, core, recurring, running and start-up costs will be considered, as will grants for buildings, feasibility studies, project, research and salaries.
RANGE OF GRANTS £100–£40,000.
SAMPLE GRANTS St Augustine – Highbury New Park (£35,000); St John's District Church (£28,000); St Mary – Ashley Road (£22,000); St Thomas – Finsbury Park (£17,000); CARIS – Islington (£7,000); Stuart Low Trust (£6,000); Choices Islington (£5,000); St George's – Tuffnell Park (£4,000); Community Languages Support Services (£3,000); Angel Shed Theatre Company (£2,000); and Single Homelessness Project (£300).
FINANCES *Year* 2009–10 *Income* £943,174 *Grants* £445,600 *Assets* £22,907,868
TRUSTEES Kevin A Streater, Chair; Cllr J Asato; Courtney Bailey; Miranda Coates; Cllr P Convery; John Durdin; Ms M Elliott; Kathleen Frenchman; Roger Goodman; Revd S Harvey; Pat Haynes; JR Trotter; M Maunsell; Ms V Mirfin; Ms D Reeves; David R Stephens; Rupert Perry; Dorothy Newton.
HOW TO APPLY Applicants should write to the correspondent requesting an application form. Applications should be in time for the trustees' meetings in April and November and should be accompanied by the organisation's accounts. The following information should be supplied: details of the work your organisation undertakes; how it falls within the geographical area of the trust; and details what the grant will fund. If you would like acknowledgement of receipt of your application please send an sae. Block grants are considered twice a year, around late April, and early November at a grants committee meeting. Recommendations are made by the grants committee at these meetings and are reviewed and authorised by

the trustees two weeks later. The trust will give brief reasons with any application that is not successful.
WHO TO APPLY TO Keith Wallace, Clerk, Reed Smith LLP, 26th Floor, Broadgate Tower, 20 Primrose Street, London EC2A 2RS *Tel* 020 3116 3624 *email* kwallace@reedsmith.com

■ The Clover Trust

CC NO 213578   **ESTABLISHED** 1961
WHERE FUNDING CAN BE GIVEN UK, and occasionally overseas, with a slight preference for West Dorset.
WHO CAN BENEFIT Registered charities.
WHAT IS FUNDED Health, disability, young people, older people and Catholic activities.
WHAT IS NOT FUNDED The arts, monuments and non-registered charities are not supported. No grants are given towards building work.
TYPE OF GRANT General running costs. Unsolicited applications which impress the trustees are given one-off grants. However, most grants are given to a 'core list' of beneficiaries.
RANGE OF GRANTS £1,000–£27,000.
SAMPLE GRANTS Friends of Children in Romania (£50,000); Downside Fisher Youth Club and Childhood First (£10,000 each); 999 Club (£7,500); Bridport Stroke Club and Orchard Vale Club (£5,000 each); Wireless for the Bedridden (£3,000); National Eczema Society (£2,000); and English Catholic History Association (£1,000).
FINANCES *Year* 2009 *Income* £223,125 *Grants* £260,000 *Assets* £4,197,190
TRUSTEES N C Haydon; S Woodhouse.
HOW TO APPLY In writing to the correspondent. Replies are not given to unsuccessful applications.
WHO TO APPLY TO G F D Wright, Trustee, DTE Business Advisory Services Limited, Park House, 26 North End Road, London NW11 7PT

■ The Robert Clutterbuck Charitable Trust

CC NO 1010559   **ESTABLISHED** 1992
WHERE FUNDING CAN BE GIVEN UK, with preference for Cheshire and Hertfordshire.
WHO CAN BENEFIT Registered charities.
WHAT IS FUNDED Personnel within the armed forces and ex-servicemen and women; sport and recreational facilities for young people benefiting Cheshire and Hertfordshire; the welfare, protection and preservation of domestic animal life benefiting Cheshire and Hertfordshire; natural history and wildlife; other charities associated with the counties of Cheshire and Hertfordshire; charities which have particular appeal to the founder, Major Robert Clutterbuck.
WHAT IS NOT FUNDED No grants to individuals.
TYPE OF GRANT Specific items and projects rather than running costs.
RANGE OF GRANTS £500–£5,000. No grants are made below £500.
SAMPLE GRANTS Sue Ryder Care (£1,800); Boys' Brigade, Henshaw's Society for the Blind and Mercyships (£1,500); Dogs Trust, David Lewis Centre, Grasslands Trust and Vincent Wildlife Trust (£1,000 each); and Leonard Cheshire Disability and Red Squirrel Survival Trust (£500 each).
FINANCES *Year* 2009–10 *Income* £34,826 *Grants* £39,431 *Assets* £1,196,870

TRUSTEES Maj. R G Clutterbuck; I A Pearson; R J Pincham.

HOW TO APPLY In writing to the correspondent. There are no application forms. Applications are acknowledged and considered by the trustees twice a year. The trustees will not normally consider appeals from charities within two years of a previous grant being approved.

WHO TO APPLY TO G A Wolfe, Secretary, 28 Brookfields, Calver, Hope Valley, Derbyshire S32 3XB *Tel* 01433 631308 *email* secretary@ clutterbucktrust.org.uk *Website* www. clutterbucktrust.org.uk

---

■ Clydpride Ltd

CC NO 295393 **ESTABLISHED** 1982

WHERE FUNDING CAN BE GIVEN Unrestricted.

WHO CAN BENEFIT Individuals and institutions benefiting Jewish people and people disadvantaged by poverty.

WHAT IS FUNDED Advancement of the orthodox Jewish faith; relief of poverty; general charitable purposes. The main focus is to support the 'renaissance of religious study and to alleviate the plight of poor scholars'.

SAMPLE GRANTS Previous beneficiaries include: Achiezer; Achisomoch Aid Company; Beis Chinuch Lebonos; Beis Soroh Scheneirer Seminary; Bnei Braq Hospital; Comet Charities Limited; EM Shasha Foundation; Friends of Mir; Gevurath Ari Torah Academy Trust; Mosdos Tchernobil; Notzar Chesed; Seed; Society of Friends of Torah; and Telz Talmudical Academy Trust.

FINANCES *Year* 2010 *Income* £1,118,233 *Grants* £1,164,965 *Assets* £14,312,126

TRUSTEES L Faust; M H Linton; A Faust.

OTHER INFORMATION A list of grant beneficiaries was not included in the trust's accounts.

HOW TO APPLY The trust states that unsolicited applications are not considered.

WHO TO APPLY TO L Faust, Secretary, Tavistock House South, Tavistock Square, London WC1H 9LG *Tel* 020 8731 7744

■ The Co-operative Foundation

CC NO 1080834 **ESTABLISHED** 2000

WHERE FUNDING CAN BE GIVEN The trading area of the Co-operative Group – United Region which has interests in the North West, south Cumbria, Yorkshire, north Midlands, Northern Ireland and North Wales.

WHO CAN BENEFIT Local groups and organisations. 'It is particularly interested in locally led and run groups which can demonstrate evidence of co-operative values and principles: self-help, equality, democracy, concern for the community.'

WHAT IS FUNDED 'Supporting community groups to find co-operative solutions to community challenges.' In support of its community-led approach the foundation has one focussed grant-making programme, the *Community Support Programme*. This programme was developed to help groups who want to 'make a difference' in their own communities, through grass roots community activity. The community can be geographically-based, such as a village, town or housing estate, or could be a community of people brought together to address a specific issue. Examples of work we may fund under the programme include: activities that encourage people to work with others who have similar needs or face similar challenges, including the development of community groups; work that aims to resolve or reduce conflict, such as community mediation or the reduction of harassment; the setting up or development of community safety schemes; provision and improvement of community facilities that allow premises and equipment to be shared between organisations; work to assist people, who would not otherwise have the opportunity, to gain access to IT equipment, training or support; development of out-reach work to offer services to the most vulnerable in society; improvement of access to information, advice and advocacy services that enable people to make informed choices about their lives or lifestyle; work which supports that undertaken by volunteers; work with communities with significant needs such as minority groups, people with disabilities and their carers, or those with special needs, mental health problems and learning disabilities.

WHAT IS NOT FUNDED No funding for: applications from outside the Co-operative Group – United Region area, including overseas applications; organisations whose activities are not recognised as charitable or philanthropic; charities that have large unrestricted reserves; national charities (unless there is a specific local project, which has been initiated by the local community benefiting from the grant); applications for salaries; replacement of statutory funding; applications from local authorities; applications from health authorities; activities that are the responsibility of local or central government; organisations that promote political parties; applications for projects which are deemed to promote a particular religious group or activity; applications to help animals; the Scout movement, including Guides, Cubs, Brownies, Beavers and Rainbows; groundwork; YMCA and YWCA; schools, including PTAs; residential homes which are the responsibility of the local authority; retrospective grants; groups not demonstrating self help; applications benefiting individuals; grants for outstanding debts or down payments for loans; groups that have received a grant from the foundation in the last twelve months; groups which are applying for more than one year's worth of funding; applications where the questions on the form have been amended or altered.

TYPE OF GRANT One-year projects – for either part or total funding, capital costs and revenue costs (but not salaries).

SAMPLE GRANTS Envision (£140,000); YWCA (£105,000); Regional Youth Work Unity North East (£93,000); Young Scot (£70,000); Changemakers (£4,000); the Prince's Trust and UnLtd (£2,000 each); and Community Arts North West, Contact, Groundwork London, Young Bristol and ICA: UK (£1,000 each).

FINANCES *Year* 2009–10 *Income* £1,153,640 *Grants* £1,973,125 *Assets* £9,805,910

TRUSTEES A Brett; P Grange; F Makinson; S Sherrington; S Howarth; P Lockley; Stephen Youd-Thomas; J Wakefield; Joyce Baruch; Mike Greenacre.

HOW TO APPLY Full guidelines, application details and application forms can be downloaded from the foundation's website. The trustees meet four times a year to approve grants, deadline dates can be found on the Co-operative website.

WHO TO APPLY TO The Charity Manager, New Century House, 6th Floor, Corporation Street, Manchester M60 4ES *Tel* 0161 246 3044 *email* foundation@coop.co.uk *Website* www.co-operative.coop/ethicsinaction/communities/fundsandfoundations/theco-operativefoundation

■ The Francis Coales Charitable Foundation

CC NO 270718 **ESTABLISHED** 1975

WHERE FUNDING CAN BE GIVEN UK, with a preference for Bedfordshire, Buckinghamshire, Hertfordshire and Northamptonshire.

WHO CAN BENEFIT Old buildings open to the public, usually churches. Organisations involved in archaeological research and related causes.

WHAT IS FUNDED The repair/restoration of buildings built before 1875; also monuments, tombs, hatchments, memorial brasses, and so on. Grants are also made towards the cost of archaeological research and related causes, the purchase of documents or items for record offices and museums, and the publication of architectural and archaeological books or papers. Assistance for structural repairs is normally given to churches and their contents in Buckinghamshire, Bedfordshire, Northamptonshire and Hertfordshire where most of the business of Francis Coales and Son was carried out with farmers. However, no territorial restriction is placed upon church monuments, and so on.

WHAT IS NOT FUNDED In respect of buildings, assistance is only given towards fabric repairs, but not to 'domestic' items such as heating, lighting, wiring, installation of facilities etc.

TYPE OF GRANT Largely one-off (or recurrent if for an ongoing application).

FINANCES *Year* 2010 *Income* £660,996 *Grants* £53,850 *Assets* £3,385,613

TRUSTEES H M Stuchfield, Chair; A G Harding; Revd B H Wilcox; I G Barnett.

HOW TO APPLY On a form which can be downloaded from the foundation's website. Trustees normally meet three times a year to consider grants. 'In respect of a building or contents, include a copy of the relevant portion only of the architect's (or conservator's) specification showing the actual work proposed. Photographs illustrating this are a necessity, and only in exceptional circumstances will an application be considered without supporting photographs here. It is of help if six copies of any supporting documentation are submitted in order that each trustee may have a copy in advance of the meeting.'

WHO TO APPLY TO Trevor Parker, Administrator, The Bays, Hillcote, Bleadon Hill, Weston-super-Mare, Somerset BS24 9JS *Tel* 01934 814009 *email* enquiries@franciscoales.co.uk *Website* franciscoales.co.uk

■ The Coalfields Regeneration Trust

CC NO 1074930 **ESTABLISHED** 1999

WHERE FUNDING CAN BE GIVEN Coalfield and former coalfield communities in England (North West and North East, Yorkshire, West Midlands and East Midlands, Kent), Scotland (West and East) and Wales.

WHO CAN BENEFIT Community and voluntary organisations who are working to tackle problems at grass-roots level within coalfield communities.

WHAT IS FUNDED Welfare of coalfield communities.

WHAT IS NOT FUNDED The following are not eligible to apply: individuals; private businesses; organisations that are in a poor financial position or whose financial management systems are not in good order. The trust's opinion on this will be based on an organisation's financial position and management systems, an analysis of their accounts and other management information, as well as contact with referees and interviews with the organisation itself; voluntary and community organisations and groups who hold 'free reserves' that total more than 12 months' operating costs and who are not contributing enough funds to the project. The trust will assess how much money the organisation has available in free reserves using information from their accounts. (Free reserves are the amounts of money an organisation hold that are not restricted by any other funder for any other purpose). The following are not eligible to apply for the Bridging the Gap programme: individuals; statutory organisations; national organisations; private businesses.

TYPE OF GRANT Usually one-off grants.

RANGE OF GRANTS Up to £100,000.

SAMPLE GRANTS Aylesham Neighbourhood Project (£210,000); Haswell and District Mencap Society – The Community Anchor (£98,000); Derbyside Rural Community Council – Wheels to Work (£89,000); The Cornforth Partnership – The Reach project (£75,000); Nottinghamshire Independent Domestic Abuse Link Workers (£66,000); Stoke On Trent and District Gingerbread Centre Ltd – Peer Mentoring (£37,000); St John's Church – A Building in Which to Serve Our Community (£10,000); Mansfield and Dukeries Irish Association – Luncheon Club (£5,000); City of Durham Air Cadets – Achieving Duke of Edinburgh's Awards (£3,800); Thornycroft Art Club – Christmas Tree Exhibition (£520).

FINANCES *Year* 2009–10 *Income* £20,523,000 *Grants* £12,186,000 *Assets* £4,394,000

TRUSTEES Peter McNestry, Chair; Kenneth Greenfield; Jim Crewdson; Prof. Anthony Crook; Dawn Davies; John Edwards; Peter Fanning; Vernon Jones; Peter Rowley; Wayne Thomas; Fran Walker; Sylvia Wileman; Nicholas Wilson.

OTHER INFORMATION The trust provides advice, support and financial assistance to community and voluntary organisations who are working to tackle problems at grass-roots level within coalfield communities. It is closely connected with the areas it serves, operating through a network of staff based at offices located within coalfield regions themselves.

HOW TO APPLY Application details are different for each programme. The trust has produced very comprehensive information booklets that should be read before applying to any fund. The application form for the first stage of applications to the level one programme is available on the foundation's website. Applicants are advised to contact their regional manager before making an application, details of which are also on the trust's website. The staff will be able to advise on the trust's application process and an appointment can be made with a member of the development team to discuss the application in more detail.

WHO TO APPLY TO Janet Bibby, Chief Executive, Silkstone House, Pioneer Close, Manvers Way, Wath Upon Dearne, Rotherham S63 7JZ *Tel* 0800 064 8560 *Fax* 01709 765599 *email* info@coalfields-regen.org.uk *Website* www.coalfields-regen.org.uk

■ The John Coates Charitable Trust

CC NO 262057   **ESTABLISHED** 1969
WHERE FUNDING CAN BE GIVEN UK, mainly southern England.
WHO CAN BENEFIT Institutions either national or of personal or local interest to one or more of the trustees.
WHAT IS FUNDED Preference is given to education, arts and culture, children, environment and health.
WHAT IS NOT FUNDED Grants are given to individuals only in exceptional circumstances.
TYPE OF GRANT Capital and recurring.
RANGE OF GRANTS £500–£10,000.
SAMPLE GRANTS Changing Faces, Great Ormond Street Hospital, Lymington Museum Trust, National Trust, Painshill Park Trust Limited, Royal Hospital for Neuro-Disability, The Royal Marsden Hospital Charity and Tommy's The Baby Charity (£10,000 each); Natural History Museum (£6,000); Action on Addiction, Age UK, Canine Partners, Chase Hospice Care for Children, Chichester Cathedral Restoration and Development Trust, Cleft Lip and Palate Association, Combat Stress, Farms for City Children, Fields in Trust, Help for Heroes, NSPCC, Pimlico Opera, Royal Albert Hall Trust, St Mungo's, Salvation Army, The Samaritans, Scope and Shakespeare's Globe (£5,000 each); Petersfield Swimming Pool, Rainbow Trust, The Solent Protection Society and Two Moors Festival Limited (£2,000 each); and Best Beginnings and The Nowhere Trust (£1,000 each).
FINANCES *Year* 2009–10 *Income* £376,111 *Grants* £362,000 *Assets* £10,286,675
TRUSTEES Mrs G F McGregor; Mrs C A Kesley; Mrs R J Lawes; Mrs P L Youngman; Mrs C P Cartledge.
HOW TO APPLY In writing to the correspondent. Small local charities are visited by the trust.
WHO TO APPLY TO Mrs R J Lawes, Trustee, PO Box 529, Cambridge CB1 0BT

■ Coats Foundation Trust

CC NO 268735   **ESTABLISHED** 1974
WHERE FUNDING CAN BE GIVEN UK.
WHO CAN BENEFIT Students on textile and thread-related training courses and research, as well as organisations benefiting such people.
WHAT IS FUNDED Preference is given, but not specifically restricted, to applicants from textile-related training courses.
TYPE OF GRANT One-off grants for capital and revenue costs.
RANGE OF GRANTS £170–£10,000.
SAMPLE GRANTS Previous beneficiaries include: Copthall School. Copthall School; Leeds University; and Nottingham Trent University.
FINANCES *Year* 2009–10 *Income* £21,950 *Grants* £85,000
TRUSTEES The Coats Trustee Company Limited.
OTHER INFORMATION The 2007–08 grant total included £66,323 paid to individuals.
HOW TO APPLY Please write, enclosing a CV and an sae, giving details of circumstances and the nature and amount of funding required. There is no formal application form. Only applicants enclosing an sae will receive a reply. Applications are considered four times a year.
WHO TO APPLY TO Sheila Macnicol, Coats plc, Coats Pensions Office, Pacific House, 70 Wellington Street, Glasgow G2 6UB *Tel* 0141 207 6820 *email* gwen.mckerrell@coats.com

■ The Cobalt Trust

CC NO 1096342   **ESTABLISHED** 2002
WHERE FUNDING CAN BE GIVEN UK and overseas.
WHO CAN BENEFIT Registered charities known to the trustees,.
WHAT IS FUNDED General charitable purposes.
TYPE OF GRANT Capital and revenue grants over 3 years.
SAMPLE GRANTS Impetus Trust (£169,000); EVPA (£26,000); Streats Limited (£14,000); Enable Ethiopia and Tree Aid (£12,000 each); Rosetrees Trust and Money for Madagascar (£10,000 each); Beat – Eating Disorders Association (£5,000); Wherever the Need (£1,000); Red Squirrel Survival Trust (£500); Wessex MS Therapy Centre (£100); and Bath RSPB (£50).
FINANCES *Year* 2009–10 *Income* £126,624 *Grants* £348,113 *Assets* £1,902,903
TRUSTEES Stephen Dawson; Brigitte Dawson; Jan Dawson.
HOW TO APPLY 'The trustees do not respond to unsolicited applications'
WHO TO APPLY TO Stephen Dawson, Trustee, 17 New Row, London WC2N 4LA

■ The Cobtree Charity Trust Ltd

CC NO 208455   **ESTABLISHED** 1951
WHERE FUNDING CAN BE GIVEN Maidstone and district.
WHO CAN BENEFIT Registered charities.
WHAT IS FUNDED The maintenance and development of Cobtree Manor Estate, and other general charitable purposes by other charities in the Maidstone and district area.
WHAT IS NOT FUNDED No support for individuals, non-registered charities and charities outside Maidstone and district.
TYPE OF GRANT Largely recurrent.
RANGE OF GRANTS Up to £10,000.
SAMPLE GRANTS The Mote Cricket Club, Maidstone Sea Cadets and Maidstone Museum Foundation (£10,000 each); Cobtree Museum of Kent Life (£5,500); The Harrietsham and Lenham Scouts (£5,000); Kent Association for the Blind and Kent Wildlife Trust (£3,500 each); St. John's Ambulance – Maidstone Division; Salvation Army – Maidstone (£2,500); Action for Children (£1,700); Five Acre Wood Special School and Macmillan Cancer Relief (£1,200); The Signalong Group (£800); Maidstone Christian Care and Boys' Brigade – North West Kent (£650).
FINANCES *Year* 2010–11 *Income* £127,683 *Grants* £115,353 *Assets* £5,028,969
TRUSTEES R J Corben; J Fletcher; L J Martin; R N Hext; D T B Wigg; M W Hardcastle; S W L Brice; M Lawrence.
HOW TO APPLY In writing to the correspondent. The trustees meet quarterly.
WHO TO APPLY TO Colin Mills, c/o Larkings (S.E.) LLP, Cornwallis House, Pudding Lane, Maidstone, Kent ME14 1NH

■ The Denise Cohen Charitable Trust

CC NO 276439   **ESTABLISHED** 1977
WHERE FUNDING CAN BE GIVEN UK.
WHO CAN BENEFIT Registered charities.
WHAT IS FUNDED Jewish; education; health and welfare of older people, infirm people and children; humanities; arts and culture.
RANGE OF GRANTS Between £9,000 and £100.

SAMPLE GRANTS Chai Cancer Charity (£9,000); Nightingale (£6,000); Jewish Woman's Aid (£4,500); Community Security Trust (£3,000); Lifeline for the Old Jerusalem (£2,500); Combat Stress (£2,000); Caring 4 Carers and British Friends of the Edith Wolfs (£1,000 each); British Friends of Rambam Medical Centre (£750); Sadler's Wells Theatre (£600); Wellbeing of Women and Royal Star and Garter Home (£500 each); Youth Aliyah-Child Rescue (£250); and British WIZO and Zionist Federation (£100 each).

FINANCES *Year* 2009–10 *Income* £93,159 *Grants* £82,430 *Assets* £2,129,715

TRUSTEES Denise Cohen; Martin D Paisner; Sara Cohen.

HOW TO APPLY In writing to the correspondent.

WHO TO APPLY TO Martin D Paisner, Trustee, c/o Berwin Leighton Paisner, Adelaide House, London Bridge, London EC4R 9HA *Tel* 020 7760 1000 *Fax* 020 7760 1111

■ The Vivienne and Samuel Cohen Charitable Trust

CC NO 255496   **ESTABLISHED** 1965

WHERE FUNDING CAN BE GIVEN UK and Israel.

WHO CAN BENEFIT Charitable organisations.

WHAT IS FUNDED Particular emphasis is given to Jewish causes; general charitable purposes, mainly education, culture and medical causes including research.

WHAT IS NOT FUNDED No grants to individuals.

SAMPLE GRANTS Ariel (£14,000); University College London (£10,000); Variety Club (£7,000); World Jewish Relief (£5,000); Hamesorah School (£4,000); the Spiro Ark (£3,000); Israel Free Loan Association and University Jewish Chaplaincy Board (£2,000 each); Chai Cancer Care, Machanaim and Royal Society of Medicine (£1,000 each).

FINANCES *Year* 2009–10 *Income* £101,927 *Grants* £182,547 *Assets* £2,859,317

TRUSTEES Dr V L L Cohen; M Y Ben-Gershon; J S Lauffer; Dr G L Lauffer.

HOW TO APPLY In writing only, to the correspondent.

WHO TO APPLY TO Dr Vivienne Cohen, Trustee, Clayton Start & Co, 5th Floor, Charles House, 108–110 Finchley Road, London NW3 5JJ *Tel* 020 7431 4200

■ The John S Cohen Foundation

CC NO 241598   **ESTABLISHED** 1965

WHERE FUNDING CAN BE GIVEN Worldwide, in practice mainly UK.

WHO CAN BENEFIT Registered charities.

WHAT IS FUNDED General charitable purposes but particularly supporting education, music and the arts and the environment, both built and natural.

TYPE OF GRANT One-off and recurring.

RANGE OF GRANTS Typically £5,000 or less; larger grants up to around £20,000.

SAMPLE GRANTS Harris Manchester College, Oxford (£40,000); Wigmore Hall (£29,000); Holburne Museum (£25,000); and the National Gallery (£20,000); Aldeburgh Music (£10,000); Garsington Opera (£7,000); Centre for Children's Books, Presteigne Festival and the Stephen Spender Memorial Trust (£5,000 each); Jewish Music Institute and Tricycle Theatre (£4,000 each); Edinburgh International Book Festival, London Chamber Music Society and the Royal Exchange Theatre – Manchester

(£3,000 each); Father Thames Trust, International Programme on the State of the Oceans and Shelter (£2,000 each); and Disasters Emergency Committee, Norfolk Wildlife Trust and Wallace Collection (£1,000 each).

FINANCES *Year* 2009–10 *Income* £480,182 *Grants* £333,542 *Assets* £6,940,205

TRUSTEES Dr David Cohen; Ms Imogen Cohen; Ms Olivia Cohen; Ms Veronica Cohen.

HOW TO APPLY In writing to the correspondent.

WHO TO APPLY TO Mrs Diana Helme, Foundation Administrator, PO Box 21277, London W9 2YH *Tel* 020 7286 6921

■ The R and S Cohen Foundation

CC NO 1078225   **ESTABLISHED** 1999

WHERE FUNDING CAN BE GIVEN Worldwide.

WHO CAN BENEFIT Educational, theatrical, operatic, medical and Jewish charitable organisations.

WHAT IS FUNDED Education and relief-in-need.

TYPE OF GRANT One-off and recurrent.

RANGE OF GRANTS £0–£747,000.

SAMPLE GRANTS Portland House Trust (£747,000); Design Museum (£40,000); Muscular Dystrophy, Royal National Institute for the Blind (£25,000 each); UJIA (£50,000); Tel-Aviv University Trust (£15,000); British Museum (£13,000); Jewish Care (£20,000); New Israel Fund (£8,000); Royal Academy of the Arts (£4,500); Tate Foundation (£5,000); WLS Charitable Fund (£1,200).

FINANCES *Year* 2010 *Income* £2,068,526 *Grants* £1,002,229 *Assets* £8,047,597

TRUSTEES Lady Sharon Harel-Cohen; Sir Ronald Cohen; Tamara Harel-Cohen; David Marks; Jonathan Harel-Cohen.

OTHER INFORMATION Grants of £1,000 or less totalled £9,000.

HOW TO APPLY In writing to the correspondent.

WHO TO APPLY TO Tess Housden, 42 Portland Place, London W1B 1NB

■ Col-Reno Ltd

CC NO 274896   **ESTABLISHED** 1977

WHERE FUNDING CAN BE GIVEN UK and Israel.

WHO CAN BENEFIT Religious and educational institutions benefiting children, young adults, students and Jewish people.

WHAT IS FUNDED Jewish religion and education.

RANGE OF GRANTS Mostly under £2,000.

SAMPLE GRANTS Society of Friends of the Torah (£16,000); Tiffert Gimzo (£7,500); Friends of Ascent (£2,400); Jerusalem Park Authority (£2,000); Friends of Yeshivat Chedvat Hatalmud (£1,600); Israel Museum – New Items Fund (£1,500); Chabad House of Hendon (£1,000); Chabad of Oxford (£720); Shaare Zedeck (£600); Yad Eliezer Trust (£200); and British Friends of Reut (£100).

FINANCES *Year* 2009–10 *Income* £95,630 *Grants* £37,930 *Assets* £1,076,426

TRUSTEES Martin Stern; Alan Stern; Keith Davis; Rhona Davis; Chaim Stern; Libbie Goldstein.

HOW TO APPLY In writing to the correspondent.

WHO TO APPLY TO The Trustees, 15 Shirehall Gardens, Hendon, London NW4 2QT

■ The Colchester Catalyst Charity

cc no 228352 **established** 1959
where funding can be given North east Essex.
who can benefit Health organisations.
what is funded Provision of support by direct contributions to health organisations for specific and well-designed projects in order to improve healthcare.
what is not funded No support for general funding, staff or running costs (usually). Retrospective funding is not considered. The charity is unable to consider applications for any item where there is an obligation for provision by a statutory authority.
type of grant One-off.
sample grants Previous beneficiaries have included Communication Aids Service, Beacon House, Balkerne Gardens Trust, Clacton Family Support, Colchester League of Friends Scanner Appeal, Colchester Toy Library, Headway Essex, St Anne's Clacton, St Helena Hospice and Tendring Shop Mobility.
finances *Year* 2009–10 *Income* £309,099 *Grants* £341,522 *Assets* £8,407,572
trustees Mr P Fitt, Chair; C Hayward; Dr E Hall; Dr M P Hickman; A W Livesley; M F Pertwee; Dr T P Rudra.
how to apply The application procedure varies for the different grants, full instructions can be obtained on the trust's website. Alternatively applicants may call or email the trust for further information on the application procedure.
who to apply to Peter Fitt, Company Secretary, 7 Coast Road, West Mersea, Colchester CO5 8QE *Tel* 01206 752545 *email* info@colchestercatalyst.co.uk *Website* www.colchestercatalyst.co.uk

■ John Coldman Charitable Trust

cc no 1050110 **established** 1995
where funding can be given UK, with a preference for Edenbridge in Kent.
who can benefit Registered charities.
what is funded General charitable purposes, particularly community and Christian groups and UK organisations whose work benefits the community, such as children's and medical charities and schools.
range of grants £250 upwards.
sample grants Great Ormond Street Hospital Children's Charity (£32,000); NSPCC Special Investigation Unit and Prince's Trust (£20,000 each); National Gardens Scheme (£18,000); Oasis International (£15,000); Citizen's Advice – Edenbridge and Westerham Branch (£12,000); Edenbridge Community Warden (£10,000); Eden Christian Trust (£7,500); Stangrove Area Community Action Group (£5,000); African Foundation (£3,000); Compaid Trust (£1,000); and Help the Hospices (£500).
finances *Year* 2009–10 *Income* £35,375 *Grants* £198,183 *Assets* £1,751,827
trustees John Coldman; Graham Coldman; Charles Warner.
other information During 2009–10 an additional £31,000 went towards the running of the Holcot Residential Centre, which operates as a hostel, holiday centre and community centre for the use of young people and others.
how to apply In writing to the correspondent.
who to apply to Charles Warner, Trustee, Bank House, Bank Street, Tonbridge, Kent TN9 1BL *Tel* 01732 770660 *Fax* 01732 362 452 *email* charles.warner@warners-solicitors.co.uk

■ The Cole Charitable Trust

cc no 264033 **established** 1972
where funding can be given Greater Birmingham, Kent and Cambridge.
who can benefit Local community projects or local branches of larger organisations. Individuals are also supported.
what is funded General charitable purposes. Grants were given in the following categories: care and social welfare; children and youth; disability; health; arts, culture and heritage; education and training; personal and community empowerment; international aid and development; and archaeology.
what is not funded No grants for large national organisations, religion, education, animal welfare, or to individuals not backed by a charity.
type of grant Small capital or project grants; normally one-off.
range of grants Up to £2,000.
sample grants Project Trust (£1,600); Saltley & Nechells Law Centre and Medical Foundation for the Care of Victims of Torture (£1,500 each); EARTH, Spadework, Books Abroad and Life Education Centres West Midlands (£1,000 each); Big Brum Theatre In Education, Cambridge Musical Festival and Bridge Trust (£500 each); Childreach (£400); and Stage 2 and Bag Books (£300 each).
finances *Year* 2009–10 *Income* £56,016 *Grants* £41,900 *Assets* £1,241,492
trustees Prof. T J Cole; G N Cole; Dr J G L Cole; T E C Cole; Dr J N Cole; A Frewin; K Hebron.
how to apply In writing to the correspondent, and must include recent annual accounts. An sae should not be sent. Two meetings per year; deadlines for applications are mid-March and mid-September.
who to apply to The Administrator, PO Box 51, Cambridge CB3 9QL *Tel* 01223 312374 *email* thecoletrust@gmail.com

■ The Colefax Charitable Trust

cc no 1017285 **established** 1993
where funding can be given Hampshire and Berkshire.
who can benefit Registered charities.
what is funded General charitable purposes.
what is not funded No grants to individuals.
sample grants Previous beneficiaries have included: Church on the Heath, Homestart, Jumbulance, Living Paintings Trust, Newbury District OAP Association, Newbury Spring Festival, Prospect Educational Trust, Reading Voluntary Action, Reliance Cancer Foundation, Southend Residents' Association and Watership Brass.
finances *Year* 2009–10 *Income* £207,924 *Grants* £134,435 *Assets* £10,184,597
trustees J E Heath; H J Krohn.
how to apply 'The trustees decide jointly which charitable institutions are to receive donations from the trust. No invitations are sought from eligible institutions.'
who to apply to Hans J Krohn, Trustee, Westbrook House, St Helens Gardens, The Pitchens, Wroughton, Wiltshire SN4 0RU

■ The John and Freda Coleman Charitable Trust

CC NO 278223   **ESTABLISHED** 1979
WHERE FUNDING CAN BE GIVEN Hampshire and Surrey and surrounding areas.
WHO CAN BENEFIT Education and training centres.
WHAT IS FUNDED The trust aims to provide: 'an alternative to an essentially academic education, to encourage and further the aspirations of young people with talents to develop manual skills and relevant technical knowledge to fit them for satisfying careers and useful employment. The aim is to develop the self-confidence of individuals to succeed within established organisations or on their own account and to impress upon them the importance of service to the community, honesty, good manners and self discipline.'
WHAT IS NOT FUNDED No grants are made to students.
TYPE OF GRANT Loans not given. Grants to 'kick start' relevant projects, capital costs other than buildings and core costs are all considered. Recurrent grants are given.
RANGE OF GRANTS Up to £20,000.
SAMPLE GRANTS Surrey SATRO (£10,500); Surrey Care Trust (£10,000); Surrey Community Development Trust (£5,000); Reigate and Redhill YMCA and Second Chance (£3,000 each); The Yvonne Arnaud Theatre Youth Drama Training (£2,000); and Step by Step (£1,000).
FINANCES *Year* 2010–11 *Income* £31,108 *Grants* £39,550 *Assets* £869,745
TRUSTEES I Williamson; Mrs J L Bird; P H Coleman; B R Coleman.
OTHER INFORMATION The following statement is taken from the trustees 2010–11 report: 'The charitable donations this year have again been targeted at the core aims of the trust in helping young people to obtain the skills they need for both work and life. Principal donations are currently directed towards a number of organisations, in Surrey and Hampshire, focussed on providing practical training, skills and support where the normal education system has failed and young people are not reaching their full potential.'
HOW TO APPLY In writing to the correspondent. Telephone calls are not welcome.
WHO TO APPLY TO Sue Poulter, Alderney House, 58 Normandy Street, Alton, Hampshire GU34 1DE *email* paul.coleman@btinternet.com

■ The Bernard Coleman Trust

CC NO 1075731   **ESTABLISHED** 1999
WHERE FUNDING CAN BE GIVEN Worldwide.
WHO CAN BENEFIT Charitable organisations.
WHAT IS FUNDED 'The objects of the charity are to provide coaching facilities to young sportsmen and sportswomen and to give donations to other similar sporting charities and grants to sporting clubs and associations. It also makes grants to medical services and to youth projects.'
RANGE OF GRANTS £500–£10,000.
SAMPLE GRANTS Chance to Shine and Royal Hospital for Neurodisability (£10,000 each); Surrey Care Trust, the Hornsby Trust and Arundel Castle Cricket Foundation (£5,000 each); National Rheumatoid Arthritis Society and UCL Hospital Charitable Foundation (£3,000 each).
FINANCES *Year* 2009–10 *Income* £122,307 *Grants* £85,626 *Assets* £568,404
TRUSTEES B Coleman; D Newton; J Fairclough; M Courtness; J Hugh-Jones.
HOW TO APPLY In writing to the correspondent.

WHO TO APPLY TO The Secretary, Moonstone, Pilgrims Way, Westhumble, Dorking, Surrey RH5 6AP *email* sheilastew@live.co.uk

■ The George Henry Collins Charity

CC NO 212268   **ESTABLISHED** 1959
WHERE FUNDING CAN BE GIVEN Within a 50-mile radius of Birmingham, or overseas.
WHO CAN BENEFIT Local charities and local branches of registered national charities in Birmingham benefiting older people, the socially isolated, or people who are ill.
WHAT IS FUNDED Wide, but the relief of illness, infirmity, old age or loneliness take preference. Trustees will consider donating one-tenth of annual income to charities for use overseas.
WHAT IS NOT FUNDED No grants to individuals.
TYPE OF GRANT One-off project funding.
RANGE OF GRANTS £250–£500, mostly £250 each.
SAMPLE GRANTS Beneficiaries included: Birmingham St Mary's Hospice, Cockermouth United Reform Church – Flood Relief, Concern Worldwide, Samaritans and Sutton Coldfield YMCA (£500 each); Adoption Support, Combat Stress, Home from Hospital Care, Kidney Research UK, Ronald McDonald House Charities and Troop Aid (£250 each); and EEIBA (£200).
FINANCES *Year* 2009–10 *Income* £46,376 *Grants* £33,900 *Assets* £1,484,518
TRUSTEES Anthony Collins, Chair; Elizabeth Davies; Andrew Waters; Roger Otto; Peter Coggan.
HOW TO APPLY In writing to the correspondent. The trustees usually meet in March, July and November.
WHO TO APPLY TO Chrissy Norgrove, c/o Martineau, No. 1 Colmore Square, Birmingham B4 6AA *Tel* 0870 763 2000

■ The E Alec Colman Charitable Fund Ltd

CC NO 243817   **ESTABLISHED** 1965
WHERE FUNDING CAN BE GIVEN UK and worldwide.
WHO CAN BENEFIT Charitable organisations, particular favour is given to those benefiting Jewish people and children.
WHAT IS FUNDED Relief of poverty; advancement of education; social welfare; and advancement of religion. The trust aims to pinpoint areas of interest and take the initiative in funding organisations working in these fields.
WHAT IS NOT FUNDED No grants to individuals.
RANGE OF GRANTS £150–£5,000.
SAMPLE GRANTS Previous beneficiaries: World Jewish Relief (£5,000); Send a Cow (£2,500); Army Cadet Force Association, the Royal British Legion and RNIB (£2,000 each); Practical Action (£1,500); the Smile Train UK (£1,200); British Friends of Ohel Sarah, the Salvation Army and Yad Vashem UK Foundation (£1,000 each); Brighton and Hove Parents and Children Group (£850); Operation New World (£750); 3H Fund (£500); At Risk Teenagers (£250); and 95th Birmingham Scout Group (£150).
FINANCES *Year* 2010–11 *Income* £12,740 *Grants* £40,000
TRUSTEES S H Colman; Mrs E A Colman; M Harris.
HOW TO APPLY In writing to the correspondent; however, the trust has stated that new beneficiaries are only considered in exceptional circumstances.

WHO TO APPLY TO A N Carless, Secretary, Colman House, 6–10 South Street, Harborne, Birmingham B17 0DB *Tel* 0121 427 7700

■ The Sir Jeremiah Colman Gift Trust

CC NO 229553   **ESTABLISHED** 1920

WHERE FUNDING CAN BE GIVEN UK, with a preference for Hampshire, especially Basingstoke.

WHO CAN BENEFIT Projects with well-established needs for support; the trust has already established priority beneficiaries.

WHAT IS FUNDED Advancement of education and literary scientific knowledge; moral and social improvement of people; maintenance of churches of the Church of England and gifts and offerings to the churches; financial assistance to past and present employees/members of Sir Jeremiah Colman at Gatton Park or other institutions associated with Sir Jeremiah Colman.

WHAT IS NOT FUNDED Grants are not made to individuals requiring support for personal education, or to individual families for welfare purposes.

SAMPLE GRANTS Warham (£7,500); National Art Collections and The Centre for Social Justice (£2,000 each); Cruse, Seeability, Wessex Counselling Service and Youth for Christ (£1,000 each).

FINANCES *Year* 2009–10 *Income* £131,017 *Grants* £121,100 *Assets* £4,756,806

TRUSTEES Sir Michael Colman; Lady Colman; Oliver Colman; Hon. Cynthia Colman; Jeremiah Colman; Sue Colman.

OTHER INFORMATION In 2009–10 grants were broken down as follows: 'special' donations (£65,000); 'annual' donations (£55,000); and 'extra' donations (£550).

HOW TO APPLY In writing to the correspondent.

WHO TO APPLY TO Mrs V R Persson, Secretary to the Trustees, Malshanger, Basingstoke, Hampshire RG23 7EY *Tel* 01256 780252

■ The Colt Foundation

CC NO 277189   **ESTABLISHED** 1978

WHERE FUNDING CAN BE GIVEN In practice UK.

WHO CAN BENEFIT Universities and research establishments benefiting research workers and students taking higher degrees.

WHAT IS FUNDED Research projects at universities and other independent research institutions into occupational and environmental health.

WHAT IS NOT FUNDED Grants are not made for the general funds of another charity, directly to individuals or projects overseas.

TYPE OF GRANT Research, project.

RANGE OF GRANTS £20,000–£100,000.

SAMPLE GRANTS Edinburgh Napier University (£96,000); National Heart and Lung Institute (£69,000); ELEGI (£52,000); University of Aberdeen (£44,000); University of Edinburgh (£42,000); Swansea University (£18,000); EPICOH 2011 (£10,000); University of Central Lancashire (£3,000); British Occupation Health Research Foundation (£1,000); Royal Society of Medicine – United States (£900); and Manchester – Jones and Scrutton (£260).

FINANCES *Year* 2010 *Income* £486,513 *Grants* £459,162 *Assets* £17,929,786

TRUSTEES Prof. David Coggon; Clare Gilchrist; Prof. A J Newman Taylor; Juliette O'Hea; Peter O'Hea; Alan O'Hea; Jerome O'Hea; Natasha Lebus; Patricia Lebus.

OTHER INFORMATION £104,000 was awarded to an unspecified number of students.

HOW TO APPLY In writing to the correspondent. Initial applications should contain sufficient information for the scientific advisers to be able to comment, and include a lay summary for the trustees' first appraisal. This lay summary is regarded as important, as the majority of the trustees do not have a medical or scientific background and this helps them with their decision making. The trustees meet twice each year, normally in May and November. Applications should reach the correspondent by 23 March and 1 October in time for these meetings so that advice can be obtained from external assessors beforehand. However, applicants can submit a single sheet 'lay summary' at any time during the year, so that advice can be given on whether the work is likely to fall within the remit of the foundation, prior to working on a full application. The foundation does not have application forms. Applicants are asked to read the following guidelines carefully and follow them when preparing an application: What is the work you would like to do; why does the work need doing; who is doing or has done similar work, and how will your work add to it; how do you intend to carry out the work, and why do you think this is the right approach; what resources will you need to do the work, and are these resources available; who will do the work, and how much time will each of the people involved devote to it; how long will the work take; how much money do you need to complete the work; and when do you plan to start?

WHO TO APPLY TO Mrs Jacqueline Douglas, Director, New Lane, Havant, Hampshire PO9 2LY *Tel* 023 9249 1400 *Fax* 023 9249 1363 *email* jackie.douglas@uk.coltgroup.com *Website* www.coltfoundation.org.uk

■ The Coltstaple Trust

CC NO 1085500   **ESTABLISHED** 2001

WHERE FUNDING CAN BE GIVEN Worldwide.

WHO CAN BENEFIT Charitable organisations.

WHAT IS FUNDED 'The relief of persons in need, poverty or distress in third world countries and the relief of persons who are homeless or in housing need in the UK or any other part of the world.'

TYPE OF GRANT Recurrent.

SAMPLE GRANTS Oxfam (£130,000); St Mungo's and Opportunity International (£50,000 each); and Sport for Life (£20,000).

FINANCES *Year* 2010–11 *Income* £207,334 *Grants* £250,000 *Assets* £4,610,676

TRUSTEES Lord Oakshott of Seagrove Bay; Dr P Oakshott; B R M Stoneham; Mrs E G Colville.

HOW TO APPLY Unfortunately the trust's funds are fully committed. 'We give to a very small number of charities on a long term basis and have recently been receiving many requests which must have taken the applicants a lot of time [. . .] which we cannot deal with.'

WHO TO APPLY TO Lord Oakshott of Seagrove Bay, Trustee, c/o Pollen House, 10–12 Cork Street, London W1S 3NP *Tel* 020 7439 4400

■ Colwinston Charitable Trust

CC NO 1049189　　　**ESTABLISHED** 1995
WHERE FUNDING CAN BE GIVEN Mostly Wales.
WHO CAN BENEFIT UK registered charities.
WHAT IS FUNDED The trustees seek to support charitable organisations working in the fields of opera/music theatre, classical music, and the visual arts. They will also consider specific project proposals for the assistance of libraries and archives. Opera/music theatre – the trust aims to widen the opportunities to enjoy and appreciate performances of opera and music theatre, especially by assisting organisations to develop new audiences for performances of the highest quality; classical music – the trust aims to widen the opportunities to enjoy and to appreciate traditional classical music, and is especially interested to support projects that deliver high quality performances to areas where provision is limited; visual arts – the trust aims to widen the opportunities to enjoy and to be stimulated by the visual arts, to foster creative endeavour and to help develop new audiences; and libraries and archives – the trust will consider applications for specific projects but are unlikely to support capital projects. 'The trust is especially interested in *exceptional* projects that demonstrate *excellence* in terms of the creative ambition of the project, the quality of the artistic product, the calibre of the participating artists, and the value of the artistic experience for audiences and/or participants.'
WHAT IS NOT FUNDED The trust will not consider applications for capital building projects, for general appeals, for retrospective funding, for conferences and seminars, websites, publications, or from individuals.
RANGE OF GRANTS £5,000 to £75,000.
SAMPLE GRANTS Welsh National Opera (£75,000); Agatha Christie's Trust (£50,000); Bampton Classical Orchestra (£15,000); Oriel Mostyn Gallery (£13,000); Sherman Cymru and Paintings in Hospitals (£10,000 each); Gregynog Festival (£8,000); Presteigne Festival of Music and the Arts (£7,000); Live Music Now (£5,000); and Tabernacle Trust (£2,000).
FINANCES *Year* 2009–10 *Income* £279,851 *Grants* £184,500 *Assets* £1,179,105
TRUSTEES Mrs A Clementson; M D Paisner; J C Prichard; M C T Prichard; R J Maskrey.
OTHER INFORMATION The trust derives its income from the royalties from the West End production of *The Mousetrap*, the Agatha Christie play, which opened in 1952.
HOW TO APPLY Full and detailed guidelines are available on the trust's website. 'In the first instance, and prior to sending any application to the trust, organisations should make contact with the Consultant Director, preferably by email, supplying a brief summary of the project and indicating the grant level being sought.' The trustees meet twice yearly (usually March and October) to consider applications and to make decisions on grants.
WHO TO APPLY TO Amanda McMurray, Consultant Director, 14 Hanover Court, Midhope Road, Woking, Surrey GU22 7UX *email* colwinston. trust@ntlworld.com *Website* www.colwinston. org.uk

■ Colyer-Fergusson Charitable Trust

CC NO 258958　　　**ESTABLISHED** 1969
WHERE FUNDING CAN BE GIVEN Churches and registered charities in Kent.
WHO CAN BENEFIT Charities and churches aiming to improve quality of life, tackle poverty, social isolation or exclusion, promote the arts and protect the natural resources and heritage of the local areas for their inhabitants.
WHAT IS FUNDED Current priority areas are: safer communities; protecting and supporting older vulnerable people; refugees and asylum seekers; caring for carers; transition to independence for young people leaving care; encouraging active living.
WHAT IS NOT FUNDED No grants to the following: animal welfare charities; individuals directly; research (except practical research designed to benefit the local community directly); hospitals or schools; political activities; commercial ventures or publications; the purchase of vehicles including minibuses; overseas travel or holidays; retrospective grants or loans; direct replacement of statutory funding or activities that are primarily the responsibility of central or local government; large capital, endowment or widely distributed appeals; applications from churches and charities outside Kent.
TYPE OF GRANT One-off, recurring, capital, core, running and start-up costs will all be considered, as will salaries, buildings, project and research costs. Funding may be given for up to three years.
RANGE OF GRANTS £500–£75,000.
SAMPLE GRANTS University of Kent (£4.5 million); Minster Abbey (£75,000); Deal Town Football Club (£40,000); St Giles Trust (£30,000); Alkham Valley Community Project (£21,000); Capel-le-Fern Village Hall (£15,000); Thanington Neighbourhood Community Centre (£12,500); Betteshanger Social Club & Community Centre (£10,000); and Volunteer Reading Help (£5,000).
FINANCES *Year* 2009–10 *Income* £600,690 *Grants* £5,131,182 *Assets* £26,238,248
TRUSTEES Jonathan Monckton, Chair; Nicholas Fisher; Robert North; Ruth Murphy.
OTHER INFORMATION A special grant of £4.5 million was made to the University of Kent during 2009–10 towards the cost of a new building for music rehearsal and performance. This was a one-off donation; grants usually total around £600,000 each year.
HOW TO APPLY All applicants must complete the on-line application form. There is no deadline for applications and all applications will be acknowledged. Trustees meet regularly during the year and decisions are usually processed within six months. All applicants will be notified in writing. The trust requests applicants, where possible, to submit any supporting material by email as scanned documents or files to admin@cfct.org.uk
WHO TO APPLY TO Jacqueline Rae, Director, Hogarth House, 34 Paradise Road, Richmond, Surrey TW9 1SE *Tel* 020 8948 3388 *email* grantadmin@cfct.org.uk *Website* www. cfct.org.uk

■ Comic Relief

CC NO 326568   **ESTABLISHED** 1985

WHERE FUNDING CAN BE GIVEN UK and overseas (mainly Africa).

WHO CAN BENEFIT UK registered charities; voluntary organisations; and self-help groups.

WHAT IS FUNDED For the period 2009–2012 the charity's UK grants programmes are focusing on the following areas: mental health; domestic and sexual abuse (young people aged 11 to 25); refugee and asylum seeking women; sport for change; sexually exploited and trafficked young people (aged 11 to 25); young people and alcohol (aged 11 to 25); young people with mental health problems (aged 11 to 25); older people and their finances; 'local communities' – this programme is being administered by the Community Foundation Network. Contact your local community foundation for further information.

WHAT IS NOT FUNDED There are certain types of work and organisations that Comic Relief does not fund. If your proposal falls into one of these categories, please do not apply: grants to individuals; medical research or hospitals; churches or other religious bodies where the monies will be used for religious purposes; work where there is statutory responsibility to provide funding; projects where the work has already taken place; statutory bodies, such as local authorities or Primary Care Trusts or organisations seeking funding to replace cuts by statutory bodies; profit-making organisations, except social enterprises; organisations who hold free reserves equivalent to the amount applied for may be turned down. The charity is also unable to fund minibuses.

TYPE OF GRANT Capital or revenue. One-off or spread over up to three years.

RANGE OF GRANTS Grants average between £25,000 and £40,000, and rarely exceed this upper limit.

TRUSTEES Peter Benett-Jones, Chair; Lenny Henry; Cilla Snowball; Claudia Lloyd; Colin Howes; Diana Barran; George Entwistle; Harry Cayton; Imelda Walsh; Jana Bennett; Jim Hytner; Joe Cerrell; Mike Harris; Richard Curtis; Suzi Aplin; Theo Sowa; Tristia Clarke; Robert Stopford Webb.

PUBLICATIONS Essential Information for applicants; Grants Strategy.

OTHER INFORMATION Of the overall grant total £19.7 million was awarded to organisations working within the UK.

HOW TO APPLY Please ensure that you have read the charity's Grant Making Principles and Essential Information for applicants. Applications are via the trust's online application process.

WHO TO APPLY TO Gilly Green, Head of UK Grants, 5th Floor, 89 Albert Embankment, London SE1 7TP *Tel* 020 7820 2000 *Fax* 020 7820 2222 *Minicom* 020 7820 2005 *email* ukgrants@comicrelief.com *Website* www.comicrelief.com

■ The Comino Foundation

CC NO 312875   **ESTABLISHED** 1971

WHERE FUNDING CAN BE GIVEN UK.

WHO CAN BENEFIT Organisations benefiting young adults and academics.

WHAT IS FUNDED Support of educational activities which encourage and enable individuals and groups to motivate and empower themselves; progressively develop their potential for the benefit of themselves and others; and

encourage a culture which affirms and celebrates both achievement and responsible practice in industry and commerce.

WHAT IS NOT FUNDED No grants to individuals or for or research projects.

TYPE OF GRANT One-off.

RANGE OF GRANTS Up to £50,000.

SAMPLE GRANTS Wigan Borough Partnership, Sheffield Hallam University, University of Winchester and Liverpool John Moores University (£50,000 each); PACE Centre (£44,000); Institute for Global Ethics UK Trust (£35,000); RSA Tipton Academy (£25,000); Local Solutions – Liverpool (£24,000); Ideas Foundation (£15,000); Potential Trust (£12,000); Youth Leaders in STEM (£10,000); Bailey Comino Scholarship (£6,000); and Foundation for Science and Technology and Values & The Classroom Teacher (£2,000 each).

FINANCES *Year* 2009–10 *Income* £264,354 *Grants* £374,541 *Assets* £4,433,854

TRUSTEES Mrs A Comino-Jones; Dr W E Duckworth; Sir Mike Tomlinson; J E Slater.

OTHER INFORMATION The trust meets these aims through its patented GRASP approach, which offers a structure for thinking in a results-driven manner through a greater pattern, design and method of thinking. Most of the funds are given towards centres which promote the GRASP approach. Further information on this can be gathered from a leaflet prepared from the trust or on their extensive website.

HOW TO APPLY Requests for support should initially be sent to the administrator by email.

WHO TO APPLY TO Diana le Clercq, Administrator, Woodlee, Park Road, Stoke Poges, Buckinghamshire SL2 4PG *Tel* 01494 722595 *email* enquire@cominofoundation.org.uk *Website* www.cominofoundation.org.uk

■ The Compton Charitable Trust

CC NO 280404   **ESTABLISHED** 1980

WHERE FUNDING CAN BE GIVEN Northamptonshire.

WHO CAN BENEFIT Charitable organisations, with a preference for those with a connection to the family estates of the Marquess of Northampton as well as those which the Marquess is a patron of.

WHAT IS FUNDED General charitable purposes.

SAMPLE GRANTS Previous beneficiaries include: Dogs Trust and Help for Heroes (£5,000 each); the Compton Wynyates Church Trust and Feldon Church Trust (£2,000 each); King Edwards VII Hospital Midhurst and St Michael Steiner School (£1,000 each); the Leukaemia Care Society (£500); NSPCC (£250); Royal British Legion – Poppy Appeal (£150); and Ghurkha Welfare Trust (£100).

FINANCES *Year* 2009–10 *Income* £22,595 *Grants* £80,000

TRUSTEES Marquess of Northampton; Lady Pamela Northampton; Earl Daniel Compton.

HOW TO APPLY In writing to the correspondent. Unsolicited applications are considered, but are usually unsuccessful.

WHO TO APPLY TO The Trustees, Moore Stephens LLP, 150 Aldersgate Street, London EC1A 4AB

■ The Douglas Compton James Charitable Trust

CC NO 1091125   **ESTABLISHED** 2002

WHERE FUNDING CAN BE GIVEN Northamptonshire.

WHO CAN BENEFIT Registered charities.

WHAT IS FUNDED General, education and social welfare. Some preference is given for Masonic charities.

TYPE OF GRANT One-off and recurrent.

RANGE OF GRANTS Up to £30,000.

SAMPLE GRANTS Grand Charity (£27,000); NHS Bedford Hospital (£12,000); Corby Women's Centre (£9,100); Lakeland Day Care Hospice and Cransley Hospital (£5,000 each); Kettering General Hospital Charity Fund and Newton in the Willows (£3,000 each); and Life Education Northamptonshire Limited, Wellingborough All Saints Scouts, Lakeland Day Care Hospice and Deafblind UK (£2,000 each).

FINANCES *Year* 2009–10 *Income* £111,189 *Grants* £108,043 *Assets* £4,382,607

TRUSTEES Jim Higham; John Humphrey; Richard Ongley; B Huckle.

HOW TO APPLY In writing to the correspondent.

WHO TO APPLY TO Louise Davies, Montague House, Chancery Lane, Thrapston, Northamptonshire NN14 4LN *Tel* 01832 732161

■ The Congleton Inclosure Trust

CC NO 244136   **ESTABLISHED** 1795

WHERE FUNDING CAN BE GIVEN The town of Congleton and the parishes of Hulme Walfield and Newbold with Astbury.

WHO CAN BENEFIT Local organisations; UK organisations with projects in the area.

WHAT IS FUNDED The relief of people who are older, impotent and poor; the relief of distress and sickness; the provision and support of facilities for recreation or other leisure-time activities; the provision and support of educational facilities; and any other charitable purpose.

WHAT IS NOT FUNDED No grants to individuals outside the beneficial area or to organisations not benefiting exclusively the people in the area of benefit.

TYPE OF GRANT Buildings, capital, core costs, feasibility studies, salaries and start-up costs will be considered. Funding may be given for up to one year.

RANGE OF GRANTS £500–£3,000 (2010).

SAMPLE GRANTS East Cheshire Hospice (£3,000); Marie Curie (£2,500); Congleton Lawn Tennis (£2,500); St John's Church (£1,500); Road Heath Band (£1,600); Lions Youth (£1,500); Youth Council (£750) and KISS and St Mary's School, Astbury (£500 each).

FINANCES *Year* 2010 *Income* £54,104 *Grants* £51,242 *Assets* £1,937,756

TRUSTEES K P Boon, Chair; J W Beardmore; Mrs J Goodier; A B McCormick; E G Pedley; Revd D Taylor; J S Wainwright; A B Watson.

OTHER INFORMATION The trust is willing to provide funding for core costs and capital costs with grants averaging £1,000–£5,000.

HOW TO APPLY On a form available from the correspondent. The trustees meet in January, April, July and October. Applications should be submitted by the first day of the month in which the trustees meet.

WHO TO APPLY TO D A Daniel, Clerk, PO Box 138, Congleton, Cheshire CW12 3SZ *Tel* 01260 273180 *email* daviddaniel@uwclub.net

■ The Congregational and General Charitable Trust

CC NO 297013   **ESTABLISHED** 1987

WHERE FUNDING CAN BE GIVEN UK.

WHO CAN BENEFIT Protestant churches and community projects, in particular those associated with United Reformed and Congregational denominations.

WHAT IS FUNDED (i) Funds for building or property projects to churches and charities of the United Reformed and Congregational denominations or other Protestant churches. (ii) Church community projects seeking funding towards their capital costs.

TYPE OF GRANT One-off for property projects and capital costs.

FINANCES *Year* 2009–10 *Income* £394,279 *Grants* £117,000 *Assets* £9,239,000

TRUSTEES Robert B Copleton, Chair; Margaret E Atkinson; David J Collett; Revd Anthony G Burnham; Revd Arnold Harrison; Revd Michael R Heaney; Revd Ifan Rh Roberts; Barrie E Smith; Stephen D Wood.

HOW TO APPLY In a form which can be downloaded from the trust's website. 'When sending your application please attach any supporting documentation – such as your church's or organisation's accounts, the project's accounts, appeal leaflets or project literature – along with your signed application form.' The closing dates for applications are 31 January and 31 July each year.

WHO TO APPLY TO David Collett, Secretary of the Trustees, Currer House, Currer Street, Bradford, West Yorkshire BD1 5BA *email* trust@congregational.co.uk *Website* www.congregational.co.uk

■ The Conscience Trust

CC NO 1044136   **ESTABLISHED** 1995

WHERE FUNDING CAN BE GIVEN UK.

WHO CAN BENEFIT Charitable organisations.

WHAT IS FUNDED 'The charity provides grants to other registered charities and organisations, primarily to assist with projects of a horticultural and eco-friendly nature.'

SAMPLE GRANTS The sole beneficiary during the year was Torbay Coast and Countryside Trust (£60,000). Previous beneficiaries have included Forna and Flora International, Garden Organic, The Miracle Trust, National Farmer Network, Organic Research Centre, Oxfam, St Christopher's Hospice, Sightsavers International, The Soil Association, The Woodland Trust and Worldwide Life Foundation.

FINANCES *Year* 2009–10 *Income* £51,652 *Grants* £60,000 *Assets* £686,468

TRUSTEES Adrian Miller; Will Michelmore; Simon Whewell; Prof. Jo Anderson.

HOW TO APPLY 'Please apply in writing, with applications to be limited to 500 words.'

WHO TO APPLY TO The Trustees, c/o Michelmores, Woodwater House, Pynes Hill, Exeter EX2 5WR

■ The Conservation Foundation

CC NO 284656   **ESTABLISHED** 1982

WHERE FUNDING CAN BE GIVEN UK and overseas.

WHO CAN BENEFIT Registered charities.

WHAT IS FUNDED Creation and management of environmental and conservation orientated projects funded by sponsorship. Income is generated to pay for the costs of managing charitable projects and supporting activities.

FINANCES *Year* 2010 *Income* £216,836
Grants £77,358 *Assets* £684,824

TRUSTEES J Senior, Chair; D A Shreeve; Prof.
D J Bellamy; J B Curtis; W F Moloney; Mrs
E A Kinmonth; Mrs L Dunn; A Nicoll; M Bennett.

OTHER INFORMATION Information about the
foundation's current projects can be found on
its website.

HOW TO APPLY In writing to the correspondent.

WHO TO APPLY TO W F Moloney, Trustee,
1 Kensington Gore, London SW7 2AR *Tel* 020
7591 3111 *email* info@conservationfoundation.
co.uk *Website* www.conservationfoundation.co.
uk

■ The Consolidated Charities for the Infirm – Merchant Taylors' Company

CC NO 214266   ESTABLISHED 1960

WHERE FUNDING CAN BE GIVEN Lewisham, Southwark,
Tower Hamlets, Hackney and environs;
occasionally Greater London. National grants
made in exceptional cases.

WHO CAN BENEFIT Charitable organisations.

WHAT IS FUNDED Relief of need, people with
disabilities, infirm, older people and children,
sheltered housing and residential care homes.

RANGE OF GRANTS £1000–£40,000.

SAMPLE GRANTS Ranyard Charitable Trust (£35,000);
Sense (£34,000); Richard House Trust
(£18,000); Tall Ships Youth Trust, The Queen's
Nursing Institute (£10,000 each); U Can Do It
(£3,600); Dressability, Disability Law Service
(£2,500 each).

FINANCES *Year* 2010 *Income* £452,268
Grants £407,147 *Assets* £9,589,707

TRUSTEES Hugh Richard Oliver-Bellasis Frags; Peter
Godfrey Magill; Andrew Graham Moss;
Christopher Morley Keville.

HOW TO APPLY In writing using the appropriate
application form which is available from the
correspondent or by visiting
www.merchanttaylors.co.uk. The charity states
that emailed enquiries are preferred and
responded to quickest.

WHO TO APPLY TO Matthew Dear, Charities Officer,
Merchant Taylors' Hall, 30 Threadneedle Street,
London EC2R 8JB *Tel* 020 7450 4440
email charities@merchant-taylors.co.uk
Website www.merchant-taylors.co.uk

■ The Cook and Wolstenholme Charitable Trust

CC NO 1091984   ESTABLISHED 2000

WHERE FUNDING CAN BE GIVEN Bournville and the
surrounding area just south of Birmingham City
Centre.

WHO CAN BENEFIT Charitable organisations.

WHAT IS FUNDED General charitable purposes, with a
preference for organisations supporting young
and older people.

SAMPLE GRANTS Previous beneficiaries included:
Sense (£3,000); Pavilion Christian Community
(£2,500); British Heart Foundation, County Air
Ambulance and St Mary's Hospice (£2,000
each); Alderbrook School (£1,500); Birmingham
Children's Hospital, Birmingham Women's
Foundation NHS Trust, Brain Tumour UK,
Brandwood Centre and Mobility Trust (£1,000
each); Cockshutt Hill Technical College and RNLI
(£500 each); and Wychall Primary School
(£250).

FINANCES *Year* 2009–10 *Income* £17,888
Grants £57,566

TRUSTEES Peter Barber; Dennis Carson; Patrick
Beasley.

HOW TO APPLY In writing to the correspondent. The
trustees meet about every six months, although
applications for grants are considered all year
round.

WHO TO APPLY TO Dennis Carson, Clerk, c/o Mills &
Reeve, 78–84 Colmore Row, Birmingham
B3 2AB

■ Gordon Cook Foundation

SC NO SC017455   ESTABLISHED 1974

WHERE FUNDING CAN BE GIVEN UK.

WHO CAN BENEFIT National curriculum agencies in
the four home nations, Local Education
Authorities, universities, colleges, schools and
clusters of schools and the voluntary sector.

WHAT IS FUNDED The foundation is dedicated to the
advancement of all aspects of education and
training which are likely to promote character
development and citizenship. In recent years the
foundation has adopted the term 'Values
Education' to denote the wide range of activity it
seeks to support.

WHAT IS NOT FUNDED Individuals are unlikely to be
funded.

TYPE OF GRANT One-off and recurring for projects and
research. Funding may be given for more than
three years.

RANGE OF GRANTS £3,000–£30,000.

SAMPLE GRANTS Previous beneficiaries include
Norham Foundation, Health Education Board for
Scotland, Citizen Foundation, North Lanarkshire
Council and Northern College.

FINANCES *Year* 2009–10 *Income* £303,458

TRUSTEES Miss A Harper, Chair; G Ross; Dr
I Sutherland; D A Adams; J Anderson.

OTHER INFORMATION Previous research indicates that
grants are made totalling around £200,000
each year.

HOW TO APPLY The trustees are proactive in looking
for projects to support and do not normally
invite or respond to unsolicited applications for
grant aid.

WHO TO APPLY TO Sharon Hauxwell, Foundation
Secretary, 3 Chattan Place, Aberdeen
AB10 6RB *Tel* 01224 571010
email gordoncook@btconnect.com
Website www.gordoncook.org

■ The Ernest Cook Trust

CC NO 313497   ESTABLISHED 1952

WHERE FUNDING CAN BE GIVEN UK.

WHO CAN BENEFIT Charitable or not for profit
organisations working through education or
training in three main areas of activity, being the
environment and the countryside, the arts,
crafts and architecture and literacy and
numeracy.

WHAT IS FUNDED Grants are given for educational
work only, focusing on children and young
people in the fields of countryside and
environment, arts and crafts, architecture,
literary and numeracy, research and other
educational projects.

WHAT IS NOT FUNDED Applicants must represent
either registered charities or not-for-profit
organisations. Grants are normally awarded on
an annual basis and will not be awarded
retrospectively. Grants are not made: to
individuals, Agricultural Colleges, independent
schools or local authorities; for building work or

refurbishment work; for youth work, social support, therapy and medical treatment, including projects using the arts for these purposes; for projects related to sports, outward bound type activities or recreation; for overseas projects; for Wildlife Trusts and for Farming & Wildlife Advisory Groups other than those which are based in counties in which the ECT owns land (Buckinghamshire, Dorset, Gloucestershire, Leicestershire and Oxfordshire).

TYPE OF GRANT Conditional; annual; one-off. Project; research; salaries; and start-up costs. Funding may be given for up to three years.

SAMPLE GRANTS Details of individual beneficiaries were not included in the trust's 2009–10 annual report, however recipients of grants from the previous year were detailed on the trust's website at the time of writing, with more recent examples no doubt available in due course. Beneficiaries previously listed here, and the purposes for which grants were made, include: Edward Barnsley Trust (£25,000), to cover the cost of an apprentice; Chetham's School of Music (£21,000), towards an early years music project; Year of Food and Farming (£20,000), towards educational work in the North East and South West; Engineering Education Scheme in Wales (£10,500), towards bursaries for the scheme; Rockingham Forest Trust (£8,000), towards the People in the Forest project; Groundwork London (£7,500), towards the cost of an education officer for the Eco Schools project; Yorkshire Agricultural Society (£7,000), towards the cost of the information boards, education adviser and information packs; Arable Group Ltd (£6,000), for bursaries for students taking part in the TAG Asset programme; and Langham Arts Trust (£4,000), towards the cost of Proms Praise for Schools.

FINANCES *Year* 2009–10 *Income* £3,222,080 *Grants* £1,302,679 *Assets* £84,805,933

TRUSTEES Anthony Bosanquet, Chair; Harry Henderson; Andrew Christie-Miller; Patrick Maclure; Miles C Tuely; Victoria Edwards.

HOW TO APPLY The ECT aims to have a 'light-touch' application process with a view to enabling small regional or local organisations to apply for support. All applicant organisations must be based and working in the UK and should be either state schools, registered charities or other recognised not-for-profit organisations. It is very important however to read the exclusions before applying. Grants are normally awarded for one year only. There are no application forms. All applicants are asked to post a covering letter on the official headed paper of the applicant organisation and also include: up to two additional sheets of A4 describing the organisation, outlining the project and specifying its educational elements and the way in which it fits in with the interests of the ECT; a simple budget for the project, outlining the way in which the grant would be spent; a list of any other funding applications; the latest annual report and accounts for the organisation (schools are not required to send one). Please do not send further supporting material or email applications, which are not accepted. Applications must be posted. Questions (not applications) can be addressed to the Grants Administrator via email or telephone.

WHO TO APPLY TO Mrs Ros Leigh, Grants Administrator, Fairford Park, Fairford, Gloucestershire GL7 4JH *Tel* 01285 712492 *Fax* 01285 713417 *email* grants@ ernestcooktrust.org.uk *Website* www. ernestcooktrust.org.uk

■ The Cooks Charity

CC NO 297913   **ESTABLISHED** 1987

WHERE FUNDING CAN BE GIVEN UK, especially City of London.

WHO CAN BENEFIT Charities and individuals.

WHAT IS FUNDED Projects concerned with catering. Any charitable purpose (with some sort of catering connection) in the City of London.

SAMPLE GRANTS Past beneficiaries have included: Academy of Culinary Arts (£55,000); Food Education At Schools Today (£42,000); Hackney Community College (£30,000); Springboard (£25,000); Ironbridge Museum (£15,000); Crisis Skylight Cafe (£12,000); Bournemouth University (£10,000); and Treloar Trust, Broadway and Pembroke House (£5,000 each).

FINANCES *Year* 2009–10 *Income* £450,684 *Grants* £224,000

TRUSTEES H F Thornton; G A V Rees; B E G Puxley.

OTHER INFORMATION At the time of writing, accounts had yet to be received at the Charity Commission. Therefore, further information was not available.

HOW TO APPLY In writing to the correspondent. Applications are considered in spring and autumn.

WHO TO APPLY TO Michael C Thatcher, Clerk and Solicitor, Coombe Ridge, Thursley Road, Churt, Farnham, Surrey GU10 2LQ *email* clerk@ cookslivery.org.uk

■ The Cookson Charitable Trust

CC NO 265207   **ESTABLISHED** 1972

WHERE FUNDING CAN BE GIVEN UK.

WHO CAN BENEFIT Charitable organisations.

WHAT IS FUNDED General charitable purposes.

RANGE OF GRANTS Up to £3,000.

SAMPLE GRANTS Beneficiaries included: King's College Cambridge (£3,000); Besom Foundation (£1,000); Bishopstone PCC (£800); Royal Marsden Hospital, Mind, Marie Curie, Live Music Now and New College Oxford (£500 each); International Musicians Seminar (£400); and Walk the Walk (£250).

FINANCES *Year* 2009–10 *Income* £36,364 *Grants* £7,983 *Assets* £252,783

TRUSTEES H R Cookson; C M Cookson.

HOW TO APPLY In writing to the correspondent.

WHO TO APPLY TO H R Cookson, Trustee, Manor Farm, Stratford Tony, Salisbury SP5 4AT

■ The Catherine Cookson Charitable Trust

CC NO 272895   **ESTABLISHED** 1977

WHERE FUNDING CAN BE GIVEN UK, with some preference for the North East of England.

WHO CAN BENEFIT Charitable organisations.

WHAT IS FUNDED General charitable purposes.

RANGE OF GRANTS Mostly £1,000 or less. A few large grants are made.

SAMPLE GRANTS Cancer Research UK (£100,000); Newcastle Diocese Education Board, the Puffin Appeal and the Stroke Association (£50,000 each); Newcastle Upon Tyne Royal Grammar School (£35,000); Great Ormond Street Hospital Children's Charity (£25,000); East Sussex Hospitals NHS Trust (£8,000); HMS Trincomalee Trust (£5,000); Royalty Theatre Sunderland (£2,000); Blind Voice UK, St Cuthberts Centre Crook and Finchale Training College (£1,000 each); Coping with Cancer Northeast, Peach Berkshire and Gangshow Newcastle and the Old Vicarage (£500 each);

Brampton Primary School, Martlett's Hospice, and Rainbow Trust Durham (£250 each); and British Dyslexics North East, Elim Church Newcastle, and Jack and Jill Pre School Nursery (£100 each).

FINANCES *Year* 2009–10 *Income* £732,517 *Grants* £481,460 *Assets* £22,419,624

TRUSTEES David S S Hawkins; Peter Magnay; Hugo F Marshall; Daniel E Sallows; Jack E Ravenscroft.

HOW TO APPLY In writing to the correspondent.

WHO TO APPLY TO Peter Magnay, Trustee, Thomas Magnay and Co, 13 Regent Terrace, Gateshead, Tyne and Wear NE8 1LU *Tel* 0191 488 7459

■ Harold and Daphne Cooper Charitable Trust

CC NO 206772   **ESTABLISHED** 1962

WHERE FUNDING CAN BE GIVEN UK.

WHO CAN BENEFIT National charities.

WHAT IS FUNDED Medical research, health and Jewish charities.

WHAT IS NOT FUNDED No grants to individuals.

TYPE OF GRANT Small one-off grants and on-going support for capital (buildings considered), project and research. Core costs and running costs are considered.

RANGE OF GRANTS One large grant; the remainder for smaller amounts.

SAMPLE GRANTS Jewish Care (£46,000); Norwood Ravenswood (£5,000); Dogs for the Disabled and Variety Club of Great Britain (£2,000 each); and Live Music Now, Marie Curie Cancer Care, Arthritis Research UK, Jewish Blind and Disabled, Moorfields Eye Hospital, Spadework, Thrive and Wheelpower (£1,000 each).

FINANCES *Year* 2009–10 *Income* £93,121 *Grants* £63,000 *Assets* £2,623,124

TRUSTEES Sally Roter; Judith Portrait; Timothy Roter; Abigail Roter; Dominic Roter.

HOW TO APPLY In writing to the correspondent; applications are not acknowledged.

WHO TO APPLY TO Alison Burton, Trust Administrator, c/o Portrait Solicitors, 1 Chancery Lane, London WC2A 1LF *Tel* 020 7092 6984

■ Mabel Cooper Charity

CC NO 264621   **ESTABLISHED** 1972

WHERE FUNDING CAN BE GIVEN UK, with a possible interest in South Devon.

WHO CAN BENEFIT Registered charities.

WHAT IS FUNDED General charitable purposes. Preference is given to projects with low overheads.

WHAT IS NOT FUNDED No grants to individuals.

RANGE OF GRANTS £100–£15,000.

SAMPLE GRANTS Christian Aid (£5,000).

FINANCES *Year* 2009–10 *Income* £52,893 *Grants* £5,000 *Assets* £1,343,254

TRUSTEES Alison Barrett; Joan Harbottle; Ian Harbottle; David John Harbottle.

HOW TO APPLY The trust states that it does not welcome, or reply to, unsolicited applications.

WHO TO APPLY TO Ian Harbottle, Trustee, Middle Manor, Lascot Hill, Wedmore BS28 4AF *Tel* 01934 712102

■ The Alice Ellen Cooper Dean Charitable Foundation

CC NO 273298   **ESTABLISHED** 1977

WHERE FUNDING CAN BE GIVEN Worldwide, with a preference for UK charities in Dorset and west Hampshire.

WHO CAN BENEFIT Registered charities.

WHAT IS FUNDED Registered charities supporting health, humanitarian causes, social disadvantage, education, religion, community, arts and culture, amateur sport and disability.

WHAT IS NOT FUNDED No grants to individuals.

TYPE OF GRANT One-off and recurring.

RANGE OF GRANTS Mostly £1,000–£10,000.

SAMPLE GRANTS The West of England School and College (£20,000); Motor Neurone Disease Association (£14,000); Powerful Information, Blanford Youth Trust and Families for Children Trust (£10,000 each); Project Harar Ethiopia (£8,000); ITACA – Ecuador (£7,500) Action for Kids and Devonshire and Dorset Military Museums Charity (£7,000 each); Help the Aged (£6,000); Link Community Development, Mseleni Children's Home, Inspire Foundation, Special Boat Service Association and Rethink (£5,000 each); Salvation Army – Bournemouth (£3,000); Special Toys Educational Postal Service (£2,000); Queen Elizabeth's Foundation for Disabled People (£1,000); and Help for Heroes (£500).

FINANCES *Year* 2009–10 *Income* £7,333,032 *Grants* £734,000 *Assets* £22,745,922

TRUSTEES John R B Bowditch; Mrs Linda J Bowditch; Rupert J A Edwards; Douglas J E Neville-Jones; Emma Blackburn.

HOW TO APPLY In writing to the correspondent. Each application should include: name and address of organisation; charity registration number; details of the project; details of the community, including area covered and numbers who will benefit from the project; details of fund raising activities and other anticipated source of grants; a copy of the latest financial accounts.

WHO TO APPLY TO Rupert J A Edwards, Trustee, Edwards and Keeping, Unity Chambers, 34 High East Street, Dorchester, Dorset DT1 1HA *Tel* 01305 251333 *Fax* 01305 251465 *email* office@edwardsandkeeping.co.uk

■ The Marjorie Coote Animal Charity Trust

CC NO 208493   **ESTABLISHED** 1954

WHERE FUNDING CAN BE GIVEN Worldwide.

WHO CAN BENEFIT Registered charities for the benefit of animals.

WHAT IS FUNDED The care and protection of horses, dogs and other animals and birds. It is the policy of the trustees to concentrate on research into animal health problems and on the protection of species, whilst continuing to apply a small proportion of the income to general animal welfare, including sanctuaries.

WHAT IS NOT FUNDED No grants to individuals.

TYPE OF GRANT One-off and recurrent.

RANGE OF GRANTS Grants are usually in the range of £500–£10,000.

SAMPLE GRANTS Animal Health Trust, RSPCA Sheffield and The Langford Trust for Animal Health & Welfare (£10,000 each); PDSA (£8,000); WWF-UK (£6,000); the Whiteley Wildlife Conservation Trust and Devon Wildlife Trust (£4,000 each); Brooke Hospital for Animals and Friends of Conservation (£3,000 each); The Gorilla organisation and Tusk Trust

(£2,500 each); Save the Rhino International (£1,000); and Alberts Horse Sanctuary and Dogs for the Disabled (£500 each).

FINANCES *Year* 2009–10 *Income* £111,479 *Grants* £108,250 *Assets* £3,187,308

TRUSTEES Sir Hugh Neill; Mrs. J P Holah; Lady Neill; Mrs. S E Browne.

HOW TO APPLY In writing to the correspondent. Applications should reach the correspondent during September for consideration in October/November.

WHO TO APPLY TO Mrs J P Holah, Trustees, Dykelands Farm, Whenby, York YO61 4SF *email* info@mcacharity.org.uk

---

■ The Marjorie Coote Old People's Charity

CC NO 226747   **ESTABLISHED** 1958

WHERE FUNDING CAN BE GIVEN South Yorkshire.

WHO CAN BENEFIT Old people of small means.

WHAT IS FUNDED The established charitable organisations which work actively for the benefit of old people in the area of jurisdiction.

WHAT IS NOT FUNDED No grants to individuals.

RANGE OF GRANTS Up to £15,000.

SAMPLE GRANTS Age Concern Sheffield, the Cavendish Centre and St Luke's Hospice (£15,000 each); and Sheffield Dial-A-Ride and Voluntary Action Sheffield (£10,000 each); The Broomgrove Trust, South Yorkshire Community Foundation and Age Concern – Rotherham (£5,000 each); British Red Cross (£2,000); Sheffield Institute for Studies on Ageing (£1,000); Deafblind UK (£500); and Drop-In Bereavement Group (£250).

FINANCES *Year* 2009–10 *Income* £98,911 *Grants* £91,200 *Assets* £2,898,934

TRUSTEES Sir Hugh Neill; Mrs J A Lee; Lady Neill; N J A Hutton.

HOW TO APPLY In writing to the correspondent during May. Appeals received at other times of the year are deferred unless for an urgent grant for a specific one-off project.

WHO TO APPLY TO Sir Hugh Neill, Trustee, Barn Cottage, Lindrick Common, Worksop, Nottinghamshire S81 8BA *Tel* 01909 562806

■ The Helen Jean Cope Trust

CC NO 1125937   **ESTABLISHED** 1998

WHERE FUNDING CAN BE GIVEN Mostly Leicestershire, but also Derbyshire and Nottinghamshire.

WHO CAN BENEFIT Registered charities only.

WHAT IS FUNDED General charitable purposes, supporting single projects.

WHAT IS NOT FUNDED No grants to individuals or unregistered charities.

TYPE OF GRANT Generally single projects.

SAMPLE GRANTS Royal Agricultural Benevolent Institution, Treetops Hospice and Philharmonia Orchestra (£10,000 each); Oaks and District Tennis Club (£7,500); Marie Curie Cancer Care (£5,000); The National Autistic Society (£3,000); Listening Books and Spina Bifida Hydrocephalus (£2,000 each); Sir John Moore Heritage Centre and Farming and Countryside Education (£1,000 each) and Shepshec Toy Library (£500).

FINANCES *Year* 2010 *Income* £117,833 *Grants* £146,315 *Assets* £3,083,754

TRUSTEES J M Carrington; D N Murphy; J M Savage; L A Brydson; G S Freckelton.

OTHER INFORMATION The Trust has an informative website.

HOW TO APPLY In writing to the correspondent.

WHO TO APPLY TO J M Carrington, Secretary, 1 Woodgate, Loughborough, Leicestershire LE11 2TY *Tel* 01509 218298 *email* info@thehelenjeancopecharity.co.uk *Website* www.thehelenjeancopecharity.co.uk

---

■ The J Reginald Corah Foundation Fund

CC NO 220792   **ESTABLISHED** 1953

WHERE FUNDING CAN BE GIVEN Leicestershire and Rutland.

WHO CAN BENEFIT Charitable organisations. However, particular favour is given to hosiery firms carrying out their business in the city or county of Leicester and Rutland.

WHAT IS FUNDED General charitable purposes, particularly for the benefit of employees and ex-employees of hosiery firms carrying on business in the city or county of Leicester and Rutland.

WHAT IS NOT FUNDED Applications from individuals are not considered unless made by, or supported by, a recognised charitable organisation.

TYPE OF GRANT One-off and recurrent.

RANGE OF GRANTS Up to £11,000.

SAMPLE GRANTS LCOS (£11,000); Army Benevolent Fund, Help for Heroes, British Forces Foundation and Marie Curie Memorial Fund (£4,000 each); Leicestershire Children's Holiday Centre (£3,000); and LOROS (£2,000).

FINANCES *Year* 2009–10 *Income* £108,597 *Grants* £92,657 *Assets* £3,894,145

TRUSTEES D P Corah; Roger Bowder; G S Makings.

HOW TO APPLY In writing to the correspondent. Trustees meet about every two months.

WHO TO APPLY TO Mrs P Fowle, Clerk, c/o Harvey Ingram Owston, 20 New Walk, Leicester LE1 6TX *Tel* 0116 254 5454

■ The Gershon Coren Charitable Foundation

CC NO 257615   **ESTABLISHED** 1968

WHERE FUNDING CAN BE GIVEN UK and the developing world.

WHO CAN BENEFIT Registered charities, particularly Jewish organisations.

WHAT IS FUNDED General charitable purposes, social welfare and Jewish causes.

RANGE OF GRANTS £500–£40,000.

SAMPLE GRANTS Gategi Village Self Help Group (£65,000); Spiro Ark (£8,000); Aish UK (£7,000); Magen David Adom UK (£5,000); Jewish Medical Association UK (£3,000); British ORT (£2,500); Kisharon (£2,000); One Voice and Smile Train (£1,000 each); and National Trust and Strongbone Children's Charitable Trust (£500).

FINANCES *Year* 2009–10 *Income* £175,209 *Grants* £157,500 *Assets* £2,457,537

TRUSTEES Muriel Coren; Anthony Coren; Walter Stanton.

HOW TO APPLY In writing to the correspondent.

WHO TO APPLY TO Muriel Cohen, Trustee, 5 Golders Park Close, London NW11 7QR

■ The Corinthian Trust

CC NO 278531   **ESTABLISHED** 1979

WHERE FUNDING CAN BE GIVEN UK and overseas.

WHO CAN BENEFIT Evangelical Christianity.

WHAT IS FUNDED The trust makes grants only to evangelical Christian organisations and individuals who are known to, or recommended to, the trustees. Nearly all the trust's grants are ongoing.

WHAT IS NOT FUNDED No grants to individuals or organisations not known to the trustees.

TYPE OF GRANT Recurrent.

RANGE OF GRANTS Up to £7,000.

SAMPLE GRANTS International Nepal Fellowship (£7,000); HIMSERVE – Siliguri, West Bengal (£5,000); Esher Green Baptist Church (£2,600); SAGOAL – Nepal (£2,000); Children Alone Trust (£1,800); and Central Asia Fellowship and Asal Chimeki – Nepal (£1,000 each).

FINANCES *Year* 2010–11 *Income* £44,636 *Grants* £51,811 *Assets* £623,243

TRUSTEES John S Bradley; Mrs Judith M Bradley; James N Bradley; David N Price.

OTHER INFORMATION The 2010–11 grant total includes £1,600 given directly to individual Christian workers.

HOW TO APPLY In writing to the correspondent, only if recommended to apply.

WHO TO APPLY TO John S Bradley, Trustee, Oregon, Avenue Road, Cobham, Surrey KT11 3HW *Tel* 01932 864665 *email* j.bradley@btinternet.com

■ Edwin Cornforth 1983 Charity Trust

CC NO 287196   **ESTABLISHED** 1983

WHERE FUNDING CAN BE GIVEN UK.

WHO CAN BENEFIT Christian Science organisations.

WHAT IS FUNDED Eight charities as stated in the will. Preference is given to certain Christian Science organisations and in practice, other charities are not considered.

WHAT IS NOT FUNDED No grants to individuals.

TYPE OF GRANT Recurrent.

SAMPLE GRANTS Previous beneficiaries included Auxiliary Committee for Retirement Homes, Claremount Fan Court Foundation Ltd, First Church of Christ – Sutton Coldfield, The Pison Trust and Vermont Trust Ltd.

FINANCES *Year* 2009–10 *Income* £21,496 *Grants* £10,000

TRUSTEES Lloyds TSB Private Banking Ltd.

HOW TO APPLY In writing to the correspondent.

WHO TO APPLY TO Lloyds TSB Private Banking Ltd, UK Trust Centre, The Clock House, 22–26 Ock Street, Abingdon, Oxfordshire OX14 5SW *Tel* 01235 232769

■ Michael Cornish Charitable Trust

CC NO 1107890   **ESTABLISHED** 2005

WHERE FUNDING CAN BE GIVEN Lincolnshire and overseas.

WHO CAN BENEFIT Preference for registered charities in the Lincolnshire area and charities involving children.

WHAT IS FUNDED General, community, youth, medical, overseas aid.

SAMPLE GRANTS Christian Partners in Africa (£20,000); The Nomad Trust (Lincoln) (£14,000); World Medical Fund for Children and Royal National Lifeboat Institution (£5,000 each); Alzheimer's Research Trust and Deafness UK (£2,500 each) and Lincolnshire

Rock Challenge and Diabetes UK (£1,000 each).

FINANCES *Year* 2010 *Income* £90,160 *Grants* £110,250 *Assets* £13,624,464

TRUSTEES Michael J Cornish, Chair; Susan M Cornish; Richard L J Vigar.

HOW TO APPLY In writing to the correspondent.

WHO TO APPLY TO Richard L J Vigar, Trustee, 15 Newland, Lincoln LN1 1XG *Tel* 01522 531341

■ The Evan Cornish Foundation

CC NO 1112703   **ESTABLISHED** 2005

WHERE FUNDING CAN BE GIVEN UK and developing countries.

WHO CAN BENEFIT Charitable organisations.

WHAT IS FUNDED General charitable purposes; overseas aid.

WHAT IS NOT FUNDED No grants for animal welfare charities, religion and political activities.

SAMPLE GRANTS Inquest, Photovoice and Twin Charity (£10,000 each); Practical Action (£9,500); AMREF and Civil Liberties Trust (£7,500); Brighton and Hove Fare Share, Extra Care and the Jenifer Trust (£5,000 each); Arts for Recovery and Rural Solar Light (£2,500 each); Village Water and Tools for Self Reliance (£1,000 each); and Power International (£700).

FINANCES *Year* 2009–10 *Income* £155,788 *Grants* £386,621 *Assets* £7,047,857

TRUSTEES Ethel Cornish; Barbara Ward; Mary Cornish; Sally Cornish; Rachel Cornish.

OTHER INFORMATION The trust supports organisations working in the following areas: education, older people, health, human rights, poverty alleviation and penal reform

HOW TO APPLY The trustees will consider applications as well as seeking out causes to support. They normally meet at least four times a year. Thet have a three step application process which can be found on the trust's website.

WHO TO APPLY TO The Trustees, c/o Provincial House, Solly Street, Sheffield S1 4BA *email* contactus@evancornishfoundation.org.uk *Website* www.evancornishfoundation.org.uk

■ Cornwall Community Foundation

CC NO 1099977   **ESTABLISHED** 2003

WHERE FUNDING CAN BE GIVEN Cornwall and the Isles of Scilly.

WHO CAN BENEFIT Local projects in Cornwall and the Isles of Scilly that engage local people in making their communities better places to live. This includes groups, projects and individuals.

WHAT IS FUNDED Community-based causes.

RANGE OF GRANTS Usually up to £10,000.

SAMPLE GRANTS Connor Downs Residents Association, Falmouth and Penryn Sea Cadets and Tywardreath Village Hall (£5,000 each); Duloe Recreational Ground Association and Carleen Panto Group (£4,000 each); Newquay Male Voice Choir and Launceston Memory Cafe (£2,000 each); St Ives Allotment (£1,500) and Penzance Youth String Orchestra (£500).

FINANCES *Year* 2010 *Income* £1,220,286 *Grants* £486,636 *Assets* £2,149,221

TRUSTEES James Williams, Chair; Oliver Baines; Mrs M Bickford-Smith; Bishop Tim Thornton; Hon Evelyn Boscawen; Lady Vanessa George; John Ede; Lady Mary Holborow; Michael Miles; Sue Guard; Daphne Skinnard; Jane Hartley; Tom Varcoe; Tim Smith; Mark Mitchell; Elaine Hunt.

HOW TO APPLY On a form available from the foundation. For general information about grants contact the grants team (tel.: 01566 779333 or email: grants@cornwallfoundation.com). Criteria, guidelines and application process are also posted on the foundation's website.

WHO TO APPLY TO Donna Martyn, Suite 1, Sheers Barton, Lawhitton, Launceston, Cornwall PL15 9NJ *Tel* 01566 779333 *email* office@cornwallfoundation.com *Website* www.cornwallfoundation.com

■ The Cornwall Historic Churches Trust

CC NO 218340   **ESTABLISHED** 1955

WHERE FUNDING CAN BE GIVEN Cornwall.

WHO CAN BENEFIT Places of Christian worship.

WHAT IS FUNDED The repair and restoration of churches, with particular regard to those of architectural or historical merit.

WHAT IS NOT FUNDED The trust is unlikely to consider the following: routine maintenance and repair work which the church community could be expected to deal with themselves; re-decoration – other than when it follows from a major restoration scheme; introduction of domestic or similar facilities within the church building; schemes which damage or adversely affect the basic building, especially its external appearance; replacement or installation of heating systems required for the comfort of the congregations; redesign and layout of the churchyard and work on tombstones – other than the restoration of specific tombstones with some significant historic connections; repair and/or maintenance of associated buildings (e.g. school rooms and church halls).

TYPE OF GRANT One-off grants.

RANGE OF GRANTS Up to £5,000. When determining the level of grant support, the trust operates a points system which takes the following factors into account: the age of the church or chapel; the merit of the building; the church's effort in two respects – (i) its participation in the CHCT's annual sponsored event and (ii) other church efforts to raise funds for the project; financial need; the church's own financial resources.

FINANCES *Year* 2010 *Income* £54,075 *Grants* £61,400 *Assets* £268,709

TRUSTEES Mrs H Briggs, Chair; The Viscountess Boyd of Merton; A H Foot; C F Hall; G J Holborow; Mrs M R C Parr; Mrs V Leslie; Dr J Mattingly.

PUBLICATIONS Leaflet on Cornish church conservation.

OTHER INFORMATION Donations were approved to 23 churches and chapels.

HOW TO APPLY On an application form available from the trust's website or from the correspondent.

WHO TO APPLY TO Simon Coy, Hon. Secretary, Dipper Bridge, Ruthernbridge, Bodmin PL30 5LU *email* mail@chct.info *Website* www.chct.info

■ The Duke of Cornwall's Benevolent Fund

CC NO 269183   **ESTABLISHED** 1975

WHERE FUNDING CAN BE GIVEN UK, with a number of grants made in the Cornwall area.

WHO CAN BENEFIT Registered charities.

WHAT IS FUNDED The relief of people in need of assistance because of sickness, poverty or age; the provision of almshouses, homes of rest, hospitals and convalescent homes; the advancement of education; the advancement of the arts and religion; and the preservation for the benefit of the public of lands and buildings.

RANGE OF GRANTS Up to £100,000. Typically under £5,000 each.

SAMPLE GRANTS the Prince's Foundation (£15,000); Business in the Community (£9,000); the Cleveland Pools Trust and Dartmoor Farmers Association (£5,000 each); Soil Association (£2,500); Wells Cathedral (£2,000); Isle of Scilly Veterinary Support Group, Shekinah Mission, Coombe Community Association and Woodland Heritage (£1,000 each).

FINANCES *Year* 2009–10 *Income* £120,928 *Grants* £116,130 *Assets* £2,761,843

TRUSTEES Hon. James Leigh-Pemberton; W R A Ross.

HOW TO APPLY In writing to the correspondent. Applicants should give as much detail as possible, especially information on how much money has been raised to date, what the target is and how it will be achieved. Applications can be made at any time. Trustees meet quarterly.

WHO TO APPLY TO Robert Mitchell, 10 Buckingham Gate, London SW1E 6LA *Tel* 020 7834 7346

■ The Cornwell Charitable Trust

CC NO 1012467   **ESTABLISHED** 1992

WHERE FUNDING CAN BE GIVEN The south west of England, with a preference for Cornwall.

WHO CAN BENEFIT Registered charities.

WHAT IS FUNDED General charitable purposes, funding projects and individuals specifically and primarily in the Cornwall area.

WHAT IS NOT FUNDED No support for travel, expeditions or university grants.

TYPE OF GRANT Project and capital.

RANGE OF GRANTS Mainly up to £5,000.

SAMPLE GRANTS Lincoln College Oxford (£25,000); The Constant Gardener Trust and Stand Proud USA (£5,000 each); The Friends of Sarah Geary, Friends of Heath Library and Medical Foundation (£2,000 each); Cornwall Hospice Care, Precious Lives Appeal, Cornwall Air Ambulance, Burgh House Trust and Morrab Library (£1,000 each).

FINANCES *Year* 2010–11 *Income* £279,777 *Grants* £55,400 *Assets* £1,104,724

TRUSTEES David Cornwell; Valerie Cornwell; Matthew Bennett; Mark Simon Bailey.

OTHER INFORMATION All grants awarded in 2010–11 were paid to organisations.

HOW TO APPLY In writing to the correspondent.

WHO TO APPLY TO Mark Bailey, Trustee, Devonshire House, 1 Devonshire Street, London W1W 5DR

■ The Sidney and Elizabeth Corob Charitable Trust

CC NO 266606   **ESTABLISHED** 1973

WHERE FUNDING CAN BE GIVEN UK.

WHO CAN BENEFIT Charitable organisations.

WHAT IS FUNDED General charitable purposes, supporting a range of causes including education, arts, welfare and Jewish charities.

WHAT IS NOT FUNDED No grants to individuals or non-registered charities.

RANGE OF GRANTS Up to £90,000.

SAMPLE GRANTS Oxford Centre for Hebrew and Jewish Studies (£47,000); Autism Speaks (£20,000); United Synagogue (£10,000); and British Technion Society, the HOPE Charity, Jewish Care, Magen David Adom UK, (£10,000 each).

Think carefully about every application. Is it justified?

465

FINANCES *Year* 2009–10 *Income* £4,161 *Grants* £287,450

TRUSTEES A L Corob; E Corob; C J Cook; J V Hajnal; S A Wechsler; S Wiseman.

HOW TO APPLY In writing to the correspondent. The trustees meet at regular intervals.

WHO TO APPLY TO The Trustees, 62 Grosvenor Street, London W1K 3JF

■ The Corona Charitable Trust

CC NO 1064320   ESTABLISHED 1997

WHERE FUNDING CAN BE GIVEN UK and overseas.

WHO CAN BENEFIT Jewish people.

WHAT IS FUNDED Jewish religious education and relief-in-need.

SAMPLE GRANTS Menorah Foundation School (£8,000); Hasmonean high School (£7,000); the ZSV Trust (£6,000); Ahavas Shalom Charity Fund (£5,000); WST Charity Limited (£2,500); and Edgware Jewish Primary School (£1,500).

FINANCES *Year* 2009–10 *Income* £43,524 *Grants* £49,168 *Assets* £76,061

TRUSTEES A Levy; A Levy; B Levy.

OTHER INFORMATION In addition, £3,000 was given out in grants of less than £1,000.

HOW TO APPLY In writing to the correspondent.

WHO TO APPLY TO A Levy, Chief Executive Officer, 16 Mayfield Gardens, Hendon, London NW4 2QA

■ The Costa Family Charitable Trust (formerly the Morgan Williams Charitable Trust)

CC NO 221604   ESTABLISHED 1964

WHERE FUNDING CAN BE GIVEN UK.

WHO CAN BENEFIT Christian organisations.

WHAT IS FUNDED Charities with which the trustees have some connection.

SAMPLE GRANTS Alpha International (£250,000); VSO (£12,000); Pentecost Festival (£10,000); the Chasah Trust and the Philo Trust (£5,000 each); British Museum (£2,000); and the Wallace Collection (£1,000).

FINANCES *Year* 2009–10 *Income* £276,903 *Grants* £299,920 *Assets* £64,367

TRUSTEES K J Costa; Mrs A F Costa.

HOW TO APPLY The trust states that only charities personally connected with the trustees are supported and absolutely no applications are either solicited or acknowledged.

WHO TO APPLY TO K J Costa, Trustee, 50 Stratton Street, London W1J 8LL *Tel* 020 7352 6592

■ The Cotton Industry War Memorial Trust

CC NO 242721   ESTABLISHED 1947

WHERE FUNDING CAN BE GIVEN UK.

WHO CAN BENEFIT Individuals and organisations.

WHAT IS FUNDED This trust makes grants to educational bodies to assist eligible students in furtherance of their textile studies, to other bodies which encourage recruitment into or efficiency in the industry or organisations otherwise researching or benefiting the cotton industry. Major support has also been given to other causes, including those related to young people and people with disabilities.

SAMPLE GRANTS Manchester University (£45,000); Adventure Farm Trust (£32,000); Texprint – Contribution to Operating Costs of Exhibition (£20,000); Primary Engineers (£15,000); the

Society of Dyers and Colourists (£10,000); Shri Krishna Temple (£5,000); and The Jack Brown Scholarship Award (£4,500).

FINANCES *Year* 2010 *Income* £296,250 *Grants* £132,500 *Assets* £5,721,608

TRUSTEES P Booth; C Trotter; Prof. A P Lockett; K Lloyd; K R Garbett; P Reid; Philip Roberts; John Reed.

OTHER INFORMATION The grants figure includes two grants to individuals of £500 each.

HOW TO APPLY In writing to the correspondent.

WHO TO APPLY TO Hilda Ball, Secretary, c/o 42 Boot Lane, Heaton, Bolton BL1 5SS *Tel* 01204 491810

■ The Cotton Trust

CC NO 1094776   ESTABLISHED 1956

WHERE FUNDING CAN BE GIVEN UK and overseas.

WHO CAN BENEFIT UK-registered charities.

WHAT IS FUNDED Relief of suffering; elimination and control of disease; people who have disabilities and disadvantaged people.

WHAT IS NOT FUNDED Grants are only given to UK-registered charities that have been registered for at least one year. No grants to animal charities, individuals, students, further education, travel, expeditions, conservation, environment, arts, new building construction, the purchase of new buildings or 'circular' appeals. The trustees will only support the purchase of computer systems and equipment if it is to be directly used by people who are disadvantaged or have disabilities, but not general IT equipment for the running of organisations.

TYPE OF GRANT Grants are primarily awarded for capital expenditure for specific projects or items of specialist equipment. A limited number of grants are awarded for running costs where the grant will provide direct support for a clearly identifiable charitable project.

RANGE OF GRANTS Usually £250–£5,000.

SAMPLE GRANTS Previously: Leicester Charity Link towards support/equipment for families (£41,000); CamFed (£15,000); Merlin (£10,000); Africa Now (£5,000); Angels International (£4,000); John Fawcett Foundation, International Medical Corps and Leukaemia Research (£2,500 each); Harvest Help (£2,250); Edinburgh Young Carers Project and International Childcare Trust (£1,500 each); Shelter, St Giles Trust and Village Service Trust (£1,000 each); People for Animal Care Trust (£750); and Youth Action Wiltshire – young carers educational project (£580).

FINANCES *Year* 2009–10 *Income* £151,149 *Grants* £193,650 *Assets* £5,730,727

TRUSTEES Joanne Burgess Congdon; Tenney Ellen Cotton; Erica Suzanne Cotton.

HOW TO APPLY In writing to the correspondent with latest accounts, evidence of charitable status, detailed budget, timetable and details of funds raised. Guidelines are available with an sae. Deadlines for applications are the end of July and the end of January, with successful applicants being notified within three months of these dates. It is regretted that only successful applications can be answered. The trustees only accept one application in a 12-month period.

WHO TO APPLY TO Joanne Burgess Congdon, Trustee, PO Box 6895, Earl Shilton, Leicester LE9 8ZE *Tel* 01455 440917

■ Country Houses Foundation

CC NO 1111049   **ESTABLISHED** 2005

WHERE FUNDING CAN BE GIVEN England.

WHO CAN BENEFIT Registered charities, building preservation trusts and private owners.

WHAT IS FUNDED The preservation of buildings of historic or architectural significance together with their gardens and grounds, for the public benefit. 'We aim to give grants for repairs and restoration work required to prevent loss or damage to historic buildings located in England, their gardens, grounds and any outbuildings. We would normally expect your building to be listed, scheduled, or in the case of a garden included in the English Heritage Register of Parks and Gardens. However, we may also make grants to projects which involve an unlisted building of sufficient historic or architectural significance or importance if it is within a conservation area.'

WHAT IS NOT FUNDED 'As a general rule we do not offer grants for the following: projects which do not have a heritage focus; alterations and improvements; routine maintenance and minor repairs; general running costs; demolitions; rent, loan or mortgage payments; buying furniture, fittings and equipment except where they have an historic relationship with the site and are relevant to the project; work carried out before a grant offer has been made in writing and accepted. We aim to give grants for repairs and restoration work required to prevent loss or damage to historic buildings located in England, their gardens, grounds and any outbuildings. We would normally expect your building to be listed, scheduled, or in the case of a garden included in the English Heritage Register of Parks and Gardens. However, we may also make grants to projects which involve an unlisted building of sufficient historic or architectural significance or importance if it is within a conservation area.' Full guidelines are available on the foundation's website.

SAMPLE GRANTS Projects supported during the year include those at: Stanford Hall – Leicestershire; Homme House near Ledbury; Red House within the Painswick Roccoco Gardens; Temple of Vaccinea in the garden of the Jenner Museum in the Vale of Berkeley; Faringdon Folly Tower; Sulgrave Manor; Tyringham Hall – Buckinghamshire; Howsham Mill; Stoneleigh Park; Launde Abbey; Woodchester Mansion and Wothorpe Towers Preservation Trust.

FINANCES *Year* 2009–10 *Income* £393,975 *Grants* £1,129,833 *Assets* £12,394,392

TRUSTEES Oliver Pearcey; Nicholas Barber; Michael Clifton; Norman Hudson; Christopher Taylor; Sir John Parsons; Mary King.

HOW TO APPLY *Pre-Application Forms* can be completed online, or in a hard copy and returned by post. The foundation tries to respond to within 28 days of receipt. If a project fits the criteria then a unique reference number will be issued which must be quoted on the *Full Application Form*. Applications can be made at anytime.

WHO TO APPLY TO David Price, Company Secretary, The Manor, Sheephouse Farm, Uley Road, Dursley, Gloucestershire GL11 5AD *Tel* 0845 402 4102 *Fax* 0845 402 4103 *email* david@countryhousesfoundation.org.uk *Website* www.countryhousesfoundation.org.uk

■ County Durham Community Foundation

CC NO 1047625   **ESTABLISHED** 1995

WHERE FUNDING CAN BE GIVEN County Durham, Darlington and surrounding areas.

WHO CAN BENEFIT Community groups and grassroots organisations seeking to improve the quality of life in their local area, particularly those aiming to combat poverty and disadvantage or promote a more equitable and just society. Applications from branches of UK organisations will only be considered if they are able to demonstrate financial independence.

WHAT IS FUNDED The foundation encourages applications from groups working in the following areas: children and young people – groups and projects that help children and young people access activities and services where they play a key role in the decision making; vulnerable people – groups and projects working with disadvantaged people, in particular providing increased access to services and facilities for people with disabilities, the homeless and the elderly; community regeneration – local partnerships plus residents and tenants' associations that aim to improve health, education, reduce crime levels (and improve community safety) and to regenerate employment, housing and the physical environment with the support of their local community; self-help groups – community based, small self-help groups who deliver basic services; environmental improvements – small-scale environmental projects particularly improvements to community held land; education, capacity and skills development – group and community-based training and education programmes, particularly for those who have had no previous access to training opportunities; health – groups and community based projects providing access to healthy eating, increased physical activity and self-help services, which aim to improve the health and well being of communities; and in particular applications from groups working in rural areas.

WHAT IS NOT FUNDED The foundation will not fund: projects outside County Durham and Darlington; national or regional charities with no independent office in County Durham or Darlington; groups that have more than one year's running costs held as free reserves; projects which should be funded by a statutory body; sponsored events; improvements to land that is not open to the general public at convenient hours; projects promoting political activities; deficit or retrospective funding; faith groups promoting religious, community based activities. Funding is not normally given for: medical research and equipment; school projects; animal welfare; general contributions to large appeals (but specific items can be funded); building or buying premises and freehold or leasehold land rights; minibuses or other vehicles; overseas travel; grants for more than one year. Some of the programmes have other exclusions. If your project is at all unusual please contact the foundation to discuss your application before submitting it.

TYPE OF GRANT Various depending on funding criteria.

FINANCES *Year* 2010–11 *Income* £2,425,659 *Grants* £1,051,524 *Assets* £8,556,952

TRUSTEES Mark I'Anson, Chair; Sir Paul Nicholson; David Watson; Michele Armstrong; Ada Burns; George Garlick; Christopher Lendrum; Andrew Martell; David Martin; Lady Sarah Nicholson; Gerry Osborne; Kate Welch.

PUBLICATIONS Newsletter and information leaflets.

HOW TO APPLY 'Community groups, non-registered charities and registered charities are all able to apply to our many funds using just one main application form. We mix-and-match applications to the most appropriate fund behind the scenes, so you don't need to worry about which fund is right for you. With the exception of the Banks Community Fund, ESF Community Grants and Surviving Winter, which have their own bespoke application forms, all our funds can be accessed using our standard application form. Please choose one of the options below to be taken to the application form. To apply for a grant you need to read our general guidelines before filling in an application form.' The full guidelines are available from the foundation's website.

WHO TO APPLY TO Barbara Gubbins, Chief Executive, Victoria House, Whitfield Court, St Johns Road, Meadowfield Industrial Estate, Durham DH7 8XL Tel 0191 378 6340 email info@cdcf.org.uk Website www.cdcf.org.uk

■ The Augustine Courtauld Trust

CC NO 226217   ESTABLISHED 1956

WHERE FUNDING CAN BE GIVEN UK, with a preference for Essex.

WHO CAN BENEFIT Registered charities benefiting people in Essex and explorers.

WHAT IS FUNDED General charitable purposes, but mostly organisations in Essex working with young people who are disadvantaged and conservation. Exploration of the Arctic and Antarctic regions are also supported. Preference is given to charities which the trust has a special interest in, knowledge of, or, association with.

WHAT IS NOT FUNDED No grants to individuals. No grants to individual churches for fabric repairs or maintenance.

TYPE OF GRANT One-off grants for projects and core costs, which may be made for multiple years if an application is submitted for each year.

RANGE OF GRANTS £500–£8,000. Normally in the range of £500–£2,000.

SAMPLE GRANTS Friends of Essex Churches Trust and Gino Watkins Memorial Trust (£9,000); Cirdan Sailing Trust (£5,000); Essex Association of Boys' Clubs (£4,500); Rural Community Council of Essex (£2,400); British Schools Exploring Society, Hope UK and Stanley Hall Opera (£1,000 each); and Association of Wheelchair Children, Braintree and Bocking Public Gardens Trust and Happy Days Children's Charity (£500 each).

FINANCES Year 2009–10 Income £126,006 Grants £62,400 Assets £1,133,450

TRUSTEES Revd A C C Courtauld; The Lord Lieutenant of Essex; The Bishop of Chelmsford; Julien Courtauld; D E Fordham; Lieutenant General Sir Anthony Denison-Smith; T J R Courtauld; W M Courtauld.

OTHER INFORMATION This trust was founded in 1956 by Augustine Courtauld, an Arctic explorer who was proud of his Essex roots. His charitable purpose was simple: 'my idea is to make available something that will do some good.'

HOW TO APPLY Applications must be submitted via the online form on the trust's website. Written applications will not be accepted.

WHO TO APPLY TO Bruce Ballard, Clerk, Birkett Ballard, No.1 Legg Street, Chelmsford, Essex CM1 1JS Website www.augustinecourtauldtrust.org

■ Coutts Charitable Trust

CC NO 1000135   ESTABLISHED 1987

WHERE FUNDING CAN BE GIVEN UK, preference is given to areas where Coutts & Co. has a physical presence, specifically London.

WHO CAN BENEFIT UK registered charities.

WHAT IS FUNDED Charities supported include those involved with helping the homeless, rehabilitation and teaching self-help (drug; alcohol; young offenders), disadvantaged adults and children, youth organisations, the elderly, medical research, heritage, education and the relief of poverty.

WHAT IS NOT FUNDED No response to circular appeals. No support for appeals from individuals or overseas projects.

TYPE OF GRANT Regular annual grants and one-off for specific projects.

RANGE OF GRANTS Most donations are in the range of £500–£1,000 'where a comparatively small amount can still make a great difference'. Many donations are between £1,000 and £2,000 with a portion of the charitable budget being used for larger donations.

SAMPLE GRANTS Charles Dickens Museum (£24,000); Samaritans (£7,000); Prostate Scotland (£6,500); DebRA (£5,000); Help for Heroes (£4,500); Little Treasures Children's Trust (£4,000); 2Simple Trust (£3,000); Amber Foundation (£2,500); 4 Sight (£1,700); Africa Challenges, Camp Horizon, PHAB, Christies Hospital, Go North Devon and Bromley Road PTA (£1,000 each).

FINANCES Year 2009–10 Income £1,288,644 Grants £863,681 Assets £728,030

TRUSTEES The Earl of Home; Mark Bevan; Sally Doyle; Gerald Bailey; Nicholas Gornall.

HOW TO APPLY In writing to the trust administrator, at any time. Applications should include clear details of the purpose for which the grant is required. Grants are made regularly where amounts between £500 and £1,000 are deemed to be appropriate. The trustees meet quarterly to consider larger donations.

WHO TO APPLY TO Kay Boland, Trust Administrator, Coutts & Co, 440 Strand, London WC2R 0QS Tel 020 7957 2822 email kay.boland@coutts.com

■ General Charity of Coventry

CC NO 216235   ESTABLISHED 1983

WHERE FUNDING CAN BE GIVEN Within the boundary of the City of Coventry.

WHO CAN BENEFIT People in need, children, young and older people, disabled (physically or mentally), people in need of social or health care and organisations that would benefit such people in the City of Coventry.

WHAT IS FUNDED Welfare; general charitable purposes; health; education & training.

WHAT IS NOT FUNDED No grants to organisations outside Coventry, or for holidays unless of a recuperative nature.

TYPE OF GRANT Pensions, relief in need and educational award bursaries.

RANGE OF GRANTS Up to £50,000.

SAMPLE GRANTS Warwickshire and Northampton Air Ambulance (£40,000); Tiny Tim's Children's Centre (£30,000); Enterprise Club for Disabled People (£25,300); Coventry Resource Centre for the Blind (£15,000); Coventry Citizens Advice Bureau, Myton Hospice (£10,000 each); Shysters inc (£5,000); The Lighthouse Christian Care Ministry (£2,500); Holbrooks Community Care Association (£1,000).

FINANCES *Year* 2010 *Income* £50,271
Grants £49,950

TRUSTEES Mr R Smith; Mr D Mason; Mr M Harris;
Mrs E Eaves; Mrs M Lancaster; Mrs M Weitzel;
Mr T McDonnell; Mr W Thomson; Cllr N Lee; Mr
D Evans; Cllr H Johnson; Mr T Proctor; Dr
C Rhodes; Cllr G Crookes; Cllr M Lapsa.

HOW TO APPLY In writing to the correspondent.
Applications are not accepted directly from the
general public for relief in need (individuals).

WHO TO APPLY TO Mrs V A Tosh, Clerk to the
Trustees, General Charities Office, Old Bablake,
Hill Street, Coventry CV1 4AN *Tel* 02476
222769 *Fax* 02476 222769 *email* cov.
genchar@virgin.net

■ Coventry Building Society Charitable Foundation

CC NO 1072244 **ESTABLISHED** 1998

WHERE FUNDING CAN BE GIVEN The Midlands.

WHO CAN BENEFIT Registered charities.

WHAT IS FUNDED A wide range of causes based, or
active, in the Midlands, with a preference for
smaller local charities.

WHAT IS NOT FUNDED No grants can be given outside
of the Midlands area. The following are not
eligible for support: large charities which enjoy
national coverage; charities with no base within
the branch area; charities with an annual
donated income in excess of £2500,000;
charities with assets over £500,000; projects
requiring ongoing commitment; large capital
projects; maintenance or building works for
buildings, gardens or playgrounds; major
fundraising; projects which are normally the
responsibility of other organisations such as
NHS and local authorities; sponsorship of
individuals; requests from individuals; replacing
funds which were the responsibility of another
body; educational institutions, unless for the
relief of disadvantage; promotion of religious,
political or military causes; sporting clubs or
organisations, unless for the relief of
disadvantage; medical research or equipment;
more than one donation to the same
organisation in a year – further applications will
be considered after a period of three years;
animal welfare.

TYPE OF GRANT One-off.

RANGE OF GRANTS Up to £3,000, but, generally
£500–£2,000.

SAMPLE GRANTS Coventry Community Responders
and Hits Homes Trust (£3,000 each); Multiple
Sclerosis Therapy Centre (South Yorkshire) Ltd.
(£2,500); Focus Banbury Counselling Service
and Crow Recycling (£2,000 each); Action for
Sick Children (£1,500); Coventry Tamil Welfare
Association and Wyken Adventure Centre
(£1,000 each) and Coten End Playground
(£450).

FINANCES *Year* 2010 *Income* £1,257,815
Grants £1,192,599 *Assets* £8,368,923

TRUSTEES M Judge; D Persaud; Ms Y J White;
S Chilton; P Walters.

HOW TO APPLY On an application form available
online or from the correspondent. This should
be returned together with any supporting
documentation. In some circumstances the
foundation may request further information
before considering the application. The trustees
meet quarterly, in February, May, August and
November.

WHO TO APPLY TO Sarah Goderidge, Secretary,
Oakfield House, Binley Business Park, Coventry

CV3 2TQ *Website* www.coventrybuildingsociety.
co.uk

■ The John Cowan Foundation

CC NO 327613 **ESTABLISHED** 1987

WHERE FUNDING CAN BE GIVEN UK (national charities)
and Surrey (community projects).

WHO CAN BENEFIT Charitable organisations.

WHAT IS FUNDED The foundation makes grants to
purely local causes apart from national
established charities. Charitable support will be
considered for: oncology, hospices, hospices at
home, medical transport, youth work,
almshouses, community and social centres,
Alzheimer's disease, arthritis and rheumatism,
cancers, heart disease, motor neurone disease,
terminal illness and sight loss.

WHAT IS NOT FUNDED No support for individuals,
community projects outside Surrey area, or
overseas projects.

RANGE OF GRANTS Usually up to £5,000.

SAMPLE GRANTS Beneficiaries included: Royal
Marsden Cancer Campaign (£2,300); South
East Cancer Help Centre, The Children's Trust,
MacMillan Cancer Support, Alzheimer's Society
and British Forces Foundation (£2,000 each);
Rainbow Children's Trust Charity and RNLI
(£1,500 each); Surrey Community Development
Trust, Dreams Come True Charity and Teenage
Cancer Trust (£1,000 each); and the Friends of
White Lodge Centre, Sense and Changing Faces
(£500 each).

FINANCES *Year* 2009–10 *Income* £39,124
Grants £33,250 *Assets* £700,975

TRUSTEES C E Foster; S J Arkoulis; J C Arkoulis.

HOW TO APPLY In writing to the correspondent.

WHO TO APPLY TO Mrs C E Foster, Trustee,
12 Kingswood Place, 119 Croydon Road,
Caterham, Surrey CR3 6DJ *Tel* 01883 344930
email joram@freenet.co.uk

■ The Michael Cowan Foundation

CC NO 1137182 **ESTABLISHED** 2010

WHERE FUNDING CAN BE GIVEN UK and the USA.

WHO CAN BENEFIT Registered charities.

WHAT IS FUNDED Medical research and teaching in
the fields of bronchial disorders and/or heart
disease; conservation projects in Santa
Barbara, California.

TRUSTEES Michael Cowan; Martin Foreman; Bryony
Cove.

OTHER INFORMATION Unfortunately no further
information was available at the time of writing
(September 2011) on the level of funding
available from the foundation.

HOW TO APPLY In writing to the correspondent.

WHO TO APPLY TO Bryony Cove, Trustee, Farrer & Co,
65–66 Lincoln's Inn Fields, London WC2A 3LH
Tel 020 3375 7000 *Fax* 020 3375 7001
email bryony.cove@farrer.co.uk

■ The Sir Tom Cowie Charitable Trust

CC NO 1096936 **ESTABLISHED** 2003

WHERE FUNDING CAN BE GIVEN City of Sunderland and
County Durham.

WHO CAN BENEFIT Young people, older people, the
infirm and disabled, poor or needy people due
to social and/or economic circumstances.

WHAT IS FUNDED General charitable purposes.

RANGE OF GRANTS Usually up to £20,000.

SAMPLE GRANTS Variety Club – DurhamTrinity Sunshine Bus (£12,000); Collierly Primary School (£6,800); Guide Dogs for the Blind (£5,000); Heel and Toe Charity (£3,000); Anthony Nolan Trust (£2,200); Friends of Weardale Community Hospital (£2,000); National Autistic Society (£1,000); Kidney Research UK (£800); and School Farm Visits (£400).

FINANCES *Year* 2009–10 *Income* £625,292 *Grants* £533,208 *Assets* £3,696,073

TRUSTEES Sir Tom Cowie; Peter Blackett; David Gray; Lady Diana Cowie.

OTHER INFORMATION In 2009–10, the largest grant by far went to Willowburn Hospice for £500,000.

HOW TO APPLY In writing to the correspondent.

WHO TO APPLY TO Loraine Maddison, Estate Office, Broadwood Hall, Lanchester, Durham DH7 0TN *Tel* 01207 529 663 *email* lorraine@ sirtomcowie.com

■ Cowley Charitable Foundation

CC NO 270682　　**ESTABLISHED** 1973

WHERE FUNDING CAN BE GIVEN Worldwide, with some preference for south Buckinghamshire and the Aylesbury area.

WHO CAN BENEFIT Registered charities.

WHAT IS FUNDED General charitable purposes.

WHAT IS NOT FUNDED No grants to non-registered charities. No grants to individuals, or for causes supposed to be serviced by public funds or with a scope considered to be too narrow.

TYPE OF GRANT One-off donations for development, capital projects and project funding.

RANGE OF GRANTS Usually £1,000–£2,000.

SAMPLE GRANTS Thinking Foundation (£20,000); Global Warming Policy (£6,000); Alzheimer's Society (£2,000); Tate Britain (£1,800); Pere Jean Zambe (£1,600); International Dark Sky Association – USA, Médecins Sans Frontières and Wordsworth Trust (£1,500 each); John Soames Museum and Hemihelp (£1,000 each); Royal Court, Save the Children and London Shakespeare Workout (£500 each); and Voluntary Services Overseas (£50).

FINANCES *Year* 2009–10 *Income* £44,233 *Grants* £52,325 *Assets* £921,700

TRUSTEES 140 Trustee Co. Ltd; Harriet M M Cullen.

HOW TO APPLY The trust states that unsolicited applications are not invited, and that the trustees carry out their own research into charities.

WHO TO APPLY TO The Secretary, 140 Trustee Co. Ltd, 36 Broadway, London SW1H 0BH *Tel* 020 7973 8044

■ The Sir William Coxen Trust Fund

CC NO 206936　　**ESTABLISHED** 1940

WHERE FUNDING CAN BE GIVEN England.

WHO CAN BENEFIT Hospitals or charitable institutions carrying out orthopaedic work.

WHAT IS FUNDED Hospitals and other charitable institutions in England carrying out orthopaedic work, particularly in respect of children.

WHAT IS NOT FUNDED No grants to individuals or non-charitable institutions.

TYPE OF GRANT One-off grants and research fellowships.

SAMPLE GRANTS Action for Kids, Brainwave, Child Care Action Trust, Fire Fighters' Charity, Motability, Neuromuscular Centre, Spinal Injuries Association, Stick and Step, The New Children's Hospital Appeal and The Orthopaedic Research Fund.

FINANCES *Year* 2009–10 *Income* £75,834 *Grants* £70,000 *Assets* £1,886,648

TRUSTEES Ian Luder; David Hugh Wootton; John Stuttard; Neil Redcliffe; Sir David Lewis; Sir Michael Savory.

OTHER INFORMATION In 2009–10 all grants were for £2,500.

HOW TO APPLY In writing to the correspondent.

WHO TO APPLY TO Rakesh Hira, The Town Clerk's Office, City of London, PO Box 270, Guildhall, London EC2P 2EJ *Tel* 020 7332 1408

■ The Lord Cozens-Hardy Trust

CC NO 264237　　**ESTABLISHED** 1972

WHERE FUNDING CAN BE GIVEN UK with a preference for Merseyside and Norfolk.

WHO CAN BENEFIT Registered charities.

WHAT IS FUNDED General charitable purposes with a particular interest in supporting medical, health, education and welfare causes.

WHAT IS NOT FUNDED No grants to individuals.

TYPE OF GRANT One-off and recurrent.

RANGE OF GRANTS Up to £20,000, mostly for smaller amounts of £5,000 or less.

SAMPLE GRANTS Norfolk and Norwich Association for the Blind and Grooms-Shaftesbury (£10,000 each); Help for Heroes and Norfolk and Norwich Families House (£5,000 each); Raleigh International Trust (£1,250); Breast Cancer Campaign, Liverpool School of Tropical Medicine, Norfolk and Norwich Association for the Blind, Prince's Trust, Salvation Army and World Association of Girl Guides and Girl Scouts (£1,000 each).

FINANCES *Year* 2009–10 *Income* £92,075 *Grants* £76,900 *Assets* £2,635,655

TRUSTEES Hon. Beryl Cozens-Hardy; J E V Phelps; Mrs L F Phelps; J J P Ripman.

HOW TO APPLY In writing to the correspondent. Applications are reviewed quarterly.

WHO TO APPLY TO The Trustees, PO Box 28, Holt, Norfolk NR25 7WH

■ The Craignish Trust

SC NO SC016882　　**ESTABLISHED** 1961

WHERE FUNDING CAN BE GIVEN UK, with a preference for Scotland.

WHO CAN BENEFIT Charitable organisations.

WHAT IS FUNDED Projects that promote the welfare of the local community, particularly through the arts, education and the environment. Projects of special interest to the trustees.

WHAT IS NOT FUNDED Running costs are not normally supported.

TYPE OF GRANT Project grants.

RANGE OF GRANTS £500–£7,500.

SAMPLE GRANTS Previous beneficiaries have included Art in Healthcare, Boilerhouse Theatre Company Ltd, Butterfly Conservation – Scotland, Cairndow Arts Promotions, Centre for Alternative Technology, Edinburgh International Book Festival, Edinburgh Royal Choral Union, Friends of the Earth Scotland, Human Rights Watch Charitable Trust and Soil Association Scotland.

FINANCES *Year* 2009–10 *Income* £151,486 *Grants* £100,000

TRUSTEES Ms M Matheson; J Roberts; Ms C Younger.

OTHER INFORMATION Despite making a written request for the accounts of this trust (including an sae) these were not provided.

HOW TO APPLY There is no formal application form; applicants should write to the correspondent. Details of the project should be included together with a copy of the most recent audited accounts.

WHO TO APPLY TO The Trustees, c/o Geoghegan and Co, 6 St Colme Street, Edinburgh EH3 6AD

■ The Craps Charitable Trust

CC NO 271492   **ESTABLISHED** 1976

WHERE FUNDING CAN BE GIVEN UK, Israel.

WHO CAN BENEFIT Charitable organisations.

WHAT IS FUNDED General charitable purposes, particularly Jewish organisations. It is not the policy of the trustees to make grants in response to appeals addressed to them, and applications will not be acknowledged.

RANGE OF GRANTS Up to £25,000.

SAMPLE GRANTS British Technion Society (£25,000); Jewish Care (£20,000); Nightingale House, Home for Aged Jews (£16,000); the New Israel Fund (£12,000); CBF World Jewish Relief (£5,000); Save the Children (£2,000); Anglo Israel Association (£1,000); and London Jewish Cultural Centre (£500).

FINANCES *Year* 2009–10 *Income* £322,941 *Grants* £178,000 *Assets* £3,817,122

TRUSTEES J P M Dent; Miss C S Dent; Miss L R Dent.

HOW TO APPLY The trust states that funds of the trust are fully committed and the trust does not invite applications for its funds.

WHO TO APPLY TO The Trustees, Grant Thornton, Chartered Accountants, 202 Silbury Boulevard, Milton Keynes MK9 1LW

■ Michael Crawford Children's Charity

CC NO 1042211   **ESTABLISHED** 1994

WHERE FUNDING CAN BE GIVEN UK.

WHO CAN BENEFIT Children and young adults, especially those disadvantaged by poverty and/or illness.

WHAT IS FUNDED Children and young people, and in particular the relief of sickness and the relief of poverty.

WHAT IS NOT FUNDED No grants for school fees and living expenses, travel and other expenses for 'year out' projects, conferences and so on.

TYPE OF GRANT Mainly capital grants.

SAMPLE GRANTS The Sick Children's Trust (£50,000).

FINANCES *Year* 2009–10 *Income* £173,726 *Grants* £64,293 *Assets* £3,231,774

TRUSTEES M P Crawford, Chair; M D Paisner; K P Dias; A Clark.

HOW TO APPLY In writing to the correspondent. Grants are made half yearly and are considered in April and October of each year. Only successful applicants will be notified.

WHO TO APPLY TO K P Dias, Trustee, Regina House, 124 Finchley Road, London NW3 5JS *Tel* 020 7433 2400 *Fax* 020 7433 2491

■ The Cray Trust

SC NO SC005592   **ESTABLISHED** 1976

WHERE FUNDING CAN BE GIVEN Mainly the east of Scotland.

WHO CAN BENEFIT Charitable organisations.

WHAT IS FUNDED General charitable purposes.

WHAT IS NOT FUNDED No support for political appeals and large UK or international charities. No grants to individuals.

RANGE OF GRANTS £100–£260,000. Average grant size in 2009–10 was less than £1,000.

SAMPLE GRANTS Previous beneficiaries included: Charitable Assets Trust; Canine Partners; Equibuddy; Equine Grass Sickness Fund; Princess Royal Trust for Carers; Alzheimer's Scotland; Cherish India; Backup Trust; Barnardo's Scotland; the Priory Church; and Rainbow RDA.

FINANCES *Year* 2009–10 *Income* £56,766 *Grants* £63,200 *Assets* £1,133,200

TRUSTEES P R Gammell; J E B Gammell.

HOW TO APPLY This trust does not accept unsolicited applications.

WHO TO APPLY TO The Trustees, c/o Springfords Accountants, Dundas House, Westfield Park, Eskbank, Midlothian EH22 3FB

■ Creative Scotland

                    ESTABLISHED 2010

WHERE FUNDING CAN BE GIVEN Scotland.

WHO CAN BENEFIT The arts.

WHAT IS FUNDED 'Creative Scotland invests in the arts, screen and creative industries for the benefit of the people of Scotland.'

TRUSTEES Sir Sandy Crombie; Gwilym Gibbons; Steve Grimond; Prof. Robin Macpherson; Prof. Gayle Macpherson; Dr Gary West; Ruth Wishart; Barclay Price.

OTHER INFORMATION Creative Scotland assumed the responsibilities and function of the Scottish Arts Council in 2010. For information regarding grants visit the website: www.creativescotland.com.

HOW TO APPLY For all information regarding grant applications visit the Creative Scotland website.

WHO TO APPLY TO 249 West George Street, Glasgow G2 4QE *Tel* 0330 333 2000 *email* enquiries@ creativesciotland.com *Website* www. creativescotland.com

---

■ The Crescent Trust

CC NO 327644   **ESTABLISHED** 1987

WHERE FUNDING CAN BE GIVEN UK.

WHO CAN BENEFIT Charitable organisations.

WHAT IS FUNDED The arts (especially larger museums), heritage and ecology. Smaller grants are mainly given in the medical field. Only specific charities of which the trustees have personal knowledge are supported.

TYPE OF GRANT One-off and recurrent.

RANGE OF GRANTS £250–£43,000.

SAMPLE GRANTS Service Funds RAF and the Attingham Trust (£10,000 each); Public Catalogue Foundation (£5,000); National Youth (£2,500); Swan Rescue Sanctuary (£2,000); Fund for Refugees (£1,000); and Shooting Star Children's Hospice (£250).

FINANCES *Year* 2009–10 *Income* £69,821 *Grants* £44,515 *Assets* £385,811

TRUSTEES J C S Tham; R A F Lascelles.

HOW TO APPLY This trust states that it does not respond to unsolicited applications.

WHO TO APPLY TO Ms C Akehurst, 9 Queripel House, 1 Duke of York Square, London SW3 4LY

■ Criffel Charitable Trust

CC NO 1040680   **ESTABLISHED** 1994
WHERE FUNDING CAN BE GIVEN UK and overseas.
WHO CAN BENEFIT Registered charities and schools.
WHAT IS FUNDED The advancement of Christianity and the relief of poverty, sickness and other needs.
TYPE OF GRANT Up to three years.
RANGE OF GRANTS Up to £50,000.
SAMPLE GRANTS Lichfield Inspires (£50,000); Tear Fund (£10,000); Links International (£5,000); and Four Oaks Methodist Church (£2,600).
FINANCES *Year* 2009–10 *Income* £64,746 *Grants* £125,295 *Assets* £847,152
TRUSTEES Jim Lees; Juliet Lees; Joy Harvey.
HOW TO APPLY All funds are fully committed. The trust states that no applications are considered or acknowledged. Please do not apply.
WHO TO APPLY TO Mr and Mrs Lees, Trustees, Ravenswood Lodge, 1a Wentworth Road, Sutton Coldfield, West Midlands B74 2SG *Tel* 0121 308 1575

■ Cripplegate Foundation

CC NO 207499   **ESTABLISHED** 1891
WHERE FUNDING CAN BE GIVEN London borough of Islington and part of the City of London.
WHO CAN BENEFIT Charitable organisations, schools and organisations working with schools and individuals.
WHAT IS FUNDED Grants which aim to improve the quality of life in the area of benefit and provide opportunities for local residents. There are three main themes: social cohesion, reducing poverty and inequality and increasing access to opportunities and making connections.
WHAT IS NOT FUNDED In the main grants programme no funding is given for: national charities or organisations outside the area of benefit; schemes or activities which would relieve central or local government of their statutory responsibilities; grants to replace cuts in funding made by the local authority or others; medical research or equipment; national fundraising appeals; advancement of religion unless the applicant also offers non-religious services to the community; animal welfare; retrospective grants; commercial or business activities; grants for events held in the church of St Giles-without Cripplegate; grants to organisations recruiting volunteers in south Islington for work overseas. In the individuals programme the following will not be funded: funeral costs; the purchase of computers; child care costs; money that has been stolen; items already bought or ordered; housing costs or council tax; repayment of debts; education needs (apart from school uniforms); wheelchairs or disability vehicles and scooters; grants for students not normally resident in the area of benefit.
TYPE OF GRANT Grants for core costs, project funding, salary costs and capital costs, often over more than one year.
RANGE OF GRANTS Up to £150,000.
SAMPLE GRANTS Help on your Doorstep and Islington Giving (£150,000 each); Islington Law Centre (£45,000); Islington Bangladesh Association (£40,000); The Maya Centre (£30,000); The Little Angel Theatre (£25,000); The Women's Therapy Centre (£15,000); Inner City Films, Islington Dyslexia Support Group and Talking News Islington (£5,000 each); Hanover Primary School (£4,300); African Swahiliphone Community Project (£4,000); Islington

Townswomen's Guild (£2,000); and Everything Is A Benefit and Arvon Road Allotments Group (£500 each).
FINANCES *Year* 2010 *Income* £2,469,386 *Grants* £2,011,153 *Assets* £31,016,526
TRUSTEES Cripplegate Foundation Limited – Sole Corporate Trustee.
OTHER INFORMATION The grant total includes over £203,000 given to individuals.
HOW TO APPLY Each programme has a different application form and deadline dates. Applicants are encouraged to telephone or email the foundation to discuss their project before making a full application. Full details of the application process are available on the foundation's helpful website.
WHO TO APPLY TO Kristina Glenn, Director, 76 Central Street, London EC1V 8AG *Tel* 020 7566 3138 *Fax* 020 7549 8180 *email* grants@cripplegate. org.uk *Website* www.cripplegate.org

■ The Violet and Milo Cripps Charitable Trust

CC NO 289404   **ESTABLISHED** 1984
WHERE FUNDING CAN BE GIVEN UK.
WHO CAN BENEFIT Charitable organisations.
WHAT IS FUNDED Prison and human rights organisations.
SAMPLE GRANTS Exceptional grant to Howard League for Penal Reform of £2 million. Other beneficiaries were: Lancaster University (£100,000); The Prison Advice and Care Trust (£50,000); Dorothy House Hospice Care, Frank Langford Charitable Trust and Trinity Hospice (£25,000 each).
FINANCES *Year* 2009–10 *Income* £2,003,005 *Grants* £2,225,000 *Assets* £734,620
TRUSTEES Anthony J R Newhouse; Richard J Lithenthal; Jennifer Beattie.
OTHER INFORMATION The trust often gives more in grants than it receives in income. Income was exceptionally high this year due to receiving £2 million from the estate of the late Lord Parmoor.
HOW TO APPLY The trust states that unsolicited applications will not receive a response.
WHO TO APPLY TO The Trustees, 52 Bedford Row, London WC1R 4LR

■ The Harry Crook Foundation

CC NO 231470   **ESTABLISHED** 1963
WHERE FUNDING CAN BE GIVEN Bristol.
WHO CAN BENEFIT Registered charities.
WHAT IS FUNDED In 2007 the trust informed us that it had decided to 'close' the fund to external application until further notice, with all available funds directed towards a single identified charity [Redland High School].
WHAT IS NOT FUNDED Medical research charities and charities serving need outside the boundaries of the City of Bristol. No grants to individuals.
SAMPLE GRANTS Redland High School (£31,000).
FINANCES *Year* 2009–10 *Income* £27,217 *Grants* £31,000 *Assets* £1,220,524
TRUSTEES R G West, Chair; J O Gough; D J Bellew; M C Manisty.
HOW TO APPLY In light of the foundation's 2007 resolution to 'close' the trust to external applications until further notice, any future applications to the trust will be ignored, 'no acknowledgement will be given, and, in particular, no consideration will be given to them.'

WHO TO APPLY TO D J Bellow, Trustee, Veale Wasbrough Lawyers, Orchard Court, Orchard Lane, Bristol BS1 5WS

■ The Cross Trust

SC NO SC008620   ESTABLISHED 1943
WHERE FUNDING CAN BE GIVEN Scotland.
WHO CAN BENEFIT Individuals and organisations.
WHAT IS FUNDED About 80% of the grants are given to individuals for educational purposes (including travel for their courses). Grants to organisations are normally made for music, drama or outdoor activities to benefit young people.
WHAT IS NOT FUNDED No retrospective applications will be considered.
TYPE OF GRANT Normally one-off, occasionally for longer periods.
FINANCES *Year* 2009–10 *Income* £172,344 *Grants* £175,000
TRUSTEES Beppo Buchanan-Smith; Hannah Buchanan-Smith; Dr R H MacDougall; Mrs Clair Orr; Dougal Philip; Mark Webster.
HOW TO APPLY Application forms and guidance notes are available from the correspondent.
WHO TO APPLY TO Kathleen Carnegie, McCash and Hunter Solicitors, 25 South Methven Street, Perth PH1 5ES *Tel* 01738 620451 *email* kathleencarnegie@mccash.co.uk *Website* www.thecrosstrust.org.uk

---

■ The Croydon Relief in Need Charities

CC NO 810114   ESTABLISHED 1962
WHERE FUNDING CAN BE GIVEN The borough of Croydon.
WHO CAN BENEFIT Local charities and individuals.
WHAT IS FUNDED General, health and welfare.
TYPE OF GRANT Recurrent.
RANGE OF GRANTS Up to £50,000.
SAMPLE GRANTS Croydon Parish Church (£50,000); St Christopher's Hospice (£39,000); Marie Curie Cancer Care (£19,000); Mencap (£12,000); Croydon Carers Centre (£10,000); Nightwatch (£9,000); Wheels for Wellbeing and MacMillan Cancer Support (£5,000 each); Theodora's Children's Trust (£4,000); Whitgift Special Needs Activity Project (£3,000); Listening Books (£1,000); and Croydon Pet PDSA Hospital (£500).
FINANCES *Year* 2009–10 *Income* £159,888 *Grants* £184,867 *Assets* £4,062
TRUSTEES N P Hepworth, Chair; Mrs M Adigun-Boaye; Mrs B E Cripps; D J Cripps; Mrs L A Talbot; Mrs C D A Trower; A Galer; Mrs M Bourne; D M Harries; D Hemmings; C Melrose.
HOW TO APPLY In writing to the correspondent.
WHO TO APPLY TO W B Rymer, Clerk, Elis David Almshouses, Duppas Hill Terrace, Croydon CR0 4BT

■ The Mayor of Croydon's Charity Fund

CC NO 1042479   ESTABLISHED 1994
WHERE FUNDING CAN BE GIVEN Croydon.
WHO CAN BENEFIT Registered charities.
WHAT IS FUNDED General charitable purposes. The grantmaking of this trust is the prerogative of whichever mayor is in office in any particular year. Two charities are chosen each year.

FINANCES *Year* 2009–10 *Income* £37,914 *Grants* £22,270 *Assets* £22,433
TRUSTEES Lea Goddard.
HOW TO APPLY Unsolicited applications cannot be considered.
WHO TO APPLY TO Lea Goddard, Head of Registration Services, The Town Hall, Katharine Street, Croydon, Surrey CR9 1DE *Tel* 020 8760 5730 *email* lea.goddard@croydon.gov.uk *Website* www.croydon.gov.uk

---

■ The Peter Cruddas Foundation

CC NO 1117323   ESTABLISHED 2006
WHERE FUNDING CAN BE GIVEN UK, with a particular interest in London.
WHO CAN BENEFIT Registered charities, hospitals and other institutions.
WHAT IS FUNDED Children and young people. 'The foundation gives priority to programmes designed to help disadvantaged and disengaged young people to pursue their education (including vocational) and more generally develop their potential whether through sport or recreation, voluntary programmes or otherwise. Preference will be given to the support of projects undertaken by charitable organisations for the benefit of such people. Consideration may be also given in certain circumstances for individual support but only on referral from appropriate sponsor organisations.'
TYPE OF GRANT One-off and recurrent grants for capital and revenue costs.
SAMPLE GRANTS The Challenge Charity Network (£400,000); The Caudwell Charitable Trust (£225,000); Duke of Edinburgh Awards (£125,000); Policy Exchange Limited (£120,000); Sheffield Institute Foundation for MND (£50,000); Mentor Foundation UK and Wicked Weather Watch (£20,000 each); Jewish Care (£16,500); Corum, Chai Cancer Care and Flying Scholarships for the Disabled (£10,000 each); and Help the Heroes and Norwood (£5,000 each).
FINANCES *Year* 2009–10 *Income* £40,290 *Grants* £1,484,673 *Assets* £2,369,180
TRUSTEES Lord David Young, Chair; Peter Cruddas; Martin Paisner.
HOW TO APPLY On an application form available to download from the foundation's website. The foundation provides guidance on how to complete the application form, also available on the website.
WHO TO APPLY TO Stephen D Cox, Administrator, 133 Houndsditch, London EC3A 7BX *Tel* 020 3003 8360 *Fax* 020 3003 8580 *email* s.cox@pcfoundation.org.uk *Website* www.petercruddasfoundation.org.uk

---

■ Cruden Foundation Ltd

SC NO SC004987   ESTABLISHED 1956
WHERE FUNDING CAN BE GIVEN Mainly Scotland.
WHO CAN BENEFIT Registered charities.
WHAT IS FUNDED General charitable purposes.
WHAT IS NOT FUNDED No grants to individuals.
TYPE OF GRANT Recurrent and one-off.
RANGE OF GRANTS Up to £15,000.
SAMPLE GRANTS Previous beneficiaries of £1,000 or more included: Edinburgh International Festival (£15,000); St Columba's Hospice (£11,000); Edinburgh Headway Group (£10,000); Marie Curie Cancer Care Scotland and Edinburgh Clothing Store (£5,000 each); Stroke Unit Support (£3,000); Edinburgh Academy Foundation (£2,500) and Children 1st (£2,000).

FINANCES *Year* 2010–11 *Income* £283,706 *Grants* £219,750

TRUSTEES N Lessels, Chair; M R A Matthews; J G Mitchell; A Johnston; M J Rowley; D D Walker; K D Reid.

HOW TO APPLY In writing to the correspondent.

WHO TO APPLY TO M J Rowley, Secretary, Baberton House, Juniper Green, Edinburgh EH14 3HN

■ The Ronald Cruickshanks Foundation

CC NO 296075   **ESTABLISHED** 1987

WHERE FUNDING CAN BE GIVEN UK, with some preference for Folkestone, Faversham and the surrounding area.

WHO CAN BENEFIT Individuals and organisations, including various local churches.

WHAT IS FUNDED General charitable purposes, but particularly for the benefit of people in financial and other need within the stated beneficial area.

TYPE OF GRANT Recurrent.

RANGE OF GRANTS £250–£8,000.

SAMPLE GRANTS Demelza House Children's Hospice, Pilgrims Hospice on the Hill and the Pilgrims Hospice – Canterbury (£8,000 each); Parish Church of St Mary & St Eanswythe – Fabric Fund (£6,000); Kent Air Ambulance (£4,500); and Barnardo's, Cats Protection and Canterbury Horse Rescue (£1,000 each); PDSA and Hearing Dogs for Deaf People (£750 each); The Genesis Appeal and Volunteer Reading Help (£500 each); and Kent Kids, Miles of Smiles, The Caldecott Foundation and Samaritans(£250 each).

FINANCES *Year* 2009–10 *Income* £134,492 *Grants* £142,570 *Assets* £1,715,154

TRUSTEES I F Cloke, Chair; J S Schilder; Mrs S E Cloke.

HOW TO APPLY In writing to the correspondent. Applications should be received by the end of September for consideration on a date coinciding closely with the anniversary of the death of the founder, which was 7 December.

WHO TO APPLY TO I F Cloke, Trustee, 34 Cheriton Gardens, Folkestone, Kent CT20 2AX *Tel* 01303 251742

■ The R D Crusaders Foundation

CC NO 1014352   **ESTABLISHED** 1992

WHERE FUNDING CAN BE GIVEN Worldwide.

WHO CAN BENEFIT Charitable organisations.

WHAT IS FUNDED The relief of poverty and sickness, particularly among children.

TYPE OF GRANT Core, capital and project funding in one-off and recurrent grants.

RANGE OF GRANTS Up to £125,000 (2010).

SAMPLE GRANTS Jewish Care (£125,000); United Jewish Israel Appeal (£100,000); Fight for Sight (£50,000); CST – Community Service Trust (£10,000); The Stroke Association (£5,000); Kindred (£2,000); Little Heroes, Pathway Project and Sainsbury's Sport Relief (£1,000 each).

FINANCES *Year* 2010 *Income* £1,363,724 *Grants* £1,418,761 *Assets* £550,000

TRUSTEES R C Desmond; Northern and Shell Services Ltd and Northern and Shell Media Group Ltd.

HOW TO APPLY In writing to the correspondent.

WHO TO APPLY TO The Trustees, The Northern and Shell Building, No. 10 Lower Thames Street, London EC3R 6EN *Tel* 020 8612 7760 *email* allison.racher@express.co.uk

■ The Cuby Charitable Trust

CC NO 328585   **ESTABLISHED** 1990

WHERE FUNDING CAN BE GIVEN UK, overseas.

WHO CAN BENEFIT Registered charities.

WHAT IS FUNDED Jewish causes.

FINANCES *Year* 2009–10 *Income* £101,639 *Grants* £107,264 *Assets* £322,746

TRUSTEES S Cuby, Chair; Mrs C Cuby; J Cuby; Mrs R Talmor.

OTHER INFORMATION No list of grant beneficiaries was included with the accounts.

HOW TO APPLY In writing to the correspondent.

WHO TO APPLY TO S Cuby, Secretary, 16 Mowbray Road, Edgware, Middlesex HA8 8JQ *Tel* 020 7563 6868

■ Cullum Family Trust

CC NO 1117056   **ESTABLISHED** 2006

WHERE FUNDING CAN BE GIVEN UK.

WHO CAN BENEFIT Registered charities and institutions.

WHAT IS FUNDED Social welfare, education and general charitable purposes.

TYPE OF GRANT One off and up to two years funding.

RANGE OF GRANTS £1,000–£5,000.

SAMPLE GRANTS Kids Company and Sussex Community Foundation (£40,000 each).

FINANCES *Year* 2009–10 *Income* £623,095 *Grants* £96,424 *Assets* £24,230,679

TRUSTEES Peter Geoffrey Cullum; Ann Cullum; Claire Louise Cullum; Simon Timothy Cullum.

OTHER INFORMATION The trust offers full project funding and will fund core and capital costs.

HOW TO APPLY In writing to the correspondent.

WHO TO APPLY TO Peter Geoffrey Cullum, Trustee, Wealden Hall, Parkfield, Sevenoaks, Kent TN15 0HX

■ The Culra Charitable Trust

CC NO 274612   **ESTABLISHED** 1977

WHERE FUNDING CAN BE GIVEN UK.

WHO CAN BENEFIT Registered charities only.

WHAT IS FUNDED General charitable purposes.

WHAT IS NOT FUNDED Grants are not given to non-registered charities or individuals.

RANGE OF GRANTS Usually between £200 and £500.

SAMPLE GRANTS Royal Air Force Benevolent Fund (£6,000).

FINANCES *Year* 2009–10 *Income* £73,612 *Grants* £28,700 *Assets* £556,018

TRUSTEES C Byam-Cook; P J Sienesi; G Needham; G Francis.

HOW TO APPLY The trust tends to support organisations known to the trustees, rather than responding to unsolicited applications. The trustees meet twice a year.

WHO TO APPLY TO Mrs Mary Kitto, 1 College Hill, London EC4R 2RA

■ The Cumber Family Charitable Trust

CC NO 291009   **ESTABLISHED** 1985

WHERE FUNDING CAN BE GIVEN Worldwide, with a preference for the developing world and Berkshire and Oxfordshire.

WHO CAN BENEFIT Individuals and organisations.

WHAT IS FUNDED Health, homelessness, disability, welfare, rural development, housing, overseas aid, Christian aid, agricultural development, youth and children's welfare and education.

About 50% of the funding given is for work overseas.

WHAT IS NOT FUNDED No grants for animal welfare. Only very few to individuals with local connections and who are personally known to the trustees are supported. Local appeals outside Berkshire and Oxfordshire are not usually supported.

TYPE OF GRANT Usually single grant, not repeated within three years. Occasionally support up to three years for a project.

RANGE OF GRANTS £250–£3,000.

SAMPLE GRANTS Bradfield Primary Project and Vale and Ridgeway Trust (£2,000 each); Amity, International Refugee Trust, Kaloko Trust, Operation New World, Practical Action, and the Unicorn School (£1,000 each); Abingdon Alzheimer's, Leys Youth Programme, Reading Deaf Centre, RoRo Sailing Project and the Friends of Hope (£500 each); and Balsam Family Project, Mareham Society and the Sunshine Club (£250 each).

FINANCES *Year* 2009–10 *Income* £43,820 *Grants* £47,000 *Assets* £781,172

TRUSTEES A R Davey; W Cumber; Mrs M J Cumber; Mrs M J Freeman; Mrs M E Tearney; Mrs J E Mearns.

HOW TO APPLY In writing to the correspondent. The trustees usually meet twice a year.

WHO TO APPLY TO Mrs M E Tearney, Secretary, Manor Farm, Marcham, Abingdon, Oxfordshire OX13 6NZ *Tel* 01865 391327 *email* mary. tearney@hotmail.co.uk *Website* www. cumberfamilycharitabletrust.org.uk

■ Cumberland Building Society Charitable Foundation

CC NO 1072435   **ESTABLISHED** 1998

WHERE FUNDING CAN BE GIVEN Cumbria, Dumfries and Galloway, Lancashire (Preston area) and Northumberland (Haltwhistle area).

WHO CAN BENEFIT Registered charities.

WHAT IS FUNDED General charitable purposes in areas where the trustees determine Cumberland Building Society operates.

WHAT IS NOT FUNDED No grants to non-registered charities and those working outside the operating area.

RANGE OF GRANTS Up to £1,000.

SAMPLE GRANTS Beneficiaries included: Recycling Lives 'Home Sweet Home' Appeal (£650) and Grizebeck Village Hall Committee (£500). Previous beneficiaries have included Children's Heart Federation, Community Action Furness, Community Transport South Lakeland, Currock House Association, DebRA, the Food Train, the Genesis Appeal, Hospice at Home, L'Arche Preston and St John Ambulance.

FINANCES *Year* 2010–11 *Income* £25,428 *Grants* £32,922 *Assets* £11,615

TRUSTEES Revd J Libby, Chair; E Amos; Mrs J Thomson; Mrs C Graham; J R Carr; Mr B Edmundson; Mrs J Booth.

OTHER INFORMATION In 2010–11 grants were made to 77 organisations totalling £33,000. A full list of donations was not available, however the accounts stated that grants were made across all geographical areas in the foundation's remit, ranging from £100 to £750, and were given to small community groups encompassing children's activities, disability support and a variety of other activities.

HOW TO APPLY In writing to the correspondent.

WHO TO APPLY TO The Secretary, Cumberland House, Castle Street, Carlisle CA3 8RX *Tel* 01228

541341 *email* charitablefoundation@ cumberland.co.uk *Website* www. cumberlandbanking.com/about/community/ charitable-foundation

■ Cumbria Community Foundation

CC NO 1075120   **ESTABLISHED** 1999

WHERE FUNDING CAN BE GIVEN Cumbria.

WHO CAN BENEFIT Organisations and individuals under several different programmes.

WHAT IS FUNDED Improving the quality of the community life of people in Cumbria, and in particular those in need by reason of disability, age, low-income or other disadvantage.

WHAT IS NOT FUNDED The following are not supported: animal welfare; deficit funding; general large appeals; boxing clubs; medical research and equipment; non-Cumbrian projects; sponsored events; replacement of statutory funding; projects that have already happened; applications where you have had a grant from that fund within the last year (except Grassroots Grants); and individuals (except for specific funds). Please contact the foundation for information on any individual restrictions on any of the grant programmes.

TYPE OF GRANT One off and recurring.

RANGE OF GRANTS About £500–£13,000.

SAMPLE GRANTS Cockermouth Flood Action Group (£150,000); Lake District Search and Rescue Association (£35,500); Young Cumbria (£35,000); West Cumbria Trades Hall Centre (£33,000); Cockermouth Town Council, Phoenix Youth Project Cleator Moor and Whitehaven Harbour Youth Project (£25,000 each); Aspatria Dream Scheme (£21,000); Workington Town Rugby League Community Development Foundation (£12,000); Cumbria Starting Point Ltd, Distington Club for Young People, Egremont Rugby Union Football Club, Keswick Flood Recover Group and Workington Life Boat Station (£10,000 each); and Appleby Chamber of Trade, Bolton Parish Hall Committee, Hospice at Home West Cumbria, Keswick Fitz Park Bowling Club, Kirkbride Church Institute, Maryport Inshore Rescue Boat, Mind in West Cumbria and Thirlmere Recreational Hall (£5,000 each).

FINANCES *Year* 2010–11 *Income* £2,768,150 *Grants* £2,663,470 *Assets* £6,759,505

TRUSTEES Sir Brian Donnelly; W Slavin; S Snyder; Ms J Stannard; C Tomlinson; J Whittle; Ian Brown; June Chapman; David Brown; James Carr; Chris Coombes; Rob Cairns; Trevor Hebdon; Bob Mather; Robin Burgess; Heike Horsburgh; Sarah Dunning; Shirley Williams; Dick Raaz; Stewart Young; Peter Stybelski; Catherine Alexander; Mike Casson.

OTHER INFORMATION The total grant figure includes £735,000 paid to individuals. A further £153,000 was spent in distributing flood bags to households and £145,000 was distributed from funds managed for other organisations.

HOW TO APPLY Application forms and clear and full guidelines for each of the foundation's programmes are available to download on the foundation's website or by contacting the correspondent directly. Applications should include the following supporting information: a copy of the organisation's governing document (not required for registered charities); a copy of the latest accounts (or bank statements covering the last quarter if the organisation has been operating for less than a year); details of an independent referee; a copy of the organisation's child protection or safeguarding policy (if the project will involve working with children and/or young people). The foundation prefers to receive applications via email, even if the supporting documents have to be sent by post. Applicants are encouraged to contact the foundation prior to making an application in order to confirm their eligibility. Applications are accepted throughout the year and decisions are usually taken within two months. Some programmes offer a faster process for small urgent projects.

WHO TO APPLY TO Andrew Beeforth, Director, Dovenby Hall, Dovenby, Cockermouth, Cumbria CA13 0PN *Tel* 01900 825760 *Fax* 01900 826 527 *email* enquiries@cumbriafoundation.org *Website* www.cumbriafoundation.org

■ The Cunningham Trust

SC NO SC013499   **ESTABLISHED** 1984
WHERE FUNDING CAN BE GIVEN Scotland.
WHO CAN BENEFIT Mostly universities.
WHAT IS FUNDED Grants are made to university departments which are carrying out academic research in the field of medicine.
WHAT IS NOT FUNDED Grants are unlikely to be made available to non-regular beneficiaries.
TYPE OF GRANT Revenue and project funding for up to two years.
SAMPLE GRANTS Previous beneficiaries have included Aberdeen University – Department of Zoology, Aberdeen University – Department of Ophthalmology, Department of Biomedical Sciences, Edinburgh University's Centre of Tropical Veterinary Medicine and St Andrew's University – School of Biomedical Sciences.
FINANCES *Year* 2009–10 *Income* £281,363 *Grants* £375,000
TRUSTEES Dr D Corner; A C Caithness; Dr D McD Greenhough.
HOW TO APPLY All applications must be submitted on the standard form.
WHO TO APPLY TO The Trustees, Murray Donald Drummond Cook LLP, Kinburn Castle, St Andrews, Fife KY16 9DR

■ The Harry Cureton Charitable Trust

CC NO 1106206   **ESTABLISHED** 2005
WHERE FUNDING CAN BE GIVEN The area covered by Peterborough and Stamford hospitals.
WHO CAN BENEFIT Individuals and organisations.
WHAT IS FUNDED Medical, Health and Sickness.
SAMPLE GRANTS Peterborough and Stamford Hospitals NHS Foundation Trust (£91,000); Peterborough NHS Primary Healthcare Trust Occupational Therapy Department (£13,000); Peterborough Community Services Team (£3,000) and Family Action, Peterborough (£1,600).
FINANCES *Year* 2008–09 *Income* £81,509 *Grants* £126,181 *Assets* £2,646,689
TRUSTEES T P S Bhullar; R C Cooper; C N Monsell; N D Plumb; S D Richards.
OTHER INFORMATION £10,000 was also given in grants towards medical research.
HOW TO APPLY On a form which can be downloaded from the trust's website.
WHO TO APPLY TO C N Monsell, Trustee, c/o Greenwoods Solicitors LLP, Monkstone House, City Road, Peterborough PE1 1JE *email* info@ harrycureton.org.uk *Website* www.harrycureton. org.uk

■ The D J H Currie Memorial Trust

CC NO 802971   **ESTABLISHED** 1990
WHERE FUNDING CAN BE GIVEN Essex.
WHO CAN BENEFIT Registered charities.
WHAT IS FUNDED General charitable purposes. The trust continues to support causes which the founder had an interest in including charities supporting people with disabilities (particularly children), conservation of the countryside, homes for the aged and sporting activities in the county.
WHAT IS NOT FUNDED No grants to individuals.
RANGE OF GRANTS £500–£1,000.
SAMPLE GRANTS Holy Family Catholic Church; Canine Partners; Asthma Relief; Accuro; National Tremor Foundation; Essex Blind Charity; Epping & Theydon Garnon; Voice; St Luke's Hospice; Motability; Fields in Trust; Study of Infant Deaths; Acorn Villages Ltd; Greenpath Ventures; Sunny Days Children Fund; Happy Days; Deafblind UK; St Helena's Hospice; Friends of Moot Hall Trust; The Sea Cadets.
FINANCES *Year* 2009–10 *Income* £470,025 *Grants* £18,000 *Assets* £288,950
TRUSTEES National Westminster Bank plc.
HOW TO APPLY In writing to the correspondent. The trustees consider applications in June each year and all applications should be submitted by the end of May. Annual accounts/last annual report to be enclosed with application. No recipient may benefit more than once every four years.
WHO TO APPLY TO The Trust Secretary, NatWest Trust Services, 5th Floor, Trinity Quay 2, Avon Street, Bristol BS2 0PT

■ The Dennis Curry Charitable Trust

CC NO 263952   **ESTABLISHED** 1971
WHERE FUNDING CAN BE GIVEN UK.
WHO CAN BENEFIT Charitable organisations.
WHAT IS FUNDED General, particular interest in conservation/environment and education. Occasional support is given to churches and cathedrals.
RANGE OF GRANTS £500–£20,000.
SAMPLE GRANTS Durrell Wildlife Conservation Trust (£20,000); University of Oxford – Dept. of Zoology, Wildlife Conservation Research Unit (£15,000); the Art Fund and Galapagos Conservation Trust (£10,000 each); Botanic Gardens Conservation International (£8,000); Project Trust (£3,000); University of Glasgow Trinidad Expedition (£1,500); Friends of Little Chalfont Library (£1,000); the Open Spaces Society (£500).
FINANCES *Year* 2009–10 *Income* £69,879 *Grants* £69,000 *Assets* £2,924,445
TRUSTEES M Curry; Mrs A S Curry; Mrs M Curry-Jones; Mrs P Edmond.
HOW TO APPLY In writing to the correspondent.
WHO TO APPLY TO N J Armstrong, Secretary to the Trust, Alliotts, 5th Floor, 9 Kingsway, London WC2B 6XF

■ The Raymond Curtis Charitable Trust

CC NO 1050295   **ESTABLISHED** 1995
WHERE FUNDING CAN BE GIVEN UK.
WHO CAN BENEFIT Registered charities.
WHAT IS FUNDED Organisations supporting children under 18 and older people.
RANGE OF GRANTS Up to £5,600.

SAMPLE GRANTS Previous beneficiaries included: The Maidenhead Synagogue (£5,600), the Variety Club of Great Britain (£5,500), Central Church of England, Hezon Yeshaya and Wizo (£1,000 each), Great Ormond Street, (£500), Galapagos Conservation Trust (£400), Spinal Research and The Children's Trust (£250 each) and the Dame Vera Lynn Trust (£150).

FINANCES *Year* 2009–10 *Income* £7,783 *Grants* £6,000

TRUSTEES Richard Curtis.

HOW TO APPLY In writing to the correspondent.

WHO TO APPLY TO R Curtis, Administrator, 8 Horseshoe Park, Pangbourne, Berkshire RG8 7JW *Tel* 0118 984 4881 *Fax* 01189 844853

■ The Manny Cussins Foundation

CC NO 219661   **ESTABLISHED** 1962

WHERE FUNDING CAN BE GIVEN Mainly UK, with some emphasis on Yorkshire.

WHO CAN BENEFIT Organisations.

WHAT IS FUNDED Welfare and care of older people and children at risk; Jewish causes; healthcare in Yorkshire and overseas; general in Yorkshire and the former county of Humberside.

WHAT IS NOT FUNDED No grants to individuals.

SAMPLE GRANTS Angels International, Christie Hospital – Children Against Cancer, Forgiveness Project, Hadassah Lodge, Leeds International Piano Competition, Leeds Jewish Education Authority, Leeds Jewish Welfare Board, Lifeline for the Old Jerusalem, Martin House Hospice, United Jewish Israel Appeal, Wheatfields Hospice and Women's International Zionist Organisation.

FINANCES *Year* 2009–10 *Income* £159,127 *Grants* £34,969 *Assets* £765,374

TRUSTEES A Reuben; A Cussins; A J Cussins; J R Cussins; Mrs. A Reuben.

HOW TO APPLY The correspondent states that applications are not sought as the trustees carry out their own research.

WHO TO APPLY TO Derek Corby, c/o Ford Campbell Freedman, 34 Park Cross Street, Leeds, LS1 2QH

■ The Cutler Trust (the Worshipful Company of Makers of Playing Cards)

CC NO 232876   **ESTABLISHED** 1943

WHERE FUNDING CAN BE GIVEN UK and City of London.

WHO CAN BENEFIT Organisations and individuals.

WHAT IS FUNDED 'The aims and objectives of the trust are: to support the City of London ('civic') charities/connected charities and City of London schools and colleges and, where relevant, inner London schools; to assist specific deserving students in their education; to support relevant, smaller charities in which Liverymen are actively involved and which they support; to support smaller charities where the trustees are able to establish an ongoing relationship.'

FINANCES *Year* 2009–10 *Income* £44,992 *Grants* £26,010 *Assets* £557,262

TRUSTEES D M Ladd; P M Cregeen; R A Howells; D C Warner; K T Heather; A J Carter.

OTHER INFORMATION The grant total in 2009–10 included £1,000 given in annuities. 'The Cutler Trust was set up on 25 October 1943 by two card manufacturers, John Waddington Limited and De La Rue Company Limited and named after the then Master, Lindsay Cutler, (whose grandsons have been apprenticed to the Livery and are now Liverymen). Consistent to the original Livery concept, it was initially for beneficiaries and dependants of those who were or had been employed in the manufacture of Playing Cards.'

HOW TO APPLY 'The trust invites applications for funding of grants from members of the Worshipful Company of Makers of Playing Cards, from educational bodies connected with the City of London, and from members of the public. The Marshall of Appeals considers the merits of the applications and seeks further information before submitting recommendations to the trustees' meeting.'
Trustees meet at least twice a year to review applications.

WHO TO APPLY TO P Bowen, Clerk to the Trustees, 8 Capell Avenue, Chorleywood, Hertfordshire WD3 5HX *Website* www.makersofplayingcards. co.uk

---

■ The Cwmbran Trust

CC NO 505855   **ESTABLISHED** 1976

WHERE FUNDING CAN BE GIVEN Cwmbran.

WHO CAN BENEFIT Local groups.

WHAT IS FUNDED Grants are made to provide social amenities for the advancement of education and the relief of poverty and sickness in the urban area of Cwmbran town. Particular support is given to local groups for older people and people who are disabled.

WHAT IS NOT FUNDED No grants are made outside of Cwmbran or to organisational running costs.

RANGE OF GRANTS £100–£10,000.

SAMPLE GRANTS Beneficiaries included: St Anne's Hospice (£10,000); Congress Theatre (£7,500); Ty Hafon Children's Hospice and Medecinema (£5,000 each); Victory Outreach UK (£2,900); Torfean People's First (£2,500); Torfaen Sea Cadets (£2,000); and All Creatures Great and Small and Blaen Bran Woodland (£1,000 each).

FINANCES *Year* 2010 *Income* £77,611 *Grants* £54,536 *Assets* £1,957,406

TRUSTEES Four co-opted Trustees; two nominated trustees; R C Grieg Nominees Ltd.

OTHER INFORMATION The grant total in 2010 includes £2,500 donated to 14 individuals.

HOW TO APPLY In writing to the correspondent. Trustees usually meet five times a year in March, May, July, October and December. Where appropriate, applications are investigated by the grants research officer. When the trustees judge it would be helpful, applicants are invited to put their case to the trustees in person. Where an application has to be dealt with urgently, for example, because of the pressure of time or of need, trustees may be contacted by letter or telephone in order that an early decision may be made.

WHO TO APPLY TO K L Maddox, Arvin Meritor HVBS (UK) Ltd, H V B S (UK) Ltd, Grange Road, Cwmbran, Gwent NP44 3XU *Tel* 01633 834040 *Fax* 01633 834051 *email* cwmbrantrust@ arvinmeritor.com

---

■ Itzchok Meyer Cymerman Trust Ltd

CC NO 265090   **ESTABLISHED** 1972

WHERE FUNDING CAN BE GIVEN UK and Israel.

WHO CAN BENEFIT Registered charities and occasional small grants to individuals – both mainly of the Jewish faith.

Think carefully about every application. Is it justified?

477

WHAT IS FUNDED Advancement of the orthodox Jewish faith, education, social welfare, relief of sickness, medical research and general.

TYPE OF GRANT Mostly recurrent.

RANGE OF GRANTS Up to £100,000.

SAMPLE GRANTS Friends of Ohr Arkiva Institute (£90,000); Vehodarto P'Nei Zoken (£50,000); Russian Immigrant Aid Fund (£44,000); Torah Supporters Fund (£25,000); and Pardes Chana Institutions (£15,000).

FINANCES *Year* 2009–10 *Income* £869,028 *Grants* £944,012 *Assets* £2,465,786

TRUSTEES Mrs H F Bondi; M D Cymerman; Mrs R Cymerman; Mrs S Heitner; L H Bondi; I Heitner; S Cymerman.

HOW TO APPLY In writing to the correspondent.

WHO TO APPLY TO I Heitner, Trustee, 497 Holloway Road, London N7 6LE *Tel* 020 7272 2255

■ The D G Charitable Settlement

cc no 1040778   **established** 1994
where funding can be given UK.
who can benefit Registered charities.
what is funded General charitable purposes to a mainly fixed list of charities.
range of grants £500–£200,000.
sample grants Beneficiaries included: Age Concern, Amnesty International, Battersea Home for Dogs, Crisis, Cancer Research UK, Environmental Investigation Agency Charitable Trust, Great Ormond Street Hospital, Greenpeace, Terrence Higgins Trust, Hoping Foundation, Medical Foundation for Victims of Torture, Otto Wolff Child Health Research, Oxfam, Prisoners Abroad, Prisoners of Conscience Appeal Fund, St Richard's Hospital Charitable Trust and Shelter.
finances *Year* 2009–10 *Income* £2,000,086 *Grants* £315,850 *Assets* £1,753,056
trustees D J Gilmour; P Grafton-Green; Ms P A Samson.
how to apply This trust does not consider unsolicited applications.
who to apply to Ms P A Samson, Trustee, PO Box 62, Heathfield, East Sussex TN21 8ZE *Tel* 01435 867604 *email* joanna.nelson@ btconnect.com

■ The D'Oyly Carte Charitable Trust

cc no 1112457   **established** 1972
where funding can be given UK.
who can benefit Registered charities only, or where it is clear the objects of the appeal are for charitable purposes.
what is funded Mainly the arts, medical/welfare charities and the environment.
what is not funded The trust is unlikely to support the following: animal welfare; applications from individuals, or for the benefit of one individual; charities requiring funding for statutory requirements; charities operating outside the UK; conferences or seminars; exhibitions; expeditions and overseas travel; general appeals; large national charities which enjoy widespread support; maintenance of religious buildings; medical research; NHS Trust hospitals for operational or building costs; recordings and commissioning of new works; religious activities; schools, nurseries and playgroups (other than those for children with special needs); support and rehabilitation from drug or alcohol abuse. Due to the volume of appeals received, the trustees have decided not to consider requests from charities that have had an application turned down until two years have elapsed after the date of rejection.
type of grant Mainly one-off.
range of grants Up to £20,000 but mostly under £5,000.
sample grants Royal Academy of Dramatic Arts (£20,000), towards bursaries; Help the Hospices (£15,000), towards an education and training programme to develop the specialist skills and expertise of doctors, nurses and hospice managers throughout the United Kingdom; Royal Northern College of Music (£10,000), towards bursaries; Tate Gallery (£5,000), to support a visual arts project for young people in the care of local authorities; British Association of Adoption & Fostering (£5,000), towards the Health Programme for children in care; Surrey Care Trust (£5,000), towards the Swingbridge Community Boat Programme's conservation projects along the waterways of Surrey; Wildlife Trust Sheffield (£4,000), towards hands-on activities for children and young people; CHASE Hospice Care for Young Children (£3,500), second and final instalment of two-year commitment towards music project for life-limited children in collaboration with the Royal Philharmonic Orchestra; and Brighton Early Music Festival (£3,500), to provide opportunities for young professional musicians to work with leading music animateurs in two major education projects.
finances *Year* 2009–10 *Income* £971,811 *Grants* £804,130 *Assets* £40,094,030
trustees Jeremy Leigh Pemberton, Chair; Francesca Radcliffe; Julia Sibley; Henry Freeland; Andrew Jackson; Michael O'Brien.
how to apply Potential applicants should write to the correspondent with an outline proposal of no more than two A4 pages. This should cover the work of the charity, its beneficiaries and the need for funding. Applicants qualifying for consideration will then be required to complete the trust's application form. The form should be returned with a copy of the latest annual report and accounts. Applications for specific projects should also include clear details of the need the intended project is designed to meet and an outline budget. The majority of applications are considered in March, July and November. The trust states that it is happy to discuss potential applications on the telephone.
who to apply to Jane Thorne, Secretary, 1 Savoy Hill, London WC2R 0BP *Tel* 020 7420 2600

■ Roald Dahl's Marvellous Children's Charity

cc no 1137409   **established** 1991
where funding can be given UK.
who can benefit Registered charities and individuals. In general, the charity aims to provide help to organisations where funds are not readily available. Preference for small or new organisations rather than long-established, large or national organisations.
what is funded 'The charity makes grants to benefit children who have the following conditions:
Neurology: acquired brain injury as the result of benign brain tumour, encephalitis, head injury, hydrocephalus, meningitis, stroke, neuro-degenerative conditions, defined as conditions in which there is progressive intellectual and/or neurological deterioration and rare and/or severe forms of epilepsy. Haematology: chronic debilitating blood diseases of childhood, excluding leukaemia and related disorders; conditions include: sickle cell anaemia, thalassaemia, haemolytic anaemia, bone marrow failure syndrome, haemophilia, thrombophilia and Von Willebrand's Disease. The charity primarily makes grants to benefit children (i.e. up to the 18th birthday). However, we may consider supporting young people between the ages of 18 and 25 (i.e. up to the 26th birthday) where a case can be made that they have specific needs

associated with their medical condition. We are looking for applications that will clearly tackle the needs and challenges children face as a result of living with the conditions listed above. We are particularly interested in: pump-priming of new specialist Paediatric nursing posts, where there is an emphasis on community care, for a maximum of 2 years. We will only consider funding posts where the applicant organisation commits to taking over funding of the post for a minimum of 3 years after our grant ends; the provision of information and/or support to children and their families; specific projects within residential and day centres to benefit children within the above-mentioned criteria; small items of medical equipment, not available from statutory sources, to enable children to be cared for in their own homes; activities to disseminate good practice in support of children living with our priority conditions; other projects which specifically benefit children and young people within the above mentioned medical criteria may be considered. Although we prefer to fund specific projects, posts and activities, we will consider providing core funding particularly in the case of very small organisations.'

WHAT IS NOT FUNDED The charity will not fund: general appeals from large, well-established charities; national appeals for large building projects; arts projects; any organisations which do not have charitable status or exclusively charitable aims (other than NHS organisations under the charity's specialist nurses programme); statutory bodies (other than NHS organisations under the charity's specialist nurses programme); school or higher education fees; organisations outside the UK; organisations for people with blood disorders which are cancer related due to the relatively large number of charities helping in the oncological field.

TYPE OF GRANT One-off, start-up costs, salaries, projects for up to two years; the range is wide.

RANGE OF GRANTS Individual: £50–£500. Organisations: up to £25,000.

SAMPLE GRANTS Society for Muco-polysaccharide Diseases (£37,000), towards a Specialist Muco-polysaccharide Disease Advocacy Worker; Sickle Cell Society (£35,000), towards the Befriending Project for Young People with Sickle Cell to support them with the transition to adulthood; Southampton General Hospital (£30,000), to establish the new post of Roald Dahl Sapphire Epilepsy Nurse Specialist; National Society for Epilepsy (£17,500), for seven Paediatric Epilepsy Information Network points in hospitals in England; Scottish Epilepsy Initiative (£10,000), towards the Young People's Fieldworker post costs for 2 years; UK Thalassaemia Society (£5,000), towards the Patient and Family National Conference; The MedicAlert Foundation (£2,000), MedicAlert service for 40 children with neurological difficulties.

FINANCES *Year* 2009–10 *Income* £576,810 *Grants* £532,712 *Assets* £1,630,847

TRUSTEES Felicity Dahl, Chair; Martin Goodwin; Roger Hills; Georgina Howson; Virginia Fisher.

OTHER INFORMATION The charity was established in 2010 to supersede the Roald Dahl Foundation following a strategic review, although the focus of the charity remains the same.

HOW TO APPLY 'First, make sure that your project or application falls within the criteria listed [in the general section]. Then contact the charity's director to discuss your proposal. If your idea fits closely within our current areas of interest you will be sent an application form to complete and return. Organisations wishing to apply for funding for specialist nurse posts must contact the charity to request a special application pack. Applications for nurse posts will not be accepted on our standard application form. Once you have completed it you should send the application form, and any attachments, together with a copy of your organisation's accounts and annual report for each of the last two years, to the address above. Applications for posts should include a copy of the proposed job description and person specification. When completing the form you should clearly demonstrate how your project fits our eligibility criteria and funding priorities. You should also clearly tell us what activities you would undertake with the funding, who will benefit (including the number of beneficiaries, their age ranges and whether they are from a specific area or community), how they will benefit (e.g. what the project will do to help, support or empower them) and how you will measure the outcomes of the project. We aim to visit as many organisations applying for funds as possible, but we may simply telephone for more information. Currently grant applications are being considered twice per year – March and September. Urgent applications may be considered between meetings – please contact the charity's director to discuss this if required.'

WHO TO APPLY TO James Fitzpatrick, Director, 81a High Street, Great Missenden, Buckinghamshire HP16 0AL *Tel* 01494 890465 *Fax* 01494 890459 *email* grants@marvellouschildrenscharity.org *Website* www.marvellouschildrenscharity.org

....

■ The Daily Prayer Union Charitable Trust Ltd

CC NO 284857   **ESTABLISHED** 1983
WHERE FUNDING CAN BE GIVEN UK.
WHO CAN BENEFIT Christians and evangelists.
WHAT IS FUNDED Evangelical Christian purposes.
WHAT IS NOT FUNDED No grants for bricks and mortar.
RANGE OF GRANTS £1,000–£7,000.
SAMPLE GRANTS Monkton Combe School (£7,000); SUMT Isle of Man (£6,000); St Andrew's Ministry Trust (£2,000); CPAS (£1,800); Jesus Lane Trust (£1,600); and UCCF (£1,000).
FINANCES *Year* 2009–10 *Income* £65,582 *Grants* £86,410 *Assets* £131,567
TRUSTEES Revd G C Grinham; Mrs F M Ashton; Mrs E D Bridger; Revd D J Jackman; Revd T J Sterry; Dr J Sudell; Mrs A V Tompson.
OTHER INFORMATION In 2009–10 £62,000 of the grant total was paid in 51 grants to individuals.
HOW TO APPLY The trust supports causes already known to the trustees. Unsolicited applications are unlikely to be successful. Trustees meet at different times throughout the year, usually around March, June and October.
WHO TO APPLY TO Mrs C Palmer, Secretary, 12 Weymouth Street, London W1W 5BY

....

■ The Daisy Trust

CC NO 283890   **ESTABLISHED** 1981
WHERE FUNDING CAN BE GIVEN Hammersmith and Fulham.
WHO CAN BENEFIT Local organisations in Hammersmith and Fulham.
WHAT IS FUNDED General charitable purposes.
WHAT IS NOT FUNDED The trust only makes grants to those residing inside the area of benefit. No

grants to individuals. No grants for general running costs or long term projects.

TYPE OF GRANT One-off.

RANGE OF GRANTS £80–£1,000.

SAMPLE GRANTS Fulham Good Neighbour Service, Sulivan Primary School and Upper Room (£1,000 each); Craven Cottage Senior Citizens Club and Royal Hospital for Neuro-disability (£500 each); Farm Lane Luncheon Club and Play Association (£250 each); and Sands End After School Childcare (£150).

FINANCES *Year* 2010 *Income* £22,859

TRUSTEES Patrick Ground; Caroline Ground; Pepita Stonor; Frances Stainton; Peter Stonor; Caroline MacKenzie.

HOW TO APPLY Application forms are available on the trust's website. Applicants are welcomed to include a one page covering letter and any leaflets or brochures about their organisation. The trust will acknowledge receipt of an application and inform as to whether or not it has been successful.

WHO TO APPLY TO Patrick Ground, Trustee, 13 Ranelagh Avenue, London SW6 3PJ *Tel* 020 7736 0131 *Fax* 020 7371 9649 *email* secretary@daisytrust.com

....

■ The Daiwa Anglo-Japanese Foundation

CC NO 299955   **ESTABLISHED** 1988

WHERE FUNDING CAN BE GIVEN UK, Japan.

WHO CAN BENEFIT Individuals and institutions (UK or Japanese) benefiting young adults, students and Japanese people – including schools, universities, grass roots and professional groups.

WHAT IS FUNDED The education of citizens of the UK and Japan in each other's culture, institutions, arts, and so on. Scholarships, bursaries and awards to enable students and academics in the UK and Japan to pursue their education abroad. Grants to charitable institutions promoting education in the UK or Japan, and research.

WHAT IS NOT FUNDED Daiwa Foundation Small Grants cannot be used for: general appeals; capital expenditure (e.g., building refurbishment, equipment acquisition, etc); consumables (e.g., stationery, scientific supplies, etc); school, college or university fees; research or study by an individual school/college/university student; salary costs or professional fees; commissions for works of art; retrospective grants; replacement of statutory funding; commercial activities. Daiwa Foundation Awards cannot be used for: any project that does not involve both a British and a Japanese partner; general appeals; capital expenditure (e.g., building refurbishment, equipment acquisition, etc); salary costs or professional fees; commissions for works of art; retrospective grants; commercial activities.

TYPE OF GRANT Outright or partnership grants, paid in sterling or Japanese yen. One year funding.

RANGE OF GRANTS £5,000–£15,000 for collaborative projects; £1,000–£5,000 for small grants.

SAMPLE GRANTS Cardiff University, School of Medicine (£12,000); Hiroshima City Culture Foundation, Imperial College London and John Innes Centre, Sainsbury Laboratory (£10,000 each); King's College London, Centre for Computing in the Humanities (£3,750); and National Galleries of Scotland (£3,000).

FINANCES *Year* 2010–11 *Income* £542,890 *Grants* £528,747 *Assets* £37,034,782

TRUSTEES Sir Michael Perry; Hiroaki Fujii; Takafumi Sato; Mami Mizutori; Sir John Whitehead; Mr Dozen; Mr Hara; Mr Everett; Merryn Somerset Webb; Sir David Brewer; Lord Brittan; Sir Peter Williams; Andrew Smithers; Akira Kyota.

HOW TO APPLY Application forms are available to download at www.dajf.org.uk. Details of deadlines and criteria for grants, awards and prizes, together with the relevant application forms and guidelines are available on the foundation's website.

WHO TO APPLY TO Prof. Marie Conte-Helm, Director General, Daiwa Foundation, Japan House, 13/14 Cornwall Terrace, London NW1 4QP *Tel* 020 7486 4348 *Fax* 020 7486 2914 *email* marie.conte-helm@dajf.org.uk *Website* www.dajf.org.uk

....

■ Oizer Dalim Trust

CC NO 1045296   **ESTABLISHED** 1994

WHERE FUNDING CAN BE GIVEN UK and overseas.

WHO CAN BENEFIT Registered charities.

WHAT IS FUNDED The alleviation of poverty amongst members of the Orthodox Jewish faith and the furtherance of Orthodox Jewish education.

FINANCES *Year* 2009–10 *Income* £160,674 *Grants* £105,620 *Assets* £58,668

TRUSTEES Mordechai Cik.

HOW TO APPLY In writing to the correspondent.

WHO TO APPLY TO Mordechai Cik, Trustee, 68 Osbaldeston Road, London N16 7DR

....

■ The Dr and Mrs A Darlington Charitable Trust

CC NO 283308   **ESTABLISHED** 1981

WHERE FUNDING CAN BE GIVEN Devon, in particular Sidmouth and east Devon.

WHO CAN BENEFIT Only registered charities.

WHAT IS FUNDED The trust mainly supports medical causes; people who are disabled; older people; and socially isolated people. Grants also given in the fields of nature conservation and preservation.

WHAT IS NOT FUNDED Applications from individuals, including students, are unlikely to be successful. Applications for donations to be used outside Devon (particularly outside Sidmouth and East Devon) are also unlikely to be successful.

TYPE OF GRANT One-off, some recurring.

RANGE OF GRANTS Up to about £15,000.

SAMPLE GRANTS Previous beneficiaries include: Peninsula Medical School Foundation, Children's Health and Exercise Research Centre, Salcombe Regis Church, Vitalise, Freedomwheels, Listening Books, Motability, West of England School and College, MS Therapy Centre, Brainwave, SSAFA, St Loyes, UBS and Countryside Foundation.

FINANCES *Year* 2009–10 *Income* £296,268 *Grants* £114,185 *Assets* £1,767,350

TRUSTEES Lloyds TSB Bank plc.

HOW TO APPLY In writing to the correspondent. The trustees regret that they cannot send replies to unsuccessful applicants. The trustees meet quarterly in March, June, September and December; applications should be received the previous month.

WHO TO APPLY TO The Trust Manager, Lloyds TSB Bank plc, UK Trust Centre, The Clock House, 22–26 Ock Street, Abingdon, Oxfordshire OX14 5SW *Tel* 01235 232734

■ Baron Davenport's Charity

CC NO 217307   **ESTABLISHED** 1930

WHERE FUNDING CAN BE GIVEN Warwickshire, Worcestershire, Staffordshire, Shropshire and West Midlands.

WHO CAN BENEFIT Individuals and charitable organisations and institutions, benefiting children, young adults, retired people, widows, and people disadvantaged by poverty.

WHAT IS FUNDED Social welfare, children and young people under the age of 25.

WHAT IS NOT FUNDED There are no exclusions, providing the applications come within the charity's objects and the applying organisation is based within the charity's beneficial area, or the organisation's project lies within or benefits people who live in the beneficial area.

TYPE OF GRANT One-off or annual grants, for capital or revenue costs.

RANGE OF GRANTS Mostly £2,500 or less.

SAMPLE GRANTS Age Concern Kingstanding and Mary Stevens Hospice (£15,000 each); Age Concern Birmingham and Laslett's Charities (£10,000 each); Douglas Macmillan Hospice (£9,000); Coventry & District Free Church Homes (£7,000); ExtraCare Charitable Trust and James Lloyd Almshouses Trust (£6,000 each).

FINANCES *Year* 2009–10 *Income* £1,106,994 *Grants* £1,072,730 *Assets* £29,167,950

TRUSTEES Christopher Hordern, Chair; Sue M Ayres; William M Colacicchi; Paul Dransfield; Philip A Gough; Rob Prichard.

OTHER INFORMATION The grant total includes £396,500 to 1,667 individuals.

HOW TO APPLY In writing to the correspondent, accompanied by the latest accounts and any project costs. Distributions take place twice a year at the end of May and November and applications should be received at the charity's office by 15 March or 15 September. All applications are acknowledged and those not within the charity's objects are advised.

WHO TO APPLY TO Mrs Marlene Keenan, Administrator, Portman House, 5–7 Temple Row West, Birmingham B2 5NY *Tel* 0121 236 8004 *Fax* 0121 233 2500 *email* enquiries@ barondavenportscharity.org *Website* www. barondavenportscharity.org

■ The Davidson (Nairn) Charitable Trust

SC NO SC024273   **ESTABLISHED** 1995

WHERE FUNDING CAN BE GIVEN Nairn area.

WHO CAN BENEFIT Social welfare organisations and all charities recognised in Scottish Law.

WHAT IS FUNDED Grants may be made towards the provision of leisure and recreation facilities, relieving poverty, assisting older people and educational concerns.

WHAT IS NOT FUNDED Only registered charities are supported or charities recognised in Scottish law.

FINANCES *Year* 2009–10 *Income* £41,145 *Grants* £50,000

TRUSTEES Iain Bain; John Anderson; William Cowie.

HOW TO APPLY On a form available from the correspondent.

WHO TO APPLY TO The Trustees, R and R Urquhart, Incorporating MacGregor and Co Solicitors, Royal Bank of Scotland Buildings, 20 High Street, Nairn IV12 4AX

■ The Davidson Family Charitable Trust

CC NO 262937   **ESTABLISHED** 1971

WHERE FUNDING CAN BE GIVEN UK.

WHO CAN BENEFIT Mainly Jewish organisations.

WHAT IS FUNDED Jewish and charitable purposes.

SAMPLE GRANTS Jewish Care (£801,000); Holburne Museum (£175,000); Museum of London (£92,000); Friends of Israel Antiquities Authority (£25,000); United Synagogue (£21,000); Emunah Child Resettlement Fund and Magon David Adom UK (£10,000 each); Friends of Ohel Torah (£6,000); Friends of Bnai Akiva and Youth Aliyah Child Rescue (£5,000 each); UJIA (£4,000); and Eastside Youth Leaders Academy and Great Ormond Street Hospital (£1,000 each).

FINANCES *Year* 2010–11 *Income* £2,128,211 *Grants* £1,346,494 *Assets* £800,749

TRUSTEES Gerald A Davidson; Maxine Y Davidson; Eve Winer.

HOW TO APPLY In writing to the correspondent.

WHO TO APPLY TO Eve Winer, Trustee, c/o Queen Anne Street Capital, 58 Queen Anne Street, London W1G 8HW *Tel* 020 72241030 *email* ewiner@wolfeproperties.co.uk

■ The Alderman Joe Davidson Memorial Trust

CC NO 202591   **ESTABLISHED** 1962

WHERE FUNDING CAN BE GIVEN UK, with a preference for Hampshire.

WHO CAN BENEFIT Local and specific national organisations and individuals benefiting: children; older people, nominated by Age Concern; and Jewish people.

WHAT IS FUNDED Charities that are named in the trust deed, people who are in need and the provision of Christmas parties. The trust also presents watches to school children for regular attendance.

TYPE OF GRANT Recurring grants given to specific organisations.

FINANCES *Year* 2009–10 *Income* £37,669 *Grants* £28,589 *Assets* £745,659

TRUSTEES K Crabbe; J Stock.

OTHER INFORMATION The trust was established to provide 'dwellings for persons over 70 years of age in necessitous circumstances preferably resident in Portsmouth for more than 25 years'.

HOW TO APPLY The trustees are only permitted to make grants to individuals or organisations that are specified in the Trust Deed.

WHO TO APPLY TO The Secretary to the Trustees, Portsmouth City Council, Civic Offices, Guildhall Square, Portsmouth PO1 2QR

■ Michael Davies Charitable Settlement

CC NO 1000574   **ESTABLISHED** 1990

WHERE FUNDING CAN BE GIVEN UK.

WHO CAN BENEFIT Organisations.

WHAT IS FUNDED General charitable purposes.

RANGE OF GRANTS Up to £15,000.

SAMPLE GRANTS Previous beneficiaries have included: BTYC Sailsports Club (£15,000); Camden Arts Centre, Camp and Trek, Marie Curie Cancer Care, North London Hospice, School Aid India and Tools for Training Overseas (£10,000 each); Médecins du Monde and the Study Gallery (£5,000 each); Architects For Aid (£3,500); Thames Wharf Charity (£2,000); the

Langford Trust for Animal Health and Welfare (£1,000); and the Architectural Association Inc. (£750).

FINANCES *Year* 2008–09 *Income* £323,229 *Grants* £299,000 *Assets* £575,679

TRUSTEES M J P Davies; K A Hawkins.

HOW TO APPLY In writing to the correspondent.

WHO TO APPLY TO K Hawkins, Administrator, Lee Associates, 5 Southampton Place, London WC1A 2DA *Tel* 020 7025 4600

....

■ The Gwendoline and Margaret Davies Charity

CC NO 235589   **ESTABLISHED** 1934

WHERE FUNDING CAN BE GIVEN UK, with particular favour given to Wales.

WHO CAN BENEFIT Registered charities only. Welsh charities are particularly favoured.

WHAT IS FUNDED General charitable purposes, with special consideration given to the arts, health and young people. Organisations in the fields of education, medical research, community care services environment and faith activities may also be considered.

WHAT IS NOT FUNDED Grants are made to registered charities only.

TYPE OF GRANT Mainly one-off, occasionally recurrent for specific capital projects.

RANGE OF GRANTS Typically up to £8,000 per organisation.

SAMPLE GRANTS Gregynog Festival (£8,000); Welsh National Opera, Abergorki Community Hall, Age Concern Montgomery and Ferndale Skate Park Ltd (£5,000 each); Bobath Children's Therapy Centre Wales and CLIC Sargent (£4,000 each); Vitalise (£3,600); Food Bank Ebbw Vale (£3,500); and Caersws Recreation Association, Mencap, Shakespeare Link and Beacon of Hope (£2,000 each).

FINANCES *Year* 2009–10 *Income* £278,889 *Grants* £114,431 *Assets* £6,366,871

TRUSTEES Rt Hon. David Davies; Dr D Lewis; Dr Denis Balsom; Dr Janet Lewis.

HOW TO APPLY The trustees consider appeals on an individual basis. There are no application forms as the trustees prefer to receive letters from applicants setting out the following information: whether the organisation is a registered charity; details of the reason for the application – the type of work and so on; the cost; how much has been raised so far towards the cost; the source of the sums raised; a copy of the last audited accounts if available; and any other information that the applicant may consider would help the application. Unsuccessful appeals are not informed unless an sae is enclosed.

WHO TO APPLY TO Mrs Susan Hamer, Secretary, The Offices, Plas Dinam, Llandinam, Powys SY17 5DQ *Tel* 01686 689172 *Fax* 01686 689172

....

■ The Hamilton Davies Trust

CC NO 1106123   **ESTABLISHED** 2004

WHERE FUNDING CAN BE GIVEN Irlam and Cadishead (in Salford) and Rixton with Glazebrook (in Warrington).

WHO CAN BENEFIT Community organisations.

WHAT IS FUNDED '(1) Youth – Supporting youth leaders and developing the youth movement with the aim of promoting links to education, sports and community initiatives and encouraging organised activities. (2) Education – Adding value to existing provision and raising

children's expectations. (3) Sport – Sport is particularly important in the development of young people and the trust has supported projects by providing funds for equipment and kit, holiday programmes and competitions. (4) Community – Support for the community by way of rebuilding and refurbishment of community buildings, supporting group work, festivals and enhancing communication between local facilities and residents.'

SAMPLE GRANTS Previous beneficiaries include: I & C Young People's Project (£18,000); Salford City Council (£14,000); Cheshire Police Authority (£11,000); St Helen's School Governors (£10,000); Salford Community Leisure (£7,500); Relate (£6,000); Moorfield Primary School (£3,000); Bridgewater School, Poorlots Allotment and St Mary's Parent Guild (£2,000 each); Fiddlers Lane Primary (£1,500); Friendly Faces, Irlam Hornets and Triton Hockey Club (£1,000 each); Friends of St Josephs (£700); St Mary's School (£500); Fridays (£300); St Mary's Parent Guild (£250); Irlam Royalettes (£225); Phoenix Gem Dance Troupe (£200); and Salford Community Leisure (£60).

FINANCES *Year* 2009–10 *Income* £993,502 *Grants* £270,593 *Assets* £3,682,828

TRUSTEES N McArthur; G Chisnall; F Cocker.

HOW TO APPLY In writing to the correspondent. Applications should include a brief outline of the project for which support is requested, the amount of funding required and details of any other funding applications that have been made. The trustees will consider all applications, with applicants being informed of their decision in writing. The trust welcomes initial telephone calls to discuss potential projects.

WHO TO APPLY TO Colette Fairfax, Secretary to the Trust, 117c Liverpool Rd, Cadishead, Manchester M44 5BG *Tel* 0161 222 4003 *email* info@hamiltondavies.org.uk

....

■ The Wilfrid Bruce Davis Charitable Trust

CC NO 265421   **ESTABLISHED** 1967

WHERE FUNDING CAN BE GIVEN UK, but mainly Cornwall; India.

WHO CAN BENEFIT Voluntary groups and registered charities.

WHAT IS FUNDED The trust presently concentrates on 'improving the quality of life for those who are physically disadvantaged and their carers'. The geographical area covered is almost exclusively Cornwall, however the main thrust of the trust's activities is now focused on India.

WHAT IS NOT FUNDED No applications from individuals are considered.

SAMPLE GRANTS Pallium India (£50,000); Cornwall Community Foundation (£6,000); Pain and Palliative Care Society Calicut (£5,000); and Médecins Sans Frontières (£1,000).

FINANCES *Year* 2009–10 *Income* £74,553 *Grants* £32,857 *Assets* £184,386

TRUSTEES W B Davis; Mrs D F Davis; Mrs D S Dickens; Mrs C A S Pierce.

HOW TO APPLY No replies are made to unsolicited applications. The correspondent has stated that the budget for many years to come is fully committed and that the trust receives hundreds of applications, none of which can be supported.

WHO TO APPLY TO W B Davis, Trustee, La Feock Grange, Feock, Truro, Cornwall TR3 6RG *Tel* 01872 862795

......

■ Davis-Rubens Charitable Trust

CC NO 263662   **ESTABLISHED** 1971

WHERE FUNDING CAN BE GIVEN UK.

WHO CAN BENEFIT Registered charities with a preference for UK-wide and Jewish charities.

WHAT IS FUNDED General charitable purposes.

WHAT IS NOT FUNDED No grants to individuals.

TYPE OF GRANT Mainly recurrent.

RANGE OF GRANTS £50–£1,000, mostly under £500.

SAMPLE GRANTS Jewish Care (£1,000); Vitalise (£750); Jewish Deaf Association (£600); Diabetes UK (£500); Musician's Benevolent Fund (£400); Trinity Hospice (£350); Greater London Fund for the Blind (£250); British Friends of the Hebrew University of Jerusalem (£200); Butler Trust (£100); and Universal Beneficent Society – UBS (£50).

FINANCES *Year* 2009–10 *Income* £23,685 *Grants* £26,000

TRUSTEES Enid Rubens; Giles Rubens; Edward Checkley.

HOW TO APPLY In writing to the correspondent, however, the trust states that applications from new charities are rarely considered.

WHO TO APPLY TO Renny Clark, Gilbert Allen and Co., Churchdown Chambers, Bordyke, Tonbridge, Kent TN9 1NR *Tel* 01732 770100

■ The Dawe Charitable Trust

CC NO 1060314   **ESTABLISHED** 1997

WHERE FUNDING CAN BE GIVEN Cambridgeshire, national, international.

WHO CAN BENEFIT Charitable organisations.

WHAT IS FUNDED Disadvantaged people and homelessness.

RANGE OF GRANTS £1,000–£100,000.

SAMPLE GRANTS Previous beneficiaries included: Prince's Trust (£50,000); St Theresa Charity and Manda Wilderness Agricultural Project (£5,000 each).

FINANCES *Year* 2009–10 *Income* £88,504

TRUSTEES Dr Peter Dawe; Lindsay Dawe; David Kerr.

HOW TO APPLY In writing to the correspondent, outlining ideas and needs.

WHO TO APPLY TO Dr Peter Dawe, Fen View, 17a Broad Street, Ely, Cambridgeshire CB7 4AJ *Tel* 0845 345 8999

■ The De Clermont Charitable Company Ltd

CC NO 274191   **ESTABLISHED** 1977

WHERE FUNDING CAN BE GIVEN UK, with a preference for north east England.

WHO CAN BENEFIT Headquarters organisations and local organisations in the north east of England.

WHAT IS FUNDED General charitable purposes, particularly those charities of special interest to the founders of this company, i.e. medical research, children and young people, service organisations and overseas disaster appeals.

WHAT IS NOT FUNDED No grants for organisations concerned with drugs and alcohol abuse.

RANGE OF GRANTS Up to £3,000.

SAMPLE GRANTS Previous beneficiaries have included: Sedburgh School Foundation, Borders Support Group, Alzheimer's Research Trust, Lowick Village Hall and Universal Beneficent Society, Brooke Hospital for Animals and Haydn Bridge High School and CLIC Sargent.

FINANCES *Year* 2009–10 *Income* £26,901 *Grants* £11,889 *Assets* £757,840

TRUSTEES Elizabeth de Clermont; Caroline Orpwood; Herbert Orpwood.

OTHER INFORMATION No grants list was available from the latest accounts.

HOW TO APPLY In writing to the correspondent.

WHO TO APPLY TO Caroline Orpwood, Bowmonthill, Mindrum, Northumberland TD12 4QW *Tel* 07890 850266

■ The Helen and Geoffrey De Freitas Charitable Trust

CC NO 258597   **ESTABLISHED** 1969

WHERE FUNDING CAN BE GIVEN UK.

WHO CAN BENEFIT Charitable organisations and voluntary umbrella bodies registered in the UK.

WHAT IS FUNDED The conservation of the countryside and environment in rural Britain; the preservation of Britain's cultural heritage; assistance to people who are underprivileged through community facilities and services, advice centres and community arts and recreation. Once a year the trustees may respond to a national or international humanitarian crisis which may be outside the terms of reference of the trust.

WHAT IS NOT FUNDED No grants to non-registered charities, individuals, or to charities on behalf of individuals. Definitely no support for charities concerned with medical or health matters, or with physical, mental or sensory impairments.

TYPE OF GRANT Usually one-off for feasibility studies, project and occasionally for start-up costs.

RANGE OF GRANTS £500–£5,000.

SAMPLE GRANTS Staffordshire Wildlife Trust and GINA (£5,000 each); Tarka Country Trust (£3,000); Dartington Hall Trust (£2,800); the Grasslands Trust, Marine Conservation Society, Nailsea Tithe Barn Trust and Suffolk Building Preservation Trust (£2,500 each); Devon Wildlife Trust (£1,500); St Michael and All Angels – London Fields (£1,500); and Community Can Cycle (£500).

FINANCES *Year* 2009–10 *Income* £18,972 *Grants* £35,000

TRUSTEES Richard Kirby; Frances de Freitas; Roger de Freitas.

HOW TO APPLY In writing to the correspondent at the following address: PO Box 18667, London, NW3 5WB. Trustees meet quarterly.

WHO TO APPLY TO Richard Kirby, Trustee, Speechly Bircham LLP, 6 New Street Square, London EC4A 3LX

■ Peter De Haan Charitable Trust

CC NO 1077005   **ESTABLISHED** 1999

WHERE FUNDING CAN BE GIVEN UK.

WHO CAN BENEFIT Charitable organisations.

WHAT IS FUNDED General charitable purposes, including organisations connected with children and young people. The current focus of the trust is social welfare, the environment and the arts.

WHAT IS NOT FUNDED 'We will not accept applications for grants: that directly replace or subsidise statutory funding; from individuals or for the benefit of one individual; for work that has already taken place; which do not have a direct benefit to the UK; for medical research; for adventure and residential courses, expeditions or overseas travel; for holidays and respite care; for endowment funds; for the promotion of a specific religion; that are part of general appeals or circulars; from applicants who have applied to us within the last 12 months. In addition to the above, we are unlikely to support: large national charities which enjoy widespread support; local organisations which are part of a wider network of others doing similar work; individual pre-schools, schools; out-of-school clubs, supplementary schools, colleges, universities or youth clubs; websites, publications, conferences or seminars.'

TYPE OF GRANT Project grants or core costs.

RANGE OF GRANTS Mostly up to £20,000.

SAMPLE GRANTS London Wildlife Trust (£400,000); Leicestershire & Rutland Wildlife Trust (£275,000); Missing People (£250,000); YouthNet (£200,000); Rainbow Trust (£100,000); New Horizon Centre (£80,000); L'Ouverture (£60,000); Bede Home Association and Cardinal Hume Centre (£30,000 each); Dandelion Trust for Children, Noah's Ark Community Café and Twelves Company (£23,000 each); Walsall Street Teams (£20,000); Accept, Exodus Project and Perthes Association (£15,000 each); Theatre in Education (£5,000); Sarum Orchestra (£4,000); Full Body and the Voice, Ice and Fire Theatre Company and the Whitechapel Art Gallery (£2,000 each); and Ascendance Repertory Company Ltd, Children's Discovery Centre and Sudden Productions (£1,000 each).

FINANCES *Year* 2010–11 *Income* £345,000 *Grants* £1,129,000 *Assets* £16,598,000

TRUSTEES Peter Charles De Haan; Janette McKay; Nikki A Crane; Dr Rob Stoneman; Carol Stone; Opus Corporate Trustees Limited.

HOW TO APPLY In writing or via email to the correspondent. Grants may be for project-based applications or to subsidise core costs. The following information should be included: a statement that you have made reference to the website; a description of the charity's aims and achievements; charity registration number; an outline and budget for the project for which funding is sought; a copy of the latest financial statements; details of funds raised and the current shortfall. Applications are considered on a continuing basis throughout the year. Major grants are awarded at the trustee meeting held quarterly in March, June, September and December. Notification of the outcome of applications will be by email. Where an email address is not available, no notification will be possible. The charity states that it is not seeking applications from wildlife trusts.

WHO TO APPLY TO Simon Johnson, Wool Yard, 54 Bermondsey Street, London SE1 3UD *Tel* 020 7232 5471 *email* sjohnson@pdhct.org.uk *Website* www.pdhct.org.uk

■ The De Laszlo Foundation

CC NO 327383   **ESTABLISHED** 1978

WHERE FUNDING CAN BE GIVEN UK and worldwide.

WHO CAN BENEFIT Arts organisations and registered charities.

WHAT IS FUNDED Promotion of the arts; general charitable purposes.

RANGE OF GRANTS It is increasingly the policy of the trustees to make a small number of targeted large grants.

SAMPLE GRANTS The De Laszlo Archive Trust (£188,000); Gordonstoun School Arts Centre (£20,000); Durham University and Royal Marsden (£10,000 each); Foundation for Liver Research (£8,000); Southampton University (£5,000); Federation of British Artists (£3,000); AGORA (£2,500); National Youth Orchestra (£1,500); Tate Foundation (£1,000); Cardboard Citizens (£500); and Chelsea Open Air Nursery School (£250).

FINANCES *Year* 2009–10 *Income* £342,614 *Grants* £321,296 *Assets* £2,819,988

TRUSTEES Damon de Laszlo, Chair; Lucy Birkbeck; Robert de Laszlo; William de Laszlo.

OTHER INFORMATION The foundation was set up to promote the advancement and promotion of education and interest in the visual arts with special reference to encouraging knowledge of the works of contemporary painters, in particular those of the late Philip de Laszlo.

HOW TO APPLY No grants to unsolicited applications.

WHO TO APPLY TO Christabel Wood, 5 Albany Courtyard, London W1J 0HF

■ The Leopold De Rothschild Charitable Trust

CC NO 212611   **ESTABLISHED** 1959

WHERE FUNDING CAN BE GIVEN UK.

WHO CAN BENEFIT Registered charities only.

WHAT IS FUNDED General charitable purposes, particularly the arts and Jewish organisations.

SAMPLE GRANTS Glyndebourne and Jewish Music Institute (£10,000 each); INTOUniversity (£3,000); Liberal Jewish Synagogue (£2,700); Aldeburgh Foundation, David Shepherd Wildlife Foundation, Jerusalem Foundation, Lord Mayor's Appeal, National Museum of Science & Industry, National Railway Museum, Newbury Spring Festival and Sir John Soane Museum (£1,000 each); and Contemporary Applied Arts, Friends of Holland Park, The Big Issue and Wiener Library (£100 each).

FINANCES *Year* 2009–10 *Income* £53,910 *Grants* £69,367 *Assets* £1,494,222

TRUSTEES Rothschild Trust Corporation Ltd.

HOW TO APPLY In writing to the correspondent.

WHO TO APPLY TO The Clerk, Rothschild Trust Corporation Ltd, New Court, St Swithin's Lane, London EC4P 4DU *Tel* 020 7280 5000

■ The Deakin Charitable Trust

CC NO 258001   **ESTABLISHED** 1968

WHERE FUNDING CAN BE GIVEN Mainly Surrey with a preference for Woking.

WHO CAN BENEFIT Mainly local charities including hospices and various religious organisations, and students seeking to extend their music education.

WHAT IS FUNDED General charitable purposes.

SAMPLE GRANTS Woking Hospice (£15,000); CHASE Children's Hospice and Phyllis Tuckwell Hospice (£7,500 each); Epworth Choir (£2,000); CPAS (£900); Alzheimer's Society and Salvation Army (£800 each); National Youth Orchestra and Action for the Blind (£500 each); Friends of the Elderly and Combat Stress (£400 each); RNLI and Theodora Children's Trust (£300 each); and Dream Makers (£200).

FINANCES *Year* 2009–10 *Income* £47,039 *Grants* £47,450 *Assets* £1,090,257

TRUSTEES Geraldine Lawson; Paul Deakin; William Hodgetts.

HOW TO APPLY In writing to the correspondent.

WHO TO APPLY TO William Hodgetts, c/o Herbert Parnell, Kingsway House, 123–125 Goldsworth Road, Woking, Surrey GU21 6LR *Tel* 01483 885700

■ William Dean Countryside and Educational Trust

CC NO 1044567 **ESTABLISHED** 1995

WHERE FUNDING CAN BE GIVEN Principally Cheshire; also Derbyshire, Lancashire, Staffordshire and the Wirral.

WHO CAN BENEFIT Individuals and organisations.

WHAT IS FUNDED The trust gives grants towards enterprises in its immediate locality which promote education in natural history, ecology and the conservation of the natural environment. For example, wildlife trusts; schools for ecological and conservation projects; and parks and pleasure grounds for similar purposes.

WHAT IS NOT FUNDED Education is not funded, unless directly associated with one of the stated eligible categories.

TYPE OF GRANT Capital, core costs, feasibility studies, one-off, project, research, and start-up costs. Funding may be given for up to two years.

RANGE OF GRANTS £100–£25,000.

SAMPLE GRANTS Cheshire Wildlife Trust (£16,000); Congleton Sustainability Group Apple Project and Lower Moss Wood Animal Hospital (£2,000 each); Bromley Farm Development Trust, Game and Wildlife Conservation Trust and Lymm Angling Club (£1,000 each); and NSPCC Show Garden RHS Tatton and Victoria School & Specialist Arts College (£500 each).

FINANCES *Year* 2010 *Income* £55,902 *Grants* £52,700 *Assets* £1,295,593

TRUSTEES David Daniel, Chair; William Crawford; John Ward; David Crawford; Margaret Williamson.

HOW TO APPLY In writing to the correspondent.

WHO TO APPLY TO Mrs Brenda Bell, St Mary's Cottage, School Lane, Astbury, Congleton, Cheshire CW12 4RG *Tel* 01260 290194 *email* bellstmarys@hotmail.com

■ The Debmar Benevolent Trust

CC NO 283065 **ESTABLISHED** 1979

WHERE FUNDING CAN BE GIVEN UK and Israel.

WHO CAN BENEFIT Jewish organisations.

WHAT IS FUNDED Jewish charitable purposes.

RANGE OF GRANTS Up to £30,000, but mostly under £1,000.

SAMPLE GRANTS Previous beneficiaries included: Beis Hamedrash Hachodosh, Chasdei Belz, Chevras Mauous Lador, Gevurath Ari, Telz Talmudical Academy, Friends of Assos Chesed, Pardes Chana, ATLIB, Bobov Institutions, Ohr Akiva Institute, Tomchei Shaarei Zion, Ponivitch Institutions, Yeshiva Shaarei Zion, Beis Yoel High School, Format Charity Trust and Manchester Kollel.

FINANCES *Year* 2009–10 *Income* £5,305,991 *Grants* £1,513,545 *Assets* £4,828,486

TRUSTEES Martin Weisz; Gella Klein; Hilary Olsberg; Rosalind Halpern; Vivienne Lewin.

OTHER INFORMATION A list a grants was not provided in the trust's latest accounts.

HOW TO APPLY In writing to the correspondent.

WHO TO APPLY TO Hilary Olsberg, Trustee, c/o Haffner Hoff LLP, 3rd Floor, Manchester House, 86 Princess Street, Manchester M1 6NP *Tel* 0161 236 4107

■ The Delius Trust

CC NO 207324 **ESTABLISHED** 1935

WHERE FUNDING CAN BE GIVEN UK.

WHO CAN BENEFIT Organisations.

WHAT IS FUNDED 'The trust promotes the music of Frederick Delius and of British composers born since 1860, by giving help towards the cost of performances, publications and recordings. In addition, assistance is occasionally offered to organisations and institutions active in this field. Priority is always given to the promotion of the works of Delius, especially those that are rarely performed.'

WHAT IS NOT FUNDED The trust will not usually make retrospective grants, nor does it consider support for capital projects. Grants are not generally made for individual performance, recording or publishing projects.

RANGE OF GRANTS £1,000 to £5,000.

FINANCES *Year* 2010 *Income* £91,343 *Grants* £53,293 *Assets* £2,494,624

TRUSTEES Musicians' Benevolent Fund (Representative: William Parker); David Lloyd-Jones; Martin Williams.

HOW TO APPLY In writing for consideration by the trustees and the advisers. See the trust's website for further details. The trust meets three times a year, in February, June and October. Applications should be received early in the month before each meeting. The trust will not usually make retrospective grants. There is no standard application form.

WHO TO APPLY TO Helen Faulkner, Secretary to the Trust, 7–11 Britannia Street, London WC1X 9JS *Tel* 020 7239 9143 *email* DeliusTrust@mbf.org.uk *Website* www.delius.org.uk

■ The Dellal Foundation

CC NO 265506 **ESTABLISHED** 1973

WHERE FUNDING CAN BE GIVEN UK.

WHO CAN BENEFIT Registered charities only.

WHAT IS FUNDED Mostly 'the welfare and benefit of Jewish people'.

WHAT IS NOT FUNDED No grants to individuals.

TYPE OF GRANT One-off.

FINANCES *Year* 2009–10 *Income* £1,031 *Grants* £100,000

TRUSTEES J Dellal; E Azouz; J Azouz; G Dellal.

OTHER INFORMATION Grants usually total around £100,000 each year.

HOW TO APPLY In writing to the correspondent.

WHO TO APPLY TO The Administrator, 25 Harley Street, London W1G 9BR

■ The Delves Charitable Trust

CC NO 231860 **ESTABLISHED** 1922

WHERE FUNDING CAN BE GIVEN UK.

WHO CAN BENEFIT General approved charities.

WHAT IS FUNDED General charitable purposes. To support approved charities by annual contributions.

WHAT IS NOT FUNDED The trust does not give sponsorships or personal educational grants.

SAMPLE GRANTS British Heart Foundation (£25,000); Action Medical Research, MacMillan Cancer Support and Médecins Sans Frontières (£10,000 each); SEQUAL Trust (£8,000); Medical Foundation for the Care of Victims of Torture (£6,000); CRISIS (£5,000); Parkinson's Disease Society (£4,000); Ghana Education Project (£3,000); Big Issue Foundation (£2,500); Sussex Wildlife Trust (£1,500);

Samaritans (£1,000); and Combat Stress (£500).

FINANCES *Year* 2009–10 *Income* £206,441 *Grants* £149,000 *Assets* £6,399,832

TRUSTEES Elizabeth Breeze; John Breeze; George Breeze; Charles Breeze; William Breeze; Mark Breeze; Catharine Mackey.

HOW TO APPLY In writing to the Trust Administrator: 'concisely explaining the objective, activities, intended public benefit and anticipated achievements. Applications are accepted on a rolling basis and reviewed by the Trustees quarterly, whose decision is final. No response is made to unsuccessful unsolicited applications.'

WHO TO APPLY TO The Trust Administrator, Luminary Finance LLP, PO Box 135, Longfield, Kent DA3 8WF

■ The Demigryphon Trust

CC NO 275821   **ESTABLISHED** 1978

WHERE FUNDING CAN BE GIVEN UK, with a preference for Scotland.

WHO CAN BENEFIT Registered charities only.

WHAT IS FUNDED General charitable purposes. The trust supports a wide range of organisations and appears to have a preference for education, medical, children and Scottish organisations.

WHAT IS NOT FUNDED No grants to individuals; only registered charities are supported.

TYPE OF GRANT Mainly one-off grants.

RANGE OF GRANTS Mostly up to £5,000.

SAMPLE GRANTS Duke of Edinburgh Award Scheme (£25,000); Game and Wildlife Conservation Trust (£5,000); Houston Tampico Sister City Association (£2,000); Welsh guards Afghanistan Appeal (£1,000); Facing Africa and Chichester Cathedral Trust (£500 each); Cancer Vaccine Institute (£250); and Macmillan Cancer Support (£50).

FINANCES *Year* 2009–10 *Income* £60,325 *Grants* £39,296 *Assets* £2,562,527

TRUSTEES The Cowdray Trust Ltd.

OTHER INFORMATION In addition, payments made to pensioners amounted to £53,000 during the year.

HOW TO APPLY No grants to unsolicited applications.

WHO TO APPLY TO The Secretary, Pollen House, 10–12 Cork Street, London W1S 3LW

■ The Denman Charitable Trust

CC NO 326532   **ESTABLISHED** 1983

WHERE FUNDING CAN BE GIVEN Bristol area and South Gloucestershire.

WHO CAN BENEFIT Organisations benefiting research workers, at-risk groups, people disadvantaged by poverty, and socially isolated people.

WHAT IS FUNDED Medical research, health and welfare.

WHAT IS NOT FUNDED No grants to individuals or non charitable organisations.

TYPE OF GRANT Pump priming rather than running costs.

RANGE OF GRANTS £150–£100,000. Mostly under £5,000.

SAMPLE GRANTS Quartet Community Foundation (£100,000); St Mary Redcliffe Organ Fund (£20,000); Daisy Garland Trust (£5,000); Bristol Grammar School (£4,000); Church Housing Trust, Jessie May Trust and Grateful Society (£2,000); Bristol Children's Help Society and St Peter's Hospice (£1,000); Brightside of Life Transplant Charity (£500); Race for Life (£150).

FINANCES *Year* 2009–10 *Income* £132,500 *Grants* £154,075

TRUSTEES Arnold Denman; Dorothy Denman; David Marsh; Sue Denman; Joanna Denman.

HOW TO APPLY In writing to the correspondent.

WHO TO APPLY TO Dorothy Denman, Mrs Dorothy Denman, Steeple Group, PO Box 1881, Old Sodbury, Bristol BS37 6WS
email dorothydenman@camers.org

■ The Denton Charitable Trust

CC NO 1054546   **ESTABLISHED** 1996

WHERE FUNDING CAN BE GIVEN UK, with a preference for West Yorkshire.

WHO CAN BENEFIT Small local and UK organisations particularly interested in benefiting children and young people, older people, people with disabilities and people with cancer.

WHAT IS FUNDED Particular interest in social welfare projects rather than arts, music, environmental or historical appeals.

WHAT IS NOT FUNDED No grants for sponsorship, educational projects funded by the state, or students looking for grants to support further education, exchange visit or overseas course.

TYPE OF GRANT One-off preferred.

RANGE OF GRANTS Up to £5,000.

SAMPLE GRANTS Previous beneficiaries include: Vizion Youth Cafe and Wesley Housing Project (£1,000 each); Shipley Women's Aid, ASBAH, International Voluntary Service, New Hope Leeds, Sangat Centre and Bradford Toy Library (£500 each); and Wharfe Valley Community Project (£100).

FINANCES *Year* 2009–10 *Income* £7,341 *Grants* £8,000

TRUSTEES Fiona Wood; John Wood; Susan Wood; Timothy Wood.

OTHER INFORMATION Individuals may also be supported in cases of direct need.

HOW TO APPLY In writing to the correspondent. The trustees meet in May and November and applications should be submitted in good time.

WHO TO APPLY TO Susan Wood, Trustee, Crook Farm, Denton, Ilkley LS29 0HD *Tel* 01943 603457

■ The Denton Wilde Sapte Charitable Trust

CC NO 1041204   **ESTABLISHED** 1994

WHERE FUNDING CAN BE GIVEN Preference for the City of London and Milton Keynes.

WHO CAN BENEFIT Normally registered charities.

WHAT IS FUNDED General charitable purposes with a preference for organisations with a legal connection, such as community law centres, or children's charities, medical charities or the arts. Preference is also given to organisations which have a connection with Denton Wilde Sapte LLP or are local to the company's offices.

WHAT IS NOT FUNDED No grants to individuals. Education and scholarships will not be funded.

TYPE OF GRANT One-off and recurrent.

RANGE OF GRANTS Previously between £75 and £6,000, usually up to £2,000.

SAMPLE GRANTS DWS Social Committee (£6,000); London Legal Support Trust and WaterAid (£2,000 each); Birkbeck College and Red Lion Boys' Club (£1,500 each); St Francis Hospice and the Whitechapel Mission (£1,000 each); Macmillan Cancer Support (£750); Action for Kids, Cyclists Fighting Cancer and Human Relief (£500 each); Children with Leukaemia and

Breast Cancer Hope (£250 each); and British Heart Foundation (£100).

FINANCES *Year* 2009–10 *Income* £83,365 *Grants* £48,130 *Assets* £120,290

TRUSTEES Mark Andrews; Virginia Glastonbury; Howard Morris.

HOW TO APPLY In writing only, to the correspondent. Trustees meet quarterly.

WHO TO APPLY TO Kathy Vanderhook, Administrator, 1 One Fleet Place, London EC4M 7WS *Tel* 020 7320 6048 *email* kathy.vanderhook@ dentonwildesapte.com

■ The Earl of Derby's Charitable Trust

CC NO 515783   **ESTABLISHED** 1984

WHERE FUNDING CAN BE GIVEN Merseyside.

WHO CAN BENEFIT Local charitable organisations, predominantly within the beneficial area.

WHAT IS FUNDED Grant giving is categorised as follows: (a) age, disablement and sickness; (b) education and youth; (c) religion; (d) racing charities; (e) general.

WHAT IS NOT FUNDED No grants to individuals.

RANGE OF GRANTS £100–£1,000; generally £750.

SAMPLE GRANTS Previous beneficiaries included: The Colonel's Fund and Liverpool University Equine Appeal (£10,000 each); Royal National Institute for the Blind – Liverpool (£5,000); Cameron House School Foundation (£2,500); Local Solutions (£1,000); St Michael's Church – Huyton, Anfield Youth Club, British Racing School and Willowbrook Hospice (£750 each); and Liver Research Trust (£500).

FINANCES *Year* 2009–10 *Income* £7,281 *Grants* £40,000

TRUSTEES C J Allan.

OTHER INFORMATION The grants total is based on previous research.

HOW TO APPLY In writing to the correspondent. Trustees meet twice a year in January and July; applicants should apply two months before the meetings.

WHO TO APPLY TO Miss S Mailtland-Titterton, Knowsley, Prescot, Merseyside L34 4AF *email* charity@knowsley.com

■ The Derbyshire Churches and Chapels Preservation Trust

CC NO 1010953   **ESTABLISHED** 1992

WHERE FUNDING CAN BE GIVEN Derbyshire.

WHO CAN BENEFIT Churches and chapels of any Christian denomination.

WHAT IS FUNDED The preservation, repair and improvement of churches and chapels in Derbyshire.

SAMPLE GRANTS Previous beneficiaries included: St. John the Baptist – Dronfield and Christ Church – Burbage (£10,000 each); St. Lawrence – Shottle (£5,500); All Saints – Elton (£3,700); St. Margaret Clitherow – Duffield (£1,000); and St. Margaret – Wormhill, Holy Trinity – Dinting Vale and Holy Trinity – Middleton by Wirksworth (£500 each).

FINANCES *Year* 2009–10 *Income* £21,306

TRUSTEES Alan Bemrose, Chair; David Garnett; Canon M A B Mallender; Dr Patrick Strange; Christopher Cunliffe.

HOW TO APPLY On a form available from the correspondent. The grants panel meets quarterly.

WHO TO APPLY TO Dr Patrick Strange, 1 Greenhill, Wirksworth, Derbyshire DE4 4EN *Tel* 01629 824904

■ Derbyshire Community Foundation

CC NO 1039485   **ESTABLISHED** 1996

WHERE FUNDING CAN BE GIVEN Derbyshire and the city of Derby.

WHO CAN BENEFIT Voluntary groups and volunteers and the people they work with in Derbyshire across a wide spectrum of activity tackling disadvantage and promoting quality of life.

WHAT IS FUNDED Community groups and voluntary organisations working to tackle disadvantage and improve quality of life. Likely priority themes are as follows: supporting families; getting back to work; health and wellbeing; young people; helping groups work; and creative community.

WHAT IS NOT FUNDED The foundation's general exclusions are: profit making organisations where individual members benefit financially (legitimate social enterprises & community interest companies can receive funding but the foundation asks that you read the additional guidelines related to this type of group structure); medical equipment; animal charities; any project which promotes faith or involves the refurbishment/building of a place of worship; statutory bodies including schools, hospitals, police etc; any project which directly replaces statutory obligations; any project which promotes a political party; projects which benefit people outside of Derbyshire; retrospective funding (grants for activities which have already taken place); and sponsored events.

TYPE OF GRANT Usually one-off, though depending on the programme and donor's wishes, the trust may give more than one grant to the same group for different projects or items. Capital, core costs, feasibility studies, research, running costs, salaries and start-up costs. Funding for up to one year will be considered.

RANGE OF GRANTS Mainly between £100 to £5,000; possibly more for managed programmes depending on their criteria.

SAMPLE GRANTS SNAP (Project Fairshare) (£133,000); Pakistan Community Centre (£37,000); Fairshare Derby Community Safety Officers (£34,000); Derby Women's Centre (£29,000); First Steps Derbyshire (£24,000); Derby City Mission, Mickleover Gymnastics Club and Viva Chamber Orchestra Ltd, £10,000 each); and Austin Community Enterprise (£7,500).

FINANCES *Year* 2009–10 *Income* £1,457,064 *Grants* £1,166,634 *Assets* £6,291,371

TRUSTEES Dr Ranjit Virma; Michael Hall; Arthur Blackwood; David Coleman; Kjell Karlsen; Nick Mirfin; Matthew Montague; Clive Moesby; Lucy Palmer; David Walker; Robin Wood; Rt Revd Alastair Redfern; Janet Birkin; Louise Pinder; Simon Ingham; Helen Bishop.

HOW TO APPLY The Foundation offers several different funds, each offering funding for a maximum of twelve months and each with a specific focus or set of criteria. Please visit the foundation's website for full details of the current grant programmes and the relevant application documents. If you require any further help in deciding which fund to apply for contact the grants team on 01773 514850. Applicants should download and complete the appropriate application form from the website and send it to the correspondent with the following supporting documents: annual accounts; bank statements; group constitution; management committee form (please download this from the website); and minutes from the last management committee meeting. Applications are passed to a member of the grants team for assessment and to prepare all of the information ready to present to the award making panel. During this time, applicants are likely to be contacted by the grants team for an informal chat about their application and their group, which helps the foundation to understand the background of the project and gives the best chance of a successful bid. The decision on whether to award a grant is made by, either a panel of independent people from the local community, who meet every eight weeks, or by a panel set up by the fund-holder, who will usually meet once every three months. Please note: the grants team are entirely independent and will not make any funding recommendations to the panels. Applicants will be informed of the decision date for their application and are invited to call the grants team or check the website, to find out the decision, two days after the panel date. You will also receive the panel decision in writing within one week of the panel date. The foundation also states that it is willing to provide full, honest feedback on all decisions and is happy to discuss any outcome with applicants.

WHO TO APPLY TO The Grants Team, Foundation House, Unicorn Business Park, Wellington Street, Ripley, Derbyshire DE5 3EH *Tel* 01773 514 850 *Fax* 01773 741 410 *email* info@derbyshirecommunityfoundation.co.uk *Website* www.derbyshirecommunityfoundation.co.uk

....

■ The J N Derbyshire Trust

CC NO 231907   **ESTABLISHED** 1944
WHERE FUNDING CAN BE GIVEN Mainly Nottingham and Nottinghamshire.
WHO CAN BENEFIT Organisations with charitable status.
WHAT IS FUNDED General charitable purposes, including: the promotion of health; the development of physical improvement; the advancement of education; and the relief of poverty, distress and sickness. Local charities receive preferential consideration.
WHAT IS NOT FUNDED No grants to individuals. Costs of study are not supported.
TYPE OF GRANT Buildings, capital, core costs, project, research, recurring and running costs, salaries, and start-up costs will be considered. Funding may be given for up to three years.
RANGE OF GRANTS Up to £10,000.
SAMPLE GRANTS Stonebridge City Farm (£10,000); the Army Benevolent Fund (£7,000); Family First, the Nottinghamshire Deaf Society and Rutland House School for Parents (£5,000 each); Volunteer Centre Broxtowe (£4,000); British Red Cross, NSPCC and St John Ambulance (£3,000 each); and Action for ME, YMCA, Relate Nottinghamshire and Nottinghamshire Water Wing (£2,500 each).
FINANCES *Year* 2009–10 *Income* £165,852 *Grants* £160,575 *Assets* £4,320,192
TRUSTEES Mrs A L Carver, Chair; S J Christophers; P R Moore; Mrs L Whittle; C J George; Mrs B Lawrie.
OTHER INFORMATION In 2009–10, grants were broken down into the following categories:

Physical health and disability	£29,000
Youth organisations	£29,000
Miscellaneous	£29,000
General medical and ambulance	£23,000
Protection and welfare of women and children	£20,000
Relief of Poverty	£18,000
Old age	£12,000
Educational	£2,000

HOW TO APPLY On a form available from the correspondent. Applications can be made at any time but trustees usually only meet to consider them twice a year in March and September. Details of the project are required. A reply is only given to unsuccessful applicants if they enclose an sae.
WHO TO APPLY TO David Parish, Secretary, The Poynt, 45 Wollaton Street, Nottingham NG1 5FW *Tel* 0115 948 9589 *email* david.parish@tenongroup.com

....

■ Devon Community Foundation

CC NO 1057923   **ESTABLISHED** 1996
WHERE FUNDING CAN BE GIVEN Devon.
WHO CAN BENEFIT Voluntary and community groups.
WHAT IS FUNDED Support primarily for voluntary and community organisations, particularly those working to relieve the effects of poverty and disadvantage.
WHAT IS NOT FUNDED The foundation does not fund: more than one application to the same fund in a 12 month period; groups we have funded before but have not returned an evaluation form when requested; no major building works associated costs; organisations that are regional or national charities (unless locally led and run); organisations that have substantial unrestricted funds; activities that promote political or religious beliefs (groups that are based in a religious building can apply, providing the activity / project is open to all people in the community); statutory bodies e.g. schools/colleges, local councils. However, 'Friends of' or Parents' Associations may be eligible to apply; organisations or activities that primarily support animals or plants; contributions to a large project where the amount applied for is less than one fifth (20%) of the total project cost; retrospective funding – this includes activities that have already taken place or repayment of money that you have already spent; consultancy fees or feasibility studies; sponsorship and/or fundraising events; contributions to an endowment; minibuses or other vehicle purchases; activities or organisations that are for personal profit or are commercial; grants for IT and associated equipment will be limited to no more than £400; overseas travel; never 100% of the project costs; no funding individuals (except from the Devonian Fund). Individual programmes may have further eligibility criteria. Please check the website or contact the foundation directly to confirm that your organisation is eligible to apply.
TYPE OF GRANT Predominantly one-off small grants for projects. Running costs and start-up costs will be considered. Funding may be given for up to one year, and very occasionally for two years.
RANGE OF GRANTS £50–£10,000.
SAMPLE GRANTS Accessible Coach Holidays, Appledore Hall Trust, Exeter Shilhay Community Limited, Exeter YMCA, Kingsbridge Playspaces Group, Refugee Support Group, Swilly Kids Club – Youth Matters and Timeout for All (£5,000 each); Turntable Furniture (£3,500); 2nd Bideford Scout Group, Children's Summer Club, Merry Go Round Toy & Leisure Library, St Budeaux Mental Health Community Group and

Alphabetical register of grant making charitable trusts

Torbay Youth Sailing Trust (£3,000 each); Combe Martin Senior Citizens, Cullompton Family Centre, Get Changed Theatre Company, Kenn Cricket Club, Ladysmith Community Action Team and Okehampton & District Duke of Edinburgh (£2,000 each); and Exeter Blue Anchor Majorettes, Health and Local Food for Families, Key Stop Luncheon Club, Tamerton Foliot Football Club and Welcombe Children's Group (£1,000 each).

FINANCES Year 2009–10 Income £2,125,229 Grants £807,055 Assets £2,140,903

TRUSTEES David Stevens; Dr Katherine Gurney; Steve Hindley; Mike Bull; Mark Haskell; Arthur Ainslie; David Searle; Peter Keech; John Sunderland; John Glasby; Caroline Marks; Nigel Arnold.

OTHER INFORMATION There were various grants under £1,000 but these were not listed in the accounts.

HOW TO APPLY The foundation's website has details of the grant schemes currently being administered and how to apply.

WHO TO APPLY TO Martha Wilkinson, The Factory, Leat Street, Tiverton, Devon EX16 5LL Tel 01884 235887 Fax 01884 243824 email grants@devoncf.com Website www.devoncf.com

----

■ The Devon Educational Trust

CC NO 220921　　**ESTABLISHED** 1988
WHERE FUNDING CAN BE GIVEN Devon.
WHO CAN BENEFIT Primarily individuals living in Devon, or whose parents live in Devon. Individuals, and organisations benefiting children, young adults and students.
WHAT IS FUNDED The education of people under the age of 25.
WHAT IS NOT FUNDED No grants for school fees and help is not normally given to people starting a second or higher degree.
RANGE OF GRANTS Up to £4,000.
SAMPLE GRANTS Sir Francis Chichester Trust (£4,100); Tiverton Market Centre, Tiverton Adventure Play Association and Little Angels (St Brannocks) Parent & Toddler Group (£500 each); Devon Portage Association (£250); Double Elephant Print (£200).
FINANCES Year 2010 Income £35,770 Grants £30,984 Assets £1,002,203
TRUSTEES Prof. W J Forsythe, Chair; Mrs J A E Cook; H B Evans; Dr C M Gillet; F J Rosamond; B W Wills-Pope; D R Wakinshaw; Mrs P Freeman.
OTHER INFORMATION In 2010, grants were made to 112 individuals totalling £25,000.
HOW TO APPLY In writing to the correspondent for an application form. Two referees will be approached for letters of support for each applicant. The trustees meet three times a year in March, July and November with a closing date four weeks before each meeting.
WHO TO APPLY TO The Clerk, PO Box 86, Teignmouth TQ14 8ZT email jc.matthews@tiscali.co.uk

----

■ The Devon Historic Churches Trust

CC NO 265594　　**ESTABLISHED** 1973
WHERE FUNDING CAN BE GIVEN Devon and diocese of Exeter.
WHO CAN BENEFIT Churches and chapels.
WHAT IS FUNDED The trust gives grants/loans for 'the preservation, repair, maintenance,

improvement and upkeep of churches in the County of Devon and the diocese of Exeter.'
WHAT IS NOT FUNDED Redundant churches/chapels, bells, plumbing, disabled facilities and routine maintenance.
TYPE OF GRANT Grants and loans.
RANGE OF GRANTS Around £100–£5,000.
SAMPLE GRANTS Westleigh (£5,000); Barnstaple – Holy Trinity (£4,000); Landkey (£3,500); Langtree (£3,000); Tipton St John (£2,000); Germansweek (£1,500); St Giles on the Heath (£1,000); Exmouth – Christchurch (£750); Marldon (£500); East Budleigh (£250); and North Tawton (£100).
FINANCES Year 2009–10 Income £124,861 Grants £69,500 Assets £1,097,447
TRUSTEES Lady Anne Boles, Chair; Earl of Devon; Nicholas Maxwell-Lawford; Carol Plumstead; Lt Cdr Christopher Tuke; Lt Col James Michie; Rosemary Howell; Judith Kauntze; John Malleson; Philip Tuckett; Penelope Dudgeon; Christopher Hewetson; Revd Dr David Keep; Lt Col Charles Rich; Mr J Mills.
HOW TO APPLY In writing to the correspondent. The trustees meet quarterly to receive reports from officers and committees and to consider grant applications.
WHO TO APPLY TO John Malleson, Clifford Lodge, Drewsteignton, Exeter EX6 6QE Tel 01647 24104 email contact@devonhistoricchurches.co.uk Website www.devonhistoricchurches.co.uk

----

■ The Duke of Devonshire's Charitable Trust

CC NO 213519　　**ESTABLISHED** 1949
WHERE FUNDING CAN BE GIVEN UK.
WHO CAN BENEFIT Registered charities only.
WHAT IS FUNDED General charitable purposes.
WHAT IS NOT FUNDED Grants are only given to registered charities and not to individuals.
RANGE OF GRANTS Typically up to £25,000.
SAMPLE GRANTS Chatsworth House Trust (£2 million); Devonshire Educational Trust (£25,000); Arkwright Society (£10,000); Fields in Trust and Bradford Diocesan (£7,000 each); Staveley Town Council (£5,500); Mercian Regimental Fund and Age UK (£4,000 each); Derbyshire Dales District Council (£2,500); RAF Benevolent Fund and Roche Court Educational Trust (£2,000 each); and the Countryside Alliance Foundation and the Meningitis Trust (£1,000 each).
FINANCES Year 2010–11 Income £235,567 Grants £2,203,087 Assets £11,306,670
TRUSTEES Duke of Devonshire; Duchess of Devonshire; Earl of Burlington; Sir Richard Beckett.
HOW TO APPLY In writing to the correspondent.
WHO TO APPLY TO The Trustees, Chatsworth, Bakewell, Derbyshire DE45 1PP

■ The Sandy Dewhirst Charitable Trust

CC NO 279161　　**ESTABLISHED** 1979
WHERE FUNDING CAN BE GIVEN UK, with a strong preference for East and North Yorkshire.
WHO CAN BENEFIT Charitable organisations and individuals connected with I J Dewhirst Holdings Limited.
WHAT IS FUNDED General and relief-in-need.
SAMPLE GRANTS Bramcote School (£50,000); Stroke Association (£20,000); All Saints Church, Driffield (£16,000); Royal British Legion (Driffield

Does the trust you have chosen match your needs? Haphazard applications waste postage and time

Branch); Help for Heroes; Driffield Boxing and Fitness Club (£1,000 each); and All Saints Church Kilham; Filey Sea Cadets TS Unseen and St Catherine's Hospice (£500 each).

FINANCES *Year* 2009 *Income* £54,796 *Grants* £123,000 *Assets* £1,535,707

TRUSTEES Timothy Dewhirst; Paul Howell.

HOW TO APPLY The trust does not accept unsolicited applications.

WHO TO APPLY TO The Secretary, Addleshaw Goddard LLP, Sovereign House, Sovereign Street, Leeds LS1 1HG

■ The Laduma Dhamecha Charitable Trust

CC NO 328678   **ESTABLISHED** 1990

WHERE FUNDING CAN BE GIVEN UK and overseas.

WHO CAN BENEFIT Organisations only.

WHAT IS FUNDED General charitable purposes including the relief of sickness and education in rural areas.

FINANCES *Year* 2009–10 *Income* £292,624 *Grants* £375,495 *Assets* £1,687,559

TRUSTEES K R Dhamecha; S R Dhamecha; P K Dhamecha.

HOW TO APPLY In writing to the correspondent.

WHO TO APPLY TO Pradip Dhamecha, Trustee, 2 Hathaway Close, Stanmore, Middlesex HA7 3NR

■ Diabetes UK

CC NO 215199   **ESTABLISHED** 1934

WHERE FUNDING CAN BE GIVEN UK.

WHO CAN BENEFIT Organisations which benefit people with diabetes.

WHAT IS FUNDED To promote and fund research into the causes and effects of diabetes, and the treatment and alleviation of the effects of diabetes to minimise the potential serious complications that can arise.

TYPE OF GRANT Equipment, fellowships, research grants, small grants, and studentships will be considered.

RANGE OF GRANTS £5,000–£40,000.

SAMPLE GRANTS Grants to institutions were broken down as follows: cause and prevention – £2.8 million; care and treatment – £3.5 million; cure – £78,000.

FINANCES *Year* 2010 *Income* £29,334,000 *Grants* £6,838,000 *Assets* £11,611,000

TRUSTEES Rekha Wadhwani; David McCance; John Grumitt; Noah Franklin; Dr Kamila Hawthorne; Julian Baust; Gill Fine; Frank Moxon; Susan Browell; Gerard Tosh; Prof. Sir George Alberti; Gavin Cookman.

HOW TO APPLY Potential applicants are first advised to read the 'Diabetes UK's research strategy' and the 'General guide to applicants', both available on the trust's website. Further information on the application process and deadlines for each specific scheme is also available on the website or by contacting the trust directly.

WHO TO APPLY TO Richard Elliott, 10 Parkway, London NW1 7AA *Tel* 020 7424 1000 *Fax* 020 7424 1001 *email* info@diabetes.org.uk *Website* www.diabetes.org.uk

■ Alan and Sheila Diamond Charitable Trust

CC NO 274312   **ESTABLISHED** 1977

WHERE FUNDING CAN BE GIVEN UK.

WHO CAN BENEFIT Registered charities only, particularly Jewish charities.

WHAT IS FUNDED Jewish causes and general charitable purposes.

WHAT IS NOT FUNDED No grants to individuals.

SAMPLE GRANTS British School of Osteopathy (£10,000); Norwood (£7,000); Anglo Israel Association (£4,900); Community Security Trust (£4,500); British WIZO (£3,400); Jewish Museum and Sidney Sussex College (£2,500 each); and Central Synagogue (£2,200).

FINANCES *Year* 2009–10 *Income* £53,307 *Grants* £43,934 *Assets* £1,451,533

TRUSTEES Alan Diamond, Chair; Sheila Diamond; Jonathan Kropman; Kate Goldberg.

HOW TO APPLY The trust states that it will not consider unsolicited applications. No preliminary telephone calls. There are no regular trustees' meetings. The trustees frequently decide how the funds should be allocated. The trustees have their own guidelines, which are not published.

WHO TO APPLY TO The Trustees, Mazars LLP, 8 New Fields, 2 Stinsford Road, Nuffield, Poole, Dorset BH17 0NF *Tel* 01202 680777

■ David and Rose Diamond Trust

CC NO 1135525   **ESTABLISHED** 2010

WHERE FUNDING CAN BE GIVEN Undefined. In practice throughout England.

WHO CAN BENEFIT Jewish organisations and individuals.

WHAT IS FUNDED The advancement of the orthodox Jewish faith; Jewish religious education; the relief of poverty amongst members of the Jewish faith and general charitable purposes.

TRUSTEES Hannah Mansoor; Aryel Mansoor; Reverend Eliyahu Shalom.

OTHER INFORMATION Hannah Mansoor is also a trustee of the JMC Trust Fund (Charity Commission no. 1054076).

HOW TO APPLY In writing to the correspondent.

WHO TO APPLY TO Mrs Hannah Mansoor, Trustee, 1 Beechwood Avenue, London N3 3AU *email* shlumi@ntlworld.com

■ The Dibden Allotments Fund

CC NO 255778   **ESTABLISHED** 1995

WHERE FUNDING CAN BE GIVEN Hythe, Fawley and Marchwood.

WHO CAN BENEFIT Grants can be made to individuals as well as organisations, including students and unemployed people.

WHAT IS FUNDED To relieve need, hardship or distress, and to invest in the community's future. Grants are awarded to individuals in need, to voluntary and charitable organisations, and to schemes benefiting children, particularly under-fives, older people and young people.

WHAT IS NOT FUNDED Scholarships to 'Schools of Excellence', such as those for the performing arts.

RANGE OF GRANTS Up to £21,000.

SAMPLE GRANTS Handy Trust (£21,000); Rethink – Forresters respite care (£10,000); Indigo – Hampshire (£6,000); Oakhaven Hospice (£3,500); St John's PCC (£2,500); Blackfield Primary School (£2,000); Planet Kids (£1,000); and Young at Heart Club (£500).

FINANCES *Year* 2009–10 *Income* £317,558 *Grants* £243,077 *Assets* £7,765,888

TRUSTEES Rosemary Dash; Malcolm Fidler; Chris Harrison; Mike Harvey (Vice Chair); Pat Hedges; Maureen McLean; Peter Parrott (Chair); Judy Saxby and Jill Tomlin.

OTHER INFORMATION £170,000 was given to individuals for general and educational purposes.

HOW TO APPLY In writing to the correspondent who will supply guidelines and application forms. A third party, such as social services, teachers, and so on, must support applications from individuals.

WHO TO APPLY TO Barrie Smallcalder, Clerk, Dibden Allotments Fund, 7 Drummond Court, Prospect Place, Hythe, Hampshire SO45 6HD *Tel* 023 8084 1305 *Fax* 023 8084 1305 *email* dibdenallotments@btconnect.com

■ The Gillian Dickinson Trust

CC NO 1094362   **ESTABLISHED** 2002

WHERE FUNDING CAN BE GIVEN County Durham, Northumberland and Tyne and Wear.

WHO CAN BENEFIT Registered charities, museums, arts and theatre groups.

WHAT IS FUNDED Arts and general charitable purposes.

RANGE OF GRANTS Up to £25,000.

SAMPLE GRANTS The Samling Foundation (£25,000); Pianoforte North Foundation (£19,000); Live Theatre (£15,000); Durham Army Cadets Force and Northern Stage (£5,000 each); Allendale Create Artists CIC (£3,500); Hexham Book Festival (£3,100); and Northumbrian Association (£1,500).

FINANCES *Year* 2009–10 *Income* £63,790 *Grants* £57,513 *Assets* £2,234,754

TRUSTEES Alexander Dickinson; Piers Dickinson; Adrian Gifford; James Ramsbotham.

HOW TO APPLY In writing to the correspondent.

WHO TO APPLY TO Patrick Evans, St Ann's Wharf, 112 Quayside, Newcastle Upon Tyne NE1 3DX *Tel* 0191 279 9628 *Fax* 0191 279 9100

■ The Dickon Trust

CC NO 327202   **ESTABLISHED** 1986

WHERE FUNDING CAN BE GIVEN North East England and Scotland.

WHO CAN BENEFIT Registered charities.

WHAT IS FUNDED General charitable purposes.

WHAT IS NOT FUNDED No support for individuals, unregistered charities or churches.

TYPE OF GRANT One-off.

RANGE OF GRANTS £500–£2,000.

SAMPLE GRANTS Holy Island Village Hall and Hopscotch Children's Charity (£2,000 each); Age Concern Gateshead, Blyth Young People's Centre LTD, Disability North, React, Skill Force, the Arkwright Scholarship Trust, St Oswald's Hospice and the Shirlie Project (£1,000 each).

FINANCES *Year* 2009–10 *Income* £53,670 *Grants* £48,000 *Assets* £1,290,932

TRUSTEES Mrs D L Barrett; Major-General R V Brims; R Y Barrett; M L Robson; A Copeman.

HOW TO APPLY Applications can be made online at the trust's website. The trustees meet twice a year in summer and winter to consider appeals. Any applications received by the end of October will be considered at the winter meeting and any applications made after that time, up to the end of May, will be considered at the summer meeting.

WHO TO APPLY TO Helen Tavroges, Dickinson Dees, St Anne's Wharf, 112 Quayside, Newcastle NE99 1SB *Tel* 0191 279 9698 *Website* www. dickontrust.org.uk

■ The Digbeth Trust

CC NO 517343   **ESTABLISHED** 1984

WHERE FUNDING CAN BE GIVEN West Midlands, principally Birmingham.

WHO CAN BENEFIT Smaller local, new and emerging voluntary and community groups, particularly those addressing exclusion and disadvantage.

WHAT IS FUNDED The trust manages a number of grant programmes that are generally targeted by area or theme, or both. See its website for current schemes.

WHAT IS NOT FUNDED General appeals, capital core costs, medical research, project running costs and grants for individuals.

TYPE OF GRANT One-off grants to enable groups to access specialist advice and services.

SAMPLE GRANTS the Healthy Lifestyles Schools Grants Programme (£87,000); the Mental Health Grants Programme (£83,000); Capacity Builders – Improving Reach (£71,500) and Capacity Builders – Modernisation (£22,000).

FINANCES *Year* 2009–10 *Income* £464,207 *Grants* £331,945 *Assets* £55,515

TRUSTEES Eddie Currall, Chair; Christopher Burrows; David Williams-Masinda; Graham Mitchell; Daina Anderson; Ben Cunningham; Mark Lynes and Mark Peters.

HOW TO APPLY The trust welcomes direct contact with groups. Application forms and guidance notes are available for the programmes it manages (this changes from time to time). Development worker support is offered to eligible groups.

WHO TO APPLY TO Tony Clabby, Secretary, Digbeth Trust Ltd, Unit F1 The Arch 48–52, Floodgate Street, Birmingham B5 5SL *Tel* 0121 753 0706 *Fax* 0121 248 3323 *email* info@ digbethtrust.org.uk *Website* www.digbethtrust. org.uk

■ The Dinwoodie Settlement

CC NO 255495   **ESTABLISHED** 1968

WHERE FUNDING CAN BE GIVEN UK.

WHO CAN BENEFIT Organisations benefiting academics and postgraduate research workers.

WHAT IS FUNDED Postgraduate medical education centres (PMCs) and research fellowships for suitably qualified medical practitioners of registrar status in general medicine or general surgery.

WHAT IS NOT FUNDED Anything falling outside the main areas of work referred to above. The trustees do not expect to fund consumable or equipment costs or relieve the NHS of its financial responsibilities.

TYPE OF GRANT Building projects will be considered. The trust's funds can be committed for three years when supporting major projects.

RANGE OF GRANTS Maximum of £1 million towards no more than one postgraduate medical centre project in an area. No more than the salary of two research workers in any one year.

SAMPLE GRANTS Kings College London (£750,000); Portsmouth Hospital (£259,000); Southport and Ormskirk Hospital (£150,000); and Imperial College London (£43,000).

FINANCES *Year* 2009–10 *Income* £323,148 *Grants* £1,202,487 *Assets* £3,498,204

TRUSTEES William A Fairbairn; Dr John M Fowler; Miss Christian Webster; Rodney B N Fisher; John A Gibson.

OTHER INFORMATION Annual figures for grants versus income may vary substantially as payments towards building costs of each project usually absorb more than one year's available income.

HOW TO APPLY The trustees state they are proactive rather than reactive in their grant-giving. Negotiating for new PMCs and monitoring their construction invariably takes a number of years.

WHO TO APPLY TO The Clerk to the Trustees, c/o Thomas Eggar, The Corn Exchange, Baffins Lane, Chichester, West Sussex PO19 1GK

■ Disability Aid Fund (The Roger and Jean Jefcoate Trust)

CC NO 1096211   **ESTABLISHED** 2002

WHERE FUNDING CAN BE GIVEN UK.

WHO CAN BENEFIT People with physical, mental or multiple disabilities or hearing or visual impairment.

WHAT IS FUNDED The following statement was taken from the trust's 2009–10 accounts and explains its grantmaking strategy: 'We support a few carefully selected local, regional and small national healthcare and disability charities for older people in Buckinghamshire and Milton Keynes and adjacent counties, especially charities which promote health and wellbeing through information, advice and practical help like developing or providing special needs technology. We look for charities showing strong support from service users and volunteers and only modest expenditure on fundraising and administration. We also provide a nationwide funding advice service for severely disabled individuals who seek special needs technology like an adapted computer for their writing or communication needs or their voluntary work. Occasionally we might also fund such equipment, but we prefer to do so through specialist charities like AbilityNet (0800 269545) which provides good independent advice on the most suitable equipment and how to get it.'

TYPE OF GRANT Building and refurbishment, equipment, training and general costs.

RANGE OF GRANTS £1,000–£20,000.

SAMPLE GRANTS Demand – Watford – for the launch of the Yorkshire premises appeal (£20,000); L'Arche Community – Bognor – to refurbish the Fieldway supported home (£6,000); Bath Institute of Medical Engineering – for general needs and St John Ambulance – improvement for wheelchair visitors (£5,000 each); MS Therapy Centre – Bristol – for electrically adjustable beds and Macular Disease Society – Andover – for a training course at Chilton (£3,000 each); Advocacy Project – London – for general needs and Help the Hospices – London – for the Drapers' company appeal (£2,000 each); and Exeter Gateway Centre – for allotment tools for people with mental disabilities (£1,000).

FINANCES *Year* 2009–10 *Income* £160,890 *Grants* £85,816 *Assets* £3,069,595

TRUSTEES Vivien Dinning, Chair; Roger Jefcoate; Valerie Henchoz; Rosemary McCloskey; Carol Wemyss.

OTHER INFORMATION The grant total in 2009–10 included £11,816 given in 11 grants to individuals.

HOW TO APPLY In writing to the correspondent.

WHO TO APPLY TO Roger Jefcoate, Trustee, 2 Swanbourne Road, Mursley, Milton Keynes MK17 0JA

■ Dischma Charitable Trust

CC NO 1077501   **ESTABLISHED** 1999

WHERE FUNDING CAN BE GIVEN Worldwide, with a strong preference for London and the south east of England.

WHO CAN BENEFIT Charitable organisations.

WHAT IS FUNDED General charitable purposes, with a preference for education, arts and culture, conservation and human and animal welfare.

WHAT IS NOT FUNDED Medical research charities.

RANGE OF GRANTS £500–£5,000.

SAMPLE GRANTS Alton College and Treloar Trust (£5,000 each); Epic Arts and International Animal Rescue (£4,000 each); Compassion in World Farming (£3,500); Listening Books, Sign Health and Wild Things (£3,000 each); Bear Baiting in Pakistan (£2,500); Action Against Hunger, Almshouse Association, ASBAH, Chernobyl Children's Project, Fields in Trust, Grasslands Trust and Marine Stewardship Council (£2,000 each); Albert Kennedy Trust, Child to Child Trust, Get Connected, Gorilla Organisation and WWF (£1,500 each); and The 999 Club (£500).

FINANCES *Year* 2010 *Income* £62,420 *Grants* £117,100 *Assets* £4,850,009

TRUSTEES Simon Robertson; Edward Robertson; Lorna Robertson Timmis; Virginia Robertson; Robertson; Arabella Brooke.

HOW TO APPLY The trustees meet half-yearly to review applications for funding. Only successful applicants are notified of the trustees' decision. Certain charities are supported annually, although no commitment is given.

WHO TO APPLY TO Linda Cousins, The Secretary, Rathbone Trust Company Ltd, c/o 159 New Bond Street, London W15 2UD *Tel* 020 7399 0820 *email* linda.cousins@rathbones.com

■ The Djanogly Foundation

CC NO 280500   **ESTABLISHED** 1980

WHERE FUNDING CAN BE GIVEN Worldwide.

WHO CAN BENEFIT Usually registered charities.

WHAT IS FUNDED Developments in medicine, education, social welfare and the arts. Welfare of older and younger people. Jewish charities.

RANGE OF GRANTS £15–£250,000.

SAMPLE GRANTS Victoria & Albert Museum (£258,500); Nottingham City Academy (£216,500); University of Nottingham (£201,500); and the Jerusalem Foundation (£201,000); Royal Collections Trust and the British Museums Development Trust (£25,000 each); Nottingham City Council (£18,500); Jewish Care (£13,500); Burlington Magazine Foundation (£5,000); Community Security Trust (£2,000); and the Chicken Shed Theatre Company (£1,000).

FINANCES *Year* 2009–10 *Income* £205,850 *Grants* £1,060,694 *Assets* £9,623,768

TRUSTEES Sir Harry Djanogly; Michael S Djanogly; Lady Carol Djanogly.

HOW TO APPLY In writing to the correspondent.

WHO TO APPLY TO Christopher Sills, Secretary, 3 Angel Court, London SW1Y 6QF *Tel* 020 7930 9845

■ The DLM Charitable Trust

cc no 328520   **established** 1990

where funding can be given UK, especially the Oxford area.

who can benefit Organisations benefiting: children; young adults; older people; medical professionals, nurses and doctors; and people with head and other injuries, heart disease or blindness.

what is funded Charities operating in Oxford and the surrounding areas, particularly charities working in the fields of: arts, culture and recreation; religious buildings; self-help groups; the conservation of historic buildings; memorials; monuments and waterways; schools; community centres and village halls; parks; various community services and other charitable purposes.

what is not funded No grants to individuals.

type of grant Feasibility studies, one-off, research, recurring costs, running costs and start-up costs. Funding of up to three years will be considered.

finances *Year* 2009–10 *Income* £131,594 *Grants* £99,000 *Assets* £5,047,085

trustees Dr E A de la Mare; Mrs P Sawyer; J A Cloke; Miss J E Sawyer.

how to apply In writing to the correspondent. Trustees meet in February, July and November to consider applications.

who to apply to J A Cloke, Trustee, c/o Cloke and Co, 475 Salisbury House, London WAll, London EC2M 5QQ *Tel* 020 7638 8992

■ The DM Charitable Trust

cc no 1110419   **established** 2005

where funding can be given UK and Israel.

who can benefit Jewish registered charities.

what is funded Social welfare and education.

finances *Year* 2009–10 *Income* £6,647,922 *Grants* £1,960,522 *Assets* £5,905,620

trustees Stephen J Goldberg, Chair; David Cohen; Patrice Klein.

other information Previous attempts to obtain a list of grants have been unsuccessful.

how to apply In writing to the correspondent.

who to apply to Stephen J Goldberg, Trustee, Ground Floor, Sutherland House, 70–78 West Hendon Broadway, London NW9 7BT *Tel* 020 8457 3258

■ Louise Dobson Charitable Trust

cc no 1022659   **established** 1986

where funding can be given UK, with some preference for West Sussex.

who can benefit Children, people with mental disabilities, religious groups and general poverty relief.

what is funded General charitable purposes with some preference for causes local to the trust.

sample grants Previous beneficiaries have included: £1,000 to CAFOD; £700 to Worth Abbey Lay Community; £650 to HCPT; £500 to Worth Abbey Parish; £450 to A and B Lourdes Fund; £350 to Inside Trust; £300 St Catherine's Hospice; £200 each to Catherington School, Catenian Association and SASBA.

finances *Year* 2010–11 *Income* £4,960 *Grants* £5,000

trustees Christopher Dobson, Chair; Stephen Leach.

how to apply In writing to the correspondent.

who to apply to C N Y Dobson, Sopers Ride, Selsfield Road, Turners Hill, Crawley, West Sussex RH10 4PP *Tel* 01342 715345

■ The Derek and Eileen Dodgson Foundation

cc no 1018776   **established** 1993

where funding can be given In practice, Brighton and Hove.

who can benefit Individuals and organisations.

what is funded Welfare of older people.

sample grants No details of grant beneficiaries were available.

finances *Year* 2009–10 *Income* £126,480 *Grants* £77,444 *Assets* £1,960,199

trustees C C K Butler, Chair; P E Goldsmith; R Prater; E Squires.

how to apply In writing to the correspondent. Trustees meet quarterly, or more frequently if necessary to assess grant applications.

who to apply to Ian W Dodd, Clerk, 8 Locks Hill, Portslade, Brighton and Hove, East Sussex BN41 2LB *Tel* 01273 419802 *email* ianw. dodd@ntlworld.com

■ The Dollond Charitable Trust

cc no 293459   **established** 1986

where funding can be given UK and Israel.

who can benefit Jewish organisations.

what is funded Jewish communities; general charitable purposes.

type of grant One-off and recurrent.

range of grants Typically £5,000–£10,000.

sample grants A list of beneficiaries was not available, although grants were broken down as follows: education/training (£1.34 million); religious education (£666,000); relief of poverty (£289,500); medical/health/sickness (£162,000); disability (£67,500); religious activities (£46,000); and general charitable purposes (£32,000).

finances *Year* 2009–10 *Income* £4,165,071 *Grants* £2,606,750 *Assets* £38,118,168

trustees Adrian Dollond; Jeffery Milston; Mellisa Dollond; Brian Dollond; Rina Dollond.

other information 'Although the constitution of the charity is broadly based, the trustees have adopted a policy of principally assisting the Jewish communities in Britain and Israel. The trustees will remain focussed on [these] main objectives – in addition, the trustees are considering a number of infrastructure (building) projects. Research is in progress and discussions are on-going with the relevant institutions.'

how to apply In writing to the correspondent.

who to apply to Jeffery Milston, Trustee, c/o FMCB, Hathaway House, Popes Drive, Finchley, London N3 1QF *Tel* 020 8346 6446 *email* gwz@fmcb.co.uk

■ Domepride Ltd

cc no 289426   **established** 1983

where funding can be given UK and overseas.

who can benefit To benefit Jewish people, at risk groups, and people who are disadvantaged by poverty or socially isolated.

what is funded Jewish causes, especially those in the welfare field. General charitable purposes.

range of grants About £500– £5,000.

SAMPLE GRANTS Previous beneficiaries include: Belz, Agudas Israel Housing Association, Chasdei Yoel, Asos Chesed, Bnos Yisroel Schools, Merkaz Torah Vochesed, Nitra and Ahavas Chesed.

FINANCES *Year* 2009–10 *Income* £23,753 *Grants* £30,000

TRUSTEES J Padwa; G Padwa; A J Cohen; E Padwa.

OTHER INFORMATION No grants list was available from the latest accounts.

HOW TO APPLY In writing to the correspondent.

WHO TO APPLY TO The Trustees, c/o 3rd Floor, Manchester House, 86 Princess Street, Manchester M1 6NG

■ The Dorcas Trust

CC NO 275494   **ESTABLISHED** 1978

WHERE FUNDING CAN BE GIVEN UK.

WHO CAN BENEFIT Designated charities specified by the trustees, benefiting children, young adults, students, Christians, and people disadvantaged by poverty.

WHAT IS FUNDED Advancement of the Christian religion, relief of poverty and advancement of education.

SAMPLE GRANTS Previous beneficiaries have included: Dorcas Developments Limited (£103,000); Navigators (£15,000), Newmarket Day Centre (£14,000), World Vision (£5,000), Mildmay Mission (£3,000), Integra (£2,000), Shaftesbury Society and Moorlands Bible College (£1,000 each); Send a Cow (£500), Chernobyl Children's Lifeline (£100) and RNIB (£50).

FINANCES *Year* 2009–10 *Income* £40,000 *Grants* £26,000 *Assets* £1,500,000

TRUSTEES J C L Broad; J D Broad; P L Butler.

OTHER INFORMATION The trustees will also consider making loans to organisations and individuals

HOW TO APPLY In writing to the correspondent, although the trust stated that applications cannot be considered as funds are already committed.

WHO TO APPLY TO I Taylor, Port of Liverpool Building, Pier Head, Liverpool L3 1NW *Tel* 0151 236 6666

■ The Dorema Charitable Trust

CC NO 287001   **ESTABLISHED** 1983

WHERE FUNDING CAN BE GIVEN UK.

WHO CAN BENEFIT Organisations benefiting children, young adults, older people, at-risk groups and socially isolated people.

WHAT IS FUNDED Medicine, health, welfare, education and religion.

TYPE OF GRANT One off and recurrent.

SAMPLE GRANTS A list of beneficiaries was not available.

FINANCES *Year* 2009–10 *Income* £1,870 *Grants* £23,000

TRUSTEES D S M Nussbaum; Mrs K M Nussbaum; S Murray-Williams.

HOW TO APPLY The trust strongly stated that unsolicited applications are not considered, describing such appeals as a waste of charitable resources.

WHO TO APPLY TO D S M Nussbaum, Trustee, 4 Church Grove, Amersham, Buckinghamshire HP6 6SH

■ Dorfred Charitable Trust

CC NO 1092347   **ESTABLISHED** 2001

WHERE FUNDING CAN BE GIVEN Worldwide.

WHO CAN BENEFIT Small UK-registered charities working in Africa, Asia and South America.

WHAT IS FUNDED Projects working to alleviate the many problems of peoples in 'poorer' countries and emergency aid in response to, for example, natural disasters or war.

TYPE OF GRANT Mainly small one-off grants.

RANGE OF GRANTS Up to £2,000.

SAMPLE GRANTS Mercury Corp (£2,000); and Health Unlimited, Lepra and CIWI (£1,500 each).

FINANCES *Year* 2009–10 *Income* £37,050 *Grants* £27,674 *Assets* £403,230

TRUSTEES Roger E Dean; Patricia J Fulker; Philip G Gardam; Revd Father Wood.

HOW TO APPLY In writing to the correspondent.

WHO TO APPLY TO Philip Gardam, Trustee, 9 Bailey Mews, Auckland Road, Cambridge CB5 8DR *Tel* 01233 510914 *email* info@dorfred-trust.org.uk *Website* www.dorfred-trust.org.uk

■ The Dorset Historic Churches Trust

CC NO 282790   **ESTABLISHED** 1960

WHERE FUNDING CAN BE GIVEN Dorset.

WHO CAN BENEFIT Churches.

WHAT IS FUNDED 'Grants or Loans towards the cost of restoring Dorset Church buildings are made in order to maintain the structure, and on some occasions other items of significant historical and architectural interest, in good repair.'

WHAT IS NOT FUNDED 'Grants or Loans will normally NOT be made for works of modernization, alteration, improvement, or demolition except where a prerequisite to make the building more suitable for community use or where rebuilding is necessary in cases of structural instability.'

TYPE OF GRANT One-off grants, mainly, but also interest-free loans for up to four years will be considered.

RANGE OF GRANTS Governed by funds available and by need.

SAMPLE GRANTS Catistock (£12,500); Christchurch Priory (£10,000); Stourton Caundle (£5,000); Shipton Gorge (£2,000) and Warmwell (£500).

FINANCES *Year* 2010 *Income* £95,265 *Grants* £78,500 *Assets* £475,847

TRUSTEES R F Adeney; E M Ashmead; B W DeMorgan; The Venerable P Evans; P F E Hodgkins; P F Moule; S R V Pomeroy; J B Sabben-Clare; D W Smith; Captain N T L L Thimbleby; A G Yeatman.

HOW TO APPLY In writing to the correspondent. Forms can be downloaded from the website.

WHO TO APPLY TO P F Moule, Hon. Secretary, Ryall's Ground, Yetminster, Sherborne, Dorset DT9 6LL *email* pandfmoule@yahoo.co.uk *Website* www.dorsethistoricchurchestrust.co.uk

■ The Dorus Trust

CC NO 328724   **ESTABLISHED** 1990

WHERE FUNDING CAN BE GIVEN Mainly UK.

WHO CAN BENEFIT Registered UK charities with a national focus benefiting people of all ages, homeless people, people with addictions, physical disabilities, cancer or diabetes, and underprivileged children.

WHAT IS FUNDED Support is given to projects including hostels, hospices, holiday accommodation, respite care, care in the

community, health counselling and some
environmental issues.

WHAT IS NOT FUNDED No grants to individuals,
expeditions, research, scholarships, charities
with a local focus, local branches of UK
charities or towards running costs.

TYPE OF GRANT Projects and one-off grants. Funding
for one year or less.

RANGE OF GRANTS £500–£15,000.

SAMPLE GRANTS Wildfowl and Wetlands Trust
(£9,000); DebRA, Just a Drop and St Raphael's
Hospice (£8,000 each); Practical Action and
Home Start Merton (£7,000 each); Crisis UK
(£6,000); Fairbridge and Switchback (£5,000
each); Landmark Trust (£4,000); and Royal
Choral Society (£3,000).

FINANCES *Year* 2009–10 *Income* £84,813
Grants £69,250 *Assets* £3,083,593

TRUSTEES C H Peacock; Mrs B Bond; A M Bond.

HOW TO APPLY This trust no longer accepts
applications.

WHO TO APPLY TO Charles H Peacock, Trustee, c/o
Charities Aid Foundation, 25 Kings Hill Avenue,
King's Hill, West Malling, Kent ME19 4TA
Tel 01732 520028

■ Double 'O' Charity Ltd

CC NO 271681   **ESTABLISHED** 1976

WHERE FUNDING CAN BE GIVEN UK and overseas.

WHO CAN BENEFIT Registered charities and
individuals.

WHAT IS FUNDED Primarily, grants towards the relief
of poverty, preservation of health and the
advancement of education. However, the charity
considers all requests for aid.

WHAT IS NOT FUNDED No grants to individuals
towards education or for their involvement in
overseas charity work.

TYPE OF GRANT Preferably one-off.

RANGE OF GRANTS Up to £50,000.

SAMPLE GRANTS Spirit of Recovery (£48,000); Avatar
Meher Baba (£33,000); Refuge (£30,000);
NAPAC (£28,000); Richmond Bridge Friendship
Club (£13,000); Arvon Foundation and One
World Action (£5,000 each); Wroxham Trust
(£3,000); Art and Soul (£2,000); and SRLV
2009 Adventure (£500).

FINANCES *Year* 2009–10 *Income* £108,307
Grants £200,440 *Assets* £120,986

TRUSTEES Peter Townshend; Karen Townshend.

OTHER INFORMATION Grants to individuals totalled
£32,000.

HOW TO APPLY In writing to the correspondent.

WHO TO APPLY TO The Trustees, c/o 4 Friars Lane,
Richmond, Surrey TW9 1NL *Tel* 020 8940 8171

■ The Doughty Charity Trust

CC NO 274977   **ESTABLISHED** 1977

WHERE FUNDING CAN BE GIVEN England, Israel.

WHO CAN BENEFIT Jewish organisations benefiting
people who are disadvantaged by poverty or who
are sick.

WHAT IS FUNDED To promote (a) the orthodox Jewish
Religion, (b) orthodox Jewish education and
(c) institutions for Jewish people who are poor,
ill and or elderly.

WHAT IS NOT FUNDED No grants to individuals.

TYPE OF GRANT Loan or grant, usually £1,000 or
less.

RANGE OF GRANTS £250–£23,000.

SAMPLE GRANTS Zichron Menachem (£25,000);
Tomchei Sharei Zion (£20,000); Beif Hayeld
(£17,000); Sylvella Charity (£12,000); FKHKS

(£10,000); JET and Achiezer (£5,000 each); and
NW London Sephardi Synagogue (£1,300).

FINANCES *Year* 2009 *Income* £213,000
Grants £136,000 *Assets* £56,475

TRUSTEES G Halibard, Chair; Mrs M Halibard.

OTHER INFORMATION Various donations of £1,000
and under amounted to £16,000.

HOW TO APPLY In writing to the correspondent.

WHO TO APPLY TO Gerald B Halibard, Trustee,
22 Ravenscroft Avenue, Golders Green, London
NW11 0RY *Tel* 020 8209 0500

■ The R M Douglas Charitable Trust

CC NO 248775   **ESTABLISHED** 1966

WHERE FUNDING CAN BE GIVEN UK with a preference
for Staffordshire.

WHO CAN BENEFIT Registered charities already in
receipt of support from the trust.

WHAT IS FUNDED The relief of poverty (including
provision of pensions) especially for present and
past employees (and their families) of Robert M
Douglas (Contractors) Ltd, and general
charitable purposes especially in the parish of
St Mary, Dunstall.

TYPE OF GRANT Mostly small grants, including
buildings, capital, core costs, one-off, research,
and recurring costs.

RANGE OF GRANTS £200–£5,000. Typically £200–
£500.

SAMPLE GRANTS Previous beneficiaries have included
Bible Explorer for Christian outreach, British Red
Cross for general purposes, Burton Graduate
Medical College to equip a new lecture theatre,
Four Oaks Methodist Church for its centenary
appeal, Lichfield Diocesan Urban Fund for
Christian mission, St Giles Hospice – Lichfield
for development, SAT-7 Trust for Christian
outreach and John Taylor High School – Barton
in Needwood for a performing arts block.

FINANCES *Year* 2009–10 *Income* £189,177
Grants £39,050 *Assets* £883,444

TRUSTEES J M Douglas; Juliet E Lees; F W Carder;
M J D Lees.

OTHER INFORMATION In 2009–10, grants totalling
£2,000 were distributed to individuals
connected with the company.

HOW TO APPLY The trust has previously stated that
its funds were fully committed.

WHO TO APPLY TO Juliet Rees, Trustee, c/o
68 Liverpool Road, Stoke-on-Trent ST4 1BG

■ The Drapers' Charitable Fund

CC NO 251403   **ESTABLISHED** 1959

WHERE FUNDING CAN BE GIVEN UK, with a special
interest in the City and adjacent parts of London
and Moneymore and Draperstown in Northern
Ireland.

WHO CAN BENEFIT Registered or exempt charities.

WHAT IS FUNDED General charitable purposes
including social welfare, education, heritage, the
arts, prisoner support and textile conservation.

WHAT IS NOT FUNDED Grants are not usually made
for: individuals; schools, colleges and
universities (except in North Wales and
Greenwich & Lewisham through The Thomas
Howell's Education Fund for North Wales and Sir
William Boreman's Foundation); churches;
almshouses; animal welfare; counselling or
advocacy; medical research/relief, hospitals or
medical centres; children's disabilities, physical
disabilities or medical conditions; holidays or
general respite care; organisations solely

assisting refugees, asylum seekers or specific cultural or ethnic groups within the UK; organisations that are not registered charities, unless exempt from registration; funds that replace or subsidise statutory funding; local branches of national charities, associations or movements; work that has already taken place; general appeals or circulars; loans or business finance.

TYPE OF GRANT One-off or recurrent grants for capital and core costs.

RANGE OF GRANTS Mostly for £10,000 or less.

SAMPLE GRANTS Foundation of Prince William and Prince Harry (£105,000); Pembroke College, Cambridge (£45,000); Baroness de Turckheim Music Fund (£35,000); Broadway (£15,000); Help for Heroes (£10,500); Startuponline Ltd (£7,500); Lattitude Global Volunteering (£6,000); and Blue Sky Development and Regeneration, Design and Manufacture for Disability and Kings Cross Brunswick Neighbourhood Association (£5,000 each).

FINANCES *Year* 2009–10 *Income* £6,105,970 *Grants* £838,977 *Assets* £29,944,338

TRUSTEES The Drapers' Company.

HOW TO APPLY Applications can be made at any time during the year. The charities committee meets four times a year (October, January, April and July). Applicants should complete the 'application summary sheet' (available to download from the website) and submit it together with a document on proposed funding. This should include detailed information about the organisation and the project/activity to be funded; full costings and project budget for the proposed work for which the grant is requested, or the organisation's income and expenditure budget for the current year (whichever is appropriate); and the most recent audited financial statements and trustees report. Applications should be submitted by post only. For full details of the application process and the trust's current priorities, applicants are advised to refer to the trust's website.

WHO TO APPLY TO Andy Mellows, Head of Charities, The Drapers' Company, Drapers' Hall, Throgmorton Avenue, London EC2N 2DQ *Tel* 020 7588 5001 *Fax* 020 7628 1988 *email* charities@thedrapers.co.uk *Website* www.thedrapers.co.uk

■ The Drayson Foundation

CC NO 1076700   **ESTABLISHED** 1999

WHERE FUNDING CAN BE GIVEN UK.

WHO CAN BENEFIT Children who are sick and in need, including social welfare services and medical welfare and research charities.

WHAT IS FUNDED Relief of sickness, with particular emphasis on children and the advancement of education.

RANGE OF GRANTS up to £33,000.

SAMPLE GRANTS National Centre for Young People with Epilepsy (£33,000).

FINANCES *Year* 2009–10 *Income* £89,612 *Grants* £33,333 *Assets* £3,584,524

TRUSTEES Lord Drayson, Lady Drayson, Clare Maurice.

HOW TO APPLY In writing to the correspondent.

WHO TO APPLY TO Clare Maurice, Trustee, 1 Threadneedle Street, London EC2R 8AY

■ Dromintee Trust

CC NO 1053956   **ESTABLISHED** 1996

WHERE FUNDING CAN BE GIVEN Worldwide.

WHO CAN BENEFIT Charitable organisations.

WHAT IS FUNDED People in need by reason of age, illness, disability or socio-economic circumstances; for charitable purposes connected with children's welfare; the advancement of health and education; research into rare diseases and disorders, in particular metabolic disorders; and for general charitable purposes.

TYPE OF GRANT One-off and recurrent.

RANGE OF GRANTS Up to £151,000.

SAMPLE GRANTS Great Ormond Street Hospital Charity (£151,000); Consolata Fathers (£35,000 in two grants); CAFOD – St Francis Community West Kenya (£34,000); Let the Children Live and the National Hospital for Neurology and Neurosurgery – Brain Tumour Unit (£25,000 each); InterCare – Medical Aid for Africa and the Parish of Dromintee and Jonesboro' (£20,000 each); Holy Cross Priory (£8,400); Atiamah Trust and International Reconstructive Plastic Surgery (Ghana) Project (£3,000 each); International Refugee Trust – Uganda (£2,600); Hospices of Hope and Home-Start International – Uganda (£2,500 each); and Feed the Children and Broom Street Children Project (£1,000 each).

FINANCES *Year* 2009–10 *Income* £323,470 *Grants* £333,907 *Assets* £1,256,097

TRUSTEES Hugh Murphy; Margaret Murphy; Robert Smith; Paul Tiernan; Mary Murphy; Patrick Murphy.

HOW TO APPLY In writing to the correspondent.

WHO TO APPLY TO Hugh Murphy, Trustee, The Manor House, Main Street, Thurnby, Leicester LE7 9PN *Tel* 0116 241 5100

■ The Dugdale Charitable Trust

CC NO 1052941   **ESTABLISHED** 1995

WHERE FUNDING CAN BE GIVEN UK, with a preference for Hampshire and West Sussex, and overseas.

WHO CAN BENEFIT Christians and Christian organisations who are personally known to the trustees.

WHAT IS FUNDED The advancement of the Methodist religion and Christian education in the UK and overseas mission, relief and development work.

RANGE OF GRANTS £0–£12,000.

SAMPLE GRANTS Waltham Chase Methodist Church; Christians Against Poverty; Mission Aviation Fellowship; WPCC; Open Doors (£5,000) each; New Life Church (£9,000); OMS International (£6,000); Winchester Family Church (£12,000); Uganda development projects (£31,000).

FINANCES *Year* 2008–09 *Income* £60,191 *Grants* £94,000 *Assets* £441,395

TRUSTEES Robert Dugdale; Bebe Dugdale; Jeremy Dugdale; Simon Dugdale.

HOW TO APPLY This trust only supports causes known personally to the trustees. Unsolicited applications are not considered.

WHO TO APPLY TO Robert Dugdale, Trustee, Yewtrees, Curbridge, Botley, Southampton SO30 2HB *Tel* 01489 788343

Think carefully about every application. Is it justified?

497

■ The Duis Charitable Trust

CC NO 800487 **ESTABLISHED** 1987
WHERE FUNDING CAN BE GIVEN Worldwide.
WHO CAN BENEFIT Children, medical, general.
WHAT IS FUNDED The trust makes grants benefiting groups largely concerned with children and Jewish causes, although this incorporates support of social welfare, education, capital library and hospital appeals.
WHAT IS NOT FUNDED No grants to individuals.
SAMPLE GRANTS Previous beneficiaries have included Norwood, Great Ormond Street Hospital, BINOH Norwood Childcare, Dulwich Picture Gallery, National Playing Fields, Down's Syndrome Association, Joint Jewish Charitable Trust, Hillel Special Purposes Fund, Breakaway Charity Committee, Children's Wish Foundation and Jewish Care.
FINANCES *Year* 2009–10 *Income* £28,982 *Grants* £32,550 *Assets* £220,937
TRUSTEES Julian Michael Fellerman and Robert Michael Gore.
HOW TO APPLY In writing to the correspondent.
WHO TO APPLY TO Robert Michael Gore, Nigel Harris, 4–6 Canfield Place, London NW6 3BT *Tel* 020 7372 2300

■ The Dulverton Trust

CC NO 206426 **ESTABLISHED** 1949
WHERE FUNDING CAN BE GIVEN Unrestricted. Mainly UK in practice. An interest in the Cotswolds. Limited support to parts of Africa. Few grants for work in London or Northern Ireland.
WHO CAN BENEFIT Mainly UK projects, some regional and local projects at a minor level.
WHAT IS FUNDED Youth and education, conservation, general welfare and to a lesser extent activities in preservation and peace and humanitarian support.
WHAT IS NOT FUNDED Grants rarely given for: individuals; museums, galleries, libraries; exhibition centres and heritage attractions; individual churches, cathedrals and other historic buildings; individual schools, colleges, universities or other educational establishments; hospices, hospitals, nursing or residential care homes; expeditions or research projects; activities outside the stated geographical scope. Support is rarely given to charities whose main beneficiaries live within Greater London or Northern Ireland. No support for the following areas of activity: health and medicine, including drug and alcohol addiction, therapy and counselling; support for people with disabilities; the arts, including theatre, music and drama; sport, including sports centres and individual playing field projects; animal welfare or projects concerning the protection of single species; expeditions and research projects; individuals volunteering overseas; conferences, cultural festivals, exhibitions and events; salaries for specific posts; major building projects, including the purchase of property or land; endowments; retrospective funding; appeals which seek to replace statutory funding.
TYPE OF GRANT Project and one-off funding. Also capital and core costs. Funding is rarely given for more than one year.
RANGE OF GRANTS £1,000–£130,000; typically £20,000.
SAMPLE GRANTS Dulverton & Michael Wills Scholarships at Oxford University (£150,000); National Churches Trust (£50,000); Army Cadet Force Association and Combat Stress (£40,000 each); Book Aid International (£36,000);

Fairbridge (£32,000); Woodland Trust (£30,000); After Adoption (£23,000), ATD Fourth World (£15,000); and the Scottish Churches Architectural Heritage Trust (£6,000).
FINANCES *Year* 2009–10 *Income* £1,762,744 *Grants* £2,793,400 *Assets* £74,462,673
TRUSTEES Christopher Wills, Chair; Sir John Kemp-Welch; Tara Douglas-Home; Lord Dulverton; Lord Gowrie; Dr Catherine Wills; Richard Fitzalan Howard; Sir Malcolm Rifkind; Dame Mary Richardson.
OTHER INFORMATION Minor grants for smaller charities working in the North East of England, Cornwall, Devon or Wales are no longer administered by the trust. The scheme is now administered by the local community foundations in these areas, namely the Community Foundation Tyne & Wear and Northumberland, Cornwall Community Foundation, Devon Community Foundation and the Community Foundation in Wales respectively.
HOW TO APPLY 'Please read the guidelines carefully, making sure that none of the exclusions apply to your charity or project. If you believe that your appeal falls within the funding policy of the trust, you are welcome to apply as follows: send your application by post to the Grants Director. The trust reserves the right not to respond to appeals by email from unfamiliar sources; there is no set application form, but you should restrict your application to two pages; make sure you include your organisation's full contact details, together with an email address and telephone number. Also please confirm your charitable status, giving the registered charity number; include a brief description of the background, aims and objectives of the charity; details of the specific purpose for which funding is sought together with the funding target; and the balance of funding outstanding at the time of the application; finally, please enclose a copy of your most recent annual report and accounts if they are not available on the Charity Commission's website. If you wish to make initial enquiries, establish eligibility, discuss time scales or need to seek further guidance about an application, please telephone the trust's office. The trustees meet four times a year to consider major appeals: in February, May, July and October. There are no deadlines or closing dates. The selection procedure can take between three to six months so it is advisable to apply in plenty of time, especially if funding is required by a certain date. Each application is considered on its merits and all will receive a reply as soon as possible, although research and consultation may delay a response from time to time. The trust will usually acknowledge receipt of your application by email, so please remember to include a current email address. If you do not have one, we will send you an acknowledgement by post. All rejected applications will receive notification and an outline explanation for the rejection will usually be given. Applications that are listed for consideration for a Major Grant will normally receive a visit from one of the trust's directors who will subsequently report to the trustees. Following the trustees' meeting, successful applicants will be notified of their award in writing. The trustees' decisions are final.'
WHO TO APPLY TO Andrew Stafford, Director, 5 St James's Place, London SW1A 1NP *Tel* 020 7629 9121 *Fax* 020 7495 6201 *email* trust@dulverton.org *Website* www.dulverton.org

■ The P B Dumbell Charitable Trust

CC NO 232770   **ESTABLISHED** 1964

WHERE FUNDING CAN BE GIVEN Occasionally worldwide, but mostly the Wolverhampton and Shropshire area.

WHO CAN BENEFIT Institutions and individuals.

WHAT IS FUNDED General charitable purposes.

WHAT IS NOT FUNDED No educational grants are given.

RANGE OF GRANTS Up to £3,000.

SAMPLE GRANTS St Peter's Church Worfield and Clocolan Peace Feeding Scheme (£3,000 each); Ironbridge Gorge Museum Trust, Compton Hospice and Beacon Centre for the Blind (£2,400 each); Ludlow Festival 2011 (£2,000); Macmillan Cancer Relief – Black Country Appeal and Midlands Air Ambulance (£1,500 each); Hope House Children's Respite Hospice (£1,000); South Shropshire Furniture Appeal and South Shropshire Youth Forum (£500 each); and West Mercia Scout County and Age Concern – Wolverhampton (£250 each).

FINANCES *Year* 2010–11 *Income* £38,533 *Grants* £29,350 *Assets* £1,010,859

TRUSTEES M H Gilbert; C F Dumbell.

OTHER INFORMATION In 2010–11 five grants were made to individuals totalling £650.

HOW TO APPLY In writing to the correspondent. The trustees meet annually in June when most grants are considered. Some applications will be considered at other times. Telephone calls are not welcomed.

WHO TO APPLY TO C F Dumbell, Trustee, Lower Hall, Worfield, Bridgnorth, Shropshire WV15 5LH *Tel* 01746 716607

■ The Dumbreck Charity

CC NO 273070   **ESTABLISHED** 1976

WHERE FUNDING CAN BE GIVEN Worldwide, especially the west Midlands.

WHO CAN BENEFIT Charitable organisations. New applications are restricted to Midlands organisations.

WHAT IS FUNDED Animal welfare and conservation; children's welfare; people who are elderly or who have mental or physical disabilities; medical causes; and general charitable purposes.

WHAT IS NOT FUNDED No grants to individuals.

TYPE OF GRANT Recurring and one-off grants.

RANGE OF GRANTS £500–£3,000, but mainly for amounts around £1,000 each.

SAMPLE GRANTS DEC Haiti Earthquake Appeal (£10,000); Worcester Cathedral for Music and Light, Macular Disease Support Group Leamington and Spear (£2,000 each); Home from Hospital Care, British Blind Sport, St Matthews Holiday Play Scheme and Birmingham Royal Ballet (£1,000 each); Momentum Midlands and the Singalong Group (£750 each); and Elgar School of Music, Trinity Christian Group, War Memorials Trust and Bowel and Cancer Research (£500 each).

FINANCES *Year* 2009–10 *Income* £241,824 *Grants* £72,500 *Assets* £3,408,188

TRUSTEES A C S Hordern; H B Carslake; Mrs J E Melling.

HOW TO APPLY In writing to the correspondent. The trustees meet annually in April/May. Unsuccessful applications will not be acknowledged. Organisations operating in the UK outside Worcestershire, Warwickshire or the West Midlands will not be supported.

WHO TO APPLY TO Mrs P M Spragg, c/o P S Accounting, 41 Sycamore Drive, Hollywood, Birmingham B47 5QX

■ Dunard Fund

CC NO 295790   **ESTABLISHED** 1986

WHERE FUNDING CAN BE GIVEN Worldwide, in practice UK with a particular interest in Scotland.

WHO CAN BENEFIT Arts, environment and humanitarian causes.

WHAT IS FUNDED Principally to the training for and performance of classical music at the highest standard and to education and display of the visual arts, also at international standard. A small percentage of the fund is dedicated to environmental and humanitarian projects.

WHAT IS NOT FUNDED Grants are only given to charities recognised in Scotland or charities registered in England and Wales.

TYPE OF GRANT The trustees prefer to engage with recipients to enable long-term development of projects and initiatives which have major and lasting significance; they are therefore less inclined to provide one-off donations.

RANGE OF GRANTS £500–£500,000.

SAMPLE GRANTS Edinburgh International Festival (£510,000); NVA Kilmahew Woodland Cardross (£200,000); London Philharmonic Orchestra (£193,000); Scottish Chamber Orchestra (£126,000); Rosslyn Chapel (£50,000); Ludus Baroque (£45,000); Academy of St Martin in the Field and Pitlochry Festival Theatre (£30,000 each); Penicuik House Preservation Trust (£25,000); Dunedin Consort (£16,000); Royal Welsh College of Music & Drama (£10,000); Sherborne Abbey (£5,000); New Town Concerts Society (£4,000); the Cockburn Association (£3,000); and Live Music Now (£1,000).

FINANCES *Year* 2009–10 *Income* £1,548,000 *Grants* £1,212,193 *Assets* £5,365,000

TRUSTEES Carol Colburn Høgel; Elisabeth Høgel; Catherine Høgel; Erik Høgel; Colin Liddell.

OTHER INFORMATION The charity is also registered with the Office of the Scottish Charity Regulator.

HOW TO APPLY No grants to unsolicited applications.

WHO TO APPLY TO Mrs Carol Colburn Høgel, Trustee, 4 Royal Terrace, Edinburgh EH7 5AB *Tel* 0131 556 4043 *Fax* 0131 556 3969

■ Ronald Duncan Literary Foundation

CC NO 266559   **ESTABLISHED** 1974

WHERE FUNDING CAN BE GIVEN UK.

WHO CAN BENEFIT Theatre and the arts.

WHAT IS FUNDED Arts and culture, general.

TYPE OF GRANT One-off and recurrent.

RANGE OF GRANTS £250–£12,000.

SAMPLE GRANTS Previous beneficiaries include: Ledbury Poetry Festival (£1,250); The Plough Arts Centre – Torrington (£900); Contact Theatre, Firefly Youth Project, Ludlow Assembly Rooms, New Writing South and Queens Theatre (£500 each); and Polka Theatre (£250).

FINANCES *Year* 2009–10 *Income* £34,113 *Grants* £3,500 *Assets* £358,392

TRUSTEES Krysia Cairns; Briony Lawson; Valerie Poulter; Anna Trussler; Karina Moreton.

HOW TO APPLY In writing to the correspondent.

WHO TO APPLY TO Briony Lawson, Secretary, Gothic House, Church Street, Charlbury, Oxfordshire OX7 3PP

■ The Dunhill Medical Trust

CC NO 294286   **ESTABLISHED** 1951

WHERE FUNDING CAN BE GIVEN UK.

WHO CAN BENEFIT Registered charities particularly those benefiting older people and academic institutions undertaking medical research.

WHAT IS FUNDED The trust's current charitable priorities are: care of older people, including rehabilitation and palliative care; and research into the causes and treatments of disease, disability and frailty associated with ageing. The trust makes grants under four programmes: research grants, general grants, serendipity awards and research training fellowships. Full guidelines are available on the trust's website.

WHAT IS NOT FUNDED The trust will not fund: organisations based outside the UK, or whose work primarily benefits people outside the UK; large national charities, with an income in excess of £10 million, or assets exceeding £100 million; issues that are already well-funded in the UK, such as heart disease, cancer or HIV/AIDS; sponsorship of individuals; sponsorship of conferences or charitable events; services or equipment that would be more appropriately provided by the National Health Service; grants to cover the revenue or capital costs of hospices*; travel or conference fees (except where these items are an integral part of a project); new or replacement vehicles (unless an integral part of a community-based development); general maintenance; institutional overheads associated with research activity (i.e. the trust will not pay the full economic cost of research activities); research via a third party (such as a fundraising charity supporting research); continuation/replacement funding where a project or post has been previously supported from statutory sources or similar.

*Although the trust does not award grants to cover the revenue or capital costs of hospices, research undertaken within a hospice setting is eligible for consideration.

TYPE OF GRANT Project grants to research groups, as well as some grants for salaries and building or equipment costs for specific projects.

RANGE OF GRANTS Up to £1 million.

SAMPLE GRANTS Previous beneficiaries include: Newcastle University, University of Oxford, University of Nottingham, University of Cambridge, Integrated Neurological Services, Neighbourly Care – Southall, Walthew House – Stockport, Age Concern – Leicestershire and Rutland, Connect – the Communication Disability Network and the Stroke Association.

FINANCES *Year* 2009–10 *Income* £2,667,139 *Grants* £2,613,777 *Assets* £95,446,180

TRUSTEES Ronald E Perry, Chair; Prof. Sir Roger M Boyle; The Rt Revd Christopher T J Chessun; Kay Glendinning; Prof. Roderick J Hay; Prof. James McEwen; Richard A H Nunneley; Timothy W Sanderson; Prof. Martin P Severs.

OTHER INFORMATION The Dunhill Medical trust is a member of the Association of Medical Research Charities.

HOW TO APPLY Applicants to the Research, Research-related and Serendipity funding programmes should complete the appropriate online *outline application form* available in the 'policies and documents' section of the trust's website. Applicants to the General Grants programme are asked to provide an initial outline (approximately two sides of A4) by post or email, including the following information: a brief description of the organisation and its status (e.g. whether it is a registered charity); who you are and what you do within the organisation; a description of the project for which funding is being sought, where it will take place and who it will involve; an outline of who will benefit from the work and why; the key outcomes and timescales; the total cost of the project/work and the specific amount being applied for from the trust. Outline applications for all programmes can be submitted at any time and those which are eligible will be invited to submit a formal application.

The formal application requirements differ depending upon the type of grant being applied for and applicants are strongly advised to visit the trust's website before making an application to ensure that they have all the relevant information. Full applications are considered by the Grants and Research Committee which meets quarterly (normally in February, May, July and November). The committee makes recommendations on whether applications should be supported and decisions are then referred to the board of trustees for approval at their quarterly meetings (normally held in March, June, September and December). Successful applicants are normally notified within two weeks of the meeting. Generally, decisions are made within three to four months.

WHO TO APPLY TO Claire Large, Administrative Director, 3rd Floor, 16–18 Marshalsea Road, London SE1 1HL *Tel* 020 7403 3299 *Fax* 020 7403 3277 *email* info@dunhillmedical.org.uk *Website* www.dunhillmedical.org.uk

■ The Houghton Dunn Charitable Trust

CC NO 261685   **ESTABLISHED** 1967

WHERE FUNDING CAN BE GIVEN UK, with an interest in Lancashire.

WHO CAN BENEFIT Registered charities only, especially those working in Lancashire.

WHAT IS FUNDED Medical, health, welfare, environment, wildlife, churches and heritage.

WHAT IS NOT FUNDED No grants to individuals.

TYPE OF GRANT Cash grants, mostly recurring. Occasional large grants for capital purposes.

SAMPLE GRANTS Previous beneficiaries have included: AMEND, Arthritis Research Campaign, Cancer BACUP, Cancer Research UK, Christie Hospital NHS Trust, East Lancashire Hospice Fund, Lancashire Wildlife Trust, Marie Curie Cancer Care, Macmillan Cancer Relief, National Eczema Society, National Trust Lake District Appeal and National Youth Orchestra.

FINANCES *Year* 2009–10 *Income* £302,788 *Grants* £292,000 *Assets* £6,049,843

TRUSTEES A M H Dunn; R C H Dunn.

OTHER INFORMATION Grants were made to 26 organisations during the year, however a list of beneficiaries were not included in the trust's accounts.

HOW TO APPLY In writing to the correspondent. There is no set time for the consideration of applications, but donations are normally made in March each year.

WHO TO APPLY TO A M H Dunn, Trustee, Carlton Place, 22 Greenwood Street, Altrincham WA14 1RZ

■ The Dunn Family Charitable Trust

CC NO 297389   **ESTABLISHED** 1987

WHERE FUNDING CAN BE GIVEN UK, with a strong preference for Nottinghamshire.

WHO CAN BENEFIT Organisations benefiting people with multiple sclerosis; environmental charities.

WHAT IS FUNDED Charities working in the fields of health facilities and buildings; support to voluntary and community organisations; MS research; conservation; bird sanctuaries and ecology.

WHAT IS NOT FUNDED Only organisations known to the trustees are supported. No grants to individuals.

TYPE OF GRANT Core costs and one-off; funding for one year or less will be considered.

RANGE OF GRANTS £100–£5,000.

SAMPLE GRANTS the Oakes Trust – Sheffield (£4,500); Nottingham multiple Sclerosis Therapy Centre Ltd (£4,000); St Luke's Hospice (£3,000); Macmillan Cancer Support (£2,500); CP Sport and Friary Drop-in Ltd (£2,000 each); Rainbow Children's Hospice (£1,500); RSPB and RNLI – Wells-next the-Sea (£1,000 each).

FINANCES *Year* 2009–10 *Income* £62,661 *Grants* £59,500 *Assets* £1,748,461

TRUSTEES A H Dunn; N A Dunn; R M Dunn.

HOW TO APPLY In writing to the correspondent.

WHO TO APPLY TO The Trustees, Rushcliffe Developments, Tudor House, 13–15 Rectory Road, West Bridgford, Nottingham NG2 6BE *Tel* 0115 945 5300 *email* nad@rushcliffe.co.uk

■ The W E Dunn Trust

CC NO 219418   **ESTABLISHED** 1958

WHERE FUNDING CAN BE GIVEN Midlands.

WHO CAN BENEFIT Charitable organisations and individuals.

WHAT IS FUNDED The general policy of the trust is to benefit people who are sick or in need and live in the Midlands, particularly Warwickshire, Staffordshire, Shropshire or Worcestershire and surrounding areas.

It is the policy of the trustees to determine at the first meeting of the trustees for the year beginning 5th April how much will be available for grants. When the amount available for grants for the coming year has been calculated the trustees determine how this total shall be divided between: needy individuals for purposes other than further education; students for further educational purposes; and to charitable organisations.

WHAT IS NOT FUNDED No grants to settle or reduce debts already incurred.

TYPE OF GRANT Buildings, capital, core costs, one-off, project and start-up costs. All funding is for up to three years.

RANGE OF GRANTS Up to £1,000.

SAMPLE GRANTS Acorns and Compton Hospice (£2,000 each); and Birmingham Hippodrome Development Trust, Ikon Gallery, Katherine House Hospice, Meningitis Trust, Shelter, St Basil's and Warwickshire and Northamptonshire Air Ambulance (£1,000 each).

FINANCES *Year* 2010–11 *Income* £135,859 *Grants* £126,475 *Assets* £4,092,871

TRUSTEES David J Corney, Chair; Leita H Smethurst; C Paul King; Jennifer A Warbrick.

OTHER INFORMATION The grant total in 2009–10 included £41,000 to individuals.

HOW TO APPLY There is a detailed policy statement on the making of grants and guidance notes and model application for sponsoring bodies making application for a grant for an individual.

Potential applicants are advised to contact the correspondent for copies of these documents in order to make an appropriate and relevant application.

Generally, applications should be in writing to the correspondent giving the name and address, some idea of the income/outgoings and any other necessary particulars of the grantee. Organisations should always enclose accounts. Grants to individuals are considered every week; grants to organisations, every three or four months.

WHO TO APPLY TO David J Corney, Trustee, The Trust Office, 30 Bentley Heath Cottages, Tilehouse Green Lane, Knowle, Solihull B93 9EL *Tel* 01564 773407

■ The Charles Dunstone Charitable Trust

CC NO 1085955   **ESTABLISHED** 2001

WHERE FUNDING CAN BE GIVEN UK and overseas.

WHO CAN BENEFIT Registered charities.

WHAT IS FUNDED General charitable purposes. 'The trustees will continue to make a small number of grants in the following areas: making lasting improvements to the lives of children with disabilities and their families; improving the prospects of prisoners on release, especially through the provision of better opportunities and services whilst in prison; making lasting improvements to the education and wellbeing of those living in disadvantaged communities, particularly young people; improving the availability of support and service for young carers.'

WHAT IS NOT FUNDED The trustees do not normally make grants to individuals.

SAMPLE GRANTS Fulwood Academy Endowment Fund (£2 million); Every Child a Chance (£225,000); St Giles Trust (£188,500); The Prince's Trust (£154,000); Shelter (£105,000); Community Links (£75,000); Greenhouse Schools (£50,000); Norfolk Community Foundation (£25,000); and Trinity Sailing (£18,000).

FINANCES *Year* 2009–10 *Income* £990,590 *Grants* £3,594,270 *Assets* £1,128,145

TRUSTEES Denis Dunstone; Adrian Bott; Nicholas Folland.

OTHER INFORMATION 'In September 2009 the trustees began funding the development and improvement of the Fulwood Academy in Preston, Lancashire. This represents a substantial commitment of time and funds over the coming 5 years at least and is likely to be the focus for much of the trust's work.'

HOW TO APPLY 'Proposals are generally invited by the trustees or initiated at their request. Unsolicited applications are not encouraged and are unlikely to be successful. The trustees prefer to support innovative schemes that can be successfully replicated or become self-sustaining.'

WHO TO APPLY TO The Trustees, H W Fisher and Company, Acre House, 11–15 William Road, London NW1 3ER *Tel* 020 7388 7000

■ Dushinsky Trust Ltd

CC NO 1020301   **ESTABLISHED** 1992

WHERE FUNDING CAN BE GIVEN Mainly Israel.

WHO CAN BENEFIT Jewish and Israeli charities.

WHAT IS FUNDED Alleviation of poverty and the furtherance of orthodox Jewish education.

SAMPLE GRANTS Previous beneficiaries have included: United Institutes of Dushinsky,

Think carefully about every application. Is it justified?

501

Minchat Yitzchok Institutions and Ish Lerehu Fund.

FINANCES *Year* 2010 *Income* £428,960 *Grants* £432,485 *Assets* £7,870

TRUSTEES S Reisner; Z Levine; M Schischa.

HOW TO APPLY The trust does not accept unsolicited applications.

WHO TO APPLY TO S Reisner, Secretary, 23 Braydon Road, London N16 6QL *Tel* 020 8802 7144

■ Mildred Duveen Charitable Trust

CC NO 1059355   **ESTABLISHED** 1996

WHERE FUNDING CAN BE GIVEN Worldwide.

WHO CAN BENEFIT Charitable organisations.

WHAT IS FUNDED General charitable purposes.

RANGE OF GRANTS Up to £7,000.

SAMPLE GRANTS Almeida Theatre (£7,000); CPRE – Wiltshire, Theatre Royal Haymarket Masterclass and Hoopers Africa Trust (£5,000 each); Monica Cantwell Trust (£3,000); Charlie Waller Memorial Trust (£2,500); the Passage (£2,000); Provincial Grand Masters Benevolent Fund – Cumberland (£1,500); PDSA, Deafblind UK, South East Cancer Help Centre, Martlets Hospice and Midlands Air Ambulance (£1,000 each); and Walk the Walk Worldwide, Cat and Rabbit Rescue Centre and Whittington Babies (£500 each).

FINANCES *Year* 2009–10 *Income* £28,678 *Grants* £50,000 *Assets* £1,118,593

TRUSTEES Peter Holgate; Adrian Houstoun; Peter Loose; John Shelford.

HOW TO APPLY In writing to the correspondent.

WHO TO APPLY TO Peter Holgate, Trustee, Devonshire House, 60 Goswell Road, London EC1M 7AD *Tel* 020 7566 4000

■ The Annette Duvollet Charitable Trust

CC NO 326505   **ESTABLISHED** 1984

WHERE FUNDING CAN BE GIVEN UK and overseas.

WHO CAN BENEFIT Registered charities supporting young people aged 14–25.

WHAT IS FUNDED General charitable purposes.

RANGE OF GRANTS Usually up to £5,000.

SAMPLE GRANTS Norfolk and Norwich Scope Association – NANSA (£5,700); Depaul Trust (£5,000); Journey of a Lifetime (£4,500); Changing Faces and Notting Hill Housing Trust (£2,000 each); Cued Speech Association, Mencap – Keynsham and Children's Trust – Tadworth (£1,000 each); and Sayers Croft Environmental Educational Trust (£500).

FINANCES *Year* 2009–10 *Income* £31,538 *Grants* £22,740 *Assets* £679,093

TRUSTEES Peter Clarke; Caroline Dawes; Richard Shuttleworth.

HOW TO APPLY In writing to the correspondent.

WHO TO APPLY TO Peter Clarke, Trustee, 18 Nassau Road, London SW13 9QE *Tel* 020 8748 5401

■ The Dwek Family Charitable Trust

CC NO 1001456   **ESTABLISHED** 1989

WHERE FUNDING CAN BE GIVEN UK, with a preference for the Greater Manchester area.

WHO CAN BENEFIT Individuals and small charities without a large fundraising profile. In previous years mainly Jewish charities have been supported.

WHAT IS FUNDED People who are in need, disabled or disadvantaged.

FINANCES *Year* 2009–10 *Income* £41,318 *Grants* £30,766 *Assets* £308,426

TRUSTEES J C Dwek; J V Dwek; A J Leon.

HOW TO APPLY In writing to the correspondent.

WHO TO APPLY TO J C Dwek, Trustee, Suite One, Courthill House, 66 Water Lane, Wilmslow, Cheshire SK9 5AP

■ The Dyers' Company Charitable Trust

CC NO 289547   **ESTABLISHED** 1984

WHERE FUNDING CAN BE GIVEN UK.

WHO CAN BENEFIT Registered charities only.

WHAT IS FUNDED General charitable purposes.

WHAT IS NOT FUNDED No grants to individuals.

RANGE OF GRANTS Up to £25,000, in practice around £500–£5,000.

SAMPLE GRANTS The Chesil Trust (£20,000); St Saviour's and St Olave's School (£18,000); Heriot-Watt University (£14,000); University of Manchester (£10,000); Society of Dyers and Colourists (£7,000); Royal College of Art (£6,000); Help for Heroes (£5,000); HANDS (£3,000); St Peter's Hospice – Bristol and Orchid Cancer Appeal (£2,000 each); City and Guilds of London Arts School and River Thames Boat Project (£1,000 each); and the Scargill Movement and PACE (£500 each).

FINANCES *Year* 2009–10 *Income* £1,064,976 *Grants* £359,463 *Assets* £8,165,779

TRUSTEES The Court of The Dyers' Company.

OTHER INFORMATION The trust also funds a bursary for a school in Norwich, for which it gave £58,000 in 2007/08.

HOW TO APPLY The trust does not welcome unsolicited applications.

WHO TO APPLY TO The Clerk, Dyers Hall, Dowgate Hill, London EC4R 2ST *Tel* 020 7236 7197

■ The James Dyson Foundation

CC NO 1099709   **ESTABLISHED** 2003

WHERE FUNDING CAN BE GIVEN UK, local community around the Dyson company's UK headquarters, in Malmesbury, Wiltshire.

WHO CAN BENEFIT Registered charities and educational institutions.

WHAT IS FUNDED Educational institutions working in the field of design, technology and engineering; charities carrying out medical or scientific research; and projects which aid the local community around Dyson, in Malmesbury, Wiltshire.

TYPE OF GRANT One-off and recurrent.

RANGE OF GRANTS Up to £350,000.

SAMPLE GRANTS 'Breast Cancer Campaigns in Various Countries' (£351,000); Bath Royal United Hospital – Neonatal Intensive Care Unit Fund (£333,000); James Dyson Award (£109,000); 21/21 Japanese Museum (£34,000); Corpus Christi Bursary (£15,000); Conservative Taskforce (£12,000); D and T Show (£8,000); University of Bath – J Fry Scholarship (£5,000); Nerd Herd (£3,500); Sparks (£2,700); and Bath Technology Centre (£137).

FINANCES *Year* 2009–10 *Income* £544,799 *Grants* £958,949 *Assets* £1,414,867

TRUSTEES Sir James Dyson; Lady Deirdre Dyson; Valerie West; Prof. Sir Christopher Frayling.

PUBLICATIONS A number of engineering and design related resources are available to download from the foundation's website.

HOW TO APPLY Applications in writing on headed paper to the correspondent. Organisations can also apply through the 'get in touch' section of the foundation's website.

WHO TO APPLY TO Grants Administrator, Tetbury Hill, Malmesbury, Wiltshire SN16 0RP *Tel* 01666 827205 *email* jamesdysonfoundation@dyson.com *Website* www.jamesdysonfoundation.com

■ EAGA Partnership Charitable Trust

CC NO 1088361   **ESTABLISHED** 2001

WHERE FUNDING CAN BE GIVEN UK and European Union.

WHO CAN BENEFIT Organisations and institutions benefiting research workers, academics and medical professionals.

WHAT IS FUNDED The trust currently provides grants to fund research and other projects within two grant programmes: the first programme aims to clarify the nature, extent and consequences of fuel poverty and offer insights into the energy efficient and cost-effective relief of fuel poverty; the second programme aims to explore issues related to vulnerable consumers and their multiple needs and preferences. It explores the overlap between fuel poverty and wider deprivation, in order to develop a better understanding of different groups of vulnerable and/or deprived consumers. The trust gives priority to funding proposals that have the potential to inform or influence national perceptions and policies and have a wide geographic focus. A project that operates at a local level will only be considered for a grant if it: clearly demonstrates innovation; identifies the policy relevance of the project; has wide applicability; and has well developed and accurately costed evaluation and dissemination plans. The work funded by the trust can be divided into three categories: policy-related research; action projects (such as practical, community based initiatives which have wider applicability); and the promotion of good practice (such as tool kits and workshops).

WHAT IS NOT FUNDED No grants for: general fund-raising appeals; projects that comprise solely of capital works; retrospective funding; energy advice provision materials; maintenance of websites; or local energy efficiency/warm homes initiatives. No grants to individuals.

TYPE OF GRANT One-off for projects and research, including reasonable overhead costs. Funding is available for up three years.

RANGE OF GRANTS The trust does not have minimum or maximum grant levels but it does encourage the co-funding of projects where appropriate.

SAMPLE GRANTS Blooming Green – for a community energy makeover (£43,000) and the University of Ulster – for research into the health impacts of fuel poverty on infants towards an action plan for intervention (£78,000).

FINANCES *Year* 2009–10 *Income* £180,357 *Grants* £121,527 *Assets* £790,288

TRUSTEES William Baker; Zoe Dick; Prof. Dave Gordon; Elizabeth Gore; Virginia Graham; Pedro Guertler; Jack Harrison; Annette Rowe.

HOW TO APPLY Application forms and detailed guidance on the application process are available on the trust's website. Meetings are held three times a year to consider submissions.

WHO TO APPLY TO Dr Naomi Brown, Trust Manager, PO Box 225, Kendal LA9 9DR *Tel* 01539 736477 *email* eagact@aol.com *Website* www.eagacharitabletrust.org

■ The Eagle Charity Trust

CC NO 802134   **ESTABLISHED** 1989

WHERE FUNDING CAN BE GIVEN UK, in particular Manchester, and overseas.

WHO CAN BENEFIT UK, international and local charities.

WHAT IS FUNDED The trust stated it supports a wide variety of charities, especially those concerned with welfare.

TYPE OF GRANT One-off, with no commitment to providing ongoing funding.

RANGE OF GRANTS Around £500–£3,000.

SAMPLE GRANTS Previously: Oxfam – Darfur and Chad (£2,500); Médecins Sans Frontières, UNICEF and Shelter (£2,000 each); British Red Cross – Bangladesh and MacMillan Cancer Support (£1,500 each); Amnesty International, Sight Savers International and Samaritans (£1,000 each); and Turning Point, Claire House and WaterAid (£500 each).

FINANCES *Year* 2009 *Income* £40,260 *Grants* £40,500 *Assets* £891,700

TRUSTEES Mrs L A Gifford; Miss D Gifford; Mrs E Y Williams; Mrs S A Nowakowski; R M E Gifford.

OTHER INFORMATION The trustees opted not to publicise a list of beneficiaries in 2009. Grants were either for £500 or £1,000, with the largest being £3,000.

HOW TO APPLY In writing to the correspondent. However, please note that unsolicited applications are not invited.

WHO TO APPLY TO The Trustees, Nairne Son and Green, 477 Chester Road, Cornbrook, Manchester M16 9HF *Tel* 0161 872 1701

■ Audrey Earle Charitable Trust

CC NO 290028   **ESTABLISHED** 1984

WHERE FUNDING CAN BE GIVEN UK.

WHO CAN BENEFIT Registered charities.

WHAT IS FUNDED General charitable purposes with some preference for animal welfare and conservation charities.

TYPE OF GRANT Mostly recurrent.

RANGE OF GRANTS Up to £10,000, in practice, £500–£4,000.

SAMPLE GRANTS Wells Hospital and Hospice Trust (£7,000); Animal Health Trust, British Red Cross Society, Royal British Legion, People's Dispensary for Sick Animals – PDSA, Age Concern England, Redwings Horse Sanctuary, Salvation Army and Oxfam (£4,000 each); Burnham Market and Norton Village Hall (£3,000); Burnham Overy PCC (£1,000); and Farming and Wildlife Advisory Group (£500).

FINANCES *Year* 2009–10 *Income* £180,999 *Grants* £86,500 *Assets* £3,827,621

TRUSTEES Paul Shiels; Roger James Weetch.

HOW TO APPLY In writing to the correspondent.

WHO TO APPLY TO Paul Shiels, c/o Moon Beaver Solicitors, 24–25 Bloomsbury Square, London WC1A 2PL *Tel* 020 7637 0661 *Fax* 020 7436 4663 *email* psheils@mail.com

■ The Earley Charity

CC NO 244823   **ESTABLISHED** 1820

WHERE FUNDING CAN BE GIVEN The Ancient Liberty of Earley (i.e. the central eastern and southern part of Reading, Earley and Lower Earley, northern Shinfield, Winnersh, Sonning and Lower Caversham).

WHO CAN BENEFIT Individuals in need and charitable and community organisations.

WHAT IS FUNDED To give aid to: the relief of distress and sickness; the relief of people who are elderly, disabled or living in poverty; the provision and support (with the object of improving the conditions of life in the interests of social welfare) of facilities for recreation and other leisure time occupation; the provision and support of educational facilities; and any other charitable purpose for the benefit of the community.

WHAT IS NOT FUNDED No nationwide appeals are considered. The trust has previously stated that it would prefer applications from local offices of national organisations.

TYPE OF GRANT One-off, project and start-up costs. Funding is available for up to one year.

RANGE OF GRANTS £250–£40,000 for organisations. £30–£2,500 for individuals.

SAMPLE GRANTS Berkshire Women's Aid (BWA) (£60,000); Age Concern Reading (£44,000); Reading Voluntary Action (RVA) (£41,000); Reading Community Welfare Rights Unit (£27,000); Readibus (£17,500); Black & Asian Service in Alcohol & Narcotics and Berkshire Maestros (£5,000 each); Geoffrey Field Junior School (£3,700); Angels Choir (£2,500); Armonico Consort (£1,500); George Palmer Primary School (£750).

FINANCES *Year* 2009–10 *Income* £1,045,016 *Grants* £447,071 *Assets* £12,703,084

TRUSTEES Robert F Ames; Mrs Leslie Owen; Mrs Miryam Eastwell; Phillip Hooper; Dr Deborah G Jenkins; Ms Bobby Richardson; Richard Rodway; David Sutton.

OTHER INFORMATION A further £13,000 was paid in grants individuals.

HOW TO APPLY In writing to the correspondent; applications are considered at any time. The trustees meet in February, May, August and November and applications should be submitted in the preceding month. No response is given to applicants from outside the beneficial area. Telephone calls or emails are welcome from applicants who wish to check their eligibility.

WHO TO APPLY TO Jane Wittig, Clerk to the Trustees, The Liberty of Earley House, Strand Way, Earley, Reading, Berkshire RG6 4EA *Tel* 0118 975 5663 *Fax* 0118 975 2263 *email* enquiries@earleycharity.org.uk *Website* www.earleycharity.org.uk

■ Earls Colne and Halstead Educational Charity

CC NO 310859   **ESTABLISHED** 1975
WHERE FUNDING CAN BE GIVEN The catchment area of the former Earls Colne and Halstead grammar schools.

WHO CAN BENEFIT Organisations for the furtherance of education, individuals and local schools.

WHAT IS FUNDED Furtherance of the education of local children and young adults.

RANGE OF GRANTS Up to £6,000.

SAMPLE GRANTS Hedingham School (£5,250); Honywood School (£4,000); Ramsey School (£2,500); Richard De Clare School (£1,700) and St Andrews (Halstead) (£1,100).

FINANCES *Year* 2009–10 *Income* £51,119 *Grants* £37,403 *Assets* £1,053,784

TRUSTEES Mrs P R Taylor, Chair; Ms S Thurgate; Mrs M M James; J M Carter; O S Forder; G C Waterer; A H Frost; Mrs A Paramor; R N Firth; J Panayi; Mrs F Murray.

OTHER INFORMATION In 2009–10 £9,000 was given in grants to individuals and £28,000 to organisations.

HOW TO APPLY In writing to the correspondent.

WHO TO APPLY TO Kaveri Woodward, Clerk to the Trustees, St Andrew's House, 2 Mallows Field, Halstead, Essex CO9 2LN *Tel* 01787 479960 *email* earlscolnehalstead.edcharity@yahoo.co.uk

■ The Earmark Trust

CC NO 267176   **ESTABLISHED** 1974
WHERE FUNDING CAN BE GIVEN UK, with a preference for charities based in Kent.

WHO CAN BENEFIT Charitable organisations, usually those personally known to the trustees.

WHAT IS FUNDED People with disabilities, children, cancer research, the arts, Christian causes and general charitable purposes.

WHAT IS NOT FUNDED Applications from individuals are seldom considered. Applications from large-scale charities, church/cathedral restoration schemes or organ rebuilding projects are also not considered.

RANGE OF GRANTS £250–£5,000.

SAMPLE GRANTS Previous beneficiaries include: Rochdale Special Needs Cycling Club (£5,000); St Luke's Hospital for the Clergy (£2,200); Laine Theatre Arts (£1,500); Willow Trust, Jubilee Sailing Trust and Kent Air Ambulance (£500); and Pestolazzi International Village Trust, Russian Immigrant Aid Fund, Scripture Union and Two Tim Two Trust (£250 each).

FINANCES *Year* 2009–10 *Income* £13,159 *Grants* £40,000

TRUSTEES F C Raven; A C M Raven.

HOW TO APPLY In writing to the correspondent.

WHO TO APPLY TO The Trustees, 8 Bidborough Court, Penshurst Road, Bidborough, Tunbridge Wells, Kent TN3 0XJ

■ East London Community Foundation

CC NO 1133535   **ESTABLISHED** 1990
WHERE FUNDING CAN BE GIVEN North East London, including Barking and Dagenham, Hackney, Havering, Newham, Redbridge, Tower Hamlets and Waltham Forest.

WHO CAN BENEFIT The community in north east London, including people who are disabled, older people and people disadvantaged by poverty; people involved in arts and cultural activities and multi-cultural groups.

WHAT IS FUNDED The foundation has a range of different funds designed for small community and voluntary groups working to help local people across East and North East London. For example, Grassroots Grants, Comic Relief and the Fair Share programme. It is important to note that grant schemes can change frequently. Please consult the foundation's website for details of current programmes and their deadlines.

WHAT IS NOT FUNDED No grants to individuals or to activities that are primarily religious or party political.

TYPE OF GRANT One-off small grants.

RANGE OF GRANTS Mostly £500–£5,000.

SAMPLE GRANTS Youth League UK (£125,000); Seedtime Projects (£89,000); Cirque Nova Ltd (£10,000); Empowering Deaf Society (£5,800); Barking and Redbridge Chinese Community, Change Community Project, Congo Promotion Arts, Redbridge Carnival Association, United Khalsa Sports Academy and White Webb Eagles under 13s (£5,000 each); Harold Wood Cricket Club, Ingrebourne Community Housing Group

Think carefully about every application. Is it justified?

505

and The Boys' Brigade, Havering & Brentwood Battalion (£3,000 each); Elm Park Regeneration Partnership and African Culture Arts & Sports Network (£2,000 each); and SSAFA Forces Help – London and North East branch.

FINANCES *Year* 2009–10 *Income* £884,126 *Grants* £770,579 *Assets* £115,228

TRUSTEES Sanjay Mazumder; David Harris; Alan Thompson; John D'Abbro; Ram Bhandari; Alex Mutyaba; Peter Caton; Jonathan Caton; Jesse Zigmund.

HOW TO APPLY The foundation's website has details of the grant schemes currently being administered. Application forms and guidance notes can be downloaded from the website or requested by telephone or letter.

WHO TO APPLY TO Anja Beinroth, Grant Manager/ Acting Director, LCCM House, Kemp Road RM8 1ST *Tel* 0300 3031203 *email* grants@ elcf.org.uk *Website* www.elcf.org.uk

■ Eastern Counties Educational Trust Limited

CC NO 310038   **ESTABLISHED** 1922

WHERE FUNDING CAN BE GIVEN Preference for Essex, Suffolk, Norfolk, Cambridgeshire and Hertfordshire.

WHO CAN BENEFIT Those with special educational needs, particularly those under 25 who have emotional and behavioural difficulties.

WHAT IS FUNDED Activities, projects or equipment which will assist the above.

WHAT IS NOT FUNDED No grants to individuals. Normally no grants are given for recurring costs.

TYPE OF GRANT One-off and recurring.

RANGE OF GRANTS Up to £20,000.

SAMPLE GRANTS The Denes High School, Lowestoft (£22,000); Manningtree High School (£17,000); Romsey Mill (£7,500); Chelmsford Prison Visitor Centre (£4,000); Bag Books (£2,500); Mendham Primary School (£1,000) and Optua (£400).

FINANCES *Year* 2009–10 *Income* £137,710 *Grants* £122,890 *Assets* £2,875,918

TRUSTEES H Anderson; Mrs V L d'Angibau; P G Glossop; L M Lepper; F V Morgan; Mrs K E Norman-Butler; A J Willis; Mrs D M Reed; Lady Singleton; Miss J S Clark; Mrs Kate Harbottle.

HOW TO APPLY An application form should be obtained from the correspondent. This provides details of information to be submitted with it. Unsuccessful applicants will not be informed unless an sae is provided.

WHO TO APPLY TO Mr A H Corin, Company Secretary, Brook Farm, Wet Lane, Boxted, Colchester, Essex CO4 5TN *Tel* 01206 273295

■ The Sir John Eastwood Foundation

CC NO 235389   **ESTABLISHED** 1964

WHERE FUNDING CAN BE GIVEN UK, but mainly Nottinghamshire in practice.

WHO CAN BENEFIT Local organisations, particularly those concerned with disabled and older people and children with special needs.

WHAT IS FUNDED General charitable purposes.

WHAT IS NOT FUNDED No grants to individuals.

RANGE OF GRANTS Mostly £4,000 or less.

SAMPLE GRANTS Nottingham Hospice (£24,000); Newark and Nottinghamshire Agricultural Society (£10,000); NSPCC (£6,000); and Age Concern –

Sybil Levin Centre, Macmillan Cancer Support and the Disability Living Centre (£5,000 each).

FINANCES *Year* 2009–10 *Income* £338,379 *Grants* £209,365 *Assets* £7,312,958

TRUSTEES Gordon G Raymond, Chair; Diana M Cottingham; Valerie A Hardingham; Constance B Mudford; David Marriott.

OTHER INFORMATION The foundation's income has reduced significantly following the cessation of trading of Adam Eastwood & Sons Limited, a company which is wholly owned by the foundation and from where income was derived.

HOW TO APPLY In writing to the correspondent.

WHO TO APPLY TO David Marriott, Secretary, PO Box 9803, Mansfield, Nottinghamshire NG18 9FT *Fax* 01623 847955

■ The Ebenezer Trust

CC NO 272574   **ESTABLISHED** 1976

WHERE FUNDING CAN BE GIVEN UK and overseas.

WHO CAN BENEFIT Registered charities.

WHAT IS FUNDED Advancement of Protestant and Evangelical tenets of the Christian faith. Activities in which the trustees are personally interested or involved.

WHAT IS NOT FUNDED No grants to individuals.

TYPE OF GRANT Occasionally interest-free loans.

RANGE OF GRANTS Up to around £10,000, in practice, between £500 and £5,000.

SAMPLE GRANTS Spacious Places and TEAR Fund (£4,000 each); Avant Ministries (£3,500); Baptist Missionary Society, Christian Concern for our Nation and Leeds Faith in Schools (£2,000 each); St Francis Hospice, Livability and Baptist Union Home Mission (£1,000 each); Bible in Literacy (£500); Treasures in Heaven Trust (£300); the Brainwave Centre (£50).

FINANCES *Year* 2009–10 *Income* £31,047 *Grants* £46,428 *Assets* £672,172

TRUSTEES Nigel Davey; Ruth Davey.

HOW TO APPLY The trust states that they 'are most unlikely to consider unsolicited requests for grants'.

WHO TO APPLY TO Nigel Davey, Trustee, Longwood Lodge, Whites Hill, Stock, Ingatestone, Essex CM4 9QB *Tel* 01277 829893

■ The EBM Charitable Trust

CC NO 326186   **ESTABLISHED** 1982

WHERE FUNDING CAN BE GIVEN UK.

WHO CAN BENEFIT Charitable organisations.

WHAT IS FUNDED General charitable purposes, especially animal welfare and research, youth development and the relief of poverty.

TYPE OF GRANT Recurring and one-off.

RANGE OF GRANTS £3,500–£200,000.

SAMPLE GRANTS British Racing School, the Royal Hospital Chelsea – Chelsea Pensioners Appeal and the Salvation Army (£200,000 each); Fairbridge (£100,000); Animal Health Trust (£50,000); Calvert Trust Exmoor (£40,000); Community Links (£35,000); Action for Kids (£30,000); The Connection (£20,000); Mayhew Animal Home (£15,000); YMCA Norfolk (£10,000); Wildlife Trust (£7,500); and the Prostate Cancer Charity (£5,000).

FINANCES *Year* 2009–10 *Income* £1,026,132 *Grants* £880,000 *Assets* £39,271,155

TRUSTEES Richard Moore; Michael Macfadyen; Stephen Hogg.

HOW TO APPLY 'Unsolicited applications are not requested as the trustees prefer to support donations to charities whose work they have

506

Does the trust you have chosen match your needs? Haphazard applications waste postage and time

researched and which is in accordance with the wishes of the settlor. The trustees do not tend to support research projects as research is not a core priority but there are exceptions. The trustees' funds are fully committed. The trustees receive a very high number of grant applications which are mostly unsuccessful.'

WHO TO APPLY TO Keith Lawrence, Secretary, Moore Stephens, 150 Aldersgate Street, London EC1A 4AB *Tel* 020 7334 9191 *Fax* 020 7651 1953

■ The Ecology Trust

CC NO 1099222   **ESTABLISHED** 2003

WHERE FUNDING CAN BE GIVEN Mainly UK and Europe.

WHO CAN BENEFIT Registered charities working on ecological and environmental initiatives, particularly, in the areas of agriculture, energy, and climate change.

WHAT IS FUNDED Support is given to projects that prevent environmental degradation and that change values and attitudes, both amongst the public and with people in positions of power. In general the trust seeks to address the causes of the environmental crisis that we face, and to tackle these, rather than to make the consequences of this crisis easier to live with.

WHAT IS NOT FUNDED The trust is unlikely to make grants to the following kinds of projects: work that has already taken place; part of general appeals or circulars; outward-bound courses, expeditions and overseas travel; capital projects (i.e. buildings and refurbishment costs); conservation of already well-supported species or of non-native species; and furniture, white goods, computer, paint, timber and scrap recycling projects.

TYPE OF GRANT One-off and recurring grants for project and core costs.

RANGE OF GRANTS Up to £100,000.

SAMPLE GRANTS School Food Matters (£100,000); Health and Environment Alliance (£46,000); Pesticides Action Network Europe (£44,000); CHEMSec (£40,000); CHEMTrust (£25,000); Campaign for Better Transport (£23,000); UK Without Incineration Network (£19,000); Grup d'Estudis de la Naturalesa/Grup Balear d'Ornitologia (GEN-GOB) Eivissa (£9,100); Amics de la Terra Eivisa (£8,200); and AirportWatch South West (£8,000).

FINANCES *Year* 2009–10 *Income* £247,034 *Grants* £322,141 *Assets* £269,885

TRUSTEES Jeremy Faull, Chair; Charles Filmer; Kenneth Richards.

HOW TO APPLY In writing to the correspondent.

WHO TO APPLY TO Jon Cracknell, Hon. Secretary, Unicorn Administration Ltd, 30–36 King Street, Maidenhead SL6 1NA

■ Eden Arts Trust

CC NO 1000476   **ESTABLISHED** 1990

WHERE FUNDING CAN BE GIVEN The Eden district of Cumbria.

WHO CAN BENEFIT Individuals and organisations benefiting: young adults and older people; artists; actors and entertainment professionals; musicians; textile workers and designers; volunteers; and writers and poets.

WHAT IS FUNDED To promote and develop the arts and art projects involving the community, and to encourage new groups.

WHAT IS NOT FUNDED Only projects/groups in the Eden district can be funded.

TYPE OF GRANT Local arts and crafts projects, days and events, feasibility studies.

RANGE OF GRANTS Up to £5,000.

SAMPLE GRANTS Highlights and Blue Jam (£2,000 each). Small grants paid totalled £4,250. A further £5,000 was spent on project costs.

FINANCES *Year* 2009–10 *Income* £112,434 *Grants* £8,240 *Assets* £124,712

TRUSTEES Mr Keith Morgan, Chair; Mr Ifor Freeman, Vice Chair; Mr Steve Huddart; Mr Terry Smith; Mr David Gaffney; Ms Heather Heron; Ms Karen MacDougall; Mr Mike Head; Mr Martin Stephenson.

OTHER INFORMATION Grants made during the year totalled £8,250 including £4,250 for 'small grants'. A further £5,000 was spent on project costs.

HOW TO APPLY Contact the trust by telephone or email for further information.

WHO TO APPLY TO Irene Faith, Executive Officer, 1 Sandgate, Penrith, Cumbria CA11 7TP *Tel* 01768 899444 *Fax* 01768 895920 *email* enquiries@edenarts.co.uk *Website* www.edenarts.co.uk

■ EDF Energy Trust (EDFET)

CC NO 1099446   **ESTABLISHED** 1996

WHERE FUNDING CAN BE GIVEN UK.

WHO CAN BENEFIT Individuals and families and voluntary and not-for-profit organisations.

WHAT IS FUNDED The trust offers two types of grants: *individual grants* – to cover the payment of gas and electricity debts and other essential household debts or costs (applicants must be EDF Energy account holders); and *organisational grants* – for organisations working in the field of money advice, debt counselling or energy efficiency advice.

WHAT IS NOT FUNDED No grants for: fines for criminal offences; educational or training needs; debts to central government departments; medical equipment, aids and adaptations; holidays; business debts; catalogues; credit cards; personal loans; deposits for secure accommodation; or overpayment of benefits.

TYPE OF GRANT Contracts and full project funding for up to three years.

SAMPLE GRANTS Bristol Debt Advice Centre, East London Financial Inclusion (£20,000 each); Brixton Advice Centre (£18,300); Money Advice Plus – East Sussex (£18,100); Thanet District CAB (£17,000); Brighton & Hove CAB (£13,800).

FINANCES *Year* 2010 *Income* £3,284,840 *Grants* £2,931,094 *Assets* £1,713,883

TRUSTEES Denice Fennell; Tim Cole; Robert Jackson; Steve Meakin; Brian Cross; Bob Richardson; Richard Sykes.

HOW TO APPLY Organisational grants: It is advisable to contact the trust for further information on future grant programmes and deadlines. Individual grants: applications can be submitted throughout the year. Applications must be made on a standard application form, which can be downloaded from the website, obtained from local advice centres such as citizen's advice bureaux or by writing to the trust. The trust also has an online application form, accessible via the website.

WHO TO APPLY TO The Trustees, EDF Energy Trust, 3rd Floor, Midgate House, Midgate, Peterborough PE1 1TN *Tel* 01733 421021 *Fax* 01733 421020 *email* edfet@charisgrants.com *Website* www.edfenergytrust.org.uk

■ The Gilbert and Eileen Edgar Foundation

CC NO 241736   **ESTABLISHED** 1965
WHERE FUNDING CAN BE GIVEN UK (and a few international appeals).
WHO CAN BENEFIT Smaller organisations.
WHAT IS FUNDED Medical Research – the promotion of medical and surgical science in all forms; care and support – helping people who are young, old and in need; fine arts – raising the artistic taste of the public in music, drama, opera, painting, sculpture and the fine arts; education in the fine arts – the promotion of education in the fine arts; religion – the promotion of religion; recreation – the provision of facilities for recreation or other leisure time activities.
WHAT IS NOT FUNDED Grants for education in the fine arts are made by way of scholarships awarded by academies and no grants are made directly to individuals in this regard.
RANGE OF GRANTS Usually £250–£6,000.
SAMPLE GRANTS Previously: Cystic Fibrosis Trust and Prostate Cancer Research Charity, Multiple Sclerosis and Prostate Cancer Research Charity (£1,000 each); Royal College of Surgeons of England (£500); NSPCC and Weston Spirit (£1,000); Books Abroad (£500); Ghurkha Welfare Trust and Nightingale House (£500 each). Brains Trust (£2,000); Not Forgotten Association (£1,000); English National Ballet (£2,000); Royal Academy of Arts – Scholarship (£6,000); Survival for Tribal Peoples and Marine Conservation Society (£500 each).
FINANCES *Year* 2009 *Income* £69,120 *Grants* £100,000
TRUSTEES Adam Gentilli; Simon Gentilli.
HOW TO APPLY In writing to the correspondent. There are no application forms.
WHO TO APPLY TO The Trustees, James Cowper LLP, North Lea House, 66 Northfield End, Henley on Thames, Oxfordshire, RG92BE *Tel* 01491 848500 *email* info@jamescowper.co.uk

■ Gilbert Edgar Trust

CC NO 213630   **ESTABLISHED** 1955
WHERE FUNDING CAN BE GIVEN Predominantly UK, limited overseas.
WHO CAN BENEFIT Registered charities, educational or cultural bodies benefiting children, medical professionals and research workers.
WHAT IS FUNDED Only charities which the trustees find worthwhile will be supported. Grants are given in the following categories: children, deaf/blind, disabled, drug abuse, handicapped, homeless, hospice, medical, overseas, research, social, youth and other.
WHAT IS NOT FUNDED No grants to individuals or non-registered charities.
RANGE OF GRANTS Mostly £500–£1,500.
SAMPLE GRANTS Samaritans, NSPCC, Simon Community and British Red Cross (£1,500 each); Prostate Cancer Charity, Macmillan Cancer Relief and National Institute of Conductive Education (£1,000 each); YMCA, Hambleden Church Council, Hospice of St Francis, Prisoners Abroad, Barts Research Trust, Woodcraft Folk, Release, Sense and Orchard Vale Trust (£500 each); and Worshipful Company of Clockmakers (£100).
FINANCES *Year* 2009–10 *Income* £37,925 *Grants* £38,600 *Assets* £940,704
TRUSTEES Simon Gentilli; Adam Gentilli; Dr Richard Solomons.

HOW TO APPLY In writing to the correspondent, with a copy of a brochure describing your work.
WHO TO APPLY TO The Trustees, c/o James Cowper LLP, North Lee House, 66 Northfield End, Henley-on-Thames, Oxfordshire RG9 2BE *Tel* 01491 848500

■ Edinburgh Children's Holiday Fund

SC NO SC010312   **ESTABLISHED** 1912
WHERE FUNDING CAN BE GIVEN Edinburgh and the Lothians.
WHO CAN BENEFIT Children.
WHAT IS FUNDED Grants are awarded to charitable and voluntary organisations that are concerned with children's welfare and provide holidays for children who are disadvantaged.
WHAT IS NOT FUNDED No grants directly to individuals.
TYPE OF GRANT One-off grants.
SAMPLE GRANTS Previous beneficiaries have included Acorn Christian Centre, Castleview Primary School, Children 1st, Drug Prevention Group, Forthview Primary School, Mother's Union Holiday Scheme, the Roses Charitable Trust, Scottish Spina Bifida Association, Stepping Stones and Uphill Ski Club.
FINANCES *Year* 2009–10 *Income* £61,411
OTHER INFORMATION This fund gives grants to organisations.
HOW TO APPLY On a form available from the correspondent. Trustees meet to consider grants in January and May. Applications should be sent in mid-December and mid-April respectively.
WHO TO APPLY TO The Secretaries, Bryce, Wilson and Co. Chartered Accountants, 22 Walker Street, Edinburgh EH3 7HR *Tel* 0131 225 5111 *Fax* 0131 220 0283

■ The Edinburgh Trust, No 2 Account

CC NO 227897   **ESTABLISHED** 1959
WHERE FUNDING CAN BE GIVEN UK and worldwide.
WHO CAN BENEFIT Registered charities only.
WHAT IS FUNDED General charitable purposes, but the trust fund and the income may be applied for the promotion and advancement of education and of the efficiency of the armed services.
WHAT IS NOT FUNDED No grants to individuals; only scientific expeditions are considered with the backing of a major society. No grants to non-registered charities.
RANGE OF GRANTS Usually £500–£3,000.
SAMPLE GRANTS International Sacred Literature Trust (£7,000); Edwina Mountbatten Trust (£3,000); the Federation of London Youth Clubs, Royal Commonwealth Ex Serviceman's League and King George Fund for Sailors (£2,500 each); King Edward VII Hospital for Officers, St George's House and the Game & Wildlife Conservancy Trust (£2,000 each); Burma Star Association, the Cutty Sark Trust, SSAFA and British Trust for Conservation Volunteers (£1,500 each); Interact Worldwide, the Sail Training Association and the Zoological Society of London (£1,000 each).
FINANCES *Year* 2009–10 *Income* £98,670 *Grants* £97,038 *Assets* £2,325,072
TRUSTEES Sir Brian McGrath; C Woodhouse; Sir Miles Hunt-Davis.
HOW TO APPLY In writing to the correspondent. The trustees meet to consider grants in April each

year. Applications must be submitted by January.

WHO TO APPLY TO The Secretary, Buckingham Palace, London SW1A 1AA *Tel* 020 7930 4832

....

■ Edinburgh Voluntary Organisations' Trust Funds

SC NO SC031561   **ESTABLISHED** 1868

WHERE FUNDING CAN BE GIVEN Edinburgh and the Lothians.

WHO CAN BENEFIT Organisations and individuals. Organisations should have an annual turnover of under £200,000. Priority is given to local charitable organisations so that a national organisation will be required to indicate need and a local presence in Edinburgh and the Lothians according to the agreed policy.

WHAT IS FUNDED The trustees have revised their grant-aid policies with effect from April 2006 recognising the difficulty that local voluntary organisations face in attaining regular funding for their main activities. Consequently, for the period 2006 to 2010 the trustees provided grants to voluntary organisations properly constituted and registered as charitable for purposes of social welfare and especially for local initiatives which benefit people in Edinburgh and the Lothians and when the organisation's aims and objectives are within trust policies, it is solvent and not in debt, and where the plan is imaginative and sound. The trustees may support main core-funding to assist progress and a grant for a genuine new development, after the first three years, may also be provided to a local organisation. Priority is given to organisations that combat inequalities and promote voluntary action. Arts or environmental tasks will only be considered where a significant social service or therapeutic intent is the main aim. Check the funds' website for up-to-date information.

WHAT IS NOT FUNDED No grants are given to or for: non-registered charities; general appeals; statutory agencies or to replace statutory funding; salaries; commercial organisations or purposes; private schools and colleges; distribution by other agencies; repairs, extensions and alterations for property or for new buildings (grants can be given for essential equipment as part of a project); organisations concerned solely with the arts (although consideration will be given to applications for work with the trust's priority groups i.e. learning difficulties, physical disability, the elderly and substance abuse).

TYPE OF GRANT One-off and recurrent for a maximum of three years.

RANGE OF GRANTS Organisations: up to £2,000 annually.

SAMPLE GRANTS Previous beneficiaries include: LIBRA, Midlothian Befriending Scheme, Lothian Autistic Society, Northfield and Willowbrae Community Services Group, Loan Head Community Services Association, Senior Action Group, Positive Help, Reality to Work and Drake Music Project in Scotland.

FINANCES *Year*-2009–10 *Income* £135,685

TRUSTEES Penny Richardson; Sandra Blake; Graeme Thom; Geoffrey Lord; Monica Langa.

OTHER INFORMATION Despite making a written request for the accounts of this trust (including an sae) these were not provided. The following entry is based on information filed with the Office of the Scottish Charity Regulator and available on the trust's useful website.

Please note: at present the Edinburgh Voluntary Organisations Council is the administrative structure for the following trusts: Miss A Beveridge's Trust, William Thyne Trust and Edinburgh Voluntary Organisations' Trust. It now administers these together and there is one application form for organisations. In addition, the trust also administers grants on behalf of Children in Need and Ponton House.

HOW TO APPLY Application forms are available from the correspondent. Applications must be submitted to Edinburgh Voluntary Organisations' Trust (EVOT) and not to the individual trusts.

WHO TO APPLY TO Janette Scappaticcio, Trust Fund Administrator, 14 Ashley Place, Edinburgh EH6 5PX *Tel* 0131 555 9100 *Fax* 0131 555 9101 *email* janettescappaticco@evoc.org.uk *Website* www.evoc.org.uk

....

■ Educational Foundation of Alderman John Norman

CC NO 313105   **ESTABLISHED** 1962

WHERE FUNDING CAN BE GIVEN Norwich and Old Catton.

WHO CAN BENEFIT Individuals who are descendants of Alderman Norman, and organisations benefiting children, young adults and students.

WHAT IS FUNDED The trust primarily supports the education of the descendants of Alderman Norman, but also supports young people, local schools and educational establishments in the area.

WHAT IS NOT FUNDED No grants to non-registered charities. No applications from outside Norwich and Old Catton will be considered.

RANGE OF GRANTS £300–£3,000.

SAMPLE GRANTS Norfolk County Council Children's Services (£3,000); Norwich Cathedral Choir Endowment Fund (£2,500); Claimants Unity Trust (£2,000); Community Action Norwich, the Whitlingham Project, Handicapped Children Action Group, the Matthew Project, the Hamlet Centre and Norwich and District Carers Forum (£500 each); and Norfolk and Norwich Chamber Music (£300).

FINANCES *Year* 2009–10 *Income* £253,059 *Grants* £220,447 *Assets* £6,037,362

TRUSTEES Revd Jonathan Boston, Chair; Roger Sandall; Dr Julia Leach; Revd Canon Martin Smith; Derek Armes; Christopher Brown; Tracey Hughes; Stephen Slack; James Hawkins; Roy Hughes; Francis Whymark.

OTHER INFORMATION In 2009–10, grants were given to descendants (£207,000); Old Catton Residents (£2,500); and organisations (£11,300).

HOW TO APPLY In writing to the correspondent. Grants to organisations are considered at the trustees meeting in May/June, however the trustees usually meet three times each year, in February, May and October.

WHO TO APPLY TO N F Saffell, Clerk, Brown and Co, The Atrium, St George's Street, Norwich NR3 1AB *Tel* 01603 629871

....

■ Edupoor Limited

CC NO 1113785   **ESTABLISHED** 2006

WHERE FUNDING CAN BE GIVEN Worldwide.

WHO CAN BENEFIT Registered charities.

WHAT IS FUNDED Projects in line with the trust's objects of, 'the advancement in education and training through the world, the relief of poverty, old age, illness, both mental and physical and

Think carefully about every application. Is it justified?

509

the relief of persons suffering from any disability, and such other charitable purpose as the association may time to time authorise'.

FINANCES *Year* 2009–10 *Income* £392,708 *Grants* £453,106

TRUSTEES Michael Shelton; Richard Fraser.

OTHER INFORMATION Accounts were on file at the Charity Commission, without a list of grants.

HOW TO APPLY In writing to the correspondent.

WHO TO APPLY TO Michael Shelton, Trustee, 50 Craven Park Road, South Tottenham, London N15 6AB

■ Dr Edwards Bishop King's Fulham Endowment Fund

CC NO 1113490   **ESTABLISHED** 1981

WHERE FUNDING CAN BE GIVEN Fulham: specifically the post code areas of SW6, part of W14 and part of W6.

WHO CAN BENEFIT Organisations or local groups that help people on low incomes who live in Fulham. Grants are also made to individuals in need.

WHAT IS FUNDED One-off projects and summer schemes.

WHAT IS NOT FUNDED 'The charity does not respond to general funding appeals but will consider matching funding raised from other sources, but not for any purpose for which statutory funding is available.'

TYPE OF GRANT Running costs, one off project grants.

RANGE OF GRANTS Up to £5,000.

SAMPLE GRANTS Bishop Creighton House, Fulham Good Neighbour Service, Fulham Citizens Advice Bureau, Fulham Legal Advice Centre, Hammersmith & Fulham Caring for Carers and Hammersmith & Fulham Mind.

FINANCES *Year* 2009–10 *Income* £360,256 *Grants* £330,000 *Assets* £8,430,087

TRUSTEES Mr M Clein; Mrs C Bailey; Mrs L Brock; Mr I Gray; Mr R Lawrence; Ms S O'Neill; Revd M Osborne; Mr A Russell Smith; Mr K Sunu; Cllr Mrs A Alford; Mr C Treloggan; Mrs B Richards and Mr M Waymouth.

OTHER INFORMATION Grants made directly to individuals totalled £200,000, from which, the majority of grants were made for relief in need purposes.

HOW TO APPLY On an application form available from the correspondent or the trust's website. The trust also requests that the following documents be included with your application: a copy of the organisation's constitution or rules; the most recent annual report and accounts or a financial statement and a brief description of your activities and a financial statement; a list of the members of your management committee; a list (if applicable) of the streets and postcodes of the people you are working with; a summary outline of the project; a budget for the project; and any appropriate estimates for materials, equipment or work. Grants to organisations are considered bi-monthly. The clerk to the trustees may ask to visit your organisation before your application is considered.

WHO TO APPLY TO Vivienne Robb, Clerk to the Trustees, Percy Barton House, 33–35 Dawes Road, Fulham, London SW6 7DT *Tel* 020 7386 9387 *Fax* 020 7610 2856 *email* clerk@debk. org.uk *Website* www.debk.org.uk

■ The W G Edwards Charitable Foundation

CC NO 293312   **ESTABLISHED** 1985

WHERE FUNDING CAN BE GIVEN UK.

WHO CAN BENEFIT Projects benefiting older people.

WHAT IS FUNDED The provision of care for older people through existing charities.

WHAT IS NOT FUNDED No grants to individuals.

TYPE OF GRANT Principally capital projects. Trustees currently prefer to give towards a named item rather than into a pool building fund.

RANGE OF GRANTS £1,000 to £10,000. Average grant about £4,000.

SAMPLE GRANTS RICE (£10,000); Alzheimer's Support, Bromley Council on Ageing, Help the Aged, Rushmore Healthy Living and Sevenoaks Almshouse Charity (£3,000 each); Age Concern Hackney, Parwich Memorial Hall, Reading YMCA, Rio Cinema and STARS (£2,000 each); and Abbeyfield Bognor Regis (£1,000 each).

FINANCES *Year* 2009–10 *Income* £90,335 *Grants* £93,806 *Assets* £2,840,247

TRUSTEES Mrs Margaret E Offley Edwards; Prof. Wendy D Savage; Mrs G Shepherd Coates; Ms Yewande Savage.

HOW TO APPLY In writing to the correspondent, including: confirmation of charitable status (charity number on letterhead will suffice); brief details of the project; budget statement for the project; current fundraising achievements and proposals for future fundraising; items of expenditure within project costing approx £1,000 to £5,000 – trustees currently prefer to give towards a named item rather than into a pool building fund; copy of latest accounts if available. There are no forms or deadlines for applications. If your project fulfils the Foundation's policy criteria, your details will be passed on to the trustees for consideration at their next meeting.

WHO TO APPLY TO Janet Brown, Clerk to the Trustees, c/o 123a Station Road, Oxted, Surrey RH8 0QE *Tel* 01883 714412 *Fax* 01883 714433 *email* janetbrown@ wgedwardscharitablefoundation.org.uk *Website* www.wgedwardscharitablefoundation. org.uk

■ The William Edwards Educational Charity

CC NO 528714   **ESTABLISHED** 1981

WHERE FUNDING CAN BE GIVEN Kenilworth.

WHO CAN BENEFIT Schools and colleges benefiting children, young adults, academics and students under the age of 25.

WHAT IS FUNDED The education of young people.

TYPE OF GRANT One-off and recurrent grants.

RANGE OF GRANTS Generally around £500 to £10,000.

SAMPLE GRANTS Kenilworth School & Sports College (£42,000); Abbotsford School (£8,600); Clinton Primary School (£7,000); Kenilworth School (£2,250) and Thorns Community Infant School (£1,000).

FINANCES *Year* 2009–10 *Income* £201,694 *Grants* £124,358 *Assets* £5,257,735

TRUSTEES Mr JA Cooke; Cllr Mrs P Edwards; Cllr J Hatfield; Captain S C Harrison; Cllr MF Coker; Cllr NJ Vincett; Cllr Mrs S Howell; Dr G Raper.

OTHER INFORMATION The 2009–10 grant total includes: grants to schools (£105,000); grants to individuals (£40,000); and bursaries for post-graduate study (£18,000).

HOW TO APPLY In writing to the correspondent. Trustees meet four times a year.

WHO TO APPLY TO J M P Hathaway, Clerk to the Trustees, Heath and Blenkinsop, 42 Brook Street, Warwick CV34 4BL *Tel* 01926 492407 *email* heath.blenkinsop@btopenworld.com

■ The Elephant Trust

CC NO 269615   **ESTABLISHED** 1975

WHERE FUNDING CAN BE GIVEN UK.

WHO CAN BENEFIT Individual artists, arts organisations and publications concerned with the visual arts.

WHAT IS FUNDED Visual arts. The priorities are to extend the frontiers of creative endeavour, to promote the unconventional and the imaginative and to make it possible for artists and arts organisations to realise and complete specific projects.

WHAT IS NOT FUNDED No education or other study grants.

TYPE OF GRANT One-off contributions to specific projects.

RANGE OF GRANTS Up to £3,500, but larger grants may be considered.

SAMPLE GRANTS Auto Italia, Bookworks, Cubitt Artists Limited, Pump House Gallery, Sheffield Contemporary Art Forum, Site Gallery, Stour Valley Arts, Studio Voltaire, Wandsworth Council (£2,000 each); and the Drawing Room and Durham Art Gallery (£1,500 each).

FINANCES *Year* 2009–10 *Income* £57,009 *Grants* £21,000 *Assets* £1,597,394

TRUSTEES Dawn Ades; Antony Forwood; Matthew Slotover; Tony Penrose; Richard Wentworth; Sarah Whitfield.

OTHER INFORMATION The trustees also administer the George Melhuish Bequest which has similar objectives.

HOW TO APPLY In writing to the correspondent. Guidelines are available. The trustees meet four times a year.

WHO TO APPLY TO Ruth Rattenbury, 512 Bankside Lofts, 65 Hopton Street, London SE1 9GZ *email* ruth@elephanttrust.org.uk

■ The George Elias Charitable Trust

CC NO 273993   **ESTABLISHED** 1977

WHERE FUNDING CAN BE GIVEN Some preference for Manchester.

WHO CAN BENEFIT Mostly Jewish organisations.

WHAT IS FUNDED Mainly Jewish causes, some smaller donations (£100–£750) to more general charitable causes, including educational needs, healthcare and the fight against poverty.

TYPE OF GRANT Capital.

RANGE OF GRANTS Usually up to £20,000, with some larger amounts considered.

SAMPLE GRANTS UK Friends of Nadar Deiah (£50,000); Ahavat Shalom (£45,000); UJIA (£30,000); Hale and District Hebrew Congregation (£24,000); JEM (£5,000); South Manchester Mikva Trust (£4,000); British Friends of Rinat Aharon (£2,500); Moracha LTD (£1,000); Chai Lifeline Cancer Trust (£300); and Friends of the Sick (£100).

FINANCES *Year* 2009–10 *Income* £292,920 *Grants* £228,694 *Assets* £132,060

TRUSTEES E C Elias; S E Elias.

HOW TO APPLY In writing to the correspondent. Trustees meet monthly.

WHO TO APPLY TO S E Elias, Trustee, Elitex House, 1 Ashley Road, Altrincham, Cheshire WA14 2DT *Tel* 0161 928 7171 *email* textiles@kshaw.com

■ The Gerald Palmer Eling Trust Company

CC NO 1100869   **ESTABLISHED** 2003

WHERE FUNDING CAN BE GIVEN Berkshire.

WHO CAN BENEFIT Charitable organisations.

WHAT IS FUNDED Christian religion, particularly the Orthodox Church; medical research and the study of medicine; and relief of sickness and poverty.

WHAT IS NOT FUNDED No grants to individuals.

TYPE OF GRANT One-off.

RANGE OF GRANTS Up to £20,000.

SAMPLE GRANTS The Mary Hare Foundation (£20,000); Convent of the Annunciation (£10,000); Brainwave (£5,000); Bede House Association (£3,000); Fledglings Family Services (£2,000); The Bishop of Winches (£1,500); Berks' Healthcare Foundation NHS Trust (£500) and Hermitage Village Hall (£250).

FINANCES *Year* 2009–10 *Income* £1,172,876 *Grants* £209,143 *Assets* £63,168,205

TRUSTEES Jasper Clutterbuck; Desmond Harrison; Robin Broadhurst; James Gardiner.

OTHER INFORMATION The trust is responsible for the long term maintenance of the character and qualities of the Eling Estate, which is the principal asset of the original endowment, and the protection and sustenance of its environment. The sum of £714,000 went towards running the estate during the year.

HOW TO APPLY In writing to the correspondent.

WHO TO APPLY TO K McDiarmid, Englefield Estate Office, Englefield Road, Theale, Reading RG7 5DU *Tel* 0118 930 2504 *email* mcd@englefield.co.uk

■ The Wilfred and Elsie Elkes Charity Fund

CC NO 326573   **ESTABLISHED** 1984

WHERE FUNDING CAN BE GIVEN Staffordshire and especially Uttoxeter, including UK-wide charities benefiting the area.

WHO CAN BENEFIT Organisations benefiting children and elderly people.

WHAT IS FUNDED The trustees have a particular interest in child welfare, the welfare of older people, organisations working with deaf people, and medical charities involved with deafness, Alzheimer's disease, Parkinson's disease and a range of other diseases. Animal welfare; infrastructure development; charity or voluntary umbrella bodies; accommodation and housing; and community facilities and services, are also considered.

WHAT IS NOT FUNDED Grants are normally made to organisations rather than to individuals.

TYPE OF GRANT Recurrent grants are given in a number of cases but more normally the grant is a one-off payment. Grants can be made for buildings, capital, core costs, project, research, running costs, salaries and start-up costs. Funding is available for up to and over three years.

RANGE OF GRANTS £500–£1,600.

SAMPLE GRANTS Childhood Eye Cancer Trust; Father Hudson's Society; Breath of Life; Juvenile Diabetes Research and Somerset Rural Music School (£1,600 each); Stafford Churches Audio Magazine (£1,000); Rays of Sunshine Children's

Charity, Cerebra and MedEquip4Kids (£800 each); Uttoxeter Methodist Church and Mad Hatter's Tea Party (£500 each).

FINANCES *Year* 2009–10 *Income* £101,763 *Grants* £51,026 *Assets* £2,280,079

TRUSTEES Royal Bank of Scotland plc.

HOW TO APPLY In writing to the correspondent.

WHO TO APPLY TO The Trust Section Manager, RBS Trust Services, Eden, Lakeside, Chester Business Park, Wrexham Road, Chester CH4 9QT *Tel* 01244 625810

■ The Maud Elkington Charitable Trust

CC NO 263929   **ESTABLISHED** 1972

WHERE FUNDING CAN BE GIVEN Mainly Desborough, Northamptonshire and Leicestershire.

WHO CAN BENEFIT Registered charities, particularly local, and local branches of UK charities and individuals through established bodies such as NHS trusts.

WHAT IS FUNDED General charitable purposes including health and welfare, especially of older people, youth and community.

WHAT IS NOT FUNDED No grants directly to individuals.

TYPE OF GRANT One-off and recurrent.

SAMPLE GRANTS Nottinghamshire County Council (£29,200 in 79 individual payments); Leicester Grammar School – Bursary (£9,500); Bromford Housing Association (£7,000 in 24 individual payments); Cynthia Spencer Hospice and Launde Abbey (£5,000 each); Cancer Research UK (£4,900); CARE Shangton (£4,600); Multiple Sclerosis Society (£3,100); Elizabeth Finn Care (£2,500); Voluntary Action Northants (£2,000); and Phoenix Furniture (£1,500).

FINANCES *Year* 2009–10 *Income* £581,635 *Grants* £431,961 *Assets* £20,497,786

TRUSTEES Roger Bowder, Chair; Allan A Veasey; Caroline A Macpherson.

OTHER INFORMATION There were 178 grants made of £1,000 or less.

HOW TO APPLY In writing to the correspondent. There is no application form or guidelines. The trustees meet every seven or eight weeks.

WHO TO APPLY TO Mrs Paula Fowle, Administrator, c/o Harvey Ingram LLP, 20 New Walk, Leicester LE1 6TX *Tel* 0116 257 6129 *Fax* 0116 255 3318 *email* paula.fowle@harveyingram.com

■ Ellador Ltd

CC NO 283202   **ESTABLISHED** 1981

WHERE FUNDING CAN BE GIVEN UK.

WHO CAN BENEFIT Jewish people.

WHAT IS FUNDED The trust supports organisations benefiting Jewish people and also Jewish individuals.

FINANCES *Year* 2009–10 *Income* £78,850 *Grants* £49,555 *Assets* £504,537

TRUSTEES Joel Schreiber; Simon Schreiber; Helen Schreiber; Rivka Schreiber.

HOW TO APPLY In writing to the correspondent.

WHO TO APPLY TO Helen Schreiber, Trustee, 20 Ashtead Road, London E5 9BH *Tel* 020 7242 3580

■ The Ellerdale Trust

CC NO 1073376   **ESTABLISHED** 1998

WHERE FUNDING CAN BE GIVEN Mainly Norfolk.

WHO CAN BENEFIT Local charitable organisations and some national charities which work with Norfolk children.

WHAT IS FUNDED Relief of poverty, distress or suffering in any part of the world, particularly amongst children.

RANGE OF GRANTS In practice, around £1,000–£20,000.

SAMPLE GRANTS Action for Kids and Rainbow Centre (£30,000 each); Break and East Anglian Children's Hospice (10,000 each); Fairbridge Merseyside (£7,000); Over the Wall (£5,000); Avon Wildlife Trust (£2,000); Brainwave and Whirlow Hall Farm Trust (£3,000 each); Scottish Spina Bifida (£2,000); CCHF (£1,000); and National Association of Toys and Leisure (£500).

FINANCES *Year* 2009–10 *Income* £393,195 *Grants* £178,500 *Assets* £6,634,652

TRUSTEES A T R Macfarlane; P C Kurthausen; S P Moores.

HOW TO APPLY In writing to the correspondent.

WHO TO APPLY TO Mary Adlard, Director of Grant-making, The Parlour, The High Street, Ketteringham, Wymondham, Norfolk NR18 9RU *Tel* 01603 813340 *email* mary.adlard@btconnect.com

■ The John Ellerman Foundation

CC NO 263207   **ESTABLISHED** 1971

WHERE FUNDING CAN BE GIVEN Mainly UK; East and Southern Africa.

WHO CAN BENEFIT UK registered charities which operate nationally or across England; local/regional charities should not apply.

WHAT IS FUNDED Health and disability; social welfare; arts and heritage; conservation.

WHAT IS NOT FUNDED 'Grants are not made for the following purposes: for or on behalf of individuals; individual hospitals and hospices; local branches of national organisations; mainstream education/establishments; purchase of vehicles; direct replacement of public funding, or deficit funding; drug or alcohol abuse; charities with an annual income less than £100,000; religious causes; friends of groups; medical research; conferences and seminars; sports and leisure facilities; domestic animal welfare; prisons and offenders; military museums at regimental/arm/corps level. The foundation will only consider applications from registered and exempt charities with a UK office. Most of our grants are for one and two years, but we will give grants for three years if a very strong case is made. Our minimum grant is £10,000. We aim to develop relationships with funded charities. We will only support charities that work – or have reach and impact – across England/UK. Those operating within a single locality, city, borough, county or region will not be considered. We believe other trusts and funders are better placed to help individuals and local or regional charities. For this reason also, applications operating exclusively in Wales, Scotland or Northern Ireland will NOT be considered.'

TYPE OF GRANT One-off or recurring. Core costs, project, running costs, salaries, and start-up costs. Funding may be given for up to three years.

RANGE OF GRANTS £10,000 minimum.

SAMPLE GRANTS Ashden Awards (£130,000), in two one-off payments towards the cost of one international award for a sustainable energy initiative in 2009 and 2010; Adoption UK (£50,000), a one-off payment towards developing Adoption UK's core work of regional support groups and to develop an accredited adoptive parent/training qualification; Fairtrade Foundation (£50,000), the second of 2 payments towards the cost of implementing the foundation's new strategy for 2008–12; Fostering Network (£42,000), a one-off payment towards the cost of supporting foster carers to set up and run voluntary foster care associations in their own localities; Combat Stress (£40,000), the first of 2 payments towards the core costs of supporting ex-Service men and women with psychological injuries; BioRegional Development Group (£30,000), the first of 2 payments towards the director's work of championing sustainable enterprise, forging new partnerships and directing strategic development across the UK; Bladder and Bowel Foundation (£30,000), the first of 2 payments towards core funding; Anti-Slavery International (£28,000*), first of 3 payments towards local partners being enabled to bring together different groups of displaced migrants in constructive problem-solving dialogue, while also advocating for their rights; One-World Action (£22,000*), second of 3 payments towards the cost of strengthening the capacity of refugee communities to respond to sexual and gender-based violence; Action for ME (£20,000), second of 3 payments towards the cost of a telephone support line, which provides employment legislation advice support; World Association of Girl Guides and Girl Scouts (£19,000*), the second of 3 payments to recruit and train 35 volunteer guide leaders and to develop and deliver training programmes to refugees and displaced girls and young women in the Republic of Chad; Elephant Family (£12,000), second of 3 payments towards the cost of creating a structured internship programme; and the English Folk Dance & Song Society (£10,000), the second of 2 payments towards the cost of a national outreach programme. (*Joint funding with the Baring Foundation).

FINANCES *Year* 2009–10 *Income* £1,442,000 *Grants* £4,194,000 *Assets* £116,824,000

TRUSTEES Lady Sarah Riddell, chair; Sue MacGregor; Dominic Caldecott; Peter Mimpriss; Tim Glass; Brian Hurwitz; Hugh Raven; Diana Whitworth.

HOW TO APPLY 'Like most other foundations, we receive many more applications than we can possibly fund. On average, only one in four of all appeals within our guidelines is successful. We recognise that preparing good applications places heavy demands on the time and resources of charities, and diverts energies from their ultimate purpose. We therefore have a two-stage application process. **Stage 1** Please first read our General Guidelines for All Applicants and then category guidelines. Please ensure that you are eligible to apply, and do not appear in the list of exclusions. Then, please send us your latest Annual Report and Audited Accounts, (include financial forecasts or estimates for financial years ended since then), together with a letter – no more than two sides of A4. This should tell us about your charity. Please include: what you do, who your beneficiaries are and where you work; examples of your work and illustrate how you match our guidelines; an explanation of your need for funding – your

turnover, reserves, main sources of income, why you need funds now, and, if you are requesting funds for a particular project, rough costings. All letters are reviewed by the Grants Manager, Director and at least one Trustee who recommend whether your proposal should be taken to the next stage. If not we will tell you at this juncture, rather than ask you to complete a full application. **Stage 2** If your proposal is recommended to the next stage, we will send you by email, an application form. You should return this to us within one month. We do not have specific deadlines for applications, as our Trustees meet regularly throughout the year. (The application form is also available on request in printed format, and we ask you to post us a printed version when applying.) On receipt of your full application, we will organise to come and see you (or meet you) and this will involve staff and/or Trustees. We do this as a matter of policy with all full applications. During or after a visit we may ask for additional information, or clarification of some issues. Your application will then be considered at the next available Board meeting which take place every two months. We will write to you as soon as possible after that with a decision.'

WHO TO APPLY TO Barbra Mazur, Grants Manager, Aria House, 23 Craven Street, London WC2N 5NS *Tel* 020 7930 8566 *Fax* 020 7839 3654 *email* enquiries@ellerman.org.uk *Website* www.ellerman.org.uk

....

■ The Ellinson Foundation Ltd

CC NO 252018   ESTABLISHED 1967

WHERE FUNDING CAN BE GIVEN Worldwide.

WHO CAN BENEFIT Jewish organisations, especially boarding schools teaching the Torah. The trust usually supports the same organisations each year.

WHAT IS FUNDED Hospitals, education and homelessness, usually with a Jewish teaching aspect.

WHAT IS NOT FUNDED No grants to individuals.

TYPE OF GRANT Capital and recurring grants.

RANGE OF GRANTS Usually up to £10,000.

SAMPLE GRANTS Kesser Yeshua Refua – Israel (£120,000); British Friends of Rinat Aharon (£30,000); Three Pillars (£20,000); Kollel Ruach Chaim – Jerusalem (£12,000); Friends of Yeshivas Brisk and Baer Hatora Ltd (£5,000 each); Institute of Torah and Charity – A Light for Israel (£2,000); and BLBH Building Fund (£1,000).

FINANCES *Year* 2009–10 *Income* £284,152 *Grants* £230,250 *Assets* £3,274,230

TRUSTEES A Ellinson; A Z Ellinson; U Ellinson.

OTHER INFORMATION Grants of less than £1,000 totalled £6,000.

HOW TO APPLY In writing to the correspondent. However, the trust generally supports the same organisations each year and unsolicited applications are not welcome.

WHO TO APPLY TO The Trustees, Messrs Robson Laidler and Co, Fernwood House, Fernwood Road, Jesmond, Newcastle upon Tyne NE2 1TJ *Tel* 0191 281 8191

■ The Edith Maud Ellis 1985 Charitable Trust

CC NO 292835   **ESTABLISHED** 1985

WHERE FUNDING CAN BE GIVEN UK, Ireland and overseas.

WHO CAN BENEFIT Edith Ellis was a passionate Quaker and worked tirelessly for international peace and reconciliation. The Edith Ellis Charitable Trust was established by her for general charitable purposes. The Trust aims to give small grants to a broad range of Quaker and other UK registered charities or Non Governmental Organisations.

WHAT IS FUNDED Grants are made to organisations that fall within following categories: UK registered charities, NGOs and social enterprises with a turnover of less than £250,000; those who can demonstrate other sources of funding for their project; and innovative charities/projects not normally able to attract regular funding. Grants are given in the following areas: Quaker work and witness; international peace and conflict resolution; interfaith and ecumenical understanding; community development work in the UK and overseas; and work with asylum seekers and refugees including internally displaced people.

WHAT IS NOT FUNDED In general the trust *does not* support the following: core funding for organisations; individuals; infrastructure organisations; conferences or seminars; ongoing work; general appeals; educational bursaries; humanitarian relief appeals; medical research and services; or organisations with a turnover exceeding £250,000.

TYPE OF GRANT Grants tend to be either: one-off; time limited in support; or; are given in the form of seed money for startup projects. Usually small grants of up to £3000 (in exceptional circumstances larger grants may be given) or interest free loans of up to £5000 repayable over 5 years.

RANGE OF GRANTS Up to £10,000.

SAMPLE GRANTS Chilterns Area Quaker meeting (£10,000); Disaster E Committee (£3,000); Wyton Meeting House (£2,000); Afghanistan & Central Asian Association, Irish School of Ecumenics and SFAC (£1,000 each); Off the Fence, Music Alive and International Rescue Committee (£500 each); and South Belfast Friends Meeting (£300).

FINANCES *Year* 2009–10 *Income* £138,825 *Grants* £41,065 *Assets* £390,529

TRUSTEES Jane Dawson; Michael Phipps; Nicholas Sims; Elizabeth Cave.

HOW TO APPLY Applications should be received by the end of January, May and September in order to be considered at one of the Trustee Meetings. It is sensible to get applications in well ahead of these dates. Late applicants will be considered in the next funding round. Successful applicants will be informed as soon as possible of the trustees' decision. If you have not heard within one calendar month of the relevant closing date you should assume you have been unsuccessful. Successful applicants will be encouraged to contribute to the trust's website in a variety of ways and may be approached to showcase the work of the trust. Applications should be made in writing to the correspondence address.

WHO TO APPLY TO Jackie Baily, Virtuosity Executive Support, Prospect House, 6 Westgate, Thirsk, North Yorkshire YO7 1QS *Website* www. theedithmellischaritabletrust.org

■ The Ellis Campbell Foundation

CC NO 802717   **ESTABLISHED** 1989

WHERE FUNDING CAN BE GIVEN Hampshire, Perth and Kinross/Tayside.

WHO CAN BENEFIT Organisations benefiting young disadvantaged people. Maintenance and preservation of buildings is also considered.

WHAT IS FUNDED Education of disadvantaged people under 25; preservation/protection/improvement of items of architectural/structural/horticultural/ mechanical heritage; encouragement of community based projects.

WHAT IS NOT FUNDED No grants to individuals. Other than the grants made annually over a period, no grants will be made more regularly than every other year. No funding for annual running costs.

TYPE OF GRANT Usually one-off funding, though grants may be given for over three to five years.

RANGE OF GRANTS Average grants of £1,300.

SAMPLE GRANTS Grants have been given previously to: Anvil Trust; Scottish Community Foundation; Prince's Trust; Bhutan Society; Meridian Trust Association; Hampshire Scouting; Hampshire Country Learning; Martin Sailing Project; Ro Ro Sailing Project; and Wheatsheaf Trust.

FINANCES *Year* 2009–10 *Income* £95,696 *Grants* £146,746 *Assets* £1,984,997

TRUSTEES M D C C Campbell, Chair; L F Campbell; J L C Campbell; Mrs A J Andrew and Mrs L G Montgomery.

OTHER INFORMATION The average donation was for £1,544.

HOW TO APPLY In writing to the correspondent. Trustees meet in April and November. Applications should be submitted before the preceding month and will only be acknowledged if they fall strictly within the trust's eligibility guidelines.

WHO TO APPLY TO Michael Campbell, Chair, Shalden Park Steading, Shalden, Alton, Hampshire GU34 4DS *Tel* 020 7297 5296 *email* karen@ elliscampbell.co.uk

■ James Ellis Charitable Trust

CC NO 1055617   **ESTABLISHED** 1996

WHERE FUNDING CAN BE GIVEN UK.

WHO CAN BENEFIT Registered medical research charities and organisations involved with health issues.

WHAT IS FUNDED The trust gives in the areas of medical research and the relief of serious illness.

TYPE OF GRANT One-off.

RANGE OF GRANTS £500–£5,000.

SAMPLE GRANTS Previous beneficiaries have included: Alzheimer's Research Trust, Down's Syndrome Research Association, Deafness Research UK, Arthritis Research Campaign, Association for Spina Bifida and Hydrocephalus, British Lung Foundation, Children's Liver Disease Foundation, Motor Neurone Disease Association and the Brain Research Trust.

FINANCES *Year* 2009–10 *Income* £19,538 *Grants* £25,000

TRUSTEES S J Ellis; J N Sheard; E Lord.

HOW TO APPLY In writing to the correspondent between November and January, for consideration in February.

WHO TO APPLY TO S J Ellis, Settlor, Barn Cottage, Botany Lane, Lepton, Huddersfield HD8 ONE *Tel* 01484 602066 *Fax* 01484 313577 *email* rukuhia@aol.com

514

Does the trust you have chosen match your needs? Haphazard applications waste postage and time

■ The Elm House Trust

CC NO 1109073　　**ESTABLISHED** 2005

WHERE FUNDING CAN BE GIVEN North Yorkshire and the north east of England.

WHO CAN BENEFIT Organisations and educational establishments in Durham and N E Yorkshire.

WHAT IS FUNDED Education and general charitable purposes.

SAMPLE GRANTS Previous beneficiaries included: Citizens Advice Bureau (£10,000); UK Melorheostosis Association (£5,000); Burton-cum-Walden Parish Council (£1,400); and Vacation Chamber Orchestra (£1,000). £1.34 million was donated to VOLT as the trust directly finances the building and development of the learning centre in Durham.

FINANCES *Year* 2010　*Grants* £17,000

TRUSTEES J O Ritchie; J P W Ritchie; R Whiteley.

OTHER INFORMATION The grants total is based on previous research.

HOW TO APPLY In writing to the correspondent.

WHO TO APPLY TO R Whiteley, 2 Greengate, Cardale Park, Harrogate HG3 1GY

■ The Elmgrant Trust

CC NO 313398　　**ESTABLISHED** 1936

WHERE FUNDING CAN BE GIVEN UK, with a preference for the South West of England.

WHO CAN BENEFIT Individuals and organisations.

WHAT IS FUNDED Encouragement of local life through education, the arts and the social sciences.

WHAT IS NOT FUNDED The following are not supported: large scale UK organisations; postgraduate study, overseas student grants, expeditions and travel and study projects overseas; counselling courses; renewed requests from the same (successful) applicant within a two-year period.

TYPE OF GRANT Primarily one-off, occasionally recurring (but not within a two-year period); core funding; no loans.

RANGE OF GRANTS £50–£5,000 (very occasionally over this). Typically £500.

SAMPLE GRANTS Dartington International Summer School (£2,000); Kinergy and the Prison Phoenix Trust (£1,000 each); Centre for the Spoken Word (£750); Dawlish Gardens Trust, the Towersey Foundation and the Daisy Garland (£500 each); and Guild of St Lawrence (£250).

FINANCES *Year* 2009–10　*Income* £84,053　*Grants* £35,917　*Assets* £1,874,967

TRUSTEES Marian Ash, Chair; Sophie Young; Paul Elmhirst; Mark Sharman.

OTHER INFORMATION In 2009–10 the grant total included £1,870 paid to five individuals.

HOW TO APPLY In writing to the correspondent, giving full financial details and, where possible, a letter of support. Initial telephone calls are welcome if advice is needed. There are no application forms. Guidelines are issued. An sae would be very helpful, although this is not obligatory. Currently, meetings are held three times a year in March, June and October. Applications need to be received one clear month prior to meeting.

WHO TO APPLY TO Angela Taylor, Secretary, The Elmhirst Centre, Dartington Hall, Totnes, Devon TQ9 6EL　*Tel* 01803 863160

■ The Elmley Foundation

CC NO 1004043　　**ESTABLISHED** 1991

WHERE FUNDING CAN BE GIVEN Herefordshire and Worcestershire.

WHO CAN BENEFIT Individuals and organisations benefiting: actors and entertainment professionals; musicians; writers and poets; and textile workers and designers; students of the arts.

WHAT IS FUNDED Arts activity.

WHAT IS NOT FUNDED No grants for endowments, loans or general appeals.

TYPE OF GRANT Capital, core costs, contracts and full project funding. Funding of up to, and over, three years will be considered.

RANGE OF GRANTS £500–£30,000.

SAMPLE GRANTS Meadow Arts (£30,000); Hereford Three Choirs (£28,000); The Public Catalogue Foundation (£10,000); Worcester Porcelain Museum (£7,000); Edgar Street Grid (£3,750); Jigsaw Community Festivals (£1,500); Somm Recordings (£1,000) and Shakespeare Schools Festival (£600).

FINANCES *Year* 2009–10　*Income* £353,462　*Grants* £332,065　*Assets* £4,465,513

TRUSTEES Deborah Ann Swallow; Diana Johnson; Sam Driver White.

OTHER INFORMATION The total grants included £17,000 for individuals.

HOW TO APPLY In writing to the correspondent, including a budget and showing other possible or existing sources of funding.

WHO TO APPLY TO Samuel Driver White, Secretary, West Aish, Morchard Bishop, Crediton, Devon EX17 6RX　*Tel* 01363 877433　*email* foundation@elmley.org.uk　*Website* www.elmley.org.uk

■ Elshore Ltd

CC NO 287469　　**ESTABLISHED** 1983

WHERE FUNDING CAN BE GIVEN Worldwide.

WHO CAN BENEFIT Jewish organisations.

WHAT IS FUNDED Advancement of religion and relief of poverty.

FINANCES *Year* 2009–10　*Income* £442,497　*Grants* £656,033　*Assets* £213,583

TRUSTEES Hersz M Lerner; Susan Yanofsky; Goldie Grahame.

HOW TO APPLY In writing to the correspondent.

WHO TO APPLY TO Hersz M Lerner, Trustee, c/o Michael Pasha & Co., 220 The Vale, Golders Green, London NW11 8SR　*Tel* 020 8209 9880

■ The Vernon N Ely Charitable Trust

CC NO 230033　　**ESTABLISHED** 1962

WHERE FUNDING CAN BE GIVEN Worldwide, with a preference for London borough of Merton.

WHO CAN BENEFIT Organisations.

WHAT IS FUNDED Christian causes, welfare, disability, children, young people and overseas grants.

WHAT IS NOT FUNDED No grants to individuals.

RANGE OF GRANTS Around £4,000.

SAMPLE GRANTS Previously: Age Concern, Cardiac Risk in the Young, Samaritans, London Sports Forum for Disabled People, Christchurch URC, Polka Children's Theatre and Community Housing Therapy (£4,000 each); British Tennis Foundation (£1,750); and West Barnes Singers and Sobell Hospice (£500 each).

FINANCES *Year* 2009–10　*Income* £44,130　*Grants* £73,750　*Assets* £1,559,567

TRUSTEES J S Moyle; D P Howorth; R S Main.

HOW TO APPLY In writing to the correspondent.
WHO TO APPLY TO Derek Howorth, Trustee, Grosvenor Gardens House, 35–37 Grosvenor Gardens, London SW1W 0BY *Tel* 020 7828 3156 *email* dph@helmores.co.uk

■ The Embleton Trust

CC NO 285274   **ESTABLISHED** 1982
WHERE FUNDING CAN BE GIVEN UK.
WHO CAN BENEFIT Organisations.
WHAT IS FUNDED Nearly all of the funds are committed to long-term projects relating to legal education and free legal advice centres.
TYPE OF GRANT One off and recurrent.
RANGE OF GRANTS Up to £25,000.
SAMPLE GRANTS City Solicitors Educational Trust (£23,000); British Institute of International and Comparative Law (£10,000); Connection at St Martins (£6,000); Amber (£3,800); Kids Company (£1,000); Simple Trust (Joshua Deller Appeal) (£500) and Mary's Meals Haiti (£225).
FINANCES *Year* 2009–10 *Income* £4,718,923 *Grants* £50,952 *Assets* £589,327
TRUSTEES Simon Martin; Charles Martin.
OTHER INFORMATION The trust is associated with and funded by partners in Macfarlanes, a firm of solicitors.
The majority of the trust's income came from Gift Aid donations.
HOW TO APPLY Unsolicited applications are not accepted.
WHO TO APPLY TO Simon Martin, Macfarlanes Solicitors, 20 Cursitor Street, London EC4A 1LT *Tel* 020 7831 9222 *email* simon.martin@ macfarlanes.com

■ The Emerton-Christie Charity

CC NO 262837   **ESTABLISHED** 1971
WHERE FUNDING CAN BE GIVEN UK.
WHO CAN BENEFIT Registered charities only.
WHAT IS FUNDED General charitable purposes. Preference is given to assist older and younger people, particularly those with disabilities or who are disadvantaged.
WHAT IS NOT FUNDED Generally no grants to individuals; religious organisations; restoration or extension of buildings; start-up costs; animal welfare and research; cultural heritage; or environmental projects.
TYPE OF GRANT Donations for capital projects and/or income requirements.
RANGE OF GRANTS Usually up to £5,000.
SAMPLE GRANTS Raising the Roof – The Greenwich Toy Library (£5,000); Awards for Young Musicians – Pathways Appeal, Canine Partners, Friends of the Elderly, Hospice at Home, Music in Hospitals, Queen Alexandra Hospital Home, RoRo Project, the Life Centre and the Treehouse Trust (£3,000 each); and Women's Health Concern (£2,000).
FINANCES *Year* 2009–10 *Income* £65,474 *Grants* £56,700 *Assets* £2,276,556
TRUSTEES Dr N A Walker; Dr C Mera-Nelson; Lt Col W D Niekirk; Dr S E Walker.
HOW TO APPLY In writing to the correspondent. A demonstration of need based on budgetary principles is required and applications will not be acknowledged unless accompanied by an sae. Trustees normally meet once a year in the autumn to select charities to benefit.
WHO TO APPLY TO The Trustees, c/o Cartmell Shepherd, Viaduct House, Carlisle CA3 8EZ *Tel* 01228 516666 *email* jmj@cartmells.co.uk

■ EMI Music Sound Foundation

CC NO 1104027   **ESTABLISHED** 1996
WHERE FUNDING CAN BE GIVEN UK and Ireland.
WHO CAN BENEFIT Individuals and organisations benefiting: children and young adults; musicians; music students; and music teachers.
WHAT IS FUNDED Non-specialist schools to fund music education; music students in full time education to fund instrument purchase; music teachers to fund courses and training. Every year EMI Music Sound Foundation awards bursaries to students at seven music colleges in the UK and Ireland. These bursaries are distributed at each college's discretion, based on criteria provided by the foundation. For more information, please contact the colleges directly (Birmingham Conservatoire, Drumtech/ Vocaltech/GuitarX – London, Institute of Popular Music – Liverpool, Irish World Music Centre – Limerick, Royal Scottish Academy of Music and Drama – Glasgow, Royal Academy – London and Royal Welsh College of Music and Drama – Cardiff).
WHAT IS NOT FUNDED No support for: applications from outside the United Kingdom and Ireland; non-school based community groups; music therapy centres, and so on; applications over £2,500.
RANGE OF GRANTS Maximum award £2,500 (for schools, individuals and music teachers). Bursaries: annual donation of £5,000 to each college.
SAMPLE GRANTS University of Limerick (£7,300); Royal Welsh College of Music and Drama, Birmingham City University, National Children's Orchestra and Brighton Institute (£5,000 each).
FINANCES *Year* 2009–10 *Income* £355,236 *Grants* £203,075 *Assets* £7,369,342
TRUSTEES Eric Nicoli, Chair; Jim Beach; John Deacon; Paul Gambaccini; Leslie Hill; David Hughes; Rupert Perry; Tony Wadsworth; Christine Walter; Charles Ashcroft.
OTHER INFORMATION During the year £125,000 was awarded to individuals and £78,000 to organisations.
HOW TO APPLY On a form which can be downloaded from the foundation's website.
WHO TO APPLY TO Janie Orr, Chief Executive, 27 Wrights Lane, London W8 5SW *Tel* 020 7795 7000 *Fax* 020 7795 7296 *email* enquiries@musicsoundfoundation.com *Website* www.musicsoundfoundation.com

■ The Emilienne Charitable Trust

CC NO 327849   **ESTABLISHED** 1988
WHERE FUNDING CAN BE GIVEN Not defined.
WHO CAN BENEFIT Charitable organisations.
WHAT IS FUNDED The trustees are particularly interested in support for charities involved in the treatment of addiction and in promoting education.
SAMPLE GRANTS Streetscene (£16,000); Wulfris Educational Foundation (£10,000); SCRATCH (£7,000); Wessex Cancer Trust (£4,000); Myositis Support Group (£2,000); and Great Oaks School (£1,500).
FINANCES *Year* 2009–10 *Income* £31,778 *Grants* £96,220 *Assets* £620,101
TRUSTEES M Howson-Green; B M Baxendale; Mrs M A Howson-Green.
OTHER INFORMATION In 2009–10 57 grants of less than £1,000 each were made to organisations totalling £38,000.
HOW TO APPLY In writing to the correspondent.

WHO TO APPLY TO M Howson-Green, Trustee, Ashton House, 12 The Central Precinct, Winchester Road, Chandlers Ford, Eastleigh, Hampshire, SO53 2GB

■ The Emmandjay Charitable Trust

CC NO 212279 ESTABLISHED 1962

WHERE FUNDING CAN BE GIVEN UK, with a special interest in West Yorkshire.

WHO CAN BENEFIT Charities and individuals.

WHAT IS FUNDED General charitable purposes, with particular favour given to helping disadvantaged people. Many different projects are supported; for example, caring for people who are physically and mentally disabled or terminally ill, work with young people and medical research. Projects which reach a lot of people are favoured.

WHAT IS NOT FUNDED 'The trust does not pay debts, does not make grants to individual students, and does not respond to circulars.' Grants are only given, via social services, to individuals if they live in Bradford.

RANGE OF GRANTS Usually £50–£10,000 (higher grants are exceptional).

SAMPLE GRANTS Previous beneficiaries have included: Abbeyfield Bradford Society, Bradford's War on Cancer, British Heart Foundation, British Red Cross, Cancer Support Centre, Caring for Life – Leeds, Marie Curie Cancer Centre, Research into Ageing and West Yorkshire Youth Association.

FINANCES Year 2009–10 Income £30,777 Grants £52,000 Assets £1,833,010

TRUSTEES Mrs Sylvia Clegg; John A Clegg; Mrs S L Worthington; Mrs E A Riddell.

HOW TO APPLY In writing to the correspondent.

WHO TO APPLY TO Mrs A E Bancroft, Administrator, PO Box 60, Otley, West Yorkshire BD23 9DP

■ Empath UK

CC NO 1135025 ESTABLISHED 2010

WHERE FUNDING CAN BE GIVEN UK.

WHO CAN BENEFIT Registered charities.

WHAT IS FUNDED General charitable purposes.

WHAT IS NOT FUNDED Grants will not be made to political projects or projects involving the advancement of religion or animal welfare. Though, the trust plans to ease this restriction in the future and allow individual donors to specify their preference for such charities.

TYPE OF GRANT Usually one-off but the trust aims to provide a stable income stream for charities and, consequently, funding is often easily renewable for longer-term projects.

TRUSTEES Peter Fayle; Alexander Le Vey.

OTHER INFORMATION Empath aims to provide donors with a new way of giving to charity. The idea is based on bringing together a large number of similar-minded donors and a large number of charities, so donors can reach all the charities they want to with however much or little they can give.

HOW TO APPLY Applications should be emailed to charity-applications@empathuk.org and include the following information: a description of the project/service; the charitable area(s) the activity tackles; and a detailed budget. Further information on the application process and reporting requirements is available on the website. The trust also has a useful e-bulletin, which includes the latest news and funding developments.

WHO TO APPLY TO Peter Fayle, Trustee, 77 Victoria Road, Cambridge CB4 3BW email peter.fayle@empathuk.org Website www.empathuk.org

■ The Worshipful Company of Engineers Charitable Trust Fund

CC NO 289819 ESTABLISHED 1984

WHERE FUNDING CAN BE GIVEN UK.

WHO CAN BENEFIT Individuals and registered charities.

WHAT IS FUNDED The trust's main aim is to support professional engineers who are in need and in the final stages of their educational qualification. Grants are also made to organisations, especially those with an engineering bias for educational purposes.

RANGE OF GRANTS £250–£5,000.

SAMPLE GRANTS RedR (£3,450); Arkwright Trust (£2,700); Ironbridge Trust (£1,000); Lord Mayor's Appeal (£500); Medical Engineering Resource Unit (£250).

FINANCES Year 2010 Income £103,039 Grants £26,269 Assets £606,625

TRUSTEES Rear Admiral D K Bawtree; Mr J H Robinson; Mr F C Price and Mr A D Roche.

HOW TO APPLY In writing to the correspondent.

WHO TO APPLY TO Air Vice Marshall G Skinner, Clerk, The Worshipful Company of Engineers, Wax Chandlers Hall, 6 Gresham Street, London EC2V 7AD Tel 020 7726 4830 Fax 020 7726 4820 email clerk@engineerscompany.org.uk Website www.engineerscompany.org.uk

■ The Englefield Charitable Trust

CC NO 258123 ESTABLISHED 1968

WHERE FUNDING CAN BE GIVEN Worldwide, in practice UK and local charities in Berkshire.

WHO CAN BENEFIT Mainly registered charities; some local schools and churches are supported.

WHAT IS FUNDED Particularly charities working in the fields of: infrastructure development; religion; residential facilities and services; arts, culture and recreation; health; conservation; education and training; and various community facilities and services.

WHAT IS NOT FUNDED Individual applications for study or travel are not considered.

TYPE OF GRANT Buildings, capital, interest-free loans, research, running costs, salaries and start-up costs. Funding for one year or less will be considered.

RANGE OF GRANTS Mainly £5,000 or less.

SAMPLE GRANTS Watermill Theatre (£10,000); Mary Hare Foundation and Museum of English Rural Life (£5,000 each); British Red Cross Berkshire Branch (£4,000); Bucklebury Memorial Hall and Lambeth Fund (£3,000 each); Kennet Opera, Kensworth Church, Morrell Room, Mortimer St John's C of E Infant School, Polish Catholic Mission Reading Parish, Thames Valley & Chiltern Air Ambulance and Volunteer Centre West Berkshire (£2,000 each); Heart Research UK, Heritage of London Trust Ltd, Highland Hospice, Swaziland Charitable Trust and West Berkshire District Council (£1,000 each); and Healing Hands India (£500).

FINANCES Year 2009–10 Income £268,730 Grants £215,862 Assets £10,578,155

TRUSTEES Sir William Benyon; James Shelley; Lady Elizabeth Benyon; Richard H R Benyon; Mrs Catherine Haig; Zoe Benyon.

HOW TO APPLY In writing to the correspondent enclosing the latest accounts, stating the charity's registered number and the purpose for which the money is to be used. Applications are considered in March and September. Only applications going before the trustees will be acknowledged.

WHO TO APPLY TO Alexander S Reid, Secretary to the Trustees, The Quantocks, North Street, Theale, Reading RG7 5EX *Tel* 0118 932 3582 *Fax* 0118 932 3748 *email* sandyreid@ englefield.co.uk

---

■ The English Schools' Football Association

CC NO 306003   **ESTABLISHED** 1904
WHERE FUNDING CAN BE GIVEN England.
WHO CAN BENEFIT Members of the association, and organisations benefiting children and young adults, sportspersons and teachers.
WHAT IS FUNDED Mental, moral and physical development of schoolchildren through association football. Assistance to teacher charities.
WHAT IS NOT FUNDED Grants are restricted to membership and teacher charities.
FINANCES *Year* 2009 *Income* £1,177,291 *Grants* £984,245 *Assets* £1,336,979
TRUSTEES P J Harding, Chair; G Smith; M R Duffield.
HOW TO APPLY In writing to the correspondent.
WHO TO APPLY TO Dawn Howard, Finance Officer, 4 Parker Court, Staffordshire Technology Park, Stafford, Staffordshire ST18 0WP *Tel* 01785 785970 *Fax* 01785 256246 *email* dawn. howard@schoolsfa.com *Website* www.esfa.co.uk

---

■ The Enkalon Foundation

IR NO XN62210   **ESTABLISHED** 1985
WHERE FUNDING CAN BE GIVEN Northern Ireland.
WHO CAN BENEFIT Grants made only to organisations for projects inside Northern Ireland.
WHAT IS FUNDED Improving the quality of life in Northern Ireland. Funding is given to cross-community groups, self help, assistance to unemployed people and groups helping people who are disadvantaged.
WHAT IS NOT FUNDED No grants to individuals unless ex-employees. No grants are given outside Northern Ireland or for travel outside Northern Ireland. Normally grants are not made to playgroups or sporting groups outside the Antrim borough area or for medical research.
TYPE OF GRANT Mainly for starter finance, single projects or capital projects.
RANGE OF GRANTS Up to £6,000 maximum but usually for around £500.
SAMPLE GRANTS Previous beneficiaries have included Council for the Homeless – Northern Ireland, Dungiven Community Resource Centre, Steeple Community Association, Tools for Solidarity and Youth Initiatives Northern Ireland.
FINANCES *Year* 2010–11 *Grants* £280,000
TRUSTEES Raymond Milnes; Peter Dalton; Mark Patterson; Stephen Montgomery; John Wallace.
OTHER INFORMATION The grant total was shared between 305 beneficiaries.
HOW TO APPLY In writing to the correspondent. There are no closing dates or application forms. Guidance notes are available from the foundation's offices. Applications, by letter, should provide the following information: description of the organisation and a copy of the constitution and rules; proposed budget and details of the project; audited accounts (if available) or statement of accounts for the most

recent; completed financial year and a copy of the latest annual report; details of charitable status; other sources of finance for the organisation at present and for the proposed project; experience and/or qualifications of staff and committee members; a list of officers and committee members; contact address and telephone number. Trustees meet four times a year and applicants will be advised as soon as practical after a meeting has taken place. All applicants, successful or unsuccessful, will be advised of the trustees' decision. Applications will not be acknowledged unless accompanied by an sae.

WHO TO APPLY TO Claire Cawley, Administrator, 25 Randalstown Road, Antrim, Northern Ireland BT41 4LJ *Tel* 028 9446 3535 *Fax* 028 9446 5733 *email* enkelonfoundation@gmail.com

---

■ Entindale Ltd

CC NO 277052   **ESTABLISHED** 1978
WHERE FUNDING CAN BE GIVEN Unrestricted.
WHO CAN BENEFIT Organisations benefiting Orthodox Jews.
WHAT IS FUNDED Orthodox Jewish charitable organisations.
TYPE OF GRANT Capital.
RANGE OF GRANTS Usually up to £150,000.
SAMPLE GRANTS British Friends of Rinat Aharon (£480,000); BHW Limited (£200,000); Moreshet Ha Torah and the Jewish Heritage Holocaust Remembrance Trust (£180,000); Menorah Grammar School (£135,000); Yesamach Levav Trust (£108,000); RS Trust (£91,000); Friends of Beis Yisroel Trust (£73,000); Telz Academy Trust (£50,000); Matono (£46,000); LTC Trust Company (£36,000); Yesodei Ha Torah Primary Girls' School (£20,000); Union of Orthodox Hebrew Congregation (£10,000); Merkaz Torah Vochessed (£3,000); and Knesses Hatorah (£1,000).
FINANCES *Year* 2009–10 *Income* £1,275,541 *Grants* £3,052,608 *Assets* £14,701,126
TRUSTEES Allan Becker; Barbara Bridgeman; Stephen Goldberg.
HOW TO APPLY In writing to the correspondent.
WHO TO APPLY TO Barbara Bridgeman, Secretary, 8 Highfield Gardens, London NW11 9HB *Tel* 020 8458 9266 *Fax* 020 8458 8529

■ The Epigoni Trust

CC NO 328700   **ESTABLISHED** 1990
WHERE FUNDING CAN BE GIVEN UK.
WHO CAN BENEFIT Registered UK charities with a national remit benefiting people of all ages, homeless people, those with addictions, physical disabilities, cancer, diabetes, and underprivileged children.
WHAT IS FUNDED Support is given to projects including hostels, hospices, holiday accommodation, respite care, care in the community, health counselling and some environmental issues.
WHAT IS NOT FUNDED No grants to individuals, expeditions, research, scholarships, charities with a local focus, local branches of UK charities or towards running costs.
TYPE OF GRANT Project and one-off. Funding for one year or less.
RANGE OF GRANTS £3,000–£17,000.
SAMPLE GRANTS Mondo Challenge Foundation (£17,000); Pallant House Gallery (£15,000); Breakthrough (£13,800); Fairbridge (£7,000);

Wheelyboat Trust (£6,000); Chichester Festival Theatre – Create and Children on the Edge (£5,000 each); and Snowdrop Trust (£3,000).

FINANCES *Year* 2010 *Income* £113,073 *Grants* £71,800 *Assets* £3,323,666

TRUSTEES C H Peacock; Mrs B Bond; A M Bond.

HOW TO APPLY This trust no longer accepts applications.

WHO TO APPLY TO Charles H Peacock, Trustee, c/o Charities Aid Foundation, 25 Kings Hill Avenue, King's Hill, West Malling, Kent ME19 4TA *Tel* 01732 520028

■ Epilepsy Research UK

CC NO 1100394 **ESTABLISHED** 1985

WHERE FUNDING CAN BE GIVEN UK.

WHO CAN BENEFIT Researchers conducting studies that will benefit people with epilepsy.

WHAT IS FUNDED 'Epilepsy Research UK annually invites applications for grants to support basic, clinical and scientific research work in the UK into the causes, treatment and prevention of epilepsy. We encourage applications on all aspects of epilepsy including basic and social science, clinical management and holistic management of patients.'

TYPE OF GRANT Projects, fellowship, research and equipment. Funding is for up to three years.

RANGE OF GRANTS Up to £150,000.

FINANCES *Year* 2010–11 *Income* £1,160,189 *Grants* £703,202 *Assets* £519,036

TRUSTEES B Akin; Prof. H Cross; Rt Hon D Cameron; J Hirst; Dr J Mumford; Dr L Nashef; Prof. B Neville; P Newman; Dr J Oxley; H Salmon; M Stevens; Dr H Wilkins; Prof. M Walker; Dr G Sills; Prof. M Kerr; S Lanyon; M Manning.

OTHER INFORMATION The grant total figure in 2010–11 represents awards committed.

HOW TO APPLY Applications are invited by advertisement in the specialist scientific press, via Epilepsy Research UK's website and Epilepsy Research UK's distribution list, the Research Register.

WHO TO APPLY TO Delphine van der Pauw, Research and Information Executive, PO Box 3004, London W4 4XT *Tel* 020 8995 4781 *Fax* 020 8995 4781 *email* info@eruk.org.uk *Website* www.epilepsyresearch.org.uk

■ The Equilibrium Foundation

CC NO 1136933 **ESTABLISHED** 2010

WHERE FUNDING CAN BE GIVEN Undefined, in practice throughout the UK.

WHO CAN BENEFIT Older people; children and young people.

WHAT IS FUNDED General charitable purposes; education and training; health; relief of poverty.

TRUSTEES Colin Lawson; Debbie Jukes; Mark Milton-Edwards; Helen Besant-Roberts.

OTHER INFORMATION There is another charity known as Equilibrium – The Bipolar Foundation, (Charity Commission no. 1117177), dedicated to improving treatment and understanding of the causes and effects of bipolar disorder ('manic-depression'). There would appear to be no connection between the two organisations.

HOW TO APPLY In writing to the correspondent.

WHO TO APPLY TO The Trustees, Equilibrium Asset Management, Brooke Court, Lower Meadow Road, Handforth, Wilmslow SK9 3ND *Tel* 0161 486 2250

■ The Equitable Charitable Trust

CC NO 289548 **ESTABLISHED** 1984

WHERE FUNDING CAN BE GIVEN Mainly UK: overseas projects can sometimes be supported.

WHO CAN BENEFIT Schools and other organisations benefiting disabled or disadvantaged children. Priority to organisations and charities with an annual income of less than £5 million.

WHAT IS FUNDED Specific projects for the educational needs of disabled or disadvantaged young people. The trust has three specific priorities: education projects or services that support the learning and development of disabled children and young people in the UK; formal education projects for disadvantaged children and young people in the UK that support delivery of the National Curriculum (i.e. curriculum enrichment projects) or that deliver accredited vocational learning that will increase employability; education projects that will help increase participation in, or improve the quality of, education for disadvantaged or disabled children and young people in developing countries.

WHAT IS NOT FUNDED The trust does not make grants towards the following: general appeals or mail shot requests for donations; informal education projects and those that are only loosely educational; projects felt to be more akin to social work than education; therapeutic treatments; supplementary schooling and homework clubs; mother tongue language classes; state maintained or voluntary aided schools, colleges or universities, either directly or via another charity (e.g. Friends, PTAs); local authorities; public schools or independent schools that are not specifically for children and young people with disabilities or special educational needs; sports education, facilities or activities (e.g. playing fields, sports clubs, or projects that are delivered through the medium of sport); projects or work related to the Olympic Games or Cultural Olympiad; salaries for posts that are not directly related to service delivery (we would not make a grant towards the salary of a fundraiser or book-keeper, for instance); minibuses; pre-school education projects (unless these are solely for the benefit of children with disabilities or special needs); individuals; bursary schemes; projects that promote religious belief or practice; holidays, recreational activities or overseas trips; capital applications for equipment or facilities that will be only partly used for education or by under 25s from disadvantaged or disabled backgrounds (e.g. outdoor education centres that also deliver recreational activities, or that are not exclusively for the use of disadvantaged or disabled children and young people); projects related to PSHE or Citizenship subjects are a low priority.

TYPE OF GRANT Project costs, capital expenditure, equipment and the salary costs of a post.

RANGE OF GRANTS £2,000–£30,000.

SAMPLE GRANTS Promoting Equality in African Schools (£23,000); Ministry of Parenting (£22,000); Africa Educational Trust (£17,000); Kibble Education and Care Centre (£15,000); School-Home Support (£10,000); Oval House (£10,000); Kids (£9,000); Jamie Oliver Foundation (£7,500); Michael Palin Centre for Stammering Children; The London Centre for Children with Cerebral Palsy (£5,000 each); Hampstead Theatre (£2,000).

FINANCES *Year* 2010 *Income* £367,575 *Grants* £842,904 *Assets* £5,960,165

TRUSTEES Brian McGeough; Roy Ranson; Peter Goddard.

HOW TO APPLY There is no form but there are very comprehensive application guidelines available on the trust's website. Accounts must be included. Trustees meet monthly.

WHO TO APPLY TO Jennie Long, Grants Officer, Sixth Floor, 65 Leadenhall Street, London EC3A 2AD *Tel* 020 7264 4993 *Fax* 020 7488 9097 *email* jennielong@equitablecharitabletrust.org.uk *Website* www.equitablecharitabletrust.org.uk

■ The Equity Trust Fund

CC NO 328103   **ESTABLISHED** 1989
WHERE FUNDING CAN BE GIVEN UK.

WHO CAN BENEFIT Theatres, theatre companies and professional theatre performers in genuine need, with special reference to members, past and present, of the union Equity.

WHAT IS FUNDED Welfare and educational grants to individuals and work performed by theatres and theatre companies.

WHAT IS NOT FUNDED No grants to non-professional performers, drama students, non-professional theatre companies, multi-arts venues, community projects or projects with no connection to the professional theatre.

TYPE OF GRANT Grants and loans.

RANGE OF GRANTS Up to £50,000, in practice, around £5,000–£10,000.

SAMPLE GRANTS Dancers' Career Development (£40,000); Lyric Theatre Hammersmith and Northern Actors Centre (£4,000 each); Attic Theatre (£2,000); High Tide Festival (£3,000); and Stone Crabs (£1,000).

FINANCES *Year* 2009–10 *Income* £350,171 *Grants* £54,000 *Assets* £8,108,067

TRUSTEES Colin Baker; Glen Barnham; James Bolam; Annie Bright; Jo Cameron Brown; Robin Browne; Oliver Ford Davies; Graham Hamilton; Frank Hitchman; Barbara Hyslop; Milton Johns; Harry Landis; Ian McGarry; Frederick Pyne; Gillian Raine; Jean Rogers; John Rubinstein; Rosalind Shanks; Ian Talbot; Josephine Tewson; Jeffry Wickham; Frank Williams; Johnny Worthy; Glen Barnham; Jo Cameron Brown; Caroline Smith.

HOW TO APPLY In the first instance please call the office to ascertain if the application is relevant. Failing that, submit a brief letter outlining the application. A meeting takes place about every six to eight weeks. Ring for precise dates. Applications are required at least two weeks beforehand.

WHO TO APPLY TO Keith Carter, Secretary, 222 Africa House, 64 Kingsway, London WC2B 6AH *Tel* 020 7404 6041

■ The Eranda Foundation

CC NO 255650   **ESTABLISHED** 1967
WHERE FUNDING CAN BE GIVEN UK.

WHO CAN BENEFIT Registered charities.

WHAT IS FUNDED The promotion of original research, and the continuation of existing research into medicine and education, fostering of the arts, and promotion of social welfare.

WHAT IS NOT FUNDED No grants to individuals.

TYPE OF GRANT Capital, project, running costs and recurring costs for up to three years.

RANGE OF GRANTS About £500–£150,000.

FINANCES *Year* 2009–10 *Income* £5,303,119 *Grants* £4,265,102 *Assets* £83,214,934

TRUSTEES Sir Evelyn de Rothschild; Renée Robeson; Leopold de Rothschild; Miss Jessica de Rothschild; Anthony de Rothschild; Sir Graham Hearne; Lady Lynn de Rothschild.

HOW TO APPLY In writing to the correspondent. Trustees usually meet in March, July and November and applications should be received two months in advance.

WHO TO APPLY TO Gail Devlin-Jones, Secretary, PO Box 6226, Wing, Leighton Buzzard, Bedfordshire LU7 0XF *Tel* 01296 689157 *email* eranda@btconnect.com

■ The Ericson Trust

CC NO 219762   **ESTABLISHED** 1962
WHERE FUNDING CAN BE GIVEN UK, developing countries, Eastern and Central Europe.

WHO CAN BENEFIT Registered charities only, benefiting: middle-aged and older people; researchers; people disadvantaged by poverty; ex-offenders and those at risk of offending; homeless people; immigrants and refugees.

WHAT IS FUNDED Older people; community projects/local interest groups, including arts; prisons, prison reform, mentoring projects, and research in this area; refugees; mental health; environmental projects and research; aid to developing countries only if supported and represented or initiated and administered by a UK registered charity.

WHAT IS NOT FUNDED No grants to individuals or to non-registered charities. Applications from the following areas are generally not considered unless closely connected with one of the above: children's and young people's clubs, centres and so on; schools; charities dealing with illness or disability (except psychiatric); or religious institutions, except in their social projects.

TYPE OF GRANT Project. Requests for core funding, running costs or particular items are considered.

RANGE OF GRANTS Up to £6,000, with most grants made at £3,000.

SAMPLE GRANTS Previous beneficiaries have included: Action on Elder Abuse, Anti-Slavery International, Ashram International, Bhopal Medical Appeal, Headway East London, Howard League for Penal Reform, the Koestler Trust, Minority Rights Group, Psychiatric Rehabilitation Association, Quaker Social Action, the Rainforest Foundation, the Relatives and Residents Association, Tools for Self Reliance and the Umalini Mary Brahma Charitable Trust.

FINANCES *Year* 2009–10 *Income* £24,733 *Grants* £50,000

TRUSTEES Miss R C Cotton; Mrs V J Barrow; Mrs A M C Cotton.

HOW TO APPLY Unsolicited applications cannot be considered as the trust has no funds available. The correspondent stated: 'We are increasingly worried by the waste of applicants' resources when they send expensive brochures at a time when we are unable to consider any new appeals and have, indeed, reduced some of our long standing grants due to the bad economic situation. It is particularly sad when we receive requests from small charities in Africa and Asia.'

WHO TO APPLY TO The Trustees, Flat 2, 53 Carleton Road, London N7 0ET *email* claudia.cotton@googlemail.com

■ The Ernest Hecht Charitable Foundation

CC NO 1095850　　　**ESTABLISHED** 2002
WHERE FUNDING CAN BE GIVEN England and Wales.
WHO CAN BENEFIT Registered charities.
WHAT IS FUNDED Support is given for: the advancement of education; relief of poverty; and advancement of religion.
FINANCES *Year* 2010 *Income* £166,145 *Grants* £87,550 *Assets* £457,572
TRUSTEES E Hecht; A P Rose; R Ward.
HOW TO APPLY In writing to the correspondent.
WHO TO APPLY TO Robert Ward, Trustee, Summit House, 170 Finchley Road, London NW3 6BP *Tel* 020 7438 6100

■ The Erskine Cunningham Hill Trust

SC NO SC001853　　　**ESTABLISHED** 1955
WHERE FUNDING CAN BE GIVEN Scotland.
WHO CAN BENEFIT Organisations registered in Scotland benefiting older people, young people, ex-service men and women, seamen, and the Church of Scotland.
WHAT IS FUNDED The Church of Scotland is the largest single focus of the trust's interest (50% of annual income). Other grants are restricted to charitable work in Scotland with older people; young people; ex-servicemen and women; seamen; Scottish interests; with priority given to charities administered by voluntary or honorary officials.
WHAT IS NOT FUNDED No grants to individuals.
TYPE OF GRANT Recurring grants to the Church of Scotland; one-off grants to individual Scottish charities.
RANGE OF GRANTS Approximately £1,000 each to individual charities.
SAMPLE GRANTS Beneficiaries have included ChildLine and Cruse Bereavement Care, The Sailors' Family Society and Venture Trust.
FINANCES *Year* 2009–10 *Income* £54,632
TRUSTEES R M Maiden; Very Revd Dr A McDonald; I W Grimmond; Very Revd J Cairns; Very Revd A McLellan; Dr A Elliot; The Church of Scotland Trust.
HOW TO APPLY In writing to the correspondent at the above address. An application form is available via email from the correspondent. There is a two-year time bar on repeat grants. The trustees do not consider applications from outside Scotland.
WHO TO APPLY TO Fred Marsh, Secretary, Department of National Mission, Church of Scotland Offices, 121 George Street, Edinburgh EH2 4YN *Tel* 0131 225 5722 *email* fmarsh@cofscotland. org.uk

■ The Esfandi Charitable Foundation

CC NO 1103095　　　**ESTABLISHED** 2004
WHERE FUNDING CAN BE GIVEN UK and overseas.
WHO CAN BENEFIT Registered charities.
WHAT IS FUNDED Jewish causes.
RANGE OF GRANTS Usually up to £50,000.
SAMPLE GRANTS Norwood (£55,000); Jewish Care (£25,000); Community Security Trust (£25,000); WST Charity LTD (£17,000); Chief Rabbinate Trust (£15,000); Jewish Community Secondary School Trust (£13,000); Ahavat Shaloh Charity Fund (£11,000); Royal National Theatre (£10,000); UK Friends of Association for Wellbeing of Israel's Soldiers (£5,000); European Council of Jewish Communities (£2,500); Achisomoch (£2,000); and the Chicken Soup Shelter, the Variety Club Children's Charity and JABE (£1,000 each).
FINANCES *Year* 2009–10 *Income* £256,549 *Grants* £235,325 *Assets* £158,445
TRUSTEES J Esfandi; Mrs D Esfandi.
HOW TO APPLY In writing to the correspondent.
WHO TO APPLY TO J Esfandi, Trustee, 36 Park Street, London W1K 2JE

■ Essex Community Foundation

CC NO 1052061　　　**ESTABLISHED** 1996
WHERE FUNDING CAN BE GIVEN Essex, Southend and Thurrock.
WHO CAN BENEFIT Any voluntary and community organisations, or any non-profit making organisation working for the benefit of people living in Essex, Southend and Thurrock. The foundation is particularly interested in small grass-roots groups.
WHAT IS FUNDED Support generally falls under the broad heading of social welfare. The foundation distributes grants through various funds. Information on current funds and their criteria is available on the foundation's website.
WHAT IS NOT FUNDED The foundation does not support the following: political activities; statutory bodies undertaking their statutory obligations, including schools; general appeals; activities which support animal welfare; projects that operate outside of Essex, or benefit non-Essex residents; retrospective funding.
TYPE OF GRANT Core costs/revenue costs, new or continuing projects, one-off initiatives and capital costs.
RANGE OF GRANTS £50–£100,000.
SAMPLE GRANTS London Bus Theatre Company (£86,000); Basildon, Billericay & Wickford CVS (£62,500); Inclusion Ventures Ltd (£60,000); Acorn Housing Association (£39,000); Chelmsford Women's Aid (£29,000); Crossroads Care Brentwood Basildon and Districts (£15,000); Hythe Community Centre Association (£11,000); Home-Start Brentwood (£10,000); Rural Community Council of Essex (£8,500); Debden Village Hall (£6,000); Essex Wildlife Trust (£5,500); and Dunmow Blind and Housebound Social Club and Severalls Concert Group (£5,000 each).
FINANCES *Year* 2009–10 *Income* £4,108,603 *Grants* £1,712,365 *Assets* £13,876,768
TRUSTEES John Spence, Chair; Peter Blanc; Jason Bartella; John Barnes; Charles Clark; Carole Golbourn; Peter Heap; Rhiannedd Pratley; Martin Hopkins; Margaret Hyde; Jonny Minter; Owen Richards; Colin Sivell; Jackie Sully.
HOW TO APPLY Essex Community Foundation manages a number of funds, many of which are tailored to the individual wishes of the donors. However, with the exception of the four funds listed below, all you have to do is complete a general application form and the foundation will find the right fund for you. Application forms are available from the foundation's office or can be downloaded from the website. Deadlines are usually twice a year on 9 January and 9 September; please contact the foundation for exact dates. Grants are awarded within three months of the deadlines. If in doubt about the suitability of your project for funding, call the foundation's grants team on 01245 356018, or email: grants@essexcf.org.uk
The four funds which use a specific application form are: Comic Relief; Thriving Third Sector Fund;

High Sheriffs' Award; and the Marion Ruth Courtauld Educational Fund. They may also have different application deadlines. Further information about each of these funds is available from the foundation's website, or by contacting the grants team, as above.

WHO TO APPLY TO Grants Team, 121 New London Road, Chelmsford, Essex CM2 0QT *Tel* 01245 355947 *Fax* 01245 246391 *email* general@essexcf.org.uk *Website* www.essexcommunityfoundation.org.uk

■ The Essex Fairway Charitable Trust

CC NO 1066858   **ESTABLISHED** 1997

WHERE FUNDING CAN BE GIVEN South east England, with a preference for Essex.

WHO CAN BENEFIT Registered charities, particularly those directly benefiting people in need. Small charities in south east England, particularly Essex, will be favoured.

WHAT IS FUNDED General charitable purposes.

WHAT IS NOT FUNDED No grants for medical research, animal welfare, the environment and political and religious purposes. No grants to large UK charities. Individuals are only considered in very exceptional circumstances.

TYPE OF GRANT One-off grants for capital and revenue costs and full project funding. Replacement of statutory funding also available.

SAMPLE GRANTS Previous beneficiaries have included Awareness of Down's Syndrome, CHESS, East Essex District Scouts Council, Fair Haven Hospice, Farleigh Hospice, Felixstowe Youth Development Group, Hamelin Trust, Headway Essex, Anne Lloyd Memorial Trust, Macmillan Cancer Relief, Martha Trust, St Christopher's School, Stepney Children's Fund and St Patrick's Trust.

FINANCES *Year* 2010 *Income* £6,253 *Grants* £150,000

TRUSTEES P W George; C J Holmes.

PUBLICATIONS A full grants list is available on request to the trust.

HOW TO APPLY Please note the following statement from the trust: 'The trust very rarely gives donations in response to applications from charities that it has not previously supported and will not reply to such applications.'

WHO TO APPLY TO K H Larkman, c/o Birkett Long, Essex House, 42 Crouch Street, Colchester, Essex CO3 3HH *Tel* 01206 217300

■ The Essex Heritage Trust

CC NO 802317   **ESTABLISHED** 1989

WHERE FUNDING CAN BE GIVEN Essex.

WHO CAN BENEFIT Any organisation, body or individual whose project will be to the benefit of the people of Essex.

WHAT IS FUNDED Grants to bodies or individuals undertaking specific work in accord with the objects of the trust, including publication or preservation of Essex history and restoration of monuments, significant structures, artefacts and church decorations and equipment.

WHAT IS NOT FUNDED No grants involving private property.

TYPE OF GRANT Mostly one-off grants for revenue and capital costs.

RANGE OF GRANTS Mainly up to £5,000.

SAMPLE GRANTS The Guildhall, Finchingfield (£10,000); Thaxted Windmill Restoration Trust and Essex County Council – Bandstand

restoration, Cliff Park, Dovercourt (£5,000 each); Messing Village Hall Committee (£4,600); The Fry Art Gallery and Chantry Chapel, Thorndon Park (£3,500); Birchanger Wood Trust and St James' the Great, Colchester – Walker Organ repair & restoration (£2,000 each); Ashdon Windmill Trust Ltd (£750) and Colchester Arts Centre (£500).

FINANCES *Year* 2010–11 *Income* £58,809 *Grants* £71,035 *Assets* £1,257,024

TRUSTEES Lord Petre; Richard Wollaston; Mark Pertwee; Peter Mamelok; James Bettley; Brian Moody; Susan Brice; Rodney Bass; Jonathan Douglas-Hughes.

PUBLICATIONS Annual newsletter.

OTHER INFORMATION The trust has been able to keep its governance costs low due to the continuing sponsorship of the salary and payroll costs of the trust's administrator by Essex County Council.

HOW TO APPLY In writing to the correspondent in the first instance. An application form will be returned for detailed completion with estimates if it is considered that the project falls within the trust's objectives. The trustees meet three times a year in March, July and November, when grant awards will be made.

WHO TO APPLY TO Sharon Hill, Administrator, Cressing Temple, Witham Road, Braintree, Essex CM77 8PD *Tel* 01376 585794 *Fax* 01376 585794 *email* eht@dsl.pipex.com *Website* www.essexheritagetrust.co.uk

■ Essex Provincial Charity Fund

CC NO 215349   **ESTABLISHED** 1932

WHERE FUNDING CAN BE GIVEN Essex.

WHO CAN BENEFIT Essex Freemasons; their dependants; central Masonic charities, and other charities.

WHAT IS FUNDED Preference for charities with a medical bias and, primarily in Essex, that assist the community in general.

WHAT IS NOT FUNDED No grants to individuals, other than those who are dependants of freemasons.

SAMPLE GRANTS Previous beneficiaries have included Broomfield Hospital – St Andrew's Centre, Grand Charity, London Chest Hospital, Macmillan Cancer Relief, Royal Masonic Trust for Girls and Boys, New Masonic Samaritan Fund and Royal Masonic Benevolent Fund.

FINANCES *Year* 2009–10 *Income* £236,572 *Grants* £38,000

TRUSTEES Peter Holland; Frederick Harris; Allan Kemp; Christopher Williams; Andrew Bishop; Paul Cohen; Kenneth Keenes; Laurie Justice.

OTHER INFORMATION The grants total is based on previous research.

HOW TO APPLY In writing to the correspondent.

WHO TO APPLY TO Kenneth Keenes, Trustee, 113 The Sorrells, Stanford-le-Hope, Essex SS17 7ES

■ The Essex Youth Trust

CC NO 225768   **ESTABLISHED** 1963

WHERE FUNDING CAN BE GIVEN Essex.

WHO CAN BENEFIT Beneficiaries include schools, youth clubs and organisations giving advice, help and information.

WHAT IS FUNDED The advancement of education for people under the age of 25 who are in need of assistance. Preference is given to those who are in need owing to 'being temporarily or permanently deprived of normal parental care or who are otherwise disadvantaged. The trustees favour organisations which develop young people's physical, mental and spiritual capacities through active participation in sports and indoor and outdoor activities. As a result they are particularly supportive of youth clubs and other organisations which provide facilities for young people to take active part in an assortment of activities as well as single activity organisations.'

WHAT IS NOT FUNDED No grants to individuals.

RANGE OF GRANTS Up to £25,000.

SAMPLE GRANTS Cirdan Sailing Trust (£57,000 in three grants); Stubbers Adventure Centre (£45,000); Essex Boys' and Girls' Clubs (£28,000 in two grants); North Avenue Youth Centre (£19,000 in three grants); Solid (£15,000); St Mark's College (£10,000); the Ark Family Resource Centre (£8,000); Frenford Clubs and Maldon Essex Mind (£5,000 each); Roots in the River (£4,000); Beyond Youth (£3,000); Motorvations Project (£2,000); Hope UK (£1,000); and Colchester Institute (£750).

FINANCES *Year* 2009–10 *Income* £420,797 *Grants* £350,881 *Assets* £6,972,880

TRUSTEES Richard Wenley; Julien Courtauld; Michael Dyer; Revd Duncan Green; William David Robson; Lady Julia Denison-Smith; Claire Coltwell; Michael Biegel; Mrs Julie Rogers.

HOW TO APPLY On a form available from the correspondent. The trustees meet on a quarterly basis.

WHO TO APPLY TO J P Douglas-Hughes, Clerk, Gepp and Sons, 58 New London Road, Chelmsford, Essex CM2 0PA *Tel* 01245 493939 *Fax* 01245 493940 *email* douglas-hughesj@gepp.co.uk

---

■ The Estelle Trust

CC NO 1101299   **ESTABLISHED** 2003

WHERE FUNDING CAN BE GIVEN Not defined, but in practice Zambia.

WHO CAN BENEFIT Organisations mostly in Zambia.

WHAT IS FUNDED Overseas aid and general charitable purposes.

RANGE OF GRANTS Usually up to £10,000.

SAMPLE GRANTS Wind pump programme in Africa (£62,000); Chipembele Wildlife Education Trust (£18,000); Arulussa School Development (£11,000); Lorry (£9,000); Queen's College Cambridge (£7,000); International Rescue Committee (£5,000); Action Age (£1,000); Kids Company (£1,000); Prostate Research Campaign UK (£250); and the Sabre Charitable Trust (£100).

FINANCES *Year* 2009–10 *Income* £131,725 *Grants* £117,930 *Assets* £1,433,403

TRUSTEES N AN E Farrow; G R Ornstein; K-M Britain; S Farrow; D Wise.

HOW TO APPLY In writing to the correspondent.

WHO TO APPLY TO Ged Ornstein, Trustee, Fisher Phillips, 170 Finchley Road, London NW3 6BP *Tel* 020 7483 6100

■ Joseph Ettedgui Charitable Foundation

CC NO 1139615   **ESTABLISHED** 2010

WHERE FUNDING CAN BE GIVEN UK and overseas.

WHO CAN BENEFIT Registered charities.

WHAT IS FUNDED General charitable purposes, with a preference for organisations working with children and young people, older people and people with disabilities.

TRUSTEES Isabel Ettedgui; Peter Ettedgui; Paul Ettedgui.

HOW TO APPLY In writing to the correspondent.

WHO TO APPLY TO Steve Harvey, Administrator, Trustee Dept, Coutts & Co, 440 Strand, London WC2R 0QS *Tel* 020 7753 1000 *email* steve. harvey@coutts.com

---

■ Euro Charity Trust

CC NO 1058460   **ESTABLISHED** 1996

WHERE FUNDING CAN BE GIVEN Worldwide, mainly India, Africa, Bangladesh and the UK.

WHO CAN BENEFIT Registered charities.

WHAT IS FUNDED The relief of poverty; to assist the vulnerable; and to assist in the advancement of education in the UK and the rest of the world.

SAMPLE GRANTS Nathani Charitable Trust (£1 million); Anjuman-I-Islam (£745,000); Moulana Hussain Ahmad Madani Charitable Trust and Charitable Society (£479,000); Jamia Isiamia Ishaatul Uloom (£465,000); and Darul U1oom Deoband (£400,000).

FINANCES *Year* 2010 *Income* £5,167,352 *Grants* £3,814,897 *Assets* £1,672,543

TRUSTEES Nasir Awan; Abdul Malik.

OTHER INFORMATION Over two thirds of the trust's grantmaking is concentrated in India.

HOW TO APPLY In writing to the correspondent.

WHO TO APPLY TO Ahmed Omer, Trustee, 51a Church Road, Edgbaston, Birmingham B15 3SJ *email* info@eurocharity.org.uk

---

■ The Patrick Evans Foundation

CC NO 1134412   **ESTABLISHED** 2010

WHERE FUNDING CAN BE GIVEN Undefined, in practice the UK.

WHO CAN BENEFIT Organisations and individuals.

TRUSTEES Mike Dennis; Alun I Evans; Mrs Catherine Evans; Miss Louise Evans; Matt Lloyd; Sean Standerwick.

HOW TO APPLY In writing to the correspondent.

WHO TO APPLY TO Mr Alun I Evans, Trustee, 31 Cronks Hill Road, Redhill RH1 6LY *email* info@patrickevansfoundation.co.uk *Website* www.patrickevansfoundation.co.uk

---

■ The Alan Evans Memorial Trust

CC NO 326263   **ESTABLISHED** 1979

WHERE FUNDING CAN BE GIVEN UK.

WHO CAN BENEFIT Registered charities only.

WHAT IS FUNDED The purchase of land and the planting of trees, shrubs and plants. The restoration of cathedrals, churches and other buildings of beauty or historical interest, to which the public can have access.

WHAT IS NOT FUNDED No grants to individuals or for management or running expenses, although favourable consideration is given in respect of the purchase of land and restoration of buildings. General appeals will not be acknowledged.

RANGE OF GRANTS £250–£1,000.

SAMPLE GRANTS Previous beneficiaries include: English Hedgerow Trust, Landmark Trust, Zoological Society of London, St Wilfrid's Church – Leeds, Thatcham Charity, Cathedral Church of the Holy Spirit – Guildford, Peterborough Cathedral Development and Preservation Trust, Wells Cathedral – Somerset, Lincoln Cathedral and the Church of Our Lord, St Mary and St Germaine – Selby Abbey.

FINANCES *Year* 2009–10 *Income* £95,565 *Grants* £77,166 *Assets* £1,576,281

TRUSTEES Coutts & Co.; David Halfhead; Deirdre Moss.

HOW TO APPLY There is no formal application form, but appeals should be made in writing to the correspondent, stating why the funds are required, what funds have been promised from other sources (for example, English Heritage) and the amount outstanding. The trust has also stated previously that it would be helpful when making applications to provide a photograph of the project. The trustees normally meet four times a year, although in urgent cases decisions can be made between meetings.

WHO TO APPLY TO The Trust Manager, Coutts & Co., Trustee Department, 440 Strand, London WC2R 0QS *Tel* 020 7753 1000

■ Sir John Evelyn's Charity

CC NO 225707   **ESTABLISHED** 1974
WHERE FUNDING CAN BE GIVEN Ancient parishes of St Nicholas Deptford and St Luke Deptford.
WHO CAN BENEFIT Charities benefiting people disadvantaged by poverty.
WHAT IS FUNDED Pensions and grants to organisations working to relieve poverty.
SAMPLE GRANTS Armada Community project (£42,000); Evelyn 190 Centre (£5,000); Henrietta and Hughes Field Young People's Project (£13,000); and St Nicholas and St Luke's (£400).
FINANCES *Year* 2010 *Income* £56,532 *Grants* £60,337 *Assets* £2,662,263
TRUSTEES Bridget Perry, Chair; Revd J K Lucas; Jasmine Barnett; Kay Ingledew; Mrs J Miller; Cllr M O'Mara; Cllr Margaret Mythen.
OTHER INFORMATION Grants to individuals totalled £365.
HOW TO APPLY In writing to the correspondent.
WHO TO APPLY TO Mrs Colette A Saunders, Clerk's Office, Armada Court Hall, 21 McMillan Street, Deptford, London SE8 3EZ *Tel* 020 8694 8953

■ The Eventhall Family Charitable Trust

CC NO 803178   **ESTABLISHED** 1989
WHERE FUNDING CAN BE GIVEN Preference for north west England.
WHO CAN BENEFIT Institutions and individuals.
WHAT IS FUNDED General charitable purposes.
WHAT IS NOT FUNDED No grants to students.
SAMPLE GRANTS Previous beneficiaries have included Aish Hatorah, ChildLine, Clitheroe Wolves Football Club, Community Security Trust, Greibach Memorial, Guide Dogs for the Blind, Heathlands Village, International Wildlife Coalition, JJCT, MB Foundation Charity, Only Foals and Horses Sanctuary, Red Nose Day, RNLI, Sale Ladies Society, Shelter and South Manchester Synagogue.
FINANCES *Year* 2009–10 *Income* £124,489 *Grants* £204,000 *Assets* £2,850,943
TRUSTEES Julia Eventhall; David Eventhall.
HOW TO APPLY In writing to the correspondent. Please note, however, previous research highlighted that the trust stated it only has a very limited amount of funds available. Telephone calls are not accepted by the trust. Trustees meet monthly to consider grants. A pre-addressed envelope is appreciated (stamp not necessary). Unsuccessful applicants will not receive a reply.
WHO TO APPLY TO The Trustees, PO Box 490, Altrincham WA14 22T

■ The Everard Foundation

CC NO 272248   **ESTABLISHED** 1976
WHERE FUNDING CAN BE GIVEN Leicestershire.
WHO CAN BENEFIT Local organisations of all sizes. Grants to UK-wide organisations must be to fund something tangibly local.
WHAT IS FUNDED General charitable purposes.
WHAT IS NOT FUNDED No grants to individuals.
TYPE OF GRANT Capital and revenue costs. Funding is available for up to three years.
RANGE OF GRANTS From £250.
SAMPLE GRANTS Leicestershire & Rutland Crimebeat Ltd (£256,000); Leicestershire Cares Ltd (£11,000); Age Concern Leicestershire & Rutland (£5,500); Help for Heroes, Leicester Theatre Trust and the Leicester Diocesan Board of Finance (£5,000 each); Special Effect (£2,500); Peterborough Diocesan Board of Finance (£2,000); Jo's Trust and Army Cadet Force Association (£1,000 each); and Edinburgh Charity Fashion show (£600).
FINANCES *Year* 2009–10 *Income* £138,230 *Grants* £327,634 *Assets* £3,045,050
TRUSTEES Richard Everard; Serena Richards; Simon J Aitkinson.
HOW TO APPLY In writing to the correspondent at any time.
WHO TO APPLY TO Richard Everard, Trustee, Castle Acres, Everard Way, Enderby, Leicester LE19 1BY

■ The Eveson Charitable Trust

CC NO 1032204   **ESTABLISHED** 1994
WHERE FUNDING CAN BE GIVEN Herefordshire, Worcestershire and the county of West Midlands (covering Birmingham, Coventry, Dudley, Sandwell, Solihull, Walsall and Wolverhampton).
WHO CAN BENEFIT Registered charities.
WHAT IS FUNDED People with physical disabilities, (including those who are blind or deaf); people with mental disabilities; hospitals and hospices; children who are in need, whether disadvantaged or with physical or mental disabilities; older people; homeless people; medical research into problems associated with any of these conditions.
WHAT IS NOT FUNDED Grants are not made to individuals, even if such a request is submitted by a charitable organisation.
TYPE OF GRANT Capital and revenue, recurring and one-off.
RANGE OF GRANTS From a few hundred pounds to £150,000; average grant around £8,000.
SAMPLE GRANTS Acorns Children's Hospice Trust (£50,000), towards nursing services at its hospice in Selly Oak, Birmingham, that provides support to life limited and life threatened children and young people; Breast Cancer Haven (£50,000), a two-year grant towards running costs of Hereford Haven that benefits people with breast cancer; Megan Baker House – Leominster (£30,000), towards the running costs of this charity that provides a free conductive education service to disabled children; Coventry & District Free Church Homes for the Elderly (£25,000), towards building extension to provide more bedrooms with improved facilities to benefit older people; Society for Mucopolysaccharide Diseases (£15,000), towards their advocacy support programme that benefits children living in the trust's area who suffer from MPS; Community Voluntary Action – Ledbury (£12,000), towards the running costs of the Mobility Centre service that benefits disabled people and older people

with mobility problems; Family Drug Support – Herefordshire (£8,000), towards work benefiting those affected by drug, alcohol and substance abuse in their families; Music in Hospitals (£6,000), towards live music performances in hospitals, hospices, homes, day care centres and special schools in the area; and Norman Laud Association – Sutton Coldfield (£4,500), towards refurbishment of bedrooms at this respite care home for children with special needs.

FINANCES *Year* 2009–10 *Income* £587,151 *Grants* £2,007,331 *Assets* £60,487,809

TRUSTEES David Pearson, Chair; Bruce Maughfling; Rt. Revd Anthony Priddis, Bishop of Hereford; Martin Davies; Louise Woodhead; Bill Wiggin; Richard Mainwaring.

HOW TO APPLY The trustees meet quarterly, usually at the end of March and June and the beginning of October and January. Applications can only be considered if they are on the trust's standard, but very simple, 'application for support' form which can be obtained from the administrator at the offices of the trust in Gloucester. The form must be completed and returned (together with a copy of the latest accounts and annual report of the organisation) to the trust's offices at least six weeks before the meeting of trustees at which the application is to be considered, in order to give time for necessary assessment procedures, often including visits to applicants. Before providing support to statutory bodies (such as hospitals and schools for people with learning difficulties), the trust requires written confirmation that no statutory funds are available to meet the need for which funds are being requested. In the case of larger grants to hospitals, the trust asks the district health authority to confirm that no statutory funding is available. Where applications are submitted that clearly fall outside the grantmaking parameters of the trust, the applicant is advised that the application cannot be considered and reasons are given. All applications that are going to be considered by the trustees are acknowledged in writing. Applicants are advised of the reference number of their application and of the quarterly meeting at which their application is going to be considered. The decisions are advised to applicants in writing soon after these meetings. Funded projects are monitored.

WHO TO APPLY TO Alex D Gay, Administrator, 45 Park Road, Gloucester GL1 1LP *Tel* 01452 501352 *Fax* 01452 302195

■ The Beryl Evetts and Robert Luff Animal Welfare Trust

CC NO 283944   **ESTABLISHED** 1981

WHERE FUNDING CAN BE GIVEN UK.

WHO CAN BENEFIT Animal charities. The trust supports the same beneficiaries each year.

WHAT IS FUNDED Veterinary research and the care and welfare of animals.

TYPE OF GRANT Priority to research projects and bursaries.

RANGE OF GRANTS Up to £65,000.

SAMPLE GRANTS Animal Welfare Trust (£65,000); Royal Veterinary College (£60,000); Blue Cross (£2,500); and Greek Animal Welfare Trust, Battersea Dogs Home, St Tiggy Winkles, Brooke Hospitals for Animals, Mayhew Animal Home, Songbird Survival, Kent Wildlife Trust, Animal Samaritan and the Cats (£1,000 each).

FINANCES *Year* 2009–10 *Income* £44,698 *Grants* £136,500 *Assets* £1,006,670

TRUSTEES Sir R Johnson; Revd M Tomlinson; J Tomlinson; R P J Price; B Nicholson; Lady Johnson; G Favot; M Condon.

HOW TO APPLY 'No applications, thank you.' The trust gives grants to the same beneficiaries each year and funds are often allocated two years in advance.

WHO TO APPLY TO The Administrator, 294 Earls Court Road, London SW5 9BB

■ The Execution Charitable Trust

CC NO 1099097   **ESTABLISHED** 2003

WHERE FUNDING CAN BE GIVEN Worldwide, in practice mainly UK.

WHO CAN BENEFIT Charitable organisations.

WHAT IS FUNDED Local organisations and community projects working in deprived areas in the UK, tackling the root causes, as well as the symptoms, of poverty and isolation.

TYPE OF GRANT One-off and recurring.

RANGE OF GRANTS Up to £400,000.

SAMPLE GRANTS ARK – local and international projects; Myeloma – UK; Peace One Day – Surrey; The Tullochan Trust – Dunbartonshire; Bryncynon Community Revival Strategy Limited – Wales; Family Action – London; South Side Family – Bedford.

FINANCES *Year* 2010 *Income* £845,728 *Grants* £958,720 *Assets* £1,001,726

TRUSTEES Jacky Joy; John R Moore; Cheryl Mustapha Whyte; Damien Devine; Peter Ward; Neil Strong.

OTHER INFORMATION Details of grants awarded were not included in the accounts.

HOW TO APPLY The trust does not consider unsolicited applications for grants. The trust has appointed New Philanthropy Capital (NPC) to proactively identify effective organisations on its behalf. To apply, visit the Execution Charitable Trust's website to fill in the online form with basic contact details and a short outline of the project.

WHO TO APPLY TO Cheryl Mustapha Whyte, Trustee, 10 Paternoster Square, London EC4M 7AL *Tel* 020 7375 2007 *email* info@ executionlimited.com *Website* www.execution-noble.com/x/charitable-interests.html

■ The Mayor of Exeter's Appeal Fund

CC NO 283469   **ESTABLISHED** 1981

WHERE FUNDING CAN BE GIVEN Exeter.

WHO CAN BENEFIT One charity is supported each year, selected by the Mayor Elect.

WHAT IS FUNDED General charitable purposes.

SAMPLE GRANTS Previous beneficiaries have included Headway Exeter, Hospice Care – Exeter, St Petrox House for the Homeless and The Ellen Tinkham School for children with special needs.

FINANCES *Year* 2009–10 *Income* £20,953 *Grants* £20,000

TRUSTEES Exeter City Council.

HOW TO APPLY In writing to the correspondent.

WHO TO APPLY TO Head of Treasury Services, Exeter City Council, Civic Centre, Paris Street, Exeter EX1 1JN *Tel* 01392 265241 *email* mayoralty@ exeter.gov.uk *Website* www.exeter.gov.uk

Think carefully about every application. Is it justified?

525

■ The Exilarch's Foundation

CC NO 275919   ESTABLISHED 1978

WHERE FUNDING CAN BE GIVEN Mainly UK.

WHO CAN BENEFIT Jewish people, educational institutions, older people, illness and relief in need.

WHAT IS FUNDED Jewish organisations; educational, medical and welfare charities.

RANGE OF GRANTS up to £4 million.

SAMPLE GRANTS Westminster Academy (£306,000); Jewish Museum (£100,000); Weizmann UK (£25,000); and Jewish Association for Business Ethics (£11,000).

FINANCES *Year* 2010 *Income* £6,320,965 *Grants* £2,833,532 *Assets* £56,982,249

TRUSTEES Naim Dangoor; David Dangoor; Elie Dangoor; Robert Dangoor; Michael Dangoor.

OTHER INFORMATION The foundation's annual report states that: 'The trustees have built up a designated reserve of £10 million for the specific purpose of assisting the setting up of educational and religious institutions in a future re-established Jewish community in Iraq. Once the position and security of that country has been stabilised it is anticipated that some Jews may chooses to live in Iraq when they will be free to pursue their religious faith without fear of persecution and discrimination.'

HOW TO APPLY The trust stated that it does not respond to unsolicited applications for grants.

WHO TO APPLY TO Naim Dangoor, Trustee, 4 Carlos Place, Mayfair, London W1K 3AW *Tel* 020 7399 0850

■ Extonglen Limited

CC NO 286230   ESTABLISHED 1982

WHERE FUNDING CAN BE GIVEN UK and Israel.

WHO CAN BENEFIT Orthodox Jewish organisations.

WHAT IS FUNDED Orthodox Jewish causes.

RANGE OF GRANTS £0–£500,000.

SAMPLE GRANTS Previously: Kol Halashon Education Programme (£470,000); Ahavas Chesed (£95,000); Pikuach Nefesh (£50,000); Kupath Gemach Chaim Bechesed Viznitz Trust (£40,000); British Friends of Nishmat Yisrael (£12,000); Children's Town Charity (£3,600).

FINANCES *Year* 2009 *Income* £510,823 *Grants* £1,072,653 *Assets* £13,098,419

TRUSTEES M Levine; Mrs C Levine; I Katzenberg.

HOW TO APPLY In writing to the correspondent.

WHO TO APPLY TO C Levine, New Burlington House, 1075 Finchley Road, London NW11 0PU *Tel* 020 8731 0777 *email* ml@rowdeal.com

■ The William and Christine Eynon Charity

CC NO 1134334   ESTABLISHED 2010

WHERE FUNDING CAN BE GIVEN Worldwide, in practice the UK.

WHO CAN BENEFIT Registered charities.

WHAT IS FUNDED General charitable purposes.

TRUSTEES William Kingdon Eynon; Christine Eynon; Ms Sophie Eynon; James Eynon.

HOW TO APPLY In writing to the correspondent.

WHO TO APPLY TO William Kingdon Eynon, Trustee, Tusker House, Newton, Porthcawl CF36 5ST *Tel* 01656 782312

■ The Matthew Eyton Animal Welfare Trust

CC NO 1003575   ESTABLISHED 1991

WHERE FUNDING CAN BE GIVEN Not defined.

WHO CAN BENEFIT Animal charities, mainly farm animal charities as opposed to wild or companion animals; vegetarians; and vegans.

WHAT IS FUNDED Animal charities, vegetarian/vegan.

TYPE OF GRANT One-off.

RANGE OF GRANTS £50–£51,000.

FINANCES *Year* 2009–10 *Income* £68,035 *Grants* £46,829 *Assets* £74,407

TRUSTEES Mrs Audrey Eyton; P A Flood.

HOW TO APPLY In writing to the correspondent.

WHO TO APPLY TO The Trustees, 7 Blackfriars Street, Canterbury, Kent CT1 2AP

■ F C Charitable Trust

CC NO 277686   **ESTABLISHED** 1978

WHERE FUNDING CAN BE GIVEN Worldwide, but mainly the UK.

WHO CAN BENEFIT Christian and welfare organisations.

WHAT IS FUNDED The trust gives support in the areas of Christian churches, missionary societies, ministers, missionaries and welfare.

WHAT IS NOT FUNDED Individuals are not eligible for grants and the trust does not normally support a charity unless it is known to the trustees.

SAMPLE GRANTS Emmanuel Church Wimbledon (£32,000 in 5 grants); The Ashton Thanksgiving Fund (£2,500 each); Stowe School Foundation and Anglican Mainstream (£1,000 each); Friends of St Ebbe's Trust (£500) and Church Society (£75).

FINANCES *Year* 2010–11 *Income* £91,283 *Grants* £48,682 *Assets* £516,855

TRUSTEES John C Vernor-Miles; The Revd Jonathan James Molyneux Fletcher.

HOW TO APPLY Applications can only be accepted from registered charities and should be in writing to the correspondent. In order to save administration costs, replies are not sent to unsuccessful applicants. For the most part, funds are fully committed.

WHO TO APPLY TO John C Vernor-Miles, Trustee, c/o Hunters, 9 New Square, Lincoln's Inn, London WC2A 3QN *Tel* 020 7412 0050

■ The F P Limited Charitable Trust

CC NO 328737   **ESTABLISHED** 1990

WHERE FUNDING CAN BE GIVEN UK, with a possible preference for Greater Manchester.

WHO CAN BENEFIT Registered charities.

WHAT IS FUNDED This trust supports educational causes, schools, religious bodies and medical appeals, giving most of its funds to regular beneficiaries.

SAMPLE GRANTS Donations were made to a variety of schools, religious institutions and medical appeals. Unfortunately a detailed list of beneficiaries was not available.

FINANCES *Year* 2008–09 *Income* £20,000 *Grants* £25,000

TRUSTEES Joshua Pine; Eli Pine.

HOW TO APPLY In writing to the correspondent.

WHO TO APPLY TO Mr Joshua Pine, Trustee, 14 Westfield Street, Salford M7 4NG *Tel* 0161 834 0456 *Fax* 0161 832 0385

■ The Faber Charitable Trust

CC NO 294820   **ESTABLISHED** 1986

WHERE FUNDING CAN BE GIVEN UK.

WHO CAN BENEFIT Jewish causes.

WHAT IS FUNDED General charitable purposes.

FINANCES *Year* 2009–10 *Income* £6,919 *Grants* £20,000

TRUSTEES Bernard Faber; Fay Faber; Benjamin Rosefelder; Jeremy Golker.

HOW TO APPLY In writing to the correspondent.

WHO TO APPLY TO H Kramer, Trustee, Citroen Wells & PartnersDevonshire House, 1 Devonshire Street, London W1W 5DR *Tel* 020 7304 2000

■ Esmée Fairbairn Foundation

CC NO 200051   **ESTABLISHED** 1961

WHERE FUNDING CAN BE GIVEN UK.

WHO CAN BENEFIT Voluntary and charitable organisations.

WHAT IS FUNDED **The Main Fund**: the cultural life of the UK, education and learning, the natural environment and enabling disadvantaged people to participate more fully in society. The foundation prioritises work that: addresses a *significant* gap in provision; develops or strengthens good practice; challenges convention or takes a risk in order to address a difficult issue; tests out new ideas or practices; takes an enterprising approach to achieving its aims; sets out to influence policy or change behaviour more widely.

Strands: the foundation also makes grants under the following two strands: *Food* – 'The aim of the Food Strand is to promote an understanding of the role of food in enhancing quality of life. It will prioritise the enjoyment and experience of food rather than its production and we seek to enable as many people in the UK as possible to access, prepare and eat nutritious, sustainable food. We are interested in work that influences policy and practice across a range of food-related areas. We expect to support a mix of practical projects that have wide significance, and some research and policy based work.'

Esmée Fairbairn Collections Fund – 'This fund is run by the Museums Association. It focuses on time-limited collections work outside the scope of an organisation's core resources. Through this fund the MA will award approximately £800,000 per year to museums, galleries and heritage organisations with two grant rounds per year. Organisations can apply for sums between £20,000 and £100,000. We are keen to fund projects at an early stage of development where it may be difficult to guarantee tangible outcomes. We want organisations that are funded to become part of a network to develop ideas, share knowledge and build a legacy. Projects that are eligible to apply include research into collections, conservation, collections review and initiatives to develop the use of collections.'

WHAT IS NOT FUNDED The foundation will not support the following: individuals or causes that will benefit only one person, including student grants or bursaries; support for a general appeal or circular; work that does not have a direct benefit in the UK; the promotion of religion; capital costs, including building work, renovations, and equipment; work that is routine or well-proven elsewhere or with a low impact; healthcare or related work such as medical research, complementary medicine, counselling and therapy, education and treatment for substance misuse; work that is primarily the responsibility of central or local government, health trusts or health authorities, or which benefits from their funding. This includes residential and day care, housing and homelessness, individual schools, nurseries and colleges, supplementary schools and vocational training; projects that primarily benefit the independent education sector; environmental projects related to animal welfare, zoos, captive breeding and animal rescue centres; individual energy efficiency or waste reduction schemes; retrospective funding, meaning support for work that has already taken place; recreational activities including outward bound courses and adventure experiences; the foundation will not normally replace or subsidise statutory income although it will make rare exceptions where the level of performance has been exceptional and where the potential impact of the work is substantial; retrospective funding; or general appeals.

TYPE OF GRANT Primarily core and project grants. Funding can be given for up to or over three years.

RANGE OF GRANTS The average grant from the Main Fund was £79,800.

SAMPLE GRANTS From the Main Fund: Bristol Old Vic Trust Ltd (£500,000), towards a five year programme to support emerging theatre artists; Family Rights Group (£300,000), towards core costs over three years for work with families of looked after children; Global Canopy Foundation (£150,000), towards the costs of surveys of forest footprint disclosure, helping companies understand their exposure to tropical deforestation; Prisoners' Education Trust (£105,000), towards the salaries of a strategic project manager, policy and communications officer and an administrator over three years; Crafts Council (£96,000), towards the costs over three years of a national project to improve ceramics education and facilities in schools; Belfast Interface Project (£90,000), towards the salary of the practice co-ordinator over three years to influence government policy regarding the regeneration of interface or 'peace line' areas, promote greater levels of sharing, address youth-led interface violence, and address membership needs; Blackburne house Group (£80,000), towards the cost of establishing a women's maintenance social enterprise, which will work closely with local housing associations, providing training opportunities and earned income; West End Refugee Service (£45,000), towards the salary of the project director over three years; Colchester and Ipswich Museum Service (£41,000), towards Out in the Open project costs which will explore perceptions of homelessness in Colchester; African Community Advice North East (£38,500), towards the salary of the development director and project costs over three years; Community Energy Practitioners Forum (£35,000), towards the costs of research and report production to map community action on climate change with a focus on the links between process and outcome; York Travellers Trust (£30,000), towards a women's education project over two years; The Men's Room (£16,000), towards the salary of a part-time arts sessional worker over two years; and Index on Censorship (£15,000), towards the core costs of the Artistic Expression and Self Censorship Programme.

FINANCES *Year* 2010 *Income* £10,606,000 *Grants* £27,618,000 *Assets* £852,311,000

TRUSTEES Tom Chandos, Chair; Felicity Fairbairn; Beatrice Hollond; James Hughes-Hallett; Thomas Hughes-Hallett; Kate Lampard; Baroness Linklater; William Sieghart; John Fairbairn; Jonathan Phillips.

OTHER INFORMATION The fund also makes grants through: a development fund for investigating new ideas or approaches; and a TASK Fund for organisations known to the trustees. The trust also runs a loan finance initiative, see the trust website for more details.

HOW TO APPLY Applying for a grant from the Main Fund. 'Please follow these three steps: 1. Read through the guidance notes, paying careful

attention to the sort of work we support – and what we do not. 2. If you think your organisation's activities could attract Esmée Fairbairn funding, go through the self-assessment checklist for eligibility [available from the foundation's website]. 3. If you can answer 'yes' to each of the self-assessment checklist questions, submit a first stage application [available from the foundation's website]. *What happens next* – We will then get back to you, aiming to acknowledge your first stage application within a week of receiving it. Within a month we will either suggest taking it to the second stage or decline to support it. If you are invited to proceed to the second stage, we will ask you for some additional information that will depend on what you have already told us and the size and complexity of the work you would like us to support. *How we assess applications?* – When considering your first stage application we are particularly interested in: How closely your application fits with one or more of our six priorities; the importance of the issue you are seeking to address; why you are the best organisation to undertake the work, including your track record; the strength and feasibility of your idea; and the overall difference that your work is likely to make. We receive many more applications than we can support. Applications should be succinct and applicants are encouraged to highlight past successes. The trust wishes to know if you intend to work with partners. Your application should demonstrate in tangible ways what you hope to achieve with our funding. Give examples if you think this will help us understand what the results will be.' The first stage application form and full guidance note is available from the trust's website. There is a different application process for the funding strands. To learn more about the strands and how to apply, visit the foundation's website.

WHO TO APPLY TO Dawn Austwick, Chief Executive, Kings Place, 90 York Way, London N1 9AG *Tel* 020 7812 3700 *Fax* 020 7812 3701 *email* info@esmeefairbairn.org.uk *Website* www.esmeefairbairn.org.uk

---

■ The Fairstead Trust

CC NO 1096359   **ESTABLISHED** 2003

WHERE FUNDING CAN BE GIVEN Worldwide.

WHO CAN BENEFIT UK registered charities and individuals.

WHAT IS FUNDED General charitable purposes.

RANGE OF GRANTS £500–£25,000.

SAMPLE GRANTS Previous beneficiaries have included: EACH (£25,000); Family Links (£15,000); Castlehaven Community Association, Nelson's Journey and St Albans Cathedral Educational Centre (£10,000 each); Cley Memorial Hall Fund (£9,000); Southwark Tigers – Football Team (£6,500); Southwark Tigers – Rugby Team (£5,000); Chance to Shine (£5,000); Afghan Connection and NNRDA (£1,000 each); and Hopefield Animal Sanctuary (£500).

FINANCES *Year* 2009–10 *Income* £23,732 *Grants* £150,000

TRUSTEES Edward Cox; Wendy Cox; Lucinda Cox; Claire Mitchell.

HOW TO APPLY In writing to the correspondent containing the following: aims and objectives of the charity; nature of appeal; total target if for a specific project; contributions received against target; registered charity number; any other relevant factors.

WHO TO APPLY TO c/o Ms L J Stoten, Payne Hicks Beach, 10 New Square, Lincoln's Inn, London WC2A 3QG

■ The Fairway Trust

CC NO 272227 **ESTABLISHED** 1976

WHERE FUNDING CAN BE GIVEN UK and worldwide.

WHO CAN BENEFIT Charities, universities, colleges and schools.

WHAT IS FUNDED Support of universities, colleges, and schools in UK and abroad; scholarships, grants and loans to postgraduates and undergraduates; grants to help religious purposes; support of clubs and recreational facilities for children and young people; preservation and maintenance of buildings of particular interest; and social welfare.

WHAT IS NOT FUNDED No grants to medical charities.

RANGE OF GRANTS £1,000–£10,000.

SAMPLE GRANTS Family Education Trust (£20,000); Clubs for Young People Northern Ireland and the Welsh National Opera (£2,000 each); Prayer Book Society (£1,250); and Sight Savers, Kids Out, Thames Philharmonic Choir and the Bishop of Wakefield (£1,000 each).

FINANCES *Year* 2009–10 *Income* £35,950 *Grants* £30,000

TRUSTEES Janet Grimstone; Ms K V M Suenson-Taylor.

OTHER INFORMATION Most of the trust's income is given out in grants each year.

HOW TO APPLY In writing to the correspondent, although the trust has previously stated 'as funds and office resources are limited it cannot be guaranteed that unsolicited applications will be answered'.

WHO TO APPLY TO Mrs J Grimstone, Trustee, The Gate House, Coombe Wood Road, Kingston-upon-Thames, Surrey KT2 7JY

■ The Fairwind Trust

CC NO 1134008 **ESTABLISHED** 2010

WHERE FUNDING CAN BE GIVEN UK and worldwide.

WHO CAN BENEFIT Registered charities.

WHAT IS FUNDED General purposes including: education/training; health; disability; prevention/relief of poverty; overseas aid/famine relief; accommodation/housing; religious activities; arts/culture/heritage/science; sport/recreation; animals; environment/conservation; economic/community development/employment.

TRUSTEES P N Howard; Mrs A Howard; Mrs L S Howard; J A Howard; W S Howard.

HOW TO APPLY In writing to the correspondent.

WHO TO APPLY TO P N Howard, c/o Whitley Stimpson LLP, 67 Hightown Road, Banbury, Oxfordshire OX16 9BE *Tel* 01295 270200

■ Faisaltex Charitable Trust

CC NO 1085973 **ESTABLISHED** 2001

WHERE FUNDING CAN BE GIVEN Worldwide.

WHO CAN BENEFIT Charitable organisations.

WHAT IS FUNDED Organisations working internationally providing religious or other education to children who are in need; the advancement of religion or public services; the relief of sickness and the preservation of good health; and the relief of poverty.

SAMPLE GRANTS The Preston Muslim Society (£40,000); The Bombay Patel Welfare Society (£31,000); Khidmat Charitable Trust (£23,000); and Angel Welfare and Education Trust and Haiti Appeal (£10,000 each).

FINANCES *Year* 2009–10 *Income* £311,971 *Grants* £325,950 *Assets* £3,332,748

TRUSTEES Arif Patel; Mrs Sabina Patel; Munaf Patel; Faisal Patel; Mrs Yasmeen Patel; Arif Barber.

OTHER INFORMATION Grants total refers to grants made to organisations in the UK. £66,000 was given in grants to overseas organisations.

HOW TO APPLY In writing to the correspondent.

WHO TO APPLY TO Arif Patel, Trustee, Faisal House, Fairways Office Park, Olivers Way, Preston PR2 9WT *Tel* 01772 704440

■ The Family Rich Charities Trust

CC NO 264192 **ESTABLISHED** 1972

WHERE FUNDING CAN BE GIVEN UK and developing countries.

WHO CAN BENEFIT Medical, welfare, arts and music charities.

WHAT IS FUNDED Beneficiaries include hospitals; organisations specialising in disease research such as epilepsy, leukaemia, cancer, Parkinson's disease and diabetes; care of people with disabilities; and disaster relief.

WHAT IS NOT FUNDED No grants to individuals.

SAMPLE GRANTS Previous beneficiaries have included the British Heart Foundation, Colon Cancer Concern, the British Epilepsy Association, Computer Aid International, the Diabetes Trust Research Fund, the Leprosy Relief Association, Marie Curie Cancer Care, Médecins Sans Frontières and Scannappeal, the Multiple Sclerosis Society and the Royal Star and Garter Home.

FINANCES *Year* 2009–10 *Income* £68,661 *Grants* £38,000

TRUSTEES Barbara Anderman; Margaret Fruchter; Tessa Goldstein; Jean Rich.

HOW TO APPLY In writing to the correspondent.

WHO TO APPLY TO Margaret Ann Fruchter, Trustee, 6 Forge Lane, Petersham Road, Richmond-upon-Thames, Surrey TW10 7BF *Tel* 020 8948 7982

■ Famos Foundation Trust

CC NO 271211 **ESTABLISHED** 1976

WHERE FUNDING CAN BE GIVEN UK and overseas.

WHO CAN BENEFIT Small local projects and established organisations benefiting children, young adults, clergy and Jewish people.

WHAT IS FUNDED Education, religion, international organisations, and general charitable purposes. The trust will consider funding: the advancement of the Jewish religion; synagogues; Jewish umbrella bodies; church schools; cultural and religious teaching and religious studies.

WHAT IS NOT FUNDED No grants to individuals.

TYPE OF GRANT One-off, core costs and running costs. Funding is given for one year or less.

RANGE OF GRANTS Up to £5,000.

SAMPLE GRANTS Medical (£10,000); education (£55,000); relief of poverty (£49,000); and places of worship (£15,000).

FINANCES *Year* 2009–10 *Income* £212,286 *Grants* £128,680 *Assets* £1,660,331

TRUSTEES Rabbi S M Kupetz; Mrs F Kupetz; I D Kupetz; J S Kupetz.

HOW TO APPLY In writing to the correspondent, at any time. The trust does not accept telephone enquiries.

WHO TO APPLY TO Rabbi S M Kupetz, Trustee, 4 Hanover Gardens, Salford, Greater Manchester M7 4FQ *Tel* 0161 740 5735

■ The Lord Faringdon Charitable Trust

CC NO 1084690   **ESTABLISHED** 2000

WHERE FUNDING CAN BE GIVEN UK.

WHO CAN BENEFIT Registered charities only.

WHAT IS FUNDED Educational grants and scholarships; hospitals and the provision of medical treatment for people who are ill; purchase of antiques and artistic objects for museums and collections which have public access; care and assistance of people who are elderly or infirm; community and economic development and housing; development and assistance of arts and sciences, physical recreation and drama; research into matters of public interest; relief of poverty; support of matters of public interest; animal care and conservation; maintaining and improving the Faringdon Collection.

WHAT IS NOT FUNDED No grants to individuals, just to registered charities.

TYPE OF GRANT Core, capital and project support considered.

SAMPLE GRANTS Institute of Cancer Research (£20,000); Autism Speaks and National Trust Buscot C & M Fund (£10,000 each); Royal Horticultural Society, Oxford Playhouse, Oxford Philomusica, Royal Choral Society, Young Musicians Symphony Orchestra, Ashmolean Museum and The Hunt Servants Fund (£5,000 each); Lifelites and Campaign for Cirencester Parish Church (£2,500 each); and Furniture Recycling Project, Living Memory Historical Museum, Cirencester Cyber Cafe, Noah's Ark Children's Venture, Swindon Counselling Service and Asthma Relief (£1,000 each).

FINANCES *Year* 2009–10 *Income* £178,581 *Grants* £137,050 *Assets* £6,328,080

TRUSTEES A D A W Forbes; Hon. J H Henderson; Mrs S J Maitland Robinson; B Cazenove.

HOW TO APPLY In writing to the correspondent.

WHO TO APPLY TO Mrs S L Lander, Secretary to the Trustees, The Estate Office, Buscot Park, Oxfordshire SN7 8BU *Tel* 01367 240786 *email* estbuscot@aol.com

■ Samuel William Farmer's Trust

CC NO 258459   **ESTABLISHED** 1929

WHERE FUNDING CAN BE GIVEN Mainly Wiltshire.

WHO CAN BENEFIT Registered charities benefiting children and older people.

WHAT IS FUNDED Charities working in the fields of residential facilities and services, infrastructure development, churches, hospices, healthcare, medical studies and research, conservation, environmental and animal sciences, education and various community facilities and services.

WHAT IS NOT FUNDED No grants to students, or for schools and colleges, endowments, inner-city welfare or housing.

TYPE OF GRANT One-off and recurrent. Buildings, project, research, running costs, salaries and start-up costs. Funding is available for up to three years.

RANGE OF GRANTS £250–£15,000.

SAMPLE GRANTS Wiltshire Air ambulance Appeal (£8,000); Great Bedwyn CE Primary School (£5,600); Farming & Countryside Education and Prospect Hospice (£2,500 each); Drews Pond

Wood project, Greatwood and The Guide Dogs for the Blind Association (£2,000 each); and South Wiltshire Intervention for Trauma, Strongbones Children's Charitable Trust and SWAN Advocacy Network (£1,000 each).

FINANCES *Year* 2010 *Income* £75,511 *Grants* £57,188 *Assets* £2,250,067

TRUSTEES Mrs J A Liddiard; W J Rendell; P G Fox-Andrews; B J Waight; C K Brockis.

OTHER INFORMATION In 2010 £6,000 was distributed in 'annual' grants: Royal Agricultural Benevolent Institution and Royal United Kingdom Beneficent (£3,000 each). £240 was awarded to individuals.

HOW TO APPLY In writing to the correspondent. Trustees meet half-yearly.

WHO TO APPLY TO Mrs M Linden-Fermor, Secretary, 71 High Street, Market Lavington, Devizes, Wiltshire SN10 4AG *Tel* 01380 813299

■ The Farmers' Company Charitable Fund

CC NO 258712   **ESTABLISHED** 1969

WHERE FUNDING CAN BE GIVEN UK.

WHO CAN BENEFIT Individuals and organisations benefiting students, and members of the Farmers' Company who are disadvantaged by poverty or in distress, socially isolated or at risk.

WHAT IS FUNDED Promotion of agriculture research and education, including scholarships; providing relief to members of the Farmers' Company in hardship or distress; providing funds for UK students travelling abroad to study agriculture; environmental issues.

RANGE OF GRANTS Usually up to £2,000.

SAMPLE GRANTS Previously: Wye College; Seale Hayne College; the Royal Agricultural Benevolent Institution; the Lord Mayor's Appeal.

FINANCES *Year* 2009–10 *Income* £119,042 *Grants* £89,705 *Assets* £1,794,314

TRUSTEES The Court of Assistants of the Worshipful Company of Farmers.

HOW TO APPLY In writing to the correspondent. The trust has various funds through which it administers different grants and awards – see the trust's websites for details.

WHO TO APPLY TO David King, Clerk, Red Copse End, Red Copse Lane, Boars Hill, Oxford OX1 5ER *Tel* 01865 321580 *Fax* 01865 321580 *email* clerk@farmerslivery.org.uk *Website* www.farmerslivery.org.uk

■ The Thomas Farr Charitable Trust

CC NO 328394   **ESTABLISHED** 1989

WHERE FUNDING CAN BE GIVEN UK, especially Nottinghamshire.

WHO CAN BENEFIT Registered charities only.

WHAT IS FUNDED General charitable purposes.

WHAT IS NOT FUNDED No grants to individuals.

RANGE OF GRANTS Up to £25,000; usually for £5,000 or less.

SAMPLE GRANTS One large donation of £100,000 was made to Maggie's Cancer Caring Centres during the year; other beneficiaries included: Base 51, Nottingham Playhouse, St Martin's Church and Nottingham Trent University (£5,000 each); Nottingham Hospice (£3,000); Vitalise (£2,500); Newark Air Museum (£1,600); War Memorials Trust (£1,000) and PSP Association, Respite Association and Notts Regional Society for Autistic Children & Adults (£500 each).

FINANCES *Year* 2009–10 *Income* £29,240,668 *Grants* £24,627,070 *Assets* £715,019,314

TRUSTEES Rathbone Trust Company Ltd; Henry J P Farr; Mrs Amanda M Farr; Barry Davys; Mrs P K Myles.

HOW TO APPLY In writing to the correspondent. Applications are considered in March and September/November.

WHO TO APPLY TO John W Thompson, 6A The Almhouses, Mansfield Road, Daybrook, Nottingham NG5 6BW *Tel* 0115 9661222

■ Walter Farthing (Trust) Limited

CC NO 220114   ESTABLISHED 1957

WHERE FUNDING CAN BE GIVEN Mid Essex.

WHO CAN BENEFIT Organisations enlarging the range (including innovative projects) and/or volume of charitable services provided in the locality.

WHAT IS FUNDED Initiation or assistance of the development of projects by undertaking or grant aiding the acquisition, erection or adaptation of buildings and the provision of initial equipment.

WHAT IS NOT FUNDED The trust does not ordinarily support the headquarters of national charities, services which public authorities are empowered to provide, individuals or current expenditure of any nature or description.

TYPE OF GRANT Capital grants.

RANGE OF GRANTS £250–£20,000.

SAMPLE GRANTS Christchurch Palers ADS (£2,500); Parc (£2,000); Christchurch URC, the Eyeless Trust, Dystonia Society, Rethink and Dream Holidays (£1,000 each); Children's Trust Tadworth, Charity Search and Vitalise (£500 each); Witham Boys' Brigade and Essex Association of Boys' Clubs (£250); and Farthing Centre (£200).

FINANCES *Year* 2009–10 *Income* £44,522 *Grants* £16,198 *Assets* £935,611

TRUSTEES Geoffrey Chivas; Christine E Sands; Michael Vandome; Francis V Whitbread; Anthea Tilsley; D J Wisbey; K M Webb.

HOW TO APPLY In writing to the correspondent. Please note that the trust states that it receives many applications that fall outside its area of interest, which cannot be considered.

WHO TO APPLY TO Michael Vandome, Trustee, Fir Tree Lane, Little Baddow, Chelmsford CM3 4SS *Tel* 01245 223465 *Fax* 01245 227810

■ Farthing Trust

CC NO 268066   ESTABLISHED 1974

WHERE FUNDING CAN BE GIVEN UK and overseas.

WHO CAN BENEFIT Individuals and charitable organisations, most of which are personally known to the trustees.

WHAT IS FUNDED General charitable purposes, with a focus on the advancement of religion, education, health and human rights and the reconciliation and promotion of religious and racial harmony, equality and diversity.

TYPE OF GRANT One-off and recurring grants.

SAMPLE GRANTS During the year grants were broken down into the following categories: overseas Christian causes (£38,000); education – UK and overseas (£37,000); UK churches (£35,000); UK Christian causes (£32,000); Christ's servants (£25,000); individuals in need – UK and overseas (£16,000); overseas general charities (£4,000); local grants (£3,700); and UK general charities (£2,500).

FINANCES *Year* 2009–10 *Income* £85,286 *Grants* £193,568 *Assets* £3,077,468

TRUSTEES C H Martin; Mrs E Martin; Mrs J Martin; Mrs A White.

HOW TO APPLY Applications and enquiries should be made in writing to the correspondent. Applicants, and any others requesting information, will only receive a response if an sae is enclosed. Most beneficiaries are known to the trustees personally or through their acquaintances, though applications from other organisations are considered.

WHO TO APPLY TO The Trustees, PO Box 277, Cambridge CB7 9DE

■ The Fassnidge Memorial Trust

CC NO 303078   ESTABLISHED 1963

WHERE FUNDING CAN BE GIVEN London borough of Hillingdon, especially the former urban district of Uxbridge.

WHO CAN BENEFIT Individuals and organisations benefiting children, older people, parents and children, carers, people with disabilities, people disadvantaged by poverty, and victims of domestic violence.

WHAT IS FUNDED Welfare of older people and families, particularly charities working in the fields of care in the community, day centres and meals provision.

WHAT IS NOT FUNDED Applications from people or organisations outside the London borough of Hillingdon are not considered.

TYPE OF GRANT Small one-off grants and start-up costs. Funding of one year or less will be considered.

RANGE OF GRANTS Up to £10,000.

SAMPLE GRANTS Previous beneficiaries include: 60+Fair; Sipson Community Association; and Hillingdon Homelessness Comfort Fund.

FINANCES *Year* 2009–10 *Income* £15,777 *Grants* £30,000

TRUSTEES David Bishop; Brian Fredericks; David Horne; Paul Harmsworth; Andrew Retter; David Routledge; David Williams; David Herriott; Richard Walker; Peter Curling; Peter Ryerson; David Yarrow.

HOW TO APPLY In writing to the correspondent.

WHO TO APPLY TO Paul Cowan, 119 Cannonbury Avenue, Pinner, Middlesex HA5 1TR *Tel* 020 8248 3372

■ Joseph Fattorini Charitable Trust 'B' Account

CC NO 200032   ESTABLISHED 1960

WHERE FUNDING CAN BE GIVEN UK, including Guernsey.

WHO CAN BENEFIT Roman Catholic, older and younger people.

WHAT IS FUNDED General charitable purposes.

RANGE OF GRANTS Up to £12,000, but in practice, between £500 and £2,000.

SAMPLE GRANTS Stonyhurst College (£12,000); Rose Charitable Trust (£2,000); Guernsey Art Community, D Day Centre, Community of Holy Fire and St Joseph Catholic Church (£1,000 each); and Sunny Days Children's Fund and Fountaine Hospital Trust (£500 each).

FINANCES *Year* 2009–10 *Income* £25,319 *Grants* £21,018 *Assets* £552,659

TRUSTEES Joseph Fattorini; Peter Fattorini.

HOW TO APPLY In writing to the correspondent.

WHO TO APPLY TO Peter Fattorini, Trustee, White Abbey, Linton in Craven, Skipton, North Yorkshire BD23 5HQ

■ The Fawcett Charitable Trust

CC NO 1013167   **ESTABLISHED** 1990

WHERE FUNDING CAN BE GIVEN UK with a preference for Hampshire and West Sussex.

WHO CAN BENEFIT Work aimed at increasing the quality of life of people with disabilities by facilitating and providing recreation opportunities.

WHAT IS NOT FUNDED Large national charities are excluded as a rule.

SAMPLE GRANTS Previously: Chichester Harbour Trust (£75,000); RYA Sailability (£65,000); Naomi House (£50,000); Wessex Children's Hospice (£30,000); St Wilfred's Hospice (£25,000); NSPCC (£20,000); Portsmouth Cathedral (£15,000); Sailing Academy and Jubilee Sailing Trust (£5,000 each); Bikeability (£1,000).

FINANCES *Year* 2008–09 *Income* £23,673 *Grants* £60,000

TRUSTEES D J Fawcett; Mrs F P Fawcett; D W Russell.

HOW TO APPLY In writing to the correspondent.

WHO TO APPLY TO Julie Fawcett, 10 Helena Close, Portslade, Brighton

■ The February Foundation

CC NO 1113064   **ESTABLISHED** 2006

WHERE FUNDING CAN BE GIVEN UK and overseas.

WHO CAN BENEFIT Charitable organisations and institutions.

WHAT IS FUNDED The foundation will consider the following organisations for the receipt of grants, equity investment or loans: charities for the benefit of persons who are making an effort to improve their lives; charities for the benefit of persons no longer physically or mentally able to help themselves; charities which protect tie environment; charities offering formal education resulting in recognised qualifications; small or minority charities where small grants will have a significant impact; companies where the acquisition of equity would be in line with the foundation's investment policy.

WHAT IS NOT FUNDED The foundation will not consider applications from the following: child care; Citizens' Advice Bureaux; community centres; environmental projects; heritage and building projects; higher education; housing associations; individuals; medical research; minibuses; NHS trusts; non-departmental government bodies; overseas projects; previously unsuccessful applicants; primary education; Scouts, Guides, Brownies, Cubs, and similar organisations; secondary education; single-faith organisations; sports clubs, unless for the mentally or physically disabled; theatre groups; village halls; youth centres.

TYPE OF GRANT One-off grants for capital and revenue costs. Loans are also considered.

FINANCES *Year* 2009–10 *Income* £420,702 *Grants* £2,873,660 *Assets* £8,155,127

TRUSTEES Richard Pierce-Saunderson; James Carleton; The February Foundation (Cayman).

OTHER INFORMATION The foundation made 24 grants to 17 organisations. A list of beneficiaries was not available.

HOW TO APPLY 'The February Foundation makes grants to selected charities. It monitors and supports the effective management of grants made. The foundation is focussed on managing its current commitments, although applications from some charities are still being accepted. Email applications are preferred. Please send details and budget of the proposed project, how many people would benefit, how those benefits might be measured (not just financially), and what the estimated cost of raising funds for the project is. It is important to include in your email application full accounts for your most recent completed financial year, and, if your accounts do not contain it, what your total fundraising costs annually are. Please note that hardcopy applications take significantly longer to process than email applications. Please do not send DVDs, CDs, glossy brochures or other additional information. It normally takes 12 weeks from application to applicants being informed of the trustees' decision. There are no application deadlines as trustees make grant decisions on a monthly basis. **Please note that less than 5% of all applications are successful.'**

WHO TO APPLY TO Richard Pierce-Saunderson, Trustee, Spring Cottage, Church Street, Stradbroke, Suffolk IP21 5HT *email* rps@thefebruaryfoundation.org *Website* www.thefebruaryfoundation.org

■ Federation of Jewish Relief Organisations

CC NO 250006   **ESTABLISHED** 1919

WHERE FUNDING CAN BE GIVEN Mainly Israel.

WHO CAN BENEFIT Jewish people, particularly those disadvantaged by poverty, socially isolated or in at risk groups, and those who are victims of war.

WHAT IS FUNDED Relief of Jewish victims of war and persecution; help wherever Jewish need exists.

SAMPLE GRANTS Grants included £4,000 for clothing shipped to Israel; and £192,000 in grants and donations for distribution by the Israel office of the charity.

FINANCES *Year* 2009–10 *Income* £40,948 *Grants* £196,220 *Assets* £218,571

TRUSTEES M Katz, Chair; A M Garfield; Mrs A Lando.

OTHER INFORMATION Founded in 1919 to assist victims of war and persecution in Europe and the Eastern Bloc. Since 1948 it has been concerned mainly in Israel with the rehabilitation, clothing, feeding and education of children of immigrant families.

HOW TO APPLY In writing to the correspondent.

WHO TO APPLY TO Alfred Garfield, Trustee, 143 Brondesbury Park, London NW2 5JL *Tel* 020 8451 3425 *Fax* 020 8459 8059

■ The John Feeney Charitable Bequest

CC NO 214486   **ESTABLISHED** 1906

WHERE FUNDING CAN BE GIVEN Birmingham.

WHO CAN BENEFIT Charitable organisations benefiting the Birmingham area.

WHAT IS FUNDED Benefit of public charities in Birmingham only; promotion of art in Birmingham only; acquisition and maintenance of open spaces near Birmingham.

WHAT IS NOT FUNDED Applications will not be accepted: from, or on behalf of, individuals; which do not directly benefit the Birmingham area or Birmingham charitable organisations; which could be considered as political or denominational. Additionally, applications from large national charities, even with a Birmingham base, are unlikely to succeed.

TYPE OF GRANT Capital.

RANGE OF GRANTS Generally £200–£5,000.

SAMPLE GRANTS Beneficiaries of grants included: City of Birmingham Symphony Orchestra

(£15,000); Elmhurst Ballet School – Scholarship fund (£10,000); Midlands Arts Centre (£7,500); Ackers Adventure (£3,500); Royal Birmingham Society of Artists and Ironbridge Gorge Museum Trust (£2,000 each); Birmingham Botanical Gardens, Theodora Children's Trust and Ikon Gallery (£1,000 each); and Cruse Bereavement (£500).

FINANCES *Year* 2009 *Income* £65,022 *Grants* £83,000 *Assets* £1,490,373

TRUSTEES C R King-Farlow; D M P Lea; S J Lloyd; Mrs M F Lloyd; H B Carslake; J R L Smith; M S Darby; Mrs S R Wright; William J E Southall; Ms Anouk Perinpanayagam.

HOW TO APPLY In writing to the correspondent by March of each year. There is no application form and no SAE is required. However, letters in support must clearly set out for what purpose, or purposes, the funding is being sought and must enclose a copy of the charity's latest accounts.

WHO TO APPLY TO Ms P J Byatt, Secretary, 55 Wychall Lane, Kings Norton, Birmingham B38 8TB *Tel* 0121 624 3865 *email* secretary@feeneytrust.org.uk

....

■ The George Fentham Birmingham Charity

CC NO 214487　　　**ESTABLISHED** 1907
WHERE FUNDING CAN BE GIVEN City of Birmingham.
WHO CAN BENEFIT Individuals and organisations benefiting young adults and people disadvantaged by poverty.
WHAT IS FUNDED Educational grants to bona fide residents of Birmingham (three-year minimum) aged 16 to 25 years of age. Particularly charities working in the fields of tertiary and higher education, and various community services and facilities, will be considered.
WHAT IS NOT FUNDED Only registered charities are supported. West Midlands organisations outside the city of Birmingham are not eligible.
RANGE OF GRANTS Up to £5,000.
SAMPLE GRANTS Marie Curie Cancer Care (£5,000); Children with Cystic Fibrosis Dream Holidays (£3,600); Happy Days Children's Charity (£3,000); Birmingham Tribunal Unit (£2,000); Elim Church, Kingstanding (£1,500) and Carrs Lane Counselling Centre, Crossroads Care Birmingham and Solihull and British Lung Foundation (£1,000 each).
FINANCES *Year* 2010 *Income* £149,145 *Grants* £142,326 *Assets* £5,161,560
TRUSTEES Mr J M Bower, Chair; Mr M Holcombe; Mrs M Martin; Mr D Ridgeway; Mrs D Duggan; Ms J Turner; Mr B Earp.
OTHER INFORMATION In 2010 grants totalling £127,000 were awarded to organisations with an additional £15,000 given to various individuals.
HOW TO APPLY On a form available from the correspondent. General grants are made in April and October, while education grants are made from September to April.
WHO TO APPLY TO Mrs Anne Holmes, c/o Cobbetts Solicitors, 1 Colmore Square, Birmingham B4 6AJ *Tel* 0845 404 2404

....

■ The A M Fenton Trust

CC NO 270353　　　**ESTABLISHED** 1975
WHERE FUNDING CAN BE GIVEN UK, preference for North Yorkshire, and overseas.
WHO CAN BENEFIT Registered charities.

WHAT IS FUNDED General charitable purposes.
WHAT IS NOT FUNDED The trust is unlikely to support local appeals, unless they are close to where the trust is based.
TYPE OF GRANT Mostly one-off.
RANGE OF GRANTS £100–£20,000.
SAMPLE GRANTS Yorkshire Count Cricket Club Charitable Youth Trust (£20,000); Hipperholme Grammar School (£10,000); Dewsbury League of Friendship (£8,000); Cleckheaton Central Methodist Church (£7,500); Tweed Foundation (£4,000); Kenmore Leonard Cheshire Disability and St John of Jerusalem Eye Hospital (£2,500 each); Ghurka Welfare Trust and Disability Action Yorkshire (£2,000 each); Age Concern Knaresborough and Crime Stoppers Trust (£1,000).
FINANCES *Year* 2010 *Income* £116,650 *Grants* £128,810 *Assets* £3,912,463
TRUSTEES James Fenton; Charles M Fenton; Charley J Fenton; Charlotte Fenton.
HOW TO APPLY In writing to the correspondent.
WHO TO APPLY TO James Fenton, Trustee, 14 Beech Grove, Harrogate, North Yorkshire HG2 0EX *Tel* 01423 504442

....

■ The Allan and Nesta Ferguson Charitable Settlement

CC NO 275487　　　**ESTABLISHED** 1977
WHERE FUNDING CAN BE GIVEN Unrestricted, with a local interest in Birmingham and Bishop's Stortford.
WHO CAN BENEFIT Organisations and individuals.
WHAT IS FUNDED Education, overseas development and world peace.
SAMPLE GRANTS AMREF (£313,000); Royal Shakespeare Company (£200,000); The Fairtrade Foundation (£112,000); Woodbrooke Quaker Study Centre (£110,000); Practical Action (£65,000); Save the Children (£35,000); Help2Read (£30,000); Amnesty International, Assist a Child to School Charity Trust, Listening Books and Stepping Stones Nigeria (£20,000 each); Care and Relief for the Young, Centre for Development & Community Welfare, and St Ethelburga's Centre for Reconciliation and Peace (£10,000 each).
FINANCES *Year* 2010 *Income* £800,280 *Grants* £3,047,385 *Assets* £28,462,798
TRUSTEES Elizabeth Banister; David Banister; Lesley Roff; Richard Tee.
OTHER INFORMATION Grants are also made towards the fees of postgraduate students who are in their final year of a postgraduate course, subject to evidence of financial hardship.
HOW TO APPLY 'Applications by charities for small to medium grants (up to a maximum of £50,000) may be submitted at any time and will be considered on a regular basis. Applications for larger grants will be considered at bi-annual meetings held in March and October and applications should be submitted at the very latest in the previous months i.e. February or September. **Please note:** No repeat applications will be considered within three years of the conclusion of the grant term. We prefer where possible that you complete and submit the on-line application form on this website and email it to us. Alternatively you may download and print out the application form, complete it and send it by letter post. See the Contact Us page for address details. Please do not extend the length of the forms, or add any attachments. Applications **MUST NOT** exceed 3 pages. Please use text size 12. Please do not apply for more

....

than one project. All applications by email will be acknowledged and considered by the Trustees within 6 to 8 weeks. If you do not hear further, after the acknowledgement, then unfortunately your application has not been successful. If the trustees do decide to award you a grant then they will contact you. No progress reports will be given and no correspondence will be entered into in the meantime.'

WHO TO APPLY TO Richard Tee, Trustee, Stanley Tee Solicitors, High Street, Bishops Stortford, Hertfordshire CM23 2LU *Tel* 01279 755200 *email* jrt@stanleytee.co.uk *Website* www.fergusontrust.co.uk

■ Elizabeth Ferguson Charitable Trust Fund

SC NO SC026240   ESTABLISHED 1988
WHERE FUNDING CAN BE GIVEN UK, with some interest in Scotland.
WHO CAN BENEFIT Organisations benefiting children and young people, particularly those who are sick.
WHAT IS FUNDED The welfare and wellbeing of children and young people. Also charities involved in medical research and hospitals where special medical equipment is needed.
WHAT IS NOT FUNDED Non-registered charities and individuals are not supported. The trust does not make grants overseas.
RANGE OF GRANTS £250–£10,000.
SAMPLE GRANTS Previous beneficiaries have included the Govan Initiative and Harmony Row Boys' Club.
FINANCES *Year* 2009–10 *Income* £260,383 *Grants* £200,000
TRUSTEES Sir Alex Ferguson; Cathy Ferguson; Huw Roberts; Ted Way; Les Dalgarno; Paul Hardman; Jason Ferguson.
HOW TO APPLY An application form and guidelines should be requested in writing from the correspondent. The committee meets to consider grants at the end of January and July. Applications should be received by December and June respectively.
WHO TO APPLY TO The Trustees, c/o 27 Peregrine Crescent, Droylsden, Manchester M43 7TA

■ The Fidelity UK Foundation

CC NO 327899   ESTABLISHED 1988
WHERE FUNDING CAN BE GIVEN Unrestricted, in practice particular preference is given to projects in Kent, Surrey, London and continental Europe.
WHO CAN BENEFIT Not for profit organisations, charities.
WHAT IS FUNDED General, giving is primarily allocated for charitable purposes in the following areas: community development, health, arts and culture and education. The trust seeks to support projects undertaken by organisations to increase proficiency, achieve goals and reach long-term self-sufficiency. Most often, funding is given for projects such as capital improvements, technology upgrades, organisational development and planning initiatives.
WHAT IS NOT FUNDED Grants are not generally made to: start-up, sectarian, or political organisations; private schools, and colleges or universities; individuals. Grants are not made for: sponsorships or benefit events; scholarships; corporate memberships; advertising and

promotional projects; exhibitions. Generally grants are not made for running costs, but may be considered on an individual basis through the foundation's small grant scheme. Grants will not normally cover the entire cost of a project. Grants will not normally be awarded to an organisation in successive years. The foundation receives many more applications for grants than it is able to fund so not all applications that fall within the guidelines will receive grants.
TYPE OF GRANT Buildings, capital, IT development, one-off grants to develop infrastructure. Funding for less than one year is considered.
RANGE OF GRANTS £1,000–£725,000.
SAMPLE GRANTS The Exeter University Foundation (£724,000); Sir John Soane's Museum (£390,000); Museum of London (£300,000); The Institute of Cancer Research (£264,000); National Maritime Museum (£229,000); The Guildhall School Development Fund, The Children's Trust (£150,000 each); The University of Cambridge (£125,000); The Photographers' Gallery (£100,000); The National Centre for Young People with Epilepsy (£97,000); In Kind Direct (£46,000); Ebony Horse Trust (£25,000); Youthnet UK (£15,000); Kidscape Campaign for Children's safety (£13,000); Thames21 (£9,000).
FINANCES *Year* 2010 *Income* £13,075,721 *Grants* £4,479,202 *Assets* £119,917,303
TRUSTEES Edward Johnson; Barry Bateman; Anthony Bolton; Richard Millar; John Owen; Sally Walden.
HOW TO APPLY In writing to the correspondent. The following documentation is required: Fidelity UK Foundation summary form (form can be downloaded from the foundation's website); organisation history and objectives; description of request and rationale, see below; itemised project budget; list of other funders and status of each request; list of directors and trustees with their backgrounds; current management accounts; most recently audited financial statements. When writing the description of your request and your rationale, please address the following questions: How does the project fit into the larger strategic plan of your organisation? What will a grant allow your organisation to achieve? How will a grant change or improve the long-term potential of your organisation? What is the implementation plan and timeline for the project? How will the project be evaluated? There are no deadlines for submitting grant proposals. All applications will normally receive an initial response within three months. The volume of requests as well as diligence of review process require a three to six month period, which should be factored into the applicant's funding plan.
WHO TO APPLY TO Susan Platts-Martin, Chief Executive, Oakhill House, 130 Tonbridge Road, Hildenborough, Tonbridge, Kent TN11 9DZ *Tel* 01732 777364 *email* foundation@fil.com *Website* www.fidelityukfoundation.org

■ The Bluff Field Charitable Trust

CC NO 1057992   ESTABLISHED 1996
WHERE FUNDING CAN BE GIVEN UK.
WHO CAN BENEFIT Charitable organisations.
WHAT IS FUNDED General charitable purposes.
SAMPLE GRANTS Previous beneficiaries have included Emmanuel Church Billericay, Leukaemia Research Fund, Risk Waters' World Trade Centre UK Appeal, St George's Hospital Medical School and Wigmore Hall Trust.
FINANCES *Year* 2010 *Income* £44 *Grants* £1,000

TRUSTEES Peter Field; Sonia Field; Stanley Salter.

OTHER INFORMATION The trust has had an income of less than £100 and an expenditure of around £1,000 for the past two years which indicates that it may be winding down. In previous years it has received substantial income from donations and Gift Aid.

HOW TO APPLY In writing to the correspondent.

WHO TO APPLY TO Peter Field, Trustee, 8 The Little Boltons, London SW10 9LP *Tel* 020 7373 1863 *email* bfct@btinternet.com

■ The Doris Field Charitable Trust

CC NO 328687   ESTABLISHED 1990

WHERE FUNDING CAN BE GIVEN UK, with a preference for Oxfordshire.

WHO CAN BENEFIT Large UK and small local organisations benefiting children and young adults; at risk groups; people who are disadvantaged by poverty or socially isolated.

WHAT IS FUNDED Medical, welfare, education and general charitable purposes.

WHAT IS NOT FUNDED It is unlikely that grants would be made for overseas projects or to individuals for higher education.

TYPE OF GRANT One-off and recurrent.

RANGE OF GRANTS £50–£50,000, mostly £5,000 or less.

SAMPLE GRANTS OCCTOPUS (£50,000); Cancer Research UK and the Thames Valley Air Ambulance Trust (£30,000 each); Maggie's Centres and Oxford Radcliffe Hospitals Charitable Trust (£5,000 each); the Mulberry Bush Organisation and Oxfordshire Netball (£2,500 each); Oxford Welsh Male Voice Choir and United Response (£2,000 each); Appleton with Eaton Parish Council and Footsteps Foundation (£1,000 each); and Charlbury Corner House, Didcot Cricket Club and Opera Anywhere (£500 each).

FINANCES Year 2009–10 Income £294,495 Grants £321,181 Assets £7,759,023

TRUSTEES N A Harper; J Cole; Mrs W Church.

HOW TO APPLY On a form available from the correspondent. Applications are considered three times a year or as and when necessary.

WHO TO APPLY TO The Trustees, c/o Morgan Cole, Buxton Court, 3 West Way, Oxford OX2 0SZ *Tel* 01865 262183

■ Fife Council/Common Good Funds and Trusts

SC NO SC019393   ESTABLISHED 1975

WHERE FUNDING CAN BE GIVEN East Fife.

WHO CAN BENEFIT Individuals in need and local community groups such as community councils and sports clubs.

WHAT IS FUNDED Arts, buildings, conservation/ environment, disability, education/training, heritage, hospitals/hospices, social welfare of people of all ages and sports and recreation.

WHAT IS NOT FUNDED The following causes are not supported: animal welfare; medical/health; medical research; overseas projects; political appeals; and religious appeals.

TYPE OF GRANT One-off grants for capital and revenue costs.

RANGE OF GRANTS Mostly under £1,000.

FINANCES Year 2009–10 Grants £70,000

OTHER INFORMATION The Office of the Scottish Charity Regulator states that the charity has ceased. The entry is based on the information

available on the council website, which states that grants are available.

HOW TO APPLY Contact the correspondent for further details. An application form and guidelines are available for the Common Good Funds but not for the trusts. Applications can be made at any time. Forms can be downloaded from the website.

WHO TO APPLY TO Andrew Ferguson, Team Leader (Democratic Services), Fife Council, Fife House, North Street, Glenrothes, Fife KY7 5LT *Tel* 0845 155 5555 (Ext 442175) *Fax* 01592 583155 *Website* www.fife.gov.uk

■ The Fifty Fund

CC NO 214422   ESTABLISHED 1963

WHERE FUNDING CAN BE GIVEN Nottinghamshire and surrounding area.

WHO CAN BENEFIT Individuals and organisations benefiting retired people; unemployed people; those in care, fostered and adopted; parents and children; one-parent families; widows and widowers; carers; disabled people; and people disadvantaged by poverty.

WHAT IS FUNDED Relief of poverty, infrastructure development, charity or voluntary umbrella bodies, advice and information on housing, respite care, and various community services.

WHAT IS NOT FUNDED No grants for education, expeditions or travel.

TYPE OF GRANT Mostly one-off grants for revenue costs and project funding.

RANGE OF GRANTS £100–£10,000.

SAMPLE GRANTS Nottinghamshire Hospice (£8,000); Army Benevolent Fund, Combat Stress, NSPCC, Shelter NHAS (£4,000 each); Salvation Army (£3,500); Barnardo's, Care for Kids, Cedar Housing, Citizens Advice Bureau – Broxtowe, Derbyshire Housing Association, Family Housing Association, Harvest Trust, I Can (£2,000 each).

FINANCES Year 2010 Income £255,680 Grants £193,347 Assets £6,844,642

TRUSTEES E W Whiles; E A Randall; Revd Canon G B Barrodale.

OTHER INFORMATION The trust also made grants to individuals which totalled £56,612.

HOW TO APPLY In writing to the correspondent.

WHO TO APPLY TO Stephen Moore, Clerk, Nelsons Solicitors, Pennine House, 8 Stanford Street, Nottingham NG1 7BQ *Tel* 0115 989 5251

■ Dixie Rose Findlay Charitable Trust

CC NO 251661   ESTABLISHED 1967

WHERE FUNDING CAN BE GIVEN UK.

WHO CAN BENEFIT Charitable organisations. Especially those concerned with children, seafarers and the blind.

WHAT IS FUNDED General charitable purposes.

TYPE OF GRANT One-off and recurrent.

RANGE OF GRANTS £1,000–£6,000.

SAMPLE GRANTS Leukaemia Research and Royal National Lifeboat Institution (£6,000 each); Cassell Hospital, Keech Hospice Care, Dorset Blind Association, St John's Wood Adventure Playground and Barnado's (£3,000 each); Family Support – Clacton and the Cleft Lip and Palate Association (£2,000 each); and Deewentside Domestic Abuse Service and Disabled Travel Service (£1,000 each).

FINANCES Year 2009–10 Income £86,394 Grants £87,000 Assets £4,081,539

TRUSTEES HSBC Trust Co. (UK) Ltd.

HOW TO APPLY In writing to the correspondent.
WHO TO APPLY TO A Fryers, Trust Manager, HSBC Trust Co. (UK) Ltd, 10th Floor, Norwich House, Nelson Gate, Commercial Road, Southampton SO15 1GX *Tel* 023 8072 2226

■ Finnart House School Trust

CC NO 220917 ESTABLISHED 1901
WHERE FUNDING CAN BE GIVEN Worldwide.
WHO CAN BENEFIT Schools and charitable organisations benefiting Jewish children and young people in need of care and/or education.
WHAT IS FUNDED Bursaries and scholarships are given to Jewish secondary school pupils and university entrants who are capable of achieving, but would probably not do so because of family and economic pressures. Also supported is work concerned with people who are disaffected, disadvantaged socially and economically through illness or neglect or in need of care and education.
TYPE OF GRANT Buildings, capital, one-off and project.
RANGE OF GRANTS Up to £12,000.
SAMPLE GRANTS Finnart Scholarship (£180,000); Jewish Free School (£12,000); King Solomon High School (£12,000); and King David High School (£1,000).
FINANCES Year 2009–10 Income £161,244 Grants £204,600 Assets £4,304,301
TRUSTEES Dame Hilary Blume; Mark Sebba; Robert Cohen; Linda Paterson; Sue Leiffer; Gideon Lyons.
OTHER INFORMATION The grant total includes £179,600 given in Finnart Scholarships to 65 students.
HOW TO APPLY Please note the following statement taken from the trust's website: 'If you are a charity (working for Jewish children in need) seeking support, please understand that the major part of Finnart's income goes to fund the Finnart Scholars. If you wish to apply, though realising the chances of success are slim, please check by telephone, email or letter before doing so. If you are a school seeking a hardship fund, please remember that our trust deed restricts our grant giving to Jewish children in need. We may also require evidence of the eligibility of any pupil. We will require a report on how any funds have been dispersed.'
WHO TO APPLY TO Peter Shaw, Clerk, PO Box 603, Edgware, Middlesex HA8 4EQ *Tel* 020 3209 6006 *email* info@finnart.org *Website* www.finnart.org

■ Gerald Finzi Charitable Trust

CC NO 313047 ESTABLISHED 1969
WHERE FUNDING CAN BE GIVEN UK.
WHO CAN BENEFIT Organisations and individuals.
WHAT IS FUNDED The trustees aim to reflect the ambitions and philosophy of the composer Gerald Finzi (1901–56), which included the general promotion of 20th century British music through assisting and promoting festivals, recordings and performances of British music. A limited number of modest grants are also offered to young musicians towards musical training.
RANGE OF GRANTS Up to £1,250.
SAMPLE GRANTS Three Choirs Festival (£1,250); Music at Tradebigge (£1,000); Finzi Friends (£830); Choral Connections, National Youth Orchestra and Royal Northern Coll of Music (£500 each); St Bride's Church and Lontano

(£250 each); and C Steel Passion and Resurrection (£100).
FINANCES Year 2009–10 Income £92,726 Grants £26,880 Assets £147,180
TRUSTEES Robert Gower, Chair; Andrew Burn; Christian Alexander; Henry Brown; Judy Digney; Jean Finzi; Sarah Moule; Stuart Ritchie; Paul Spicer.
OTHER INFORMATION The grant total includes £5,200 given in grants to organisations.
HOW TO APPLY In writing to the correspondent.
WHO TO APPLY TO Elizabeth Pooley, Administrator, PO Box 137, Stour Row, Shaftesbury, Dorset SP7 0WX *email* admin@geraldfinzi.org *Website* www.geraldfinzi.org

■ Firtree Trust

CC NO 282239 ESTABLISHED 1981
WHERE FUNDING CAN BE GIVEN UK and abroad.
WHO CAN BENEFIT Christian organisations.
WHAT IS FUNDED Religious education and the advancement of the Protestant and Evangelical tenets of the Christian faith.
TYPE OF GRANT One year grants for capital and revenue costs.
RANGE OF GRANTS Up to £3,000.
SAMPLE GRANTS Harvest Christian Fellowship Trust (£3,000); Open Doors (£2,600); Christians Against Poverty and FEBA (£2,000 each); Sat-7 Trust Ltd (£1,500); Warlingham Methodist Trust (£1,200); Titus Trust (£1,300); Tearfund and United Christian Broadcasters (£1,000 each); and UCCF (£750).
FINANCES Year 2009–10 Income £34,754 Grants £32,425 Assets £21,951
TRUSTEES Maurice John Turner; Margaret Helen Turner; James Stephen Turner; Paul Turner; Elizabeth Turner.
OTHER INFORMATION In 2009–10, grants totalling £11,000 were given to 37 individuals.
HOW TO APPLY In writing to the correspondent.
WHO TO APPLY TO James Turner, 12 Purley Bury Avenue, Purley, Surrey CR8 1JB *Tel* 020 8668 1994

■ The Margaret Fisher Charitable Trust

CC NO 286256 ESTABLISHED 1982
WHERE FUNDING CAN BE GIVEN Shaftesbury in Dorset.
WHO CAN BENEFIT Older people; people with disabilities.
WHAT IS FUNDED Social welfare, health and housing.
WHAT IS NOT FUNDED The trustees do not make donations to individuals.
SAMPLE GRANTS During the year the trust awarded one large grant to the Abbeyfield Bursary Fund (£50,000) and smaller grants of £6,000 for Abbeyfield Kent Society's Who Cares appeal and £750 to the Margaret Fisher House.
FINANCES Year 2009–10 Income £25,235 Grants £65,468 Assets £1,641,847
TRUSTEES Josephine Jane Gisborne; Payne Hicks Beach Trustees.
HOW TO APPLY In writing to the trustees, including a set of the latest report and accounts.
WHO TO APPLY TO Josephine Jane Passmore, Trustee, Payne Hicks Beach, 10 New Square, Lincoln's Inn, London WC2A 3QG *Tel* 020 7465 4300

■ The Sir John Fisher Foundation

CC NO 277844   **ESTABLISHED** 1979

WHERE FUNDING CAN BE GIVEN UK, with a preference for charities in the Furness peninsula and adjacent area and local branches of national charities.

WHO CAN BENEFIT National and local registered charities.

WHAT IS FUNDED The foundation has six main areas of interest: maritime; medical and disability; education; music; arts; and community projects in and around Barrow-in-Furness.

WHAT IS NOT FUNDED The trustees will generally not fund: individuals; sponsorship; expeditions; promotion of religion; places of worship; animal welfare; retrospective funding; pressure groups; community projects outside Barrow-in-Furness and surrounding area (except occasional projects in Cumbria or North Lancashire or if they fall within one of the other categories supported by the foundation).

TYPE OF GRANT Capital and revenue funding for up to three years.

RANGE OF GRANTS Mostly under £10,000.

SAMPLE GRANTS *Local beneficiaries included*: Lancaster University (£119,000 in total); Barrow District Scouts (£40,000); Cancercare (£35,000 in total); St Mathews Community Hall (£29,000); the Wordsworth Trust (£20,000); Blackwell Sailing (£15,000); Lakeland Art Trust (£12,000); Dance Resource Ltd (£10,000); Rumic Foundation Trust (£8,500); Citizens Advice – South Lakeland (£6,300); Resolve Mediation Service (£3,000); Kidsafe UK (£1,500); and the Ulverston Outsiders (£100). *National beneficiaries included*: National Maritime Museum – Cornwall (£60,000 in total); University of Dundee (£25,000); London Handel Society Ltd (£15,000); Chemical Industries Education Centre (£12,000); Imperial War Museum (£10,000); Barnardo's (£7,500); Changing Faces (£5,000); British Wireless for the Blind Fund (£2,500); and Brain and Spinal Injury Centre (£500).

FINANCES *Year* 2009–10 *Income* £1,185,898 *Grants* £895,624 *Assets* £34,135,408

TRUSTEES Daniel P Tindall, Chair; Diane S Meacock; Sir David Hardy; Rowland F Hart Jackson.

HOW TO APPLY Application forms are available from the secretary or to download from the foundation's website. Completed applications should be submitted together with all relevant information (set out on the application form) to the secretary at least six weeks in advance of the next trustees' meeting. The trustees meet at the beginning of May and the beginning of November each year. Urgent grants for small amounts (less than £4,000) can be considered between meetings, but the trustees would expect an explanation as to why the application could not be considered at a normal meeting. Applicants are welcome to contact the secretary for an informal discussion before submitting an application for funding. The trustees expect to receive feedback from the organisations they support, to help in their decision making process. Organisations are asked to provide a brief one page report about nine months after receipt of a grant (or when the specific project assisted has been completed). A feedback form is available from the foundation's website.

WHO TO APPLY TO Dr David Hart Jackson, Trust Secretary, Heaning Wood, Ulverston, Cumbria LA12 7NZ *Tel* 01229 580349 *email* info@sirjohnfisherfoundation.org.uk *Website* www.sirjohnfisherfoundation.org.uk

■ Fisherbeck Charitable Trust

CC NO 1107287   **ESTABLISHED** 2004

WHERE FUNDING CAN BE GIVEN Worldwide.

WHO CAN BENEFIT Registered charities worldwide.

WHAT IS FUNDED The advancement of the Christian religion; support for the provision of accommodation for the homeless; the relief of poverty; the advancement of education; conservation of the environment and the preservation of heritage.

WHAT IS NOT FUNDED Grants are only made to individuals known to the trust or in exceptional circumstances.

TYPE OF GRANT One-off and recurrent.

RANGE OF GRANTS Up to £50,000.

SAMPLE GRANTS Tear Fund (£48,000); Christian Viewpoint for Men (£45,000); Urban Saints (£40,000); Bible Society (£30,000); Evangelical Alliance (£21,000); Release International (£20,000); Hope for Lugazi (£15,000); Resource (£15,000); Church Pastoral Aid Society (£6,000); and St Peter's Church Appeal (£5,000).

FINANCES *Year* 2009–10 *Income* £492,423 *Grants* £462,500 *Assets* £238,991

TRUSTEES I R Cheal; Mrs J Cheal; M Cheal.

HOW TO APPLY In writing to the correspondent, although please note: 'We are a small family trust and having built up a portfolio of donees (who we access yearly), we rarely add or subtract more or less than about five changes.'

WHO TO APPLY TO The Trustees, Home Farm House, 63 Ferringham Lane, Ferring, Worthing, West Sussex BN12 5LL *Tel* 01903 241027 *email* ian@roffeyhomes.com

■ The Fishmongers' Company's Charitable Trust

CC NO 263690   **ESTABLISHED** 1972

WHERE FUNDING CAN BE GIVEN UK, however this refers to charities whose objects extend worldwide in England. In practice, mainly the City of London and its adjacent boroughs.

WHO CAN BENEFIT Registered charities and individuals (for educational grants only).

WHAT IS FUNDED General. In practice, education, relief of poverty and disability, in particular assistance to almshouses, fishery related bodies, environment and heritage.

WHAT IS NOT FUNDED No grants to individuals except for educational purposes.

RANGE OF GRANTS Up to £300,000.

SAMPLE GRANTS Gresham's School (£281,000); Jesus Hospital Almshouses (£100,000); Harrietsham Almshouses (£50,500); Rivers & Fisheries Trusts of Scotland (£21,500); New Model School (£20,000); Salmon & Trout Association (£11,500); Bristol Charities (£10,000); Royal College of Music (£8,000); Royal National Mission to Deep Sea Fishermen (£7,000); Against Breast Cancer (£5,000); Bermuda Institute of Ocean Sciences (£4,000); Prostate UK and St Mungo's (£2,000 each); and the British Museum and Age Concern Westminster (£1,000 each).

FINANCES *Year* 2009–10 *Income* £1,626,258 *Grants* £773,220 *Assets* £18,301,906

TRUSTEES K S Waters; P T R Woodward; Court of the Worshipful Company of Fishmongers.

OTHER INFORMATION £91,500 was distributed to individuals during the year.

HOW TO APPLY In writing to the correspondent. Meetings take place three times a year, in March, June/July and November, and applications should be received a month in

Think carefully about every application. Is it justified?

537

advance. No applications are considered within three years of a previous grant application being successful. Unsuccessful applications are not acknowledged.

WHO TO APPLY TO Peter Woodward, Clerk, The Fishmongers' Company, Fishmongers' Hall, London Bridge, London EC4R 9EL *Tel* 020 7626 3531 *Fax* 020 7929 1389 *email* clerk@fishhall.org.uk *Website* www.fishhall.org.uk

....

■ Marc Fitch Fund

CC NO 313303   **ESTABLISHED** 1956
WHERE FUNDING CAN BE GIVEN UK.
WHO CAN BENEFIT Both individuals and institutions benefiting young adults, research workers and students.
WHAT IS FUNDED Publication and research in archaeology, historical geography, history of art and architecture, heraldry, genealogy, surnames, catalogues of and use of archives (especially ecclesiastical) and other antiquarian, archaeological or historical studies. In many cases, the awards enable work to be undertaken, or the results published either in print or on-line form, which would not otherwise be achieved.
WHAT IS NOT FUNDED No grants are given towards foreign travel or for research outside the British Isles (unless the circumstances are exceptional); building works; mounting exhibitions; or general appeals. No awards are made in connection with vocational or higher education courses or to people reading for higher degrees.
TYPE OF GRANT Mainly publication costs and incidental research expenses.
RANGE OF GRANTS Institutions: usually up to £10,000.
SAMPLE GRANTS Manorial Documents Register (£10,000); Tate Gallery (£8,500); Institute of Historical Research – Centre for Metropolitan History (£8,500); Lambeth Palace Gallery (£7,000); Wordsworth Trust (£6,000); North West Wales Dendrochronology Project (£5,000); Victoria County History (£4,500); National Archives (£4,000); British School at Rome (£3,000); North Yorkshire County Record Office (£2,500); Corpus Vitrearum Medii Aevi (£2,000); Northmoor Trust for Countryside Conservation (£1,500); Tayside and Fife Archaeological Committee (£1,300); South Ainsty Archaeological Society (£1,000); and Centre for English Local History – Leicester (£500).
FINANCES *Year* 2009–10 *Income* £184,048 *Grants* £105,696 *Assets* £5,011,981
TRUSTEES David White; Lindsay Allason-Jones; Alan Scott Bell; Andrew Howard Murison; Dr Helen Forde; Dr John Blair; Prof. David Hey; Michael Hall.
OTHER INFORMATION The grant total includes £23,146 given in research grants to individuals.
HOW TO APPLY In writing to the correspondent, providing a brief outline of the project. The Council of Management meets twice a year, in spring and autumn, to consider applications. The deadlines for receipt of completed applications and references are 1 March and 1 August. The fund requests that any application enquiries be made well in advance of these deadlines as the application process is likely to take at least a few weeks to complete.

WHO TO APPLY TO Christopher Catling, Director, 19 The Avenue, Cirencester, Gloucestershire GL7 1EJ *Tel* 01608 811944 *email* admin@marcfitchfund.org.uk *Website* www.marcfitchfund.org.uk

....

■ The Fitton Trust

CC NO 208758   **ESTABLISHED** 1928
WHERE FUNDING CAN BE GIVEN UK.
WHO CAN BENEFIT Registered charities only.
WHAT IS FUNDED General charitable purposes.
WHAT IS NOT FUNDED No grants to individuals.
RANGE OF GRANTS Usually £100–£250; occasionally £1,000 or more.
SAMPLE GRANTS King's Medical Research Trust (£2,100).
FINANCES *Year* 2009–10 *Income* £84,973 *Grants* £69,200 *Assets* £1,610,614
TRUSTEES Dr R P A Rivers; D V Brand; R Brand; K J Lumsden; E M Lumsden; L P L Rivers.
HOW TO APPLY In writing to correspondent. The trustees meet three times each year, usually in April, August and December. The trust states: 'No application considered unless accompanied by fully audited accounts. No replies will be sent to unsolicited applications whether from individuals, charities or other bodies.'
WHO TO APPLY TO Mrs Rosalind Gordon-Cumming, The Secretary, PO Box 649, London SW3 4LA

....

■ The Earl Fitzwilliam Charitable Trust

CC NO 269388   **ESTABLISHED** 1975
WHERE FUNDING CAN BE GIVEN UK, with a preference for areas with historical family connections, chiefly in Cambridgeshire, Northamptonshire and Yorkshire.
WHO CAN BENEFIT Organisations benefiting: children and young adults; clergy; ex-service and service people; volunteers; Christians; Church of England; at risk groups; disabled people; people living in rural areas; victims of abuse and crime; victims of man-made or natural disasters; and people with cancer, diabetes, head and other injuries, leprosy, mental illness, spina bifida and hydrocephalus. Projects and charities connected in some way with or which will benefit rural life and communities including churches.
WHAT IS FUNDED Preference for charitable projects in areas with historical family connections, chiefly in Cambridgeshire, Northamptonshire and Yorkshire. Particularly charities working in the fields of: accommodation and housing; infrastructure, support and development; Christian outreach; churches; religious umbrella bodies; arts, culture and recreation; health facilities and buildings; cancer research; conservation and environment; schools and colleges; and various community facilities and services.
WHAT IS NOT FUNDED No grants to individuals.
TYPE OF GRANT Buildings, capital, endowments, one-off, project and research. Funding of one year or less will be considered.
RANGE OF GRANTS Usually £100–£5,000.
SAMPLE GRANTS York Minster Fund, Peterborough Cathedral Trust and Liver Research Trust (£5,000 each); Ryedale In-Touch Group, Macmillan Cancer Support, Deafblind UK and Addenbrooke's Charitable Trust (£2,500 each); East Anglia's Children's Hospice, Northamptonshire Association for the Blind and Prince's Trust (£2,000 each); Helpston and

Etton Community Association and Nene Valley Archaeological Trust (£1,000 each); Renewable Heritage Trust and Farm Crisis Network (£500); and Habitat for Humanity and Historic Churches Trust (£250 each).

FINANCES *Year* 2009–10 *Income* £135,283 *Grants* £99,744 *Assets* £10,562,738

TRUSTEES Sir Philip Naylor-Leyland; Lady Isabella Naylor-Leyland.

HOW TO APPLY In writing to the correspondent. Trustees meet about every three months.

WHO TO APPLY TO R W Dalgleish, Secretary to the Trustees, Estate Office, Milton Park, Peterborough PE6 7AH *Tel* 01733 267740 *email* agent@miltonestate.co.uk

....

■ Bud Flanagan Leukaemia Fund

CC NO 1092540   **ESTABLISHED** 1969

WHERE FUNDING CAN BE GIVEN UK.

WHO CAN BENEFIT Hospitals and similar organisations carrying out research, diagnosis and treatment of leukaemia and allied diseases; people with leukaemia and their families and dependants.

WHAT IS FUNDED Promotion of clinical research into the treatment and possible cure of leukaemia and allied diseases and the publication of the results of all such research. Relief of people with leukaemia and allied diseases and the relief of poverty and distress among their families and dependants. The policy is to make donations to hospitals and similar institutions for equipment or research into leukaemia and allied diseases so that as many people as possible benefit.

WHAT IS NOT FUNDED The fund does not normally make grants to welfare charities or to individuals.

TYPE OF GRANT Capital (including buildings), project and research. Funding can be for up to three years.

RANGE OF GRANTS Usually up to £10,000.

SAMPLE GRANTS The Royal Marsden Hospital (£40,000); Help for Heroes (£200) and St Catharine's Hospice (£100).

FINANCES *Year* 2010 *Income* £103,660 *Grants* £40,355 *Assets* £633,233

TRUSTEES Joseph Goodman; K Kaye; Martin King; Tony Robinson.

HOW TO APPLY In writing to the correspondent.

WHO TO APPLY TO Julie Rudland-Wood, 10 Royal Sovereign View, Eastbourne, East Sussex BN23 6EQ *Tel* 01323 642843 *email* budflanagan-fund@hotmail.co.uk *Website* www.bflf.org.uk

....

■ The Rose Flatau Charitable Trust

CC NO 210492   **ESTABLISHED** 1959

WHERE FUNDING CAN BE GIVEN UK.

WHO CAN BENEFIT Registered charities.

WHAT IS FUNDED Jewish and other organisations which relieve those in need by reason of youth, age, disability, ill health and social circumstances.

WHAT IS NOT FUNDED No grants to individuals.

RANGE OF GRANTS £100–£15,000.

SAMPLE GRANTS Brantwood Trust (£10,000); British Red Cross, Cherry Trees and Children's Trust Tadworth (£5,000 each); Institute of Cancer Research, New Horizons Research and Nightingales (£2,500 each); London Catalyst and Royal Hospital Disability (£2,000 each); and MacMillan Cancer Support and St Mary's Wrestwood Trust (£1,000 each).

FINANCES *Year* 2009–10 *Income* £70,893 *Grants* £85,500 *Assets* £1,663,403

TRUSTEES Naomi Woolf; A E Woolf; N L Woolf.

HOW TO APPLY The trust stated: 'Our funds are fully committed to the foreseeable future'. Speculative applications will therefore be fruitless.

WHO TO APPLY TO The Trustees, Friend-James, Chartered Accountants, 169 Preston Road, Brighton BN1 6AG *Tel* 01273 562563

....

■ The Ian Fleming Charitable Trust

CC NO 263327   **ESTABLISHED** 1971

WHERE FUNDING CAN BE GIVEN UK.

WHO CAN BENEFIT Individual musicians and registered charities benefiting medical professionals, research workers and scientists. Support is also given to at risk groups, and people who are disabled, disadvantaged by poverty or socially isolated.

WHAT IS FUNDED Income is allocated equally between: national charities actively operating for the support, relief and welfare of men, women and children who are disabled or otherwise in need of help, care and attention, and charities actively engaged in research on human diseases; and music education awards under a scheme administered by the Musicians Benevolent Fund and advised by a committee of experts in the field of music.

WHAT IS NOT FUNDED No grants to individuals except under the music education award scheme. No grants to purely local charities.

RANGE OF GRANTS £1,000–£3,000.

SAMPLE GRANTS Apex Trust, Diabetes UK and Stroke Association (£2,000 each); Camphill Family and Salvation Army (£1,500 each); and Centrepoint and Variety Club Children's Charity (£1,000 each).

FINANCES *Year* 2009–10 *Income* £95,774 *Grants* £77,000 *Assets* £2,515,670

TRUSTEES A A I Fleming; N A M McDonald; A W W Baldwin; A H Isaacs.

OTHER INFORMATION The grant total in 2009–10 consisted of £31,000 to organisations and £46,000 to individuals through the music educational awards scheme.

HOW TO APPLY In writing to the correspondent.

WHO TO APPLY TO A A I Fleming, Trustee, Haysmacintyre, Fairfax House, 15 Fulwood Place, London WC1V 6AY *Tel* 020 7969 5500 *email* mjones@haysmacintyre.com

....

■ The Joyce Fletcher Charitable Trust

CC NO 297901   **ESTABLISHED** 1987

WHERE FUNDING CAN BE GIVEN England, almost entirely South West.

WHO CAN BENEFIT England/wide and south west charities. This trust will consider funding for the benefit of all ages; musicians; volunteers; those in care, fostered and adopted; one-parent families; parents and children; people with disabilities; those living in rural areas; and socially isolated people.

WHAT IS FUNDED Music in the community and in a special needs context; children's welfare; and charities in the south west. Currently main areas of interest are institutions and organisations specialising in music education and performance, special needs education and performance involving music, and charities for children's welfare. Arts, culture and recreation;

art galleries and cultural centres; community centres and village halls; theatres' and opera houses' education programmes; and other charitable purposes are all considered for funding.

WHAT IS NOT FUNDED Grants to individuals and students are exceptionally rare; applications are not sought. No support for areas which are the responsibility of the local authority. No support is given to purely professional music/arts promotions. No support for purely medical research charities.

TYPE OF GRANT Recurring expenses; capital; or new projects.

RANGE OF GRANTS £450–£5,000, occasionally more.

SAMPLE GRANTS Welsh National Opera (£5,000); Wiltshire Music Centre (£4,000); Buxton Festival, Drake Music Project and Iford Arts (£3,000 each); Bath Area Play Project, Bath Fringe Festival, Bath Mozartfest and Jessie's Fund (£2,000 each); Project Trust and Hope and Homes for Children (£1,000 each); and National Trust (£600).

FINANCES *Year* 2009–10 *Income* £58,599 *Grants* £71,050 *Assets* £2,107,628

TRUSTEES R A Fletcher; W D R Fletcher; Susan C Sharp; S P Fletcher.

HOW TO APPLY In writing to the correspondent before 1 November each year. Applications are considered in the months of October and November. There are no application forms. Letters should include the purpose for the grant, an indication of the history and viability of the organisation and a summary of accounts. Preliminary telephone calls are accepted. Acknowledgements are only given if the application is being considered or if an sae is sent.

WHO TO APPLY TO R A Fletcher, Trustee, 68 Circus Mews, Bath BA1 2PW *Tel* 01225 314355

■ The Roy Fletcher Charitable Trust

CC NO 276498   **ESTABLISHED** 1978

WHERE FUNDING CAN BE GIVEN Shropshire.

WHO CAN BENEFIT Local organisations.

WHAT IS FUNDED Children and young people; older people; disadvantage. The trust also established The Roy Fletcher Centre to house caring agencies and provide office space, meeting and counselling rooms; this is now run independently of the trust.

WHAT IS NOT FUNDED The trust is unlikely to fund projects eligible for statutory funding, applicants not seeking funds from elsewhere, UK charities, operating costs, building repairs or educational grants. The trust no longer supports individuals.

RANGE OF GRANTS Up to £1 million, in practice – up to £100,000.

SAMPLE GRANTS The West Cornwall Youth Trust (£1 million); Rainbow Hospice (£87,000); T & W Grassroots (£30,000); CCS Grassroots (£46,000); K21 Appeal (£22,000); W2W (£17,000); Starlight (£15,000); Confide and Prince's Trust (£10,000 each); Age Concern Shropshire (£5,000); ShelterBox, DEC – Haiti and Médecins Sans Frontières (£5,000 each); and Fletcher Memorial Church (£3,000).

FINANCES *Year* 2009–10 *Income* £71,607 *Grants* £1,303,983 *Assets* £6,178,835

TRUSTEES Mrs R A Coles; Mrs G M Mathias; Mrs E J Fletcher-Cooper; D N Fletcher.

HOW TO APPLY In writing to the correspondent only. The trustees meet three times a year in early January, May and October, and requests for funding should be received at least four weeks before each meeting. The trust does not welcome telephone enquiries to The Roy Fletcher Centre (which is a separate organisation).

WHO TO APPLY TO Mrs I Cowen, c/o Roy Fletcher Centre, 12–17 Cross Hill, Shrewsbury, Shropshire SY1 1JE *email* info@royfletchertrust.org.uk *Website* www.royfletchertrust.org.uk

■ Florence's Charitable Trust

CC NO 265754   **ESTABLISHED** 1973

WHERE FUNDING CAN BE GIVEN UK, with a preference for Rossendale in Lancashire.

WHO CAN BENEFIT Mainly local organisations, or local branches of UK organisations, benefiting employees or former employees of the shoe trade and people who are elderly or disadvantaged by poverty. Support may be given to children and young adults.

WHAT IS FUNDED General charitable purposes, especially establishment, maintenance and support of places of education; relief of sickness of infirmity for older people; and relief of poverty of anyone employed or formerly employed in the shoe trade.

WHAT IS NOT FUNDED No grants to individuals for educational fees, exchange visits or gap year activities.

TYPE OF GRANT Mainly recurrent grants.

RANGE OF GRANTS £50–£30,000.

SAMPLE GRANTS Previous beneficiaries have included: Pioneer Community Club; Bacup Family Centre; Whitworth Water Ski; Rossendale Search and Rescue; Rossendale United Junior Football Club; North West Air Ambulance; British Heart Foundation; Rochdale Special Needs; Macmillan Cancer Support; Children with AIDS; Sense; Tenovus; All Black Netball Fund; Sport Relief and Heart of Lancashire appeal. A number of local primary schools and playgroups also benefited.

FINANCES *Year* 2009–10 *Income* £57,533 *Grants* £99,563 *Assets* £999,006

TRUSTEES C C Harrison; A Connearn; G D Low; R D Uttley; S Holding; M Kelly; A Jepson.

HOW TO APPLY In writing only to the correspondent (no telephone calls allowed). To save on administration costs, unsuccessful applications will not be acknowledged even if an sae is provided.

WHO TO APPLY TO B Terry, Secretary to the Trustees, E Suttons and Sons, PO Box 2, Riverside, Bacup, Lancashire OL13 0DT

■ The Flow Foundation

CC NO 328274   **ESTABLISHED** 1989

WHERE FUNDING CAN BE GIVEN UK.

WHO CAN BENEFIT Registered charities.

WHAT IS FUNDED The trust makes grants to support child welfare, education, environment, Jewish, and medical causes.

RANGE OF GRANTS Up to £20,000.

SAMPLE GRANTS Previous beneficiaries have included After Adoption, Brain Research Trust, British Friends of Haifa University, British ORT, Chicken Shed Theatre Company, Honey Pot Charity, International Centre for Child Studies, Jewish Care, Norwood, Royal Pharmaceutical Society, Tate Gallery Foundation, Toynbee Hall Foundation, Unite for the Future, Variety Club Children's Charity, Weizmann Institute Foundation and West London Synagogue.

FINANCES *Year* 2009–10 *Income* £11,448
Grants £117,000
TRUSTEES Mrs N Shashou; Mrs Nina Sowerbutts;
H Woolf; Mrs J Woolf.
HOW TO APPLY In writing to the correspondent on
one sheet of paper only.
WHO TO APPLY TO Mrs Nita Sowerbutts, Trustee,
22 Old Bond Street, London W1S 4PY *Tel* 020
7499 9099

....

■ The Mrs Yvonne Flux Charitable Trust

CC NO 1136459   ESTABLISHED 2010
WHERE FUNDING CAN BE GIVEN UK.
WHO CAN BENEFIT Individuals and organisations.
WHAT IS FUNDED General charitable purposes.
TRUSTEES Yvonne Flux; Susan Boyle.
HOW TO APPLY In writing to the correspondent.
WHO TO APPLY TO C Dodds, c/o Stephenson Smart &
Co, 22–26 King Street, King's Lynn, Norfolk
PE30 1HJ *Tel* 01553 774104 *Fax* 01553
692602

....

■ The Gerald Fogel Charitable Trust

CC NO 1004451   ESTABLISHED 1991
WHERE FUNDING CAN BE GIVEN UK.
WHO CAN BENEFIT Mainly headquarters organisations
benefiting: children and older people, those in
care, fostered and adopted, Jewish people and
homeless people.
WHAT IS FUNDED Charities working in the fields of:
the advancement of the Jewish religion;
synagogues; and cultural and religious teaching.
The trust may also fund residential facilities,
arts activities, care in the community, hospices,
hospitals, cancer research and campaigning on
health issues.
WHAT IS NOT FUNDED No grants to individuals or non-
registered charities.
TYPE OF GRANT One-off and recurrent.
SAMPLE GRANTS Chai Cancer Care – nine grants
(£9,000); World Jewish Relief (£6,000); Jewish
Care (£5,000); Community Security Trust
(£2,500); London Jewish Cultural Centre
(£1,000).
FINANCES *Year* 2009–10 *Income* £67,783
Grants £44,949 *Assets* £873,399
TRUSTEES J G Fogel; B Fogel; S Fogel; D Fogel.
OTHER INFORMATION Small grants below £1,000
each totalled £5,000.
HOW TO APPLY In writing to the correspondent.
WHO TO APPLY TO J Clay, Accountant, Morley and
Scott, Lynton House, 7–12 Tavistock Square,
London WC1H 9LT

....

■ The Follett Trust

CC NO 328638   ESTABLISHED 1990
WHERE FUNDING CAN BE GIVEN UK and overseas, with
a preference for Stevenage in the UK.
WHO CAN BENEFIT Individuals and organisations
benefiting children and young adults, actors and
entertainment professionals, musicians, textile
workers and designers, writers and poets, at
risk groups and people disadvantaged by
poverty; medical research and hospital projects;
people with disabilities.
WHAT IS FUNDED Education; individual students in
higher education (including theatre); disability
and health; trusts for writers and publishers;
and international relief work.

RANGE OF GRANTS Usually up to £20,000.
FINANCES *Year* 2009–10 *Income* £161,553
Grants £150,701 *Assets* £46,038
TRUSTEES Brian Mitchell; Ken Follett; Barbara
Follett.
HOW TO APPLY The trust states, 'A high proportion of
donees come to the attention of the trustees
through personal knowledge and contact rather
than by written application. Where the trustees
find it impossible to make a donation they rarely
respond to the applicant unless a stamped
addressed envelope is provided.'
WHO TO APPLY TO Brian Mitchell, Trustee/
Administrator, Po Box 4, Knebworth, Herts
SG3 6UT

....

■ The Football Association National Sports Centre Trust

CC NO 265132   ESTABLISHED 1972
WHERE FUNDING CAN BE GIVEN UK.
WHO CAN BENEFIT County football associations,
football clubs and other sports associations.
WHAT IS FUNDED The provision, maintenance and
improvement of facilities for use in recreational
and leisure activities.
TYPE OF GRANT One-off grants towards community-
based projects.
RANGE OF GRANTS £5,000–£25,000.
FINANCES *Year* 2010 *Income* £24,504
Grants £90,000
TRUSTEES Geoff Thompson; Barry Bright; Raymond
Berridge; William Annable; Jack Perks.
HOW TO APPLY In writing to the correspondent.
WHO TO APPLY TO Mike Appleby, Secretary, The
Football Association, Wembley Stadium, London
HA9 0WS *Tel* 0844 980 8200 *email* mike.
appleby@thefa.com

....

■ The Football Association Youth Trust

CC NO 265131   ESTABLISHED 1972
WHERE FUNDING CAN BE GIVEN UK.
WHO CAN BENEFIT County football associations,
schools, universities and other sports
associations benefiting young people who play
football or other sports.
WHAT IS FUNDED The organisation or provision of
facilities which will enable young people under
the age of 21 in the UK to play association
football or other games and sports including the
provision of equipment, lectures, training
colleges, playing fields or indoor
accommodation.
TYPE OF GRANT One-off.
SAMPLE GRANTS Girls' Centre of Excellence
(£1 million); schools and universities
(£204,500); county football associations
(£77,500); 'other' (£1,300).
FINANCES *Year* 2009–10 *Income* £37,305
Grants £1,284,956 *Assets* £1,276,713
TRUSTEES Raymond G Berridge; Barry W Bright;
Geoff Thompson; Jack Perks.
HOW TO APPLY In writing to the correspondent.
Grants are made throughout the year. There are
no application forms, but a copy of the most
recent accounts should be sent.
WHO TO APPLY TO Mike Appleby, Secretary, The
Football Association, Wembley Stadium, London
HA9 0WS *Tel* 0844 980 8200 *email* mike.
appleby@thefa.com

Think carefully about every application. Is it justified?

541

■ The Football Foundation

CC NO 1079309   **ESTABLISHED** 2000

WHERE FUNDING CAN BE GIVEN England.

WHO CAN BENEFIT Grass roots of football. It also funds educational and community projects.

WHAT IS FUNDED The grass roots advisory group works at an infrastructure level to deliver modern facilities in parks, local leagues and schools throughout the country. Local football partnerships have been established to ensure that all relevant groups have a voice in how football is delivered in their communities. The community and education panel aims to promote community and education initiatives and enhance football's role as a positive force in society.

SAMPLE GRANTS London Borough of Hackney (£1.9 million); North East Lincolnshire Council (£1 million); Evesham United Football Club (£700,000); City of Wolverhampton College (£557,000); South Manchester Sports Club (£495,000); Stoke Gabriel Football Club (£453,000); Oakworth Juniors Football Club (£416,000); Tresham Institute of Further & Higher Education (£300,000); Welbeck Miners Welfare Trust (£259,500); London Borough of Hillingdon (£250,000); Mole Valley District Council (£198,000); Norfolk County FA (£157,000); Witchford Village College (£121,000); and Norton Parish Council (£100,000).

FINANCES *Year* 2009–10 *Income* £46,907,000 *Grants* £40,472,000 *Assets* £9,386,000

TRUSTEES Richard Scudamore; Roger Burden; Peter McCormick; Philip Smith; Clive Sterling.

OTHER INFORMATION See the foundation's website for full details of the current schemes.

HOW TO APPLY Application forms and guidance notes are available on request directly from the foundation or downloadable from the website.

WHO TO APPLY TO Robert Booker, Director of Finance, Whittington House, 19–30 Alfred Place, London WC1E 7EA *Tel* 0845 345 4555 *Fax* 0845 345 7057 *email* enquiries@footballfoundation.org.uk *Website* www.footballfoundation.org.uk

■ The Forbes Charitable Foundation

CC NO 326476   **ESTABLISHED** 1983

WHERE FUNDING CAN BE GIVEN UK.

WHO CAN BENEFIT Charities benefiting adults with learning disabilities.

WHAT IS FUNDED Welfare causes.

TYPE OF GRANT Capital rather than revenue projects.

RANGE OF GRANTS Usually up to £10,000.

SAMPLE GRANTS Leicester City Council-Special Olympics (£50,000); Cottage and Rural Enterprises Ltd (£8,000); See Ability (£5,000); Mires Beck Nursery (£3,000); Wirral Autistic Society (£2,600); and Merseyside Tuesday Club (£1,000).

FINANCES *Year* 2009–10 *Income* £936,695 *Grants* £95,037 *Assets* £3,057,552

TRUSTEES C G Packham, Chair; I Johnson; R Bunting; N J Townsend; J M Waite; J. W. Williamson; R Warburton.

HOW TO APPLY In writing to the correspondent. Applications are considered in June and November.

WHO TO APPLY TO The Secretary to the Trustees, 14 Nursery Court, Kibworth Harcourt, Leicester LE8 0EX

■ The Forces Trust

CC NO 211529   **ESTABLISHED** 1924

WHERE FUNDING CAN BE GIVEN UK.

WHO CAN BENEFIT Registered military charities.

WHAT IS FUNDED Military charities. The trustees prefer to assist people (disabled, injured and disadvantaged) rather than institutions or the preservation of buildings.

WHAT IS NOT FUNDED No grants to any non-naval or military charities, individuals, scholarships or education generally.

TYPE OF GRANT Capital, one-off, project, research and recurring costs. Funding of up to two years.

RANGE OF GRANTS £500–£25,000, typically £2,500.

SAMPLE GRANTS Previous beneficiaries included: British Limbless Ex-Service Men's Association, Erskine Hospital, Gordon Highlanders London Association Benevolent Fund, League of Remembrance, Scottish National Institution for the War Blinded, Sir Oswald Stoll Foundation, SSAFA-Forces Help Cumbria and St David's Nursing Home.

FINANCES *Year* 2009–10 *Income* £42,500 *Grants* £55,096

TRUSTEES Capt. A P C Niekirk; Lieu. Col. W D Niekirk; Brig. R E Nugee; B E V Bowater.

HOW TO APPLY In writing to the correspondent at any time, preferably on one side of A4.

WHO TO APPLY TO Joanna Jeeves, Viaduct House, Victoria Viaduct, Carlisle CA3 8EZ *Tel* 01228 516666 *email* joanna.jeeves@cartmells.co.uk

■ Ford Britain Trust

CC NO 269410   **ESTABLISHED** 1975

WHERE FUNDING CAN BE GIVEN Local to the areas in close proximity to Ford Motor Company Limited's locations in the UK. These are Essex (including East London), Bridgend, Southampton and Daventry.

WHO CAN BENEFIT Registered charities; schools/PTAs (non-fee paying, state sector schools only); non-profit organisations (including small clubs and societies).

WHAT IS FUNDED Education, the environment, children, disabilities, youth education and projects that benefit the local communities that Ford operates in. Grants are typically one-off and fall into two categories: small grants – for amounts up to £250; and large grants – for amounts over £250 and usually up to £3,000.

WHAT IS NOT FUNDED Grant applications are not considered if they support the following purposes or activities: major building works; sponsorship or advertising; research; overseas projects; travel; religious projects; political projects; purchase of second hand vehicles; third party fundraising initiatives (exceptions may be made for fundraising initiatives by Ford Motor Company Limited employees and retirees). National charities are assisted rarely and then only when the purpose of their application has specific benefit to communities located in close proximity to Ford locations.

TYPE OF GRANT Contributions to capital projects (e.g. refurbishments); capital expenditure items (e.g. furniture/equipment/computers); contributions towards the purchase or leasing of new Ford vehicles (up to a maximum of £2,000); and general funds (small grants up to £250 only).

RANGE OF GRANTS Most grants range between £250 and £3,000.

SAMPLE GRANTS Thames Gateway Youth Football Programme (£10,000); and Harold Hill Youth Football Club, 1st Miskin Mill Scout Group, St

Mary's Primary School and Woodbridge High School (£3,000 each).

FINANCES *Year* 2009–10 *Income* £192,064 *Grants* £163,679 *Assets* £220,802

TRUSTEES Michael Callaghan; David Russell; Michael Brophy; Jennifer Ball; Dr June-Alison Sealy; Mitra Janes.

HOW TO APPLY On a form available from the correspondent or to download from the website. Applications for large grants should include a copy of the organisation's most recent report and accounts. Small grant applications are considered in March, June, September and November and should be submitted by the 1st of each month. Applications for large grants are considered in May and September and again should be submitted by the 1st of each month.

WHO TO APPLY TO Andy Taylor, Room 1/445, c/o Ford Motor Company Limited, Eagle Way, Brentwood, Essex CM13 3BW *Tel* 01277 252551 *email* fbtrust@ford.com *Website* www.ford.co.uk/fbtrust

....

■ The Oliver Ford Charitable Trust

CC NO 1026551   **ESTABLISHED** 1993

WHERE FUNDING CAN BE GIVEN UK.

WHO CAN BENEFIT Neighbourhood-based community projects, students and institutions. Children, young persons or adults who have learning disabilities or learning difficulties.

WHAT IS FUNDED The trust aims to educate the general public and advance knowledge of the history and techniques of interior decoration, the design of fabrics and other decorative materials and landscape gardening. Charities providing housing, educational or training facilities for children, young persons or adults who have learning disabilities or learning difficulties.

TYPE OF GRANT One-off.

RANGE OF GRANTS Usually up to £10,000.

SAMPLE GRANTS Norwood Ravenswood (£20,000); L'Arche (£5,000); Hansel Foundation (£2,500); Norman Laud Association (£1,500); and Independent Options (£700).

FINANCES *Year* 2009–10 *Income* £95,878 *Grants* £50,597 *Assets* £2,453,927

TRUSTEES Lady Wakeham; Martin Levy.

OTHER INFORMATION In 2009–10 grants were also given to students at the Furniture & History Society (£2,795); the Royal Horticultural Society (£5,000); and the Victoria & Albert Museum (£17,810).

HOW TO APPLY In writing to the correspondent. Trustees meet in March and October.

WHO TO APPLY TO Matthew Pintus, 20 Cursitor Street, London EC4A 1LT *Tel* 020 7831 9222

....

■ Fordeve Ltd

CC NO 1011612   **ESTABLISHED** 1992

WHERE FUNDING CAN BE GIVEN UK.

WHO CAN BENEFIT Organisations benefiting Jews, at risk groups and people who are unemployed, disadvantaged by poverty or socially isolated. Support may also be given to people who are disabled, homeless, immigrants or refugees.

WHAT IS FUNDED Jewish causes and relief of need.

SAMPLE GRANTS Previous beneficiaries include: the Gertner Charitable Trust; Lubavitch Foundation; the Yom Tov Assistance Fund; the Society of Friends of the Torah; Lolev Charitable Trust; Beth Jacob Grammar School for Girls.

FINANCES *Year* 2009–10 *Income* £123,243 *Grants* £203,080 *Assets* £686,000

TRUSTEES Jeremy Kon; Helen Kon.

HOW TO APPLY In writing to the correspondent.

WHO TO APPLY TO Jeremy Kon, Trustee, c/o Gerald Kreditor & Co, Hallswelle House, 1 Hallswelle Road, London NW11 0DH *Tel* 020 8209 1535

....

■ The Forest Hill Charitable Trust

CC NO 1050862   **ESTABLISHED** 1995

WHERE FUNDING CAN BE GIVEN UK and overseas.

WHO CAN BENEFIT Organisations and individuals.

WHAT IS FUNDED Christian causes.

RANGE OF GRANTS Grants usually range between £1,000 and £2,000.

SAMPLE GRANTS LiNX (£22,000) and Great Parks Chapel (£12,000).

FINANCES *Year* 2009–10 *Income* £242,912 *Grants* £238,700 *Assets* £3,212,301

TRUSTEES H F Pile, Chair; Mrs P J Pile; R S Pile; Mrs M S Tapper; M Thomas.

OTHER INFORMATION All other grants of £5,000 or less amounted to £205,000.

HOW TO APPLY The trustees have previously stated that their aim was to maintain regular and consistent support to the charities they are currently supporting. New requests for funding are therefore very unlikely to succeed and unsolicited applications are rarely considered.

WHO TO APPLY TO Mrs P J Pile, Secretary to the Trustees, 104 Summercourt Way, Brixham, Devon TQ5 0RB *Tel* 01803 852857 *email* horacepile@tiscali.co.uk

....

■ The Lady Forester Trust

CC NO 241187   **ESTABLISHED** 1979

WHERE FUNDING CAN BE GIVEN Shropshire.

WHO CAN BENEFIT Primarily, the residents of the Parish of Wenlock and then the inhabitants of the County of Shropshire.

WHAT IS FUNDED Residents who are sick, convalescent, disabled or infirm where help is not readily available to them from other sources.

RANGE OF GRANTS Up to £30,000.

SAMPLE GRANTS St Dunstan's, Llandudno (£9,500); Combat Stress (£6,000); County Air Ambulance (£5,000); Marie Curie Cancer Care (£4,000); NSPCC (£2,000) and Surestart's Additional Needs Group (£1,000).

FINANCES *Year* 2010 *Income* £136,813 *Grants* £108,750 *Assets* £4,362,510

TRUSTEES Lady Forester, Chair; Mrs Alice Stoker; Mrs Libby Collinson; John Michael Dugdale; Henry Carpenter; Lord Forester; The Lady Forester MRICS and Mrs J Stewart.

OTHER INFORMATION The grant total included £55,000 to organisations and £37,000 to approximately 70 individuals.

HOW TO APPLY Trustees meet on a quarterly basis to consider applications and will consider unsolicited applications. Grants for individuals are usually recommended by GPs or social workers. Application should be made in writing to the correspondent.

WHO TO APPLY TO Lady Forester, Chair, Willey Estates, The Estate Office, Willey Park, Willey, Broseley, Shropshire TF12 5JJ *Tel* 01952 884318

■ The Foresters' Fund for Children

CC NO 327449 **ESTABLISHED** 1987
WHERE FUNDING CAN BE GIVEN UK.
WHO CAN BENEFIT Non-profit making organisations, charities and agencies.
WHAT IS FUNDED Projects related to improving the quality of life of children and for specific education needs.
FINANCES *Year* 2009–10 *Income* £18,432 *Grants* £30,000
TRUSTEES Tom Ball, Chair; Alex Clark; Darren Hanney; Paul Bayliss; Lonija Balgavis; Jason Alexander.
HOW TO APPLY In writing to the correspondent, or via an application form available from the fund's website. Applications are considered by the trustees at their quarterly meetings.
WHO TO APPLY TO The Grants Secretary, PO BOX 98, Penperlleni, Pontypool NP4 4BQ *Tel* 01873 880379 *email* grants@forestersfundforchildren. org.uk *Website* www.forestersfundforchildren. org.uk

■ The Foresters' Charity Stewards UK Trust

CC NO 328604 **ESTABLISHED** 1990
WHERE FUNDING CAN BE GIVEN UK.
WHO CAN BENEFIT Individuals and institutions benefiting older people, disabled people and communities as a whole.
WHAT IS FUNDED To improve quality of life and the environment of the community at large.
TYPE OF GRANT One-off grants for capital and revenue costs.
SAMPLE GRANTS Previous beneficiaries have included: Abbeyfield, AOF Education Awards Fund, AOF Foresters' Home, AOF Yorkshire Convalescent Home, Mayor of Scarborough's Charity, North Middlesex Hospital, RNLI and Taste for Adventure.
FINANCES *Year* 2010 *Income* £4,189 *Grants* £45,000
TRUSTEES Graham D Lloyd; Barbara Lloyd; Carole Shuttle; Derek Shuttle; Richard Biddlecombe; Pat Biddlecombe; Graham Lale.
HOW TO APPLY In writing to the correspondent.
WHO TO APPLY TO Graham D Lloyd, Trustee, Littlecroft, 8 The Marches, Kingsfold, Horsham, West Sussex RH12 3SY

■ Forever Manchester (The Community Foundation for Greater Manchester)

CC NO 1017504 **ESTABLISHED** 1993
WHERE FUNDING CAN BE GIVEN Greater Manchester.
WHO CAN BENEFIT Registered charities and small, locally run community or voluntary groups who seek to improve the circumstances in economically and socially excluded areas in Greater Manchester facing disadvantage.
WHAT IS FUNDED General charitable purposes including health; welfare; education; people with disabilities; older people; youth and children. Improving the quality of life and helping to build stronger communities across Greater Manchester.
WHAT IS NOT FUNDED The foundation will not support: organisations and projects outside the Greater Manchester area; organisations trading for profit or intending to redistribute grant awards; major capital requests, i.e. building and construction work; requests that will replace or enhance statutory provision; academic or medical research & equipment; overseas travel; primary purpose of request is to promote religious or political beliefs; retrospective grants – (projects/activities that have already taken place); projects that fall within statutory sector responsibility; sponsorship or fundraising events; contributions to larger/major appeals. (Where the application sum would not cover at least 75% of the total project cost); holidays and social outings. (Except in cases of specific disablement or proven benefit to a community or group of people); local branches of national charities unless locally managed, financially autonomous and not beneficiaries of national marketing or promotion; more than one application at a time for the same project.
TYPE OF GRANT One-off; project. Start-up costs will be considered.
RANGE OF GRANTS Mostly under £5,000 but can be up to £40,000, dependent upon scheme.
SAMPLE GRANTS Tindall Street Allotments (£40,000); Groundwork – Oldham and Rochdale (£22,000); Brinnington Samba band (£5,000); Men Behaving Dadly (£4,800); Hope Carr Morris Dancers (£3,700); Abraham Moss Warriors JFC (£2,500); Chorlton Park Regeneration Group; Have Your Say Community Publishing Project (£2000 each); Droylsden Amateur Boxing Club (£1,600); Caribbean Elders (£900).
FINANCES *Year* 2010–11 *Income* £8,603,830 *Grants* £4,521,354 *Assets* £9,409,571
TRUSTEES John Sandford; Chris Hirst; Richard Hogben; Tony Burns; Simon Webber; Jo Farrell; Han-Son Lee; Sandra Lindsay; Natalie Qureshi.
PUBLICATIONS Guidelines; information packs.
HOW TO APPLY The foundation's website provides full guidelines for each of the programmes for which organisations can apply. It also provides application and monitoring forms for each programme. If you are applying for a grant for the first time, or if you would like advice before making an application, contact the foundation for any advice. Applications will only be accepted if submitted on the foundation's application form. All sections of the form must be completed even if the information is supplied in the form of a report, leaflet and so on. The foundation prefers not to receive applications by fax; completed forms should be returned by post. The decision of the foundation's trustees is final and no discussion will be entered into. The foundation will, however, try to provide helpful feedback to both successful and unsuccessful applicants.
Applicants are requested to provide copies of the constitution, and a copy of the latest, relevant annual accounts and the last two bank statements with their applications. Decisions are almost always given within three months but the exact time will often depend on a number of factors and not just when the appropriate committee next meets. One of the foundation's grants administrators may contact you for further information or to discuss your application with you. Contact the foundation directly for up-to-date information on deadlines for programmes and the dates of panel meetings.
WHO TO APPLY TO Nick Massey, Chief Executive Officer, 5th Floor, Speakers House, 39 Deansgate, Manchester M3 2BA *Tel* 0161 214 0940 *Fax* 0161 214 0941 *email* enquiries@communityfoundation.co.uk *Website* www.forevermanchester.com

■ Gwyneth Forrester Trust

cc no 1080921   **established** 2000
where funding can be given England and Wales.
who can benefit Charitable organisations.
what is funded The trustees support a specific charitable sector each year.
what is not funded No grants to individuals.
type of grant One-off.
finances *Year* 2009–10 *Income* £384,645 *Grants* £425,000 *Assets* £21,139,414
trustees Wendy J Forrester; Anthony J Smee; Michael B Jones; Christopher Perkins.
other information No information was available on the future focus of the trust's grant-making as 'once the charitable sector is chosen, we research that sector and produce a list of possibles and then contact the individual charities to discuss with them their particular needs and any specific projects they have in hand. These are then discussed and the final grant list is decided.'
how to apply The trust has previously stated that 'applications for aid cannot be considered'.
who to apply to Christopher Perkins, Trustee, Lancaster House, 7 Elmfield Road, Bromley, Kent BR1 1LT *Tel* 020 8461 8014

■ The Donald Forrester Trust

cc no 295833   **established** 1986
where funding can be given UK and overseas.
who can benefit Charities benefiting people who are sick or disabled, particularly older people and children.
what is funded Medical welfare and relief; overseas; children and youth; old people's welfare; hospitals and hospices, physical and mental disability; blind and deaf; community care and social welfare; medical research; animal and bird welfare; services and ex-services; maritime; and culture, heritage, environment and sport.
what is not funded No grants to individuals.
type of grant One off and recurrent.
range of grants £5,000–£15,000.
sample grants Great Ormond Street Hospital Children's Charity and Disasters Emergency Committee (£15,000 each); RSPCA, NSPCC, and the Blond McIndoe Research Foundation (£10,000 each); and Battersea Dogs and Cats Home, Marine Conservation Society, National Deaf Children's Society, Foundation for the Study of Infant Deaths, Volunteer Reading Help, Housing the Homeless Central Fund, Moorfields Eye Hospital Development Fund, RNLI, Down's Syndrome Association, Psychiatry Research Trust, Mental Health Foundation, Friends of the Elderly, Médecins Sans Frontières, Royal British Legion and All Souls Clubhouse (£5,000 each).
finances *Year* 2009–10 *Income* £889,431 *Grants* £845,000 *Assets* £7,742,083
trustees Wendy J Forrester, Anthony J Smee; Michael B Jones; Hilary J Porter; Christopher A Perkins.
how to apply The trust supports a substantial number of charities on a regular basis. We are informed that regrettably, detailed applications, which place 'an intolerable strain' on administrative resources, cannot be considered. It is suggested that very brief details of an application should be submitted to the correspondent on one side of A4. The trustees normally meet twice a year to consider and agree on the grants which are paid half yearly. There are no specific requirements under the trust deed and over the years the trustees have supported a wide range of national and international charities and endeavoured to achieve a balance between the large institutions and the smaller charities that experience greater difficulty in fund raising. The trustees have developed a fairly substantial list of charities that are supported on a regular basis, but new proposals, both regular and 'one-off' are considered at each meeting.
who to apply to Christopher A Perkins, Trustee, Lancaster House, 7 Elmfield Road, Bromley, Kent BR1 1LT *Tel* 020 8461 8014

■ The Anna Rosa Forster Charitable Trust

cc no 1090028   **established** 1996
where funding can be given Worldwide.
who can benefit Charitable organisations.
what is funded Medical research, animal welfare, famine relief.
range of grants Usually between £2,500 and £3,500.
sample grants Previous beneficiaries include: Alzheimer's Research Trust, Cancer Research UK, British Red Cross, Farm Africa, Cats Protection League, CARE International UK, Motor Neurone Disease Association, the Donkey Sanctuary, PDSA, RSPCA, International Spinal Research Trust and the World Medical Fund.
finances *Year* 2009–10 *Income* £67,633 *Grants* £69,105 *Assets* £1,998,283
trustees R W Napier; A W Morgan.
how to apply In writing to the correspondent.
who to apply to R W Napier, Trustee, c/o R W Napier Solicitors, Floor E, Milburn House, Dean Street, Newcastle upon Tyne NE1 1LF *Tel* 0191 230 1819

■ The Fort Foundation

cc no 1028639   **established** 1993
where funding can be given North east Lancashire.
who can benefit Organisations supporting young people and individuals.
what is funded Training for industry and life extra curriculum activities.
what is not funded Education fees.
type of grant One–off.
sample grants Marine Society & Sea Cadets (£5,000); Foulridge Parish Council; St John's Hospice, London and Special Boat Services Association (£1,250 each); and Pendle Croquet Club (£1,000).
finances *Year* 2010–11 *Income* £103,159 *Grants* £18,735 *Assets* £221,060
trustees E S Fort; I Wilson; Mrs. S Friedlander.
other information Around £1,500 of the grants total was awarded to individuals.
how to apply In writing to the correspondent.
who to apply to Anne Hartley, Administrator, Fort Vale Engineering Ltd, Calder Vale Park, Simonstone Lane, Simonstone, Burnley BB12 7ND *Tel* 01282 440000

■ The Forte Charitable Trust

cc no 326038   **established** 1982
where funding can be given UK and overseas.
who can benefit Community-based projects and national organisations and institutions.
what is funded The Roman Catholic faith, Alzheimer's disease and senile dementia.
finances *Year* 2009–10 *Grants* £120,000

Think carefully about every application. Is it justified?

545

TRUSTEES Hon. Sir Rocco Forte; Hon. Olga Polizzi di Sorrentino; G F L Proctor; Lowndes Trustees Ltd.

OTHER INFORMATION Information was provided by the trust.

HOW TO APPLY In writing to the correspondent.

WHO TO APPLY TO Mrs Heather McConville, Lowndes House, Lowndes Place, London SW1X 8DB *Tel* 020 7235 6244 *email* hmcconville@roccofortehotels.com

■ Lord Forte Foundation

CC NO 298100   **ESTABLISHED** 1987
WHERE FUNDING CAN BE GIVEN UK.
WHO CAN BENEFIT Educational establishments.
WHAT IS FUNDED Training courses and research in the field of hotel management, catering and the travel and tourism industries.
RANGE OF GRANTS £1,000–£7,000.
SAMPLE GRANTS University of Bedfordshire (£7,000); Thames Valley University (£5,600); Leeds City College, Llandrillo College, the Bournemouth and Poole College Foundation, Fifteen Foundation and Westminster Kingsway College (£5,000 each); Crisis UK (£3,900); and Bournemouth University and the University of Strathclyde (£1,300 each).
FINANCES *Year* 2009–10 *Income* £55,832 *Grants* £44,025 *Assets* £2,124,530
TRUSTEES Hon Sir Rocco Forte, Chair; Lord Janner; Hon Olga Polizzi di Sorrentino; George Proctor; Nick Scade; Andrew McKenzie.
HOW TO APPLY In writing to the correspondent.
WHO TO APPLY TO Heather McConville, Foundation Administrator, Lowndes House, Lowndes Place, Belgrave Square, London SW1X 8DB *Tel* 020 7235 6244 *email* hmcconville@roccofortecollection.com

■ Foundation for Management Education

CC NO 313388   **ESTABLISHED** 1960
WHERE FUNDING CAN BE GIVEN UK.
WHO CAN BENEFIT UK business schools and management studies departments benefiting young adults, older people and students.
WHAT IS FUNDED Improvement of quality and relevance of management education and development, by encouraging and supporting innovation in management education in the leading UK business schools and colleges; enhancing the supply and quality of management teachers; encouraging the development of research into management education and teaching methods; and supporting innovative developments in management education for managers operating within a highly competitive environment.
WHAT IS NOT FUNDED Individual applications for further studies cannot be supported.
SAMPLE GRANTS Previous beneficiaries include the universities of Surrey, Bath, Cambridge and Nottingham, and the London School of Economics.
FINANCES *Year* 2009–10 *Income* £42,390 *Grants* £101,404 *Assets* £159,545
TRUSTEES Geoffrey Armstrong; Valerie Boakes; Tim Boswell; Robert Lintott; G C Olcott; David Thomas; Lord J E Tomlinson of Walsall; James Watson; John Wybrew; Miss P B Graham; J L James; J Colley; M Flanagan; Dr P Hahn; Dr J Hodges; Dr B Howieson; Dr O Mathias; S Pepper.

HOW TO APPLY Unsolicited applications are not encouraged.

WHO TO APPLY TO The Director, TBAC Business Centre, Avenue Four, Station Lane, Witney OX28 4BN *Tel* 01993 848722 *email* fme@lineone.net *Website* www.management-education.org.uk

■ The Four Winds Trust

CC NO 262524   **ESTABLISHED** 1971
WHERE FUNDING CAN BE GIVEN Worldwide.
WHO CAN BENEFIT Registered charities and people working in religion.
WHAT IS FUNDED Christian and overseas aid organisations, but grants are also given to retired evangelists and to missionaries and their dependants.
RANGE OF GRANTS Up to approximately £5,000.
SAMPLE GRANTS Ashbury Free Church (£5,100); Counties Evangelistic Work (£3,000); South Road Church (£1,500); Forest Hill Community Church (£1,200); Swindon Youth for Christ (£1,100); and OM Algeria (£1,000).
FINANCES *Year* 2009–10 *Income* £42,088 *Grants* £39,466 *Assets* £772,247
TRUSTEES Philip Charters; Mary Charters; Peter John Charters; Simon Charters; Frances Charters.
OTHER INFORMATION The grant total includes grants made to individual evangelists and missionaries totalling £6,300.
HOW TO APPLY The trust was set up for purposes in which the trustees have a personal interest and the funds are earmarked for these purposes. Unsolicited requests are unlikely to be considered.
WHO TO APPLY TO Philip Charters, Trustee, Four Winds, Church Lane, Ashbury, Swindon SN6 8LZ *Tel* 01793 710431

■ The Foyle Foundation

CC NO 1081766   **ESTABLISHED** 2000
WHERE FUNDING CAN BE GIVEN UK.
WHO CAN BENEFIT Registered charities and state schools.
WHAT IS FUNDED **Main Grants Scheme**
'*Arts:* The foundation seeks applications that make a strong artistic case for support in either the performing or visual arts. Our Arts programme has a twofold purpose to help sustain the arts and to support projects that particularly help to deliver artistic vision. We look for value for money and sustainability in projects that we support. Typical areas of support include: helping to make the arts more accessible by developing new audiences, supporting tours, festivals and arts educational projects; encouraging new work and supporting young and emerging artists; building projects that improve or re-equip existing arts venues (rather than construction of new facilities, although this will not be excluded); projects that reduce overheads or which help generate additional revenue. Generally, we make grants for specific projects/activities. We will consider applications for core funding (but generally only from smaller organisations or from those not receiving recurrent revenue funding from the Arts Council or local authorities). Please note that community arts activity will not generally be supported. *Learning:* The foundation will support projects which facilitate the acquisition of knowledge and which have a long-term strategic impact. Key areas for support are: libraries, museums and archives; special educational needs and learning difficulties; projects that

546

Does the trust you have chosen match your needs? Haphazard applications waste postage and time

reduce overheads or which help generate additional revenue will also be considered. For state funded schools our main initiative will be The Foyle School Libraries Scheme [special guidance notes are available from the foundation's website]. Dedicated schools catering for those with Special Educational Needs (SEN) may also be supported. Private schools will not generally be supported. Citizenship, esteem-building, training, skills acquisition to aid employment, independent living, early learning projects or playgroups will not generally be considered. **Small Grants Scheme** Our Small Grants Scheme is designed to support smaller charities in the UK, especially those working at grass roots and local community level, in any field, across a wide range of activities. Please note we are not able to support individuals. Applications are welcomed from charities that have an annual turnover of less than £100,000 per annum. Larger or national charities will normally not be considered under this scheme. Nor will the Scheme generally support charities that are able to consistently to generate operational surpluses or which have been able to build up unrestricted reserves to a level equivalent to three months turnover. If applying on behalf of a state school please refer to the state schools webpage [on the foundation's website]. Please note that competition for funding is intense and we receive many more applications that we are able to fund.'

WHAT IS NOT FUNDED No grants to individuals, organisations which are not registered charities or for international work. No retrospective funding.

TYPE OF GRANT Capital, revenue and project funding.

RANGE OF GRANTS Up to £300,000.

SAMPLE GRANTS Major grants in 2010: Cheltenham Art Gallery & Museum Development Trust (£300,000), towards the £6.3 million development to expand the museum to show more of its collections and provide improved public and education facilities; Chetham's School of Music – Manchester (£250,000), towards the creation of a new state-of-the-art music and academic building; London Academy of Music and Dramatic Art (£250,000), towards the fundraising campaign to mark the 150th anniversary of LAMDA and the capital redevelopment of the Talgarth site; Royal Welsh College of Music and Drama – Cardiff (£250,000), towards their new facilities which include a new concert hall, theatre and drama rehearsal studios; Turner Contemporary Art Trust – Margate (£250,000), towards the new contemporary visual arts gallery; The Courtauld Institute of Art Fund – London (£150,000 over three years), towards cataloguing and combining its separate holdings to create and open up the Renaissance and Baroque Special Collections; City & Guilds of London Art School (£125,000), towards Phase 1 of work on the Kennington site, for the refurbishment and improvements to a row of six Grade 2 listed Georgian terrace houses; The National Gallery – London (£125,000), to purchase an ATR-FTIR imaging system to analyse the material components of paintings, inform conservation treatment and research how paintings were created; Scott Polar Research Institute – Cambridge (£125,000), towards the refurbishment of the Polar Museum and its associated curatorial and storage spaces; Museum of London (£112,000), towards creation of the new Inspiring London Gallery, part of the redevelopment of the lower floor galleries; Black Cultural Archives – London (£100,000), towards

the Raleigh Hall Development Project to create a national black heritage and archive centre; The Cambridge Foundation – Cambridge (£100,000), towards the extension for Kettle's Yard Museum expanding their educational and outreach provision; English Heritage (£100,000), towards the conservation, digitisation and display of a collection of 95,000 images from the Aerofilms Collection; and Historic Royal Palaces – London (£100,000), towards the re-development of Kensington Palace and opening up its environs and the expansion of public access to the building.

FINANCES *Year* 2009–10 *Income* £3,600,775 *Grants* £5,218,000 *Assets* £74,138,576

TRUSTEES Michael Smith; Kathryn Skoyles; Sir Peter Duffell; Roy Amlot.

HOW TO APPLY 'Please note that competition is intense; we receive many more applications than we are able to fund. Also the Foundation only supports charities and is not able to support individuals. Guidelines and application forms are available [from the foundation's website]. Charities wishing to make an application for funding should download and read the appropriate guidelines for applicants before completing and signing the appropriate application form and sending this together with the supporting information requested. Applications are acknowledged by email or by post within two weeks of receipt. If you do not receive this acknowledgement, please contact the foundation to confirm safe receipt of your request. *When to Apply:* Applications are accepted all year round. We have no deadlines. Except for capital projects, it may take up to four months, occasionally longer, to receive a decision from the trustees, so please apply well in advance of your funding requirements. *Capital Projects:* Please note for capital projects seeking more than £50,000 the foundation will now only consider these twice per year in the spring and autumn. Therefore it could be six months or more before we take a decision on your project. **Small Grants Scheme** *How much can you apply for?:* We plan to make one year grants of between £1,000 and £10,000 to charities which can demonstrate that such a grant will make a significant difference to their work. If you cannot demonstrate this, your application will be declined. No multi-year funding awards will be made. *Other Information:* There are no deadlines for submission. Applications will be received at all times but it may take up to four months to obtain a decision from trustees. Please apply well in advance of your requirements. All applications will be acknowledged but in order to reduce administration, usually we will not send declination letters. If you have not heard from the foundation within four months of your application being acknowledged, you should assume that your application has been unsuccessful.'

WHO TO APPLY TO David Hall, Chief Executive, Rugby Chambers, 2 Rugby Street, London WC1N 3QU *Tel* 020 7430 9119 *Fax* 020 7430 9830 *email* info@foylefoundation.org.uk *Website* www. foylefoundation.org.uk

■ The Isaac and Freda Frankel Memorial Charitable Trust

CC NO 1003732 **ESTABLISHED** 1991
WHERE FUNDING CAN BE GIVEN UK and overseas, particularly Israel.
WHO CAN BENEFIT Established organisations benefiting children, young adults and people disadvantaged by poverty. People of many different religions and cultures will be funded, but preference is given to Jewish people.
WHAT IS FUNDED Jewish charities, medicine and health, education, religion and the relief of poverty.
WHAT IS NOT FUNDED No grants to individuals or students, for expeditions or scholarships.
TYPE OF GRANT One-off and recurrent grants.
RANGE OF GRANTS £1,000 or less.
FINANCES *Year* 2009–10 *Income* £26,692 *Grants* £47,180 *Assets* £420,145
TRUSTEES M D Frankel; G Frankel; J Steinhaus; J Silkin.
HOW TO APPLY In writing to the correspondent.
WHO TO APPLY TO M D Frankel, Secretary, 33 Welbeck Street, London W1G 8LX *Tel* 020 7872 0023

■ The Elizabeth Frankland Moore and Star Foundation

CC NO 257711 **ESTABLISHED** 1968
WHERE FUNDING CAN BE GIVEN UK.
WHO CAN BENEFIT Charitable organisations.
WHAT IS FUNDED General charitable purposes.
SAMPLE GRANTS Star Appeal – East Lothian (£25,000); Kids Company (£15,000); BLESMA, Eye Hope, The Hansel Foundation and Salvation Army Scotland (£10,000 each); Barnardo's Scotland, Special Forces Benevolent Fund and SANDS (£5,000 each); Royal Blind Society (£2,500); Accord Hospice and Glasgow Lodging House Mission (£1,000 each); Search and Rescue Dog Association, UK Youth and Wiltshire Air Ambulance Appeal (£500 each).
FINANCES *Year* 2009–10 *Income* £186,339 *Grants* £236,250 *Assets* £8,775,528
TRUSTEES J Cameron; R A Griffiths; A E Ely; Dr David Spalton.
HOW TO APPLY In writing to the correspondent. Trustees meet twice a year.
WHO TO APPLY TO Marianne Neuhoff, c/o Neuhoff & Co, 11 Towcester Road, Whittlebury, Northamptonshire, NN 12 8XU *Tel* 01327 858171

■ Sydney E Franklin Deceased's New Second Charity

CC NO 272047 **ESTABLISHED** 1973
WHERE FUNDING CAN BE GIVEN Worldwide. Priority is given to developing world projects.
WHO CAN BENEFIT Small charities with low income (under £300,000).
WHAT IS FUNDED Relief of poverty and disability and the protection of endangered species. Priority is given to projects supporting children in the developing world, education and communities working towards self sufficiency.
TYPE OF GRANT One-off and project grants.
RANGE OF GRANTS Typical grant £500–£3,000.
SAMPLE GRANTS Previous beneficiaries include: Kerala Federation for the Blind, Water for Kids, Narwhal/Niaff, United Charities Fund, Ashram International, Books Abroad, Children of the Andes, Kaloko Trust, Microloan Foundation,

Tools for Self Reliance, Tree Aid, Window for Peace UK, Forest Peoples Project, African Initiatives, Lake Malawi Projects, World Medical Fund and Gwalior Children's Hospital.
FINANCES *Year* 2009–10 *Income* £19,974 *Grants* £30,000
TRUSTEES Dr Rodney Franklin; Natasha Franklin; Caroline Holliday.
OTHER INFORMATION Limited information was available from the Charity Commission website. The grant total of £30,000 is estimated.
HOW TO APPLY Donations may only be requested by letter, including a copy of latest accounts, and these are placed before the trustees at their meeting which is normally held at the end of each year. Applications are not acknowledged.
WHO TO APPLY TO Dr Rodney Franklin, Trustee, c/o 39 Westleigh Avenue, London SW15 6RQ

■ The Jill Franklin Trust

CC NO 1000175 **ESTABLISHED** 1988
WHERE FUNDING CAN BE GIVEN Worldwide.
WHO CAN BENEFIT Charitable organisations, not necessarily registered charities, benefiting: disabled people; carers; ex-offenders and those at risk of offending; people with a mental illness; refugees and asylum-seekers.
WHAT IS FUNDED Self-help groups etc for people with a mental illness or learning difficulties; holidays for carers to provide respite from their caree – this is mainly as a block grant to the Princess Royal Trust for Carers; organisations helping and supporting asylum seekers and refugees coming to the UK; restoration of churches of architectural importance; grants to prisoners for education and training – this is given as a block grant to the Prisoners Education Trust; Camden Bereavement Service, with which Jill Franklin was closely associated.
WHAT IS NOT FUNDED Grants are not given to: appeals for building work; endowment funds; branches of a national organisations, and to the centre itself (unless it is a specific grant, probably for training in the branches); replace the duties of government, local authorities or the NHS; encourage the 'contract culture', particularly where authorities are not funding the contract adequately; religious organisations set up for welfare, education etc. of whatever religion, unless the service is open to and used by people from all denominations; overseas projects; 'heritage schemes' animal charities; students, nor to any individuals nor for overseas travel; medical research.
TYPE OF GRANT One-off, project, recurring costs, running costs and start-up costs. Funding for up to three years will be considered.
SAMPLE GRANTS Linden Lodge School (£20,000); Camden City Islington and Westminster Bereavement Services (£12,000); Princess Royal Trust for Carers (£7,000); Pevsner Book Trust (£2,250); Kiloran Trust, Hoffman Foundation for Autism and Respite Association (£1,000 each).
FINANCES *Year* 2009–10 *Income* £171,226 *Grants* £94,092 *Assets* £1,524,142
TRUSTEES Andrew Franklin; Norman Franklin; Sally Franklin; Sam Franklin; Tom Franklin.
HOW TO APPLY In writing to the correspondent, enclosing a copy of the latest annual report and accounts and a budget for the project. Organisations based outside the UK should provide the name, address and telephone number of a correspondent or referee in the UK. 'The trustees tend to look more favourably on an appeal which is simply and economically

prepared: glossy, 'prestige' and mail sorted brochures do not impress the trustees.' Unsolicited enquiries are not usually acknowledged. 'We have very little uncommitted cash, and so most applications are rejected, for the only reason that we have insufficient money.'

WHO TO APPLY TO N Franklin, Trustee, Flat 5, 17–19 Elsworthy Road, London NW3 3DS *Tel* 020 7722 4543 *email* info@jill-franklin-trust.org.uk *Website* www.jill-franklin-trust.org.uk

■ The Gordon Fraser Charitable Trust

CC NO 260869   **ESTABLISHED** 1966

WHERE FUNDING CAN BE GIVEN UK, with a preference for Scotland.

WHO CAN BENEFIT Registered charities.

WHAT IS FUNDED At present the trustees are particularly interested in help for children and young people, the environment and in assisting organisations associated with the arts. Other charitable purposes will also be considered.

WHAT IS NOT FUNDED No grants are made to organisations which are not recognised charities, or to individuals.

TYPE OF GRANT Grants are usually one-off, though funding for up to three years may be considered.

RANGE OF GRANTS £100–£12,000, typical grant £250–£750.

SAMPLE GRANTS Ballet West (£9,000); the MacRoberts Arts Centre (£7,000); the Aberlour Child Care Trust and Scottish Museums Council (£6,000 each); Scottish International Piano Competition (£5,500); Mull Theatre (£3,000); KilMartin House Trust and National Library of Scotland (£2,000 each); Paisley Festival Company, the Hebridean Trust and Sense Scotland (£1,000 each).

FINANCES *Year* 2009–10 *Income* £178,762 *Grants* £144,450 *Assets* £2,705,907

TRUSTEES Mrs Margaret A Moss; William F T Anderson.

HOW TO APPLY In writing to the correspondent. Applications are considered in January, April, July and October. Grants towards national or international emergencies can be considered at any time. All applicants are acknowledged; an sae would, therefore, be appreciated.

WHO TO APPLY TO Claire Armstrong, Administrator, Gaidrew Farmhouse, Drymen, Glasgow G63 0DN

■ The Hugh Fraser Foundation

SC NO SC009303   **ESTABLISHED** 1960

WHERE FUNDING CAN BE GIVEN UK, especially western or deprived areas of Scotland.

WHO CAN BENEFIT Registered charities working in many different sectors principally hospitals, schools and universities, arts organisations and organisations working with the disabled, the underprivileged and the aged.

WHAT IS FUNDED Medical facilities and research; relief of poverty and assistance for older and infirm people; education and learning; provision of better opportunities for people who are disadvantaged; music and the arts; encouragement of personal development and training of young people.

WHAT IS NOT FUNDED Grants are only awarded to individuals in exceptional circumstances (see 'information').

TYPE OF GRANT Capital and revenue grants for up to three years, sometimes longer. Start-up costs.

RANGE OF GRANT Up to £100,000.

SAMPLE GRANTS Inspiring Scotland (£200,000); Marie Curie Cancer Care – The Big Build (£100,000); and Scottish Ballet and the Edinburgh University Development Trust – Royal School of Veterinary Studies (£50,000 each).

FINANCES *Year* 2009–10 *Income* £1,644,824 *Grants* £1,365,950 *Assets* £54,387,394

TRUSTEES Dr Kenneth Chrystie; Belinda Ann Hanson; Patricia Fraser; Blair Smith.

OTHER INFORMATION Note: In 2007 the Hugh Fraser Foundation merged with the Emily Fraser Trust, a related charity. As a result the trustees will, in exceptional circumstances, also help individuals and the dependents of individuals who were or are engaged in the drapery and allied trades and the printing, publishing, books and stationary, newspaper and allied trades in the UK.

HOW TO APPLY In writing to the correspondent. The trustees meet on a quarterly basis to consider applications.

WHO TO APPLY TO Katrina Muir, Trust Administrator, Turcan Connell WS, Princes Exchange, 1 Earl Grey Street, Edinburgh EH3 9EE *Tel* 0131 228 8111

■ The Joseph Strong Frazer Trust

CC NO 235311   **ESTABLISHED** 1939

WHERE FUNDING CAN BE GIVEN Unrestricted, in practice, England and Wales.

WHO CAN BENEFIT Registered charities only.

WHAT IS FUNDED General charitable purposes, with broad interests in the fields of medical and other research, social welfare, people with disabilities, children, hospitals, education, maritime, youth, religion and wildlife.

WHAT IS NOT FUNDED No grants to individuals.

TYPE OF GRANT One-off, capital and recurring costs.

SAMPLE GRANTS Combat Stress received £3,000 while grants of £2,000 were paid to 46 organisations including: Addaction, Archway Project, British Retinitis Pigmentosa Society, Carers UK, Counsel & Care for the Elderly, Downside Fisher Youth Club, Iris Fund, Leonard Cheshire Wales & West, Prostate Cancer Charity, Royal School for the Blind Liverpool and Welsh National Opera. There were a further 115 grants to organisations of less than £2,000 which were not detailed in the accounts.

FINANCES *Year* 2009–10 *Income* £400,186 *Grants* £218,000 *Assets* £11,923,448

TRUSTEES Sir William A Reardon Smith, Chair; David A Cook; R M H Read; William N H Reardon Smith; William I Waites.

HOW TO APPLY In writing to the correspondent. Trustees meet twice a year, usually in March and September. Application forms are not necessary. It is helpful if applicants are concise in their appeal letters, which must include an sae if acknowledgement is required.

WHO TO APPLY TO The Trustees, Floor A, Milburn House, Dean Street, Newcastle upon Tyne NE1 1LE *Tel* 0191 232 8065 *Fax* 0191 222 1554 *email* uf@joseph-miller.co.uk

■ The Louis and Valerie Freedman Charitable Settlement

cc no 271067   **established** 1976

where funding can be given UK, especially Buckinghamshire.

who can benefit National and local (Burnham in Buckinghamshire) charities.

what is funded Health, welfare and equine interests in which the Freedman family have a particular interest. Local education and youth charities are also supported.

what is not funded No grants to individuals. Only registered charities are considered for support.

range of grants Usually around £5,000 to £10,000.

sample grants Burnham Health Promotion Trust (£50,000); Prostrate Research Campaign UK and The PSP Association (£10,000 each); and Care International, Children's Trust, Helena Kennedy Foundation, Every Child a Chance, Newlife Foundation for Disabled Children and Red Cross Haiti Earthquake Appeal (£5,000 each).

finances *Year* 2009–10 *Income* £109,399 *Grants* £100,000 *Assets* £3,652,402

trustees M A G Ferrier; F H Hughes.

how to apply There is no application form. Applications should be in writing to the correspondent and they will not be acknowledged. Notification of a failed application will only be given if an sae is enclosed.

who to apply to F H Hughes, Trustee, c/o Bridge House, 11 Creek Road, Hampton Court, East Molesey, Surrey KT8 9BE *Tel* 020 8941 4455

■ The Michael and Clara Freeman Charitable Trust

cc no 1125083   **established** 2008

where funding can be given UK and overseas.

what is funded General charitable purposes.

range of grants £23,000–£750.

sample grants Help for Heroes (£23,000); Balliol College – University of Oxford (£7,500); Chipping Norton Theatre (£5,000); Combat Stress and the British Legion (£2,500); Kids Company and St Giles' Trust (£2,000 each); and Mary's Meals (£1,000).

finances *Year* 2009–10 *Income* £275,433 *Grants* £62,775 *Assets* £2,182,801

trustees Michael Freeman; Clara Freeman; Laura Freeman; Edward Freeman.

other information The annual accounts for this financial year states: 'The trustees have pledged a gift of £450,000 to Balliol College, Oxford towards the permanent endowment of one of the Classical Literature Fellowships, conditional upon the College being able to raise the balance of the capital required.'

how to apply In writing to the correspondent.

who to apply to Michael Freeman, Trustee, 9 Connaught Square, London W2 2HG

■ The Freemasons' Grand Charity

cc no 281942   **established** 1980

where funding can be given England, Wales and overseas.

who can benefit Charities benefiting freemasons and their dependants; medical research, hospices and other charities concerned with general welfare especially of young and older people and overseas emergency aid.

what is funded Consideration is only given to charities whose work covers the whole of England and Wales; London charities (no other local charities should apply); freemasons of the United Grand Lodge of England, their widows and certain other dependants; hospices; social welfare organisations, organisations supporting vulnerable people including the young and older people, medical research and emergency aid.

what is not funded Local charities (i.e. serving an individual city or region) should apply to the provincial grand lodge of the region in which they operate, (these are listed in telephone directories, usually under 'freemasons' or 'masons'). Those not eligible for a grant are: individuals (other than for the relief of 'poor and distressed freemasons and their poor and distressed dependants'); charities that serve an individual region or city, for example, a regional hospital, local church, day centre or primary school; organisations not registered with the Charity Commission, except some exempt charities; activities that are primarily the responsibility of central or local government or some other responsible body; organisations or projects outside of England and Wales; animal welfare, the arts or environmental causes; charities with sectarian or political objectives; charities that are deemed to hold funds in excess of their requirements.

range of grants Up to £250,000.

sample grants Soldiers, Sailors, Airmen and Families Association (SSAFA)-Forces Help – to be distributed to each of the provinces for presentation locally (£250,000); Grants for Air Ambulances and similar rescue services – 22 grants across the UK and channel islands (£192,000); The Cambridge Foundation – to fund research into the use of alemtuzumab in treating multiple sclerosis (£100,000); Pakistan Floods via British Red Cross (£50,000); Association for Spina Bifida Hydrocephalus – to fund research into the use of in utero MRI (£40,000); Childhood First – to fund a family placement and support scheme in Norfolk (£20,000); Kidscape – to fund workshops for children at risk of becoming bullies (£15,000); Refuge (£5,000); Disability Law Service (£3,000); Survivors of Bereavement by suicide (£2,000); and London Narrow Boat Project (£1,500).

The fund awarded £600,000 to a total of 226 hospices across England, Wales, the Isle of Man and the Channel Islands. The majority of grants were between £1,000–£3,000.

finances *Year* 2009–10 *Income* £22,265,600 *Grants* £2,521,200 *Assets* £62,270,700

trustees Grahame Elliott; Roderic Mitchell; Peter Griffiths; Sir Stuart Hampson; Paul Richards; Michael Turnbull; John Hornblow; Raymond Larkin; Ian MacBeth; Reginald Rivett; John Woolway; Dr David Mccormick; Raymond Lye; Charles Assad Akle; Tom Hedderson; Dr Richard Dunstan; Geoff Tuck; Terry Baker; Dr Kevin Williams; Laurie Justice; Roger Richmond; Nigel Buchanan; Nigel Pett; Anthony Wood; Timothy Dallas-Chapman; Judge Hone; Roger Needham; Alexander Stewart.

publications Booklet, Information on Masonic Charities.

how to apply Application forms are available from the charity's office or from its website. This form must be completed in full accompanied by a copy of the latest annual report and full audited accounts; these must be less than 18 months old.

Hospice grant applications are made on a separate form, available from either the appropriate provincial grand lodge or the trust's office.

Applications may be submitted at any time throughout the year and are considered at meetings held in January, April and July. Acknowledgement of receipt will be made by post. Applications are not accepted for 'emergency grants' which are made as 'the need arises' and at the trustees' discretion.

WHO TO APPLY TO Ms Laura Chapman, Chief Executive, Freemasons Hall, 60 Great Queen Street, London WC2B 5AZ *Tel* 020 7395 9261 *Fax* 020 7395 9295 *email* info@the-grand-charity.org *Website* www.grandcharity.org

·····································

■ The Thomas Freke and Lady Norton Charity

CC NO 200824   **ESTABLISHED** 1990
WHERE FUNDING CAN BE GIVEN Only within the parishes of Hannington, Inglesham, Highworth, Stanton Fitzwarren, Blunsdon St Leonards and Castle Eaton.
WHO CAN BENEFIT Local communities and organisations benefiting children, young adults and Christians.
WHAT IS FUNDED Buildings or equipment for churches, schools, youth and community facilities. The trust is willing to consider emergency or unforeseen expenditure. Funding may also be given to community centres, village halls, recreation grounds and sports centres.
WHAT IS NOT FUNDED No grants are given for ordinary running expenses. No applications from outside the beneficial area can be considered.
TYPE OF GRANT Capital.
FINANCES *Year* 2009–10 *Income* £8,473,658 *Grants* £10,511,975 *Assets* £9,600,055
TRUSTEES Mrs Lorna Wallace; Mrs Valerie J Davies; Dr Keith T Scholes; John M E Scott; Edwin R Cole.
HOW TO APPLY In writing to the correspondent for help with capital projects such as building improvements development or, provision of specialist equipment. Clear outline details of the project and accurate estimated costs are required. Trustees meet four times a year to consider applications. The correspondent has previously stated that: 'There have been many applications from outside the beneficial area that cannot be supported.'
WHO TO APPLY TO Barry T Compton, Clerk, 23 Chedworth Gate, Broome Manor, Swindon SN3 1NE *email* barry.compton@btinternet.com

·····································

■ The Charles S French Charitable Trust

CC NO 206476   **ESTABLISHED** 1959
WHERE FUNDING CAN BE GIVEN North east London and south west Essex.
WHO CAN BENEFIT Registered charities.
WHAT IS FUNDED General charitable purposes, including community services and facilities.
WHAT IS NOT FUNDED Only registered charities are supported.
RANGE OF GRANTS Usually £1,000–£10,000.
SAMPLE GRANTS Loughton Youth Project (£22,000); Pioneer Sailing Trust (£6,000); Marie Curie Cancer Care and Foundation for Study of Infant Death (£3,000 each); EFD Citizens Advice Bureau Loughton and Chelmsford Boy's Club (£2,000 each) and Asthma Relief at work in SW Essex and British Wireless for Blind (£1,000 each).

FINANCES *Year* 2009–10 *Income* £162,095 *Grants* £126,990 *Assets* £7,282,381
TRUSTEES W F Noble; M P W Scarth; J Thomas; R Foster.
HOW TO APPLY In writing to the correspondent, including a copy of the latest accounts. The trustees meet four times a year. The trust invites applications for grants and donations from local charities and these applications are reviewed against the trust's objects, with grants and donations being awarded at the trustee's discretion.
WHO TO APPLY TO W F Noble, Trustee, 169 High Road, Loughton, Essex IG10 4LF *email* office@csfct.org.uk *Website* www.csfct.org.uk

·····································

■ The Anne French Memorial Trust

CC NO 254567   **ESTABLISHED** 1963
WHERE FUNDING CAN BE GIVEN Diocese of Norwich (Norfolk and north Suffolk).
WHO CAN BENEFIT Christians, clergy and local charities.
WHAT IS FUNDED Any charitable purpose in the beneficial area, especially church-related causes.
TYPE OF GRANT One-off, project, research and feasibility.
SAMPLE GRANTS Non-clergy gifts (£14,000); Gifts to clergy (£44,000); Youth and training (£16,000); Training of clergy (£5,000); Building maintenance (£40,000); Building maintenance (£40,000); Diocesan expenses (£24,000).
FINANCES *Year* 2010–11 *Income* £207,729 *Grants* £170,467 *Assets* £6,263,442
TRUSTEES Lord Bishop of Norwich.
HOW TO APPLY The trust states that 'in no circumstances does the Bishop wish to encourage applications for grants'.
WHO TO APPLY TO Christopher Dicker, c/o Lovewell Blake, Sixty Six, North Quay, Great Yarmouth, Norfolk NR30 1HE

·····································

■ The Freshfield Foundation

CC NO 1003316   **ESTABLISHED** 1991
WHERE FUNDING CAN BE GIVEN UK.
WHO CAN BENEFIT Registered charities.
WHAT IS FUNDED Environment, climate change and, to a less extent, healthcare. The foundation's annual report includes the following information about the trustees' plans for the future: 'The following strategy was agreed to increase the level of grantmaking: maintain the donations to UK sustainable development at £500,000 per annum; explore the idea of giving between £100,000 and £500,000 per annum to overseas disaster relief. Other ideas for future giving were discussed [at the 2010 trustees' meeting], including: music education with a link to social and health benefits; funding the fitting of improved insulation to the homes of disadvantaged families.'
SAMPLE GRANTS Sustrans (£200,000); Friends of the Earth (£180,000); Formby Land Trust for the Formby Pool Project (£150,000); Forestry Stewardship Council (£60,000); Osteopathic Centre for Children and the New Economics Foundation (£40,000 each); Centre for Tomorrow's Company (£35,000); Afghan Connection and Cambridge University (£30,000 each); Campaign for Better Transport and the Soil Association (£20,000 each); and Cree Valley Community Woodland Trust (£15,000).
FINANCES *Year* 2009–10 *Income* £1,759,992 *Grants* £820,000 *Assets* £5,877,779

TRUSTEES Paul Kurthausen; Patrick A Moores; Mrs Elizabeth J Potter.

HOW TO APPLY In writing to the correspondent, although the trust states that 'the process of grant making starts with the trustees analysing an area of interest, consistent with the charity's aims and objectives, and then proactively looking for charities that they think can make the greatest contribution'. With this in mind, a letter of introduction to your organisation's work may be more appropriate than a formal application for funding.

WHO TO APPLY TO Paul Charles Kurthausen, c/o MacFarlane and Co., Cunard Building, Water Street, Liverpool L3 1DS *Tel* 0151 236 6161 *Fax* 0151 236 1095 *email* paulk@macca.co.uk

■ The Freshgate Trust Foundation

CC NO 221467   **ESTABLISHED** 1962

WHERE FUNDING CAN BE GIVEN Mainly Sheffield and South Yorkshire.

WHO CAN BENEFIT Organisations benefiting: people of all ages; actors and entertainment professionals; musicians; textile workers and designers; writers and poets; at risk groups; people disadvantaged by poverty and socially isolated people. Both innovatory and established bodies may be considered.

WHAT IS FUNDED Local appeals working in the fields of: education (including travel and training); medical (both psychological and physical); recreation; music and arts; welfare and social care; heritage.

WHAT IS NOT FUNDED The trust restricts its grants to UK charitable organisations and does not deal with applications from individuals, national appeals or for church fabric unless used for a wider community purpose.

TYPE OF GRANT Capital (including buildings), core costs, endowments, feasibility studies, interest free loans, one-off, project, research, running costs, recurring costs, salaries and start-up costs. Funding for up to three years will be considered.

FINANCES *Year* 2009–10 *Income* £105,985 *Grants* £54,504 *Assets* £2,885,327

TRUSTEES J F B Hopkins; J E Parkin; Miss E Murray; D R Stone; I Walker; J C Mould; Mrs V A Linnemann; Ms H Dobson; P Else; U Fitch.

HOW TO APPLY In writing to the correspondent, by early February, June and October each year. Applications are not normally acknowledged.

WHO TO APPLY TO Jonathan Robinson, Secretary, Jonathan Robinson, The Hart Shaw Building, Europa Link, Sheffield Business Park, Sheffield, South Yorkshire *Tel* 0114 251 8850 *Fax* 0114 251 8851

■ The Friarsgate Trust

CC NO 220762   **ESTABLISHED** 1955

WHERE FUNDING CAN BE GIVEN UK, with a strong preference for West Sussex, especially Chichester.

WHO CAN BENEFIT UK and East and West Sussex organisations, especially those already supported by the trust.

WHAT IS FUNDED General charitable purposes, especially education and welfare of children and young people and care of people who are elderly or in need.

WHAT IS NOT FUNDED Local organisations outside Sussex are unlikely to be supported.

RANGE OF GRANTS Up to £20,000, with most grants ranging between £500–£2,000.

SAMPLE GRANTS CYE Sailing Centre, the Honey Pot Charity and St Barnabus Hospice (£2,000 each); Enterprise Educational Trust, Sussex Autistic Trust and the Association of Wheelchair Children (£1,000 each); and Life Centre, Pallant House Gallery and Whizz Kidz (£500 each).

FINANCES *Year* 2009–10 *Income* £86,790 *Grants* £196,880 *Assets* £2,913,452

TRUSTEES A C Colenutt; T J Bastow; Mrs V Higgins.

HOW TO APPLY In writing to the correspondent. Applicants are welcome to telephone first to check they fit the trust's criteria.

WHO TO APPLY TO Miss Amanda King-Jones, The Corn Exchange, Baffins Lane, Chichester, West Sussex Po19 1GE *Tel* 01243 786111 *Fax* 01243 775640

■ The Friends Hall Farm Street Trust

CC NO 209818   **ESTABLISHED** 1893

WHERE FUNDING CAN BE GIVEN Birmingham and district.

WHO CAN BENEFIT Charitable organisations. Grants are made to organisations and individuals known to the trustees or recommended through the religious Society of Friends.

WHAT IS FUNDED Religion and education, primarily Quaker concerns.

WHAT IS NOT FUNDED Applications from outside the beneficial area cannot be considered.

FINANCES *Year* 2009–10 *Income* £24,665 *Grants* £80,000

TRUSTEES Stuart Morton; Eric Adams; John Bodycote; Roger Gough; Annette Gough; David Taylor.

HOW TO APPLY In writing to the correspondent. Applications should be submitted between March and October for consideration in October/November. Ineligible applications will not receive a reply.

WHO TO APPLY TO Stuart Morton, Trustee, 1 Witherford Way, Selly Oak, Birmingham B29 4AY *Tel* 0121 472 5305 *email* stuart46@googlemail.com

■ Friends of Biala Ltd

CC NO 271377   **ESTABLISHED** 1964

WHERE FUNDING CAN BE GIVEN UK and overseas.

WHO CAN BENEFIT Jewish organisations and registered charities.

WHAT IS FUNDED Religious institutions of the orthodox Jewish faith, and the relief of poverty.

SAMPLE GRANTS Previous beneficiaries include: Friends of Biala Israel, Aguda Hadadit, Yeshiva Beis Ephraim, Gemach Ezra Hadadit and Freebee Foundation Limited.

FINANCES *Year* 2009–10 *Income* £10,950 *Grants* £65,000

TRUSTEES B Z Rabinovitch; Mrs T Weinberg.

OTHER INFORMATION Due to the trust's low income in 2009–10, only basic financial information was available from the Charity Commission. The grant total of £65,000 is an estimation based on this information.

HOW TO APPLY In writing to the correspondent.

WHO TO APPLY TO The Secretary, Rosenthal and Co, 106 High West Street, Gateshead, Tyne and Wear NE8 1NA *Tel* 0191 477 2814

■ Friends of Boyan Trust

CC NO 1114498 **ESTABLISHED** 2006
WHERE FUNDING CAN BE GIVEN Worldwide.
WHO CAN BENEFIT Orthodox Jews.
WHAT IS FUNDED Jewish causes.
SAMPLE GRANTS Previously: Gomlei Chesed of Chasidei Boyan (£84,000); Mosdot Tiferet Yisroel Boyan (£31,000); Kimcha De'Pischa Boyan (£21,000); Kimcha De'Pischa Beitar Ilit (£13,000); Chevras Mo'oz Ladol (£12,000); Kolel Avrechim Boyan, Betar Ilit (£6,000); Ezer Mikoidesh Foundation (£2,000); Beis Rizhin Trust (£1,500); and Yad Vochessed (£1,000).
FINANCES *Year* 2010 *Income* £296,901 *Grants* £283,128 *Assets* £18,429
TRUSTEES J Getter; M Freund; N Kuflik.
HOW TO APPLY In writing to the correspondent.
WHO TO APPLY TO Jacob Getter, Trustee, 23 Durley Road, London N16 5JW *Tel* 020 8809 6051

■ The Friends of Kent Churches

CC NO 207021 **ESTABLISHED** 1950
WHERE FUNDING CAN BE GIVEN County of Kent, particularly the dioceses of Canterbury and Rochester.
WHO CAN BENEFIT Churches of architectural merit and historical interest.
WHAT IS FUNDED The upkeep of their fabric and the preservation of fixtures of importance.
WHAT IS NOT FUNDED No grants for reordering, new extensions, toilets and kitchens; heating, redecorating and rewiring; bells, clocks and organs.
TYPE OF GRANT Building. Interest-free loans are considered.
RANGE OF GRANTS £250–£20,000.
SAMPLE GRANTS Grants approved included: St Mildred – Canterbury, St Nicholas – St Nicholas at Wade (£10,000 each); Newnham – St Peter and St Paul and Ruckinge – St Mary Magdalene (£7,500 each); Newington – St Nicholas (£5,000); Kilndown Christchurch (£3,000); and St Botolph – Lullington (£1,000).
FINANCES *Year* 2010 *Income* £183,032 *Grants* £142,000 *Assets* £501,107
TRUSTEES Charles Banks; Charles Oliver; Mary Gibbins; Paul Smallwood; Angela Parish; Leslie Smith; Jane Bird; Richard Latham; Jane Boucher.
HOW TO APPLY In writing to the correspondent.
WHO TO APPLY TO Jane Bird, Parsonage Farm House, Hampstead Lane, Yalding, Maidstone ME18 6HG *Tel* 01622 815569 *Website* www.friendsofkentchurches.co.uk

■ Friends of Muir Group

CC NO 1100471 **ESTABLISHED** 2002
WHERE FUNDING CAN BE GIVEN UK.
WHO CAN BENEFIT Individuals, community groups and charitable organisations benefiting Muir Group residents in areas where they live or work.
WHAT IS FUNDED Priority is given to young people, older people and communities.
WHAT IS NOT FUNDED No grants for: the settling of debts; the promotion of political activities; general public appeals; the ongoing costs for Credit Unions (although start up grants are considered); the support of individual religions to the exclusion of other religions (however initiatives that promote tolerance and understanding of different faiths and cultures are actively supported).

TYPE OF GRANT Capital grants, revenue costs and full project funding.
RANGE OF GRANTS £500–£16,000.
FINANCES *Year* 2009–10 *Income* £27,903 *Grants* £33,498 *Assets* £58,413
TRUSTEES Richard Hoffman, Chair; David Booth; Adrienne Berkson; Martyn Delaney; Leslie Patterson; Robert Robertson; C Babbs.
OTHER INFORMATION The majority of grants made during the year, were spent on 'Sport and Play' (£16,000).
HOW TO APPLY Please note the following statement from the trust: 'We receive many applications from organisations that have failed to read our application guidelines and criteria. We also insist that applications are made through our application forms and not in the form of a letter.' Guidance notes and application forms are available on request from the correspondent and can also be downloaded from the trust's website.
WHO TO APPLY TO Andrew Hunt, Secretary, Old Government House, Dee Hills Park, Chester, Cheshire CH3 5AR *Tel* 01244 313613 *email* andrew.hunt@muir.org.uk *Website* www.muir.org.uk

■ Friends of Wiznitz Limited

CC NO 255685 **ESTABLISHED** 1948
WHERE FUNDING CAN BE GIVEN UK and overseas.
WHO CAN BENEFIT Registered charities.
WHAT IS FUNDED Mainly Jewish education and relief of poverty.
RANGE OF GRANTS Up to £264,000.
SAMPLE GRANTS Igud Mosdos Wiznitz (£264,000); L'Hachzicom Ve'lehachyosom (£187,000); CMA Trust Ltd (£95,000); and Mosdos Wiznitz (£89,000).
FINANCES *Year* 2009–10 *Income* £713,961 *Grants* £721,090 *Assets* £953,289
TRUSTEES H Feldman; E Kahan; R Bergmann; S Feldman.
OTHER INFORMATION In 2009–10 grants were divided between: religious education (£480,000); relief of poverty (£232,000); advancement of religion (£7,500); and medical (£1,600).
HOW TO APPLY In writing to the correspondent.
WHO TO APPLY TO E Gottesfeld, 8 Jessam Avenue, London E5 9DU

■ Friends Provident Charitable Foundation

CC NO 1087053 **ESTABLISHED** 2002
WHERE FUNDING CAN BE GIVEN UK.
WHO CAN BENEFIT Groups and organisations working with disadvantaged people.
WHAT IS FUNDED The foundation 'currently works to create the conditions throughout the UK for improved access to appropriate financial services for those who are currently excluded, particularly those on low incomes or otherwise vulnerable to market failure'. Friends Provident Tradition: 'The foundation also carries forward a legacy of giving by the Friends Provident Group. Trustees have determined that a proportion (currently up to 15%) of the foundation's funds may be committed in line with previous gifts to charity made by the Group. The current criteria for giving are: medical research aimed at preventative medicine; charities/causes that were related to the regions where Friends Provident operated as an employer, including the City of London; Quaker initiatives.'

RANGE OF GRANTS £10,000–£80,000.

SAMPLE GRANTS Personal Finance Research Centre – University of Bristol and MyBnk (£80,000 each); TaxAid and Age UK (£70,000 each); Jackie Wells & Associates (£45,000); Centre for Responsible Credit, University of Salford and Hyde Charitable Trust – Debt advice (£40,000 each); Institute for Public Policy Research (£18,000); and ResPublica (£15,000).

FINANCES *Year* 2009–10 *Income* £894,093 *Grants* £782,169 *Assets* £24,060,525

TRUSTEES Ashley Taylor, Chair; Nick Perks; Jenny Shellens; Whitni Thomas; Mike Hampton; Diane Coyle; Jim Gilbourne.

HOW TO APPLY See the foundation's website for up-to-date details of their giving policy.

WHO TO APPLY TO The Company Secretary, Danielle Walker Palmour, Pixham End, Surrey, Dorking, Surrey RH4 1QA *Tel* 0845 268 3388 *email* foundation.enquiries@friendsprovident.co.uk *Website* www.friendsprovidentfoundation.org

■ The Frognal Trust

CC NO 244444 ESTABLISHED 1964

WHERE FUNDING CAN BE GIVEN UK.

WHO CAN BENEFIT Registered charities benefiting older people, children and people with disabilities or sight loss.

WHAT IS FUNDED The trustees' current grant-making policy is to make relatively small grants to as many qualifying charities as possible. Particularly charities working in the fields of: residential facilities and services; cultural heritage; hospices; nursing homes; ophthalmological research; conservation; heritage; parks; and community services. Other charitable purposes will be considered.

WHAT IS NOT FUNDED The trust does not support: any animal charities; the advancement of religion; charities for the benefit of people outside the UK; educational or research trips; branches of national charities; general appeals; individuals.

TYPE OF GRANT Buildings, capital, one-off, research and start-up costs will be considered.

RANGE OF GRANTS £200–£3,500.

SAMPLE GRANTS Previous beneficiaries have included: Action Medical Research, Aireborough Voluntary Services to the Elderly, Canniesburn Research Trust, Elderly Accommodation Counsel and Leeds Society for Deaf and Blind People, Friends of the Elderly, Gloucestershire Disabled Afloat Riverboat Trust, National Rheumatoid Arthritis Society, Royal Liverpool and Broad Green University Hospitals, Samantha Dickson Research Trust, Stubbers Adventure Centre, Wireless for the Bedridden Society and Yorkshire Dales Millennium Project.

FINANCES *Year* 2009–10 *Income* £71,089 *Grants* £29,545 *Assets* £2,123,805

TRUSTEES Philippa Blake-Roberts; Jennifer Helen Fraser; P Fraser.

HOW TO APPLY In writing to the correspondent. Applications should be received by February, May, August and November, for consideration at the trustees' meeting the following month.

WHO TO APPLY TO Donor Grants Officer, Steynings House, Summerlock Approach, Salisbury, Wiltshire SP2 7RJ

■ T F C Frost Charitable Trust

CC NO 256590 ESTABLISHED 1966

WHERE FUNDING CAN BE GIVEN UK and overseas.

WHO CAN BENEFIT Research associates of recognised centres of excellence in ophthalmology.

WHAT IS FUNDED Research in ophthalmology by establishing research fellowships and supporting specific projects.

WHAT IS NOT FUNDED There are no available resources for the relief of blind people or people suffering from diseases of the eye.

RANGE OF GRANTS Around £5,000–£35,000.

SAMPLE GRANTS Previous beneficiaries have included: University of Southampton – Professor Andrew Lotery, University of Bristol – Chair in Experimental Ophthalmology and the Rayne Institute St Thomas' Hospital – Professor John Marshall.

FINANCES *Year* 2009–10 *Income* £79,972 *Grants* £16,434 *Assets* £2,677,102

TRUSTEES Thomas Frost; Michael Miller; Prof. John Marshall; Dr Elizabeth Graham.

HOW TO APPLY In writing to the correspondent. Trustees meet twice a year.

WHO TO APPLY TO John Holmes, Holmes and Co Accountants, 10 Torrington Road, Claygate, Esher, Surrey KT10 0SA *Tel* 01372 465378 *email* holmes_and_co@hotmail.com

■ The Patrick Frost Foundation

CC NO 1005505 ESTABLISHED 1991

WHERE FUNDING CAN BE GIVEN Worldwide, but only through UK charities.

WHO CAN BENEFIT Registered charities.

WHAT IS FUNDED The relief and welfare of people of small means and the less fortunate members of society, and assistance for small organisations where a considerable amount of self-help and voluntary effort is required.

WHAT IS NOT FUNDED No grants to individuals or non-UK charities.

TYPE OF GRANT One-off donations.

RANGE OF GRANTS Mainly £5,000 or less.

SAMPLE GRANTS London Narrow Boat Project, Humberside Police Authority and The Smile Train UK (£20,000 each); Dogs for the Disabled, Opportunity International and Toynbee Hall (£10,000 each); Chance for Children, Deafblind UK and Family Holiday Association (£5,000 each); and Acorn Christian Foundation and Medical Foundation for the Care of Victims of Torture (£4,000 each).

FINANCES *Year* 2009–10 *Income* £312,695 *Grants* £252,000 *Assets* £4,918,516

TRUSTEES Mrs Helena Frost; Donald Jones; Luke Valner; Dominic Tayler.

HOW TO APPLY In writing to the correspondent, accompanied by the last set of audited accounts. The trustees regret that due to the large number of applications they receive, they are unable to acknowledge unsuccessful applications.

WHO TO APPLY TO Mrs Helena Frost, Trustee, c/o Trowers and Hamlins LLP, Sceptre Court, 40 Tower Hill, London EC3N 4DX *Tel* 020 7423 8000 *Fax* 020 7423 8001

■ Maurice Fry Charitable Trust

CC NO 327934 ESTABLISHED 1988

WHERE FUNDING CAN BE GIVEN UK and overseas.

WHO CAN BENEFIT Registered charities benefiting at risk groups, and people disadvantaged by poverty or socially isolated. Support is given to medical professionals, research workers, scientists, academics and writers and poets. Support may also be given to refugees, and victims of famine, man-made or natural disasters and war.

WHAT IS FUNDED General charitable purposes. Currently the main areas of interest are welfare, humanities, environmental resources, and international causes.

WHAT IS NOT FUNDED No grants to individuals.

RANGE OF GRANTS £500–£2,500.

SAMPLE GRANTS Médecins Sans Frontières and British Red Cross (£8,000 each); The Maypole Project (£4,000); Royal Marsden Cancer Campaign, Friends of the Earth Trust, Amnesty International and Southbank Centre (£2,000 each); and Carers Bromley, Bromley Mencap, St Christopher's Hospice and FROK (£1,000 each).

FINANCES *Year* 2009–10 *Income* £37,355 *Grants* £32,000 *Assets* £1,118,295

TRUSTEES L E A Fry; Mrs F Cooklin; Mrs L Weaks; Sam Cooklin-Smith.

HOW TO APPLY The trust states that it does not respond to unsolicited applications.

WHO TO APPLY TO L E A Fry, Trustee, 98 Savernake Road, London NW3 2JR

■ Mejer and Gertrude Miriam Frydman Foundation

CC NO 262806   **ESTABLISHED** 1971

WHERE FUNDING CAN BE GIVEN UK and overseas.

WHO CAN BENEFIT Organisations benefiting children, young adults, students, teachers and governesses. Support is given to Jewish people, and particular favour is given to Jewish charities.

WHAT IS FUNDED New and established charitable projects for study and research, including scholarships, fellowships, professorial chairs, lectureships, prizes, awards and the cost of purchasing or erecting any building or land required for such projects. Support in these areas is given to organisations and institutions only. Individuals are not supported under any circumstances.

WHAT IS NOT FUNDED No grants to individuals for scholarships or any other purpose.

RANGE OF GRANTS Up to £4,000.

SAMPLE GRANTS Previous beneficiaries include: North West London Jewish Day School, Jewish Care, Norwood Ravenswood, Kisharon, Chai Cancer Care, Kesser Torah, Friends of Yeshiva O H R Elchanan, the Merephdi Foundation, Institute for Higher Rabbinicial Studies and Talia Trust for Children.

FINANCES *Year* 2009–10 *Income* £41,198 *Grants* £36,600 *Assets* £88,088

TRUSTEES Keith Graham; David H Frydman; Gerald B Frydman; Louis J Frydman.

HOW TO APPLY In writing to the correspondent.

WHO TO APPLY TO David H Frydman, Trustee, Westbury Chartered Accountants, 145–157 St John Street, London EC1V 4PY *Tel* 020 7253 7272

■ The Fuellers Charitable Trust Fund

CC NO 288157   **ESTABLISHED** 1983

WHERE FUNDING CAN BE GIVEN UK, particularly City of London.

WHO CAN BENEFIT City of London charities and organisations supporting education and

research into energy technology and conservation.

WHAT IS FUNDED General charitable purposes, research and dissemination, conservation.

SAMPLE GRANTS Regular donations are given to organisations including the Basil Watson Memorial, Stockwell Park School, Big Issue Foundation, British Paralympics Association, RLNI, City of London Sea Cadets, Guildhall School of Music & Drama and Action Aid.

FINANCES *Year* 2010 *Income* £16,653 *Grants* £15,000

TRUSTEES James Hill; David Port; John Bainbridge; Michael Husband; Nigel Draffin; Stuart Goldsmith; Russel Warburton.

HOW TO APPLY In writing to the correspondent.

WHO TO APPLY TO Russel Warburton, 29 Cromwell Place, Cranleigh GU6 7LF *Tel* 014832 71467 *email* clerk@fuellers.co.uk

---

■ The Fulmer Charitable Trust

CC NO 1070428   **ESTABLISHED** 1998

WHERE FUNDING CAN BE GIVEN Worldwide, especially the developing world and Wiltshire.

WHO CAN BENEFIT Registered charities worldwide, especially in the developing world and Wiltshire.

WHAT IS FUNDED General charitable purposes.

WHAT IS NOT FUNDED No support for gap year requests.

RANGE OF GRANTS Up to £15,000, but mostly for £500–£3,000.

SAMPLE GRANTS Sight Savers and Sense (£11,000 each); Save the Children and Shelter (£10,000 each); NSPCC and the Sequal Trust (£9,000 each); Age Concern and Macmillan Cancer Relief (£8,000 each); the Brain Research Trust, Brainwave and Extracare (£7,000 each); I.M.P.S., the Leys Youth Programme and TRAX (£5,000 each); Coventry Cathedral Development Trust (£4,000); Disasters Emergency Committee (£3,000); Bath and District Samaritans, Bibles for Children, Book Aid International, Karen Hill Tribes Trust, Sailors Society and Topsy Foundation (£2,000 each); Traidcraft, Y Care International and Youth Action Wiltshire (£1,750 each); Zimbabwe A National Emergency – ZANE (£1,500); Able Child Africa, Acid Survivors Trust International, Food for the Hungry UK, Kenyan Children's Project, Lamb Health Care Foundation, Transrural Trust (£1,000 each); King's Care (£500); and Salisbury & South Wiltshire Museum (£100).

FINANCES *Year* 2009–10 *Income* £435,068 *Grants* £423,017 *Assets* £5,648,549

TRUSTEES J S Reis; Mrs S Reis; Mrs C Mytum; Miss E J Reis.

HOW TO APPLY In writing to the correspondent. Very few unsolicited applications are accepted.

WHO TO APPLY TO The Trustees, Estate Office, Street Farm, Compton Bassett, Calne, Wiltshire SN11 8SW *Tel* 01249 760410 *Fax* 01249 760410

■ Worshipful Company of Furniture Makers Charitable Fund

CC NO 270483   **ESTABLISHED** 1975

WHERE FUNDING CAN BE GIVEN UK.

WHO CAN BENEFIT Individuals and organisations.

WHAT IS FUNDED Causes directly connected to furniture, funding design competitions, prototypes and visits to exhibitions or factories and offering bursaries to students at colleges.

WHAT IS NOT FUNDED No grants will be made to individuals due to a decision by the trustees to focus on organising tours and courses to 'benefit a much larger number of young furniture people'.

RANGE OF GRANTS £200–£5,000.

SAMPLE GRANTS Design Student's Industrial Tour (£5,200); The Woods Awards (£5,000); FIT (£4,000); Retails Course (£3,700); Bucks Chilterns University College (£3,000) and Oxford and Cherwell College (£2,000).

FINANCES *Year* 2009–10 *Income* £341,128 *Grants* £126,141 *Assets* £1,080,390

TRUSTEES Sir John Perring; Roger H Richardson; Martin Jourdan.

HOW TO APPLY In writing to the correspondent.

WHO TO APPLY TO Mrs Jan A Wright, Clerk, Furniture Makers' Hall, 12 Austin Friars, London EC2N 2HE *Tel* 020 7256 5558 *Fax* 020 7256 5155 *email* clerk@furnituremakers.org.uk *Website* www.furnituremakers.co.uk

....

■ The Fuserna Foundation

CC NO 1107895   **ESTABLISHED** 2005

WHERE FUNDING CAN BE GIVEN UK and overseas.

WHO CAN BENEFIT Children and older people.

WHAT IS FUNDED Relief-in-need and mental and physical illness.

WHAT IS NOT FUNDED The foundation will not generally consider projects that include the following: animals; religious activities/ institutions; general appeals.

SAMPLE GRANTS National Gallery (£3 million); William J Clinton Foundation UK (£194,000); Fuserna Foundation – US (£136,000); Metropolitan Opera (£102,000); Africa Foundation (£25,000); Reprieve (£15,000); Brainwave (£5,000); and Barton Training Trust (£2,000).

FINANCES *Year* 2009 *Income* £3,430,521 *Grants* £3,522,046

TRUSTEES Louise Creasly; Ariadne Getty; Patrick Maxwell.

OTHER INFORMATION In regard to the foundation's largest grant of £3 million to the National Gallery it stated: 'We would not normally consider such a large donation to a high profile arts charity. However the trustees consider that the retention of these artworks in Great Britain is of the utmost importance and of the overall benefit to the general public and therefore contributed to the successful retention of Diana and Actaeon.'

HOW TO APPLY The foundation asks for all initial applications to be in writing and to include the following: background information about the charity or charitable project in question; details of the project that currently requires funding including the objective of the project and full operational details of how that objective will be achieved; a copy of your most recent financial statutory accounts; details of the budget outlined in respect of the project; details of existing sources of finance, including donations from other charitable trusts and details of other fund raising activities in place in respect of raising the funds needed for the project. 'Upon receipt of the above information, a member of the foundation's day to day operational staff may wish to visit the charity prior to presenting its application to the trustees or alternatively to commence discussions with you. Further to this your application will be put forward to the trustees of the Fuserna Foundation for their consideration.'

WHO TO APPLY TO The Trustees, Sixth Floor, 6 Chesterfield Gardens, Mayfair, London

W1J 5BQ *Tel* 020 7409 3900 *email* info@ fusernafoundation.org *Website* www. fusernafoundation.org

■ The G D Charitable Trust

CC NO 1096101 **ESTABLISHED** 2002
WHERE FUNDING CAN BE GIVEN Worldwide.
WHO CAN BENEFIT Registered charities.
WHAT IS FUNDED Animal welfare, the environment, disability, homelessness.
WHAT IS NOT FUNDED No grants to individuals.
SAMPLE GRANTS the Whitely Fund for Nature (£50,000); the Aspinall Foundation and the Eve Appeal (£10,000 each); Naomi House Children's Hospice (£2,000); and Brook Hospital for Animals and Royal Parks Foundation (£1,000 each).
FINANCES *Year* 2009–10 *Income* £134,554 *Grants* £74,000 *Assets* £3,528,762
TRUSTEES George Lincoln Duffield; Natasha Velvet Duffield; Alexander Seamus Fitzgibbons.
HOW TO APPLY In writing to the correspondent.
WHO TO APPLY TO The Trustees, c/o Bircham Dyson Bell LLP, 50 Broadway, Westminster, London SW1H 0BL *Tel* 020 7227 7000

■ Gableholt Limited

CC NO 276250 **ESTABLISHED** 1978
WHERE FUNDING CAN BE GIVEN UK.
WHO CAN BENEFIT Jewish organisations.
WHAT IS FUNDED Advancement of the orthodox Jewish faith.
FINANCES *Year* 2009–10 *Income* £1,074,712 *Grants* £29,101 *Assets* £21,195,102
TRUSTEES S Noe; Mrs E Noe; C Lerner; P Noe; A E Bude.
HOW TO APPLY In the past this trust has stated that 'in the governors' view, true charitable giving should always be coupled with virtual anonymity' and for this reason they are most reluctant to be a party to any publicity. Along with suggesting that the listed beneficiaries might also want to remain unidentified, they also state that the nature of the giving (to orthodox Jewish organisations) means the information is unlikely to be of much interest to anyone else. Potential applicants would be strongly advised to note these comments.
WHO TO APPLY TO Mrs E Noe, Secretary, 115 Craven Park Road, London N15 6BL *Tel* 020 8802 4782

■ The Galanthus Trust

CC NO 1103538 **ESTABLISHED** 2004
WHERE FUNDING CAN BE GIVEN UK and overseas.
WHO CAN BENEFIT Registered charities and individuals.
WHAT IS FUNDED Medical, developing countries, environment, conservation.
RANGE OF GRANTS UK and overseas.
SAMPLE GRANTS Previously grants had been distributed between three categories: medical and healthcare, projects in the third world and environment and welfare.
FINANCES *Year* 2009–10 *Income* £5,127 *Grants* £100,000
TRUSTEES S F Rogers; Mrs J M Rogers.
OTHER INFORMATION During the year, the trust had a total expenditure of £113,606.

HOW TO APPLY In writing to the correspondent. 'All requests for grants are considered carefully by the trustees. The trustees decide whether to donate and the amount to donate.'
WHO TO APPLY TO Mrs J M Rogers, Trustee, West Farm House, Newton Tony, Salisbury SP4 0HF *Tel* 01980 629345 *email* galanthustrust@yahoo.co.uk

■ The Galbraith Trust

CC NO 1086717 **ESTABLISHED** 2001
WHERE FUNDING CAN BE GIVEN The administrative area of Lancaster City Council.
WHO CAN BENEFIT Charitable organisations.
WHAT IS FUNDED General charitable purposes.
RANGE OF GRANTS £250–£2,000.
SAMPLE GRANTS Previous beneficiaries included: Archbishop Hutton After School Fun Club, Bare Necessities Pre-School Playgroup, Bolton-le-Sands Village Hall, Lancashire Outward Bound Association and Night Owls (£1,500 each); Friendship Centre (£1,000); 1st Heysham Guides and Community Learning Network (£800 each); St Barnabas Housebound Club (£600); Lancaster and Garstang Division Girl Guiding and Stage Struck Youth Theatre (£500 each); and Greenfield Court residents Association (£300).
FINANCES *Year* 2010–11 *Income* £18,696 *Grants* £33,000
TRUSTEES Ms K F Gordon, Chair; J W Wilson; M V L Harris; Mrs I E Bowker; M W Burrow; P G Crowther.
OTHER INFORMATION The grants total is based on previous research. 25 grants were given.
HOW TO APPLY Application forms may be obtained from the Lancaster District Council for Voluntary Service at the following address: Trinity Community Centre, Middle Street, Lancaster LA1 1JZ.
WHO TO APPLY TO Lancaster CVS, Blackhurst Swainson Goodier, Aalborg Square, Lancaster LA1 1GG *email* email@lancastercvs.org.uk

■ The Gale Family Charitable Trust

CC NO 289212 **ESTABLISHED** 1984
WHERE FUNDING CAN BE GIVEN UK, mainly Bedfordshire.
WHO CAN BENEFIT Registered charities, with a preference for Bedfordshire-based charities.
WHAT IS FUNDED Churches and church ministries, community life in Bedfordshire and general charitable purposes.
WHAT IS NOT FUNDED Grants are rarely given to individuals.
FINANCES *Year* 2009–10 *Income* £212,955 *Grants* £135,250 *Assets* £5,399,648
TRUSTEES G D Payne, Chair; J Tyley; J Williams; A J Ormerod; Mrs D Watson; R Beard; W Browning; D Stanton.
HOW TO APPLY In writing to the correspondent. Grants are distributed once a year and applications should be made by May for consideration in July.
WHO TO APPLY TO G Garner, Administrator, Garner Associates, Northwood House, 138 Bromham Road, Bedford MK40 2QW *Tel* 01234 354 508 *Fax* 01234 349 588 *email* ggg@garnerassociates.co.uk

■ The Angela Gallagher Memorial Fund

CC NO 800739   **ESTABLISHED** 1989

WHERE FUNDING CAN BE GIVEN UK and international organisations based in the UK.

WHO CAN BENEFIT Registered charities benefiting: children; Christians; Roman Catholics; and those suffering from paediatric diseases. Support will also go to people disadvantaged by poverty; people with disabilities; victims of famine and disasters; and victims of abuse.

WHAT IS FUNDED The aim of the fund is to help children within the UK. The fund will also consider Christian, humanitarian and educational projects worldwide. Particularly charities working in the fields of: special needs education; day centres; holidays and outings; and Catholic bodies. Small charities which do not have access to large corporate donors are given priority. International disasters are aided by way of CAFOD and Red Cross only.

WHAT IS NOT FUNDED Donations will not be made to the following: older people; scientific research; hospitals and hospices; artistic and cultural appeals; animal welfare; or building and equipment appeals. No grants to individuals.

TYPE OF GRANT One-off grants for core costs.

RANGE OF GRANTS Usually £500–£1,000.

SAMPLE GRANTS Grants of £1,000 each were made to Anglo-Peruvian Child Care Mission, Cathedral Camps, Derby Toc H Children's Camp, North East Help Link, Over the Wall, The BTT John Fawcett Foundation, The Singalong Group and The Spiti Projects. Remaining donations were mostly for £500 each and included those to African Village Support, Bahia Street Trust, Bibles for Children, Children of Fiji, Cirencester Cyber Cafe, Clothing Solutions, Kidz Club – Leeds, Merthyr Tydfil Children Contact Centre, Mosaic, One in a Million, Rutland Sailability, Sail, Shelterbox for Haiti, Sunny smiles, Thumbs Up Club and Women in Need in Jinja.

FINANCES *Year* 2010 *Income* £37,995 *Grants* £32,500 *Assets* £1,504,555

TRUSTEES N A Maxwell-Lawford; Diana R Moss; Wendy Manfield; H Rising.

HOW TO APPLY In writing to the correspondent, for consideration at trustees' meetings twice a year. Applicants must include a set of accounts or the appeal will not be considered. Applications are not acknowledged without an sae.

WHO TO APPLY TO Diana R Moss, Secretary, Church Cott, The Green, Mirey Lane, Woodbury, Devon EX5 1DX *Tel* 01395 232097

■ The Gamlen Charitable Trust

CC NO 327977   **ESTABLISHED** 1988

WHERE FUNDING CAN BE GIVEN UK.

WHO CAN BENEFIT Organisations benefiting law students and trainee solicitors.

WHAT IS FUNDED Legal education, general charitable purposes.

TYPE OF GRANT Grants for scholarships, bursaries and prizes.

RANGE OF GRANTS Up to £7,500.

SAMPLE GRANTS Christ Church (Law Fellowship) (£39,000); City Solicitors Educational Trust (£5,000); Newbury Spring Festival (£4,000); Grange Park Opera (£3,000); and Garsington Opera (£2,000).

FINANCES *Year* 2009–10 *Income* £127,420 *Grants* £53,512 *Assets* £27,991

TRUSTEES R G Stubblefield; P G Eaton; J W M Chadwick.

HOW TO APPLY The trust does not accept unsolicited applications.

WHO TO APPLY TO J W M Chadwick, Trustee, c/o Thomas Eggar LLP, Newbury House, 20 Kings Road West, Newbury, Berkshire RG14 5XR *Tel* 01635 571000

■ The Gamma Trust

SC NO SC004330   **ESTABLISHED** 1965

WHERE FUNDING CAN BE GIVEN UK, with a possible preference for Scotland.

WHO CAN BENEFIT Registered charities.

WHAT IS FUNDED General charitable purposes.

WHAT IS NOT FUNDED No grants to individuals.

TYPE OF GRANT Project, research and recurring costs.

SAMPLE GRANTS Previous beneficiaries have included British Red Cross, British Heart Foundation, Cancer Research Campaign and Erskine Hospital.

FINANCES *Year* 2009–10 *Income* £62,513 *Grants* £60,000

HOW TO APPLY In writing to the correspondent for consideration quarterly.

WHO TO APPLY TO The Trust Secretary, c/o Mazars CYB Services Limited, 90 St Vincent Street, Glasgow G2 5UB *Tel* 0141 225 4953 *email* glasgowtrustteam@mazars.co.uk

■ The Gannochy Trust

SC NO SC003133   **ESTABLISHED** 1937

WHERE FUNDING CAN BE GIVEN Scotland, with a preference for the Perth and Kinross area.

WHO CAN BENEFIT Organisations which meet the OSCR Charity Test.

WHAT IS FUNDED The trust's grant-making mission is: 'to make a positive difference for the benefit of people living in Scotland, with a preference for Perth and Kinross'. It has four grant-making themes: (1) inspiring young people; (2) improving the quality of life of the disadvantaged and vulnerable; (3) supporting and developing community amenities; (4) care for the natural and man-made environment. NOTE: Themes 3 and 4 are restricted to Perth and Kinross.

WHAT IS NOT FUNDED 'General applications for funds will not be considered – applications must be specific, and preferably for a project with a defined outcome, not general running costs; donations will not be made to individuals; donations will only be made to organisations which meet the OSCR Charity Test; projects where the benefit of a donation will be realised outside Scotland; donations will rarely be made to projects that do not demonstrate an element of self or other funding; donations will not be made that contribute to an organisation's healthy reserves or endowments; applications will seldom be considered for more than a 3-year commitment; applications will not be considered for holidays, with the exception of those for the disabled and disadvantaged living in Perth & Kinross where the project has a tangible recreational or educational theme; applications will not be considered for animal welfare projects, with the exception of wildlife projects within Perth & Kinross that meet the sub-themes within theme 4; applications will not be considered from schools for recreational facilities unless there will be a demonstrable and sustained community involvement, preferably for the disadvantaged or vulnerable; applications from pre-school groups, play schemes, after school clubs and parent-teacher associations; applications will not be considered from cancer and other health-related charities unless they demonstrate that their project directly provides tangible relief from suffering and direct patient benefit; applications from places of worship will not be considered unless there is a distinct community benefit through use as a community centre or village hall, and where there is not a similar facility nearby; applications will not be considered from charities re-applying within a year of their previous appeal or award, or instalment thereof; applications will not be considered where funding would normally be provided by central or local government; waste disposal/landfill, pollution control and renewable energy projects will not be considered if they are the sole purpose of the project, and unless they meet the criteria within theme 4; applications will not be considered for political or lobbying purposes.'

SAMPLE GRANTS Horsecross Arts Ltd – Perth (£3 million); Kibble Education and Care Centre (£300,000); Perth Festival of the Arts (£260,000); Erskine and Royal Scottish Geographical Society (£75,000 each); Madderley Community Association, Quality of Life Trust – Village Halls and William Simpson's Home (£50,000); and Church of Scotland Viewpark parish and Rollo Park Trust (£40,000 each).

FINANCES *Year* 2009–10 *Income* £4,942,494 *Grants* £2,040,535 *Assets* £119,708,140

TRUSTEES Dr Russell Leather, Chair; Mark Webster; Dr James H F Kynaston; Ian W McMillan; Stewart N Macleod; John Markland.

HOW TO APPLY On a form which can be downloaded from the trust's website. Full guidelines are available.

WHO TO APPLY TO Fiona Russell, Secretary, Kincarrathie House Drive, Pitcullen Crescent, Perth PH2 7HX *Tel* 01738 620653 *email* admin@gannochytrust.org.uk *Website* www.gannochytrust.org.uk

■ The Ganzoni Charitable Trust

CC NO 263583 **ESTABLISHED** 1971

WHERE FUNDING CAN BE GIVEN Suffolk.

WHO CAN BENEFIT Registered charities.

WHAT IS FUNDED General charitable purposes.

WHAT IS NOT FUNDED Grants to individuals will not be considered. Applications from outside Suffolk are not normally considered and will not be acknowledged.

TYPE OF GRANT A number of the grants are recurring; the remainder will normally be one-off.

RANGE OF GRANTS £50–£20,000.

SAMPLE GRANTS St Augustine's Church (£20,000); St Edmuntsbury Cathedral (£15,000); St Marys Church, Bentley (£5,000); All Saints Church, Chelsworth (£2,000); Bramford Road Methodist Church and British School of Osteopathy (£1,000 each); Children with Leukaemia (£500); Friston Village Hall (£250) and Multiple Sclerosis North Suffolk (£100).

FINANCES *Year* 2009–10 *Income* £117,472 *Grants* £111,995 *Assets* £3,111,197

TRUSTEES Hon. Mary Jill Ganzoni; Hon. Charles Boscawen; Nicholas Ridley.

HOW TO APPLY In writing to the correspondent. Telephone calls are not encouraged. There are no application forms, guidelines or deadlines. No SAE is required unless material is to be returned.

WHO TO APPLY TO Hon. C R Boscawen, Trustee, Birketts LLP, 24–26 Museum Street, Ipswich IP1 1HZ *Tel* 01473 232300

■ The Worshipful Company of Gardeners of London

CC NO 222079 **ESTABLISHED** 1962

WHERE FUNDING CAN BE GIVEN Mainly City of London.

WHO CAN BENEFIT Horticultural organisations.

WHAT IS FUNDED The fund supports charitable activities connected with horticulture in all its forms and within the City of London.

RANGE OF GRANTS £100–£5,500.

SAMPLE GRANTS London Children's Flower Association and Gardening for the Disabled (£5,000 each); London Gardens Society and Royal Fund for Gardner's Children (£4,000 each); Flowers in the City (£2,500); Lord Major's Appeal (£1,000); Reeds School Foundation Appeal, Army Benevolent Fund and Fairbridge (£500 each).

FINANCES *Year* 2009–10 *Income* £73,179 *Grants* £54,375 *Assets* £433,463

TRUSTEES N A Chalmers, Chair; Alan D Wiltshire; W B Fraser; Mrs N L Robinson; Guy R C Petty; Ramsay Shewell-Cooper; Sir Gavin Arthur; Venerable P A Delaney; M L E Dowlen; B S Porter; D R Caspi.

HOW TO APPLY In writing to the correspondent.

WHO TO APPLY TO Trevor Faris, Clerk, 25 Luke Street, London EC2A 4AR *Tel* 020 7739 6404 (PA to the Clerk) or ext. 6696 (Assistant Clerk) *Fax* 020 7613 3412 *email* paclerk@gardenerscompany.org.uk *Website* www.gardenerscompany.org.uk

■ The Samuel Gardner Memorial Trust

CC NO 261059 **ESTABLISHED** 1970

WHERE FUNDING CAN BE GIVEN Harrow on the Hill.

WHO CAN BENEFIT Organisations and charitable groups.

WHAT IS FUNDED Music and music education; the arts and heritage; preservation of landscaped public spaces. There is an emphasis on the encouragement of young people.

WHAT IS NOT FUNDED No grants to individuals.

SAMPLE GRANTS Arthur Gardner Scholarship (£22,000).

FINANCES *Year* 2009–10 *Income* £39,796 *Grants* £33,738 *Assets* £1,370,841

TRUSTEES Timothy Brown; Marion Friend; Ms Ursula Jones; Timothy J Lines; John A Stenhouse.

HOW TO APPLY In writing to the correspondent.

WHO TO APPLY TO Mrs Pauline McAlpine, SBM & Company, 117 Fentman Road, London SW8 1JZ *Tel* 020 7582 9473 *email* pauline@sbmandco.com

■ The Garnett Charitable Trust

CC NO 327847 **ESTABLISHED** 1988

WHERE FUNDING CAN BE GIVEN South west England and Northern Ireland.

WHO CAN BENEFIT Registered charities.

WHAT IS FUNDED Health, hospices, environmental causes and animal welfare groups, arts, culture and recreation.

WHAT IS NOT FUNDED No grants to unsolicited applications. Most funds are earmarked and speculative applications will not be considered.

RANGE OF GRANTS £5–£10,000.

SAMPLE GRANTS Previous beneficiaries included: All Hallows' School – Cranmore, CARE International, Design Museum, Ireland Fund of Great Britain, National Gallery Trust, St Michael's Parish and Save the Children.

FINANCES *Year* 2009–10 *Income* £5,814
Grants £25,262
TRUSTEES A J F Garnett; Mrs P Garnett; Sandra
Brown; Fiona Vincent.
HOW TO APPLY No grants to unsolicited applications.
WHO TO APPLY TO Fiona Vincent, Trustee, 2 Temple
Back East, Temple Quay, Bristol BS1 6EG
Tel 0117 917 3022

■ Garrick Charitable Trust

CC NO 1071279   ESTABLISHED 1998
WHERE FUNDING CAN BE GIVEN UK.
WHO CAN BENEFIT Registered charities.
WHAT IS FUNDED Institutions which are seeking to
further theatre (including dance), literature or
music.
RANGE OF GRANTS Usually £2,500, exceptionally up
to £10,000.
SAMPLE GRANTS Orange Tree Theatre, Dance
Umbrella, Two Moors Festival and National
Academy of Writing (£5,000 each); Poetry
School (£3,000); Opera UK Limited, National
Youth Ballet, Royal Society of Literature,
Sinfonietta Production, Tobacco Factory Theatre
and Lyric Players Theatre Productions Limited
(£2,500 each); Tete a Tete (£2,100); Appledore
Book Festival (£1,300); Sticking Place (£1,000);
and Sibmas (£300).
FINANCES *Year* 2009–10 *Income* £141,926
Grants £124,365 *Assets* £4,567,711
TRUSTEES John Nigel Newton; David Sigall; Stephen
Waley-Cohen; Roger Braban; Stephen Peter Aris.
HOW TO APPLY Initial applications are reviewed by
the trustees who decide whether or not to send
an application form. Trustees meet quarterly.
WHO TO APPLY TO Fiona Murray, Trust Administrator,
Garrick Club, 15 Garrick Street, London
WC2E 9AY *Tel* 020 7395 4111
email charitabletrust@garrickclub.co.uk

■ Garvan Limited

CC NO 286110   ESTABLISHED 1980
WHERE FUNDING CAN BE GIVEN UK.
WHO CAN BENEFIT Jewish organisations.
WHAT IS FUNDED The advancement of religion in
accordance with the Orthodox Jewish faith and
the relief of poverty.
FINANCES *Year* 2009–10 *Income* £239,496
Grants £68,242 *Assets* £1,180,898
TRUSTEES A Ebert; L Ebert.
HOW TO APPLY In writing to the correspondent.
WHO TO APPLY TO The Trustees, Flat 9, Windsor
Court, Golders Green Road, London NW11 9PP

■ The Gatsby Charitable
Foundation

CC NO 251988   ESTABLISHED 1967
WHERE FUNDING CAN BE GIVEN Unrestricted.
WHO CAN BENEFIT Registered charities only. Many
beneficiary organisations are specialist research
institutes.
WHAT IS FUNDED **Plant Science**: to develop basic
research in fundamental processes of plant
growth and development and molecular plant
pathology, to encourage young researchers in
the field of plant science in the UK;
Neuroscience: to support world-class research
in the area of neural circuits and behaviour, and
in the area of theoretical neuroscience; and to
support activities which enhance understanding
in this field; **Science and Engineering**

Education: to support improvement in
educational opportunity in the UK for a
workforce that can better apply technology for
wealth creation by incubating innovative
programmes in the field of science and
engineering education and promoting excellence
in teaching and learning; **Africa**: to promote
economic development and income generation
through selected programmes supporting small
scale manufacturing and enterprise and market
sector development in selected African
countries; **Institute for Government**: an
independent centre available to politicians and
the civil service, focused on making government
more effective; **The Arts**: to support the fabric
and programming of institutions with which
Gatsby's founding family has long connections;
Mental Health: to improve the quality of life for
people with long-term problems by improved
delivery of services.
WHAT IS NOT FUNDED Generally, the trustees do not
make grants in response to unsolicited
applications or to individuals.
TYPE OF GRANT One-off and recurring grants.
SAMPLE GRANTS University of Cambridge
(£31 million); Sainsbury Laboratory – Norwich
(£5 million); Institute for Government
(£4.8 million); Gatsby Technical Education
(£2.96 million); Royal Shakespeare Theatre and
RSC (£2.25 million); Tanzania Gatsby Trust
(£2 million); Frenchay Hospital (£1.2 million);
Royal Society (£1 million); Two Blades
Foundation (£939,000); New Engineering
Foundation £740,000); Harvard University
(£601,000); Centre for Cities (£400,000);
Hebrew University of Jerusalem (£271,000);
Chamber Orchestra of Europe (£250,000);
Kenya Gatsby Trust (£211,000); University of
York (£201,000); Shakespeare Birthplace Trust
(£100,000); and African Agricultural Capital
(£75,000).
FINANCES *Year* 2009–10 *Income* £34,771,000
Grants £33,015,000 *Assets* £460,792,000
TRUSTEES Bernard Willis; Sir Andrew Cahn; Miss
Judith Portrait.
OTHER INFORMATION The trust is one of the
Sainsbury Family Charitable Trusts which share
a common administration. An application to one
is taken as an application to all.
HOW TO APPLY Proposals are generally invited by the
trustees or initiated at their request. Unsolicited
applications are not encouraged and are unlikely
to be successful.
WHO TO APPLY TO Peter Hesketh, Director, Allington
House, 1st Floor, 150 Victoria Street, London
SW1E 5AE *Tel* 020 7410 0330 *Fax* 020 7410
0332 *email* contact@gatsby.org.uk
Website www.gatsby.org.uk

■ Gatwick Airport Community
Trust

CC NO 1089683   ESTABLISHED 2001
WHERE FUNDING CAN BE GIVEN Parts of East and West
Sussex, Surrey and Kent but particularly
communities directly affected by operations at
Gatwick Airport. A map of the area of benefit
can be seen on the website.
WHO CAN BENEFIT Environmental and community
projects in the area of benefit.
WHAT IS FUNDED Priority categories for support are:
the development of young people; art projects
including amateur drama, music and art;
sporting facilities; environmental improvement
and conservation; improvements to community
facilities such as village halls; support for

people who are disabled; support for people who are elderly; and the encouragement of additional volunteering or giving in the area.

WHAT IS NOT FUNDED The trustees will not consider projects that involve any of the following categories: projects or beneficiaries that are completely or largely outside the area of benefit (less attention is given to applications from areas not directly affected by the airport); recurrent expenditure or running costs, ongoing maintenance or deficits; salaries or training costs, except start-up costs in relation to an additional amenity or service being established that will be self-sustaining thereafter; costs that should be funded from other sources, e.g. public bodies; applications from organisations that have statutory responsibilities such as local authorities, hospitals, schools, unless it is a project that is over and above their core activities; the purchase of land or buildings. Grants will not be made to organisations that are working to make a profit for shareholders, partners or sole owners, nor to individuals. Grants will not normally be made where it is evident that little or no effort has been made to raise funds elsewhere.

TYPE OF GRANT The trust favours applications that involve one-off capital or project costs, rather than ongoing maintenance, salaries or training costs.

RANGE OF GRANTS £250–£5,000.

SAMPLE GRANTS Grants were listed by project type which included: 'Community facilities' (£43,000); 'Young adults' (£42,000); 'Sports and recreation' (£27,000); 'Disabled/disadvantaged' (£22,000) and 'Elderly' (£4,500).

FINANCES *Year* 2009–10 *Income* £170,861 *Grants* £179,500 *Assets* £5,012

TRUSTEES Mike Roberts, Chair; Kay Hammond; Neil Matthewson; John Mortimer; Michael Sander; James Smith; Christopher Chadburn-Hersey; Helyn Clack; Gillian Dewdney; Ian Revell.

OTHER INFORMATION The majority of grant applications were successful with 114 out of 131 applications being accepted.

HOW TO APPLY Application forms are available during the period each year when applications are being accepted (see below) by contacting the trust by telephone or writing to: GACT, PO Box 464, Tunbridge Wells, Kent TN2 9PU. Forms can also be downloaded from the website. Applications are invited once a year, usually between January and March. Grants are paid by the end of May. Further information can be found on the trust's website. Telephone queries are welcomed.

WHO TO APPLY TO Rosamund Quade, Trust Secretary, c/o Public Affairs, 7th Floor, Destinations Place, Gatwick Airport, West Sussex RH6 0NP *Tel* 01892 826088 *Website* www.gact.org.uk

■ The Robert Gavron Charitable Trust

CC NO 268535   **ESTABLISHED** 1974
WHERE FUNDING CAN BE GIVEN Mainly UK.
WHO CAN BENEFIT Mainly small charities.
WHAT IS FUNDED The principal fields of interest continue to include health and welfare (including charities for people with disabilities), prisons and prison reform, arts and arts education, education and social policy and research. Much of the funding follows the trustees' own charitable involvement. The trust generally makes a small number of substantial grants

together with a larger number of smaller donations.

WHAT IS NOT FUNDED The trust does not give donations to individuals or to large national charities.

TYPE OF GRANT One-off; project; research; recurring cost; and salaries. Funding can be given for up to three years.

RANGE OF GRANTS £25–£100,000.

SAMPLE GRANTS Menerbes Sports Centre (£179,000); King Alfred School (£100,000); Arab Israel Children's Tennis Charity (£76,500); and Barbados Cricket Association (£41,000); Runnymede Trust (£25,000); Friends of Highgate Cemetery (£15,000); REFRESH (£10,000); Rainbow Drama Group (£5,000); Holocaust Educational Trust (£1,000); and Jewish Community Centre UK (£300).

FINANCES *Year* 2009–10 *Income* £646,357 *Grants* £261,847 *Assets* £8,573,705

TRUSTEES Lord Robert Gavron; Charles Corman; Lady Katharine Gavron; Jessica Gavron; Sarah Gavron.

HOW TO APPLY Although the trust indicates that its funds are fully committed and that it would have difficulty in considering further appeals, particularly due to the current financial climate, some new projects may be supported. Organisations should apply in writing only to the correspondent. Please enclose a stamped addressed envelope and latest accounts. There are no regular dates for trustees' meetings, but they take place about five times a year.

WHO TO APPLY TO Ms Yvette Dear, Secretary, 44 Eagle Street, London WC1R 4FS *Tel* 020 7400 4300 *Fax* 020 7400 4245

■ Jacqueline and Michael Gee Charitable Trust

CC NO 1062566   **ESTABLISHED** 1997
WHERE FUNDING CAN BE GIVEN UK.
WHO CAN BENEFIT Charitable organisations, with a preference for Jewish groups.
WHAT IS FUNDED Almost exclusively health, arts and educational charities. Social welfare causes may be considered.
TYPE OF GRANT Project grants, one-off or long-term.
RANGE OF GRANTS Usually up to £10,000.
SAMPLE GRANTS Royal Opera House (£17,000); Philip and Nicola Gee Charitable Trust, Purcell School, Chai-Lifeline Cancer Care and Dalaid (£10,000 each); Royal National Theatre (£5,000); British Emunah (£3,300); Jewish Leadership Council (£2,500); St John's Hospice (£2,200); United Synagogue (£1,800); Heart Cells Foundation (£1,500); Camphill Village Trust (£1,400); WIZO UK (£1,100); SSAFA – Forces Help and Grange Park Opera (£1,000 each); Drugsline (£500); and Swiss Global Artistic Foundation (£100).
FINANCES *Year* 2009–10 *Income* £125,021 *Grants* £108,818 *Assets* £68,493
TRUSTEES Michael Gee; Jacqueline Gee.
HOW TO APPLY In writing to the correspondent.
WHO TO APPLY TO Michael Gee, Trustee, 27 Berkeley House, 15 Hay Hill, London W1J 8NS *Tel* 020 7493 1904

■ The General Nursing Council for England and Wales Trust

CC NO 288068   ESTABLISHED 1983
WHERE FUNDING CAN BE GIVEN England and Wales.
WHO CAN BENEFIT Universities and other public bodies benefiting nurses.
WHAT IS FUNDED Public bodies undertaking research into matters directly affecting nursing or the nursing profession.
TYPE OF GRANT One-off or annually towards revenue costs.
SAMPLE GRANTS One grant totalling £50,000 'towards advancing the science and art of nursing at South Bank University'.
FINANCES *Year* 2009–10 *Income* £99,173 *Grants* £50,000 *Assets* £2,583,492
TRUSTEES Sir Ron de Witt; Prof. Dame Betty Kershaw; Dame Jacqueline Docherty; Prof. C Gerrish; Ms C Rees-Williams; Prof. J Ellis.
OTHER INFORMATION Out of fifteen applications received, one was successful receiving a grant of £50,000.
HOW TO APPLY In writing to the correspondent, by 30 April for June meeting, by 30 September for November meeting.
WHO TO APPLY TO Dr Sam Koroma, Secretary, 83 Victoria Road, Lower Edmonton, London N9 9SU *Tel* 020 8345 5379 *email* gnct@koroma5824.fsnet.co.uk

■ Generations Charitable Trust

CC NO 1110565   ESTABLISHED 2005
WHERE FUNDING CAN BE GIVEN London Borough of Merton and overseas.
WHO CAN BENEFIT Local causes in the Borough of Merton and also in developing countries.
WHAT IS FUNDED Projects helping children who need it the most; those who have disabilities, are disadvantaged, or struggle with ill health. Projects in the areas of environmental protection and conservation are also supported.
TYPE OF GRANT Capital costs, full project and unrestricted funding for up to, and in some cases over, three years.
RANGE OF GRANTS Up to £50,000.
SAMPLE GRANTS World Land Trust, Global Hospital and Research Centre and Save the Children – Haiti (£50,000 each); Right to Dream, Network 81 and In-Touch (£10,000 each); Sports Relief 2010 (£8,000); Shooting Stars Children's Hospice (£7,000); MARE Hostel (£6,300); and Scope, Variety Club of Jersey, the Sing-along Group and Tree Aid (£5,000 each).
FINANCES *Year* 2009–10 *Income* £192,398 *Grants* £367,062 *Assets* £37,843
TRUSTEES Robert Finch, Stephen Finch; Rohini Finch.
HOW TO APPLY In writing to the correspondent
WHO TO APPLY TO Rohini Finch, Trustee, 36 Marryat Road, Wimbledon, London SW19 5BD *Tel* 020 8946 7760 *email* rfinch@rfinch.plus.com *Website* www.generationsct.co.uk

■ J Paul Getty Jr Charitable Trust

CC NO 292360   ESTABLISHED 1985
WHERE FUNDING CAN BE GIVEN UK, mainly England.
WHO CAN BENEFIT Mainly registered charities. Priority is likely to be given to projects in the less prosperous parts of the country, particularly outside London and the south east, and to those which cover more than one beneficial area.

WHAT IS FUNDED Projects which will 'help to relieve poverty, support disadvantaged people, and effect long-term change where help is not readily available from the public or private purse'. The trust also provides some funding for the arts, and towards the conservation of the natural and built environment.
WHAT IS NOT FUNDED Grants are not given for: individuals; organisations based outside of the UK; schools, universities or public sector organisations; routine maintenance, repairs, refurbishment or modernisation costs, or large-scale development projects, such as church restoration work or the construction of new village halls and local community centres; medical care or general health and wellbeing programmes; one-off events, residential or adventure trips. Priority is likely to be given to projects in the less prosperous parts of the country, particularly outside London and the south east, and to those which cover more than one beneficial area. Please remember this trust has no connection with the Getty Foundation in the USA.
TYPE OF GRANT Capital or recurrent; core funding and salaries are considered. Main grants of over £5,000 and small grants of under £5,000.
RANGE OF GRANTS Up to £250,000 (over three years).
SAMPLE GRANTS Social Finance (£300,000); Women's Diversionary Fund (£175,000); Restorative Solutions (£200,000); Shannon Trust (£150,000); Kensington Palace (£250,000); Abbotsford (£150,000); War Memorials Trust (£25,000); National Cataloguing Scheme (£60,000); Infobuzz Ltd (£45,000); Cardboard Citizens (£90,000); Housing for Women (£80,000); Wells Cathedral (£75,000); Ethnic Minority Training Project (£60,000); The Civil Liberties Trust (£50,000); Trinity Winchester (£30,000); Hackfall Trust (£7,000).
FINANCES *Year* 2010 *Income* £1,086,079 *Grants* £9,463,248 *Assets* £43,075,864
TRUSTEES Christopher Gibbs, Chair; Lady Getty; Vanni Treves; Christopher Purvis.
OTHER INFORMATION This trust has no connection with the Getty Foundation in the USA. In accordance with the express wishes of Sir Paul Getty Jr, the trustees decided in 2011 to wind down the trust within the next five years. It is likely that the trust will close to new applications within the next two years, and at least 6 months notice will be provided on the website
HOW TO APPLY Applications must be submitted using the online form accessible through the trust's website. There are no 'closing dates', and all applicants should receive an initial response within 12 weeks. The form will ask you to provide: information on the work of the organisation; details of the organisation's size and income; an overview of the project/work for which funding is required; the daytime contact details of someone with whom the trust can discuss the application. When starting an application for the first time applicants will be asked to complete a short 'eligibility quiz' to check that their project falls within the trust's criteria. If successful you will be able to begin the full application (guidance on completing the form is given within the form itself). If the project is short-listed for a grant of over £5,000, the trust will request more detailed information about the charity and the specific project. Full application guidelines are available on the trust's website.

562

Does the trust you have chosen match your needs? Haphazard applications waste postage and time

WHO TO APPLY TO Elizabeth Rantzen, Director, 1 Park Square West, London NW1 4LJ *Tel* 020 7486 1859 *Website* www.jpgettytrust.org.uk

■ The Gibbs Charitable Trust
CC NO 207997 ESTABLISHED 1946
WHERE FUNDING CAN BE GIVEN UK with a preference for the south of England and worldwide.
WHO CAN BENEFIT Organisations benefiting Methodists are given particular attention.
WHAT IS FUNDED Primarily to support Methodist charities; also areas of social or educational concern. Grants are normally made to projects of which the trustees have personal knowledge. Also supported are international causes and creative arts, especially those which use the arts for personal development.
WHAT IS NOT FUNDED A large number of requests are received by the trust from churches undertaking improvement, refurbishment and development projects, but only a few of these can be helped. In general, Methodist churches are selected, sometimes those the trustees have particular knowledge of. Individuals and animal charities are not supported.
TYPE OF GRANT Buildings, capital and project grants will be considered.
RANGE OF GRANTS Almost all grants in the range £500–£10,000.
SAMPLE GRANTS Village Aid for Youth and Women's Empowerment (£6,000); Biblical Literacy – University of Durham (£5,000); Oxfam – West African peace project (£4,000); Africa Now (£3,000); Llangynidr Village Hall – for Tennis Courts (£2,000); Shakespeare at the Tobacco Factory – Bristol(£1,000); Sudden Productions (£750); Daventry Project (£500).
FINANCES *Year* 2009–10 *Income* £104,623 *Grants* £93,400 *Assets* £1,981,728
TRUSTEES John N Gibbs, Chair; James Gibbs; Andrew Gibbs; Celia Gibbs; Elizabeth Gibbs; Jessica Gibbs; John E Gibbs; Juliet Gibbs; Patience Gibbs; Rebecca Gibbs; William Gibbs; James D Gibbs.
HOW TO APPLY The trust has no application forms, although an application cover sheet is available on the trust's website along with a policy and guidelines page. Requests should be made in writing to the correspondent. The trustees meet three times a year, after Christmas, near Easter and late summer. Unsuccessful applicants are not normally notified. The trustees do not encourage telephone enquiries or speculative applications. They also state that they are not impressed by applicants that send a huge amount of paperwork.
WHO TO APPLY TO Dr James M Gibbs, Trustee, 8 Victoria Square, Clifton, Bristol BS8 4ET *email* jamesgibbs@btinternet.com *Website* www.gibbstrust.org.uk

■ Simon Gibson Charitable Trust
CC NO 269501 ESTABLISHED 1975
WHERE FUNDING CAN BE GIVEN UK and local charities in East Anglia and South Wales.
WHO CAN BENEFIT Registered or exempt charities.
WHAT IS FUNDED General.
WHAT IS NOT FUNDED No grants to individuals.
TYPE OF GRANT One-off or recurring, core costs, running costs, project, research, buildings and capital. Funding may be given for up to three years.
RANGE OF GRANTS £1,000 to £10,000, but most grants fall in the range £3,000 to £5,000.

SAMPLE GRANTS Ely Cathedral Appeal Fund, Prostate Cancer Charity, Save the Children Fund, St Nicholas Hospice Bury St Edmunds and the Prince's Trust (£10,000 each); New Astley Club Endowment Fund (£6,000); Addenbrooke's Charitable Trust, Campaign to Protect Rural England, Crimestoppers, Help For Heroes, National Ankylosing Spondylitis Society and the Welsh National Opera (£5,000 each); Action for Children, Blue Cross Animal Centre Cambridge, Flying Scholarship for the Disabled, Listening Books and Save The Rhino (£3,000 each); and the Temple Trust (£1,000).
FINANCES *Year* 2009–10 *Income* £544,346 *Grants* £579,458 *Assets* £12,785,430
TRUSTEES Bryan Marsh; Angela Homfray; George Gibson; Deborah Connor; John Homfray.
HOW TO APPLY 'There are no application forms. Charities applying to the trust should make their application in writing in whatever way they think best presents their cause.' It acknowledges all applications but does not enter into correspondence with applicants unless they are awarded a grant. The trustees meet in May and applications should be received by March.
WHO TO APPLY TO Bryan Marsh, Trustee, Wild Rose House, Llancarfan, Vale of Glamorgan CF62 3AD *Tel* 01446 781459 *email* marsh575@btinternet.com

■ The G C Gibson Charitable Trust
CC NO 258710 ESTABLISHED 1969
WHERE FUNDING CAN BE GIVEN UK.
WHO CAN BENEFIT Registered charities and 'authorities'.
WHAT IS FUNDED General charitable purposes, in practice, mainly art, music & education; health, hospices & medical research; community & other social projects; religion.
WHAT IS NOT FUNDED No grants to individuals.
TYPE OF GRANT Capital, research, running and core costs.
RANGE OF GRANTS £1,000–£20,000; mostly £1,000–£3,000.
SAMPLE GRANTS St Nicholas Hospice (£14,000); Botanic Garden Conservation Ltd, Ely Cathedral and Royal Welsh College of Music and Drama (£10,000 each); Friends of Horsmonden Church, Haiti Appeal and Help for Heroes (£5,000 each); Anti-Slavery International and Northampton Hope Centre (£2,000 each); and Campaign to Protect Rural Hampshire (£1,000).
FINANCES *Year* 2009–10 *Income* £502,759 *Grants* £574,000 *Assets* £11,734,646
TRUSTEES Simon Gibson; Jane M Gibson; Robert D Taylor; Martin Gibson; Lucy Kelly; Anna Dalrymple.
HOW TO APPLY In writing to the correspondent by October each year. Trustees meet in November/December. Successful applicants will receive their cheques during January. Organisations that have already received a grant should re-apply describing how the previous year's grant was spent and setting out how a further grant would be used. In general, less detailed information is required from national charities with a known track record than from small local charities that are not known to the trustees. NB 'Due to the volume of applications, it is not possible to acknowledge each application, nor is it possible to inform unsuccessful applicants.'
WHO TO APPLY TO Karen Griffin, c/o Deloitte PCS LTD, 5 Callaghan Square, Cardiff CF10 5BT *Tel* 029 2026 0000 *email* kagriffin@deloitte.co.uk

■ Lady Gibson's Charitable Trust

CC NO 261442   **ESTABLISHED** 1970
WHERE FUNDING CAN BE GIVEN Overseas and the UK, with a preference for East Sussex, Kent, Surrey and West Sussex.
WHO CAN BENEFIT Registered charities.
WHAT IS FUNDED General charitable purposes, including arts, culture and recreation.
WHAT IS NOT FUNDED No grants to individuals or non-registered charities.
TYPE OF GRANT One-off capital grants; funding for up to two years are considered.
RANGE OF GRANTS £20–£11,000.
SAMPLE GRANTS Withyham Parochial Church Council (£11,000); Royal National Theatre (£1,500); Royal Academy Trust (£1,300); Blond McIndoe Centre (£1,000); Bowles (£500); Chichester Cathedral Restoration and Development Trust (£350); Combat Stress (£250); London Philharmonic Orchestra (£120); Southbank Centre (£45); and Friends of Friendless Churches (£20).
FINANCES *Year* 2010–11 *Income* £17,182 *Grants* £23,500
TRUSTEES The Cowdray Trust Limited.
OTHER INFORMATION Applications for grants will only be acknowledged if a donation is to be sent.
HOW TO APPLY In writing to the correspondent. Acknowledgements will only be sent if a grant is being made.
WHO TO APPLY TO Laura Gosling, c/o Millbank Financial Services Ltd, Pollen House, 10–12 Cork Street, London W1S 3LW *Tel* 020 7439 9061 *email* charity@mfs.co.uk

■ The Harvey and Hilary Gilbert Charitable Trust

CC NO 296293   **ESTABLISHED** 1986
WHERE FUNDING CAN BE GIVEN UK.
WHO CAN BENEFIT Registered charities.
WHAT IS FUNDED General charitable purposes.
SAMPLE GRANTS Previous beneficiaries included: Jewish Care (£10,000); Prostate Cancer Care and World Jewish Relief (£5,000 each); Friends of the Royal Marsden (£2,000); Jewish Blind and Disabled (£500) and Great Ormond Street Hospital Children's Charity (£100).
FINANCES *Year* 2008–09 *Income* £25,656 *Grants* £29,450 *Assets* £3,676
TRUSTEES Harvey Gilbert; Claire Abrahams.
OTHER INFORMATION Accounts for the last two financial years were not available to view.
HOW TO APPLY In writing to the correspondent.
WHO TO APPLY TO Harvey Gilbert, Trustee, 7 Spaniards Park, Columbas Drive, Hampstead, London NW3 7JD

■ The Girdlers' Company Charitable Trust

CC NO 328026   **ESTABLISHED** 1988
WHERE FUNDING CAN BE GIVEN UK, with a preference for City and East End of London, and Hammersmith and Peckham.
WHO CAN BENEFIT Registered charities benefiting children, young adults, academics, students and teachers.
WHAT IS FUNDED Medicine and health, education, welfare, youth welfare, heritage, environment, humanities and Christian religion.
WHAT IS NOT FUNDED Applications will only be considered from registered charities. Whilst it is extremely rare for grants to be made to

individuals, the trustees will consider applications from, or on behalf of, a person who is disabled or disadvantaged needing financial support to enable their participation in a course of training or study leading to employment.
TYPE OF GRANT One-off and recurrent.
RANGE OF GRANTS Mostly up to £10,000.
SAMPLE GRANTS Leyton Orient Community Sports Programme (£40,000); London Youth (£37,500); London Youth – 2012 Project (£20,000); Queen Elizabeth Foundation and Resource Information Service (£10,000 each); Bosence Farm Community (£8,000); Ashburnham Christian Trust and Haven House Foundation (£5,000 each); The Voices Foundation (£3,000); Alone in London, Barons Court Project, Children's Safety Education Foundation, Fulham Good Neighbour Service, Manton Village Hall and West London Action for Children (£1,000 each); Milford and Villages Day Care Centre (£800); Retired Greyhound Trust (£700); Back-up Trust, Chicken Shed Theatre Trust, The Cranston Library and Together for Sudan (£500); and The Parish Church of St Margaret the Queen – Buxted (£400).
FINANCES *Year* 2009–10 *Income* £874,824 *Grants* £793,261 *Assets* £5,527,572
TRUSTEES Court of the Company of Girdlers.
HOW TO APPLY The trust operates an open application process for circa £50,000 of its total grant making. Of this £30,000 is awarded to between 25 and 30 charities whose beneficiaries reside in Hammersmith or Peckham. Around 20 awards are made, of approximately £1,000, to charities in the UK where the charity has an annual income less than £1 million.'
Applicants should write to the correspondent. To be considered for a donation please cover each of the following points: the beneficial area under which a grant is sought; a brief summary of the organisation's background and aims; the specific nature of the request, highlighting the change you wish to bring about; how you will know if you have achieved these changes; your charity registration number. Applications from charities whose beneficiaries reside in Hammersmith or Peckham are considered annually. Each April and November the trustee considers general applications with 10 donations of approximately £1,000 being made on each occasion. The closing dates are the last Friday in January and August. Successful applicants are unlikely to be awarded a further donation within the following 5 years. Successful applicants will be informed in May and December.
WHO TO APPLY TO John Gahan, Charities Manager, Girdlers' Hall, Basinghall Avenue, London EC2V 5DD *Tel* 020 7448 4851 *Fax* 020 7628 4030 *email* john@girdlers.co.uk

■ The Glass-House Trust

CC NO 1017426   **ESTABLISHED** 1993
WHERE FUNDING CAN BE GIVEN Unrestricted, but UK in practice.
WHO CAN BENEFIT Registered charities and institutions.
WHAT IS FUNDED Housing, the built environment, art and child development.
WHAT IS NOT FUNDED Grants are not normally made to individuals.
RANGE OF GRANTS £1,200–£176,000.
SAMPLE GRANTS Glass-House Community Led Design (£390,000); A Space (£55,000); Transform Drug Policy Foundation (£50,000); Resonance

FM (£45,000); HACT: The Housing Action Charity (£35,000); Akany Avoko, Madagascar (£15,000); and WAM Foundation (£5,000).

FINANCES *Year* 2009–10 *Income* £504,376 *Grants* £483,858 *Assets* £11,071,856

TRUSTEES Alexander Sainsbury; Timothy Sainsbury; Jessica Sainsbury; Elinor Sainsbury; Miss Judith Portrait.

OTHER INFORMATION The trust is one of the Sainsbury Family Charitable Trusts which share a common administration. An application to one is taken as an application to all.

HOW TO APPLY See the guidance for applicants in the entry for the Sainsbury Family Charitable Trusts. A single application will be considered for support by all the trusts in the group. However, in the case of this trust, 'trustees initiate proposals to be considered and do not encourage unsolicited approaches'.

WHO TO APPLY TO Alan Bookbinder, Director, Allington House, 1st Floor, 150 Victoria Street, London SW1E 5AE *Tel* 020 7410 0330 *Fax* 020 7410 0332 *Website* www.sfct.org.uk

---

■ The B and P Glasser Charitable Trust

CC NO 326571   **ESTABLISHED** 1984

WHERE FUNDING CAN BE GIVEN UK and worldwide.

WHO CAN BENEFIT Registered charities.

WHAT IS FUNDED General charitable purposes, particularly health and disability charities, and Jewish organisations.

WHAT IS NOT FUNDED No grant to individuals or students.

RANGE OF GRANTS £500–£8,000.

SAMPLE GRANTS Practical Action (£8,000), Nightingale House (£7,500), Jewish Care (£5,500); Royal National Institute for the Blind and Sight Savers International and (£5,000 each); Ian Rennie Hospice at Home (£2,500); Camphill Village Trust (£2,000); Help the Aged (£1,500); Gurkha Welfare Trust and The Samaritans – Chiltern branch (£500 each).

FINANCES *Year* 2009–10 *Income* £75,781 *Grants* £65,500 *Assets* £2,007,055

TRUSTEES J D H Cullingham; M J Glasser; J A Glasser.

OTHER INFORMATION Grants totalling £65,000 were awarded to 25 organisations.

HOW TO APPLY In writing to the correspondent. To keep administrative costs to a minimum the trust is unable to reply to unsuccessful applicants.

WHO TO APPLY TO B S Christer, Stafford Young Jones, The Old Rectory, 29 Martin Lane, London EC4R 0AU

■ The Glastonbury Trust Limited

CC NO 1078170   **ESTABLISHED** 1999

WHERE FUNDING CAN BE GIVEN UK.

WHO CAN BENEFIT Individuals, schools and other community groups in providing learning experiences that focus on emotional well-being and spiritual growth.

WHAT IS FUNDED Projects that address the needs of the wider community, particularly those that support family and community cohesion.

WHAT IS NOT FUNDED No funding for individual academic study or gap year projects.

RANGE OF GRANTS Up to about £10,000.

SAMPLE GRANTS In 2008 donations were made to the following: Isle of Avalon Foundation (£9,600); Avalon Library (£3,900); and Goddess Temple (£3,700). In addition to the above grants, £12,000 was given under the category 'secondary schools', £1,900 to 'primary schools' and a further £1,500 to 'other' causes.

There was unfortunately no examples of donations for 2010.

FINANCES *Year* 2010 *Income* £31,876 *Grants* £22,000 *Assets* £567,713

TRUSTEES GW Bishop; DMP Jones; S Martin; G Mills; S Strong; RA Weelen.

HOW TO APPLY Please note the following advice on the trust's website. 'The trust can consider applications for grants at any of its quarterly meetings. The grant process begins with potential applicants contacting the Executive Director, Chris Trwoga, by telephone or email to discuss the proposed project and to see whether it is likely to fall within the trust's funding criteria and is either charitably educational or charitably religious. Trustee meetings are held in March, June, September and December, so it is important that applicants contact the trust at least six weeks before the next trustees meeting in order to prepare the application for possible consideration at the meeting. The trust does not insist on match funding or partnership with other organisations in grant applications. If the trust agrees to fund a project, successful applicants will sign a contract agreeing to timescale and agreed outputs. Payment will generally be made in arrears on completion of specific targets, although advance payments can be made if the trust can be ensured that this money can be returned in the case of non-completion of the project.'

WHO TO APPLY TO Chris Trwoga, Executive Director, 2–4 High Street, Glastonbury BA6 9DU *Tel* 01458 831399 *email* contact@glastonburytrust.co.uk *Website* www.glastonburytrust.co.uk

---

■ Global Care

CC NO 1054008   **ESTABLISHED** 1996

WHERE FUNDING CAN BE GIVEN Overseas.

WHO CAN BENEFIT Children and families in one world's poorest countries through relief and development. People of many religions, cultures and social circumstances will be supported.

WHAT IS FUNDED Trustees favour children's charities already supported by them working in the poorest countries and the advancement of Christian education.

FINANCES *Year* 2009–10 *Income* £838,135 *Grants* £688,453 *Assets* £903,064

TRUSTEES Mark Curran, Chair; Norman Lochhead; Rachel Murrill; Paul Slater; Sue Matejtschuk; Margaret Patterson; Raymond Neal.

OTHER INFORMATION Trustees continue to support projects they seek themselves therefore applications for new grants will not be considered at this time.

HOW TO APPLY Applications are not recommended. Trustees seek out projects to support, as appropriate, and new grants cannot be considered.

WHO TO APPLY TO John White, Chief Executive Officer, Steve Murrill, Global Care, 2 Dugdale Road, Coventry CV6 1PB *Tel* 024 7660 1800 *Fax* 024 7660 1444 *email* info@globalcare.org.uk *Website* www.globalcare.org.uk

■ Global Charities (formerly GCap Charities)

cc no 1091657　　　　**established** 1978
where funding can be given Greater London; UK.
who can benefit Community organisations and registered charities.
what is funded Projects supporting disadvantaged children and young people; or those with an illness or disability.
what is not funded Each individual branch has specific exclusions, generally however the charities will not fund: individual children or families; retrospective funding; statutory funding – funding for schools or health projects that would otherwise be covered by designated statutory funding from the local authority; salaried posts; deficit funding or repayment of loans; medical research; purchase of a minibus; trips abroad; distribution to other organisations; religious activities; political groups; general structural changes to buildings; projects which are part of a larger charity and are not separately constituted; core funding for a national or regional charity.
type of grant Capital; core costs; one-off; project; running costs.
range of grants Mostly under £10,000. Larger grants are made very occasionally.
sample grants Previous beneficiaries included: Prince's Foundation for Children and the Arts (£100,000); Missing People (£61,000); and Impact Initiatives (£25,000); Sixth Sense Theatre (£7,500); Cambourne Youth Partnership (£5,000); Havens Hospices – Essex (£3,000); Bangladeshi Parents Association (£2,100); Howbury Friends (£1,800); and Centrepoint – Hammersmith and Fulham (£1,600).
finances *Year* 2010–11 *Income* £4,056,169 *Grants* £2,498,500 *Assets* £1,320,899
trustees Martin George, Chair; Nigel Atkinson; Moira Swinbank; Paul Soames; James Wilkins; Cary Wakefield.
how to apply The charity provides the following guidance on its website:
'If you have a general enquiry regarding any of our appeals funds please contact us (Tel: 020 7054 8391).We are always glad to answer questions from any organisation, charity or group on our grants process. Help a Capital Child in London has two annual small grants funding rounds. We attempt to fund as many eligible applications as possible, although this is always limited to the funds raised in the year. Details are given on www.capitalfm.com/charity, as well as how to apply for an application form. The form is reviewed and updated by our grants panel in conjunction with the overall Board to ensure the application process is as accessible as possible and to ensure applicants are guided though our funding criteria.'
who to apply to Sophie Marks, PA to MD, Charities and Communities, 30 Leicester Square, London WC2H 7LA *Tel* 020 7054 8391
email charities@thisisglobal.com *Website* www.thisisglobal.com/charities

■ Gloucestershire Community Foundation

cc no 900239　　　　**established** 1989
where funding can be given Gloucestershire.
who can benefit Charitable organisations and social enterprises.
what is funded Combating disadvantage in Gloucestershire.

type of grant Revenue and full project funding.
sample grants Dean Forest Hospice (£10,000); Woolaston Skatepark Group, The Door Youth Project, Moreton Rangers FC, Soudley Recreation Group and Village Hall, Stroud Valley Woodcraft Folk (£5,000 each); FOD Food Makers (£2,500).
finances *Year* 2010 *Income* £1,263,652 *Grants* £485,609 *Assets* £4,611,982
trustees S Preston; L Archer; G Bruce; I Brothwood; J Carr; A Chambers; G Cole; C Evans; R Graham; R Head; T Hitchins; H Lovatt; T Standing; B Thornton; C J Wakeman; J Winstanley.
publications Children in the Community – Making Things Better teachers' pack.
how to apply Information sheets, guidelines and an application forms are available from the correspondent. Staff are pleased to discuss any potential project applications. The foundation operates other funds and administers a number of grant making trusts. Please see its website for up-to-date details.
who to apply to The Grants Development Manager, British Energy, Barnett Way, Barnwood, Gloucester GL4 3RS *Tel* 01452 656386 *email* jane.jarman@british-energy.com or darien.parkes@british-energy.com *Website* www.gloucestershirecommunityfoundation.co.uk

■ The Gloucestershire Historic Churches Trust

cc no 1120266　　　　**established** 1980
where funding can be given Gloucestershire.
who can benefit Churches and chapels.
what is funded 'GHCT is a charity which raises funds to help places of Christian worship of all denominations with repairs and improvements to the fabric of the buildings and their contents, as well as to their surrounding churchyards. Our aim is to help keep the 500 plus churches and chapels in the county alive, not only as places of worship and active centres of community life, but also as buildings which make a huge impact on the landscape of Gloucestershire and help to draw visitors to the county.'
what is not funded No grants are made for routine maintenance.
type of grant One-off, but repeat applications will be considered.
range of grants £250–£10,000, typical grants between £1,000 and £4,000.
sample grants St John Baptist Church, Cirencester (£12,000); St Mary's Church, Hawkesbury, St Martin's Church, Horsley (£10,000 each); St Mary's Church, Dymock (£8,000); St Peter's Church, Rodmarton, Holy Trinity Church, Amberley (£4,000 each); Holy Trinity, Badgeworth, St Mary's Church, Berkeley, Christ Church, Bretton (£1,000 each).
finances *Year* 2010 *Income* £137,653 *Grants* £100,250 *Assets* £1,191,432
trustees Ian Phillips; Ben Woods; Philip Kendell; Helen Whitbread.
how to apply Application forms and full guidelines can be downloaded from the trust's website.
who to apply to B Woods, Chair of Grants Committee, 5 Fleet Place, London EC4M 7RD *Tel* 020 7203 8841 *email* grants@ghct.org.uk *Website* www.ghct.org.uk

■ Worshipful Company of Glovers of London Charity Fund

CC NO 269091   **ESTABLISHED** 1975

WHERE FUNDING CAN BE GIVEN UK with a preference for the City of London.

WHO CAN BENEFIT Glovers and glove-related projects; general charitable purposes.

WHAT IS FUNDED The trust makes grants mainly towards the provision of gloves, or to causes that are related to the City of London.

RANGE OF GRANTS Up to £5,000.

SAMPLE GRANTS British Glove Association – prizes/donations and Museum of London (£2,500 each); Crisis (£2,000) and Lord Major Treloar School (£1,500).

Grants made for bursaries were: City of London School for Girls (£4,600); St Paul's Cathedral School (£4,250); King Edwards School (£3,800); Guildhall School of Music and Drama (£2,100) and Church of St Margaret in Lothbury (£1,500).

FINANCES *Year* 2009–10 *Income* £66,068 *Grants* £36,962 *Assets* £696,066

TRUSTEES Worshipful Company of Glovers of London.

OTHER INFORMATION Grants were made to both organisations and individuals totalling £37,000.

HOW TO APPLY In writing to the correspondent.

WHO TO APPLY TO Mrs Monique Hood, Clerk, 73 Clapham Manor Street, London SW4 6ds *Tel* 020 7622 2167 *Fax* 020 7622 0316

■ GMC Trust

CC NO 288418   **ESTABLISHED** 1965

WHERE FUNDING CAN BE GIVEN UK, predominantly in the West Midlands.

WHO CAN BENEFIT Organisations benefiting children, young adults and older people.

WHAT IS FUNDED Primarily medical research and healthcare, also causes related to inner city deprivation. Income is substantially committed to a range of existing beneficiaries.

WHAT IS NOT FUNDED No grants to individuals, or to local or regional appeals outside the West Midlands. The trust does not respond to national appeals, except where there are established links.

TYPE OF GRANT One-off.

RANGE OF GRANTS Potentially up to £25,000, but most grants are between £100 and £5,000.

SAMPLE GRANTS Birmingham Settlement (£6,000); Sense (£5,100); Runnymede Trust (£5,000); King's College Cambridge and Birmingham Women's NHS Foundation Trust Charities (£2,500 each); Mind and King's Lynn Arts Centre (£2,000 each); Depaul Trust, Dodford Children's Holiday Farm, Practical Action, Save the Children and Princess Royal Trust for Carers (£1,000 each); Derek Johnson Leukaemia Fund, No Panic, Royal Birmingham Society of Artists, Shelter and Abbeyfield Society (£500 each); Schools Outreach (£250); and Christian Aid (£100).

FINANCES *Year* 2009–10 *Income* £154,537 *Grants* £60,550 *Assets* £2,426,169

TRUSTEES Sir A Cadbury; B E S Cadbury; M J Cadbury; Mrs C E Fowler-Wright.

HOW TO APPLY In writing to the correspondent. The trust largely supports projects which come to the attention of its trustees through their special interests and knowledge. General applications for grants are not encouraged.

WHO TO APPLY TO Rodney Pitts, Secretary, Flat 4, Fairways, 1240 Warwick Road, Knowle, Solihull, West Midlands B93 9LL *Tel* 01564 779971 *Fax* 01564 770499

■ The GMW Charitable Trust

CC NO 1135184   **ESTABLISHED** 2010

WHERE FUNDING CAN BE GIVEN National and overseas.

WHO CAN BENEFIT Charitable organisations.

WHAT IS FUNDED The relief of poverty, the advancement of religion, the relief and support of animals of all kinds and for general charitable purposes.

TRUSTEES George Watterson; Maureen Watterson.

OTHER INFORMATION The trust's objects also allow it to 'establish or secure' a community centre and manage it in furtherance of its objects. It should be noted that if the trust does choose to go down this route it is likely to have much less money available for grantmaking.

HOW TO APPLY In writing to the correspondent.

WHO TO APPLY TO George Watterson, Trustee, Kanzan, Legh Road, Knutsford, Cheshire WA16 8LS *email* georgewatterson1@ googlemail.com

■ The GNC Trust

CC NO 211533   **ESTABLISHED** 1960

WHERE FUNDING CAN BE GIVEN UK, with preferences for Birmingham and Cornwall.

WHO CAN BENEFIT Registered charities.

WHAT IS FUNDED To support those charities which the trustees have special interest in, knowledge of or association with.

WHAT IS NOT FUNDED No grants are made to national appeals, London-based charities or to individuals.

RANGE OF GRANTS £20–£10,000; mostly for £1,000 or less.

SAMPLE GRANTS Lymington Museum Trust (£60,000); National Youth Ballet (£25,000); St John of Jerusalem Eye Hospital (£15,000); Downing College (£5,000) Friends of Bournville Cantlor (£3,000); National Trust (£2,300) and Milton Abbey School and St Francis Church, Bournville (£2,000 each).

FINANCES *Year* 2010 *Income* £43,050 *Grants* £143,151 *Assets* £1,526,747

TRUSTEES G T E Cadbury; R J Cadbury; Mrs P J Richmond-Watson; Mrs I J Williamson.

OTHER INFORMATION All grants were made to institutions.

HOW TO APPLY In writing to the correspondent at any time. There are no application forms and applications are not acknowledged.

WHO TO APPLY TO Mrs P M Spragg, c/o P S Accounting, 41 Sycamore Drive, Hollywood, Birmingham B47 5QX *Tel* 0121 265 5000

■ The Meir Golda Trust

CC NO 1041256   **ESTABLISHED** 1994

WHERE FUNDING CAN BE GIVEN UK.

WHO CAN BENEFIT Particular favour is given to Jewish charities, but charities benefiting followers of all faiths are considered. People with illnesses of any kind are a priority.

WHAT IS FUNDED General charitable purposes; the arts; conservation; animal facilities and services; synagogues and Jewish bodies.

FINANCES *Year* 2009–10 *Income* £13,340 *Grants* £1,000

TRUSTEES Joseph Gutstein.

HOW TO APPLY In writing to the correspondent.

WHO TO APPLY TO Joseph Gutstein, 17 Highfield Road, London NW11 9LS *Tel* 020 8731 9393

■ The Sydney and Phyllis Goldberg Memorial Charitable Trust

cc no 291835   ESTABLISHED 1985
WHERE FUNDING CAN BE GIVEN UK.
WHO CAN BENEFIT Organisations benefiting, research workers, at risk groups, and people who are disabled, disadvantaged by poverty or socially isolated.
WHAT IS FUNDED Medical research, welfare and disability.
TYPE OF GRANT One-off, some recurrent.
RANGE OF GRANTS Usually up to £15,000.
SAMPLE GRANTS Previously: £13,500 each to Children of St Mary's Intensive Care Department of Child Health, the British Stammering Association, the Dystonia Society, Children with Special Needs Foundation, Life Centre and the Prostate Cancer Charity; and £7,500 to the Isaac Goldberg Charity Trust.
FINANCES Year 2009–10 Income £61,325 Grants £0 Assets £3,163,611
TRUSTEES H G Vowles; M J Church; C J Pexton.
OTHER INFORMATION The 2009–10 trustee report states: 'However, no distributions were made during the current year', despite there being an expenditure of £10,000 on administration.
HOW TO APPLY In writing to the correspondent. Telephone requests are not appreciated. Applicants are advised to apply towards the end of the calendar year.
WHO TO APPLY TO M J Church, Trustee, Coulthards Mackenzie, 17 Park Street, Camberley, Surrey GU15 3PQ Tel 01276 65470

■ The Golden Bottle Trust

cc no 327026   ESTABLISHED 1985
WHERE FUNDING CAN BE GIVEN Worldwide.
WHO CAN BENEFIT Registered charities.
WHAT IS FUNDED General charitable purposes with a preference for charities supporting the environment, health, education, religion, the arts and developing countries.
WHAT IS NOT FUNDED No grants for individuals or organisations that are not registered charities.
TYPE OF GRANT 'One-off' and recurring.
RANGE OF GRANTS Up to £10,000 with larger grants for charities that the Hoare family have a personal relationship with.
SAMPLE GRANTS The Bulldog Trust and The Henry C Hoare Charitable Trust (£40,000) and West Country Rivers Trust (£7,000); St Dunstan-in-the-West (£50,000); Hand and Hand International (£50,000); Exeter Cathedral; Find Your Feet; Jesus College Cambridge; Temple Music Foundation; Trinity Hospice; Warrior Programme (£10,000 each); Opportunity International (£7,000).
FINANCES Year 2008–09 Income £558,037 Grants £623,149 Assets £7,553,588
TRUSTEES Messrs Hoare Trustees (H C Hoare; D J Hoare; R Q Hoare; A S Hoare; V E Hoare; S M Hoare; A S Hopewell.).
OTHER INFORMATION The most recent accounts were not available to view at the Charity Commission.
HOW TO APPLY In writing to the correspondent. Applications are considered from bank staff and external registered charities.
WHO TO APPLY TO Miss J Moore, Messrs Hoare Trustees, 37 Fleet Street, London EC4P 4DQ Tel 020 7353 4522 Fax 020 7353 4521 email enquiries@hoaresbank.co.uk

■ Golden Charitable Trust

cc no 263916   ESTABLISHED 1972
WHERE FUNDING CAN BE GIVEN UK with a preference for West Sussex.
WHO CAN BENEFIT Registered charities.
WHAT IS FUNDED Literature, English Literature, the conservation of printed books and manuscripts, and libraries and museums, church restoration and medical research.
WHAT IS NOT FUNDED No grants to individuals.
TYPE OF GRANT Endowment, sometimes recurring.
RANGE OF GRANTS Up to £20,000, usually between £100–£2,500.
SAMPLE GRANTS Previous beneficiaries include: Westminster Synagogue, Petworth Cottage Nursing Home, Music Mind Spirit Trust, Wordsworth Trust, Langdon Foundation, Chichester Cathedral Trust, Royal School of Needlework, Inter-Cultural Youth Exchange, Reform Foundation Trust, Macmillan Cancer Trust, Dermatitis and Allied Diseases Research Trust, Helen and Douglas House and Cancer Research UK.
FINANCES Year 2009–10 Income £19,550 Grants £45,000
TRUSTEES Sara Solnick; Jeremy Solnick.
OTHER INFORMATION Due to the trust's low income in 2009–10, only basic financial information was available from the Charity Commission.
HOW TO APPLY In writing to the correspondent.
WHO TO APPLY TO Lewis Golden, Secretary to the Trustees, Little Leith Gate, Angel Street, Petworth, West Sussex GU28 0BG Tel 01798 342434

■ The Jack Goldhill Charitable Trust

cc no 267018   ESTABLISHED 1974
WHERE FUNDING CAN BE GIVEN UK.
WHO CAN BENEFIT Registered charities benefiting those in need.
WHAT IS FUNDED Human need causes and visual arts.
WHAT IS NOT FUNDED No support for individuals or new applications.
SAMPLE GRANTS Previous beneficiaries have included CST, City and Guilds of London School of Art, Jack Goldhill Award Fund, JNF Charitable Trust, Jewish Care, Joint Jewish Charitable Trust, Nightingale House, Royal Academy of Arts, Royal London Hospital, Tate Gallery, Tricycle Theatre Co., West London Synagogue and Atlantic College.
FINANCES Year 2009–10 Income £84,268 Grants £25,247 Assets £581,752
TRUSTEES G Goldhill; J A Goldhill; M L Goldhill.
OTHER INFORMATION A list of grants has not been included with the accounts filed at the Christy Commission in recent years.
HOW TO APPLY The trustees have a restricted list of charities to whom they are committed and no unsolicited applications can be considered.
WHO TO APPLY TO Jack Goldhill, Trustee, 85 Kensington Heights, Campden Hill Road, London W8 7BD Tel 020 7727 4326

■ The Goldmark Trust

cc no 1072901   ESTABLISHED 1998
WHERE FUNDING CAN BE GIVEN UK.
WHO CAN BENEFIT Registered charities.
WHAT IS FUNDED General charitable purposes.
RANGE OF GRANTS Typically up to £5,000.

SAMPLE GRANTS Children's Hospices UK and NCYPE (£2,500 each); Foundation for Conductive Education (£2,000); Autism West Midlands (£1,500); Birmingham Royal Ballet, Discover Children's Centre and Tourettes Action (£1,000 each).

FINANCES *Year* 2009–10 *Income* £109,882 *Grants* £55,500 *Assets* £2,459,314

TRUSTEES A O M Goldsmith; P L Luckett; M J Snell.

HOW TO APPLY In writing to the correspondent. The trustees meet at least twice a year.

WHO TO APPLY TO Graham Cole, 30 St Giles, Oxford OX1 3LE

■ The Goldsmiths' Arts Trust Fund

CC NO 313329   ESTABLISHED 1965

WHERE FUNDING CAN BE GIVEN UK.

WHO CAN BENEFIT Registered charities.

WHAT IS FUNDED The arts by the encouragement of the art of design and good craftsmanship.

RANGE OF GRANTS £1,000–£36,000.

SAMPLE GRANTS Goldsmiths' Craft and Design Council (£36,000); University College for the Creative Arts (£15,000); Royal College of Art (£7,000) and University of Central England (£1,000). Bursaries and grants to colleges/ students totalled £38,000.

FINANCES *Year* 2009–10 *Income* £10,044,893 *Grants* £96,694 *Assets* £84,993

TRUSTEES Court of Assistants of the Goldsmiths' Company; Susan Bailey.

HOW TO APPLY In writing to the correspondent.

WHO TO APPLY TO The Clerk, The Goldsmiths' Company, Goldsmiths' Hall, Foster Lane, London EC2V 6BN *Tel* 020 7606 7010 *Fax* 020 7606 1511 *email* the.clerk@ thegoldsmiths.co.uk *Website* www. thegoldsmiths.co.uk

■ The Goldsmiths' Company Charity

CC NO 1088699   ESTABLISHED 1961

WHERE FUNDING CAN BE GIVEN UK, with a special interest in London charities.

WHO CAN BENEFIT Registered charities, schools, individuals connected with the trade of goldsmithing, silversmithing and jewellery, and Londoners in need. Grants are made to London-based or national charities, but not to local provincial charities. Where charities are members, branches or affiliates of an association, appeals are accepted from the governing body or head office of that association only. In the case of church restoration, block grants are made to the Historic Churches Preservation Trust and therefore appeals from individual churches will not normally be considered.

WHAT IS FUNDED Support of the goldsmiths' craft, education, and general charitable purposes (including general welfare, medical welfare, youth, heritage, church, and arts.).

WHAT IS NOT FUNDED Applications are not normally considered on behalf of medical research; animal welfare; memorials to individuals; overseas projects; individual housing associations; endowment schemes; charities with a turnover of more than £10 million.

TYPE OF GRANT Buildings, capital, salaries, core, project, start-up and running costs. Funding is occasionally 3 year, but usually one-off.

RANGE OF GRANTS £500 upwards.

SAMPLE GRANTS University of Cambridge – Department of Material Science and Metallurgy (£173,000); National Churches Trust (£50,000); London Borough of Lambeth – for the support of individuals (£25,000); Refugee Council and School Home Support (£15,000 each); Children's Hospices UK (£10,000); Royal Air Force Disabled Holiday Trust (£6,000); Changing Faces, The Young Vic and Country Holidays for Inner City Kids (£5,000 each); and New Horizon Youth Centre (£3,000).

FINANCES *Year* 2009–10 *Income* £3,232,203 *Grants* £3,583,974 *Assets* £89,293,851

TRUSTEES Goldsmith's Company Trustee: Tim Schroder; Scott Shepherd; Bruno Schroder; Sir John Rose; David Peake; Lord Stuart Sutherland; Bryan Toye; Henry Wyndham; Sir Alfred Wiggin; Michael Wainwright; Richard Vanderpump; Richard Helly; William Parente; Richard Came; Dame Lynne Brindley; The Hon. Mark Bridges; Richard Agutter; Lord Roger Cunliffe; Martin Drury; George MacDonald; Prof. Richard Himsworth; Rupert Hambro; Hector Miller; Arthur Galsworthy.

HOW TO APPLY Applications should be made by letter, no more than two sides of A4 in length, highlighting the case for the company to give its support. The letter should be accompanied by the completed application form, which can be downloaded from the company's website. The form may be retyped, but should follow the same format and length (three sides of A4). All questions should be answered. Do not cut and paste information on the form. Legible handwritten applications are acceptable. The charity's most recent annual report and audited accounts (or financial report required by the Charities Act) should also be included. Applications are considered monthly, except in August and September, and there is usually a three to four month delay between receipt of an appeal and a decision being made. Applications from any organisation, whether successful or not, are not normally considered more frequently than every three years. Any enquiries should be addressed to the correspondent.

WHO TO APPLY TO Miss H Erskine, Charity Administrator, Goldsmiths' Hall, Foster Lane, London EC2V 6BN *Tel* 020 7606 7010 *Fax* 020 7606 1511 *email* charity@ thegoldsmiths.co.uk *Website* www. thegoldsmiths.co.uk/charities

■ The Golsoncott Foundation

CC NO 1070885   ESTABLISHED 1998

WHERE FUNDING CAN BE GIVEN UK.

WHO CAN BENEFIT Arts organisations.

WHAT IS FUNDED The trust states its objects as follows: 'to promote, maintain, improve and advance the education of the public in the arts generally and in particular the fine arts and music. The fostering of the practice and appreciation of the arts, especially amongst young people and new audiences, is a further specific objective.'

WHAT IS NOT FUNDED No grants to individuals.

TYPE OF GRANT One-off and some recurring grants.

RANGE OF GRANTS £200–£5,000.

SAMPLE GRANTS Marian Consort (£4,000); Lake Land Arts (£2,500); New London's Children's Choir and Little Angel Theatre (£2,000 each); Gainsborough House and Shakespeare at the Tobacco Factory (£1,000 each); Hexham Abbey (£750); Magdalen Farm Strings (£500); Wildfire Folk (£200); and Purbeck Strings (£100).

Think carefully about every application. Is it justified?

569

FINANCES *Year* 2009–10 *Income* £64,177
Grants £50,250 *Assets* £1,663,069

TRUSTEES Penelope Lively, Chair; Josephine Lively; Stephen Wick; Dr Harriet Harvey Wood.

HOW TO APPLY The trustees meet quarterly to consider applications, in February, May, August and November. Applications should be sent to the correspondent by the end of the month preceding the month of the trustees meeting. They should include the following: (1) A clear and concise statement of the project, whether the award sought will be for the whole project or a component part. Is the applicant organisation of charitable status? (2) Evidence that there is a clear benefit to the public, i.e. does the project conform with the declared object of the trust. (3) The amount requested should be specified, or a band indicated. Is this the only source of funding being sought? All other sources of funding should be indicated, including those that have refused funding. (4) If the grant requested is part of the match-funding required by the Heritage Lottery Foundation (HLF) following an award, state the amount of that award and the percentage of match-funding required by the HLF and the completion date. (5) Wherever possible an annual report and accounts should accompany the application, as may other supporting information deemed relevant. Second or further applications will not be considered until a minimum of 12 months has elapsed since determination of the previous application, whether successful or not.

WHO TO APPLY TO Hal Bishop, Administrator, 53 St Leonard's Rd, Exeter EX2 4LS *Tel* 01392 252855 *email* golsoncott@btinternet.com *Website* www.golsoncott.org.uk

■ Golubovich Foundation

CC NO 1113965   **ESTABLISHED** 2006

WHERE FUNDING CAN BE GIVEN UK.

WHO CAN BENEFIT UK centres of excellence.

WHAT IS FUNDED The foundation seeks to foster relationships between Russia and the UK in the area of performing arts. This is done mainly through encouraging established UK arts centres to identify and develop the talents of young Russian nationals.

RANGE OF GRANTS Up to £75,000.

SAMPLE GRANTS Trinity College of Music London (£75,000); University of the Arts London (£65,000).

FINANCES *Year* 2009–10 *Income* £171,000 *Grants* £140,000 *Assets* £7,765

TRUSTEES Alexei Golubovich; Olga Mirimskaya; Andrey Lisyanski; Arkadiy Golubovich.

OTHER INFORMATION During the year £31,000 was spent on governance costs.

HOW TO APPLY In writing to the correspondent.

WHO TO APPLY TO Tim Lewin, c/o MVL Business Services, 15a High Street, Battle, East Sussex TN33 0AE *Tel* 01424 830 723 *email* tim. lewin@btinternet.com

■ The Good Neighbours Trust

CC NO 201794   **ESTABLISHED** 1960

WHERE FUNDING CAN BE GIVEN UK, with preference for Bristol, Somerset and Gloucestershire.

WHO CAN BENEFIT Registered charities whose principal activity is to assist people with physical or mental disabilities.

WHAT IS FUNDED Principally in respect of specific projects on behalf of people who are mentally or physically disabled.

WHAT IS NOT FUNDED Support is not given for overseas projects; general community projects*; individuals; general education projects*; religious and ethnic projects*; projects for unemployment and related training schemes*; projects on behalf of offenders and ex-offenders; projects concerned with the abuse of drugs and/or alcohol; wildlife and conservation schemes*; and general restoration and preservation of buildings, purely for historical and/or architectural. (*If these projects are mainly or wholly for the benefit of people who have disabilities then they may be considered.) Ongoing support is not given, and grants are not usually given for running costs, salaries, research and items requiring major funding. Loans are not given.

TYPE OF GRANT One-off for specific projects. Ongoing, research, core funding and major funding appeals are not supported.

RANGE OF GRANTS Usually between £250–£2,500.

SAMPLE GRANTS Children's Hospice South West (£10,000); Avon Riding Centre For the Disabled and St Peter's Hospice (£1,000 each); Keynsham and District Mencap Society and Whizz-Kidz – London (£500 each); and Theodora Children's Trust and Listening Books (£250 each).

FINANCES *Year* 2010 *Income* £83,178 *Grants* £76,750 *Assets* £2,569,956

TRUSTEES G V Arter, Chair; J C Gurney; P S Broderick; J L Hudd.

HOW TO APPLY The trust does not have an official application form. Appeals should be made in writing to the secretary. Telephone calls are not welcome. The trust asks that the following is carefully considered before submitting an application – appeals must: be from registered charities; include a copy of the latest audited accounts available (for newly registered charities a copy of provisional accounts showing estimated income and expenditure for the current financial year); show that the project is 'both feasible and viable' and, if relevant, give the starting date of the project and the anticipated date of completion; include the estimated cost of the project, together with the appeal's target-figure and details of what funds have already been raised and any fundraising schemes for the project. The trustees state that 'where applicable, due consideration will be given to evidence of voluntary and self-help (both in practical and fundraising terms) and to the number of people expected to benefit from the project'. They also comment that their decision is final and 'no reason for a decision, whether favourable or otherwise, need be given' and that 'the award and acceptance of a grant will not involve the trustees in any other commitment'. Appeals are dealt with on an ongoing basis, but the trustees meet formally four times per year usually in March, June, September and December.

WHO TO APPLY TO P S Broderick, Secretary, 16 Westway, Nailsea, Bristol BS48 2NA *Tel* 01275 851051 *email* gntbristol@aol.com

■ Nicholas and Judith Goodison's Charitable Settlement

CC NO 1004124   **ESTABLISHED** 1991

WHERE FUNDING CAN BE GIVEN UK.

WHO CAN BENEFIT Registered charities.

WHAT IS FUNDED Arts and arts education; mostly commitments to previously supported charities. Other causes may be considered.

WHAT IS NOT FUNDED No grants to individuals.
TYPE OF GRANT Recurrent capital grants. One-off grants may be considered.
RANGE OF GRANTS £200–£20,000, although most grants are for £2,000 or less.
SAMPLE GRANTS Victoria and Albert Museum – Ceramic Galleries and Courtauld Institute of Art (£20,000 each); Fitzwilliam (£7,100); Academy of Ancient Music (£5,000); Handel House (£4,000); Tate Gallery (£3,500); English National Opera (£2,500); British Museum (£2,000); Burlington Magazine Travel Scholarship (£1,200); MEMO and Attingham Trust (£1,000 each); Wigmore Hall (£500); World Monuments Fund (£350); and Venice in Peril (£200).
FINANCES *Year* 2009–10 *Income* £47,953 *Grants* £69,739 *Assets* £1,273,329
TRUSTEES Nicholas Goodison; Judith Goodison; Katharine Goodison.
HOW TO APPLY The trust states that it cannot respond to unsolicited applications.
WHO TO APPLY TO Nicholas Goodison, Trustee, PO Box 2512, London W1A 5ZP

■ The Everard and Mina Goodman Charitable Foundation

CC NO 220474   **ESTABLISHED** 1962
WHERE FUNDING CAN BE GIVEN UK and Israel.
WHO CAN BENEFIT Registered charities only.
WHAT IS FUNDED As well as supporting causes related to the Jewish faith, this trust also makes grants for: the relief of poverty; the advancement of education; children and youth; medicine and health; and rehabilitation and training.
WHAT IS NOT FUNDED No grants to individuals.
SAMPLE GRANTS Previous beneficiaries include: British Friends of Bar-Ilan University – Life Sciences Faculty, Variety Club – Sunshine Coach Appeal, British Friends of Laniado Hospital, Child Resettlement Fund, Institute for Jewish Policy Research, Western Marble Arch Synagogue, Smile Train UK, Jewish Women's Aid, National Autistic Society and High Blood Pressure Foundation.
FINANCES *Year* 2009–10 *Income* £14,657 *Grants* £35,000
TRUSTEES Dr Everard Goodman; Mina Goodman; Michael Goodman; Suzanne Goodman; David Goodman.
OTHER INFORMATION In 2006 the foundation's income increased significantly due to a substantial donation from the settlor, Everard Goodman, former chief executive of property company Tops Estates. Although, a substantial part of this went to the Faculty of Life Sciences at Bar-Ilan University in Israel (£2 million), the foundation's increase in income allowed the level of general grantmaking to rise significantly. Although income and expenditure have been reduced somewhat in recent years.
HOW TO APPLY In writing to the correspondent.
WHO TO APPLY TO Dr Everard Goodman, Trustee, Flat 5, 5 Bryanston Court, London W1H 7HA *Tel* 020 7355 3333

■ The Goodman Foundation

CC NO 1097231   **ESTABLISHED** 2003
WHERE FUNDING CAN BE GIVEN UK, excluding Scotland.
WHO CAN BENEFIT Registered charities.

WHAT IS FUNDED General, social welfare, older people, health and disability.
FINANCES *Year* 2009–10 *Income* £377,294 *Grants* £143,407 *Assets* £12,326,111
TRUSTEES L J Goodman; C Goodman; R M Cracknell; L Tidd.
OTHER INFORMATION In 2009–10 grants were given in the following categories: Third world and disasters (£60,000); Poor, elderly, sick and disabled (£53,000); Other (£18,000); Children's charities (£12,000).
HOW TO APPLY In writing to the correspondent.
WHO TO APPLY TO The Trustees, c/o APB, Unit 6290, Bishops Court, Solihull Parkway, Birmingham Business Park, Birmingham B37 7YB

■ Mike Gooley Trailfinders Charity

CC NO 1048993   **ESTABLISHED** 1995
WHERE FUNDING CAN BE GIVEN UK.
WHO CAN BENEFIT Charitable organisations.
WHAT IS FUNDED Medical research and general charitable purposes.
WHAT IS NOT FUNDED Grants are not made to overseas charities or to individuals.
RANGE OF GRANTS £100–£100,000.
SAMPLE GRANTS Previous beneficiaries have included: Alzheimer's Society (£400,000); Prostate Cancer Charity (£100,000); and the Second World War Experience Centre (£40,000).
FINANCES *Year* 2009–10 *Income* £104,405 *Grants* £350,733 *Assets* £9,424,844
TRUSTEES Mark Bannister; Michael D W Gooley; Bernadette M Gooley; Tristan P Gooley; Fiona Gooley; Louise Breton.
OTHER INFORMATION A list of grants was not included in the charity's recent accounts.
HOW TO APPLY In writing to the correspondent.
WHO TO APPLY TO Louise Breton, Trustee, Trailfinders Ltd, 9 Abingdon Road, London W8 6AH *Tel* 020 7938 3143 *Fax* 020 7937 6059

■ Leonard Gordon Charitable Trust

CC NO 1075185   **ESTABLISHED** 1999
WHERE FUNDING CAN BE GIVEN England and Wales.
WHO CAN BENEFIT Jewish organisations.
WHAT IS FUNDED Religion, education and welfare.
FINANCES *Year* 2009–10 *Income* £10,708 *Grants* £30,000
TRUSTEES Leonard Gordon, Chair; Michael Gordon; Jan Fidler.
HOW TO APPLY In writing to the correspondent.
WHO TO APPLY TO Leonard Gordon, Chair, 17 Park Street, Salford M7 4NJ *Tel* 0161 792 3421

■ The Gosling Foundation Limited

CC NO 326840   **ESTABLISHED** 1962
WHERE FUNDING CAN BE GIVEN Worldwide. In practice UK.
WHO CAN BENEFIT Registered charities.
WHAT IS FUNDED The relief of poverty, suffering and distress; provision of facilities for recreation and other leisure-time occupation (in the interests of social welfare); naval and service charities; advancement of education; furtherance of other charitable purposes.
RANGE OF GRANTS Mainly £100–£5,000, but up to £200,000.
SAMPLE GRANTS Marine Society and Sea Cadets (£200,000); Duke of Edinburgh's Award (£103,000 in 2 grants); SSAFA Forces Help (£100,500); Great Steward of Scotland's

Dumfries House Trust (£75,000); National Museum of the Royal Navy (£70,000); Britannia Association and St Martin-in-the-Fields (£50,000 each); Tennis Foundation (£42,000 in 3 grants); Annual National Service for Seafarers and the Foundation for Liver Research (£25,000 each); Queen Elizabeth Castle of Mey Trust (£20,000); Entertainment Artistes Benevolent Fund (£12,000 in 2 grants); Special Olympics Leicestershire (£10,000); Action for ME and the Nordoff-Robbins Music Therapy Centre (£7,000 each); Bud Flanagan Leukaemia Fund (£6,000); Hampshire & Wight Trust for Maritime Archaeology, Bobarth Children's Therapy Centre Wales and Hearing Dogs for Deaf People (£5,000 each); Cherubim Music Trust (£3,000); British Association for Adoption & Fostering (£2,000 each); and Game and Wildlife Conservation Trust (£1,000).

FINANCES *Year* 2009–10 *Income* £4,899,749 *Grants* £1,905,200 *Assets* £91,243,002

TRUSTEES Sir Donald Gosling; Ronald F Hobson; Adam P Gosling.

HOW TO APPLY In writing to the correspondent. The grant making policies of the foundation are 'regularly reviewed' and currently are: applications should fall within the objects of the foundation; there is no minimum limit for any grant; all grants will be approved unanimously; the charity will only make grants to individuals in exceptional circumstances.

WHO TO APPLY Miss Anne Yusof, Secretary, 21 Bryanston Street, Marble Arch, London W1H 7PR *Tel* 020 7495 5599

■ The Gough Charitable Trust

CC NO 262355   **ESTABLISHED** 1970

WHERE FUNDING CAN BE GIVEN UK, with a possible preference for Scotland.

WHO CAN BENEFIT Registered charities only, usually working in the areas outlined below, benefiting children, young adults and the Church of England.

WHAT IS FUNDED Youth projects; Episcopal or Church of England projects; preservation of the countryside.

WHAT IS NOT FUNDED No support for non-registered charities and individuals including students.

TYPE OF GRANT Usually one-off but some ongoing.

SAMPLE GRANTS Previously: Irish Guards Lieutenant Colonels Fund, Prince of Wales Lodge No 259 Benevolent Fund, The Lifeboat Service Memorial Book Trust, National Army Development Trust, Household Brigade Benevolent Fund, Lloyds Charities Fund, Lloyds Benevolent Fund, Crown and Manor Boys' Club and Trinity Hospice. No indication was given on the size of these donations.

FINANCES *Year* 2009–10 *Income* £24,962 *Grants* £20,000

TRUSTEES Lloyds Bank plc.

HOW TO APPLY In writing to the correspondent at any time. No acknowledgements are sent. Applications are considered quarterly.

WHO TO APPLY To The Trust Manager, Lloyds TSB Private Banking Ltd, UK Trust Centre, 22–26 Ock Street, Abingdon OX14 5SW *Tel* 01235 232712

■ The Gould Charitable Trust

CC NO 1035453   **ESTABLISHED** 1993

WHERE FUNDING CAN BE GIVEN UK.

WHO CAN BENEFIT Registered charities only.

WHAT IS FUNDED General charitable purposes, with a preference for charities working in the field of self-help.

WHAT IS NOT FUNDED No grants to individuals.

RANGE OF GRANTS Usually up to £5,000.

SAMPLE GRANTS One to One (£5,000); Alzheimer's Research Trust, NSPCC and FCED Foundation Philippines (£2,000 each); Child Hope (£600); Médecins Sans Frontières, Friends of Hebrew University, and New Israel Fund (£500 each); SOS Children and Jewish World Relief (£300 each); and Project Trust and Hackney Quest (£200 each).

FINANCES *Year* 2009–10 *Income* £22,725 *Grants* £50,000

TRUSTEES Mrs J B Gould; L J Gould; M S Gould; S Gould; S H Gould.

HOW TO APPLY In writing to the correspondent, although the trust states: 'We never give donations to unsolicited requests on principle.'

WHO TO APPLY To S Gould, Trustee, Cervantes, Pinner Hill, Pinner, Middlesex HA5 3XU

■ The Hemraj Goyal Foundation

CC NO 1136483   **ESTABLISHED** 2010

WHERE FUNDING CAN BE GIVEN UK and overseas.

WHO CAN BENEFIT Grants to organisations; children and young people; women; people with disabilities.

WHAT IS FUNDED General charitable purposes; social welfare, women's rights, education and disability.

TRUSTEES Avnish Goyal; Mala Ararwal; Vidya Goyal.

OTHER INFORMATION The foundation is a family run charity led by the young people in the family, supported by the older family members. Avnish Goyal is also a trustee of The Care Professionals Benevolent Fund (Charity Commission no. 1132286), established in October 2009 and registered with the Commission in the same month.

HOW TO APPLY In writing to the correspondent.

WHO TO APPLY To Avnish Goyal, Trustee, 2 Kingfisher House, Woodbrook Crescent, Radford Way, Billericay, Essex CM12 0EQ *email* info@hgf.org.uk

■ The Grace Charitable Trust

CC NO 292984   **ESTABLISHED** 1985

WHERE FUNDING CAN BE GIVEN UK.

WHO CAN BENEFIT Registered charities, including Christian organisations.

WHAT IS FUNDED General charitable purposes, Christian, education, medical and social welfare.

RANGE OF GRANTS £1,000–£10,000.

FINANCES *Year* 2009–10 *Income* £849,562 *Grants* £1,029,165 *Assets* £2,402,035

TRUSTEES Mrs G J R Payne; E Payne; Mrs G M Snaith; R B M Quayle.

OTHER INFORMATION A further £5,000 was given in grants to individuals.

HOW TO APPLY The trust states: 'Grants are made only to charities known to the settlors and unsolicited applications are, therefore, not considered.'

WHO TO APPLY To Mrs G J R Payne, Trustee, Swinford House, Nortons Lane, Great Barrow, Chester CH3 7JZ *Tel* 01928 740773

■ A B Grace Trust

CC NO 504332 **ESTABLISHED** 1975
WHERE FUNDING CAN BE Garstang and Preston.
WHO CAN BENEFIT Charitable organisations.
WHAT IS FUNDED General charitable purposes.
TYPE OF GRANT Recurrent.
SAMPLE GRANTS St Mary's & St Michael's Church,
Bonds; St Helen's Church, Churchtown; United
Reformed Church, Garstang; Guide Dogs for the
Blind; RSPCA (£4,100 each); St Peter's Parish
Church, Scorton; RNLI; RSPB; Christ Church,
Over Wyresdale (£5,125 each).
FINANCES *Year* 2009–10 *Income* £41,033
Grants £41,000 *Assets* £970,848
TRUSTEES Anthony H Blunt; Thomas I Balmain;
Valerie M Wilson.
HOW TO APPLY 'The charity's trust deed sets out very
specifically who are beneficiaries are to be and
consequently we are unable to consider any
grant applications.'
WHO TO APPLY TO Antony Blunt, Trustee,
31 Yewlands Drive, Garstang, Preston PR3 1JP

■ The Graff Foundation

CC NO 1012859 **ESTABLISHED** 1991
WHERE FUNDING CAN BE GIVEN UK and worldwide.
WHO CAN BENEFIT Charitable organisations.
WHAT IS FUNDED General charitable purposes.
TYPE OF GRANT One-off and recurrent.
RANGE OF GRANTS £500–£314,000.
SAMPLE GRANTS The museum of Contemporary art
(£148,000); The Tel Aviv Museum of Art
(£314,000); Tate Foundation (£5,000); Guys
and St. Thomas charity (£1,500).
FINANCES *Year* 2010 *Income* £680,654
Grants £469,276 *Assets* £3,844,664
TRUSTEES Laurence Graff; Francois Graff; Anthony
Kerman.
HOW TO APPLY In writing to the correspondent.
WHO TO APPLY TO Anthony Kerman, 28 Albemarle
Street, London WC2N 6RH *Tel* 020 7539 7272

■ A and S Graham Charitable Trust

CC NO 288220 **ESTABLISHED** 1983
WHERE FUNDING CAN BE GIVEN UK.
WHAT IS FUNDED Education, social welfare, the arts,
children and young people.
FINANCES *Year* 2009–10 *Income* £35,966
Grants £36,891 *Assets* £6,696
TRUSTEES Andrew Graham; Sandra Graham;
Natasha Graham; Emma Graham; Laura
Graham.
OTHER INFORMATION Grants were made to both
organisations and individuals totalling £37,000.
HOW TO APPLY In writing to the correspondent.
WHO TO APPLY TO Keith Hardy, Smith Pearman, Hurst
House, Ripley, Surrey GU23 6AY *Tel* 01483
225457 *Fax* 01483 211023 *email* keithhardy@
smithpearman.com

■ The Grahame Charitable Foundation Limited

CC NO 1102332 **ESTABLISHED** 1969
WHERE FUNDING CAN BE GIVEN UK and overseas.
WHO CAN BENEFIT Organisations benefiting: children,
young adults, older people and Jewish people.
WHAT IS FUNDED The advancement of the Jewish
religion; health facilities and buildings, medical
studies and research; special schools; cultural
and religious teaching; and community services.
WHAT IS NOT FUNDED No grants to individuals.

TYPE OF GRANT Capital, core costs, interest-free
loans, one-off, recurring costs and start-up
costs. Funding for up to two years may be
considered.
RANGE OF GRANTS £100–£60,000.
SAMPLE GRANTS British Friends of the Shaare Zedek
Medical Centre (£60,000); and United Jewish
Israel Appeal (£38,000).
FINANCES *Year* 2009 *Income* £82,504
Grants £231,265 *Assets* £1,225,862
TRUSTEES A Grahame; J M Greenwood.
HOW TO APPLY The trustees allocate funds on a long-
term basis and therefore have none available
for other applicants.
WHO TO APPLY TO Mrs G Grahame, Secretary,
5 Spencer Walk, Hampstead High Street,
London NW3 1QZ *Tel* 020 7794 5281

■ Grampian Police Diced Cap Charitable Fund

SC NO SC017901 **ESTABLISHED** 1991
WHERE FUNDING CAN BE GIVEN Within the Grampian
police force area only.
WHO CAN BENEFIT Charitable organisations.
WHAT IS FUNDED General charitable purposes.
WHAT IS NOT FUNDED National charities and those
outside the beneficial area cannot be
supported.
FINANCES *Year* 2009–10 *Income* £116,303
Grants £35,000
TRUSTEES Susan Barclay; Betty Bates; Alan Findlay;
David Mclean; Neil McHattie; Colin Menzies;
Davie Threadgold.
HOW TO APPLY In writing to the correspondent.
WHO TO APPLY TO Robbie Ross, The Secretary,
Queen Street, Aberdeen AB10 1ZA
Website www.dicedcap.org

■ The Granada Foundation

CC NO 241693 **ESTABLISHED** 1965
WHERE FUNDING CAN BE GIVEN North west England.
WHO CAN BENEFIT Organisations.
WHAT IS FUNDED Encouragement and promotion of
the study, practice and appreciation of the fine
arts and the methods and means of their
dissemination; encouragement and promotion of
the study and application of the sciences;
promotion and advancement of education;
promotion and provision of facilities for
recreation or other leisure time occupation in
the interests of social welfare.
WHAT IS NOT FUNDED No grants will be given for
general appeals, individuals (including for
courses of study), expeditions, overseas travel
or youth clubs/community associations.
RANGE OF GRANTS Up to £20,000.
SAMPLE GRANTS Buxton Festival (£20,000);
Merseyside Dance Initiative (£4,000); National
Wildflower Centre and Horse and Bamboo
Theatre (£3,000 each); Music in Hospitals,
Manchester City Galleries Trust and Live Music
Now (£2,000 each); Design Initiative, Citadel
Arts Centre and Manchester Jazz Festival
(£1,000 each).
FINANCES *Year* 2009–10 *Income* £120,476
Grants £93,584 *Assets* £3,556,625
TRUSTEES Advisory Council: Sir Robert Scott, Chair;
Lord Bernstein; Lady Manduell; Prof. Denis
McCaldin; Mrs Margaret Kenyon; Philip
Ramsbottom; Miss Kathy Arundale; Prof.
Jennifer Latto; Christopher Kerr.
HOW TO APPLY On an application form, available in
writing from the correspondent, giving an outline

Think carefully about every application. Is it justified?

573

of the project. Detailed information can be added when the formal application is submitted. Details of the next trustees' meeting will be given when an application form is sent (trustees meet three times a year at irregular intervals). All letters are acknowledged. 'The Advisory Council interprets the guidelines in a flexible way, realising that it cannot hope to achieve a true balance across all the areas of activity. The council does, however, examine the context of each application and tries to make grants in areas where the benefit will be most widely felt.'

WHO TO APPLY TO Mrs Irene Langford, Administrator, PO Box 3430, Chester CH1 9BZ *Tel* 01244 661867 *email* irene.langford@btconnect.com *Website* www.granadafoundation.org

■ Grand Charitable Trust of the Order of Women Freemasons

CC NO 1059151   **ESTABLISHED** 1996

WHERE FUNDING CAN BE GIVEN UK and overseas.

WHO CAN BENEFIT Registered charities.

WHAT IS FUNDED General charitable purposes. This trust donates about half its grant total to causes related to the Order of Women Freemasons, including individual members and their dependants. The remaining half is donated to external charities.

SAMPLE GRANTS £57,000 to Adelaide Litten Charitable Trust.

FINANCES *Year* 2009–10 *Income* £175,279 *Grants* £132,608 *Assets* £756,397

TRUSTEES B I Fleming-Taylor; M J P Masters; H I Naldrett; J S Brown; Z D Penn.

HOW TO APPLY In writing to the correspondent. Applications should be submitted by the end of July each year for consideration by the trustees.

WHO TO APPLY TO Mrs Joan Sylvia Brown, Trustee, 27 Pembridge Gardens, London W2 4EF *Tel* 020 7229 2368 *Website* www.owf.org.uk

■ The Grand Order of Water Rats' Charities Fund

CC NO 292201   **ESTABLISHED** 1889

WHERE FUNDING CAN BE GIVEN UK.

WHO CAN BENEFIT Organisations benefiting: actors and entertainment professionals and their dependants.

WHAT IS FUNDED Assistance to members of the variety and light entertainment profession who are in need. Also supplying medical equipment to certain hospitals and institutions.

WHAT IS NOT FUNDED No grants to students.

TYPE OF GRANT One-off and recurrent.

SAMPLE GRANTS Previous grants included those made to Actors Church Union, British Legion Wales, Bud Flanagan Leukaemia Fund, Cause for Hope, Northwick Park Hospital and Queen Elizabeth Hospital for Children.

FINANCES *Year* 2009 *Income* £139,997 *Grants* £63,602 *Assets* £1,518,910

TRUSTEES Chas McDevitt, Chair; Wyn Calvin; Roy Hudd; Kaplan Kaye; Keith Simmons; Ken Joy.

HOW TO APPLY In writing to the correspondent. The trustees meet once a month.

WHO TO APPLY TO John Adrian, Secretary, 328 Gray's Inn Road, London WC1X 8BZ *Tel* 020 7407 8007 *email* charities@gowr.net *Website* www. gowr.net

■ The Grange Farm Centre Trust

CC NO 285162   **ESTABLISHED** 1984

WHERE FUNDING CAN BE GIVEN The London Metropolitan Police District and Epping Forest.

WHO CAN BENEFIT Charitable organisations, including scout groups etc.

WHAT IS FUNDED Recreation and leisure activities.

WHAT IS NOT FUNDED No grants to individuals and usually no grants to applications received from local authorities.

RANGE OF GRANTS £550–£20,000.

SAMPLE GRANTS St John's Wood Adventure Playground; Positive Youth for the Community; Chigwell Community Trust; The Archway Project; Cherry Aide; National Autistic; Impact Theatre Company; Redbridge Sports Centre; Friends of Battersea Park and Vauxhall City Farm.

FINANCES *Year* 2009–10 *Income* £216,319 *Grants* £129,443 *Assets* £9,810,148

TRUSTEES A Pelican; R D Neville; Mrs E Webster; M Tomkin; C Huckle; R E Flaxman; Mrs A Wheeler; Mr P Smith; Mr R Church.

HOW TO APPLY In writing to the correspondent giving a brief outline of what the grant will be used for. After initial consideration that the application falls within both the area of benefit and the objects of the trust, an application form will be sent to the applicant for completion which will then be considered in greater detail by the trustees.

WHO TO APPLY TO N E Gadsby, Clerk, c/o 181 High Street, Epping, Essex CM16 4BQ *Tel* 01992 578642 *Fax* 01992 572586

■ Grantham Yorke Trust

CC NO 228466   **ESTABLISHED** 1975

WHERE FUNDING CAN BE GIVEN The (old) West Midlands metropolitan county area.

WHO CAN BENEFIT People under the age of 25 who are in need and were born within the old West Midlands metropolitan county area, and youth organisations benefiting such people.

WHAT IS FUNDED Education, including providing outfits, clothing, tools, instruments, equipment or books to help such people on leaving school, university and so on, to prepare for, or enter a profession or trade.

WHAT IS NOT FUNDED No grants are given towards anybody aged 25 and over.

RANGE OF GRANTS Generally £50–£5,000.

SAMPLE GRANTS All Saints Youth Project, Performances Birmingham and St Basil's (£5,000 each); Birmingham Phab Camps and St Francis Church & Community Centre (£4,000 each); New Hope Mentoring Programme (£3,000); Friends of Victoria School (£2,500) and Youth Action Network (£2,000).

FINANCES *Year* 2009–10 *Income* £232,803 *Grants* £113,871 *Assets* £5,733,226

TRUSTEES Howard Belton, Chair; Peter Jones; Tim Clarke; Miss Elspeth Insch; Sam Monaghan; Fred Rattley; Philip Smiglarski; Barbara Welton; Revd Pamela Ogilvie; P Mannion.

OTHER INFORMATION Grants were made to 63 organisations and 11 individuals totalling £116,000.

HOW TO APPLY In writing to the correspondent. The trustees meet four times a year, in March, June, September and December.

WHO TO APPLY TO Mrs Christine Norgrove, Appeals Clerk, Martineau Johnson, No. 1 Colmore Square, Birmingham B4 6AA *Tel* 0870 763 2000

■ GrantScape

CC NO 1102249   **ESTABLISHED** 2004
WHERE FUNDING CAN BE GIVEN UK.
WHO CAN BENEFIT Environmental and community-based projects.
WHAT IS FUNDED Its generic grantmaking policy is as follows: GrantScape will only make grants in line with its charitable objectives; grants will be made on a justifiable and fair basis to projects which provide best value; grants will be made to projects that improve the life of communities and the environment; GrantScape will make available specific criteria for each of the grant programmes that it manages. All grants are subject to meeting the generic grant-making criteria as well as the specific grant programme criteria.
WHAT IS NOT FUNDED Specific exclusions apply to each programme – see General for details.
FINANCES *Year* 2009–10 *Income* £1,006,469 *Grants* £1,081,256 *Assets* £2,823,884
TRUSTEES Dave Bramley; Doug De Freitas; Shirley Baines; Chris Brown; Alan Loynes; Alastair Singleton; Sheila Torrance.
OTHER INFORMATION New grant programmes are introduced from time to time – check the charity's website for up-to-date information.
HOW TO APPLY Applications are made electronically via the charity's website.
WHO TO APPLY TO Mr S Hargreaves, Whitsundoles, Broughton Road, Salford, Milton Keynes MK17 8BU *Tel* 01908 247630 *email* helpdesk@grantscape.org.uk *Website* www.grantscape.org.uk

■ The J G Graves Charitable Trust

CC NO 207481   **ESTABLISHED** 1930
WHERE FUNDING CAN BE GIVEN Mainly Sheffield.
WHO CAN BENEFIT Registered charities.
WHAT IS FUNDED Charities working in the fields of: provision of parks and open spaces; libraries and art galleries; advancement of education; general benefit of people who are sick or poor; and such other charitable purposes as the trustees see fit. The income is mainly applied to local (Sheffield) charities for capital purposes rather than running costs.
WHAT IS NOT FUNDED Grants are generally not made to or for the benefit of individuals.
TYPE OF GRANT Mainly for capital and one-off for start-ups. Some for running costs.
RANGE OF GRANTS Up to £5,000.
SAMPLE GRANTS Trinity Day Care Trust, Hillsborough Tabernade Congregational Church and Aspire (£2,000 each); Girlguiding UK and Galvanize Festival (£1,500) and Under the Stars (£1,250).
FINANCES *Year* 2009–10 *Income* £115,953 *Grants* £72,310 *Assets* £4,223,541
TRUSTEES T H Reed, Chair; R S Sanderson; R T Graves; S Hamilton; D S W Lee; Mrs A C Womack; G W Bridge; P Price; Mrs J Lee; Dr D R Cullen; J C Bramah.
OTHER INFORMATION Grants were made to 70 organisations with the majority of grants being under £1,000.
HOW TO APPLY In writing to the correspondent, to reach the secretary by 31 March, 30 June, 30 September or 31 December. Applications should indicate whether the applicant is a registered charity, include audited accounts and include a statement giving such up-to-date information as is available with regard to the income and any commitments the organisation has.

WHO TO APPLY TO R H M Plews, Secretary, 2nd Floor, Fountain Precinct, Balm Green, Sheffield S1 2JA *Tel* 0114 276 7991 *Fax* 0114 223 1717

■ The Gray Trust

CC NO 210914   **ESTABLISHED** 1962
WHERE FUNDING CAN BE GIVEN Nottinghamshire, especially Linby and Southall.
WHO CAN BENEFIT Organisations benefiting older people, retired people, ex-service and service people, and people who are disadvantaged by poverty or disability.
WHAT IS FUNDED General charitable purposes, primarily for the benefit of older people, charitable purposes in the parishes of Linby and Papplewick and the surrounding area, and to provide sheltered accommodation for older people in Sherwood House and cottages.
WHAT IS NOT FUNDED Grants are not made to individuals and seldom for applications from outside Nottinghamshire.
RANGE OF GRANTS £500–£69,000.
SAMPLE GRANTS Friends of the Elderly (£69,000); Age Concern Nottingham (£10,000); Papplewick & Linby Day Centre (£2,000); Family Care, Friary Drop In, Independent Age, NSPCC and Macmillan (£1,000 each); Nottinghamshire Coalition for Disabled People (£800); Myasthenia Gravis Association and Rutland House School for Parents (£500 each).
FINANCES *Year* 2009–10 *Income* £129,872 *Grants* £137,576 *Assets* £5,171,713
TRUSTEES Clare Hardstaff; Bella St Clair Harlow; Richard B S Stringfellow; Revd. Can. Keith H Turner.
OTHER INFORMATION Grants for the year totalled £138,000 including a large grant of £69,000 to Friends of the Elderly. The majority of grants ranged between £500 and £1,000.
HOW TO APPLY In writing to the correspondent by letter of application together with most recent accounts.
WHO TO APPLY TO Kelly Boorman, Trust Co-ordinator, Smith Cooper Nottingham, 309–329 Haydn Road, Sherwood, Nottingham NG5 1HG *Tel* 0115 960 7111 *Fax* 0115 969 1313 *email* kelly.boorman@smithcooper.co.uk

■ The Great Britain Sasakawa Foundation

CC NO 290766   **ESTABLISHED** 1985
WHERE FUNDING CAN BE GIVEN UK and Japan.
WHO CAN BENEFIT Voluntary, educational and cultural organisations and registered charities benefiting citizens of UK and Japan. Emphasis on younger people and on projects benefiting groups of people rather than individuals.
WHAT IS FUNDED Advancement of the education of the citizens of the UK and Japan in each other's institutions, people, history, language, culture, and society and in each other's intellectual, artistic and economic life. Research, exchanges, seminars, courses, publications and cultural events may all be funded. The foundation has a special scheme for joint research in medicine and health (the Butterfield Awards).
WHAT IS NOT FUNDED Grants are not made to individuals applying on their own behalf. The foundation will consider proposals from organisations that support the activities of individuals, provided they are citizens of the UK or Japan. No grants are awarded for the construction, conservation or maintenance of

land and buildings, student fees or travel in connection with study for a qualification.

TYPE OF GRANT Mainly one-off; also project and research, maximum term three years. No funding for core-costs.

RANGE OF GRANTS £750–£30,000.

FINANCES *Year* 2010 *Income* £1,097,020 *Grants* £399,787 *Assets* £23,075,458

TRUSTEES Earl of St Andrew, Chair; Hiroaki Fujii; Prof. Nozomu Hayashi; Michael French; Jeremy Brown; Prof. Harumi Kimura; Yohei Sasakawa; Prof. Shoichi Watanabe; Sir John Boyd; Prof. Peter Mathias; Prof. David Cope; Taysuya Tanami.

OTHER INFORMATION The foundation is rarely able to consider grants for the total cost of any project and encourages applicants to seek additional support from other donors.

HOW TO APPLY The foundation expresses a strong preference for emailed applications. A form will be emailed on request, and is also available from the foundation's website where detailed information is given about the foundation's grant giving and application procedures. Application forms are also available from both the London headquarters or from the Tokyo office at: The Nippon Foundation Bldg 4F, 1–2–2 Akasaka Minato-ku, Tokyo 107–0052. The application form requires the following information: a summary of the proposed project and its aims, including dates, its likely impact and long-term sustainability; the total cost of the project and the amount of the desired grant, together with a note of other expected sources of funds; and a description of what elements of the project grant funding has been requested for (the foundation prefers to support identifiable activities rather than general overheads). Organisations should be registered charities, recognised educational institutions, local or regional authorities, churches, media companies, publishers or other bodies that the foundation may approve. Telephone enquiries or personal visits are welcomed by the foundation's staff to discuss eligibility in advance of any formal application. The awards committee meets in London in February, May and October. Applications should be received by December, March and August. Awards meetings in Tokyo are held in April and October, with applications to be submitted by February and September. School applicants are requested to first file an application with Connect Youth International, Japan Exchange Programme, 10 Spring Gardens, London SW1A 2BN (which is part of the British Council), to which the foundation grants external finance, aimed at encouraging exchanges (both ways) for schools in Great Britain and Japan, (their website is: www.connectyouthinternational.com). All applicants are notified shortly after each awards committee meeting of the decisions of the trustees. Those offered grants are asked to sign and return an acceptance form and are given the opportunity to say when they would like to receive their grant. Please note: the foundation receives requests for two to three times the amount of money it actually has available for grants and many applicants receive much less than they asked for.

WHO TO APPLY TO Stephen McEnally, Chief Executive, Dilke House, 1 Malet Street, London WC1E 7JN *Tel* 020 7436 9042 *Fax* 020 7355 2230 *email* grants@gbsf.org.uk *Website* www.gbsf.org.uk

■ The Great Stone Bridge Trust of Edenbridge

CC NO 224309   **ESTABLISHED** 1964

WHERE FUNDING CAN BE GIVEN The parish of Edenbridge, Kent.

WHO CAN BENEFIT Organisations, and individuals under 25 for educational purposes.

WHAT IS FUNDED Education and general charitable purposes in the parish of Edenbridge.

TYPE OF GRANT Some recurrent.

TRUSTEES A Russell; R Davison; R Cunnington; D Leigh; G Jackman; J Hodson; C Burges; R Parsons; M Elliot; C Pearman; P Deans.

OTHER INFORMATION The grant total also includes £1,500 in grants to schools in Edenbridge.

HOW TO APPLY In writing to the correspondent.

WHO TO APPLY TO William Ross, Clerk, 8 Church Lane, East Grinstead, West Sussex RH19 3BA *Tel* 01342 323687

■ The Great Torrington Town Lands Charity

CC NO 202801   **ESTABLISHED** 1971

WHERE FUNDING CAN BE GIVEN Great Torrington, Devon.

WHO CAN BENEFIT Individuals and organisations, including clubs, societies and churches.

WHAT IS FUNDED People in need and general charitable purposes.

FINANCES *Year* 2009–10 *Income* £264,959 *Grants* £40,440 *Assets* £5,987,018

TRUSTEES Mrs T Batty; S M Blake; Dr H E Cramp; B M Davies; Mr H Martin; E W J Kelly; Mrs S Lambert; G Lee; J B Nash; Mrs E Norridge; R Rumbold; A J Stacey; T R Sutton; Mrs E Weeks.

OTHER INFORMATION Grants totalling £40,000 were divided into five categories.

HOW TO APPLY In writing to the correspondent.

WHO TO APPLY TO Chris Styles, Town Hall Office, High Street, Torrington, Devon EX38 8HN *Tel* 01805 623517 *Fax* 01805 623517

■ The Constance Green Foundation

CC NO 270775   **ESTABLISHED** 1976

WHERE FUNDING CAN BE GIVEN England, with a preference for West Yorkshire.

WHO CAN BENEFIT Registered charities, and organisations recognised as charitable, benefiting children; young adults and older people; service and ex-service people; seafarers and fishermen; unemployed people; those in care, fostered and adopted; at risk groups; disabled people; people disadvantaged by poverty; homeless people; victims of famine and war; and people with autism, cancer, epilepsy, head and other injuries, multiple sclerosis, prenatal conditions, terminal illness or tropical diseases.

WHAT IS FUNDED Some preference is given to charities operating in Yorkshire. In previous years grants have been made mainly, but not exclusively, to national organisations in the fields of social welfare and medicine, with special emphasis on support of young people in need and mentally and physically disabled people. Preference for charities working in the fields of residential facilities and services, health and social care professional bodies, councils for voluntary service, special schools and special needs education, medical research and various community facilities and services.

WHAT IS NOT FUNDED Sponsorship of individuals is not supported.

TYPE OF GRANT Capital, special project, buildings and one-off funding of one year or less.

RANGE OF GRANTS Typically up to £10,000.

SAMPLE GRANTS British Red Cross Haiti Appeal (£10,000); Brainwave, Martin House Hospice – Wetherby and the Libra Foundation (£5,000 each); Family Holiday Association (£3,000); Friends of Michael Sobell House (£2,000); KIDS (£1,500); and Transplant Active and Women in Prison (£1,000 each).

FINANCES *Year* 2009–10 *Income* £339,343 *Grants* £136,000 *Assets* £8,060,521

TRUSTEES M Collinson; Col. H R Hall; Mrs M L Hall; Mrs S Collinson.

OTHER INFORMATION In 2009–10 grants were distributed as follows:

Category	%	£
Medical and social care	62	£86,000
Children and young persons	11	£22,000
'Disabled and aged'	16	£15,000
Homeless	10	£13,000
Church and community projects	1	£1,000

HOW TO APPLY At any time in writing to the correspondent (no special form of application required). Applications should include clear details of the need the intended project is designed to meet, plus an outline budget.

WHO TO APPLY TO S Hall, FCM Limited, Centenary House, La Grande Route de St Pierre, St Peter, Jersey JE3 7AY *Tel* 01534 487757 *Fax* 01534 485261 *email* management@fcmtrust.com

■ The Philip Green Memorial Trust

CC NO 293156   **ESTABLISHED** 1985

WHERE FUNDING CAN BE GIVEN UK and overseas, with a preference for Israel and Nepal.

WHO CAN BENEFIT Charitable organisations.

WHAT IS FUNDED Young and older people, people with disabilities, people in need.

SAMPLE GRANTS Colnbrook School (£20,000); Jewish Community Secondary School (£15,000); Community Security Trust (£12,000); Norwood (£31,000); Namaste Children's Home and London Ex-Boxers Association (£1,000).

FINANCES *Year* 2009–10 *Income* £310,614 *Grants* £80,523 *Assets* £100,601

TRUSTEES D Kosky; M Campbell; S Paskin.

OTHER INFORMATION D Kosky is also a trustee of Friends of the Museum of the History of Polish Jews (Charity Commission no. 1087537) and Kosky Seal Charitable Charity (Charity Commission no. 1014309).
The accounts state that Mr C Paskin and Mrs N Paskin are both employed as administrators of the trust.

HOW TO APPLY In writing to the correspondent.

WHO TO APPLY TO The Committee, 105 Trafalgar House, Grenville Place, Mill Hill, London NW7 3SA *Tel* 020 8906 8732 *email* info@pgmt.org.uk *Website* www.pgmt.org.uk

■ The Green Room Charitable Trust

CC NO 1134766   **ESTABLISHED** 2010

WHERE FUNDING CAN BE GIVEN Not defined. In practice, UK.

WHO CAN BENEFIT Social enterprises.

WHAT IS FUNDED General charitable purposes, environmental causes.

TRUSTEES Tom Prickett; Dino Morra; Andrew Ferry.

OTHER INFORMATION The trust is currently arranging funding from a few large donors and researching a broad spectrum of sectors in order to better define its area of interest. Over the next five years, the trust will largely focus on investing in social enterprises, setting up a few regular payments to select charities, and developing its goals for the longer term through this.

HOW TO APPLY At present the trust is only considering applications for grants from environmental charities and only via email.

WHO TO APPLY TO Tom Prickett, Trustee, 30 Cavendish Gardens, Trouville Road, London SW4 8QW *email* thegreenroommct@yahoo.co.uk

■ Philip and Judith Green Trust

CC NO 1109933   **ESTABLISHED** 2005

WHERE FUNDING CAN BE GIVEN UK and Africa.

WHO CAN BENEFIT Registered charities.

WHAT IS FUNDED Christian and missionary work.

RANGE OF GRANTS £2,000–£104,000.

SAMPLE GRANTS Hope Through Action (£105,000); Bible Society (£30,000); African Enterprises (£15,000); Greyfriars Church (£8,300); Stewardship Services (£6,600); Rinell Carey Holmquist (£2,200); and Mission Aviation (£2,000).

FINANCES *Year* 2009–10 *Income* £84,977 *Grants* £178,672 *Assets* £69,595

TRUSTEES Philip Green; Judith Green.

OTHER INFORMATION Other grants of smaller amounts were made totalling £8,400, however these were not listed in the charity's accounts. A grant of £1,700 was also made to an individual.

HOW TO APPLY In writing to the correspondent.

WHO TO APPLY TO Philip Green, Trustee, Marchfield, Flowers Hill, Pangbourne, Berkshire RG8 7BD

■ Mrs H R Greene Charitable Settlement

CC NO 1050812   **ESTABLISHED** 1845

WHERE FUNDING CAN BE GIVEN UK, with a preference for Norfolk and Wistanstow in Shropshire.

WHO CAN BENEFIT Individuals and institutions, particularly those benefiting at risk groups, and people who are disadvantaged by poverty or socially isolated.

WHAT IS FUNDED Welfare and general charitable purposes.

SAMPLE GRANTS Previous beneficiaries included: St Michael's Hospital Bartestree, Norfolk and Norwich Clergymen's Widows' and Children's Charity, Brittle Bone Society, Children's Food Fund, Macmillan Cancer Relief, Muscular Dystrophy Group, Orbis, Beeston Church Organ, Friends of Norwich Cathedral, Horsford and St Faith's Scout Group and Litcham Parochial Church Council.

FINANCES *Year* 2009–10 *Income* £71,054 *Grants* £55,445 *Assets* £2,144,303

TRUSTEES A C Briggs; Revd J B Boston; D A Moore.

OTHER INFORMATION A recent list of grants has not been included in the accounts filed at the Charity Commission.

HOW TO APPLY The trust states that it does not respond to unsolicited applications.

WHO TO APPLY TO N G Sparrow, Trust Administrator, Birketts LLP, Kingfisher House, 1 Gilders Way, Norwich, Norfolk NR3 1UB *Tel* 01603 232300

Think carefully about every application. Is it justified?

577

■ Greenham Common Community Trust Limited

CC NO 1062762   ESTABLISHED 1997

WHERE FUNDING CAN BE GIVEN West Berkshire and northern Hampshire with particular interest in Newbury.

WHO CAN BENEFIT Community organisations and individuals.

WHAT IS FUNDED General charitable purposes.

WHAT IS NOT FUNDED Grants are only made within the trust's geographical area of operation.

RANGE OF GRANTS £100–£19,000.

SAMPLE GRANTS The Open Studios Scheme (£4,000); The Corn Exchange (£3,500); Proteus Theatre Company (£1,500); Newbury Nomads (£1,000) and West Berkshire Writers (£400). Berkshire Association of Youth Clubs (£26,000); West Berks CAB (£19,000); LSP Greener sub Partnership (£15,000); Children First West Berkshire (£10,000) and Army Benevolent Fund (£5,000). Chieveley Parish Council (£10,000); Thames and Kennett Narrowboat Trust (£3,800); West Berkshire Mencap (£3,500); Vitalise (£2,350) and Saturday Fun School (£900). Berkshire County Blind Association (£10,000); NHS Berkshire West (£7,500); Alzheimer's Society WB (£7,000); Berkshire MS Therapy Centre and Berkshire Autistic Society (£1,000 each) and Newbury and District Crossroads (£500).

FINANCES *Year* 2009–10 *Income* £5,635,679 *Grants* £1,883,082 *Assets* £45,460,328

TRUSTEES Sir P Michael, Chair; D Bailey; G Mather; P Bryant; M Morris; P Pockney; J Robinson; Ms O Ni-Chionna.

HOW TO APPLY On a form available by telephoning the trust. Grants should be submitted by December/January for consideration in February. Applications can also be made via the trust website.

WHO TO APPLY TO Stuart Tagg, Chief Executive, Liberty House, The Enterprise Centre, New Greenham Park, Newbury, Berkshire RG19 6HW *Tel* 01635 817444 *Fax* 01635 817555 *email* enquiries@greenham-common-trust.co.uk *Website* www.greenham-common-trust.co.uk

■ Naomi and Jeffrey Greenwood Charitable Trust

CC NO 275633   ESTABLISHED 1978

WHERE FUNDING CAN BE GIVEN UK.

WHO CAN BENEFIT Mainly Jewish organisations.

WHAT IS FUNDED General charitable purposes.

RANGE OF GRANTS £25–£10,000.

SAMPLE GRANTS Previous beneficiaries have included B'nai B'rith of England, Community Security Trust, Conquer and Learn, Friends of the Sick, National Jewish Chaplaincy Board, Hillel House Manchester, Jewish Care, Jewish Literary Trust, Sunderland Kolel, UJIA, Walk the Walk Worldwide, World Jewish Relief and ZSV Trust – Food Lifeline.

FINANCES *Year* 2009–10 *Income* £22,828 *Grants* £20,000

TRUSTEES J M Greenwood; Mrs N Greenwood.

HOW TO APPLY In writing to the correspondent.

WHO TO APPLY TO J M Greenwood, Trustee, Flat 6, Summit Lodge, 9 Lower Terrace, London NW3 6RF *Tel* 020 7431 5779

■ Wiles Greenworld Charitable Trust

CC NO 1136634   ESTABLISHED 2010

WHERE FUNDING CAN BE GIVEN Undefined, in practice national.

WHO CAN BENEFIT Registered charities.

WHAT IS FUNDED The environment, conservation or heritage.

TRUSTEES T G Robins; M James.

HOW TO APPLY In writing to the correspondent.

WHO TO APPLY TO T G Robins, Trustee, Walmgate Road, Perivale, Greenford, Middlesex UB6 7LN *Website* www.wilesgreenworld.co.uk

■ Greggs Foundation (formerly Greggs Trust)

CC NO 296590   ESTABLISHED 1987

WHERE FUNDING CAN BE GIVEN UK, with a preference for the North East of England, and in the regions of Greggs Plc's Divisional Charity Committees.

WHO CAN BENEFIT The trustees are committed to equal opportunities and anti-discriminatory practice and wish to encourage applications from disadvantaged groups of all kinds including ethnic minorities, people with disabilities and other minorities, without prejudice as to racial origin, religion, age, gender or sexual orientation. Recent grants have included support for work with homeless people, older people, young people, children and women, including unemployed people, for people with disabilities and ethnic and multi-cultural groups.

WHAT IS FUNDED Applications from small community-led organisations and self-help groups are more likely to be successful than those from larger and well-staffed organisations and those that have greater fundraising capacity. Projects in the fields of the arts, the environment, conservation, education and health will be considered so long as they have a social welfare focus and/or are located in areas of deprivation.

WHAT IS NOT FUNDED Major grants are not made for: animal welfare; capital projects including the purchase, construction and refurbishment of buildings; events such as conferences, seminars and exhibitions, expeditions and overseas travel, fee-charging residential homes, nurseries and care facilities; festivals; performance and other entertainment activities; fundraising events; holidays and outings; hospitals, health service trusts, medically related appeals and medical equipment; individuals other than through the Hardship Fund; large, well-staffed organisations with a greater fundraising capacity; loans or repayments of loans; national organisations and their regional branches; mini-buses other than community transport schemes; research – academic and medical; religious promotion; replacement of statutory funds; retrospective grants; schools other than for pre-school and after school clubs and activities promoting parental and community involvement; sponsorship – organisations and individuals; sports kit equipment; uniformed organisations such as Scouts, Guides and Sea Cadets. The following are not supported through the hardship fund: payment of debt; computer equipment; sponsorship; overseas expeditions.

TYPE OF GRANT Core costs, running costs, project, start-up costs, recurring costs, salaries, one-off. Funding may be given for up to three years.

RANGE OF GRANTS Major grant for core costs and salaries between £10,000–£15,000. One off grants to small organisations or low cost budget grants between £1,000–£10,000. Hardship Fund grants for necessities between £50–£150.

SAMPLE GRANTS Major grants included: Eastern Ravens Trust, North East Special Needs Network, Single Homeless Action in Derwentside, Hadston House (£45,000 each); Eastlea Community Centre (£41,200); Gateshead Carers Association (£27,400); George's Community Cafe, Fenham Association of Residents (£15,000).

FINANCES *Year* 2010 *Income* £1,464,241 *Grants* £1,453,162 *Assets* £10,419,506

TRUSTEES Andrew Davison, Chair; Felicity Deakin; Richard Hutton; Peter McKendrick; Fiona Nicholson; Annemarie Norman; Lesley Spuhler; Melanie Nicholson.

HOW TO APPLY In writing to the correspondent. Applicants for major grants are asked to set out their application briefly in a letter, giving full address, phone/fax number and a contact name, the purpose of the application, the amount requested, and details of other applications for the same purposes. More information about the project may be provided in supporting documents. The following should be included: a copy of your latest audited annual report and accounts/financial statement; a budget for the organisation for the current year and a budget for which the application is made; details of your organisation's bank account in which you would like us to pay any grant which might be approved and a copy of a recent bank statement. The trust advises that you do not overload you application with attachments. Send only relevant information and check that your envelope has the correct postage. It is advisable to take a copy of your application and retain it for your own records. Full guidelines are available on request from the trust or downloaded from the website. Requests for major grants are assessed in March, June, September and November and applications should be sent in two months prior to meeting dates. The trust aims to respond to applications for small grants within approximately two months and to acknowledge applications for major grants in the same period. Applicants will be informed if their applications have not been selected for further consideration.

WHO TO APPLY TO Foundation Manager, Fernwood House, Clayton Road, Jesmond, Newcastle upon Tyne NE2 1TL *Tel* 0191 212 7626 *email* greggsfoundation@greggs.co.uk *Website* www.greggsfoundation.org.uk

■ The Gretna Charitable Trust

CC NO 1020533   **ESTABLISHED** 1993
WHERE FUNDING CAN BE GIVEN UK, with a preference for Hertfordshire and London.
WHO CAN BENEFIT Registered charities.
WHAT IS FUNDED Seedcorn grants or specific needs.
WHAT IS NOT FUNDED The trust will not provide support to fund salaries or administration costs.
TYPE OF GRANT On-going and one-off.
RANGE OF GRANTS Up to £6,000.
SAMPLE GRANTS Beneficiaries included: Lord Major's Appeal (£6,000); Basketmakers Company – Charitable Trust (£1,750); St Albans Cathedral (£4,000); Royal British Legion (£500); University of Hertfordshire Scholarship (£2,000); St Mary's Essendon (£4,250); Potters Bar Cricket (£1,000); Nicholas Biddle Choir (£1,000) and Potters Bar Museum (£500).

FINANCES *Year* 2009–10 *Income* £43,025 *Grants* £57,239 *Assets* £1,483,816
TRUSTEES H R Walduck; Mrs S M C Walduck; A H E P Walduck; C B Bowles.
HOW TO APPLY This trust does not encourage applications.
WHO TO APPLY TO The Trustees, Imperial London Hotels Limited, Russell Square, London WC1B 5BB

■ The Greys Charitable Trust

CC NO 1103717   **ESTABLISHED** 2004
WHERE FUNDING CAN BE GIVEN UK and locally in Oxfordshire.
WHO CAN BENEFIT Charitable organisations.
WHAT IS FUNDED 'The trustees seek to make donations to other charities and voluntary bodies for the benefit of Church of England preservation projects, other charities dealing with historical preservation, both local to Oxfordshire and nationally, and may seek to make donations to the arts.'
SAMPLE GRANTS Rotherfield Greys PCC (£11,000 in three grants); the National Trust (£9,000 in two grants); Institute of Economic Affairs (£5,000); the Royal Opera House (£4,000 in two grants); Vincent's Club – Oxford University (£3,000 in two grants); Save Canterbury Cathedral (£2,000); the Art Fund (£1,500); and the Landmark Trust (£1,000).
FINANCES *Year* 2009–10 *Income* £28,446 *Grants* £61,500 *Assets* £993,760
TRUSTEES J S Brunner; T B H Brunner.
HOW TO APPLY In writing to the correspondent, the trustees usually meet twice a year.
WHO TO APPLY TO The Trustees, c/o Lawrence Graham LLP, 4 More London, Riverside, London SE1 2AU

■ Grimmitt Trust

CC NO 801975   **ESTABLISHED** 1989
WHERE FUNDING CAN BE GIVEN Birmingham and district and areas where trustees have a personal connection.
WHO CAN BENEFIT Local charities and organisations, local branches of UK charities and individuals.
WHAT IS FUNDED Culture and education, community, children and youth, medical and health, overseas, and older people.
RANGE OF GRANTS Up to £15,000 but mostly less than £2,000.
SAMPLE GRANTS Methodist Relief and Development Fund (£15,000); City of Birmingham Symphony Orchestra (£14,000); WaterAid (£10,000); Walk Through the Bible Ministries (£7,500); Go Africa (£7,000); Birmingham Law Centre and Midlands Art Centre (£5,000 each); Wellbeing of Women (£4,000); Barton Training Trust (£3,000); and Edwards Trust, Walsall Hospice, St John the Evangelist – Sparkhill and Acacia (£2,000 each).
FINANCES *Year* 2009–10 *Income* £268,822 *Grants* £232,650 *Assets* £6,374,171
TRUSTEES Patrick Welch; Sue Day; Leon Murray; David Owen; Tim Welch; Jenny Dickins; Sarah Wilkey.
OTHER INFORMATION In 2009–10, smaller grants of less than £2,000 were made to 172 organisations, totalling £98,000, and four grants were made to individuals during the year.
HOW TO APPLY Potential applicants should contact the secretary who will advise on the best way to design a grant request and to ensure that all the necessary information is included. The

trustees meet three times a year to consider applications.

WHO TO APPLY TO Kate Chase, Secretary, Orchard House, 4a St Catherines Road, Blackwell, Worcestershire B60 1BN *Tel* 0121 445 2197 *email* admin@grimmitt-trust.org.uk

■ The Grocers' Charity

CC NO 255230   **ESTABLISHED** 1968
WHERE FUNDING CAN BE GIVEN UK.
WHO CAN BENEFIT Registered charities only.
WHAT IS FUNDED The charity's charitable aims are broad-ranging, encompassing education, the church, the relief of poverty, medicine, support for the arts, heritage, the elderly, young people and those with disabilities.
Support is more commonly given to cathedrals, churches & other ecclesiastical bodies, hospices, schools & other educational establishments when there is a specific close or long-standing connection with The Grocers' Company.
WHAT IS NOT FUNDED Only UK-registered charities are supported. Individuals cannot receive grants directly, although grants can be given to organisations on their behalf. Support is rarely given to the following unless there is a specific or long-standing connection with the Grocers' Company: cathedrals, churches and other ecclesiastical bodies, hospices, schools and other educational establishments, research projects.
TYPE OF GRANT Both capital and revenue projects. Non-recurring grants of limited size. Core costs, one-off, running costs and salaries will be considered. Funding may be given for up to one year.
RANGE OF GRANTS £1,500–£132,000.
SAMPLE GRANTS Oundle School for bursaries (£154,000); Dementia UK and The FOCUS Kensington & Chelsea Foundation (£50,000 each); The Coldstream Guards (£34,000); the Elms – Colwall (£22,000); Samaritans (£20,000); Combat Stress (£11,000); the Concertina Charitable Trust (£10,000); St Mary, Bow – Mile End (£7,000); Reed's School (£6,500); Flintshire Mental Health Advocacy, the Forget Me Not Club, National Trust for Scotland and Starlight Children's Foundation (£5,000 each); New London Orchestra and SPECIAL (£3,000 each); Shakespeare at the Tobacco Factory (£2,000); and Cherry Trees (£1,500).
FINANCES *Year* 2009–10 *Income* £965,645 *Grants* £973,409 *Assets* £12,376,048
TRUSTEES The Grocers' Trust Company Limited administers the Charity and the Directors of that company are the Master and Second Warden of the Grocers' Company, together with the Chairmen of the Education and Charities Committee and the Finance Committee. The Master and Second Warden together with eight other Members of the Court of Assistants, all of whom are elected for a fixed term of office, form the Education and Charities Committee which is responsible for grant-making.
HOW TO APPLY Applications for grants can be considered from UK registered charities only and must comply with current guidelines, including restrictions, as detailed in the Grocers' Charity Annual Review and on the Grocers' Company website: www.grocershall.co.uk The company's website states: 'Before making an application, please read our Charity Policy and Guidelines. Please complete the Initial Enquiry Form. You can either submit it online or print it out and send it to: The Charity Administrator,

Grocers' Hall, Princes Street, London, EC2R 8AD.
Please do not send any further information at this stage. We will review your enquiry and contact you if we wish to take your application further. We regret we are unable to acknowledge receipt of enquiries.'
WHO TO APPLY TO Anne Blanchard, Charity Administrator, Grocers' Hall, Princes Street, London EC2R 8AD *Tel* 020 7606 3113 *Fax* 020 7600 3082 *email* anne@grocershall. co.uk *Website* www.grocershall.co.uk

■ The M and R Gross Charities Limited

CC NO 251888   **ESTABLISHED** 1967
WHERE FUNDING CAN BE GIVEN UK and overseas.
WHO CAN BENEFIT Jewish organisations.
WHAT IS FUNDED Organisations supporting the orthodox Jewish religion and Jewish education.
SAMPLE GRANTS Atlas Memorial Limited; United Talmudical Associates Limited, a grant making organisation which distributes smaller grants made by the trust; Chevras Tsedokoh Limited; Kolel Shomrei Hachomoth; Telz Talmudical Academy; Talmud Torah Trust; Gevurah Ari Torah Academy Trust; Friends of Yeshivas Brisk; Beis Ruchel Building Fund; Beth Hamedresh Satmar Trust; Kehal Chareidim Trust; Daas Sholem; Craven Walk Beis Hamedrash; Union of Orthodox Hebrew Congregations; and Yetev Lev Jerusalem.
FINANCES *Year* 2009–10 *Income* £6,754,878 *Grants* £3,343,064 *Assets* £22,210,815
TRUSTEES Mrs Rifka Gross; Mrs Sarah Padwa; Michael Saberski.
OTHER INFORMATION A recent list of grants was not available.
HOW TO APPLY In writing to the organisation. Applications are assessed on a weekly basis and many of the smaller grants are dealt with through a grant making agency, United Talmudical Associates Limited.
WHO TO APPLY TO Mrs Rivka Gross, Secretary, Cohen Arnold and Co., New Burlington House, 1075 Finchley Road, London NW11 0PU *Tel* 020 8731 0777 *Fax* 020 8731 0778

■ The Grove Charitable Trust

CC NO 279110   **ESTABLISHED** 1979
WHERE FUNDING CAN BE GIVEN UK and overseas.
WHO CAN BENEFIT Jewish people and people disadvantaged by poverty.
WHAT IS FUNDED Organisations advancing education in and the religion of orthodox Jewish faith, and the relief of poverty.
RANGE OF GRANTS £50–£10,000.
SAMPLE GRANTS Previously, £10,000 to Friends of Laniado Hospital; £5,000 to Pardes House School; £3,500 to Achisomoch Aid Co. Ltd; £3,000 to Society of Friends of the Torah; £2,000 to Friends of Mir Yeshiva; £1,200 each to Beth Shmnel Synagogue and Keren Hatorah; £500 each to Friends of Bobor and Gertner Charitable Trust; £360 to Emuua Education Centre.
FINANCES *Year* 2009 *Income* £405,323 *Grants* £6,830 *Assets* £285,919
TRUSTEES M Bodner; Mrs S Bodner; A Denderowicz.
HOW TO APPLY In writing to the correspondent.
WHO TO APPLY TO Mrs R Bodner, Chair, 40 Highfield Gardens, London NW11 9HB *Tel* 020 8455 0388

■ The GRP Charitable Trust

CC NO 255733 **ESTABLISHED** 1968
WHERE FUNDING CAN BE GIVEN UK.
WHO CAN BENEFIT Organisations already known to the trust.
WHAT IS FUNDED Jewish, general.
WHAT IS NOT FUNDED No grants to individuals.
RANGE OF GRANTS Typically up to £80,000.
SAMPLE GRANTS Oxford Centre for Hebrew and Jewish Studies (£50,000); Jewish Care (£20,000); British ORT (£17,000); United Jewish Israel Appeal (£10,000); Barts and the London Charity and the Politics and Economics Research Trust (£5,000 each); the Fare Share Foundation (£2,500); Jerusalem Foundation (£1,000); Oxford Playhouse Trust (£500); Spotlight Appeal (£200); and St Peter's Trust for Kidney, Bladder and Prostrate Research (£100).
FINANCES *Year* 2009–10 *Income* £176,107 *Grants* £158,275 *Assets* £4,818,019
TRUSTEES Kleinwort Benson Trustees Ltd.
OTHER INFORMATION The GRP of the title is George Richard Pinto, a London banker who established the trust.
HOW TO APPLY In writing to the correspondent. However, the trustees prefer to provide medium-term support for a number of charities already known to them, and unsolicited applications are not acknowledged. Trustees meet annually in March.
WHO TO APPLY TO The Secretary, Kleinwort Benson Trustees Ltd, PO Box 57005, 30 Gresham Street, London EC2V 7PG *Tel* 020 3207 7356

■ The David and Marie Grumitt Foundation

CC NO 288826 **ESTABLISHED** 1984
WHERE FUNDING CAN BE GIVEN UK, with a preference for London.
WHO CAN BENEFIT Registered charities, with a preference for charities supporting homeless people.
WHAT IS FUNDED General charitable purposes.
WHAT IS NOT FUNDED Previous beneficiaries include: Jesuit Missions (£6,000) and St Ann's Church (£3,000); CAFOD, The Diocese of Arundel and Brighton (£2,000 each); Catholic Children's Society, LIFE, The Manna Society (£1,000 each).
TYPE OF GRANT Often recurring.
RANGE OF GRANTS £1,000–£6,000.
FINANCES *Year* 2009–10 *Income* £19,808 *Grants* £30,000
TRUSTEES The Governor and Company of the Bank of Scotland; Marie Grumitt.
HOW TO APPLY This trust has stated that the income of the foundation is fully committed for the foreseeable future and it does not respond to unsolicited applications.
WHO TO APPLY TO Marion Bisset, Trustee Tax Manager, Bank of Scotland, Tax & Trustee Services, Donaldson House, 97 Haymarket Terrace, Edinburgh EH12 5HD *Tel* 0131 313 7908 *Fax* 0131 313 7950 *email* marion.bisset@mazars.co.uk

■ The Bishop of Guildford's Foundation

CC NO 1017385 **ESTABLISHED** 1993
WHERE FUNDING CAN BE GIVEN Diocese of Guildford.
WHO CAN BENEFIT Voluntary and community groups who are linked with a church or faith community, or engaged in a project working in partnership with a church or faith community. Organisations don't have to be registered charities but do have to have a constitution or set of rules, and a bank account, or be supported by an organisation that has these.
WHAT IS FUNDED Community projects. The purpose of the foundation's grants programme is to support projects and partnerships through which church or faith linked groups meet local needs or get involved in community development and regeneration. Priority will be given to projects and partnerships which build communities' own capacity to meet local needs, especially in relation to those who are excluded or vulnerable. It normally expects those funded to obtain funding and/or support in kind from other sources and will only fund the entire costs of a project on an exceptional basis. It aims to help projects access funding from other sources. It will act as a first funder, enabling new projects to unlock other funds. It aims to achieve a balance between strategic grants, which make an impact on project development and sustainability, and small grants, which enable particular activities to take place.
WHAT IS NOT FUNDED Funding is not normally given to assist individuals directly, or for capital costs, or for projects which have already occurred.
TYPE OF GRANT Small grants, usually up to £2,000 and larger strategic grants, usually up to £10,000. Applications for funding for more than one year can be considered, especially where this enables projects to apply for other funding.
RANGE OF GRANTS £500–£32,000.
SAMPLE GRANTS Previously: Partnership Development Project (£32,000); North East Hampshire Development (£27,000); Faith Communities Capacity (£21,000); Camberley Churches and Lakeview (£10,000 each); South East England Faiths Forum (£7,000); the Vine (£4,200); Watts Gallery (£4,200); Ebbisham Association (£2,000); Emmaus House (£400); and Thames Housing Project (£350).
FINANCES *Year* 2009–10 *Income* £19,676 *Grants* £80,000
TRUSTEES Rt Revd Christopher Hill, Bishop of Guildford; Revd Canon Christopher Rich; Geoffrey Riggs; Martin Lee.
OTHER INFORMATION The foundation works in partnership with staff from the diocesan Department for Social Responsibility, including a development team assigned to work with the foundation.
HOW TO APPLY On a form available either as a paper copy or by email. There are two application forms; one for grant applications for up to £2,000; and another for applications for larger projects. Applications are welcomed at any time. The foundation's development team can provide advice and assistance in making an application. Beneficiaries must have a bank or building society account. Full guidelines are available from the foundation. Trustees meet quarterly to consider applications.
WHO TO APPLY TO Jane Schofield, Diocesan House, Quarry Street, Guildford, Surrey GU1 3XG *Tel* 01483 237866 *email* jane.schofield@cofeguildford.org.uk *Website* www.bgf.org.uk

■ The Guildry Incorporation of Perth

SC NO SC008072 **ESTABLISHED** 1210

WHERE FUNDING CAN BE GIVEN Perth, Guildtown and surrounding areas.

WHO CAN BENEFIT Members of the Guildry; residents of Perth and surrounding area who are in need.

WHAT IS FUNDED The main purpose of the trust is to provide support for its members and their families. Charitable donations are also made to local causes at the discretion of the committee. The trust's main aims are to relieve poverty; aid the advancement of education and health, as well as aid the advancement of the arts, sports, environmental protection and recreational activities in the specified area.

WHAT IS NOT FUNDED Any appeals outside Perth.

SAMPLE GRANTS Previous beneficiaries included: the Diabetes Research Campaign; Guildtown Community Association; Perth Access Cars; Perthshire Rugby Club; and Family Mediation.

FINANCES *Year* 2009–10 *Income* £204,495

TRUSTEES Gordon Bannerman; Michael Norval; Alastair Anderson; Alexander Sneddon; Ian Nicol; Rae Pattillo; Alistair Barn; Louis Flood; Dr Ronald McDougall.

HOW TO APPLY In writing to the correspondent. 'Requests for charitable donations may be made to the Guildry by members and close members of their family. Additionally, any other individuals living in, or organisations located in, either Perth or Guildtown, may apply for a donation.' The trust meets to consider grants on the last Tuesday of every month.

WHO TO APPLY TO Lorna Peacock, Secretary, 42 George Street, Perth, Perthshire PH1 5JL *Tel* 01738 623195

■ The Walter Guinness Charitable Trust

CC NO 205375 **ESTABLISHED** 1961

WHERE FUNDING CAN BE GIVEN UK with a preference for Wiltshire and overseas.

WHO CAN BENEFIT Charitable organisations only.

WHAT IS FUNDED The trust is unlikely to be able to support anything it is not already in touch with, but would be interested to hear from charities concerned with research, education, communities and ecology.

WHAT IS NOT FUNDED No grants to individuals.

TYPE OF GRANT Normally one-off.

RANGE OF GRANTS £1,000–£10,000.

SAMPLE GRANTS NSPCC (£10,000); Andover Mind, Hunt Servants Fund and National Society for Epilepsy (£4,000 each); Oxford Medical Students Elective Trust (£3,000); Friends of the Elderly, Prisoners Advice Service, RNIB and Sailors Society (£2,000 each); and Asylum Aid, Brainwave, Charity Search, Children's Safety Education Foundation and Diabetes UK South West (£1,000 each).

FINANCES *Year* 2009–10 *Income* £164,866 *Grants* £134,658 *Assets* £6,355,208

TRUSTEES Hon. F B Guinness; Hon. Mrs R Mulji; Hon. Catriona Guinness.

HOW TO APPLY In writing to the correspondent. Replies are only sent when there is a positive decision. Initial telephone calls are not possible. There are no application forms, guidelines or deadlines. No SAE is required.

WHO TO APPLY TO The Secretary, Biddesden House, Andover, Hampshire SP11 9DN

■ The Gunter Charitable Trust

CC NO 268346 **ESTABLISHED** 1974

WHERE FUNDING CAN BE GIVEN UK.

WHO CAN BENEFIT Local and UK organisations.

WHAT IS FUNDED General charitable purposes including the countryside, medical and wildlife causes.

WHAT IS NOT FUNDED No support for unsolicited applications.

RANGE OF GRANTS Typically up to £20,000.

SAMPLE GRANTS Marie Stopes International (£8,000); Woodland Trust (£4,500); Médecins Sans Frontières (£4,000); the Great Bustard Group (£3,000); the New Bridge Foundation and Womankind Worldwide (£2,000 each); the Smile Train UK and Sandleheath Sea Scouts (£1,000 each); Oxfam (£650); Plantlife International (£350); Royal National Mission for Deep Sea Fishermen (£250).

FINANCES *Year* 2009–10 *Income* £111,046 *Grants* £82,739 *Assets* £2,081,246

TRUSTEES J de C Findlay; R G Worrall.

HOW TO APPLY Applications are considered by the trustees twice a year. No unsolicited applications are accepted, and all such applications are immediately returned to the applicant.

WHO TO APPLY TO The Trustees, c/o Forsters, 31 Hill Street, London W1J 5LS *Tel* 020 7863 8333

■ The Gur Trust

CC NO 283423 **ESTABLISHED** 1961

WHERE FUNDING CAN BE GIVEN Worldwide.

WHO CAN BENEFIT Individuals and organisations benefiting children, young adults, students and Jewish people.

WHAT IS FUNDED Advancement of education and the orthodox Jewish religion.

SAMPLE GRANTS Previous beneficiaries have included Beis Yaacov Casidic Seminary, Beth Yaacov Town, Bnei Emes Institutions, Central Charity Fund, Gur Talmudical College, Kollel Arad, Yeshiva Lezeirim, Pri Gidulim, Maala and Mifal Gevura Shecehessed.

FINANCES *Year* 2009–10 *Income* £54,356 *Grants* £42,415 *Assets* £1,367,659

TRUSTEES David Cymerman; M Mandel; S Morgenstern.

HOW TO APPLY In writing to the correspondent. The trust has previously stated that: 'Funds are raised by the trustees. All calls for help are carefully considered and help is given according to circumstances and funds then available.'

WHO TO APPLY TO The Trustees, 206 High Road, London N15 4NP *Tel* 020 8801 6038

■ Dr Guthrie's Association

SC NO SC009302 **ESTABLISHED** 1986

WHERE FUNDING CAN BE GIVEN Scotland, with a preference for Edinburgh.

WHO CAN BENEFIT Not-for-profit organisations benefiting disadvantaged children and young people under 22 years of age.

WHAT IS FUNDED The care and welfare of young people.

WHAT IS NOT FUNDED No grants to individuals, or in support of: projects of an environmental nature; mainstream activities and statutory requirements of schools, universities and hospitals; large-scale building projects; historic restoration; retrospective funding.

RANGE OF GRANTS £250–£1,000.

SAMPLE GRANTS Abernethy Trust, Citylife Ministries Ltd, City Youth Café, Glasgow City Mission, Happy Days Children's Charity, Reality Adventure Works in Scotland, Riptide Music Studios, Tall Ships Youth Trust, Turning Point Scotland and Visibility (£1,000 each); ChildLine Scotland (£750); Red School Youth Centre (£700); and Bibles for Children (£500).

FINANCES *Year* 2009–10 *Income* £36,730

TRUSTEES J M P Galbraith, Chair; Mrs S Crane; Mrs R Derby; P J Derby; Mrs A M G Hepburn; Ms E Marquis.

HOW TO APPLY Applications are considered by the trustees three times a year (approximately) in February, June and October.

WHO TO APPLY TO Fiona Watson, Secretary and Treasurer, PO BOX 28838, Edinburgh EH15 2XZ *Tel* 0772 901 8214 *email* drguthrie@tiscali.co.uk *Website* www.scott-moncrieff.com/charitable_trusts/page5.html

■ The H and J Spack Charitable Trust

CC NO 1087689   **ESTABLISHED** 2001
WHERE FUNDING CAN BE GIVEN Worldwide.
WHO CAN BENEFIT Charities and organisations working in the worldwide community.
WHAT IS FUNDED Jewish and general charitable purposes.
RANGE OF GRANTS Up to £3,000.
SAMPLE GRANTS Previous grants included: £3,000 each to Jewish Care and United Jewish Israel Appeal; £2,000 to New London Synagogue; £1,500 to Defending Jewish Community Security Trust; £1,000 to Royal Mencap Society; £900 to Dementia Relief Trust; £100 each to Langdon Foundation, Nightingale Care for Life and Prostate Cancer (£500 each), Cancer Research UK and Care of China's Orphaned & Abandoned.
FINANCES *Year* 2009–10 *Income* £22,500 *Grants* £22,000
TRUSTEES Arvind Raichand Shah; Harvey Montague Spack; Mrs Judith Anne Spack.
HOW TO APPLY In writing to the correspondent.
WHO TO APPLY TO Harvey Montague Spack, 28 Hill Street, London W1J 5NW

■ The H and M Charitable Trust

CC NO 272391   **ESTABLISHED** 1976
WHERE FUNDING CAN BE GIVEN UK, with some preference for Kent.
WHO CAN BENEFIT Charities concerned with seamanship, including welfare education.
WHAT IS FUNDED 'Resources are committed on a regular annual basis to organisations who have come to rely upon [the trust] for their funding.'
SAMPLE GRANTS Previous beneficiaries included: Arethusa Venture Centre, Fairbridge – Kent, Guide Dogs for the Blind, Hand in Gillingham, Jubilee Sailing Trust, Kent Air Ambulance, North London Hospice, RSPCA, Royal Engineers Association, Royal National Lifeboat Association and Royal Star and Garter Home.
FINANCES *Year* 2009–10 *Income* £68,642 *Grants* £80,000 *Assets* £2,694,893
TRUSTEES Pamela M Lister; D Harris; J Lister.
HOW TO APPLY The trustees said they do not wish their trust to be included in this guide since it leads to disappointment for applicants. Unsolicited applications will not be successful.
WHO TO APPLY TO David Harris, Trustee, Abbey House, 342 Regents Park Road, London N3 2LJ *Tel* 020 8445 9104

■ H and T Clients Charitable Trust

CC NO 1104345   **ESTABLISHED** 2004
WHERE FUNDING CAN BE GIVEN England and Wales.
WHO CAN BENEFIT Organisations.
WHAT IS FUNDED General charitable purposes.
FINANCES *Year* 2009–10 *Income* £236,705 *Grants* £96,643 *Assets* £168,246
TRUSTEES H M Lask; R M Harris; M Webber.
HOW TO APPLY In writing to the correspondent.
WHO TO APPLY TO H M Lask, Trustee, 65 New Cavendish Street, London W1G 7LS

■ H C D Memorial Fund

CC NO 1044956   **ESTABLISHED** 1995
WHERE FUNDING CAN BE GIVEN Worldwide.
WHO CAN BENEFIT Organisations benefiting the environment and people who are in need. Especially, people disadvantaged by poverty, education or ill-health and people with disabilities.
WHAT IS FUNDED Health, education, community, environment, development aid abroad, and other social and educational work in the UK and the Republic of Ireland.
WHAT IS NOT FUNDED The following are not supported: evangelism or missionary work; individuals; nationwide emergency appeals; animal, cancer and children's charities. The fund stresses that it receives applications for gap year funding which are always unsuccessful as grants are never made to individuals.
TYPE OF GRANT Can be one-off or recurring, including core costs, buildings and start-up costs. Funding may be given for up to three years.
RANGE OF GRANTS £1,000–£154,000; average grant: £10,000–£20,000.
SAMPLE GRANTS Beneficiaries overseas included: Practical Action – Sudan (£60,000); CAFOD – Ethiopia (£57,000); Angels International – Malawi (£23,000); Donald Woods Foundation – South Africa (£50,000); Build IT and Concern in Africa (£20,000 each); Rwanda Aid and Target Tuberculosis – Timor (£10,000 each); and Leaves of Hope – Belarus (£5,000). Beneficiaries in the UK included: Newhaven Community Development Association, for people with disabilities (£30,000); Dartington Hall Trust and Refugee Support Group Devon, for refugees (£20,000 each); Green Light Trust (£16,000); Refugee Women of Bristol (£5,000); and Thanington Neighbourhood Resource Centre (£2,000).
FINANCES *Year* 2009–10 *Income* £647,612 *Grants* £638,500 *Assets* £547,942
TRUSTEES Nicholas Debenham, Chair; Bill Flinn; Harriet Lear and Joanna Lear; Jeremy Debenham; Catherine Debenham.
OTHER INFORMATION £129,000 to organisations in the UK (2009–10)
HOW TO APPLY In writing to the correspondent, although please note that the trust has a preference for seeking out its own projects and only very rarely responds to general appeals. 'Unsolicited applications are not encouraged. They are acknowledged, but extremely rarely receive a positive response. No telephone enquiries, please.'
WHO TO APPLY TO Harriet Lear, Secretary and Trustee, Knowlands Farm Granary, Barcombe, Lewes, East Sussex BN8 5EF

■ The H P Charitable Trust

CC NO 278006   **ESTABLISHED** 1979
WHERE FUNDING CAN BE GIVEN UK.
WHO CAN BENEFIT Orthodox Jewish charities.
WHAT IS FUNDED Jewish charitable purposes.
SAMPLE GRANTS Previous beneficiaries included: Craven Walk Charities, Emuno Educational Centre Ltd, Gur Trust, Ponivez, Yad Eliezer, Yeshuas Caim Synagogue and Yetev Lev.
FINANCES *Year* 2009–10 *Income* £181,000 *Grants* £5,660 *Assets* £1,542,609
TRUSTEES A Piller; Mrs H Piller; A Zonszajn.
HOW TO APPLY In writing to the correspondent.
WHO TO APPLY TO Aron Piller, Trustee, 26 Lingwood Road, London E5 9BN *Tel* 020 8806 2432

■ The Hackney Parochial Charities

CC NO 219876 **ESTABLISHED** 1904
WHERE FUNDING CAN BE GIVEN The London Borough of Hackney.
WHO CAN BENEFIT Organisations benefiting children, young adults and people disadvantaged by poverty may be considered. Community organisations can also benefit.
WHAT IS FUNDED Community and education projects which benefit people in Hackney who are poor.
TYPE OF GRANT One-off and recurrent.
RANGE OF GRANTS Up to £50,000.
SAMPLE GRANTS St Joseph Hospice (£50,000); Hackney Marsh (£15,000); St John Church (£8,000); Hackney Winter Shelter (£6,300); Muslim Community and Open Door Care Trust (£5,000 each); Headway and The Learning Foundation (£3,000); Quaker Social and Alone in London (£2,000 each).
FINANCES *Year* 2009–10 *Income* £186,554 *Grants* £231,254 *Assets* £4,675,225
TRUSTEES Chair, Revd R Wickham; Miss P Hibbs; Cllr G N Taylor; Mrs V Edwards; Mrs M Cannon; Ms N Baboneau; H Deadman; P Ottino.
OTHER INFORMATION Other grants under £2,000 amounted to £60,000.
HOW TO APPLY In writing to the correspondent. The trustees will consider written applications for grants and project funding from individuals and organisations that are in line with the charity's objectives and are within the area of benefit at their discretion.
WHO TO APPLY TO Robin Sorrell, Clerk to the Trustees, 2 The Broadway, 157 High Street, Chipping Ongar, Essex CM5 9JD *Tel* 01277 365532 *Fax* 01277 899067 *email* rsorrell@sorrells.org.uk

■ The Hadfield Trust

CC NO 1067491 **ESTABLISHED** 1998
WHERE FUNDING CAN BE GIVEN Cumbria.
WHO CAN BENEFIT Organisations benefiting children, young adults and older people; unemployed people; parents and children; one parent families; and widows and widowers.
WHAT IS FUNDED Charities concerned with social needs, youth employment, help for older people, the arts and the environment. Particularly supported are those working in the fields of accommodation and housing; support and development; arts, culture and recreation; health; conservation; education and training; and social care and development.
WHAT IS NOT FUNDED The following would not normally be considered for a grant: applicants from outside the county of Cumbria; individuals; any form of sponsorship; religious bodies; political organisations; pressure groups; feasibility studies; schools seeking specialist status; where funding from statutory bodies is, or should be available.
TYPE OF GRANT Capital projects preferred; buildings will be considered and funding is generally for one year or less.
RANGE OF GRANTS Minimum £50.
SAMPLE GRANTS Beneficiaries included: Cumbrian Farmers Network (£4,000); Allerdale CAB (£3,000); Kendal & South Lakes Shop Mobility, Quondam Arts, The Broughton Beck Room (£2,000 each); The Pro Nobis Singers, South Cumbria Family Forum, Carlisle Festival (£1,000 each); West Cumberland Choral Society (£500); Roadhead Public Hall (£50).
FINANCES *Year* 2009 *Income* £309,705 *Grants* £219,498 *Assets* £5,929,852

TRUSTEES Roy Morris; William Rathbone; Alan Forsyth; Andrew Morris; Andrew Forsyth.
PUBLICATIONS A leaflet setting out the aims and objectives of the trust (available on request).
HOW TO APPLY A completed application form is always required and is available from the trust's website or offices. The completed application form should be sent to the administrator together with a copy of the applicant's most recent accounts to reach the trust not later than the deadline for the relevant meeting. The deadlines are always the 1st of the month preceding that of the trustees' meeting i.e. 1 February, 1 June and 1 October. If the application form gives insufficient space for your project to be described, up to 2 sheets of A4 paper can be accepted. The policy of the trust is that capital funding is strongly preferred but some revenue requests will be accepted in particular circumstances. If in any doubt about the best way to complete the application form, including the size of the grant to be requested, applicants are strongly advised to telephone the administrator who will be glad to advise. 'In reaching their decision the trustees have the benefit of advice from the Advisory Panel which meets some weeks before them to discuss in detail the applications. The Advisory Panel, under the chairmanship of Alan Forsyth, is made up of people resident in Cumbria and drawn from all parts of the county who have wide experience and knowledge of the charitable sector.'
WHO TO APPLY TO Michael Hope, Administrator, 3 College Path, Formby, Liverpool L37 1LH *Tel* 01704 834887 *email* admin@hadfieldtrust.org.uk *Website* www.hadfieldtrust.org.uk

■ The Hadley Trust

CC NO 1064823 **ESTABLISHED** 1997
WHERE FUNDING CAN BE GIVEN UK, especially London.
WHO CAN BENEFIT Registered charities.
WHAT IS FUNDED The trust's objects allow it to assist in creating opportunities for people who are disadvantaged as a result of environmental, educational or economic circumstances or physical or other handicap to improve their situation, either by direct financial assistance, involvement in project and support work, or research into the causes of and means to alleviate hardship.
FINANCES *Year* 2009–10 *Income* £4,372,586 *Grants* £2,023,354 *Assets* £75,642,909
TRUSTEES Janet Hulme; Philip Hulme.
HOW TO APPLY In writing to the correspondent.
WHO TO APPLY TO Carol Biggs, Trust Administrator, Gladsmuir, Hadley Common, Barnet, Hertfordshire EN5 5QE *Tel* 020 8447 4577 *Fax* 020 8447 4571 *email* carol@hadleytrust.org

■ The Hadrian Trust

CC NO 272161 **ESTABLISHED** 1976
WHERE FUNDING CAN BE GIVEN Within the boundaries of the old counties of Northumberland and Durham, this includes Tyne and Wear and the former county of Cleveland (north of the Tees).
WHO CAN BENEFIT Organisations benefiting people of all ages; unemployed people; volunteers; people in care, or who are fostered or adopted; one-parent families; and widows and widowers. Typical grants are to councils of voluntary service, advice and counselling services, women's projects, youth clubs and schools,

Think carefully about every application. Is it justified?

585

charities for people who are disabled, older people, arts and environmental projects, church restoration and block grants for individuals in need.

WHAT IS FUNDED Social welfare and other charitable projects within the boundaries of the old counties of Northumberland and Durham (this includes Tyne and Wear). The main headings under which applications are considered are: social welfare; youth; women; the elderly; the disabled; ethnic minorities; the arts; the environment; education and churches.

WHAT IS NOT FUNDED General appeals from large UK organisations and smaller bodies working outside the beneficial area are not considered.

TYPE OF GRANT Usually one-off for a special project or part of a project. The average grant is £1,000. Buildings, capital, project, research, recurring costs, as well as running costs, salaries and start-up costs will be considered. Funding of up to three years will be considered.

RANGE OF GRANTS £500–£3,000.

SAMPLE GRANTS 20,000 Voices, Alnwick (£3,000); Open Door North East, Children's Foundation, Newcastle, The Irene Taylor Trust, (Music in Prisons) London, National Rheumatoid Arthritis Society and Mind in Gateshead (£2,000 each); Bardon Mill and Henshaw Community Projects Group, Embleton Cygnets Nursery, Northumberland Scout Council and Unity Organisation, Sunderland (£1,000 each); Outlookers Theatre Group, Kimblesworth, Stranton FC, Hartlepool and St. James the Great Parish Church, Darlington (£500 each).

FINANCES *Year* 2009–10 *Income* £164,406 *Grants* £189,750 *Assets* £5,208,716

TRUSTEES B J Gillespie, Chair; J B Parker; P A Dodgson; R H M Hargreave; K L H Winskell; J C Dias.

OTHER INFORMATION A total of 161 grants were made including 4 grants to individuals.

HOW TO APPLY In writing to the correspondent setting out details of the project, the proposed funding, a list of any other applications being made (with the result if known) and a copy of the latest annual report/accounts. Applications are considered at meetings usually held in October, January, March and July each year, or as otherwise required. There is no application form but an information sheet is available on request. Eligible applications will be acknowledged and given a date when the application will be considered. Successful applicants will hear within two weeks of the meeting; no further correspondence is sent to unsuccessful applicants. To help assess the effectiveness of their grantmaking the trustees welcome reports from successful applicants on how the grant has been spent and how it has helped the project, especially if a repeat application is being considered. Applications for individuals should be sent to: Greggs Charitable Trust, Fernwood House, Clayton Road, Jesmond, Newcastle upon Tyne NE2 1TL.

WHO TO APPLY TO John Parker, Pauline Dodgson, The Hadrian Trust, PO Box 785, Whitley Bay NE26 9DW *Tel* 07815 785074 *email* enquiries@hadriantrust.co.uk *Website* www.hadriantrust.co.uk

■ The Doris Louise Hailes Charitable Trust

CC NO 1134434   **ESTABLISHED** 2010

WHERE FUNDING CAN BE GIVEN Undefined, in practice in the UK.

WHO CAN BENEFIT Registered charities.

WHAT IS FUNDED The advancement of health and saving of lives, disability, and animals.

SAMPLE GRANTS Under its main clause it is set up to assist the following charities: the PDSA – Peoples Dispensary For Sick Animals – Telford (CC no. 208217); the RSPB – Bedfordshire; Royal Society For The Protection Of Birds (CC no. 207076); the Heart Foundation (CC no. 225971); the Arthritis Society, RNIB (CC no. 226227); the RAF Benevolent Fund (CC no. Number 264436); and any other like minded charities.

TRUSTEES HSBC Trust Co (UK) Ltd.

HOW TO APPLY In writing to the correspondent.

WHO TO APPLY TO HSBC Trust Co (UK) Ltd, Norwich House, 10th Floor, Nelson Gate, Commercial Road Southampton, SO15 1GX

■ The Alfred Haines Charitable Trust

CC NO 327166   **ESTABLISHED** 1986

WHERE FUNDING CAN BE GIVEN Birmingham and West Midlands (including Staffordshire and Warwickshire).

WHO CAN BENEFIT Mainly smaller charities.

WHAT IS FUNDED Christian social action. Grants were broken down into the following categories: family support and counselling; youth and children's work; humanitarian and overseas aid; medically disadvantaged; care for older people and people with disabilities; homeless; and holidays for disadvantaged children and teenagers.

WHAT IS NOT FUNDED No support for activities which are primarily the responsibility of central or local government or some other responsible body; animal welfare; church buildings – restoration, improvements, renovations or new ones; environmental – conservation and protection of wildlife and landscape; expeditions and overseas trips; hospitals and health centres; individuals, including students (on the rare occasions that individuals are supported, the person has to be recommended by someone known to the trustees and the funding should be of long-term benefit to others); large national charities; it is unusual for the trust to support large national charities even where there is a local project; loans and business finance; medical research projects; promotion of any religion other than Christianity; or school, universities and colleges. Projects overseas or outside the West Midlands, whether Christian or not, will only be considered where the applicants are known to a trustee or are recommended by someone known to a trustee who has first-hand knowledge of the work.

TYPE OF GRANT Generally one-off. Specific projects rather than general running costs.

SAMPLE GRANTS A list of beneficiaries was not available.

FINANCES *Year* 2009–10 *Income* £23,919 *Grants* £140,000

TRUSTEES A L Gilmour; G L H Moss.

HOW TO APPLY In writing to the trustees, quoting ref: DSC. Applications should include a brief description of the activities of the organisation; details of the project and its overall cost; what

586

Does the trust you have chosen match your needs? Haphazard applications waste postage and time

funds have already been raised and how the remaining funds are to be raised; a copy of the latest accounts including any associated or parent organisation; any other leaflets or supporting documentation. When considering whether to apply for funding, advice (if needed) can be obtained from the administrator prior to writing. Replies are only sent where further information is required. No telephone calls or correspondence will be entered into for any proposed or declined applications. Successful applicants are required to complete an official receipt and produce a report on the project, usually after 10 months. Successful applicants are advised to leave at least 10 months before applying for further support.

WHO TO APPLY TO J A Gilmour, Administrator, Dale Farm, Worcester Lane, Sutton Coldfield B75 5PR *Tel* 0121 323 3236

■ The Hale Trust

CC NO 313214   **ESTABLISHED** 1970
WHERE FUNDING CAN BE GIVEN Surrey, Sussex, Kent and Greater London.
WHO CAN BENEFIT Individuals and registered charities in the area defined above. The trust will consider children and young adults (up to the age of 25) who have disabilities and students for recognised courses who are disadvantaged by poverty, including unemployed people and volunteers.
WHAT IS FUNDED There is a tendency to support local projects where the trust can see the use the money is put to.
WHAT IS NOT FUNDED The trust does not give grants for: the purchase, repair or furnishing of buildings; basic equipment or teachers' salaries, which by law are the responsibility of the education authorities; performances, exhibitions or festivals; youth projects or foreign travel; conferences or seminars; university or medical research; establishing funds for bursary or loan schemes; stage, film or video production costs, or commercial publications; supplementary schools or mother tongue teaching; general fundraising campaigns or appeals; or retrospective grants to help pay off overdrafts or loans. The trust will not remedy the withdrawal or reduction of statutory funding.
TYPE OF GRANT One-off and reoccurring.
RANGE OF GRANTS Up to £5,000.
SAMPLE GRANTS Hindleap Warren (£4,600); Edenbridge Holiday Activities Scheme (£1,300); St George Hanworth Youth Club (£900); Brighton and Hove Parents' and Children's Group (£730); Tower Hamlets Parents Centre (£600); Brighton and Hove Unwaged Advice and Rights Centre; Project Reach (£430 each).
FINANCES *Year* 2010 *Income* £38,252 *Grants* £32,241 *Assets* £1,093,593
TRUSTEES Sheila Henderson; John Tuke; Diana Whitmore; John Burns; Jocelyn Broughton; Julia Cole; David Macfarlane.
OTHER INFORMATION Grants to individuals cannot exceed £1,200 each year or last for more than three years and the total amount allocated from the income of the trust for this purpose in any one year is strictly limited.
HOW TO APPLY In writing to the correspondent. The trustees meet in February, June and October so it is advisable to apply in time for these meetings.
WHO TO APPLY TO Mrs J M Broughton, Secretary, Rosemary House, Woodhurst Park, Oxted, Surrey RH8 9HA

■ E F and M G Hall Charitable Trust

CC NO 256453   **ESTABLISHED** 1968
WHERE FUNDING CAN BE GIVEN South east England.
WHO CAN BENEFIT Charities concerned with children and older people; disability and medical charities; churches; and others.
WHAT IS FUNDED General charitable purposes.
WHAT IS NOT FUNDED No grants to individuals.
TYPE OF GRANT One-off and recurrent.
RANGE OF GRANTS £50–£3,000.
SAMPLE GRANTS Dorothy Karen Trust (£3,000); Christian Aid (£1,450); Save the Children (£750); Médecins Sans Frontières (£650) and The Friends of Canterbury Cathedral, Great Ormond Street Hospital and Shelter (£500 each).
FINANCES *Year* 2009–10 *Income* £51,008 *Grants* £27,649 *Assets* £1,030,547
TRUSTEES Anthony E F Hall; Moira G Hall; Ian F Hall.
OTHER INFORMATION The trust made 110 grants ranging from £50 up to £3,000. The majority of grants made were between £100 and £500. No grants to individuals.
HOW TO APPLY In writing to the correspondent, although the trust had previously stated that its funds are already allocated to selected charities.
WHO TO APPLY TO Moira Hall, Trustee, Mrs Moira Gladys Hall, Holmsley House, Holtye Common, Cowden, Edenbridge, Kent *Tel* 01342 850571

■ The Edith Winifred Hall Charitable Trust

CC NO 1057032   **ESTABLISHED** 1996
WHERE FUNDING CAN BE GIVEN UK, with a preference for Northamptonshire.
WHO CAN BENEFIT Registered charities.
WHAT IS FUNDED General charitable purposes.
SAMPLE GRANTS Balscote Village Hall (£80,000); Luton Churches Education Trust (£75,000); Friends of St Paul's Church – Bedford (£60,000); the Country Trust and Reach Out Projects (£50,000 each); All Saints Church with St Katherine and St Peter (£20,000); Keystone Escape Youth Centre (£14,000); St Peter's Church – Lowick (£10,000); and St Leonard Fabric Fund and Leicester and Rutland Crime Beat Limited (£5,000 each).
FINANCES *Year* 2009–10 *Income* £111,037 *Grants* £612,148 *Assets* £2,263,798
TRUSTEES D Reynolds; D Endicott; P P Reynolds; L C Burgess-Lumsden.
HOW TO APPLY In writing to the correspondent.
WHO TO APPLY TO D Endicott, Trustee, Spratt Endicott, 52–54 South Bar Street, Banbury, Oxfordshire OX16 9AB *Tel* 01295 204000

■ Robert Hall Charity

CC NO 1015493   **ESTABLISHED** 1992
WHERE FUNDING CAN BE GIVEN West Walton, Wisbech and Walsoken in Cambridgeshire.
WHO CAN BENEFIT Organisations particularly those benefiting children and young adults.
WHAT IS FUNDED General charitable purposes, including charities working with hospices and hospitals, medical research, conservation and campaigning, education and various community services and facilities.
WHAT IS NOT FUNDED No grants to individuals.

TYPE OF GRANT Range of grants including buildings, capital, recurring costs and start-up costs. Funding for up to three years may be available.

SAMPLE GRANTS West Walton Parish Church (£19,000); Angles Theatre (£10,000); Cancer Research UK and Friends of Wisbech Hospitals (£7,000 each); St Peter's Church of England Junior School (£5,000); West Walton Village Hall (£4,000); Alzheimer's Society (£3,000); Fenland Mencap (£2,000); Downham Market High School (£1,500); and 3rd Wisbech Guides Group (£1,000).

FINANCES *Year* 2009–10 *Income* £36,997 *Grants* £33,353 *Assets* £28,439

TRUSTEES D W Ball; E A Plater; B A Lyons; D Walker; D Turner.

HOW TO APPLY In writing to the correspondent. Applications are considered at twice yearly trustees' meetings.

WHO TO APPLY TO D Ball, Trustee, Frasers Solicitors, 29 Old Market, Wisbech, Cambridgeshire PE13 1ND *Tel* 01945 468700 *Fax* 01945 468 709 *email* d.ball@frasers-solicitors.com

---

■ The Hamamelis Trust

CC NO 280938　　　**ESTABLISHED** 1980

WHERE FUNDING CAN BE GIVEN UK, but with a special interest in the Godalming and Surrey areas.

WHO CAN BENEFIT UK charities involved in medical research or conservation projects.

WHAT IS FUNDED Medical research in the UK; and specific projects for conservation of the countryside in the UK.

WHAT IS NOT FUNDED Projects outside the UK are not considered. No grants to individuals.

TYPE OF GRANT Project.

RANGE OF GRANTS Up to £10,000.

SAMPLE GRANTS the Chiddingfold Conservation Trust (£15,000); SOIL Association and Friends of the Earth (£4,000 each); Blond McIndoe Research Foundation, Bowel Cancer Research and Wildfowl and Wetlands Trust (£2,000 each); Busbridge Infants School (£1,500); Rural Life Centre and the Bluebell Railway Trust (£1,000 each); and Plantlife (£500).

FINANCES *Year* 2009–10 *Income* £79,490 *Grants* £85,000 *Assets* £2,948,606

TRUSTEES Mrs L Dadswell; Dr A F M Stone; Ms L J Stone.

HOW TO APPLY In writing to the correspondent. All applicants are asked to include a short summary of the application along with any published material and references. Unsuccessful appeals will not be acknowledged. Dr Adam Stone, one of the trustees, who is medically qualified, assesses medical applications.

WHO TO APPLY TO Mrs L Dadswell, Trustee, c/o Penningtons Solicitors LLP, Highfield, Brighton Road, Godalming, Surrey GU7 1NS *Tel* 01483 791800

■ Hamilton Wallace Trust

CC NO 1052453　　　**ESTABLISHED** 1996

WHERE FUNDING CAN BE GIVEN UK.

WHO CAN BENEFIT Registered charities.

WHAT IS FUNDED General charitable purposes.

RANGE OF GRANTS £500–£1,000.

SAMPLE GRANTS Previous beneficiaries included: Diabetes UK; Brainwave, Crohn's in Childhood Research Association, Dyslexia Action, Independent Age, Motor Neurone Disease Association and Young Minds; and Disabled

Living Foundation, Nightstop UK and Step by Step.

FINANCES *Year* 2010–11 *Income* £22,709 *Grants* £20,000

TRUSTEES Timothy Calder; Peter Phillips.

HOW TO APPLY In writing to the correspondent. Trustees meet twice a year to consider appeals, in November and May of each year, and it would be helpful for any appeals to be received about a month before the meetings.

WHO TO APPLY TO Peter Phillips, Rubinstein Phillips Lewis LLP, 19 Buckingham Street, London WC2N 6EF *Tel* 020 7925 2244

■ Paul Hamlyn Foundation

CC NO 1102927　　　**ESTABLISHED** 1987

WHERE FUNDING CAN BE GIVEN UK and India.

WHO CAN BENEFIT Registered charities and organisations.

WHAT IS FUNDED The foundation aims to address issues of inequality and disadvantage, particularly in relation to children and young people. Its main areas of interest are arts, education and learning in the UK and local organisations supporting vulnerable groups of people, especially children, in India.

WHAT IS NOT FUNDED In the UK the foundation does not support: individuals or proposals for the benefit of one individual; funding for work that has already started; general circulars/appeals; proposals about property or which are mainly about equipment or other capital items; overseas travel, expeditions, adventure and residential courses; promotion of religion; animal welfare; medical/health/residential or day care; proposals from organisations outside the UK, except under our India programme; proposals that benefit people living outside the UK, except under the India programme. 'We are unlikely to support: endowments; organisations to use our funding to make grants; websites, publications, seminars unless part of a wider proposal.' In India, the foundation does not support: individuals or proposals for the benefit of one individual; retrospective (funding for work that has already started); general circulars/appeals; proposals that solely concentrate on the purchasing of property, equipment or other capital items; overseas activities, including travel, expeditions, adventure and residential courses.

TYPE OF GRANT Grants are usually one-off, for a specific project or for a specific part of a project, and funding is normally given for one year only.

RANGE OF GRANTS Usually up to £30,000 each.

SAMPLE GRANTS Eastside Projects (£360,000), to develop and underpin Eastside Projects and programming costs – full funding will be determined on successful year one and the development of a sustainable business and fundraising plan for Eastside Projects; Contact Theatre Company (£200,000), support for 'Future Fires', an innovative programme using the best international practice to develop creative young leaders who will design and deliver projects in their own communities; New Writing North (£150,000), to support an innovative programme of activities and new partnerships to engage North East readers with quality literature events and activities; CEWC – Cymru (£58,000), to extend the use of a proven classroom method for developing speaking and listening skills through establishing whole-school practices and inter-school networks; and Council for Assisting Refugee Academics (£10,000), towards the publication and dissemination of a practical guide for higher education institutions in providing more effective support to refugee and at risk academics.

FINANCES *Year* 2009–10 *Income* £11,239,000 *Grants* £18,700,000 *Assets* £548,326,000

TRUSTEES Jane Hamlyn, Chair; Michael Hamlyn; Robert Boas; James Lingwood; Baroness Estelle Morris; Claus Moser; Anthony Salz; Peter Wilson-Smith; Tim Bunting.

HOW TO APPLY The foundation's guidance on its application procedure is particularly detailed and helpful:

'Applicants should submit an application using the outline application form which can be completed online. It will be acknowledged automatically by email. You will hear from us within four weeks whether or not we accept your outline application and wish to take it forward. If we accept your outline application, a member of our staff will contact you to progress your proposal. You will normally be asked to send further details about the proposed work which should include the following information – in this order and up to a maximum of eight pages in total: what do you aim to achieve? (please describe in approx 50 words); how will you achieve your aim(s)? (please describe in approx 50 words); how your specific objectives link with the aims of the scheme to which you are applying; job description (if you are applying for funding for a post); anticipated problems and how you will address them; start date and length of work; who will undertake the work?; number of beneficiaries; total budget for this work; exact breakdown of how PHF money would be spent; other funders/fundraising; monitoring and evaluation plans; dissemination strategy; sustainability/future funding; independent referee; appropriate letters of support.'

'Please ensure that the above information reaches us by email. You can send any additional supporting information by post if necessary. In addition to the details requested above, we would also like you to send us: an annual report and audited financial statements or equivalent (ideally electronically); name of your organisation's Chief Executive or equivalent. We will then assess your application. This may involve correspondence and meetings between our staff and your representatives, and may also include consultation with our trustees, advisers and independent referees. We will normally complete the assessment within two to three months of receiving the further details as listed above. The assessed proposal will then go to a decision making meeting. Applications for up to £10,000 are normally considered by staff. Applications over £10,000 and up to £150,000 are normally considered by the relevant programme committee. Applications for over £150,000, or applications which are novel or potentially contentious, are considered first by the relevant programme committee and then by the full board of trustees. The programme committees and the full board of trustees meet four times a year. We do not publish meeting dates. Please allow six months between making an outline application and the start date for the work you propose to carry out with our funding, or longer if the proposal is particularly large or complex. We will not consider applications from organisations outside the UK, or applications to help people who live outside the UK. This does not apply to our India programme.'

WHO TO APPLY TO Tony Davey, Information and Resources Officer, 5–11 Leeke Street, London WC1X 9HY *Tel* 020 7812 3300 *Fax* 020 7812 3310 *email* information@phf.org.uk *Website* www.phf.org.uk

....

■ The Helen Hamlyn Trust

CC NO 1084839   **ESTABLISHED** 2000

WHERE FUNDING CAN BE GIVEN Worldwide.

WHO CAN BENEFIT Organisations working in the fields of: medical, the arts and culture, education and welfare, heritage and conservation in India, international humanitarian affairs and healthy ageing. Within these areas of activity the trust also supports a number of projects with a design focus which are undertaken by the Helen Hamlyn Research Centre at the Royal College of Art, London.

WHAT IS FUNDED Individual projects aim to: support innovation in the medical arena; increase access to the arts and support the professional development of artists from the fields of music and the performing arts; increase intercultural understanding; provide opportunities for young people to develop new interests and practical skills which will contribute to their education and their future lives and to create opportunities for young offenders to acquire practical skills which will support their personal development for their future lives and reduce re-offending; conserve heritage in India for public access and cultural activities; support good practice in the humanitarian sector through educational programmes; and provide practical support to enable the elderly to maintain their independence for as long as possible.

SAMPLE GRANTS Imperial College, London (The Hamlyn Centre for Robotic Surgery) (£1 million); The Design Dimension Educational Trust (£275,000); The Royal Horticultural Society (£83,0000; The Society for the Advancement of Philosophical Enquiry and Reflection in Education (£64,000); Royal Opera House, Covent Garden (£48,000); Safe Ground (£10,000); and INTACH UK (£5,000).

FINANCES *Year* 2009–10 *Income* £2,864,706 *Grants* £1,945,970 *Assets* £4,605,782

TRUSTEES Lady Hamlyn; Dr Kate Gavron; Dr Shobita Punja; Brendan Cahill; Margaret O'Rorke; Anthony Edwards; Dr Deborah Swallow; Mark Bolland.

HOW TO APPLY 'The trustees bring forward recommendations for projects to support.'

WHO TO APPLY TO John Roche-Kuroda, Trust Administrator and Secretary, 129 Old Church Street, London SW3 6EB *Tel* 020 7351 5057 *Fax* 020 7352 3284 *email* john.rochekuroda@helenhamlyntrust.org

....

■ Sue Hammerson's Charitable Trust

CC NO 235196   **ESTABLISHED** 1957

WHERE FUNDING CAN BE GIVEN UK, with a slight preference for London.

WHO CAN BENEFIT Registered charities benefiting people disadvantaged by poverty, medical professionals, research workers and scientists.

WHAT IS FUNDED General charitable purposes. Particular consideration is given to the advancement of medical learning and research and to the relief of sickness and poverty. Substantial support is given to Lewis W Hammerson Memorial Home.

WHAT IS NOT FUNDED No grants to individuals.

RANGE OF GRANTS £100–£151,000, most grants are under £1,000.

SAMPLE GRANTS Lewis W Hammerson Memorial Home (£151,000); NA and GA Lightman Charitable Trust (£8,000); West London Synagogue (£6,900); National Theatre (£6,500); English National Opera (£6,000); Royal Academy of Arts (£3,500); Bobby Moore Fund for Cancer Research (£2,500); Diabetes UK (£2,000); St John's Hospice (£1,300); Shalom Foundation (£1,000); Alzheimer's Society (£750); Youth Aliyah Child Rescue and Motability (£500 each); CHASE (£250); Independent Age (£200); and Breadline Africa (£100).

FINANCES *Year* 2009–10 *Income* £242,123 *Grants* £256,225 *Assets* £7,280,077

TRUSTEES Sir Gavin Lightman; David Hammerson; Patricia Beecham; Peter Hammerson; Anthony Bernstein; Anthony Thompson; Rory Hammerson.

HOW TO APPLY In writing to the correspondent.

WHO TO APPLY TO The Trustees, c/o H W Fisher & Co, Chartered Accountants, Acre House, 11–15 William Road, London NW1 3ER *Tel* 020 7388 7000

■ The Hammonds Charitable Trust

CC NO 1064028   **ESTABLISHED** 1997

WHERE FUNDING CAN BE GIVEN Mainly Birmingham, London, Leeds, Bradford and Manchester.

WHO CAN BENEFIT Registered charities only.

WHAT IS FUNDED General charitable purposes.

RANGE OF GRANTS Usually up to £10,000.

SAMPLE GRANTS Business in the Community (£9,250); the Royal National Institute for Deaf People (£7,000); the Nordoff-Robbins Music Therapy Centre (£5,000); Orchid (£4,000); NSPCC (£3,400); the Prince's Trust (£2,500); Crohn's and Colitis in Childhood (£2,000); Shaare Zedek UK and the Healing Foundation (£1,000 each); Elim Church (£500); Brathay Trust (£300); Birmingham Centre for Arts Therapies (£200); Guy's Gift (£100); and Dodford Children's Holiday Farm (£70).

FINANCES *Year* 2009–10 *Income* £66,630 *Grants* £124,015 *Assets* £105,039

TRUSTEES S M Gordon; J S Forrest; S R Miller; S Kelly.

OTHER INFORMATION This trust was formerly known as The Hammond Suddards Edge Charitable Trust.

HOW TO APPLY This trust does not accept unsolicited applications.

WHO TO APPLY TO Linda Sylvester, Hammonds Solicitors, Rutland House, 148 Edmund Street, Birmingham B3 2JR *email* linda.sylvester@hammonds.com *Website* www.hammonds.com

---

■ The Hampshire and Islands Historic Churches Trust

CC NO 299633   **ESTABLISHED** 1988

WHERE FUNDING CAN BE GIVEN Hampshire, Isle of Wight and the Channel Islands.

WHO CAN BENEFIT Churches – interior and exterior.

WHAT IS FUNDED The restoration, preservation, repair, maintenance and improvement of churches, including monuments, fittings and furniture, in the area specified above.

WHAT IS NOT FUNDED Specific areas only.

RANGE OF GRANTS Up to £6,000.

SAMPLE GRANTS Wherwell – St Peter & Holy Cross (£6,000); Ventnor (IOW) – St Catherine (£5,000); Gosport Methodist Church, North Waltham – St Michael, Weston – Holy Trinity (£3,000 each); Highclere – St Michael & All Angels (£1,500); Bramdean – St Simon & St Jude, Newnham – St Nicholas (£500 each).

FINANCES *Year* 2010 *Income* £53,571 *Grants* £32,500 *Assets* £77,071

TRUSTEES Nick Jonas, Chair; Corinne Bennett; Revd John Cranmer; Ven. Adrian Harbidge; John Steel; Lady Joan Appleyard.

OTHER INFORMATION From the grant total, the trust also raised £42,600 as a result of the annual Bike Ride fundraising event.

HOW TO APPLY In writing to the correspondent. Grants are paid out only on submission of architects' certificates and receipted fee accounts, so there is sometimes a considerable delay between the trust offering a grant and actually making the payment.

WHO TO APPLY TO The Secretary, Hampshire Record Office, Sussex Street, Winchester, Hampshire SO23 8TH *Tel* 01962 760230 *Website* www.hampshirehistoricchurches.org.uk

---

■ Hampshire and Isle of Wight Community Foundation

CC NO 1100417   **ESTABLISHED** 2002

WHERE FUNDING CAN BE GIVEN Hampshire and Isle of Wight.

WHO CAN BENEFIT Individuals and organisations.

WHAT IS FUNDED General charitable purposes.

WHAT IS NOT FUNDED Specified locations only.

RANGE OF GRANTS £1,000–£15,000.

SAMPLE GRANTS Southampton Voluntary Services (£14,250); Island Youth Water Activities Centre (£9,000); Community Action Hampshire (£8,000); The Boleh Trust (£6,000); The Source Young People's Charity, The Students Exploring Marriage Trust, Groundwork Solent's Mix-Up Youth Project (£5,000 each).

FINANCES *Year* 2010 *Income* £2,236,580 *Grants* £126,526 *Assets* £4,355,483

TRUSTEES Tom Floyd; Pat James; John Barwick; Lena Samuels; Carole damper; Marcelle Speller; Chris Martin; Michael Woodhall; Miles Brown; Jonathan Moseley; Alistair Stokes; Rebecca Kennelly.

HOW TO APPLY Application forms can be downloaded from the foundation's website.

WHO TO APPLY TO Toni Shaw, Chief Executive Officer, Sun Alliance House, Wote Street, Basingstoke, Hampshire RG21 1LU *Tel* 01256 776101 *email* info@hantscf.org.uk *Website* www.hantscf.org.uk

---

■ The Hampstead Wells and Campden Trust

CC NO 1094611   **ESTABLISHED** 1971

WHERE FUNDING CAN BE GIVEN The former metropolitan borough of Hampstead; organisations covering a wider area but whose activities benefit Hampstead residents among others may also apply.

WHO CAN BENEFIT Organisations, institutions and individuals in Hampstead and Camden, benefiting children, young adults and older people, parents and children, ethnic minority groups, at risk groups, people who are disabled or disadvantaged by poverty, ex-offenders and those at risk of offending, refugees, homeless people, socially isolated people, and victims of abuse and domestic violence.

WHAT IS FUNDED The relief of people in need who are sick, convalescent, have disabilities or are infirm, and the relief generally of people in need or distress.

WHAT IS NOT FUNDED Grants may not be made towards the payment of rates or taxes, or in principle where statutory bodies have the responsibility to help.

TYPE OF GRANT One-off to individuals and organisations, some recurring.

SAMPLE GRANTS Royal Free Hospital (£27,000); Marie Curie Cancer Care (£18,000); Camden Community Law Centre (£15,000); Camden CAB (£12,500); Central & Cecil Housing Trust, Kingsgate Community Association, Mind in Camden, Tavistock for Couple Relationships (£10,000 each); Brandon Centre, Camden Arts Centre, Home Start Camden (£7,500 each); Food Chain (£3,000).

FINANCES *Year* 2010 *Income* £898,386 *Grants* £445,758 *Assets* £15,808,401

TRUSTEES Gaynor Bassey; Geoff Berridge; Michael Bieber; Linda Chung; Diana Dick; Francoise Findlay; Dennis Finning; Ian Harrison; Gaynor Humphreys; Alistair Jacks; David Sloman; Jocelyne Tobin; Revd Stephen Tucker; Alistair Voaden; George Webster; Christina Williams; Gareth Wilson.

OTHER INFORMATION In 2010, grants totalling £211,000 were awarded to individuals whilst £238,000 was awarded to organisations.

HOW TO APPLY Applications may be made at any time. The trustees meet eight times a year and in addition requests for smaller grants are considered at more frequent intervals. There is no application form (for organisations), but 'it is imperative to show, preferably with statistical information, how many people in the former metropolitan borough of Hampstead have been or will be helped by the project … Applications may be discussed with the staff of the trust prior to their submission'.

WHO TO APPLY TO Mrs Sheila A Taylor, Director/Clerk to the Trustees, 62 Rosslyn Hill, London NW3 1ND *Tel* 020 7435 1570 *Fax* 020 7435 1571 *email* grant@hwct.co.uk *Website* www. hwct.org.uk

···

■ Hampton Fuel Allotment Charity

CC NO 211756   **ESTABLISHED** 1811

WHERE FUNDING CAN BE GIVEN Hampton, the former borough of Twickenham, and the borough of Richmond (in that order). Individual grants only in the first two areas.

WHO CAN BENEFIT Community groups, voluntary organisations and individuals.

WHAT IS FUNDED Grants towards fuel costs; essential equipment; not for profit organisations which support those in need; hospitals and hospices; organisations supporting people with disabilities; social welfare; housing; education; community.

WHAT IS NOT FUNDED The charity is unlikely to support grants to individuals for private and post-compulsory education; adaptations or building alterations for individuals; holidays, except in cases of severe medical need; decoration, carpeting or central heating; anything which is the responsibility of a statutory body; national general charitable appeals; animal welfare; religious groups, unless offering a non-religious service to the community; commercial and business activities;

endowment appeals; political projects; retrospective capital grants.

TYPE OF GRANT Various including capital, one-off and loans.

RANGE OF GRANTS £100–£60,000.

SAMPLE GRANTS Richmond Citizens Advice Bureau Service (£60,000); Teddington Methodist Church & Community Centre – building improvements (£50,000); Age Concern Richmond (£50,000); St Stephen's Church – building extension (£50,000); London Borough of Richmond upon Thames Early Years and Childcare, and Richmond Youth Partnership (£45,000 each); Landmark Arts Centre (£17,000); National Autistic Society Richmond Branch (£6,000); Royal Hospital for Neuro-Disability (£4,000); Marble Hill Playcentres (£3,000); Mediation in Divorce (£2,000); Vietnamese Community Association in South West London (£1,800); Hampton Village Youth Football Club (£1,000); and Churches together in Teddington (£500).

FINANCES *Year* 2009–10 *Income* £1,766,680 *Grants* £1,720,052 *Assets* £43,367,113

TRUSTEES David Parish, Chair; Revd Derek Winterburn; Jonathan Cardy; David Cornwell; Stuart Leamy; Geoffrey Clarkson; Jamie Mortimer; P Williams; George Hunter; Marie Martin; Jane Young.

OTHER INFORMATION Of the grant total £904,00 was made in grants to organisations and £816,000 was paid in grants to individuals.

HOW TO APPLY In writing to the clerk on the application form available from the trust or its website, local vicarages, the Greenwood centre and the Citizens Advice Bureau together with guidelines for completing it. Health and social workers also have them for applying on behalf of their service users. Please do not send requests by email. On receipt of your application form the clerk will review it and may wish to ask further questions before submitting it to the trustees for consideration. All eligible applications will be considered. The individual grants panel meets every 2 months to consider applications. In urgent cases grants may be given in between these meetings. The board meets annually to decide the following year grant and household income levels. The general grants panel also meets every 2 months to consider applications from organisations. Communication concerning major projects is encouraged prior to application submission.

WHO TO APPLY TO M J Ryder, Clerk, 15 High Street, Hampton, Middlesex TW12 2SA *Tel* 020 8941 7866 *email* info@hamptonfuelcharity.co.uk *Website* www.hfac.co.uk

···

■ The W A Handley Charitable Trust

CC NO 230435   **ESTABLISHED** 1963

WHERE FUNDING CAN BE GIVEN Northumberland and Tyneside.

WHO CAN BENEFIT Registered charities only.

WHAT IS FUNDED General charitable purposes with preference for the alleviation of distress, crisis funding, pump-priming finance and operating expenses.

WHAT IS NOT FUNDED No grants to individuals. Grants are only made to registered charities.

TYPE OF GRANT Buildings; capital; core costs; endowments; feasibility studies; one-off; project; research; running costs; recurring costs; salaries; and start-up costs. Funding is available for up to one year.

RANGE OF GRANTS £1,000–£5,000.

SAMPLE GRANTS Cathedral Church of St Nicholas, Newcastle upon Tyne (£200,000); SSAFA Help for Heroes (£25,000); Gateshead Young Women's Outreach (£6,000); Prostate Research Campaign UK, Northumbria Youth Action, St Oswald's Hospice and Aquila Way (£5,000 each); Disability North and Combat Stress (£3,000); Salvation Army and NSPCC (£2,250); and Age Concern Newcastle, Children's Society and Listening Books (£1,000 each).

FINANCES *Year* 2009–10 *Income* £332,815 *Grants* £519,650 *Assets* £8,206,067

TRUSTEES Anthony Glenton; David Milligan; William Dryden; David Irvin.

OTHER INFORMATION No grants to individuals.

HOW TO APPLY In writing to the correspondent, quoting the applicant's official charity number and providing full back-up information. Grants are made quarterly in March, June, September and December.

WHO TO APPLY TO David Milligan, Trustee, c/o Ryecroft Glenton, 32 Portland Terrace, Jesmond, Newcastle upon Tyne NE1 1QP *Tel* 0191 281 1292 *email* davidmilligan@ryecroft-glenton.co.uk

■ Beatrice Hankey Foundation Ltd

CC NO 211093   **ESTABLISHED** 1949

WHERE FUNDING CAN BE GIVEN UK and overseas.

WHO CAN BENEFIT Institutions benefiting Christians.

WHAT IS FUNDED The advancement of the Christian religion, especially training missionaries. Study and training courses in Eastern Europe.

WHAT IS NOT FUNDED No grants for buildings or equipment.

TYPE OF GRANT Recurrent.

RANGE OF GRANTS Up to £14,000.

SAMPLE GRANTS Lagan College (£14,000); Corrymeela Community (£3,500); St Alfege's School Project (£3,000); The Dalitsu Trust – Malawi (£2,000); Friends of Burma (£1,500); and Mathieson Music Trust (£1,000).

FINANCES *Year* 2010 *Income* £46,206 *Grants* £35,150 *Assets* £1,056,949

TRUSTEES Revd David Faulks; H W Bright; Revd David Savill; T Halliday; A Y Stewart; H Walker; Canon David Haokip; Christine Legg; Pamela Macey; Wendy Hill; Selina Ormond; Daphne Sampson; Margaret Faulks; Crispin Wedell.

HOW TO APPLY Unsolicited applications cannot be considered.

WHO TO APPLY TO Melanie Churchill, Secretary, 11 Staverton Road, Werrington, Peterborough, Cambridgeshire PE4 6LY *Tel* 01733 571794

■ The Hanley Trust

CC NO 299209   **ESTABLISHED** 1987

WHERE FUNDING CAN BE GIVEN UK, with a preference for Corby and Rutland.

WHO CAN BENEFIT Registered charities benefiting at-risk groups, people disadvantaged by poverty and socially isolated people.

WHAT IS FUNDED Organisations concerned with social welfare and disadvantage.

WHAT IS NOT FUNDED Grants are not made to individuals or to non-registered charities.

RANGE OF GRANTS Up to a maximum of £4,000, with most grants made between £250 and £2,500.

SAMPLE GRANTS Butler Trust and Irene Taylor Trust (£2,500 each); Uppingham PCC (£2,000); Helen Arkell Dyslexia Centre and Shelter (£1,000 each); Young Minds, the Royal National Mission to Deep Sea Fishermen and Deafness Research UK (£500 each); Conservation Foundation,

Ladywood Furniture Project and Suffolk Punch Trust (£250 each); and Corby Furniture Turnabout Foundation (£100).

FINANCES *Year* 2009–10 *Income* £32,514 *Grants* £29,950 *Assets* £1,023,999

TRUSTEES Hon. Sarah Price, Chair; Hon. Samuel James Butler; William Swan.

HOW TO APPLY In writing to the correspondent.

WHO TO APPLY TO Hon. Mrs Sarah Price, Trustee, 21 Buckingham Gate, London SW1E 6LS

■ The Kathleen Hannay Memorial Charity

CC NO 299600   **ESTABLISHED** 1988

WHERE FUNDING CAN BE GIVEN UK.

WHO CAN BENEFIT Registered charities, universities and schools.

WHAT IS FUNDED General charitable purposes, particularly Christian causes, health, social welfare and education. The trust will consider funding, for example: community development; support to voluntary and community organisations; support to volunteers; social care professional bodies; the advancement of the Christian religion; churches including conservation of church buildings; Anglican and Free Church umbrella bodies; music; health; church schools; special schools; education and training; medical research; religion; social sciences; specialist research; and social care and development.

WHAT IS NOT FUNDED No grants to individuals or non-registered charities.

TYPE OF GRANT One-off grants for capital and revenue costs.

RANGE OF GRANTS £4,000 – £150,000.

SAMPLE GRANTS The Pennies Foundation (£150,000); the Story Museum and the Save the Children Fund (£50,000 each); and the Children's Fire & Burn Trust (£40,000).

FINANCES *Year* 2009–10 *Income* £183,770 *Grants* £580,805 *Assets* £12,953,822

TRUSTEES Jonathan F Weil; Simon P Weil; Christian Alison K Ward; Laura Watkins.

HOW TO APPLY In writing to the correspondent. The trustees usually meet in March (applications should be submitted in February).

WHO TO APPLY TO G Fincham, Administrator, 15 Suffolk Street, London SW1Y 4HG *Tel* 020 7036 5685

■ The Doughty Hanson Charitable Foundation

CC NO 1080755   **ESTABLISHED** 2000

WHERE FUNDING CAN BE GIVEN Unrestricted.

WHO CAN BENEFIT Registered charities.

WHAT IS FUNDED The relief of poverty distress and suffering, advancing education and appreciation in the arts and science, furthering religious work and other charitable purposes in any part of the world.

SAMPLE GRANTS Private Equity Foundation (£37,500); Voluntariado Jesus con los Ninos (£20,000); Parkinson's Disease Society (£15,000); Women's Aid (£10,000); NSPCC (£5,500); Afghan Action (£1,000); Breast Cancer Campaign (£230).

FINANCES *Year* 2010 *Income* £247,759 *Grants* £246,759 *Assets* £2,027

TRUSTEES Nigel Doughty; Richard Hanson; Stephen Marquardt; Richard Lund; Graeme Stening.

HOW TO APPLY In writing to the correspondent – the grants committee meets about four times a year. Only successful applicants receive a response.

WHO TO APPLY TO Julie Foreman, Secretary, PO Box 31064, London SW1Y 5ZP

■ Lord Hanson Foundation

CC NO 1077014   ESTABLISHED 1999
WHERE FUNDING CAN BE GIVEN Worldwide.
WHO CAN BENEFIT Charitable organisations.
WHAT IS FUNDED General charitable purposes.
RANGE OF GRANTS Up to £13,000.
SAMPLE GRANTS Raisa Gorbachev Foundation (£12,000); Hanson Research Trust (£10,000); Royal College of Radiologists, Help for Heroes and Imperial College Health Care Charity Fund (£1,000) and The Children's Charity (£500).
FINANCES Year 2009–10 Income £45,529 Grants £25,500 Assets £53,889
TRUSTEES Jonathan G. A. Azis; Alan Hagdrup; The Hon Robert Hanson.
HOW TO APPLY In writing to the correspondent.
WHO TO APPLY TO Miss Gillian Ryan, 31 Wilton Row, London SW1X 7NS Tel 020 7245 6996

■ The Haramead Trust

CC NO 1047416   ESTABLISHED 1995
WHERE FUNDING CAN BE GIVEN Worldwide, in practice, developing countries, UK and Ireland and locally in the east Midlands.
WHO CAN BENEFIT Registered charities and individuals and families in need of direct assistance.
WHAT IS FUNDED Children, social welfare, education, people with disabilities, homeless people, medical assistance, victims and oppressed people and religious activities.
TYPE OF GRANT Core support, building/renovation, equipment, vehicles and project support will all be considered.
RANGE OF GRANTS £1,000–£130,000.
SAMPLE GRANTS Action Aid (£130,000); Leicestershire Leicester & Rutland Community (£60,000); Launde Abbey and Menphys (£50,000 each); and Brainwave, Concern Worldwide, De Paul Trust, Duke of Edinburgh's Award, Emmaus, International Childcare Trust, Laura Centre, Leicester Rape Crisis, Raleigh International, Scope and World Orthopaedic Concern (£10,000 each).
FINANCES Year 2009–10 Income £644,866 Grants £870,200 Assets £237,349
TRUSTEES Simon P Astill; Mrs Winifred M Linnett; Michael J Linnett; Robert H Smith; David L Tams; Revd Joseph A Mullen.
OTHER INFORMATION Grants between £5,000 and £9,999 totalled £436,500; grants of less than £5,000 totalled £33,700.
HOW TO APPLY In writing to the correspondent. The trustees meet every couple of months and may visit funded projects for monitoring purposes or to assess for future grants.
WHO TO APPLY TO Michael J Linnett, Trustee, Park House, Park Hill, Gaddesby, Leicestershire LE7 4WH

■ Miss K M Harbinson's Charitable Trust

WHERE FUNDING CAN BE GIVEN UK and developing countries.
WHO CAN BENEFIT Development organisations.
WHAT IS FUNDED International development.
RANGE OF GRANTS £1,000–£9,000.
SAMPLE GRANTS Previous beneficiaries have included ActionAid, British Red Cross Worldwide Fund for Nature, Breadline Africa, Care Britain, Ethopiaid Intermediate Technology, Marie Stopes International, Oxfam, Romanian Orphanage Trust, Sight Savers International, UNICEF.
FINANCES Year 2009–10 Income £151,495
TRUSTEES A Maguire; G L Harbinson; R Harbinson.
OTHER INFORMATION Up-to-date information was unavailable for this trust.
HOW TO APPLY In writing to the correspondent.
WHO TO APPLY TO The Secretary, 190 St Vincent Street, Glasgow G2 5SP Tel 0141 204 2833

■ Harbo Charities Limited

CC NO 282262   ESTABLISHED 1981
WHERE FUNDING CAN BE GIVEN UK.
WHO CAN BENEFIT Charities, and scholastic and religious institutions.
WHAT IS FUNDED General charitable purposes and Jewish causes, particularly those which provide financial support and basic necessities to 'the poor', support Jewish education and places of worship for the Jewish community and provide relief of sickness and disability.
SAMPLE GRANTS Previous beneficiaries have included: Beis Chinuch Lebonos Girls' School, Beth Rochel d'Satmar, Bobov Trust, Chevras Maoz Ladol, Craven Walk Charitable Trust, Edgware Yeshiva Trust, Keren Yesomim, Kollel Shomrei HaChomoth, Tevini Limited, Tomchei Shabbos, Yad Eliezer, Yesode Ha Torah School and Yeshiva Chachmay Tsorpha.
FINANCES Year 2009–10 Income £104,100 Grants £97,381 Assets £760,483
TRUSTEES Harry Stern; Barbara Stern; Harold Gluck.
HOW TO APPLY In writing to the correspondent.
WHO TO APPLY TO The Trustees, c/o Cohen Arnold, New Burlington House, 1075 Finchley Road, London NW11 0PU Tel 020 8731 0777

■ The Harborne Parish Lands Charity

CC NO 219031   ESTABLISHED 1699
WHERE FUNDING CAN BE GIVEN The ancient parish of Harborne, which includes parts of Harborne, Smethwick, Bearwood and Quinton.
WHO CAN BENEFIT All grants must benefit people living within the parish.
WHAT IS FUNDED Charities working in the fields of: accommodation and housing; infrastructure and technical support; infrastructure development; healthcare; health facilities and buildings; physical and mental disability organisations; schools; education and training; community centres and village halls; playgrounds and community services; individual need and other charitable purposes.
TYPE OF GRANT Buildings, capital, core costs, interest-free loans, one-off, project, running costs, salaries and start-up costs. Funding for up to one year will be considered.
RANGE OF GRANTS £300–£18,000.

Think carefully about every application. Is it justified?

593

SAMPLE GRANTS Cares Sandwell (£18,000); St Albans Community Centre (£8,500); Ask Big Dave CIC Anti-Bullying (£6,500); Friends of Clathorpe Haven, Lift & WHF Community Project and Focus Birmingham (£5,000); Sandwell Young Carers (£3,500); Home Start Birmingham & Sandwell, Sense and All Nations Steel Band (£2,000).

FINANCES *Year* 2009–10 *Income* £1,032,619 *Grants* £224,936 *Assets* £13,833,490

TRUSTEES Cllr J E C Alden; Cllr P Hollingworth; Mr P John; M Lloyd; J S Gregory; Mrs V Montague-Smith; Mr F Wayt; R Horton; Mrs R Silber; Mr A Lawrence; Cllr V Silvester.

OTHER INFORMATION During the period 1 July 2009 to 30 June 2010 134 grants to individuals were approved, the total value of goods provided being £55,000.

HOW TO APPLY In writing to the correspondent. An exact map of the beneficial area can be obtained from the trust (or on its website) and should be consulted before an application is submitted. Further information can be obtained from the trust's website.

WHO TO APPLY TO Miss L J Bending, Clerk to the Trustees, 109 Court Oak Road, Harborne, Birmingham B17 9AA *Tel* 0121 426 1600 *Fax* 0121 428 2267 *email* theclerk@hplc.fednet.org.uk *Website* www.harborneparishlandscharity.org.uk

■ The Harbour Charitable Trust

CC NO 234268 **ESTABLISHED** 1962

WHERE FUNDING CAN BE GIVEN UK.

WHO CAN BENEFIT Organisations benefiting children, young adults and students. Support may also be given to teachers and governesses, medical professionals, research workers, parents and children and one-parent families.

WHAT IS FUNDED Childcare, education and healthcare, and other charitable organisations.

WHAT IS NOT FUNDED Grants are given to registered charities only.

SAMPLE GRANTS Grants were made in the following categories: Joint Jewish Charitable Trust (£38,000); healthcare (£40,000); education (£6,000); aged care (£4,000); childcare (£2,000); and other donations (£13,000).

FINANCES *Year* 2009–10 *Income* £291,187 *Grants* £102,811 *Assets* £3,464,934

TRUSTEES Mrs B B Green; Mrs Z S Blackman; Mrs T Elsenstat; Mrs E Knobil.

HOW TO APPLY In writing to the correspondent.

WHO TO APPLY TO The Trustees, Barbican House, 26–34 Old Street, London EC1V 9QQ

■ The Harbour Foundation

CC NO 264927 **ESTABLISHED** 1970

WHERE FUNDING CAN BE GIVEN Worldwide, with a preference for London.

WHO CAN BENEFIT Organisations and individuals.

WHAT IS FUNDED There is a preference for at risk groups, people disadvantaged by poverty, people who are homeless, refugees and people who are socially isolated. Support may also be given to research workers and students.

TYPE OF GRANT Recurring costs.

RANGE OF GRANTS Up to £200,000.

SAMPLE GRANTS Royal College of Music, London; Tel Aviv Foundation, Israel (£15,000 each).

FINANCES *Year* 2009–10 *Income* £1,494,796 *Grants* £482,254 *Assets* £55,924,172

TRUSTEES S R Harbour; A C Humphries; D Harbour; Rex Harbour.

HOW TO APPLY In writing to the correspondent. Applications need to be received by February, as trustees meet in March.

WHO TO APPLY TO The Trustees, 1 Red Place, London W1K 6PL *Tel* 020 7456 8180

■ The Harding Trust

CC NO 328182 **ESTABLISHED** 1989

WHERE FUNDING CAN BE GIVEN Mainly, but not exclusively, north Staffordshire and surrounding areas.

WHO CAN BENEFIT To benefit actors and entertainment professionals; musicians; textile workers and designers; writers and poets; at risk groups; people who are ill or disadvantaged by poverty; and socially isolated people. Consideration will be given to national charities if there is a good reason for doing so.

WHAT IS FUNDED To give to smaller rather than larger charities. Charities supported are in most cases connected with music and the arts but local welfare charities and hospices are also given support.

TYPE OF GRANT One-off and recurrent.

SAMPLE GRANTS Previous grants beneficiaries included: Donna Louise Trust, Douglas Macmillan Hospice, Harding Trust Piano Recitals, Katharine House Hospice, Patrons Victoria Hall Organ, St John's Ambulance, Stoke on Trent Festival, Stoke on Trent Music School – Education Scheme, Wolverhampton Civic Hall Orchestra and Wolverhampton Recital Series.

FINANCES *Year* 2009–10 *Income* £116,152 *Grants* £120,600 *Assets* £3,561,032

TRUSTEES G G Wall; J P C Fowell; M N Lloyd; G B Snow.

HOW TO APPLY In writing to the correspondent. The trustees meet annually in spring/early summer. Accounts are needed for recurrent applications.

WHO TO APPLY TO Peter O'Rourke, Brabners Chaffe Street, Horton House, Exchange Flags, Liverpool L2 3YL *Tel* 0151 600 3000 *email* peter.orourke@brabnerscs.com

■ William Harding's Charity

CC NO 310619 **ESTABLISHED** 1978

WHERE FUNDING CAN BE GIVEN Aylesbury in Buckinghamshire.

WHO CAN BENEFIT Older people, those in the charity's almshouse accommodation and young people under the age of 25 to further their education.

WHAT IS FUNDED To assist young people in education, including at an individual level, by providing scholarships, maintenance allowances, travel awards and grants for equipment. At a wider level, grants are made to the LEA for Aylesbury schools to fund equipment in addition to that which can be provided by the authority. The charity also provides relief in need and for the general benefit of Aylesbury residents.

WHAT IS NOT FUNDED 'All persons and organisations not based in Aylesbury Town.'

TYPE OF GRANT One-off and capital.

RANGE OF GRANTS £500–£200,000 (organisations).

SAMPLE GRANTS Skill Centre UK (£15,000); Aylesbury Grammar School and Aylesbury Citizens Advice Bureau (£10,000 each); and Gerald Simmonds Healthcare (£6,000); Aylesbury Homestarts (£5,000); Grange Youth Centre (£3,500); Girl Guide Bucks (£2,250); Yours Social Club (£1,500); Jansel's 60 Club (£1,250) and Thursday Morning Club (£1,100).

FINANCES *Year* 2010 *Income* £691,447
Grants £304,890 *Assets* £23,341,878

TRUSTEES Bernard Griffin, Chair; William Chapple; Mrs Freda Roberts; Leslie Sheldon; Mrs Betty Foster; John Vooght; Mrs Kathleen Brooker; Mrs Penni Thorne; Roger Evans.

OTHER INFORMATION Grants to organisations totalled £220,000. Grants were also made to 143 individuals totalling £85,000.

HOW TO APPLY In writing to the correspondent. Trustees meet on a monthly basis to consider and determine applications for charitable assistance.

WHO TO APPLY TO J Leggett, Parrott and Coales LLP, 14 Bourbon Street, Aylesbury, Buckinghamshire HP20 2RS *Tel* 01296 318501 *Website* www.whardingcharity.org.uk

---

■ The Hare of Steep Charitable Trust

CC NO 297308   **ESTABLISHED** 1987

WHERE FUNDING CAN BE GIVEN UK, with preference for the south of England, especially Petersfield and East Hampshire.

WHO CAN BENEFIT Registered charities only.

WHAT IS FUNDED Charities which benefit the community, in particular the advancement of social, cultural, medical, educational and religious projects.

WHAT IS NOT FUNDED No funding for overseas charities, students, visits abroad or political causes.

TYPE OF GRANT Mainly annual contributions but one-off grants are made for special projects.

RANGE OF GRANTS £250–£2,000.

SAMPLE GRANTS Previous beneficiaries include: £1,500 each to Alzheimer's Disease Society, Arthritis and Rheumatism Council – Petersfield, British Heart Foundation, Rainbow House Trust and SSAFA.

FINANCES *Year* 2009–10 *Income* £41,363
Grants £49,250 *Assets* £145,101

TRUSTEES P L F Baillon; J S Grenfell; J R F Fowler; S M Fowler; S E R Johnson-Hill.

HOW TO APPLY 'The trustees already support as many charities as they could wish and would certainly not welcome any appeals from others. Unsolicited requests are not acknowledged.'

WHO TO APPLY TO Mrs S M Fowler, Hon. Secretary, 56 Heath Road, Petersfield, Hampshire GU31 4EJ *Tel* 01730 267953

■ The Harebell Centenary Fund

CC NO 1003552   **ESTABLISHED** 1991

WHERE FUNDING CAN BE GIVEN UK.

WHO CAN BENEFIT UK and small charitable organisations benefiting children, older people, carers, people who have a disability and animals.

WHAT IS FUNDED Neurological research and animal welfare. This includes charities working in the fields of health, medical studies and research, conservation, heritage, special needs education and holidays and outings.

WHAT IS NOT FUNDED No grants are made towards infrastructure or to individuals.

TYPE OF GRANT One-off, core costs, research, recurring costs, running costs and funding for one year or less will be considered.

RANGE OF GRANTS Up to £4,000.

FINANCES *Year* 2009–10 *Income* £69,066
Grants £65,000 *Assets* £1,985,571

TRUSTEES J M Denker; M I Goodbody.

HOW TO APPLY In writing to the correspondent. Unsolicited applications are not requested, as the trustees prefer to make donations to charities whose work they have come across through their own research.

WHO TO APPLY TO Ms P J Chapman, 50 Broadway, London SW1H 0BL *Tel* 020 7227 7000 *email* pennychapman@bdb-law.co.uk

---

■ The Hargrave Foundation

CC NO 1106524   **ESTABLISHED** 2004

WHERE FUNDING CAN BE GIVEN Worldwide.

WHO CAN BENEFIT Registered charities.

WHAT IS FUNDED General, medical, welfare.

RANGE OF GRANTS Up to £10,000.

SAMPLE GRANTS Institute of Healing of Memories (£38,000); Reform Research Trust (£20,000); British Liver Trust, Prostate Cancer Charity, Writers & Scholars Educational Trust and English Pen (£10,000 each). Grants were also made to other charities amounting to £32,000.

FINANCES *Year* 2009–10 *Income* £151,083
Grants £129,283 *Assets* £2,851,597

TRUSTEES Stephen Hargrave; Dominic Moseley; Mark Parkin.

OTHER INFORMATION In 2009–10 an additional £5,000 was given in grants to individuals.

HOW TO APPLY In writing to the correspondent.

WHO TO APPLY TO Stephen Hargrave, Trustee, 47 Lamb's Conduit Street, London WC1N 3NG

■ The Kenneth Hargreaves Charitable Trust

CC NO 223800   **ESTABLISHED** 1957

WHERE FUNDING CAN BE GIVEN UK, with a preference for Wetherby area of Leeds.

WHO CAN BENEFIT Registered charities benefiting children, young adults, students, medical professionals, community workers, research workers, teachers and project workers.

WHAT IS FUNDED Health, social welfare, arts, education, the environment and conservation.

WHAT IS NOT FUNDED No grants to individuals. Applications for core funding or salaries are rarely considered.

TYPE OF GRANT Preference is given to capital rather than revenue funding.

RANGE OF GRANTS Usually £100–£2,000.

SAMPLE GRANTS Yorkshire Cancer Centre (£25,000); Children with Leukaemia (£2,000); Selby Abbey Trust (£1,000); Hepworth Art Gallery (£500); Yorkshire Foundation For Conservation & Craftsmen (£250); and Barn Owl Trust (£100).

TRUSTEES Dr Ingrid Roscoe; Mrs M Hargreaves-Allen; Mrs Sheila Holbrook; P R P Chadwick.

OTHER INFORMATION Small one-off grants, especially to groups using volunteers.

HOW TO APPLY In writing to the correspondent including clear details of the intended project, an outline budget and an annual report. The trustees meet quarterly. Only successful applicants will be acknowledged.

WHO TO APPLY TO Mrs Sheila Holbrook, Hon. Treasurer, The Hollies, 67 Millbeck Green, Collingham, Nr Wetherby, Yorkshire LS22 5AG

■ The Harris Charitable Trust

CC NO 292652 **ESTABLISHED** 1966

WHERE FUNDING CAN BE GIVEN UK, with a preference for Merton.

WHO CAN BENEFIT Registered charities known to the trustees.

WHAT IS FUNDED General charitable purposes.

RANGE OF GRANTS £50–£3,000.

SAMPLE GRANTS Past beneficiaries obtaining grants of over £1,000 each have included those made to: the British Heart Foundation; Cancer Research; Freeways Trust; MS Society – Merton; Noah's Ark Trust and Rochester Cathedral Trust.

TRUSTEES Diana Harris; Colin Harris; Dr Andrew Harris; Thomas Harris.

HOW TO APPLY The trust does not respond to unsolicited applications.

WHO TO APPLY TO Mrs Diana Harris, 101 Church Road, Wimbledon, London SW19 5AL

■ The Harris Charity

CC NO 526206 **ESTABLISHED** 1883

WHERE FUNDING CAN BE GIVEN Lancashire, with a preference for the City of Preston (formally the borough of Preston.).

WHO CAN BENEFIT Young people.

WHAT IS FUNDED Charities benefiting individuals, children and young people under 25, in the Lancashire area.

TYPE OF GRANT Capital projects and provision of equipment are preferred.

RANGE OF GRANTS £30 to £4,000.

SAMPLE GRANTS Brownedge St. Mary's & The Coppice School and Holy Cross High School (£4,000); Leyland (St Mary's) Scout Group (£3,000); St.Cuthbert's Playgroup & Youth Group (£1,000) and Friends of Stoneyholme Park (£300).

FINANCES *Year* 2009–10 *Income* £100,117 *Grants* £105,000 *Assets* £2,996,208

TRUSTEES W S Huck; E J Booth; Miss B Banks; S R Fisher; T Scott; S B R Smith; S Huck; Mrs R Jolly; K Mellalieu; Mrs A Scott; Mrs N Fielden.

OTHER INFORMATION During the year, £56,000 was given in grants to individuals.

HOW TO APPLY Application forms are available from the trustees, on which the applicant is invited to submit a summary of their proposal. The trustees meet quarterly to discuss grant applications that are approved twice a year in March and September. Each candidate is informed of the outcome of their application and if successful will be asked to provide the trustees with the relevant documents and/or invoices so that the funds can be released.

WHO TO APPLY TO P R Metcalf, Secretary, Richard House, 9 Winckley Square, Preston, Lancashire PR1 3HP *Tel* 01772 821021 *Fax* 01772 259441 *email* harrischarity@mooreandsmalley.co.uk

■ The Harris Family Charitable Trust

CC NO 1064394 **ESTABLISHED** 1997

WHERE FUNDING CAN BE GIVEN UK.

WHO CAN BENEFIT Charitable organisations.

WHAT IS FUNDED Health issues and the alleviation of sickness.

FINANCES *Year* 2009–10 *Income* £10,573 *Grants* £381,982

TRUSTEES R M Harris; Loretta Harris; Charlotte Emma Harris.

HOW TO APPLY 'The charity invites applications for funding of projects through various sources. The applications are reviewed by the trustees who ensure that they are in accordance with the charity's objectives.'

WHO TO APPLY TO R M Harris, Trustee, 65 New Cavendish Street, London W1G 7LS *Tel* 020 7467 6300

■ The Edith Lilian Harrison 2000 Foundation

CC NO 1085651 **ESTABLISHED** 2000

WHERE FUNDING CAN BE GIVEN UK.

WHO CAN BENEFIT Registered charities.

WHAT IS FUNDED General charitable purposes.

SAMPLE GRANTS Alzheimer's Society (£29,500); and Cardiac Risk in the Young – CRY and Salisbury Hospice (£20,000 each).

FINANCES *Year* 2009–10 *Income* £71,799 *Grants* £69,500 *Assets* £2,629,274

TRUSTEES Geoffrey Peyer; Clive Andrews; Paul Bradley.

HOW TO APPLY In writing to the correspondent. The trustees meet quarterly. At each regular meeting, applications for grants are considered and duly dealt with.

WHO TO APPLY TO Geoffrey Peyer, Trustee, TWM Solicitors, 40 West Street, Reigate, Surrey RH2 9BT *Tel* 01737 221212 *Fax* 01737 240120 *email* reigate.reception@twmsolicitors.com

■ The Harrison and Potter Trust

CC NO 224941 **ESTABLISHED** 1970

WHERE FUNDING CAN BE GIVEN Leeds (pre-1974 boundary).

WHO CAN BENEFIT Individuals, or organisations supporting people in need who are resident in Leeds.

WHAT IS FUNDED Individuals can be given grants for heat, lighting, equipment, clothing and holidays. Organisations or projects concerned with homeless, older people, young mothers and unemployed people are supported.

WHAT IS NOT FUNDED The trust cannot commit to repeat grants.

TYPE OF GRANT One-off and project.

FINANCES *Year* 2010 *Income* £243,108 *Grants* £32,462 *Assets* £4,380,614

TRUSTEES G Whitehead, Chair; Dr I A Blomfield; P G Wooler; W J A Smith; Mrs H A Vinall; Mrs J V White; Lord Mayor of Leeds; Vicar of Leeds; Local Authority Representative.

HOW TO APPLY In writing to the correspondent to be considered in February, May, August and November. Individuals must write requesting an application form and these will be considered monthly.

WHO TO APPLY TO Miss A S Duchart, Clerk, Wrigleys Solicitors, 19 Cookridge Street, Leeds LS2 3AG *Tel* 0113 204 5710

■ The John Harrison Charitable Trust

CC NO 277956 **ESTABLISHED** 1979

WHERE FUNDING CAN BE GIVEN UK.

WHO CAN BENEFIT Organisations concerned with multiple sclerosis.

WHAT IS FUNDED Multiple Sclerosis support and research.

SAMPLE GRANTS Multiple Sclerosis Trust (£8,000). Previous beneficiaries have included: Andover &RD MS Soc (£885); Whizz Kidz (£5,000).
FINANCES *Year* 2010–11 *Income* £76,857 *Grants* £8,000 *Assets* £1,734,025
TRUSTEES Judy Sebba; Iris Sebba; Sian Crookes.
HOW TO APPLY In writing to the correspondent.
WHO TO APPLY TO David Hull, PO Box 326, Bedford MK40 3XU *Tel* 01234 266657

....

■ The Peter Harrison Foundation

CC NO 1076579   **ESTABLISHED** 1999
WHERE FUNDING CAN BE GIVEN UK and south east England.
WHO CAN BENEFIT Registered charities, community amateur sports clubs, friendly or provident societies and organisations in Scotland and Northern Ireland recognised by the Inland Revenue.
WHAT IS FUNDED Charitable activities capable of demonstrating an existing high level of committed voluntary members with strong self-help activities together with well-planned and thought out projects under the following categories: Opportunities Through Sport Programme – support for sporting activities or projects which provide opportunities for children and young people who have disabilities or those who are disadvantaged, to fulfil their potential, and for other personal and life skills to be developed; Special Needs and Care Programme for Children and Young People – only for organisations in south east England; Opportunities Through Education Programme – applications not invited. Grants are also made through the Trustees' Discretionary Programme – again, invitations are not invited.
WHAT IS NOT FUNDED General appeals; retrospective funding; individuals; other grant-making bodies to make grants on its behalf; projects that replace statutory funding; projects that are the responsibility of the central or local government; holidays in the UK or abroad and expeditions; outdoor activity projects such as camping or outward bound expeditions; overseas projects; projects solely for the promotion of religion.
RANGE OF GRANTS £100–£100,000.
SAMPLE GRANTS British Paralympic Association (£75,000); the Orpheus Trust (£53,000); Reigate and Redhill YMCA (£50,000); the Rose Road Association and SeeAbility (£45,000 each); Lake District Calvert Trust (£40,000); Access Sport (£35,000); Royal Caledonian Curling Club (£30,000); Carers First (£21,000); Poole Sailability (£20,000); the National Autistic Society (£19,000); Brittle Bone Society (£11,000); Different Strokes (£9,800); and Sportability (£7,500).
FINANCES *Year* 2009–10 *Income* £2,954,418 *Grants* £1,967,447 *Assets* £38,738,770
TRUSTEES Peter Harrison, Chair; Joy Harrison; Julia Harrison-Lee; Peter Lee.
HOW TO APPLY The foundation has a two stage application process.
Step 1: Initial enquiry
Potential applicants are asked to first read the information on eligibility and grant programmes available on the foundation's website. If your project meets the criteria for one of the open programmes (i.e. Opportunities through Sport or Special Needs and Care for Children and Young People), then complete the online initial enquiry form. This can be found in the 'application process' section of the foundation's website. Applications are processed as quickly as possible, but please be aware that the foundation receives a large number of applications and it may sometimes take up to two months for an initial enquiry form to be considered. Applications are first assessed by the foundation's staff. If it is felt the project will be of interest, they will arrange either to visit the project or to conduct a telephone discussion with the applicant about it. Depending on the outcome of these discussions, you may then be invited to submit a full application. If your initial enquiry is not successful you will be notified by email. The foundation receives many more applications than it is able to support and unfortunately have turn down many good proposals, even though they meet the criteria. No feedback is given on unsuccessful applications.
Step 2: Full application
Applicants should only submit a full application form if their initial enquiry has been successful. Completed forms should be sent by post to the correspondent. If an application is successful the applicant will normally be contacted by telephone followed by a grant offer letter. The letter will explain the conditions which apply to all grant awards and also set out any special conditions which apply to your organisation. It will also confirm details of how and when you will receive the grant and how payment is made. If an application is unsuccessful the applicant will be informed by letter. The main reason for not funding projects is the volume of applications received. Organisations supported by the foundation are required to show how they have used the grant and, depending on the grant amount and the nature of the project, may be asked to undertake a review and evaluation of the project being funded. This will normally be on completion of the project, but for charities receiving their grant in several instalments, interim reports may be requested. Full details of the monitoring information required are given in the foundation's grant offer letter. The foundation aims to ensure that all grant applications that are eligible for consideration within the foundation's grants criteria are given equal consideration, irrespective of gender, sexual orientation, race, colour, ethnic or national origin, or disability.
WHO TO APPLY TO John Ledlie, Director, Foundation House, 42–48 London Road, Reigate, Surrey RH2 9QQ *Tel* 01737 228000 *Fax* 01737 228 001 *email* enquiries@peterharrisonfoundation. org *Website* www.peterharrisonfoundation.org

....

■ The Spencer Hart Charitable Trust

CC NO 800057   **ESTABLISHED** 1988
WHERE FUNDING CAN BE GIVEN UK and overseas.
WHO CAN BENEFIT Registered charities.
WHAT IS FUNDED General charitable purposes.
RANGE OF GRANTS Most grants made in region of £100 to £5,000.
SAMPLE GRANTS The League of the Helping Hand and Norwood (£5,000 each); Most Mira and Wigmore Hall Trust (£1,000 each); Pancreatic Cancer Research Fund (£750); and RNLI (£250).
FINANCES *Year* 2010 *Income* £32,895 *Grants* £19,200
TRUSTEES J S Korn; I A Burman.
HOW TO APPLY In writing to the correspondent.
WHO TO APPLY TO J S Korn, Trustee, Laytons, Carmelite, 50 Victoria Embankment, Blackfriars, London EC4Y OLS *Tel* 020 7842 8000 *Fax* 020 7842 8080 *email* london@laytons.com

■ The Hartley Charitable Trust

CC NO 800968 **ESTABLISHED** 1989
WHERE FUNDING CAN BE GIVEN Unrestricted.
WHO CAN BENEFIT Organisations.
WHAT IS FUNDED General charitable purposes.
WHAT IS NOT FUNDED No grants to individuals.
TYPE OF GRANT One-off and recurrent grants for core costs, projects, research and salaries, for one year or less.
RANGE OF GRANTS £1,000–£30,000.
SAMPLE GRANTS Alzheimer's Society (£30,000); National Association of Clubs for Young People (£15,000); Open Arms Malawi (£7,000); Royal National Lifeboat Institute (£5,800); Senior Volunteer Network Trust and Celtic Storm – Cornwall Powerchair Football Club (£5,000); Marie Curie Cancer Care, Martin House and Yorkshire Cancer Research (£1,000).
FINANCES *Year* 2009–10 *Income* £61,713 *Grants* £70,793 *Assets* £1,738,747
TRUSTEES Charles Richard Hartley; Mrs Jane Hartley; Mrs Peta Elizabeth Hillard Hyland.
HOW TO APPLY In August 2011 the trust told us: 'We are fully committed for 4–5 years. It would be better if you indicated this in your publications and website, as organisations and individuals are wasting money in putting applications to us.'
WHO TO APPLY TO Mr Rick Hartley, Sunnyside Farm, Brearton, Harrogate, Yorkshire HG3 3BX *Tel* 01423 869369 *Fax* 01423 525313 *email* hartleycharitabletrust@hotmail.com

■ The N and P Hartley Memorial Trust

CC NO 327570 **ESTABLISHED** 1987
WHERE FUNDING CAN BE GIVEN Unrestricted with a preference for West Yorkshire.
WHO CAN BENEFIT Organisations benefiting people who are disabled, elderly or terminally ill, children and young people, medical research and the environment.
WHAT IS FUNDED The trust supports individuals and community organisations benefiting people who have disabilities, older people, young people and people who are sick, including the provision of medical facilities and care for all age groups. Particular attention is given to smaller charities and individuals in need where relatively small donations may have the greatest impact. It will support both old and new causes.
WHAT IS NOT FUNDED The trust does not support the arts or animal welfare. Grants are not made for non-vocational higher education.
TYPE OF GRANT One-off and recurring.
SAMPLE GRANTS Previous beneficiaries included: St George's Crypt; South Yorkshire Community; Mercy Ships; and Hainworth Wood Community Centre.
FINANCES *Year* 2008–09 *Income* £16,099 *Grants* £90,000
TRUSTEES Mrs V B Watson; Dr James Jason Procter; John Kirman; Mrs Gwen Procter.
HOW TO APPLY In writing to the correspondent. Applications are considered at meetings held twice a year, although urgent cases can be considered outside these meetings. Relevant accounts or budget should be enclosed. Reapplications from previous beneficiaries are welcomed.
WHO TO APPLY TO The Administrator, 24 Holywell Lane, Leeds LS17 8HA

■ The Alfred And Peggy Harvey Charitable Trust

CC NO 1095855 **ESTABLISHED** 2003
WHERE FUNDING CAN BE GIVEN UK, with a strong preference for Kent, Surrey and South East London.
WHO CAN BENEFIT Mostly registered charities.
WHAT IS FUNDED The trust has four main objects: the advancement and funding of medical and surgical studies and research; the care of the elderly and the provision of accommodation for the elderly; the care of and provision of financial support for disabled children and young people and for children and young people suffering from the lack of stable family upbringing or other social or educational disadvantages; and the care of blind and deaf people.
RANGE OF GRANTS £1,000–£10,000.
SAMPLE GRANTS Macular Disease Society (£10,000); Country Holidays For Inner City Kids (£6,400); Lighthouse Educational Scheme (£4,700); E-Learning Foundation (£4,000); Hope UK (£3,800); Children's Country Holiday Fund (£3,500); Kidscape (£3,000); Happy Days (£2,500); Action for Kids (£2,000); and Child Victims of Crime (£1,000).
FINANCES *Year* 2009–10 *Income* £84,041 *Grants* £53,314 *Assets* £329,794
TRUSTEES Colin John Russell; John Duncan; Kevin James Custis.
HOW TO APPLY In writing to the correspondent.
WHO TO APPLY TO The Trustees, c/o Manches LLP, Aldwych House, 81 Aldwych, London WC2B 4RP *Tel* 020 7404 4433

■ William Geoffrey Harvey's Discretionary Settlement

CC NO 800473 **ESTABLISHED** 1968
WHERE FUNDING CAN BE GIVEN Unrestricted with some preference for north west England.
WHO CAN BENEFIT Registered charities.
WHAT IS FUNDED Animal facilities and services to promote the well-being of, and prevent cruelty to, animals and birds.
WHAT IS NOT FUNDED Please note, the trustees state that the settlor Mrs Harvey gave them 'a clear indication of the causes she favoured and [they] are guided by that for the moment at least'. New applicants will not be considered.
TYPE OF GRANT Running costs and capital expenditure.
RANGE OF GRANTS £10,000–£40,000.
SAMPLE GRANTS People's Dispensary for Sick Animals (£40,000); St Tiggywinkles (£26,000); The Donkey Sanctuary (£24,000); Dog's Trust (£20,000) and Home of Rest for Horses (£10,000).
FINANCES *Year* 2009–10 *Income* £131,719 *Grants* £87,000 *Assets* £551,042
TRUSTEES G J Hull (chair), F R Shackleton; S A Hull, N J Joyce.
OTHER INFORMATION The trustees aim to provide grants to charities favoured by the Harvey family. These grants are intended to fund projects that, without the funding, would not materialise.
HOW TO APPLY Previously the trust has stated that the settlor Mrs Harvey gave them 'a clear indication of the causes she favoured and [they] are guided by that for the moment at least', therefore new applicants will not be considered for the time being.
WHO TO APPLY TO F A Sherring, Mrs N Joyce, Usher Spiby & Co, 76 Manchester Road, Denton,

Manchester M34 3PS *Tel* 0161 432 8307
email sa.hull4harvey@gmail.com

....

■ The Edward Harvist Trust Fund

cc no 211970   **ESTABLISHED** 1994
WHERE FUNDING CAN BE GIVEN The London boroughs of Barnet, Brent, Camden, Harrow and the City of Westminster.
WHO CAN BENEFIT Registered charities.
WHAT IS FUNDED General charitable purposes.
RANGE OF GRANTS Up to £16,000.
SAMPLE GRANTS PACE (£15,000); Ijad Dance Company (£8,000); Camden Somali Forum (£5,000); Mary Ward Legal Centre (£4,100); St John's Wood Crypt Youth Club (£3,000); Barnet Play Association (£1,500); Iran Institute (£1,100); Friends of Canons Park (£500); and Carramea (£260).
FINANCES *Year* 2009–10 *Income* £261,005 *Grants* £253,000 *Assets* £7,330,096
TRUSTEES Mr Leslie Sussman, Chairman (London borough of Barnet); Cllr Mrs Gwyneth Hampson (City of Westminster); Cllr Mr Owen Cock (London borough of Harrow); Mr Richard Eden (London borough of Camden); Mr Alan Mendoza (London borough of Brent).
OTHER INFORMATION Income is distributed to the local authorities in proportion to the length of the Edgware Road passing through their area. In 2009–10 this was as follows: London borough of Barnet – (31%) £78,000; London borough of Brent – (27%) £70,000; City of Westminster – (25%) £63,000; London borough of Camden – (11%) £27,000; London borough of Harrow – (6%) £14,000.
HOW TO APPLY In writing to the relevant local authority. Do not write to the correspondent.
WHO TO APPLY TO Jennifer Hydari, London Borough of Harrow, Finance Department, PO Box 21, Civic Centre, Harrow *Tel* 020 8424 1393

....

■ The Haskel Family Foundation

cc no 1039969   **ESTABLISHED** 1993
WHERE FUNDING CAN BE GIVEN UK.
WHO CAN BENEFIT Jewish people and research workers.
WHAT IS FUNDED The charity is currently funding projects concerned with social policy research and Jewish communal life.
RANGE OF GRANTS Usually up to £12,000.
SAMPLE GRANTS Aldeburgh Music (£15,000); Liberal Judaism and the Rosetree Trust (£5,000 each); Children Leukaemia (£3,500); Jewish Research (£1,100) and The Rainbow Trust (£500).
FINANCES *Year* 2009 *Income* £28,872 *Grants* £30,100 *Assets* £536,168
TRUSTEES A M Davis; S Haskel; M Nutman; Lord Haskel.
HOW TO APPLY **This trust states that it does not respond to unsolicited applications.**
WHO TO APPLY TO Lord Simon Haskel, 12 Rosemont Road, Richmond-upon-Thames, Surrey TW10 6QL *Tel* 020 8948 7711

....

■ Hasluck Charitable Trust

cc no 1115323   **ESTABLISHED** 2006
WHERE FUNDING CAN BE GIVEN UK.
WHO CAN BENEFIT Children and young people, people with disabilities.
WHAT IS FUNDED Health, welfare, disability, youth, overseas aid.
RANGE OF GRANTS Up to £6,000.

SAMPLE GRANTS Regular beneficiaries (see the 'Other information' section) received £6,000 each. One-off grants were made to: World Vision (£4,000); Kent Air Ambulance, London Narrow Boat Project and Children's Liver Disease Foundation (£1,500 each); Credit Action, Beat Bullying and Friends of the Elderly (£1,000 each).
FINANCES *Year* 2009–10 *Income* £125,809 *Grants* £93,600 *Assets* £1,170,392
TRUSTEES Matthew James Wakefield; John Billing.
OTHER INFORMATION Half of the income received by the trust is allocated to eight charities (Barnardo's, Mrs R H Hotblacks Michelham Priory Endowment Fund, International Fund for Animal Welfare, Macmillan Cancer Relief, the Riding for the Disabled Association, RNLI, RSPB and Scope), which are of particular interest to the settlor. The remaining monies are distributed to such charitable bodies as the trustees decide.
HOW TO APPLY In writing to the correspondent. 'Distributions are generally made in January and July, although consideration is given to appeals received at other times of the year.'
WHO TO APPLY TO John Billing, Trustee, Rathbone Trust Company Limited, 159 New Bond Street, London W1S 2UD *Tel* 020 7399 0447 *email* john.billing@rathbones.com

....

■ The Hathaway Trust

cc no 1064086   **ESTABLISHED** 1997
WHERE FUNDING CAN BE GIVEN Unrestricted.
WHO CAN BENEFIT Registered charities and individuals.
WHAT IS FUNDED The trust tends to support Jewish organisations and causes.
RANGE OF GRANTS £1,000–£13,000.
SAMPLE GRANTS Beneficiaries included: Toimchei Shabbos Manchester (£13,000); Meleches Machsheves (£5,500); Sayser (£4,200); Kol Yom Trust Ltd (£4,000); Manchester Swallow (£3,600) and Ahavas Tzdedoka Vochesed (£1,500). The trust also made 'other grants' totalling £21,000.
FINANCES *Year* 2009–10 *Income* £72,123 *Grants* £72,539 *Assets* £77,444
TRUSTEES Mr N Younger; Mrs M Younger; Rabbi S Schwalbe.
OTHER INFORMATION During the year, the trust became involved in a variety of new projects and activities aimed at youths in the area of Greater Manchester 'who have yet to find their place in society'. The aim being to help them realize their potential, develop their skills and capabilities to participate and contribute to society.
HOW TO APPLY The trustees have stated previously that they have adopted a proactive approach to funding and now only fund projects with which they have a personal connection, therefore unsolicited requests will not be considered.
WHO TO APPLY TO The Trustees, 12 Hereford Drive, Prestwich, Manchester M25 0JA

....

■ The Maurice Hatter Foundation

cc no 298119   **ESTABLISHED** 1987
WHERE FUNDING CAN BE GIVEN Unrestricted.
WHO CAN BENEFIT Educational bodies, particularly those with Jewish links, and registered charities.
WHAT IS FUNDED Education, medical research and social welfare.
TYPE OF GRANT Grants, often recurring; loans.

SAMPLE GRANTS British Friends of Haifa University (£354,000); World ORT (£134,000); Ray Tye Medical Foundation (£68,000); University College London Intellectual Property (£50,000); Traditional Alternatives Foundation (£25,000); Norwood Ravenswood (£10,000); and Nightingales House (£5,000).

FINANCES *Year* 2009–10 *Income* £486,994 *Grants* £1,076,756 *Assets* £6,242,337

TRUSTEES Sir Maurice Hatter; Ivor Connick; Jeremy S Newman; Richard Hatter.

HOW TO APPLY Unsolicited applications will not be considered.

WHO TO APPLY TO The Trustees, c/o Smith and Williamson Limited, 1 Bishops Wharf, Walnut Tree Close, Guildford, Surrey GU1 4RA *Tel* 01483 407100

■ The M A Hawe Settlement

CC NO 327827   ESTABLISHED 1988

WHERE FUNDING CAN BE GIVEN UK, with a preference for the north west of England, particularly the Fylde coast area.

WHO CAN BENEFIT UK and local organisations and schemes benefiting people of all ages, women, at-risk groups, and children who are ill or disabled, people who are socially isolated, homeless or disadvantaged by poverty.

WHAT IS FUNDED Welfare of older people, women and children, disability, homelessness and other charitable purposes.

TYPE OF GRANT One-off, some recurrent.

RANGE OF GRANTS Usually up to £1,000.

SAMPLE GRANTS Kensington House Trust Limited (£1,800,000); The Cross and Passion Sisters (£5,500); Haiti Earthquake and Holy Cross Church and Soup Kitchen, (£1,000 each); Kenyan Orphan Project (£500); Home Start Fund Day and Claremont School (£250 each); and Rev Ballard – Sri Lanka (£200).

FINANCES *Year* 2009–10 *Income* £76,935 *Grants* £1,811,341 *Assets* £3,410,179

TRUSTEES M A Hawe; Mrs G Hawe; M G Hawe.

OTHER INFORMATION The trustees have decided to put Kensington House on the market and will use the proceeds to develop the new Daisy Chain Project at Normoss Farm which provides holidays in Blackpool for the families of children who have special needs.

HOW TO APPLY In writing to the correspondent.

WHO TO APPLY TO M A Hawe, Trustee, 94 Park View Road, Lytham St Annes, Lancashire FY8 4JF *Tel* 01253 796888

■ The Hawerby Trust

CC NO 1133740   ESTABLISHED 2010

WHERE FUNDING CAN BE GIVEN UK and overseas.

WHO CAN BENEFIT Registered charities.

WHAT IS FUNDED General charitable purposes.

FINANCES *Year* 2009–10 *Income* £9,044 *Grants* £9,000

TRUSTEES Wynne Phillip Morgan Griffiths; Pamela Griffiths; Kate Morgan Griffiths; William Morgan Griffiths; Nicholas Morgan Griffiths; Max Morgan Griffiths; Robert Penrose; Coutts & Co.

HOW TO APPLY In writing to the correspondent.

WHO TO APPLY TO Coutts & Co, Trustee Dept, 440 Strand, London WC2R 0QS *Tel* 020 7663 6825

■ The Hawthorne Charitable Trust

CC NO 233921   ESTABLISHED 1964

WHERE FUNDING CAN BE GIVEN UK, especially Hereford and Worcester.

WHO CAN BENEFIT Organisations benefiting young people and older people, medical professionals and people disadvantaged by poverty.

WHAT IS FUNDED The trustees make donations, generally on an annual basis, to a large number of charities mainly concerned with the care of young people and older people, the relief of pain, sickness and poverty, the advancement of medical research, particularly into the various forms of cancer, research into animal health, the arts, disability and heritage.

WHAT IS NOT FUNDED Grants are given to registered charities only. No grants to individuals.

TYPE OF GRANT Often recurring.

RANGE OF GRANTS Usually up to £8,000.

SAMPLE GRANTS The Dyson Perrins Museum Trust (£8,000); Army Benevolent Fund and Welland pre-school (£5,000 each); Motor Neurone Disease Association, Battersea Dogs and Cats Home and National Trust (£3,000 each); London Library, Combat Stress and Hospice Care Kenya (£2,500 each); Woodland Trust, Crusaid and Mobility Trust (£2,000 each); Dogs Trust, S.P.A.C.E. and Music Space West Midlands (£1,000 each); and Cambridge Cancer Research Fund, Prostate Appeal and Herefordshire Mind (£250 each).

FINANCES *Year* 2009–10 *Income* £161,200 *Grants* £124,150 *Assets* £6,895,970

TRUSTEES Mrs A S C Berington; R J Clark.

HOW TO APPLY In writing to the correspondent, including up-to-date accounts. Applications should be received by October for consideration in November.

WHO TO APPLY TO Mrs Evaline Sarbout, c/o Baker Tilly, 25 Farringdon Street, London EC4A 4AB *Tel* 020 3201 8298

■ The Dorothy Hay-Bolton Charitable Trust

CC NO 1010438   ESTABLISHED 1992

WHERE FUNDING CAN BE GIVEN UK, with a preference for the South East of England and overseas.

WHO CAN BENEFIT Charities working with people who are blind or deaf, particularly children, young people and elderly people.

WHAT IS FUNDED Welfare needs.

WHAT IS NOT FUNDED The trust states that it does not generally give to individuals.

TYPE OF GRANT One-off and ongoing.

RANGE OF GRANTS Up to £3,500.

SAMPLE GRANTS Previous beneficiaries included: Hearing Dogs for the Deaf (£3,500); Action for Blind People, Sussex Lantern and Telephones for the Blind (£2,500); Eyeless Trust (£1,500); British Blind Sport and Esther Benjamin's Trust (£1,250); East Sussex Association for the Blind (£1,000); The Seeing Ear (£750); and East Kent Cycling Club (£250).

FINANCES *Year* 2009–10 *Income* £23,788 *Grants* £40,000

TRUSTEES Brian E Carter; Stephen J Gallico.

HOW TO APPLY In writing to the correspondent.

WHO TO APPLY TO Brian E Carter, Trustee, c/o F W Stephens, 3rd Floor, 24 Chiswell Street, London EC1Y 4YX *Tel* 020 7382 1820 *email* brian.carter@fwstephens.co.uk

■ The Haymills Charitable Trust

CC NO 277761   **ESTABLISHED** 1979

WHERE FUNDING CAN BE GIVEN UK, but particularly the west of London and Suffolk, where the Haymills group is sited.

WHO CAN BENEFIT Organisations benefiting children and young adults; former employees of Haymills; at-risk groups, people who are disadvantaged by poverty and socially isolated people.

WHAT IS FUNDED The trust seeks to support projects which are not widely known, and therefore likely to be inadequately funded. Main support is given to registered charities operating in areas lying in and to the west of London and in Suffolk. Grants fall into four main categories: education – schools, colleges and universities; medicine – hospitals, associated institutions and medical research; welfare – primarily to include former Haymills staff, people in need, or who are otherwise distressed or disadvantaged; and youth – support for schemes to assist in the education, welfare and training of young people. A limited number of applications will be considered which can show they are committed to further education and training, preferably for employment in the construction industry.

WHAT IS NOT FUNDED No personal applications will be considered unless endorsed by a university, college or other appropriate authority.

SAMPLE GRANTS Beneficiaries included: Merchant Taylors' School for the Geoffrey Cox Scholarships (£30,000); and the Royal College of Physicians and the British Red Cross (£5,000 each).
In addition, research societies supported included Cancer, Plastic Surgery and Ischaemia. League of Friends at Ealing, Central Middlesex and Bournemouth Eye Hospitals have continued to be supported as well as the London and St John's Ambulances.
Payments in the past have also been made to support retired employees of Haymills Contractors Ltd.

FINANCES *Year* 2009–10 *Income* £170,428 *Grants* £230,275 *Assets* £6,802,093

TRUSTEES W G Underwood, Chair; E F C Drake; I W Ferres; J A Sharpe; J L Wosner; I R Brown.

HOW TO APPLY In writing to the correspondent, but note the comments in the general section. Trustees meet at least twice a year, usually in March and October. Applications are not acknowledged.

WHO TO APPLY TO I W Ferres, Secretary, 7 Wildwood, Northwood HA6 2DB *Tel* 01923 825989 *email* ian.w.ferres@btinternet.com

■ The Charles Hayward Foundation

CC NO 1078969   **ESTABLISHED** 1961

WHERE FUNDING CAN BE GIVEN Worldwide, in practice mainly UK with some overseas funding.

WHO CAN BENEFIT Registered charities.

WHAT IS FUNDED Predominantly capital costs for organisations undertaking projects which are preventative or provide early intervention; developmental or innovative; promote or continue good practice and add value to existing services. Priority areas: People with disabilities, early intervention, medical research, medical, older people, art, preservation & environment, community, hospices, criminal justice, overseas, youth at risk.

WHAT IS NOT FUNDED Grants are not made for: academic chairs; bursaries; church restoration; computers; education; endowment funds; environmental and animal sciences; fund-raising activities; general repairs; non-medical academic research; paying off loans; revenue funding or core costs, general funding, continuing funding and replacement funding; replacement of government or lottery funding or activities primarily the responsibility of central or local government or any other responsible body; travel, outings or holidays.

TYPE OF GRANT Capital cost of buildings, extensions, adaptations, equipment and furnishings. Occasionally project funding for start-up or development.

RANGE OF GRANTS Generally £1,000–£25,000.

SAMPLE GRANTS Amber Trust Wiltshire (£200,000); St Gemma's Hospice (£30,000); Wells Cathedral and College of St Barnabas, Surrey (£25,000 each); Phoenix Cinema, London (£20,000); Women's Work, Derby (£16,000); SOVA – Supporting Others Through Volunteer Action (£15,000); Caledonia Youth (£10,000); Holderness Road Methodist Church (£4,000); Islington Somali Community (£3,000); Proteus Theatre Company Limited (£2,000); and Solihull Bereavement Counselling Service (£1,500).

FINANCES *Year* 2010 *Income* £1,934,591 *Grants* £1,771,192 *Assets* £49,320,504

TRUSTEES I F Donald; Mrs J M Chamberlain; Sir Jack Hayward; Mrs S J Heath; B D Insch; J N van Leuven; Miss A T Rogers; Mr R Hayward; Mr A J Heath.

OTHER INFORMATION 'The trustees amend their policy from time to time. Up-to-date guidelines for applicants can be downloaded from our website. They may also be obtained by sending an sae to the foundation's offices specifying either General Guidelines or Overseas Guidelines.'

HOW TO APPLY 'There is no application form. Your initial application should be made in writing to the Administrator, Dorothy Napierala. It should provide the details listed below. You may add any enclosures that help to describe your organisation or the project. We will advise you whether more information is required. All applications will receive an acknowledgement. However, as there is often a waiting list, and the trustees meet only four times a year to consider applications, you may have a wait of several months before you receive a decision. Please note that there are always many more applications than we are able to fund out of our limited resources. You are advised to read these guidelines very carefully, as inappropriate applications waste time. Details required in your application: Name and location of Organisation; Contact details; Description of Organisation – Provide a description of your present work and the priorities you are addressing. Quantify the scale of your operation – how many people do you help and how? Description of Proposed Project – Describe the project you are undertaking, detailing the number of people and groups who will benefit and how. Specify how life will be improved for the target group; Project Cost – For larger projects give a breakdown of the costs. Capital and revenue costs should be kept separate. For a capital project, include only information on the capital costs; Funds raised and pledged – Give a breakdown of the funds raised to date towards your target, separating capital and revenue, where applicable. Include the amount of any of your own funds or reserves going into the project, and any money you intend to borrow; Outstanding Shortfall – Specify the amount of money you still need for capital and revenue separately; Timetable – State the timetable for the project; when it will start and be finished; Accounts – Include one set of your

Think carefully about every application. Is it justified?

601

latest audited accounts. Small grants – please note that applications for the small grant scheme need only be up to 4 pages plus accounts.'

WHO TO APPLY TO Dorothy Napierala, Hayward House, 45 Harrington Gardens, London SW7 4JU *Tel* 020 7370 7063 *Website* www. charleshaywardfoundation.org.uk

■ Headley-Pitt Charitable Trust

CC NO 252023   **ESTABLISHED** 1955
WHERE FUNDING CAN BE GIVEN Mainly Ashford, Kent.
WHO CAN BENEFIT Older people and those in need.
WHAT IS FUNDED Quaker projects. The trust also administers 10 bungalows for the benefit of older people in the community.
WHAT IS NOT FUNDED Sport or animal projects.
TYPE OF GRANT One-off.
RANGE OF GRANTS Up to £2,000.
FINANCES *Year* 2009–10 *Income* £61,709 *Grants* £25,545 *Assets* £2,391,384
TRUSTEES Mrs S D Pitt; H C Pitt; J R Pitt; R W Pitt.
OTHER INFORMATION In 2009–10 grants to institutions totalled £8,300 and grants to individuals totalled £17,000.
HOW TO APPLY In writing to the correspondent.
WHO TO APPLY TO Mrs Thelma Pitt, Administrator, Old Mill Cottage, Ulley Road, Kennington, Ashford, Kent *email* thelma.pitt@headley.co.uk

■ The Headley Trust

CC NO 266620   **ESTABLISHED** 1973
WHERE FUNDING CAN BE GIVEN Unrestricted.
WHO CAN BENEFIT Registered charities working in the areas listed. The trust prefers to support innovative schemes that can be successfully replicated or become self-sustaining.
WHAT IS FUNDED Arts and heritage – UK: support for a wide variety of built conservation or heritage projects. Arts and heritage – overseas – restoration of buildings, statuary or paintings, primarily in Central and Eastern Europe, supporting the capacity of new heritage NGOs, and training the next generation of conservation and heritage professionals. Developing countries: priority is given to projects in sub-Saharan Anglophone Africa and Ethiopia. Focus areas include water/sanitation projects, environmental projects, education and literacy projects, health projects and community and voluntary sector development. Education: provision of bursary support, particularly for artistic or technical skills training, or performing opportunities for talented young artists, including the disadvantaged or disabled. Health and social welfare: support for a broad range of health and social welfare projects, particularly supporting elderly people of limited means, especially with their housing needs, or help carers of an ill or disabled relative. Also, parenting education projects; and occasional health research into specialist areas of particular interest to the trustees.
WHAT IS NOT FUNDED Individuals; expeditions.
TYPE OF GRANT One-off, capital and project over three years or less.
RANGE OF GRANTS Average grant size was £16,400 in 2010.
SAMPLE GRANTS Tate St Ives (£1 million); University of Durham (£120,000); Alzheimer's Society (£75,000); Orbis International (£60,000); Interact Reading Service (£50,000); Coventry Cathedral and Sing for your Life (£40,000 each); British Library (£34,000); Croatian

Conservation Institute (£25,000); Textile Conservation Centre Foundation (£24,000); Woodbridge Tide Mill Trust (£20,000); Diocese of Newcastle (£15,500); Venice in Peril Fund (£12,500); Save the Children UK (£10,000); Marie Curie Cancer Care (£7,500); and Shrewsbury Museum & Art Gallery (£6,000).
FINANCES *Year* 2010 *Income* £2,420,000 *Grants* £3,746,524 *Assets* £76,350,000
TRUSTEES Sir Timothy Sainsbury; Lady Susan Sainsbury; Timothy James Sainsbury; J R Benson; Judith Portrait.
OTHER INFORMATION The trust is one of the Sainsbury Family Charitable Trusts which share a common administration. An application to one is taken as an application to all.
HOW TO APPLY The Museums' Treasure Acquisition Scheme has its own application form, available from the Headley Museums Archaeological Acquisition Fund website, www.headley-archaeology.org.uk. For information on the small Aids for Disabled Fund, ring the trust on 020 7410 0330. Otherwise, see the guidance for applicants in the entry for the Sainsbury Family Charitable Trusts. A single application will be considered for support by all the trusts in the group. However, for this as for many of the trusts, 'the trustees take an active role in their grant-making, employing a range of specialist staff and advisers to research their areas of interest and bring forward suitable proposals. Many of the trusts work closely with their chosen beneficiaries over a long period to achieve particular objectives. It should therefore be understood that the majority of unsolicited proposals we receive will be unsuccessful. Applications should be sent by post with a description (strictly no more than two pages please, as any more is unlikely to be read) of the proposed project, detailing: the organisation – explaining its charitable aims and objectives, and giving its most recent annual income and expenditure, and current financial position. Please do not send a full set of accounts; the project requiring funding – why it is needed, who will benefit and in what way; the funding – breakdown of costs, any money raised so far, and how the balance will be raised. All applications will receive our standard acknowledgement letter. If your proposal is a candidate for support from one of the trusts, you will hear from us within 8 weeks of the acknowledgement. Applicants who do not hear from us within this time must assume they have been unsuccessful.'
WHO TO APPLY TO Alan Bookbinder, Director, Allington House, 1st Floor, 150 Victoria Street, London SW1E 5AE *Tel* 020 7410 0330 *Fax* 020 7410 0332 *Website* www.sfct.org.uk

■ Heagerty Charitable Trust

CC NO 1033543   **ESTABLISHED** 1994
WHERE FUNDING CAN BE GIVEN UK and overseas.
WHO CAN BENEFIT Catholic organisations and registered charities.
WHAT IS FUNDED General charitable purposes.
WHAT IS NOT FUNDED The trust says it identifies causes it wishes to support itself and unsolicited applications are not considered.
RANGE OF GRANTS Up to £15,000.
SAMPLE GRANTS Beneficiaries include: Worth Abbey – medical centre in Irundu (£15,000); Worth Abbey – conversion of parish hall/carpentry workshop (£13,000) and St Raphael's Nursing Home (£2,000).

FINANCES *Year* 2009–10 *Income* £26,825
Grants £36,500 *Assets* £674,324
TRUSTEES J S Heagerty; Miss P Smith;
P J P Heagerty; Mrs V C M Heagerty; Mrs
C M J Milne.
HOW TO APPLY The trust says it identifies causes it
wishes to support itself and unsolicited
applications are not considered.
WHO TO APPLY TO J S Heagerty, Trustee, Walstead
Grange, Lindfield, Surrey RH16 2QQ *Tel* 01444
483863

■ May Hearnshaw's Charity

CC NO 1008638   **ESTABLISHED** 1992
WHERE FUNDING CAN BE GIVEN UK, particularly South
Yorkshire, North Nottinghamshire, Derbyshire,
East Lancashire or Cheshire areas.
WHO CAN BENEFIT Registered charities.
WHAT IS FUNDED General with a preference for the
promotion of education, advancement of religion
and the relief of poverty and sickness.
TYPE OF GRANT One-off, with grants for buildings,
core costs, research, recurring costs, running
costs and salaries all considered. Funding may
be given for up to three years.
RANGE OF GRANTS £500–£5,000.
SAMPLE GRANTS Holmesfield Scouts (£5,000);
Neurocare – Sheffield Hallamshire Hospital
(£4,100 in two grants); Action for Kids
(£3,500); National Kidney Foundation (£3,000);
Yorkshire Air Ambulance (£2,500); Meadowhead
Community Learning Trust, Stroke Association
and Barnardo's (£2,000 each); Tansley
Methodist Church, Independent Age, Shelter
Housing Difficulties, Christians Against Poverty
and Ecclesall Live at Home Scheme (£1,000
each); and NORSACA (£750).
FINANCES *Year* 2009–10 *Income* £70,972
Grants £29,388 *Assets* £1,847,723
TRUSTEES Marjorie West; Michael Ferreday; Richard
Law; William Munro; D C Law.
HOW TO APPLY 'The trustees usually meet three
times a year when they decide on and make
major grants to charitable organisations but may
decide to make grants at any time. They do not
include in their consideration appeals received
direct from individuals.'
WHO TO APPLY TO Michael Ferreday, Trustee, Barber
Harrison and Platt, 2 Rutland Park, Sheffield
S10 2PD

■ The Heart of England Community Foundation

CC NO 1117345   **ESTABLISHED** 1995
WHERE FUNDING CAN BE GIVEN The city of Coventry
and Warwickshire.
WHO CAN BENEFIT Community-based groups and
activities benefiting a wide range of social
circumstances.
WHAT IS FUNDED General charitable purposes, in
particular for the benefit of the local community
in Warwickshire and the city of Coventry and
people who are disabled, and to promote social
and economic development. This includes
residential facilities and services, community
arts and recreation, respite care and care for
carers, support and self-help groups, community
services, social issues advice and information
and health advocacy.
WHAT IS NOT FUNDED Grants will not usually be
considered for the following: general and major
fundraising; individuals; educational institutions
except where the institution or project is aimed

at the relief of disadvantage; promotion of
religious causes except where the institution or
the project is aimed at relief of disadvantage;
medical research; organisations with no
permanent presence in the beneficial area;
animal welfare; political activity; organisations
with substantial reserves relative to turnover;
sports clubs except where the institution or the
project is aimed at relief of disadvantage;
salaries and other core costs.
TYPE OF GRANT Buildings, capital, core costs,
feasibility studies, one-off, project, research,
development costs, salaries, and start-up costs.
Funding is available for up to one year.
RANGE OF GRANTS £100–£7,000.
SAMPLE GRANTS Blaze Community Foundation and
Metal Dog Media Ltd (£12,000 each); Ford
Residents Association and Southam Gymnastics
(£5,000 each); Coventry Jesus Centre (£3,000);
Tile Hill Trojans Basketball Club (£2,700);
Somali Youth Community (£2,500); Milan Group
(£2,000); Breakaway Holiday Project and
Coventry Action for Autism Group (£1,000
each); Sea Cadet Corps (Leamington & Warwick)
(£750); Alzheimer's Society Coventry and the
Children's Care Campaign (£500 each); The
Abbeyfield Society and Charterhouse District
Scout Council (£250 each); and Youth of 2Day –
Leavers Care Group (£150).
FINANCES *Year* 2009–10 *Income* £2,092,848
Grants £1,296,806 *Assets* £2,579,153
TRUSTEES John Atkinson, Chair; Peter Deeley; Mrs
Margaret Backhouse; Mrs Sally Carrick; Andrew
Corner; Stewart Fergusson; David Green; Brian
Holt; Donald Hunter; Zamurad Hussain; Lady
Jane Liggins; Susan Ong; Ven. Michael Paget-
Wilkes; Peter Shearing; John Taylor.
OTHER INFORMATION The priorities of the trustees
are reviewed annually; applicants are
encouraged to contact the foundation by
telephone to obtain up-to-date information on
current priorities. Only one grant will be given to
an organisation in any one year from the
foundation.
HOW TO APPLY Application forms may be downloaded
from the foundation's website, or you can call
on 024 7688 4386 and a copy will be sent it to
you. Although guidance on how to complete the
application form is included within the form
itself, you are encouraged to telephone the
foundation to discuss your project in advance of
applying. Grants Officers, who cover specific
geographical areas and funds, will be pleased to
assist you. None of the foundation's grant
programmes run to deadlines, however
applicants should expect an answer within 12
weeks. Applicants to the grassroots programme
should expect to hear within 15 days.
WHO TO APPLY TO Ms Catherine Mulkern, Director,
Pinley House, Sunbeam Way, PO BOX 227,
Coventry CV3 1ND *Tel* 024 7688 4386
Fax 024 7688 4640 *email* info@
heartofenglandcf.co.uk *Website* www.
heartofenglandcf.co.uk

■ The Heathcoat Trust

CC NO 203367   **ESTABLISHED** 1945
WHERE FUNDING CAN BE GIVEN Local causes in and
around Tiverton, Devon.
WHO CAN BENEFIT Local organisations to Tiverton
and individual grants to employees and
pensioners of the Heathcoat group of
companies.
WHAT IS FUNDED Welfare, educational.
TYPE OF GRANT Recurring and one-off.
RANGE OF GRANTS Usually less than £1,000.

FINANCES *Year* 2009–10 *Income* £684,470
Grants £115,080 *Assets* £19,301,273

TRUSTEES Sir Ian Heathcoat Amory; M J Gratton;
J Smith; Mr C Dunster; Mr S Butt.

OTHER INFORMATION A further £454,000 went to
individuals.

HOW TO APPLY In writing to the correspondent. There
are application forms for certain education
grants.

WHO TO APPLY TO Mr E W Summers, Secretary, The
Factory, Tiverton, Devon EX16 5LL *Tel* 01884
254949 *Website* www.heathcoat.co.uk

■ Heathside Charitable Trust

CC NO 326959   **ESTABLISHED** 1985

WHERE FUNDING CAN BE GIVEN UK.

WHO CAN BENEFIT Charitable organisations,
especially Jewish groups.

WHAT IS FUNDED General charitable purposes.

RANGE OF GRANTS £1,000–£141,100.

SAMPLE GRANTS Previously: Joint Jewish Charitable
Trust (£141,000); Jewish Education Defence
Trust and Community Security Trust (£25,000
each); Jewish Care (£15,000); and British
Friends of Jaffa Institute, GRET and Motivation
(£10,000 each).

FINANCES *Year* 2010 *Income* £378,457
Grants £640,260 *Assets* £3,035,154

TRUSTEES Sir Harry Solomon; Lady Judith Solomon;
Geoffrey Jayson; Louise Jacobs; Juliet Solomon;
Daniel Solomon.

OTHER INFORMATION In recent years, a list of grants
has not been included in the trust's accounts.

HOW TO APPLY In writing to the correspondent, at
any time. Trustees meet four times a year.

WHO TO APPLY TO Sir Harry Solomon, Trustee,
Hillsdown House, 32 Hampstead High Street,
London NW3 1QD *Tel* 020 7431 7739

■ The Charlotte Heber-Percy Charitable Trust

CC NO 284387   **ESTABLISHED** 1981

WHERE FUNDING CAN BE GIVEN Worldwide, with a
preference for Gloucestershire.

WHO CAN BENEFIT Registered charities.

WHAT IS FUNDED General charitable purposes.

WHAT IS NOT FUNDED No grants to individuals.

RANGE OF GRANTS Mostly between £500–5,000.

FINANCES *Year* 2009–10 *Income* £212,071
Grants £251,350 *Assets* £5,571,283

TRUSTEES C S Heber Percy; J A Prest.

HOW TO APPLY The correspondent stated that
unsolicited applications are not required.

WHO TO APPLY TO The Administrator, Rathbone Trust
Company Limited, 159 New Bond Street,
London W1S 2UD *Tel* 020 7399 0820

■ The Hedera Charitable Trust

CC NO 1139607   **ESTABLISHED** 2010

WHERE FUNDING CAN BE GIVEN UK.

WHO CAN BENEFIT Registered charities.

WHAT IS FUNDED General charitable purposes.

TRUSTEES Ross Brawn; Jean Brawn; Coutts & Co.

OTHER INFORMATION The settlor of the trust is Ross
Brawn, who has been involved in Formula 1
motor racing for many years, notably with the
Brawn GP team, with whom he won the world
championship in 2009. It was reported in early
2011 that he made around £100 million from
the sale of the Honda F1 team, which he bought

for £1. He is currently the head of the Mercedes
GP team.

HOW TO APPLY In writing to the correspondent.

WHO TO APPLY TO Coutts & Co, Trustee Dept,
440 Strand, London WC2R 0QS *Tel* 020 7663
6838

■ Percy Hedley 1990 Charitable Trust

CC NO 1000033   **ESTABLISHED** 1990

WHERE FUNDING CAN BE GIVEN UK with a preference
for Northumberland and Tyne and Wear.

WHO CAN BENEFIT Charitable organisations.

WHAT IS FUNDED General charitable purposes.

RANGE OF GRANTS Up to £5,000, but the majority of
grants are for £500.

SAMPLE GRANTS Percy Headley Foundation (£5,000);
Newcastle Royal Grammar School Bursary Fund
and Central Newcastle High School GDST
Bursary Fund (£3,000 each); St Oswald's
Hospice, Anaphylaxis Campaign and Samaritans
– Newcastle (£1,000 each); Employment
Opportunities, Combat Stress, Girl Guiding –
North Tyneside, Koestler Trust, Natural History
Society of Northumberland, Newcastle Dog and
Cat Shelter, Age UK, British Blind Sport,
Embleton Cygnets Nursery, National Youth
Orchestra, Perthes Association and Woodland
Trust (£500 each); and Bamburgh Church – St
Aidan's (£250).

FINANCES *Year* 2009–10 *Income* £46,720
Grants £46,750 *Assets* £1,321,182

TRUSTEES John Armstrong; Bill Meikle; Fiona
Ruffman.

HOW TO APPLY In writing to the correspondent.
Trustees meet twice a year.

WHO TO APPLY TO John Armstrong, Trustee,
10 Castleton Close, Newcastle upon Tyne
NE2 2HF *Tel* 0191 281 5953

■ The Hedley Denton Charitable Trust

CC NO 1060725   **ESTABLISHED** 1996

WHERE FUNDING CAN BE GIVEN North east England.

WHO CAN BENEFIT Charitable organisations, including
those operating overseas.

WHAT IS FUNDED General charitable purposes.

RANGE OF GRANTS £250–£1,000.

SAMPLE GRANTS Beneficiaries included: British Blind
Fund, Camp and Trek UK, Girlguiding in
Wickham and Hexham Abbey Arts (£250); The
Samaritans of Northumbria, ORBIS, and St
Mary's Church (£500); Rift Valley Justice
Project, North East Promenaders Against
Cancer, Great North Air Ambulance and
Alzheimer's Research (£1,000).

FINANCES *Year* 2009–10 *Income* £55,013
Grants £37,750 *Assets* £960,955

TRUSTEES I H Nicholson, Chair; Miss D M Wild;
C M Watts; C Nicholson.

OTHER INFORMATION Grants made totalled £37,000
ranging from £250–£1,000.

HOW TO APPLY In writing to the correspondent.

WHO TO APPLY TO I H Nicholson, Trustee, MR I.H.
Nicholson, Iain Nicholson & Co, 5 West Road,
Ponteland, Newcastle upon Tyne NE20 9ST
Tel 01661 823863 *Fax* 01661 823724
email law@iainnicholson.co.uk

....

■ The Hedley Foundation

cc no 262933 **established** 1971

where funding can be given UK only.

who can benefit Registered charities benefiting young people including their education, training and health; disabled people and the terminally ill.

what is funded Organisations working with young people, local church and community projects, organisations concerned with people who are disabled or seriously ill and medical equipment.

what is not funded Grants are made to UK registered charities only. No support for individuals, churches and cathedrals, core revenue costs, salary or transport funding, or for very large appeals.

type of grant Grants for specific projects only, mostly one-off but a limited number of recurring grants for up to three years are given. No revenue or salary funding.

range of grants £1,000–£15,000; average grant £3,000.

sample grants Beneficiaries included: Abbeyfield (Reading) Society, Aberlour Child Care Trust;, Academy Performance Ensemble; Access 2 Watersports, Action Medical Research, Adventure Limited, Air Training Corp ATC, Brookside Primary School, Brunswick Boys' Club, Buckingham Army Cadet League, Cumbria Cerebral palsy, Cuttleslowe Community Association, Daisy Chain, Friends of Holbeach School, Goal Line Youth Trust, Godalming Band, Magdalen Village Hall – Norfolk, Myton Hospices, Northern Ireland Cancer Fund for Children, Ocean Youth Trust, Raleigh International, RASCAL, Scouts, Sea Cadets, Wells Town Tennis Club and Youth Create.

finances *Year* 2009–10 *Income* £1,294,986 *Grants* £748,473 *Assets* £29,264,990

trustees John F Rodwell, Chair; Patrick R Holcroft; George R Broke; Lt Col. Peter G Chamberlin; Lorna B Stuttaford; Angus Fanshawe; Lt. Col. Andrew Ford; David Byam-Cook.

how to apply Application forms are downloadable from the foundation's website. Once completed in typescript, the form should be printed off and sent by post to the appeals secretary named above, accompanied by a recent copy of your accounts and your email address. Please note that the foundation is unable to return any enclosures that are sent in with applications. The trustees meet six times a year. The closing date for a meeting is three weeks beforehand. All applications will be acknowledged, but, in the case of those short-listed, not until after they have been considered by the trustees. The trustees usually meet in January, March, May, July, September and November. A list of meeting dates for the current year is also published on the foundation's website.

The foundation receives many more applications than it can fund and urges that applicants should not be surprised, or too disappointed, if they are unsuccessful.

who to apply to Pauline Barker, Appeals Secretary, 1–3 College Hill, London EC4R 2RA *Tel* 020 7489 8076 *email* pbarker@hedleyfoundation. org.uk *Website* www.hedleyfoundation.org.uk

....

■ The H J Heinz Company Limited Charitable Trust

cc no 326254 **established** 1982

where funding can be given UK.

who can benefit Organisations benefiting children and young adults, at-risk groups, people disadvantaged by poverty and socially isolated people.

what is funded The trust typically supports medicine, welfare, education (food technology and nutrition in particular), conservation, community relations and the arts. UK bodies are more likely to be favoured than local groups unless local applicants operate in the immediate vicinity of the company's main operating locations.

what is not funded No grants to individuals. Requests for political or denominational causes or for advertising are not considered.

type of grant One-off.

range of grants £5,000–£10,000.

sample grants Wigan & Leigh Hospice (£10,000); Community Cancer Care, Nelson's Journey, Hope House Children's Hospice (£5,000 each).

finances *Year* 2009 *Income* £84,632 *Grants* £54,769

trustees D Heinz; N Perry; S Cowdroy; N Dickie; C Finney; R Knee; M Laikin; C Middlehurst; R Munby; R Neo; C Humphries.

how to apply In writing to the address below, no follow-up telephone calls. Applications are considered once or twice a year. Applicants whether successful or unsuccessful are informed of the trustees' decisions.

who to apply to Elizabeth Keane, Trust Secretary, Hayes Park South Building, Hayes End Road, Hayes, Middlesex UB4 8AL *Tel* 020 848 2223 *email* charitable.trust@uk.hjheinz.com *Website* www.heinz.co.uk

....

■ The Hellenic Foundation

cc no 326301 **established** 1982

where funding can be given UK.

who can benefit Organisations and individuals, to advance education in the cultural tradition and heritage of Greece, particularly in the subjects of education, philosophy, the arts and science.

what is funded Projects involving education, research, music and dance, books and library facilities, and university symposia.

what is not funded The foundation is unable to offer scholarships or grants to cover tuition fees and living expenses.

range of grants Up to £15,000.

sample grants Previously: Royal Academy Byzantine exhibition (£15,000); Theatro Technis (£1,000); and Aghia Shophia School (£200).

finances *Year* 2010 *Income* £21,406 *Grants* £23,199

trustees Stamos J Fafalios; Nicos H Sideris; Constantinos I Caroussis; Mary Bromley; George J D Lemos; Louisa Williamson; Joanna Caroussis; Nikki Chandris; Pantelis Michelakis.

how to apply In writing to the correspondent.

who to apply to The Secretary, 150 Aldersgate Street, London EC1A 4AB *Tel* 020 7251 5100

....

■ The Michael and Morven Heller Charitable Foundation

cc no 327832 **established** 1988

where funding can be given Worldwide.

who can benefit Organisations benefiting academics, medical professionals, research workers, scientists, students and teachers.

what is funded Medical, education and scientific research.

what is not funded No support for individuals.

range of grants £5,000–£100,000.

SAMPLE GRANTS Education (£166,000); Humanitarian (£31,000); and Research (£20,000).
FINANCES *Year* 2009–10 *Income* £302,275 *Grants* £217,374 *Assets* £3,872,282
TRUSTEES Michael Heller; Morven Heller; W S Trustee Company Limited.
HOW TO APPLY In writing to the correspondent.
WHO TO APPLY TO M A Heller, Trustee, Carlton House, 22a St James's Square, London SW1Y 4JH *Tel* 020 7415 5000 *Fax* 020 7415 0611

■ The Simon Heller Charitable Settlement

CC NO 265405 **ESTABLISHED** 1972
WHERE FUNDING CAN BE GIVEN Worldwide.
WHO CAN BENEFIT Organisations benefiting academics, medical professionals, research workers, scientists, students and teachers.
WHAT IS FUNDED Medical research and scientific and educational research.
WHAT IS NOT FUNDED No grants to individuals.
SAMPLE GRANTS Previously: Institute for Jewish Policy Research (£35,000); Jewish Care (£30,000), Aish Hatora (£15,000 in two grants), Spiro Institute (£13,000), Scopus (£12,000 in two grants) and Chief Rabbinate Charitable Trust (£10,000).
FINANCES *Year* 2009–10 *Income* £384,590 *Grants* £355,250 *Assets* £7,256,503
TRUSTEES M A Heller; Morven Heller; W S Trustee Company Limited.
HOW TO APPLY In writing to the correspondent.
WHO TO APPLY TO The Trustees, Carlton House, 22a St James' Square, London SW1Y 4JH *Tel* 020 7415 5000

■ Help the Homeless

CC NO 271988 **ESTABLISHED** 1975
WHERE FUNDING CAN BE GIVEN UK.
WHO CAN BENEFIT Small-medium and/or new, registered charities with a turnover of less than £1 million a year. Grants to larger charities are considered if the project is suitably innovative and it is only possible for a large organisation to develop it.
WHAT IS FUNDED Projects which assist individuals in their return to mainstream society, rather than simply offer shelter or other forms of sustenance.
WHAT IS NOT FUNDED Charities with substantial funds are not supported. No grants to individuals.
TYPE OF GRANT Capital costs.
RANGE OF GRANTS Normally up to £3,000. Trustees will also consider applications for larger pump priming grants for major and innovative projects.
SAMPLE GRANTS Wellspring – Stockport (£30,000); Pilsdon Community (£5,000); Bridge Trust Corporation (£4,300); Streetwork UK and the Amber Foundation (£3,000 each); One25 Limited (£2,800); Hornsey YMCA (£2,600); Pavement (£2,000); Clock Tower Sanctuary – Brighton (£1,800); Causeway Irish Housing Association (£1,400); and Burntwood Pathway Project (£1,000).
FINANCES *Year* 2009–10 *Income* £60,423 *Grants* £85,145 *Assets* £1,151,485
TRUSTEES F J Bergin; T S Cookson; L A Bains; T Rogers; P Fullerton; J Rose.
HOW TO APPLY Application forms can be downloaded from the trust's website. The quarterly deadlines for applications each year are: 31

March, 30 June, 30 September and 31 December.
WHO TO APPLY TO Terry Kenny, Secretary, 6th Floor, 248 Tottenham Court Road, London W1T 7QZ *Fax* 020 7636 1428 *email* hth@help-the-homeless.org.uk *Website* www.help-the-homeless.org.uk

■ Help the Hospices

CC NO 1014851 **ESTABLISHED** 1984
WHERE FUNDING CAN BE GIVEN UK and overseas.
WHO CAN BENEFIT Hospices, palliative care units and their staff.
WHAT IS FUNDED Grant programmes vary, please go to www.helpthehospices.org.uk for up-to-date details of open and forthcoming programmes.
TYPE OF GRANT One-off and recurrent.
FINANCES *Year* 2009–10 *Income* £6,073,000 *Grants* £362,000 *Assets* £7,163,000
TRUSTEES Rt Hon Lord Howard of Lympne; Peter Holliday; Sally Taylor; Bay Green; Paul Dyer; Dr Ros Taylor; Beverley Brooks; Gary Hawkes; Marina Phillips; Sheila Tonge; Isabelle Whaite; Peter Ellis; Shaun O'Leary; Sue Newman.
OTHER INFORMATION The grant total represents funding given to both individuals and organisations during the year.
HOW TO APPLY The website provides guidelines for each programme and clear information on application procedures and deadlines. Depending on the programme, application forms can be downloaded or completed through the online application system.
WHO TO APPLY TO Grants Team, 34–44 Britannia Street, London WC1X 9JG *Tel* 020 7520 8277 *Fax* 020 7278 1021 *email* info@helpthehospices.org.uk *Website* www.helpthehospices.org.uk

■ The Helping Foundation

CC NO 1104484 **ESTABLISHED** 2004
WHERE FUNDING CAN BE GIVEN Greater London and Greater Manchester.
WHO CAN BENEFIT Institutions and registered charities.
WHAT IS FUNDED The advancement of education according to the tenets of the Orthodox Jewish Faith; the advancement of the Orthodox Jewish Religion and the relief of poverty amongst the elderly or persons in need, hardship or distress in the Jewish Community.
TYPE OF GRANT Recurrent grants.
RANGE OF GRANTS Mostly up to around £50,000.
SAMPLE GRANTS Asser Bishvil Foundation (£2 million); British Friends of Ezrat Yisrael (£670,000); Notzar Chesed (£236,500); New Rachmistrivka Synagogue Trust (£201,000); TTT (£198,500); Emuno Educational Centre (£163,000); United Talmudical Associates (£160,000); BCG CT (£105,000); Friends for the Centre for Torah Education Centre (£57,000); Toimchei Shabbos Manchester (£30,000); Gateshead Kollel (£20,000); Beis Naduorna (£10,000); and Law of Truth (£5,500).
FINANCES *Year* 2010 *Income* £17,840,617 *Grants* £4,634,864 *Assets* £59,990,649
TRUSTEES Benny Stone; David Neuwirth; Rabbi Aubrey Weis; Mrs Rachel Weis.
HOW TO APPLY In writing to the correspondent.
WHO TO APPLY TO Benny Stone, Trustee, 1 Allandale Court, Waterpark Road, Salford M7 4JN

■ The Hemby Trust

CC NO 1073028   **ESTABLISHED** 1998
WHERE FUNDING CAN BE GIVEN Merseyside and Wirral.
WHO CAN BENEFIT Charitable organisations.
WHAT IS FUNDED Social needs, community facilities and services, youth and employment, schools and colleges, help for older people, health, the arts, culture and recreation, the environment and church buildings.
WHAT IS NOT FUNDED Grants will not be given to political organisations, pressure groups or individuals, feasibility studies, organisations outside Merseyside or Wirral, or to replace statutory funding.
TYPE OF GRANT Capital grants.
RANGE OF GRANTS £250–£3000.
SAMPLE GRANTS Beneficiaries included: Action on Addiction (£1,050); Autism Initiatives, British Red Cross, Home Start, Help for Heroes – RS Clare & Co (£1,000); Garston Adventure Playground (£650); Benagl Sports Association (£500); Adult Dyslexia Access, Aidis Trust (£250).
FINANCES *Year* 2009–10 *Income* £7,462,642 *Grants* £6,926,640 *Assets* £220,626,536
TRUSTEES R A Morris; C J L Tod; A T Morris; N A Wainwright.
HOW TO APPLY Applicants should write to the correspondent for a leaflet which sets out the aims and objectives of the trust and an application form which should be returned with a copy of the applicant's latest accounts. A date will be given for the return of the form if it is to be discussed by the trustees at their next meeting. The trustees meet at the end of March, July and November. Applications are not acknowledged, but the applicant is welcome to telephone the administrator (01704 834887) to check it has been received.
WHO TO APPLY TO Michael Hope, Rathbone Investment Management, Port of Liverpool Building, Pier Head, Liverpool L3 1NW *Tel* 01704 834887 *Website* www.hembytrust. org.uk

■ The Christina Mary Hendrie Trust for Scottish and Canadian Charities

SC NO SC014514   **ESTABLISHED** 1975
WHERE FUNDING CAN BE GIVEN Scotland and Canada.
WHO CAN BENEFIT Charities benefiting young people and older people.
WHAT IS FUNDED Charities connected with young people and older people. Cancer charities are also supported.
WHAT IS NOT FUNDED Grants are not given to individuals. Only organisations known to the trustees can be considered.
RANGE OF GRANTS Typical grants £1,000–£5,000.
SAMPLE GRANTS William Simpson's Home (£40,000); Barnardo's Scotland (£22,500); Black Watch (£25,000); Elgin Youth Development Group, Place 2 Be and Queen Victoria School (£15,000 each); Canine Partners and Rock Trust (£10,000 each); Aberlour, Alzheimer's Research Trust and Edinburgh Young Carers Project (£5,000 each); Alcohol Focus Scotland (£2,000); and Junction and Royston Youth Project (£1,000 each).
FINANCES *Year* 2009–10 *Income* £223,398 *Grants* £287,992 *Assets* £6,342,794
TRUSTEES Sir Alistair Irwin, Chair; Anthony Cox; Arabella Cox; Charles Cox; Mary-Rose Grieve;

Susie Hendrie; Miss Caroline Irwin; John K Scott-Moncrieff.
HOW TO APPLY In writing to the correspondent.
WHO TO APPLY TO Alan Sharp, Secretary, Anderson Strathern Solicitors, 1 Rutland Court, Edinburgh EH3 8EY *Tel* 0131 270 7700 *Fax* 0131 270 7788 *Website* www.christinamaryhendrietrust. com

■ The Henley Educational Charity

CC NO 309237   **ESTABLISHED** 1604
WHERE FUNDING CAN BE GIVEN Henley-on-Thames and the parishes of Bix and Rotherfield Greys in Oxfordshire and Remenham in Berkshire only.
WHO CAN BENEFIT Individuals and organisations concerned with the education of children, young adults and people who are disadvantaged. State-maintained schools and colleges in the area defined above.
WHAT IS FUNDED Grants are given to alleviate financial hardship, to support particular educational initiatives and courses and to help meet the cost of educational visits, books and equipment at a local school or college.
WHAT IS NOT FUNDED Applicants for individual grants must be under 25 years of age, and must either be resident in the area of benefit or have attended a state-maintained school in the area for at least two years.
TYPE OF GRANT Mainly one-off grants for core and capital support; also project funding.
RANGE OF GRANTS All applications considered individually.
SAMPLE GRANTS Gillots (£29,000); Henley Youth Centre (£9,000); Trinity (£3,500); Sacred Heart (£2,000); Nettlebed (£1,000); Crazies Hill (£900) and Henley Outdoor Play Scheme (£250).
FINANCES *Year* 2009–10 *Income* £104,315 *Grants* £94,754 *Assets* £2,843,642
TRUSTEES Mrs G Dodd; A Follet; Mrs M S T Hall; Mrs E Hodgkin; W Parrish; Mrs M Smith; Mrs R G Whittaker; the Mayor of Henley; the Rector of Henley.
OTHER INFORMATION The area of benefit is restricted to the parishes of Henley, Bix, Remenham and Rotherfield Greys or the applicants must currently attend or have attended for a minimum of two years the nominated schools within the above areas. Individual applicants must be under 25 years of age.
HOW TO APPLY Apply in writing to the correspondent Mrs Claire Brown, for an application form. Full details of the application for grants can be found on the charity's web site at www.henleyeducationaltrust.com.
WHO TO APPLY TO Mrs Claire Brown, Clerk, Syringa Cottage, Horsepond Road, Gallowstree Common, Reading, Berkshire RG4 9BP *Tel* 0118 972 4575 *email* henleyeducationalcharity@hotmail.co.uk

■ The Tim Henman Charitable Foundation

CC NO 1083055   **ESTABLISHED** 2001
WHERE FUNDING CAN BE GIVEN UK.
WHO CAN BENEFIT Registered charities.
WHAT IS FUNDED General charitable purposes and medical research.
SAMPLE GRANTS Previous beneficiaries include: Teenage Cancer Trust (£70,000); Wessex Children's Hospice Trust and Ucare (£2,500 each); Les Ecoles de L'Espoir (£2,000).

FINANCES *Year* 2009–10 *Income* £20,090
TRUSTEES Jan Felgate; Lucy Henman; Tim Henman.
HOW TO APPLY The trustees tend to select charities for support based on their own experience and knowledge. It receives a high number of requests which have to be refused.
WHO TO APPLY TO Neil Grainger, Talent Financial Ltd, Chiswick Gate, 3rd Floor, 598–608, Chiswick High Road, London W4 5RT *Tel* 020 8104 1002

■ Philip Henman Trust

CC NO 1054707   **ESTABLISHED** 1986
WHERE FUNDING CAN BE GIVEN Worldwide.
WHO CAN BENEFIT UK-registered charities concerned with long term overseas development.
WHAT IS FUNDED Grants are aimed at established major UK registered charity (normally defined as having an income of over £100,000 per annum). The funding from the trust should be important to the project, normally accounting for between 20% and 80% of the total project budget. The project should be partly funded by other sources, voluntary work and central office administration costs can be counted as other source funding.
WHAT IS NOT FUNDED The trust does not fund ongoing concerns.
TYPE OF GRANT Partnership grants for three to five years. Projects must start and finish within five years.
RANGE OF GRANTS £3,000–£5,000 per year. A maximum of £25,000 over the course of the project.
SAMPLE GRANTS Overseas aid (£34,057); Medical and community work (£5,000); Individuals (£1,135); Other (£145).
FINANCES *Year* 2009–10 *Income* £59,480 *Grants* £40,337 *Assets* £1,828,093
TRUSTEES Joseph Charles Clark; David James Clark; Jason Colin Duffey.
HOW TO APPLY Applications are only considered once a year – the deadline is always 10 September. Applications are no longer accepted by post. Please use the online form (available on the 'Applications' page) to submit a request for funding.
WHO TO APPLY TO Joseph Charles Clark, Trustee, 16 Pembury Road, Tonbridge TN9 2HX *Tel* 01732 362227 *email* info@pht.org.uk *Website* www.pht.org.uk

■ Esther Hennell Charitable Trust

CC NO 261477   **ESTABLISHED** 1970
WHERE FUNDING CAN BE GIVEN UK.
WHO CAN BENEFIT Registered charities.
WHAT IS FUNDED General.
WHAT IS NOT FUNDED No grants to individuals.
SAMPLE GRANTS Previous beneficiaries include: Emmanuel Church Wimbledon, Strangers' Rest Mission, Shaftesbury Society, Whitefield Christian Trust, Barnabas Fund, Interserve, Tear Fund, AIM, South Asian Concern and Crosslinks UK.
FINANCES *Year* 2009–10 *Income* £20,889 *Grants* £25,000
TRUSTEES Esther J Hennell; Jane Ann Hunt; Nicholas W Smith.
HOW TO APPLY In writing to the correspondent.
WHO TO APPLY TO Nicholas W Smith, Trustee, Currey and Co, 21 Buckingham Gate, London SW1E 6LS *Tel* 020 7802 2700

■ The G D Herbert Charitable Trust

CC NO 295998   **ESTABLISHED** 1986
WHERE FUNDING CAN BE GIVEN UK.
WHO CAN BENEFIT Registered charities.
WHAT IS FUNDED The trust supports medicine, health, welfare and environmental resources. It mainly gives regular grants to a set list of charities, with a few one-off grants given each year.
TYPE OF GRANT Mainly recurrent.
RANGE OF GRANTS Up to £2,500.
SAMPLE GRANTS Previous beneficiaries of 'special donations' included: Ashford and Tenterden Samaritans, Children's Fire and Burn Trust, The Queen Alexandra Hospital Home, National ME Centre for Fatigue Syndromes, The Rainbow Centre, St Raphael's Hospice and Deafness Research UK (£2,000 each).
Previous beneficiaries of 'regular donations' included: The National Trust, Friends of the Elderly, Marie Curie Cancer Care, PDSA, Royal College of Surgeons of England, Royal Hospital for Neuro-Disability and The Woodland Trust (£2,500 each); Ogbourne St Georges PCC and Wiltshire Wildlife Trust (£500 each).
FINANCES *Year* 2009–10 *Income* £46,210 *Grants* £58,500 *Assets* £1,840,742
TRUSTEES M E Beaumont; J M Cuxson.
OTHER INFORMATION 'Regular donations' were made to 25 organisations in 2009–10.
HOW TO APPLY No applications are invited other than from those charities currently supported by the trust.
WHO TO APPLY TO Mrs J M Cuxson, Trustee, Barnards Inn, 86 Fetter Lane, London EC4A 1EN *Tel* 020 7405 1234

■ The Joanna Herbert-Stepney Charitable Settlement (also known as The Paget Charitable Trust)

CC NO 327402   **ESTABLISHED** 1986
WHERE FUNDING CAN BE GIVEN Worldwide, with an interest in Loughborough.
WHO CAN BENEFIT Normally only British registered charities.
WHAT IS FUNDED Sheer need is paramount, and, in practice, nothing else can be considered. There is a preference for the unglamorous, for maximum achievement with minimal resources. Priorities include the developing world, deprived children, old age, 'green' projects, and animal welfare. The trust does sometimes give ongoing support, thus leaving fewer funds for new applicants.
WHAT IS NOT FUNDED The trust states that 'sheer need is paramount, in practice, nothing else is considered'. Grants are only given to registered UK charities. Overseas projects can only be funded via UK charities; no money can be sent directly overseas. The trust does not support individuals (including students), projects for people with mental disabilities, medical research or AIDS/HIV projects.
RANGE OF GRANTS £50–£5,000.
SAMPLE GRANTS Manacare Foundation (£7,600); Oxfam (£7,000); Tibet Relief Fund of UK (£3,325); International Development Partnerships and Soil Association (£3,000 each); Children's Family Trust, Vitalise, Mali Medics and Medical Foundation for Care of Victims (£2,000 each); Contact the Elderly, FARM Africa, Friends of Student Educational Trust and Mexico Child Link (£1,000 each) and

Marie Stopes International, Mother's Union and St Cuthbert's Hospice (£500 each).

FINANCES *Year* 2009–10 *Income* £154,000 *Grants* £225,425 *Assets* £6,826,081

TRUSTEES Joanna Herbert-Stepney; Lesley Mary Blood; Meg Williams.

OTHER INFORMATION No grants to individuals.

HOW TO APPLY In writing to the correspondent; there is no application form. The trustees meet in spring and autumn. The trust regrets that it cannot respond to all applications.

WHO TO APPLY TO Joanna Herbert-Stepney, Trustee, Old Village Stores, Dippenhall Street, Crondall, Farnham, Surrey GU10 5NZ *Tel* 01252 850253

■ The Anne Herd Memorial Trust

SC NO SC014198   **ESTABLISHED** 1990

WHERE FUNDING CAN BE GIVEN Scotland, with a preference for Tayside, the City of Dundee and Broughty Ferry.

WHO CAN BENEFIT People who are visually impaired.

WHAT IS FUNDED Organisations working in the beneficial area with visually impaired individuals.

RANGE OF GRANTS Up to £20,000.

FINANCES *Year* 2009–10 *Income* £3,839,300

TRUSTEES B Neil Bowman; Mrs Pamela M M Bowman; Mrs Elizabeth N McGillivray; Rory W H Hudson; Mrs Elizabeth M Breckon; Robert J Wild.

HOW TO APPLY In writing to the correspondent. Trustees meet once a year to consider grants, usually in June. Applications should be received by March/April.

WHO TO APPLY TO The Trustees, Bowman Scottish Lawyers, 27 Bank Street, Dundee DD1 1RP

■ The Herefordshire Community Foundation

CC NO 1094935   **ESTABLISHED** 2002

WHERE FUNDING CAN BE GIVEN Herefordshire.

WHO CAN BENEFIT Community and voluntary groups and individuals in Herefordshire.

WHAT IS FUNDED General charitable purposes.

RANGE OF GRANTS Up to £22,000.

SAMPLE GRANTS Beneficiaries included: DIAL South Worcestershire (two grants) (£21,000); Asha Wyre Centre (£12,000); 2XL Youth Projects (£9,900); Homestart Herefordshire (£7,400); Caribbean Roots Connection (£6,000) and Hope Support Services (£5,000).

FINANCES *Year* 2009–10 *Income* £22,930 *Grants* £303,535 *Assets* £240,659

TRUSTEES W L Banks; Mrs C J Forrester; W Lindesay. Miss S Evans; Ms B Parkinson.

HOW TO APPLY In writing to the correspondent.

WHO TO APPLY TO David Barclay, Director, The Fred Bulmer Centre, Wall Street, Hereford HR4 9HP *Tel* 01432 272550 *email* dave.barclay@ herefordshire-cf.co.uk

---

■ The Herefordshire Historic Churches Trust

CC NO 511181   **ESTABLISHED** 1954

WHERE FUNDING CAN BE GIVEN Old county of Herefordshire.

WHO CAN BENEFIT All Christian places of worship.

WHAT IS FUNDED The restoration, preservation, repair, maintenance and improvement of churches, their contents and their churchyards in Herefordshire.

WHAT IS NOT FUNDED 'Grants are available for most activities associated with structural repairs and maintenance, but certain items such as heating and decoration are excluded'.

TYPE OF GRANT Buildings.

RANGE OF GRANTS Up to £10,000.

SAMPLE GRANTS Beneficiaries included the parishes of: Yarpole, Ross (£10,000); Alemely Quakers (£7,500); Satunton on Arrow (£5,000); Marden (£3,000); Whitborne (£2,500); Hereford St Peters (£2,000) and Letton (£1,000).

FINANCES *Year* 2009–10 *Income* £68,603 *Grants* £64,250 *Assets* £75,180

TRUSTEES Earl of Darnley, Chair; David Furnival; H C Moore; Archdeacon of Hereford; Miss Susan Bond; R H Peers; S Arbuthnott; Ven Malcolm Colmer; Ali Hayden Jones.

HOW TO APPLY In writing to the correspondent. Deadlines for applications are 15 March and 15 September.

WHO TO APPLY TO David Furnival, The Woodhouse, Staplow, Ledbury, Herefordshire HR8 1NP *Tel* 01531 640030 *email* furnivald@aol. com/davidfurnival@tiscali.co.uk *Website* www. herefordhistoricchurchestrust.org.uk

---

■ The Heritage of London Trust Ltd

CC NO 280272   **ESTABLISHED** 1980

WHERE FUNDING CAN BE GIVEN All 33 London boroughs.

WHO CAN BENEFIT Listed buildings in London.

WHAT IS FUNDED The restoration of buildings of architectural importance. Grants are mainly given for skilled restoration of notable features of listed buildings, generally (though not exclusively) external work. Examples of buildings assisted are churches, community centres, almshouses, theatres, hospitals, museums and educational establishments.

RANGE OF GRANTS Up to £20,000.

SAMPLE GRANTS St.Mary's Ilford (£5,000); Pembroke House, Southwalk (£4,000); St Thomas the Apostle (£1,300).

FINANCES *Year* 2009–10 *Income* £127,320 *Grants* £159,000 *Assets* £538,616

TRUSTEES The Hon. Edward Vaizey Hon. Nicholas Assheton, Chair; Sir John Lambert; Ronald Barden; Nicholas Bell; Mrs Bridget Cherry; Cllr Robert Davies; Martin Drury; John Dudley Fishburn; Katharine Goodison; Jonathan Gestetner; Norman Howard; Cllr Denise Jones; Frances Lloyd; Derek Lutyens; Michael Medlicott; Cllr Bob Skelly; Dame Valerie Strachan; Cllr Nigel Sumner. Norman Howard.

PUBLICATIONS Map: *Historic Buildings in Covent Garden.*

HOW TO APPLY Initial contact should be by telephone. If the project seems eligible, guidance notes will be sent to the applicant who should make a formal application in writing. Board meetings are held in January, May and September.

WHO TO APPLY TO Diana Beattie, Director, Heritage of London Trust, 34 Grosvenor Gardens, London SW1W 0DH *Tel* 020 7730 9472 *Fax* 020 7117 1125 *email* info@heritageoflondon.com *Website* www.heritageoflondon.com

■ **The Hertfordshire Community Foundation**

CC NO 299438 **ESTABLISHED** 1988
WHERE FUNDING CAN BE GIVEN Hertfordshire.
WHO CAN BENEFIT Individuals and organisations which benefit local people. Many are smaller, less well-known groups or less 'popular' causes that often find it extremely difficult to obtain funds elsewhere.
WHAT IS FUNDED To support the work of local charities and voluntary groups for the benefit of the community, with the following particular concerns: disadvantaged children and families; developing young people; access to education, training and employment; the needs of older people; and other community needs. Grants are made for a variety of needs including: running costs; training; staff costs; equipment; and new initiatives.
WHAT IS NOT FUNDED No grants are made towards: political groups; animal welfare; projects that are solely environmental; statutory agencies; medical research; religious activities; individuals, except within the terms of certain funds.
TYPE OF GRANT Project grants up to £5,000 for specific purpose, start-up or development. Small grants of £500 on a one-off basis – usually for small groups. Small individual grants up to £300 for children within very specific areas.
RANGE OF GRANTS £100–£10,000 per year for up to three years.
SAMPLE GRANTS Previous beneficiaries include: Citizens Advice Bureau – Hertfordshire, Broxbourne and East Hertfordshire Credit Union, Hertfordshire PASS, Satsang Mandal, Hitchin Town Bowls Club, Age Concern Hertfordshire, Hertfordshire Area Rape Crisis and Sexual Abuse Centre, Dacorum Indian Society, Neomari Beadcraft Training Services, Grandparents' Association, and Alzheimer's Disease Society.
FINANCES *Year* 2009–10 *Income* £2,964,063 *Grants* £1,036,023 *Assets* £4,854,048
TRUSTEES J Stuart Lewis, Chair; Kate Belinis; Jo Connell; Gerald Corbett; David Fryer; Pat Garrard; Mike Master; Caroline McCaffrey; Brig John Palmer; John Peters; Cllr Richard Roberts; Penny Williams.
PUBLICATIONS Leaflets; newsletter; guidelines for applicants.
OTHER INFORMATION For further information on the grant programmes currently available please consult the foundation's website.
HOW TO APPLY Ideally, applications should be made online via the foundation's website. However, if it is not possible to apply online, contact the foundation and they will send an application pack by post or email. An initial telephone call or email to check eligibility is also welcomed.
WHO TO APPLY TO Christine Mills, Grants Manager, Foundation House, 2–4 Forum Place, Fiddlebridge Lane, Hatfield, Hertfordshire AL10 0RN *Tel* 01707 251351 *email* grants@hertscf.org.uk *Website* www.hertscf.org.uk

■ **The Hesed Trust**

CC NO 1000489 **ESTABLISHED** 1990
WHERE FUNDING CAN BE GIVEN UK and overseas.
WHO CAN BENEFIT Christian charities benefiting children, young adults, older people, clergy, students, Christians and evangelists.
WHAT IS FUNDED Christian charitable purposes. The trust will consider funding the advancement of religion and the Free Church umbrella bodies.

WHAT IS NOT FUNDED No support for expeditions and individual requests.
TYPE OF GRANT One-off grants, for one year or less.
RANGE OF GRANTS Up to £45,000.
SAMPLE GRANTS Ministries without Borders (£42,000); All Nations Church (£24,000); Blackpool Church and City Church Coventry (£10,000 each); and Covenant Life Church Leicester (£750).
FINANCES *Year* 2009–10 *Income* £180,189 *Grants* £87,154 *Assets* £81,032
TRUSTEES P Briggs; R Eagle; G Rawlings; J C Smith.
HOW TO APPLY The trust states that no applications are now being considered.
WHO TO APPLY TO G Rawlings, Secretary, 14 Chiltern Avenue, Cosby, Leicestershire LE9 1UF *Tel* 0116 286 2990 *email* glynrawlings@btopenworld.com

■ **The Hesslewood Children's Trust (Hull Seamen's and General Orphanage)**

CC NO 529804 **ESTABLISHED** 1982
WHERE FUNDING CAN BE GIVEN East Yorkshire and North Lincolnshire.
WHO CAN BENEFIT Individuals and organisations in the area defined above, benefiting children and young adults under 25. Support will be given to people in care, or who are fostered or adopted; people who are disabled; people disadvantaged by poverty; ex-offenders and people at risk of offending; homeless people; people living in both rural and urban areas; socially isolated people; and victims of abuse and crime.
WHAT IS FUNDED To provide aid for young individuals in need and to support youth organisations for holidays. Particularly supported are charities working in the fields of education, housing and accommodation, and arts, culture and recreation.
WHAT IS NOT FUNDED No grants to benefit people over the age of 25 will be made.
TYPE OF GRANT One-off. Funding may be given for up to one year.
RANGE OF GRANTS Up to £21,000.
SAMPLE GRANTS Beneficiary groups included: Hull Compact Ltd. (£21,000); N Ferriby Riding for Disabled (£8,000); Dyslexia Association (£5,000); Endsleigh Holy Child Primary School (£4,500); Barnardo's Sibling Support Service (£2,000); Braveheart Sport Foundation (£1,000).
FINANCES *Year* 2009–10 *Income* £88,646 *Grants* £101,793 *Assets* £2,375,702
TRUSTEES I D Graham, Chair; R M S Allenby; Dr C Woodyatt; Capt. E Howlett; D Turner; Revd T Boyns; Mrs G Munn; M Mitchell; E W Gilbert; Dr C Jones; Mrs D Lidgett; Dr D Nicholas; P Evans; Capt. P. Watts.
OTHER INFORMATION Payments to individuals totalled £36,000.
HOW TO APPLY On a form available from the correspondent, with a telephone number if possible. The trustees meet to consider applications at least three times a year. No replies are given to ineligible organisations. This trust informed us that it promotes its work through its own avenues, receiving more applications than it can support.
WHO TO APPLY TO R E Booth, Secretary, c/o Graham and Rosen Solicitors, 8 Parliament Street, Hull HU1 2BB *Tel* 01482 323123

■ The Bernhard Heuberger Charitable Trust

CC NO 294378   **ESTABLISHED** 1986
WHERE FUNDING CAN BE GIVEN Worldwide.
WHO CAN BENEFIT Jewish organisations benefiting Jewish people.
WHAT IS FUNDED Jewish charitable purposes.
SAMPLE GRANTS C.M.M (£80,000); Beis Harnadrash (£7,500); Gateshead Jewish High School (£6,000); Kemble Charitable Trust (£4,000); Hendon United Synagogue (£2,400); Binoh (£2,000); JFS School (£1,700) Congregation Ateres ZVI Trust, the Hebrew University and Norwood (£1,000 each).
FINANCES *Year* 2008–09 *Income* £48,922 *Grants* £108,359 *Assets* £2,255,275
TRUSTEES D H Heuberger; S N Heuberger.
OTHER INFORMATION Other small charitable donations amounted to £1,800.
HOW TO APPLY In writing to the correspondent.
WHO TO APPLY TO The Trustees, 12 Sherwood Road, London NW4 1AD

■ Hexham and Newcastle Diocesan Trust (1947)

CC NO 235686   **ESTABLISHED** 1867
WHERE FUNDING CAN BE GIVEN Diocese of Hexham and Newcastle, overseas.
WHO CAN BENEFIT Roman Catholic organisations.
WHAT IS FUNDED This trust supports the advancement of the Roman Catholic religion in Hexham and Newcastle by both initiating its own projects and giving grants to other organisations.
TYPE OF GRANT One-off and re-occurring.
RANGE OF GRANTS Up to £300,000.
SAMPLE GRANTS Bede Chair of Catholic Theology (£700,000); CAFOD Development and emergency aid (£259,000); Catholic Education Service (£45,000); Peru Mission (£60,000); Peter's Pence; Sick and Retired Priests (£25,000 each); Apostleship of the Sea (£18,000); Domestic grants (£13,000); Racial Justice (£8,000); Survive MIVA (£7,000); and Catholic Agency for Social Concerns (£2,000).
FINANCES *Year* 2009–10 *Income* £19,946,000 *Grants* £1,788,000 *Assets* £63,198,000
TRUSTEES Revd Canon Seamus Cunningham; Monsignor Gerard Lavender; Revd James O'Keefe; Revd Philip Quinn; Revd Martin Stempczyk; Revd Christopher Jackson.
HOW TO APPLY Please contact the correspondent.
WHO TO APPLY TO Kathleen Smith, St Cuthberts House, West Road, Newcastle upon Tyne NE15 7PY *Tel* 0191 243 3300 *Fax* 0191 243 3309 *email* office@rcdhn.org.uk *Website* rcdhn.org.uk

■ The P and C Hickinbotham Charitable Trust

CC NO 216432   **ESTABLISHED** 1947
WHERE FUNDING CAN BE GIVEN UK, with a preference for Leicestershire and Rutland.
WHO CAN BENEFIT Registered charities only. Particular favour is given to Quakers.
WHAT IS FUNDED The trust generally supports local (Leicester, Leicestershire and Rutland) charities and Quaker activities in a wider field.
WHAT IS NOT FUNDED No grants to individuals applying for bursary-type assistance or to large UK charities.
TYPE OF GRANT Usually one-off grants.

RANGE OF GRANTS Up to £15,000, most grants made between £1,000 and £2,000.
SAMPLE GRANTS Rainbows Children's Hospice (£5,000); De Montfort University (£2,600); The Mummers Foundation and The Woodland Trust (£2,000); Society of Friends – Leicester PM (£1,600); and Belgrave Playhouse Cruise Bereavement Care and NSPCC (£1,000 each).
FINANCES *Year* 2009–10 *Income* £65,494 *Grants* £58,757 *Assets* £3,291,047
TRUSTEES Catherine Hickinbotham; Roger Hickinbotham; Rachel Hickinbotham; Anna Steiger.
HOW TO APPLY In writing to the correspondent, giving a brief outline of the purpose of the grant. Replies will not be sent to unsuccessful applicants.
WHO TO APPLY TO Roger Hickinbotham, Trustee, 9 Windmill Way, Lyddington, Oakham, Leicestershire LE15 9LY *Tel* 01572 821236 *email* rogerhick@gmail.com

■ The Rosalind Hicks Charitable Trust

CC NO 1050135   **ESTABLISHED** 1995
WHERE FUNDING CAN BE GIVEN Devon.
WHO CAN BENEFIT Charitable organisations.
WHAT IS FUNDED General charitable purposes.
RANGE OF GRANTS £500–£5,000.
SAMPLE GRANTS Interact (£5,000); Home Farm Trust and Chew Lake Association of Disabled Sailors (£2,000 each); Muir Maxwell and the Flavel Centre (£1,500 each); Devon Wildlife Trust, Calvert Trust and CHICKS (£1,000 each); Sense (£650) and PDSA (£500).
FINANCES *Year* 2010–11 *Income* £42,500 *Grants* £22,320 *Assets* £616,095
TRUSTEES N J Wollen; T A W Gregory; Mrs A Clementson; Lady J F Cassels and J M Mallowan.
HOW TO APPLY In writing to the correspondent.
WHO TO APPLY TO The Trustees, c/o Hooper & Wollen, 30 The Terrace, Torquay TQ1 1BS *Tel* 01803 213251 *Fax* 01803 296871

■ The Higgs Charitable Trust

CC NO 267036   **ESTABLISHED** 1982
WHERE FUNDING CAN BE GIVEN UK, with a preference for the former county of Avon.
WHO CAN BENEFIT Mostly medical research trusts or foundations. Organisations benefiting children, young adults, older people and people who are disadvantaged by poverty or homeless.
WHAT IS FUNDED Mainly research into deafness carried out by private charitable foundations. Also considered are charities working in the fields of religious buildings; housing and accommodation; animal facilities and services; conservation and campaigning; and education and training.
TYPE OF GRANT One-off and research. Funding for more than three years will be considered.
RANGE OF GRANTS Up to £18,000.
SAMPLE GRANTS TWJ Foundation (£18,000).
FINANCES *Year* 2009–10 *Income* £27,406 *Grants* £18,350 *Assets* £884,028
TRUSTEES D W M Campbell; T W Higgs; Mrs L Humphris; P Humphris.
HOW TO APPLY In writing to the correspondent, not less than two months before the annual general meeting in November.
WHO TO APPLY TO Anthony Nash, 24 Queen Square, Bath BA1 2HY *Tel* 01225 750 000

■ Alan Edward Higgs Charity

CC NO 509367   **ESTABLISHED** 1979

WHERE FUNDING CAN BE GIVEN Within 25 miles of the centre of Coventry only.

WHO CAN BENEFIT Registered charities where their activity will benefit young people either directly, through their family, or through the provision of facilities or services to the community.

WHAT IS FUNDED Activities or projects that contribute to the amelioration of deprivation.

WHAT IS NOT FUNDED No grants for individuals or the funding of services usually provided by statutory services, medical research, travel outside the UK or evangelical or worship activities.

TYPE OF GRANT One-off capital for buildings and equipment; will consider both core and revenue funding of projects.

RANGE OF GRANTS Typically £500–£30,000.

SAMPLE GRANTS Alan Higgs Centre Trust (£460,000); Coventry Institute of Creative Enterprise (£40,000); The Living Environment Trust (£28,000); Belgrade Theatre (£20,000); Family Holiday Association (£10,000); Shakespeare Hospice Appeal (£5,000); Guideposts Trust (£3,000); and the RSPB (£1,000).

FINANCES *Year* 2009–10 *Income* £521,393 *Grants* £211,114 *Assets* £17,918,980

TRUSTEES Peter J Davis; Marilyn F Knatchbull-Hugessen; Andrew Young.

OTHER INFORMATION During 2009–10, 39 grants were awarded. The average grant was for £5,400.

HOW TO APPLY In writing to the clerk to the trustees, along with: a copy of the latest audited accounts; charity number (if registered); a detailed description of the local activities for the benefit of which the grant would be applied; the specific purpose for which the grant is sought; a copy of the organisation's policy that ensures the protection of young or vulnerable people and a clear description of how it is implemented and monitored.

WHO TO APPLY TO Peter Knatchbull-Hugessen, Clerk, Ricoh Arena Ltd, Phoenix Way, Coventry CV6 6GE *Tel* 024 7622 1311 *email* clerk@higgscharity.org.uk

■ The High Sheriff's Police Trust for the County of West Midlands (Building Blocks)

CC NO 1075800   **ESTABLISHED** 1999

WHERE FUNDING CAN BE GIVEN West Midlands Police catchment area.

WHO CAN BENEFIT Children and young people in all matters relating to alcohol, drug and solvent abuse.

WHAT IS FUNDED Crime prevention projects in partnership with the police.

WHAT IS NOT FUNDED No grants towards personal applications, circular and capital appeals. No grants outside the benefit area.

SAMPLE GRANTS Barnados Dudley Community Routes (£18,000); Walsall Street Teams – The Nemiah Project (£9,400).

FINANCES *Year* 2009–10 *Income* £19,794 *Grants* £30,000

TRUSTEES C Birchall; J Hesketh; P Gormley; D Smith; Mrs A Worley.

HOW TO APPLY Application forms are available on the trust's website. Applicants must have a police partner or a statement of support for the project. The trustees consider applications three times a year.

WHO TO APPLY TO Ann Penfold, Lloyd House, Colmore Circus, Queensway, Birmingham B4 6NQ *Tel* 0845 1135000 *email* a.penfold@west-midlands.pnn.police.uk *Website* www.buildingblockscharity.co.uk

■ Highcroft Charitable Trust

CC NO 272684   **ESTABLISHED** 1975

WHERE FUNDING CAN BE GIVEN UK and overseas.

WHO CAN BENEFIT Organisations benefiting Jewish people, especially people disadvantaged by poverty.

WHAT IS FUNDED The advancement and study of the Jewish faith and the Torah. The relief of poverty and advancement of education among people of the Jewish faith.

RANGE OF GRANTS Up to £10,000.

SAMPLE GRANTS Previous beneficiaries included: Chevras Maoz Ladal, Kol Yaacov, SOFT and Tevini (£10,000 each); Friends of Beer Miriam, Institute For Higher Rabbinic Studies and Kollel Ohr Yechiel (£5,000 each); Kollel Chibas Yerushalayim (£4,200); Craven Walk Charity Trust (£2,500); London Friends of Kamenitzer (£2,000).

FINANCES *Year* 2009–10 *Income* £111,874 *Grants* £107,483 *Assets* £405,903

TRUSTEES Rabbi R Fischer; Mrs S L Fischer.

HOW TO APPLY In writing to the correspondent.

WHO TO APPLY TO Rabbi R Fischer, Trustee, 15 Highcroft Gardens, London NW11 0LY

■ The Hilden Charitable Fund

CC NO 232591   **ESTABLISHED** 1963

WHERE FUNDING CAN BE GIVEN UK and developing countries.

WHO CAN BENEFIT Charities, voluntary organisations and NGOs. In the UK most grant aid is directed to registered charities. Overseas projects will either work with a UK charity partner or show relevant local legal status. Preference is given to smaller organisations rather than large national charities. Scottish charities are only funded through a block grant to Scottish Community Foundation which they distribute to the sector.

WHAT IS FUNDED Priorities in the UK are homelessness, asylum seekers and refugees, penal affairs and disadvantaged young people. For projects in developing countries, priorities are projects which focus on community development, education, and health.

WHAT IS NOT FUNDED Grants are not normally made for well established causes or to individuals, and overseas grants concentrate on development aid in preference to disaster relief.

TYPE OF GRANT Capital, revenue and recurring. Also running costs and project costs.

RANGE OF GRANTS Average grant £4,700.

SAMPLE GRANTS Scottish Community Foundation (£33,000); Tanzania Development Trust – Tanzania (£20,000 in two grants); Joint Council for the Welfare of Immigrants – London (£15,000); Tolerance International UK – London and Church Mission Society – Bangladesh (£7,000 each); Foundation of the Simon Bolivar Experimental United World College of Agriculture – Venezuela (£6,800); Detention Advice Service – London (£6,000); BOAZ Trust – Manchester (£5,600); Barts and the London NHS Trust (£5,300); Soundmix – London and Shekinah Torbay – Torquay (£5,000 each); Congo Action – D R of Congo (£4,000); Littlehampton Churches Together Homelink (£3,500); Alternatives to

Violence Project (£3,000); Food Skills Limited – London (£2,500); Francis Clarissa Charitable Foundation – Philippines (£1,500); Inter Care – Ghana (£1,200); and Bondo Fund – Kenya (£1,000).

FINANCES *Year* 2009–10 *Income* £333,873 *Grants* £438,350 *Assets* £11,409,535
TRUSTEES J R A Rampton; Prof. C H Rodeck; Prof. M B H Rampton; Mrs E K Rodeck; A J M Rampton; Miss E J Rodeck; Ms C S L Rampton; C H Younger; Prof. D S Rampton; Ms M E Baxter; Miss E M C Rampton.
HOW TO APPLY 'When making an application, grant seekers should bear in mind the points below. We expect all applicants to complete the application form. Your case for funds should be concise (no more than 2 sides of A4), but supporting documentation is essential. Please ensure your application includes enclosures of: your most recent independently inspected accounts; your most recent annual report; projected income and expenditure for the current financial year. Please be clear in your application form about when the proposed work is to commence, and give the relevant timetable.' Your application for funds should cover the following: clear explanation about who is responsible for managing the project; a coherent plan of how the work is going to be carried out together with relevant budgets. Project budgets should be presented in the context of the overall income and expenditure of the applicant NGO/Charity; a plan of how the work is going to be maintained and developed in the future by involving relevant agencies and attracting money and resources; an explanation of why the local project seeks the help of a UK agency; details of local costs (e.g. salaries of state-employed teachers and medical personnel, cost of vehicles, petrol etc) and notes of any problems over exchange rates or inflation; an account of the political, economic, religious and cultural situation in the country/area; a brief comment on the extent to which the project can rely on government and local state funding in the country concerned; details of monitoring and evaluation.
Applicants from the UK applying for funds for their project partners must complete both the UK Application Form and the Overseas Partner Profile Form. Application forms, including one for Summer Playschemes, are available from the trust's website or offices. Please note that forms must be submitted to the secretary by post as hard copies; forms submitted by email or other electronic means are not accepted. Applicants are advised to ensure that they have read the application guidelines at the top of the form prior to completion. Potential applicants in Scotland should contact the Scottish Community Foundation, 22 Carlton Road, Edinburgh EH8 8DP; Tel: 0131 524 0300; website: www.scottishcf.org
WHO TO APPLY TO Rodney Hedley, Secretary, 34 North End Road, London W14 0SH *Tel* 020 7603 1525 *Fax* 020 7603 1525 *email* hildencharity@hotmail.com *Website* www.hildencharitablefund.org.uk

■ The Hill Charitable Trust
CC NO 1137072   **ESTABLISHED** 2008
WHERE FUNDING CAN BE GIVEN Worldwide, in practice, Havant, Hampshire.
WHO CAN BENEFIT Organisations.

WHAT IS FUNDED General charitable purposes – currently this is a very small trust supporting local activities.
TRUSTEES Philip James Hill; Wendy Ann Enid Hill; Jane Hill; Matthew Hill.
OTHER INFORMATION The trustees also have the option to accumulate all or any part of the income of the charity for a period of 21 years from the date of its establishment.
HOW TO APPLY In writing to the correspondent.
WHO TO APPLY TO The Trustees, 3 Marrelswood Gardens, Purbrook, Waterlooville, Hampshire PO7 5RS *email* gauntlettandhill@gmail.com

■ The Derek Hill Foundation
CC NO 801590   **ESTABLISHED** 1989
WHERE FUNDING CAN BE GIVEN UK.
WHO CAN BENEFIT Organisations and individuals.
WHAT IS FUNDED The promotion of arts and culture.
TYPE OF GRANT Bursaries and travel costs.
SAMPLE GRANTS The British School at Rome (£9,000); Welsh National Opera (£5,000); Memorial Arts Charity (£2,500); Llanfyllin Festival Association (£2,000); Royal College of Music (£1,500); National Arts Collection (£1,000); and Lyme Regis Organ Appeal (£300).
FINANCES *Year* 2009–10 *Income* £26,743 *Grants* £28,281 *Assets* £1,393,435
TRUSTEES Rathbone Trust Company Limited; Earl of Gowrie; Lord Armstrong of Ilminster; Mrs Josephine Batterham; Ian Patterson.
OTHER INFORMATION Grants to five individuals totalled £34,000
HOW TO APPLY In writing to the correspondent.
WHO TO APPLY TO The Trustees, c/o Rathbone Trust Company Limited, 159 New Bond Street, London W1S 2UD

■ The Charles Littlewood Hill Trust
CC NO 286350   **ESTABLISHED** 1978
WHERE FUNDING CAN BE GIVEN UK, with a preference for Nottinghamshire and Norfolk.
WHO CAN BENEFIT Charitable organisations in the UK, particularly those in Norfolk and Nottinghamshire.
WHAT IS FUNDED General charitable purposes.
WHAT IS NOT FUNDED Applications from individuals are not considered. Grants are seldom made for repairs of parish churches outside Nottinghamshire.
TYPE OF GRANT Applications for starter finance are encouraged. Grants are seldom made to endowment or capital funds.
RANGE OF GRANTS £1,000–£15,000, but usually of £5,000 or less.
SAMPLE GRANTS **Norfolk – 19 grants totalling £72,500:** YMCA Norfolk (£7,500); NORCAS (£5,000); Norfolk Eating Disorders Association (£3,000) and Purfleet Trust and St Edmunds Society (£1,000). **Nottinghamshire – 25 grants totalling £70,500:** Maggie's Nottingham (£10,000); St John Waterwing (£6,000); Nottinghamshire Hospice (£5,000); The Army Benevolent Fund – Nottinghamshire (£3,000); Family Care (£2,000) and St Peter's Church – Toton (£1,000). **Elsewhere – 14 grants totalling £19,100:** The Arkwright Scholarships (£3,600); Leonard Cheshire Disability (£2,000); Marie Curie Cancer Care and The Heather Trust (£1,000 each). Other grants in aggregate totalled £20,000.
FINANCES *Year* 2010 *Income* £188,942 *Grants* £182,000 *Assets* £4,093,766

Think carefully about every application. Is it justified?

613

TRUSTEES C W L Barratt; W F Whysall; T H Farr; N R Savory.

OTHER INFORMATION No grants to individuals.

HOW TO APPLY In writing to the correspondent, including the latest set of audited accounts, at least one month before trustees' meetings in March, July and November. Unsuccessful applications will not be notified.

WHO TO APPLY TO W F Whysall, Trustee, Berryman Shacklock LLP, Park House, Friar Lane, Nottingham NG1 6DN *Tel* 0115 945 3700 *Fax* 0115 948 0234

■ Hille Pandana

CC NO 1134461   **ESTABLISHED** 2010

WHERE FUNDING CAN BE GIVEN Undefined, in practice local.

WHO CAN BENEFIT Registered charities.

WHAT IS FUNDED Health; the arts; heritage; science; and sport.

TRUSTEES Jonathan Prevezer; Richard Luck-Hille.

HOW TO APPLY In writing to the correspondent.

WHO TO APPLY TO Jonathan W Prevezer, Trustee, c/o Citroen Wells Chartered Accountants, Devonshire House, 1 Devonshire Street, London W1W 5DR *Tel* 020 7304 2000

■ The Hillingdon Community Trust

CC NO 1098235   **ESTABLISHED** 2003

WHERE FUNDING CAN BE GIVEN The London borough of Hillingdon.

WHO CAN BENEFIT Community organisations.

WHAT IS FUNDED Supports community projects, education, the relief of poverty and advocacy in the beneficial area.

WHAT IS NOT FUNDED No grants to individuals, public bodies, religious bodies or organisations that have already received funding in respect of a completed project.

TYPE OF GRANT One-off; recurrent.

RANGE OF GRANTS Small grants: £500–£7,500. Main grants: upto £75,000.

SAMPLE GRANTS Benificiaries include: Green Corridor (£45,000); Age Concern Hillingdon (£35,000); Community Cancer Care (£26,000); Crown Centre for the Deaf (£24,000); Sahan Society (£16,000); Jupiter House Foyer (£10,000); Hayes Hawks, Heathrow Special Needs Farm, Dash (£7,500); Hillingdon Asian Women's Group (£5,300); Tageero (£4,000) and Harlington Football Club (£2,700).

FINANCES *Year* 2009–10 *Income* £1,100,000 *Grants* £692,622 *Assets* £1,637,747

TRUSTEES David Brough, Chair; Tony Eginton; Tim Hughes; Elaine Jacobs; Douglas Mills; Christine Taylor; Ian Campbell; Jody Hawley; Isabel King; Colin Lowen; D Crofts; M Gorman; D Sandhu and K Wallis.

OTHER INFORMATION Grants approved for the year were: Small grants – £98,000 Main grants – £594,000

HOW TO APPLY Small grants scheme – Application forms are available from the trust or can be can downloaded from the trust's website. Main grants scheme – This is a two-stage process. Initially, applicants complete a two-sided expression of interest form. These are considered by the Main Grants Sub-Committee and the trustees, who shortlist applicants with a reasonable likelihood of being funded. These applicants are then invited to complete and submit a full application for a main grant. Forms are available from the trust or can be can

downloaded from the trust's website, which also has details of application deadlines.

WHO TO APPLY TO Christine Little, Trust Administrator, Ms Christine Little, Barra Hall, Wood end, Green Road, Hayes, Middlesex *Tel* 020 8581 1676 *email* info@ hillingdoncommunitytrust.org.uk *Website* www. hillingdoncommunitytrust.org.uk

---

■ The Hillingdon Partnership Trust

CC NO 284668   **ESTABLISHED** 1982

WHERE FUNDING CAN BE GIVEN The London borough of Hillingdon.

WHO CAN BENEFIT Organisations benefiting people of all ages, at risk groups, people disadvantaged by poverty and socially isolated people.

WHAT IS FUNDED The trust aims: to build links between the local community and the business sector to secure funding for community initiatives and projects; to relieve people resident in Hillingdon who are sick, disabled, elderly, poor or in other social and economic circumstances; to provide, or assist in providing, equipment and facilities not normally provided by the local authority for the purpose of advancing education or relieving people in need.

FINANCES *Year* 2009–10 *Income* £464,894 *Grants* £65,000 *Assets* £96,570

TRUSTEES Dr D Neave; M J Taylor; J H Crowe; Air Cmdr P Thomas, Chair; J A Watts; M A Wisdom; Prof. H S Wolff; Ann Banks; A Kanjee; N Smith; Miranda Clarke; Nicholas Hurd; John Randall; Peter O'Reilly and David Routledge.

OTHER INFORMATION 'In general the trust does not itself make grants. It does make appeals to its business supporters on behalf of needy organisations and exceptionally, individuals, and the business partners may then provide funds direct to the applicant. Exceptionally, the trust may meet a need by arranging the purchase of necessary items and delivering the essential items to an applicant.'

HOW TO APPLY On a form available from the correspondent.

WHO TO APPLY TO John Matthews, Chief Executive, Mr John Matthews, Room 22–25 Building 219, Epsom Square, London Heathrow Airport, Hillingdon, Middlesex *Tel* 020 8897 3611 *Fax* 020 8897 3613 *email* johnmatthewshpt@ lineone.net

---

■ R G Hills Charitable Trust

CC NO 1008914   **ESTABLISHED** 1982

WHERE FUNDING CAN BE GIVEN UK and overseas.

WHO CAN BENEFIT Local and national registered charities.

WHAT IS FUNDED General charitable purposes with some preference for the fields of health, poverty and education.

RANGE OF GRANTS Up to £5,000.

SAMPLE GRANTS Fauna and Flora International (£3,800); Motor Neurone Disease Association (£3,500); Blonde McIndoe Research Foundation and Fynvola (£3,000 each); Spurgeons, Mission to Seafarers and Salvation Army – Canterbury Corps (£2,500 each); International Animal Rescue, Crime Diversion Scheme and Farm Africa (£2,000 each); Combat Stress (£1,900); Best Beginnings (£1,500); Cardboard Citizens (£1,200); and Toynbee Hall, Welcome Day Centre, Mental Health Foundation and L'Arche Overseas Development Fund (£1,000 each).

FINANCES *Year* 2009–10 *Income* £102,498 *Grants* £96,625 *Assets* £2,863,252

TRUSTEES David Pentin; Harvey Barrett.

HOW TO APPLY In writing to the correspondent.

WHO TO APPLY TO Harvey Barret, Trustee, Furley Page, 39 St Margaret's Street, Canterbury, Kent CT1 2TX *Tel* 01227 763939

······································

■ Hinchley Charitable Trust

CC NO 1108412   **ESTABLISHED** 1973

WHERE FUNDING CAN BE GIVEN UK and overseas.

WHO CAN BENEFIT Mainly evangelical Christian organisations, including Christian youth organisations and Christian organisations in local communities.

WHAT IS FUNDED General charitable purposes, with particular reference to evangelical Christian work, such as the training of Christian leaders, holistic mission and evangelism and Christian influence in the public sphere.

TYPE OF GRANT One-off and recurring, usually for projects, but capital and core costs are considered.

RANGE OF GRANTS Up to £23,000.

SAMPLE GRANTS Urban Saints – formerly Crusaders Union (£23,000); Langham Partnership (£13,000); Cleenish Renewal (£10,000); LICC (£8,000); Emmanual International (£7,500); and St Edmunds College and Willowfield Community Project (£5,000 each).

FINANCES *Year* 2009–10 *Income* £149,928 *Grants* £109,500 *Assets* £2,439,329

TRUSTEES Prof. Brian Stanley; John Levick; Mark Hobbs; Roger Northcott.

OTHER INFORMATION The grant total shows a partial recovery from 2008–09 when the trust could only make grants of £84,000 but grantmaking has yet to return to 2007–08 levels when £140,000 was distributed. As part of the trust's strategy to maintain the effectiveness of its grantmaking during this period, it has reduced the number of grants made while increasing the value of those grants. In 2009–10, for example, 56 per cent of grants were over £5,000, compared with only 27 per cent in 2008–09.

HOW TO APPLY The trustees adopt a proactive approach to grant making meaning unsolicited applications are rarely supported.

WHO TO APPLY TO Prof. Brian Stanley, Chair, 10 Coplow Terrace, Coplow Street, Birmingham B16 0DQ *Tel* 0121 455 6632 *email* bs217@cam.ac.uk

······································

■ Lady Hind Trust

CC NO 208877   **ESTABLISHED** 1951

WHERE FUNDING CAN BE GIVEN Mainly Nottinghamshire and Norfolk; UK.

WHO CAN BENEFIT Registered and exempt charities, including churches.

WHAT IS FUNDED General charitable purposes with a preference for health, disability, medical and social welfare charities, with churches and animal welfare charities also being supported.

WHAT IS NOT FUNDED Grants are not awarded to individuals.

TYPE OF GRANT Core and project support.

RANGE OF GRANTS Up to £20,000, but mostly £1,000 to £5,000.

SAMPLE GRANTS Oliver Hind Club (£17,500); Maggie's Nottingham, Nottinghamshire Community Safety Trust, The Hamlet Centre Trust – Norfolk and Norfolk Family Mediation Service (£10,000 each); The Norfolk Churches Trust, Lincolnshire & Nottinghamshire Air Ambulance, Nottinghamshire Historic Churches Trust and NSPCC – Nottinghamshire (£7,500

each). More typical grants of £5,000 or less included those to: Rutland House School for Parents, Nottinghamshire Deaf Society, RSPCA – Radcliffe Animal Shelter, Nottingham Pregnancy Crisis Centre, Nottingham Youth Orchestra, YWCA Nottingham, Norwich Cathedral Choir Endowment Fund, Norfolk Community Foundation, Buckingham Emergency Food Appeal, North Walsham Multisports Club, National Rheumatoid Arthritis Society, Rainbows Children's Hospice, British Trust for Ornithology, Orchid Cancer Appeal and Shelter.

FINANCES *Year* 2009–10 *Income* £377,302 *Grants* £382,204 *Assets* £11,663,298

TRUSTEES Charles W L Barratt; Tim H Farr; Nigel R Savory.

HOW TO APPLY Applications, in writing and with latest accounts, must be submitted at least one month in advance of trustee meetings held in March, July and November. Unsuccessful applicants are not notified. 'The trustees consider all written applications made to them by charitable organisations. Such applications are reviewed by every trustee prior to the trustees' four-monthly meetings and are discussed at such meetings. Grants are awarded at such meeting to those organisations which the trustees collectively consider to be worthy of their support. Grants are awarded principally to institutions based on their level of need and with a geographical bias towards Nottinghamshire and Norfolk.'

WHO TO APPLY TO John Thompson, Administrator, c/o Shakespeares Solicitors, Park House, Friar Lane, Nottingham NG1 6DN *Tel* 0115 945 3700 *Fax* 0115 948 0234 *email* ladyhind@btinternet.com

······································

■ The Hinduja Foundation

CC NO 802756   **ESTABLISHED** 1989

WHERE FUNDING CAN BE GIVEN Worldwide.

WHO CAN BENEFIT Registered charities.

WHAT IS FUNDED Health-care, educational charities, scarcity relief, poverty alleviation, art and culture, sports, social, economic and international development-related research.

RANGE OF GRANTS Up to £11,000.

SAMPLE GRANTS International Society for Krishna Consciousness (£10,800); Women's India Association, BAPS Swaminarayan Sanstha (£5,000 each); Chain of Hope (£3,000); The Marathon of Marathons Trust, Malayalee Association of UK, Savitri Waney Charitable Trust (£1,000 each); The Loomba Trust (£100).

FINANCES *Year* 2010 *Income* £141,825 *Grants* £45,595 *Assets* £141,100

TRUSTEES S P Hinduja; G P Hinduja; P P Hinduja; S S P Hinduja.

HOW TO APPLY In writing to the correspondent.

WHO TO APPLY TO The Trustees, c/o New Zealand House, 80 Haymarket, London SW1Y 4TE *email* foundation@hindujagroup.com *Website* hindujagroup.com

······································

■ Stuart Hine Trust

CC NO 326941   **ESTABLISHED** 1985

WHERE FUNDING CAN BE GIVEN UK and overseas.

WHO CAN BENEFIT Evangelical Christian organisations, supported by Stuart Hine during his lifetime or by the trustees since his death.

WHAT IS FUNDED The support of Christian ministry.

SAMPLE GRANTS Wycliff Bible Translators (£150,000).

······································

FINANCES *Year* 2009–10 *Income* £137,256 *Grants* £187,715 *Assets* £205,622

TRUSTEES Raymond Bodkin; Amelia Gardner; Philip Johnson; Jonathan Birdwood Juby; Leonard Chipping.

PUBLICATIONS During the year the trust finished the writing and design of a booklet: *How Great Thou Art! – The Inspiring Story of Stuart K. Hine and the Making of a Classic Christian Hymn.* This will be published in the near future.

OTHER INFORMATION The trust receives its income mainly from royalties from the song 'How Great Thou Art' written by Stuart Hine.

HOW TO APPLY The trust states that 'unsolicited requests for funds will not be considered'. Funds are basically distributed in accordance with the wishes of the settlor.

WHO TO APPLY TO Raymond Bodkin, Trustee, 'Cherith', 23 Derwent Close, Hailsham, East Sussex BN27 3DA *Tel* 01323 843948

■ The Hinrichsen Foundation

CC NO 272389   **ESTABLISHED** 1976

WHERE FUNDING CAN BE GIVEN UK.

WHO CAN BENEFIT Organisations benefiting musicians; individual musicians.

WHAT IS FUNDED Assisting contemporary composition and its performance, and musicological research. The trustees are aware that financial assistance is often necessary to create the opportunities for both composition and research. They are equally aware that the results of composition or research need to be made known and that financial assistance is often necessary for the production of performance materials, for the publication of the results of research and for performances of new compositions to take place.

WHAT IS NOT FUNDED The trust does not support study courses, including those at postgraduate level. Grants are not given for instruments, equipment or recordings.

TYPE OF GRANT Usually one-off for a specific project or part of a project.

RANGE OF GRANTS Variable, generally between £500 and £2,000.

SAMPLE GRANTS Previously: Huddersfield Contemporary Music Festival (£5,000); Dartington International Summer School and Spitalfields Festival (£2,000 each); Birmingham Contemporary Music Group and Kettle's Yard (£1,500 each); Swaledale Festival and York Late Music Festival (£1,000 each); The Red Violin (£750); Dmitri Ensemble (£500); and Pro Nobis Singers (£450).

FINANCES *Year* 2009 *Income* £216,329 *Grants* £0 *Assets* £335,731

TRUSTEES P Standford, Chair; T Berg; Dr J Cross; Dr Linda Hirst; Sue Lubbock; K Potter; P Strang; Prof. S Walsh; Mrs T Estell.

OTHER INFORMATION Currently the trust has suspended its grant giving program due to issues surrounding income generation. The trust's website should be checked for updates.

HOW TO APPLY On a form that can be downloaded from the foundation's website. Trustees meet quarterly.

WHO TO APPLY TO The Secretary, PO Box 309, Leatherhead, Surrey KT22 2AT *email* hinrichsen.foundation@editionpeters.com *Website* www.hinrichsenfoundation.org.uk

■ The Hintze Family Charitable Foundation

CC NO 1101842   **ESTABLISHED** 2003

WHERE FUNDING CAN BE GIVEN England and Wales.

WHO CAN BENEFIT Churches, museums, galleries, libraries, schools and charitable organisations.

WHAT IS FUNDED The trust operates in the following areas: promoting access to museums, libraries and art galleries; supporting Christian churches in England and Wales, particularly the Diocese of Southwark; the relief of sickness and people with terminal illnesses; and the provision of resources and equipment for schools, colleges and universities (in particular to enable the acquisition and retention of antiquarian books to be used as a learning resource).

TYPE OF GRANT Capital and revenue funding, mostly over 2–5 years.

SAMPLE GRANTS National Gallery (£2 million); Ridley Hall (£900,000); Catholic Conference for England & Wales (£540,000); the Prince's Foundation for the Built Environment (£219,500); Victoria & Albert Museum (£200,000); Glyndebourne Arts Trust (£150,000); and the Institute of Economic Affairs (£100,000).

FINANCES *Year* 2010 *Income* £5,944,613 *Grants* £4,224,914 *Assets* £2,694,757

TRUSTEES Michael Hintze; David Swain; Brian Hannon.

HOW TO APPLY The trust offers the following application guidance in its latest accounts: 'The foundation invites applications for grants or commitments from charities which serve the objects of the foundation. No specific format is required for applications. Applications, along with potential donations and commitments identified by the chief executive and the trustees, are considered in formal trustee meetings.'

WHO TO APPLY TO Oliver Hylton, Trustee, 5th Floor, 33 Chester Street, London SW1X 7BL *Tel* 020 7201 6862

■ The Hitchin Educational Foundation

CC NO 311024   **ESTABLISHED** 1965

WHERE FUNDING CAN BE GIVEN Unrestricted, in practice, Hertfordshire.

WHO CAN BENEFIT Individuals and local organisations benefiting children, young adults and students under the age of 25 years.

WHAT IS FUNDED The advancement of education and training.

WHAT IS NOT FUNDED No support for second degrees or the purchase of certain books.

TYPE OF GRANT One-off.

RANGE OF GRANTS Up to £35,000.

SAMPLE GRANTS Beneficiaries included: Hitchin Boys' School (£35,000), the Priory School and Hitchin Girls' School (£30,000 each); and Hertfordshire Educational Foundation (£300). Other miscellaneous grants were given to unnamed recipients totalling £19,000.

FINANCES *Year* 2009–10 *Income* £108,207 *Grants* £114,000 *Assets* £1,310,111

TRUSTEES Mr D Hitchcock – Chairman; Mr D Ashley – Vice Chairman; Mr M Brown; Mr P Loach; Mrs F Manning; Mr R Slater; Dr R Lee; Mr C Minton; Revd M Roden; Mr D Chapallaz; Mr A F Kingston-Splatt; Mr N K Brook; Mrs S J Wren; Mr D Miller; Mrs J Wood and Mrs S Cracknell.

OTHER INFORMATION Applicants must have lived in Hitchin or attended a Hitchin school for at least two years. In 2009–10 a further £19,000 was given for miscellaneous grants.

HOW TO APPLY Apply in writing to the correspondent for an application form.

WHO TO APPLY TO Brian Frederick, Clerk, 33 Birch Close, Broom, Biggleswade SG18 9NR *Tel* 01767 313892 *Fax* 01462 681509

■ The Henry C Hoare Charitable Trust

CC NO 1088669   **ESTABLISHED** 2001
WHERE FUNDING CAN BE GIVEN UK.
WHO CAN BENEFIT Charitable organisations.
WHAT IS FUNDED General charitable purposes.
TYPE OF GRANT One-off and annual donations.
SAMPLE GRANTS Previous beneficiaries have included: Trinity College Cambridge (£25,000); Transform Drug Policy Foundation, Foundation for People with Learning Disabilities (£20,000 each); For Dementia (£15,000); and The Abby CEVA Primary School (£7,000).
FINANCES *Year* 2009–10 *Income* £163,945 *Grants* £224,725 *Assets* £3,460,899
TRUSTEES Henry C Hoare; Messrs Hoare Trustees.
HOW TO APPLY In writing to the correspondent.
WHO TO APPLY TO C Hoare and Co, 37 Fleet Street, London EC4P 4DQ *Tel* 020 7353 4522

■ The Eleemosynary Charity of William Hobbayne

CC NO 211547   **ESTABLISHED** 1962
WHERE FUNDING CAN BE GIVEN Support is first given to causes in Hanwell and any surplus is then donated to causes in the borough of Ealing.
WHO CAN BENEFIT Specific beneficiaries as stated in the trust's deed; Organisations and individuals in (a) Hanwell, then (b) borough of Ealing.
WHAT IS FUNDED General charitable purposes, including the relief of need and hardship.
RANGE OF GRANTS Up to about £7,500.
SAMPLE GRANTS Beneficiaries included: St Mary's Church Hanwell (£7,500); Ealing and Brentwood Consolidated Charity (£5,000); Hanwell neighbourly care scheme (£4,800) and Educational Charity of William Hobbayne (£3,000).
FINANCES *Year* 2009–10 *Income* £133,888 *Grants* £29,600 *Assets* £2,577,987
TRUSTEES Revd Matthew Grayshon, Chair; Mark Cosstick; Roy Price; Allison Rockley; John Sawyer; Susan Stiff; Angela Wallis; Nicholas Robinson; Robert Coomber; David Muir.
OTHER INFORMATION £7,600 was paid in grants to individuals.
HOW TO APPLY In writing to the correspondent.
WHO TO APPLY TO Caroline Lumb, Clerk, Mrs Caroline Lumb, The William Hobbayne Community Centre, St. Dunstans Road, London W7 2HB *Tel* 020 8810 0277 *Fax* 020 8579 2921

■ The Hobson Charity Limited

CC NO 326839   **ESTABLISHED** 1985
WHERE FUNDING CAN BE GIVEN UK.
WHO CAN BENEFIT Registered charities only, particularly those benefiting people of all ages, students, teachers, at risk groups, people disadvantaged by poverty and socially isolated people.
WHAT IS FUNDED Relief of poverty and distress among people who are elderly and poor; the provision of recreation and leisure facilities; and

the advancement of education and other charitable purposes.
WHAT IS NOT FUNDED No grants to individuals, except in exceptional circumstances.
TYPE OF GRANT One-off and recurrent.
RANGE OF GRANTS £1,000–£150,000.
SAMPLE GRANTS Westminster Abbey (£250,000 in 4 grants); Royal Opera House (£150,000); RNLI (£105,000 in 4 grants); SSAFA and Queenswood School (£100,000 each); White Ensign Association (£90,000 in 2 grants); Great Steward of Scotland's Dumfries House Trust (£75,000); Outward Bound Trust (£60,000 in 2 grants); Churchill Archives Centre, Tate Millbank and the Foundation for Liver Research (£50,000 each); STOP – Trafficking UK (£35,000 in 2 grants); Children in the Arts, White Lodge Redevelopment and the British School of Osteopathy (£25,000 each); Centrepoint and the Swan Sanctuary (£10,000 each); and the British Association of Adoption & Fostering, Jewish Lads' and Girls' Brigade and Christian Youth Enterprise (£5,000 each).
FINANCES *Year* 2009–10 *Income* £17,142,248 *Grants* £2,172,114 *Assets* £14,939,345
TRUSTEES Deborah Hobson; Sir Donald Gosling; Sir Ronald F Hobson; Lady Hobson; J Richardson.
HOW TO APPLY In writing to the correspondent. The trustees meet quarterly.
WHO TO APPLY TO Deborah Hobson, Trustee and Secretary, Hildane Properties Limited, 7th Floor, 21 Bryanston Street, Marble Arch, London W1H 7PR *Tel* 020 7495 5599

■ Hockerill Educational Foundation

CC NO 311018   **ESTABLISHED** 1977
WHERE FUNDING CAN BE GIVEN UK, with a preference for the dioceses of Chelmsford and St Albans.
WHO CAN BENEFIT Organisations benefiting young adults, older people, academics, students, teachers and educational support staff, Christians and the Church of England.
WHAT IS FUNDED The foundation makes grants in the field of education in three main areas: individual grants to support the education and training of teachers; grants to organisations to support teachers and research and development in religious education; and grants to develop the church's educational work in the dioceses of Chelmsford and St Albans. The trustees will normally consider applications from corporate bodies or institutions associated with education on Christian principles. There is a religious dimension to all education, but the trustees would expect any activity, course, project or research supported to be of real benefit to religious education and/or the church's educational work. They will give priority to imaginative new projects which will enhance the Church of England's contribution to higher and further education and/or promote aspects of religious education in schools.
WHAT IS NOT FUNDED Grants are not given for general appeals for funds, 'bricks and mortar' building projects or purposes that are the clear responsibility of another body.
TYPE OF GRANT Renewable for up to three years, or occasionally a maximum of five years, subject to satisfactory progress reports.
FINANCES *Year* 2009–10 *Income* £263,043 *Grants* £213,515 *Assets* £4,914,909
TRUSTEES Ven. Trevor Jones, Chair; Rt Revd Stephen Cottrell; Rt Revd Dr Alan Smith; Lesley Barlow; Rt Revd Paul Bayes; Colin Bird; Ven.

Think carefully about every application. Is it justified?

617

Elwin Cockett; Rob Fox; Jonathan Longstaff; Revd Coralie McCluskey; Canon Harry Marsh; Rt Revd Christopher Morgan; Hannah Potter; Canon Jonathan O Reynolds; Janet Scott.

OTHER INFORMATION The grant total includes £51,715 given to individuals.

HOW TO APPLY On a form available to download from the website. Applications should include some official documentation, such as the most recent annual report and accounts, which clearly show the status, objects and ideals of the organisation and its financial position, and an sae. They should be submitted by 31 March each year. Grants are usually awarded between July and September.

WHO TO APPLY TO Derek J Humphrey, Secretary, 3 The Swallows, Harlow, Essex CM17 0AR *email* info@hockerillfoundation.org.uk *Website* www.hockerillfoundation.org.uk

■ Matthew Hodder Charitable Trust

CC NO 1042741   **ESTABLISHED** 1994
WHERE FUNDING CAN BE GIVEN Worldwide.
WHO CAN BENEFIT Organisations and individuals.
WHAT IS FUNDED The trust's charitable concern is with: book publishing; literacy and literature; reading; the book trade (including the provision of books); arts education (including music); provision of financial support for educational purposes; Christian endeavour.
WHAT IS NOT FUNDED Health (unless reading related); social welfare; environment; politics.
TYPE OF GRANT Funding for up to three years for capital and core costs.
RANGE OF GRANTS Up to £1,000.
FINANCES *Year* 2009–10 *Income* £36,913 *Grants* £34,200 *Assets* £929,494
TRUSTEES Mark Hodder-Williams, Chair; Tim Biggs-Davison; Roger Spurling; Timothy Ford; Anthony Brown.
OTHER INFORMATION The trust has no geographical limits and makes grants to individuals and organisations.
HOW TO APPLY In writing to the correspondent.
WHO TO APPLY TO Mark Hodder-Williams, Chair of Trustees, Little Birches, 38 Greenhill Road, Otford, Sevenoaks, Kent TN14 5RS *Tel* 01959 522180

■ The Sir Julian Hodge Charitable Trust

CC NO 234848   **ESTABLISHED** 1964
WHERE FUNDING CAN BE GIVEN UK.
WHO CAN BENEFIT Registered charities benefiting people of all ages. Support may also be given to people who are disabled, medical professionals, research workers, scientists, students and teachers and governesses. Support may also be given to people with cancer, paediatric diseases, polio and tuberculosis.
WHAT IS FUNDED General charitable purposes, especially medical research in cancer, polio, tuberculosis and diseases of children. General advancement of medical and surgical science, the advancement of education, religion, and the relief of older people and people who are disabled.
WHAT IS NOT FUNDED No grants to individuals or companies.
RANGE OF GRANTS £500–£5,000.
SAMPLE GRANTS Hope House Children's Hospices (£5,000); The St John of Jerusalem Eye

Hospital (£3,000); Compton Hospice, Headway and National Autistic Society (£2,000 each); Albrighton Trust, Derby Kids Camp, Good Companions Bolton, Guide Dogs, Walsall Disability Centre and Youth for Christ (£1,000 each).
FINANCES *Year* 2009–10 *Income* £50,261 *Grants* £62,500 *Assets* £1,349,080
TRUSTEES Julian J Hodge; Joyce Harrison; Derek L Jones; Margaret Cason; Eric M Hammonds.
HOW TO APPLY In writing to the correspondent. The trust invites applications for grants from charitable institutions. Institutions submit a summary of their proposals to the trustees in a specific format. Applications for grants are considered by the trustees against its objectives.
WHO TO APPLY TO Joyce Harrison, Trustee, Ty Gwyn, Lisvane Road, Lisvane, Cardiff CF14 0SG

■ The Jane Hodge Foundation

CC NO 216053   **ESTABLISHED** 1962
WHERE FUNDING CAN BE GIVEN Unrestricted, in practice UK with a preference for Wales.
WHO CAN BENEFIT UK registered charities and those exempt from registration.
WHAT IS FUNDED Medical and surgical science, studies and research; education; religion; and general charitable purposes.
WHAT IS NOT FUNDED No grants to individuals.
TYPE OF GRANT One-off and recurring grants and loans.
RANGE OF GRANTS Up to £140,000.
SAMPLE GRANTS Cardiff University – Macro Economics (£137,000 in three grants); George Thomas Memorial Trust (£58,000 in two grants); Tenovus (£30,000); Cardiff University – Merit Prizes (£14,000 in two grants); Ty Hafan (£8,000); Age UK (£6,000); Great Western Society Ltd, Bobath Cymru, Race Equality First, Shelter Cymru and Archdiocese of Cardiff – St Mary's Priory (£5,000 each); Plan International UK (£4,000); the Owl Fund (£3,000); and Missionary Sisters of the Holy Rosary, British Heart Foundation and Corpus Christi Catholic High School (£2,500 each).
FINANCES *Year* 2009–10 *Income* £558,604 *Grants* £584,525 *Assets* £27,737,680
TRUSTEES Eric Hammonds; Julian Hodge; Joyce Harrison; Derek Jones; Ian Davies; Margaret Cason.
OTHER INFORMATION The foundation described its grantmaking in the 2009–10 accounts: 'From the applications for grants received in the year, applications in respect of £585,000 (2009: £935,000) met the criteria required and amounts were granted to the charities concerned. The level of grants made each year can vary since there is a process of assessment and approval before grants can be made and grants may cover a period of more than one year. [] Actual donations paid in the year including amounts committed in prior years, amounted to £625,000.'
HOW TO APPLY In writing to the correspondent. Applications for grants are considered by the trustees at regular meetings throughout the year. Applications are acknowledged.
WHO TO APPLY TO Margaret Cason, Secretary, Ty Gwyn, Lisvane Road, Lisvane, Cardiff CF14 0SG *Tel* 029 2076 6521 *email* dianne.lydiard@ janehodgefoundation.co.uk

■ The J G Hogg Charitable Trust

CC NO 299042   **ESTABLISHED** 1987
WHERE FUNDING CAN BE GIVEN UK.
WHO CAN BENEFIT To benefit people in need and animals in need.
WHAT IS FUNDED Humanitarian causes, overseas charities, wild and domestic animal welfare causes.
WHAT IS NOT FUNDED No grants to individuals. Registered charities only are supported.
SAMPLE GRANTS Previously: Kids Company and Oxfam (£15,000 each); Medicinema and Teddy Bear Air Care (£10,000 each); and Addiction Recovery Foundation (£7,000).
FINANCES *Year* 2009–10 *Income* £19,420 *Grants* £100,000
TRUSTEES Sarah Jane Houldsworth; Joanna Wynfreda Turvey.
HOW TO APPLY In writing to the correspondent. To keep administration costs to a minimum, the trust is unable to reply to unsuccessful applicants.
WHO TO APPLY TO C M Jones, Trustees' Accountant, Chantrey Vellacott DFK, Russell Square House, 10 -12 Russell Square, London WC1B 5LF *Tel* 020 7509 9000 *email* cjones@cvdfk.com

■ The Holbeck Charitable Trust

CC NO 1113089   **ESTABLISHED** 2006
WHERE FUNDING CAN BE GIVEN Worldwide, preference for York.
WHO CAN BENEFIT Registered charities.
WHAT IS FUNDED (1) The advancement of medical research; (2) the advancement of education; (3) the advancement of the Christian religion; (4) people in need; (5) the preservation of buildings or sites of historic or architectural importance. 'The trust receives both solicited and unsolicited applications for funding. The trustees are also encouraged to identify suitable charities, including local organisations as well as national organisations in need of funding for specific projects.'
WHAT IS NOT FUNDED No grants to animal charities or individuals. Unsolicited applications for large capital projects or medical research projects are not supported.
TYPE OF GRANT One-off grants for capital funding, core costs, salaries, contracts and replacement of statutory funding. Full project funding and unrestricted funding is also considered.
FINANCES *Year* 2009–10 *Income* £81,000 *Grants* £599,000 *Assets* £6,366,000
TRUSTEES G C Horsfield; F A Horsfield; J R Lane; V A Denman; C L Horsfield.
HOW TO APPLY In writing to the correspondent including the latest annual report and accounts. The trustees meet quarterly.
WHO TO APPLY TO The Trustees, c/o Rollits, Rowntree Wharf, Navigation Road, York YO1 9WE

■ The Holden Charitable Trust

CC NO 264185   **ESTABLISHED** 1972
WHERE FUNDING CAN BE GIVEN UK, with a preference for the Manchester area.
WHO CAN BENEFIT Organisations benefiting Jewish people. Children, young adults and students may benefit.
WHAT IS FUNDED Jewish charitable purposes with emphasis on the advancement of education.
SAMPLE GRANTS Broom Foundation (£59,000); Ohel Bnei Yaakob (£50,000); Ohr Yerushalayim

Synagogue (£33,000); Friends of Beis Eliyahu Trust (£24,000); the FED (£7,500); and King David's School (£5,000).
FINANCES *Year* 2009–10 *Income* £247,515 *Grants* £346,969 *Assets* £835,213
TRUSTEES David Lopian; Marion Lopian; Michael Lopian.
OTHER INFORMATION Grants of less than £5,000 each amounted to £66,996.
HOW TO APPLY In writing to the correspondent.
WHO TO APPLY TO The Clerk, c/o Lopian Gross Barnett and Co., Cardinal House, 20 St Mary Parsonage, Manchester M3 2IG *Tel* 0161 832 8721

■ John Holford's Charity

CC NO 223046   **ESTABLISHED** 1984
WHERE FUNDING CAN BE GIVEN The parishes of Clutton and Middlewich, the borough of Congleton and that part of Astbury that lies outside the borough.
WHO CAN BENEFIT Mostly individuals, also organisations including schools.
WHAT IS FUNDED Relief in need and educational visits and trips.
FINANCES *Income* £39,113 *Grants* £19,328 *Assets* £539,661
TRUSTEES Mrs Anita Lockett; Revd Ian Bishop; Revd Jonathan Sharples; Mrs Rosamund Mahon; E S Tudor Evans; Revd David Taylor; Mrs Jane Shelmerdine.
OTHER INFORMATION Up to 5% of the income can be used for relief-in-need in the parish of Clutton, with the remainder divided equally between the parish of Middlewich, the borough of Congleton and the part of Astbury outside the borough of Congleton.
HOW TO APPLY In writing to the correspondent.
WHO TO APPLY TO The Clerk, Birch Cullimore, Friars, White Friars, Chester CH1 1XS *Tel* 01244 356789 *email* kerris.owen@cullimoredutton. co.uk

■ The Hollands-Warren Fund

CC NO 279747   **ESTABLISHED** 1977
WHERE FUNDING CAN BE GIVEN Maidstone.
WHO CAN BENEFIT Residents of the borough of Maidstone who are in genuine need.
WHAT IS FUNDED Temporary medical and nursing services and/or domestic help for residents.
RANGE OF GRANTS Up to £43,000.
SAMPLE GRANTS Twilight Nursing Service (£43,000) and Heart of Kent Hospice (£13,000).
TRUSTEES Kim Harrington; D W H Bell; A S Palmer; J C M Sankey.
HOW TO APPLY In writing to the correspondent.
WHO TO APPLY TO Kim Harrington, Somerfield House, 59 London Road, Maidstone, Kent ME16 8JH *Tel* 01622 690691 *email* kimharrington@ brachers.co.uk

■ The Hollick Family Charitable Trust

CC NO 1060228   **ESTABLISHED** 1997
WHERE FUNDING CAN BE GIVEN UK and overseas.
WHO CAN BENEFIT Registered charities.
WHAT IS FUNDED General charitable purposes.
TYPE OF GRANT One-off and recurrent.
RANGE OF GRANTS £1,000–£12,000.
SAMPLE GRANTS AMREF (£12,000); London Citizens (£7,500); Real Action and King's Head (£5,000

each); Scene and Heard (£2,000); Amref Christmas Concert (£1,500) and Aid to Gaza, Notting Hill Churches Homeless Concern and Macmillan (£1,000 each).

FINANCES *Year* 2009–10 *Income* £163,384 *Grants* £66,857 *Assets* £1,074,033

TRUSTEES Lord Hollick; Lady Hollick; Hon. C D Hollick; C M Kemp; D W Beech; Hon. G L Hollick; Hon. A M Hollick; T Kemp, C M Kemp.

OTHER INFORMATION Grants for less than £1,000 totalled £8,000.

HOW TO APPLY In writing to the correspondent.

WHO TO APPLY TO D W Beech, Solicitor, c/o Peter Bryan and Co, Foxglove House, 166 Piccadilly, London W1J 9EF *Tel* 020 7493 4932

■ The Holliday Foundation

CC NO 1089931 **ESTABLISHED** 2002

WHERE FUNDING CAN BE GIVEN United Kingdom.

WHO CAN BENEFIT Organisations and individuals.

WHAT IS FUNDED General charitable purposes.

SAMPLE GRANTS Charsfield Recreation Ground, Help the hospices (£5,000); Sparkles Home Sri Lanka (£2,500); The Easy Anglian Academy (£1,200); The Newbury Spring Festival (£1,000).

FINANCES *Income* £25,129 *Grants* £11,949 *Assets* £1,361,461

TRUSTEES D W J Garrett; Mrs J M Garrett; J A Cave; A R Wilson; M V H Llewellyn.

OTHER INFORMATION The trustees review requests for grants and may request further information or visit applicants before deciding whether to make a payment. The trustees will follow up the use of grants where relevant.

HOW TO APPLY In writing to the correspondent.

WHO TO APPLY TO The Trustees, Salisbury Partners LLP, 25 Hill Street, London W1J 5LW

■ The Dorothy Holmes Charitable Trust

CC NO 237213 **ESTABLISHED** 1964

WHERE FUNDING CAN BE GIVEN UK, with a preference for Dorset.

WHO CAN BENEFIT UK registered charities benefiting young adults and older people; people who are sick; clergy; ex-service and service people; legal professionals; unemployed people; volunteers; parents and children; one-parent families; widows and widowers; at risk groups; carers; and people who are disabled.

WHAT IS FUNDED Charities working in the fields of advice and information on housing; emergency and short-term housing; residential facilities; respite and sheltered accommodation; information technology and computers; civil society development; support of voluntary and community organisations; health professional bodies; and religion will be considered. Support is also given to healthcare; hospices and hospitals; cancer research; church buildings; heritage; secondary schools and special schools; counselling on social issues; and income support and maintenance.

WHAT IS NOT FUNDED Only applications from registered charities will be considered.

TYPE OF GRANT Buildings; capital; core costs; one-off; project; research; recurring costs; running costs; salaries; and start-up costs. Funding for up to and over three years will be considered.

RANGE OF GRANTS Up to £6,000.

SAMPLE GRANTS Previous beneficiaries included: Wallingford School (£6,000); Children in Touch,

Crisis and Christmas and RNLI (£5,000 each); Hyman Cen Foundation (£4,000); Army Benevolent Fund (£3,000); Action on Elder Abuse and CLIC Sargent Cancer Fund (£2,000 each); National Autistic Society and Raleigh International (£1,000 each); and Royal Free Hospital Retirement Fellowship (£300).

FINANCES *Year* 2010–11 *Income* £22,068 *Grants* £60,216

TRUSTEES Miss M Cody; Dr S Roberts; J Roberts.

HOW TO APPLY In writing to the correspondent, preferably in January to March each year.

WHO TO APPLY TO Michael Kennedy, Smallfield Cody and Co, 5 Harley Place, Harley Street, London W1G 8QD *Tel* 020 7636 6100

■ The Holmes Family Trust (Sheffield)

CC NO 1139716 **ESTABLISHED** 2011

WHERE FUNDING CAN BE GIVEN UK.

WHO CAN BENEFIT Registered charities.

WHAT IS FUNDED General charitable purposes, Christian causes and children and young people.

TRUSTEES Adrian Holmes; Michelle Rigby; Andrew Robertson; Richard Holmes.

OTHER INFORMATION The lead trustee, Adrian Holmes, is an entrepreneur and former chief executive of Employability and Skills Group, which provides vocational skills training and the Welfare to Work programme on behalf of the UK government.

HOW TO APPLY In writing to the correspondent.

WHO TO APPLY TO Adrian Holmes, Trustee, Bank Green House, Fox Lane, Millthorpe, Derbyshire S18 7WG

■ The Holst Foundation

CC NO 283668 **ESTABLISHED** 1981

WHERE FUNDING CAN BE GIVEN UK.

WHO CAN BENEFIT Mainly musicians.

WHAT IS FUNDED To promote public appreciation of the musical works of Gustav and Imogen Holst and to encourage the study and practice of the arts. Funds are almost exclusively for the performance of music by living composers.

WHAT IS NOT FUNDED No support for the recordings or works of Holst that are already well supported, nor for capital projects. No grants to individuals for educational purposes.

RANGE OF GRANTS Usually up to £30,000.

SAMPLE GRANTS NMC Recordings (£123,000); University of York music Press (£7,500); Aldeburgh Music (£5,000); Birmingham Contemporary Music Group (£4,000); Cheltenham Music Society and Huddersfield Festival (£1,000 each).

FINANCES *Year* 2009–10 *Income* £73,667 *Grants* £174,483 *Assets* £1,386,222

TRUSTEES Rosamund Strode, Chair; Noel Periton; Prof. Arnold Whittall; Peter Carter; Andrew Clements; Julian Anderson.

HOW TO APPLY In writing to the correspondent. Trustees meet four times a year. There is no application form. Seven copies of the application should be sent. Applications should contain full financial details and be as concise as possible. Funding is not given retrospectively.

WHO TO APPLY TO The Grants Administrator, 179 Great Portland Street, London W1W 5LS *Tel* 020 8673 4215 (answerphone only) *email* holst@dpmail.co.uk

■ P H Holt Foundation

CC NO 1113708   **ESTABLISHED** 1955
WHERE FUNDING CAN BE GIVEN UK, with a preference for Merseyside.
WHO CAN BENEFIT Wherever possible, grants are paid to or through registered charities.
WHAT IS FUNDED General charitable purposes in the UK, especially Merseyside, particularly when original work or work of special excellence is being undertaken.
WHAT IS NOT FUNDED No grants for: individuals; sectarian causes; appeals for help with minibuses, holidays and animal welfare work; organisations based outside of Merseyside (in some circumstances help may be given to organisations in parts of Cheshire, Halton and West Lancashire which have strong links with Merseyside).
TYPE OF GRANT One-off and recurrent.
RANGE OF GRANTS Up to £10,000.
SAMPLE GRANTS Speke Baptist Church (£10,000); Lodestar Theatre Company (£6,000); Collective Encounters and Liverpool Arts Interface Ltd (£5,000 each); Plaza Community Cinema (£4,400); Garston and District Community Council (£3,000); Hurricane Film Foundation (£2,500); Creative Ideas in Action and Merseyside Refugee and Asylum Seekers Pre and Post Natal Support Group (£2,000 each); Steps to Freedom (£1,500); Kensington Remembers, Outward Bound Trust and Runnymede Trust (£1,000 each); China Pearl, Inter-Faith Network for UK, Rotunda Community College and Elim Christian Centre (£500 each); and Friends of the Lake District and John Muir Trust (£250 each).
FINANCES *Year* 2009–10 *Income* £199,695 *Grants* £78,530 *Assets* £12,833,666
TRUSTEES Neil Kemsley, Chair; Tilly Boyce; Martin Cooke; Paige Earlam; Nikki Eastwood; Anthony Hannay; Derek Morris; Ken Ravenscroft.
HOW TO APPLY In writing to the correspondent including, as appropriate, a budget, annual report and accounts and indications of who else is supporting the work or willing to recommend it. Full and detailed guidance notes are available from the foundation.
WHO TO APPLY TO Roger Morris, Secretary, Room 607, India Buildings, Liverpool L2 0RA *Tel* 0151 473 4693 *Fax* 0151 473 4693

■ The Edward Holt Trust

CC NO 224741   **ESTABLISHED** 1955
WHERE FUNDING CAN BE GIVEN UK with a preference for Greater Manchester.
WHO CAN BENEFIT General charitable purposes/ projects.
WHAT IS FUNDED Primarily the maintenance of a block of 10 flats in Didsbury, Manchester, for retired people. Preference to charities which the trustees have special interest in, knowledge of or association with, including cancer, neurological and ageing research.
TYPE OF GRANT Buildings, capital, project and research. Funding is available for up to three years.
SAMPLE GRANTS Christie Hospital NHS Trust – Communication Skills Training Unit (£5,000).
FINANCES *Year* 2009–10 *Income* £214,761 *Grants* £95,195 *Assets* £6,612,895
TRUSTEES Richard Kershaw, Chair; Mike Fry; David Tully; Edward Tudor-Evans; Angela Roden.
OTHER INFORMATION Holt House expenditure totalled to £78,000 including the cost of refurbishments carried out in the year.

HOW TO APPLY 'Unsolicited grant requests are not currently being considered as the trustees are targeting the income to specific longer term projects.'
WHO TO APPLY TO Bryan Peak, Secretary, 22 Ashworth Park, Knutsford, Cheshire WA16 9DE *Tel* 01565 651086 *email* edwardholt@btinternet.com

■ The Holywood Trust

SC NO SC009942   **ESTABLISHED** 1981
WHERE FUNDING CAN BE GIVEN Dumfries and Galloway.
WHO CAN BENEFIT Young people, the disabled and those suffering from ill health in Dumfries and Galloway. Grants are made both to individuals and to organisations.
WHAT IS FUNDED 'The Holywood Trust assists organisations working with or for young people in Dumfries and Galloway. It does this by means of secondment of staff, management and administrative support, assisting with fund-raising activity as well as direct financial support.'
TYPE OF GRANT One-off, capital and recurring (usually limited to three years) depending on need.
RANGE OF GRANTS £10–£50,000.
FINANCES *Income* £127,154,700
TRUSTEES Mrs E A Nelson, Chair; C A Jencks; J J G Brown; A M McLeod; B J K Weatherall; Ms L L Fox.
HOW TO APPLY On a form available from the correspondent. Applications are considered by the trustees at least three times a year.
WHO TO APPLY TO Richard Lye, Trust Administrator, Mount St Michael, Craigs Road, Dumfries DG1 4UT *Tel* 01387 269176 *Website* www.holywood-trust.org.uk

■ The Homelands Charitable Trust

CC NO 214322   **ESTABLISHED** 1962
WHERE FUNDING CAN BE GIVEN UK.
WHO CAN BENEFIT Registered charities benefiting children, particularly people in at risk groups, or who are victims of abuse or domestic violence. Support may also be given to clergy, medical professionals and research workers.
WHAT IS FUNDED General charitable purposes in accordance with the settlor's wishes. Special emphasis is given to the General Conference of the New Church, medical research and the care and protection of children. Hospices are also supported.
WHAT IS NOT FUNDED No grants to individuals.
SAMPLE GRANTS General Conference of the New Church (£68,000); Broadfield Memorial Fund (£15,000); New Church College (£11,000); Bournemouth Society (£10,000); Jubilee Sailing Trust, Manic Depression Fellowship and National Children's Homes (£2,400 each); and the Attic Charity – Youth Project, Bikeability, Eyeless Trust and Pestalozzi (£1,600 each).
FINANCES *Year* 2009–10 *Income* £517,038 *Grants* £239,000 *Assets* £6,452,850
TRUSTEES D G W Ballard; N J Armstrong; Revd C Curry; R J Curry.
HOW TO APPLY In writing to the correspondent.
WHO TO APPLY TO N J Armstrong, Trustee, c/o Alliotts, 4th Floor, Imperial House, 15 Kingsway, London WC2B 6UN *Tel* 020 7240 9971

Think carefully about every application. Is it justified?

621

■ The Homestead Charitable Trust

CC NO 293979   **ESTABLISHED** 1986
WHERE FUNDING CAN BE GIVEN UK.
WHO CAN BENEFIT Actors and entertainment professionals, musicians, textile workers and designers, writers and poets, Christians, at risk groups, people disadvantaged by poverty, and socially isolated people.
WHAT IS FUNDED Medical, health and welfare, animal welfare, Christianity and the arts.
TYPE OF GRANT Some recurring.
RANGE OF GRANTS Up to £10,000.
SAMPLE GRANTS CVS (£10,000); Stroke Association and UN World Food Programme (£5,000 each); Sight Savers (£180); and WaterAid (£100).
FINANCES *Year* 2009–10 *Income* £209,545 *Grants* £31,628 *Assets* £5,219,645
TRUSTEES Sir C Bracewell-Smith; Lady N Bracewell-Smith.
OTHER INFORMATION The trust fund of the Sir Charles Bracewell-Smith Voluntary Settlement worth £1.6 million was transferred to the trust in October 2004.
HOW TO APPLY In writing to the correspondent.
WHO TO APPLY TO Lady Nina Bracewell-Smith, Trustee, Flat 7, Clarence Gate Gardens, Glentworth Street, London NW1 6AY *Tel* 020 7258 1051

■ The Mary Homfray Charitable Trust

CC NO 273564   **ESTABLISHED** 1977
WHERE FUNDING CAN BE GIVEN UK, with a preference for Wales.
WHO CAN BENEFIT Registered charities.
WHAT IS FUNDED General charitable purposes.
RANGE OF GRANTS Up to £5,000.
SAMPLE GRANTS Thomas Mansel Franklen Trust (£5,000); Age Concern, Salvation Army, Shelter – Cymru, Amelia Trust Farm and Wallich Clifford Community (£3,000 each); Coram Family, National Botanic Garden of Wales and Kiloran Trust (£2,000 each); Maes-y-Dyfan and Army Benevolent Fund (£1,000 each); and Y Bont (£500).
FINANCES *Year* 2009–10 *Income* £33,421 *Grants* £50,000 *Assets* £1,405,320
TRUSTEES Angela Homfray; Simon Gibson; Josephine Homfray.
HOW TO APPLY In writing to the correspondent. Applications should be made towards the end of the year, for consideration at the trustees' meeting in February or March each year.
WHO TO APPLY TO Angela Homfray, Trustee, 5 Callaghan Square, Cardiff CF10 5BT *Tel* 029 2026 0000

■ Sir Harold Hood's Charitable Trust

CC NO 225870   **ESTABLISHED** 1962
WHERE FUNDING CAN BE GIVEN Worldwide.
WHO CAN BENEFIT Roman Catholic charities and churches.
WHAT IS FUNDED Charities dealing with the advancement of the Roman Catholic faith through religious buildings, religious umbrella bodies and other Roman Catholic organisations.
WHAT IS NOT FUNDED No grants to individuals.
TYPE OF GRANT One-off and recurring.
RANGE OF GRANTS Up to £30,000.
SAMPLE GRANTS Prison Advice & Care Trust (£30,000); Craig Lodge Trust (£25,000); Duchess of Leeds Foundation (£20,000); Diocese of Brentwood (£15,000); St Joseph's Pastoral Centre (£12,000); Venerable English College – Rome (£10,000); Maryvale Institute – Birmingham (£8,000); Apostleship of the Sea (£6,000); Catholic Children's Society – Westminster and Saint John of God Care Services (£5,000 each); San Jose Retreat Centre – Chile (£4,000); Young Christian Workers (£3,000); Ten Ten Theatre (£2,000); and the Dominican Sisters of St Joseph (£1,000).
FINANCES *Year* 2009–10 *Income* £518,257 *Grants* £481,900 *Assets* £24,840,064
TRUSTEES Dom James Hood; Anne-Marie Blanco; Nicholas True; Margaret Hood; Christian Elwes.
HOW TO APPLY In writing to the correspondent. The trustees meet once a year to consider applications, usually in November.
WHO TO APPLY TO Margaret Hood, Trustee, Haysmacintyre, Fairfax House, 15 Fulwood Place, London WC1V 6AY *Tel* 020 7722 9088

■ Hope For Youth (Formerly Women Caring Trust)

CC NO 264843   **ESTABLISHED** 1972
WHERE FUNDING CAN BE GIVEN Northern Ireland.
WHO CAN BENEFIT Integrated schools; community playgroups; play buses; youth clubs; women's groups; cross-community holiday schemes benefiting children and young adults.
WHAT IS FUNDED Cross-community projects that give disadvantaged 11–18 year olds in Northern Ireland the opportunity to work together on practical projects that foster teamwork, creativity and personal development, especially within the arts or in the great outdoors. Education, arts, media, sport, recreation.
WHAT IS NOT FUNDED No grants for individuals, large capital expenditure or salaries, organisations solely for the welfare of physically or mentally disabled people, or drug or alcohol related projects. No grants for holidays outside the island of Ireland.
TYPE OF GRANT Recurring costs funded for up to one year.
RANGE OF GRANTS £200–£2,000.
SAMPLE GRANTS Music Theatre for Youth, Youth Initiatives, Appletree Childcare, Careers 'N' Kids, Drumaness Cross Community Playgroup, Old Library Trust, Significance Women's Initiative, St Vincent de Paul, The Diamond Centre.
FINANCES *Year* 2010 *Income* £22,042 *Grants* £70,000
TRUSTEES Ion Montgomery (Chairman); Mr Johnny Andrews; Mrs Nicholas Argles; Mr Peter Cooke (Vice Chairman); Miss Julia Corkey; Mr Marc Cramsie; The Viscount Crichton; Mrs David Lindsay; Mrs William Montgomery; Lady Nicholson; The Viscount Gough; Miss Emma Nicholson; Jonathan Shillington.
OTHER INFORMATION Details of 2012 grant round to be made available on website.
HOW TO APPLY Online application form providing full details of the project. Copies of accounts showing simple details of income and expenditure should be emailed or posted to the trust. The trustees meet four or five times a year and receive many more applications than can be accepted.

WHO TO APPLY TO Ion Montgomery, Chairman, c/o Cherton Enterprise Ltd, Unit 8, Belmont Business Park, 240 Belmont Road, Belfast *Tel* 028 9076 9966 *email* angela.dickson@cherton.co.uk *Website* www.hopeforyouthni.com

■ The Hope Trust

SC NO SC000987   ESTABLISHED 1912
WHERE FUNDING CAN BE GIVEN Worldwide, with a preference for Scotland.
WHO CAN BENEFIT Individuals and organisations benefiting Christians; Church of England; evangelists; Methodists; Quakers; Unitarians and people with a substance addiction.
WHAT IS FUNDED The provision of education and the distribution of literature to combat the misuse and effects of drink and drugs and to promote the principles of Reformed Churches; charities concerned with the advancement of the Christian religion, Anglican bodies, Free Church, rehabilitation centres and health education.
WHAT IS NOT FUNDED No grants to gap year students, scholarship schemes or to any individuals, with the sole exception of PhD students of theology studying at Scottish universities. No grants for the refurbishment of property.
TYPE OF GRANT Core costs, one-off funding, project, research, recurring costs, running costs, salaries, start-up costs and funding for more than three years will be considered.
RANGE OF GRANTS £100–£6,000.
SAMPLE GRANTS Previous beneficiaries have included Church of Scotland Priority Areas Fund, World Alliance of Reformed Churches, National Bible Society for Scotland, Feed the Minds and Waldensian Mission Aid.
FINANCES *Year* 2009 *Income* £171,000 *Grants* £150,000
TRUSTEES Prof. G M Newlands; Prof. D A S Ferguson; Revd G R Barr; Revd Dr Lyall; Carole Hope; Revd Gillean McLean.
HOW TO APPLY In writing to the correspondent. The trustees meet to consider applications in June and December each year. Applications should be submitted by mid-May or mid-November each year.
WHO TO APPLY TO The Secretary, Drummond Miller, 31–32 Moray Place, Edinburgh EH3 6BZ *Tel* 0131 226 5151 *email* rmiller@drummond-miller.co.uk

■ HopMarket Charity

CC NO 244569   ESTABLISHED 1964
WHERE FUNDING CAN BE GIVEN The city of Worcester.
WHO CAN BENEFIT 'Needy' people in the city of Worcester. 'Needy' is defined as those 'who, by reason of poverty, sickness or infirmity, whether young or old, are in need of financial assistance, care or attention'. People of all ages, volunteers, and people who are disabled or disadvantaged by poverty.
WHAT IS FUNDED The trust has adopted the following guidelines: 'That as a general principle the funds should be allocated to either capital or revenue projects which fall within the purposes of the charity and which will generate further support for the community. Where revenue funding is made, such support should not imply any ongoing commitment except where the trustees specifically indicate otherwise. Emphasis should be placed on assisting applications which have an affinity to matters which are within the council's sphere of activity.'

WHAT IS NOT FUNDED No grants to, or on behalf of, individuals.
RANGE OF GRANTS £750–£27,400.
SAMPLE GRANTS Worcester Housing and Benefits Advice (£27,400); Noah's Ark Trust (£13,000); Perdiswell Young People's Club (10,000); Mentor Link (£6,920); YMCA (£5,610); Ethnic Access Link Scheme (£2,100); Shopmobility Worcester (£1,450) and Worcester Contact Centre (£750).
FINANCES *Year* 2009–10 *Income* £198,653 *Grants* £95,048 *Assets* £1,215,739
TRUSTEES The City Council.
OTHER INFORMATION Grant applications are administered by the Head of Financial Services, Graveney House, Farrier Street, Worcester.
HOW TO APPLY On a form available from the correspondent. Applications should be submitted by the beginning of January or August for consideration in March or September respectively.
WHO TO APPLY TO Ms D Porter, Administrator, Worcester City Council: Development, Orchard House, Farrier Street, Worchester WR1 3BB *Tel* 01905 722019 *Fax* 01905 722028 *email* corporateservices@cityofworcester.gov.uk

■ The Horizon Foundation

CC NO 1118455   ESTABLISHED 2007
WHERE FUNDING CAN BE GIVEN Unrestricted.
WHO CAN BENEFIT Registered charities.
WHAT IS FUNDED General, education, women and children.
SAMPLE GRANTS There were six grants made to three organisations which were: Eton College; University of Essex; and Pembroke College. Although the amount received by each recipient was not disclosed in the brief report filed with the Charity Commission. Previous beneficiaries have included: Atlantic College, Lessons with Love, Mongolian Children's Aid Foundation, and The Hotchkiss School.
FINANCES *Year* 2009–10 *Income* £68,100 *Grants* £67,844 *Assets* £77,086
TRUSTEES Kirkland Caroline Smulders; Patrick Lance Smulders; Coutts & Co.
HOW TO APPLY In writing to the correspondent.
WHO TO APPLY TO Coutts & Co, Trustee Dept, 440 Strand, London WC2R 0QS *Tel* 020 7663 6814

■ The Cuthbert Horn Trust

CC NO 291465   ESTABLISHED 1985
WHERE FUNDING CAN BE GIVEN UK.
WHO CAN BENEFIT Registered charities.
WHAT IS FUNDED General charitable purposes.
WHAT IS NOT FUNDED No grants are made to individuals.
TYPE OF GRANT One-off and recurrent.
RANGE OF GRANTS £1,000–£10,000.
SAMPLE GRANTS Farms for City Children, International Bee Research Association, Progressive Farming Trust (£4,000 each); the Fishermans Mission, Sevenoaks Symphony Orchestra and Ovingdean Hall School (£3,000 each); and the Charleston Trust and Norwegian Locomotive Trust (£2,000).
FINANCES *Year* 2009 *Income* £356,132 *Grants* £50,000 *Assets* £1,280,607
TRUSTEES AA Flint; H Flint; P H Marr-Johnson; Capita Trust Co Ltd.
HOW TO APPLY There are no application forms to complete; applicants should provide in writing as much background about their charity or

cause as possible. Applications need to be received by December as the trustees meet as soon as possible after the financial year end. Only successful applications will be notified.

WHO TO APPLY TO Laurie Wilson, Trust Manager, Capita Trust Company Limited, Phoenix House, 18 King William Street, London EC4N 7HE *Tel* 020 7800 4126 *email* trusts@capitatrust.co.uk

■ The Antony Hornby Charitable Trust

CC NO 263285   **ESTABLISHED** 1971

WHERE FUNDING CAN BE GIVEN Unrestricted with a preference for London and the Home Counties.

WHO CAN BENEFIT Registered charities.

WHAT IS FUNDED General charitable purposes, in particular supporting charities involved in medical activities, education and welfare.

WHAT IS NOT FUNDED No grants to individuals. Only registered charities are supported. No grants to localised building projects.

RANGE OF GRANTS £250–£21,000.

SAMPLE GRANTS Youth Talk (£21,000); Marine Society; Brain Tumour UK (£2,000); Help for Heroes (£1,500); Chelsea Pensioners Appeal; St Albans Bereavement Trust; Maggie's Centre, Oxford (£1,000); Disability Snow Sports (£500); Roh Foundation (£330).

FINANCES *Year* 2009–10 *Income* £37,903 *Grants* £38,580 *Assets* £1,150,056

TRUSTEES Marie Antoinette Hall; Mark Antony Loveday; Michael Wentworth-Stanley; Jane Wentworth-Stanley.

HOW TO APPLY The trust has stated that it is fully committed and does not usually add new names to its list of beneficiaries unless it is a charity known to the trustees, or a very special appeal.

WHO TO APPLY TO Paul Langdon, Saffrey Champness, Lion House, 72–75 Red Lion Street, London WC1R 4GB *Tel* 020 7841 4000

■ The Horne Foundation

CC NO 283751   **ESTABLISHED** 1981

WHERE FUNDING CAN BE GIVEN Mainly Northamptonshire.

WHO CAN BENEFIT Preference is given to local organisations benefiting young adults, children and older people, especially people disadvantaged by poverty, with occasional grants also made to UK organisations.

WHAT IS FUNDED Predominantly large grants towards major educational projects that involve new buildings and regular smaller donations to local projects in the Northampton and Oxfordshire area and student bursaries for higher education through Northampton schools.

WHAT IS NOT FUNDED The foundation prefers organisations without religious affiliation.

TYPE OF GRANT Capital and project grants.

RANGE OF GRANTS £1,500–£10,000.

SAMPLE GRANTS Marie Curie, Prince's Trust Third Tranche, Crisis Christmas, Ise Community College Specialist (£10,000); Botanic Gardens Oxford (£8,000); Boys' Brigade (£4,000); Full Circle Oxford (£1,500).

FINANCES *Year* 2009–10 *Income* £206,932 *Grants* £253,500 *Assets* £6,595,690

TRUSTEES E J Davenport; Mrs R M Harwood; C A Horne.

OTHER INFORMATION In 2009–10 grants were given to 3 national appeals, 6 organisations and 85 individual students.

Grants given to students were in the form of bursaries for higher education through Northampton schools.

HOW TO APPLY In writing to the correspondent at any time.

WHO TO APPLY TO Mrs R M Harwood, Secretary, PO Box 6165, Newbury RG14 9FY *email* hornefoundation@googlemail.com

■ The Horne Trust

CC NO 1010625   **ESTABLISHED** 1992

WHERE FUNDING CAN BE GIVEN UK and the developing world.

WHO CAN BENEFIT Charities, hospices and charitable projects.

WHAT IS FUNDED Homelessness, hospices (particularly children's hospices), medical support and development of self-reliant technology in Africa and the developing world.

RANGE OF GRANTS £1,000–£40,000.

SAMPLE GRANTS Demelza House Children's Hospice, Humberstone Hydrotherapy Pool and World Medical Fund (£10,000 each); AbilityNet, Share Community and Woodlands Hospice – Liverpool (£7,500); Laura Campbell-Preston Trust (£6,700); Deafblind UK, FACT, and Young Minds (£5,000 each); Winfield Trust, Disability Aid Fund Whitby Dog Rescue (£1,000 each).

FINANCES *Year* 2009–10 *Income* £343,473 *Grants* £491,700 *Assets* £6,235,905

TRUSTEES J T Horne; J L Horne; N J Camamile.

HOW TO APPLY Normally in writing to the correspondent, although the trust has stated that currently unsolicited applications cannot be supported.

WHO TO APPLY TO J T Horne, Trustee, Kingsdown, Warmlake Road, Chart Sutton, Maidstone, Kent ME17 3RP *Tel* 01622 842638 *email* mail.jh@horne-trust.org.uk

■ The Worshipful Company of Horners' Charitable Trusts

CC NO 292204   **ESTABLISHED** 1985

WHERE FUNDING CAN BE GIVEN Mainly in London.

WHO CAN BENEFIT Registered charities, educational establishments and individuals.

WHAT IS FUNDED General charitable purposes; education in plastics; and scholarships and bursaries in education.

RANGE OF GRANTS £1,000–£25,000.

SAMPLE GRANTS Smile Train (£25,000); Polymer Study Tours (£20,000); University of Reading (£15,000); Students Design (£10,000); Ralph Anderson Lecture (£5,000); Lord Mayor's Appeal (£3,000); Tower Hamlet's Mission, National Association for Colitis and Crohn's (£2,500 each); and Arts University College Bournemouth (£2,000). Other grants for under £1,000 each amounted to £5,000.

FINANCES *Year* 2010 *Income* £93,831 *Grants* £108,639 *Assets* £1,767,559

TRUSTEES R Anstis; N K Greene; D A Williams; D M Spofforth; M S C Baird; C T Baird; C T Richards; G Scott; K Featherstone; K Pinker; C Thompson.

OTHER INFORMATION Other grants for under £1,000 each amounted to £5,000.

HOW TO APPLY In writing to the correspondent.

WHO TO APPLY TO Iain McGrory, Clerk to the Trustees, Le Bourg, St Meard De Gurcon, France, 24610 *Tel* 07802 733122 *email* horners.clerk@btinternet.com *Website* www.horners.org.uk

■ Hornsey Parochial Charities

CC NO 229410 **ESTABLISHED** 1890

WHERE FUNDING CAN BE GIVEN Ancient parish of Hornsey in part of the boroughs of Hackney and Haringey.

WHO CAN BENEFIT Individuals and organisations benefiting people disadvantaged by poverty.

WHAT IS FUNDED Supporting those in need and also assisting with education expenses for those young people under the age of 25 years. Financial assistance is granted to individuals and local organisations through bursaries, maintenance allowances, clothing, instruments and books.

WHAT IS NOT FUNDED Residential qualification needed (must have lived in ancient parish of Hornsey for at least a year). No commitment to continuous grants.

SAMPLE GRANTS The charities administered a combined grants total of £86,000 given to numerous causes in the beneficial area. Full details of grants were withheld on the grounds of protecting the confidentiality of the recipients.

FINANCES *Year* 2010 *Income* £96,663 *Grants* £85,908 *Assets* £2,941,236

TRUSTEES Revd P Henderson; E Griffiths; J Hudson; A Jones; P Kenyon; V Manheim; L Marshall; B Simon; K Jones; A Gillespie; C O'Brien; P Lanning.

HOW TO APPLY In writing to the correspondent or by downloading an application form from the website. Initial enquiries by email are welcome.

WHO TO APPLY TO The Clerk to the Trustees, PO Box 22985, London N10 3XB *Tel* 020 8352 1601 *Fax* 020 8352 1601 *email* hornseypc@blueyonder.co.uk *Website* hornseycharities.com

■ The Hospital of God at Greatham

CC NO 1123540 **ESTABLISHED** 1973

WHERE FUNDING CAN BE GIVEN Darlington, Durham, Gateshead, Hartlepool, Newcastle upon Tyne, Northumberland, North Tyneside, South Tyneside, Stockton on Tees and Sunderland.

WHO CAN BENEFIT Charities, voluntary organisations and individuals. The trust supports children, young adults, older people, at risk groups, carers, people who are disabled, disadvantaged by poverty, homeless or socially isolated, victims of abuse and domestic violence, and people with Alzheimer's disease, epilepsy and hearing loss.

WHAT IS FUNDED Preference is given to projects concerned with local initiatives aimed at disadvantaged people, particularly charities working in the field of social care and with local communities.

WHAT IS NOT FUNDED No grants for: capital projects; building work; education, travel or adventure projects; hospices; medical equipment; work outside the beneficial area; UK organisations with no base in the north east of England; training, conferences or feasibility studies.

TYPE OF GRANT One-off, capital, core funding, running costs and salaries. Funding for one year or more will be considered.

RANGE OF GRANTS £500–£8,000.

SAMPLE GRANTS Bishop of Durham Discretionary Fund (£7,000); West View Project (£3,000); The National Autistic Fund, Sunderland & North Durham Society for the Blind and North East Help Link (£2,000 each); People and Drugs Ltd, Breast Cancer Survival Trust and Linking Women of Africa (£1,000 each).

FINANCES *Income* £2,732,970 *Grants* £95,179 *Assets* £38,452,992

TRUSTEES Mrs S Mitchell, Chair; Ven I Jagger; Ven G Miller; B Winter; J Allen; S Croft; J De Martino; M Poole; P Shields; P Sinclair; JH Madden.

OTHER INFORMATION The charity's main work is the provision of almshouse accommodation and residential care. Grants are made from surplus funds.

HOW TO APPLY Applications should be made to the correspondent in writing. The grants committee meets three times a year. Applications should include in no more than two pages giving the following information: the objects of the charity; description of, and budget for the project and the specific work for which funding is sought; a copy of the latest audited accounts. The correspondent is happy to answer initial telephone enquiries.

WHO TO APPLY TO David Granath, The Estate Office, Greatham, Hartlepool TS25 2HS *Tel* 01429 870247 *email* david.granath@hospitalofgod.org.uk *Website* www.hospitalofgod.org.uk

■ The Hospital Saturday Fund

CC NO 1123381 **ESTABLISHED** 1987

WHERE FUNDING CAN BE GIVEN UK, the Republic of Ireland, the Channel Islands and the Isle of Man.

WHO CAN BENEFIT Hospitals, hospices, medically-associated charities and welfare organisations providing similar services worldwide, but mostly in the UK and Republic of Ireland. Individuals can also be directly supported.

WHAT IS FUNDED Medical care and research to organisations; specialist equipment, welfare and scholarships to individuals.

WHAT IS NOT FUNDED Unless there are exceptional circumstances, organisations are not supported in successive years.

TYPE OF GRANT One-off grants. Organisations are rarely supported in successive years.

RANGE OF GRANTS Usually up to £3,000.

FINANCES *Year* 2010 *Income* £27,892,862 *Grants* £354,643 *Assets* £19,956,564

TRUSTEES John Greenwood; Jane Laidlaw Dalton; Michael Boyle; John Randel; David Thomas.

OTHER INFORMATION In 2010 the trust made grants to individuals totalling £5,000.

HOW TO APPLY Hospitals, hospices and medically-related charities are invited to write detailed letters or to send a brochure with an accompanying letter. There is a form for individuals to complete available from the personal assistant to the trust administrator.

WHO TO APPLY TO Keith R Bradley, Chief Executive, 24 Upper Ground, London SE1 9PD *Tel* 020 7928 6662 *email* charity@hsf.eu.com

■ The Sir Joseph Hotung Charitable Settlement

CC NO 1082710 **ESTABLISHED** 2000

WHERE FUNDING CAN BE GIVEN Worldwide.

WHO CAN BENEFIT Charitable organisations.

WHAT IS FUNDED General charitable purposes.

SAMPLE GRANTS British Museum (£1 million); School of Oriental and African Studies (£180,000); Atlantic College (£135,000); London Symphony Orchestra, the Council for Assisting Refugee Academics and Yesh Din Volunteers (£50,000 each); Rushmore Healthy Living (£10,000); and International Spinal Research Trust (£1,200).

FINANCES *Year* 2009–10 *Income* £2,632,398 *Grants* £1,476,355 *Assets* £2,256,263

TRUSTEES Sir Joseph E Hotung; Sir Robert D H Boyd; Victoria F Dicks; Michael Gabriel; Joseph S Lesser.

HOW TO APPLY The trust has previously stated that: 'the trustees have their own areas of interest and do not respond to unsolicited applications'.

WHO TO APPLY TO Sir Joseph Hotung, Trustee, c/o Alison Holmes, HSBC Private Bank (UK) Ltd, 78 St James' Street, London, SWIA 1JB

....

■ Houblon-Norman/George Fund

CC NO 213168   **ESTABLISHED** 1944

WHERE FUNDING CAN BE GIVEN UK.

WHO CAN BENEFIT Organisations benefiting academics and research workers.

WHAT IS FUNDED Research into the interaction and function of financial and business institutions, the economic conditions affecting them, and the dissemination of knowledge thereof. Fellowships are tenable at the Bank of England. The research work is intended to be full-time work, and teaching or other paid work must not be undertaken during the tenure of the fellowship, without the specific consent of the trustees. In considering applications the trustees will pay particular regard to the relevance of the research to current problems in economics and finance.

TYPE OF GRANT Research fellowship.

FINANCES *Year* 2009–10 *Income* £57,793 *Grants* £70,161 *Assets* £1,790,896

TRUSTEES C R Bean; Brendan Barber; Andrew Haldane.

HOW TO APPLY On an application form available from the website.

WHO TO APPLY TO The Secretary, Bank of England, Threadneedle Street, London EC2R 8AH *Tel* 020 7601 3778 *Fax* 020 7601 4423 *email* ma-hngfund@bankofengland.co.uk *Website* www.bankofengland.co.uk/research/houblonnorman/index.htm

....

■ The House of Industry Estate

CC NO 257079   **ESTABLISHED** 1968

WHERE FUNDING CAN BE GIVEN Borough of Bedford.

WHO CAN BENEFIT People who are in need and local organisations.

WHAT IS FUNDED Local organisations concerned with unemployed people, youth, counselling and housing.

WHAT IS NOT FUNDED Funds are not given in relief of taxes or other public funds. No recurrent grants are given.

TYPE OF GRANT One-off.

SAMPLE GRANTS Previous beneficiaries included: Bedford Community Rights; Bedfordshire Garden Carers; Bedford Pilgrims Housing Association; Kempston Summer School; and King's Arms Project.

FINANCES *Year* 2009–10 *Income* £19,675,958 *Grants* £82,294 *Assets* £357,596,058

TRUSTEES Phil Merryman, Chair; Pat Olney; Colleen Atkins; Apu Baggchi; Roger Gwynne Jones; David Sawyer; Sallyanne Smith.

OTHER INFORMATION 'The trustees may pay for such items, services or facilities by way of donations or subscriptions to institutions or organisations which provide or which undertake, in return, to provide such items, services or facilities for such persons.'

HOW TO APPLY In writing to Susan Audin – Head of Benefits & Community Welfare.

WHO TO APPLY TO Director of Finance, Director of Finance and Corporate Services, Bedford

Borough Council, Cauldwell Street, Bedford MK42 9AP *Tel* 01234 267422

....

■ The Reta Lila Howard Foundation

CC NO 1041634   **ESTABLISHED** 1994

WHERE FUNDING CAN BE GIVEN UK and Republic of Ireland.

WHO CAN BENEFIT Children up to the age of 16.

WHAT IS FUNDED Innovative projects that benefit children, and projects concerned with 'the education of young people or to ameliorate their physical and emotional environment'.

WHAT IS NOT FUNDED Grants are not given to individuals, organisations which are not registered charities, or towards operating expenses, budget deficits, (sole) capital projects, annual charitable appeals, general endowment funds, fundraising drives or events, conferences, or student aid.

RANGE OF GRANTS £5,000–£45,000.

SAMPLE GRANTS Countryside Education Trust (£70,000); Barnardo's (£68,500); Civitas (£60,000); The Tree Council (£53,000); Farms for City Children (£40,000); Children's Hospice Association Scotland (£35,000); Teach First (£30,000); New Forest Museum & Library (£20,000); The Bridge End Community Centre (£15,000); and Bibles for Children (£10,000).

FINANCES *Income* £217,289 *Grants* £275,605 *Assets* £13,650,922

TRUSTEES Emma Adamo; Christian Bauta; Charles Burnett; Garfield Mitchell; Alannah Weston; Graham Weston; Claudia Hepburn; Melissa Murdoch.

HOW TO APPLY The trust states that it does not accept unsolicited applications, since the trustees seek out and support projects they are interested in.

WHO TO APPLY TO The Company Secretary, Jamestown Investments Ltd, 4 Felstead Gardens, Ferry Street, London E14 3BS *Tel* 020 7537 1118 *email* jamestown@btinternet.com

....

■ The Daniel Howard Trust

CC NO 267173   **ESTABLISHED** 1974

WHERE FUNDING CAN BE GIVEN UK and Israel.

WHO CAN BENEFIT Charities benefiting: children; young adults; actors and entertainment professionals; musicians; textile workers and designers; and writers and poets.

WHAT IS FUNDED Culture, education, the environment and welfare. Particularly Jewish causes.

WHAT IS NOT FUNDED Grants are only made to registered charities. No grants to individuals.

TYPE OF GRANT Recurrent and one-off.

RANGE OF GRANTS £500–£52,000.

SAMPLE GRANTS World Jewish Relief – Metuna (£30,000); The Israel Family Therapy Advancement Fund (£25,000); Friends of Daniel for Rowing (£20,000); International Scholarship Foundation Charitable Trust (£20,000 in two grants); British Friends of the IGDCB and The British Friends of Israel Philharmonic (£15,000 each); and Tel Aviv University and Weizmann Institute Foundation (£10,000 each).

FINANCES *Year* 2008–09 *Income* £129,894 *Grants* £375,320 *Assets* £7,427,013

TRUSTEES Dame Shirley Porter; Linda Streit; Steven Porter; Brian Padgett; Andrew Peggie.

HOW TO APPLY In writing to the correspondent.

WHO TO APPLY TO Sarah Hunt, St James's House, 3rd Floor, 23 King Street, London SW1Y 6QY *Tel* 020 78395169

■ The Clifford Howarth Charity Trust

CC NO 264890   **ESTABLISHED** 1972

WHERE FUNDING CAN BE GIVEN UK, with a preference for Lancashire (Burnley/Rossendale).

WHO CAN BENEFIT Local and UK-registered charities which were supported by the founder.

WHAT IS FUNDED General charitable purposes.

WHAT IS NOT FUNDED Only registered charities will be supported. No grants to individuals, for scholarships or for non-local special projects.

TYPE OF GRANT One-off.

RANGE OF GRANTS £1,000–£20,000.

SAMPLE GRANTS Previous beneficiaries included: Cumbria Cerebral Palsy (£15,000); St Marys Hospice (£5,000); St Nicholas Church – Newchurch (£3,000); Hospice in Rossendale (£2,500); and Ulverstone Inshore Rescue, Beaver Scouts, Spurgeons and Burnley Garrick Club (£2,000 each).

FINANCES *Year* 2009–10 *Income* £17,283 *Grants* £30,000

TRUSTEES James Howarth; Judith Howarth; Cara Tinning.

HOW TO APPLY The charity states that grants are only made to organisations known to the trustees, and that applications are unlikely to be successful.

WHO TO APPLY TO James Howarth, Trustee, 14A Hall Garth, Kelbeck, Barrow in Furness, Cumbria LA13 0QT

■ The Howe Family Foundation

CC NO 1136256   **ESTABLISHED** 2010

WHERE FUNDING CAN BE GIVEN Undefined.

WHO CAN BENEFIT Organisations and individuals.

WHAT IS FUNDED General charitable purposes.

TRUSTEES Caroline Howe; Graham Howe.

OTHER INFORMATION A request to the correspondent for further information on the foundation did not produce a response.

HOW TO APPLY In writing to the correspondent.

WHO TO APPLY TO Sylvie Nunn, c/o Wrigleys Solicitors LLP, 19–21 Cookridge Street, Leeds LS2 3AG *Tel* 0113 204 5726 *email* sylvie.nunn@wrigleys.co.uk

■ HTA Sheba Foundation UK

CC NO 1135473   **ESTABLISHED** 2010

WHERE FUNDING CAN BE GIVEN Undefined, in practice national.

WHO CAN BENEFIT Charitable organisations.

WHAT IS FUNDED 'Any charitable purpose for the benefit of the community, including the relief of poverty, advancement of education, in the interest of social welfare, to meet the needs of disabled, children, widows, elderly, people in need, orphans, health and homelessness, as well as the relief of natural disasters.'

TRUSTEES Ashuk Uddin; Muhammad Ashraful; Salma Hashim.

HOW TO APPLY In writing to the correspondent.

WHO TO APPLY TO Ashuk Uddin, Trustee, 199 Caulfield Road, London E6 2DH

■ The Hudson Foundation

CC NO 280332   **ESTABLISHED** 1980

WHERE FUNDING CAN BE GIVEN UK, with a preference for the Wisbech area.

WHO CAN BENEFIT Individuals and organisations benefiting older people and those who are infirm, especially in the Wisbech area.

WHAT IS FUNDED The relief of people who are elderly or infirm.

RANGE OF GRANTS Up to £80,000.

SAMPLE GRANTS Wisbech Parish Church of St Peter and St Paul (£80,000); Ely Diocesan Board of Finance (£64,000); Wisbech St Mary Sports and Community Centre (£30,000); Wisbech Grammar School (£29,000); Wisbech Swimming Club (£8,400); Methodist Homes for the Aged (£6,200); Alzheimer's Society (£1,200); Wisbech and Fenland Museum (£250); and Wisbech Music Society (£150).

FINANCES *Year* 2009–10 *Income* £947,154 *Grants* £132,813 *Assets* £1,783,604

TRUSTEES Hayward A Godfrey; David W Ball; Stephen G Layton.

HOW TO APPLY In writing to the correspondent. Trustees meet quarterly.

WHO TO APPLY TO David W Ball, Trustee, 1–3 York Row, Wisbech, Cambridgeshire PE13 1EA

■ The Huggard Charitable Trust

CC NO 327501   **ESTABLISHED** 1987

WHERE FUNDING CAN BE GIVEN UK, with a preference for South Wales.

WHO CAN BENEFIT Older people, people who are disabled, people who are disadvantaged by poverty.

WHAT IS FUNDED Advancement of religion, the relief of poverty, disability and the welfare of older people.

RANGE OF GRANTS Up to £12,000.

SAMPLE GRANTS Previously: Amelia Methodist Trust, Vale of Glamorgan, Bro Morgannwg NHS Trust, CURE Fund – Cardiff, Laparoscopy Laser Fund – UHW, SWS Cymru and Whitton Rosser Trust – Vale of Glamorgan.

FINANCES *Year* 2009–10 *Income* £6,740 *Grants* £30,000

TRUSTEES Mrs A Helme; S J Thomas.

HOW TO APPLY The trustees are not inviting applications for funds.

WHO TO APPLY TO S J Thomas, Trustee, Blacklands Farm, Five Mile Lane, Bonvilston, Cardiff CF5 6TQ

■ The Geoffrey C Hughes Charitable Trust

CC NO 1010079   **ESTABLISHED** 1992

WHERE FUNDING CAN BE GIVEN UK.

WHO CAN BENEFIT Actors and entertainment professionals and musicians.

WHAT IS FUNDED This trust is essentially interested in two areas: nature conservation/environment and performing arts, particularly ballet or opera with a bias towards modern work.

WHAT IS NOT FUNDED No grants to individuals.

FINANCES *Year* 2009–10 *Income* £6,152 *Grants* £15,000

TRUSTEES J R Young; P C M Solon; W A Bailey.

OTHER INFORMATION In 2009–10 the trust had a total expenditure of £15,000.

HOW TO APPLY In writing to the correspondent.

WHO TO APPLY TO P C M Solon, Trustee, c/o Mills & Reeve, Francis House, 112 Hills Road, Cambridge CB2 1PH *Tel* 01223 222290

■ The Hull and East Riding Charitable Trust

CC NO 516866 **ESTABLISHED** 1985

WHERE FUNDING CAN BE GIVEN Hull and the East Riding of Yorkshire.

WHO CAN BENEFIT Registered charities only, with a possible preference for organisations working with children/youth, medical/disability and welfare.

WHAT IS FUNDED General charitable purposes.

WHAT IS NOT FUNDED Grants are not normally given to individuals. No grants to organisations or causes of a political nature, or for religious purposes, although requests for maintenance of significant religious buildings may be considered. If a donation has been made the trustees would not expect to receive a further request from the recipient in the immediate future.

TYPE OF GRANT The trust prefers to fund the capital costs of a project, but will consider funding revenue costs over a limited period of time.

RANGE OF GRANTS £100–£15,000.

SAMPLE GRANTS Hull Truck Theatre, Humberside Police Authority (£10,000); National Probation Service (£9,000); Prison me? no way trust (£5,500); Hull Boys' Club, Mires Beck Nursery (£5,000); The Green Team (£750); Longhill Primary School (£250) and Quay Scrabble Club (£200).

FINANCES *Year* 2009–10 *Income* £237,149 *Grants* £218,149 *Assets* £6,023,250

TRUSTEES Mrs K Field; Mrs M R Barker; A M Horsley.

HOW TO APPLY In writing to the correspondent, including the aims of the project and benefits hoped for, the costs involved with budgets/accounts as appropriate, the contribution sought from the trust and details of other funds raised. The trustees meet in May and November and requests for donations will only be considered at those meetings. Applications must be received by 30 April and 31 October. The trust states: 'It is unlikely that the trustees would support the total cost of a project and applicants should be able to demonstrate that funds have been raised or are in the process of being raised from other sources.'

WHO TO APPLY TO J R Barnes, Secretary and Administrator, Greenmeades, Kemp Road, Swanland, East Yorkshire HU14 3LY *Tel* 01482 634664 *email* john@barnes1939.karoo.co.uk

■ Hulme Trust Estates (Educational)

CC NO 532297 **ESTABLISHED** 1964

WHERE FUNDING CAN BE GIVEN Greater Manchester.

WHO CAN BENEFIT Educational establishments.

WHAT IS FUNDED This trust supports educational establishments in the Greater Manchester area.

TYPE OF GRANT Grants awarded to schools and universities in the Greater Manchester area.

SAMPLE GRANTS Brasenose College (£74,000); Manchester University (£37,000); William Hulmes GS, Bury GS, Hulme GS Oldham (£4,600 each); Manchester HS for Girls (£3,800); Manchester GS (£770).

FINANCES *Year* 2010 *Income* £182,734 *Grants* £174,599 *Assets* £7,195,882

TRUSTEES DJ Claxton; TA Hoyle; I Thompson; Prof. R Cashmore; P Sidwell; JR Heaton; Mrs J Robinson; P Parker; I Rankin.

HOW TO APPLY In writing to the correspondent.

WHO TO APPLY TO J M Shelmerdine, Secretary, Butcher Barlow, 31 Middlewich Road, Sandbach CW11 1HW *Tel* 01270 762521

■ Human Relief Foundation

CC NO 1126281 **ESTABLISHED** 1995

WHERE FUNDING CAN BE GIVEN Somalia, Ethiopia, Chechnya, Bosnia, Kosovo, Kashmir, Pakistan, India, Bangladesh, Afghanistan and Palestine and other regions requiring urgent relief/aid.

WHO CAN BENEFIT Organisations benefiting at risk groups, carers, people who are disabled, people disadvantaged by poverty, refugees, victims of famine, man-made or natural disasters and war. Medical professionals, scientists, unemployed people and volunteers will be supported.

WHAT IS FUNDED General charitable purposes for the relief of poverty, sickness and to protect and preserve good health, and advance education of those in need from impoverished countries, in particular Somalia, Bosnia, Iraq, Bangladesh and Lebanon. Infrastructure, support and development and cultural activity are also funded.

WHAT IS NOT FUNDED No grants to individuals, or for medical expenses, tutors or examination fees.

SAMPLE GRANTS Previous beneficiaries included: Red Crescent U A E; Qatar Charitable Society, Muslim Aid; Islamic Trust; Elrahm Trust; Saudi Arabia (Muslim World League); Darfur Health Clinics; Isakhel Hospital Pakistan; Well Project, Iraq.

FINANCES *Year* 2010 *Income* £2,065,029 *Grants* £1,307,426 *Assets* £1,628,397

TRUSTEES Dr Haytham Al-Khaffaf; Wael Musabbeh; Fared Sabri; Dr Nooh Al-Kaddo; Dr Haytham Al-Rawi.

OTHER INFORMATION A list of recent grants was not included in the accounts.

HOW TO APPLY In writing to the correspondent.

WHO TO APPLY TO Kassim Tokan, Secretary, PO Box 194, Bradford, West Yorkshire BD7 1BQ *Tel* 01274 392727 *Fax* 01274 739992 *Website* www.hrf.org.uk

■ Humanitarian and Charitable One Trust (HACOT)

CC NO 1134249 **ESTABLISHED** 2010

WHERE FUNDING CAN BE GIVEN Worldwide, with some preference for India and Kenya.

WHO CAN BENEFIT Registered charities.

WHAT IS FUNDED The trust has the following charitable objectives: the advancement of education; the relief of sickness and need by such means as decided by the trustees including the provision of suitable advice and counselling; prevention or relief of poverty anywhere in the world for the public benefit by providing or assisting in the provision of education, training, health care projects and all the necessary support designed to enable individuals to generate a sustainable income and be self-sufficient; relief of financial hardship; the relief of unemployment by such means as the trustees think fit including the provision of micro finance or assistance to find employment; and the relief of poverty and need by providing or assisting with the provision of low cost housing these objects shall be primarily advanced in India and Kenya but are not restricted to this area and will be undertaken for the public benefit irrespective of gender, nationality, race, religion or colour.

TRUSTEES Dr Amir Lakha; Mohamed Lalji; Rafik Mawji.
HOW TO APPLY In writing to the correspondent.
WHO TO APPLY TO Dr Amir Lakha, Trustee, 10 Bayhurst Drive, Northwood, Hillingdon HA6 3SA *Tel* 01923 824877 *email* info@hacot.org *Website* hacot.org

··

■ The Humanitarian Trust

CC NO 208575   **ESTABLISHED** 1946
WHERE FUNDING CAN BE GIVEN Worldwide, mainly Israel.
WHO CAN BENEFIT Organisations and individuals.
WHAT IS FUNDED 'The trustees consider grant applications from organisations and individuals in the UK and abroad, especially in the fields of education, health, social welfare, civil society, Jewish communal life and general charitable purposes.'
TYPE OF GRANT One-off grants.
RANGE OF GRANTS up to £10,000.
SAMPLE GRANTS Previously grants included those made to: Friends of the Hebrew University of Jerusalem towards: the Humanitarian Trust Fellowship and the M Gunsbourg Memorial Scholarships (£10,000 each). Other beneficiaries included: New Israel Fund (£6,000); Institute for Jewish Policy Research (£5,000); University of Oxford (£4,500); Jerusalem Foundation Bilingual School, Association for Civil Rights in Israel and The Samaritans (£2,000 each); King's College London, University of Dundee and University of Birmingham (£500 each).
FINANCES *Year* 2009–10 *Income* £131,994 *Grants* £100,000
TRUSTEES Jacques Gunsbourg; Pierre Halban; Anthony Lerman.
OTHER INFORMATION Approximate total grant-giving.
HOW TO APPLY In writing to the correspondent, including annual report and accounts, projected budgets and future plans. Applications are considered at trustees' meetings in March and October.
WHO TO APPLY TO Mrs M Myers, Secretary, 27 St James's Place, London SW1A 1NR *Tel* 020 7409 1376

··

■ The Humberside Charitable Health Trust

CC NO 1091814   **ESTABLISHED** 2002
WHERE FUNDING CAN BE GIVEN Kingston upon Hull, East Yorkshire and North East Lincolnshire.
WHO CAN BENEFIT Organisations.
WHAT IS FUNDED Healthcare provision (including facilities and equipment), medical research and medical education.
SAMPLE GRANTS Beneficiaries included: St John Ambulance (£100,000); Macmillian Cancer Support (£50,000); Dove House Hospice (£30,000); Motor Neurone Disease Association, Hull and East Yorkshire Riding Institute for the Blind, Tweendykes school (£5,000); Barnardo's (£2,500).
FINANCES *Year* 2009–10 *Income* £91,160 *Grants* £221,498 *Assets* £4,233,552
TRUSTEES R D King; K Gorton; Mrs J Bielby; F M Burton; Prof. P W R Lee; A Milner; S L Smith; Mrs W Thomas, Mr A Mould.
OTHER INFORMATION 'The charity carried out its objectives by inviting applications for grant aid and considering all those received.'

HOW TO APPLY In writing to the correspondent. The trustees meet bi-monthly.
WHO TO APPLY TO Roger King, Secretary, Roger King, Help for Health, Baker Tilly, 2 Humber Quays, Wellington Street West, Hull *Tel* 01964 550725 *email* info@helphealth.org.u

··

■ The Michael and Shirley Hunt Charitable Trust

CC NO 1063418   **ESTABLISHED** 1997
WHERE FUNDING CAN BE GIVEN UK and overseas.
WHO CAN BENEFIT Prisoners and/or their families, and people charged with criminal offences and held in custody. Also, animals which are unwanted, sick or ill-treated.
WHAT IS FUNDED Relief of need, hardship or distress of prisoners and/or their families; animal welfare; general charitable purposes.
WHAT IS NOT FUNDED No grants for capital projects, support costs, fines, bail, legal costs, rent deposits and so on.
TYPE OF GRANT One-off.
RANGE OF GRANTS £50–£10,000.
SAMPLE GRANTS DEC Haiti Earthquake Appeal (£10,000); St Barnabus Hospice (£5,000); Macmillan Cancer Support and Prisoners Families and Friends Service (£2,500 each); East Sussex WRAS, Eden Animal Rescue, S.H.A.R.P., and Wood Green Animal Shelters, (£2,000 each); and Action for Prisoners Families, Capricorn Animal Rescue, Lincolnshire Trust for Cats, National Probation Service, Sussex and Willows Animal Sanctuary (£1,000 each).
FINANCES *Year* 2009–10 *Income* £223,497 *Grants* £64,400 *Assets* £5,582,036
TRUSTEES W J Baker; C J Hunt; S E Hunt; D S Jenkins; K D Mayberry.
HOW TO APPLY In writing to the correspondent. The trustees meet to consider applications 'as and when necessary, and at least annually'.
WHO TO APPLY TO Mrs D S Jenkins, Trustee, Ansty House, Henfield Road, Small Dole, West Sussex BN5 9XH *Tel* 01903 817116 *Fax* 01903 879995

··

■ The Albert Hunt Trust

CC NO 277318   **ESTABLISHED** 1979
WHERE FUNDING CAN BE GIVEN UK.
WHO CAN BENEFIT Registered charities.
WHAT IS FUNDED Projects that enhance the physical and mental welfare of individuals, or group of individuals.
WHAT IS NOT FUNDED No grants for research or overseas work.
RANGE OF GRANTS Up to £50,000.
SAMPLE GRANTS Royal School for the Blind (£50,000); Chiltern MS Centre (£41,000); Marie Curie Cancer Care (£30,000); East Anglia Children's Hospice and Lorica Trust (£25,000 each); St Barnabus Hospice (£20,000); St Christopher's Hospice (£15,000); Fiveways School (£11,000); Little Sisters of the Poor – Dundee, RNIB, Clock Tower Sanctuary and Garwood Foundation (£10,000 each); YMCA, West Sussex Learning Link, Wigtownshire Women's Aid, Trinity Hospice and the Salvation Army (£5,000 each); Teenage Cancer Trust Scotland and Northern Ireland, Union Chapel Project and Hospice at Home – Cumbria (£2,000 each); and Green Light Trust and Disability North (£1,000 each).

Think carefully about every application. Is it justified?

········
629

FINANCES *Year* 2009–10 *Income* £1,297,007 *Grants* £1,352,896 *Assets* £44,677,010

TRUSTEES Coutts and Co; Richard Collis; Breda McGuire.

HOW TO APPLY In writing to the correspondent. All appeals should be by letter containing the following: aims and objectives of the charity; nature of appeal; total target if for a specific project; contributions received against target; registered charity number; any other relevant factors. The correspondent has stated that no unsolicited correspondence will be acknowledged, unless an application receives favourable consideration. Trustees meet in March, July and November although appeals are considered on an ongoing basis.

WHO TO APPLY TO The Senior Manager, Coutts & Co, Trustee Department, 440 Strand, London WC2R 0QS *Tel* 020 7663 6825 *Fax* 020 7663 6794

....

■ The Hunter Foundation

SC NO SC027532 ESTABLISHED 1998

WHERE FUNDING CAN BE GIVEN UK and overseas.

WHO CAN BENEFIT Charitable organisations.

WHAT IS FUNDED Educational initiatives aimed largely at children; relief of poverty; community development. Focus in the developed world is to invest in national educational programmes that challenge the system wide issues which prevent children from achieving their potential. In the developing world the focus is on investing in holistic developments that embed solutions within communities and countries, again with education being central.

RANGE OF GRANTS £10,000 £750,000.

SAMPLE GRANTS Previous beneficiaries include: Determined to Succeed, the Children's Charity, Make Poverty History, Band Aid for Village Reach Mozambique, Cash for Kids at Christmas Charitable Trust, Maggie Care Centre, Retail Trust, Variety Club, NCH Action for Children Scotland, Cancer Research, Prince's Scottish Youth Business Trust and Children in Need.

FINANCES *Year* 2009–10 *Income* £1,080,677 *Grants* £750,000

TRUSTEES Sir Tom Hunter, Chair; Lady Marion Hunter; Jim McMahon; Robert Glennie; Vartan Gregorian.

OTHER INFORMATION Despite making a written request for the accounts of this foundation these were not provided. The following entry is based on the details filed with the Office of the Scottish Charity Regulator. At the time of writing the trust's website was not functioning. Since the financial crisis of 2007/08 the investment company West Coast Capital went into administration which impacted on the trust as its income was partially tied to the profitability of that company. Following this the spokesperson for the founder of the trust, stated that: 'The foundation will be leaner and meaner going forward, but [...] hopefully he's got another 40 years to invest £1bn in the common good. He is not withdrawing that challenge'

HOW TO APPLY The foundation offers the following application guidance on its website: 'The Hunter Foundation proactively sources programmes for investment, or works with partners to develop new programmes where a gap or clear need is identified. As such it is very rare indeed for THF to fund unsolicited bids, however if you wish to apply please complete a maximum two page summary outlining how your project fits with our aims and objectives and email it to

info@thehunterfoundation.co.uk. This summary should include: summary of project; impact of project; any independent evaluation undertaken of your project/programme; if this is a local programme how it could be scaled to become a national programme; current sources of funding; and funding sought from the Hunter Foundation. Please note: we do not have a large staff and thus we will not consider meetings in advance of this information being provided. If your project appears to be of initial interest, we will then contact you to discuss this further.'

WHO TO APPLY TO Sir Tom Hunter, Trustee, Marathon House, Olympic Business Park, Drybridge Road, Dundonald, Ayrshire KA2 9AE *email* info@thehunterfoundation.co.uk *Website* www.thehunterfoundation.co.uk

....

■ Miss Agnes H Hunter's Trust

SC NO SC004843 ESTABLISHED 1954

WHERE FUNDING CAN BE GIVEN Scotland (apart from specified medical research).

WHO CAN BENEFIT Organisations benefiting people of all ages, including unemployed people, volunteers, people who are in care, fostered or adopted, parents and children, and one-parent families. Also supported are carers, people who are disabled, people disadvantaged by poverty, homeless people, socially isolated people and people who are ill.

WHAT IS FUNDED Charities assisting people who are blind or visually impaired; help to disabled people, including those affected by physical disability or illness and those with mental health problems or learning disabilities; training and education for disadvantaged people; research into the cause, cure or alleviation for cancer or arthritis or supporting people with these conditions.

WHAT IS NOT FUNDED No grants to individuals, or to organisations under the control of the UK government. The trust does not support grant giving bodies or umbrella organisations.

TYPE OF GRANT Mainly one-off, buildings, capital, core costs, feasibility studies, projects, research and start-up costs will be considered.

RANGE OF GRANTS £200–£10,000; typical grant £3,000–£6,000.

SAMPLE GRANTS Breakthrough Breast Cancer and Visability (£10,000 each); Anthony Nolan Trust (£8,200); Grampian Society for the Blind Trust (£7,000); Alzheimer's Research Trust (£6,000); Scottish Spina Bifida Association (£5,000); Children 1st (£4,000); Contact a Family (£3,000); and PBC Foundation (£2,000).

FINANCES *Year* 2009–10 *Income* £634,665 *Grants* £340,000 *Assets* £17,998,609

TRUSTEES N D S Paterson; W F MacTaggart; A P Gray; Mrs A M Campbell.

HOW TO APPLY In writing to the correspondent. The trustees meet twice a year to allocate grants and the closing dates for receipt of applications are 9 February for the May meeting and 1 August for the November meeting.

WHO TO APPLY TO Mrs Jane Paterson, Grants Administrator, c/o Pagan Osborne, 55–56 Queen Street, Edinburgh EH2 3PA *Tel* 0131 538 5496 *email* grants@agneshunter.org.uk *Website* www.agneshunter.org.uk

....

■ The Huntingdon Foundation

CC NO 286504 **ESTABLISHED** 1984
WHERE FUNDING CAN BE GIVEN Mainly UK, some giving in the US.
WHO CAN BENEFIT Organisations benefiting Jewish people.
WHAT IS FUNDED Jewish organisations, particularly schools.
WHAT IS NOT FUNDED No grants to individuals.
RANGE OF GRANTS About £1,000 to £60,000.
SAMPLE GRANTS Yavneh College; Yesodey Hatorah Schools; Sylvella Charity Limited; Edgware Jewish Primary School; Morasha Jewish Primary School; Aish; Noam Primary School; and Bais Yaccov Primary School.
FINANCES *Year* 2009–10 *Income* £1,068,902 *Grants* £287,691 *Assets* £10,572,202
TRUSTEES Benjamin Perl, Chair; Dr Shoshana Perl; R Jeidel (USA); Jonathan Perl; Naomi Sorotzkin; Joseph Perl.
OTHER INFORMATION The accounts do not list the amounts given to individual recipient organisations.
HOW TO APPLY In writing to the correspondent. The trustees meet several times a year.
WHO TO APPLY TO Benjamin Perl, 8 Goodyers Gardens, London NW4 2HD *Tel* 020 8202 2282

■ Huntingdon Freemen's Charity

CC NO 1044573 **ESTABLISHED** 1993
WHERE FUNDING CAN BE GIVEN Huntingdon.
WHO CAN BENEFIT Individuals and organisations.
WHAT IS FUNDED Relief in need (including sickness and healthcare provision); provision of pensions; educational needs; and recreational needs.
WHAT IS NOT FUNDED No applications from outside the boundaries of Huntingdon.
RANGE OF GRANTS Up to £25,000.
SAMPLE GRANTS Commemoration Hall (£25,000); Natural High (£8,560); Huntingdonshire Music School (£3,600); St Barnabas Furniture Project (£3,600); Disability Information Service (DISH) (£3,500); and Huntingdon Tennis Club and Huntingdon Citizens Advice Bureau (£2,500 each).
FINANCES *Year* 2009–10 *Income* £469,941 *Grants* £258,469 *Assets* £12,226,529
TRUSTEES Edward G Bocking, Chair; Michael A Bloomfield; Brian S Bradshaw; James D Fell, Jonathon Hampstead; John R Hough; Mrs Laine Kadic; A Turnill; and A Mackender-Lawrence.
OTHER INFORMATION In 2009–10 grants were made totalling £258,000, and distributed evenly amongst relief in need (£88,000), education (£84,000) and recreation (£86,000). No large grants were approved during the year (£50,000 or more).
HOW TO APPLY In writing to the correspondent.
WHO TO APPLY TO David Kerr, Clerk to the Trustees, 37 High Street, Huntingdon, Cambridgeshire PE29 3AQ *Tel* 01480 414909 *email* huntingdonfreemens@tiscali.co.uk *Website* www.huntingdonfreemen.org.uk

■ John Huntingdon's Charity

CC NO 203795 **ESTABLISHED** 1972
WHERE FUNDING CAN BE GIVEN The parish of Sawston.
WHO CAN BENEFIT This charity makes grants for the relief of need, hardship and distress in the parish of Sawston.

WHAT IS FUNDED The charity provides housing and family support services. Grants are made to both organisations and individuals.
RANGE OF GRANTS Up to £10,000.
SAMPLE GRANTS Cogwheel Adult Counselling (£1,000); Centre 33 (young people's drop in and counselling (£2,100); Alzheimer's Society Singing for the Brain project (£2,000); STARS 9children's bereavement counselling (£500); Camsight visual impairment (£500).
FINANCES *Year* 2010 *Income* £372,362 *Grants* £25,966 *Assets* £7,672,678
TRUSTEES Thomas Butler; Sally Hatton; Susan Reynolds; Reg Cullum; Christine Ingham; Eugene Murray; Eleanor Clapp; Catherine Gilmore; Alan Partridge; Josephine Shickell; David Basilington.
HOW TO APPLY In writing to the correspondent.
WHO TO APPLY TO Revd Mary Irish, Charity Manager, John Huntingdon House, Tannery Road, Sawston, Cambridge CB22 3UW *Tel* 01223 830599 *email* office@johnhuntingdon.org.uk *Website* www.johnhuntingdon.org.uk

■ Hurdale Charity Limited

CC NO 276997 **ESTABLISHED** 1978
WHERE FUNDING CAN BE GIVEN Worldwide.
WHO CAN BENEFIT Organisations benefiting Jewish people.
WHAT IS FUNDED Jewish organisations that promote the Orthodox Jewish way of life.
WHAT IS NOT FUNDED In writing to the trustees.
TYPE OF GRANT One-off and recurring.
RANGE OF GRANTS Up to £250,000.
SAMPLE GRANTS Previous beneficiaries include: Mesifta; Chevras Moaz Ladol; Yetev Lev Jerusalem Trust; Vyoel Moshe Trust; Beis Ruchel; Kollel Rabinow; Craven Walk Beis Hamedresh Trust; Ezras Bis Yisroel; Mosdos Belz Bnei Brak; Pesach Project Trust; Shaarei Chesed; Kehal Chasidei Bobov; Hachzakos Torah V'chesed; Medical Aid Trust; Yeshiva Law of Trust; and Zichron Yechezkal Trust.
FINANCES *Year* 2009–10 *Income* £2,426,134 *Grants* £2,002,221 *Assets* £18,838,903
TRUSTEES Mrs Eva Oestreicher; Pinkas Oestreicher; David Oestreicher; Abraham Oestreicher; Jacob Oestreicher; Benjamin Oestreicher.
HOW TO APPLY In writing to the correspondent.
WHO TO APPLY TO Abraham Oestreicher, Trustee, Cohen Arnold and Co., New Burlington House, 1075 Finchley Road, London NW11 0PU

■ The Hutton Foundation

CC NO 1106521 **ESTABLISHED** 2004
WHERE FUNDING CAN BE GIVEN Worldwide.
WHO CAN BENEFIT Charitable organisations.
WHAT IS FUNDED Christian causes.
SAMPLE GRANTS Previously: the Catholic Trust for England and Wales and Hampshire (£100,000 each); NSPCC (£34,000); Catholic Bishops Conference (£25,000); Aid to the Church in Need (£25,000); and International Theologies Institute (£21,000).
FINANCES *Year* 2010 *Income* £28,362 *Grants* £133,344 *Assets* £1,896,800
TRUSTEES Graham Hutton; Amanda Hutton; Richard Hutton; James Hutton.
HOW TO APPLY In writing to the correspondent.
WHO TO APPLY TO Graham Hutton, Trustee, Spring Cottage, Cranes Road, Sherborne St John, Hampshire RG24 9HY

■ The Huxham Charitable Trust

cc no 1000179   established 1990

where funding can be given Mainly Albania and Kosova.

who can benefit Registered UK charities; Christian organisations, refugees.

what is funded Development work.

finances *Year* 2009–10 *Income* £55,228 *Grants* £66,519 *Assets* £135,032

trustees Revd Deacon; Revd Percy; Mr Corney; Mr Hawkins.

other information Grants to organisations and individuals totalled £80,000, with £67,000 being made to organisations.

how to apply The trust stated it is has been unable to support any new organisations in recent years.

who to apply to Adrian W Huxham, Thatcher Brake, 37 Whidborne Avenue, Torquay TQ1 2PG *Tel* 01803 380399

■ The Nani Huyu Charitable Trust

cc no 1082868   established 2000

where funding can be given UK, particularly but not exclusively within 50 miles of Bristol.

who can benefit Welfare organisations.

what is funded 'To assist people who are underprivileged, disadvantaged or ill, young people in matters of health, accommodation and training and those requiring assistance or medical care at the end of their lives.'

finances *Year* 2009–10 *Income* £142,494 *Grants* £141,500 *Assets* £3,757,598

trustees S Whitmore; Ben Whitmore; Charles Thatcher; Maureen Whitmore.

how to apply In writing to the correspondent.

who to apply to The Trustees, Rusling House, Butcombe, Bristol BS40 7XQ *Tel* 01275 474433 *email* maureensimonwhitmore@ btinternet.com

■ The P Y N and B Hyams Trust

cc no 268129   established 1974

where funding can be given Worldwide.

who can benefit Organisations, especially those benefiting Jewish people.

what is funded Jewish organisations and general charitable purposes.

finances *Year* 2009–10 *Income* £83,271 *Grants* £49,260 *Assets* £1,095,121

trustees Mrs M Hyams; D Levy; N Shah.

how to apply In writing to the correspondent, but please note, the trust states that funds are fully committed and unsolicited applications are not welcomed.

who to apply to N Shah, Trustee, Lubbock Fine, Russell Bedford House, City Forum, 250 City Road, London EC1V 2QQ *Tel* 020 7490 7766

■ The Hyde Charitable Trust – Youth Plus

cc no 289888   established 1984

where funding can be given The areas in which the Hyde Group operates (currently London, Kent, Surrey, Sussex and Hampshire).

who can benefit Schools and registered charities.

what is funded Youth Plus is 'mainly interested in innovative projects seeking to address problems faced by children and young people in areas typified by social deprivation. These areas will often have high levels of unemployment and disenchantment within the community and offer very few prospects for young people.

what is not funded No funding for: projects outside of the area where Hyde is working – no areas outside the South East of England; sporting, social or fund-raising events; medical research, hospices, residential homes for the elderly; any other projects which the trustees deem to fall outside the trust's main criteria.

sample grants The following causes and initiatives were supported as follows: £65,000 to family support/parenting; £46,000 to Young Pride Awards; £39,000 to Holiday play fund; £10,000 to Jobs plus; £5,000 to New business; £2,000 to Sustainability and environmental; £6,000 to other causes.

finances *Year* 2009–10 *Income* £167,000 *Grants* £164,000 *Assets* £2,581,000

trustees Peter Matthew; Stephen Hill; Patrick Elliott; Geron Walker; Martin Wheatley; Derek Biggs; Baroness Kishwer Falkner.

other information 'Youth Plus is supported by Hyde Plus, Hyde's economic and community regeneration arm. Hyde Plus administers the grants and supports groups in the development of projects seeking Youth Plus funding.'

how to apply The trust has recently informed us that it can no longer accept unsolicited applications.

who to apply to The Trustees, Hollingsworth House, 181 Lewisham High Street, London SE13 6AA *Tel* 020 8297 7575 *email* youthplus@hyde-housing.co.uk *Website* www.youthplus.co.uk

■ The Idlewild Trust

CC NO 268124 **ESTABLISHED** 1974
WHERE FUNDING CAN BE GIVEN UK.
WHO CAN BENEFIT Registered charities only.
WHAT IS FUNDED The encouragement of excellence in the performing and fine arts and the preservation for the benefit of the public of buildings and items of historical interest or national importance. Occasional support is given to bodies for educational bursaries in these fields and for conservation of the natural environment.
WHAT IS NOT FUNDED Grants to registered charities only. No grants are made to individuals. The trust will not give to: repetitive UK-wide appeals by large charities; appeals where all, or most, of the beneficiaries live outside the UK; local appeals unless the artistic significance of the project is of more than local importance; appeals whose sole or main purpose is to make grants from the funds collected; endowment or deficit funding.
TYPE OF GRANT Buildings, core costs, endowments, feasibility studies, one-off, projects, research and start-up costs.
RANGE OF GRANTS £500–£5,000. Average grant £2,000.
FINANCES *Year* 2010 *Income* £150,157 *Grants* £128,805 *Assets* £4,361,761
TRUSTEES Lady Judith Goodison, Chair; J A Ford; M Wilson; J Ouvry; Dr T Murdoch.
HOW TO APPLY On a form available from the correspondent, or as a download from the trust's website. This can be sent via post or emailed as a Microsoft Word file. Applications should include the following information: Applications should include the following information: budget breakdown (one page); most recent audited accounts; a list of other sponsors, including those applied to; other relevant information. Potential applicants are welcome to telephone the trust on Tuesdays or Wednesdays between 10am and 4pm to discuss their application and check eligibility. Trustees meet twice a year, usually in March and November. All eligible applications, which are put forward to the trustees, are acknowledged; other applications will not be acknowledged unless an sae is enclosed. Applications from organisations within 18 months of a previous grant will not be considered.
WHO TO APPLY TO Mrs Angela Hurst, Administrator, 1a Taylors Yard, 67 Alderbrook Street, London SW12 8AD *Tel* 020 8772 3155 *email* info@idlewildtrust.org.uk *Website* www.idlewildtrust.org.uk

■ The Iliffe Family Charitable Trust

CC NO 273437 **ESTABLISHED** 1977
WHERE FUNDING CAN BE GIVEN UK and Worldwide.
WHO CAN BENEFIT The majority of donations are made to charities already known to the trustees. Thereafter, preference is given to charities in which the trust has a special interest.
WHAT IS FUNDED Medical, activities for people who are disabled, heritage organisations, and education.
WHAT IS NOT FUNDED No grants to individuals and rarely to non-registered charities.
RANGE OF GRANTS Usually up to £40,000.
SAMPLE GRANTS Marine Society & Sea Cadets (£30,000); Royal Shakespeare Company and Bradfield Foundation (£20,000); Game & Wildlife Conservation Trust (£15,000); Arthur Rank Centre (£12,000); Jubilee Sailing Trust (£10,000); Priors Court Foundation (£5,000); Ufton Court Education Centre (£1,000); FAAOA (£900); and Elizabeth Finn Care (£500).
FINANCES *Year* 2009–10 *Income* £204,255 *Grants* £219,400 *Assets* £1,247,817
TRUSTEES N G E Petter; G A Bremner; Lord Iliffe; Hon. Edward Iliffe.
HOW TO APPLY In writing to the correspondent. Only successful applications will be acknowledged. Grants are considered at ad hoc meetings of the trustees, held throughout the year.
WHO TO APPLY TO The Secretary to the Trustees, Barn Close, Yattendon, Berkshire RG18 0UX *Tel* 01635 203929

■ Impetus Trust

CC NO 1094681 **ESTABLISHED** 2002
WHERE FUNDING CAN BE GIVEN Worldwide, in practice UK.
WHO CAN BENEFIT Registered charities and social enterprises, which work with people who are economically disadvantaged and are at a critical stage in their strategic development; have a turnover of at least £250,000; have operated and produced accounts for the last three years; and have a headquarters and a significant portion of their management in England.
WHAT IS FUNDED Distinctive charities, which aim to break the cycle of economic disadvantage and improve levels of education, skills and employability. The charities supported have to both want and need the integrated package of support the trust offers to make them stronger and more sustainable when that support is removed.
WHAT IS NOT FUNDED Grants are not made to organisations in the following areas: those focusing on animals, culture and heritage rather than people; umbrella organisations/networks; services that are conditional upon the acceptance, profession or observance of a particular religious position; projects substantially/exclusively working in the areas of research or advocacy; those seeking funding for a particular project/building.
TYPE OF GRANT S*trategic core funding* – usually from three-to-five years, to scale up social impact; *hands-on management support* – executive overview and support in implementing agreed strategy, including monthly meetings with the charity's chief executive and other senior executives, providing a sounding board, challenge and support; monitoring progress against business plan objectives and agreed milestones; *specialist expertise* – targeted on specific areas for development and growth – delivered on a project basis by the highly skilled Impetus pro bono expert pool.
RANGE OF GRANTS £100,000–£500,000 over three to five years.
SAMPLE GRANTS Street League (£125,000); Fairtrade Foundation (£95,000); Blue Sky (£75,000); FRC Group (£38,000); COUI – Teens and Toddlers, IntoUniversity and Camfed International (£25,000 each); Keyfund

Think carefully about every application. Is it justified?

633

(£17,000); St Giles Trust (£13,000); Speaking Up, Beat and NPL (£5,000 each); and Leap Confronting Conflict (£2,500).

FINANCES *Year* 2009–10 *Income* £3,831,147 *Grants* £454,592 *Assets* £2,497,354

TRUSTEES Louis G Elson, Chair; Nat Sloane; Amelia Howard; Andy Hinton; Stephen Dawson; Stephen Lambert; Ian Meakins; Chris Underhill; Craig Dearden-Phillips.

HOW TO APPLY In the first instance, applicants should complete the 'eligibility checker' on the trust's website and submit a brief expression of interest. The trust will then be in contact if it wishes to pursue the application any further. If so, the assessment process will include a detailed due diligence assessment covering all aspects of the charity's operations, including meetings with the organisation's trustees and management as well as site visits and analysis of financial data.

WHO TO APPLY Claire Kelly, 20 Flaxman Terrace, London WC1H 9PN *Tel* 020 3384 3940 *email* info@impetus.org.uk *Website* www.impetus.org.uk

■ The Indigo Trust

CC NO 1075920   **ESTABLISHED** 1999

WHERE FUNDING CAN BE GIVEN UK and overseas.

WHO CAN BENEFIT Organisations or programmes that have the potential to bring about systematic change both in prisons and within the criminal justice system more widely.

WHAT IS FUNDED Prisons and criminal justice. The trust wishes to fund programmes in the areas of: improved use of resources in the sector, particularly in resettlement and education; the development of innovation and best practice in the sector, particularly in terms of the use of the web and new technologies; research and dissemination to support the areas above. .

WHAT IS NOT FUNDED Grants are not usually made to individuals.

SAMPLE GRANTS Impetus Trust (£72,000); New Philanthropy Capital (£63,000); Open Book (£45,000); My Society (£40,000); Butler Trust (£36,000); University of Cambridge – Robinson College (£10,000); and the Sainsbury Archive (£3,000).

FINANCES *Year* 2009–10 *Income* £117,061 *Grants* £270,980 *Assets* £7,364,310

TRUSTEES Francesca Sainsbury; Dominic Flynn; Bernard Chi-Chung Fung.

OTHER INFORMATION In 2009–10 a grant of £1,300 was also made but not listed.

HOW TO APPLY See the guidance for applicants in the entry for the Sainsbury Family Charitable Trusts. A single application will be considered for support by all the trusts in the group. However, please see comments above regarding the selection of beneficiaries.

WHO TO APPLY Alan Bookbinder, Director, Allington House, 1st Floor, 150 Victoria Street, London SW1E 5AE *Tel* 020 7410 0330 *Fax* 020 7410 0332 *Website* www.sfct.org.uk

■ Infinity Capital Trust

CC NO 1134183   **ESTABLISHED** 2010

WHERE FUNDING CAN BE GIVEN Worldwide.

WHO CAN BENEFIT Individuals and organisations.

WHAT IS FUNDED The relief of poverty among persons of the Jewish faith in any part of the world; the advancement of the Jewish religion in any part of the world; the advancement of the education of the public in any part of the world in the knowledge of the Jewish religion and Jewish history and culture; other charitable purposes for the benefit of persons of the Jewish faith in any part of the world as the trustees shall from time to time decide.

TRUSTEES Rabbi Naftali Chaim Blau; Brian Blau; Judith Wilk.

HOW TO APPLY In writing to the correspondent. The trust has stated that it plans to allow its capital to build up and, consequently, will not be making grants in the near future.

WHO TO APPLY TO Brian Blau, Trustee, Foframe House, 35–37 Brent Street, London NW4 2EF

■ The Ingram Trust

CC NO 1040194   **ESTABLISHED** 1994

WHERE FUNDING CAN BE GIVEN UK and overseas, especially Surrey.

WHO CAN BENEFIT Established registered charities only.

WHAT IS FUNDED General charitable purposes. The trust prefers to support specific projects including special services and equipment. It will support major UK charities together with some local ones in the county of Surrey. Normally the policy is to support a limited number of charities (usually less than 20), but with a longer-term commitment to each.

WHAT IS NOT FUNDED No grants to non-registered charities or to individuals. No charities specialising in overseas aid are considered except those dedicated to encouraging self help or providing more permanent solutions. No animal charities except those concerned with wildlife conservation.

RANGE OF GRANTS Up to £75,000.

SAMPLE GRANTS WWF – UK (£75,000); ActionAid (£50,000); the National Theatre (£30,000); St Mungo's (£20,000); St Giles Trust (£15,000); and Disability Challengers and Pimlico Opera (£10,000 each).

FINANCES *Year* 2009–10 *Income* £206,065 *Grants* £672,000 *Assets* £12,179,936

TRUSTEES C J Ingram; Mrs J E Ingram; Ms C M Maurice.

HOW TO APPLY In writing to the correspondent, although the trust states that it receives far more worthy applications than it is able to support.

WHO TO APPLY TO Joan Major, Administrator, c/o 8th Floor, 101 Wigmore Street, London W1U 1QU *email* theingramtrust@sandaire.com

■ The Inland Waterways Association

CC NO 212342   **ESTABLISHED** 1946

WHERE FUNDING CAN BE GIVEN UK and Ireland.

WHO CAN BENEFIT Organisations promoting the restoration of inland waterways (such as canal and river navigations).

WHAT IS FUNDED (1) Construction, especially works relating to the restoration of navigation such as locks, bridges, aqueducts, culverts, weirs, pumps, excavation, dredging, lining, and so on; (2) administration – support for a particular purpose, such as a project officer, a funding appeal or for promotional literature or events; (3) professional services, such as funding of feasibility studies or detailed work on engineering, economic or environmental issues; (4) land purchase; (5) research on matters affecting waterway restoration, including original research, reviews of research undertaken by others and literature reviews; (6) education, such as providing information to local authorities or agencies to promote the nature and benefits of waterway restoration.

WHAT IS NOT FUNDED No grants to individuals. No retrospective grants for projects where expenditure has already been incurred or committed.

TYPE OF GRANT Capital, feasibility studies, one-off grants, project and research grants. Funding can be given over a number of years.

RANGE OF GRANTS Up to £15,000. In exceptional cases, larger grants can be made.

SAMPLE GRANTS Previously: The Driffield Navigation Trust (£7,500); Lichfield & Hatherton Canals Restoration Trust and Caldon & Uttoxeter Canal Trust (£5,000 each); British Waterways (£2,500); Rolle Canal and North Devon Waterways Society, Wiltshire and Berkshire Canal Trust and Foxton Locks Partnership (£2,000 each); and River Gipping Trust (£1,000).

FINANCES *Year* 2010 *Income* £1,501,888 *Grants* £85,000 *Assets* £276,907

TRUSTEES The Council of the Association; Doug Beard; Ray Carter; Leslie Etheridge; John Fletcher; Anthony Harrison; Michael Palmer; John Pomfret; Paul Strudwick; Vaughan Welch; Ian West.

OTHER INFORMATION Charitable expenditure during the year totalled approximately £800,000 of which a large amount (£575,000) was designated to 'campaign and restoration costs' which included 'donations and grants' of £85,000.

HOW TO APPLY In writing to the correspondent. Applications should comply with the 'Guidelines for Applicants', also available from the correspondent. Each applicant should provide a full description of its proposal, show that the organisation can maintain a satisfactory financial position and demonstrate that it is capable of undertaking the proposed project. Applications for up to £2,000 are assessed under a simplified procedure – each application should demonstrate that the grant would be used to initiate or sustain a restoration scheme or significantly benefit a specific small project. Applications for over £2,000 should demonstrate that the grant would be applied to one of the types of projects (1–6). Applicants should also demonstrate the extent to which the project satisfies one or more of the following conditions: the grant would unlock (lever) a grant several times larger from another body; the grant would not replace grants available from other sources; the project does not qualify for grants from major funding sources; the grant would enable a key project to be undertaken which would have a significant effect on the prospect of advancing the restoration and gaining funds from other sources for further restoration projects; the result of the project would have a major influence over the progress of a number of other restoration projects; The Inland Waterways Association Restoration Committee would have a major influence in the management of the project, including monitoring of expenditure.

WHO TO APPLY TO The Chair of the IWA Restoration Committee, Island House, Moor Road, Chesham, Buckinghamshire HP5 1WA *Tel* 01923 711114 *Fax* 01923 897000 *email* iwa@waterways.org.uk *Website* www.waterways.org.uk

■ The Inlight Trust

CC NO 236782   **ESTABLISHED** 1957
WHERE FUNDING CAN BE GIVEN UK.

WHO CAN BENEFIT Registered charities benefiting people from many different religions.

WHAT IS FUNDED Donations are made on a non-denominational basis to charities providing valuable contributions to spiritual development and charities concerned with spiritual healing and spiritual growth through religious retreats.

WHAT IS NOT FUNDED Grants are made to registered charities only. Applications from individuals, including students, are ineligible. No grants are made in response to general appeals from large national organisations. Grants are seldom available for church buildings.

TYPE OF GRANT Usually one-off for a specific project or part of a project. Bursary schemes eligible. Core funding and/or salaries are rarely considered.

RANGE OF GRANTS Up to £20,000.

SAMPLE GRANTS Drukpa UK (£10,000); St Albans Cathedral Music Trust (£5,000): Christians in Care (£3,000); and Acorn Christian Healing Foundation (£2,000).

FINANCES *Year* 2009–10 *Income* £218,152 *Grants* £100,000 *Assets* £5,207,709

TRUSTEES Sir T Lucas; Mrs W Collett; S Neil; R Wolfe; D Hawkins; Mrs J Hayward.

HOW TO APPLY In writing to the correspondent including details of the need the intended project is designed to meet plus an outline budget and the most recent available annual accounts of the charity. Only applications from eligible bodies are acknowledged. Applications must be accompanied by a copy of your trust deed or of your entry in the Charity Commission register. They are considered four times a year. Only successful applicants are informed.

WHO TO APPLY TO The Trustees, PO Box 2, Liss, Hampshire GU33 6YP *Tel* 01730 894120

■ The Inman Charity

CC NO 261366   **ESTABLISHED** 1970
WHERE FUNDING CAN BE GIVEN UK.

WHO CAN BENEFIT 'The directors operate a grant giving policy, providing funds for such charitable object or institution as the directors think fit. In addition to supporting a wide range of charitable organisations, the charity makes a regular payment (normally £15,000 per annum) to the Victor Inman Bursary Fund at Uppingham School of which the settlor had been a lifelong supporter.'

WHAT IS FUNDED Previously, the main areas of interest have been older people, medical research, hospices and disability.

WHAT IS NOT FUNDED No grants to individuals.

RANGE OF GRANTS Most grants were of £5,000 or less.

SAMPLE GRANTS The Roy Castle Lung Cancer Foundation and Fight for Sight (£5,000 each); World Cancer Research Fund and Gurkha Welfare Trust (£4,000 each); Redbridge Concern Mental Health (£3,000); the Dystonia Society and Right Employment (£2,500 each); Missing People (£1,500); and Optua (£500).

FINANCES *Year* 2010 *Income* £155,514 *Grants* £283,000 *Assets* £4,927,833

TRUSTEES A L Walker; Miss B M A Strother; M R Matthews; Prof. J D Langdon.

HOW TO APPLY In writing to the correspondent accompanied by the charity's latest report and full accounts. Applications should contain the following: aims and objectives of the charity;

nature of the appeal; total target if for a specific project; contributions received against target; registered charity number; any other relevant factors.

WHO TO APPLY TO The Trustees, Payne Hicks Beech, 10 New Square, Lincoln's Inn, London WC2A 3QG

■ The Inner London Magistrates Court Poor Box and Feeder Charity

CC NO 1046214   **ESTABLISHED** 1995
WHERE FUNDING CAN BE GIVEN Inner London.
WHO CAN BENEFIT Individuals and organisations.
WHAT IS FUNDED Relief of need, hardship or distress.
WHAT IS NOT FUNDED Not directly for the relief of rates, taxes or other public funds.
RANGE OF GRANTS Usually £250 to £15,000.
SAMPLE GRANTS Inner London Probation Services – Christmas Donations (£15,000) and Relief Payments (£3,600); Prisoners' Family and Friends (£10,000); West London Churches Homeless Concern, Broadway Day Centre and Addaction (£5,000 each); Accord Centre (£2,000); Camberwell Youth and West London youth (£1,000 each).
FINANCES *Year* 2009–10 *Income* £101,019 *Grants* £49,426 *Assets* £3,164,521
TRUSTEES T Workman; R Mangnall; N Evans; Mrs P Sinclair; Q Purdy; K Griffiths.
OTHER INFORMATION Under a Charity Commission scheme of 1995, this new charity now administers the amalgamated assets of the poor box funds of 16 previous London magistrates' courts, as well as a number of other associated trusts. These old trusts covered the courts of Bow Street, Camberwell Green, Clerkenwell, Greenwich, Hampstead, Highbury Corner, Horseferry Road, Inner London, Marlborough Street, Marylebone, Old Street, South Western, Thames, Tower Bridge, West London and Woolwich.
HOW TO APPLY In writing to the correspondent.
WHO TO APPLY TO Paula Carter, Administrator, City of Westminster Courts, 7th Floor, 65 Romney Street, London SW1P 3RD *Tel* 020 7805 1132

■ The Innocent Foundation

CC NO 1104289   **ESTABLISHED** 2004
WHERE FUNDING CAN BE GIVEN India, Vietnam, Indonesia, Peru, Kenya and Uganda.
WHO CAN BENEFIT Community based projects and non-government organisations in the developing countries where the Innocent Drinks company sources fruit. Organisations must have UK representation or be registered to receive foreign funds.
WHAT IS FUNDED Projects enabling people dependant on subsistence agriculture to build sustainable futures.
WHAT IS NOT FUNDED No grants to individuals. Funding is not currently available in the UK.
TYPE OF GRANT Most funds are allocated in three year partnerships.
SAMPLE GRANTS Find your Feet (£40,000); Farm Africa (£23,000); Action Aid (£19,000); War on Want (£12,000); Microloan Foundation (£10,000); Plan International (£8,000); Guanacaste (£7,600); ADD (£7,000); Practical Action (£5,600); and APD (£750).
FINANCES *Year* 2009 *Income* £31,562 *Grants* £177,478 *Assets* £993,543
TRUSTEES Adam Balon; Jon Wright; Richard Reed.

OTHER INFORMATION The Innocent Foundation was set up by Innocent Drinks in 2004. Each year the company gives at least 10% of its profits to charity, the majority to the foundation.
HOW TO APPLY The foundation states that 'most partnerships come from research and not speculative enquiry'. As such, it asks potential applicants to discuss the project with them first before submitting a detailed proposal.
WHO TO APPLY TO The Secretary, The Goldhawk Estate, Brackenbury Road, London W6 0BA *Website* www.innocentfoundation.org

■ The International Bankers Charitable Trust (The Worshipful Company of International Bankers)

CC NO 1087630   **ESTABLISHED** 2001
WHERE FUNDING CAN BE GIVEN UK with preference for inner London.
WHO CAN BENEFIT Registered charities only.
WHAT IS FUNDED 'The company will seek to promote recruitment and development of employees in the financial services industry with particular emphasis on those younger people in the immediate area of the city who would not normally be able to aspire to a city job.'
WHAT IS NOT FUNDED The following areas are excluded from company grants: large projects towards which any contribution from the company would have limited impact; general appeals or circulars; replacement of statutory funds; salaries; counselling; course fees for professionals; medical research; fundraising events and sponsorship.
TYPE OF GRANT The company may support: (a) specific projects where a donation from the company would cover either a significant proportion of the cost or an identified element of it; (b) long-term funding of scholarships and/or bursaries.
FINANCES *Year* 2009–10 *Income* £123,318 *Grants* £83,950 *Assets* £814,772
TRUSTEES The Worshipful Company of International Bankers.
OTHER INFORMATION 'As a representative of the major commercial activity in the city, banking and financial services, the company combines the traditions of the City Livery Companies with a modern outlook on the financial services sector. With more than 600 members, drawn from over 250 companies and institutions and with almost 50 nationalities represented, the company has a truly international character.'
HOW TO APPLY On a form with can be downloaded from the trust's website. Previous grant recipients must allow two years from the date the original grant was awarded to reapply.
WHO TO APPLY TO Tim Woods, Clerk, 3rd Floor, 12 Austin Friars, London EC2N 2HE *Tel* 020 7374 0214 *email* tim.woods@ internationalbankers.co.uk *Website* www. internationalbankers.co.uk

■ International Spinal Research Trust

CC NO 281325   **ESTABLISHED** 1980
WHERE FUNDING CAN BE GIVEN UK and overseas.
WHO CAN BENEFIT Academic institutions undertaking research into spinal cord injury.
WHAT IS FUNDED A wide range of research activities are funded, with the sole aim of ending the

permanence of paralysis caused by spinal cord injury, such as clinical-based programmes and PhD studentships.

WHAT IS NOT FUNDED No commercial organisations or private individuals are funded.

RANGE OF GRANTS £175,000 on average.

FINANCES *Year* 2009–10 *Income* £1,830,621 *Grants* £773,251 *Assets* £986,930

TRUSTEES David Allan; Frances Blois; Martin Curtis; Diana Garnham; Prof. Charles Greenough; Philippa Herbert; John Hick; Dr Lee Illis; Jane Pelly; Dr Ruth McKernan; Prof. Frank Walsh; David Thomson.

HOW TO APPLY The trust advertises in publications such as the British Medical Journal, The Lancet, Nature and Science for people to apply to work on specific research topics. Applications should be made in the form of a letter of intent, of approximately two sides of A4 in length. All applications are reviewed by the Scientific Committee, assisted where appropriate by other scientists in the field. Some applicants will then be invited to make a full application. Unsolicited applications will not be considered.

WHO TO APPLY TO The Head of Research, Unit 8a Bramley Business Centre, Station Road, Bramley, Guildford, Surrey GU5 0AZ *Tel* 01483 898786 *email* info@spinal-research.org *Website* www.spinal-research.org

■ The Inverforth Charitable Trust

CC NO 274132   **ESTABLISHED** 1977

WHERE FUNDING CAN BE GIVEN UK.

WHO CAN BENEFIT UK-wide charities only.

WHAT IS FUNDED General charitable purposes.

RANGE OF GRANTS All grants given ranged from £500 to £2,000.

SAMPLE GRANTS Previous beneficiaries have included: Help for Heroes (£5,000); Helriot Hospice Homecare and CHASE Hospice Care for Children (£2,000 each); the ART Fund, British Lung Foundation, Voluntary Services Overseas and National Youth Orchestra of Great Britain (£1,500 each); National Playbus Association, Kidscape, Contact the Elderly and Farms for City Children (£1,000 each); and Book Aid International, Bowel Cancer UK and the Gurkha Welfare Trust (£500 each).

FINANCES *Year* 2010 *Income* £38,579 *Grants* £0 *Assets* £4,120,443

TRUSTEES Elizabeth Lady Inverforth; Dr Andrew Weir; Hon. Mrs C Kane.

OTHER INFORMATION No grants were made in 2010.

HOW TO APPLY In writing to the trustees.

WHO TO APPLY TO The Secretary, 58A Flood Street, London SW3 5TE *Tel* 0870 770 2657

■ Investream Charitable Trust

CC NO 1097052   **ESTABLISHED** 2003

WHERE FUNDING CAN BE GIVEN In practice the UK and Israel.

WHO CAN BENEFIT Registered charities.

WHAT IS FUNDED Jewish, education, relief of poverty, medical and community.

SAMPLE GRANTS Beneficiaries included: Jewish Care, Moreshet Hatorah, Cosmon Belz, Chana, Project Seed, Menorah High School for Girls, Train for Employment and Woodstock Sinclair Trust. Individual grant amounts were not disclosed in the accounts.

FINANCES *Year* 2009–10 *Income* £436,561 *Grants* £644,350 *Assets* £374,082

TRUSTEES Mark Morris; Graham S Morris.

HOW TO APPLY In writing to the correspondent.

WHO TO APPLY TO The Trustees, Investream Ltd, 38 Wigmore Street, London W1U 2RU *Tel* 020 7486 2800

■ The Ireland Fund of Great Britain

CC NO 327889   **ESTABLISHED** 1988

WHERE FUNDING CAN BE GIVEN Ireland and Great Britain.

WHO CAN BENEFIT Organisations benefiting people disadvantaged by poverty.

WHAT IS FUNDED Peace, reconciliation, cultural activity and the alleviation of poverty among Irish communities north and south of the border and in GB.

WHAT IS NOT FUNDED Grants are generally not given for: general administration costs; travel or accommodation costs; payments for buildings or land; general appeals i.e. applications must be made for clearly specified purposes; other grant making trusts; payments for vehicles; medical expenses. No multi-annual awards.

RANGE OF GRANTS £1,500–£10,000.

SAMPLE GRANTS Coventry Irish Society, Irish Community Care Merseyside, Aisling Return to Ireland Project, Cricklewood Homeless Concern, Solace Women's Aid (£10,000 each); The Hibernian Society, Milton Keynes Irish Welfare Support Group, Immigrant Counselling & Psychotherapy (£7,000 each); Irish Arts Foundation (£6,000); Tyneside Irish Centre (£5,000); Southwark Irish Pensioners Project (£4,500); St John Bosco Club (£2,000); and Tara Irish Pensioners (£1,500).

FINANCES *Year* 2010 *Income* £1,168,920 *Grants* £863,355 *Assets* £613,112

TRUSTEES Sheila Bailey; Seamus McGarry; Basil Geoghegan; Peter Kiernan; John Rowan; Ruth McCarthy; Ivan Fallon; Michael Casey; Ruari Conneely; Conor Foley; Zach Webb; Eileen Kelliher.

HOW TO APPLY Application forms and full details of how to apply are available from the IFGB website.

WHO TO APPLY TO Sheila Bailey, 2nd Floor, Wigglesworth House, 69 Southwark Bridge Road, London SE1 9HH *Tel* 020 7940 9850 *Fax* 020 7378 8376 *email* info@irelandfund.org *Website* www.irlfunds.org/great_britain

■ The Irish Youth Foundation (UK) Ltd (incorporating The Lawlor Foundation)

CC NO 328265   **ESTABLISHED** 1989

WHERE FUNDING CAN BE GIVEN UK.

WHO CAN BENEFIT Community-based organisations working directly with young Irish people.

WHAT IS FUNDED Projects benefiting young Irish people or enhancing their personal and social development, especially if they are disadvantaged or in need. A wide range of projects are supported which include: help for the homeless; employment and training schemes; help for women and children escaping violence; repatriation schemes; help for young offenders; cross community initiatives; help to combat discrimination; professional counselling and advocacy; educational, cultural and social activities; and drug rehabilitation.

WHAT IS NOT FUNDED The foundation generally does not support: projects for people over 25; general appeals; large/national charities; academic research; alleviating deficits already incurred; individuals; capital bids; or overseas travel.

TYPE OF GRANT Programme development grants; seeding grants; grants to upgrade premises and/or equipment and small grants.

RANGE OF GRANTS Grants for organisations in England, Scotland and Wales fall into the following three categories: Small grants for up to £2,500; Medium grants for over £2,500 and under £12,000; Large grants for one year or more ranging from £12,000–£25,000. The Irish Youth Foundation (UK) and the Irish Youth Foundation (Ireland) have established a joint fund to provide support for community and voluntary groups in Northern Ireland. Grants for organisations in Northern Ireland are up to £5,000.

SAMPLE GRANTS Brent Adolescent Centre – London (£15,000 in two grants for three years); Irish Community Care – Merseyside (£12,000); London Gypsy and Traveller Unit (£9,000); The National Deaf Children's Society, Northern Ireland (£4,500); Artillery Youth Centre – Belfast and Irish Arts Foundation – Leeds (£4,000 each); Drake Music Project – Newry (£3,500); Warwickshire Schools Gaelic Athletics Association (£2,000); Down Community Arts – Downpatrick (£3,000); Headliners – Derry (£2,500); and Our Lady Queen of Peace Youth Club – Belfast and Liverpool Irish Festival Society (£1,000 each).

FINANCES *Year* 2010 *Income* £190,576 *Grants* £197,324 *Assets* £2,252,524

TRUSTEES John O'Neill, Chair; John Dwyer; Fred Hucker; Virginia Lawlor; Mary Clancy; Mark Gilbert; David Murray; Jim O'Hara.

OTHER INFORMATION Irish Youth Foundation (UK) Ltd merged with the Lawlor Foundation (on 30 June 2005). The work of the Lawlor Foundation towards the advancement of education in Northern Ireland continues with support for Irish students and educational organisations.

HOW TO APPLY Applications are assessed on an annual basis and application forms are only available during the annual round either on the website or by request. The application period is short as forms are only available during December and January, with grant awards being made the following April. Applications are assessed on the following requirements: need; continuity; track record/evaluation; disadvantaged young people; innovativeness; funding sources; and budgetary control. Faxed or emailed applications are not considered. Unsolicited applications outside the annual round of grant applications will not be considered or acknowledged.

WHO TO APPLY TO Linda Tanner, The Irish Cultural Centre, Blacks Road, Hammersmith, London W6 9DT *Tel* 020 8748 9640 *email* info@iyf.org.uk *Website* www.iyf.org.uk

---

The Ironmongers' Foundation

CC NO 238256   **ESTABLISHED** 1964

WHERE FUNDING CAN BE GIVEN UK with some preference for inner London.

WHO CAN BENEFIT 'The Ironmongers' Company aims to help people who are disadvantaged to improve their ability to make the most of life. We wish to support projects that develop and nurture the motivation and skills necessary to take advantage of opportunities.'

WHAT IS FUNDED Projects benefiting: children and young people up to the age of 25; educational activities; specific projects with clear aims and objectives to be met within a planned timescale.

The company's support should make a recognisable difference; therefore preference will be given to requests which cover a significant element of the cost and to those from smaller organisations.

WHAT IS NOT FUNDED No grants towards: large projects towards which any contribution from the Company would have limited impact; general appeals or circulars; replacement of statutory funds; general running costs (a reasonable proportion of overheads will be accepted as part of project costs); counselling; course fees for professionals; medical research; fundraising events and sponsorship; retrospective appeals and projects starting before the date of the relevant Committee meeting.

TYPE OF GRANT The trustees will consider making grants over more than one year to longer term projects, subject to a satisfactory evaluation of progress at the end of each year.

RANGE OF GRANTS Mostly £1,000–£10,000.

SAMPLE GRANTS St John – Bethnal Green (£6,000); the Industrial Trust (£4,500); University of Birmingham (£3,500); the National Trust (£2,000); and Lincoln Cathedral (£1,250).

FINANCES *Year* 2009–10 *Income* £135,086 *Grants* £160,308 *Assets* £2,192,024

TRUSTEES Worshipful Ironmongers' Company.

HOW TO APPLY The company's 'Grant Application Summary Sheet' must be completed and returned including a description of the project, of no more than three A4 pages. Summary sheets can be downloaded from the fund's website. The Appeals Committee meets twice a year in March and October. The deadlines for receipt of applications are 31 January and 31 August respectively. Please note that applications are not accepted by email. Grants must be spent within twelve months from the date of the award.

WHO TO APPLY TO Helen Sant, Charities Administrator, Ironmongers' Hall, Barbican, London EC2Y 8AA *Tel* 020 7776 2311 *Fax* 020 7600 3519 *email* helen@ironhall.co.uk *Website* www.ironhall.co.uk

---

Irshad Trust

CC NO 1056468   **ESTABLISHED** 1996

WHERE FUNDING CAN BE GIVEN UK and overseas.

WHO CAN BENEFIT Institutions involved in Islamic research and similar educational activities.

WHAT IS FUNDED Promotion of education in an Islamic environment.

SAMPLE GRANTS £703,000 to Islamic College for Advanced Studies; £55,000 in donations to similar organisations.

FINANCES *Year* 2009 *Income* £1,228,357 *Grants* £757,939 *Assets* £1,832,422

TRUSTEES Mohsen Mohammadi Araghi; Abolhossein Moezi; Mohammed Saeed Bahmanpour; Prof. Abolfazl Ezzati; Dr Mohammed Jafar Elmi; Dr Syed Naqi Hassan Kirmani.

HOW TO APPLY Beneficiaries are selected by the trustees who make personal contact with potential donors.

WHO TO APPLY TO The General Secretary, 133 High Road, Willesden, London NW10 2SW *Tel* 020 8451 9993 *email* sbahmanpour@islamic-college.ac.uk *Website* www.islamic-college.ac.uk

■ The Charles Irving Charitable Trust

CC NO 297712   **ESTABLISHED** 1987
WHERE FUNDING CAN BE GIVEN Mainly Gloucestershire.
WHO CAN BENEFIT Charitable organisations.
WHAT IS FUNDED Disability, mental health, older people in the local community, local community projects, homelessness, victim support and the resettlement of offenders.
WHAT IS NOT FUNDED Research, expeditions, computers or equipment are not supported unless benefiting people who are disabled.
TYPE OF GRANT Capital, project and recurring.
RANGE OF GRANTS Mostly in the rage of £50–£1,000. Larger grants are sometimes made.
FINANCES *Year* 2009–10 *Income* £77,799 *Grants* £58,207 *Assets* £1,743,601
TRUSTEES A P Hilder; Mrs J E Lane; D J Oldham; P W Shephard.
HOW TO APPLY In writing to the correspondent, giving details of the proposed project, its total cost and the amount (if any) already raised or promised from other sources. In 2007–08 the trusted noted 'a decline in the number of grants awarded because of a decline in the number of applications received'.
WHO TO APPLY TO Mrs J E Lane, Trustee and Secretary, PO Box 868, Cheltenham, Gloucestershire GL53 9WZ *Tel* 01242 234848

■ Irwin Trust

CC NO 1061646   **ESTABLISHED** 1997
WHERE FUNDING CAN BE GIVEN UK and overseas.
WHO CAN BENEFIT Charities concerned with Christianity, relief of sickness, promotion of health, advancement of education and benefit to the community.
WHAT IS FUNDED General charitable purposes.
SAMPLE GRANTS Goldhill Baptist Church (£10,000); The School of Pharmacy and LICC (£5,000 each); Barnabas Fund and Relief for Oppressed People Everywhere (£4,000 each); Release International (£3,000); Worldshare (£2,000); Global Connections (£1,000); and DCI Trust and Moorlands College (£500 each).
FINANCES *Year* 2009–10 *Income* £23,375 *Grants* £39,000
TRUSTEES T R Irwin; Mrs E J Irwin.
HOW TO APPLY In writing to the correspondent.
WHO TO APPLY TO T R Irwin, Trustee, Kleinwort Benson, 14 St George Street, London W1S 1FE *Tel* 020 3207 7338 *Fax* 020 3207 7665

■ The ISA Charity

CC NO 326882   **ESTABLISHED** 1985
WHERE FUNDING CAN BE GIVEN UK.
WHO CAN BENEFIT Registered charities only.
WHAT IS FUNDED Causes related to the arts, health and education in the broadest sense. This can include both UK and overseas initiatives. The charity selects various organisations which help to find the individual beneficiaries.
FINANCES *Year* 2009–10 *Income* £31,150 *Grants* £30,224 *Assets* £1,655,346
TRUSTEES R Paice; Mrs M Paice; Miss A Paice.
HOW TO APPLY The charity's website included the following statement: 'The charity adopts a venture philanthropy approach and identifies its own projects. It does not accept funding requests from individuals, organisations or other charities. As a consequence it will not acknowledge any unsolicited funding requests.'

WHO TO APPLY TO R Paice, Trustee, 2 The Mansion, Northwick Park, Blockley, Moreton-in-Marsh Gl56 9RJ *Website* www.isacharity.org

■ The Isaacs Charitable Trust

CC NO 264590   **ESTABLISHED** 1972
WHERE FUNDING CAN BE GIVEN UK and Israel.
WHO CAN BENEFIT Registered charities.
WHAT IS FUNDED Jewish charities and general charitable purposes, particularly medical causes. The trustees tend to support favoured projects.
TYPE OF GRANT Recurrent and one-off.
RANGE OF GRANTS £500–£6,000.
SAMPLE GRANTS Previous beneficiaries have included Jewish Care, the Child Resettlement Fund Emunah, the Marie Curie Foundation, Friends of Laniado UK, Norwood Children and Families Trust, Nightingale House, Cancer Research UK, British Heart Foundation, Furniture Trades Benevolent Association, North Western Reform Synagogue, Royal National Lifeboat Institution and Scope.
FINANCES *Year* 2009–10 *Income* £23,693 *Grants* £24,000
TRUSTEES Adam Isaacs; David Isaacs; Stephen Goldberg.
HOW TO APPLY This trust's income is fully committed to its current list of donees. New applications are not considered.
WHO TO APPLY TO David Isaacs, Trustee, Flat 26 Leamington House, 23 Stonegrave, Edgware HA8 7TN *Tel* 020 8958 7854

■ The J Isaacs Charitable Trust

CC NO 1059865   **ESTABLISHED** 1996
WHERE FUNDING CAN BE GIVEN England and Wales.
WHO CAN BENEFIT Charitable organisations.
WHAT IS FUNDED General charitable purposes.
RANGE OF GRANTS Up to £100,000.
SAMPLE GRANTS Jewish Care (£200,000); the Jewish Museum London (£100,000); Community Security Trust (£75,000); Greenhouse Schools Project (£25,000); Policy Exchange Ltd (£15,000); UCLH Fund (£7,500); UK Jewish Film (£5,000); and Royal National Theatre (£1,000).
FINANCES *Year* 2009–10 *Income* £31,166 *Grants* £595,107 *Assets* £16,582,633
TRUSTEES Jeremy Isaacs: Joanne Isaacs; Helen Eastick.
HOW TO APPLY In writing to the correspondent.
WHO TO APPLY TO Peter Katz, c/o Touch Group PLC, Saffron House, 6–10 Kirby Street, London EC1N 6TS *email* peter.katz@touchgroupplc.com

■ The Isle of Anglesey Charitable Trust

CC NO 1000818   **ESTABLISHED** 1990
WHERE FUNDING CAN BE GIVEN Isle of Anglesey.
WHO CAN BENEFIT Organisations in Anglesey.
WHAT IS FUNDED The provision of amenities and facilities; the preservation of buildings; the conservation and protection of the land; the protection and safeguarding of the environment.
WHAT IS NOT FUNDED Individuals.
TYPE OF GRANT One-off and recurring.
RANGE OF GRANTS 1,000–£270,000.
SAMPLE GRANTS Menai Bridge Community Centre (£8,000); Brynteg Village Hall (£7,000); Llangoed Village Hall (£6,500); Llanddanielfab Community Centre (£6,000); Children's Park

Newborough (£5,000); Holyhead Weightlifting Club (£4,000); Newborough Institute and David Hughs Community Centre Beaumaris (£3,000 each); Trearddur Bay Community Centre (£2,000); and Rhosneigr Evangelical Church and Amlwch Port Hall (£1,000 each).

FINANCES *Year* 2009–10 *Income* £428,765 *Grants* £357,188 *Assets* £15,530,961

TRUSTEES E Schofield; R G Parry; David Bowles; David Elis-Williams; Lynn Ball.

HOW TO APPLY In writing to the correspondent with an application form, following advertisements in the local press in February. The trustees meet twice a year and the grants committee decides upon an annual grants programme.

WHO TO APPLY TO David Elis-Williams, Treasurer, Isle of Anglesey County Council, County Offices, Llangefni, Anglesey LL77 7TW *Tel* 01248 752607 *Fax* 01248 752696 *email* gvwfi@ anglesey.gov.uk

....

■ Isle of Dogs Community Foundation

CC NO 802942   **ESTABLISHED** 1990

WHERE FUNDING CAN BE GIVEN London Borough of Tower Hamlets.

WHO CAN BENEFIT Community and voluntary organisations serving the area defined above or having direct impact on the area.

WHAT IS FUNDED General, including community development, education and training and employment.

WHAT IS NOT FUNDED IDCF will not fund: individuals; projects with primarily religious activities; projects with primarily political activities; projects or activities that are a statutory service; activities that are the responsibility of the local or health authorities; activities that have already taken place.

TYPE OF GRANT The foundation's current policy is to offer: 'Fast track' grants up to £800 – normally for one-off projects or capital needs; 'Standard' grants of between £800 and £10,000 – for general purposes, capital items, or running costs; and 'Large' grants over £10,000 per annum for multiple years, for larger, well established organisations.

RANGE OF GRANTS Mainly £100–£10,000.

FINANCES *Year* 2009–10 *Income* £1,304,981 *Grants* £1,230,590 *Assets* £5,254,882

TRUSTEES Sister Christine Frost; Gabrielle Harrington; Mohammed Shahid Ali;.Stella Bailey; Rita Bensley; Howard Dawber; Elizabeth Passey; Timothy Archer; Elizabeth Cowie; Muge Dindjer; David Edgar; Duke Chifiero; Gareth Stephens.

HOW TO APPLY The foundation's website has details of the grant schemes currently being administered. Please note: the foundation asks that grant seekers discuss their potential applications with the director, Tracey Betts, before any application is submitted.

WHO TO APPLY TO Tracy Betts, Director, Jack Dash House, 2 Lawn House Close, Isle of Dogs, London E14 9YQ *Tel* 020 7345 4444 *Fax* 020 7538 4671 *email* admin@idcf.org *Website* www.idcf.org

....

■ The ITF Seafarers Trust

CC NO 281936   **ESTABLISHED** 1981

WHERE FUNDING CAN BE GIVEN UK and overseas.

WHO CAN BENEFIT Seafarers of all nations and their dependants.

WHAT IS FUNDED Seafaring organisations; and the social welfare of seafarers of all nations, their families and dependants.

TYPE OF GRANT Buildings, capital, one-off, project, training and education.

RANGE OF GRANTS Up to £1,500,000.

SAMPLE GRANTS Seafarer's Rights International (£3,000,000); World Maritime Museum – Sweden (£157,000); International Sports for Seafarers – UK (£82,500); Sailor's Society – India (£75,000); Mission to Seafarers – Brazil (£49,500) International Committee for Seafarer's Welfare – UK (£30,000); Port Welfare Committee – India (£25,000); Apostleship of the Sea – Singapore (£21,000); Mission to Seafarers – France (£18,000); International Seamen's Centre – USA (£15,500); Seafarers House – Puerto Rico (£12,500); Universal Seafarers Christian Welfare Association – India (£11,000); and Mission to Seafarers – Australia (£10,100).

FINANCES *Income* £2,522,195 *Grants* £345,883 *Assets* £24,162,198

TRUSTEES T Broome; D Cockroft; R Crow; P Crumlin; D Heindel; R Howard; L Lindgren; B Orrell; G Stevenson.

HOW TO APPLY On a form available from the correspondent. Applications must be supported by an ITF affiliated seafarers' or dockers' trade union and have a proven record of dealing with seafarers' welfare.

WHO TO APPLY TO Tom Holmer, Administrative Officer, 49–60 Borough Road, London SE1 1DR *Tel* 020 7403 2733 *Fax* 020 7357 7871 *email* trust@itf.org.uk *Website* www.itfglobal.org.uk

■ J A R Charitable Trust

CC NO 248418   **ESTABLISHED** 1966
WHERE FUNDING CAN BE GIVEN Worldwide.
WHO CAN BENEFIT Organisations benefiting older people, students, Roman Catholics, missionaries, and people disadvantaged by poverty.
WHAT IS FUNDED The advancement of the Roman Catholic faith; education for people under 30; and the provision of food, clothing and accommodation for people in need over 55.
WHAT IS NOT FUNDED The trust does not normally support a charity unless it is known to the trustees and it does not support individuals.
TYPE OF GRANT One-off and recurring.
RANGE OF GRANTS £1,000–£4,000.
SAMPLE GRANTS Oxford Oratory and the Passage (£4,000 each); Liverpool Archdiocesan Youth Pilgrimage, the Venerable English College Rome and Catholic Children's Society (£3,000 each); Friends of Turnaini, Little Sisters of the Poor and Church of St James (£2,000 each); and Tongabezi Trust School, Court Meadow School and Marriage Care (£1,000 each).
FINANCES *Year* 2010–11 *Income* £71,773 *Grants* £68,000 *Assets* £2,415,094
TRUSTEES Philip R Noble; Revd William Young; Revd Paschal Ryan.
HOW TO APPLY In writing to the correspondent. Please note that the trust's funds are fully committed to regular beneficiaries and it states that there is very little, if any, for unsolicited appeals. In order to save administration costs replies are not sent to unsuccessful applicants.
WHO TO APPLY TO Philip R Noble, Trustee, Hunters, 9 New Square, London WC2A 3QN *Tel* 020 7412 0050

■ The J J Charitable Trust

CC NO 1015792   **ESTABLISHED** 1992
WHERE FUNDING CAN BE GIVEN Unrestricted.
WHO CAN BENEFIT Charities benefiting children with learning difficulties particularly dyslexia, ex-offenders and people at risk of offending.
WHAT IS FUNDED Literacy: to improve the effectiveness of literacy teaching in the primary and secondary education sectors for children with general or specific learning difficulties, including dyslexia, and to do the same through agencies working with ex-offenders or people at risk of offending. Environment UK: to support environmental education, particularly supporting projects displaying practical ways of involving children and young adults. Support is rarely given to new educational resources in isolation from the actual process of learning and discovering. More interest is shown in programmes which enable schools to take on the benefits of education for sustainable development across the whole school and beyond, into the local community. Particularly, those projects which help pupils and teachers develop a sense of ownership over time. There is also an interest in sustainable agriculture and bio-diversity; and sustainable transport, energy efficiency and renewable energy in wider society. Environment overseas: to support community-based agriculture projects which aim to help people to help themselves in an environmentally sustainable way. General: especially the education and social welfare of children who are disadvantaged.
WHAT IS NOT FUNDED No grants for: individuals; educational fees; or expeditions. The trust only funds registered charities or activities with clearly defined charitable purposes.
RANGE OF GRANTS £3,000–£124,000.
SAMPLE GRANTS London Libraries Development Agency, towards the expansion of Outside Story, promoting reading and library support among homeless people and others at risk (£124,000); British Dyslexia Association, towards the mentoring training and development scheme and the local association and membership development scheme (£98,000); Sustainability and Environmental Education – SEEd, towards core costs (£90,000); Koru Foundation, to increase capacity for delivering more renewable energy projects in the developing world (£75,000); the Ashden Awards, towards a UK award at the 2010 Ashden Awards (£70,000); Movement for Ecological Learning and Community Action – MELCA Ethiopia, to expand work with communities as they protect their local environment (£60,000); the Ministry of Stories, towards the London replication of 826 Valencia, a creative reading and writing store for children in San Francisco (£30,000); the Mayhem Company, towards performance work with young people in Southwark through the South Bank Centre (£26,000); Public Interest Research Centre Ltd, for research on the value of the UK's offshore renewable resource (£10,000); and University College London, for research on Germany's pay-as-you-save loan schemes for domestic energy efficiency retro-fitting to inform the plans of the UK Department of Energy and Climate Change (£3,100).
FINANCES *Year* 2009–10 *Income* £2,549,301 *Grants* £764,625 *Assets* £31,562,905
TRUSTEES John Julian Sainsbury; Mark Sainsbury; Judith Portrait; Lucy Guard.
OTHER INFORMATION The trust is one of the Sainsbury Family Charitable Trusts which share a common administration. An application to one is taken as an application to all.
HOW TO APPLY See the guidance for applicants in the entry for the Sainsbury Family Charitable Trusts. A single application will be considered for support by all the trusts in the group. However, for this as for many of the trusts, the following statement from the Sainsbury Family website should be noted: 'the trustees take an active role in their grant-making, employing a range of specialist staff and advisers to research their areas of interest and bring forward suitable proposals. Many of the trusts work closely with their chosen beneficiaries over a long period to achieve particular objectives. It should therefore be understood that the majority of unsolicited proposals we receive will be unsuccessful.'
WHO TO APPLY TO Alan Bookbinder, Director, Allington House, 1st Floor, 150 Victoria Street, London SW1E 5AE *Tel* 020 7410 0330 *Fax* 020 7410 0332 *email* info@sfct.org.uk *Website* www.sfct.org.uk

■ The J R S S T Charitable Trust

CC NO 247498   **ESTABLISHED** 1955
WHERE FUNDING CAN BE GIVEN UK.
WHO CAN BENEFIT Organisations or individuals undertaking research or action in fields which

Think carefully about every application. Is it justified?

641

relate directly to the non-charitable work of the Joseph Rowntree Reform Trust Ltd. Academics and research workers may benefit.

WHAT IS FUNDED The trust works in close association with the Joseph Rowntree Reform Trust Ltd, which is a non-charitable trust of which all the trustees of The JRSST Charitable Trust are directors, in supporting the development of an increasingly democratic and socially just UK.

WHAT IS NOT FUNDED No student grants are funded.

TYPE OF GRANT Specific project finance in particular fields of trust interest.

SAMPLE GRANTS Institute for Government (£50,000); Democratic Audit (£14,000); Northern Ireland Family Planning Association (£10,000); and Demos, Mysociety and Reuters Institute (£5,000 each).

FINANCES Year 2010 Income £93,711 Grants £130,965 Assets £2,784,671

TRUSTEES Christine J Day; Christopher J Greenfield; Paedar Cremin; Mandy Cormack; Lord Archy Kirkwood; Andrew Neal.

OTHER INFORMATION Examples of beneficiaries given are of grants that have been approved, rather than paid.

HOW TO APPLY The trustees meet quarterly. They do not invite applications.

WHO TO APPLY TO Tina Walker, The Garden House, Water End, York YO30 6WQ *Tel* 01904 625744 *Fax* 01904 651502 *email* info@jrrt.org.uk *Website* www.jrrt.org.uk

....

■ The Jabbs Foundation

CC NO 1128402   ESTABLISHED 2009

WHERE FUNDING CAN BE GIVEN UK and overseas.

WHO CAN BENEFIT Registered charities; universities and educational/research institutions.

WHAT IS FUNDED Medical research; education; enhancing family relationships.

SAMPLE GRANTS £756,500 over 5 years to a leading English University to fund an exchange programme for medical staff with a leading US research hospital; Grants of £600,000 to fund specific medical research projects into the incidence and treatment of pituitary tumours and chronic kidney disease; £500,000 to a leading English University towards the costs of its new music centre; £50,000 to a leading UK charity specialising in relationship counselling.

FINANCES Year 2009–10 Income £3,166,147 Grants £2,465,210 Assets £691,443

TRUSTEES Mr R Daniels; Alexander Wright.

OTHER INFORMATION No specific beneficiary organisations detailed in the accounts.

HOW TO APPLY In writing to the correspondent.

WHO TO APPLY TO Mr R Daniels, PO BOX 16067, Harborne, Birmingham, West Midlands B32 9GP *Tel* 0121 428 2593

....

■ Elizabeth Jackson Charitable Trust

CC NO 1083421   ESTABLISHED 1999

WHERE FUNDING CAN BE GIVEN Warwickshire and surrounding areas, particularly Barston (Solihull) and Great Rollright (Oxfordshire).

WHO CAN BENEFIT Organisations and individuals.

WHAT IS FUNDED General charitable purposes.

RANGE OF GRANTS Usually £2,000 to £5,000.

SAMPLE GRANTS Beneficiaries were: Great Rollright School (£15,000); Animal Health Trust (£5,000); ARC Addington Fund (£3,000); and Motor Neurone Disease Association, Multiple Sclerosis Society, Marie Curie Cancer Care,

Warks and Northants Medical Air Ambulance and the Medical Research Fund (£2,000 each).

FINANCES Year 2009–10 Income £28,503 Grants £33,000 Assets £827,342

TRUSTEES Robin S Ogg; James P H Davy; Jeremy S Seel.

HOW TO APPLY In writing to the correspondent.

WHO TO APPLY TO Thomas Charles Incledon McKenzie, Olympus House, Olympus Avenue, Tachbrook Park, Warwick CV34 6RJ *Tel* 01926 886688

....

■ Jacobs Charitable Trust

CC NO 264942   ESTABLISHED 1972

WHERE FUNDING CAN BE GIVEN Unrestricted.

WHO CAN BENEFIT Registered charities and community groups.

WHAT IS FUNDED Jewish causes and the arts.

RANGE OF GRANTS Up to £10,000.

SAMPLE GRANTS Central Synagogue Central Charities Fund (£10,000); Royal Opera House and Central Synagogue Yom Kippur Appeal (£5,000 each); British ORT (£2,000); Palm Beach Country Club Federation and Washington Institute (£630 each); British Technion Society (£150); and Food Lifeline and Central Synagogue Yahrzeit (£100 each).

FINANCES Year 2009–10 Income £35,046 Grants £23,608 Assets £49,531

TRUSTEES Lord Jacobs, Chair; Lady Jacobs; Marla Kosec.

HOW TO APPLY In writing to the correspondent.

WHO TO APPLY TO The Rt Hon the Lord Jacobs, Chair, 9 Nottingham Terrace, London NW1 4QB *Tel* 020 7486 6323

....

■ The Ruth and Lionel Jacobson Trust (Second Fund) No 2

CC NO 326665   ESTABLISHED 1984

WHERE FUNDING CAN BE GIVEN UK, with a preference for North East England.

WHO CAN BENEFIT Organisations benefiting people of all ages, medical professionals, parents and children, people with disabilities, people who are sick, people who have had strokes or who are terminally ill, homeless people, refugees and victims of famine.

WHAT IS FUNDED Organisations working in the fields of holiday accommodation and residential facilities, support for voluntary organisations, the Jewish religion, health, animal/bird sanctuaries and nature reserves, special needs education and speech therapy and various community facilities and services.

WHAT IS NOT FUNDED No grants for individuals. Only registered charities will be supported.

TYPE OF GRANT One-off, project and research. Funding is available for one year or less.

RANGE OF GRANTS £50–£10,000; typical grant £100–£500.

SAMPLE GRANTS WIZO UK (£13,000).

FINANCES Year 2009–10 Income £46,222 Grants £13,000 Assets £1,133,911

TRUSTEES Anne Jacobson; Malcolm Jacobson.

HOW TO APPLY In writing to the correspondent. Please enclose an sae. Applications are considered every other month.

WHO TO APPLY TO The Trustees, 14 The Grainger Suite, Dobson House, The Regent Centre, Newcastle upon Tyne NE3 3PF

■ Jaffe Family Relief Fund

CC NO 208560   **ESTABLISHED** 1970
WHERE FUNDING CAN BE GIVEN UK.
WHO CAN BENEFIT Registered charities.
WHAT IS FUNDED People in need.
WHAT IS NOT FUNDED No grants to charities for anything which is not direct relief of poverty in UK.
SAMPLE GRANTS Previously grants have been made to the following organisations: Bryson House, Catholic Children's Society, Campden Charities, Central Family Service Units, Providence Row, SSAFA Forces Help, West London Action for Children and West London Family Service Unit.
FINANCES *Year* 2009–10 *Income* £47,106
Grants £46,794 *Assets* £1,129,426
TRUSTEES Dr B P Levitt; Dr R R Jacobson; Mrs G A Haworth.
HOW TO APPLY In writing to the correspondent, but the trust states that 'funds are unlikely to allow us to add to the list of beneficiaries'.
WHO TO APPLY TO Robin Jacobson, Trustee, 24 Manor Way, Beckenham, Kent BR3 3LJ *Tel* 020 0650 8125

■ John James Bristol Foundation

CC NO 288417   **ESTABLISHED** 1983
WHERE FUNDING CAN BE GIVEN Worldwide, in practice the city of Bristol, UK.
WHO CAN BENEFIT Usually only charitable bodies that can clearly show that they are benefiting Bristol residents.
WHAT IS FUNDED Education, health and the elderly are the key focus areas.
WHAT IS NOT FUNDED No grants to individuals.
RANGE OF GRANTS £50–£150,000.
SAMPLE GRANTS Vassall Centre Trust (£151,000); Bristol Grammar School and the Red Maid's School (£33,000 each); St James Priory Project (£31,000); Barton Hill Settlement (£30,000); Barnardo's – Bristol BASE Project (£25,000); Jessie May Trust, Feed the Children and St Ursula's School (£20,000 each); Marie Curie Cancer Care (£19,000); Cotham School (£15,000); Motability (£10,000); Age Concern – Bristol (£8,900); Caring at Christmas (£5,000); St Dunstan's (£3,000); InterAct (£2,500); Relate – Avon (£1,500); and Canynges Society (£1,000).
FINANCES *Year* 2009–10 *Income* £1,266,707
Grants £1,153,249 *Assets* £51,072,739
TRUSTEES Joan Johnson; David Johnson; Elizabeth Chambers; John Evans; Andrew Jardine; Andrew Webley; John Haworth.
HOW TO APPLY The trustees meet quarterly in February, May, August and November to consider appeals received by 15 January, April, July and October as appropriate. There is no application form and appeals **must be submitted by post**, to the chief executive on no more than two sides of A4. Supporting information, sent by the applicant with their appeal, is available to the trustees at their meeting. All appeal applications are acknowledged, stating the month in which the appeal will be considered by the trustees. If further information is required it will be requested and a visit to the applicant may be made by a representative of the foundation.
WHO TO APPLY TO Julia Norton, Chief Executive, 7 Clyde Road, Redland, Bristol BS6 6RG *Tel* 0117 923 9444 *Fax* 0117 923 9470 *email* info@johnjames.org.uk *Website* www.johnjames.org.uk

■ The Susan and Stephen James Charitable Settlement (also known as

the Stephen James Charitable Trust)

CC NO 801622   **ESTABLISHED** 1988
WHERE FUNDING CAN BE GIVEN UK.
WHO CAN BENEFIT Registered charities; Jewish organisations.
WHAT IS FUNDED General charitable purposes.
RANGE OF GRANTS £60–£20,000.
SAMPLE GRANTS Norwood Ravenswood (£16,400); Jewish Care (£15,250); Community Security Trust (£10,000); Nightingale (£6,000); World Jewish Relief (£5,250); Dementia UK (£3,200); Wizo UK (£3,000); Kol Nidre Appeal (£2,000); United Synagogue (£1,900); Heart Cells Foundation (£1,500); and Prostate Cancer Care (£1,100); Magan David Adom (£1,000); Jewish Women's Aid (£750); Tree House (£500); St John's Hospice (£250); and JAMI (£100).
FINANCES *Year* 2010 *Income* £84,102
Grants £73,437 *Assets* £23,932
TRUSTEES S M James; Mrs S R James.
HOW TO APPLY In writing to the correspondent.
WHO TO APPLY TO S M James, Trustee, 4 Turner Drive, London NW11 6TX *Tel* 020 7486 5838

■ The James Trust

CC NO 800774   **ESTABLISHED** 1989
WHERE FUNDING CAN BE GIVEN UK and overseas.
WHO CAN BENEFIT Principally Christian organisations benefiting Christians, young adults, older people, people disadvantaged by poverty, disaster victims, and refugees.
WHAT IS FUNDED Churches, Christian organisations and individuals. Support is primarily to Christian causes, the advancement of the Christian religion and Anglican diocesan and Free Church umbrella bodies.
WHAT IS NOT FUNDED No grants to individuals not personally known to the trustees.
TYPE OF GRANT One-off, capital, projects, recurring costs, salaries and start-up costs. Funding is available for up to three years.
RANGE OF GRANTS Usually up to £10,000.
SAMPLE GRANTS Previously, Archbishops Council (£10,000); Above Bar Church (£7,700); Food For the Hungry (£5,000); UCCF (£3,600); Crusaders (£4,100); Tearfund (£1,900); Christian Aid (£1,300); Bible Society (£800); Church Missionary Society (£500); and Cancer Research (£200).
FINANCES *Year* 2009–10 *Income* £40,145
Grants £96,748 *Assets* £135,029
TRUSTEES R J Todd; G Blue.
HOW TO APPLY In writing to the correspondent. Unsolicited applications are not acknowledged.
WHO TO APPLY TO R J Todd, Trustee, 27 Radway Road, Upper Shirley, Southampton, Hampshire SO15 7PL *Tel* 023 8078 8249

■ The Marjory Jameson Trust

CC NO 1135470   **ESTABLISHED** 2010
WHERE FUNDING CAN BE GIVEN Undefined, in practice national and overseas.
WHO CAN BENEFIT Organisations.
WHAT IS FUNDED The advancement of health and the saving of lives, including establishing nursing/care homes; the advancement of education, including setting up, managing and supporting schools; and the advancement of the Christian faith by establishing, promoting and supporting churches or other Christian organisations.

TRUSTEES Elizabeth Frances Bailey; Colin Dundonald Jameson.
HOW TO APPLY In writing to the correspondent.
WHO TO APPLY TO Colin Dundonald James, 2 Applegarth, Wymondham, Norfolk NR18 0BZ

■ The Jarman Charitable Trust

CC NO 239198   ESTABLISHED 1964
WHERE FUNDING CAN BE GIVEN Birmingham and district.
WHO CAN BENEFIT Organisations benefiting children, young adults, older people, one-parent families, at-risk groups, homeless people.
WHAT IS FUNDED Welfare work, church building extension schemes and general social services in the Birmingham district. This includes convalescent homes, hospices, hospitals, nursing homes, rehabilitation centres, cancer research, community centres and village halls, day centres, holidays and outings, youth work and playschemes.
WHAT IS NOT FUNDED There is a preference for registered charities. No grants to individuals.
TYPE OF GRANT Annual donations and one-off payments.
SAMPLE GRANTS Previous beneficiaries include Coventry Day Centre for the Homeless, Friendship Project for Children, St Anne's Hostel for Men, St Paul's Church, Samaritans – Birmingham, Shakespeare Hospice and Victim Support – East Birmingham.
FINANCES Year 2010 Income £83,533 Grants £37,550 Assets £709,822
TRUSTEES Dr G M Jarman; Mrs S Chilton; Mrs I Jarman.
HOW TO APPLY In writing to the correspondent by the first week in February or the first week in September. Trustees meet in spring and autumn. The trust does not want telephone calls and will not acknowledge applications even if an sae is enclosed. Accounts and/or budgets should be included.
WHO TO APPLY TO Mrs S M Chilton, Trustee, 52 Lee Crescent, Edgbaston, Birmingham, West Midlands B15 2BJ Tel 0121 2472 622 email jarmanct@hotmail.com

■ The Barbara Joyce Jarrald Charitable Trust

CC NO 1135228   ESTABLISHED 2010
WHERE FUNDING CAN BE GIVEN Worldwide.
WHO CAN BENEFIT Registered charities.
WHAT IS FUNDED Health and animal welfare.
TRUSTEES NatWest Trust Services.
HOW TO APPLY In writing to the correspondent.
WHO TO APPLY TO NatWest Trust Services, 5th Floor, Trinity Quay 2, Avon Street, Bristol BS2 0PT Tel 0117 940 3283

■ The John Jarrold Trust

CC NO 242029   ESTABLISHED 1965
WHERE FUNDING CAN BE GIVEN UK and overseas, but mostly Norfolk.
WHO CAN BENEFIT Organisations benefiting academics, research workers and students.
WHAT IS FUNDED General charitable purposes of all kinds and in particular of education and research in all or any of the natural sciences. Social welfare, arts, education, environment/conservation, medical research, churches. Funds currently very limited.

WHAT IS NOT FUNDED Educational purposes that should be supported by the state will not be helped by the trust. Local groups outside Norfolk are very unlikely to be supported unless there is a personal connection to the trust. Individual educational programmes and gap year projects are not supported.
TYPE OF GRANT One-off.
RANGE OF GRANTS Usually up to £5,000.
SAMPLE GRANTS Beneficiaries included: Hamlet Centre and YMCA Norfolk (£25,000 each); Arkwright Scholarship and Norfolk & Norwich Festival (£5,000 each); Britten Sinfonia (£2,500); Age Concern, East Anglian Air Ambulance, Hebron Trust, Leeway Norwich Women's Aid, Norfolk Association for the Disabled, Norfolk Deaf Association, Poppy Centre Trust, Real Health Action, Against Breast Cancer, Asperger East Anglia, Blood Pressure Association, Brain Research Trust, Fight For Sight, Scout Group, 1st Blofield & Brundall St Stephen's Church Norwich (£1,000 each); Sailors' Families' Society, Stalham Community Gym and Feed the Minds (£500 each); and Hellesdon High School, Sewell Park College, Sprowston Community High School and Wymondham College (£25 each).
FINANCES Year 2009–10 Income £186,683 Grants £159,208 Assets £1,465,035
TRUSTEES A C Jarrold, Chair; R E Jarrold; P J Jarrold; Mrs D J Jarrold; Mrs J Jarrold; Mrs A G Jarrold; Mrs W A L Jarrold; L C Jarrold.
HOW TO APPLY Trustees meet in January and June each year and applications should be made in writing by the end of November and April respectively. Grants of up to £250 can be made between meetings.
WHO TO APPLY TO Caroline Jarrold, Secretary, Jarrold and Sons Ltd, Whitefriars, Norwich NR3 1SH Tel 01603 677360 email caroline.jarrold@jarrold.com Website www.jarrold.com

■ Jay Education Trust

CC NO 1116458   ESTABLISHED 2006
WHERE FUNDING CAN BE GIVEN Worldwide.
WHO CAN BENEFIT Jewish organisations.
WHAT IS FUNDED 'The objects of the charity are: the relief of poverty in the Jewish Community worldwide; the advancement of religious education according to the beliefs and values of the Jewish Faith worldwide and any charitable purpose at the discretion of the trustees for the benefit of the community.'
SAMPLE GRANTS Previous beneficiaries included: Mifalei Tzedoko Vochesed; United Talmudical Associates; British Friends Of Igud Hakolelim B'Yerushalayim; Lolev Charitable Trust; Toldos Aharon Israel; Edupoor Ltd; Chachmei Tzorfat Trust; Heichel Aharon; Friends of Sanz Institutions; Yad Vochessed; Zedokoh Bechol Eis; Belz Yeshiva London; Jewish Seminary For Girls; and Comet Charities Ltd.
FINANCES Year 2009–10 Income £1,457,020 Grants £471,000 Assets £2,000,000
TRUSTEES Rabbi Alfred Schechter; Gabriel Gluck; Shlomo Z Stauber.
HOW TO APPLY In writing to the correspondent.
WHO TO APPLY TO Rabbi Alfred Schechter, Trustee, 37 Filey Avenue, London N16 6JL

■ JCA Charitable Foundation

CC NO 207031   **ESTABLISHED** 1891
WHERE FUNDING CAN BE GIVEN Israel.
WHO CAN BENEFIT Projects benefiting Jewish people, particularly children and those living in rural areas.
WHAT IS FUNDED The foundation helps the development of new settlements in Israel, the Kibbutzim and Moshavim, contributes to the resettlement of Jewish people in need, fosters viable agricultural and rural life to support them, and encourages other trusts and foundations to join it in partnership to fulfil its ideals. New projects in education and agricultural research are now the main interests of the JCA.
WHAT IS NOT FUNDED Grants are not awarded for individual students' tuition fees in Israel or elsewhere.
TYPE OF GRANT Loans, grants and feasibility studies. Funding may be given for one year or less.
SAMPLE GRANTS Migal Galilee Technology Centre ($164,500); Eshel Hanasi Youth Village ($150,000); Aro Volcani Centre ($74,500); Kibbutz Shomria ($50,000); Ein Shemer Greenhouse ($45,000); the Mariculture Centre ($44,000); Ben Gurion Heritage Institute ($30,000); Kibbutz Ravid ($17,500); Ran Munitz Model Farm ($13,500); and Eyal Policar ($5,000).
FINANCES Year 2009 *Income* £2,841,000 *Grants* £1,546,699 *Assets* £26,542,000
TRUSTEES Sir Stephen Waley-Cohen, President; A Philippson; Y Admoni; R Brickner; J Capelluto; Prof. Yona Chen; Efraim Halevy; J Jakobi; Mme Beatrice Jouan; Issac Lidor; Dr Shimon Ravid; Mark Sebba; Mrs Hana Smouha; Guy Wallier; S Arad.
OTHER INFORMATION The amounts given in Sample Grants relate to US dollars.
HOW TO APPLY Full proposals should be sent to the office in Israel. For further information contact the correspondent.
WHO TO APPLY TO Timothy R Martin, Company Secretary, The Victoria Palace Theatre, Victoria Street, London SW1E 5EA *Tel* 020 7828 0600 *Fax* 020 7828 6882 *email* thejcafoundation@ aol.com *Website* www.jca-is.org.il

■ The Jeffrey Charitable Trust

SC NO SC015990   **ESTABLISHED** 1972
WHERE FUNDING CAN BE GIVEN Scotland and elsewhere.
WHO CAN BENEFIT Organisations benefiting seafarers and fishermen, volunteers, and people in care, or who are fostered or adopted.
WHAT IS FUNDED Primarily this trust is concerned with medical research, and carer organisations. It also considers holiday and respite accommodation; health; conservation; independent and special schools; tertiary, higher and special needs education; community facilities and transport; and emergency care for refugees and their families.
WHAT IS NOT FUNDED Animal-related charities, medical electives and projects eligible for statutory support are not considered.
TYPE OF GRANT One-off and recurring grants are most commonly made for capital, buildings, core costs, endowment, project, research, running costs, salaries and start-up costs. Funding is available for up to three years.
RANGE OF GRANTS £250–£20,000; typical grant £1,000–£1,500.
SAMPLE GRANTS £20,000 to Glasgow Royal Infirmary for HTR project – diabetes centre; £5,000 to

Dunstans Home for the War-blinded for general purposes; £2,500 each to Morrison's Academy Appeal for bursary provision and Donaldson School for the Deaf for a development project; £2,000 each to Erskine Hospital for general purposes, Princess Royal Trust for Carers for general purposes, and Edinburgh Breast Cancer Foundation for general purposes; £1,359 to Salvation Army for general purposes; £1,000 each to Capability Scotland for general purposes and Crieff Parish Church for hall refurbishment.
FINANCES Year 2009–10 *Income* £56,129 *Grants* £50,000
TRUSTEES R B A Bolton; R S Waddell; Mrs M E Bolton; Dr A C MacCuish.
HOW TO APPLY In writing to the correspondent, although due to continuing support to long-term projects and anticipated repeat grants to other organisations, new requests for assistance are unlikely to be successful.
WHO TO APPLY TO Robert B A Bolton, 29 Comrie Street, Crieff, Perthshire PH7 4BD *Tel* 01764 652224 *Fax* 01764 653999

■ Rees Jeffreys Road Fund

CC NO 217771   **ESTABLISHED** 1950
WHERE FUNDING CAN BE GIVEN UK.
WHO CAN BENEFIT Universities, research bodies, academic staff and students, as well as proposals for roadside rest projects.
WHAT IS FUNDED The trustees will consider funding lectureships and postgraduate bursaries over an academic year; research projects; physical roadside projects; and transport and alternative transport. Only subjects directly related with road and transportation will be considered.
WHAT IS NOT FUNDED Grants are not given to environmental projects not related to highways, individual works for cycle tracks or works of only local application. Also, operational and administrative staff costs are rarely considered.
TYPE OF GRANT Some one-off capital, some bursaries and others for research and lectureships including salaries and, in some cases, running costs and endowments. Funding is available for up to five years.
RANGE OF GRANTS Up to £24,000.
SAMPLE GRANTS The fund offers the following commentary on its grantmaking in the 2010 accounts: 'The largest proportion of this sum related to bursary awards, which remained a key priority for trustees during 2010, providing vital support and encouragement to nine highly impressive candidates, who, it is anticipated, will make a significant impact upon the UK transport world in future years. Grants for physical projects continued to rely upon the long-standing relationship which the fund has with Wildlife Trusts, and in 2010 the partnership resulted in financial support for four schemes in England and Wales []. The fund's chairman has continued to express a desire to extend the number of research grant recipients. The trustees see the support that they can give to projects which can influence UK transport policy as a core objective, and they would very much wish to encourage more applicants in this area.' During the year major awards under this heading went to the Road Safety Foundation and to the Sir Colin Buchanan Archive project.
FINANCES Year 2010 *Income* £31,974 *Grants* £166,570 *Assets* £6,769,221
TRUSTEES David Bayliss, Chair; Mike Cottell; Tony Depledge; Ann Frye; Prof. Mike McDonald; Prof. Stephen Glaister; David Hutchinson; Martin Shaw.

HOW TO APPLY Applications should be made in writing to the Fund Secretary and include the following details: the purpose for which funding is sought – outlining the objects, relevance and the proposed methodology of the project including the names of the principal participants; the expected costs by category, along with the project timetable; evidence of the willingness of other parties (where the project requires their contribution or participation) to get involved. Applications should not be more than three A4 pages. All necessary supporting material and a digital version of the application should also be submitted. The trustees meet five times a year, usually in January, April, July, September and November (please see the fund's website for specific dates). The deadline for submission of applications or other agenda items is normally a fortnight before the meeting.

WHO TO APPLY TO Brian Smith, Fund Secretary, Merriewood, Horsell Park, Woking, Surrey GU21 4LW *Tel* 01483 750758 *email* briansmith@reesjeffreys.org *Website* www.reesjeffreys.co.uk

■ The Nick Jenkins Foundation

CC NO 1135565   ESTABLISHED 2010
WHERE FUNDING CAN BE GIVEN England & Wales; India; Ethiopia.
WHO CAN BENEFIT Organisations.
WHAT IS FUNDED General charitable purposes.
TRUSTEES Rosemary Connor Rafferty; Alison Clare Jenkins; Nicholas David Jenkins.
HOW TO APPLY In writing to the correspondent.
WHO TO APPLY TO Nicholas David Jenkins, Bapton Manor, Bapton, Warminster, Wiltshire BA12 0SB

■ The Jenour Foundation

CC NO 256637   ESTABLISHED 1968
WHERE FUNDING CAN BE GIVEN UK, with a special interest in Wales.
WHO CAN BENEFIT Registered charities only.
WHAT IS FUNDED General charitable purposes. Both UK charities and local charities in Wales are supported.
WHAT IS NOT FUNDED No support for individuals.
RANGE OF GRANTS Usually up to £8,000.
SAMPLE GRANTS Atlantic College (£8,000 each); Welsh National Opera and British Heart Foundation (£7,000 each); Red Cross International (£5,000 each); George Thomas Society (£4,000); Llandovery College (£3,000); St Woolos Cathedral (£2,000); Society for Welfare of Horses and Ponies (£1,000); and Send a Cow Appeal (£500).
FINANCES *Year* 2009–10 *Income* £111,442 *Grants* £105,500 *Assets* £2,967,593
TRUSTEES Sir P J Phillips; G R Camfield; D M Jones.
HOW TO APPLY Applications should be in writing and reach the correspondent by February for the trustees' meeting in March.
WHO TO APPLY TO The Trustees, Deloitte and Touche, Blenhein House, Fitzalan Court, Newport Road, Cardiff CF24 0TS *Tel* 029 2026 4348

■ The Jephcott Charitable Trust

CC NO 240915   ESTABLISHED 1965
WHERE FUNDING CAN BE GIVEN Worldwide.
WHO CAN BENEFIT 'We like to make grants which will make a difference, preference will be given to charities or projects which are having difficulty getting started, or raising funds from other

sources.' The financial situation of the organisation is taken into account (85% of income should be directly applied to advancing its charitable objectives).

WHAT IS FUNDED Funding priorities: population control – support for schemes, particularly educational ones, which help to control excessive growth in population; the natural environment – projects involved in conserving the natural environment (it does not support projects involving animal welfare or heritage sites or buildings); education – projects will be considered benefiting people of all ages and backgrounds; healthcare projects.

WHAT IS NOT FUNDED The trust does not support: organisations whose administrative expenses form more than 15% of their annual income; individuals; animal welfare; heritage; projects which require long-term funding are not normally considered.

TYPE OF GRANT Pump-priming – helping to get an organisation up and running, or make a significant step forward. Project costs – capital rather than running costs are preferred.

RANGE OF GRANTS Grants are made in the range of £2,000–£10,000, and in exceptional cases only, up to £20,000. The trust prefers to make one-off donations to get many projects started, rather than support fewer projects charities over a long period.

SAMPLE GRANTS Toe in the water and Kariandusi School Trust (£25,000 each); Starehe UK (£15,000) Building Blocks (£9,000); Berkeley Reforestation Trust (£9,000); Tree for Cities (£4,000); and Human Relief (£2,500).

FINANCES *Year* 2009–10 *Income* £205,009 *Grants* £209,053 *Assets* £4,518,237
TRUSTEES Lady Jephcott, Chair; Judge A North; M Jephcott; K Morgan; Mrs D Ader; Mrs C Thomas.

HOW TO APPLY Full and detailed guidelines and application forms can be downloaded from the trust's website. Trustees meet twice a year (in April and October) and must have detailed financial information about each project before they will make a decision. Only applications from eligible bodies are acknowledged, when further information about the project may be requested. Monitoring of grant expenditure is a requirement of all successful grants and donations from the trust.

WHO TO APPLY TO Dr Felicity Gibling, The Threshing Barn, Ford, Kingsbridge, Devon TQ7 2LN *Website* www.jephcottcharitabletrust.org.uk

■ The Jerusalem Trust

CC NO 285696   ESTABLISHED 1982
WHERE FUNDING CAN BE GIVEN Unrestricted.
WHO CAN BENEFIT Organisations working for the promotion of Christianity in the fields detailed below.
WHAT IS FUNDED *Evangelism and Christian mission in the UK* – particularly Christian projects that develop new ways of working with children and young people; in church planting and evangelistic projects, including those that undertake Christian work with prisoners, ex-prisoners and their families. *Christian education* – including the development of Christian curriculum resource materials for schools in RE and across the curriculum; the recruitment and development of Christian teachers in all subjects; and adult lay Christian training and education. *Christian evangelism and relief work overseas* – specifically the provision of support for indigenous training centres and the provision

of Christian literature in Central and Eastern Europe and Anglophone sub-Saharan Africa. *Christian media* – support for media projects that promote Christianity as well as training and networking projects for Christians working professionally in, or considering a career in, the media. *Christian art* – specifically a small number of commissions of works of works of art for places of worship.

WHAT IS NOT FUNDED Trustees do not normally make grants towards building or repair work for churches. Grants are not normally made to individuals.

RANGE OF GRANTS Up to £250,000.

SAMPLE GRANTS Jerusalem Productions Ltd, for disbursement by Jerusalem Productions during the calendar years 2010–2011 (£250,000); University of York, towards Christianity and Cathedrals, to include a DVD, four pilot projects in cathedrals and an app for mobiles (£177,000); Tearfund, towards the costs of supporting the Kale Haywet Church's development programme in Ethiopia (£131,000); Kainos Community, towards the cost of the organisation's long term development programme (£100,000); Churches' National Adviser in Further Education, towards the costs of All Faiths and None working in further education colleges (£70,000); Lapido Media, towards core costs (£60,000); Bible Reading Fellowship, towards the costs of employing a regional coordinator for Messy Church (£50,000); Institute for Bible Translation, towards the costs of translation work for Russia and the Commonwealth of Independent States (£30,000); National Gallery, towards the interpretation and education costs of the Gallery's exhibition in 2011, Devotion by Design – Italian Renaissance Alterpieces before 1500 (£45,000); pubchurch.co.uk, towards the organisation's charitable activity (£23,000); HCJB UK, towards the costs of Spotlight (£16,000); and Biblical Frameworks, towards developing resources (£7,500).

FINANCES *Year* 2010 *Income* £2,664,000 *Grants* £2,521,000 *Assets* £84,531,000

TRUSTEES Rt Hon. Sir Timothy Sainsbury; Lady Susan Sainsbury; Dr V E Hartley Booth; Phillida Goad; Dr Peter Frankopan.

OTHER INFORMATION The trust is one of the Sainsbury Family Charitable Trusts which share a common administration. An application to one is taken as an application to all.

HOW TO APPLY See the guidance for applicants in the entry for the Sainsbury Family Charitable Trusts. A single application will be considered for support by all the trusts in the group. However, for this as for many of the trusts, 'proposals are generally invited by the trustees or initiated at their request'.

WHO TO APPLY TO Alan Bookbinder, Director, Allington House, 1st Floor, 150 Victoria Street, London SW1E 5AE *Tel* 020 7410 0330 *Fax* 020 7410 0332 *email* jerusalemtrust@sfct.org.uk *Website* www.sfct.org.uk

··

■ Jerwood Charitable Foundation

CC NO 1074036   **ESTABLISHED** 1999
WHERE FUNDING CAN BE GIVEN UK.

WHO CAN BENEFIT Organisations benefiting young adults, actors, artists, musicians, research workers, writers, dancers and choreographers, directors, producers and film makers.

WHAT IS FUNDED Project and programme support across the arts throughout the UK. The foundation host an open grants programme as well as proactively funding the Jerwood Visual Arts series of events.

WHAT IS NOT FUNDED The Jerwood charitable Foundation will not consider applications for: building or capital costs (including purchase of equipment); projects in the fields of religion or sport; animal rights or welfare; study fees or course fees; general fundraising appeals which are likely to have wide public appeal; appeals to establish endowment funds for other charities; appeals for matching funding for National Lottery applications; grants for the running and core costs of voluntary bodies; projects which are of mainly local appeal or identified with a locality; medical or mental health projects; social welfare, particularly where it may be considered a government or local authority responsibility; retrospective awards; projects outside Great Britain; schools which are trying to attain Special Schools Status; general touring, production or staging costs; environmental or conservation projects; musical instruments; informal education or community participation projects; education or participation projects for those who have not yet left formal education.

The foundation may, where there are very exceptional circumstances, decide to waive an exclusion.

TYPE OF GRANT Principally one-off, usually incorporating challenge funding, but will sometimes be prepared to maintain support if consistency will secure better results.

RANGE OF GRANTS Lower range will be around £5,000–£10,000, and the more substantial grants usually ranging from £10,000–£50,000; but up to £100,000.

SAMPLE GRANTS Sadler's Wells, Jerwood Studio and Artangel (£100,000 each); Royal Court and Jerwood New Playwrights (£75,000 each); Young Vic and Jerwood Assistant Directors Programme (£50,000 each); Dance UK and Dancers' Health and Take Five (£40,000 each); Royal Society of Literature and the RSL Jerwood Awards for Non-Fiction (£28,000 each); The Opera Group and Incubator (£22,000 each); Performing Arts Labs – Movement and Meaning Lab (£15,000); Aurora Orchestra, Jerwood Commissions and Circus Space: Creative Exchanges (£10,000 each); PRS for Music Foundation and New Music 20 x 12 (£8,000 each); Wittering Productions: Where are they now? (£6,000); and Brian Lobel: Carpe Minuta Prima (£4,800).

FINANCES *Year* 2010 *Income* £979,311 *Grants* £1,227,520 *Assets* £27,015,285

TRUSTEES Tim Eyles, Chair; Katherine Goodison; Juliane Wharton; Anthony Palmer; Sarah Vine; Thomas Grieve; Rupert Tyler; Phyllida Earle.

HOW TO APPLY Initial applications should include: a short proposal, not more than two sides of A4, outlining a description of the organisation's aims or a short biography for individuals, and a description of the specific project for which funding is sought and the opportunity it seeks to fulfil; a detailed budget for the project, identifying administrative, management and central costs details of funding already in place for the project, including any other trusts or sources which are being or have been approached for funds; and, if funding is not in place, details of how the applicant plans to secure the remaining funding. The trustees may decide to contact the applicants for further information including: details of the management and staffing structure, including trustees; and the most recent annual report and audited accounts of the organisation, together with current management accounts if relevant to the project. However, the trust asks that this information is **not** sent unless it is requested. Applications may be made online via the website. Alternatively applicants can send proposals by post. The foundation may wish to enter into discussions and/or correspondence with the applicant which may result in modification and/or development of the project or scheme. Any such discussion or correspondence will not commit the foundation to funding that application. Applications are assessed throughout the year. Successful applicants will be invited to report to the foundation at the completion of their project and to provide photographs of the work or project supported. As the foundation receives a large number of applications, it is not always possible to have preliminary meetings to discuss possible support before a written application is made.

WHO TO APPLY TO Shonagh Manson, Director, 171 Union Street, Bankside, London SE1 0LN *Tel* 020 7261 0279 *email* info@jerwood.org *Website* www.jerwoodcharitablefoundation.org

■ Jesus Hospital Charity

CC NO 1075889   **ESTABLISHED** 1679
WHERE FUNDING CAN BE GIVEN Barnet.
WHO CAN BENEFIT Individuals; and local organisations benefiting people of all ages, academics, research workers, scientists, students, unemployed people, volunteers, families, at risk groups, carers, people who are disabled, people with a medical condition or disease, people who are disadvantaged by poverty or who are socially isolated, and victims of abuse, crime and domestic violence.
WHAT IS FUNDED This trust will consider funding: almshouses; support to voluntary and community organisations; support to volunteers; respite care and care for carers; support and self-help groups; ambulances and mobile units; special needs education; training for work; costs of study; academic subjects, sciences and research; and community services.
WHAT IS NOT FUNDED No grants for relief of rates, taxes or other public funds. No provision of almshouse accommodation to anyone male or under the age of 50. No grants outside the Barnet area.
TYPE OF GRANT Capital and one-off. Funding is available for one year or less. Each case is considered on its merits.
SAMPLE GRANTS The Valley Centre (£1,000); Chipping Barnet Day Centre for the Elderly (£1,000); Rotary Club of Barnet and East Barnet – Christmas Day Lunches (£1,000); High Barnet Good Neighbour Scheme (£1,000).
FINANCES *Year* 2010 *Income* £505,084 *Grants* £12,247 *Assets* £9,224,485
TRUSTEES Neil Kobish; Brenda Sandford; P J Mellows; William Carrington; Ian Lawless; Revd Canon Hall Speers; Catherine Cavanagh; Stephen Payne; Dr Ian Johnston; Malcolm Bye; M Relfe; Ian Lawless; Janet Hulme.
HOW TO APPLY Application forms are available to download on the charity's website. Trustees meet every 2 months to consider applications.
WHO TO APPLY TO Simon Smith, Clerk to the Visitors (Trustees), Ravenscroft Lodge, 37 Union Street, Barnet, Hertfordshire EN5 4HY *Tel* 020 8440 4374 *Website* www.jesushospitalcharity.org.uk

■ Jewish Child's Day

CC NO 209266   **ESTABLISHED** 1947
WHERE FUNDING CAN BE GIVEN Worldwide. In practice, mainly Israel and UK.
WHO CAN BENEFIT Organisations caring for Jewish children.
WHAT IS FUNDED Charitable purposes of direct benefit to Jewish children who are disadvantaged, suffering or in need of special care.
WHAT IS NOT FUNDED Individuals are not supported. Grants are not given towards general services, building or maintenance of property or staff salaries.
TYPE OF GRANT 'One-off' and recurring.
RANGE OF GRANTS Up to £70,000.
SAMPLE GRANTS Federation of Jewish Services (£70,000); Givat Ada and Leeds Jewish Welfare Board (£60,000 each); Kol Israel (£20,000); Friends of Givat Ada's Children's Home (£18,000); Mantas Arava (£10,000); Nitzan (£8,000); Reut Sderot Association (£5,000); and Orr Shalom (£2,000).
FINANCES *Year* 2009–10 *Income* £1,287,979 *Grants* £846,963 *Assets* £646,596
TRUSTEES Joy Moss, Chair; June Jacobs; Stephen Moss; Virginia Campus; David Clayton; Francine Epstein; Susie Olins; Amanda Ingram; Gaby Lazarus; David Collins.
HOW TO APPLY If your organisation meets JCD's criteria, you could apply for a grant ranging from £500 to £5,000 towards the cost of small or medium size items of equipment or a project that will directly benefit children. The committee considers applications in February, June and September each year. Completed application forms should be sent together with a set of audited accounts by 31 December, 30 April and 31 July accordingly. To apply for a grant from JCD please contact Jackie Persoff on 020 8446 8804 or jackie.persoff@jcd.uk.com.
WHO TO APPLY TO Daniel Burger, Executive Director, 5th Floor, 707 High Road, North Finchley, London N12 0BT *Tel* 020 8446 8804 *Fax* 020 8446 7370 *email* info@jcd.uk.com *Website* www.jcd.uk.com

■ The Jewish Youth Fund

CC NO 251902   **ESTABLISHED** 1937
WHERE FUNDING CAN BE GIVEN UK.
WHO CAN BENEFIT Jewish youth clubs, centres, movements and groups.
WHAT IS FUNDED Jewish youth work projects, equipment and premises.
WHAT IS NOT FUNDED Grants are not made in response to general appeals. Formal education is not supported.
TYPE OF GRANT Grants are made for a whole variety of Jewish youth work projects. Loans are sometimes offered towards the cost of building.
RANGE OF GRANTS £1,000–£6,500 (2009–10).
SAMPLE GRANTS Step by Step (£6,500); B'nai Akiva UK and JAT (£5,000 each); The BBYO Charitable Trust (£2,500); Bushey Youth (£1,800) and London Jewish Cultural Centre (£1,000).
FINANCES *Year* 2009–10 *Income* £375,306 *Grants* £184,091 *Assets* £3,540,910
TRUSTEES Lady Morris of Kenwood; Adam D Rose; Phillipa Strauss; Lord Jonathan Morris; David Goldberg.
HOW TO APPLY On an application form available from the correspondent, enclosing a copy of the latest accounts and an annual report.

WHO TO APPLY TO Julia Samuel, Secretary, Third Floor, 24 Chiswell Street, London EC1Y 4YX *Tel* 020 7443 5169 *email* info@jyf.org.uk

....

■ The JMK Charitable Trust

CC NO 274576　**ESTABLISHED** 1977
WHERE FUNDING CAN BE GIVEN Worldwide.
WHO CAN BENEFIT Registered charities only, benefiting the appreciation of art and music, also assisting religious organisations to help relations with other faiths.
WHAT IS FUNDED There is a preference for charities concerned with Art and Music.
RANGE OF GRANTS £500–£10,000.
SAMPLE GRANTS English Touring Opera (£10,000); Royal Academy of Music – Scholarship (£5,000); Royal Academy of Music – Pavarotti Prize (£3,000); Royal Opera House (£2,500); Royal Academy of Arts (£2,000); Diva Opera and Keeping Kids Company (£1,000 each); West London Synagogue (£500) and Friends Royal Academy (£100).
FINANCES *Year* 2009–10 *Income* £6,449,461 *Grants* £36,861 *Assets* £199,033,840
TRUSTEES Mrs J M Karaviotis; J Karaviotis.
HOW TO APPLY In writing to the correspondent. No acknowledgement of receipt is given.
WHO TO APPLY TO The Trustees, Chantrey Vellacott DFK, Prospect House, 58 Queen's Road, Reading, Berkshire RG1 4RP *Tel* 0118 952 4700

....

■ The Joanies Trust

CC NO 1097803　**ESTABLISHED** 2003
WHERE FUNDING CAN BE GIVEN UK.
WHO CAN BENEFIT Registered charities.
WHAT IS FUNDED Grants are given to organisations working with young people aged 11 to 25, especially projects that lead to employment, accreditation, further education, training and integration. In particular the trust looks for innovation and entrepreneurship. The event can be one-off or part of a programme. The trust looks for strong evidence of how closely applicants consult young people in developing their service, and for any community involvement or local financial support.
WHAT IS NOT FUNDED Funding is not given for: national organisations, even if the project is local; general appeals and activities which collect funds for subsequent redistribution; individuals; promotion of religion; services run by statutory or public authorities, or that replace statutory funding; minibuses; UK organisations; animal charities; projects that have taken place or have started before the deadline; projects that are based outside the UK; outings, trips, or fun days.
TYPE OF GRANT Grants for running costs, both project and core costs, and capital costs.
SAMPLE GRANTS The Garage Trust Ltd (£1,400); Zoom In Ltd and Sussex Association of Spina Bifida (£1,300 each); Springfield Community Flat (£1,200); Wales Millennium Centre (£1,100); Cinderford Art Space, City Gateway and The Young Vic (£1,000 each); Theatre Royal Stratford East and Wren Music (£900 each); Choysez (£800); and Dorset Youth Association (£500).
FINANCES *Year* 2009 *Income* £37,019 *Grants* £34,939 *Assets* £786,689
TRUSTEES Alan Lloyd; Peter Arscott; Vivien Arscott.
HOW TO APPLY The trustees will only consider applications which are submitted on the trust's

application form; this is now only available to download as a PDF file from the trust's website in order to keep administration and postage costs as low as possible. Applicants are asked to print out and fill in the application form, and send it to the trust's address for the attention of 'the administrator', along with a copy of their annual accounts. 'Applications will benefit by showing how a project supports this particular age group. Those that are succinct and that give direct answers to the questions in the application form stand a greater chance of success.'
WHO TO APPLY TO Peter Arscott, Secretary, PO Box 42, Ledbury, Herefordshire HR8 1WH *Tel* 01531 633345 *email* info@joaniestrust.org.uk *Website* www.joaniestrust.org.uk

....

■ The Harold Joels Charitable Trust

CC NO 206326　**ESTABLISHED** 1957
WHERE FUNDING CAN BE GIVEN UK and US.
WHO CAN BENEFIT Jewish organisations only, with a possible preference for USA.
WHAT IS FUNDED General charitable purposes.
RANGE OF GRANTS £50–£20,000.
SAMPLE GRANTS Previous beneficiaries in the US included: The American Jewish Committee, Emunah of America, Family Law Connection, Florida Holocaust Museum, Florida Studio Theatre, Gocio Elementary School, Jewish Family and Children's Service, Temple Beth Sholom, Women's Resource Centre of Sarasota County World, Jewish Congress and Young Judea. Previous beneficiaries in the UK included: Bet Elazraki Home, British Friend of the Hebrew University, Chai Cancer Care, Hampstead Synagogue, I Rescue, Jewish Care, National Theatre, Royal Academy of Arts, the Tel Aviv Foundation, Tricycle Theatre Co Ltd, United Synagogue and World Jewish Relief.
FINANCES *Year* 2009–10 *Income* £24,433 *Grants* £30,000
TRUSTEES H Joels; Dr N Joels; Mrs V Joels; N E Joels.
OTHER INFORMATION The grant total includes grants made in the US.
HOW TO APPLY In writing to the correspondent.
WHO TO APPLY TO H Joels, Trustee, 11a Arkwright Road, London NW3 6AA *email* hjoles7@aol.com

....

■ The Jonathan Joels Charitable Trust

CC NO 278408　**ESTABLISHED** 1978
WHERE FUNDING CAN BE GIVEN UK and overseas.
WHO CAN BENEFIT Registered charities.
WHAT IS FUNDED General charitable purposes.
RANGE OF GRANTS Up to $18,000.
SAMPLE GRANTS Previously, figures provided by the trust on grants awarded were quoted in US dollars and included: $34,800 to UJA Federation of Bergen County and North Hudson, $8,500 to Congregation Ahavath Torah, $8,000 to Moriah School of Englewood, $6,700 to Ramaz School, $3,600 to Ramaz Special Educational Fund, $3,300 to Jewish Community Center on the Palisades, $2,200 to Emunah of America and $1,900 to Shaare Zedek Medical Center in Jerusalem.
Grants of less than $1,000 included: Sinai Special Needs Institute, Jewish Home and Rehabilitation Center, Boys Town Jerusalem Foundation of America, Jewish Family Service,

East Hill Synagogue, United Lifeline/Kav Lachayim, Yeshiva Chanoch Lenaar, Yeshiva Ohr Hatalmud of Englewood, Chai Lifeline, AZTUM, League for the Hard of Hearing, National Jewish Council for the Disabled, SCAT, Keser Dovid Inc, Chabad Center of Fort Lee, Friends of the Israeli Defence Forces, Lakewood Cheder School and Friends of the Lubavitch of Bergen County.

FINANCES *Year* 2009–10 *Income* £18,131 *Grants* £19,000

TRUSTEES J Joels; N E Joels; H Joels; Debra Joels.

HOW TO APPLY In writing to the correspondent.

WHO TO APPLY TO The Trustees, BBK Partnership, 1 Beauchamp Court, Victors Way, Barnet, Herts EN5 5TZ *Tel* 020 8216 2520 *Fax* 020 8216 2521

■ The Nicholas Joels Charitable Trust

CC NO 278409   **ESTABLISHED** 1978

WHERE FUNDING CAN BE GIVEN UK and overseas.

WHO CAN BENEFIT Registered charities only, with a preference for Jewish charities.

WHAT IS FUNDED General charitable purposes.

RANGE OF GRANTS Up to £9,000.

SAMPLE GRANTS Previously: World Jewish Relief (£9,000); Norwood (£5,300); Emunah (£4,300); United Jewish Israel Appeal (£3,800); Jewish Care (£2,000); Zionist Federation (£1,000); United Synagogue (£900); I Rescue (£750); Chinese Disaster Fund (£500); Jewish Women's Aid (£200); and Friends of the Tate Gallery (£100).

FINANCES *Year* 2009–10 *Income* £13,769 *Grants* £19,815

TRUSTEES N Joels; H Joels; Mrs A Joels.

HOW TO APPLY In writing to the correspondent.

WHO TO APPLY TO N Joels, Trustee, 20 Copse Wood Way, Northwood HA6 2UF *Tel* 01923 841376

■ The Norman Joels Charitable Trust

CC NO 206325   **ESTABLISHED** 1957

WHERE FUNDING CAN BE GIVEN UK, Israel and the Middle East.

WHO CAN BENEFIT Registered charities only.

WHAT IS FUNDED General charitable purposes.

RANGE OF GRANTS £100–£3,500.

SAMPLE GRANTS Previous beneficiaries have included: Friends of Magen David Action in Great Britain, Jewish Aid Committee, Jewish Care, Joint Jewish Charitable Trust, New London Synagogue, Norwood Ravenswood, The Spiro Institute and World Jewish Relief.

FINANCES *Year* 2009–10 *Income* £24,885 *Grants* £24,374

TRUSTEES Jessica L Joels; Norman Joels; Harold Joels; Myriam Joels.

HOW TO APPLY In writing to the correspondent.

WHO TO APPLY TO The Trustees, Grunberg and Co Ltd, 10 - 14 Accommodation Road, London NW11 8EP *Tel* 020 8458 0083 *Fax* 0208 458 0783

■ The Joffe Charitable Trust

CC NO 270299   **ESTABLISHED** 1968

WHERE FUNDING CAN BE GIVEN The Gambia, Kenya, Malawi, Mozambique, South Africa, Tanzania, Uganda, Zambia and Zimbabwe.

WHO CAN BENEFIT Registered charities with good quality leadership, clear objectives and realistic project budgets.

WHAT IS FUNDED The alleviation of poverty and protection/advancement of human rights mainly in the developing world, (poverty for this purpose could include some forms of suffering such as mental or physical disability and lack of education).

WHAT IS NOT FUNDED No grants for: emergency relief, the arts, conflict resolution, formal education, micro credit, work directly in the field of HIV/Aids, individuals, large charities with income of over £5 million per annum.

TYPE OF GRANT Grants and loans for up to three years.

RANGE OF GRANTS Around £5,000–£40,000.

SAMPLE GRANTS Ubulele (£51,000); Acid Survivors Trust and Global Witness (£30,000 each); Tourism Concern (£27,000); BUILD (£20,000); Centre for Innovation in Voluntary Action (£17,000); Transparency International (£15,000); APT Enterprise Development (£13,000); One Voice Europe (£10,000); and Tomorrow's Company (£7,500).

FINANCES *Year* 2009–10 *Income* £386,496 *Grants* £367,500 *Assets* £11,650,738

TRUSTEES Lord Joel Joffe; Lady Vanetta Joffe; Deborah Joffe; Nick Maurice; Mark Poston.

HOW TO APPLY Firstly, applicants must complete an online application form available through the website. The trust aims to respond to applicants within one month if they have been successful. If so, they will be asked to submit a more detailed proposal, including: objectives and specific targets; information on how they will measure results; information on the sustainability of the work planned; CV of the chief executive or key person in the organisation; evidence of demand and fit to other initiatives in the geographic area; the latest audited accounts, sent as a hard copy; the most recent annual review, if applicable, sent as a hard copy. The trust aims to let all stage two applicants have a decision within four months of receiving their proposal.

WHO TO APPLY TO Linda Perry, Trust Manager, Liddington Manor, The Street, Liddington, Swindon SN4 0HD *Tel* 01793 790203 *email* joffetrust@lidmanor.co.uk *Website* www.joffecharitabletrust.org

■ The Elton John Aids Foundation

CC NO 1017336   **ESTABLISHED** 1993

WHERE FUNDING CAN BE GIVEN Unrestricted. Countries vary from year to year.

WHO CAN BENEFIT Organisations helping those people living with HIV/AIDS, or running AIDS prevention programmes.

WHAT IS FUNDED The provision of focused and sustainable funding to frontline programmes that help alleviate the physical, emotional and financial hardship of those living with, affected by or at risk of HIV/AIDS.

WHAT IS NOT FUNDED For both UK and international grants the foundation will not fund: academic or medical research; conferences; grants to individuals; repatriation costs; retrospective funding.

TYPE OF GRANT Revenue and specific projects. Core costs; one-off, running costs; and salaries. Funding may be given for one year or up to three years.

RANGE OF GRANTS £200–£1.3 million.

SAMPLE GRANTS The Food Chain (£116,000); Terrence Higgins Trust (£445,000); University of

Liverpool (£23,000); CARE International UK (£143,000); Tamil Nadu Voluntary Health Association (£200); AIDS Foundation of South Africa (£15,700); Thohoyandou Victim Empowerment Trust (£6,000); Bwindi Community Hospital (£97,000); Centre for Infectious Disease Research in Zambia (£26,000); Grassroots Soccer (£233,000); Johannesburg Child Welfare Society (£5,800); and UK Ukrainian AIDS Response (£31,000).

FINANCES *Year* 2010 *Income* £9,203,560 *Grants* £7,417,891 *Assets* £26,708,064

TRUSTEES Sir Elton John, Chair; David Furnish; Lynette Jackson; Frank Presland; Anne Aslett; Marguerite Littman; Johnny Bergius; James Locke; Rafi Manoukian; Scott Campbell.

OTHER INFORMATION Visit the foundation's excellent website for full information.

HOW TO APPLY The foundation's website has an interactive map which you can use to click on a country you are interested in. This will take you to a page containing an overview of the country and the foundation's work within it, some examples of previous projects, details of the current grant strategy for that country and the application procedure. Interested organisations should complete a 'concept note' (available to download from the website) and email it to grants@ejaf.com.

WHO TO APPLY TO Robert Key, Executive Director, 1 Blythe Road, London W14 0HG *Tel* 020 7603 9996 *Fax* 020 7348 4848 *email* admin@ejaf.com *Website* www.ejaf.com

■ The Michael John Trust

CC NO 293571   ESTABLISHED 1986

WHERE FUNDING CAN BE GIVEN UK.

WHO CAN BENEFIT Scientific research, education, health, disability – UK.

WHAT IS FUNDED Registered charities.

RANGE OF GRANTS Usually £200 to £3,000.

SAMPLE GRANTS Beneficiaries were: Sheffield University (£167,000); Chadsgrove School and Specialist Sports College (£10,000); the Snowdon Award Scheme (£3,000); the Science and Technology Foundation Trust (£2,000); and Help the Aged (£1,500). Other grants below £1,000 totalled £4,300.

FINANCES *Year* 2009–10 *Income* £130,118 *Grants* £187,766 *Assets* £2,067,479

TRUSTEES Dr H P Jost; Mrs M J Jost; M J O Kettle; R Worby.

HOW TO APPLY In writing to the correspondent. The trustees meet quarterly.

WHO TO APPLY TO Dr Peter Jost, Trustee, Angel Lodge Chambers, 57 London Road, Enfield, Middlesex EN2 6SW *Tel* 020 3213 1030 *email* michaeljohntrust@btconnect.com

■ The Lillie Johnson Charitable Trust

CC NO 326761   ESTABLISHED 1985

WHERE FUNDING CAN BE GIVEN UK, with a preference for the West Midlands.

WHO CAN BENEFIT Charities concerned with children, young people and medical causes.

WHAT IS FUNDED Medical and welfare causes.

WHAT IS NOT FUNDED No support for individuals.

SAMPLE GRANTS LEC – Worcester (£60,000); Web Care (£13,000); West House School (£10,000); Cancer Care and St Mary's and St Margaret's (£5,000 each); Solihull Samaritans (£4,000); Barnardo's, Castle Bromwich hall Gardens,

Focus Parkinson's Society and Primrose Hospital (£1,000 each).

FINANCES *Year* 2009–10 *Income* £193,831 *Grants* £183,327 *Assets* £5,231,601

TRUSTEES V M C Lyttle; P W Adams; J W Desmond; Mrs V C Adams.

HOW TO APPLY Applications are only considered from charities which are traditionally supported by the trust. The trust stated that it is inundated with applications it cannot support and feels obliged to respond to all of these.

WHO TO APPLY TO J W Desmond, Trustee, Heathcote House, 39 Rodbourne Road, Harborne, Birmingham B17 0PN

■ The Johnson Foundation

CC NO 518660   ESTABLISHED 1987

WHERE FUNDING CAN BE GIVEN Merseyside.

WHO CAN BENEFIT Registered charities benefiting medical professionals, carers, people who are disabled or disadvantaged by poverty, and victims of abuse.

WHAT IS FUNDED Medicine and health, education, relief of poverty and youth projects,.

WHAT IS NOT FUNDED Grants are not normally given to individuals.

TYPE OF GRANT One-off, recurrent, core costs, project and research.

SAMPLE GRANTS Birkenhead School Scholarship (£35,000); Cardiothoracic Centre (£15,000); Life Education Centres (£10,000); New Brighton Rugby Junior Development (£5,000); Lord Mayor's Charity Appeal (£4,000); Women's Enterprising Breakthrough (£2,500); Royal Navy and Marine Charity (£2,000); Empowering Youth Foundation and Harvest Trust for Deprived Children (£1,500 each); and Henshaw Society for the Blind and Local Solutions (£1,000 each).

FINANCES *Year* 2009–10 *Income* £139,963 *Grants* £94,298 *Assets* £1,849,708

TRUSTEES P R Johnson; C W Johnson.

OTHER INFORMATION The trust stated: 'Whilst this trust is prepared to help larger charities, it prefers to support small, local organisations unable to afford professional fundraisers with grants from about £250 to £1,000.' In 2009–10, other grants and donations (25 less than £1,000) amounted to £6,143.

HOW TO APPLY In writing to the correspondent. The trustees meet monthly.

WHO TO APPLY TO P R Johnson, Trustee, Westmount, Vyner Road South, Birkenhead, Wirral CH43 7PN *Tel* 0151 653 1700

■ The Johnson Group Cleaners Charity

CC NO 802959   ESTABLISHED 1990

WHERE FUNDING CAN BE GIVEN Merseyside only.

WHO CAN BENEFIT Registered local charities benefiting: children, young adults and older people; at risk groups; carers; people disadvantaged by poverty; ex-offenders and those at risk of offending; homeless people; victims of abuse and domestic violence; and people with substance misuse problems.

WHAT IS FUNDED Merseyside charities, including Councils for Voluntary Service, care in the community and holidays and outings.

WHAT IS NOT FUNDED No grants to national charities or individuals.

TYPE OF GRANT Core costs, one-off, project and running costs.

RANGE OF GRANTS Up to £80,000, usually £5,000 or less.

SAMPLE GRANTS Previously: Johnson Group Welfare Charity (£80,000); Bootle YMCA, Stroke Association, Salvation Army and Claire House (£5,000 each); Royal School for the Blind, Slightline Vision and Merseyside Holiday Services (£3,000 each); Rainbow Charity Children's Hospice (£750); Halton Haven Hospice and Merseyside Gymnastic Club (£500 each); Wellchild (£250).

FINANCES *Year* 2009–10 *Income* £1,717 *Grants* £0 *Assets* £136,383

TRUSTEES Yvonne Monaghan; Karen Castle; Christopher Sander; Margo Green.

OTHER INFORMATION This trust is connected to the Johnson Charitable Trust, they have the same trustees and the accounts for this trust were included in those for the Johnson Charitable Trust. The trust reported that they gave no grants in the previous year due to the low income.

HOW TO APPLY In writing only to the correspondent.

WHO TO APPLY TO Yvonne Monaghan, Abbots Park, Monks Way, Preston Brook, Cheshire WA7 3GH *Tel* 01928 704600

■ The Johnnie Johnson Trust

CC NO 200351   **ESTABLISHED** 1961

WHERE FUNDING CAN BE GIVEN UK, with a preference for the West Midlands.

WHO CAN BENEFIT To benefit children and young adults.

WHAT IS FUNDED Heritage and training/adventure breaks for children, youth and welfare organisations.

SAMPLE GRANTS £95,000 to Johnnie Johnson Adventure Trust; and £200 to 1st Shirley Scouts.

FINANCES *Year* 2010 *Income* £107,594 *Grants* £95,200 *Assets* £3,567,616

TRUSTEES P V Johnson; P E T Johnson; Mrs J S Fordham; G W Ballard.

OTHER INFORMATION Over the last few years, the trust's funds have mostly been given to Johnnie Johnson Adventure Trust, which provides adventure/training for children.

HOW TO APPLY In writing to the correspondent. Please note that most funds go to the trust's sister charity and very little is available to other organisations.

WHO TO APPLY TO Christopher R Jackson, 3 Crumpfields Lane, Webheath, Redditch, Worcestershire B97 5PN *Tel* 01527 544722

■ The Johnson Wax Ltd Charitable Trust

CC NO 200332   **ESTABLISHED** 1961

WHERE FUNDING CAN BE GIVEN 20 mile radius of Frimley Green, Surrey.

WHO CAN BENEFIT Local charities.

WHAT IS FUNDED Health, education, local community, environment, arts, sports.

WHAT IS NOT FUNDED No grants to individuals.

RANGE OF GRANTS £4,000 average.

FINANCES *Year* 2009–10 *Income* £171,535 *Grants* £238,470 *Assets* £309,879

TRUSTEES Mrs R Gillingham; Mrs C Hyde; Mrs J Thake.

HOW TO APPLY In writing to the correspondent including the following information: the amount requested and what it is needed for; – details of how the grant will benefit a broad cross-section of the Frimley Green community and meet a clear social need within it.

WHO TO APPLY TO Jan Jewers, S C Johnson Wax Ltd, Frimley Green, Camberley, Surrey GU16 7AJ *Tel* 01276 852422 *email* jjewers@scj.com

---

■ The Joicey Trust

CC NO 244679   **ESTABLISHED** 1965

WHERE FUNDING CAN BE GIVEN Unrestricted, but in practice, the county of Northumberland and the old metropolitan county of Tyne and Wear.

WHO CAN BENEFIT Registered charities operating in Northumberland and Tyne and Wear or groups with a specific project within the area defined above. The trust will consider funding organisations benefiting people of all ages, seafarers and fishermen, people who are in care, fostered or adopted and one-parent families.

WHAT IS FUNDED This trust will consider funding activities within the following fields: residential facilities and services; a range of infrastructure, technical support and development; charity or voluntary umbrella bodies; religious buildings; music, dance and theatre; healthcare, facilities and buildings; conservation; education and training; and community facilities and services. UK appeals are not normally supported unless there is specific evidence of activity benefiting the local area.

WHAT IS NOT FUNDED The trust states that it will not support 'bodies not having registered charitable status; personal applications; individuals; groups that do not have an identifiable project within the beneficial area'.

TYPE OF GRANT One-off for capital and revenue projects, with preference for discrete projects over running costs. Also start-up costs, buildings, core costs, projects and salaries.

RANGE OF GRANTS Up to £5,000 with very occasional larger grants.

SAMPLE GRANTS Riding for the Disabled Association (£10,000); Shilbottle Community Hall (£5,000); Calvert Trust Kielder (£2,000); Gateway into the Community, The Fire Fighting Charity, Cancer Connections, Blyth Valley CVA, Acorn and Mencap (£1,000 each) and Browsden Village Hall, Project Trust, Dreams Holidays (£400 each).

FINANCES *Year* 2009–10 *Income* £237,157 *Grants* £248,013 *Assets* £6,747,364

TRUSTEES Rt Hon. Lord Joicey; Rt Hon. Lady Joicey; Hon. A H Joicey; R H Dickinson.

HOW TO APPLY There is no application form and applications should be made in writing to the correspondent. Trustees' meetings are held in January and July and applications should be received not later than the end of November and the end of May respectively. Applications should include a brief description of the project and must include a copy of the previous year's accounts and, where possible, a copy of the current year's projected income and expenditure. In the case of large projects, an indication should be given of how the major sources of funding are likely to be secured, including reference to any Community Fund grant applied for/received. Unsuccessful applicants will not be informed unless an sae is provided.

WHO TO APPLY TO N A Furness, Appeals Secretary, Dickinson Dees LLP, St Ann's Wharf, 112 Quayside, Newcastle Upon Tyne NE99 1 SB *Tel* 0191 279 9662 *Fax* 0191 230 8921 *email* sylvia.hepplewhite@dickinson-dees. com

■ The Jones 1986 Charitable Trust

cc no 327176 **established** 1986
where funding can be given UK, mostly Nottinghamshire.
who can benefit Registered charities.
what is funded People with disabilities, welfare of older people, welfare of younger people, education and purposes beneficial to the community.
what is not funded No grants to individuals.
range of grants Up to around £100,000, but mostly between £4,000 and £25,000.
sample grants Queens Medical Centre Nottingham – University Hospital NHS Trust (£80,000); Cope Children's Trust (£40,000); The Ruddington Framework Knitters Museum (£26,000); Age Concern Nottingham and Nottinghamshire (£25,000); Winged Fellowship (£24,000); Nottinghamshire Hospice (£23,000); Framework Housing Association (£20,000); Rutland House School for Parents (£15,000); National Head Injuries Association (Headway) (£12,000); Nottingham Deaf Society and The Place2be (£10,000 each); Prince of Paste Anglers (£8,000); Elizabeth Finn Care and The Boys' Brigade: Nottinghamshire Battalion (£5,000 each); Nottingham Society for Autistic Children and Adults (£2,000); and Deafblind UK (£1,000).
finances *Year* 2009–10 *Income* £567,465 *Grants* £512,956 *Assets* £19,475,348
trustees Robert Heason; Richard Stringfellow; John David Pears.
how to apply In writing to the correspondent. The trust invites applications for grants by advertising in specialist press. Applications are considered for both capital and/or revenue projects as long as each project appears viable.
who to apply to David Lindley, Smith Cooper, Haydn House, 309–329 Haydn Road, Sherwood, Nottingham NG5 1HG *Tel* 0115 960 7111 *Fax* 0115 969 1313

■ Dezna Robins Jones Charitable Foundation

cc no 1104252 **established** 2004
where funding can be given Preference for Wales.
who can benefit Local medical charities.
what is funded Medical, general charitable purposes.
sample grants Previously: Cancer Care Cymru (£462,000); University Hospital of Wales – Cardiff (£138,000); Cory band (£72,000); and Performance Arts Education (£48,000).
finances *Year* 2009–10 *Income* £4 *Grants* £997
trustees B W R Jones; Alexia Cooke; Louise Boobyer.
how to apply In writing to the correspondent. Trustees meet at least twice a year.
who to apply to Bernard Jones, Trustee, Greenacres, Laleston, Bridgend, Mid Glamorgan CF32 OHN *Tel* 01656 768584

■ The Marjorie and Geoffrey Jones Charitable Trust

cc no 1051031 **established** 1995
where funding can be given UK, preference south west of England.
who can benefit Registered charities.
what is funded General charitable purposes.
range of grants £1,000–£5,000.

sample grants Torbay Coast and Countryside Trust (£4,000); Pilgrim BM45 Trust Ltd, Living Paintings and Teign Heritage (£3,000 each); Children's Hospice South West and Fire Services Benevolent Fund (£2,500); Deafblind UK and West Country Rivers (£2,000 each); and Rural Stress South West, The Two Moors Festival and Apollo Football Club (£1,000 each).
finances *Year* 2009–10 *Income* £23,898 *Grants* £39,087
trustees N J Wollen; W F Coplestone Boughey; P M Kay; E M J Richards.
how to apply In writing to the correspondent. The trustees meet four times a year to consider applications.
who to apply to N J Wollen, Trustee, Carlton House, 30 The Terrace, Torquay, Devon TQ1 1BN *Tel* 01803 213251 *email* nigel.wollen@hooperwollen.co.uk

■ The Muriel Jones Foundation

cc no 1135107 **established** 2010
where funding can be given Undefined.
who can benefit Registered charities.
what is funded General charitable purposes.
trustees Richard Brindle; Katie Brindle.
other information Richard Brindle is also a trustee of Crossflow Limited, a charity which supports people in the countries of the Himalayas through the advancement of health and education.
how to apply In writing to the correspondent.
who to apply to The Administrator, Coutts and Co, 440 Strand, London WC2R 0QS *Tel* 020 7663 6838

■ The Jordan Charitable Foundation

cc no 1051507 **established** 1995
where funding can be given UK national charities, Herefordshire and Sutherland, Scotland.
who can benefit UK national charities and local charities and community groups in Herefordshire and Sutherland, Scotland.
what is funded General charitable purposes.
type of grant One-off, capital and core costs will be considered.
range of grants Up to £50,000.
sample grants Taste for Adventure (£50,000); Headway – Herefordshire (£30,000); Mind – Herefordshire (£26,000); Martha Trust (£20,000); County Air Ambulance Trust (£15,000); Alzheimer's Research Trust, Brooke Hospital for Animals and the Samaritans (£10,000 each); Sutherland Schools Pipe Band (£6,000); RNLI, Atlantic Salmon Trust, National Trust for Scotland and Age Concern (£5,000 each); International Animal Rescue and Loth Helmsdale Flower Show Society (£2,000 each); and Northlands Creative Glass (£1,000).
finances *Year* 2010 *Income* £844,004 *Grants* £433,984 *Assets* £44,505,854
trustees Sir George Russell; Ralph Stockwell; Christopher Jan Andrew Bliss; Simon Paul Jennings; David Geoffrey Barker; Anthony Brierley.
how to apply In writing to the correspondent.
who to apply to Ralph Stockwell, Trustee, Rawlinson & Hunter, 8th Floor, 6 New Street Square, New Fetter Land, London EC4A 3AQ *Tel* 020 7842 2000 *email* jordan@rawlinson-hunter.com

Think carefully about every application. Is it justified?

653

■ The Joron Charitable Trust

CC NO 1062547   **ESTABLISHED** 1997
WHERE FUNDING CAN BE GIVEN UK.
WHO CAN BENEFIT Registered charities.
WHAT IS FUNDED 'The charity's policy is to make grants to registered charities in the fields of education, medical research and other charities who can demonstrate that the grants will be used effectively.'
SAMPLE GRANTS Roan Charitable Trust (£1 million); The Princess Royal Trust for Carers (£150,000); the Wilderness Foundation (£137,000); Hammersmith Hospital (£110,500); Child's Dream Foundation (£64,000); St Christopher's Hospice (£25,000); and Great Ormond Street Children's Hospital (£5,000).
FINANCES *Year* 2009–10 *Income* £1,266,325 *Grants* £1,675,159 *Assets* £874,998
TRUSTEES Bruce D G Jarvis; Mrs Sandra C Jarvis; Joseph R Jarvis.
HOW TO APPLY 'There is no formal grants application procedure. The trustees retain the services of a charitable grants advisor and take account of the advice when deciding on grants.'
WHO TO APPLY TO Bruce D G Jarvis, Chair, 115 Wembley Commercial Centre, East Lane, North Wembley, Middlesex HA9 7UR *Tel* 020 8908 4655

■ The J E Joseph Charitable Fund

CC NO 209058   **ESTABLISHED** 1946
WHERE FUNDING CAN BE GIVEN London, Manchester, Israel, India and Hong Kong.
WHO CAN BENEFIT Jewish people who are poor and in need.
WHAT IS FUNDED Jewish community organisations, especially those catering for people who are socially disadvantaged and young people.
WHAT IS NOT FUNDED No grants to individuals. No support for capital projects.
TYPE OF GRANT Outright cash grants frequently on an annual basis. Very occasionally loans.
RANGE OF GRANTS £500–£10,000.
SAMPLE GRANTS The Future Generation Fund (£13,000); Od Yosef Hai Yeshiva (£7,000); Edinburgh House (Home for Elderly) (£6,000); Kisharon Day School, Spanish and Portuguese Synagogue Welfare Board and University Jewish Chaplaincy Board (£5,000 each); Ilford Synagogue (Eastern) (£3,000); and Hospital Kosher Meals (£2,000).
FINANCES *Year* 2010–11 *Income* £121,860 *Grants* £129,060 *Assets* £4,296,746
TRUSTEES F D A Mocatta, Chair; P Sheldon; J H Corre; J S Horesh; S Frosh; Robert Shemtob; Susan Kendal.
HOW TO APPLY In writing to the correspondent, including a copy of the latest accounts. The trustees respond to all applications which are first vetted by the secretary. The trust stated that many applications are unsuccessful as the number of appeals exceeds the amount available from limited income.
WHO TO APPLY TO Roger J Leon, Secretary, Flat 10, Compass Close, Edgware, Middlesex HA8 8HU *Tel* 020 8958 0126

■ The Lady Eileen Joseph Foundation

CC NO 327549   **ESTABLISHED** 1987
WHERE FUNDING CAN BE GIVEN UK.
WHO CAN BENEFIT Mainly UK organisations benefiting at-risk groups and people who are disadvantaged by poverty or socially isolated.
WHAT IS FUNDED Largely welfare and medical causes. General charitable purposes are also supported.
TYPE OF GRANT One-off.
RANGE OF GRANT Up to £10,000.
SAMPLE GRANTS Previous beneficiaries included: Second Chance (£7,500); Coldstream Guards Association (£6,500); Alzheimer's Research Trust and Friends of the Home Physiotherapy Service (£5,000 each); Havens Hospices (£4,500); Ellenor Foundation and Queen Alexandra Hospital (£3,000 each); Independent Age and Wellbeing of Women (£2,000 each); and Cystic Fibrosis Trust, Foundation for the Prevention of Blindness and Action for Kids (£1,000 each).
FINANCES *Year* 2009–10 *Income* £22,194 *Grants* £35,672
TRUSTEES Judith M Sawdy; Thurlstan W Simpson; Gael Lynn Simpson.
HOW TO APPLY The trust states that unsolicited requests will not be considered.
WHO TO APPLY TO Thurlstan W Simpson, Trustee, Colbrans Farm, Cow Lane, Laughton, Lewes BN8 6BZ

■ The Josh Charitable Trust

CC NO 1107060   **ESTABLISHED** 2004
WHERE FUNDING CAN BE GIVEN UK, Israel and Australia.
WHO CAN BENEFIT Registered charities.
WHAT IS FUNDED General charitable purposes.
FINANCES *Year* 2009–10 *Income* £75,443 *Grants* £61,484 *Assets* £25,221
TRUSTEES Joel Cope; Shoshana Raizelle Cope.
HOW TO APPLY In writing to the correspondent.
WHO TO APPLY TO The Trustees, 1 Lancaster Drive, Prestwich, Manchester M25 0HZ

■ JTH Charitable Trust

SC NO SC000201   **ESTABLISHED** 1989
WHERE FUNDING CAN BE GIVEN Scotland, in particular west Scotland and Glasgow.
WHO CAN BENEFIT Individuals and organisations.
WHAT IS FUNDED Grants are given to a range of organisations, including universities, cultural bodies and those caring for people who are sick. Support may also be given to charities working in the fields of community services, community centres and village halls, special needs education, voluntary and community organisations and volunteers.
WHAT IS NOT FUNDED The following are not usually supported: medical electives, second or further qualifications, payment of school fees or costs incurred at tertiary educational establishments.
TYPE OF GRANT Some grants are made to individuals for educational purposes. Core costs, one-off, project, research, running costs and start-up costs will be considered.
RANGE OF GRANTS £100–£10,000.
SAMPLE GRANTS Previous beneficiaries have included Crossroads (Scotland) Care Attendance Scheme and East Park Home for Inform Children, Royal Blind Asylum and School, University of Glasgow and University of Strathclyde.

FINANCES *Year* 2010–11 *Income* £166,795 *Grants* £250,000

TRUSTEES Gordon M Wyllie; Christine C Howat.

HOW TO APPLY In writing to the correspondent. There is no application form for organisations. Applications should contain a summary not longer than one side of A4, backed up as necessary with schedules. A copy of the latest accounts and/or business plan should be included. Costs and financial needs should be broken down where possible. It should be clear what effect the grant will have and details of other grants applied for or awarded should be given. Evidence that the project will enhance the quality of life of the clients and that they are involved in the decision making must be included. 'Applications should include evidence of charitable status, current funding, and the use you are making of that. Projects should be demonstrated to be practical and business-like. It is a condition of any grant given that a report be made as to how the funds have been used. Grants not used for the purposes stated must be returned.' Successful applicants should not reapply in the following year. Unsuccessful applicants are not acknowledged due to the large number of applications received by the trust. The trustees meet to consider grants in March, June, September and December. Applications should be received in the preceding month.

WHO TO APPLY TO Lynne Faulkner, Biggart Baillie LLP, Dalmore House, 310 St Vincent Street, Glasgow G2 5QR *Tel* 0141 228 8000 *Fax* 0141 228 8310 *email* lfaulkner@biggartbaillie.co.uk

■ The Judith Trust

CC NO 1063012   **ESTABLISHED** 1997

WHERE FUNDING CAN BE GIVEN UK.

WHO CAN BENEFIT Organisations concerned with people with a learning disability and mental health needs.

WHAT IS FUNDED Multi-disciplinary preventative and innovative approaches to help those with learning disabilities and mental health problems, especially women, children and Jewish people.

WHAT IS NOT FUNDED No grants to individuals.

TYPE OF GRANT One-off, project and research. Funding may be given for up to three years.

SAMPLE GRANTS Previous beneficiaries have included: Living in the Community Project (£26,000) and 'Healthcare needs and experiences of care' (£11,000).

FINANCES *Year* 2009–10 *Income* £18,306 *Grants* £77,725

TRUSTEES Dr Annette Lawson; Peter Lawrence; George Lawson; Charlotte Collins; Geraldine Holt; Colin Samson.

PUBLICATIONS Joined Up Care: good practice in services for people with learning disabilities and mental health needs.

OTHER INFORMATION Accounts for the financial year 2009–10 were received but not required by the Charity Commission as the income was below £25,000.

HOW TO APPLY In writing to the correspondent; however, please note that most grants are made through experts and advisors. The trust does not accept unsolicited applications for funding, but is pleased to hear from organisations who wish the trust to be aware of their work.

WHO TO APPLY TO Dr A R Lawson, Trustee, 5 Carriage House, 88–90 Randolph Avenue, London W9 1BG *Tel* 020 7266 1073 *Fax* 020 7289 5804 *email* judith.trust@lineone.net *Website* www.judithtrust.org.uk

■ The Cyril and Eve Jumbo Charitable Trust

CC NO 1097209   **ESTABLISHED** 2003

WHERE FUNDING CAN BE GIVEN Worldwide.

WHO CAN BENEFIT Charitable organisations.

WHAT IS FUNDED The objectives of the trust are: fresh water projects; projects that deal with grass roots and front line action, and that set up sustainable, ongoing projects so that people can increase their independence and create their own livelihoods; projects that help children (particularly those in countries recovering from war and trauma), older people and people with disabilities/special needs.

SAMPLE GRANTS Wherever the Need (£25,000); Médecins Sans Frontières and MKA Charity Challenge (£5,000 each); Trax (£2,000) Afrikaya, Army Benevolent Fund, British Heart Foundation, Combat Stress and St George's Hospital (£1,000); Help in Action (£900); Jack Wallace (£500); and Voluntary Services Overseas (£200).

FINANCES *Year* 2009–10 *Income* £137,386 *Grants* £57,125 *Assets* £1,909,337

TRUSTEES Geoffrey Allan Margolis; Rafiq Ahmed Hayat; Michaela Justice; Fred Kindall.

HOW TO APPLY Unsolicited applications are not always accepted. Please check the trust's website for up-to-date details.

WHO TO APPLY TO The Trustees, 56a Poland Street, London W1F 7NN *email* info@ mumbojumboworld.com

■ The Anton Jurgens Charitable Trust

CC NO 259885   **ESTABLISHED** 1969

WHERE FUNDING CAN BE GIVEN UK with a preference for the south east of England.

WHO CAN BENEFIT UK registered charities.

WHAT IS FUNDED The welfare of children and young people; youth organisations; centres, clubs and institutions; community organisations; day centres and nurseries; and general welfare organisations.

TYPE OF GRANT Generally one-off.

RANGE OF GRANTS £1,000–£15,000.

SAMPLE GRANTS Silcester Parochial Council (£25,000); Highland Hospice (£15,000); Ability Net, Kid's Company and Royal School for Deaf Children – Margate (£10,000 each); child Link Adoption Society (£8,000); the Fifth Trust (£6,000); Bucks Disability Information Network and Queen Alexandra Hospital Home (£5,000 each); Hope House (£4,000); Haemophilia Society (£3,000); Barnabas Adventure Centres and Vitalise (£2,000 each); and Bury Shopmobility (£1,000).

FINANCES *Year* 2009–10 *Income* £255,615 *Grants* £296,520 *Assets* £6,332,414

TRUSTEES Eric M C Deckers; R Jurgens; Frans A V Jurgens; F A W Jurgens; Maria E Edge-Jurgens; M A J Jurgens; I L M van Oosten Slingeland.

HOW TO APPLY In writing to the correspondent. The trustees meet twice a year in June and October. The trustees do not enter into correspondence concerning grant applications beyond notifying successful applicants.

WHO TO APPLY TO Maria E Edge-Jurgens, Trustee, Saffrey Champness, Lion House, 72–75 Red Lion Street, London WC1R 4GB *Tel* 020 7841 4000 *Fax* 020 7841 4100

■ Jusaca Charitable Trust

CC NO 1012966   **ESTABLISHED** 1992

WHERE FUNDING CAN BE GIVEN UK, overseas and Israel.

WHO CAN BENEFIT Registered charities.

WHAT IS FUNDED Jewish, arts, research, religion, housing.

TYPE OF GRANT Mainly recurrent.

FINANCES *Year* 2009–10 *Income* £92,497 *Grants* £167,803 *Assets* £1,345,077

TRUSTEES Ralph Neville Emanuel; Sara Jane Emanuel; Carolyn Leonora Emanuel; Maurice Seymour Emanuel; Diana Clare Franklin; Donald Franklin; Rachel Paul.

OTHER INFORMATION The trust aims to distribute at least 50% of donations to Jewish charities in the UK, overseas and Israel, and of the remainder about 40% to be donation to charities operating in the UK and about 60% outside the UK. The majority of grants are given to the same organisations each year in order to provide a long term stream of funding.

HOW TO APPLY Grants are made at the discretion of the trustees. Unsolicited applications are not encouraged.

WHO TO APPLY TO The Trustees, 17 Ashburnham Grove, London SE10 8UH

The Bernard Kahn Charitable Trust

CC NO 249130   **ESTABLISHED** 1965
WHERE FUNDING CAN BE GIVEN UK and Israel.
WHO CAN BENEFIT Organisations benefiting Jewish people, children and young adults, people disadvantaged by poverty, teachers, governesses and rabbis.
WHAT IS FUNDED Relief of, and assistance to, Jewish people to alleviate poverty; the advancement of religion and education.
RANGE OF GRANTS £25–£45,000.
SAMPLE GRANTS Achisomoch Aid Company Ltd, Gevuras Ari Trust and Orthodox Council of Jerusalem Limited (£20,000 each); Tely (£15,000); Friends of Be'er Miriam and Marbeh Torah Trust (£11,000 each); Beth Hamedrash Elyon Golders Green Limited (£4,500); Margenita D'Avrohom (£1,500); British Friends of Yeshivath – Ofakim (£900); Lopian Sofer (£750); Yeshivas Shaarei Torah (£500); Tel Hai Fund (£300); the Friends of Neve Yerushalaym Seminary Trust (£200); and Yad Ezrah – Helping Hand (£100).
FINANCES *Year* 2008–09 *Income* £84,000 *Grants* £114,320 *Assets* £1,711,857
TRUSTEES C B Kahn; S Fuehrer, Y E Kahn.
HOW TO APPLY In writing to the correspondent.
WHO TO APPLY TO The Trustees, 24 Elmcroft Avenue, London NW11 0RR

The Stanley Kalms Foundation

CC NO 328368   **ESTABLISHED** 1989
WHERE FUNDING CAN BE GIVEN UK and overseas.
WHO CAN BENEFIT Organisations and individuals involved with: orthodox Jewish education in the UK and Israel; the arts; medicine; and other secular and religious programmes.
WHAT IS FUNDED Encouragement of orthodox Jewish education in the UK and Israel, particularly by providing scholarships, fellowships and research grants. Other areas supported include the arts, medicine and other programmes, both secular and religious.
TYPE OF GRANT One-off, research, project, bursaries and scholarships.
SAMPLE GRANTS Previously: Dixons City Academy (£25,000), Milliken Community High (£23,000), Royal Opera House Foundation (£17,000), Jewish Care (£14,000) and Jewish National Fund (£12,000); Norwood (£7,600), British Friends of Haifa University (£7,200), Keren Klita (£7,000), Civitas, Centre for Social Justice, Institute of Economic Affairs, Jewish Policy Research, Royal Academy Trust (£5,000 each), Stephen Wise Temple (£4,500), the Kabbalah Centre (£2,900), Anglo Israel Association (£2,000), British ORT (£1,500) and St James Conversation Trust (£1,000).
FINANCES *Year* 2009–10 *Income* £69,927 *Grants* £69,352
TRUSTEES Lord Stanley Kalms; Lady Pamela Kalms; Stephen Kalms.
HOW TO APPLY In writing to the correspondent, but note that most of the trust's funds are committed to projects supported for a number of years.

WHO TO APPLY TO Mrs Jane Hunt-Cooke, 84 Brook Street, London W1K 5EH *Tel* 020 7499 3494

The Kalou Foundation

CC NO 1135173   **ESTABLISHED** 2010
WHERE FUNDING CAN BE GIVEN Worldwide.
WHO CAN BENEFIT Individuals and organisations.
WHAT IS FUNDED The provision of facilities in the interests of social welfare for recreation or other leisure time occupation of individuals who have need of such facilities by reason their youth, age, infirmity or disability, financial hardship or social circumstances; the relief of sickness worldwide; other general charitable purposes as determined by the trustees.
TRUSTEES Salomon Kalou; Jan De Visser; Constance Kalou.
OTHER INFORMATION This foundation was established in 2010 by the Chelsea and Ivory Coast footballer Salomon Kalou.
HOW TO APPLY In writing to the correspondent.
WHO TO APPLY TO Stephen Claus, Clerk to the Trustees, Brabners Chaffe Street LLP, Horton House, Exchange Flags, Liverpool L2 3YL *Tel* 0151 600 3000 *email* stephen.claus@brabnerscs.com

The Karenza Foundation

CC NO 264520   **ESTABLISHED** 1972
WHERE FUNDING CAN BE GIVEN England and Wales.
WHO CAN BENEFIT Charitable organisations.
WHAT IS FUNDED General charitable purposes.
RANGE OF GRANTS Larger grants can be up to £30,000.
SAMPLE GRANTS Previously Charities Aid Foundation (£30,000); Liver Cancer Surgery Appeal (£2,500); and Aid to Children Everywhere and St Catherine's Hospice (£1,000 each).
FINANCES *Year* 2009–10 *Income* £25,385 *Grants* £0 *Assets* £532,269
TRUSTEES Mr E J Uren; Mrs A F Uren.
OTHER INFORMATION In 2009–10 no grants were given. However, in previous years grants have totalled around £30,000.
HOW TO APPLY In writing to the correspondent.
WHO TO APPLY TO The Trustees, No. 1 Dorset Street, Southampton, Hampshire SO15 2DP

The Boris Karloff Charitable Foundation

CC NO 326898   **ESTABLISHED** 1985
WHERE FUNDING CAN BE GIVEN Worldwide.
WHO CAN BENEFIT UK and local charities benefiting actors, musicians and people disadvantaged by mental or physical illness.
WHAT IS FUNDED General charitable purposes.
WHAT IS NOT FUNDED Charities with large resources are not supported.
RANGE OF GRANTS £100–£10,000.
SAMPLE GRANTS Royal Theatrical Fund, RADA – Boris Karloff Scholarship Fund and Cinema and Television Benevolent Fund (£10,000 each); Shakespeare Global Trust (£6,500); LAMDA – the London Academy of Music and Dramatic Arts, Surrey County Cricket and the Royal Shakespeare Community (£5,000 each); and the Royal National Theatre (£4,000).
FINANCES *Year* 2009–10 *Income* £51,716 *Grants* £55,500 *Assets* £2,157,554
TRUSTEES Ian D Wilson; P A Williamson; O M Lewis.
HOW TO APPLY In writing to the correspondent.

WHO TO APPLY TO The Trustees, Peachey and Co., 95 Aldwych, London WC2B 4JF *Tel* 020 7316 5200

■ The Ian Karten Charitable Trust

CC NO 281721   **ESTABLISHED** 1980
WHERE FUNDING CAN BE GIVEN Great Britain and Israel, with some local interest in Surrey and London.
WHO CAN BENEFIT People with disabilities attending CTEC Centres, and students who have been awarded Karten Scholarships by universities or conservatoires.
WHAT IS FUNDED The establishment by suitable charities of centres for computer-aided training, education and communication (CTEC Centres) for people with severe physical, sensory or cognitive disabilities, or with mental health problems; scholarships for postgraduate study and research in selected subjects at selected universities and for postgraduate training of musicians of outstanding talent at selected conservatoires; and the trust makes occasional small donations to some charities in Surrey and London.
WHAT IS NOT FUNDED No grants to individuals.
TYPE OF GRANT Projects: sometimes funded over a period of two years; charities: normally one-off, but in some cases repeated annually; universities: scholarships.
RANGE OF GRANTS £50–£150,000.
FINANCES *Year* 2009–10 *Income* £254,095 *Grants* £1,149,013 *Assets* £7,033,348
TRUSTEES Ian H Karten, Chair; Mrs Mildred Karten; Tim Simon; Angela Hobbs.
OTHER INFORMATION In 2009–10 further funding was given for scholarships to nine institutions, including Haifa University and University College London, totalling £84,000; an individual scholarship of £900; and the sum of £5,300 was also given in small grants.
HOW TO APPLY The trust currently only considers grants to charities supported in the past. Individual scholarships are no longer available directly to students, instead the trust's chosen universities select the Karten Scholarships themselves. The trustees meet every six weeks to consider applications.
WHO TO APPLY TO Timothy Simon, Administrator, The Mill House, Newark Lane, Ripley, Surrey GU23 6DP *Tel* 01483 225020 *Fax* 01483 222420 *email* iankarten@btinternet.com *Website* www.karten-network.org.uk

■ The Kasner Charitable Trust

CC NO 267510   **ESTABLISHED** 1974
WHERE FUNDING CAN BE GIVEN UK and Israel.
WHO CAN BENEFIT Jewish organisations.
WHAT IS FUNDED Jewish charitable purposes.
RANGE OF GRANTS £25–£20,000.
SAMPLE GRANTS The Gevourah Ari Torah Academy Trust and The Sunderland Kolel (£20,000 each); United Jewish Appeal (£10,000); British Friends of Bnei Bracha Hospital (£5,000); S.O.F.T. (£4,000), Yesoda Hatorah School (£1,250); and British Friends of Nishmas Yisroel, British Friends of Shemaya Trust, British Friends of the Hebrew University, British Friends of Tiferet Shlomo, Friends of Lubavitch Scotland, Friends of Melachos Schomayim, Friends of Ohel Torah Trust, Talmud Torahs Torat Emet, and The JNF Charitable Trust (£100 each).
FINANCES *Year* 2009–10 *Income* £126,569 *Grants* £96,547 *Assets* £734,371

TRUSTEES Elfreda Erlich; Baruch Erlich; Josef Kasner; Judith Erlich.
HOW TO APPLY In writing to the correspondent. The trust gives grants to most of the organisations that apply. Certain organisations are investigated personally by the trustees and may receive larger grants.
WHO TO APPLY TO Josef Kasner, Trustee, 1a Gresham Gardens, London NW11 8NX *Tel* 020 8455 7830

■ The Kass Charitable Trust

CC NO 1006296   **ESTABLISHED** 1991
WHERE FUNDING CAN BE GIVEN UK.
WHO CAN BENEFIT Organisations.
WHAT IS FUNDED The trust now focuses on 'poverty and education for disadvantaged children'.
RANGE OF GRANTS Up to £11,000.
SAMPLE GRANTS British Friends of Mercaz Hatorah (£5,000).
FINANCES *Year* 2009–10 *Income* £39,812 *Grants* £40,336 *Assets* £13,179
TRUSTEES David Elliot Kass; Mrs Shulamith Malkah Sandler.
OTHER INFORMATION Grants totalled £40,000, of which £26,000 was given in grants to over 500 organisations. £6,000 was given to 'provide support for a needy family'.
HOW TO APPLY In writing to the correspondent.
WHO TO APPLY TO D E Kass, Trustee, 37 Sherwood Road, London NW4 1AE *Tel* 020 8371 3111 *email* dkass@vintange.co.uk

■ The Kathleen Trust

CC NO 1064516   **ESTABLISHED** 1997
WHERE FUNDING CAN BE GIVEN UK, with a preference for London.
WHO CAN BENEFIT Organisations benefiting young musicians.
WHAT IS FUNDED Typically course fees or instrument costs for outstanding young musicians.
SAMPLE GRANTS Previously organisation grants have been awarded to: Oxford Chamber Music Festival; and British Kidney Patient Association (Young Clarinetist).
FINANCES *Year* 2009–10 *Income* £24,720 *Grants* £61,828
TRUSTEES E R H Perks; Sir O C A Scott; Lady P A Scott; Mrs C N Withington.
OTHER INFORMATION The trust's main grant-making priority is individuals.
HOW TO APPLY In writing to the correspondent.
WHO TO APPLY TO E R H Perks, Trustee, Currey and Co, 21 Buckingham Gate, London SW1E 6LS *Tel* 020 7828 4091

■ The Michael and Ilse Katz Foundation

CC NO 263726   **ESTABLISHED** 1971
WHERE FUNDING CAN BE GIVEN Worldwide.
WHO CAN BENEFIT International and UK schemes and organisations benefiting Jewish people, at risk groups, and people who are disadvantaged by poverty or socially isolated.
WHAT IS FUNDED Primarily Jewish organisations. Medical/disability and welfare charities are also supported.
TYPE OF GRANT One-off and recurring.
RANGE OF GRANTS Up to £20,000.
SAMPLE GRANTS Jewish Care (£25,000); Community Security Trust (£14,000); Norwood Children and

Families First (£10,000); Bournemouth Orchestral Society (£8,000); The Worshipful Company of Butchers (£4,000); Nightingale House for Aged Jews (£1,500); Hillel Foundation and Magen David Adom UK (£2,000 each); Bournemouth Reform Synagogue, Holocaust Education Trust, MacMillan Cancer Relief, and Tel Aviv Sourasky Medical Centre (£1,000 each).

FINANCES *Year* 2009–10 *Income* £206,000 *Grants* £94,300 *Assets* £887,927

TRUSTEES Norris Gilbert; Osman Azis.

HOW TO APPLY In writing to the correspondent

WHO TO APPLY TO Osman Azis, Trustee, The Counting House, Trelill, Bodmin, Cornwall PL30 3HZ *Tel* 01208 851814

■ The Katzauer Charitable Settlement

CC NO 275110 **ESTABLISHED** 1977

WHERE FUNDING CAN BE GIVEN UK, but mainly Israel.

WHO CAN BENEFIT Jewish people.

WHAT IS FUNDED Jewish organisations, predominantly in Israel.

RANGE OF GRANTS Up to £30,000.

SAMPLE GRANTS Previous beneficiaries included: Chabad Ra'anana (£26,000); Moriah Community and Meir Hospital (£10,000); Nahalat Yehiel (£6,000); Mercaz Hatorah (£4,000); Rabbi K Gross (£3,800); KollelRalanana (£3,200); Friends of Lubavitch (£2,900); Beit Hatavshil (£1,000).

FINANCES *Year* 2009–10 *Income* £3,066 *Grants* £46,000

TRUSTEES Gordon C Smith; Mrs E Moller; M S Bailey; W Lian.

HOW TO APPLY In writing to the correspondent.

WHO TO APPLY TO Gordon C Smith, Trustee, Citroen Wells & Partners, Devonshire House, 1 Devonshire Street, London W1W 5DR *Tel* 020 7304 2000 *email* walter.lian@citroenwells.co.uk

■ The Kaufman Charitable Trust

CC NO 1136996 **ESTABLISHED** 2010

WHERE FUNDING CAN BE GIVEN England and Wales; Israel.

WHO CAN BENEFIT Organisations.

WHAT IS FUNDED Education; relief or prevention of poverty; advancement of the orthodox Jewish faith; disability; general charitable purposes.

TRUSTEES Pauline Kaufman; L I Kaufman.

HOW TO APPLY In writing to the correspondent.

WHO TO APPLY TO L I Kaufman, 100 Princes Park Avenue, London NW11 0JX *Tel* 020 8209 9880

■ The C S Kaufman Charitable Trust

CC NO 253194 **ESTABLISHED** 1967

WHERE FUNDING CAN BE GIVEN UK.

WHO CAN BENEFIT Organisations benefiting Jewish people.

WHAT IS FUNDED Mainly Jewish organisations.

WHAT IS NOT FUNDED No grants to individuals.

RANGE OF GRANTS Up to £30,000.

SAMPLE GRANTS Tomchei Yotzei Anglia (£20,000); Ezer Mikoidesh Foundation (£15,000); Kollel Sha'rei Shlomo (£10,000 in two grants); Tomchei Torah Family Relief (£5,000); Jewish Teacher Training College (£3,000 in two grants); SOFT (£1,000 in four grants); Yeshiva Tiferes Yaakov (£750); and ZVT (£150).

FINANCES *Year* 2009–10 *Income* £91,954 *Grants* £79,429 *Assets* £887,924

TRUSTEES I I Kaufman; Mrs L L Kaufman; J J Kaufman; S Kaufman.

OTHER INFORMATION Many of the grants recipients received more than one grant each during the year.

HOW TO APPLY In writing to the correspondent.

WHO TO APPLY TO C S Kaufman, 162 Whitehall Road, Gateshead, Tyne and Wear NE8 1TP

■ The Geoffrey John Kaye Charitable Foundation

CC NO 262547 **ESTABLISHED** 1971

WHERE FUNDING CAN BE GIVEN UK and overseas.

WHO CAN BENEFIT Jewish people.

WHAT IS FUNDED Jewish organisations and other charitable purposes.

TYPE OF GRANT Largely recurrent.

SAMPLE GRANTS UJIA (£26,000); Animal shelter A.C (£20,000); and JNF 1,000.

FINANCES *Year* 2009–10 *Income* £56,006 *Grants* £58,009 *Assets* £995,876

TRUSTEES G J Kaye; Mrs S Rose; J Pears.

OTHER INFORMATION In 2009–10, a donation totalling £11,000 was also given to one individual.

HOW TO APPLY In writing to the correspondent. Please note the foundation has previously stated that funds were fully committed.

WHO TO APPLY TO Robert Shaw, Chartered Account, 7 St John's Road, Harrow, Middlesex HA1 2EY *Tel* 020 8863 1234 *email* charity@mmrca.co.uk

■ The Emmanuel Kaye Foundation

CC NO 280281 **ESTABLISHED** 1980

WHERE FUNDING CAN BE GIVEN UK and overseas.

WHO CAN BENEFIT Organisations benefiting medical professionals, research workers, scientists, Jewish people, at-risk groups, people who are disadvantaged by poverty and socially isolated people.

WHAT IS FUNDED Medical research, welfare and Jewish organisations.

WHAT IS NOT FUNDED Only registered charities are supported.

RANGE OF GRANTS £50–£25,000.

SAMPLE GRANTS Previously: St James Conservation Trust (£6,000); Imperial College London and Nightingale (£5,000 each); Royal Academy of Arts and St Michaels Hospice – North Hampshire (£2,500 each); Jewish Care, the Holocaust Education Trust, Shaare Zedek UK, Community Links Trust, Laniado UK and UK Friends of Magen David Adom (£2,000 each); and Caius (£1,500).

FINANCES *Year* 2009–10 *Income* £19,326 *Grants* £15,000

TRUSTEES David Kaye; Lady Kaye; John Forster; Michael Cutler.

HOW TO APPLY In writing to the correspondent.

WHO TO APPLY TO The Secretary to the Trustees, Oakleigh House, High Street, Hartley Wintney, Hampshire RG27 8PE *Tel* 01252 843773

■ The Caron Keating Foundation

CC NO 1106160 **ESTABLISHED** 2004

WHERE FUNDING CAN BE GIVEN UK.

WHO CAN BENEFIT Small but significant cancer charities and support groups.

WHAT IS NOT FUNDED No grants to individuals.

SAMPLE GRANTS One main grant was made this year to Action Cancer Belfast (£25,000).

FINANCES *Year* 2009–10 *Income* £217,228 *Grants* £55,000 *Assets* £799,814

TRUSTEES M Keating; G Hunniford.

OTHER INFORMATION A number of grants for less than £20,000 were made totalling £30,000.

HOW TO APPLY In writing to the correspondent.

WHO TO APPLY TO The Secretary, PO Box 122, Sevenoaks, Kent TN13 1UM *email* info@caronkeating.org *Website* www.caronkeating.org

■ The Soli and Leah Kelaty Trust Fund

CC NO 1077620   **ESTABLISHED** 1999

WHERE FUNDING CAN BE GIVEN England and Wales.

WHO CAN BENEFIT Registered charities.

WHAT IS FUNDED General, education, overseas aid, religion.

FINANCES *Year* 2009–10 *Income* £36,200 *Grants* £29,468 *Assets* £33,783

TRUSTEES David Lerer; Fredrick Kelaty; Sharon Mozel Kelaty.

HOW TO APPLY In writing to the correspondent.

WHO TO APPLY TO F S Kelaty, Secretary, Block O, OCC Building, London N4 1TJ *Tel* 020 8800 2000 *email* freddy.kelaty@asiatic.co.uk

■ The Kelly Family Charitable Trust

CC NO 1102440   **ESTABLISHED** 2004

WHERE FUNDING CAN BE GIVEN UK.

WHO CAN BENEFIT Registered charities that support and encourage family welfare and cohesion.

WHAT IS FUNDED 'The trust has decided to prioritise its funding in favour of charities whose activities involve all or most family members in initiatives that support and encourage the family to work as a cohesive unit in tackling problems that face one or more of its members. The overall objective is to reinforce the potential benefit and support that family members as a unit can give to each other. Applications are also welcomed from sports and health-related charities whose activities comply with the above criteria.'

WHAT IS NOT FUNDED The following will not be considered: non-registered charities; grants directly to individuals; national charities (only regional projects will be considered); general appeals; organisations with specific religious or political agendas.

TYPE OF GRANT Capital and revenue grants; core funding as well as project-based grants.

RANGE OF GRANTS £1,000–£5,000.

SAMPLE GRANTS The beneficiaries during the year were: 3D Drumchapel; Addaction; Cambridge Mediation; Circle; Families First; Guys Gift; HomeStart Havant; Made of Money Project; MOSAC; Multi-Cultural Family Base; Norfolk Playvan; Parent to Parent; Positive Help; Richmond's Hope; The Zone; and Westminster Befriend a Family.

FINANCES *Year* 2009–10 *Income* £126,380 *Grants* £122,016 *Assets* £2,696,340

TRUSTEES Annie Kelly; Brian Mattingley; Jenny Kelly; Sheldon Cordell; Michael Field; Emma Maier.

OTHER INFORMATION Applications are welcomed from sports and health-related charities and particularly from relatively new organisations to help them become established.

HOW TO APPLY Applications should be made using the application form, which can be downloaded from the trust's website. Applications should be

sent by email, and should be supported by annual accounts where available. Grants are awarded twice a year to charities and are usually for amount between £1,000 and £5,000, but the trustees will consider requests for higher amounts. Applications must be submitted by 1 March and 1 September to be considered at the subsequent meeting. The trustees will ask for more detail for those applications that pass the initial screening and may visit the projects they wish to support.

WHO TO APPLY TO Stuart Armstrong, Administrator, 8 Mansfield Place, Edinburgh EH3 6NB *Tel* 0131 315 4879 *email* s.armstrong@kfct.org *Website* www.kfct.org.uk

■ Kelsick's Educational Foundation

CC NO 526956   **ESTABLISHED** 1723

WHERE FUNDING CAN BE GIVEN Lakes parish (Ambleside, Grasmere, Langdale and part of Troutbeck).

WHO CAN BENEFIT Organisations and individuals under 25 years of age.

WHAT IS FUNDED Educational needs of individuals; organisations providing educational benefit to those under 25. School activities such as educational visits, field trips, music lessons. Academic courses and apprenticeships including equipment.

WHAT IS NOT FUNDED Holidays, course items without receipts.

TYPE OF GRANT Capital and project support, for longer than three years.

RANGE OF GRANTS Usually £50–£3,000. With large grants of up to £50,000 given to schools.

SAMPLE GRANTS £111,000 to individuals; and £119,000 to organisations.

FINANCES *Year* 2009–10 *Income* £353,153 *Grants* £229,823 *Assets* £6,543,233

TRUSTEES Mr N F Hutchinson, Chair; N M Tyson; Mrs L A Dixon; Mrs H M Fuller; Mr P Jackson; Mr J O Halstead; Mrs J Renouf; Mr N C Martin; Canon W R F Coke; Mr R Curphey.

OTHER INFORMATION The Kelsick Foundation office is open Monday-Friday: 9.30 to 12.30.

HOW TO APPLY Application forms are available from the correspondent and from the website.

WHO TO APPLY TO P G Frost, Clerk, Kelsick Centre, St Mary's Lane, Ambleside, Cumbria LA22 9DG *Tel* 01539 431289 *Fax* 01539 431292 *email* john@kelsick.plus.com *Website* www.kelsick.org.uk

■ The Kemp–Welch Charitable Trust

CC NO 263501   **ESTABLISHED** 1972

WHERE FUNDING CAN BE GIVEN UK.

WHO CAN BENEFIT National and local charities.

WHAT IS FUNDED Medical research, parochial church councils, care and welfare of both children and the elderly and educational establishments, arts and culture, wildlife and the environment.

RANGE OF GRANTS £100 to £10,000.

SAMPLE GRANTS Beneficiaries included: Winchester College (£10,000); Royal Horticultural Society and Scottish Countryside Alliance Educational Trust (£2,500 each); Little Hallingbury Parochial Church Council (£1,500); Youth Concern Trust (£1,250); National Portrait Gallery (£1,000); Children with Leukaemia and Help for Heroes (£500 each); and Ace Africa UK, Essex Young

Musicians Trust and Stanley Hall Opera (£250 each).

FINANCES *Year* 2009–10 *Income* £31,019 *Grants* £28,650 *Assets* £57,307

TRUSTEES Sir John Kemp–Welch; Lady Diana Elisabeth Kemp–Welch.

HOW TO APPLY No unsolicited applications.

WHO TO APPLY TO Sir John Kemp–Welch, Trustee, Little Hallingbury Place, Wrights Green Lane, Little Hallingbury, Bishop's Stortford, Hertfordshire CM22 7RE *Tel* 01279 722455

■ The Kay Kendall Leukaemia Fund

CC NO 290772   **ESTABLISHED** 1984

WHERE FUNDING CAN BE GIVEN Unrestricted.

WHO CAN BENEFIT Organisations conducting research into and treatment of leukaemia.

WHAT IS FUNDED Medical research into and treatment of leukaemia.

WHAT IS NOT FUNDED Circular appeals for general support are not funded.

TYPE OF GRANT Research, capital, equipment.

SAMPLE GRANTS Cambridge Institute for Medical Research (£896,000); Institute of Cancer Research (£680,500); Imperial College London (£229,000); The Rayne's Institute (£180,000); Royal Bournemouth Hospital (£150,000); Doncaster & Bassetlaw Hospitals NHS Foundation Trust (£75,000); Paterson Institute for Cancer Research (£53,500); University Hospitals Morecambe Bay Hospitals NHS Trust (£35,000); Bolton Hospitals NHS Trust (£20,000); and Aintree University Hospitals NHS Foundation Trust (£18,500).

FINANCES *Year* 2009–10 *Income* £1,667,000 *Grants* £5,229,000 *Assets* £40,067,000

TRUSTEES Judith Portrait; Timothy J Sainsbury; Christopher Stone.

OTHER INFORMATION The trust is one of the Sainsbury Family Charitable Trusts which share a common administration. An application to one is taken as an application to all.

HOW TO APPLY A preliminary letter or telephone call to the administration offices of the Kay Kendall Leukaemia Fund may be helpful to determine whether or not a proposal is likely to be eligible. Application forms are available by contacting the trust's office. Research Proposal: 'Applicants should complete the approved Application Form and include a research proposal (aims, background, plan of investigation, justification for budget). The research proposal should be 3–5 single-spaced pages for project grants (excluding references, costings and CV) and up to 10 single-spaced pages for programme grants. Applications should be submitted by email in addition to the provision of a hard copy with original signature. The trustees will take account of annual inflation and of salary increases related to nationally negotiated pay scales and these should not be built into the application. Salaries should generally be on nationally agreed scales. Tenured or non time-limited appointments will not be supported. The trustees may, from time to time, set special conditions for the award of a grant. Final decision on the award of a grant is made by the trustees, having taken into account advice from their scientific advisers. The trustees consider proposals twice each year, normally May and October. To allow for the refereeing process, new full proposals for the May meeting should be received by 28 February and for the October/

November meeting by 15 July. Late applications may be deferred for 6 months.'

WHO TO APPLY TO Alan Bookbinder, Director, Allington House, 1st Floor, 150 Victoria Street, London SW1E 5AE *Tel* 020 7410 0330 *Fax* 020 7410 0332 *email* info@kklf.org.uk *Website* www.kklf.org.uk

---

■ William Kendall's Charity (Wax Chandlers' Company)

CC NO 228361   **ESTABLISHED** 1559

WHERE FUNDING CAN BE GIVEN Greater London and the London borough of Bexley.

WHO CAN BENEFIT Charitable organisations in Greater London working for relief of need; in Bexley, charitable organisations generally.

WHAT IS FUNDED Most donations are for relief of need in London.

WHAT IS NOT FUNDED Grants are not normally made to large charities, charities whose accounts disclose substantial reserves or non-registered charities. Grants are not made to replace cuts in funding made by local authorities or others, schemes or activities which would be regarded as relieving central or local government of their statutory responsibilities or cover deficits already incurred.

TYPE OF GRANT One-off or recurring.

RANGE OF GRANTS £500–£25,000, typical grant £5,000.

SAMPLE GRANTS Grants from the Bexley Fund included those made to: Bexley Accessible Transport Scheme (£5,000); Bexley Trust for Adult Students and Bexley Women's Aid (£2,000 each); and Carers' Support Bexley (£1,000).

FINANCES *Year* 2009–10 *Income* £75,883 *Grants* £113,555 *Assets* £3,010,971

TRUSTEES Wax Chandlers' Company.

OTHER INFORMATION Grants to 6 individuals from the Persons in Need Fund totalled £5,000

HOW TO APPLY The company undertakes its own research and does not respond to unsolicited applications.

WHO TO APPLY TO The Clerk to the Wax Chandlers' Company, Wax Chandlers' Hall, 6 Gresham Street, London EC2V 7AD *Tel* 020 7606 3591 *Fax* 020 7600 5462 *email* info@chandlers.ndonet.com *Website* www.waxchandlers.org.uk/charity

---

■ The Kennedy Charitable Foundation

CC NO 1052001   **ESTABLISHED** 1995

WHERE FUNDING CAN BE GIVEN Unrestricted, but mainly Ireland with a preference for County Mayo and County Sligo.

WHO CAN BENEFIT Registered charities and individuals.

WHAT IS FUNDED Predominantly organisations connected with the Roman Catholic faith, mainly in Ireland.

RANGE OF GRANTS £200–£50,000; typical grant £1,000–£5,000.

SAMPLE GRANTS Newman Institute (£87,000); Ballintubber Abbey Trust (£23,000); Lower Shankhill Community Association (£18,000); Elizabeth Hardie Ferguson Trust (£10,000); St Ann's Hospice (£6,000); Archdiocese of Cardiff and Diocese of Hexham and Newcastle (£5,000 each); Destination Florida, Lancaster Roman Catholic Diocese Trustees and St Vincent de Paul Society – Wythenshawe (£2,000 each);

East Belfast Mission and Society of African Missions (£1,000 each); Leukaemia Research (£500); and NSPCC (£100).

FINANCES *Year* 2009–10 *Income* £122,812 *Grants* £261,471 *Assets* £250,624

TRUSTEES Patrick James Kennedy; Kathleen Kennedy; John Gerard Kennedy; Patrick Joseph Francis Kennedy; Anna Maria Kelly.

HOW TO APPLY The foundation says that 'unsolicited applications are not accepted'.

WHO TO APPLY TO The Trustees, 12th Floor, Bank House, Charlotte Street, Manchester M1 4ET *Tel* 0161 236 8191 *Fax* 0161 236 4814 *email* kcf@pye158.freeserve.co.uk

----

■ The Kennel Club Charitable Trust

CC NO 327802   **ESTABLISHED** 1988

WHERE FUNDING CAN BE GIVEN UK.

WHO CAN BENEFIT Registered charities or research bodies benefiting dogs; research workers and vets; and people who are disabled blind or deaf where dogs are involved (e.g. in support of human beings).

WHAT IS FUNDED The trust describes its objects as 'science, welfare and support'. It supports the furthering of research into canine diseases and hereditary disorders of dogs and also organisations concerned with the welfare of dogs in need and those which aim to improve the quality of life of humans by promoting dogs as practical or therapeutic aids.

WHAT IS NOT FUNDED The trust does not give grants directly to individuals; veterinary nurses can apply to the British Veterinary Nursing Association where bursaries are available. The trustees tend not to favour funding the costs of building work.

TYPE OF GRANT One-off and recurring for set periods.

RANGE OF GRANTS The trust gives both ongoing and one-off grants, generally up to £35,000 each a year for research and of up to £10,000 each for support of dogs and those who care for them or benefit from them.

FINANCES *Year* 2010 *Income* £846,574 *Grants* £777,918 *Assets* £2,779,514

TRUSTEES M Townsend, Chair; M Herrtage; W H King; J Spurling; Mrs J Ziman.

OTHER INFORMATION Further information is available at the trust's website.

HOW TO APPLY In writing to the administrator, including latest accounts. Please state clearly details of the costs for which you are requesting funding, and for what purpose and over what period the funding is required. The trustees meet three or four times a year.

WHO TO APPLY TO Mrs Cas Oakes, 1–5 Clarges Street, Piccadilly, London W1J 8AB *Tel* 020 7518 1037 *email* dholford@the-kennel-club.org.uk *Website* www.mad4dogs.org.uk

----

■ Kent Community Foundation

CC NO 1084361   **ESTABLISHED** 2001

WHERE FUNDING CAN BE GIVEN Kent.

WHO CAN BENEFIT Local charities, community groups and voluntary organisations and individuals.

WHAT IS FUNDED Improving the quality of life for people in Kent. The foundation administers a number of funds established by individuals, families and companies. In addition it has its own general fund which enables it to support voluntary groups which fall outside the stated criteria of these funds.

RANGE OF GRANTS £100–£600,000.

FINANCES *Year* 2009–10 *Income* £6,034,435 *Grants* £2,831,897 *Assets* £5,726,906

TRUSTEES Peter Hardy, Chair; Arthur Gulland; Laura Jones; Eric Watts; Alan Rogers; Fiona Sunley; Bella Coltrain; Amanda Cottrell; Peter Lake.

OTHER INFORMATION A member of the Community Foundation Network, Kent Community Foundation is a charitable foundation set up to encourage philanthropy for the benefit of the people of Kent.

HOW TO APPLY Further information on applications can be obtained from the Grants Team.

WHO TO APPLY TO The Grants Team, 23 Evegate Park Barn, Evegate, Smeeth, Kent TN25 6SX *Tel* 01303 814500 *email* admin@kentcf.org.uk *Website* www.kentcf.org.uk

----

■ The Nancy Kenyon Charitable Trust

CC NO 265359   **ESTABLISHED** 1972

WHERE FUNDING CAN BE GIVEN UK.

WHO CAN BENEFIT Registered charities only.

WHAT IS FUNDED General charitable purposes. Primarily for people and causes known to the trustees.

WHAT IS NOT FUNDED Grants not usually made to individuals.

RANGE OF GRANTS Up to £11,000.

SAMPLE GRANTS Nancy Oldfield Trust (£10,500); the Rainbow Farm Trust (£8,500); Nehemiah Project (£3,000); The Good Shepherd Project, Cheltenham Youth for Christ and The Starfish Cafe, Cambodia (£2,000 each); Cheltenham Youth for Christ and the Starfish Cafe – Cambodia (£2,000 each); Emthonjeni Trust, Epic Arts and Cheltenham Open Door (£1,000 each); and Uganda Shoe Box Appeal (£400).

FINANCES *Year* 2009–10 *Income* £37,330 *Grants* £41,150 *Assets* £1,430,121

TRUSTEES Lucy Phipps; Maureen Kenyon; Christopher Kenyon; Sally Kenyon; Peter Kenyon.

OTHER INFORMATION £6,000 was also awarded to individuals in 2009–10.

HOW TO APPLY In writing to the correspondent at any time. Applications for causes not known to the trustees are considered annually in December.

WHO TO APPLY TO Alison Smith, Brook Financial Management Ltd, Meads Barn, Ashwell Business Park, Ilminster, Somerset TA19 9DX *Tel* 01460 259852

■ Keren Association

CC NO 313119   **ESTABLISHED** 1961

WHERE FUNDING CAN BE GIVEN UK.

WHO CAN BENEFIT Organisations benefiting children, young adults and Jewish people.

WHAT IS FUNDED The advancement of education; the provision of religious instruction and training in traditional Judaism; general charitable purposes.

SAMPLE GRANTS Previous beneficiaries include: Beis Aharon Trust, Yeshivah Belz Machnovke, U T A, Yetev Lev Jerulalem, Lomdei Tom h Belz Machnovke, Friends of Beis Yaakov, Yeshlvat Lom dei Torah, Friends of Arad, Kupat Gmach Vezer Nlsuin, Clwk Yaakov and British Heart Foundation.

FINANCES *Year* 2009–10 *Income* £7,530,788 *Grants* £6,485,496 *Assets* £35,481,873

TRUSTEES E Englander, Chair; Mrs S Englander; P N Englander; S Z Englander; B Englander; J S Englander; Mrs H Z Weiss; Mrs N Weiss.

OTHER INFORMATION A list of grant recipients was not included in the accounts.

HOW TO APPLY In writing to the correspondent.

WHO TO APPLY TO Mrs S Englander, Trustee, 136 Clapton Common, London E5 9AG

■ Kermaville Ltd

CC NO 266075   ESTABLISHED 1973

WHERE FUNDING CAN BE GIVEN UK, Israel.

WHO CAN BENEFIT Organisations benefiting Jewish people.

WHAT IS FUNDED Advancement of religion according to the orthodox Jewish faith and general charitable purposes.

SAMPLE GRANTS Previous beneficiaries include: Yeshivas Imrei Chaim Spinka, Bais Rochel D'Satmar, Keren Tzedoka Vechessed, Kollel Congregation Yetev Lev, Kollel Atzei Chaim, United Talmudical Association, Ponevez Beth Hamedrash and Lolev Charitable Trust.

FINANCES *Year* 2009–10 *Income* £21,431 *Grants* £25,000

TRUSTEES L Rabinowitz.

HOW TO APPLY In writing to the correspondent.

WHO TO APPLY TO M Freund, 3 Overlea Road, London E5 9BG *Tel* 020 8806 5783

■ E and E Kernkraut Charities Limited

CC NO 275636   ESTABLISHED 1978

WHERE FUNDING CAN BE GIVEN UK.

WHO CAN BENEFIT Charitable organisations.

WHAT IS FUNDED General charitable purposes, Jewish and education.

FINANCES *Year* 2009–10 *Income* £930,171 *Grants* £743,507 *Assets* £5,788,075

TRUSTEES Eli Kernkraut, Chair; Esther Kernkraut; Joseph Kernkraut; Jacob Kernkraut.

OTHER INFORMATION Accounts were on file at the Charity Commission, but without a list of grants.

HOW TO APPLY In writing to the correspondent.

WHO TO APPLY TO The Trustees, c/o Cohen Arnold, New Burlington House, 1075 Finchley Road, London NW11 0PU *Tel* 020 8731 0777

■ The Peter Kershaw Trust

CC NO 268934   ESTABLISHED 1974

WHERE FUNDING CAN BE GIVEN Greater Manchester and North Cheshire for social welfare and school bursaries. Research and youth work not defined.

WHO CAN BENEFIT Registered charities benefiting young adults and older people, carers and people who are disadvantaged by poverty, homeless or socially isolated.

WHAT IS FUNDED Social welfare; medical research; grants to medical and other institutions, bursaries for schools.

WHAT IS NOT FUNDED No grants to individuals or for building projects.

TYPE OF GRANT One-off or core costs. Also research, running costs, salaries and start-up costs. Funding may be given for up to three years.

RANGE OF GRANTS Up to £25,000.

SAMPLE GRANTS H-Pan and Stonehouse Gang (£15,000 each); Fairbridge, Sycamore Project and United Estates of Wythenshawe (£10,000 each); Mustard Tree (£8,000); Bolton School and Manchester High School for Girls (£6,000 each); Barnabus, Jigsaw and m13 Youth Project (£5,000 each); St Bede's (£3,500);

Cornerstone Day Centre (£2,000); Booth's Centre and Salford Child Contract Centre (£1,000 each); and Christie Hospital (£250).

FINANCES *Year* 2009–10 *Income* £194,622 *Grants* £156,020 *Assets* £6,345,274

TRUSTEES R P Kershaw, Chair; Mrs H F Kershaw; Mrs M L Rushbrooke; D Tully; Mrs R Adams; T Page.

OTHER INFORMATION David Tully and Peter Kershaw are also trustees of Edward Holt Trust (Charity Commission no. 224741) and The Booth Charities (Charity Commission no. 221800); David Tully is also a trustee of CHR Charitable Trust (Charity Commission no. 213579); and Tim Page is also a trustee of Cheadle Royal Industries Charitable Trust (Charity Commission no. 509813).

HOW TO APPLY In writing to the correspondent, however the trust is always oversubscribed. The trustees normally meet twice a year in May and November to consider recommendations for grant aid which will be disbursed in June and December respectively.

WHO TO APPLY TO Bryan Peak, Secretary and Trustee, 22 Ashworth Park, Knutsford, Cheshire WA16 9DE *Tel* 01565 651086 *email* pkershawtrust@btinternet.com

■ The Kessler Foundation

CC NO 290759   ESTABLISHED 1984

WHERE FUNDING CAN BE GIVEN UK.

WHO CAN BENEFIT Charitable organisations, with a preference for Jewish organisations.

WHAT IS FUNDED The foundation will assist organisations which may be devoted to: the advancement of Jewish religion, learning, education and culture; the improvement of inter-faith, community and race relations, and the combating of prejudice; the alleviation of the problems of minority and disadvantaged groups; the protection, maintenance and monitoring of human rights; the promotion of health and welfare; the protection and preservation of records and objects with special significance to the Jewish and general community; or the encouragement of arts, literature and science including archaeology, natural history and protection of the environment with special reference to the Jewish community.

WHAT IS NOT FUNDED In general the foundation will not support the larger well-known charities with an income in excess of £100,000, and will not provide grants for social, medical and welfare projects which are the responsibility of local or national government.

RANGE OF GRANTS Up to £2,000.

SAMPLE GRANTS Previous beneficiaries have included: Jewish Council for Racial Equality, Asylum Aid and Bedouin Women for Themselves (£2,000 each); International Council of Jewish Women (£1,500); Project Harar Ethiopia (£1,200); Peace Child Israel, Makor Charitable Trust, Jewish Bereavement Counselling Service and Theatre Objektiv (£1,000 each); Friends of Israel Educational Foundation and Quest New London Synagogue (£750 each); Ipswich Community Playbus and Aid for Romanian Orphanages (£500 each); and Arts to Share (£250).

FINANCES *Year* 2008–09 *Income* £16,789 *Grants* £10,000

TRUSTEES G Horwitz, Chair; Mrs J Jacobs; Prof. M Geller; Mr N P J Saphir; Mrs J F Mayers; P Morgenstern.

HOW TO APPLY On a form available from the correspondent. The trustees meet at least twice a year in June and December. Applicants will be notified of decisions as soon as possible after then.

WHO TO APPLY TO Gwen Horwitz, Jewish Chronicle Newspaper Ltd, 25 Furnival Street, London EC4A 1JT

....

■ Keswick Hall Trust

CC NO 311246   **ESTABLISHED** 1968
WHERE FUNDING CAN BE GIVEN England, Wales, East Anglia.
WHO CAN BENEFIT University of East Anglia, its teachers and students (especially student teachers) and corporate organisations in the dioceses of Ely, Norwich and St Edmundsbury and Ipswich.
WHAT IS FUNDED Grants to support the education and training of religious education (RE) teachers and students, corporate grants to support the teaching of RE, and research and development grants in that subject.
WHAT IS NOT FUNDED The trust does not make grants for buildings, courses in pastoral work or courses which are purely for personal interest. Retrospective applications will not be considered. If an application is received from a student who has already started a course, but has not yet completed it, the application will not be regarded as a retrospective application. The trustees state that they give priority to their own initiatives.
RANGE OF GRANTS Up to £8,000.
FINANCES *Year* 2009–10 *Income* £214,462 *Grants* £64,559 *Assets* £3,959,408
TRUSTEES Ven. John Cox; Revd Canon T Elbourne; T Haydn; A Mash; Mr D Hicks; Revd P Richmond; Mr D Briggs; D Bartlett; D Broom; M McGarvie.
HOW TO APPLY Grant applications should be received by the beginning of the months of January, May or September each year and must be made online at the Keswick Hall Charity website.
WHO TO APPLY TO Malcolm Green, PO Box 307, Woodbridge IP13 6WL *Tel* 07760 433409 *email* admin@keswickhalltrust.org.uk *Website* www.keswickhalltrust.org.uk

....

■ The Ursula Keyes Trust

CC NO 517200   **ESTABLISHED** 1985
WHERE FUNDING CAN BE GIVEN Chester, but occasionally other areas.
WHO CAN BENEFIT Individuals and institutions benefiting at risk groups, and people who are disadvantaged by poverty, socially isolated or sick.
WHAT IS FUNDED The purpose of the trust is to support the financial needs of various organisations and individuals in the Chester area, particularly in the fields of health and social care. A wide range of causes are supported, including cultural and leisure projects, particularly when matched by other fundraising efforts. Funds are mainly directed at the cost of capital projects and equipment rather than as a source of funding for on-going running costs or salaries. National charities are also considered for support if there is a clear link to a local beneficiary.
WHAT IS NOT FUNDED No support for students or political groups.
TYPE OF GRANT Small and large grants.
RANGE OF GRANTS Most are for under £10,000.
SAMPLE GRANTS Hospice of the Good Shepherd (£50,000); Claire House and Clatterbridge

(£10,000 each); Upton High School and the Wingate Centre (£5,000 each); Vision 4 Children (£3,000); Age Concern (£2,500); Wirral Girl Guides, Spinal Injuries Association and Lache Park (£2,000 each); and Children's Centre, RNIB and Shelter (£1,000 each).
FINANCES *Year* 2009 *Income* £294,648 *Grants* £129,282 *Assets* £5,246,727
TRUSTEES J F Kane, Chair; Dr R A Owen; H M Shaw; Dr A E Elliot; J R Leaman; J D Brimelow; Dr G Sissons.
OTHER INFORMATION Grants were also made to individuals totalling £17,500.
HOW TO APPLY In writing to the correspondent.
WHO TO APPLY TO Sharon Bakewell, Administrator to the Trustees, c/o Baker Tilly, Steam Mill, Chester, Cheshire CH3 5AN *Tel* 01244 505100 *Fax* 01244 505101 *Website* www.ursula-keyes-trust.org.uk

....

■ The Kiawah Charitable Trust

CC NO 1107730   **ESTABLISHED** 2005
WHERE FUNDING CAN BE GIVEN Primarily sub Saharan Africa and southern India.
WHO CAN BENEFIT Charitable organisations.
WHAT IS FUNDED Young people whose lives are vulnerable due to health and/or education issues.
SAMPLE GRANTS Sight Savers International (£47,000); Hope and Homes for Children (£40,000); and Railway Children (£30,000).
FINANCES *Year* 2009–10 *Income* £492,372 *Grants* £116,594 *Assets* £837,728
TRUSTEES Peter Smitham; Lynne Smitham; Vic Miles.
HOW TO APPLY 'The trustees consider any applications received for grants and adopt a proactive approach in seeking worthy causes requiring support.'
WHO TO APPLY TO Anne Marie Piper, c/o Farrer and Co, 65–66 Lincoln's Inn Fields, London WC2A 3LH *Tel* 020 7242 2022

....

■ The Robert Kiln Charitable Trust

CC NO 262756   **ESTABLISHED** 1970
WHERE FUNDING CAN BE GIVEN UK, with a special interest in Hertfordshire and Bedfordshire. Occasionally overseas.
WHO CAN BENEFIT Organisations benefiting archaeologists and small environmental organisations.
WHAT IS FUNDED General charitable purposes with a preference for small organisations.
WHAT IS NOT FUNDED Applications from individuals, large national appeals, churches, schools or artistic projects (such as theatre groups) will not be considered.
TYPE OF GRANT Usually one-off, or instalments for particular projects.
RANGE OF GRANTS £250–£2,500. Mostly £500.
SAMPLE GRANTS Beneficiaries receiving grants of £1,000 each or more included: Bucks Archaeological Society (£1,500); Global Heritage Fune (£1,000); Hertford Symphony Orchestra (£3,250); South West Maritime Archaeology Group (£2,000).
FINANCES *Year* 2009–10 *Income* £43,942 *Grants* £34,490 *Assets* £839,017
TRUSTEES S W J Kiln; Mrs B Kiln; Dr N P Akers; Mrs J Akers.
OTHER INFORMATION The trust stated: 'Most of the income is allocated to regular beneficiaries, where relationship has been built up over many years (55%). The trustees are keen to support

new projects, particularly those from small local organisations. The trustees support many charities where they have a particular interest.'

HOW TO APPLY In writing to the correspondent, setting out as much information as seems relevant and, if possible, costings and details of any other support. The trust no longer has twice-yearly distribution meetings and will endeavour to distribute funds within one month of receiving applications, subject to funds being available. The trust does not acknowledge receipt of applications unless an sae is enclosed.

WHO TO APPLY TO Mrs Sarah Howell, Secretary to the trustees, 15a Bull Plain, Hertford SG14 1DX *Tel* 01992 554962 *email* kilntrust@hemscott. net

■ The Eric and Margaret Kinder Charitable Trust

CC NO 1136528   **ESTABLISHED** 2010

WHERE FUNDING CAN BE GIVEN UK with a preference for North West England.

WHO CAN BENEFIT Individuals and organisations with some preference for children and young people.

WHAT IS FUNDED Priorities are the advancement of education of young people in music in the North West and assisting in the treatment of Alzheimer's disease.

TRUSTEES M Harris; Ms K M Allen; E Kinder; C W Kinder.

HOW TO APPLY In writing to the correspondent.

WHO TO APPLY TO Wrigleys Solicitors LLP, 17–21 Cookridge Street, Leeds LS2 3AG *Tel* 0113 204 5724

■ The King Henry VIII Endowed Trust – Warwick

CC NO 232862   **ESTABLISHED** 1964

WHERE FUNDING CAN BE GIVEN The former borough of Warwick only.

WHO CAN BENEFIT Half the income goes to Warwick churches, 30% to Warwick Independent Schools Foundation and 20% for the 'Town Share' – general charitable purposes for the inhabitants of the town of Warwick.

WHAT IS FUNDED General charitable purposes in the former borough of Warwick (in effect now covered by the postcode area CV34). (The grant total in this entry only applies to the grants for general charitable purposes.).

RANGE OF GRANTS £300–£75,000.

SAMPLE GRANTS Warwick Hospital Cancer Ward Appeal (£75,000); Newburgh Primary School (£36,000); Warwick Tennis Club (£15,000); Senior Citizens Holiday Club (£9,000); and Warwick International Festival (£3,000).

FINANCES *Year* 2010 *Income* £1,486,186 *Grants* £211,375 *Assets* £25,879,243

TRUSTEES Trustees' names not disclosed – dispensation given.

OTHER INFORMATION A total of £1.6 million was distributed during the year.

HOW TO APPLY In writing to the correspondent. Trustees meet to make grants six times a year.

WHO TO APPLY TO Jonathan Wassall, Clerk and Receiver, 12 High Street, Warwick CV34 4AP *Tel* 01926 495533 *Fax* 01926 401464 *email* jwassall@kinghenryviii.org.uk *Website* www.kinghenryviii.org.uk

■ King Sturge Charitable Trust

CC NO 1133593   **ESTABLISHED** 2010

WHERE FUNDING CAN BE GIVEN Worldwide.

WHO CAN BENEFIT Registered charities.

WHAT IS FUNDED General charitable purposes.

TRUSTEES Richard Batten; Simon Bailey.

OTHER INFORMATION King Sturge is a supplier of property services to owners and occupiers in the UK industrial, office, retail, hotels & leisure, healthcare and residential sectors.

HOW TO APPLY In writing to the correspondent.

WHO TO APPLY TO Simon Bailey, Trustee, King Sturge, 30 Warwick Street, London W1B 5NH

■ The King/Cullimore Charitable Trust

CC NO 1074928   **ESTABLISHED** 1999

WHERE FUNDING CAN BE GIVEN UK.

WHO CAN BENEFIT Charitable organisations.

WHAT IS FUNDED General charitable purposes.

RANGE OF GRANTS From £500 up to £100,000.

SAMPLE GRANTS Prostate Cancer (£100,000); Jubilee Sailing Trust (£25,000); Study Group Sea Turtles and Woodrow High House (£20,000 each); Crisis, Leonard Cheshire Foundation and Woodland Trust (£10,000 each); and Countryside Foundation for Education and Music in Hospitals (£5,000 each).

FINANCES *Year* 2009–10 *Income* £310,391 *Grants* £228,500 *Assets* £5,407,975

TRUSTEES P A Cullimore; C Gardner; C J King; A G McKechnie.

HOW TO APPLY In writing to the correspondent.

WHO TO APPLY TO P A Cullimore, Trustee, 52 Ledborough Lane, Beaconsfield, Buckinghamshire HP9 2DF *Tel* 01494 678811

■ The King's Fund

CC NO 1126980   **ESTABLISHED** 1897

WHERE FUNDING CAN BE GIVEN London.

WHO CAN BENEFIT Voluntary or statutory organisations in the health sector in or serving Greater London.

WHAT IS FUNDED Through the Partners for Health in London funding and development programme, focusing initially on four areas: end-of-life care, sexual health, mental health advocacy and integrated health care; delivering, on behalf of the Department of Health, the current Enhancing the Healing Environment programmes and developing new areas of application; delivering a national awards scheme to identify and promote best practice in community organisations working to improve health; developing analytical tools to be used throughout the National Health Service.

The objects of the fund are the promotion of health and the alleviation of sickness for the benefit of the public, by working with and for healthcare organisations.

TYPE OF GRANT One-off grants are available.

FINANCES *Year* 2010 *Income* £14,094,000 *Grants* £91,000 *Assets* £145,688,000

TRUSTEES Sir Christopher Kelly; Mr Strone Macpherson; Mr Simon Stevens' Dr Penny Dash' Dame Jacquelie Doherty; Ms Judith Goffe; Prof. Julian Le Grand; Mr David Wooton.

OTHER INFORMATION The King's Fund is a leading independent health care charity, set up in 1897 by the Prince of Wales, later King Edward VII, to support the improvement of the health of Londoners and health care in London. Today it fulfils this mission through a range of activities, including research and policy analysis as well as grantmaking – which accounts for about one-quarter of its charitable expenditure.

HOW TO APPLY Applicants are advised to check the fund's website or contact them directly for the latest information on current funding programmes.

WHO TO APPLY TO Kate Batlin, The Funding and Development Department, 11–13 Cavendish Square, London W1G 0AN *Fax* 020 7307 2809 *email* website@kingsfund.org.uk *Website* www.kingsfund.org.uk

---

■ The Kingsbury Charity

CC NO 205797 **ESTABLISHED** 1986

WHERE FUNDING CAN BE GIVEN Ancient parish of Kingsbury.

WHO CAN BENEFIT Older people in need.

WHAT IS FUNDED Organisations in the ancient parish of Kingsbury.

FINANCES *Year* 2009 *Income* £279,903 *Grants* £15,750 *Assets* £8,284,068

TRUSTEES Gwendoline Tookey; Revd Clive Morton, Chair; Valerie Pope; Julia Day; Rose Peacock; Terence Hopkins.

HOW TO APPLY In writing to the correspondent.

WHO TO APPLY TO Philomena Hughes, Hon Secretary, 29 Bowater Crescent, London NW9 0XD *Tel* 020 8205 9712

■ The Mary Kinross Charitable Trust

CC NO 212206 **ESTABLISHED** 1957

WHERE FUNDING CAN BE GIVEN UK.

WHO CAN BENEFIT Registered charities benefiting research workers, young people and people disadvantaged by poverty.

WHAT IS FUNDED General charitable purposes. Donations confined to projects which the trust promotes and manages, particularly in the areas of medical research, to benefit the communities of which trustees have direct knowledge: youth, mental health and penal affairs. Grants made under the heading of youth are often made with crime prevention in mind.

WHAT IS NOT FUNDED No grants to individuals.

TYPE OF GRANT Capital projects, core costs and recurring.

FINANCES *Year* 2010–11 *Income* £710,786 *Grants* £699,162 *Assets* £28,444,029

TRUSTEES Elizabeth Shields, Chair; Fiona Adams; Neil Cross; Jonathan Haw; Robert McDougall.

HOW TO APPLY 'Because the trustees have no office staff and work from home, they prefer dealing with written correspondence rather than telephone calls from applicants soliciting funds.' Please note: unsolicited applications to this trust are very unlikely to be successful.

WHO TO APPLY TO Fiona Adams, Trustee, 36 Grove Avenue, Moseley, Birmingham B13 9RY

■ Kinsurdy Charitable Trust

CC NO 1076085 **ESTABLISHED** 1999

WHERE FUNDING CAN BE GIVEN UK.

WHO CAN BENEFIT Registered charities.

WHAT IS FUNDED General charitable purposes.

RANGE OF GRANTS Up to £7,500.

SAMPLE GRANTS RABI, RNLI and Alzheimer's Society (£7,500 each); Save the Children, Age Concern, Guide Dogs, WWF – UK, Macmillan Cancer Support, British Red Cross and the Samaritans

(£6,000 each); and League of Friends – West Berkshire Hospice (£3,500).

FINANCES *Year* 2009–10 *Income* £167,017 *Grants* £110,000 *Assets* £1,620,013

TRUSTEES R P Tullett; A H Bartlett.

HOW TO APPLY The trustees do not respond to unsolicited requests.

WHO TO APPLY TO The Trustees, c/o Cheviot Asset Management Limited, 90 Long Acre, London WC2E 9RA *Tel* 020 7438 5600

■ Kirkley Poor's Land Estate

CC NO 210177 **ESTABLISHED** 1976

WHERE FUNDING CAN BE GIVEN The parish of Kirkley and the former borough of Kirkley.

WHO CAN BENEFIT Individuals and organisations.

WHAT IS FUNDED Welfare and disability. The trust administers a grocery voucher scheme enabling people of pensionable age in Kirkley to receive a grant each winter to purchase groceries. It cooperates with Kirkley High School to make grants to former pupils whose parents have low incomes to help with their expenses at university or other further education establishments. All funding has to be calculated to reduce identified need, hardship or distress.

WHAT IS NOT FUNDED No grants to well known charities or only to local branches.

TYPE OF GRANT One-off.

RANGE OF GRANTS Up to £3,575.

SAMPLE GRANTS Past beneficiaries have included: St. John's Housing Trust; the Waveney Women's Refuge; Waveney Counselling Service; Kirkley Church – St. Peter & St. John, Pakefield Church; Waveney Rape & Abuse; Waveney Crossroads; Salvation Army – Kirkley Branch; Lowestoft Club for the Elderly and Kirkley Pre-school.

FINANCES *Year* 2009–10 *Income* £81,994 *Grants* £24,621 *Assets* £1,730,374

TRUSTEES Mrs J Van-Pelt, Chair; Mr M Cook; Mr R Castleton; Mr A Shepherd; Revd A White.

OTHER INFORMATION In total, individuals received £17,000; including 729 vouchers given to older people in Kirkley for the purchase of groceries in the winter.

HOW TO APPLY In writing to the correspondent. Trustees meet two to three times a year.

WHO TO APPLY TO Lucy Walker, Clerk, 23 Alexandra Road, Lowestoft, Suffolk NR32 1pp *Tel* 01502 514964

■ The Richard Kirkman Charitable Trust

CC NO 327972 **ESTABLISHED** 1988

WHERE FUNDING CAN BE GIVEN UK, with a preference for Hampshire.

WHO CAN BENEFIT Registered charities and individuals.

WHAT IS FUNDED General charitable purposes, however the trustees are considering financing various plans for alleviating drug addiction.

RANGE OF GRANTS Up to £3,000.

SAMPLE GRANTS British Limbless Ex-Servicemen Association (£4,000); Enham Trust (£3,000); British Diabetic Association and Stroke Association (£2,000 each); and Haemophilia Society and Police Dependants Trust (£1,500 each).

FINANCES *Year* 2009–10 *Income* £50,017 *Grants* £45,672 *Assets* £1,513,883

TRUSTEES M Howson-Green; Mrs F O Kirkman; B M Baxendale; D A Hoare; Mrs M Howson-Green.

OTHER INFORMATION In 2009–10 the total grants figure includes 29 grants of £1,000 or less, given to organisations and totalling £21,000.

HOW TO APPLY The trust carries out its own research for beneficiaries and does not respond to applications by post or telephone.

WHO TO APPLY TO M Howson-Green, Trustee, Ashton House, 12 The Central Precinct, Winchester Road, Chandlers Ford, Eastleigh, Hampshire, SO53 2GB *Tel* 023 8027 4555 *Fax* 023 8027 5766

■ Kirschel Foundation

CC NO 1067672   **ESTABLISHED** 1998

WHERE FUNDING CAN BE GIVEN UK.

WHO CAN BENEFIT Registered charities.

WHAT IS FUNDED The trust states that its aims and objectives are 'to provide benefits to underprivileged persons, who may be either disabled or lacking resources'. In practice this includes many Jewish organisations.

RANGE OF GRANTS Up to £50,000.

SAMPLE GRANTS Ahavat Shalom Charity Fund (£95,000); Jewish Learning Exchange (£55,000); Friends of Shamir and Tikkun (£40,000 each); Anshei Shalom Friends of Lubavitch Scotland (£18,000 each); Achisomoch (£12,000); Norwood Children's and Families Trust (£10,000); Lolev Charitable Trust (£7,000); Kabbalah Centre, Kisharon and Variety Club (£5,000 each); BSD and Camp Simcha (£3,000 each); Children with Leukaemia, Make a Wish and Seed (£2,500 each); Bas Melech, Evelina Children's Hospital Appeal and Keren Moisdos Eretz Yisroel (£2,000 each); and Keen London, Palace for All and Shooting Star (£1,000 each).

FINANCES *Year* 2009–10 *Income* £250,900 *Grants* £563,886 *Assets* £107,024

TRUSTEES Laurence Grant Kirschel; Ian Lipman; Stephen Pinshaw.

OTHER INFORMATION In 2009–10, the total of all other donations, individually less than £1,000 each was £7,000.

HOW TO APPLY In writing to the correspondent.

WHO TO APPLY TO Stephen Pinshaw, Trustee, 26 Soho Square, London W1D 4NU *Tel* 020 7437 4372

■ Robert Kitchin (Saddlers' Company)

CC NO 211169   **ESTABLISHED** 1891

WHERE FUNDING CAN BE GIVEN City of London and contiguous boroughs.

WHO CAN BENEFIT Organisations and student welfare.

WHAT IS FUNDED Education and general charitable purposes.

RANGE OF GRANTS £500 to £100,000.

SAMPLE GRANTS City University London (£97,000); St Ethelburga's Centre for Reconciliation and Peace (£33,000); London Borough of Tower Hamlets – maths project (£10,000); Beormund Primary School (£5,400); Skill Force (£5,000); and City of London School, City of London School for Girls, City of London Freemen's School and Reed's School (£650 each).

FINANCES *Year* 2009–10 *Income* £141,671 *Grants* £140,281 *Assets* £3,078,938

TRUSTEES Saddlers' Company.

OTHER INFORMATION Each year the charity gives a fixed percentage to two organisations – City University receives 50 per cent of net income, while St Ethelburga's Centre for Reconciliation and Peace receives 15 per cent of net income. The remaining 35 per cent is distributed at the discretion of the trustees.

HOW TO APPLY In writing to the correspondent. However, the discretionary element of the trust's income is fully committed each year and the trustees are unable to respond to applications.

WHO TO APPLY TO The Clerk to the Trustees, Saddlers' Company, Saddlers' Hall, 40 Gutter Lane, London EC2V 6BR *Tel* 020 7726 8661 *email* clerk@saddlersco.co.uk

■ Ernest Kleinwort Charitable Trust

CC NO 229665   **ESTABLISHED** 1963

WHERE FUNDING CAN BE GIVEN UK, mainly Sussex and overseas.

WHO CAN BENEFIT Registered charities.

WHAT IS FUNDED The main fields of work are wildlife and environmental conservation, disability, medical research, welfare of older people and welfare of young people.

WHAT IS NOT FUNDED The trust will not consider funding: large national charities having substantial fundraising potential, income from legacies and or endowment income; organisations not registered as charities or those that have been registered for less than a year; pre-school groups; out of school play schemes including pre-school and holiday schemes; projects which promote a particular religion; charities not funded by any other charity; very small and narrowly specialised activities; local authorities; individuals or charities applying on behalf of individuals; general requests for donations; expeditions or overseas travel; campaigning organisations; charities whose main aim is to raise funds for other charities; charities with substantial cash reserves.

TYPE OF GRANT Grants for start-up, capital costs and ongoing expenses for up to five years.

RANGE OF GRANTS Up to £70,000, but mostly for £10,000 or less.

SAMPLE GRANTS Tusk Trust (£100,000); Cheiley Heritage School (£75,000); The River Trust (£70,000); World Wildlife Fund UK (£50,000); 3 Towns Shopmobility (£30,000); Federation of London Youth Clubs (£21,500); East Sussex Disability Association (£17,500); Raleigh International (£15,000); Livability and City Gate Community Projects (£10,000 each); Disabilities Trust and Wildfowl and Wetlands Trust (£7,500 each); Buglife and Scope (£5,000); Treloar Trust and the Living Paintings Trust (£2,000 each); and Monkey Sanctuary, the Stroke Association and Sussex Chorus (£1,000 each).

FINANCES *Year* 2009–10 *Income* £1,258,300 *Grants* £1,209,710 *Assets* £48,466,928

TRUSTEES Sir Simon Robertson, Chair; Richard Ewing; Alexander Kleinwort; Lady Madeleine Kleinwort; Marina Kleinwort; Sir Richard Kleinwort; Sir Christopher Lever.

HOW TO APPLY In writing to the correspondent. Applications should be no longer than two A4 sides, and should incorporate a short (half page) summary. Applications should also include a detailed budget for the project and the applicant's most recent audited accounts. If accounts show a significant surplus or deficit of

Kleinwort

income, please explain how this has arisen. Applicants must also complete and include an Accounts Summary form, which is available on the trust's website.

WHO TO APPLY TO Nick R Kerr-Sheppard, Administrator, c/o Kleinwort Benson Trustees Limited, 14 St George Street, London W1S 1FE *Tel* 020 3207 7008 *Website* www.ekct.org.uk

■ The Marina Kleinwort Charitable Trust

CC NO 1081825   **ESTABLISHED** 2000
WHERE FUNDING CAN BE GIVEN UK.
WHO CAN BENEFIT Arts organisations.
WHAT IS FUNDED Arts projects.
WHAT IS NOT FUNDED No grants to individuals.
SAMPLE GRANTS RADA (£6,500); Almeida Theatre Co Ltd and The Old Vic (£5,000 each); The Clonter Farm Music Trust and Endymion Ensemble (£3,000 each); Natural History Museum and the Royal Court (£2,500 each); and Live Music Now (£1,000).
FINANCES *Year* 2009–10 *Income* £47,730 *Grants* £49,484 *Assets* £1,261,725
TRUSTEES Miss Marina Rose Kleinwort, Chair; David James Roper Robinson; Miss Zenaida Yanowsky; Mrs Tessa Elizabeth Bremmer.
HOW TO APPLY The trustees' current policy is to consider written appeals from charities working in the field of the arts, but only successful applications are notified of the trustees' decision. The trustees do not normally respond favourably to appeals from individuals, nor to those unconnected with the arts. The charity requests a copy of the most recent report and financial statements from applicants.
WHO TO APPLY TO Miss Emily Verdeyen, Kleinwort Benson, 30 Gresham Street, London EC2V 7PG *Tel* 020 3207 7109 *email* emily.verdeyen@kleinwortbenson.com

■ The Sir James Knott Trust

CC NO 1001363   **ESTABLISHED** 1990
WHERE FUNDING CAN BE GIVEN Tyne and Wear, Northumberland, County Durham inclusive of Hartlepool but exclusive of Darlington, Stockton-on-Tees, Middlesbrough, Redcar and Cleveland.
WHO CAN BENEFIT Registered charities only.
WHAT IS FUNDED Support of the welfare of people who are disadvantaged, the young, the elderly, people with disabilities, education and training, medical care, historic buildings, the environment, music and the arts and seafarers' and services' charities.
WHAT IS NOT FUNDED Individuals, replacement of funding withdrawn by local authorities or organisations that do not have an identifiable project within the beneficial area.
SAMPLE GRANTS Diocese of Newcastle (£20,000 in total); Northumbria Historic Churches Trust (£17,500); Durham Association of Clubs for Young People and Puffin Appeal (£10,000 each); YMCA-North East, Yorkshire & NE Lincolnshire Regions (£8,000); Durham University (£7,500); Astley Community High School, Berwick upon Tweed Preservation Trust, Collingwood 2010 Festival Committee, Durham Wildlife Trust and Phoenix Futures (£5,000 each); Corbridge Youth Initiative (£4,000); Action Foundation, Berwick Youth Project and Sacriston Cricket Club (£3,000 each); Action for Children, BLISS Mediation Services, Bubble Foundation UK and Kidney Research UK

(£2,000 each); and Bamburgh Castle Cricket Club and Cruse Bereavement Care – Tyneside Branch (£1,500 each).
FINANCES *Year* 2009–10 *Income* £1,302,556 *Grants* £873,814 *Assets* £38,362,858
TRUSTEES Prof. Oliver James; Charles Baker-Cresswell; Sarah Riddell; Ben Speke.
HOW TO APPLY In writing to the correspondent, giving a brief description of the need, with relevant consideration to the following points: what type of organisation you are and how you benefit the community; how you are organised and managed; how many staff/volunteers you have; if a registered charity, please provide your registered number, if not you will need to submit the name and registered number of a charity which is prepared to administer funds on your behalf; what relationship, if any, do you have with similar or umbrella organisations; please provide details of your main funding source; please provide full details of the project you are currently fundraising for, including the cost, the amount required and when the funds are needed; please give details of who else you have approached and what response have you had; please confirm whether you have you applied to the Big Lottery Fund (if not, state why not); and please enclose a copy of your latest trustee report and accounts (if you are a new organisation then provide a copy of your latest bank statement). Not all the questions/points may apply to you, but they give an idea of what the trustees may ask when considering applications. Applicants may be contacted for further information. Trustees normally meet in spring, summer and autumn. Applications need to be submitted at least three months before a grant is required. However, if your application is for a grant of less than £1,000, this can usually be processed outside meetings and usually within 1 month.
WHO TO APPLY TO Vivien Stapley, Secretary, 16–18 Hood Street, Newcastle upon Tyne NE1 6JQ *Tel* 0191 230 4016 *Fax* 0191 230 2817 *email* info@knott-trust.co.uk *Website* www.knott-trust.co.uk

■ The Kobler Trust

CC NO 275237   **ESTABLISHED** 1963
WHERE FUNDING CAN BE GIVEN UK.
WHO CAN BENEFIT Registered charities. Grants given to individuals only in exceptional circumstances.
WHAT IS FUNDED General charitable purposes with emphasis on the arts and Jewish causes.
WHAT IS NOT FUNDED Grants are only given to individuals in exceptional circumstances.
TYPE OF GRANT No restrictions. These vary from small grants on a one-off basis for a specific project to a continuing relationship.
RANGE OF GRANTS £500–£50,000.
SAMPLE GRANTS Jewish Aids Trust Brighton Dome & Festival Limited and Sadler's Wells (£15,000 each); Pavilion Opera Educational Trust (£12,000); UK Jewish Film Festival and West London Synagogue Interfaith Project (£10,000 each); Royal Academy of Music (£5,000); Rich Mix and St Giles Trust (£2,000 each); Soho Theatre Company, Spadework and Touchstones 12 (£1,000 each); and Thomas Hospice Care (£500).
FINANCES *Year* 2009–10 *Income* £81,536 *Grants* £164,950 *Assets* £2,930,434
TRUSTEES A Xuereb; A H Stone; Ms J L Evans; J W Israelsohn.
HOW TO APPLY Applications should be in writing and incorporate full details of the charity for which

funding is requested. Acknowledgements are not generally sent out to unsuccessful applicants.

WHO TO APPLY TO Ms J L Evans, Trustee, c/o Lewis Silkin LLP, 5 Chancery Lane, Clifford's Inn, London EC4A 1BL

....

■ The Kohn Foundation

CC NO 1003951   **ESTABLISHED** 1991
WHERE FUNDING CAN BE GIVEN UK and overseas.
WHO CAN BENEFIT Registered charities.
WHAT IS FUNDED General charitable purposes, especially education, Jewish religion, relief of poverty, care of people who are sick or who have a mental illness, medical research, and the arts (particularly music).
SAMPLE GRANTS The Royal Society (£300,000); Manchester University (£25,000); Imperial College (£15,000) and National Osteoporosis Society (£5,000).
Jesus College Oxford (£12,000); Nash Concert Society (£2,500) and Rudolph Kemp Society (£1,500).
Emunah (£18,000); Jewish Music Institute (£6,250) and Jewish Care (£5,000).
FINANCES *Year* 2010 *Income* £846,853
Grants £651,442 *Assets* £1,277,790
TRUSTEES Dr Ralph Kohn, Chair; Zahava Kohn; Anthony A Forwood.
HOW TO APPLY In writing to the correspondent.
WHO TO APPLY TO Dr R Kohn, Trustee, Wilkins Kennedy & Co, Brdige House, 4 Borough High Street, London SE1 9QR

....

■ Kollel and Co. Limited

CC NO 1077180   **ESTABLISHED** 1999
WHERE FUNDING CAN BE GIVEN Worldwide.
WHO CAN BENEFIT Jewish organisations.
WHAT IS FUNDED The objects of the charity are the: advancement of education and religion in accordance with the doctrines of the Jewish religion; and the relief of poverty.
RANGE OF GRANTS Up to £128,000.
SAMPLE GRANTS Ezer V'hatzolah (£128,000); Tchaba Kollel (£60,000); Hadras Kodesh Trust and Shaarei Chesed – London (£45,000 each); and Satmar Kollel (Antwerp) Ltd (£44,000).
FINANCES *Year* 2009–10 *Income* £476,406
Grants £516,517 *Assets* £2,028,429
TRUSTEES S Low; J Lipschitz; Z Rothschild.
HOW TO APPLY Grants are made upon application by the charity concerned. Grants are made in amounts thought appropriate by the directors/trustees.
WHO TO APPLY TO A Low, Secretary, Lieberman and Co, 2L Cara House, 339 Seven Sisters Road, London N15 6RD

....

■ The KPMG Foundation

CC NO 1086518   **ESTABLISHED** 2001
WHERE FUNDING CAN BE GIVEN UK.
WHO CAN BENEFIT Refugees, young offenders, children and young people who have been in care, children and young people with dyslexia/literacy difficulties.
WHAT IS FUNDED Registered charities.
SAMPLE GRANTS School Home Support (£83,000); ICAN (£80,000); Every Child a Chance and Blue Sky Development and Regeneration (£50,000 each); The Fostering Network (£37,500); Helena Kennedy Foundation and Oval House (£25,000 each); East Potential and National Literacy Trust

(£20,000); Watts Gallery (£19,000); Young Vic (£17,000); Theatre Royal Plymouth (£15,000) and The Amber Foundation (£12,000).
FINANCES *Year* 2009–10 *Income* £564,391
Grants £484,449 *Assets* £5,687,747
TRUSTEES John Griffith-Jones, Chair; Gerry Acher; Sir John Cassels; Helena Kennedy; Dr Ashley Steel; Surinder Arora; Lisa Harker; Claire Le Masurier; Neil Sherlock.
HOW TO APPLY Application forms can be downloaded from KPMG the website in PDF and Word format. 'The KPMG Foundation considers applications for the General Grants programme once a year. Throughout the year, we capture all organisations keen to apply for funding on a database. When the Trustees agree their funding date at the end of each year for the following year, we write to all organisations on our database providing them with details of the funding date, when applications must be submitted and any specific criteria defined by the Trustees. If you would like your details added to our database then please email us at kpmg@kpmg.co.uk'
'The trustees meet four times a year. Once a year the trustees will assess all applications and make their funding decisions. If the trustees are keen to progress your application a project/site visit may be undertaken by either one of the trustees or one of the support team. In addition, the trustees may request that a Financial due diligence assessment be undertaken, by the Foundation Treasurer, of the charitable organisation seeking funding.'
WHO TO APPLY TO Jo Clunie, Director, KPMG, 15 Canada Square, London E14 5GL
email kpmgfoundation@kpmg.co.uk
Website www.kpmg.co.uk/about/foundation

....

■ The Kreditor Charitable Trust

CC NO 292649   **ESTABLISHED** 1985
WHERE FUNDING CAN BE GIVEN UK, with preferences for London and North East England.
WHO CAN BENEFIT Jewish organisations and UK welfare organisations benefiting Jewish people, at risk groups, and people who are disadvantaged by poverty or socially isolated.
WHAT IS FUNDED Jewish organisations working in education and social and medical welfare.
SAMPLE GRANTS Previous beneficiaries have included: Academy for Rabbinical Research, British Diabetic Association, British Friends of Israel War Disabled, Fordeve Ltd, Jerusalem Ladies' Society, Jewish Care, Jewish Marriage Council Kosher Meals on Wheels, London Academy of Jewish Studies, NW London Talmudical College, Ravenswood, RNID and UNICEF UK.
FINANCES *Year* 2009–10 *Income* £70,306
Grants £101,579 *Assets* £55,200
TRUSTEES P M Kreditor; M P Kreditor; Sharon Kreditor.
HOW TO APPLY In writing to the correspondent.
WHO TO APPLY TO Paul M Kreditor, Gerald Kreditor and Co., Chartered Accountants, Hallswelle House, 1 Hallswelle Road, London NW11 0DH
Tel 020 8209 1535 *Fax* 020 8209 1923
email admin@gerald-kreditor.co.uk

....

■ The Kreitman Foundation

CC NO 269046   **ESTABLISHED** 1975
WHERE FUNDING CAN BE GIVEN UK.
WHO CAN BENEFIT Registered charities and other tax exempt charitable organisations benefiting children, young adults and older people, people

who are disabled and people disadvantaged by poverty.

WHAT IS FUNDED Education, health and welfare and animal conservation.

WHAT IS NOT FUNDED No grants to individuals.

TYPE OF GRANT Capital and core costs.

RANGE OF GRANTS £2,500–£105,000.

SAMPLE GRANTS Middlesex University received £105,000 and Hile Pandana received £2,500.

FINANCES *Year* 2009–10 *Income* £157,296 *Grants* £108,000 *Assets* £4,915,720

TRUSTEES Mrs Jill Luck-Hille; P M Luck-Hille.

HOW TO APPLY To the correspondent in writing. The trustees seem to have a list of regular beneficiaries and it may be unlikely that any new applications will be successful.

WHO TO APPLY TO Citroen Wells, Devonshire House, 1 Devonshire Street, London W1W 5DR

■ The Neil Kreitman Foundation

CC NO 267171   **ESTABLISHED** 1974

WHERE FUNDING CAN BE GIVEN Worldwide, in practice UK, USA and Israel.

WHO CAN BENEFIT Registered or exempt charities.

WHAT IS FUNDED Arts and culture; education; health and social welfare; Jewish causes.

WHAT IS NOT FUNDED No grants to individuals.

TYPE OF GRANT Primarily general funds with some small capital grants and core costs.

RANGE OF GRANTS Generally £500–£30,000.

SAMPLE GRANTS University of Washington (£132,000); British Museum (£70,000); Independent Shakespeare Company (£39,000); Sierra Club Foundation (£32,000); The Ancient India and Iran Trust (£14,000); Royal Numismatic Society (£12,500); Los Angeles County Museum of Art and Save the Children (£10,000 each); International PEN Foundation (£7,000); and Ziyaret Tepe Archaeological Trust (£5,000).

FINANCES *Year* 2009–10 *Income* £464,735 *Grants* £435,248 *Assets* £23,248,988

TRUSTEES Neil R Kreitman; Gordon C Smith.

HOW TO APPLY In writing to the correspondent.

WHO TO APPLY TO Gordon C Smith, Trustee, Citroen Wells & Partners, Devonshire House, 1 Devonshire Street, London W1W 5DR *Tel* 020 7304 2000 *Fax* 020 7304 2020 *email* gordon. smith@citreonwells.co.uk

■ The Heinz, Anna and Carol Kroch Foundation

CC NO 207622   **ESTABLISHED** 1962

WHERE FUNDING CAN BE GIVEN UK.

WHO CAN BENEFIT Individuals with chronic illnesses; disabled people; people who are disadvantaged by poverty; homeless people; victims of abuse and domestic violence; and victims of war.

WHAT IS FUNDED The foundation exists to support people who have suffered injustice and relieve hardship amongst people with medical conditions.

WHAT IS NOT FUNDED No grants are made to students or for holidays. Overseas applications or projects are not considered.

RANGE OF GRANTS Up to £10,000.

SAMPLE GRANTS Previous beneficiaries include: Bath Institute of Medical Engineering, Brainwave, Breakthrough Breast Cancer, Eyeless Trust, Northern Friends of ARMS, VISCERAL and University College London.

FINANCES *Year* 2009–10 *Income* £146,344 *Grants* £75,565 *Assets* £4,077,748

TRUSTEES Mrs M Cottam; Dr A Kashti; D Lang; X Lang; Ms A Page; C Rushbrook; J Seagrim.

HOW TO APPLY Appeals are considered monthly. Applications on behalf of individuals must be submitted through a recognised body, such as social services, GP/consultant, CAB or welfare rights. Applications always receive a reply – please include an sae.

WHO TO APPLY TO Mrs H Astle, PO Box 5, Bentham, Lancaster LA2 7XA *Tel* 01524 263001 *Fax* 01524 262721 *email* hakf50@hotmail.com

■ Kupath Gemach Chaim Bechesed Viznitz Trust

CC NO 1110323   **ESTABLISHED** 2005

WHERE FUNDING CAN BE GIVEN UK and Israel.

WHO CAN BENEFIT Registered charities.

WHAT IS FUNDED Jewish causes.

RANGE OF GRANTS Up to £256,000.

SAMPLE GRANTS BHW Ltd – for the advancement of religion (£256,000); and Tchabe Kollel Ltd – for education (£37,000).

FINANCES *Year* 2009–10 *Income* £297,409 *Grants* £463,531 *Assets* £2,574

TRUSTEES Israel Kahan; Saul Weiss; Alexander Pifko.

OTHER INFORMATION During the year, a further £112,754 went to individuals.

HOW TO APPLY In writing to the correspondent.

WHO TO APPLY TO Saul Weiss, Trustee, 171 Kyverdale Road, London N16 6PS *Tel* 020 8442 9604

■ The Kyte Charitable Trust

CC NO 1035886   **ESTABLISHED** 1994

WHERE FUNDING CAN BE GIVEN UK.

WHO CAN BENEFIT Organisations benefiting medical professionals and research workers. Support may go to at risk groups, and people who are disadvantaged by poverty or socially isolated.

WHAT IS FUNDED Medical research, community services.

RANGE OF GRANTS Up to £27,000.

SAMPLE GRANTS United Jewish Israel Appeal (£27,000); Jewish Care (£21,000); Community Security Trust and Norwood Ravenswood (£15,000 each) and Myeloma UK (£1,000).

FINANCES *Year* 2009–10 *Income* £131,047 *Grants* £123,233 *Assets* £18,811

TRUSTEES D M Kyte; T M Kyte; J L Kyte; I J Kyte.

HOW TO APPLY In writing to the correspondent.

WHO TO APPLY TO The Trustees, Business Design Centre, 52 Upper Street, London N1 0QH *Tel* 020 7704 7791

■ The Late Sir Pierce Lacy Charity Trust

cc no 1013505   **ESTABLISHED** 1992

WHERE FUNDING CAN BE GIVEN UK and overseas.

WHO CAN BENEFIT The trust only supports the Roman Catholic Church or associated institutions which are registered charities and does not fund requests from individuals.

WHAT IS FUNDED Medicine and health, welfare, education, religion and general charitable purposes. Particularly charities working in the field of infrastructure development, residential facilities and services, Christian education, Christian outreach, Catholic bodies, charity or voluntary umbrella bodies, hospices, rehabilitation centres, advocacy, education and training, community services and community issues.

WHAT IS NOT FUNDED The trust only supports the Roman Catholic Church or associated institutions.

TYPE OF GRANT Recurrent small grants of £1,000 or less, buildings, capital, core costs, project, research, start-up costs and funding for more than three years may be considered.

RANGE OF GRANTS Most are less than £500.

SAMPLE GRANTS Previously: £1,400 to Crusade of Rescue; £920 to St Francis 'Children's Society; £810 to Poor Mission Fund; £800 to St Cuthbert's Mayne RC School as a special donation; £720 to Society of St Vincent De Paul; £610 to Poor Mission Fund; £550 to Catholic Children's Society; £530 to St Francis's Leprosy Guild.

FINANCES *Year* 2009–10 *Income* £22,278 *Grants* £25,757

TRUSTEES Aviva Insurance Ltd.

HOW TO APPLY In writing to the correspondent, at any time.

WHO TO APPLY TO Aviva, Trustee Department, Aviva, Trustee Department, Pitheavlis, Perth PH2 0NH *Tel* 01738 895590 *Fax* 01738 895903

■ The K P Ladd Charitable Trust

cc no 1091493   **ESTABLISHED** 2002

WHERE FUNDING CAN BE GIVEN UK and overseas.

WHO CAN BENEFIT Churches and other organisations.

WHAT IS FUNDED 'It is the trustees' present intention that the fund will be applied to support Christian charities and other charitable organisations involved in religious activities. This will be done by supporting churches, missionary work and other organisations both in the UK and overseas.'

RANGE OF GRANTS Up to £20,000. Usually £2,000.

SAMPLE GRANTS Beneficiaries included: London Institute for Contemporary Christianity (£21,000); Eastbury Church Northwood Trust (£19,300); Kepplewray Trust (£6,000); Tonbridge Church (£3,000); SOS Bosnia, London City Mission, Salvation Army and Wycliffe Bible Translators, European Evangelical Alliance and Livability (£2,000 each); Emmanuel Church Northwood (£1,000).

FINANCES *Year* 2009–10 *Income* £275,137 *Grants* £82,531 *Assets* £1,465,028

TRUSTEES Roger Cooper; Brian Ladd; Kenneth Ladd.

HOW TO APPLY 'The trust is fully committed and does not reply to unsolicited requests'.

WHO TO APPLY TO Roger Cooper, Trustee, 2 Wolsey Road, Northwood HA6 2HS *Tel* 01923 829982

■ John Laing Charitable Trust

cc no 236852   **ESTABLISHED** 1962

WHERE FUNDING CAN BE GIVEN UK.

WHO CAN BENEFIT Existing and former employees of John Laing plc who are in need; 'charitable organisations, or in exceptional circumstances from not-for-profit companies'.

WHAT IS FUNDED More recently, the trust has concentrated its support on charities which support the following main themes: education; community regeneration; disadvantaged young people; homelessness with a particular emphasis on day centres; and environment.

WHAT IS NOT FUNDED No grants to individuals (other than to Laing employees and/or their dependants).

TYPE OF GRANT Usually one-off, but a small number are supported for an agreed period, often up to three years.

RANGE OF GRANTS £250–£25,000.

SAMPLE GRANTS National Communities Resource Centre (£50,000); ContinYou (£35,000); Young Enterprise London (£30,000); Prince's Trust (£29,000); Victim Support, Croydon Commitment, Hertfordshire Groundwork and Learning Thro' Landscapes (£25,000 each); National Literacy Trust and The Reading Agency (£20,000 each); Kidscape and Springboard for Children (15,000 each); Church Action on Poverty, Fairshare, and Groundswell (£10,000 each); Depaul Trust (£7,500); CRASH (£6,000); Bentilee Dad's Group, Child Victims of Crime, Clouds of Hope, Discover, Maryland Primary School Quaker Social Action and Self Help Housing (£5,000 each); Upper Room and Wood Street Mission (£2,500 each).

FINANCES *Year* 2010 *Income* £1,701,000 *Grants* £307,000 *Assets* £50,568

TRUSTEES C M Laing; Sir Martin Laing; D C Madden; R I Sumner; P Jones; D Whipp; L Krige.

OTHER INFORMATION In addition to the grant total, £631,000 was distributed to about 573 individuals who were either current or former employees of John Laing plc.

HOW TO APPLY In writing to the correspondent. The trust does not have an application form and applicants are asked to keep the initial request as brief as possible. There is no deadline for receipt of applications. All applications are dealt with on a rolling basis. The trust says that all applications are acknowledged.

WHO TO APPLY TO Michael Hamilton, Secretary, 33 Bunns Lane, Mill Hill, London NW7 2DX *Tel* 020 8959 7321 *email* michael.a.hamilton@laing.com *Website* www.laing.com/lct.htm

■ Maurice and Hilda Laing Charitable Trust

cc no 1058109   **ESTABLISHED** 1996

WHERE FUNDING CAN BE GIVEN UK and overseas.

WHO CAN BENEFIT Registered charities.

WHAT IS FUNDED The advancement of the Christian religion and the relief of poverty both in the UK and overseas. In practice grants awarded fall into three main categories: to organisations seeking to promote Christian faith and values through evangelistic, educational and media activities at home and overseas; to organisations seeking to express Christian faith through practical action to help people in need, for example, those with disabilities, the homeless, the sick, young people, prisoners and ex-offenders; to organisations working to relieve poverty overseas, with a particular emphasis on helping children who are vulnerable or at risk; evangelical activities, theological training and the promotion of Christianity in the UK and overseas. In most cases these grants to overseas projects are made through UK registered charities who are expected to monitor and evaluate the projects on behalf of the trust, providing progress reports at agreed intervals.

WHAT IS NOT FUNDED No grants to groups or individuals for the purpose of education, travel, attendance at conferences or participation in overseas exchange programmes. No grants towards church restoration or repair.

TYPE OF GRANT Usually one-off grants to capital costs or project funding on a one-off or recurring basis. A few grants towards the core costs of national organisations.

RANGE OF GRANTS Up to £650,000.

SAMPLE GRANTS United Learning Trust (£100,000); Anglican Centre, Doha, Qatar (£100,000); The 2011 Trust (King James Bible Trust) (£100,000); The Salvation Army UK (£650,000) Ethiopian Graduate School of Theology (£50,000); Credit Action (£40,000); YMCA UK National Council (£25,000); Launde Abbey (£30,000); Scripture Union (£25,000); Bible Reading Fellowship (£25,000); Tearfund (£50,000); Release International (£25,000); Mission Aviation Fellowship (£50,000); Christian Youth Enterprises Sailing Centre (£50,000); and St Madoc Christian Youth Camp (£43,000).

FINANCES *Year* 2010 *Income* £1,510,104 *Grants* £2,504,930 *Assets* £34,043,388

TRUSTEES Andrea Currie; Peter Harper; Robert Harley; Ewan Harper; Charles Laing; Stephen Ludlow.

OTHER INFORMATION See the entry for the Laing Family Foundations for the work of the group as a whole.

Please note: in 2006 the trust made the decision to work towards winding up the trust over a 10–15 year period. As such, there will be a controlled increase in the level of future grant expenditure.

HOW TO APPLY In writing to the correspondent. One application only is needed to apply to this or the Kirby Laing Foundation, Martin Laing Foundation or Beatrice Laing Charitable Trust. Multiple applications will still only elicit a single reply, even then applicants are asked to accept non-response as a negative reply on behalf of all these trusts, unless an sae is enclosed. After the initial sifting process, the Maurice and Hilda Laing Trust follows its own administrative procedures. Each application should contain all the information needed to allow such a decision to be reached, in as short and straightforward a way as possible.

Specifically, each application should say: what the money is for; how much is needed; how much has already been found; and where the rest of the money is to come from. The trustees meet quarterly to consider applications for grants above £10,000. In most cases the trust's administrators will have met with applicants and prepared reports and recommendations for the trustees. Applications for smaller amounts are considered on an ongoing basis throughout the year. The administrators are authorised to make such grants without prior consent up to a maximum of £100,000 in each quarter, the grants to be reported to the trustees and approved retrospectively at the following quarterly meeting.

WHO TO APPLY TO Elizabeth Harley, Secretary, 33 Bunns Lane, Mill Hill, London NW7 2DX *Tel* 020 8238 8890

....

■ The Christopher Laing Foundation

CC NO 278460   **ESTABLISHED** 1979

WHERE FUNDING CAN BE GIVEN UK, with a particular interest in Hertfordshire.

WHO CAN BENEFIT Applications from headquarter organisations and local organisations will be considered.

WHAT IS FUNDED General charitable purposes, arts and culture, environment, health and sport, with a preference for local projects in Hertfordshire.

WHAT IS NOT FUNDED Donations are only made to registered charities.

TYPE OF GRANT Recurrent and one-off. Grants are given for core support, capital funding and project, seed and feasibility funding. Loans may be given.

SAMPLE GRANTS Charities Aid Foundation (£50,000); the Lord's Taverners (£30,000 in two grants); Fields in Trust (£25,000); Hertfordshire Groundwork (£15,000 in two grants); Alastair Hignall Multiple Sclerosis Fund (£10,000); Sport Aid and Worshipful Company of Paviors (£5,000 each).

FINANCES *Year* 2009–10 *Income* £193,360 *Grants* £179,500 *Assets* £5,884,937

TRUSTEES Christopher M Laing; John Keeble; Peter S Jackson; Diana C Laing.

HOW TO APPLY In writing to the correspondent.

WHO TO APPLY TO Paula Doraisamy, Trust Consultant, c/o TMF Management UK Ltd, 400 Capability Green, Luton LU1 3AE *Tel* 01582 439200 *email* paula.doraisamy@tmf-group.com

....

■ The David Laing Foundation

CC NO 278462   **ESTABLISHED** 1979

WHERE FUNDING CAN BE GIVEN Worldwide.

WHO CAN BENEFIT Organisations benefiting children, including those who are in care, fostered or adopted; one-parent families; and people who are disabled.

WHAT IS FUNDED The policy is to support charities aiding children, people from broken homes, and people who are physically and mentally disabled; with further donations to bodies supporting the improvement of the arts, education and training, overseas aid, social welfare and sports and recreation.

WHAT IS NOT FUNDED No grants to individuals.

TYPE OF GRANT Grants are not normally recurrent on a regular annual basis unless forming phases of a larger donation. Some charities are closely associated with the foundation and would benefit more frequently. Starter finance, recurring expenses or single projects are considered. Sometimes a small grant plus an interest-free loan.

SAMPLE GRANTS Previously: Northamptonshire Community Foundation (£120,000 in three grants); Grove House Hospice (£21,000); International Organ Festival (£15,000); Lord's Taverners (£6,500 in four grants); St John Ambulance (£6,000); Peterborough Cathedral (£5,000); British Olympic Foundation (£4,700 in three grants); Firfield Primary School PTA, Game Conservancy Trust, Hertfordshire Agricultural

Society and Interact Reading Service (£2,000 each).

FINANCES *Year* 2009–10 *Income* £100,807 *Grants* £258,000 *Assets* £4,356,289

TRUSTEES David Eric Laing; John Stuart Lewis; Richard Francis Dudley Barlow; Frances Mary Laing.

OTHER INFORMATION When supporting larger charities the support will be at headquarters and local levels as, for instance, in support of Save the Children Fund where donations to headquarters will aid the African famine appeal, but support is also given to local branches.

HOW TO APPLY In writing to the correspondent. Trustees meet in March, June, October and December, although applications are reviewed weekly. Due to the large number of applications received, and the relatively small number of grants made, the trust is not able to respond to all requests.

WHO TO APPLY TO David E Laing, Trustee, Fermyn Woods Hall, Brigstock, Northamptonshire, NN 14 3JA *Tel* 01536 373886

■ The Kirby Laing Foundation

CC NO 264299   **ESTABLISHED** 1972
WHERE FUNDING CAN BE GIVEN Unrestricted, but mainly UK.

WHO CAN BENEFIT Registered charities benefiting disadvantaged sections of the community including people with disabilities or mental illness, people disadvantaged by poverty, and socially isolated people; UK and overseas mission societies.

WHAT IS FUNDED Advancement of the Christian faith, youth development, medical research, care and health organisations, social welfare.

WHAT IS NOT FUNDED No grants to individuals; no travel grants; no educational grants. The foundation rarely gives grants for the running costs of local organisations.

TYPE OF GRANT Usually capital costs or project funding on a one-off or recurring basis.

RANGE OF GRANTS £100–£120,000.

SAMPLE GRANTS Leicester Cathedral (£100,000); Great Britain Trust (£65,000); Oriel College and the University of Hertfordshire (£50,000 each); Institution of Civil Engineers (£35,000); Youth for Christ and the National Hospital for Neurology and Neurosurgery (£25,000 each); Mines Advisory Group (£15,000); The Art Fund (£10,000); and UK Sailing Academy, St Christopher's Hospice and the British Limbless Ex service Men's Association (£5,000 each).

FINANCES *Year* 2010 *Income* £1,734,005 *Grants* £1,429,990 *Assets* £46,772,566

TRUSTEES Lady Isobel Laing; David E Laing; Simon Webley; Revd Charles Burch.

HOW TO APPLY One application only is needed to apply to this or the Beatrice Laing Trust or Maurice and Hilda Laing Charitable Trust. Multiple applications will still only elicit a single reply. These trusts make strenuous efforts to keep their overhead costs to a minimum. As they also make a very large number of grants each year, in proportion to their income, the staff must rely almost entirely on the written applications submitted in selecting appeals to go forward to the trustees. Each application should contain all the information needed to allow such a decision to be reached, in as short and straightforward a way as possible. Specifically, each application should say: what the money is for; how much is needed; how much has already been found; where the rest is to come from. Unless there is reasonable

assurance on the last point the grant is unlikely to be recommended. The trustees meet four times a year to consider the award of grants of over £20,000. Decisions on smaller grants are made on an ongoing basis.

For all grants above £5,000 the foundation asks for a report from the charity one year after the grant has been made, describing briefly how the grant has been spent and what has been achieved. For larger and multi-year grants more detailed reports may be required. Where a grant is paid in instalments the usual practice is not to release the second and subsequent instalments until a review of progress has been satisfactorily completed.

WHO TO APPLY TO Elizabeth Harley, Secretary, 33 Bunns Lane, Mill Hill, London NW7 2DX *Tel* 020 8238 8890 *Fax* 020 8238 8897

■ The Martin Laing Foundation

CC NO 278461   **ESTABLISHED** 1979
WHERE FUNDING CAN BE GIVEN UK and worldwide.
WHO CAN BENEFIT Registered charities.

WHAT IS FUNDED General charitable purposes, including environment and conservation, young people and the elderly, but most grants go to charities and projects which the trustees have a personal connection to.

SAMPLE GRANTS Beneficiaries included: Home Farm Trust Limited (£250,000); Students' Education Trust (£20,000); Malta Aviation Museum Foundation and WWF-UK (£10,000 each); Action for M E, Bird College, CPRE Norfolk, Cowes Community Partnership, The Poppy Centre Trust and The Pushkin Prizes (£5,000 each); Flimkien ghal Ambient Ahjar (£3,000); and The Malta Hospice Movement (£1,000).

FINANCES *Year* 2009–10 *Income* £189,280 *Grants* £444,636 *Assets* £5,598,355

TRUSTEES Sir John Martin Laing; Colin Fletcher; Edward Charles Laing; Nicholas Gregory; Lady Stephanie Stearn Laing.

OTHER INFORMATION Exceptional gift of £250,000 to Home Farm Trust Ltd in 2009–10.

HOW TO APPLY The trust states: 'The trustees receive an enormous and increasing number of requests for help. Unfortunately the trustees are only able to help a small proportion of the requests and consequently they limit their support to those charities where they have a personal connection or interest in their activities.'

WHO TO APPLY TO Ms Elizabeth Ann Harley, 33 Bunns Lane, London NW7 2DX *Tel* 020 8238 8890

■ The Beatrice Laing Trust

CC NO 211884   **ESTABLISHED** 1952
WHERE FUNDING CAN BE GIVEN UK and overseas.
WHO CAN BENEFIT Mainly registered charities.

WHAT IS FUNDED The welfare of people who are homeless, children, older people, socially excluded and people with physical, mental or learning disabilities. Grants to projects overseas are concentrated upon building the capacity to provide long-term solutions to the problems faced by countries in the developing world, rather than emergency aid. Grants towards the advancement of the evangelical Christian faith are made by the trustees through the JW Laing Trust.

WHAT IS NOT FUNDED No grants to individuals; no travel grants; no educational grants.

RANGE OF GRANTS Most grants are between £500 and £8,000, occasionally larger.

SAMPLE GRANTS Home Farm Trust (£50,000); National Star College, Wirral Autistic Society, Impact Foundation and Open Door St Albans (£25,000 each); Chailey Heritage School (£20,000); DEMAND (£15,000); Cumbria Community Foundation (£13,000); and Garwood Foundation, Oxfam, Book Aid International and Scottish Veterans' Garden City Association (£10,000 each).

FINANCES *Year* 2009–10 *Income* £1,509,817 *Grants* £1,215,800 *Assets* £41,028,419

TRUSTEES Sir Martin Laing; David E Laing; Christopher M Laing; Charles Laing; Paula Blacker; Alexandra Gregory.

OTHER INFORMATION See the entry for the Laing Family Foundations for the work of the group as a whole.

HOW TO APPLY In writing to the correspondent. One application only is needed to apply to this or the Kirby Laing Foundation, Martin Laing Foundation or Maurice and Hilda Laing Charitable Trust. Applicants are asked to accept non-response as a negative reply on behalf of all these trusts, unless a stamped addressed envelope is enclosed. Applications are considered monthly. Specifically, each application should say: what the money is for; how much is needed; how much has already been found; and where the rest of the money is to come from. Unless there is reasonable assurance on the last point the grant is unlikely to be recommended. Where larger grants are contemplated, meetings and visits are often undertaken by the trust's staff.

WHO TO APPLY TO Elizabeth Harley, Secretary, 33 Bunns Lane, Mill Hill, London NW7 2DX *Tel* 020 8238 8890

■ The Lambert Charitable Trust

CC NO 257803   **ESTABLISHED** 1969

WHERE FUNDING CAN BE GIVEN UK and Israel.

WHO CAN BENEFIT There is a preference for people of the Jewish faith.

WHAT IS FUNDED Each year, nominally one half of the income is given to organisations in Israel, one third to Jewish organisations based in the UK and one sixth to health and welfare charities in the UK.

TYPE OF GRANT One-off and recurrent.

RANGE OF GRANTS £250–£15,000.

SAMPLE GRANTS Jewish Care (£15,000); Action Medical Research, Medical Foundation for the Care of Victims of Torture, Meningitis Research Foundation, and Quaker Social Action (£2,000 each); Crossroads Caring for Carers Headway and Jewish Association for the Mentally Ill (£1,000); and Ponevez Yeshivah Israel (£250).

FINANCES *Year* 2009–10 *Income* £85,467 *Grants* £57,250 *Assets* £3,064,138

TRUSTEES M Lambert; Prof. H P Lambert; Jane Lambert; O E Lambert; D J R Wells.

HOW TO APPLY In writing to the correspondent before July for payment by 1 September.

WHO TO APPLY TO George Georghiou, Mercer and Hole Trustees Ltd, 72 London Road, St Albans, Hertfordshire AL1 1NS *Tel* 01727 869141

■ Community Foundation for Lancashire

CC NO 1123229   **ESTABLISHED** 2005

WHERE FUNDING CAN BE GIVEN Lancashire.

WHO CAN BENEFIT Registered charities and community groups.

WHAT IS FUNDED Social welfare and general charitable purposes.

FINANCES *Year* 2009–10 *Income* £169,105 *Grants* £22,500 *Assets* £152,561

TRUSTEES Peter Robinson; Arthur Roberts; David Sanderson; Terry Hephrun; Peter Butterfield; Pam Barker; Tom Hoyle; Graham Burgess; Deborah Ashton.

HOW TO APPLY For application details, please see the foundation's website.

WHO TO APPLY TO Cathy Elliott, Chief Executive, The Bungalow, Davyfield Road, Blackburn BB1 2LX *Tel* 01254 585056 *email* info@lancsfoundation. org.uk *Website* www.lancsfoundation.org.uk

■ Lancashire Environmental Fund

CC NO 1074983   **ESTABLISHED** 1998

WHERE FUNDING CAN BE GIVEN Lancashire.

WHO CAN BENEFIT Environmental organisations.

WHAT IS FUNDED Environmental projects which meet the criteria of the ENTRUST scheme.

WHAT IS NOT FUNDED All projects must satisfy at least one objective of the Landfill Tax Credit Scheme. For more information about the scheme contact Entrust, the regulatory body, by visiting their website at www.entrust.org.uk or telephoning 0161 972 0074.

TYPE OF GRANT One-off and recurrent.

RANGE OF GRANTS £3,000 to £30,000.

SAMPLE GRANTS Thornton Methodist Church and The Woodlands – Clayton le Moors (£30,000 each); Longholme Methodist Church – Rawtenstall (£25,000); Martin Mere, The Secret Garden – Penwortham and Yarrow Valley – Chorley (£15,000 each); Willow Lane – Lancaster (£9,000); and Briercliffe Memorial Bowling Green – Burnleyl (£5,000).

FINANCES *Year* 2009–10 *Income* £916,257 *Grants* £796,276 *Assets* £2,576,034

TRUSTEES Gary Mayson; P Greijenberg; D Tattersall; Albert Atkinson; Roger Hardman.

HOW TO APPLY Guidance notes and application forms for each funding strand are available from the correspondent or may be downloaded from the fund's website. Completed forms should contain all possible relevant material including maps, photographs, plans, and so on. The board meets quarterly in January, April, July and October. Staff are willing to have informal discussions before an application is made. Potential applicants are strongly advised to visit the website before contacting the trust.

WHO TO APPLY TO Andy Rowett, Administration Officer, The Barn, Berkeley Drive, Bamber Bridge, Preston, Lancashire PR5 6BY *Tel* 01772 317247 *Fax* 01772 628849 *email* andyrowett@lancsenvfund.org.uk *Website* www.lancsenvfund.org.uk

■ Duchy of Lancaster Benevolent Fund

CC NO 1026752   **ESTABLISHED** 1993

WHERE FUNDING CAN BE GIVEN The county palatine of Lancashire (in Lancashire, Greater Manchester and Merseyside), and elsewhere in the country where the Duchy of Lancaster has historical links such as land interests and church livings.

WHO CAN BENEFIT Individuals and organisations.

WHAT IS FUNDED General charitable causes, but especially youth and education, welfare of people who are disabled or elderly, community help, religion.

TYPE OF GRANT Mainly one-off grants for specific projects. Recurrent grants occasionally given.

RANGE OF GRANTS Up to £10,000, but usually £50–£5,000.

SAMPLE GRANTS Lancaster University Bursary Fund (£9,000); East Lancashire Women's Refuge and Life Education Centre (£5,000 each); Barthomley Bowling Club (£2,000); Florence Institute (£1,500); Braile Chess Association, Deafblind UK, RNIB and Walthew House (£1,000 each).

FINANCES *Year* 2009–10 *Income* £399,825 *Grants* £373,298 *Assets* £10,325,682

TRUSTEES Lord Charles Shuttleworth; Sir Alan Reid; Hon. Justice David Richards; Dame Lorna Muirhead; Robert Hildyard; Chris Adcock; Warren Smith; Geoffrey Driver.

OTHER INFORMATION The Duchy of Lancaster Jubilee Trust (Charity Commission No. 1085881) is administered from the same address and mainly gives towards the Queen's Chapel of Savoy.

HOW TO APPLY In writing to the appropriate lieutenancy office (see below), at any time. Applications should be by letter, including as much information as possible. All applications are acknowledged. Lancashire lieutenancy: County Hall, Preston, Lancashire LPRI 8XJ. Greater Manchester lieutenancy: Byrum House, Quay Street, Manchester M3 30D. Merseyside lieutenancy: PO Box 144, Royal and Sun Alliance Building, New Hall Place, Old Hall Street, Liverpool L69 3EN.

WHO TO APPLY TO Chris Adcock, Duchy of Lancaster Office, 1 Lancaster Place, Strand, London WC2E 7ED *Tel* 020 7269 1707 *Fax* 020 7269 1710 *email* info@duchyoflancaster.co.uk *Website* www.duchyoflancaster.org.uk

....

■ The Lancaster Foundation

CC NO 1066850   **ESTABLISHED** 1997

WHERE FUNDING CAN BE GIVEN UK and overseas, with a local interest in Clitheroe.

WHO CAN BENEFIT Only charities personally known to the trustees.

WHAT IS FUNDED Christian charities only.

SAMPLE GRANTS Grand at Clitheroe (£868,000); The Message Trust (£325,000 in total); Open Arms International (£240,000); Sparrow Ministries (£130,000); Mission Aviation Fellowship (£62,000); Cross Polinate (£21,000); Christians Against Poverty (£18,000); Exstreet Kenya Musical Instruments (£5,500); Ignition (£2,500); and Open Doors UK (£1,000).

FINANCES *Year* 2009–10 *Income* £1,854,473 *Grants* £2,009,650 *Assets* £50,057,315

TRUSTEES Rosemary Lancaster; Dr John Lancaster; Steven Lancaster; Julie Broadhurst.

HOW TO APPLY The trust has previously stated: 'We do not consider applications made to us from organisations or people unconnected with us. All our donations are instigated because of personal associations. Unsolicited mail is, sadly, a waste of the organisation's resources.'

WHO TO APPLY TO Rosemary Lancaster, Trustee, c/o Text House, 152 Bawdlands, Clitheroe, Lancashire BB7 2LA *Tel* 01200 444404

....

■ LandAid Charitable Trust

CC NO 295157   **ESTABLISHED** 1986

WHERE FUNDING CAN BE GIVEN UK.

WHO CAN BENEFIT Homeless organisations.

WHAT IS FUNDED Provision of accommodation, assistance with refurbishment projects, running training, life skills and other educational programmes and start-up funding for schemes that might not otherwise get off the ground.

WHAT IS NOT FUNDED No funding for staff costs, unless the project is of limited duration or the applicant has shown how such costs will be met on an ongoing basis. No grants to individuals.

TYPE OF GRANT One-off.

RANGE OF GRANTS £5,000–£25,000.

SAMPLE GRANTS New Horizons Youth Centre (£8,800); Robert Blair Primary School (£7,500); Astell Foundation (£6,500); Chartered Surveyors Training Trust (£5,300); and Booth Centre, Space Trust and Canterbury Housing Advice Centre (£5,000 each).

FINANCES *Year* 2009–10 *Income* £873,273 *Grants* £43,118 *Assets* £281,009

TRUSTEES Robin Broadhurst, Chair; Michael Slade; Liz Peace; Jeremy Newsum; David Taylor; Robert Bould; Lynette Lackey; Tim Roberts; Robert Noel.

OTHER INFORMATION The trust also supports 'Foundations for Life', an innovative partnership between LandAid and Centrepoint which aims to deliver real help to homeless young people.

HOW TO APPLY Organisations should apply online through the trust's website. Supporting documentation, including a copy of the latest annual report and financial statements, is required.

WHO TO APPLY TO Lucy-Jayne Cummings, Administrator, St Albans House, 5th Floor, 57–59 Haymarket, London SW1Y 4QX *Tel* 020 3102 7190 *email* enquiries@landaid.org *Website* www.landaid.org

....

■ The Jack Lane Charitable Trust

CC NO 1091675   **ESTABLISHED** 2002

WHERE FUNDING CAN BE GIVEN Gloucestershire and Wiltshire.

WHO CAN BENEFIT Registered charities.

WHAT IS FUNDED General charitable purposes.

RANGE OF GRANTS Up to £2,500.

FINANCES *Year* 2009–10 *Income* £55,034 *Grants* £45,284 *Assets* £1,818,126

TRUSTEES Mr J A G Toogood; R White; Ms S Friday; Mrs C MacLachlan; Mr D C Crampton; Mr T G Newman; Mr M A Wright.

HOW TO APPLY In writing to the correspondent or through the trust's website.

WHO TO APPLY TO J A G Toogood, Trustee, Forrester & Forrester, 59 High Street, Malmesbury, Wiltshire SN16 9AH *Tel* 01666 822671 *Fax* 01666 823548 *email* admin@jacklane.co. uk *Website* www.jacklane.co.uk

....

■ The Allen Lane Foundation

CC NO 248031   **ESTABLISHED** 1966

WHERE FUNDING CAN BE GIVEN UK.

WHO CAN BENEFIT Organisations whose work is with groups who may be perceived as unpopular such as asylum seekers, lesbian, gay bisexual or transgender people, gypsies and travellers, offenders and ex-offenders, older people, people experiencing mental health problems and people experiencing violence or abuse.

WHAT IS FUNDED The provision of advice, information and advocacy; community development; neighbourhood mediation, conflict resolution and alternatives to violence; research and education aimed at changing public attitudes or policy; social welfare aimed at making a long-term difference and empowering users.

WHAT IS NOT FUNDED The foundation does not currently make grants for academic research; addiction, alcohol or drug abuse; animal welfare or animal rights; arts or cultural or language projects or festivals; work with children, young people and families; endowments or contributions to other grantmaking bodies; holidays or holiday play schemes; housing; hospices and medical research; individuals; museums or galleries; overseas travel; particular medical conditions or disorders; physical or learning disabilities; private and/or mainstream education; promotion of sectarian religion; publications; purchase costs of property, refugee community groups working with single nationalities; restoration or conservation of historic buildings or sites; sports and recreation; therapy, counselling; vehicle purchase; work relating to particular medical conditions of illness; work which the trustees believe is rightly the responsibility of the state; work outside the United Kingdom; work which will already have taken place before a grant is agreed; work by local organisations with an income of more than £100,000 per annum or those working over a wider area with an income of more than £250,000. The foundation will not normally make grants to organisations which receive funding (directly or indirectly) from commercial sources where conflicts of interest for the organisation and its work are likely to arise.

TYPE OF GRANT Generally for one year only, although longer term funding of up to three years may be offered sometimes. Project or core costs.

RANGE OF GRANTS Usually £500–£15,000.

SAMPLE GRANTS Student Action for Refugees – core costs of a national organisation (£15,000); Restorative Justice Consortium – towards core costs of this national organisation (£15,000); Allied Resource Community – running costs of the Tools for Self Reliance project in Middlesbrough (£9,000); Links Project – towards running costs of a project for asylum seekers, refugees and migrant communities (£7,500); Broken Rainbow – core costs of national organisation for lesbian, gay, bisexual and transgender people who experience domestic violence (£6,000); Women's Community Support Network – core costs of this project supporting women offenders in Belfast (£5,000); Network for Surviving Stalking – towards core costs (£5,000); Polish Community Association Wakefield – towards the cost of weekend advice and provision (£4,500); North Manchester Black Health Forum – towards the active citizens project aiming to empower older people and those with mental health problems (£4,000); and One Voice 4 Travellers – single grant towards the cost of the 'Breaking the cycle of abuse' project in East Anglia (£3,000).

FINANCES *Year* 2010–11 *Income* £480,351 *Grants* £717,881 *Assets* £16,731,112

TRUSTEES Clare Morpurgo; John Hughes; Christine Teale; Zoe Teale; Guy Dehn; Juliet Walker; Jane Walsh; Fredrica Teale; Lea Morpurgo.

PUBLICATIONS Every year the foundation hosts a lecture in memory of Sir Allen Lane. Since 1999 the text of each lecture each year has been published on the foundation's website.

OTHER INFORMATION 'The trustees regret that applications far outstrip the funds available and not all good or appropriate projects can be offered funding, even though they may fall well within current funding priorities. A rejection may be no reflection on the value of the project.'

HOW TO APPLY There is no formal application form, but when sending in an application the foundation asks that you complete the registration form (available on the website) and return it with your application. Applications should be no more than four sides of A4 but the budget may be on extra pages. It should be accompanied by your last annual report and accounts (if applicable) and the budget for the whole organisation (and the project budget if they are different) for the current year. The foundation now no longer has application deadlines. Applications are now processed continually. When the foundation has received your application they will usually be in touch within two weeks either to: ask for any further information; to tell you whether the application will be going forward to the next stage of assessment and what the timetable for a final decision will be; or to inform you that they are unable to help. The time it takes to process an application and make a grant is usually between two and six months.

WHO TO APPLY TO Tim Cutts, Executive Secretary, 90 The Mount, York YO24 1AR *Tel* 01904 613223 *Fax* 01904 613133 *email* info@allenlane.org.uk *Website* www.allenlane.org.uk

---

■ The Langdale Trust

CC NO 215317 **ESTABLISHED** 1960

WHERE FUNDING CAN BE GIVEN Worldwide, but with a special interest in Birmingham.

WHO CAN BENEFIT Registered charities.

WHAT IS FUNDED Youth organisations, medical, environment and social needs.

TYPE OF GRANT Annual for general and specific use.

RANGE OF GRANTS £1,000–£9,000.

SAMPLE GRANTS Yorkshire Swan and Wildlife Rescue Hospital (£9,000); Rainforest Concern (£6,000); The One Foundation (£5,000); Oxfam (£4,000); Prisoners Abroad (£3,000); Survival International (£2,000) and Tall Ships Youth Trust, Galapagos Conservation Trust and Apprentices are MAD (£1,000 each).

FINANCES *Year* 2009–10 *Income* £117,165 *Grants* £130,000 *Assets* £3,459,620

TRUSTEES Jethro Elvin; Timothy R Wilson; Teresa Whiting.

HOW TO APPLY In writing to the correspondent. The trustees meet in July.

WHO TO APPLY TO Mrs C G O'Brien, Secretary, c/o Cobbetts Solicitors, One Colmore Square, Birmingham B4 6AJ *Tel* 0845 404 2404

■ The Langley Charitable Trust

CC NO 280104 **ESTABLISHED** 1980

WHERE FUNDING CAN BE GIVEN UK and worldwide, with a preference for the West Midlands.

WHO CAN BENEFIT Individuals and groups benefiting Christians, at risk groups, people who are disadvantaged by poverty, socially isolated or sick.

WHAT IS FUNDED Advancement of the gospel and Christianity; welfare and health.

WHAT IS NOT FUNDED No grants to animal or bird charities.

RANGE OF GRANTS £25–£1 million.

SAMPLE GRANTS Northamptonshire Association of Youth Clubs (£1 million); Wide horizons (£15,000); Friends of Ludhiana (£25,000); United Christian Broadcaster (£500); Trauma Heading Workshop; Bible Society (£100 each); Manna House (£150); St Andrews Hospice Airdrie; St Giles Hospice (£25 each); Soul Survivor (£400); British Red Cross (£250).

FINANCES *Year* 2009 *Income* £183,322 *Grants* £1,042,550 *Assets* £5,291,270

TRUSTEES J P Gilmour; Mrs S S Gilmour.

HOW TO APPLY In writing to the correspondent. 'The trustees only reply where they require further information and so on. Neither telephone calls nor correspondence will be entered into concerning any proposed or declined applications.'

WHO TO APPLY TO The Trustees, Wheatmoor Farm, 301 Tamworth Road, Sutton Coldfield, West Midlands B75 6JP *Tel* 0121 308 0165

■ The Langtree Trust

CC NO 232924   **ESTABLISHED** 1963

WHERE FUNDING CAN BE GIVEN Gloucestershire.

WHO CAN BENEFIT Organisations benefiting the local community; occasionally to individuals if then of direct benefit to the community.

WHAT IS FUNDED General charitable purposes in Gloucestershire only. Priority is given to church projects, youth groups and people who are disabled or disadvantaged. The arts have a lower priority.

WHAT IS NOT FUNDED No grants are given in response to general appeals from large UK organisations. No grants for education.

TYPE OF GRANT Usually one-off for a specific project.

RANGE OF GRANTS £50–£1,000.

FINANCES *Year* 2009–10 *Income* £106,485 *Grants* £44,845 *Assets* £1,292,307

TRUSTEES Col P Haslam, Chair; Dr R E Way; G J Yates; Mrs A M Shepherd; Miss S Birch; Mrs K Bertram.

HOW TO APPLY In writing to the correspondent giving a simple, clear statement of the need with the costs of the project, what funding has so far been achieved and/or a recent copy of the annual accounts. Expensive, extensive, glossy appeal brochures are not appreciated. The trustees meet four to six times a year to decide the grant allocation. In exceptional circumstances a grant may be made between meetings. Please note that the address is a postal address and Randall and Payne cannot answer any telephone queries.

WHO TO APPLY TO Mrs K Bertram, Secretary, Randall & Payne, Rodborough Court, Walkley Hill, Stroud GL5 3LR

■ The LankellyChase Foundation

CC NO 1107583   **ESTABLISHED** 2005

WHERE FUNDING CAN BE GIVEN UK.

WHO CAN BENEFIT Charitable organisations.

WHAT IS FUNDED The following is taken from a press release, which is available in full on the foundation's website:

'After many years of working to improve the quality of people's lives in the UK, the LankellyChase Foundation has decided to intensify its focus on social disadvantage. From April 2012, the foundation will concentrate exclusively on bringing about change to improve the quality of life of people who face severe and multiple disadvantage. It has become increasingly clear that a significant number of people have been failed by attempts to tackle disadvantage and social exclusion. These are people who face a number of social disadvantages simultaneously, and who are poorly served by services and systems that are limited to individual needs and that struggle to provide effective or appropriate support for the whole person (sometimes called 'deep exclusion'). LankellyChase and many others have funded practice which shows that effective, sustainable and creative approaches to severe and multiple disadvantage are possible. In recognition of the scale and urgency of this challenge, the foundation has decided to place at the heart of its mission a single and sustained drive to bring about change that will improve the quality of life of people who face **severe and multiple disadvantage**. We will therefore be developing a number of proactive **special initiatives** that will try to get under the skin of severe and multiple disadvantage, tackle systemic failure and promote solutions that are both preventative and transformational. These initiatives will be developed in close partnership with organisations and individuals in the field, and they will typically combine grant making, research, learning and policy development. We also recognise that many organisations working with people who face severe and multiple disadvantage don't fit neatly into categories and require flexible funding in order to thrive. So we are moving away from our current programme approach, and are developing an **Open Grants scheme** that will offer funding to organisations that are working to build the capabilities of people who face severe and multiple disadvantage. We expect to launch this in **summer 2012**. The foundation has been working in the criminal justice system for more than twenty years, and we have helped fund many innovative services that have gone on to be regarded as best practice. This work has convinced us that people who face severe and multiple disadvantage need to be supported to avoid the criminal justice system altogether, and that our efforts and resources need to be concentrated at an early stage in their lives and in the system. We have therefore decided that our first Special Initiative should focus on ways of addressing severe and multiple disadvantage before people are drawn into offending. Details will be announced in **summer 2012**.'

Applicants are advised to consult the foundation's website for further news of the reorientation of grantmaking.

WHAT IS NOT FUNDED The foundation receives many more applications from worthwhile projects than it can hope to fund and as a consequence it does not support the following areas of work which are in addition to those specifically mentioned in the guidelines to the current programmes: access to buildings; advancement of religion; after school and homework clubs; animal charities; breakfast clubs; bursaries and scholarships; child befriending schemes; circular appeals; expeditions/overseas travel; festivals; formal education including schools, colleges and universities; general counselling; holidays/ holiday centres; hospitals and hospices; individual youth clubs; individuals – including students; medical care and medical research; mother and toddler groups/playgroups; museums/galleries; organisations working with particular medical conditions; other grant making organisations; research; sport; work that has already taken place; work which is primarily the responsibility of central or local government, education or health authorities.

TYPE OF GRANT Capital, revenue and full project funding for up to three years.

RANGE OF GRANTS Mainly £10,000 to £15,000. Occasionally up to £135,000.

SAMPLE GRANTS Family Action – London (£135,000); Clean Break (£100,000); Bright – London (£75,000); Kirckman Concert Society – London (£70,000); Women's Support Network – Belfast (£60,000); East Kent Rapeline, Canterbury (£57,000); Gorebridge Community Development Trust – Scotland (£50,000); Calderdale CAB – Halifax (£48,000); Red Dog Productions – Stroud; and Walsall Street Teams – Walsall (£45,000 each); Asylum Welcome – Oxford; and Justice First – Stockton on Tees (£30,000 each); Signpost and Rite Direkshon – Bristol (£20,000); Lateef Social Enterprise – Birmingham (£15,000); and St Mary at the Quay – Ipswich (£5,000).

FINANCES *Year* 2010–11 *Income* £4,365,005 *Grants* £5,754,280 *Assets* £124,060,841

TRUSTEES Nicholas Tatman (Chair); Ann Stannard; Dodie Carter; Paul Cotterill; Leo Fraser-Mackenzie; Victoria Hoskins; Marion Janner; Andrew Robinson; Kanwaljit Singh; Clive Martin; Peter Latchford; Morag Burnett; Alison Leverett-Morris.

HOW TO APPLY Application forms are available from the foundation's office or website. Please post the following with the application: an itemised income and expenditure budget for the work for which funding is requested, a supporting letter (no more than 2 sides of A4) and the organisation's most recent annual report and/or accounts. Please note the foundation's revised programme focus. Applicants are encouraged to contact the foundation for advice if necessary.

WHO TO APPLY TO Peter Kilgarriff, Chief Executive, 1 The Court, High Street, Harwell, Didcot, Oxfordshire OX11 0EY *Tel* 01235 820044 *Fax* 01235 432720 *email* enquiries@lankellychase.org.uk *Website* www.lankellychase.org.uk

■ The Lanvern Foundation

CC NO 295846   **ESTABLISHED** 1986

WHERE FUNDING CAN BE GIVEN UK.

WHO CAN BENEFIT Organisations concerned with health and education, with a preference for children's organisations.

WHAT IS FUNDED Trustees favour registered, medical and education charities.

WHAT IS NOT FUNDED Absolutely no grants to individuals.

TYPE OF GRANT Single projects preferred. Capital expenditure.

RANGE OF GRANTS Up to £125,000.

SAMPLE GRANTS The Moorfields Eye Hospital (£125,000); The Marchant-Holliday School (£5,000).

FINANCES *Year* 2009 *Income* £107,548 *Grants* £130,000 *Assets* £2,702,275

TRUSTEES J C G Stancliffe; A H Isaacs.

HOW TO APPLY In writing to the correspondent.

WHO TO APPLY TO J C G Stancliffe, Trustee, P O Box 34475, London W6 9YB *Tel* 020 8741 2930

■ The R J Larg Family Charitable Trust

SC NO SC004946   **ESTABLISHED** 1970

WHERE FUNDING CAN BE GIVEN UK but generally Scotland, particularly Tayside.

WHO CAN BENEFIT Organisations benefiting children, young adults, students and people who are disabled or who have a disease or medical condition.

WHAT IS FUNDED Grants are made for cancer research, amateur music and youth organisations including university students' associations. Funding may also be given to churches, conservation, respite care, hospices, MS and neurological research, care in the community and other community facilities. Other charitable purposes will be considered.

WHAT IS NOT FUNDED Grants are not available for individuals.

TYPE OF GRANT Generally one-off, some recurring. Buildings, core costs, running costs, salaries and start-up costs will be considered. Funding may be given for up to two years.

RANGE OF GRANTS £250–£5,000; typical grant £1,000–£2,000.

SAMPLE GRANTS Previous beneficiaries include High School – Dundee, Whitehall Theatre Trust, Macmillan Cancer Relief – Dundee and Sense Scotland Children's Hospice.

FINANCES *Year* 2009–10 *Income* £140,000 *Grants* £100,000

TRUSTEES R W Gibson; D A Brand; Mrs S A Stewart.

OTHER INFORMATION Income and grants total figures are approximate amounts provided by the trust.

HOW TO APPLY In writing to the correspondent. Trustees meet to consider grants in February and August.

WHO TO APPLY TO The Trustees, Whitehall House, Yeaman Shore, Dundee DD1 4BJ

■ Largsmount Ltd

CC NO 280509   **ESTABLISHED** 1979

WHERE FUNDING CAN BE GIVEN UK and overseas.

WHO CAN BENEFIT Institutions providing religious education in accordance with the doctrine and principles of traditional Judaism and organisations set up to provide for the Jewish needy.

WHAT IS FUNDED Jewish charitable purposes, mainly education.

TYPE OF GRANT Capital and reoccurring.

SAMPLE GRANTS Previously: MYR Charitable Trust (£235,000).

FINANCES *Year* 2009 *Income* £526,332 *Grants* £154,431 *Assets* £3,488,341

TRUSTEES Z M Kaufman; Naomi Kaufman; Simon Kaufman.

OTHER INFORMATION Accounts were overdue at the Charity Commission. Accounts for previous years were available without a list of grants.

HOW TO APPLY In writing to the correspondent.

WHO TO APPLY TO Simon Kaufman, Trustee, 50 Keswick Street, Gateshead NE8 1TQ *Tel* 0191 490 0140

■ The Lark Trust

CC NO 327982   **ESTABLISHED** 1988

WHERE FUNDING CAN BE GIVEN Bristol.

WHO CAN BENEFIT Registered charities benefiting people of all ages.

WHAT IS FUNDED Support in the areas of counselling, psychotherapy and the visual arts.

WHAT IS NOT FUNDED No grants to individuals.

TYPE OF GRANT Generally one-off.

RANGE OF GRANTS £100/£5,000.

SAMPLE GRANTS Beneficiaries included: Positive Action on Cancer (£3,000); St Peter's Hospice Trust (£2,000); Kinergy, One25 and Rainbow Centre (£1,500 each); Bridge Foundation, Katherine House Hospice, North Somerset Crossroads and AGBI (£1,000 each); Bristol Chan Group (£400).

FINANCES *Year* 2009–10 *Income* £96,983 *Grants* £28,460 *Assets* £1,489,508

TRUSTEES Iris Tute; George Tute; Martin Mitchell.

HOW TO APPLY Initially in writing to the correspondent, who will check eligibility and then send a form which must be completed. Trustees do not accept information from charities wishing to build a relationship with them. Applications should be received by the end of January for consideration in March.

WHO TO APPLY TO Alice Meason, c/o Quartet Community Foundation, Royal Oak House, Royal Oak Avenue, Bristol BS1 4AH *Tel* 0117 989 7700 *Fax* 0117 989 7701

■ Laslett's (Hinton) Charity

CC NO 233696   **ESTABLISHED** 1879

WHERE FUNDING CAN BE GIVEN Worcestershire and surrounding area.

WHO CAN BENEFIT Children, older people, clergy and people who are disadvantaged by poverty.

WHAT IS FUNDED Church repairs; general benefit of people who are poor, including homes for older people and educating children; relief of sickness, hospitals and general charitable purposes in Worcestershire and surrounding area.

SAMPLE GRANTS Previous beneficiaries have included St James' – Dudley, Worcester Cathedral, All Saints – Bromsgrove, Little Malvern Priory, St James' – Dudley, St Michael's – Tenbury Wells, St Stephen's – Worcester, St Barnabas – Worcester, St George's – Kidderminster, St Michael's – Hanley Childs, Throckmorton Chapel, St Edmund's – Dudley, St Clement's – Worcester, St Nicholas – Dormston, YMCA, Maggs Day Centre, Age Concern, Armchair, Cactus, Home-Start, Perdisell YPLC, Salvation Army, Sunfield – Stourbridge and Worcester Action for Youth.

FINANCES *Year* 2010 *Income* £521,517 *Grants* £28,050 *Assets* £10,178,476

TRUSTEES J B Henderson, Chair; E W Bonnett; E A Pugh-Cook; R A F Smith; R J R Young; J Panter; A E Lodge; A P Baxter; T J Bridges; S P Inman; M Jones; T King.

OTHER INFORMATION This trust has recently been focussing on the refurbishments of its properties in the hope of generating greater income in the following years, therefore has not been giving many grants that do not further this aim. This position is currently under review.

HOW TO APPLY In writing to the correspondent. Trustees meet quarterly to consider applications.

WHO TO APPLY TO I C Pugh or Mary Barker, Hallmark Hulme LLP, 4 and 5 Sansome Place, Worcester WR1 1UQ

■ Lauchentilly Charitable Foundation 1988

CC NO 299793   **ESTABLISHED** 1988

WHERE FUNDING CAN BE GIVEN UK and Republic of Ireland.

WHO CAN BENEFIT Small local projects, UK and established organisations benefiting children, young adults and people disadvantaged by poverty.

WHAT IS FUNDED Advancement of education, religion, relief of poverty and general charitable purposes.

WHAT IS NOT FUNDED No grants to individuals, including students, or to non-registered charities.

TYPE OF GRANT One-off and recurrent.

RANGE OF GRANTS £50–£10,000, usually £2,500 or less.

SAMPLE GRANTS Previous grant beneficiaries have included: Prince of Wales's Charitable Foundation; Macmillan Cancer Relief; Newton Toney Memorial Hall; Recreational Ground; Friends of Newton Toney School; Museum of Garden Hospital; Archie Foundation; Chelsea Physic Garden Company; Drukpa Kargyuad Trust; Friends of the Rotunda; Grange Park Opera; Newton Toney; PCC Iveagh Trust; Alzheimer's Society; Canine Partners for Independence; Crimestoppers Trust; Ormiston Children and Families Trust; Sandy Gill Afghanistan Appeal; League of Friends of the Ipswich Hospital NHS Trust; St Gregory's Foundation; Salisbury House.

FINANCES *Year* 2009–10 *Income* £15,351 *Grants* £13,892

TRUSTEES Countess of Iveagh; Cowdray Trust Ltd.

OTHER INFORMATION Accounts had been received at the Charity Commission but were not available for viewing online

HOW TO APPLY In writing to the correspondent including an sae. Only successful applications will be acknowledged.

WHO TO APPLY TO Laura Gosling, c/o Millbank Financial Services LtdPollen House, 10–12 Cork Street, London W1S 3LW *Tel* 020 7439 9061 *email* charity@mfs.co.uk

■ Laufer Charitable Trust

CC NO 275375   **ESTABLISHED** 1961

WHERE FUNDING CAN BE GIVEN UK.

WHO CAN BENEFIT Jewish organisations and charities personally known to the trustees.

WHAT IS FUNDED General charitable purposes.

WHAT IS NOT FUNDED No grants to individuals, as grants are only made to registered charities.

TYPE OF GRANT Recurrent core costs for up to one year.

RANGE OF GRANTS Any new grants made would not exceed £50 as the trust has a number of outstanding commitments which will absorb its income for the foreseeable future.

FINANCES *Year* 2009–10 *Income* £89,107 *Grants* £33,545 *Assets* £836,168

TRUSTEES S W Laufer; Mrs D D Laufer; S C Goulden; R Aarons; M Hoffman.

OTHER INFORMATION 'As this is a small charity, new beneficiaries are only considered in exceptional circumstances as the income is already allocated for some years to come.'

HOW TO APPLY In view of the ongoing support for an existing group of charities, applications are not recommended.

WHO TO APPLY TO R Aarons, Trustee, 342 Regents Park Road, London N3 2LJ *Tel* 020 8343 1660

■ The Lauffer Family Charitable Foundation

CC NO 251115　　**ESTABLISHED** 1965

WHERE FUNDING CAN BE GIVEN Commonwealth countries, Israel and USA.

WHO CAN BENEFIT Educational and medical charities benefiting students.

WHAT IS FUNDED Education, medical and cultural causes.

WHAT IS NOT FUNDED No support for individuals.

TYPE OF GRANT Starter finance and recurrent for five years.

SAMPLE GRANTS Jewish Learning Exchange (£20,000); Hasmonean High School (£15,000); British Friends of Sarah Herzog Memorial Hospital (£10,000); United Joint Israel Appeal (£6,000); Spiro Ark (£5,000); and British Friends of Ezer Mizion (£1,200).

FINANCES *Year* 2009–10 *Income* £138,483 *Grants* £213,720 *Assets* £5,254,137

TRUSTEES Mrs R R Lauffer; J S Lauffer; G L Lauffer; R M Lauffer.

HOW TO APPLY In writing to the correspondent; applications are considered once a year.

WHO TO APPLY TO J S Lauffer, Trustee, Clayton Stark & Co, 5th Floor, Charles House, 108–110 Finchley Road, London NW3 5JJ *Tel* 020 7431 4200 *email* bethlauffer@lineone.net

■ Mrs F B Laurence Charitable Trust

CC NO 296548　　**ESTABLISHED** 1976

WHERE FUNDING CAN BE GIVEN Worldwide.

WHO CAN BENEFIT Organisations benefiting ex-service and service people, retired people, unemployed people and disadvantaged members of society within the UK or overseas to whom the UK owes a duty of care.

WHAT IS FUNDED The aid and support of people who are chronically ill and people who are disabled. The support of justice and human rights organisations and the protection of the environment and wildlife. Charities working in the fields of accommodation and housing legal services, publishing and printing, support to voluntary and community organisations, volunteer bureaux, community arts and recreation, community facilities, special schools and special needs education and literacy will also be considered.

WHAT IS NOT FUNDED No support for individuals. The following applications are unlikely to be considered: appeals for endowment or sponsorship; overseas projects, unless overseen by the charity's own fieldworkers; maintenance of buildings or landscape; provision of work or materials that are the responsibility of the state; where administration expenses, in all their guises, are considered by the trustees to be excessive; or where the fundraising costs in the preceding year have not resulted in an increase in the succeeding years donations in excess of these costs.

TYPE OF GRANT Core costs, one-off, project and start-up costs. Funding is for one year or less.

SAMPLE GRANTS Gurkha Welfare Trust and ZANE – Zimbabwe a National Emergency (£3,000 each); Seafarers UK and Barnado's (£2,500 each); Blue Cross, Stroke Association and Winston's Wish (£2,000 each); BHEST, Carers UK and Women for Women (£1,500 each); and Children with Leukaemia (£1,300).

FINANCES *Year* 2009–10 *Income* £72,379 *Grants* £83,500 *Assets* £2,254,969

TRUSTEES Caroline Fry; Camilla Carr; Elizabeth Lyle.

OTHER INFORMATION Smaller grants of £1,000 or less totalled £28,750.

HOW TO APPLY In writing to the correspondent, including the latest set of accounts. Only registered charities will be considered.

WHO TO APPLY TO The Trustees, BM Box 2082, London WC1N 3XX

■ The Kathleen Laurence Trust

CC NO 296461　　**ESTABLISHED** 1987

WHERE FUNDING CAN BE GIVEN UK.

WHO CAN BENEFIT General charities with specific projects and events.

WHAT IS FUNDED General charitable purposes. The trust particularly favours smaller organisations and those raising funds for specific requirements such as medical research, associations connected with disability and learning difficulties, organisations helping people who are sick, older people and children.

WHAT IS NOT FUNDED No donations are made for running costs, management expenses or to individuals.

TYPE OF GRANT One-off and recurrent grants.

RANGE OF GRANTS £500–£30,000.

SAMPLE GRANTS Action for Kids, Age Concern, Colchester Cat Rescue, Heart Research UK, Institute of Cancer Research, Just Different, Marfan Trust, Prostate Cancer Charity, Roy Castle Lung Cancer Foundation, Sunnybank Trust and West Norfolk Schools for Parents.

FINANCES *Year* 2009–10 *Income* £886,346 *Grants* £113,500 *Assets* £2,985,113

TRUSTEES Coutts and Co.

HOW TO APPLY In writing to the correspondent. Trustees meet in January and June.

WHO TO APPLY TO Trust Manager, Coutts and Co, Trustee Department, 440 Strand, London WC2R 0QS *Tel* 020 7753 1000 *Fax* 020 7753 1090

■ The Law Society Charity

CC NO 268736　　**ESTABLISHED** 1974

WHERE FUNDING CAN BE GIVEN Worldwide.

WHO CAN BENEFIT Organisations protecting people's legal rights and lawyers' welfare as well as projects from charities without an identifiable legal connection.

WHAT IS FUNDED Charitable activities in the furtherance of law and justice. This includes: charitable educational purposes for lawyers and would-be lawyers; legal research; promotion of an increased understanding of the law; and charities concerned with the provision of advice, counselling, mediation services connected with the law, welfare directly/indirectly of solicitors, trainee solicitors and other legal and Law Society staff and their families.

TYPE OF GRANT One-off and recurrent grants.

SAMPLE GRANTS Previous beneficiaries have included: The Citizenship Foundation (£90,000); LawCare Limited (£82,500); Howard League for Penal Reform (£17,500); Environmental Law Foundation and Solicitors' Benevolent Society (£15,000 each); Nottinghamshire Law Society and Working Families (£10,000 each); Asylum Support Appeals Project (£7,500); Book Aid International (£6,400); Peace Brigades International and Youthnet UK (£5,000 each).

FINANCES *Year* 2009–10 *Income* £16,527 *Grants* £491,139

TRUSTEES The Law Society Trustees Ltd.

HOW TO APPLY In writing to the correspondent. Applications are considered at quarterly trustees' meetings, usually held in April, July, September and December.

WHO TO APPLY TO Andrew Dobson, Company Secretary, 113 Chancery Lane, London WC2A 1PL *Tel* 020 7316 5597 *email* lawsocietycharity@lawsociety.org.uk *Website* www.lawsociety.org.uk

---

■ The Edgar E Lawley Foundation

CC NO 201589   **ESTABLISHED** 1961

WHERE FUNDING CAN BE GIVEN UK, with a preference for the West Midlands.

WHO CAN BENEFIT Older people, disability, children, community, hospices and medical in the UK.

WHAT IS FUNDED Charities involved in the provision of medical care and services to older people, children's charities, and those involved with the advancement of medicine and medical research.

WHAT IS NOT FUNDED No grants to individuals.

TYPE OF GRANT One-off.

RANGE OF GRANTS £500 upwards; typical grant £1,000–£1,500.

SAMPLE GRANTS Acorns Children's Hospice, Aston & Birchfield Community Association, Extra Care Charitable Trust, Gospel Oak Community Centre, Guide Dogs, Home from Hospital Care, Lifelites, Redditch Association for the Blind, Walsall Hospice, Who Cares Trust and Zoe's Place for Baby Hospice.

FINANCES *Year* 2010–11 *Income* £197,609 *Grants* £227,000 *Assets* £4,167,224

TRUSTEES J H Cooke, Chair; Mrs G V H Hilton; P J Cooke; F S Jackson.

HOW TO APPLY Applications should be made in writing to the correspondent by 31 October. Applicants should outline the reasons for the grant request and the amount of grant being sought. Any supporting information that adds to the strength of the application should be included. The trustees make grant decisions in January. The foundation regrets that it is not possible, unless a stamped addressed envelope has been provided, to communicate with unsuccessful applicants and if a grant has not been received by mid August then it has not been possible to fund it.

WHO TO APPLY TO F S Jackson, Trustee, P.O. Box 456, Esher KT10 1DP *Tel* 01372 805760 *email* frankjackson1945@yahoo.com *Website* www.edgarelawleyfoundation.org.uk

---

■ The Herd Lawson and Muriel Lawson Charitable Trust

CC NO 1113220   **ESTABLISHED** 1975

WHERE FUNDING CAN BE GIVEN Mainly Cumbria.

WHO CAN BENEFIT Charitable organisations.

WHAT IS FUNDED This trust supports organisations benefiting older people in need, particularly those who are members of evangelical or Christian Brethren churches. A number of other named organisations receive support each year.

SAMPLE GRANTS Beneficiaries included: British Red Cross Society and WWF – UK (£21,000 each); the Christian Workers Relief Fund (£15,000); West Cumbria Hospice (£7,000) the Hospice of St Mary of Furness (£4,500); Ambleside Baptist Church (£4,500); Spring Mount Fellowship (£3,000); Ambleside Welfare Charity (£2,500) the Universal Beneficent Society (£1,500); and Heron Corn Mill Project (£400).

FINANCES *Year* 2009–10 *Income* £209,911 *Grants* £84,000 *Assets* £1,615,595

TRUSTEES John Scott; Peter Matthews; Robert Holme Barker; Edmund Herd.

HOW TO APPLY The trust receives more applications than it can deal with and does not seek further unsolicited appeals. 'The trustees have established a number of charities to whom they make grants each year and they very rarely make any donations to other charities.'

WHO TO APPLY TO J D Scott, The Estate Office, 14 Church Street, Ambleside, Cumbria LA22 0BT *Tel* 015394 34758

■ The Lawson Beckman Charitable Trust

CC NO 261378   **ESTABLISHED** 1970

WHERE FUNDING CAN BE GIVEN UK.

WHO CAN BENEFIT Mainly headquarters organisations.

WHAT IS FUNDED Jewish organisations, welfare, education, the arts and general purposes.

WHAT IS NOT FUNDED No grants to individuals.

TYPE OF GRANT One-off and recurrent.

RANGE OF GRANTS £250–£100,000.

SAMPLE GRANTS Jewish Care (£100,000), Norwood Ravenswood (£10,000), Nightingale House and United Jewish Israel Appeal (£5,000 each); Dalaid Limited and Project Seed (£2,500 each); and World Jewish Relief (£600).

FINANCES *Year* 2009–10 *Income* £107,485 *Grants* £133,367 *Assets* £1,786,507

TRUSTEES M A Lawson; F C Katz; L R Stock.

HOW TO APPLY In writing to the correspondent, but please note that grants are allocated two years in advance.

WHO TO APPLY TO Melvin Lawson, Trustee, A Beckman plc, PO Box 1ED, London W1A 1ED *Tel* 020 7637 8412 *Fax* 020 7436 8599

■ The Raymond and Blanche Lawson Charitable Trust

CC NO 281269   **ESTABLISHED** 1980

WHERE FUNDING CAN BE GIVEN UK, with an interest in West Kent and East Sussex.

WHO CAN BENEFIT Registered charities benefiting children, young adults and older people, including people with disabilities.

WHAT IS FUNDED This trust will consider funding: arts activities and education; building preservation; hospice at home; nursing service; local hospices; hospitals; cancer research; community centres and village halls; guide dogs; care in the community; and armed service charities and benevolent associations.

WHAT IS NOT FUNDED No support for churches or individuals.

TYPE OF GRANT One-off, project and research. Funding is available for up to one year.

RANGE OF GRANTS £250–£5,000. Typically £500–£1,000.

SAMPLE GRANTS The three largest grants during the year were for £5,000 and awarded to the following charities: Royal British Legion, Citizens Advice Bureau and Marden Memorial Village Hall.
Smaller grants included: Weald of Kent Hospice (£3,000); St Georges Community Children's Project and Royal London Society for the Blind (£2,000 each); Multiple Sclerosis Society and Independence at Home and League of Friends of Pembury Hospital (£1,000 each).

FINANCES *Year* 2009–10 *Income* £106,649
Grants £127,440 *Assets* £1,539,553
TRUSTEES Mrs S Hill and Mr P Thomas.
HOW TO APPLY In writing to the correspondent.
WHO TO APPLY TO 28 Barden Road, Tonbridge, Kent
TN9 1TX *Tel* 01732 352183 *Fax* 01732 352
621

■ The Carole and Geoffrey Lawson Foundation

CC NO 801751   ESTABLISHED 1989
WHERE FUNDING CAN BE GIVEN Worldwide, in practice,
UK.
WHO CAN BENEFIT Registered charities.
WHAT IS FUNDED Child welfare, poverty, arts,
education, research and Jewish organisations.
WHAT IS NOT FUNDED In principal, no grants to
individuals.
RANGE OF GRANTS £500–£115,000.
SAMPLE GRANTS Previous beneficiaries included:
World ORT Trust (£113,000); the Prince's Trust
(£33,000); Chase Children's Hospice Service
(£29,000); St David's Care in the Community
(£15,000); and Jewish Care (£13,000);
Community Security Trust and World Jewish
Relief (£10,000 each); Nightingale Home
(£8,000); King Silver Lining Appeal (£5,000);
Young Enterprise (£3,500); Meath Epilepsy
Trust (£2,000); and Royal Opera House, the
Sanctuary and Coexistence Trust (£1,000 each).
FINANCES *Year* 2009–10 *Income* £5,906
Grants £30,000
TRUSTEES Geoffrey C H Lawson; Carole Lawson;
Harold I Connick; Edward C S Lawson; Jeremy
S Lawson.
OTHER INFORMATION Grant making was significantly
reduced this year (£30,000 2009–10)
compared with the previous year (£298,000
2007/08).
HOW TO APPLY In writing to the correspondent.
WHO TO APPLY TO Geoffrey Lawson, Trustee,
Stilemans, Munstead, Godalming, Surrey
GU8 4AB *Tel* 01483 420757

■ The Mason Le Page Charitable Trust

CC NO 1054589   ESTABLISHED 1996
WHERE FUNDING CAN BE GIVEN London area.
WHO CAN BENEFIT Organisations benefiting people
with cancer and medical research.
WHAT IS FUNDED General charitable purposes, with a
preference for supporting charities working in
cancer research and care in the London area.
WHAT IS NOT FUNDED No grants to Individuals.
SAMPLE GRANTS Previous beneficiaries include:
£3,000 each to Barry Reed Oncology
Laboratory, St Barts, CORE, St Joseph's
Hospice; £2,000 to Breast Cancer Campaign;
Harlington Hospice Middlesex, Prostate Cancer
Research Centre, and Prostate Cancer Research
Campaign UK; £1,000 each to Dulwich Helpline,
St Christopher's Hospice and Trinity Hospice.
FINANCES *Year* 2009–10 *Income* £19,549
Grants £35,000
TRUSTEES David Morgan; Andrew John Francis
Stebbings.
HOW TO APPLY In writing to the correspondent.
WHO TO APPLY TO Andrew Stebbings, The
Administrator, Pemberton Greenish LLP,
45 Cadogan Gardens, London SW3 2TB
Tel 020 7591 3333 *Fax* 020 7591 3300
email charitymanager@pglaw.co.uk

■ The Leach Fourteenth Trust

CC NO 204844   ESTABLISHED 1961
WHERE FUNDING CAN BE GIVEN UK with some
preference for south west England.
WHO CAN BENEFIT Grants to registered charities only.
WHAT IS FUNDED Charities working in the fields of:
residential facilities and services; missionary
work; conservation and environment; and
community services. Support may be given to:
professional bodies; councils for voluntary
service; hospice at home; respite care;
ambulances and mobile units; medical
equipment; medical research; alternative
medicine; professional and specialist training;
and special needs education. Trustees mainly
seek out their own ventures to support.
WHAT IS NOT FUNDED Only registered charities based
in the UK are supported (the trust only gives
overseas via a UK-based charity). No grants to:
individuals, including for gap years or trips
abroad; private schools other than for people
with disabilities or learning difficulties; no pet
charities.
TYPE OF GRANT Buildings, capital, core costs, one-
off, project, research, running costs, recurring
costs, salaries and start-up costs will be
considered. Funding may be given for more than
three years.
RANGE OF GRANTS £500–£5,000.
SAMPLE GRANTS Merlin (£15,000); Plan International
UK (£4,000); Army Benevolent Fund (£3,000);
Salvation Army (£2,500); Mercy Ships and
Youth Action Wiltshire (£2,000); and British
Blind Sport, Countryside Restoration Trust,
React and The Princess Royal Trust for Carers
(£1,000 each).
FINANCES *Year* 2009–10 *Income* £92,791
Grants £106,000 *Assets* £2,836,333
TRUSTEES W J Henderson; Mrs J M M Nash;
G S Ward; Roger Murray-Leach.
HOW TO APPLY In writing to the correspondent.
Applications for a specific item or purpose are
favoured. Only successful appeals can expect a
reply. A representative of the trust occasionally
visits potential beneficiaries. There are bi-annual
meetings of trustees in summer and late
autumn. Grants tend to be distributed twice a
year but exceptions are made.
WHO TO APPLY TO Guy Ward, Trustee, Barron &
Barron, Chartered Accountants, Bathurst House,
86 Micklegate, York YO1 6LQ *Tel* 01904
628551 *Fax* 01904 623 533 *email* info@
barronyork.co.uk

■ The David Lean Foundation

CC NO 1067074   ESTABLISHED 1997
WHERE FUNDING CAN BE GIVEN UK.
WHO CAN BENEFIT Charitable organisations.
WHAT IS FUNDED Promotion and advancement of
education and to cultivate and improve public
taste in the visual arts, particularly in the field
of film production, including screenplay writing,
film direction and editing. The foundation
supports scholarships at the National Film and
Television School, Leighton Park School and
other institutions.
TYPE OF GRANT One-off and recurrent grants.
RANGE OF GRANTS £500–£135,000.
SAMPLE GRANTS National Film and Television School
(£135,000 for lectures/scholarships); British
Academy of Film and Television (£67,000);
British Film Institute (£49,000); Royal Academy
of Arts (£23,000 for schools/public lectures);
University of Southampton (£20,000 for
archives); Royal Holloway University of London

(£16,500 for David Lean award/scholarships); and Leighton Park School (£500 for scholarships).
FINANCES *Year* 2010 *Income* £389,926 *Grants* £310,832 *Assets* £390,963
TRUSTEES A A Reeves; J G Moore.
HOW TO APPLY Scholarship grants for students attending the National Film and Television School, Royal Holloway or Leighton Park School, are normally only awarded on the recommendation of the course provider with the trustees. Other applications for grants that would meet the aims of the foundation are invited in writing, enclosing full details of the project and including financial information and two references.
WHO TO APPLY TO The Trustees, KJD Freeth LLP, Churchill House, Regent Road, Stoke-on-Trent ST1 3RQ *Tel* 01782 202020 *Fax* 01782 266060 *email* aareeves@kjd.co.uk *Website* www.davidleanfoundation.org

■ The Leathersellers' Company Charitable Fund

CC NO 278072   **ESTABLISHED** 1979
WHERE FUNDING CAN BE GIVEN UK, particularly London.
WHO CAN BENEFIT Registered charities only.
WHAT IS FUNDED Charities associated with the Leathersellers' Company, the leather and hide trades, education in leather technology and for the welfare of poor and sick former workers in the industry and their dependants. Thereafter financial support is provided to registered charities associated with the City of London and its environs in the fields of education and sciences, relief of those in need, people with disabilities, children and youth, medicine and health, the arts, the church and the environment.
TYPE OF GRANT One-off and recurrent grants.
RANGE OF GRANTS £500–£60,000.
SAMPLE GRANTS Colfe's School (£60,000); Prendergast Hilly Fields College (£50,000); Chatham Historic Dockyard and SSAFA (£30,000 each); The Leather Conservation Centre (£28,000); Fitzwilliam College and St Catherine's College (£27,000 each); National Churches Trust and the Mary Rose Trust (£25,000 each); Rainbow Trust, Until the Violence Stops and Cancer & Bio-detection Dogs (£20,000 each); and the Kids' Cookery School, New Horizon Youth Centre, Michael Palin Centre for Stammering Children and Prison Advice & Care Trust (£15,000 each).
FINANCES *Year* 2009–10 *Income* £1,444,000 *Grants* £1,218,000 *Assets* £37,471,000
TRUSTEES The Leathersellers Company.
OTHER INFORMATION £209,000 was awarded to 107 individuals for educational and scientific purposes.
HOW TO APPLY 'Appeals must be from registered charities operating within the UK. Priority will be given to charities connected with leather, the leather trade, and the London area due to the company's long associations there. We will also consider charities that are based throughout the United Kingdom.' Applications are online via the trust's website. Successful applicants to the main grants programme will typically have to pass through a four stage process, which can take up to 9 months: Initial assessment – applicants will hear whether they have been successful or unsuccessful within 6 weeks; consideration by the grants committee; possible

visit by committee working group for a detailed assessment; and grants committee final decision.
WHO TO APPLY TO Mr David Santa-Olalla, Administrator, 21 Garlick Hill, London EC4V 2AU *Tel* 020 7330 1444 *Fax* 020 7330 1445 *email* dmsantao@leathersellers.co.uk *Website* www.leathersellers.co.uk

■ The Leche Trust

CC NO 225659   **ESTABLISHED** 1963
WHERE FUNDING CAN BE GIVEN UK.
WHO CAN BENEFIT Individuals and organisations benefiting: the arts, architecture and overseas students during last six months of their PhD courses.
WHAT IS FUNDED '(i) the promotion of amity and good relations between Britain and third world countries by financing visits to such countries by teachers or other appropriate persons, or providing financial assistance to students from overseas especially those in financial hardship during the last six months of their postgraduate doctorate study in the UK or those engaged in activities consistent with the charitable objects of the trust; (ii) assistance to academic, educational or other organisations concerned with music, drama, dance and the arts; (iii) the preservation of buildings and their contents and the repair and conservation of church furniture (including such items as monuments, but excluding structural repairs to the church fabric); preference is to be given to buildings and objects of the Georgian period; (iv) assistance to conservation in all its aspects, including in particular museums and encouraging good practice in the art of conservation by supporting investigative and diagnostic reports; (v) the support of charitable bodies or organisations associated with the preservation of the nation's countryside, towns, villages and historic landscapes.'
WHAT IS NOT FUNDED No grants are made for: religious bodies; overseas missions; schools and school buildings; social welfare; animals; medicine; expeditions; or British students other than music students.
TYPE OF GRANT For a specific purpose and not recurrent, including building costs.
RANGE OF GRANTS £170–£30,000.
SAMPLE GRANTS Sir John Soane's Museum – London (£30,000); SAVE Europe's Heritage (£10,000); Painswick Rococo Garden Trust, St Alkmund's Church – Shrewsbury (£5,000 each); College of Arms – London (£3,000); The National Trust – Erdigg (£4,000); The Hebridean Trust, Osterley Park, The Royal College of Surgeons of England (£2,500 each); Lichfield Festival and London Song Festival (£1,000 each).
FINANCES *Year* 2009–10 *Income* £283,425 *Grants* £315,504 *Assets* £5,742,793
TRUSTEES Dr Ian Bristow; The Hon. Mrs Felicity Guinness; Simon Jervis; Lady Greenstock; Martin Williams; Simon Wethered; Mrs Caroline Laing.
OTHER INFORMATION Included in the grant total is £18,760 given to individual students.
HOW TO APPLY In writing to the secretary. Trustees meet three times a year, in February, June and October; applications need to be received the month before.
WHO TO APPLY TO Mrs Louisa Lawson, Secretary, 84 Cicada Road, London SW18 2NZ *Tel* 020 8870 6233 *Fax* 020 8870 6233 *email* info@lechetrust.org *Website* www.lechetrust.org

■ The Arnold Lee Charitable Trust

cc no 264437   **established** 1972
WHERE FUNDING CAN BE GIVEN UK.
WHO CAN BENEFIT Organisations benefiting children, young adults and Jewish people. Support may also be given to rabbis, medical professionals, students, teachers and governesses. Very occasional grants may be made to individuals.
WHAT IS FUNDED Established charities of high repute working in the fields of education, health and religious purposes.
WHAT IS NOT FUNDED Grants are rarely made to individuals.
SAMPLE GRANTS Previously: Joint Jewish Charitable Trust (£34,000); Project SEED (£7,500); Jewish Care (£6,500; Lubavich Foundation (£5,000); The Home of Aged Jews (£2,500); Friends of Akim and Yesodey Hatorah School (£2,400 each).
FINANCES *Year* 2010–11 *Income* £103,804 *Grants* £100,850 *Assets* £1,624,004
TRUSTEES Edward Michael Lee; Alan Lee.
HOW TO APPLY In writing to the correspondent.
WHO TO APPLY TO Hazlems Fenton LLP, Palladium House, 1–4 Argyll Street, London W1F 7LD *Tel* 020 7437 7666

■ The William Leech Charity

cc no 265491   **established** 1972
WHERE FUNDING CAN BE GIVEN Northumberland, Tyne and Wear, Durham and overseas.
WHO CAN BENEFIT Registered charities.
WHAT IS FUNDED Small charities with a high proportion of unpaid volunteers, organisations working in deprived areas for the benefit of local people, particularly those which encourage people to help themselves, the promotion of community involvement and Christian charitable purposes.
WHAT IS NOT FUNDED No grants for: community centres and similar (exceptionally, those in remote country areas may be supported); running expenses of youth clubs (as opposed to capital projects); running expenses of churches (this includes normal repairs, but churches engaged in social work, or using their buildings largely for 'outside' purposes, may be supported); sport; the arts; individuals or students; organisations which have been supported in the last 12 months (it would be exceptional to support an organisation in two successive years, unless support had been confirmed in advance); holidays, travel, outings; minibuses (unless over 10,000 miles a year is expected); schools; and housing associations.
TYPE OF GRANT One-off and recurring grants, loans, running costs.
RANGE OF GRANTS £100–£50,000; most grants are for £1,000 or less.
SAMPLE GRANTS University of Newcastle upon Tyne Cardiovascular Stem Cell Research Department (£200,000), towards lab refurbishment and equipment. Other beneficiaries of larger grants included: Diocese of Newcastle Hirst Academy (£50,000); County Durham Foundation Grass Roots Challenge (£25,000); Northumberland County Blind Association and Partners in the Community (£10,000 each); Hexham & Newcastle Diocese Peru Mission (£7,000 in total); Mylambaverly Sri Lanka Playschool (£5,000); Mityana Community Development Foundation – Uganda (£4,000 in total); and Jitegemee School Building Project – Tanzania (£2,000). More typical grants of £1,000 or less included those to: Action for Children; Audio Visual Arts North East; Deafblind UK; Felling Male Voice Choir; Listening Books; The Woodland Trust; and YMCA Newcastle upon Tyne.
FINANCES *Year* 2009–10 *Income* £447,761 *Grants* £401,579 *Assets* £13,968,098
TRUSTEES Prof. Peter H Baylis; Cyril Davies; Adrian Gifford; Roy Leech; Richard Leech; N Sherlock; David Stabler; Barry Wallace; Prof. Chris Day.
HOW TO APPLY **The Main Fund:** 'As it is the intention of the trustees to favour support for those charities who help others by utilising the generous time and skills of volunteers, they accept applications in the short form of a letter, rather than expecting the completion of a complicated application form, which may seem daunting to some applicants. In order to safe-guard our charity status, it is important that we are accountable for how funds are distributed. As such, the following protocols exist for making and investigating applications. Please note we only accept applications from registered charities, and the registered charity address must be included in the application process. For large grants and multiple grants, trustees would like to see as much supporting information as possible, and in rare cases, they may wish to interview the applicant. Your applications must include: a description of the project that the charity is undertaking, who it hopes to help, and any evidence which will support the need for this particular project; how much the project will cost, capital and revenue, with an indication of the amounts involved; how much the charity has raised so far, and where it expects to find the balance; the type of support sought; i.e. small grant, multiple grant, loan, etc.; how much does it cost to run the charity each year, including how much of the revenue is spent on salaries and employees. Where does the revenue come from? How many paid workers are there, how many volunteers are there.'
The Lady Leech Fund: 'Applications to this fund should be submitted in a letter containing: the name, address and registration number of the charity; the name and contact details of the person who is authorised by the charity to apply for funding; a description of the project that the charity is undertaking, who it hopes to help, and any evidence which will support the need for this particular project; how much the project will cost, capital and revenue, with an indication of the amounts involved; how much the charity has raised so far, and where it expects to find the balance; a description of the connection between the Developing World Project, and the people in the North East of England; how much does it cost to run the charity each year, including how much of the revenue is spent on salaries and employees. Where does the revenue come from? How many paid workers are there? How many volunteers are there?'
Application letters can be written and submitted on the charity's website.
WHO TO APPLY TO Mrs Kathleen M Smith, Secretary, Saville Chambers, 5 North Street, Newcastle upon Tyne NE1 8DF *Tel* 0191 243 3300 *Fax* 0191 243 3309 *email* enquiries@williamleechcharity.org.uk *Website* www.williamleechcharity.org.uk

■ The Lord Mayor of Leeds Appeal Fund

CC NO 512441   ESTABLISHED 1982
WHERE FUNDING CAN BE GIVEN Leeds.
WHO CAN BENEFIT The charities selected by the lord mayor during her/his year of office.
WHAT IS FUNDED Charitable causes.
SAMPLE GRANTS £49,000 was awarded between The Create Foundation CiC; The Samaritans of Leeds; and Middleton Park Equestrian Centre RDA.
FINANCES *Year* 2009–10 *Income* £50,476 *Grants* £49,344 *Assets* £63,072
TRUSTEES Peter Gruen; Ann Blackburn; John M Proctor; Susan Bentley.
HOW TO APPLY The fund does not accept unsolicited applications.
WHO TO APPLY TO Paul Gilmartin, Leeds City Council, Corporate Financial Management, Selectapost 3, Civic Hall, Leeds LS1 1JF *Tel* 0113 247 4283

■ Leeds Building Society Charitable Foundation

CC NO 1074429   ESTABLISHED 1999
WHERE FUNDING CAN BE GIVEN Areas where the society's branches are located.
WHO CAN BENEFIT Organisations benefiting the homeless, local community centres, younger people, older people, individuals with disabilities, and deaf and/or blind people.
WHAT IS FUNDED Charities which have benefited include those working in the following areas: provision of shelter, support and resettlement programmes; for the homeless; centres offering facilities for the local community with emphasis on the young and elderly; provision of work experience and skills training for young people with special needs; educational and recreational projects for the deaf and blind; provision of transport for the physically disabled; practical care for the terminally ill; recreational and educational opportunities for children and young people from disadvantaged backgrounds.
WHAT IS NOT FUNDED The following are not eligible for grants: restoration of buildings, including churches; playgroups, Scout or Guide associations; environmental charities (unless there is a benefit to a disadvantaged community); religious, political or military purposes; overseas charities or projects; individuals, including sponsorship; animal welfare projects; medical research or equipment.
TYPE OF GRANT One-off for capital projects.
RANGE OF GRANTS £250–£1,000.
FINANCES *Year* 2010 *Income* £104,530 *Grants* £105,105 *Assets* £13,141
TRUSTEES Paul D Taylor, Chair; Ann Shelton; Gary Brook; Robert Wade; Martin J Richardson.
HOW TO APPLY In writing to the correspondent. The trustees meet four times a year in March, June, September and December. The trust is unable to consider applications if support has been provided in the last two years.
WHO TO APPLY TO Sally Smith, Secretary, 105 Albion Street, Leeds, West Yorkshire LS1 5AS *Tel* 0113 216 7296 *Fax* 0113 225 7549 *email* ssmith@leeds-holbeck.co.uk *Website* www.leedsbuildingsociety.co.uk/foundation

■ The Leeds Community Foundation

CC NO 1096892   ESTABLISHED 2005
WHERE FUNDING CAN BE GIVEN Leeds.
WHO CAN BENEFIT Community groups and registered charities.
WHAT IS FUNDED Social welfare and general charitable purposes.
RANGE OF GRANTS Usually from below £1,000 to £50,000.
FINANCES *Year* 2009–10 *Income* £2,695,221 *Grants* £4,049,679 *Assets* £10,202,788
TRUSTEES Andrew Wriglesworth, Chair; Martin Dean; Uell Kennedy; Kevin O'Connor; Steve Rogers; Helen Thomson; Julie Meakin; Nicholas Burr; Kimberly O'Callaghan; Patrick Salami-Spencer; Steve Smith.
OTHER INFORMATION The Leeds Community Foundation aimed to distribute a total of £3 million in 2010–11.
HOW TO APPLY The foundation's website has details of the grant schemes currently being administered and how to apply.
WHO TO APPLY TO The Grants and Community Manager, 51a St Paul's Street, Leeds LS1 2TE *Tel* 0113 2422426 *email* info@leedscommunityfoundation.org.uk *Website* www.leedscommunityfoundation.org.uk

■ Leicester Charity Link (formerly The Leicester Charity Organisation Society)

CC NO 209464   ESTABLISHED 1876
WHERE FUNDING CAN BE GIVEN The city of Leicester, Leicestershire and Rutland.
WHO CAN BENEFIT Individuals and organisations.
WHAT IS FUNDED General charitable purposes.
SAMPLE GRANTS Grants to: Leicestershire Palliative and Cancer Care Teams which help patients and their carers; individuals in need; grants to a few organisations through the Local Network Fund and other trusts under its administration.
FINANCES *Year* 2009–10 *Income* £420 *Grants* £1,000
TRUSTEES Mrs Ann M Brennan, Chair; Mrs Rosemary Freer; Rodney J Hudson; Clive E Smith; Mrs Caroline M Wessel; Anthony H Jarvis; Mrs R M Ingam; Veronica Tordimah; Mrs Catherine Boulton.
HOW TO APPLY In writing to the correspondent.
WHO TO APPLY TO James Munton, 20a Millstone Lane, Leicester LE1 5JN *Tel* 0116 222 2200 *Fax* 0161 222 2201 *email* info@charity-link.org *Website* www.charity-link.org

■ Leicestershire Historic Churches Trust

CC NO 233476   ESTABLISHED 1964
WHERE FUNDING CAN BE GIVEN Leicestershire.
WHO CAN BENEFIT Churches and chapels.
WHAT IS FUNDED The restoration, preservation, repair, maintenance and improvement of churches and chapels, their churchyards and contents.
WHAT IS NOT FUNDED No grants for electrical work, disability access, reordering of the interior, redecorating, toilets or kitchen facilities, extensions, school or other ancillary buildings.
FINANCES *Year* 2009–10 *Income* £79,945 *Grants* £36,265 *Assets* £111,972
TRUSTEES R H Bloor; Hon. Lady Brooks; C B Byford; T Y Cocks; J M Hemes; Revd D N Hole;

J Ireland; D Knowles; Fr Fabian Radcliffe;
B W Wilford; R J Wood.

HOW TO APPLY In writing to the correspondent. The
trustees meet twice a year, usually in April and
October. Applications should be submitted by 1
March and 1 September. Churches and chapels
have three years in which to claim a grant once
a grant has been awarded.

WHO TO APPLY TO Janet Arthur, Chair, 20 Gumley
Road, Smeeton Westerby, Leicester LE8 0LT
Tel 0116 279 3995 *email* chairman@lhct.org.
uk *Website* www.lhct.org.uk

■ The P Leigh-Bramwell Trust 'E'

CC NO 267333   **ESTABLISHED** 1973
WHERE FUNDING CAN BE GIVEN UK, with a preference
for Bolton.

WHO CAN BENEFIT Registered charities, schools,
universities and churches benefiting children,
young adults, students and Methodists.

WHAT IS FUNDED Specific regular allocations, leaving
little opportunity to add further charities.
Support is particularly given to Methodist
churches and Bolton-based organisations.

WHAT IS NOT FUNDED No grants to individuals.

TYPE OF GRANT Mainly recurrent grants to
established beneficiaries.

RANGE OF GRANTS £100–£30,000.

SAMPLE GRANTS King's College School (£30,000);
Leigh-Bramwell Fund (£23,000); The Methodist
Church – Bolton (£11,000); Rivington Parish
Church (£7,500); The Unicorn School (£7,000);
and The Methodist Church – Delph Hill and The
Methodist Church – Breightmet (£3,400 each);
RNLI (£2,000); Barnabus, Bolton Choral Union,
Bolton Deaf Society, ChildLine North West, NCH
Bypass, West London Mission and YWCA (£500
each).

FINANCES *Year* 2009–10 *Income* £88,933
Grants £88,260 *Assets* £1,863,680

TRUSTEES Mrs H R Leigh-Bramwell; Mrs J Leigh
Mitchell; B H Leigh-Bramwell.

HOW TO APPLY In writing to the correspondent;
however, please note that previous research
suggests that there is only a small amount of
funds available for unsolicited applications and
therefore success is unlikely.

WHO TO APPLY TO Mrs L Cooper, Secretary, W and J
Leigh and Co., Tower Works, Kestor Street,
Bolton BL2 2AL *Tel* 01204 521771

■ The Kennedy Leigh Charitable Trust

CC NO 288293   **ESTABLISHED** 1983
WHERE FUNDING CAN BE GIVEN Israel and UK.
WHO CAN BENEFIT Registered charities only.
WHAT IS FUNDED Projects and causes which will
improve and enrich the lives of all parts of
society, not least those of the young, the needy,
the disadvantaged and the underprivileged. The
trust's objects require three-quarters of its
grant-making funds to be distributed to
charitable institutions within Israel, with the
remainder being distributed in the UK and
elsewhere.

WHAT IS NOT FUNDED No grants to individuals.

TYPE OF GRANT Capital projects and running costs.
Usually up to three years, with the possibility of
renewal.

RANGE OF GRANTS £1,000 and over.

SAMPLE GRANTS Yemin Orde (£50,000); Weizmann
Institute (£45,000); Oxford Centre for Hebrew
Studies (£25,000); Hebrew University Rehovol

Campus Library (£20,000); and Jewish Care and
the Community Security Trust (£10,000 each).

FINANCES *Year* 2009–10 *Income* £431,033
Grants £814,723 *Assets* £17,572,647

TRUSTEES Lesley Berman; Anthony Foux; Geoffrey
Goldkorn; Angela L Sorkin; Michael Sorkin;
Carole Berman.

HOW TO APPLY The trust stated in its 2009–10
accounts: 'The funds available for distribution
outside of Israel are all but committed for the
foreseeable future to several UK charities. The
trustees are therefore unable to consider
applications for funding from charitable
organisations outside of Israel at this time.' The
trust has more recently stated that funds are
fully committed.

WHO TO APPLY TO Naomi Shoffman, Administrator,
ORT House, 126 Albert Street, London
NW1 7NE *Tel* 020 7267 6500 *email* naomi@
klct.org

■ Morris Leigh Foundation

CC NO 280695   **ESTABLISHED** 1980
WHERE FUNDING CAN BE GIVEN UK.
WHO CAN BENEFIT Charitable organisations, with a
strong preference for Jewish/Israeli
organisations.

WHAT IS FUNDED General charitable purposes,
including the arts and humanities, education,
culture and health and welfare causes.

TYPE OF GRANT Grants and long-term loans.

RANGE OF GRANTS £50–£5,000.

SAMPLE GRANTS Nightingale House and Purcell
School (£5,000 each); New Israel Fund, British
Friends of Ohel Sarah and My Israel (£500
each); and Brainstrust (£300).

FINANCES *Year* 2009–10 *Income* £32,310
Grants £11,800 *Assets* £1,590,292

TRUSTEES Martin D Paisner; Howard D Leigh.

HOW TO APPLY In writing to the correspondent.

WHO TO APPLY TO Tina Grant-Brook, Administrator,
40 Portland Place, London W1B 1NB *Tel* 020
7908 6000

■ The Leigh Trust

CC NO 275372   **ESTABLISHED** 1976
WHERE FUNDING CAN BE GIVEN UK and overseas.
WHO CAN BENEFIT Registered charities benefiting
children; young adults; older people;
unemployed people; volunteers; people who are
in care, fostered or adopted; ethnic minority
groups; at risk groups; people disadvantaged by
poverty; ex-offenders and those at risk of
offending; refugees; socially isolated people;
people living in urban areas; victims of abuse
and crime; and people with substance abuse
problems.

WHAT IS FUNDED Grants can be given to legal
services, support to voluntary and community
organisations, support to volunteers, health
counselling, support and self-help groups, drug
and alcohol rehabilitation, education and
training, social counselling, crime prevention
schemes, community issues, international rights
of the individual, advice and information (social
issues), asylum seekers, racial equality and
other charitable causes.

WHAT IS NOT FUNDED The trust does not make grants
to individuals.

TYPE OF GRANT Buildings, capital, core costs, one-
off, project, recurring costs, running costs,
salaries and start-up costs. Funding is available
for up to three years.

RANGE OF GRANTS £500–£5,000.

SAMPLE GRANTS Shelter (£10,000); Birmingham Law Centre (£6,000); Hebron Trust, ASAP, REALLITY, Remedi, Justice First and The Anna Freud Centre (£5,000 each); Tower Hamlets Mission, Church Action on Poverty, Article 1, Renecassin, Not Shut Up Limited and Leeway Women's Aid £3,000 each); Refugee Support Group Devon and New Bridge (£2,000 each); Open Hands Coventry, Barwaqa Relief Organisation, Glenthorne Quaker Centre and OSW (£1,500 each).

FINANCES *Year* 2009–10 *Income* £79,796 *Grants* £96,140 *Assets* £2,833,969

TRUSTEES Hon. David Bernstein; Dr R M E Stone; Caroline Moorehead.

HOW TO APPLY Organisations applying for grants must provide their most recent audited accounts, a registered charity number, a cash flow statement for the next 12 months, and a stamped addressed envelope. Applicants should state clearly on one side of A4 what their charity does and what they are requesting funding for. They should provide a detailed budget and show other sources of funding for the project.

WHO TO APPLY TO The Trustees, Begbies Chettle Agar, Epworth House, 25 City Road, London EC1Y 1AR *Tel* 020 7628 5801 *Fax* 020 7628 0390

■ Mrs Vera Leigh's Charity

CC NO 274872   **ESTABLISHED** 1976

WHERE FUNDING CAN BE GIVEN UK.

WHO CAN BENEFIT Organisations only.

WHAT IS FUNDED General charitable purposes.

WHAT IS NOT FUNDED No grants to individuals.

TYPE OF GRANT One-off.

RANGE OF GRANTS £250–£2,000.

SAMPLE GRANTS DEC Haiti Earthquake (£2,000); Royal British Legion (£1,700); British Heart Foundation (£1,250); Cystic Fibrosis Trust and Marie Curie Cancer Care (£1000 each); Christian Aid, Save the Children, The Stroke Association, Multiple Sclerosis Society (£750 each); Army Benevolent Funds, Make a Wish Campaign (£500 each); Alzheimer's Society, The Grange Centre, National Rifle Association (£250).

FINANCES *Year* 2009–10 *Income* £27,279 *Grants* £19,200

TRUSTEES J H Woollcombe; T A Cole.

HOW TO APPLY In writing to the correspondent, although the trust states that unsolicited applications are not considered.

WHO TO APPLY TO Penningtons Solicitors LLP, Highfield, Brighton Road, Godalming, Surrey GU7 1NS

■ The Lennox and Wyfold Foundation

CC NO 1080198   **ESTABLISHED** 2000

WHERE FUNDING CAN BE GIVEN Unrestricted.

WHO CAN BENEFIT Registered charities.

WHAT IS FUNDED General charitable purposes.

SAMPLE GRANTS Eton College (£100,000), toward its endowment fund; and Maggie's Centre (£25,000), towards the development of a new cancer centre at Churchill Hospital. Unfortunately, no other beneficiaries were listed in the accounts. Previous beneficiaries included: Breakthrough Breast Cancer; Absolute Return for Kids; RNIB; Deafblind UK; Amber Foundation; Tusk Trust; Elephant Family; St George's Chapel – Windsor; Bucklebury Memorial Hall; Chipping

Norton Theatre and Friends Trust; Gloucestershire Air Ambulance; Mary Hare Foundation; and Reform Research Trust.

FINANCES *Year* 2009–10 *Income* £313,994 *Grants* £618,500 *Assets* £34,011,422

TRUSTEES Lennox Hannay; Adam Flemming; Christopher Fleming; Caroline Wilmot-Sitwell.

HOW TO APPLY In writing to the correspondent.

WHO TO APPLY TO G Fincham, Secretary, Fleming Family & Partners Ltd, 15 Suffolk Street, London SW1Y 4HG *Tel* 020 7036 5000 *Fax* 020 7036 5601

■ The Leonard Trust

CC NO 1031723   **ESTABLISHED** 1993

WHERE FUNDING CAN BE GIVEN Overseas and UK, with a preference for Winchester.

WHO CAN BENEFIT Registered charities.

WHAT IS FUNDED Christian, overseas aid.

WHAT IS NOT FUNDED No grants to individuals. Medical research or building projects are no longer supported.

TYPE OF GRANT Usually one-off.

RANGE OF GRANTS £1,000–£5,000.

SAMPLE GRANTS Tower Hamlets Mission (£25,000); Christian Aid (£6,000); L'Arche Overseas Development Fund (£5,000); Chernobyl Children (£3,000); and Brendon Care and Credit Action (£2,000 each).

FINANCES *Year* 2010 *Income* £27,075 *Grants* £42,670 *Assets* £175,574

TRUSTEES Dominic Gold; Christopher Smiley.

HOW TO APPLY Unsolicited applications cannot be considered.

WHO TO APPLY TO Tessa E Feilden, 18 Edgar Road, Winchester, Hampshire SO23 9TW *Tel* 01962 854800

■ The Erica Leonard Trust

CC NO 291627   **ESTABLISHED** 1985

WHERE FUNDING CAN BE GIVEN Mainly Surrey and occasionally overseas.

WHO CAN BENEFIT Registered charities only.

WHAT IS FUNDED General charitable purposes.

WHAT IS NOT FUNDED Only able to support registered charities.

RANGE OF GRANTS Most grants are for £1,000 or less.

SAMPLE GRANTS Phoenix Trust (£9,000); Wells for India (£4,000); Leonard Trust (£2,000); Gauchers Association (£1,000); Cherry Trees (£750); Marie Curie Cancer Care (£500); and FMDM (£250).

FINANCES *Year* 2009–10 *Income* £18,822 *Grants* £38,000

TRUSTEES R C E Grey; A C Kemp; R Beeston; A Lodge.

HOW TO APPLY In writing to the correspondent.

WHO TO APPLY TO Richard C E Grey, Trustee, Old Farmhouse, Farnham Road, Elstead, Surrey GU8 6DB *Tel* 01252 702230 *email* rcegrey@ aol.com

■ The Mark Leonard Trust

CC NO 1040323   **ESTABLISHED** 1994

WHERE FUNDING CAN BE GIVEN Worldwide, but mainly UK.

WHO CAN BENEFIT Organisations benefiting the environment, children and young adults.

WHAT IS FUNDED Environment: environmental education, particularly supporting projects displaying practical ways of involving children and young adults, as well as sustainable transport, energy efficiency and renewable energy. Youth work: the rehabilitation of young people who have become marginalised and involved in anti-social or criminal activities, as well as extending and adding value to the existing use of school buildings and encouraging greater involvement of parents, school leavers and volunteers in extra-curricular activities. General charitable purposes.

WHAT IS NOT FUNDED Grants are not normally made to individuals.

RANGE OF GRANTS £10,000–£100,000.

SAMPLE GRANTS Sustainable Restaurant Association (£100,000); Grow Organisation and the Ashden Awards (£50,000 each); Fight for Peace (£35,000); Sustainability and Environmental Education (£30,000); Worldwide Volunteering for Young People and Youth at Risk (£25,000 each); East Potential (£23,000); Federation of City Farms and Community Gardens (£22,500); Charles Darwin Trust and Green Alliance (£20,000 each); People and Planet (£17,000); and City University and Medical Relief and Emergency International (£10,000 each).

FINANCES *Year* 2009–10 *Income* £1,132,065 *Grants* £483,513 *Assets* £12,305,655

TRUSTEES Zivi Sainsbury; Judith Portrait; John Julian Sainsbury; Mark Sainsbury.

HOW TO APPLY 'Proposals are generally invited by the trustees or initiated at their request. Unsolicited applications are discouraged and are unlikely to be successful, unless they are closely aligned to the trust's areas of interest.' A single application will be considered for support by all the trusts in the Sainsbury family group.

WHO TO APPLY TO Alan Bookbinder, Director, Allington House, 1st Floor, 150 Victoria Street, London SW1E 5AE *Tel* 020 7410 0330 *Fax* 020 7410 0332 *Website* www.sfct.org.uk

···········

■ Lesley Lesley and Mutter Trust

CC NO 1018747   **ESTABLISHED** 1989

WHERE FUNDING CAN BE GIVEN Dorset.

WHO CAN BENEFIT Parkinson's Disease Association, Chest Heart and Stroke Association, Multiple Sclerosis Society, Muscular Dystrophy Group of Great Britain, Royal National Institute for the Blind, Rowcroft Hospice for Torbay and Guide Dogs for the Blind (Devon Area Branch).

WHAT IS FUNDED Recipients are named in the trust deed and only those organisations can be funded.

TYPE OF GRANT Recurrent.

SAMPLE GRANTS The trust supports the same recipients year after year. New applicants are therefore not welcome. In 2010 the trust had assets of £170,000 and an income of £214,000. Grants were made totalling £39,000. Each year grants are distributed as follows: 35% to Chest Heart and Stroke Association; 35% to Parkinson's Disease Society; 6% to Guide Dogs for the Blind (Devon Area Branch); 6% to Multiple Sclerosis Society; 6% to Muscular Dystrophy Group of Great Britain; 6% to Rowcroft Hospice for Torbay; 6% to Royal National Institute for the Blind.

FINANCES *Year* 2010 *Income* £213,753 *Grants* £38,713 *Assets* £179,214

TRUSTEES Lloyds TSB Private Banking Ltd.

HOW TO APPLY Applications are not welcome.

WHO TO APPLY TO Miss Emily Parry, Lloyds Private Banking Limited, UK Trust Centre, The Clock House, 22–26 Ock Street, Abingdon, Oxfordshire OX14 5SW *Tel* 01235 232688

···········

■ Leukaemia and Lymphoma Research Fund

CC NO 216032   **ESTABLISHED** 1960

WHERE FUNDING CAN BE GIVEN UK.

WHO CAN BENEFIT Hospitals and university medical centres which benefit medical professionals, nurses and doctors; students; and people with leukaemia.

WHAT IS FUNDED Improving treatments, finding the cures and preventing all forms of leukaemia, Hodgkin's disease and other lymphomata, myelomata, the myelodysplasias and aplastic anaemia.

TYPE OF GRANT Capital (equipment), feasibility study, recurring costs, research and salaries.

RANGE OF GRANTS £45,000–£4.5 million.

SAMPLE GRANTS Beneficiaries included: University of Birmingham (£3.5 million); University College London (£2.4 million); Imperial College London (£2 million); University of Cambridge, University of Southampton and Babraham Institute (£1.1 million each); University of Sheffield (£1 million); Kings College London (£800,000).

FINANCES *Year* 2009–10 *Income* £19,135,000 *Grants* £17,848,312 *Assets* £23,771,000

TRUSTEES The Earl Cadogan, Chair; P Burrell; G Brocklebank; A Dart; M Clarke; M Cockayne; A Knowles; R Delderfield; M Williams; J Wells; J House; J Reeve.

HOW TO APPLY On an application form available from the trust.

WHO TO APPLY TO Dr David Grant, Scientific Director, 39–40 Eagle Street, London WC1R 4TH *Tel* 020 7405 0101 *Fax* 020 7242 1488 *email* info@beatbloodcancers.org *Website* www.beatbloodcancers.org

···········

■ The Leverhulme Trade Charities Trust

CC NO 288404   **ESTABLISHED** 1983

WHERE FUNDING CAN BE GIVEN UK.

WHO CAN BENEFIT Charities connected with and benefiting commercial travellers, grocers or chemists, their wives, widows and children, especially those disadvantaged by poverty.

WHAT IS FUNDED Benevolent societies, educational institutions and research costs.

WHAT IS NOT FUNDED No capital grants. No response is given to general appeals.

TYPE OF GRANT One-off and recurrent grants.

SAMPLE GRANTS Royal Pinner School Foundation (£480,000); Girl's Day School Trusts (£276,000); Caravan (£150,000); UCTA Samaritan Fund (£130,000); Pharmacy Practice Research Trust (£125,000); and Provision Trade Benevolent Institution (£24,000).

FINANCES *Year* 2010 *Income* £1,802,000 *Grants* £1,690,000 *Assets* £46,685,000

TRUSTEES Sir Michael Perry, Chair; N W A Fitzgerald; P J-P Cescau; A S Ganguly; P Polman.

OTHER INFORMATION During the year 82 applications for undergraduate bursaries were received and 82 were approved as grants. A further 25 postgraduate grants were approved.

HOW TO APPLY By letter to the correspondent. All correspondence is acknowledged. The trustees meet in February and applications need to be received by the preceding October. Undergraduate bursary applications should be directed to the relevant institution.

WHO TO APPLY TO Paul Read, Secretary, 1 Pemberton Row, London EC4A 3BG *Tel* 020 7042 9881 *email* pread@leverhulme.ac.uk *Website* leverhulme-trade.org.uk

■ The Leverhulme Trust

CC NO 288371 **ESTABLISHED** 1925
WHERE FUNDING CAN BE GIVEN Unrestricted.
WHO CAN BENEFIT Universities and other institutions of higher and further education; registered charities; and individuals.
WHAT IS FUNDED Grants are made to institutions for specific research undertakings, for schemes of international academic interchange and for education.
WHAT IS NOT FUNDED When submitting an application to the trust, applicants are advised that the trust does not offer funding for the following costs, and hence none of these items may be included in any budget submitted to the trust: core funding or overheads for institutions; individual items of equipment over £1,000; sites, buildings or other capital expenditure; support for the organisation of conferences or workshops, which are not directly associated with International Networks, Early Career Fellowships or Philip Leverhulme Prizes; exhibitions; contributions to appeals; endowments; a shortfall resulting from a withdrawal of or deficiency in public finance; UK student fees where these are not associated with a Research Project Grant bid or with Fine and Performing Arts schemes detailed in the Guidelines for Applicants.
TYPE OF GRANT One-off, project, research, recurring, running costs and salaries.
SAMPLE GRANTS Oxford University (£4.8 million); Leicester University (£2 million); Warwick University (£1.4 million); Reading University (£1.2 million); Edinburgh University (£895,000); Southampton University (£762,000); York University (£692,000); Liverpool University (£592,000); University of East Anglia (£530,000); British Museum (£429,000); Sheffield University (£377,000); and the Natural History Museum (£348,000).
FINANCES *Year* 2009–10 *Income* £59,115,000 *Grants* £53,395,000 *Assets* £1,587,548,000
TRUSTEES Sir Michael Perry, Chair; Patrick J P Cescau; Niall W A Fitzgerald; Dr Ashok S Ganguly; Paul Polman.
PUBLICATIONS Full and detailed information is available in the trust's 'Guidelines for Applicants'.
HOW TO APPLY Each programme, scholarship and award has its own individual application deadline and procedure. Full guidelines and application procedures for each award scheme are available from the trust directly or via its website.
WHO TO APPLY TO Paul Read, Secretary, 1 Pemberton Row, London EC4A 3BG *Tel* 020 7042 9881 *email* enquiries@leverhulme.org.uk *Website* www.leverhulme.org.uk

■ Lord Leverhulme's Charitable Trust

CC NO 212431 **ESTABLISHED** 1957
WHERE FUNDING CAN BE GIVEN UK especially, Cheshire, Merseyside and South Lancashire.
WHO CAN BENEFIT Registered and exempt charities.
WHAT IS FUNDED General charitable purposes. Priority is given to certain charitable organisations and trusts in Cheshire and Merseyside, particularly educational organisations, welfare charities, youth organisations, the arts, churches, and organisations benefiting older people and people with disabilities.
WHAT IS NOT FUNDED No grants to non-charitable organisations.
TYPE OF GRANT Recurrent, one-off and capital.
RANGE OF GRANTS Up to £200,000.
SAMPLE GRANTS Bolton School (£320,000 in total); Lady Lever Art Gallery (£60,000 in total); Royal College of Surgeons (£50,000); and the Prince's Youth Business Trust (£21,500).
FINANCES *Year* 2009–10 *Income* £653,604 *Grants* £660,324 *Assets* £24,661,275
TRUSTEES A E H Heber-Percy; A H S Hannay.
HOW TO APPLY The trust states: 'Priority is given [. . .] to applications from Cheshire, Merseyside and South Lancashire and the charities supported by the settlor in his lifetime. Others who do not meet those criteria should not apply without prior invitation but should, on a single sheet, state briefly their aims and apply fully only on being asked to do so. A handful of charities have heeded this warning and telephoned our administrator but the continuing volume of applications from charities which plainly do not meet the stated criteria suggests that many applicants do not concern themselves with their target's policies.'
WHO TO APPLY TO Mrs S Edwards, Administrator, Leverhulme Estate Office, Hesketh Grange, Manor Road, Thornton Hough, Wirral CH63 1JD *Tel* 0151 336 4828 *Fax* 0151 353 0265

■ The Joseph Levy Charitable Foundation

CC NO 245592 **ESTABLISHED** 1965
WHERE FUNDING CAN BE GIVEN UK and Israel.
WHO CAN BENEFIT Registered charities benefiting children and young people, older people, health, medical research.
WHAT IS FUNDED Health and community care, religion, social welfare, education, arts, culture and sport.
WHAT IS NOT FUNDED No grants to individuals, under any circumstances.
TYPE OF GRANT Project, research, salaries and start-up costs. Funding may be given for up to and over three years.
RANGE OF GRANTS £250–£60,000.
SAMPLE GRANTS Cystic Fibrosis Holiday Fund (£58,000); Cystic Fibrosis Trust (£47,000); English Blind Golf (£40,000); Jewish Council for Racial Equality (£20,000); London Youth (£10,000); Oxford Centre for Jewish Studies (£5,000); and University of St Andrews (£3,000).
FINANCES *Year* 2009–10 *Income* £794,830 *Grants* £898,893 *Assets* £16,707,005
TRUSTEES Mrs Jane Jason; Peter L Levy; Melanie Levy; Claudia Giat; James Jason.
HOW TO APPLY 'The trustees wish to inform you that due to current commitments, the foundation is no longer able to accept unsolicited applications.'
WHO TO APPLY TO Sue Nyfield, Director, 1st Floor, 1 Bell Street, London NW1 5BY *email* info@jlf.org.uk *Website* www.jlf.org.uk

■ Lewis Family Charitable Trust

CC NO 259892 **ESTABLISHED** 1962
WHERE FUNDING CAN BE GIVEN UK and Israel.
WHO CAN BENEFIT Charitable bodies and research institutions.
WHAT IS FUNDED Medical research, particularly into possible treatments for cancer, Jewish community work, general medical support,

Think carefully about every application. Is it justified?

689

educational funding, support for the elderly and child care.

WHAT IS NOT FUNDED No grants to individuals.

TYPE OF GRANT Potentially up to three years funding but mostly one-off.

RANGE OF GRANTS Up to £80,000.

SAMPLE GRANTS Institute of Cancer Research (£80,000); Jewish Care (£56,000); United Jewish Israel Appeal (£50,000); Reform Judaism (£30,000); Weizmann Institute (£25,000); University of Nottingham (£14,000); Policy Exchange Limited, Child Resettlement Fund and Alzheimer's Research Trust (£10,000 each); Casa Shalom (£7,000); UJS Hillel (£5,000); Amutat Orr Shalom (£4,400); Dermatrust, Cancer Backup and Camp Simcha (£2,000 each); Ben Gurion University (£1,600); and Royal British Legion and Kisharon (£1,000 each).

FINANCES *Year* 2009–10 *Income* £1,696,240 *Grants* £551,248 *Assets* £6,070,912

TRUSTEES David Lewis; Julian Lewis.

HOW TO APPLY In writing to the correspondent.

WHO TO APPLY TO The Secretary, Chelsea House, West Gate, Ealing, London W5 1DR *Tel* 020 8991 4601

■ The John Spedan Lewis Foundation

CC NO 240473   **ESTABLISHED** 1964

WHERE FUNDING CAN BE GIVEN UK.

WHO CAN BENEFIT The focus is on applications for small projects connected with the natural sciences, in particular horticulture, environmental education, ornithology and conservation, and from organisations benefiting, in the first instance, children, young adults and research workers.

WHAT IS FUNDED Charitable purposes, in the first instance reflecting the particular interests of John Spedan Lewis, namely horticulture, ornithology, entomology and associated educational and research projects. The trustees will also consider applications from organisations for imaginative and original educational projects aimed at developing serious interest and evident talent, particularly among young people.

WHAT IS NOT FUNDED Local branches of national organisations, or for salaries, medical research, welfare projects, building works or overseas expeditions.

TYPE OF GRANT Mostly one-off donations. Salaries not funded.

RANGE OF GRANTS £60–£12,000.

SAMPLE GRANTS Learning through Landscapes (£12,000); Cumbria Wildlife Trust (£7,500); Derbyshire Wildlife Trust (£6,000); National Museums Liverpool and University of Sussex (£5,000 each); Freshwater Biological Association, The British Trust for Ornithology and The Grasslands Trust (£4,000 each); and The Charleston Trust and People's Trust for Endangered Species (£1,000 each).

FINANCES *Year* 2009–10 *Income* £94,167 *Grants* £84,987 *Assets* £2,179,355

TRUSTEES Charlie Mayfield, Chair; David Jones; Dr Vaughan Southgate; Simon Fowler; Miss Tessa Colman.

OTHER INFORMATION One individual donation was to fund the final year of a PhD student at the University of Reading.

HOW TO APPLY In writing to the correspondent with latest report and accounts and a budget for the proposed project.

WHO TO APPLY TO Ms Bridget Chamberlain, Secretary, Partnership House, Carlisle Place, London SW1P 1BX *Tel* 020 7592 6121 *email* bridget_chamberlain@johnlewis.co.uk

■ The Sir Edward Lewis Foundation

CC NO 264475   **ESTABLISHED** 1972

WHERE FUNDING CAN BE GIVEN UK and overseas, with a preference for Surrey.

WHO CAN BENEFIT Registered charities.

WHAT IS FUNDED General charitable purposes.

WHAT IS NOT FUNDED Grants are generally only given to charities, projects or people known to the trustees. No grants are given to individuals.

RANGE OF GRANTS £500–£38,000,.

SAMPLE GRANTS FareShare (£20,000); The Children's Trust Tadworth; Focus Kensington & Chelsea Foundation; and Ridgegate Home (£10,000 each); Gurkha Welfare Trust, The David Shepherd Wildlife Foundation and St Anthony's Foundation (£5,000 each); The Rugby Clubs (£4,000); Council for Music in Hospitals (£3,000); Ophthalmic Aid to Eastern Europe and Musicians Benevolent Fund (£2,500 each); UK Antarctic Heritage Trust and Trinity Hospice (£2,000 each); Cary Dickinson Breast Cancer and Shipwrecked Fisherman's Society (£1,500 each); RNLI and Soundaround (£1,000 each); and Barnardo's and The Uphill Ski Club (£500 each).

FINANCES *Year* 2009–10 *Income* £477,435 *Grants* £180,200 *Assets* £7,513,374

TRUSTEES R A Lewis; K W Dent; Christine J A Lewis; Sarah J N Dorin.

OTHER INFORMATION The trust makes one substantial donation every two or three years, as well as smaller donations each year.

HOW TO APPLY In writing to the correspondent. The trustees meet every six months.

WHO TO APPLY TO Darren Wing, Rawlinson and Hunter, The Lower Mill, Kingston Road, Ewell, Surrey KT17 2AE *Tel* 020 7842 2000

■ John Lewis Partnership General Community Fund

CC NO 209128   **ESTABLISHED** 1961

WHERE FUNDING CAN BE GIVEN UK.

WHO CAN BENEFIT Registered charities.

WHAT IS FUNDED UK and local registered charities benefiting children and young adults, at risk groups, people who are sick or who have disabilities, people disadvantaged by poverty and those who are socially isolated. Medical professionals and research workers may be considered for funding.

WHAT IS NOT FUNDED Loans are not made and sponsorship is not undertaken. Grants are not made for the promotion of religion, political organisations, advertising or to individuals.

TYPE OF GRANT One-off and recurring grants.

RANGE OF GRANTS £250–£50,000.

SAMPLE GRANTS British Red Cross and Retail Trust (£50,000 each); Textile Industry Children's Trust (£25,000); Salisbury Playhouse (£20,000); Royal Academy of Music and Royal College of Music (£15,000); National Association of Youth Orchestras (£14,000); The Royal British Legion (£10,000); Driving Dotty and the Royal Exchange Theatre (£5,000 each); and Bobath Children's Therapy Centre, Different Strokes and DARE (UK) (£1,000 each).

FINANCES *Year* 2009–10 *Income* £435,455 *Grants* £435,494 *Assets* £0

TRUSTEES Mr John Parker; Mr Charlie Mayfield; Mr David Barclay; Mr Ian Hiscock; Mr Mark Wilson.

HOW TO APPLY The trust provided the following information: 'As a co-owned business, the partnership has recently made a decision to focus its support on smaller charities in the communities in which we trade and where our partners [employees] work, rather than making large donations from head office. We are, therefore, asking that all enquiries be made to the local branch of John Lewis or Waitrose, where partners will be deciding which organisations they would like to support. Although the emphasis will primarily be on making a meaningful difference to smaller, local charities, partners may equally wish to support larger, national charities where there is a strong relationship with the local community.'

WHO TO APPLY TO Justine Little, Partnership House, Carlisle Place, London SW1P 1BX *email* justine_little@johnlewis.co.uk

■ The Lewis Ward Trust

CC NO 1100891   **ESTABLISHED** 2003

WHERE FUNDING CAN BE GIVEN UK and overseas.

WHO CAN BENEFIT Children, particularly those with special needs or disabilities, are deprived or terminally ill or are lacking adequate nutrition and education.

WHAT IS FUNDED Special projects for children run locally, nationally and internationally. Hospices and special therapy units for children and organisations caring for lepers.

RANGE OF GRANTS Generally £1,000.

SAMPLE GRANTS No list of beneficiary organisations was available.

FINANCES *Year* 2009 *Income* £788 *Grants* £8,412

TRUSTEES Margaret Waugh; Revd Gareth Jones (Chair); Revd Anthony Innes; Kevin Ward; Stephanie Cheetham; Bernard Cheetham.

HOW TO APPLY In writing to the correspondent. 'The trustees meet twice a year, when appeals for grants are considered and depending on monies available, donations are sent to those organisations it is felt are in greatest need.'

WHO TO APPLY TO Margaret Waugh, Trustee, 2 Abraham Court, Lutton Close, Oswestry SY11 2TH *Tel* 01691 688892

■ Liberum Foundation

CC NO 1137475   **ESTABLISHED** 2010

WHERE FUNDING CAN BE GIVEN Undefined but in practice the UK.

WHO CAN BENEFIT Organisations and individuals.

WHAT IS FUNDED General charitable purposes including education/training; the prevention or relief of poverty; sport/recreation and community development/employment.

WHAT IS NOT FUNDED Adult health; hospitals; animals; older people; the armed services; housing; heritage; environment; and religion.

FINANCES *Year* 2011 *Assets* £60,000

TRUSTEES Ms Carolyn Doherty; Simon Stilwell; Antony Scawthorn.

OTHER INFORMATION In 2011 funds held were in the region of £60,000.

HOW TO APPLY In writing to the Secretary.

WHO TO APPLY TO Justine Rumens, Secretary to the Foundation, Ropemaker Place, Level 12, 25 Ropemaker Street, London EC2Y 9LY *Tel* 020 3100 2000 *email* info@liberumfoundation.com

■ Lichfield Conduit Lands

CC NO 254298   **ESTABLISHED** 1982

WHERE FUNDING CAN BE GIVEN Lichfield.

WHO CAN BENEFIT Organisations and people under 25 who are in education.

WHAT IS FUNDED General charitable purposes.

RANGE OF GRANTS Up to £20,000.

SAMPLE GRANTS Beneficiaries included: The Chapter of Lichfield Cathedral (£10,000); Lichfield District Council – parks project (£3,000); Lichfield and District Talking Newspaper, King Edward VI School (£2,000); Lichfield Bowling Club (£1,000); Lichfield Rugby UFC's under 16s (£300).

FINANCES *Year* 2009 *Income* £27,065 *Grants* £25,280 *Assets* £993,070

TRUSTEES J Russell (Chair); J D Shaw, C P Ablitt; Revd D K Beedon; Mrs D English; A D Thompson; Mrs K Duncan Brown; B Twivey; R W White; Mrs M G Boyle; J J R Powell; T J Thomas.

OTHER INFORMATION Grants were made to individuals totalling £1,800.

HOW TO APPLY Application forms are available from the reception at Ansons, along with a map of the beneficial area. They are considered four times a year

WHO TO APPLY TO S R James, The Warden, Ansons LLP Solicitors, St Mary's Chambers, 5 Breadmarket Street, Lichfield WS13 6LQ *Tel* 01543 263456 *Fax* 01543 250942 *email* sjames@ansonsllp.com

■ The Liebreich Foundation

CC NO 1136835   **ESTABLISHED** 2010

WHERE FUNDING CAN BE GIVEN Undefined, in practice UK and overseas.

WHO CAN BENEFIT Charities and other voluntary organisations.

WHAT IS FUNDED General charitable purposes.

TRUSTEES M D J Liebreich; Dr J B W Levy; N J Newman.

OTHER INFORMATION Michael Liebreich is also a trustee of St Mark's Hospital Foundation (Charity Commission No. 1088119). Accounts not due at the Charity Commission for this new charity.

HOW TO APPLY In writing to the correspondent.

WHO TO APPLY TO M D J Liebreich, Trustee, 11 Pembridge Mews, London W11 3EQ *email* info@liebreichfoundation.org *Website* www.liebreichfoundation.org

■ Lifeline 4 Kids

CC NO 200050   **ESTABLISHED** 1961

WHERE FUNDING CAN BE GIVEN Worldwide.

WHO CAN BENEFIT Organisations supporting children who are disabled (up to 18 years old), such as hospitals, homes, special schools and so on. Individuals and their families are also supported.

WHAT IS FUNDED To assist children who are disabled by providing equipment and services.

WHAT IS NOT FUNDED Building projects, research grants and salaries will not be funded.

TYPE OF GRANT Equipment purchased by the trust. No cash grants are given.

SAMPLE GRANTS Previous grants included: £5,000 to Central Middlesex Hospital, towards equipment for its outdoor play area; £2,500 to the Living Paintings Trust, funding the production of 20 copies of a new Living Picture Book; £2,400 to the New Jumbulance Travel Trust, providing two portable instant resuscitation packs; £2,000 to Vision Aid, providing a specialised flat screen video magnifier; £1,500 to the Lothian Autistic Society, for equipment for its various play schemes.

FINANCES *Year* 2010 *Income* £186,653 *Grants* £132,263 *Assets* £659,226

TRUSTEES Roger Adelman, Chair; Paul Maurice; Beverley Emden; Mrs Roberta Harris; Irving Millman; Jeffrey Bonn.

HOW TO APPLY Applications for help indicating specific requirements and brief factual information must initially be made in writing, addressed to the Investigations Officer, or by email (appeals@lifeline4kids.org). Each request will be acknowledged and provided it meets the charity's criteria, an application form will be sent by post. Appeals are discussed and decided upon at monthly meetings. If appropriate, the appeal will be investigated personally by one of the charity's members. If approved, a maximum sum is allocated and the charity will take full responsibility for the purchase and safe delivery of the approved item. Initial telephone calls from applicants are not welcome.

WHO TO APPLY TO Roger Adelman, 215 West End Lane, West Hampstead, London NW6 1XJ *Tel* 020 794 1661 *Fax* 020 7794 1161 *email* rda@lifeline4kids.org *Website* www.lifeline4kids.org

■ The Lightbridge Foundation

CC NO 1134678   **ESTABLISHED** 2010
WHERE FUNDING CAN BE GIVEN Worldwide.
WHO CAN BENEFIT Registered charities.
WHAT IS FUNDED General charitable purposes, though some preference is given to projects involving children and young people.
TRUSTEES Robert Levesque; John Munn; Andrew Morris; Ray Tunsich.
OTHER INFORMATION This foundation is closely linked with the cleaning and maintenance company Lightbridge Support Services Limited.
HOW TO APPLY In writing to the correspondent.
WHO TO APPLY TO Robert Levesque, Trustee, 1–2 Stangate House, Stanwell Road, Penarth, Vale of Glamorgan CF64 2AA

■ The Thomas Lilley Memorial Trust

CC NO 1039529   **ESTABLISHED** 1960
WHERE FUNDING CAN BE GIVEN UK, with some preference for the Newbury area and Isle of Man.
WHO CAN BENEFIT Individuals and organisations.
WHAT IS FUNDED General charitable purposes.
WHAT IS NOT FUNDED No grants are made to individuals for educational or gap year activities.
RANGE OF GRANTS Usually up to £2,000.
SAMPLE GRANTS Beneficiaries of grants of £450 included: All Saints Church, Cuddesdon, Riding for the Disabled, Samaritans, Isle of Man, Action Medical Research, Army Benevolent Fund, Greater London Fund for the Blind, National Deaf Children's Society, Shelter and Voluntary Services Overseas.
FINANCES *Year* 2009–10 *Income* £30,889 *Grants* £20,700 *Assets* £799,378
TRUSTEES John F Luke; Peter T A Lilley.
OTHER INFORMATION The amount available each year in individual grants in determined by the trust's income for that year.

HOW TO APPLY In writing to the correspondent.
WHO TO APPLY TO N Buckley Sharp, c/o Moors Andrew Thomas, Clarence Moors House, 94 Wilderspool Causeway, Warrington, Cheshire WA4 6PU *Tel* 01925 652999

■ The Limbourne Trust

CC NO 1113796   **ESTABLISHED** 2006
WHERE FUNDING CAN BE GIVEN UK and overseas.
WHO CAN BENEFIT Communities throughout the world.
WHAT IS FUNDED Environment, welfare, and arts organisations, particularly where meeting the trust's objectives concerning the advancement of education, the protection of health, and the relief of poverty, distress and sickness.
SAMPLE GRANTS Chicks (£13,000); Norfolk and Norwich Families House and Journey of a Lifetime Trust (£12,000 each); EACH (£10,000); Vauxhall City Farm (£10,000); Whirlow Hall Farm Trust (£5,500); Aldeburgh Music (£5,000); Grasslands Trust (£4,000); Buckingham Emergency Fund Appeal (£1,000); and Metfield United Charities (£660).
FINANCES *Year* 2009–10 *Income* £85,956 *Grants* £87,515 *Assets* £2,235,596
TRUSTEES Elisabeth Thistlethwayte; Katharine Thistlethwayte; Jennifer Lindsay; Jane Chetwynd Atkinson; Jocelyn Magnus.
HOW TO APPLY 'The trustees will seek to identify those projects where the greatest and widest benefit can be attained, and usually will only consider written applications and, where necessary, make further enquiries.' Trustees meet three times a year.
WHO TO APPLY TO Elisabeth Anne Thistlethwayte, Trustee, Downs Farm, Homersfield, Harleston, Norwich IP20 0NS

■ Limoges Charitable Trust

CC NO 1016178   **ESTABLISHED** 1991
WHERE FUNDING CAN BE GIVEN UK, with a preference for Birmingham.
WHO CAN BENEFIT Registered charities.
WHAT IS FUNDED Education, health and welfare, heritage and community, animals, youth, environment and nautical projects.
RANGE OF GRANTS £50–£18,000; mostly £200–£1,000.
SAMPLE GRANTS Birmingham Museum and Art Gallery (£18,000 in two grants); Moseley Community Development Trust and Moseley Street Wardens (£10,000 each); Edward's Trust Limited (£6,000 in two grants); THSH, University of Birmingham, National Memorial Arboretum and Birmingham Early Music Festival (£2,000 each); and St Ildiernas Church (£1,600).
FINANCES *Year* 2009–10 *Income* £30,620 *Grants* £85,571 *Assets* £861,673
TRUSTEES Mike Dyer; Albert Kenneth Dyer; Judy Ann Dyke; Andrew Milner.
HOW TO APPLY In writing to the correspondent.
WHO TO APPLY TO Judy Ann Dyke, Trustee, c/o Tyndallwoods Solicitors, 29 Woodbourne Road, Edgbaston, Birmingham B17 8BY *Tel* 0121 693 2222 *Fax* 0121 693 0844

■ The Linbury Trust

CC NO 287077   **ESTABLISHED** 1973
WHERE FUNDING CAN BE GIVEN Unrestricted.
WHO CAN BENEFIT Charities working in the fields listed below.

WHAT IS FUNDED Arts and arts education, especially support for dance and dance education. Medical research into chronic fatigue syndrome, and occasionally other 'unfashionable' areas. Drug abuse, provision of hands-on care to treat and rehabilitate drug users, particularly those which work with young people and the families of drug users. Education, especially support for best practice in the identification and teaching of children and young people with literacy problems, especially dyslexia. Environment and heritage, particularly historical buildings and major art institutions. Social welfare, especially for work helping young people disadvantaged by poverty, educational achievement or difficult family backgrounds, or who are involved in the criminal justice system. Also support for initiatives that improve quality of life of older people and through which they are helped to continue living in their own home. Developing countries, including humanitarian aid, social welfare and educational opportunities.

WHAT IS NOT FUNDED No grants to individuals.

TYPE OF GRANT Running costs, project.

SAMPLE GRANTS Stowe School (£1.5 million); Holburne Museum of Art and Royal Welsh College of Music & Drama (£250,000); Institute for Historical Research Trust (£127,500); University of Buckingham (£90,000); Shakespeare Schools Festival (£75,000); Foundation Training Company and the Palestine Association for Children's Encouragement of Sports (£50,000 each); and the Royal Liverpool University Hospital (£40,000).

FINANCES *Year* 2009–10 *Income* £6,203,000 *Grants* £5,647,000 *Assets* £151,339,000

TRUSTEES Lord Sainsbury of Preston Candover; Lady Sainsbury; Sir Martin Jacomb; Sir James Spooner.

OTHER INFORMATION The trust is one of the Sainsbury Family Charitable Trusts which share a common administration. An application to one is taken as an application to all.

HOW TO APPLY See the guidance for applicants in the entry for the Sainsbury Family Charitable Trusts. A single application will be considered for support by all the trusts in the group. Please note: 'the trustees take a proactive approach towards grant-making; accordingly, unsolicited applications to the trust are not usually successful'.

WHO TO APPLY TO Alan Bookbinder, Director, Allington House, 1st Floor, 150 Victoria Street, London SW1E 5AE *Tel* 020 7410 0330 *Fax* 020 7410 0332 *Website* www.linburytrust.org.uk

■ Lincolnshire Community Foundation

CC NO 1092328   **ESTABLISHED** 2002

WHERE FUNDING CAN BE GIVEN Lincolnshire.

WHO CAN BENEFIT Organisations supporting people in Lincolnshire General charitable purposes.

WHAT IS FUNDED General charitable purposes.

TYPE OF GRANT One-off and up to 3 years funding.

FINANCES *Year* 2010–11 *Income* £1,364,732 *Grants* £653,897 *Assets* £1,827,603

TRUSTEES Jean Burton; David Close; Richard Ferens; Jim Hopkins; Dr Cheryle Berry; S Cousins; Mrs J Hiles; Mrs B Jones; Mrs E Milligan-Manby and P Scott.

HOW TO APPLY Please visit the foundation's website for details of current grant schemes. Application forms can be downloaded from the foundation's website or requested by phone.

WHO TO APPLY TO Gordon Hunter, Director, 4 Mill House, Carre Street, Sleaford, Lincolnshire NG34 7TW *Tel* 01529 305825 *email* lincolnshirecf@btconnect.com *Website* www.lincolnshirecf.co.uk

■ The Lincolnshire Old Churches Trust

CC NO 509021   **ESTABLISHED** 1953

WHERE FUNDING CAN BE GIVEN Lincolnshire.

WHO CAN BENEFIT Churches, principally Christian churches, of any denomination.

WHAT IS FUNDED The preservation, repair and maintenance of churches over 100 years old in the area defined above, to exclude wind and weather, achieve safety and security and to ensure the preservation of those features which make old churches unique.

WHAT IS NOT FUNDED No grants for ritual or gravestone repair.

RANGE OF GRANTS £500–£10,000.

SAMPLE GRANTS Details of beneficiary churches were not available.

FINANCES *Year* 2009–10 *Income* £135,302 *Grants* £85,200 *Assets* £298,844

TRUSTEES P Sandberg, Chair; Baroness Willoughby de Eresby; Nevile Camamile; Mrs J Ware; D Wellman; D Lawrence; Mrs R Lindop; A Seton; C Hammant; R D Underwood; Revd C Knowles; R Critchlow; G Cook; Mrs Mona Dickinson; Mrs Henrietta Reeve; Anthony Worth; Mrs Linda Lord.

HOW TO APPLY On a form available from the correspondent.

WHO TO APPLY TO N J Camamile, Treasurer, Tower House, Lucy Tower Street, Lincoln LN1 1XW *Tel* 01522 551200

■ The Lind Trust

CC NO 803174   **ESTABLISHED** 1990

WHERE FUNDING CAN BE GIVEN UK.

WHO CAN BENEFIT Churches, charities and individuals involved in social action, community and Christian service.

WHAT IS FUNDED Christian service and social action.

SAMPLE GRANTS The Open Youth Trust (£190,000); and other charities not listed. The trustees in 2009–10 have made commitments to donate £5,000 per year for two years to the Prince's Trust and £5,000 per year for two years to the Matthew Project.

FINANCES *Year* 2009–10 *Income* £3,105,087 *Grants* £1,053,637 *Assets* £14,702,400

TRUSTEES Leslie C Brown; Dr Graham M Dacre; Gavin C Wilcock; Mrs Julia M Dacre; Russell B Dacre; Samuel E Dacre.

OTHER INFORMATION No breakdown of the total amount given in 2009–10 was given in the accounts.

HOW TO APPLY In writing to the correspondent at any time. However, the trust commits most of its funds in advance, giving the remainder to eligible applicants as received.

WHO TO APPLY TO Gavin Croft Wilcox, Trustee, Tithe Barn, Attlebridge, Norwich, Norfolk NR9 5AA *Tel* 01603 262626

Think carefully about every application. Is it justified?

693

■ Lindale Educational Foundation

CC NO 282758   **ESTABLISHED** 1981

WHERE FUNDING CAN BE GIVEN UK and overseas.

WHO CAN BENEFIT Roman Catholic organisations benefiting children, young adults and students.

WHAT IS FUNDED Charities which aim to advance education in accordance with Christian principles and ideals within the Roman Catholic tradition, in particular those organisations that train priests. Most grants are already allocated to specific charities.

WHAT IS NOT FUNDED No grants to individuals.

TYPE OF GRANT Recurrent.

SAMPLE GRANTS Netherhall Educational Association Centre for Retreats and Study (eight grants totalling £56,500); Thornycroft Hall (four grants totalling £20,200).

FINANCES *Year* 2009–10 *Income* £76,694 *Grants* £76,760 *Assets* £30,350

TRUSTEES Netherhall Educational Association; Dawliffe Hall Educational Foundation; Greygarth Association.

HOW TO APPLY In writing to the correspondent, but note that most funds are already committed.

WHO TO APPLY TO J Valero, 6 Orme Court, London W2 4RL *Tel* 020 7243 9417

■ The Linden Charitable Trust

CC NO 326788   **ESTABLISHED** 1985

WHERE FUNDING CAN BE GIVEN UK, with a preference for West Yorkshire.

WHO CAN BENEFIT Registered charities and arts organisations.

WHAT IS FUNDED Currently, the trust's policy is to benefit charities specialising in cancer relief and research, those particularly involved with hospices, those involved in arts and also a wider range of charities based in and around Leeds.

The trustees have agreed (2009–10) to make a regular donation to Leeds International Pianoforte Competition of £10,000 per year.

WHAT IS NOT FUNDED No grants to individuals.

RANGE OF GRANTS Up to £20,000.

SAMPLE GRANTS Leeds International Pianoforte Competition (£10,000); Macmillan Cancer Relief (£5,000); Marie Curie Cancer Care (£3,000); Leeds Lieder, Martin House Hospice and Mission for Seafarers (£2,000 each); Caring for Life, Combat Stress and Live Music Now (£1,000 each); and Listening Books (£500).

FINANCES *Year* 2009–10 *Income* £55,238 *Grants* £63,500 *Assets* £2,420,200

TRUSTEES Miss M H Pearson; J F H Swales; G L Holbrook.

HOW TO APPLY In writing to the correspondent.

WHO TO APPLY TO Miss M H Pearson, Trustee, c/o Baker Tilly, The Waterfront, Salts Mill Road, Shipley BD17 7EZ *Tel* 01274 536400

■ Lindenleaf Charitable Trust

CC NO 1124672   **ESTABLISHED** 2008

WHERE FUNDING CAN BE GIVEN UK and overseas.

WHO CAN BENEFIT General charitable purposes in particular, children and young people; community development.

WHAT IS FUNDED Registered charities.

SAMPLE GRANTS Previously: Impetus Trust (£25,000); and Broadway Homelessness and Support and Crisis (£2,500 each).

FINANCES *Year* 2009–10 *Income* £23,783 *Grants* £6,401

TRUSTEES Henry Charles.

HOW TO APPLY In writing to the correspondent.

WHO TO APPLY TO Paul Greatbatch, 344 Fulham Road, London SW10 9UH *email* paul_greatbatch@hotmail.com

■ The Enid Linder Foundation

CC NO 267509   **ESTABLISHED** 1974

WHERE FUNDING CAN BE GIVEN Unrestricted.

WHO CAN BENEFIT Registered charities benefiting children, older people and people who are disabled; universities and teaching hospitals.

WHAT IS FUNDED The aims of the foundation are: to fund research and teaching related to all areas of medicine by way of medical electives and general support costs to students and chosen medical universities; to assist in the funding of chosen research fellowship schemes which are of particular interest to the trustees; to distribute in full, in accordance with the governing Trust Deed, all the income available each year; to maintain resources at a reasonable level in order to continue to provide general charitable assistance in the foreseeable future. The main objectives for the year are shaped by these strategic aims with a view to maintaining both a stable medical electives scheme at universities, to support the research fellowship schemes and to continue funding chosen general charitable causes.

TYPE OF GRANT One-off and recurrent.

SAMPLE GRANTS Royal College of Surgeons (£100,000); National Children's Orchestra (£65,000 in total); Victoria & Albert Museum (£30,000); Médecins Sans Frontières (£20,000); Bath University (£15,000); Bath Intensive Care Baby Unit and Help for Heroes (£10,000 each); Beatrix Potter Society (£7,000); Chauncy Maples Malawi Trust and the Stroke Association (£5,000 each); and the Prostate Society (£1,000).

FINANCES *Year* 2010–11 *Income* £470,981 *Grants* £462,500 *Assets* £13,368,000

TRUSTEES Jack Ladeveze; Audrey Ladeveze; M Butler; C Cook; Jonathan Fountain.

OTHER INFORMATION Direct charitable expenditure, other than the trust's normal grantmaking, included £71,500 to 'teaching hospitals and universities'.

HOW TO APPLY In writing to the correspondent. Although unsolicited applications are accepted, the trust states that it prefers to support organisations whose work it has researched.

WHO TO APPLY TO Martin Pollock, Secretary, Moore Stephens LLP, 150 Aldersgate Street, London EC1A 4AB *Tel* 020 7334 9191 *Fax* 020 7248 3408 *email* martin.pollock@moorestephens.com

■ The Linmardon Trust

CC NO 275307   **ESTABLISHED** 1977

WHERE FUNDING CAN BE GIVEN UK, with a preference for Nottinghamshire.

WHO CAN BENEFIT Registered charities.

WHAT IS FUNDED General charitable purposes.

WHAT IS NOT FUNDED Registered charities only. No grants to individuals.

RANGE OF GRANTS £500–£3,000.

SAMPLE GRANTS Jubilee Sailing Trust (£3,000); Children with Leukaemia, Young Minds and Children's Liver Disease Foundation (£2,000 each); and 3H Fund, Princess Royal Trust for Carers, React, Martha Trust and Streatham Youth and Community Trust (£1,000 each).

FINANCES *Year* 2009–10 *Income* £787,438 *Grants* £14,000 *Assets* £1,183,835

TRUSTEES HSBC Trust Company (UK) Ltd.

HOW TO APPLY In writing to the correspondent. The trustees meet quarterly, generally in February, May, August and November. Grants are made throughout the year.

WHO TO APPLY TO Lee Topp, Trust Manager, HSBC Trust Co UK Ltd, Norwich House, Nelson Gate, Commercial Road, Southampton SO15 1GX *Tel* 023 8072 2240

■ The Ruth and Stuart Lipton Charitable Trust

CC NO 266741　　　ESTABLISHED 1973

WHERE FUNDING CAN BE GIVEN UK, with a preference for London.

WHO CAN BENEFIT Preference for organisations benefiting Jewish people.

WHAT IS FUNDED Jewish charities and charitable purposes.

WHAT IS NOT FUNDED No grants to individuals.

RANGE OF GRANTS £100–£30,000.

SAMPLE GRANTS Nightingale (£9,500); Royal Opera House (£7,000); Jewish Care (£5,500); United Synagogue (£4,000); British Technion Society (£500); Well Being of Women (£250); and Help for Heroes (£100).

FINANCES *Year* 2009–10 *Income* £30,491 *Grants* £37,287 *Assets* £562,364

TRUSTEES Sir S Lipton; Lady Lipton; N W Benson.

OTHER INFORMATION There is no minimum limit for any grant and all grants must be approved unanimously by the trustees.

HOW TO APPLY In writing to the correspondent.

WHO TO APPLY TO N W Benson, Trustee, Lewis Golden and Co., 40 Queen Anne Street, London W1G 9EL *Tel* 020 7580 7313

■ The Lister Charitable Trust

CC NO 288730　　　ESTABLISHED 1981

WHERE FUNDING CAN BE GIVEN UK and overseas.

WHO CAN BENEFIT Registered charities which work with young people.

WHAT IS FUNDED General charitable purposes.

WHAT IS NOT FUNDED Applications from individuals, including students, are ineligible. No grants are made in response to general appeals from large UK organisations or to smaller bodies working in areas outside its criteria.

TYPE OF GRANT Usually one-off for specific project or part of a project. Core funding and/or salaries rarely considered. Funding may be given for up to one year.

SAMPLE GRANTS The European Nature Trust (£88,000); University of Miami (£64,000); Home Start Ashford (£10,000); Embercombe (£3,000); The Juvenile Diabetes Research Foundation (£2,500); Light Dragons (£2,000); and Sport Relief (£1,000).

FINANCES *Year* 2009–10 *Income* £173,106 *Grants* £170,987 *Assets* £7,512,586

TRUSTEES Noel A V Lister; David A Collingwood; Penny A Horne; Paul A Lister; Sylvia J Lister.

HOW TO APPLY In writing to the correspondent. Applications should include clear details of the need the intended project is designed to meet, plus an outline budget. Only applications from eligible bodies are acknowledged, when further information may be requested.

WHO TO APPLY TO Nicholas Yellowlees, Accountant, 43 High Street, Marlow, Buckinghamshire SL7 1BA *Tel* 01628 477879 *email* info@ apperleylimited.co.uk

■ Frank Litchfield Charitable Trust

CC NO 1038943　　　ESTABLISHED 1994

WHERE FUNDING CAN BE GIVEN Mostly in and around Cambridge.

WHO CAN BENEFIT Charitable organisations.

WHAT IS FUNDED Medical services and relief of poverty amongst those involved in agriculture.

RANGE OF GRANTS Up to £12,000.

SAMPLE GRANTS Beneficiaries included: Therfield Recreation Ground (£12,000); Tomotherapy and Cambridge University (£10,000); Headway Cambridgeshire (£7,500); The Cogwheel Trust (£5,000); and Happy Days and Richmond Fellowship Cambridge (£1,000 each).

FINANCES *Year* 2009–10 *Income* £66,593 *Grants* £54,620 *Assets* £1,785,695

TRUSTEES M T Womack; D M Chater; P Gooderham.

HOW TO APPLY In writing to the correspondent. This trust receives more applications each year than it is able to fund.

WHO TO APPLY TO Michael Womack, Trustee, 12 De Freville Avenue, Cambridge CB4 1HR *Tel* 01223 358012

■ The Andrew and Mary Elizabeth Little Charitable Trust

SC NO SC011185　　　ESTABLISHED 1935

WHERE FUNDING CAN BE GIVEN Mainly Glasgow and the surrounding area.

WHO CAN BENEFIT Organisations based in Scotland such as infirmaries, hospitals, homes for the aged, orphanages and other such institutions, which provide direct or indirect help to disadvantaged people.

WHAT IS FUNDED Welfare needs.

SAMPLE GRANTS Previous beneficiaries have included Ayrshire Hospice, Glasgow City Mission, Glasgow Marriage Guidance Council, Glasgow Old People's Welfare Committee, St Margaret's of Scotland Adoption Society and Strathclyde Youth Club Association.

FINANCES *Year* 2010 *Income* £56,315

HOW TO APPLY In writing to the correspondent. Trustees meet to consider grants once a month. Individuals should provide financial details of income support.

WHO TO APPLY TO The Trustees, Low Beaton Richmond Solicitors, Sterling House, 20 Renfield Street, Glasgow G2 5AP

■ The Second Joseph Aaron Littman Foundation

CC NO 201892　　　ESTABLISHED 1961

WHERE FUNDING CAN BE GIVEN UK.

WHO CAN BENEFIT Registered charities only.

WHAT IS FUNDED General charitable purposes with special preference for academic and medical research.

WHAT IS NOT FUNDED Applications from individuals are not considered.

SAMPLE GRANTS Littman Library of Jewish Civilisation (£208,000); The Spiro Ark (£10,000); Hadassah UK (£5,000); Westminster Synagogue (£3,500); The Misholin Children's Centre and JNF (£2,500 each); and Libra Foundation (£250).

FINANCES *Year* 2009–10 *Income* £300,258 *Grants* £251,441 *Assets* £5,456,888

TRUSTEES Mrs C C Littman; R J Littman; Glenn Hurstfield.

HOW TO APPLY The trust's funds are fully committed and no new applications are considered.

WHO TO APPLY TO Glenn Hurstfield, Trustee, Berkeley Law (Ref: GCH/L2556/1), 19 Berkeley Street, London W1J 8ED

■ The George John and Sheilah Livanos Charitable Trust

CC NO 1002279   **ESTABLISHED** 1985
WHERE FUNDING CAN BE GIVEN UK.
WHO CAN BENEFIT Registered charities.
WHAT IS FUNDED Medical research and equipment, health, medical charities for children or older people, marine charities and general charitable purposes.
WHAT IS NOT FUNDED No grants to individuals or non-registered charities.
TYPE OF GRANT One-off and recurring grants. Capital grants.
RANGE OF GRANTS £1,000–£90,000.
SAMPLE GRANTS St Mary's Hospital (£90,000); The Watts Gallery (£54,000); Parkinson's Disease Society (£50,000); University of Dundee – Child Health Studentship (£29,000); Ekklesia Project Fakenham (£24,000); Breakthrough Breast Cancer and London Youth (£10,000 each); Disasters Emergency Committee and Paul D'Auria Cancer Support Centre (£7,500 each); British Liver Trust, Crimestoppers, Demand, Langalanga Scholarship Fund and the Cirdan Sailing Trust (£5,000 each); Stubbers (£2,000) and Whitechapel Mission (£1,000).
FINANCES *Year* 2010 *Income* £118,347 *Grants* £350,687 *Assets* £2,661,824
TRUSTEES Philip N Harris; Timothy T Cripps; Anthony S Holmes.
HOW TO APPLY 'Unsolicited applications are considered but the trustees inevitably turn down a large number of applications.'
WHO TO APPLY TO Philip N Harris, Trustee, Jeffrey Green Russell, Waverley House, 7–12 Noel Street, London W1F 8GQ *Tel* 020 7339 7000

■ Liverpool Charity and Voluntary Services

CC NO 223485   **ESTABLISHED** 1970
WHERE FUNDING CAN BE GIVEN Merseyside only.
WHO CAN BENEFIT Registered charities.
WHAT IS FUNDED General charitable purposes.
SAMPLE GRANTS Grants are categorised through the CVS's main objectives as follows: Well managed and governed: £331,130; Well resourced: £671,409; Well represented: £49,901.
FINANCES *Year* 2009–10 *Income* £6,111,619 *Grants* £1,122,811 *Assets* £6,874,547
TRUSTEES William Fulton; Charles Feeny; Sue Newton, Chair; Roger Morris; Philip Love; Hilary Russell; Mark Blundell; Andrew Lovelady; Christine Reeves; Dil Daly; Heather Akehurst; Adeyinka Olushonde; Perminder Bal.
OTHER INFORMATION The charity acts in a similar manner to a community foundation, administrating the giving of much smaller charitable trusts.
HOW TO APPLY In writing to the correspondent. An application should be made to the charity that will then pass it on to a relevant trust for consideration.

WHO TO APPLY TO The Grants Team, Liverpool Charity and Voluntary Services, 151 Dale Street, Liverpool L2 2AH *Tel* 0151 227 5177 *email* info@lcvs.org.uk *Website* www.lcvs.org.uk

■ Liverpool Sailors' Home Trust

CC NO 515183   **ESTABLISHED** 1984
WHERE FUNDING CAN BE GIVEN Merseyside.
WHO CAN BENEFIT Organisations benefiting seafarers, fishermen, ex-service and service people and sea cadets.
WHAT IS FUNDED Charities engaged in maritime activities and based in Merseyside.
WHAT IS NOT FUNDED No grants to individuals.
TYPE OF GRANT One-off and capital grants will be considered.
SAMPLE GRANTS Previous grants have included: £9,000 to The Royal Merchant Navy School Foundation, £4,000 each to Sail Training Association and Fairbridge Merseyside, £2,000 to Sea Cadet Corps – Ellesmere Port, £1,500 each to RNLI – New Brighton and RNLI – Hoylake and West Kirby, and £1,000 each to BISS and Sea Cadet Corps – Liverpool Mersey Unit.
FINANCES *Year* 2009–10 *Income* £2,408 *Grants* £18,000
TRUSTEES D G Beazley, Chair; Mrs L P Cook; P O Copland; S Sutherland; I Higby; T Hart; J R Hulmes.
HOW TO APPLY In writing to the correspondent. Trustees meet to consider grants in March, applications should be sent by 20 January.
WHO TO APPLY TO Mrs L Gidman, Secretary, Room 19, 2nd Floor, Tower Building, 22 Water Street, Liverpool L3 1AB *Tel* 0151 227 3417 *Fax* 0151 227 3417 *email* enquiries@rlsoi-uk.org

■ Jack Livingstone Charitable Trust

CC NO 263473   **ESTABLISHED** 1971
WHERE FUNDING CAN BE GIVEN UK and worldwide, with a preference for Manchester.
WHO CAN BENEFIT Registered charities benefiting Jewish people, at risk groups, and people who are ill, disadvantaged by poverty or socially isolated.
WHAT IS FUNDED Jewish charities and general charitable purposes.
TYPE OF GRANT One-off and recurrent.
RANGE OF GRANTS Up to £10,000.
SAMPLE GRANTS Manchester City Art Gallery (£10,000); R Chritake Trust (£6,000); King David School, SO Community Security and Morris F Homes (£5,000 each); London FDN Patrons and Manchester Jewish Federation (£3,000 each); British Friends (£1,500); and Stockdales, Southport New Synagogue, Israel Children's Tennis Centers and Aish Hatorah (£1,000 each).
FINANCES *Year* 2009–10 *Income* £84,770 *Grants* £66,633 *Assets* £2,023,836
TRUSTEES Janice Livingstone; Terence Livingstone; Brian White.
HOW TO APPLY The trust does not respond to unsolicited applications.
WHO TO APPLY TO Janice Livingstone, Trustee, Westholme, The Springs, Bowdon, Altrincham, Cheshire WA14 3JH *Tel* 0161 928 3232

■ The Elaine and Angus Lloyd Charitable Trust

CC NO 237250   **ESTABLISHED** 1964

WHERE FUNDING CAN BE GIVEN UK, with a preference for Surrey, Kent and the South of England.

WHO CAN BENEFIT Individuals, local, regional and UK organisations benefiting children, young adults, at risk groups, people disadvantaged by poverty and socially isolated people.

WHAT IS FUNDED Health and welfare organisations, churches and education.

WHAT IS NOT FUNDED No support for overseas aid.

TYPE OF GRANT Recurrent and one-off.

RANGE OF GRANTS Below £1,000–£5,000.

SAMPLE GRANTS EHAS (£4,000); Alive and Kicking and Positive Initiative Trust (£2,500 each); Brighton and Hove Parents and Children's Group, Monday to Wednesday Club, Rhema Partnership Mission Hospital and Rhema Religious and Charitable Trust (£2,000 each); the Grange Centre and the Willow Foundation (£1,000 each).

FINANCES *Year* 2009–10 *Income* £86,419 *Grants* £73,126 *Assets* £2,288,270

TRUSTEES C R H Lloyd; A S Lloyd; J S Gordon; Sir Michael Craig-Cooper; Mrs V E Best; J S Lloyd; Mrs Philippa Satchwell Smith; Revd R J Lloyd.

OTHER INFORMATION Grants to individuals totalled £5,600

HOW TO APPLY In writing to the correspondent. The trustees meet regularly to consider grants.

WHO TO APPLY TO Ross Badger, 3rd Floor, North Side, Dukes Court, 32 Duke Street, St James's, London *Tel* 020 7930 7797

■ The Charles Lloyd Foundation

CC NO 235225   **ESTABLISHED** 1964

WHERE FUNDING CAN BE GIVEN The Roman Catholic Dioceses of Menevia and Wrexham.

WHO CAN BENEFIT Roman Catholics.

WHAT IS FUNDED The upkeep of Roman Catholic churches, houses, convents and monasteries, the advancement of religion and the promotion and advancement of music, either religious or secular.

TYPE OF GRANT One-off.

SAMPLE GRANTS Welshpool Catholic Church (£42,000); the Carmelites – Dolgellau (£25,000); Abergele Catholic Church (£7,000); and Tywyn Catholic Church (£2,000).

FINANCES *Year* 2009–10 *Income* £44,901 *Grants* £78,000 *Assets* £1,244,303

TRUSTEES Revd C D S Lloyd; P Walters; T V Ryan; R C A Thorn.

HOW TO APPLY In writing to the correspondent. The trust asks for 'evidence of hardship'. Unsuccessful applications are not acknowledged.

WHO TO APPLY TO Vincent Ryan, Trustee, 8–10 Grosvenor Road, Wrexham, Clwyd LL11 1BU *Tel* 01978 291000 *Fax* 01978 290493 *email* vincentryan@allingtonhughes.co.uk

■ The Lloyd Fund

CC NO 295018   **ESTABLISHED** 1986

WHERE FUNDING CAN BE GIVEN UK.

WHO CAN BENEFIT Charitable organisations.

WHAT IS FUNDED General charitable purposes.

SAMPLE GRANTS Previous grant recipients have included DEC and Médecins Sans Frontières (£1,500 each), Middle East Relief and Reprieve (£1,000 each), Prospex (£500), Queille Music Trust (£150) and Womankind (£45).

FINANCES *Year* 2009–10 *Income* £15,673 *Grants* £19,000

TRUSTEES Stephen Lloyd; Lorna Lloyd; Toby Lloyd; James Lloyd; Edward Lloyd.

HOW TO APPLY Unsolicited applications are unlikely to be successful as the trustees have a settled grant-making programme and funds are very limited.

WHO TO APPLY TO Stephen Lloyd, Trustee, Bates Wells and Braithwaite, Scandinavian House, 2–6 Cannon Street, London EC4M 6YH *Tel* 020 7551 7711 *email* s.lloyd@bwbllp.com

■ Lloyd's Charities Trust

CC NO 207232   **ESTABLISHED** 1953

WHERE FUNDING CAN BE GIVEN UK, with particular interest in East London.

WHO CAN BENEFIT Charitable organisations.

WHAT IS FUNDED General charitable purposes, with a specific fund for education, training and enterprise.

WHAT IS NOT FUNDED No grants for any appeal where it is likely that the grant would be used for sectarian purposes or to local or regional branches of charities where it is possible to support the UK organisation. Support is not given to individuals.

SAMPLE GRANTS The Prince's Trust (£66,000); Bromley By Bow Centre (£50,000); DEC Haiti Earthquake Appeal; Tower Hamlets' Education Business Partnership (£40,000); Chilean Red Cross Chile Earthquake Appeal (£20,000–£30,000 each); East London Small Business Centre (£15,000); Maritime London Officer Cadet Scholarship; Reed's School and Mulberry School for Girls (£5,000–£15,000 each).

FINANCES *Year* 2010 *Income* £490,168 *Grants* £430,657 *Assets* £2,506,040

TRUSTEES Ms Holly Bellingham; Grahame Chilton; Graham White; David Gittings; Lawrence Holder; John Spencer; Iain Wilson; Ms Sue Langley; Rupert Atkin; Charles Harbord-Hamond.

HOW TO APPLY Funds permitting, Lloyd's Charities Trust makes ad hoc donations. However, the majority of funds are committed to supporting the partnership charities the trust works with. The trust has previously stated that as funds are committed over a three-year period 'we are unable to respond positively to the numerous appeals we receive'. Applications are not currently being invited for partner charity status.

WHO TO APPLY TO Mrs Vicky Mirfin, Secretary, One Lime Street, London EC3M 7HA *Tel* 020 7327 6075 *Fax* 020 7327 6368 *email* communityaffairs@lloyds.com *Website* www.lloyds.com

■ Lloyds TSB Foundation for England and Wales

CC NO 327114   **ESTABLISHED** 1986

WHERE FUNDING CAN BE GIVEN England and Wales.

WHO CAN BENEFIT Registered charities benefiting people who are disabled or disadvantaged.

WHAT IS FUNDED Education and training and social and community needs through the Community Programme.

WHAT IS NOT FUNDED The foundation does not fund the following types of organisations and work: *Organisations:* organisations that are **not** registered charities; second or third tier organisations (unless there is evidence of direct benefit to disadvantaged people); charities that mainly work overseas; charities that mainly give funds to other charities, individuals or other organisations; hospitals, hospices or medical centres; rescue services; schools, colleges and universities.

Types of work: activities which a statutory body is responsible for; capital projects, appeals, refurbishments; environmental work, expeditions and overseas travel; funding to promote religion; holidays or trips; loans or business finance; medical research, funding for medical equipment or medical treatments; sponsorship or funding towards a marketing appeal or fundraising activities; work with animals or to promote animal welfare.

TYPE OF GRANT One-off for a specific project, core funding, two or three year funding. Also capital, recurring costs, running costs and salaries.

RANGE OF GRANTS £500–£25,000.

SAMPLE GRANTS During 2010 the foundation made 908 grants to organisations. A full list of grants is available from the foundation's website.

FINANCES *Year* 2010 *Income* £26,063,000 *Grants* £24,463,000 *Assets* £33,741,000

TRUSTEES Prof. Ian Diamond, Chair; Janet Bibby; Rob Devey; Pavita Cooper; Alan Leaman; Rosemary Stevenson; Philip Grant; Mohammad Naeem; Lord Sandy Leitch; Sir Clive Booth; Dame Denise Platt.

HOW TO APPLY 'Step 1 – Read our guidelines: Please check our guidelines and individual criteria for the programme you are interested in so that you are clear what is and is not funded; **Step 2 – Check if your charity is eligible:** Before you apply you need to complete our short charity eligibility questionnaire which you can find on our website. If you don't have access to the internet or would prefer to talk to us first, please call 0870 411 1223. Please note that charity eligibility does not mean that your work meets the criteria for all of our programmes; **Step 3 – We will contact you to discuss whether your work is eligible:** If your charity is eligible, one of our team will contact you to discuss whether the work you are seeking funding for fits within our guidelines – and if it does to discuss the next steps; **Step 4 – Assessment:** If your work is eligible for consideration and you are applying for a grant of over £5,000, your local Grant Manager will visit you to discuss your funding requirements. If you are applying for a grant of under £5,000, the Grant Manager will carry out a telephone assessment. Assessment visits take one to two hours, and your local Grant Manager will discuss a range of issues relevant to your potential application, including: your governance; your finances; your evidence of need; your work; and the difference it will make to your users/ beneficiaries. The Grant Manager will tell you whether or not to proceed with an application. If you are advised to apply, they will help you to make the best application; **Step 5 – Complete the application form:** If your local Grant Manager recommends that you complete an application form, they will give you a copy of the form. You will need to read the accompanying guidance notes and include: a copy of your most recent annual report and full signed accounts. These should be signed as approved on behalf of your Management Committee or equivalent. You must make sure your charity annual returns are up to date and registered with the Charity Commission – we will check this when we assess your application. (If your records are not up to date this could delay your application being processed); a copy of your charity's most recent bank statement so that we can verify the account details; the relevant job description if

you are applying for funding towards the cost of a post, a copy of your equal opportunities policy or if you do not have one, information about your commitment to equal opportunities. We will also need to know about the other governance policies that you have in place that are relevant to your work; **Step 6 – Return your application form to us:** You will need to submit a signed copy of the form together with the supporting documents to us; **Step 7 – The decision on your application:** We respond to all applications that we receive and it takes from three to six months for a decision to be made on your application. Your local Grant Manager will tell you when you are likely to hear the decision. *Common reasons for unsuccessful applications* The foundation cannot fund all eligible applications even if they are of a high quality because each year the total amount requested by charities exceeds the money that we have available. Other reasons for the foundation not being able to make a grant include: charities' core work not being sufficiently focused on our mission; applications not falling within our guidelines; charities not filling in the application form properly; charities not having up to date annual returns or accounts filed with the Charities Commission or other relevant regulatory bodies. *When can I reapply?* If you receive a grant, you will not be eligible to apply for another grant from the Community Programme for another two years from receipt of the grant (or from receipt of the final payment if it has been two or three-year funding). If your application is unsuccessful, you must wait for a year before you apply again.'

WHO TO APPLY TO Mrs Linda Kelly, Chief Executive, Pentagon House, 52–54 Southwark Street, London SE1 1UN *Tel* 0870 411 1223 *Fax* 0870 411 1224 *email* enquiries@ lloydstsbfoundations.org.uk *Website* www. lloydstsbfoundations.org.uk

···

■ Lloyds TSB Foundation for Northern Ireland

IR NO XN72216   **ESTABLISHED** 1986

WHERE FUNDING CAN BE GIVEN Northern Ireland.

WHO CAN BENEFIT Charities registered with HM Revenue and Customs, benefiting children, young adults, older people, volunteers and people who are unemployed, homeless, living in rural communities, disabled or disadvantaged by poverty. Constituted groups with charitable purposes, but not registered as a charity and have an annual income of less than £2,000, may apply for a grant of up to £1,000.

WHAT IS FUNDED Underfunded voluntary organisations which enable people who are disabled and people who are disadvantaged through social and economic circumstances, to make a contribution to the community. The trustees regret that, as the funds available are limited, they cannot support all fields of voluntary and charitable activity. The two main objectives to which funds are allocated are: (a) social and community needs; (b) education and training. For full details of the foundation's funding objectives go to the website.

WHAT IS NOT FUNDED Grants are not usually given for: organisations that are not recognised as a charity by HM Revenue and Customs; individuals, including students; animal welfare; environmental projects including those that deal with geographic and scenic issues – however, the trustees may consider projects that improve the living conditions of disadvantaged

698

Does the trust you have chosen match your needs? Haphazard applications waste postage and time

individuals and groups; activities that are normally the responsibility of central or local government or some other responsible body; schools, universities and colleges (except for projects specifically to benefit students with special needs); hospitals and medical centres; sponsorship or marketing appeals; fabric appeals for places of worship; promotion of religion; activities that collect funds for subsequent redistribution to others; endowment funds; fundraising events or activities; corporate affiliation or membership of a charity; loans or business finance; expeditions or overseas travel; construction of an extension to buildings; salary or training costs for the pre-school sector. Please note: organisations must have a total income of less than £250,000 to be eligible to apply to the Standard Grant Programme.

TYPE OF GRANT Capital, core costs, one-off, project, recurring costs, salaries and start-up costs. Funding is usually one-off, but support for two years or more is considered.

RANGE OF GRANTS Normally a maximum of £5,000, but larger amounts are considered.

SAMPLE GRANTS Carntogher Community Association – towards the salary and travel expenses of a Volunteer Co-ordinator (£6,700); Chinese Welfare Association – towards the salary of the welfare rights officer (£6,000); Reco (NI) Ltd – towards the salary of a workshop joiner (£5,000); Belfast Samaritans – to support the publicity campaign (£5,000); Strabane & Lifford Lesbian Gay Bisexual & Transgender Group – towards governance and strategic planning training (£3,300); and Castlederg Childcare Services – towards security and CCTV (£1,000). International grants included: Africare – towards improvements at a children's hospital in Uganda (£20,000); War on Want – irrigation projects and farmer training in Malawi (£12,500); Grooms-Shaftesbury – towards a spinal chord rehabilitation centre in Nepal (£10,000); Romanian Partnership Committee – to support young orphans in and out of orphanages in Romania (£5,000); and Camara Education UK Ltd – for computer facilities and teacher training in Zambia (£3,200).

FINANCES *Year* 2010 *Income* £1,918,629 *Grants* £1,682,560 *Assets* £2,791,442

TRUSTEES Paddy Bailie, Chair; Tony Reynolds, Deputy Chair; Robert Agnew; Angela Colhoun; Hugh Donnelly; Janine Donnelly; James Grant; Janet Leckey; Jim McCooe; Brian Scott.

HOW TO APPLY The foundation offers the following advice on applying to the Standard Grant Programme on its website:
Who can apply? – 'The Standard Grant Programme is open to any organisation that is registered as a charity with HM Revenue and Customs. Constituted groups with charitable purpose, but not registered as a charity and have an annual income of less than £2,000, may apply for a grant of up to £1,000.'
How to apply? – 'The application pack should be downloaded from the foundation website. The downloaded application form is in Microsoft WORD format to enable it to be completed on screen before printing off a hard copy. The application form should then be signed and dated by the three required signatories, before attaching copies of the required supporting documents.' The trust website also provides detailed guides and advice for applicants.
When to apply? – 'The closing dates for applications are normally the second Friday of January, April, July and October. Always check the website for the latest closing dates, as they may change due to statutory holidays. Applications will be accepted until 5pm on each closing date. Applicants are required to leave one year between applications whether they are successful or unsuccessful. Organisations who have received three years consecutive funding must leave two years before reapplying. All applicants will be informed in writing of the decision approximately ten weeks from the closing date for applications. Unfortunately, demands made on the foundation always out-strip the funds available, and this means that many good applications, whilst meeting the criteria, will still be unsuccessful.' Please note: the application process for other programmes may differ. Organisations are advised to contact the foundation for details, as appropriate.

WHO TO APPLY TO Sandara Kelso-Robb, Executive Director, 2nd Floor, 14 Cromac Place, Gasworks, Belfast BT7 2JB *Tel* 028 9032 3000 *Fax* 028 9032 3200 *email* info@ lloydstsbfoundationni.org *Website* www. lloydstsbfoundationni.org

··

■ Lloyds TSB Foundation for Scotland

SC NO SC009481   **ESTABLISHED** 1986

WHERE FUNDING CAN BE GIVEN Scotland and overseas.

WHO CAN BENEFIT Recognised charities which provide support to the Scottish community, enabling people, primarily those in need, to become active members of society and to improve their quality of life.

WHAT IS FUNDED The foundation's current programmes are: Henry Duncan Awards; and the Partnership Drugs Initiative. The foundation is in the process of reviewing its Capacity Building programme for 2012 and beyond – potential applicants should check the foundation's website for current information.

WHAT IS NOT FUNDED The foundation will not support: charities with an income of more than £500,000 per annum; organisations which are not formally recognised as charities in Scotland; charities which pay their board members or have paid employees who also hold a position as Director on the Board. This principle also applies to charities operating as collectives; individuals – including students; animal welfare; initiatives that are focused on sport, the arts or the environment, except where the subject is being used as a vehicle to engage with at risk or disadvantaged groups to increase life skills; conservation and protection of flora and fauna; mainstream activities and statutory requirements of hospitals and medical centres; schools, universities and colleges; sponsorship or marketing appeals; establishment/ preservation of endowment funds; activities that collect funds for subsequent grant making to other organisations and/or individuals; expeditions or overseas travel; major building projects/capital appeals; historic restoration/ historic publications; retrospective funding; promotion of religion/church fabric appeals; hobby groups; one-off events such as gala days.

TYPE OF GRANT Mostly one-off. However the foundation will consider grants over two or three years. Grants are made for buildings, capital, core costs, feasibility studies, project, research, recurring costs, running costs, salaries and start-up costs.

FINANCES *Grants* £2,000,000

TRUSTEES Christine Lenihan, Chair; Martin Cheyne; Prof. Sir John P Arbuthnott; Prof. Sandy

Cameron; James G D Ferguson; Paul Hardie; Jane Mackie; Maria McGill; Ian Small.

OTHER INFORMATION Recent financial information was not available at the time of writing, although it is expected that previous levels of grantmaking will be maintained, totalling around £2 million each year.

HOW TO APPLY Application forms for all programmes, complete with comprehensive guidance notes, are available from the foundation. These can be requested by telephone, by email, or through its website. Foundation staff are always willing to provide additional help. Check the foundation's website for details of upcoming application deadlines.

WHO TO APPLY TO Karen Brown, Administrator and Secretary, Riverside House, 502 Gorgie Road, Edinburgh EH11 3AF *Tel* 0131 444 4020 *Fax* 0131 444 4099 *email* enquiries@ltsbfoundationforscotland.org.uk *Website* www.ltsbfoundationforscotland.org.uk

■ Lloyds TSB Foundation for the Channel Islands

CC NO 327113   **ESTABLISHED** 1986
WHERE FUNDING CAN BE GIVEN The Channel Islands.
WHO CAN BENEFIT Organisations benefiting children and young people; older people; volunteers; at risk groups; people who are unemployed, carers, disabled, disadvantaged by poverty or homeless; and victims of abuse and domestic violence.

WHAT IS FUNDED The main aims of the foundation are to assist disadvantaged and disabled people and to promote social and community welfare within the Channel Islands. A wide range of activities are supported, and the following examples are meant as a guide only: advice services – addictions (particularly substance misuse rehabilitation), bereavement, counselling, emergency and rescue services, family support, helplines, homelessness, housing, parenting; community relations – crime prevention (particularly activities involving young people), mediation, promotion of volunteering, rehabilitation of offenders, victim support, vulnerable young people; community facilities and services – after school clubs, community centres, family centres, older people's clubs, playschemes, transport, youth organisations; cultural enrichment – improving participation in and access to the arts and national heritage; activities with an educational focus for all ages; improvements to buildings of historic or architectural value which increase their benefit to the community; projects which have a strong focus on benefit to people and the social environment; disabled people – advocacy, carers, day centres, information and advice, sheltered accommodation, transport; promotion of health – day care, information and advice, mental health, holistic medicine, home nursing, hospices. The trustees will, on an exceptional basis, also fund research projects in health related areas. The foundation also supports education and training, particularly activities which enhance learning opportunities for disabled and disadvantaged people of all ages.

WHAT IS NOT FUNDED No grants for: organisations which are not recognised charities; activities which are primarily the responsibility of the Insular authorities in the Islands or some other responsible body; activities which collect funds to give to other charities, individuals or other organisations; animal welfare; corporate

subscription or membership of a charity; endowment funds; environment – conserving and protecting plants and animals, geography and scenery; expeditions or overseas travel; fabric appeals for places of worship; fundraising events or activities; hospitals and medical centres (except for projects which are clearly additional to statutory responsibilities); individuals, including students; loans or business finance; promotion of religion; schools and colleges (except for projects that will benefit disabled students and are clearly additional to statutory responsibilities); sponsorship or marketing appeals; international appeals – trustees may from time to time consider a limited number of applications from UK registered charities working abroad.

TYPE OF GRANT Depends on merit, but usually one-off for a specific project, operational costs, salaries and start-up costs. Funding of up to three years may be considered.

RANGE OF GRANTS £1,000–£110,000.

SAMPLE GRANTS Action for Children Guernsey Youth Housing (£111,000); Autism Jersey (£105,000); Drug Concern (£98,000); Guernsey Women's Refuge (£60,000); Weston Health Care Foundation (£50,000); St Mark's Church (£30,000); Headway Jersey (£25,000); St Stephen's Community Centre Millennium Trust (£15,000); Jersey Army Cadet Force League (£10,000); Communicate Guernsey (£5,000); and Sailaway (£1,000).

FINANCES Year 2010 *Income* £1,093,349 *Grants* £977,500 *Assets* £1,174,859

TRUSTEES Sir Rocky Goodall; Advocate Susan Pearmain; Pauline Torode; John Boothman; Stephen Jones; Dr John Furguson; Patricia Tumelty; Martin Fricker.

HOW TO APPLY Applications are only accepted on the foundation's own form. These, along with guidelines, are available from its website or from the foundation's office in Jersey and can be returned at any time. They must be returned by post as the foundation does not accept forms that have been emailed or faxed. All applications are reviewed on a continual basis. The trustees meet three times a year to approve donations. Decision-making processes can therefore take up to four months. Applications up to £5,000 are normally assessed within one month and all applicants are informed of the outcome of their application. Applicants are encouraged to discuss their project with one of the foundation's staff before completing an application form. This will help ensure that your project is within its criteria and that you are applying for an appropriate amount. You will also be informed of when you should hear a decision.

WHO TO APPLY TO John Hutchins, Executive Director, PO Box 160, 25 New Street, St Helier, Jersey JE4 8RG *Tel* 01534 845889 *email* john.hutchins@lloydstsbfoundations.org.uk *Website* www.ltsbfoundationci.org

■ Llysdinam Charitable Trust

CC NO 255528   **ESTABLISHED** 1968
WHERE FUNDING CAN BE GIVEN Wales.
WHO CAN BENEFIT Registered charities.
WHAT IS FUNDED The advancement of education in the natural sciences, particularly botany and biology; the advancement (so far as legally charitable) of horticulture, agriculture and silviculture; the advancement of the Christian religion in Wales and in particular by support of the Church of Wales; and the relief of poverty in

Wales and particularly in the parishes of Llysdlnam, Llanfihangel-Bryn-Pabuan and Llanafan Fawr in the county of Brecon and the parish of Llanyre in the county of Radnor.

WHAT IS NOT FUNDED No grants to individuals.

TYPE OF GRANT Normally recurrent.

RANGE OF GRANTS £180–£16,000.

SAMPLE GRANTS University of Wales – Cardiff (£16,000); Llysdinam Field Centre (£11,000); Powys Arts Forum and Shakespeare Link (£2,000 each); National Gardens Scheme (£1,300); Llandokery College Arts Centre and Combat Stress (£1,000 each); Cyrnryd Rhan (£800); the Sequel Trust (£750); Wales Air Ambulance (£210); and NSPCC (£180).

FINANCES *Year* 2009–10 *Income* £119,038 *Grants* £39,106 *Assets* £4,438,147

TRUSTEES Mary Elster; Norman Tyler; Emma Birkmyre.

HOW TO APPLY The trust has previously stated that it is overloaded with applications and does not welcome unsolicited applications.

WHO TO APPLY TO The Trustees, Rees Richards and Partners, Druslyn House, De La Beche Street, Swansea SA1 3HH *Tel* 01792 650705 *Fax* 01792 468 384 *email* post@reesrichards. co.uk

---

■ Localtrent Ltd

CC NO 326329   **ESTABLISHED** 1982

WHERE FUNDING CAN BE GIVEN UK, with some preference for Manchester.

WHO CAN BENEFIT Charities benefiting Jewish people and the advancement of the Jewish faith.

WHAT IS FUNDED The trustees will consider applications from organisations concerned with orthodox Jewish faith education and the relief of poverty.

SAMPLE GRANTS Chasdei Yoel Charitable Trust (£53,000) and Kesser Torah School (£4,000).

FINANCES *Year* 2009–10 *Income* £216,857 *Grants* £173,027 *Assets* £245,672

TRUSTEES Hyman Weiss; Mina Weiss; Philip Weiss; Zisel Weiss; Bernardin Weiss; Yocheved Weiss.

HOW TO APPLY In writing to the correspondent.

WHO TO APPLY TO A Kahan, Administrator, Lopian Gross Barnett and Co, 6th Floor, Cardinal House, 20 St Mary's Parsonage, Manchester M3 2LG *Tel* 0161 832 8721 *Fax* 0161 835 3085

■ The Locker Foundation

CC NO 264180   **ESTABLISHED** 1972

WHERE FUNDING CAN BE GIVEN UK and overseas.

WHO CAN BENEFIT Organisations benefiting Jewish people. General charitable purposes with preference for the welfare of the sick and those with disabilities and the teaching of the Jewish religion.

WHAT IS FUNDED Jewish charities, Synagogues, schools and colleges and Jewish education studies.

RANGE OF GRANTS £100–£100,000.

SAMPLE GRANTS Magen David Adom (£100,000); Kahal Chassidim Babov (£60,000); British Friends of Israel War Disabled (£35,000); Ezer Mizion (£25,000); Chai Cancer Care and WIZO (£20,000 each); Jewish Blind and Disabled and Jewish Care (£15,000 each); World Jewish Relief (£10,000); North London Hospice (£6,000); Wolfson Hillel Primary School (£5,000); Birmingham Jewish Community Care (£2,000); St John's Wood Synagogue and Zionist Federation (£1,000 each); Jewish

Women's Week British WIZO (£200); and St Peter & St James Hospice (£100).

FINANCES *Year* 2009–10 *Income* £539,746 *Grants* £500,543 *Assets* £4,533,931

TRUSTEES I Carter; M Carter; Mrs S Segal.

HOW TO APPLY In writing to the correspondent.

WHO TO APPLY TO Irving Carter, Trustee, 28 High Road, East Finchley, London N2 9PJ *Tel* 020 8455 9280

■ The Loftus Charitable Trust

CC NO 297664   **ESTABLISHED** 1987

WHERE FUNDING CAN BE GIVEN UK and overseas.

WHO CAN BENEFIT Jewish organisations benefiting children, young adults and students.

WHAT IS FUNDED Jewish organisations working in the areas of welfare, education and religion.

RANGE OF GRANTS £**SAMPLE GRANTS** Chabad Lubavitch (£25,000); Norwood (£21,500); Kisharon and UK Friends of AWIS (£20,000 each); Community Security Trust (£15,000); and British Friends of Sulam (£12,500); One Family (£7,800); Lubavitch Foundation (£7,500); Chief Rabbinate Trust Magen David Adom UK and Nightingale House (£5,000 each); British Friends of Affa Institute (£4,000); and JNF Charitable Trust and TZEDEK (£2,500 each).

FINANCES *Year* 2009–10 *Income* £264,283 *Grants* £260,532 *Assets* £26,044

TRUSTEES R I Loftus; A L Loftus; A D Loftus.

HOW TO APPLY The trustees state that all funds are committed and unsolicited applications are not welcome.

WHO TO APPLY TO Anthony Loftus, Trustee, Asher House, Blackburn Road, London NW6 1AW *Tel* 020 7604 5900

■ The Lolev Charitable Trust

CC NO 326249   **ESTABLISHED** 1982

WHERE FUNDING CAN BE GIVEN Worldwide.

WHO CAN BENEFIT Individuals and organisations.

WHAT IS FUNDED Orthodox Jewish causes.

FINANCES *Year* 2009 *Income* £2,919,096 *Grants* £224,000 *Assets* £36,746

TRUSTEES Abraham Tager; Eve Tager; Michael Tager.

OTHER INFORMATION £2.7 million was also given in grants to individuals.

HOW TO APPLY In writing to the correspondent.

WHO TO APPLY TO Abraham Tager, Trustee, 14a Gilda Crescent, London N16 6JP

■ The Trust for London (formerly the City Parochial Foundation)

CC NO 205629   **ESTABLISHED** 2004

WHERE FUNDING CAN BE GIVEN The Metropolitan Police District of London and the City of London.

WHO CAN BENEFIT Organisations providing advice, information and individual advocacy, especially those which are user-led or which encourage user involvement, participation and which lead to user empowerment. Organisations developing, promoting and providing education, training and employment schemes. Organisations which are attempting to develop initiatives which tackle violence and hate crimes against the target groups; applications will be considered for work with people who commit crimes and violence as well as work with the victims of it. Organisations who support and help settle asylum seekers, migrants and refugees.

Think carefully about every application. Is it justified?

701

WHAT IS FUNDED Work that aims to bring about policy changes relating to discrimination, isolations and violence and improving people's quality of life; second tier and infrastructure organisations which meet the needs of the targeted groups; projects involving working together with others to meet the needs of their members.

WHAT IS NOT FUNDED The foundation will not support proposals: which do not benefit Londoners; that directly replace or subsidise statutory funding (including contracts); that are the primary responsibility of statutory funders such as local and central government and health authorities; from individuals, or which are for the benefit of one individual; for mainstream educational activity including schools; for medical purposes including hospitals and hospices; for the promotion of religion; for umbrella bodies seeking to distribute grants on the trust's behalf; for work that has already taken place; for general appeals; for large capital appeals (including buildings and minibuses); or from applicants who have been rejected by us in the last six months.

The foundation is unlikely to support proposals: from large national charities which enjoy widespread support; for work that takes place in schools during school hours; where organisations have significant unrestricted reserves (including those that are designated). Generally up to six months expenditure is normally acceptable; or where organisations are in serious financial deficit.

TYPE OF GRANT Core and management costs; work that aims to change policy.

RANGE OF GRANTS Usually £15,000–£80,000 often up to three years.

SAMPLE GRANTS Bail for Immigration Detainees (£140,000); London Voluntary Service Council (£139,000); Hammersmith and Fulham Law Centre (£116,000); Evelyn Oldfield Unit (£100,000); Disability Alliance (£90,000); Farsophone Association (£80,000); Eaves Housing for Women (£75,000); Anti-Slavery International (£75,000); Zacchaeus 2000 Trust (£64,000); Mind (The National Association for Mental Health) (£50,000); Kanlungan Filipino Consortium (£36,000); Trees for Cities (£34,000); Waltham Forest Somali Women's Association(£21,000); and Downright Excellent (£18,000). £632,000 was awarded under the special initiatives programme in 2010. This included grants to: Changing Minds (£300,000); Africans Unite Against Child Abuse (£60,000); Africa Policy Research Network (£47,000); and Churches' Child Protection Advisory Service (£40,000).

FINANCES *Year* 2010 *Income* £8,299,513 *Grants* £10,393,711 *Assets* £226,888,560

TRUSTEES Trust for London Trustee.

OTHER INFORMATION The trust administers two main funds – the central fund, whose broad aim is to tackle poverty in London; and the city church fund. The latter fund provides funds to six dioceses of the Church of England within the beneficial area. Of the total grants disbursed, £4.2 million came from the city church fund.

HOW TO APPLY The foundation's funding guidelines for 2010–12 are available to download from its website. Alternatively contact the foundation's office for hard copies. It is strongly recommended that potential applicants read the guidelines before making an application. There is a three-stage application process: *Stage one* – An initial proposal to be submitted by post. There are three closing dates for proposals to be submitted by – you may submit your proposal at any time but it will only be assessed once the next closing date has passed. Closing dates are: 7 February for the June Grants Committee; 30 May for the October Grants Committee; 5 October for the February Grants Committee. *Stage two* – All organisations whose initial proposals are shortlisted will be visited by the foundation to assess their suitability for funding. *Stage three* – The grants committee will make the final decision on all funding requests. Applicants will be contacted within 10 days of the committee meeting. The whole process can take approximately four and a half months from the closing date for successful applicants.

WHO TO APPLY TO Bharat Mehta, Chief Executive and Clerk to the Trustees, 6–9 Middle Street, London EC1A 7PH *Tel* 020 7606 6145 *Fax* 020 7600 1866 *email* info@trustforlondon.org.uk *Website* www.trustforlondon.org.uk

....

■ London Catalyst (formerly The Metropolitan Hospital-Sunday Fund)

CC NO 1066739   **ESTABLISHED** 1872

WHERE FUNDING CAN BE GIVEN Greater London, within the boundaries of the M25.

WHO CAN BENEFIT Hospitals, homes and medical charities outside the NHS who are also registered charities; NHS hospitals throughout London; clients of social workers; individuals in need.

WHAT IS FUNDED Projects working with people on low incomes are favoured, as is work that assists adults. It is interested to hear from organisations working with minority ethnic and other faith communities, including refugees and asylum seekers. Themes the programme will fund are: community transport – such as modifications to existing or proposed transport (but not the purchase of minibuses), transportation costs to allow people to access activities and volunteer driving training; specialist equipment – such as hoists, slings, pressure mattresses, adjustable beds, special wheelchairs, mobility aids and so on; respite breaks and holidays – meeting the costs of breaks and holidays for people with health problems or disabilities and supporting respite programmes for carers; start-up costs – in exceptional cases, new organisations meeting an unmet need may receive revenue grants in their first two years to help them 'get off the ground' supporting volunteers – costs of volunteer training and involvement where this will add value to services for Londoners who are sick or have disabilities, and their carers; and arts and health – arts projects forming part of health recovery programmes, including those for older people.

WHAT IS NOT FUNDED No grants to: hospitals and homes within the NHS, including specialist clinics and appeals relating to NHS hospitals and special units; charitable organisations not registered with the Charity Commission; hospital league of friends for NHS and independent hospitals; government departments; or individuals.

TYPE OF GRANT Project and one-off.

RANGE OF GRANTS Usually £1,000–£3,000.

SAMPLE GRANTS Beneficiaries included: Mind in Camden (£15,000); Southall Community Alliance (£9,000); Holy Cross Centre and Community CIC (£8,000 each); Headway North London, Somali Health Advocacy Project and the Chinese Healthy Living Centre (£3,000 each);

Complementary Cancer Care Trust, Praxis and RHND (£2,000); St Mary's Hospital, Springfield Hospital and Richmond Home Treatment Team (£300 each).

FINANCES *Year* 2009–10 *Income* £390,554 *Grants* £325,749 *Assets* £10,127,837

TRUSTEES John Cornes; Charles Davidson; Revd Paul Regen; Canon Grahame Shaw; Dr Steve Mowle, Chair; Helal Uddin Abbas; Katharine Barber; Yoke Hopkins.

OTHER INFORMATION This entry only refers to grants made to organisations. It operates smaller funds for individuals.

HOW TO APPLY Forms and guidance can be downloaded from the charity's website or requested by phone or letter. Applications and other grant enquiries are acceptable via email. All applications are reviewed against eligibility criteria and then considered by the grants scrutiny committee before presenting to the trustees for approval.

WHO TO APPLY TO Graham Lawrence, Company Secretary, c/o The Peabody Trust, Minster Court, 45 Westminster Bridge Road, London SE1 7JB *Tel* 020 7021 4633 *email* london.catalyst@peabody.org.uk *Website* www.londoncatalyst.org.uk

····················

■ The London Community Foundation (formerly Capital Community Foundation)

CC NO 1091263   **ESTABLISHED** 2002

WHERE FUNDING CAN BE GIVEN The London boroughs including the City of London.

WHO CAN BENEFIT Community organisations benefiting unemployed people, volunteers, people disadvantaged by poverty, refugees and people living in urban areas.

WHAT IS FUNDED Community based projects enhancing the quality of life of people in the community and addressing discrimination and disadvantage. Each scheme run by the foundation has its own local grant criteria and awards panel.

WHAT IS NOT FUNDED Generally, no grants for individuals, political groups or activities which promote religion.

TYPE OF GRANT Normally one-off for core costs, feasibility studies, project, running costs, salaries and start up costs. Funding is available for up to two years on some programmes. Most are up to one year.

RANGE OF GRANTS Small grant programmes up to £5,000. Large grants up to £50,000.

SAMPLE GRANTS Food Skills Ltd., (£50,000); Bench Outreach (£48,000 in total); Cystic Fibrosis (£33,000); Ilderton Foundation, Fresh Visions People Ltd., Mosaic Clubhouse and Springfield Community Flat After School Club (£25,000 each); Cricket for Change, Snow-Camp, Southwark Tigers Rugby Club and Tideway Sailability (£10,000 each); The Dodds Fund (£8,000); Latin American House and Highbury Roundhouse Youth & Community Centre (£7,000 each); Emmaus South Lambeth Community and Indoamerican Refugee and Migrant Organisation (£5,000 each); Centre Point Corporation CIC and Foundations UK (£4,000 each); Bounce Theatre Company (£2,000); Allianz Community Fund (£1,000); and The Capital Community Foundation Fund (£500).

FINANCES *Year* 2009–10 *Income* £4,175,272 *Grants* £2,594,123 *Assets* £5,377,849

TRUSTEES Carole Souter, Chair; Gordon Williamson; Ade Sawyerr; Clive Cutbill; Michael Brophy; William Moore; Nicholas Hammond; Toni Cupal; Juliet Wedderburn; Stephen Jordan; Donovan Norris; Martin Richards; Grant Gordon; Davina Judelson.

OTHER INFORMATION The foundation is primarily the local distributor of funds from a number of government programmes under a variety of different schemes.

HOW TO APPLY In order to apply for a grant from the foundation your organisation must have: a management committee of at least 3 people who are not related and are not paid wages by your group; a governing document (e.g. constitution or Memorandum & Articles of Association); a bank account with at least 2 unrelated signatories for transactions (Pass Book accounts or those which permit only cash withdrawals are not accepted); a child protection policy and procedures if you will be working with children.

As the foundation offers funds on behalf of different donors, you may apply to each and every programme for which your group is eligible. However, the criteria do vary for each grant programme, so be sure to read the guidance carefully. If you are unsure about your eligibility, please call the grants team on Tel: 020 7582 5117 before making an application. Application forms and guidance notes specific to each programme are available from the foundation and/or the website. Each programme has its own set of closing dates. All applications must reach Capital Community Foundation by 5pm on that date.

WHO TO APPLY TO Gordon Williamson, Trustee, 357 Kennington Lane, London SE11 5QY *Tel* 020 7582 5117 *Fax* 020 7582 4020 *email* enquiries@londoncf.org.uk *Website* www.londoncf.org.uk

····················

■ The London Law Trust

CC NO 1115266   **ESTABLISHED** 1968

WHERE FUNDING CAN BE GIVEN UK.

WHO CAN BENEFIT Registered charities benefiting children and young people.

WHAT IS FUNDED The alleviation of illness and disability in children and young people; and the encouragement in young people of the qualities of leadership and service to the community. The trust may also support charities working in the fields of education and residential facilities and services.

The trustees also support The London Law Trust Medal, in association with King's College London. The Medal carries with it an eighteen-month Research Career Establishment Fellowship which is funded jointly by the trustees and the College. The Fellowship is awarded for research in medicine or dentistry which is designed to impact on patient care. Candidates are selected on merit by a panel constituted by the College and including up to two trustees of The London Law Trust. Two Medals may be awarded in any year.

WHAT IS NOT FUNDED Applications from individuals, including students, are ineligible.

TYPE OF GRANT Usually one-off grants for or towards specific projects. Buildings, capital, core costs, research, running costs, recurring costs, salaries and start-up costs will also be considered. Funding may be given for up to three years.

RANGE OF GRANTS £500–£5,000; typical grant £3,000.

SAMPLE GRANTS Previous beneficiaries have included: BRIC, British Lung Foundation, Deans & Canons of Windsor, Great Ormond Street and

St George's Hospital Medical School (£5,000 each); Envision (£3,000); Activenture and Swan Syndrome (£2,500 each); and Circomedia (£1,000).

FINANCES *Year* 2009–10 *Income* £128,013 *Grants* £142,500 *Assets* £3,530,162

TRUSTEES Prof. Anthony R Mellows; R A Pellant; Sir Michael Hobbs; Sir Ian Gainsford.

OTHER INFORMATION Grants were made to organisations totalling £67,500.

HOW TO APPLY Usually, in writing to the correspondent. However, the Secretary to the Trust has informed us (August 2011) that 'The funds for the London Law Trust are fully committed for the present and for the foreseeable future. Therefore the trust regrets that it is unable to consider any new applications for grants at the moment.' The trustees employ a grant advisor whose job is to evaluate applications. Grant applicants are requested to supply detailed information in support of their applications. The grant advisor makes on-site visits to all applicants and makes a written report.
The directors of the trust meet twice a year to consider the grant advisor's individual visit reports together with the application form, latest accounts and other supporting information. Most grants are awarded in late Autumn.

WHO TO APPLY TO G D Ogilvie, Secretary, Hunters, 9 New Square, Lincoln's Inn, London WC2A 3QN *Tel* 020 7412 0050 *email* londonlawtrust@hunters-solicitors.co.uk *Website* www.thelondonlawtrust.org

■ London Legal Support Trust

CC NO 1101906   **ESTABLISHED** 2004

WHERE FUNDING CAN BE GIVEN London and the Home Counties.

WHO CAN BENEFIT Voluntary sector legal agencies in London and the Home Counties that employ solicitors or retain the services of solicitors as volunteers to provide free legal advice to poor or disadvantaged members the public; and network organisations that support the above agencies.

WHAT IS FUNDED (i) Legal services and projects that encourage or provide co-operation between voluntary sector agencies and volunteers from private practice. (ii) Crisis intervention to 'keep the doors open' when funding cuts threaten the closure of a voluntary sector legal agency and when the trustees consider that short term funding may lead to sustainable recovery. (iii) One-off capital support to increase the capacity of an agency to deliver its service. (iv) Creation of new social welfare legal and pro bono provision in London and the Home Counties.

WHAT IS NOT FUNDED The trust does not fund: non charitable activity; applications for which the trustees feel that Legal Services Commission funding is suitable and practical within a reasonable time frame, except where the trust's funding is to be used to lever matched funding.

RANGE OF GRANTS £100–£35,000.

SAMPLE GRANTS Beneficiaries included: Surrey Law Centre (£35,000); The Royal Courts of Justice Advice Bureau (£31,000); Tower Hamlets Law Centre (£26,000); Bar Pro Bono Unit and Free Representation Unit (£15,000); Rights of Women (£8,000); Notradame Refugee Centre (£7,000); Prisoners Advice Service (£5,000); and Sutton Citizen's Advice (£700).

FINANCES *Year* 2009–10 *Income* £743,302 *Grants* £330,907 *Assets* £302,465

TRUSTEES Julian Clark; Richard Dyton; Peter Gardner; Graham Huntley; Steve Hynes; Joy Julien; Michael Smyth; Marc Sosnow; Fraser Thomas; Jeremy Thomas.

HOW TO APPLY In writing to the correspondent stating what is needed and why. Applicants should enclose annual accounts and annual report. Please check the trust's website for availability and full guidelines.

WHO TO APPLY TO Emma Shaw, c/o Allen & Overy, 1 New Change, London EC4M 9QQ *Tel* 020 3088 3656 *email* chair@ londonlegalsupporttrust.org.uk *Website* londonlegalsupporttrust.org.uk

■ The London Marathon Charitable Trust

CC NO 283813   **ESTABLISHED** 1982

WHERE FUNDING CAN BE GIVEN Mainly London, but also City of Birmingham and South Northamptonshire.

WHO CAN BENEFIT Organisations involved with sports, recreation and leisure, including schools.

WHAT IS FUNDED Recreational facilities in London. Grants have been made towards the establishment of play areas and nature trails; improvements to existing leisure facilities; provision of MUGAs (Multi Use Games Areas); and to various rowing organisations to provide new accommodation and boats. Grants are aimed to benefit both the able bodied and people with disabilities and include the sports of athletics, cricket, tennis, gymnastics, sailing, football, boxing, and climbing.

WHAT IS NOT FUNDED Grants cannot be made to 'closed' clubs or schools, unless the facility is available for regular public use. No grants are made for recurring or revenue costs. Individuals are not supported.

RANGE OF GRANTS £750–£732,000.

SAMPLE GRANTS Most grants made in London, via borough councils. LM Playing Field Chase Lodge – ground purchase and improvements (£732,000); LM Playing Field Mottingham – all-weather court (£256,000); Lee Valley Regional Park – indoor track upgrade at Lee Valley Stadium (£174,000); Jo Richardson Community School, Barking & Dagenham – dual use fitness suite (£150,000); London 2012 Legacy Stadia – development of pool lift for disabled (£90.000); and Liverpool Sailing Club – rebuild slipway (£25,000).

FINANCES *Year* 2009–10 *Income* £4,785,636 *Grants* £3,789,053 *Assets* £15,417,005

TRUSTEES Bernard Atha; Simon Cooper; Eileen Gray; Dame Mary Peters; Joyce Smith; John Graves; James Dudley Henderson Clarke; John Austin; John Disley; Sir Rodney Walker; John Bryant.

OTHER INFORMATION The trust has no connection to the fundraising efforts of the individuals involved in the race, who raise over £40 million each year for their chosen good causes.

HOW TO APPLY On a form available from the correspondent. Applications are welcomed from London Boroughs and independent organisations, clubs and charities. The trustees meet once a year; the closing date is usually the end of August.

WHO TO APPLY TO David Golton, Secretary, Kestrel House, 111 Heath Road, Twickenham TW1 4AH *Tel* 020 8892 6646 *Fax* 020 8892 6478 *email* lmct@ffleach.co.uk

■ The William and Katherine Longman Trust

cc no 800785   **ESTABLISHED** 1988
WHERE FUNDING CAN BE GIVEN UK.
WHO CAN BENEFIT Registered charities.
WHAT IS FUNDED General charitable purposes.
WHAT IS NOT FUNDED Grants are only made to registered charities.
TYPE OF GRANT One-off and recurrent.
RANGE OF GRANTS £1,000–£30,000.
SAMPLE GRANTS Previous beneficiaries include: Vanessa Grant Trust; World Child Cancer Fund; Hope Education Trust; RADA; Action for ME; The Children's Society; Age Concern – Kensington & Chelsea; RSPCA; St Mungo's; and Prisoners Abroad.
FINANCES *Year* 2009–10 *Income* £101,859 *Grants* £195,000 *Assets* £3,457,714
TRUSTEES W P Harriman; A C O Bell.
HOW TO APPLY The trustees believe in taking a proactive approach in deciding which charities to support and it is their policy not to respond to unsolicited appeals.
WHO TO APPLY TO Mrs G Feeney, Charles Russell LLP, 8–10 New Fetter Lane, London EC4A 1RS *Tel* 020 7203 5196

■ The Lord's Taverners

cc no 306054   **ESTABLISHED** 1950
WHERE FUNDING CAN BE GIVEN Unrestricted, in practice, UK.
WHO CAN BENEFIT Cricket clubs affiliated to a National Governing Body, individual schools or other organisations directly involved in the organisation of youth cricket and which have a genuine need for assistance.
WHAT IS FUNDED Youth cricket, minibuses for organisations supporting young people with disabilities and sports and recreational equipment for young people with special needs.
WHAT IS NOT FUNDED Youth cricket: Only one application in any 12 month period. The following is not normally grant aided: building or renovation of pavilions; sight screens; bowling machines; mowers/rollers; overseas tours; clothing; refreshments; trophies. Sport for young people with special needs: the following will not normally be considered for a grant: capital costs; general grants; running costs including salaries; individuals (although applications will be considered for equipment to enable an individual to participate in a team/group recreational activity); holidays/overseas tours. Minibuses: homes, schools and organisations catering for young people with special needs under the age of 25 years, are entitled to only one minibus per location, although applications are accepted for a replacement.
SAMPLE GRANTS No grants list was available.
FINANCES *Year* 2009–10 *Income* £6,752,668 *Grants* £2,814,037 *Assets* £3,377,407
TRUSTEES John Ayling; John Barnes; Leo Callow; Mike Gatting; Robert Powell; Sally Surridge; Tom Rodwell; Robert Griffiths; David East; Christine Colbeck; Martin Smith.
HOW TO APPLY The trust committee meets regularly to review applications for grant aid. All applications must be presented on the appropriate application forms and should be submitted to the secretary. Application forms with detailed application instructions for the different grant schemes are available from the secretary or on the trust's website.
WHO TO APPLY TO Nicky Pemberton, Head of Foundation, 10 Buckingham Place, London SW1E 6HX *Tel* 020 7821 2828 *Fax* 020 7821 2829 *email* foundation@lordstaverners.org *Website* www.lordstaverners.org

■ The Loseley and Guildway Charitable Trust

cc no 267178   **ESTABLISHED** 1973
WHERE FUNDING CAN BE GIVEN International and UK, with an interest in Guildford.
WHO CAN BENEFIT Organisations benefiting people with various disabilities and terminal illness, children and victims of natural disasters.
WHAT IS FUNDED Compassionate causes, mainly local or causes with which various members of the More-Molyneux family and trustees are associated.
WHAT IS NOT FUNDED No grants to non-registered charities.
RANGE OF GRANTS £25–£5,000.
SAMPLE GRANTS CHASE and Disability Challengers (£5,000 each); Brooke Hospital, Cherry Trees, Crisis, Gurkha Welfare Trust, National Society for Epilepsy, Phyllis Tuckwell Hospice, RNLI and Wells for India (£1,000 each).
FINANCES *Year* 2009–10 *Income* £63,165 *Grants* £40,493 *Assets* £1,188,640
TRUSTEES Maj. James More-Molyneux, Chair; Susan More-Molyneux; Michael More-Molyneux; Alexander More-Molyneux; Glye Hodson.
OTHER INFORMATION Grant recipients of £1,000 or over were listed in the accounts.
HOW TO APPLY In writing to the correspondent. The trustees meet in February, May and September to consider applications. However, due to commitments, new applications for any causes are unlikely to be successful.
WHO TO APPLY TO Mrs Julia Barnes, Secretary, The Estate Offices, Loseley Park, Guildford, Surrey GU3 1HS *Tel* 01483 405114 *Fax* 01483 302 036 *email* charities@loseleypark.co.uk *Website* www.loseley-park.com/charities.asp

■ The Lotus Foundation

cc no 1070111   **ESTABLISHED** 1998
WHERE FUNDING CAN BE GIVEN UK, especially London and Surrey; occasionally overseas.
WHO CAN BENEFIT Established or newly-formed charities.
WHAT IS FUNDED The primary objectives of the trust are: 'to support those charities that fall within our aims, [i.e.] children and youth, medical, substance abuse and domestic violence, education, animal welfare and community charities'.
WHAT IS NOT FUNDED No response to circular appeals. No grants to individuals, non-registered charities, charities working outside of the foundation's areas of interest, or for research purposes.
TYPE OF GRANT One-off and Recurrent.
RANGE OF GRANTS £200–£32,000.
SAMPLE GRANTS Great Ormond Street Tick Tock Club (£25,000); Whizz Kids (£10,000); Marie Curie Cancer Care (£10,000); Médecins Sans Frontières (£20,000); Action on Addiction (£5,000); RAPT (£32,000); Gosden House School (£1,000); Battersea Dogs and Cats Home (£10,000); Cranleigh Lions Club (£2,000); Samaritans (£1,000).
FINANCES *Year* 2010 *Income* £216,097 *Grants* £201,200 *Assets* £72,342
TRUSTEES Mrs B Starkey; R Starkey; Mrs E Turner.

HOW TO APPLY In writing to the correspondent giving a brief outline of the work, amount required and project/programme to benefit. The trustees prefer applications which are simple and economically prepared rather than glossy 'prestige' and mail sorted brochures. Note: In order to reduce administration costs and concentrate its efforts on the charitable work at hand, unsolicited requests will no longer be acknowledged by the foundation.

WHO TO APPLY TO Barbara Starkey, Trustee, c/o Startling Music Ltd, 90 Jermyn Street, London SW1Y 6JD *Tel* 020 7930 5133 *Website* www.lotusfoundation.com

---

■ The Lower Green Foundation

CC NO 1137862   **ESTABLISHED** 2010
WHERE FUNDING CAN BE GIVEN Worldwide.
WHO CAN BENEFIT Organisations and individuals.
WHAT IS FUNDED General charitable purposes.
TRUSTEES L Billett; Ms M Sajitz; S C S Beecham.
OTHER INFORMATION Laurence Billett is also a trustee for Hampstead Theatre Limited (Charity Commission no. 218506)
HOW TO APPLY In writing to the correspondent.
WHO TO APPLY TO Pam Henness, 3 Willow Street, London EC2A 4BH *email* info@lowergreen.com

---

■ The Lowy Mitchell Foundation

CC NO 1094430   **ESTABLISHED** 2002
WHERE FUNDING CAN BE GIVEN Worldwide.
WHO CAN BENEFIT Charitable organisations chosen at the trustees' discretion.
WHAT IS FUNDED General and Jewish charitable purposes.
RANGE OF GRANTS £100–£20,000.
SAMPLE GRANTS Grants were categorised as follows: Community and Welfare £16,150; Arts and Culture £30,000; Education Science and Technology £2,500; Medical and Disability £11,000; Children and Youth £150; Religious £2,300; and Other £900. Beneficiaries included: Portobello Media (£20,000); Community Security Trust (£10,000); UK Jewish Film Festival (£5,000); Help for Heroes (£2,000); The Amos Bursary (£1,500); National Theatre (£1,250); Batsheva Dance Company (£1,000); and Pratham UK and Jewish Community Centre (£150 each).
FINANCES *Year* 2009–10 *Income* £30,025 *Grants* £62,877 *Assets* £518,322
TRUSTEES Lord Mitchell; Lady Mitchell; A J Weiner; A Delew.
HOW TO APPLY In writing to the correspondent.
WHO TO APPLY TO Lady Lowy Mitchell, Administrator, 3 Elm Row, London NW3 1AA *Tel* 020 7431 1534

■ The C L Loyd Charitable Trust

CC NO 265076   **ESTABLISHED** 1973
WHERE FUNDING CAN BE GIVEN UK, with a preference for Berkshire and Oxfordshire.
WHO CAN BENEFIT Neighbourhood-based community projects and UK organisations benefiting at risk groups, and people who are disabled, disadvantaged by poverty or socially isolated.
WHAT IS FUNDED General charitable purposes. Local charities in Berkshire and Oxfordshire, UK health and welfare charities and UK animal welfare charities.
WHAT IS NOT FUNDED In writing to the correspondent. Grants are made several times each month.

TYPE OF GRANT One-off and recurrent.
RANGE OF GRANTS Up to £50,000; mostly £1,000 or less.
SAMPLE GRANTS County Buildings Protection Trust (£27,000); Ardington & Lockinge PCC (£20,000); King Alfred Educational Charity and Leighton House (£5,000 each); King Alfred's School (£3,500); Christian Aid (£2,000); Ardington & Lockinge Churches (£1,600); Injured Jockey's Fund (£1,100); and William Rowden Trust and National Hospital Development Fund (£1,000 each).
FINANCES *Year* 2009–10 *Income* £72,857 *Grants* £77,053 *Assets* £2,242,361
TRUSTEES Mrs A Loyd; T C Loyd; C L Lord.
OTHER INFORMATION Other grants of less than £1,000 amounted to £9,000.
HOW TO APPLY In writing to the correspondent. Grants are made several times each month.
WHO TO APPLY TO C L Loyd, Trustee, Betterton House, Lockinge, Wantage, Oxfordshire OX12 8QL *Tel* 01235 833265

■ LSA Charitable Trust

CC NO 803671   **ESTABLISHED** 1989
WHERE FUNDING CAN BE GIVEN UK.
WHO CAN BENEFIT Individuals and institutions benefiting horticultural researchers, students and people working in horticulture, and former tenants and employees of the former Land Settlement Association Ltd, who are in need.
WHAT IS FUNDED Horticultural research, the promotion of horticultural knowledge, and the relief of poverty.
FINANCES *Year* 2009–10 *Income* £55,802 *Grants* £38,830 *Assets* £1,277,227
TRUSTEES S R V Pomeroy, Chair; B E G Howe; P Hadley; C F Woodhouse; A M M Ross; D J P Price.
HOW TO APPLY For organisations: in writing to the correspondent. Grants to individuals for the relief of poverty are made through the Royal Agricultural Benevolent Institution.
WHO TO APPLY TO Cheryl Boyce, c/o Farrer and Co, 66 Lincoln's Inn Fields, London WC2A 3LH *Tel* 020 7242 2022

■ The Marie Helen Luen Charitable Trust

CC NO 291012   **ESTABLISHED** 1984
WHERE FUNDING CAN BE GIVEN UK, with a preference for Wimbledon.
WHO CAN BENEFIT Charitable organisations.
WHAT IS FUNDED The trust supports both UK and local charities concerned with cancer relief, homelessness and the relief of hardship, pain and suffering. Grants are also given to relieve developing world poverty.
RANGE OF GRANTS Up to £5,000.
SAMPLE GRANTS Beneficiary organisations included: Kingston University Student Hardship Fund (£5,000); Macmillan Cancer Relief, Crisis and Mpemba Orphanage in Malawi (£2,000 each); Marie Curie Cancer Care, St Mungo's, Headway, Beating Bowel Cancer and Tenovus (£1,000 each).
FINANCES *Year* 2009–10 *Income* £36,426 *Grants* £36,500 *Assets* £960,496
TRUSTEES S V Perera; R R Littleton; M G Whitehead.
OTHER INFORMATION Grants to both individuals and organisations
HOW TO APPLY In writing to the correspondent.

WHO TO APPLY TO Richard R Littleton, Trustee, Hillcroft, 57 Langley Avenue, Surbiton, Surrey KT6 6QR *Tel* 020 8946 3979 *email* richard@esppos.com

■ Robert Luff Foundation Ltd

CC NO 273810   **ESTABLISHED** 1977
WHERE FUNDING CAN BE GIVEN UK.
WHO CAN BENEFIT Medical research charities.
WHAT IS FUNDED Medical research.
RANGE OF GRANTS Up to £150,000.
SAMPLE GRANTS Cystic Fibrosis Trust (£150,000); Royal Brompton Hospital (£110,000); Bowel Disease Research Foundation (£80,000); British Lung Foundation (£60,000); International Spinal Research Trust (£50,000); Alzheimer's Society, Osteopathic Centre for Children, Sheffield Health Authority Trust Fund and Blonde McIndoe Research Foundation (£40,000 each); N W London Hospital Trust (£30,000).
FINANCES *Year* 2009 *Income* £456,889 *Grants* £858,000 *Assets* £23,487,881
TRUSTEES Sir Robert Johnson; Lady Johnson; R P J Price; Ms G Favot; Mrs J Tomlinson; Revd Matthew Tomlinson; Mrs M Condon; B D Nicholson.
HOW TO APPLY The foundation makes its own decisions about what causes to support. It has stated that 'outside applications are not considered, or replied to'.
WHO TO APPLY TO Michael D Lock, Secretary, The Garth, Wood Lane, Stanmore, Middlesex HA7 4JZ *Tel* 020 8954 9006 *email* md.lock@virgin.net

■ Henry Lumley Charitable Trust

CC NO 1079480   **ESTABLISHED** 2000
WHERE FUNDING CAN BE GIVEN UK and overseas.
WHO CAN BENEFIT Charities which are known to at least one trustee.
WHAT IS FUNDED Medical, educational and relief of poverty/hardship.
TYPE OF GRANT Mainly recurrent.
RANGE OF GRANTS £1,000–£20,000.
SAMPLE GRANTS Royal College of Surgeons (£20,000); Cancer Research UK, Stroke Association and Broderers Charitable Appeal (£5,000 each); Asthma UK, British Liver Trust and Meningitis Research Fund (£4,000 each); Ghurka Welfare Trust, Friends of St Michael's Hospice, Royal British Legion and Royal Star, Garter Home for Disabled Ex-service Men and Women and Wellbeing of Women (£2,500 each); and Royal School of Needlework (£1,000).
FINANCES *Year* 2010 *Income* £75,684 *Grants* £119,000 *Assets* £3,476,650
TRUSTEES Henry Lumley; Peter Lumley; Robert Lumley; James Porter.
HOW TO APPLY In writing to the correspondent.
WHO TO APPLY TO Peter Lumley, Trustee, c/o Lutine Leisure Ltd, Windlesham Golf Club, Bagshot, Surrey GU19 5HY *Tel* 01276 472273

■ Lady Lumley's Educational Foundation

CC NO 529625   **ESTABLISHED** 1959
WHERE FUNDING CAN BE GIVEN Pickering, Sinnington and Thornton Dale.
WHO CAN BENEFIT Lady Lumley School, schools and other places of learning, charitable organisations and individuals.
WHAT IS FUNDED Education, special benefits not provided by the LEA, provision of recreational facilities for young people and financial assistance to enable study of music or other arts.
FINANCES *Year* 2009–10 *Income* £82,435 *Grants* £121,287 *Assets* £2,012,451
TRUSTEES Mrs S R Wass, Chair; G Acomb; R Bramley; C M Cooper; R H Towler; Mrs S Whalley; W W Garbutt; Mrs M R Lowe; A Wilson.
HOW TO APPLY The trustees meet at least three times a year to consider applications which should be made in writing to the correspondent.
WHO TO APPLY TO D C Fitzgerald, Clerk to the Governors, 1 The Mount, Thornton Dale, Pickering, North Yorkshire YO18 7TF *Tel* 01751 472121 *Fax* 01751 475132 *email* dcf@ellis-lakin.co.uk

■ Paul Lunn-Rockliffe Charitable Trust

CC NO 264119   **ESTABLISHED** 1972
WHERE FUNDING CAN BE GIVEN UK with a preference for Hampshire.
WHO CAN BENEFIT Mainly smaller and locally based charities and those which may be known to the trustees, or members of their family.
WHAT IS FUNDED The trust makes grants in the following categories: aged; children; disabled; education and students; family; mission; needy, drug addicts, homeless and unemployed people; prisoners; radio/mission; third world; youth; and 'others'. Each year the trustees allocate a proportion of the funds for donation to be applied to charities not previously supported and for special one-off causes.
WHAT IS NOT FUNDED The trustees will not fund individuals; for example, student's expenses and travel grants. Repair and maintenance of historic buildings are also excluded for support.
TYPE OF GRANT Core costs, one-off and start-up costs. Funding for more than three years will be considered.
RANGE OF GRANTS £300–£1,000.
SAMPLE GRANTS Christians Against Poverty and British Red Cross (£1,000 each); Church Urban Fund, Langley House Trust and Community of Holy Fire – Zimbabwe Children (£600 each); Action for Elder Abuse, Children Country Holiday Fund, Shepherds Down School, Hope Pregnancy Crisis, Street Pastors, Society of St Dismas, Touchstones 12, Hour of Revival, Appropriate Technology Asia, Fairbridge Solent and Armed Forces Christian Union (£500 each); Way to Life, Consequences, Friends of the Family and People International (£400 each); and Gateway Club (£300).
FINANCES *Year* 2009–10 *Income* £35,045 *Grants* £37,100 *Assets* £759,973
TRUSTEES Jacqueline Lunn-Rockliffe; James Lunn-Rockliffe; Bryan Boult.
HOW TO APPLY The trust encourages preliminary phone calls to discuss applications. It will generally only reply to written correspondence if an sae has been included.

WHO TO APPLY TO Jacqueline Lunn-Rockliffe, Trustee, 4a Barnes Close, Winchester, Hampshire SO23 9QX *Tel* 01962 852949 *Fax* 01962 852949

■ C F Lunoe Trust Fund

CC NO 214850   **ESTABLISHED** 1960
WHERE FUNDING CAN BE GIVEN UK.
WHO CAN BENEFIT Universities and ex-employees (and their dependants) of Norwest Holst Group Ltd.
WHAT IS FUNDED Universities associated with the construction industry.
SAMPLE GRANTS ICE Quest Fund (£38,000); Leeds University (£50,000) and Leeds University (£10,000) C F Lunoe Memorial Lecture (£3,000). Payments to individuals totalled £30,000.
FINANCES *Year* 2008–09 *Grants* £60,625
TRUSTEES J A Bosdet, Chair; P H Lunoe; R F Collins; J E Ellis; G V Smith; J A Jefkins; J A Dodson; T Parks.
OTHER INFORMATION In 2008–09 a further £30,000 was given to 14 individuals.
HOW TO APPLY In writing to the correspondent. However, the majority of the trust's funds go to organisations already known to the trustees and as a result new applications are likely to be unsuccessful.
WHO TO APPLY TO Peter Lunoe, Trustee, 29 Box Lane, Hemel Hempstead, Hertfordshire HP3 0DH *Tel* 01442 252236

■ The Ruth and Jack Lunzer Charitable Trust

CC NO 276201   **ESTABLISHED** 1978
WHERE FUNDING CAN BE GIVEN UK.
WHO CAN BENEFIT Organisations benefiting children, young adults and students are given priority.
WHAT IS FUNDED Jewish organisations, educational institutions and the arts. Other charitable purposes will be considered.
TYPE OF GRANT Mainly recurrent.
RANGE OF GRANTS £100–10,000.
SAMPLE GRANTS Kahal Chassidim Bobov (£14,000) and Yesoday Hatorah Schools (£6,200); Lubavich Foundation (£5,500); Adath Yikroet Synagogue and Moreshet Hatorah (£3,000 each); Beis Yehudis Moscow (£1,000); Closehelm Limited and Community Concern Limited (£500 each); Federation of Synagogues (£200); and Collel Chibath Yerushatayim (£100).
FINANCES *Year* 2009–10 *Income* £51,000 *Grants* £49,375 *Assets* £42,773
TRUSTEES J V Lunzer; Martin D Paisner.
HOW TO APPLY In writing to the correspondent. Unsuccessful applicants are not acknowledged.
WHO TO APPLY TO Martin D Paisner, Trustee, c/o Berwin Leighton Paisner, Adelaide House, London Bridge, London EC4R 9HA *Tel* 020 7760 1000 *Fax* 020 7760 1111

■ Lord and Lady Lurgan Trust

CC NO 297046   **ESTABLISHED** 1987
WHERE FUNDING CAN BE GIVEN UK and South Africa.
WHO CAN BENEFIT Medical charities, older people, children and the arts.
WHAT IS FUNDED The registered objects of this trust are: the relief and medical care of older people; medical research, in particular cancer research

and the publication of the useful results of such research; the advancement of education including education in the arts for the public benefit by the establishment of educational and artistic bursaries; other charitable purposes at the discretion of the trustees.
WHAT IS NOT FUNDED No support for organisations in Scotland. No grants to individuals or for expeditions.
TYPE OF GRANT One-off and recurrent.
RANGE OF GRANTS £1,000–£5,000.
SAMPLE GRANTS Royal College of Music (£10,000); English National Opera and Queen's University – Belfast (£2,000 each); Greater Shankhill Business Forum (£1,540); and Deafblind UK, Help the Aged, Macmillan Cancer Relief, Oesophageal Patients Association, St Joseph's Hospice and Water Aid (£1,000 each).
FINANCES *Year* 2010 *Income* £27,167 *Grants* £75,582 *Assets* £1,045,828
TRUSTEES Simon Ladd; Andrew Stebbings; Diana Graves; Brendan Beder.
HOW TO APPLY Complete the downloadable application form which is available on the trust's website. Please read the grant policy on the website before completing the form. Trustees meet three or four times a year.
WHO TO APPLY TO Mrs Diana Burke, 45 Cadogan Gardens, London SW3 2AQ *Tel* 020 7591 3333 *Fax* 020 7591 3300 *email* charitymanager@ pglaw.co.uk *Website* www.lurgantrust.org

■ The Lyndhurst Trust

CC NO 235252   **ESTABLISHED** 1964
WHERE FUNDING CAN BE GIVEN UK and overseas, with preferences for north east England and the developing world.
WHO CAN BENEFIT Evangelistic Christian organisations, especially those operating where people have never had the opportunity of hearing the gospel. Those involved in difficult areas for Christian witness. Charities ministering to the needs of the disadvantaged in society are also funded.
WHAT IS FUNDED Charities connected with the propagation of the gospel or the promotion of the Christian religion; the distribution of bibles and other Christian religious works; the support of Christian missions; the provision of clergy; the maintenance of churches and chapels; work with disadvantaged people in society. Funds are given worldwide; there is a preference for the developing world, and in the UK a preference for the north east of England. It tends to support specific charities on a regular basis.
WHAT IS NOT FUNDED No support for individuals or buildings.
TYPE OF GRANT Recurring.
RANGE OF GRANTS £500–£20,000.
SAMPLE GRANTS Sowing Seeds (£8,000); Message Trust (£7,000); Northumbria Community (£6,000); St Luke's Church (£5,000); Friends International (£3,000); St Barnabus Church and Icthus Christian Fellowship (£2,000 each); and Guildford Town Centre Chaplaincy – Street Angels, street Pastors and Youth for Church NE (prison work) (£1,000 each).
FINANCES *Year* 2010 *Income* £46,275 *Grants* £69,000 *Assets* £1,473,575
TRUSTEES Revd Dr R Ward; Jane Hinton; Ben Hinton; Sally Tan.
HOW TO APPLY In writing to the correspondent, enclosing an sae if a reply is required. Requests are considered half-yearly.
WHO TO APPLY TO The Secretary, PO Box 615, North Shields, Tyne and Wear NE29 1AP

Every application represents a cost to you and to the trust

■ The Lynn Foundation

CC NO 326944   **ESTABLISHED** 1985
WHERE FUNDING CAN BE GIVEN UK and overseas.
WHO CAN BENEFIT Registered charities, institutions benefiting musicians, textile workers and designers, and artists. Older people and people who are disabled will also benefit.
WHAT IS FUNDED Promotion and encouragement of music, art, Masonic charities, disability, and charities concerned with children and older people.
TYPE OF GRANT One-off grants for core, capital and project support. Loans are also made.
RANGE OF GRANTS Usually £500–£1,000.
SAMPLE GRANTS No grants list was available, although support was broken down as follows: Disabled adults – 138 grants totalling £69,000; Disabled children – 133 grants totalling £66,000; Youth sponsorship – 52 grants totalling £31,000; The arts – 8 grants totalling £25,000; Medical research – 39 grants totalling £19,000; Music – 35 grants totalling £18,000; Hospices – 35 grants totalling £18,000; and 4 Sundry grants totalling £2,000.
FINANCES *Year* 2009–10 *Income* £300,303 *Grants* £248,969 *Assets* £4,666,343
TRUSTEES Guy Parsons, Chair; J F Emmott; Dr P E Andry; P R Parsons; Ian Fair; John Sykes.
HOW TO APPLY In writing to the correspondent.
WHO TO APPLY TO Guy Parsons, Chair of the Trustees, Blackfriars, 17 Lewes Road, Haywards Heath, West Sussex RH17 7SP *Tel* 01444 454773 *Fax* 01444 456192

■ The Lynwood Trust

CC NO 289535   **ESTABLISHED** 1984
WHERE FUNDING CAN BE GIVEN UK and overseas.
WHO CAN BENEFIT Organisations benefiting children, older people and people who are disabled.
WHAT IS FUNDED Advancement of religion and other charitable purposes including churches and missionary organisations.
WHAT IS NOT FUNDED No grants to individuals.
TYPE OF GRANT One-off and recurrent.
SAMPLE GRANTS Previous beneficiaries include: Africa Inland Mission, Amersham Christian Housing Association, Church of Christ, Evangelical Alliance, London Bible College and St Paul's Church – Rusthall.
FINANCES *Year* 2009–10 *Income* £23,638 *Grants* £30,000
TRUSTEES Miss J S Barling; C R Harmer.
HOW TO APPLY In writing to the correspondent.
WHO TO APPLY TO C R Harmer, Trustee, Salatin House, 19 Cedar Road, Sutton, Surrey SM2 5DA *Tel* 020 8652 2700 *Fax* 020 8652 2719 *email* colin@harmerslater.biz

■ John Lyon's Charity

CC NO 237725   **ESTABLISHED** 1578
WHERE FUNDING CAN BE GIVEN The London boroughs of Barnet, Brent, Camden, Ealing, Kensington and Chelsea, Hammersmith and Fulham, Harrow and the Cities of London and Westminster.
WHO CAN BENEFIT Schools and registered charities working with children and young people.
WHAT IS FUNDED Education, training, arts, sport, youth clubs, disability and counselling services, all aimed at improving the lives of children and young people in the charity's beneficial area.
WHAT IS NOT FUNDED Grants are restricted to the London boroughs of Harrow, Barnet, Brent, Ealing, Camden, City of London, City of Westminster, Hammersmith & Fulham and Kensington & Chelsea. Grants are not made: to individuals; for research, unless it is action research designed to lead directly to the advancement of practical activities in the community; for feasibility studies; for medical care and resources; in response to general charitable appeals, unless they can be shown to be of specific benefit to children and young people in one or more of the geographical areas listed; as direct replacements for the withdrawal of funds by statutory authorities for activities which are primarily the responsibility of central or local government; to umbrella organisations to distribute to projects which are already in receipt of funds from the charity; for the promotion of religion or politics; for telephone helplines; as core funding for national charities; for advice and information services; to housing associations.
TYPE OF GRANT Capital costs, revenue costs and recurring costs up to three years. Buildings, core costs, project, salaries and start-up costs.
RANGE OF GRANTS Up to £250,000.
SAMPLE GRANTS London Diocesan Board for Schools (£250,000); Continyou (£80,000); City Literary Institute (£75,000); Phoenix Cinema Trust (£70,000); Harrow Club W10 (£54,000); Skill Force (£52,500); HAFPAC, Tate Gallery, Kentish Town Community Centre, London Jewish Cultural Centre (£50,000 each); St Gregory's Catholic Science College (£48,000); HAFD (£36,000); Arts Depot, British Museum, Tricycle Theatre Company, Mousetrap Theatre Projects, Roxeth Primary School (£35,000 each); Unicorn Theatre (£33,000); Wigmore Hall and Urban Partnership Group (£30,000 each).
FINANCES *Year* 2010–11 *Income* £6,277,617 *Grants* £4,477,448 *Assets* £221,285,107
TRUSTEES The Governors of Harrow School.
HOW TO APPLY The charity's main and small grants programmes have a two stage application process: Stage One – Initial Proposal: Please write to the Grants Office with the following information: a summary of the main purpose of the project; details of the overall amount requested; the timescale of your project; some indication of how funds from the charity would be allocated. The trust has produced guidelines on how best to write the initial proposal which can be accessed on the website. Trustees meet to decide three times a year in March, June and November. There is no stage two for small grants of less than £2,000. Applications are made by initial proposal letter and the grants team will be in touch if more information is required.
Stage Two – Application Form: If your Initial Proposal is assessed positively, you will be advised whether you will need to complete an application form. Forms are required for all applications to the Main Grants Programme, Access to Opportunity and for requests of over £2,000 to the Small Grants Programme. If you qualify for Stage Two you will be advised by your Grants Officer when your application form must be returned. Applications by fax or email will not be accepted.
The John Lyon's Access to the Arts Fund
The John Lyon Access to the Arts Fund has a **single stage** application process and requests are made by application form. Applications can be made at any time. Application forms are available via the charity's website.

WHO TO APPLY TO The Grants Office, 45 Cadogan Gardens, London SW3 2TB *Tel* 020 7591 3330 *Fax* 020 7591 3412 *email* info@johnlyonscharity.org.uk *Website* www.johnlyonscharity.org.uk

■ The Lyons Charitable Trust

CC NO 1045650 **ESTABLISHED** 1995
WHERE FUNDING CAN BE GIVEN UK.
WHO CAN BENEFIT Registered charities.
WHAT IS FUNDED Health, medical research, children in need and charities concerned with animals.
TYPE OF GRANT Recurrent.
RANGE OF GRANTS £3,000–£20,000.
SAMPLE GRANTS The 11 beneficiaries each year are: The Royal Marsden Hospital and Macmillan Cancer Relief, Helen House, St. Thomas Hospital and Streetsmart, CLIC, One25 Ltd., Cambridge Curwen Print Study Centre, Cats Protection League, Children with Aids and Walthamstow Stadium Greyhound.
FINANCES *Year* 2009–10 *Income* £65,979 *Grants* £0 *Assets* £1,666,189
TRUSTEES M Scott Gibbon; J Scott Gibbon; G Whitelock Read; Robin Worby.
OTHER INFORMATION Historically, the same 11 charities are supported each year. In 2009–10 no grants were made but we trust this is a one-off and that grant-making will resume.
HOW TO APPLY The trust has stated that it is closed to new applications.
WHO TO APPLY TO Michael Scott Gibbon, Trustee, 74 Broad Walk, London N21 3BX *Tel* 020 8882 1336

■ The Sir Jack Lyons Charitable Trust

CC NO 212148 **ESTABLISHED** 1960
WHERE FUNDING CAN BE GIVEN UK and Israel.
WHO CAN BENEFIT Charities benefiting children and young people; actors and entertainment professionals; musicians; students; textile workers and designers; writers and poets; at risk groups; those disadvantaged by poverty, and people who are socially isolated.
WHAT IS FUNDED Relief in need, arts, education and humanities. Jewish charities are also supported.
WHAT IS NOT FUNDED No grants to individuals.
TYPE OF GRANT Mainly recurrent.
RANGE OF GRANTS £200–£50,000.
SAMPLE GRANTS UJIA – Tel Hal Academic College (£67,500); Youth Futures in Beer Sheva (£61,000), Beer Sheva Start Up and Sparks of Science (£30,000 each); UJIA (£25,000); Jerusalem Foundation (£24,000); Beit Halohem Geneva (£11,000); and University of York Celebration Prize (£1,500).
FINANCES *Year* 2009–10 *Income* £189,289 *Grants* £250,680 *Assets* £3,224,527
TRUSTEES Lady Roslyn Marion Lyons; M J Friedman; D S Lyons; Miss A R J Maude-Roxby; P D Mitchell; Belinda Lyons-Newman.
HOW TO APPLY In writing to the correspondent. In the past the trust has stated: 'In the light of increased pressure for funds, unsolicited appeals are less welcome and would waste much time and money for applicants who were looking for funds which were not available.'
WHO TO APPLY TO Paul Mitchell, Gresham House, 5–7 St. Pauls Street, Leeds LS1 2JG *Tel* 01332 976789

■ The Joy and Malcolm Lyons Foundation

CC NO 1050689 **ESTABLISHED** 1995
WHERE FUNDING CAN BE GIVEN UK.
WHO CAN BENEFIT Jewish and Israeli organisations.
WHAT IS FUNDED Jewish charitable purposes.
TYPE OF GRANT Mainly recurrent.
RANGE OF GRANTS £10–£20,000.
SAMPLE GRANTS Previous beneficiaries include: Sage, L'Ecole Juive du Cannes, Chai Cancer Care, Lubavitch Foundation, Child Resettlement Fund, Noam Primary School, British Friends of Ezer Mizion, Jewish Care, Camp Simcha and British Emunah.
FINANCES *Year* 2009–10 *Income* £11,558 *Grants* £38,000
TRUSTEES Malcolm Lyons; Joy Lyons; Jeremy Newman.
OTHER INFORMATION Accounts were received at the Charity Commission but were unavailable to view. Grants totalled around £38,000.
HOW TO APPLY The trust does not consider unsolicited applications.
WHO TO APPLY TO Jeremy Newman, Trustee, BDO, 55 Baker Street, London W1U 7EU *Tel* 020 7893 2602

■ The Lyras Family Charitable Trust

CC NO 328628 **ESTABLISHED** 1990
WHERE FUNDING CAN BE GIVEN UK, Greece, worldwide.
WHO CAN BENEFIT Beneficiaries include: people disadvantaged by poverty and members of the Greek Orthodox religion.
WHAT IS FUNDED (a) Disaster funds worldwide; (b) the relief of poverty; (c) the advancement of religion, in particular within the country of Greece; and (d) other charitable purposes.
RANGE OF GRANTS Up to £5,500.
SAMPLE GRANTS St Sophia's School (£5,000); The Greek Orthodox Charity Organisation (£2,500); Monastery of St John the Baptist and Foundation for Paediatric Osteopathy (£2,000 each); Multiple Sclerosis Society, British Diabetic Association and Alzheimer's Society (£1,000 each); and RNLI and The Smile Train (£500 each).
FINANCES *Year* 2009–10 *Income* £26,194 *Grants* £17,855 *Assets* £709,310
TRUSTEES John C Lyras; John M Lyras; Richard Moore.
HOW TO APPLY In writing to the correspondent, although the trust states that its funds are fully committed and unsolicited applications are not requested.
WHO TO APPLY TO Richard Mason, Secretary, Moore Stephens, 150 Aldersgate Street, London EC1A 4AB *Tel* 020 7334 9191

■ Sylvanus Lyson's Charity

CC NO 202939 **ESTABLISHED** 1980
WHERE FUNDING CAN BE GIVEN Diocese of Gloucester.
WHO CAN BENEFIT Individuals and organisations benefiting people of all ages, clergy, and Church of England.
WHAT IS FUNDED Religious and charitable work in the areas of youth, community, relief for widows, clergy and people in need.
WHAT IS NOT FUNDED The present policy is to make no grants for the repair or maintenance and improvement of churches or other buildings, other than in very exceptional circumstances.

TYPE OF GRANT Recurrent and one-off.

RANGE OF GRANTS Usually £1,000 to £5,000 with a few larger grants.

SAMPLE GRANTS Diocesan Board of Finance (£32,000); Gloucester Cathedral Stone Masons (£20,000); Gloucester Night Stop (£10,000); Holy Trinity – Tewkesbury (£4,500); Cheltenham Youth for Christ (£4,250); St Paul's PCC (£3,750); Pioneer Minister (£3,000).

FINANCES *Year* 2009–10 *Income* £8,364,446 *Grants* £135,178 *Assets* £492,132

TRUSTEES B V Day, Chair; G V Doswell; Rt Revd J S Went; Revd B C E Coker.

OTHER INFORMATION In addition grants to clergy, widows and others totalled £21,000.

HOW TO APPLY In writing to the correspondent.

WHO TO APPLY TO A Holloway, c/o Rowberry Morris Solicitors, Morroway House, Station Road, Gloucester GL1 1DW *Tel* 01452 301903

■ The M and C Trust

CC NO 265391   **ESTABLISHED** 1973
WHERE FUNDING CAN BE GIVEN UK.
WHO CAN BENEFIT Mainly Jewish organisations benefiting Jewish people, at risk groups, people disadvantaged by poverty, and socially isolated people.
WHAT IS FUNDED Primarily Jewish and welfare organisations.
WHAT IS NOT FUNDED No grants to individuals.
TYPE OF GRANT One-off and recurrent grants.
RANGE OF GRANTS £2,500–£20,000.
SAMPLE GRANTS Jewish Care, Norwood and One Voice Europe (£20,000 each); World Jewish Relief, Connect and Jewish Children's Holiday Fund (£10,000 each); and Deaf Blind UK and Princess Royal Trust (£5,000 each).
FINANCES *Year* 2009–10 *Income* £117,777 *Grants* £186,000 *Assets* £4,464,264
TRUSTEES Kate Bernstein; Rachel J Lebus; Julia Marks.
HOW TO APPLY In writing to the correspondent, but the trust states that funds are currently earmarked for existing projects. In order to keep administration costs to a minimum, they are unable to reply to any unsuccessful applications.
WHO TO APPLY TO Chris Jones, Secretary, c/o Chantrey Vellacott DFK, Russell Square House, 10–12 Russell Square, London WC1B 5LF *Tel* 020 7509 9000 *Fax* 020 7509 9219

■ The M D and S Charitable Trust

CC NO 273992   **ESTABLISHED** 1977
WHERE FUNDING CAN BE GIVEN UK and Israel.
WHO CAN BENEFIT Organisations benefiting Jewish people. Support is given to rabbis, children and young adults, students, teachers and people disadvantaged by poverty.
WHAT IS FUNDED Trustees are primarily interested in Jewish causes for either the relief of poverty or the advancement of education or religion.
RANGE OF GRANTS Below £4,000–£28,000.
SAMPLE GRANTS Yeshivat Kolel Breslaw (£28,000); Ichud Mosdos Gur (£23,000); Emunah Education Centre (£22,000); Yeshivat Magen Avrohom(£11,000); Centre for Torah Education Trust, Mercaz Lechinuch Torami (£10,000 each); Hechel Moishe Fund and Tomchey Torah Yeshivat Rasbi (£5,000 each).
FINANCES *Year* 2008–09 *Income* £163,763 *Grants* £209,305 *Assets* £2,335,066
TRUSTEES M D Cymerman; Mrs S Cymerman.
HOW TO APPLY In writing to the correspondent.
WHO TO APPLY TO Martin D Cymerman, Trustee, 15 Riverside Drive, Golders Green Road, London NW11 9PU *Tel* 020 7272 2255

■ The M K Charitable Trust

CC NO 260439   **ESTABLISHED** 1966
WHERE FUNDING CAN BE GIVEN Unrestricted, in practice mainly UK.
WHO CAN BENEFIT Orthodox Jewish organisations.
WHAT IS FUNDED Support of orthodox Jewish organisations.

FINANCES *Year* 2009–10 *Income* £1,240,671 *Grants* £288,695 *Assets* £6,678,688
TRUSTEES Z M Kaufman; S Kaufman; A Piller; D Katz.
HOW TO APPLY In writing to the correspondent. The trust accepts applications for grants from representatives of orthodox Jewish charities, which are reviewed by the trustees on a regular basis.
WHO TO APPLY TO Simon Kaufman, Trustee, c/o Cohen Arnold and Co., New Burlington House, 1075 Finchley Road, Regent Street, Temple Fortune, London *Tel* 020 8731 0777

■ The Madeline Mabey Trust

CC NO 326450   **ESTABLISHED** 1983
WHERE FUNDING CAN BE GIVEN UK and overseas.
WHO CAN BENEFIT Registered charities, including UK registered charities and international charities.
WHAT IS FUNDED Principally medical research and children's welfare and education.
WHAT IS NOT FUNDED No grants to individuals.
SAMPLE GRANTS A list of grant beneficiaries was unavailable.
FINANCES *Year* 2009–10 *Income* £245,809 *Grants* £337,250 *Assets* £271,183
TRUSTEES Alan G Daliday; Bridget A Nelson; Joanna L Singeisen.
HOW TO APPLY In writing to the correspondent. Please note, unsuccessful applications are not acknowledged.
WHO TO APPLY TO Joanna Singeisen, Trustee, Madeline Mabey Trust, Woodview, Tolcarne Road, Beacon, Camborne TR14 9AB *Tel* 0120 971 0304

■ The E M MacAndrew Trust

CC NO 290736   **ESTABLISHED** 1984
WHERE FUNDING CAN BE GIVEN UK.
WHO CAN BENEFIT Charitable organisations.
WHAT IS FUNDED Medical and children's charities.
RANGE OF GRANTS £500–£5,000.
SAMPLE GRANTS Calibre (£4,000); Bucks Association for the Care of Offenders (£3,000); St Laurence Room Development Fund, Toe in the Water and Chilterns MS Centre (£2,000 each); and Anxiety UK, Cancer and Bio-detection Dogs and Puzzle Pre School Playgroup (£1,000 each).
FINANCES *Year* 2009–10 *Income* £49,200 *Grants* £38,000 *Assets* £990,169
TRUSTEES Amanda Nicholson; J K Nicholson; Sally Grant; Verity Webster.
HOW TO APPLY The trustees state that they do not respond to any unsolicited applications under any circumstances, as they prefer to make their own decisions as to which charities to support.
WHO TO APPLY TO J P Thornton, Administrator, J P Thornton and Co., The Old Dairy, Adstockfields, Adstock, Buckingham MK18 2JE *Tel* 01296 714886 *Fax* 01296 714711

■ The Macdonald-Buchanan Charitable Trust

CC NO 209994   **ESTABLISHED** 1952
WHERE FUNDING CAN BE GIVEN UK, with a slight preference for Northamptonshire.
WHO CAN BENEFIT Registered charities, with a small preference for those benefiting young people in Northamptonshire.
WHAT IS FUNDED General charitable purposes with a preference for charities which the trust has

special interest in, knowledge of or association with.

WHAT IS NOT FUNDED No grants to individuals.

TYPE OF GRANT Mainly recurrent.

RANGE OF GRANTS £50–£15,000.

SAMPLE GRANTS Langham Hospital Trust (£80,000); Carriejo Charity and Orrin Charitable Trust (£30,000 each); British Racing School (£20,000); Oracle Cancer Trust (£10,000); Scotts Guards Colonel's Fund (£3,000); and Artists General Benevolent Institution, Hearing Dogs for the Deaf, Migraine Trust, Order of St John, Salvation Army and Sightsavers International (£400 each).

FINANCES *Year* 2010 *Income* £123,328 *Grants* £224,760 *Assets* £3,233,115

TRUSTEES Capt. John Macdonald-Buchanan, Chair; A J Macdonald-Buchanan; A R Macdonald-Buchanan; H J Macdonald-Buchanan; Mrs M C A Philipson.

OTHER INFORMATION The majority of grants were for £400.

HOW TO APPLY In writing to the correspondent, for consideration once a year. Appeals will not be acknowledged.

WHO TO APPLY TO Miss Linda Cousins, Rathbone Trust Co. Ltd, 159 New Bond Street, London W1S 2UD *Tel* 020 7399 0820 *email* linda.cousins@rathbone.com

■ The R S Macdonald Charitable Trust

SC NO SC012710   **ESTABLISHED** 1978

WHERE FUNDING CAN BE GIVEN Scotland.

WHO CAN BENEFIT Charities and institutions working in the areas of research and support of neurological conditions, visual impairment, child welfare and animal welfare.

WHAT IS FUNDED The care and welfare of individuals suffering from neurodevelopmental or neurodegenerative disorders; the care and welfare of individuals who are either blind or suffering from visual impairment; research into neurological and ophthalmic disorders; the care and welfare of children and young persons under the age of eighteen years who have been or are in danger of being abused physically, sexually or mentally; the prevention of cruelty to animals.

WHAT IS NOT FUNDED Grants are not given to non-registered charities or individuals.

TYPE OF GRANT One-off, recurring costs, project and research will be considered. Funding may be given for up to three years and can be revenue or capital funding.

RANGE OF GRANTS Average grants are about £20,000.

SAMPLE GRANTS Children 1st (£70,000 in total), towards several projects; University of St Andrew's (£50,000), for research into neuro-degeneration caused by Alzheimer's disease and stroke trauma; University of Aberdeen (£42,000), for a Parkinson's disease research project; Sense Scotland (£30,000), for the TouchBase cafe; Scottish Spina Bifida Association (£20,000), to fund a post; Grampian Society for the Blind (£15,000), for a communication technology project; Safe Space (£10,000), towards revenue costs; Quarriers (£5,000), towards an initiative for children and young people affected by parental substance abuse; and the Greyhound Awareness League (£3,000), towards revenue costs.

FINANCES *Year* 2009–10 *Income* £1,703,546 *Grants* £1,091,425 *Assets* £54,217,088

TRUSTEES Richard Sweetman, Chair; Richard K Austin; Donald Bain; Fiona Patrick; John Rafferty.

HOW TO APPLY 'Applicants are invited to apply by letter; there is no application form. The trustees request that, except in relation to medical or social research, the application letter should not exceed two pages in length. It should explain (as appropriate) what and how the need to be addressed has been identified, the costs involved and the extent to which support has been sought from other sources, the outcome hoped for and how that outcome is to be measured. It should also demonstrate how the subject of the application meets the charitable objects of the trust. Where an application is for help with revenue costs for a particular service there should be an explanation of how this will continue following the expiry of the award. Along with your letter you may enclose separate papers, providing background information and/or more detailed financial information. If there is a current DVD providing an insight into the work of your organisation you may wish to submit this. In addition to the application letter you are required to complete and submit (a) a copy of the applicant's most recently audited accounts and (b) an Organisation Information Sheet. This can be downloaded from the trust's website or obtained from the trust's secretary.'

WHO TO APPLY TO Richard K Austin, Secretary, 21 Rutland Square, Edinburgh EH1 2BB *Tel* 0131 228 4681 *email* secretary@rsmacdonald.com *Website* www.rsmacdonald.com

■ The Macfarlane Walker Trust

CC NO 227890   **ESTABLISHED** 1963

WHERE FUNDING CAN BE GIVEN UK, with priority for Gloucestershire.

WHO CAN BENEFIT Individuals, registered charities and institutions benefiting: former employees of Walker-Crosweller; musicians; actors and entertainment professionals; artists; students; and scientists.

WHAT IS FUNDED Grants to former employees, and their families, of Walker, Crosweller and Co Ltd; provision of educational facilities particularly for scientific research; encouragement of music, drama and the fine arts. Also support for community facilities and services, and charities in the fields of conservation, alternative transport, and recreation.

WHAT IS NOT FUNDED No grants for expeditions, medical expenses, nationwide appeals, animal charities or educational fees.

TYPE OF GRANT Feasibility studies, one-off, project, research, running costs and start-up costs. Funding for up to and over three years will be considered.

RANGE OF GRANTS Up to £2,000.

SAMPLE GRANTS Vicar's Relief Fund (£8,000); The Family Haven (£3,000); and Music Space (£2,700).

FINANCES *Year* 2009–10 *Income* £25,861 *Grants* £24,046 *Assets* £642,070

TRUSTEES D F Walker; N G Walker; Miss C Walker.

HOW TO APPLY In writing to the correspondent giving the reason for applying, and an outline of the project with a financial forecast. An sae must accompany the initial application.

WHO TO APPLY TO Sophie Walker, Secretary, 4 Shooters Hill Road, Blackheath, London SE3 7BD *Tel* 020 8858 4701 *email* sophiewalker@mac.com

Think carefully about every application. Is it justified?

713

■ The Mackay and Brewer Charitable Trust

cc no 1072666   established 1998
WHERE FUNDING CAN BE GIVEN UK.
WHO CAN BENEFIT Charitable organisations.
WHAT IS FUNDED General charitable purposes.
SAMPLE GRANTS £7,250 each to Hampshire Association for the Care of the Blind, Macmillan Cancer Trust, Marie Curie Cancer Care, National Trust for Scotland, PDSA, Open Doors, Salvation Army, and St John Ambulance.
FINANCES *Year* 2009–10 *Income* £74,687 *Grants* £58,000 *Assets* £20,914
TRUSTEES HSBC Trust Co. (UK) Ltd.
HOW TO APPLY In writing to the correspondent.
WHO TO APPLY TO The Clerk, c/o HSBC Trust Co. (UK) Ltd, 10th Floor, Norwich House, Nelson Gate, Commercial Road, Southampton SO15 1GX *Tel* 02380 723344

■ The Mackintosh Foundation

cc no 327751   established 1988
WHERE FUNDING CAN BE GIVEN Worldwide. In practice, mainly UK.
WHO CAN BENEFIT Registered charities.
WHAT IS FUNDED Priority is given to the theatre and the performing arts. Also funded are children and education; medicine; homelessness; community projects; the environment; HIV/AIDS; refugees; and other charitable purposes.
WHAT IS NOT FUNDED Religious or political activities are not supported. Apart from the foundation's drama award and some exceptions, applications from individuals are discouraged.
TYPE OF GRANT Capital, project and recurring costs up to three years.
RANGE OF GRANTS Up to £30,000.
SAMPLE GRANTS Sylvia Young Theatre School (£32,500); Charlton Musgrove Memorial Hall (£25,000); American Music Center (£17,000); Royal Academy of Music (£10,000); Kids Company (£6,000); Breakthrough Breast Cancer (£5,000); Marefat Education Centre (£4,500); Cambodian Child's Dream Foundation and Lochaber Fisheries Trust (£3,000 each); NSPCC (£2,500); and Afghan Connection (£2,000).
FINANCES *Year* 2009–10 *Income* £80,045 *Grants* £476,590 *Assets* £9,921,152
TRUSTEES Sir Cameron Mackintosh, Chair; Nicholas Mackintosh; Nicholas Allott; D Michael Rose; Robert Noble; Bart Peerless; Thomas Schonberg; F Richard Pappas.
HOW TO APPLY In writing to the correspondent outlining details of the organisation, details of the project for which funding is required and a breakdown of the costs involved. Supporting documents should be kept to a minimum and SAE enclosed if materials are to be returned. The trustees meet in May and October in plenary session, but a grants committee meets weekly to consider grants of up to £10,000. The foundation responds to all applications in writing and the process normally takes between 4–6 weeks.
WHO TO APPLY TO Nicholas Mackintosh, Appeals Director, 1 Bedford Square, London WC1B 3RB *Tel* 020 7637 8866 *Fax* 020 7436 2683 *email* info@camack.co.uk

■ The MacRobert Trust

sc no SC031346   established 1943
WHERE FUNDING CAN BE GIVEN UK, mainly Scotland.
WHO CAN BENEFIT Recognised charitable organisations benefiting children, young adults and older people, ex-service and service people, seafarers and fishermen, and volunteers. Also artists, musicians, textile workers and designers, and writers and poets. At risk groups, carers, disabled people, people disadvantaged by poverty, and socially isolated people will also be considered.
WHAT IS FUNDED Currently, the major categories under which the trustees consider support are: science and technology; youth; services and sea; ex-servicemen's and ex-servicewomen's hospitals and homes; education; disability; community welfare. The minor categories are: agriculture and horticulture; arts and music; medical care; and Tarland and Deeside.
WHAT IS NOT FUNDED Grants are not normally provided for: religious organisations (but attention will be given to youth/community services provided by them, or projects of general benefit to the whole community); organisations based outside the United Kingdom; individuals; general appeals or mailshots; political organisations; student bodies as opposed to universities; fee-paying schools, apart from an Educational Grants Scheme for children who are at, or who need to attend, a Scottish independent secondary school and for which a grant application is made through the Head Teacher; expeditions, except those made under the auspices of recognised bodies such as the British Schools Exploring Society (BSES); community and village halls other than those local to Tarland and Deeside; retrospective grant; and departments within a university, unless the appeal gains the support of, and is channelled through, the principal.
TYPE OF GRANT Core/revenue costs, project. Capital including buildings, feasibility studies, one-off, research, recurring and running costs, and salaries. Funding may be given for one year or more.
RANGE OF GRANTS Mostly £5,000–£10,000.
SAMPLE GRANTS Erskine Hospital (£120,000); Tarand Welfare Trust (£75,000); Mid Deeside Limited (£25,000); Cairngorms Outdoor Access Trust and Combat Stress (£20,000 each); The Trust for St John's Kirk of Perth (£15,000); Greenock Arts Guild Limited (£10,000); The Royal Institution of Great Britain (£9,000); The Royal Marines Association (£8,000); Glasgow Shettleston New Church of Scotland (£5,000); Orange Tree Theatre Limited (£3,000); Musically Active Dudes (£2,000): and Marie Curie Cancer Care (£500).
FINANCES *Year* 2010–11 *Income* £2,155,395 *Grants* £657,661 *Assets* £74,075,205
TRUSTEES W G Morrison, Chair; S Campbell; C D Crole; K Davis; J D Fowlie; Group Capt. D A Needham; C W Pagan; J C Swan; H B Wood; J H Strickland.
PUBLICATIONS Leaflet – Advice to Applicants for Grants.
OTHER INFORMATION The education total includes £24,000 awarded to 14 students from 12 separate schools in educational grants.
HOW TO APPLY The application form and full guidelines can be downloaded from the website, although applications must be posted. The trustees meet to consider applications twice a year in March and November. To be considered, applications must be received for the March

Does the trust you have chosen match your needs? Haphazard applications waste postage and time

meeting by 31 October previously and for the October meeting by 31 May previously.

Time bars: Unsuccessful applicants must wait for at least one year from the time of being notified before re-applying. Successful applicants must wait for at least two years from the time of receiving a donation before re-applying. When a multi-year donation has been awarded, the time bar applies from the date of the final instalment. Withdrawn applications do not normally face a time bar.

The trust stresses the importance of including an informative covering letter; completing *all* sections of the application form and asks that applicants maintain a process of dialogue with the trust: 'We deal with many hundreds of worthy applications each year. If we have to chase you for information, you will understand that our interest might wane.' A further list of additional guidance and feedback on the application procedure is available on the trust website. Applicants are informed of the trustees' decision, and if successful, payments are made immediately after each meeting.

WHO TO APPLY TO Air Comm. R W Joseph, Administrator, Cromar, Tarland, Aboyne, Aberdeenshire AB34 4UD *Tel* 01339 881444 *Website* www.themacroberttrust.org.uk

■ The Mactaggart Third Fund

SC NO SC014285   **ESTABLISHED** 1969
WHERE FUNDING CAN BE GIVEN UK and abroad.
WHO CAN BENEFIT Charitable organisations.
WHAT IS FUNDED General charitable purposes.
TYPE OF GRANT One-off.
RANGE OF GRANTS £100–£50,000.
SAMPLE GRANTS St Mary's Paddington Charitable Trust (£50,000); Amazon Conservation Team – Orito Sanctuary Project (£28,000); WPSI – UK (£25,000); Bahamas National Trust (£16,000); Friends of the Environment (£15,000); Mactaggart Community Cybercafé (£11,000); Ella Edgar School of Dancing (£6,300); Angling for Youth Development (£5,200); Medical Aid for Palestinians (£3,000); Scottish Countryside Alliance Education Trust (£2,000); The Red Squirrel Survival Trust (£1,000); and Seeing Ear (£750).
FINANCES *Year* 2009–10 *Income* £472,601 *Grants* £311,172 *Assets* £11,125,345
TRUSTEES Sandy Mactaggart; Robert Gore; Fiona Mactaggart; Andrew Mactaggart; Sir John Mactaggart.
HOW TO APPLY 'The trustees are solely responsible for the choice of charitable organisations to be supported. Trustees are proactive in seeking out charities to support and all projects are chosen on the initiative of the trustees. Unsolicited applications are not supported.'
WHO TO APPLY TO The Trustees, One Red Place, London W1K 6PL *Website* www. mactaggartthirdfund.org

■ Ian Mactaggart Trust

SC NO SC012502   **ESTABLISHED** 1969
WHERE FUNDING CAN BE GIVEN UK, with a preference for Scotland.
WHO CAN BENEFIT Charitable organisations.
WHAT IS FUNDED The trust supports a wide range of activities including: education and training, culture and the relief of people who are poor, sick, in need or disabled.
WHAT IS NOT FUNDED Unsolicited requests for donations are discouraged.

RANGE OF GRANTS £100–£50,000.
SAMPLE GRANTS University of Miami – Miami Project (£50,000); Robin Hood Foundation (£28,000); University of Glasgow Trust (£18,000); Oxfordshire Community Foundation and Alzheimer's Society (£15,000 each); KIPP NY inc (£10,000); Muirhead Outreach Project (£7,000); Institute for Public Policy Research (£6,000); Game and Wildfire Conservation Trust (£5,000); Checkerboard Foundation (£4,300); the Promise (£3,000); Women's Aid (£2,000); NSPCC (£1,800); Coisir Og Ghadhlig Ile (£1,000); Ashmolean Museum (£750); Scottish Ballet Ruby Slipper Fund (£500); Islay, Jura and Colonsay Agricultural Association (£300); Sheppard Trust (£200); and Boltons Association (£100).
FINANCES *Year* 2009–10 *Income* £470,977 *Grants* £215,171 *Assets* £7,896,844
TRUSTEES Sir John Mactaggart; Philip Mactaggart; Jane Mactaggart; Fiona Mactaggart; Lady Caroline Mactaggart; Leora Armstrong.
HOW TO APPLY The trustees are committed to seeking out charitable organisations that they wish to support and therefore they do not respond to unsolicited applications.
WHO TO APPLY TO The Trustees, 2 Babmaes Street, London SW1Y 6HD *Website* www. ianmactaggarttrust.org/index.htm

■ James Madison Trust

CC NO 1084835   **ESTABLISHED** 2000
WHERE FUNDING CAN BE GIVEN UK.
WHO CAN BENEFIT Charities and educational institutions.
WHAT IS FUNDED 'The objects of the charity are to support and promote studies of federal government whether within or among states and of related subjects, including the processes that may lead towards the establishment of such government, and to support or promote education and dissemination of knowledge of these subjects. These objects govern all decisions of trustees without the need for further specific annual objectives.'
TYPE OF GRANT Seminars, conferences, studies and publications.
RANGE OF GRANTS £3,500–£155,000.
SAMPLE GRANTS Previous beneficiary organisations have included: University of Kent (£102,000); Federal Trust (£94,000); University of Edinburgh (£30,000); Unlock Democracy, University of Middlesex (£19,000); London Metropolitan University (£7,500); and University of Cardiff (£5,000). Previous projects funded by grants have included: Comparative Devolution (£155,000); Centre for Federal Studies (£106,000); Federal Trust Projects (£105,000); Additional Constitutionalism (£24,000); Autonomy Website, Regions of England (£19,000); European Foreign & Security Policy (£7,500); Welsh Papers (£5,000); Climate Change Research and Book of Federal Studies 06 (£3,500).
FINANCES *Year* 2009–10 *Income* £18,947 *Grants* £86,000
TRUSTEES Robert Emerson; Ernest Wistrich; John Pinder; John Bishop; Richard Corbett.
HOW TO APPLY In writing to the correspondent. The trustees meet approximately every six weeks to approve grants.
WHO TO APPLY TO D Grace, Secretary to the Trustees, 68 Furnham Road, Chard TA20 1AP *Tel* 01460 67368

■ **The Magdalen and Lasher Charity**

cc no 211415 established 1951

where funding can be given Hastings.

who can benefit Individuals, and organisations benefiting elderly and young people, and people disadvantaged by poverty.

what is funded Pensions for elderly people in Hastings; playschemes; primary, secondary and special schools; purchase of books, travel and maintenance in schools; literacy; health care, facilities and buildings; community services.

type of grant One-off; one year or less.

sample grants Emmaus Hastings & Rother (£5,000); Athelstan Nursery (£3,000); St Clements & All Saints (£2,000); Clive Vale Social Club (£750); Halton Baptist Church (£685) Grass Roots Open Writers (GROW) (£310); Methodist Church and Ore Church Mice Playgroup (£300 each) and Treasure Seekers Playgroup (£250).

finances Year 2010–11 Income £1,383,743 Grants £120,330 Assets £11,766,224

trustees Ian Michael Steel, Chair; Gareth N Bendon; John H Bilsby; Revd Robert Featherstone; Michael J Foster; Nicola J Harris; Donald Burrows; Jill Cooper; Richard Stevens; Clive R Morris; Susan M Parsons; Joy A Waite; Trevor E Webb; Jennifer Clare Blackburn; John Hodges; Susan Phillips; Nikki Port.

how to apply In writing to the correspondent.

who to apply to Gill Adamson, 132 High Street, Hastings, East Sussex TN34 3ET Tel 01424 452646 email mlc@oldhastingshouse.co.uk Website www.magdalenandlasher.co.uk

■ **Magdalen Hospital Trust**

cc no 225878 established 1963

where funding can be given UK.

who can benefit Registered charities benefiting: deprived children and young adults up to 25 years; those in care, fostered and adopted; parents and children; one-parent families; people disadvantaged by poverty; and people with HIV/AIDS.

what is funded Projects for deprived and disabled children and young people, including literacy, special needs education, training for work and personal development, clubs, crime prevention, emergency care, playschemes, and counselling.

what is not funded No grants to non-registered charities, individuals, charities with an income in excess of £150,000 or national charities.

type of grant One-off; project; start-up funding; one year or less.

range of grants £500–£2,000; typically £1,000.

sample grants Hope's Place and Blue Horizon's (£2,000 each); Birmingham University Guild of Students, Friends of the Family, Network for Surviving Stalking, Youth for Youth, Young and Free (£1,000 each); and Musical Keys (£500).

finances Year 2009–10 Income £38,595 Grants £15,400 Assets £751,283

trustees Mrs B M Gregory; Mrs B Lucas; Revd R Mitchell; Ven. F R Hazell; Mrs D Lazenby; Hon. E Wood; Dr E Offerman; Mrs L Wood.

how to apply An application form and guidelines are available. An sae is required.

who to apply to Mrs Norma Hazell, Flat 27, Ramsay Hall, 9–13 Byrom Road, Worthing BN11 3HN Tel 01451 821140 email correspondent@magdalentrust.org.uk Website www.magdalentrust.org.uk

■ **The SV and PE Magee Family Charitable Trust**

cc no 1135130 established 2010

where funding can be given Worldwide.

who can benefit Charitable organisations.

what is funded Religious activities.

trustees NatWest Trust Services.

how to apply In writing to the correspondent.

who to apply to The Administrator, NatWest Trust Services, 5th Floor, Trinity Quay 2, Avon Street, Bristol BS2 0PT Tel 0117 940 3283

■ **The Magen Charitable Trust**

cc no 326535 established 1984

where funding can be given UK.

who can benefit Registered charities.

what is funded Jewish and educational organisations.

sample grants Previous beneficiaries have included Manchester Yeshiva Kollel, Talmud Educational Trust, Bnos Yisroel School and Mesifta Tiferes Yisroel.

finances Year 2009–10 Income £234,060 Grants £131,210 Assets £1,513,934

trustees Jacob Halpern; Mrs Rose Halpern.

how to apply In writing to the correspondent.

who to apply to The Trustees, New Riverside, 439 Lower Broughton, Salford M7 2FX Tel 0161 792 2626

■ **Mageni Trust**

cc no 1070732 established 1998

where funding can be given UK.

who can benefit Arts organisations; registered charities.

what is funded Primarily arts projects and other general charitable purposes.

type of grant One-off and recurrent.

range of grants Up to £10,000.

sample grants Charities Aid Foundation (£10,000); Farms for City Children and LPO Thomas Beecham Group (£5,000 each); BYMT (£4,500); National Theatre, Tools for Self Reliance and National Youth Orchestra (£2,500 each); DAGE and Foundation for Young Musicians (£2,000); LPO Annual Appeal (£1,000); Primavera (£600); Derby Toc H Camp and Greenwich and Bexley Hospice (£500 each); and LSO Benefactor (£350).

finances Year 2009–10 Income £40,797 Grants £38,950 Assets £1,148,739

trustees Garfield Collins; Gillian Collins; Stephen Hoare.

how to apply In writing to the correspondent.

who to apply to Garfield Collins, Trustee, 5 Hyde Vale, Greenwich SE10 8QQ Tel 020 8469 2683 email garfcollins@gmail.com

■ **The Brian Maguire Charitable Trust**

cc no 1091978 established 2002

where funding can be given Worldwide.

who can benefit Organisations.

what is funded General charitable purposes.

range of grants £200–£5,000.

sample grants Wheel Power and Cornwall Mobility Centre (£5,000 each); the Peace Hospice – Starlight Walk (£2,000); The National Trust, Parapet Breast Unit and The Salvation Army (£1,000 each); Barrow Romania Action Group and Galloway's Society for the Blind (£500 each); Disability Recreation Unity Movement (£300); and Watford Philharmonic (£200).

FINANCES *Year* 2009–10 *Income* £72,794 *Grants* £24,385 *Assets* £2,207,069

TRUSTEES Margaret Craik Maguire; Martin William Bennett; Burges Salmon Trustees Ltd.

HOW TO APPLY 'Applications are considered by the trustees and donations are made based on the merits of the applications.'

WHO TO APPLY TO The Trustees, Burges Salmon LLP, 1 Glass Wharf, Bristol BS2 0ZX *Tel* 0117 939 2000

■ The Mahavir Trust (also known as the K
S Mehta Charitable Trust)

CC NO 298551   **ESTABLISHED** 1988

WHERE FUNDING CAN BE GIVEN UK.

WHO CAN BENEFIT Registered charities, social enterprises and hospitals.

WHAT IS FUNDED General, medical, animal welfare, relief of poverty, overseas aid, religion.

TYPE OF GRANT Unrestricted.

RANGE OF GRANTS Usually of the order of £250.

SAMPLE GRANTS Infrastructure to promote Jain philosophy (£30,000); relief of poverty, sickness and distress (£13,000); advancement of education in rural areas (£7,200); Jain religion (£6,300); promotion of humane behaviour towards animals and vegetarianism (£4,900); relief of financial need for victims of natural disaster (£1,300).

FINANCES *Year* 2009–10 *Income* £117,477 *Grants* £62,691 *Assets* £360,537

TRUSTEES Jay Mehta; Nemish Mehta; Pravin Mehta; Pushpa Mehta; Kumud Mehta; Sudha Mehta; Sheena Mehta Sabharwal; Kumar Mehta.

HOW TO APPLY In writing to the correspondent.

WHO TO APPLY TO Jay Mehta, Trustee, 19 Hillersdon Avenue, Edgware, Middlesex HA8 7SG *Tel* 020 8958 4883 *email* mahavirtrust@googlemail.com

---

■ The Makin Charitable Trust

CC NO 1089832   **ESTABLISHED** 2001

WHERE FUNDING CAN BE GIVEN Preference for Merseyside.

WHO CAN BENEFIT Registered charities.

WHAT IS FUNDED 'Learning, religion, the arts and general philanthropy.'

RANGE OF GRANTS Up to £75,000.

SAMPLE GRANTS Liverpool Hope University (£75,000); Merseyside Jewish Community Care (£50,000); and Liverpool Old Hebrew Congregation (£30,000). A further 24 grants totalling £26,000 were made to organisations for religious, educational and philanthropic purposes.

FINANCES *Year* 2009–10 *Income* £129,331 *Grants* £181,332 *Assets* £470,192

TRUSTEES Rex Makin; Shirley Makin; Robin Makin.

HOW TO APPLY In writing to the correspondent.

WHO TO APPLY TO c/o E Rex Makin & Co., Leigh Street, Whitechapel, Liverpool L1 1HQ *Tel* 0151 709 4491

■ Malbin Trust

CC NO 1045174   **ESTABLISHED** 1995

WHERE FUNDING CAN BE GIVEN Worldwide.

WHO CAN BENEFIT Organisations.

WHAT IS FUNDED Jewish, general charitable purposes.

SAMPLE GRANTS Previously: £10,000 to Chasidei Belz Institutions.

FINANCES *Year* 2008–09 *Income* £65,788 *Grants* £92,334 *Assets* £550,575

TRUSTEES Benjamin Leitner; Margaret Leitner; Jehuda Waldman.

HOW TO APPLY In writing to the correspondent.

WHO TO APPLY TO Benjamin Leitner, Trustee, 8 Cheltenham Crescent, Salford M7 4FP *Tel* 0161 792 7343

■ The Mallinckrodt Foundation

CC NO 1058011   **ESTABLISHED** 1996

WHERE FUNDING CAN BE GIVEN Worldwide.

WHO CAN BENEFIT Registered charities and charitable organisations.

WHAT IS FUNDED General charitable purposes.

RANGE OF GRANTS £2,000–£11,000.

SAMPLE GRANTS Vatican Library (£16,000); Christian Responsibility for Public Affairs and Companions of Windsor (£5,000 each); and Young Musicians Symphony Orchestra (£1,000).

FINANCES *Year* 2009–10 *Income* £49,743 *Grants* £26,840 *Assets* £3,148,621

TRUSTEES G W Mallinckrodt; Mrs C B Mallinckrodt; L St J T Jackson.

HOW TO APPLY The foundation does not seek or respond to unsolicited applications.

WHO TO APPLY TO Sally Yates, 31 Gresham Street, London EC2V 7QA

■ Man Group plc Charitable Trust

CC NO 275386   **ESTABLISHED** 1978

WHERE FUNDING CAN BE GIVEN UK and overseas, with some preference for London.

WHO CAN BENEFIT Registered charities.

WHAT IS FUNDED General charitable purposes in the UK and overseas with some preference for causes near to or linked to the business of Man Group Plc.

WHAT IS NOT FUNDED The trust does not normally support: large national charities; charities who use outside fund-raising organisations; charities whose administration costs are thought to be excessive; animal charities; applicants who have applied within the previous 12 months; requests that directly replace statutory funding; individuals (unless under a sponsorship scheme); endowment funds; charities where the main purpose is to promote religious beliefs.

SAMPLE GRANTS Beneficiaries included: TreeHouse and Merlin – Haiti earthquake emergency response (£250,000 each); Tomorrow's People (£200,000); London Youth Rowing (£150,000); Dyslexia Action and Refuge (£100,000 each); Impetus trust (£55,000); I CAN and Wave Trust (£50,000 each); Unicorn Theatre, Action on Addiction and Chance to Shine (£30,000 each); Young Vic (28,000); Action on Elder Abuse, Teenage Cancer Trust and Contact the Elderly (£25,000 each); Young Minds and MapAction (£20,000 each); Birkbeck College and Inspire (£15,000 each); National Literacy Trust (£12,000); Crossroads and Canine Partners (£10,000 each); and Friends of all Hallows (£100).

FINANCES *Year* 2009–10 *Income* £5,745,060 *Grants* £4,752,870 *Assets* £7,686,254

TRUSTEES Jonathan Aisbitt; John Angell; M Chambers; P Clarke, chair; Catherine O'Keefe; Jasveer Singh.

HOW TO APPLY The trust has stated that it does not accept unsolicited applications.

WHO TO APPLY TO L Clarke, Secretary to the Trust, Man Group Plc, Sugar Quay, Lower Thames Street, London EC3R 6DU *Tel* 020 7144 1000 *email* charitabletrust@mangroupplc.com *Website* www.mangroupplc.com

■ Manchester Airport Community Trust Fund

CC NO 1071703   **ESTABLISHED** 1997
WHERE FUNDING CAN BE GIVEN The area which is most affected by the Manchester Airport. This includes South Manchester and Tameside, Trafford, Stockport, the borough of Macclesfield and the borough of Congleton up to but not including the towns of Macclesfield and Congleton, Vale Royal, and up to but not including Northwich.
WHO CAN BENEFIT Established groups or charities able to demonstrate clear financial records.
WHAT IS FUNDED Projects which: encourage tree planting, afforestation, landscaping and other environmental improvements or heritage conservation; promote social welfare through recreation, sport and leisure; provide better appreciation of the natural and urban environment; and promote the use of the natural environment as a safe habitat for flora and fauna. Projects must be for the benefit of the whole community or a substantial section of it, with preference given to those that have considered the needs of people who have disabilities or who are elderly. Preference is given to those projects with volunteer involvement.
WHAT IS NOT FUNDED Applications from individuals or organisations working for profit are not considered. Projects must be over and above core activities and statutory requirements. The fund will not support applications for: running costs, salaries and expenses, general repair and maintenance, general sponsorship, office costs, office equipment, events, administration, general medical costs, uniforms, individual's sports kit, out of school clubs, or the purchase of land or buildings; projects considered by the trustees to be the statutory responsibility of local councils and government departments will not be supported; money for items already purchased or work already done; schools and churches benefiting just pupils and worshippers. Projects must demonstrate access and benefit to the wider community. Membership groups, clubs, societies and sports clubs will be considered on their own merits, particularly looking at community access and membership fees.
RANGE OF GRANTS Mostly £500–£5,000.
SAMPLE GRANTS St Michael's Parish Community Hall (£5,000); Starlight Performing Arts Academy (£3,000); West Indian Sports and Social Community Centre and St Paul's Parish Hall (£2,500 each); Cheshire Youth Pantomime Society (£2,000); Northmore Live at Home Scheme (£1,000); The Furniture Station (£700) Pickmere Parish Council (£500).
FINANCES *Year* 2009–10 *Income* £135,418 *Grants* £153,689 *Assets* £31,560
TRUSTEES Andrew Cornish, Chair; Ms Julie Armstrong; Anthony Burns; James Pearson; John N Pantall; Bill Harrison; Malcolm Byram; Don Stockton.
HOW TO APPLY Generally, awards are for up to £5,000 towards a project and the trustees prefer to offer part funding to complement a group's own fundraising or grant raising.

Applications are considered for particular items or works that allow the project to increase community benefit. Applications from not-for-profit groups or organisations working to improve the environment or social welfare in communities within the area of benefit. The project should offer open access to all and demonstrate wide, lasting benefit to all members of the community regardless of race, gender, age, ability or religion. The items or works the group seeks funds for should clearly bring community benefit. Trustees prefer to support groups that have volunteer involvement. If you would like any advice or need an application form please contact the fund administrator. You can also get an application form on-line from www.manchesterairport.co.uk. Trustees meet quarterly. You should return your completed form to the Administrator no later than the first Friday of March, June, September or December for consideration by the trustees the following month. Successful groups will usually receive a cheque a month after the trustees' meeting. Groups must send original invoices / receipts for the works or goods you purchased within 3 months of receiving the grant cheque.
WHO TO APPLY TO Jonathan Green, Trust Fund Administrator, The Community Relations Department, Manchester Airport Plc, 3th Floor, Olympic House, Manchester M90 1QX *Tel* 0161 489 5281 *Fax* 0161 489 3467 *email* trust.fund@manairport.co.uk *Website* www.manchesterairport.co.uk

■ The Manchester Guardian Society Charitable Trust

CC NO 515341   **ESTABLISHED** 1984
WHERE FUNDING CAN BE GIVEN Greater Manchester.
WHO CAN BENEFIT Preference is usually shown to smaller charities.
WHAT IS FUNDED General charitable purposes. The emphasis is very much on support in the Greater Manchester area.
WHAT IS NOT FUNDED The trust does not give to individuals.
TYPE OF GRANT Primarily small, single, capital projects.
RANGE OF GRANTS £100–£2,500.
SAMPLE GRANTS 5th Urmston Scout Group and The Message Trust (£2,000 each); (£1,000 each); BASIC (£1,500); Bury People First (£1,400); Bolton Bulls Wheelchair Basketball Club, Depaul Trust and Disability Sports Events (£1,000 each); ADD Action Project, Body Positive North West (£750 each); Aspull RFC, Community Ambassadors, Dream Connection and Churches on the Mount (£500 each); Barhill Residents Association (£250).
FINANCES *Year* 2009–10 *Income* £94,231 *Grants* £79,190 *Assets* £3,467,071
TRUSTEES D Burton; L Worsley; W R. Lees-Jones; W J Smith; D G Wilson; J P Wainwright; P F Goddard; K Ahmed; K Hardinge; J A H Fielden; D Hawkins; P Lochery.
HOW TO APPLY On a form available from the correspondent. Applications are considered on the first Monday in March, June, September and December; they must arrive 14 days before these dates. The trustees do not welcome repeat applications within two years.
WHO TO APPLY TO J J Swift, Clerk to the Trustees, Cobbetts, 58 Mosley Street, Manchester M2 3HZ *Tel* 0845 404 2404 *Fax* 0845 404 2414

■ Lord Mayor of Manchester's Charity Appeal Trust

cc no 1066972 **ESTABLISHED** 1997
WHERE FUNDING CAN BE GIVEN The City of Manchester.
WHO CAN BENEFIT Registered charities.
WHAT IS FUNDED General charitable purposes.
RANGE OF GRANTS Usually £500.
SAMPLE GRANTS Family Holidays (£16,732); Manchester Gateway Centre (£750); Happy Days, RNIB, Wood Street Mission, St John Ambulance, Barnabus, Deafblind UK, South West Division Ranger Unit, PSU Manchester, Indian Senior Citizens Centre and Mancunian Amateur Boxing Club (£500 each).
FINANCES *Year* 2009–10 *Income* £57,721 *Grants* £28,532 *Assets* £641,824
TRUSTEES The Mayor; The Mayor's Consort; Chief Executive; The Deputy Executive Member for Children's Services; City Treasurer; W Egerton; C Bird; A Burden.
HOW TO APPLY Application forms are available from the Mayor's office. Applications are considered quarterly.
WHO TO APPLY TO Anita Scallan, Head of Lord Mayor's Office, Lord Mayor's Suite, Town Hall, Albert Square, Manchester M60 2LA *Tel* 0161 234 3375 *Fax* 0161 274 7113 *email* a. scallan@manchester.gov.uk

■ The Mandeville Trust

cc no 1041880 **ESTABLISHED** 1994
WHERE FUNDING CAN BE GIVEN UK.
WHO CAN BENEFIT Organisations.
WHAT IS FUNDED General charitable purposes.
SAMPLE GRANTS Previously: University College London (£26,000) and Imperial College (£20,000) for research purposes; the Berkshire Community Foundation (£10,000). Other smaller grants totalled £2,500.
FINANCES *Year* 2009–10 *Income* £14,000 *Grants* £11,869
TRUSTEES Robert Cartwright Mandeville; Pauline Maude Mandeville; Peter William Murcott; Justin Craigie Mandeville.
HOW TO APPLY In writing to the correspondent.
WHO TO APPLY TO R C Mandeville, Trustee, The Hockett, Hockett Lane, Cookham Dean, Berkshire SL6 9UF *Tel* 01628 484272

■ The Manifold Charitable Trust

cc no 229501 **ESTABLISHED** 1962
WHERE FUNDING CAN BE GIVEN UK.
WHO CAN BENEFIT Registered charities only.
WHAT IS FUNDED Education, historic buildings, environmental conservation and general. The trust has previously focused much attention on the preservation of churches, however following the death in 2007 of its founder, Sir John Smith, the trust is now allocating most of its grants for educational purposes. The trust still makes grants to the Historic Churches Preservation Trust for onward distribution to churches; however it would seem that the amount has been reduced on previous years.
WHAT IS NOT FUNDED Applications are not considered for improvements to churches as this is covered by a block grant to the Historic Churches Preservation Trust. The trust regrets that it does not give grants to individuals for any purpose.
TYPE OF GRANT One-off; recurring.
SAMPLE GRANTS Eton College (around £421,000). Previous beneficiaries have included: Historic

Churches Preservation Trust (£140,000 in total); Thames Hospice Care (£50,000); Imperial College (£15,000); Berkeley Castle Charitable Trust and Maidenhead Heritage Trust (£10,000 each); Berkshire Medical Heritage Centre (£7,500); Gislingham PCC (£6,000); Household Cavalry Museum Trust (£5,000); Brompton Ralph PCC (£4,500); Morrab Library (£2,500); and Richmond Building Preservation Society, Askham PCC and Westray Heritage Trust (£1,000 each).
FINANCES *Year* 2010 *Income* £490,212 *Grants* £495,053 *Assets* £8,629,760
TRUSTEES Manifold Trustee Company Limited.
OTHER INFORMATION In 2010 approximately 85% of grants were awarded to Eton College (around £421,000).
HOW TO APPLY The trust has no full-time staff, therefore general enquiries and applications for grants should be made in writing only, by post or by fax and not by telephone. The trust does not issue application forms. Applications should be made to the correspondent in writing and should: state how much money it is hoped to raise; if the appeal is for a specific project state also (a) how much it will cost (b) how much of this cost will come from the applicant charity's existing funds (c) how much has already been received or promised from other sources and (d) how much is therefore still being sought; list sources of funds to which application has been or is intended to be made (for example local authorities, or quasi-governmental sources, such as the national lottery); if the project involves conservation of a building, send a photograph of it and a note (or pamphlet) about its history; send a copy of the charity's latest income and expenditure account and balance sheet. Applications are considered twice a month, and a reply is sent to most applicants (whether successful or not) who have written a letter rather than sent a circular.
WHO TO APPLY TO Helen Niven, Studio Cottage, Windsor Great Park, Windsor, Berkshire SL4 2HP *email* helen.niven@cumberlandlodge. ac.uk

■ W M Mann Foundation

sc no SC010111 **ESTABLISHED** 1992
WHERE FUNDING CAN BE GIVEN Scotland and other areas of the UK.
WHO CAN BENEFIT organisations based in Scotland or serving the Scottish community.
WHAT IS FUNDED The arts, education, music, health, care and sport.
RANGE OF GRANTS £100 to £10,000.
FINANCES *Year* 2011 *Income* £223,620
TRUSTEES W M Mann; B M Mann; A W Mann; S P Hutcheon.
HOW TO APPLY In writing to the trustees.
WHO TO APPLY TO Bruce M Mann, Trustee, 201 Bath Street, Glasgow G2 4HZ *Tel* 0141 248 4936 *Fax* 0141 221 2976 *email* mail@ wmmanngroup.co.uk *Website* www. thewmmannfoundation.org.uk

■ R W Mann Trust

cc no 1095699 **ESTABLISHED** 1959
WHERE FUNDING CAN BE GIVEN UK, but grants are practically all confined to organisations in Tyne and Wear, with a preference for North Tyneside.
WHO CAN BENEFIT Local activities or local branches of national charities benefiting children, young adults, older people, academics, seafarers and

fishermen, students, teachers and governesses, unemployed people, volunteers, those in care, fostered and adopted, parents and children, one-parent families, widows and widowers, at risk groups, carers, people with disabilities, people disadvantaged by poverty, ex-offenders and those at risk of offending, homeless people, people living in urban areas, and victims of abuse, crime and domestic violence. People with Alzheimer's disease, autism, cancer, cerebral palsy, Crohn's disease, mental illness, motor neurone disease, multiple sclerosis, muscular dystrophy, sight loss and all terminal diseases will be considered.

WHAT IS FUNDED Charities working in the fields of: accommodation and housing; information technology and computers; infrastructure development; professional bodies; charity and umbrella bodies; arts and art facilities; theatre; the visual arts; arts activities and education; cultural activity; health; conservation and environment; education and training; and social care and development. Other charitable purposes will be considered.

WHAT IS NOT FUNDED 'The trust will not support: large well-established national charities; individuals; church buildings except where they are used for community groups; projects or groups which can attract public funds or which appeal to Community Fund grants or national charitable trusts or other sources except if there is a particular part of the project which other sources would be unlikely to fund; deficits already incurred or to replace statutory funding.'

TYPE OF GRANT Recurrent expenditure, capital or single expenditure. Core costs, feasibility studies, interest-free loans, one-off and project funding, recurring costs, running costs, and salaries up to two years will be considered.

RANGE OF GRANTS £50–£5000; usually £1,000 or below.

SAMPLE GRANTS Northumberland Clubs for Young People (£4,500); Depaul UK, Fairbridge in Tyne and Wear, Whitley Bay Development Trust and St Paul's Community Partnership (£3,000 each); North Tyneside YMCA (£2,500); Young Enterprise North East, Whitley Bay District Scout Council, SSAFA Forces Help – North East, Skills for People, North Tyneside Carer's Centre, North Shields Live at Home Scheme, Newcastle CVS and Families in Care (£2,000 each); St Luke's Institute, Whizz Kidz and Woodland School (£1,000 each); Eastfield Estates Community Association and Jamboree (£750 each); North Tyneside Disability Forum (£700); Action Aid and Action for Sick Children (£500 each); Kidney Research Fund (£250).

FINANCES *Year* 2009–10 *Income* £79,563 *Grants* £128,110 *Assets* £2,300,531

TRUSTEES Mrs Judy Hamilton, Chair; Guy Javens; Mrs Monica Heath.

HOW TO APPLY In writing to the correspondent, with an sae. The Trustees meet monthly. Applicants will usually hear if their application has been successful within two months.

WHO TO APPLY TO John Hamilton, PO Box 119, Gosforth, Newcastle upon Tyne NE3 4WF *Tel* 0191 284 2158 *Fax* 0191 285 8617 *email* john.hamilton@onyx.octacon.co.uk *Website* www.rwmanntrust.org.uk

■ The Leslie and Lilian Manning Trust

CC NO 219846   **ESTABLISHED** 1960

WHERE FUNDING CAN BE GIVEN The north east of England.

WHO CAN BENEFIT Principally charities with local affinities benefiting at risk groups, and people who are disadvantaged by poverty, socially isolated, sick or disabled.

WHAT IS FUNDED Principally health and welfare.

WHAT IS NOT FUNDED No grants to individuals.

RANGE OF GRANTS Usually £500–£2,000.

SAMPLE GRANTS St Oswald's Hospice (£2,000 in two grants); Cornerstone, Mental After Care Association, Northumbria Coalition Against Crime and RNID (£1,000 each); and Northumbria Youth Action (£500).

FINANCES *Year* 2009–10 *Income* £23,046 *Grants* £25,000

TRUSTEES D Jones; N Sherlock; K L Andersen.

HOW TO APPLY In writing to the correspondent by January for consideration in March.

WHO TO APPLY TO David Jones, Trustee, David Jones, 44 Midhurst Road, Newcastle upon Tyne NE12 9NU *Tel* 01912 847661

■ The Manoukian Charitable Foundation

CC NO 1084065   **ESTABLISHED** 2000

WHERE FUNDING CAN BE GIVEN Worldwide.

WHO CAN BENEFIT Registered charities.

WHAT IS FUNDED Social welfare, education, medical, the arts, 'Armenian matters'.

SAMPLE GRANTS Royal Opera House – Thurrock (£750,000); Armenian Apostolic Holy Church (£589,000); Elton John's AIDS Foundation (£102,000); Cherie Blair Foundation for Women (£100,000); Chronic Care Centre (£65,000); Action Innocence (£32,500); British Lebanese Association (£30,000); Jenkins Penn Haitian Relief Organisation (£17,000); and Our Lady of Lebanon Church (£10,000).

FINANCES *Year* 2010 *Income* £1,550,000 *Grants* £1,894,632 *Assets* £54,201

TRUSTEES Mrs Tamar Manoukian; Anthony Bunker; Steven Press; Dr Armen Sarkissian.

HOW TO APPLY 'Requests for grants are received from the general public and charitable and other organisations through their knowledge of the activities of the foundation and through personal contacts of the settlor and the trustees.' The trustees meet at least once per year.

WHO TO APPLY TO Anthony Bunker, Trustee, c/o Berwin Leighton Paisner, Adelaide House, London Bridge, London EC4R 9HA *Tel* 020 7760 1000

■ Maranatha Christian Trust

CC NO 265323   **ESTABLISHED** 1972

WHERE FUNDING CAN BE GIVEN UK and overseas.

WHO CAN BENEFIT Christian organisations and individuals.

WHAT IS FUNDED The promotion of education among young persons and the relief of poverty, particularly among those professing the Christian religion or working to promote such religion.

RANGE OF GRANTS £500–£10,000.

SAMPLE GRANTS Previous beneficiaries include: Christian Action Research and Education, Vanessa Grant Memorial Trust, Cafe Africa Trust, Micah Trust, Friends of St Andrew's

Church, Office for International Diplomacy, Concordis International, Cheer, Re Source, Forty-Three Trust and Christians in Entertainment.

FINANCES *Year* 2009–10 *Income* £28,321 *Grants* £61,500 *Assets* £855,583

TRUSTEES Alan Bell; Revd Lyndon Bowring; Rt Hon. Viscount Brentford.

OTHER INFORMATION Unusually, a list of beneficiaries was not included in the latest accounts.

HOW TO APPLY In writing to the correspondent, but please note that the trust does not consider unsolicited applications.

WHO TO APPLY TO The Secretary, 208 Cooden Drive, Bexhill-on-Sea, East Sussex TN39 3AH *Tel* 01424 844741

■ Marbeh Torah Trust

CC NO 292491   **ESTABLISHED** 1985

WHERE FUNDING CAN BE GIVEN UK and Israel.

WHO CAN BENEFIT Jewish charities.

WHAT IS FUNDED Furtherance of orthodox Jewish religious education and relief of poverty.

RANGE OF GRANTS £3,500–£81,000.

SAMPLE GRANTS Yeshiva Marbeh Torah (£81,000); Chazon Avraham Yitzchak (£38,000); Tashbar (£25,000); Kol Eitan (£11,600); Mishkenos Yaakov (£10,000); Shaarei Limund (£6,800); Torat Bezalel (£6,400); Yad Gershon and Margenita De Avraham (£6,000 each); Kollel Oneg Shabbos (£4,000); and Kol Zvi (£3,500).

FINANCES *Year* 2010 *Income* £216,580 *Grants* £217,250 *Assets* £100

TRUSTEES Moishe Chaim Elzas; Jacob Naftoli Elzas; Simone Elzas.

HOW TO APPLY In writing to the correspondent.

WHO TO APPLY TO M C Elzas, Trustee, 116 Castlewood Road, London N15 6BE

■ The Marcela Trust

CC NO 1127514   **ESTABLISHED** 2009

WHERE FUNDING CAN BE GIVEN UK.

WHO CAN BENEFIT Research institutions.

WHAT IS FUNDED Medical research.

TYPE OF GRANT Research grants; capital projects.

SAMPLE GRANTS Nuffield Orthopaedic Centre Appeal (£500,000), to fund an extension to the Botnar Research Centre; Consensus Action on Salt and Health (£200,000), for research; and the Open Eyes Foundation (£100,000), for research into the treatment of retinoblastoma.

FINANCES *Year* 2009–10 *Income* £73,449,968 *Grants* £800,000

TRUSTEES Brian Groves; Dawn Rose; Dr Martin Lenz; Mark Spragg.

HOW TO APPLY In writing to the correspondent, although potential applicants should be aware that grant recipients may be pre-determined by the directors of OMC Investments Limited.

WHO TO APPLY TO Josephine Paxton, OMC Investments Limited, 2nd Floor, 14 Buckingham Street, London WC2N 6DF *Tel* 020 7925 8095

■ Marchig Animal Welfare Trust

CC NO 802133   **ESTABLISHED** 1989

WHERE FUNDING CAN BE GIVEN Worldwide.

WHO CAN BENEFIT Organisations and individuals that make positive contributions in protecting animals and promoting and encouraging practical work in preventing animal cruelty and suffering.

WHAT IS FUNDED There are no restrictions on the geographical area of work (with the exception of the USA and Canada), types of grants or potential applicants, but all applications must be related to animal welfare and be of direct benefit to animals. Projects supported by the trust have included mobile spay/neuter clinics, alternatives to the use of animals in research, poster campaigns, anti-poaching programmes, establishment of veterinary hospitals, clinics and animal sanctuaries.

WHAT IS NOT FUNDED The trust will reject any application failing to meet its criteria. Additionally, applications relating to educational studies or other courses, expeditions, payment of salaries, support of conferences and meetings, or activities that are not totally animal welfare related, will also be rejected.

TYPE OF GRANT Based on project.

RANGE OF GRANTS Based on project.

SAMPLE GRANTS In 2010 the trust made a number of grants to organisations and individuals at home and abroad. Projects included: spay/neuter programmes and their promotion in the UK, Tanzania, Gibraltar, Greece, Spain, South Africa, Romania, Israel and India; provision of a vehicle for rescued animals in the Philippines; improving the welfare of dairy cows and their calves; exploring the use of 'human cells' to replace animals in pesticide toxicity trials; assisting with the construction, renovation, maintenance and ongoing operations of animal shelters in the UK, India, Gibraltar, Philippines, Thailand, Israel and Greece; support was provided for animal welfare and protection education programmes in Romania, Yugoslavia and Tanzania; in addition, support was given for the purchase of veterinary medicines, equipment and for the provision of care to relieve the suffering of animals in a number of countries. A major grant was awarded to the Royal (Dick) School of Veterinary Studies in Edinburgh to establish an International Centre for Animal Welfare Education'.

FINANCES *Year* 2010 *Income* £2,674,410 *Grants* £554,414 *Assets* £17,598,094

TRUSTEES Mrs Jeanne Marchig; Dr Jerzy A Mlotkiewicz; Colin Moor; Les Ward.

OTHER INFORMATION As well as giving grants, the trust also makes Marchig Animal Welfare Trust Awards. These awards, which take the form of a financial donation in support of the winner's animal welfare work, are given in either of the following two categories: (a) The development of an alternative method to the use of animals in experimental procedures and the practical implementation of such an alternative resulting in a significant reduction in the number of animals used in experimental procedures; (b) Practical work in the field of animal welfare resulting in significant improvements for animals either nationally or internationally.

HOW TO APPLY On an application form available from the correspondent or via the website.

WHO TO APPLY TO Colin Moor, 10 Whitehorn Close, Ash, Aldershot GU12 6NZ *Tel* 0131 225 6039 *Fax* 0131 220 6377 *email* info@marchigtrust. org *Website* www.marchigtrust.org

■ The Stella and Alexander Margulies Charitable Trust

CC NO 220441   **ESTABLISHED** 1970

WHERE FUNDING CAN BE GIVEN UK.

WHO CAN BENEFIT Institutions benefiting Jewish people.

WHAT IS FUNDED Jewish charities, the arts, general charitable purposes.

RANGE OF GRANTS Generally £50–£3,000.

SAMPLE GRANTS Jerusalem Foundation (Mount Herzl) (£645,000); Alma Hebrew College (£30,000); Royal Opera House Foundation (£25,000); Community Security Trust (£6,000); Nightingale House (£5,000); YMER (£2,000); and Royal Academy of Arts and Tate Foundation (£1,000 each).

FINANCES *Year* 2009–10 *Income* £231,352 *Grants* £724,729 *Assets* £8,308,503

TRUSTEES Marcus J Margulies; Martin D Paisner; Sir Stuart Lipton; Alexander M Sorkin; Leslie D Michaels.

HOW TO APPLY In writing to the correspondent.

WHO TO APPLY TO Leslie Michaels, Trustee, 34 Dover Street, London W1S 4NG *Tel* 020 7343 7200 *Fax* 020 7343 7201

■ The Marianne Foundation

CC NO 1136999 **ESTABLISHED** 2010

WHERE FUNDING CAN BE GIVEN Developing countries.

WHO CAN BENEFIT Organisations working with children and young people.

WHAT IS FUNDED Education and training.

TRUSTEES Edward Seymour; Raffaella Taylor-Seymour; Susan Johns; Stephen Gee; Jenefer Greenwood.

HOW TO APPLY In writing to the correspondent. 'We will never give cash donations directly to institutions. We will assess carefully where our support will be most valuable and then set about devising the most suitable solutions, financing and organising the projects rather than handing over a lump sum.'

WHO TO APPLY TO Edward Seymour, Trustee, Sutton Grey, Wick Road, Oaksey, Malmesbury, Wiltshire *Tel* 01666 577100 *email* info@ themariannefoundation.org *Website* www. themariannefoundation.org

■ Mariapolis Limited

CC NO 257912 **ESTABLISHED** 1968

WHERE FUNDING CAN BE GIVEN UK and overseas.

WHO CAN BENEFIT Organisations and individuals.

WHAT IS FUNDED Christian ecumenism and the International Focolare Movement.

SAMPLE GRANTS Pia Associazione Maschile Opera di Maria (£323,000); family welfare grants (£1,500); Anglican Priests Training Fund (£1,000); Focolare Trust (£408); and 'other' (£1,600).

FINANCES *Year* 2009–10 *Income* £521,438 *Grants* £327,097 *Assets* £2,451,731

TRUSTEES Timothy King; Manfred Kochinky; Barry Redmond.

OTHER INFORMATION This trust promotes the international Focolare Movement in the UK, and grant making is only one area of its work. It works towards a united world and its activities focus on peace and cooperation. It has a related interest in ecumenism and also in overseas development. Activities include organising conferences and courses, and publishing books and magazines.

HOW TO APPLY In writing to the correspondent.

WHO TO APPLY TO Rumold Van Geffen, 38 Audley Road, London W5 3ET *Tel* 020 8991 2022 *email* rumold@btconnect.com

■ Market Harborough and The Bowdens Charity

CC NO 1041958 **ESTABLISHED** 1994

WHERE FUNDING CAN BE GIVEN The parishes of Market Harborough, Great Bowden and Little Bowden.

WHO CAN BENEFIT Organisations and individuals.

WHAT IS FUNDED The trust supports a wide range of large and small projects, giving towards supporting the community, the improvement of the environment, the arts, healthcare, heritage and relief-in-need.

WHAT IS NOT FUNDED No grants towards sporting projects or to replace statutory funding.

RANGE OF GRANTS £5,000–£15,000.

SAMPLE GRANTS Harborough Town Football Club (£40,000); P.A.T.H. (£22,000); Market Harborough C of E Primary School and Voluntary Action South Leicestershire (£17,500 each); Robert Smyth School (£15,000); Farndon Fields Primary School (£11,000); St Nicholas Church Hall (£7,500); Arts Fresco (£5,000); and Harborough Millennium Chorus (£1,500).

FINANCES *Year* 2010 *Income* £551,523 *Grants* £360,525 *Assets* £15,354,439

TRUSTEES I C Wells, Chair; T Banks; Dr J Jones; D Battersby; J C Clare; Mrs J Hefford; Mrs J Roberts; G Stamp; M Stamp; A F Trotter; A E Walker; Mrs J A Williams; Mrs L Rhodes; P E Beardsmore; G R Hartopp.

OTHER INFORMATION The trust works in informal administrative partnerships with organisations and other funding bodies to pursue schemes in line with its main areas of work. Grants were also made to 130 individuals totalling over £106,000.

HOW TO APPLY On a form available from the correspondent. Potential applicants are welcome to contact the correspondent directly for further guidance.

WHO TO APPLY TO J G Jacobs, Steward, Godfrey Payton & Co, 149 St Mary's Road, Market Harborough, Leicestershire LE16 7DZ *Tel* 01858 462467 *Fax* 01858 431898 *email* admin@mhbcharity.co.uk *Website* www. mhbcharity.co.uk

■ The Michael Marks Charitable Trust

CC NO 248136 **ESTABLISHED** 1966

WHERE FUNDING CAN BE GIVEN UK and overseas.

WHO CAN BENEFIT Registered charities.

WHAT IS FUNDED Conservation, environment and culture.

WHAT IS NOT FUNDED Grants are given to registered charities only. No grants to individuals or profit organisations.

RANGE OF GRANTS Generally £1,000–£25,000.

SAMPLE GRANTS British Museum (£25,000); British Library (£19,000); Sainsbury Institute (£12,000); Woodland Trust, National Theatre, Burlington Magazine and Academy of Ancient Music (£10,000 each); St Pancras Community Trust (£7,700); Spitalfields Music (£7,500); Benaki Museum (£6,000); Royal Horticultural Society (£4,500); Polish Association of the Knights of Malta (£3,000); and Scottish Poetry Library and Greek Archdiocese of Thyateria and Great Britain (£2,000 each).

FINANCES *Year* 2009–10 *Income* £203,253 *Grants* £162,927 *Assets* £5,834,837

TRUSTEES Marina, Lady Marks; Prof. Sir Christopher White; Noel Annesley.

HOW TO APPLY In writing to the correspondent. Applications should include audited accounts, information on other bodies approached and details of funding obtained. The trustees meet twice a year, usually in January and July, to consider applications. Requests will not receive a response unless they have been successful.

who to apply to The Trustees, 5 Elm Tree Road, London NW8 9JY *Tel* 020 7286 4633 *Fax* 020 7289 2173

■ The Marks Family Foundation

cc no 1137014   **established** 2010
where funding can be given UK.
who can benefit Organisation working with children and young people and older people.
what is funded General charitable purposes, with a preference for health, arts and culture.
type of grant Usually one-off, unrestricted grants.
trustees David Marks; Selina Marks.
other information The settlor of the foundation, David Marks, is a partner in Apax Partners LLP private equity investment group and also a trustee of the Apax Foundation and the R and S Cohen Foundation.
how to apply The trust has recently stated that it is overwhelmed by the number of unsolicited applications received.
who to apply to David Marks, Trustee, 10 Green Street, London W1K 6RP *email* dmarkstax@aol.com

■ The Ann and David Marks Foundation

cc no 326303   **established** 1983
where funding can be given Worldwide with a preference for Manchester.
who can benefit Jewish charities.
what is funded Jewish charitable purposes.
range of grants Up to £3,000.
sample grants Finchley Jewish School (£4,000); UJIA £3,000); and Magen (£1,500).
finances *Year* 2010 *Income* £70,668 *Grants* £31,994 *Assets* £596,973
trustees D L Marks; Mrs A M Marks; Dr G E Marks; A H Marks; M Purcell.
how to apply Previous research suggested that the trust's funds are mostly committed and unsolicited applications are not welcome.
who to apply to D L Marks, Trustee, Mutley House, 1 Ambassador Place, Stockport Road, Altrincham, Cheshire WA15 8DB *Tel* 0161 941 3183 *email* davidmarks@mutleyproperties.co.uk

■ The Hilda and Samuel Marks Foundation

cc no 245208   **established** 1965
where funding can be given UK and Israel.
who can benefit Voluntary organisations and charitable groups benefiting Jewish people of all ages. Support is given to those helped by the Jewish Blind Society.
what is funded General charitable purposes; the relief and assistance of poor and needy persons; education; advancement of Judaism and assistance to synagogues and Jewish bodies; community facilities and services; health.
what is not funded No grants to individuals.
type of grant Buildings and other capital; core costs; project; start-up costs.
sample grants The ALYN Pediatric and Adolescent Rehabilitation Centre in Jerusalem (£25,000).

finances *Year* 2009–10 *Income* £110,763 *Grants* £170,584 *Assets* £3,134,947
trustees S Marks; Mrs H Marks; D L Marks; Mrs R D Selby.
how to apply The trust primarily supports projects known to the trustees and its funds are fully committed. Therefore unsolicited applications are not being sought.
who to apply to D L Marks, Trustee, Mutley House, 1 Ambassador Place, Stockport Road, Altrincham, Cheshire WA15 8DB *Tel* 0161 941 3183 *Fax* 0161 927 7437 *email* davidmarks@mutleyprperties.co.uk

■ J P Marland Charitable Trust

cc no 1049350   **established** 1995
where funding can be given UK.
who can benefit Registered charities.
what is funded General charitable purposes.
range of grants Up to £16,000.
sample grants Natural History Museum (£16,000); Guggenheim UK Charitable Trust (£5,500); The Sports Nexus (£5,000); Hospitaller Ltd (£2,000); and Tickets for Troops (£3,000).
finances *Year* 2009–10 *Income* £45,493 *Grants* £35,270 *Assets* £355,555
trustees Lord J Marland; Lady P M Marland; Mrs C J Law; Mr M Marland; Mr H Marland.
how to apply In writing to the correspondent.
who to apply to J P Marland, Odstock Manor, Odstock, Salisbury SP5 4JA *Tel* 01722 329781 *email* jmarland@jltgroup.com

■ Marmot Charitable Trust

cc no 1106619   **established** 2004
where funding can be given Worldwide.
who can benefit 'Green' and peace organisations.
what is funded Environment, sustainability, nuclear disarmament and non-proliferation.
range of grants £1,200–£15,000.
sample grants British American Security Information Council (£15,000); Friends of the Earth Trust and Unit for Research into Changing Institutions (£10,000); Martin Ryle Trust (Scientists for Global Responsibility)(£5,000); Poverty and Environment Trust (Sustainable Communities Act); Margaret Hayman Charitable Trust (Talkworks); and Tree Aid (£2,000).
finances *Year* 2009–10 *Income* £366,599 *Grants* £99,317 *Assets* £2,526,705
trustees Jean Barlow; Martin Gillett; Jonathan Gillett.
how to apply In writing to the correspondent.
who to apply to The Secretary, c/o B M Marmot, London WC1N 3XX

■ The Marr-Munning Trust

cc no 261786   **established** 1970
where funding can be given Worldwide, mainly developing world.
who can benefit Organisations benefiting refugees, people disadvantaged by poverty, and victims of famine, war and man-made or natural disasters.
what is funded Overseas aid projects, particularly those likely to improve economic and educational work. Provision of water supplies and general medical care. Refugee works and language schools are also supported.
what is not funded No grants to individuals or for work taking place within the UK.
type of grant Recurrent and one-off.
range of grants Up to £14,000.

SAMPLE GRANTS Marr-Munning Asram – India
(£14,000); Aysanew Kassa Trust (£11,000);
Médecins Sans Frontières (£10,000); Africa
Equipment for School (£5,400); CAFOD
(£5,000); UNICEF (£4,500); World Orthopaedic
Concern (£4,000); Homeless International and
Joliba Trust (£3,000 each); Build It International
(£2,500); Rural Solar Lighting, the Spiti Project
and Mercy Ships (£2,000 each); Action for
Children in Conflict and VETAID (£1,500 each);
and Ss. Cyril and Methodious University
(£1,000).

FINANCES *Year* 2009–10 *Income* £578,438
Grants £229,065 *Assets* £12,426,580

TRUSTEES Glen Barnham; Marianne Elliott; Julian
Kay; Guy Perfect; David Strachan; Pierre
Thomas; Martin Sarbicki; Dr Geetha Oommen.

HOW TO APPLY The trustees meet quarterly on
average and usually review applications twice
yearly, in the spring and autumn. Sometimes a
request may be carried forward to a later
meeting. However, emergency appeals may be
considered at any meeting. Applications should
be concise, ideally limited to no more than 2
sides of A4 plus a project description, budget
and summary accounts or annual report. Clear
financial information is essential, and
applications from small or new organisations
may benefit from reference to any better-known
supporters or partners. Charitable or equivalent
status of the applicant organisation should be
made clear. **Please note**: Any other supporting
literature should be kept to a minimum. Do not
waste stamps on an sae; the trust regrets that
it does not have the administrative resources at
present to return papers or respond to
telephone or email enquiries (a website is under
consideration). A trustee has agreed to look at
the requests each month and where necessary
seek further information. Otherwise, applicants
will normally only hear if their bid has been
successful which may be more than 6 months
from receipt of application.

WHO TO APPLY TO Donford Gleeson, Trust
Administrator, 9 Madeley Road, Ealing, London
W5 2LA *Tel* 020 8998 7747 *Fax* 020 8998
9593 *email* dongleeson@tiscali.co.uk

■ The Michael Marsh Charitable Trust

CC NO 220473   **ESTABLISHED** 1958

WHERE FUNDING CAN BE GIVEN Birmingham,
Staffordshire, Worcestershire, Warwickshire,
Coventry, Wolverhampton and associated towns
in the Black Country.

WHO CAN BENEFIT Organisations benefiting children
and young people, people who are elderly, at
risk groups and people who are disabled,
disadvantaged by poverty or socially isolated.

WHAT IS FUNDED Health and welfare charities,
community-based organisations, education and
training and religious activities.

WHAT IS NOT FUNDED No grants towards animals or
entertainment charities. Grants to individuals
are only given through charitable institutions on
their behalf.

TYPE OF GRANT Generally recurrent.

RANGE OF GRANTS Usually £300–£10,000.

SAMPLE GRANTS Queen Elizabeth Hospital
Birmingham (£50,000); The Extracare charitable
Trust (£7,500); Enterprise Education Trust
(£4,000); Birmingham Fellowship of the
Handicapped (£3,500); Christchurch pre-school
(£2,500); Birmingham Settlement, St Matthew's
Holiday Fairbridge, Volunteer Reading Help and

Primrose Hospice (£2,000 each); The
Anaphylaxis Campaign (£1,000); Whiz-Kidz
(£500); and St Basil's (£300).

FINANCES *Year* 2009–10 *Income* £176,906
Grants £137,847 *Assets* £3,419,115

TRUSTEES Peter Gary Barber; Lee Nuttall; Susan
Bennett.

HOW TO APPLY In writing to the correspondent.
Trustees meet in June and December,
considering all applications received in the
preceding six months. However, they will
consider on an ad-hoc basis any applications
that they consider should not be retained until
their next scheduled meeting.

WHO TO APPLY TO Clerk to the Trust, c/o Mills and
Reeve, 78–84 Colmore Row, Birmingham
B3 2AB *Tel* 0870 600 0011 *Fax* 0121 456
8483 *email* marsh.charity@mills-reeve.com

■ The Marsh Christian Trust

CC NO 284470   **ESTABLISHED** 1981

WHERE FUNDING CAN BE GIVEN UK.

WHO CAN BENEFIT Registered charities only.

WHAT IS FUNDED General charitable purposes;
housing advice and information; holiday
accommodation; sheltered accommodation;
arts, culture and recreation; schools and
colleges; education and training; day centres;
emergency care; community holidays and
outings; family planning clinics; support and
self-help groups; well woman clinics; Christian
education; missionaries and evangelicals;
Quakerism; conservation of flora and fauna,
historic buildings, nature reserves and
woodlands; animal facilities and services;
environmental and animal sciences;
conservation and campaigning.

WHAT IS NOT FUNDED No grants can be made to
individuals or for sponsorships. No start-up
grants. No support for building funds, ordinary
schools, colleges, universities or hospitals, or
research.

TYPE OF GRANT Annual; more than three years.

RANGE OF GRANTS Generally £250–£4,000, with
responses to new applications being at the
lower end of this scale.

SAMPLE GRANTS Bible Reading Fellowship, Christians
Against Poverty, English Speaking Union of the
Commonwealth and Prisoners Abroad (£1,000
each); Cruse Bereavement Care (£900);
Addaction and Historic Chapels Trust (£800
each); Impact Foundation (£700); Awareness
Foundation (£600); London Early Years
Foundation and London Philharmonic Orchestra
(£500 each); Lloyd's Patriotic Fund (£450);
Migraine Action and Mind (£400 each); The
Charleston Trust (£275); and Little and David
Construction and Small Woods Association
(£100 each).

FINANCES *Year* 2009–10 *Income* £469,109
Grants £156,413 *Assets* £6,076,209

TRUSTEES B P Marsh; R J C Marsh; Miss
N C S Marsh; Mrs. L Ryan; Miss A Marsh.

OTHER INFORMATION The trust also runs a portfolio of
awards with a number of internationally and
nationally recognised organisations such as
Barnardo's, the National Trust and the
Zoological Society of London. In 2009–10, 27
awards were made and totalled £55,000.

HOW TO APPLY In writing to the correspondent,
including a copy of the most recent accounts.
Decisions are made at monthly trustee
meetings. The trustees attempt to visit each
long-term recipient at least once every three
years to review the work done, to learn of future
plans and renew acquaintance with those

responsible for the charity. Advice on fund-raising and other organisational problems is also offered free of charge by the trust.

WHO TO APPLY TO Brian Peter Marsh, Trustee, 2nd Floor, 36 Broadway, London SW1H 0BH *Tel* 020 7233 3112 *Website* www.marshchristiantrust.org

■ The Charlotte Marshall Charitable Trust

CC NO 211941 **ESTABLISHED** 1962
WHERE FUNDING CAN BE GIVEN UK.
WHO CAN BENEFIT Registered charities, institutions benefiting Roman Catholics, children, young adults and students.
WHAT IS FUNDED Educational and religious objects for Roman Catholics.
WHAT IS NOT FUNDED No grants are given to individuals.
RANGE OF GRANTS £300–£8,000.
SAMPLE GRANTS St Winifred's Centre – Sheffield (£8,000); St Gregory's Youth and Community Centre – Liverpool and St Mary's Star of the Sea (£6,000 each); Sacred Heart Primary School and St Mary Magdalen Catholic School (£5,000 each); Scottish Marriage Care (£4,000); St James Priory Project – Bristol and Westminster Children's Society (£3,000 each); Speak Out Hounslow (£1,500); Independent Age (£1,000): and Birmingham Settlement and Derby TOC H (£500 each).
FINANCES *Year* 2009–10 *Income* £119,271 *Grants* £110,000 *Assets* £522,000
TRUSTEES Mrs E M Cosgrove; J Crosgrove; K B Page; J M Russell; Rachel Cosgrove.
HOW TO APPLY On a form available from the correspondent. Completed forms must be returned by 31 December for consideration in March.
WHO TO APPLY TO The Trustees, Sidney Little Road, Churchfields Industrial Estate, St Leonards on Sea, East Sussex TN38 9PU *Tel* 01424 856655

■ The Jim Marshall Charitable Trust

CC NO 328118 **ESTABLISHED** 1989
WHERE FUNDING CAN BE GIVEN Milton Keynes.
WHO CAN BENEFIT Charitable organisations.
WHAT IS FUNDED General charitable purposes, mainly for the benefit of children, young people, families and people who are disabled or sick.
RANGE OF GRANTS £1,000–£25,000.
SAMPLE GRANTS Previous beneficiaries have included: MK Victors Boxing Club, Luton and Bedfordshire Youth Association and Action 4 Youth (£25,000); Foundation for Promoting the Art of Magic (£5,000); Comedians' Golfing Society (£2,500); Hazeley School Charitable Trust (£2,000); Nathan Edwards Mobility Bike Fund (£1,100); and Music Alive, Brainwave and Music for All (£1,000 each).
FINANCES *Year* 2010 *Income* £1,032 *Grants* £28,000
TRUSTEES Dr James Marshall, Chair; Kenneth Saunders; Brian Charlton; Jonathon Ellery; Victoria Marshall.
HOW TO APPLY In writing to the correspondent at any time.
WHO TO APPLY TO Simpson Wreford and Co, Wellesley House, Duke of Wellington Avenue, London SE18 6SS *Tel* 020 8317 6460

■ The D G Marshall of Cambridge Trust

CC NO 286468 **ESTABLISHED** 1982
WHERE FUNDING CAN BE GIVEN Predominantly Cambridge and Cambridgeshire.
WHO CAN BENEFIT Community projects, local appeals and local charities benefiting disabled people and people disadvantaged by poverty.
WHAT IS FUNDED Charitable causes in and around Cambridge.
WHAT IS NOT FUNDED Unsolicited applications are not supported.
SAMPLE GRANTS The Cambridge Foundation (£900,000); Jesus College (£100,000); Prince's Charities (£10,000); the Air League (£6,000 each); Arkwright Scholarship Trust (£3,600); Cambridge and County folk Museum (£2,000); Alopecia UK (£750); and Combat Stress and The Prince's Trust (£500 each); and NSPCC (£250).
FINANCES *Year* 2009–10 *Income* £195,990 *Grants* £1,057,597 *Assets* £1,822,950
TRUSTEES M J Marshall; J D Barker; W C M Dastur; R Marshall.
HOW TO APPLY The trust has stated that it does not respond to unsolicited applications.
WHO TO APPLY TO Ms Sarah Moynihan, Airport House, The Airport, Newmarket Road, Cambridgeshire CB5 8RY *Tel* 01223 373 273

■ Marshall's Charity

CC NO 206780 **ESTABLISHED** 1627
WHERE FUNDING CAN BE GIVEN England and Wales with preference for Kent, Surrey, Lincolnshire and Southwark.
WHO CAN BENEFIT Anglican churches and parsonage buildings.
WHAT IS FUNDED Improvement work to parsonages in England and Wales, repairs to existing Anglican churches in Kent, Surrey and Lincolnshire (as the counties were defined in 1855).
WHAT IS NOT FUNDED No grants to churches outside the counties of Kent, Surrey and Lincolnshire, as defined in 1855. No church funding for the following: cost of church halls and meeting rooms; kitchens; decorations – unless they form part of qualifying repair or improvement work; furniture and fittings; work to bells, brasses or clocks; private chapels or monuments; stained glass – although work to repair ferraments can be supported; grounds, boundary walls and fences; external lighting.
TYPE OF GRANT Building and other capital works; interest-free loans.
RANGE OF GRANTS Up to £20,000. Grants to churches usually £3,000 to £5,000. Grants to parsonages usually £1,000 to £4,000.
SAMPLE GRANTS St Lawrence – Aylesby; St Andrew – Deal; All Saints – Elsham; St Michael – Hernhill; St Bartholomew – Keelby; Holy Trinity – Milton Regis; St Botolph's – Quarrington; and St Mary the Virgin – Swineshead.
FINANCES *Year* 2009–10 *Income* £1,201,486 *Grants* £743,086 *Assets* £15,623,664
TRUSTEES Anthea Nicholson, Chair; Colin Bird; David Lang; Michael Dudding; Colin Stenning; Stephen Clark; Gina Isaac; Bill Eason; Jeremy Hammant; John Heawood; Surbhi Malhotra; Revd Jonathan Rust; Ven. Christine Hardman; Tony Guthrie; Lesley Bosman.
HOW TO APPLY Applicants should write a letter or send an email to the correspondent, giving the name and location of the Church and a brief (30 – 40 words maximum) description of the proposed work. If appropriate the charity will

then send out an application form. Applications for parsonage grants should be made by the relevant Diocesan Parsonage Board. Trustees usually meet in January, April, July and October.

WHO TO APPLY TO Richard Goatcher, Clerk, Marshall House, 66 Newcomen Street, London Bridge, London SE1 1YT *Tel* 020 7407 2979 *Fax* 020 7403 3969 *email* grantoffice@marshalls.org.uk *Website* www.marshalls.org.uk

■ Marshgate Charitable Settlement

CC NO 1081645   **ESTABLISHED** 2000
WHERE FUNDING CAN BE GIVEN England and Wales.
WHO CAN BENEFIT Christian, educational and medical charities.
WHAT IS FUNDED There is an interest in work with children.
SAMPLE GRANTS Greyfriars Church (£22,000); The Philo Trust (£8,200); Stewardship and Tearfund (£5,000 each); and Bible Society, Marie Curie Cancer Care and Retrak (£500 each).
FINANCES *Year* 2009–10 *Income* £187 *Grants* £28,489
TRUSTEES C S H Hampton; M J Hampton; R Hambler.
HOW TO APPLY In writing to the correspondent.
WHO TO APPLY TO Clifford Hampton, Trustee, Highmoor Hall, Henley-on-Thames, Oxfordshire RG9 5DH *Tel* 01491 641543 *Fax* 01491 641098

■ Sir George Martin Trust

CC NO 223554   **ESTABLISHED** 1956
WHERE FUNDING CAN BE GIVEN Largely Yorkshire with particular emphasis on Leeds and Bradford.
WHO CAN BENEFIT Organisations benefiting children, young adults and older people; dance and ballet; music; theatre; opera companies; schools and colleges; education and training; community facilities and services; religious buildings; conservation.
WHAT IS FUNDED Education, social welfare, general charitable purposes, especially in Yorkshire. The trust assists a very wide range of charitable causes with a number of awards to schools and groups working with young people. Emphasis is placed on projects located in north and west Yorkshire and occasionally in Cumbria.
WHAT IS NOT FUNDED Full guidelines detailing what is and is not funded by the trust are available from the correspondent.
TYPE OF GRANT Grants for capital rather than revenue projects. Grants are not repeated to any charity in any one-year; the maximum number of consecutive grants is three, though a one-off approach to grant applications is preferred. Average donation is just over £1,230.
RANGE OF GRANTS Usually £100–£5,000 with some larger grants.
SAMPLE GRANTS Wade's Charity (£50,000); Woodhouse Grove School (£12,500); Harrogate Homeless Project (£4,000); Northern Ballet Theatre, Little Heroes, Cumbria Community Foundation and Fire Fighters Charity (£2,000 each), Adel Parish Church (£1,000); Addingham Gala Friends, BATI About Kids and Keighly CVS (£500 each); and Wordsworth Trust (£200).
FINANCES *Year* 2009–10 *Income* £186,244 *Grants* £150,350 *Assets* £6,171,248
TRUSTEES T D Coates, Chair; M Bethel; R F D Marshall; P D Taylor; Ms Janet Martin.

HOW TO APPLY The trust meets four times a year to consider applications. Applications should be made in writing to the secretary. Applications that are not within the guidelines cannot be answered due to substantial increase in costs. Applications that are relevant will be acknowledged and, following meetings, successful applicants will be told of the grants they are to receive. Unsuccessful applicants will not be informed. The trust is unable to consider applications from organisations without charitable status. Telephone calls are not encouraged as the office is not always staffed – it is better to write, fax or email.
WHO TO APPLY TO Jane Aldridge, Secretary, Netherwood House, Skipton Road, Ilkley, West Yorkshire LS29 9RP *Tel* 01943 831019 *Fax* 01943 831 570 *email* sirgeorgemartintrust@care4free.net

■ John Martin's Charity

CC NO 527473   **ESTABLISHED** 1714
WHERE FUNDING CAN BE GIVEN Evesham and 'certain surrounding villages' only.
WHO CAN BENEFIT Individuals and charitable or voluntary organisations and schools benefiting the residents of Evesham.
WHAT IS FUNDED Propagation of the Christian gospel – the charity helps with the expenses of designated local clergy, PCCs and St Andrew's Church of England First School in Hampton; promotion of education – grants are made to all state schools and the college in Evesham to support special needs education, in addition to considering other educational projects; relief in need – grants are made for the benefit of children, single parent families, people with disabilities and people who have fallen on hard times for a variety of circumstances beyond their control; health – support is given to health projects, particularly those helping people with chronic health problems.
WHAT IS NOT FUNDED No grants for the payment of rates or taxes, or otherwise to replace statutory benefits.
TYPE OF GRANT Equipment – normally paid against an agreed invoice, either direct to the supplier or by direct credit to the organisation's bank account; project or on-going costs – normally paid in stages by direct credit; general expenditure – normally paid by direct credit.
RANGE OF GRANTS £200–£29,000.
SAMPLE GRANTS St Andrews PCC – Hampton (£29,000); Citizens Advice – Wychavon (£20,000); St Richard's Hospice and All Saints' PCC – Evesham (£18,000 each); Acquired Aphasia Trust (£14,000); Prince Henry's High School (£11,000); Hampton First School (£8,800); Evesham College (£6,100); Shop Mobility – Evesham (£3,000); Noah's Ark Trust (£2,500); St Mary's Primary School (£1,300); and Breast Cancer Haven (£200).
FINANCES *Year* 2009–10 *Income* £715,960 *Grants* £587,663 *Assets* £18,321,452
TRUSTEES Nigel Lamb; John Smith; Richard Emson; Revd Barry Collins; Cyril Scorse; Revd Andrew Spurr; Cllr Diana Raphael; Cllr Frances Smith; Joyce Turner; Julie Westlake; John Wilson; Revd Mark Binney; Catherine Evans; Gabrielle Falkiner.
OTHER INFORMATION The grant total includes £189,350 to schools and organisations. The remaining £398,313 was given to individuals.
HOW TO APPLY Grant applications are considered from organisations in, or supporting, the town of Evesham where the requested support is

726

Does the trust you have chosen match your needs? Haphazard applications waste postage and time

considered to fit within the governing schemes of the charity. Application periods close on 1 March, 1 June, 1 September and 20 November. Forms are available from the correspondent or via the 'downloads' page at: www.johnmartins.org.uk/downloads.html. Applicants are asked to provide the following with their application: the latest set of annual accounts; latest bank statement showing the current balance and name of the organisation; any relevant literature about the organisation e.g. a leaflet or flyer.

Details of the application procedure for individuals are also contained on the trust's website.

WHO TO APPLY TO John Daniels, Clerk, 16 Queen's Road, Evesham, Worcestershire WR11 4JN *Tel* 01386 765440 *Fax* 01386 765340 *email* enquiries@johnmartins.org.uk *Website* www.johnmartins.org.uk

■ The John Mason Family Trust

CC NO 1136856   **ESTABLISHED** 2010
WHERE FUNDING CAN BE GIVEN North West England, with a preference for the diocese of Chester; overseas.
WHO CAN BENEFIT Registered charities.
WHAT IS FUNDED Education, social welfare, religious activities and overseas aid.
TRUSTEES John Philip Mason; Joan Linda Mason.
HOW TO APPLY In writing to the correspondent.
WHO TO APPLY TO The Trustees, Aaron & Partners LLP, 5–7 Grosvenor Court, Foregate Street, Chester CH1 1HG *Tel* 01244 405555 *Fax* 01244 405566 *email* enquiries@ aaronandpartners.com

■ The Mason Porter Charitable Trust

CC NO 255545   **ESTABLISHED** 1968
WHERE FUNDING CAN BE GIVEN UK.
WHO CAN BENEFIT Grants are made only to charities known to the settlor.
WHAT IS FUNDED General charitable purposes, particularly Christian causes.
SAMPLE GRANTS Hoylake Cottage Hospital (£50,000); Abernethy Trust Ltd and Cliff College (£10,000 each); ECG Trust (£5,000); Just Care (£4,000); Proclaim Trust (£3,000); St Luke's Methodist Church Hoylake; (£2,000); and Share Jesus International and Wirral Christian Centre (£1,000 each).
FINANCES *Year* 2009–10 *Income* £111,272 *Grants* £105,110 *Assets* £1,591,651
TRUSTEES Sue Newton, Chair; Mark Blundell; Dil Daly; Adeyinka Olushonde; Charles Feeny; William Fulton; Prof. Phillip Love; Andrew Lovelady; Christine Reeves; Hilary Russell; Heather Akehurst; Perminder Bal.
HOW TO APPLY The trust states that it only makes grants to charities known to the settlor and unsolicited applications are not considered.
WHO TO APPLY TO The Trustees, Liverpool Charity and Voluntary Services, 151 Dale Street, Liverpool L2 2AH *Tel* 0151 227 5177

■ The Nancie Massey Charitable Trust

SC NO SC008977   **ESTABLISHED** 1989
WHERE FUNDING CAN BE GIVEN Scotland, particularly Edinburgh and Leith.
WHO CAN BENEFIT Registered charities.
WHAT IS FUNDED Young people; elderly people; education; the arts; and medical research.
WHAT IS NOT FUNDED Grants are not given to individuals.
TYPE OF GRANT Capital, core costs and salaries.
RANGE OF GRANTS £500–£2,000, but can be larger.
SAMPLE GRANTS Scottish National Portrait Gallery (£25,000); Alzheimer's Research Trust and the Queen's Hall (£15,000 each); Edinburgh and Lothian Council on Alcohol, Hearts & Minds, and the Marie Curie Build Appeal (£5,000 each); and Children 1st; SSAFA Forces Help; Greenbank Parish Church; Marie Curie Memorial Foundation; and St Columba's Hospital.
FINANCES *Year* 2009–10 *Income* £221,514 *Grants* £146,000 *Assets* £5,791,892
TRUSTEES Gavin Morton; M F Sinclair; E Wilson.
HOW TO APPLY Write to the correspondent requesting an application form. Trustees meet three times a year in February, June and October. Applications need to be received by January, May or September.
WHO TO APPLY TO Gavin Morton, Trustee, c/o Chiene and Tait, Cairn House, 61 Dublin Street, Edinburgh EH3 6NL *Tel* 0131 558 5800 *Fax* 0131 558 5899

■ The Mathew Trust

SC NO SC016284   **ESTABLISHED** 1935
WHERE FUNDING CAN BE GIVEN City of Dundee, Angus, Perth and Kinross and Fife.
WHO CAN BENEFIT Registered charities.
WHAT IS FUNDED The advancement of education of adults; advancement of vocational and professional training; relief of poverty by providing assistance in the recruitment of people who are unemployed, or who are likely to become unemployed in the near future.
FINANCES *Year* 2011 *Income* £198,661
TRUSTEES D B Grant, Chair; G S Lowden; A F McDonald; Prof. P Howie; The Lord Provost of the City of Dundee.
HOW TO APPLY In writing to the correspondent.
WHO TO APPLY TO Fiona Bullions, Henderson Loggie, Chartered Accountants, Royal Exchange, Panmure Street, Dundee DD1 1DZ

■ Matliwala Family Charitable Trust

CC NO 1012756   **ESTABLISHED** 1992
WHERE FUNDING CAN BE GIVEN UK and overseas, especially Bharuch – India.
WHO CAN BENEFIT Charitable organisations.
WHAT IS FUNDED The advancement of education for pupils at Matliwala School of Baruch in Gujarat – India, including assisting with the provision of equipment and facilities; advancement of the Islamic religion; relief of sickness and poverty; advancement of education.
SAMPLE GRANTS Various projects in Bharuch, Gujarat – India (£650,000); advancement of the Islamic religion – UK (£100,000); and advancement of education – overseas (£3,400).
FINANCES *Year* 2009–10 *Income* £309,786 *Grants* £753,400 *Assets* £4,419,942

TRUSTEES Ayub Vali Bux; Usman Salya; Abdul Aziz Vali Patel; Yousuf Bux; Ibrahim Vali Patel.
HOW TO APPLY In writing to the correspondent.
WHO TO APPLY TO Ayub Vali Bux, Trustee, 9 Brookview, Fulwood, Preston PR2 8FG *Tel* 01772 706501

■ The Matt 6.3 Charitable Trust
CC NO 1069985   **ESTABLISHED** 1998
WHERE FUNDING CAN BE GIVEN UK.
WHO CAN BENEFIT Christian organisations.
WHAT IS FUNDED Christian charitable purposes.
SAMPLE GRANTS Christian Centre (Humberside) Limited (£358,000); European Gospel Mission Limited (£65,000); and The Ice House Christian Centre (£2,000).
FINANCES *Year* 2009–10 *Income* £262,247 *Grants* £461,187 *Assets* £7,057,152
TRUSTEES Christine Ruth Barnett; Doris Dibdin; T P Dibdin; R O Dauncey.
OTHER INFORMATION Includes £21,000 to individuals.
HOW TO APPLY The trust does not accept unsolicited applications. Funds are committed to ongoing projects.
WHO TO APPLY TO I H Davey, Progress House, Progress Park, Cupola Way, Off Normanby Road, Scunthorpe, North Lincolnshire *Tel* 01724 863666

■ The Violet Mauray Charitable Trust
CC NO 1001716   **ESTABLISHED** 1990
WHERE FUNDING CAN BE GIVEN UK.
WHO CAN BENEFIT Registered charities.
WHAT IS FUNDED General charitable purposes, particularly medical charities and Jewish organisations.
WHAT IS NOT FUNDED No grants to individuals.
RANGE OF GRANTS Usually £1,000–£6,000.
SAMPLE GRANTS Mango Tree and Tzedek (£5,000 each); Médecins Sans Frontières (£4,000); Employment Resource Centre and Jewish Care (£3,000 each); Merlin and Shelterbox (£2,000 each); Kids Company and National Animal Welfare Trust (£1,000 each); and Concertina Charitable Trust (£500).
FINANCES *Year* 2009–10 *Income* £39,659 *Grants* £49,000 *Assets* £1,738,805
TRUSTEES Alison Karlin; John Stephany; Robert Stephany.
HOW TO APPLY In writing to the correspondent.
WHO TO APPLY TO John Stephany, Trustee, 9 Bentinck Street, London W1U 2EL *Tel* 020 7935 0982

■ The Maxell Educational Trust
CC NO 702640   **ESTABLISHED** 1990
WHERE FUNDING CAN BE GIVEN Telford and The Wrekin.
WHO CAN BENEFIT Students between the ages of 9 and 25, and teachers.
WHAT IS FUNDED Education, in particular projects with industrial or technological content.
SAMPLE GRANTS Previous beneficiaries have included Shropshire Campus of the University of Wolverhampton to establish an Electronic Design Centre, Southall Special School for computers and software for pupils to produce a school newspaper, Ercall Wood School to establish the Maxell Music Technology Centre and Wrockwardine Wood School to establish the Controlled Technology Centre.
FINANCES *Year* 2008–09 *Income* £1,365 *Grants* £1,400
TRUSTEES Mike Lowe; Ian Jamieson.
HOW TO APPLY In writing to the correspondent.
WHO TO APPLY TO Ian Jamieson, Maxell Europe Ltd, Apley, Telford TF1 6DA *Tel* 01952 522222

■ The Maxwell Family Foundation
CC NO 291124   **ESTABLISHED** 1965
WHERE FUNDING CAN BE GIVEN UK.
WHO CAN BENEFIT Registered charities in the fields of health, medical research, and the relief of people who are elderly, are sick or who have disabilities.
WHAT IS FUNDED An established list of charities is supported.
WHAT IS NOT FUNDED The trust states explicitly that there is no support for unsolicited applications. It clearly abides by this policy and we would urge readers who do not know the trustees personally not to write to the trust.
RANGE OF GRANTS Usually £3,500 or under.
SAMPLE GRANTS Deafblind UK (£10,000); British Institute for Brain Injured Children (£5,0000); The Army Benevolent Fund (£3,000); National Eye Research Centre (£2,500); Bristol Children's Help Society (£1000); The Extra Care Charitable Trust (£500); Dolphin Society (£250); and British Wireless for the Blind fund (£150).
FINANCES *Year* 2010 *Income* £27,734 *Grants* £60,500 *Assets* £2,311,975
TRUSTEES E M Maxwell; P M Maxwell.
HOW TO APPLY Applications are neither sought nor acknowledged. There appears little purpose in applying to this trust as no application will be supported unless accompanied by a personal request from someone known by the trustees.
WHO TO APPLY TO E M Maxwell, Trustee, 181 Whiteladies Road, Clifton, Bristol BS8 2RY *Tel* 0117 962 6878

■ Evelyn May Trust
CC NO 261038   **ESTABLISHED** 1970
WHERE FUNDING CAN BE GIVEN UK.
WHO CAN BENEFIT Registered charities, mainly headquarters organisations, especially those benefiting elderly people, children, medical professionals, research workers, and people disadvantaged by sickness and poverty.
WHAT IS FUNDED Currently the main areas of interest are elderly people, children, medical projects and natural disaster relief, but support is given to a variety of registered charities.
WHAT IS NOT FUNDED No grants to individuals, including students, or to general appeals or animal welfare charities.
TYPE OF GRANT Often one-off for a specific project, but support for general purposes is also given.
SAMPLE GRANTS Previous beneficiaries include: Queen Alexandra Hospital (£3,000); Child Hope, Children's Heart Foundation, NSPCC Trust, Frishta Children's Village, Child Health Advocacy International, Children in Crisis, Richards House (£2,000 each) and Tabor centre (£1,000).
FINANCES *Year* 2010 *Income* £26,166 *Grants* £57,000
TRUSTEES Ms Lisa Webb; Ms K Gray; Ms J Tabersham.
HOW TO APPLY In writing to the correspondent.
WHO TO APPLY TO Ms Kim Gray, c/o Pothecary Witham Weld Solicitors, 70 St George's Square, London SW1V 3RD *Tel* 020 7821 8211

■ Mayfair Charities Ltd

CC NO 255281   **ESTABLISHED** 1968

WHERE FUNDING CAN BE GIVEN UK and overseas.

WHO CAN BENEFIT Registered charities benefiting Orthodox Jews, particularly children and young adults.

WHAT IS FUNDED Education, religion and medical welfare charities which support Orthodox Judaism.

TYPE OF GRANT Capital and running costs.

RANGE OF GRANTS Typically £500–£2,500, although large donations are also made.

SAMPLE GRANTS Previous beneficiaries include: SOFT; Beth Jacob Grammar School For Girls Ltd; Merkaz Lechinuch Torani; Ohr Akiva Institute; Kollel Chibas Yerushalayim; Mesivta Letzeirim; Chevras Maoz Ladal; Congregation Ichud Chasidim; Chaye Olam Institute; United Talmudical Association; Talmud Torah Zichron Gavriel; Friends of Bobov; Regent Charities Ltd; Comet Charities Ltd; Woodstock Sinclair Trust; Yesodei Hatorah School; Beis Aharon Trust; Ezer Mikodesh Foundation; Gateshead Jewish Teachers Training College; Edgware Foundation; Heritage House; Kiryat Sanz Jerusalem; and PAL Charitable Trust.

FINANCES *Year* 2009–10 *Income* £4,053,000 *Grants* £5,983,000 *Assets* £54,125,000

TRUSTEES Benzion S E Freshwater, Chair; D Davis; Solomon I Freshwater.

OTHER INFORMATION Grants were made to over 600 organisations. A recent list of beneficiaries was unavailable.

HOW TO APPLY In writing to the correspondent.

WHO TO APPLY TO Mark Jenner, Secretary, Freshwater House, 158–162 Shaftesbury Avenue, London WC2H 8HR *Tel* 020 7836 1555 *email* mark.jenner@highdorn.co.uk

■ The Mayfield Valley Arts Trust

CC NO 327665   **ESTABLISHED** 1988

WHERE FUNDING CAN BE GIVEN Unrestricted, but with a special interest in Sheffield and South Yorkshire.

WHO CAN BENEFIT Charities concerned with music and the promotion and presentation of musical events and activities.

WHAT IS FUNDED Support is concentrated on certain beneficiaries, with remaining funds to established chamber music venues.

WHAT IS NOT FUNDED No grants to students.

TYPE OF GRANT Up to three years for core costs.

SAMPLE GRANTS Wigmore Hall (£40,000); Live Music Now (£35,000); York Early Music Foundation (£30,000); Music in the Round (£20,000); and Prussia Cove (£10,000).

FINANCES *Year* 2009–10 *Income* £115,060 *Grants* £135,000 *Assets* £2,171,604

TRUSTEES A Thornton; J R Thornton; Mrs P M Thornton; D Whelton; D Brown; J R Rider.

HOW TO APPLY The trust states that no unsolicited applications are considered.

WHO TO APPLY TO P J Kennan, Administrator, Hawsons, Pegasus House, 463a Glossop Road, Sheffield S10 2QD *Tel* 0114 266 7141

■ Mazars Charitable Trust

CC NO 287735   **ESTABLISHED** 1983

WHERE FUNDING CAN BE GIVEN UK and overseas.

WHO CAN BENEFIT Organisations with charitable purposes.

WHAT IS FUNDED Support is normally only given to projects which are nominated to the management committee by the partners and staff of Mazars (chartered accountants).

WHAT IS NOT FUNDED No grants to individuals, large national charities (rarely), applications from a particular national charity within three years of an earlier grant, or for on-going funding. Unsolicited appeals are rarely considered.

TYPE OF GRANT Single strategic projects; one-off; research; building; and capital. Funding is for one year or less.

RANGE OF GRANTS £55–£19,000.

SAMPLE GRANTS UK Youth (£25,000); Chickenshed and Parkinson's Disease Society of the United Kingdom (£15,000 each); The Johari Foundation (£12,000); Hope HIV and The Waterside Charitable Trust (£10,000 each); Emmanuel Global Network (UK) Limited, Hope for Konya and Redbridge Breast Funds (£5,000 each); and Sense and The National Deafblind & Rubella Association (£2,250 each).

FINANCES *Year* 2010 *Income* £226,709 *Grants* £271,957 *Assets* £73,692

TRUSTEES Alan T H Edwards, David J Evans, Peter R Hyatt and Robert H Neate.

HOW TO APPLY The trustees operate through the management committee who meet annually to consider nominations for national (major) grants. Some funds are allocated to ten regional 'pots' whose appointed representatives approve smaller grant nominations from within their own region. Nominations for national grants must be known to and be sponsored by team members of Mazars LLP and comply with stated criteria. Applicants known to team members of Mazars LLP can obtain a copy of the stated criteria upon request to the trust administrator. National and regional criteria are regularly reviewed but, in general, the trustees consider that the national grant-making policy should avoid core funding. Most national grants are therefore made towards one-off projects covering a defined period. Successful national nominations cannot normally be repeated within three years

WHO TO APPLY TO Bryan K Rogers, Trust Administrator, 1 Cranleigh Gardens, South Croydon CR2 9LD *Tel* 020 8657 3053

■ The Robert McAlpine Foundation

CC NO 226646   **ESTABLISHED** 1963

WHERE FUNDING CAN BE GIVEN UK.

WHO CAN BENEFIT Registered charities and hospitals.

WHAT IS FUNDED Children with disabilities, older people, medical research, social welfare.

WHAT IS NOT FUNDED The trust does not like to fund overheads. No grants to individuals.

RANGE OF GRANTS Up to £90,000.

SAMPLE GRANTS The Ewing Foundation (£80,000); Age Concern (£40,000); Sevenoaks School Charity and From Boyhood to Manhood Foundation (£25,000 each); and Community Self Build Agency, Merchants Academy Withywood and The Towers School and Sixth Form Centre (£20,000 each); The Respite Association (£15,000); Berkshire Community Foundation, Children's Aid Team and Dulwich Helpline (£10,000 each); The Pirate Club (£5,000); and Greenfingers Appeal (£2,500).

FINANCES *Year* 2009–10 *Income* £463,427 *Grants* £448,373 *Assets* £12,974,547

TRUSTEES Hon. David McAlpine; Malcolm H D McAlpine; Kenneth McAlpine; Cullum McAlpine; Adrian N R McAlpine.

HOW TO APPLY In writing to the correspondent at any time. Considered annually, normally in November.

WHO TO APPLY TO Brian Arter, Eaton Court, Maylands Avenue, Hemel Hempstead, Hertfordshire HP2 7TR *Tel* 01442 233444

■ The McDougall Trust

CC NO 212151   **ESTABLISHED** 1959

WHERE FUNDING CAN BE GIVEN UK and overseas.

WHO CAN BENEFIT Organisations or individuals carrying out charitable work including research in accord with the trust's objects.

WHAT IS FUNDED The knowledge, study and research of: political or economic science and functions of government and the services provided to the community by public and voluntary organisations; methods of election of and the selection and government of representative organisations whether national, civic, commercial, industrial or social; and representative democracy, its forms, functions and development and also its associated institutions. Special priority is given to electoral research projects.

WHAT IS NOT FUNDED No grants to any political party or commercial organisation, for an individual's education, for social welfare matters, or for general appeals, expeditions or scholarships.

TYPE OF GRANT Usually one-off for a specific project or part of a project or work programme. Applications for small 'pump-priming' grants are welcomed. Feasibility studies and research grants are also considered.

RANGE OF GRANTS Minimum grant £250.

SAMPLE GRANTS The Institute of Welsh Affairs; Wilton Park Trust; and Queens University Belfast.

FINANCES *Year* 2009–10 *Income* £53,033 *Grants* £28,650 *Assets* £885,339

TRUSTEES Patrick Noon; Prof. Ron Johnston; Elizabeth Collingridge; Ruth Farmer; David Hill; Michael Meadowcroft; Peter Morley; Nigel Siederer; Michael Steed (Chair).

PUBLICATIONS Representation: Journal of Representative Democracy, (quarterly).

OTHER INFORMATION The trustees have established a library called the Lakeman Library for Electoral Studies at the address below. This is available for the use of research workers and the public generally on conditions laid down by the trustees. The trustees also sponsor several prizes in conjunction with the Political Studies Association and the Politics Association.

HOW TO APPLY In writing to the correspondent, including annual accounts. Trustees normally meet six times a year. Brief details of proposal needed. Initial enquiries by telephone accepted. Two deadlines for receipt of applications: 1 May and 1 October. Applications received after a deadline may be held over for consideration at the trustees' discretion.

WHO TO APPLY TO Paul Wilder, Trust Secretary, 6 Chancel Street, London SE1 0UX *Tel* 020 7620 1080 *Fax* 020 7928 1528 *email* admin@mcdougall.org.uk *Website* www.mcdougall.org.uk

■ The A M McGreevy No 5 Charitable Settlement

CC NO 280666   **ESTABLISHED** 1979

WHERE FUNDING CAN BE GIVEN UK, with a preference for the Bristol and Bath area.

WHO CAN BENEFIT Registered charities.

WHAT IS FUNDED General charitable purposes.

WHAT IS NOT FUNDED No support for individuals.

SAMPLE GRANTS NSPCC (£25,000); Prostate Cancer Charity (£2,000); and the Stroke Association (£500).

FINANCES *Year* 2009–10 *Income* £27,137 *Grants* £27,500 *Assets* £2,186,329

TRUSTEES Avon Executor and Trustee Co. Ltd; Anthony McGreevy; Elise McGreevy-Harris; Katrina Paterson.

HOW TO APPLY In writing to the correspondent.

WHO TO APPLY TO Karen Ganson, Trust Administrator, KPMG, 100 Temple Street, Bristol BS1 6AG *Tel* 0117 905 4000

■ The McKenna Charitable Trust

CC NO 1050672   **ESTABLISHED** 1995

WHERE FUNDING CAN BE GIVEN England and Wales.

WHO CAN BENEFIT Organisations and individuals.

WHAT IS FUNDED Health, disability, education, children, arts/culture, general.

SAMPLE GRANTS National Film and Television School (£50,000); Georgia's Teenage Cancer Appeal and The Royal Free Hampstead Charities (£5,000 each); CWMT (£2,600); Nordoff Robins Music Therapy (£1,500); and Animals Asia Foundation (Moon Bear) (£500).

FINANCES *Year* 2009–10 *Income* £87,500 *Grants* £64,620 *Assets* £26,780

TRUSTEES P A McKenna; Mrs. M E A McKenna; J L Boyton; H R Jones.

HOW TO APPLY The 2009–10 trustees' report and accounts states: 'The trustees will consider applications for grants from individuals and charitable bodies on their merits but will place particular emphasis on the educational needs and the provision of support for disabled people.'

WHO TO APPLY TO J L Boyton, Trustee, Ingenious Asset Management, 15 Golden Square, London W1F 9JG *Tel* 020 7319 4000

■ Martin McLaren Memorial Trust

CC NO 291609   **ESTABLISHED** 1985

WHERE FUNDING CAN BE GIVEN UK.

WHO CAN BENEFIT Horticulture students.

WHAT IS FUNDED Horticultural scholarships.

RANGE OF GRANTS £50–£12,000.

SAMPLE GRANTS Previous beneficiaries include: Art and Christianity Enquiry Trust, Horticultural Scholarships Fund, European Gardens, St John's Smith Square, Combe PCC, ESU Music Scholarship Fund, Queen Mary's Clothing Guild, Macmillan Cancer Relief, The PCC Busbridge Church and Fairbridge Garden Society.

FINANCES *Year* 2009–10 *Income* £21,880 *Grants* £25,000

TRUSTEES Sir Kenneth Carlisle; William Francklin; Revd Richard Mclaren; Nancy Gordon Mclaren; Robert Blower.

HOW TO APPLY In writing to the correspondent.

WHO TO APPLY TO Michael McFadyen, Administrator, c/o Charles Russell Solicitors, 5 Fleet Place, London EC4M 7RD *Tel* 020 7203 5269 *Fax* 020 7203 0200

■ The Helen Isabella McMorran Charitable Foundation

CC NO 266338   **ESTABLISHED** 1973

WHERE FUNDING CAN BE GIVEN UK.

WHO CAN BENEFIT Registered charities benefiting children, young adults and older people; those in care, fostered and adopted; Christians,

Church of England; people with disabilities; people disadvantaged by poverty; homeless and socially isolated people.

WHAT IS FUNDED Older people's welfare, Christian education, churches, the arts, residential facilities and services, social and moral welfare, special schools, cultural and religious teaching, special needs education, health, medical and religious studies, conservation, animal welfare, bird sanctuaries and heritage.

WHAT IS NOT FUNDED No grants to individuals.

TYPE OF GRANT One-off.

RANGE OF GRANTS £500–£2,000.

SAMPLE GRANTS Previous beneficiaries include: Christian Aid, Marine Conservation, Moon Bear Rescue, National Association for Crohn's Disease, National Children's Bureau, React, St Matthews PCC, St Nicholas Church, Sense International and Stoneham Housing Association.

FINANCES *Year* 2009–10 *Income* £22,479 *Grants* £28,000

TRUSTEES NatWest Trust Services.

HOW TO APPLY In writing to the correspondent. Brief guidelines are available. The closing date for applications is February each year.

WHO TO APPLY TO NatWest Trust Services, 5th Floor, Trinity Quay 2, Avon Street, Bristol BS2 0PT *Tel* 0117 940 3283

....

■ D D McPhail Charitable Settlement

CC NO 267588   **ESTABLISHED** 1974

WHERE FUNDING CAN BE GIVEN UK.

WHO CAN BENEFIT Registered charities, especially those benefiting people who are elderly or disabled.

WHAT IS FUNDED Medical research and welfare.

TYPE OF GRANT Mainly recurrent.

RANGE OF GRANTS Mostly £2,000–£10,000.

SAMPLE GRANTS Association of Wheelchair Children (£170,000); Combat Stress (£150,000); Meningitis Research Foundation (£53,000); Demand (£25,000); Princess Royal Carers Trust (£20,000); Vocal Eyes (£10,000); Sir William Burrough School (£5,000); and Barbara Bus Fund, International League for the Protection of Horses, BLISS, National Society for Epilepsy, Hospice in the Weald and the Kidney Association Children's Holiday Fund (£2,000 each).

FINANCES *Year* 2009–10 *Income* £957,308 *Grants* £511,000 *Assets* £8,200,040

TRUSTEES Julia Noble; Patricia Cruddas; Catherine Charles-Jones; Christopher Yates; Tariq Kazi; Michael Craig; Mary Meeks.

OTHER INFORMATION In 2009–10 the trust had an unusually high income of £957,000 (£303,000 in 2008–09), due to a 'recoup of investment impairment' worth £721,000.

HOW TO APPLY In writing to the correspondent.

WHO TO APPLY TO Mrs Sheila Watson, Administrator, PO Box 285, Pinner, Middlesex HA5 3FB

....

■ The Mears Foundation

CC NO 1134941   **ESTABLISHED** 2010

WHERE FUNDING CAN BE GIVEN UK, India, Indonesia, South Africa, Romania and Sri Lanka.

WHO CAN BENEFIT Charities, voluntary bodies and individuals.

WHAT IS FUNDED Projects in the following areas: economic, community, people development and employment; education and training; overseas aid and famine relief; sport and recreation; environment, conservation and heritage. The foundation follows four 'guiding principles' in its grant-making: to improve the lives of people living within our communities; to help build community cohesion and integration; to provide career and skills development opportunities to those needing them the most; to be a positive contributor to the environment.

FINANCES *Year* 2010 *Income* £87,093

TRUSTEES Judith Dacey; Kenneth Mantock; Margaret Devine; Donna Ellis; Sally Ann Clarke; Gary Pelling.

OTHER INFORMATION This foundation was established as the next 'logical step' following the successful delivery of two international relief projects in India in 2008 and Sri Lanka in 2009 by Mears Group plc, the social housing and domiciliary care company.

HOW TO APPLY In writing to the correspondent.

WHO TO APPLY TO Judith Dacey, Trustee, Mears Group plc, Unit 1390, Montpellier Court, Gloucester Business Park, Brockworth, Gloucester GL3 4AH *Tel* 01452 634600 *Website* www.mearsgroup.co.uk

....

■ The James Frederick and Ethel Anne Measures Charity

CC NO 266054   **ESTABLISHED** 1973

WHERE FUNDING CAN BE GIVEN West Midlands.

WHO CAN BENEFIT All categories within the West Midlands area.

WHAT IS FUNDED General charitable purposes. Applicants must usually originate in the West Midlands and show evidence of self-help in their application. Trustees have a preference for disadvantaged people.

WHAT IS NOT FUNDED Trustees will not consider funding students who have a full local authority grant and want finance for a different course of study. Applications by individuals in cases of hardship will not usually be considered unless sponsored by a local authority, health professional or other welfare agency.

TYPE OF GRANT Recurrent grants are occasionally considered. The trustees favour grants towards the cost of equipment.

RANGE OF GRANTS £100–£1,600.

SAMPLE GRANTS Farms for City Children (£7,500); Royal Wolverhampton School (£2,400); Bluecoat School (£1,500); and Sightsavers (£1,000); Birmingham and Midland Limbless Ex-Service Association, BID – Services with deaf people in the West Midlands, Stratford-upon-Avon Athletic Club and Stratford-upon-Avon Shakespeare Hospice (£500 each); All Saints Sea Scouts – Sutton Coldfield, Edwards Trust – Birmingham and Tall Ships Youth Trust – Coventry and Warwicks Branch (£400 each); Birmingham Festival Choral Society and Birmingham Settlement, (£300 each); Small Heath Play Centre, Stratford-upon-Avon Writers Circle and T S Coventry – Sea Cadets (£250 each); Birmingham Focus on Blindness (£200); and Warwick Hospital Cancer Ward (£175).

FINANCES *Year* 2009–10 *Income* £32,199 *Grants* £30,200 *Assets* £1,068,447

TRUSTEES J P Wagg; M P Green; D A Seccombe; R S Watkins.

HOW TO APPLY In writing to the correspondent. No reply is sent to unsuccessful applicants unless an sae is enclosed. The trustees meet quarterly.

WHO TO APPLY TO Mrs S E Darby, 2nd Floor, 33 Great Charles Street, Birmingham B3 3JN

....

■ The Medlock Charitable Trust

CC NO 326927 **ESTABLISHED** 1985

WHERE FUNDING CAN BE GIVEN Overwhelmingly the areas of Bath and Boston in Lincolnshire.

WHO CAN BENEFIT Small local projects and established organisations benefiting children, adults and young people.

WHAT IS FUNDED General charitable purposes, especially education, medicine, research and social services for the benefit of the local community.

WHAT IS NOT FUNDED No grants to individuals or students.

TYPE OF GRANT One-off capital and revenue grants for up to two years.

RANGE OF GRANTS Mainly less than £10,000.

SAMPLE GRANTS The Well's Palace Appeal (£150,000), to make the palace more accessible to visitors and provide a new education centre and cafe; and Bath University (£100,000), to replace an old Astroturf facility with a modern state-of-the-art surface; Quartet Community Foundation (£80,000); SS Great Britain Trust (£75,000); the Boshier-Hinton Foundation (£60,000); Forever Friends Appeal (£51,000); The Prince's Trust (£25,000); Hayesfield School (£18,000); Somerset 500 Club (£15,000); Julian House, Southern Spinal Injuries Trust, Royal Air Force Benevolent Fund and Centrepoint Outreach (£10,000 each); John Cabot Academy (£8,000); Bristol Care & Repair (£7,000); St Saviour's Church of England Junior School (£6,000); Bath Preservation Trust, Boston and District Athletic Club, NSPCC and the Clara Cross Rehab Unit (£5,000 each); Bristol Children's Help Society (£3,000); The Anchor Society and the Thera Trust (£2,000 each); and Castle Primary School, Mid-Somerset Festival, Avon Outward Bound Association and Centre for Deaf People (£1,000 each).

FINANCES *Year* 2009–10 *Income* £791,515 *Grants* £1,092,231 *Assets* £26,485,638

TRUSTEES Leonard Medlock; Jacqueline Medlock; David Medlock; Peter Carr.

HOW TO APPLY In writing to the correspondent. 'The trustees have identified the City of Bath and the borough of Boston as the principal but not exclusive areas in which the charity is and will be proactive. These areas have been specifically chosen as the founder of the charity has strong connections with the City of Bath, the home of the charity, and has family connections of long standing with the borough of Boston. To date the charity has supported and funded a number of projects in these areas by making substantial grants. These grants have been made to fund projects in the areas of education, medicine, research and social services all for the benefit of the local community. During the year, the trustees also receive many applications for assistance from many diverse areas in the United Kingdom. These are all considered sympathetically.'

WHO TO APPLY TO Leonard Medlock, Trustee, c/o Hebron & Medlock Ltd, St Georges Lodge, 33 Oldfield Road, Bath, Avon BA2 3ND *Tel* 01225 428221

■ The Anthony and Elizabeth Mellows Charitable Settlement

CC NO 281229 **ESTABLISHED** 1980

WHERE FUNDING CAN BE GIVEN UK.

WHO CAN BENEFIT UK bodies benefiting: children and young adults; actors and entertainment professionals; musicians; textile workers and designers; and writers and poets.

WHAT IS FUNDED The acquisition of objects to be used or displayed in houses of the National Trust or churches of the Church of England; the encouragement of hospices and medical research; support of the arts; the training and development of children and young people. The trustees can only consider projects recommended to them by those UK institutions with whom they are in close cooperation.

WHAT IS NOT FUNDED Applications from individuals, including students, are ineligible.

TYPE OF GRANT Generally single projects.

SAMPLE GRANTS Royal Opera House Foundation (£2,900); Heath Chapel (£2,000); The Order of St John (£1,900); National Art Collection Fund (£1,125); and St Martin-in-the-Fields (£500).

FINANCES *Year* 2010–11 *Income* £32,355 *Grants* £20,679 *Assets* £703,706

TRUSTEES Prof. Anthony R Mellows; Mrs Elizabeth Mellows.

HOW TO APPLY Applications are considered when received, but only from UK institutions. No application forms are used. Grants decisions are made three times a year when the trustees meet to consider applications.

WHO TO APPLY TO Prof. Anthony Mellows, Trustee, 22 Devereux Court, Temple Bar, London WC2R 3JR *Tel* 020 7583 8813

■ Melodor Ltd

CC NO 260972 **ESTABLISHED** 1970

WHERE FUNDING CAN BE GIVEN UK and overseas.

WHO CAN BENEFIT Orthodox Jewish institutions.

WHAT IS FUNDED Jewish causes, such as education (including adult education), relief of poverty and the advancement of religion in accordance with the orthodox Jewish faith.

TYPE OF GRANT One-off grants and loans.

RANGE OF GRANTS Up to £30,000.

SAMPLE GRANTS Previous beneficiaries include: Centre for Torah Education Trust, Beis Rochel, Chasdei Yoel, Beth Hamedrash Hachodosh, Yeshivas Ohel Shimon, Beis Minchas Yitzhok, Talmud Torah Education Trust, Dushinsky Trust, Kollel Chelkas Yakov, Yetev Lev, Delman Charitable Trust, Ovois Ubonim and Friends of Viznitz.

FINANCES *Year* 2009–10 *Income* £174,192 *Grants* £143,797 *Assets* £751,460

TRUSTEES Hyman Weiss; Philip Weiss; Zisel Weiss; Pinchas Neumann; Yocheved Weiss; Eli Neumann; Esther Henry; Henry Neumann; Janet Bleier; Maurice Neumann; Miriam Friedlander; Rebecca Delange; Rivka Ollech; Rivka Rabinowitz; Pesha Kohn; Yehoshua Weiss.

HOW TO APPLY In writing to the correspondent.

WHO TO APPLY TO Bernardin Weiss, Secretary, 10 Cubley Road, Salford M7 4GN *Tel* 0161 720 6188

■ The Melow Charitable Trust

CC NO 275454 **ESTABLISHED** 1978

WHERE FUNDING CAN BE GIVEN UK and overseas.

WHO CAN BENEFIT Jewish charities.

WHAT IS FUNDED Jewish charitable purposes.

RANGE OF GRANTS Up to £107,000.

SAMPLE GRANTS The largest grants were to: Friends of Kollel Satmar (Antwerp) Ltd (£107,000); Ezer V'Hatzalah Ltd (£81,000); Lolev Charitable Trust (£75,000); Tchaba Kollel (£50,000); and Rehabilitation Trust (£38,000).

FINANCES *Year* 2010 *Income* £1,431,542 *Grants* £620,897 *Assets* £9,763,686
TRUSTEES J Low; Miriam Spitz; Esther Weiser.
HOW TO APPLY In writing to the correspondent.
WHO TO APPLY TO J Low, 21 Warwick Grove, London E5 9HX *Tel* 020 8806 1549

■ Meningitis Trust

CC NO 803016   **ESTABLISHED** 1986
WHERE FUNDING CAN BE GIVEN UK.
WHO CAN BENEFIT Organisations researching meningitis.
WHAT IS FUNDED Research into all aspects of the disease.
FINANCES *Year* 2009–10 *Income* £3,065,515 *Grants* £257,637 *Assets* £1,457,841
TRUSTEES Bernadette McGhie; Gill Noble; James Wilson; Mike Hall; Peter Johnson; Bob Johnson; Les Green; Richard Greenhalgh; James Kilmister; Alastair Irvine; Prof. Keith Cartwright; Mitchell Wolfe; Eddie Wilson.
OTHER INFORMATION Of the grant total, £258,000 was made in financial support grants to individuals and £65,000 was distributed to organisations as research grants.
HOW TO APPLY Application forms are available from the correspondent. Requests for financial support are reviewed regularly by the Financial Grants Review Panel.
WHO TO APPLY TO Financial Grants Officer, Fern House, Bath Road, Stroud, Gloucestershire GL5 3TJ *Tel* 01453 768000 *Fax* 01453 768001 *email* helpline@meningitis-trust.org *Website* www.meningitis-trust.org

■ Menuchar Ltd

CC NO 262782   **ESTABLISHED** 1971
WHERE FUNDING CAN BE GIVEN UK.
WHO CAN BENEFIT Jewish organisations.
WHAT IS FUNDED Advancement of religion in accordance with the orthodox Jewish faith, and relief of people in need.
WHAT IS NOT FUNDED No grants to non-registered charities or to individuals.
TYPE OF GRANT Primarily one-off.
SAMPLE GRANTS List of beneficiaries unavailable.
FINANCES *Year* 2009–10 *Income* £635,250 *Grants* £307,491 *Assets* £484,505
TRUSTEES Norman Bude; Gail Bude.
HOW TO APPLY In writing to the correspondent.
WHO TO APPLY TO The Trustees, c/o Barry Flack & Co, Knight House, 27–31 East Barnet Road, Barnet EN4 8RN *Tel* 020 8275 5186

■ The Menzies Charity Foundation

CC NO 1136667   **ESTABLISHED** 2010
WHERE FUNDING CAN BE GIVEN Worldwide.
WHO CAN BENEFIT Registered charities working with children and young people and people with disabilities.
WHAT IS FUNDED General charitable purposes.
TRUSTEES Peter Noyce; Julie Adams; Tom Govan.
HOW TO APPLY In writing to the correspondent.
WHO TO APPLY TO Peter Noyce, Trustee, Menzies LLP, 62 Goldsworth Road, Woking, Surrey GU21 6LQ *Tel* 01483 755000 *Fax* 01483 599238 *email* pnoyce@menzies.co.uk

■ Mercaz Torah Vechesed Limited

CC NO 1109212   **ESTABLISHED** 2005
WHERE FUNDING CAN BE GIVEN Worldwide.
WHO CAN BENEFIT Charitable organisations and individuals.
WHAT IS FUNDED The advancement of the orthodox Jewish faith, orthodox Jewish religious education, and the relief of poverty and infirmity amongst members of the orthodox Jewish community.
FINANCES *Year* 2009–10 *Income* £1,011,738 *Grants* £965,461 *Assets* £25,800
TRUSTEES Jacob Moishe Grosskopf; Joseph Ostreicher; Mordche David Rand.
PUBLICATIONS The trust states that, 'a full list of the material grants made by the charity during the year is available on application in writing to the trustees at the Principal Office'. A request has been sent by this organisation but a reply is yet to be received.
HOW TO APPLY In writing to the correspondent.
WHO TO APPLY TO Joseph Ostreicher, Secretary, 28 Braydon Road, London N16 6QB *Tel* 020 8880 5366

■ Brian Mercer Charitable Trust

CC NO 1076925   **ESTABLISHED** 1999
WHERE FUNDING CAN BE GIVEN UK and overseas.
WHO CAN BENEFIT Charitable organisations.
WHAT IS FUNDED Advancement of education, promotion of medical and scientific research.
TYPE OF GRANT Mainly recurrent.
RANGE OF GRANTS £1,000 to £50,000.
SAMPLE GRANTS Fight for Sight and British Council for the Prevention of Blindness (£50,000 each); Sightsavers International (£25,000); Computer Aid International (£19,000); Macular Disease Society and Macmillan Cancer Relief (£15,000 each); DEC Haiti Earthquake Appeal and Vision Aid (£10,000 each); Micro Loan Foundation and North West Air Ambulance (£5,000 each); Burnley College and Cardinal Newman College (£2,500 each); and St Paul's PCC – Lindale (£1,000).
FINANCES *Year* 2009–10 *Income* £528,769 *Grants* £360,262 *Assets* £20,978,764
TRUSTEES Christine Clancy; Kenneth Merrill; Alan Rowntree; Roger Duckworth; Mary Clitheroe.
HOW TO APPLY In writing to the correspondent. Trustees meet at least twice yearly to allocate grants.
WHO TO APPLY TO Alan Rowntree, Trustee, c/o Beever and Struthers, Central Buildings, Richmond Terrace, Blackburn BB1 7AP *Tel* 01254 686600 *Website* www. beeverstruthers.co.uk

■ The Mercers' Charitable Foundation

CC NO 326340   **ESTABLISHED** 1982
WHERE FUNDING CAN BE GIVEN UK; strong preference for London and the West Midlands.
WHO CAN BENEFIT Registered or exempt charities.
WHAT IS FUNDED General welfare, the elderly, conservation, arts, Christian faith activities, educational institutions.
WHAT IS NOT FUNDED These should be read alongside the specific exclusions for the particular category into which an application falls. Excluded appeals: animal welfare charities; endowment appeals; projects that are primarily political; activities that are the responsibility of the local, health or education authority or other

Think carefully about every application. Is it justified?

733

similar body; activities that have already taken place; other grant making trusts; sponsorship or marketing appeals; loans or business finance; and general or mailshot appeals.

Capital projects: This is restricted to appeals that are within the last 20% of their target. No capital projects are funded under the Education programme.

TYPE OF GRANT Building and other capital grants with certain restrictions; feasibility studies; one-off grants; project and research grants; recurring and start-up costs. Grants given for up to three years.

RANGE OF GRANTS Usually £5,000–£15,000, but up to £430,000.

SAMPLE GRANTS Beneficiaries included: St Paul's School (£430,000); Gresham College (£322,000); Prior's Court Foundation (£50,000); Every Child a Chance Trust (£35,000); Peter Symonds' College (£34,000); Sandwell Academy and Treloar Trust (£30,000 each); Hexham Abbey (£21,000); Southside Young Leaders' Academy (£20,000); First Story Ltd (£15,000); Age Concern Westminster (£12,000); London Citizens (£11,000); Baxter College, London Philharmonic Orchestra, Finsbury Park Homeless Families Project, Tate Gallery and The Ethics Academy (£10,000 each).

FINANCES *Year* 2010–11 *Income* £5,968,000 *Grants* £2,962,471 *Assets* £10,094,000

TRUSTEES The Mercers' Company.

HOW TO APPLY Applications can be made online via the foundation's website. In addition applicants are required to post: The organisation's most recent statutory report and accounts (produced not later than 10 months after the end of the financial year); and a copy of your organisation's bank statement, dated within the last three months.

Grants officers are happy to give advice by telephone or email. Applicants must submit applications 4 weeks prior to committee meetings. Applications will be acknowledged within 10 working days. Committees meet regularly throughout the year. For up to date committee meeting dates please consult the trust's website for each grant programme. Approval of successful applications may take up to 4 weeks from the date of the meeting at which your applications is considered. 'Where possible, applicants awarded, or being considered for, a grant over £10,000 will receive a visit either from staff or from members of the Mercers' Company.' Please note: This trust is under the trusteeship of the Mercers' Company and one application to the Company is an application to all its trusts including the Charity of Sir Richard Whittington and the Earl of Northampton's Charity.

WHO TO APPLY TO The Clerk, Mercers' Hall, Ironmonger Lane, London EC2V 8HE *Tel* 020 7726 4991 *Fax* 020 7600 1158 *email* mail@ mercers.co.uk *Website* www.mercers.co.uk

■ The Merchant Taylors' Company Charities Fund

CC NO 1069124   **ESTABLISHED** 1941
WHERE FUNDING CAN BE GIVEN UK, especially inner London.

WHO CAN BENEFIT Organisations benefiting children, older people, actors and entertainment professionals, medical professionals, musicians, substance abuse, carers, people who are disabled, and homeless people.

WHAT IS FUNDED Areas that may be considered are the arts, social care and community development, disability, older people, poverty, medical studies and research, chemical dependency, homelessness, children, and education, with priority for special needs.

TYPE OF GRANT One-off grants or three-year tapering grants.

RANGE OF GRANTS £1—£10,000.

SAMPLE GRANTS Sparks (£50,000); St Mungo's and East Potential (£10,000 each); Hope & Homes (£6,400); Guildhall School of Music (£6,000); UNLOCK (£5,000); Dean Close School and St Helen's Church – Bishopsgate (£2,000 each); St Paul's Cathedral of Friends and St Margaret's Church – Lee (£1,000 each); St Michael's – Cornhill, St Paul's Cathedral Choir School and Royal School of Needlework (£500 each).

FINANCES *Year* 2010 *Income* £261,691 *Grants* £72,350 *Assets* £592,992

TRUSTEES Sir David Brewer; Mr. Richard Wingate Edward Charlton and Mr. Christopher Morley Keville.

HOW TO APPLY Awards are restricted at present to charities nominated by the Livery Committee.

WHO TO APPLY TO Matthew Dear, Charities Officer, Merchant Taylors' Hall, 30 Threadneedle Street, London EC2R 8JB *Tel* 020 7450 4440 *email* charities@merchant-taylors.co.uk *Website* www.merchanttaylors.co.uk

■ The Merchant Venturers' Charity

CC NO 264302   **ESTABLISHED** 1972
WHERE FUNDING CAN BE GIVEN Bristol.

WHO CAN BENEFIT Local and regional organisations and local branches of national organisations particularly those supporting the young, aged and disadvantaged; and some individuals.

WHAT IS FUNDED Any charitable purpose which enhances the quality of life for all, including learning and the acquisition of skills by supporting education; supporting community activity; and assisting in the preservation of open spaces and heritage.

TYPE OF GRANT Some recurrent.

SAMPLE GRANTS Prince's Trust (£19,000); St Mary Redcliffe Organ Appeal (£5,000); and Withywood Community School Leadership Programme (£2,500).

FINANCES *Year* 2010 *Income* £377,007 *Grants* £234,019 *Assets* £5,928,893

TRUSTEES The Standing Committee of the Society of Merchant Venturers of Bristol.

HOW TO APPLY In writing to the correspondent. A sub-committee of the trustees meets bi-annually while the trustees meet monthly and can, if necessary, consider any urgent business at that meeting.

WHO TO APPLY TO Richard Morris, The Society of Merchant Venturers, Merchants' Hall, The Promenade, Clifton, Bristol BS8 3NH *Tel* 0117 973 8058 *Fax* 0117 973 5884 *email* enquiry@ merchantventurers.com

■ The Merchants' House of Glasgow

SC NO SC008900   **ESTABLISHED** 1605
WHERE FUNDING CAN BE GIVEN Glasgow and the west of Scotland.

WHO CAN BENEFIT Registered charities benefiting seamen, pensioners and young people (aged 10 to 30) in full-time education.

WHAT IS FUNDED Seamen's missions, general charitable purposes, and grants to pensioners and young people in education.

WHAT IS NOT FUNDED The trust will not, unless in exceptional circumstances, make grants to: individuals; churches other than Glasgow Cathedral; organisations that have received support in the two years preceding an application.

TYPE OF GRANT Capital projects.

RANGE OF GRANTS Up to £4,000.

SAMPLE GRANTS Previous grant recipients have included: Erskine Hospital, the National Youth Orchestra of Scotland, Scottish Motor Neurone Disease, the Castle Howard Trust, Delta, the National Burns Memorial Homes, Quarriers Village and Shelter.

FINANCES *Year* 2009 *Income* £930,274

TRUSTEES The Directors.

HOW TO APPLY In writing to the correspondent at any time, supported by copy of accounts and information about the organisation's principal activities.

WHO TO APPLY TO The Directors, 7 West George Street, Glasgow G2 1BA *Tel* 0141 221 8272 *Fax* 0141 226 2275 *email* theoffice@ merchantshouse.org.uk *Website* www. merchantshouse.org.uk

■ Mercury Phoenix Trust

CC NO 1013768   **ESTABLISHED** 1992

WHERE FUNDING CAN BE GIVEN Worldwide.

WHO CAN BENEFIT Registered charities benefiting people with AIDS and the HIV virus.

WHAT IS FUNDED Relief of poverty, sickness and distress of people affected by AIDS and the HIV virus, and to stimulate awareness of the virus throughout the world.

WHAT IS NOT FUNDED No funding for individuals or travel costs.

TYPE OF GRANT One-off, capital, project, running costs.

RANGE OF GRANTS Up to £15,000.

SAMPLE GRANTS Save The Children – UK (£15,000); Preana – Nepal (£12,000); Care International – UK and Gemini – UK (£10,000 each); British Red Cross – UK (£9,200); Mfesane – South Africa (£8,000); Christian Social Services – South Africa (£7,000); OGLM – US (£4,500); Sawed Trust – India and Rural Consciousness Unit – Bangladesh (£4,000 each); Social Welfare Environment and Conservation – Nepal (£3,500); and Dhiverse – India (£1,000).

FINANCES *Year* 2009–10 *Income* £254,846 *Grants* £202,913 *Assets* £1,283,951

TRUSTEES Brian May; Henry James Beach; Mary Austin; Roger Taylor.

HOW TO APPLY Application forms are available on request to 'funding@mercuryphoenixtrust.com'. In addition to a completed application form, the trust requires the following documents: a budget; registration certificate; audited accounts for the last financial year; constitution or memorandum and articles of association; annual report; and equal opportunities policy.

WHO TO APPLY TO Peter Chant, Administrator, 22 Cottage Offices, Latimer Park, Latimer, Chesham, Buckinghamshire HP5 1TU *Tel* 01494 766799 *email* mercuryphoenixtrust@ idrec.com *Website* www.mercuryphoenixtrust. com

■ The Mersey Docks and Harbour Company Charitable Fund

CC NO 206913   **ESTABLISHED** 1811

WHERE FUNDING CAN BE GIVEN Merseyside.

WHO CAN BENEFIT Seafaring, registered charities on Merseyside.

WHAT IS FUNDED The relief of people who are sick, disabled and retired in the dock service or the families of those who were killed in service; and to benefit charities in the town or port of Liverpool.

RANGE OF GRANTS £25–£24,000.

SAMPLE GRANTS Community Foundation for Merseyside (£24,000); The Mersey Mission to Seafarers (£10,000); Plaza Community Cinema (£3,000); National Museums Liverpool (££2,000); Seafarers UK (£1,000); The Ark (£500) and Marie Curie Cancer Care (£150).

FINANCES *Year* 2010 *Income* £50,191 *Grants* £44,138 *Assets* £34,247

TRUSTEES G E Hodgson; M Whitworth.

HOW TO APPLY In writing to the correspondent.

WHO TO APPLY TO C R Marrison Gill, Secretary, The Mersey Docks and Harbour Company, Maritime Centre, Port of Liverpool, Liverpool L21 1LA

■ Community Foundation for Merseyside

CC NO 1068887   **ESTABLISHED** 1998

WHERE FUNDING CAN BE GIVEN Merseyside, Halton and Lancashire.

WHO CAN BENEFIT Charitable organisations.

WHAT IS FUNDED General charitable purposes, community, regeneration. The foundation manages funds on behalf of parent donors. Funding priorities will vary considerably depending on the requirements of these donors.

WHAT IS NOT FUNDED Each fund administered by the trust has separate guidelines and exclusionary criteria which are available directly from the trust's website.

SAMPLE GRANTS Halton Voluntary Action – to promote youth volunteering in the Halton area (£7,000 from the Local Network Fund); Jo Jo Mind & Body – to provide educational classes for young people with learning difficulties (£7,000 from the Local Network Fund); The Zero Centre – to fund a drop-in centre for victims of domestic abuse (£6,600 from the Local Network Fund); Liverpool Academy of Art – to provide running costs for art exhibitions (£5,000 from the Arts & Culture Fund); Fire Support Network – to develop a community garden (£500 from Unilever Green Machine); and Liverpool Greenbank Wheelchair Basketball Club – to offer introductory sports sessions to people with disabilities (£500 from Alliance & Leicester).

FINANCES *Year* 2010–11 *Income* £6,474,925 *Grants* £3,576,794 *Assets* £5,511,499

TRUSTEES Sue Langfield, Administrator. Michael Eastwood; Abi Pointing; Andrew Wallis; Robert Towers; William Bowley; Sally Yeoman; David McDonnell; Jayne Pugh.

OTHER INFORMATION The foundation manages funds on behalf of parent donors. Funding priorities will vary considerably depending on the requirements of these donors.

HOW TO APPLY Most of the trust's funds can now be applied for online using a standard form. Royal London fund applications must be submitted directly to the fund and the John Goore fund has a separate application form available on the trust website.

The trust's website states that, during the application process, 'you will be asked to give information on what your organisation needs. Information on our fund guidelines is below, on submission of your application we will determine which fund your project proposal meets. If your project proposal does not fit one of our funds at the time of submission, your application will be WITHDRAWN. If your application is withdrawn, if your organisation needs change, or if our fund portfolio changes you can reapply after 12 weeks of your original submission, however there is no guarantee of funding.' Applications must also include the following documents: constitution, accounts, bank statements and safeguarding policy (where applicable). Unless your organisation has received a grant from the foundation in the last 12 months you *must* submit these documents, otherwise your application will not be considered. The website also states: 'We ask you to identify a theme for your project and outcome indicators which will be compared when monitoring successful grants.' A list of themes and outcome indicators may be downloaded from the website. Full guidelines and application forms for individual funds are available from the foundation's website.

WHO TO APPLY TO Cathy Elliott, Chief Executive, Third Floor, Stanley Building, 43 Hanover Street, Liverpool L1 3DN *Tel* 0151 232 2444 *Fax* 0151 232 2445 *email* info@cfmerseyside. org.uk *Website* www.cfmerseyside.org.uk

■ The Zachary Merton and George Woofindin Convalescent Trust

CC NO 221760   **ESTABLISHED** 1956

WHERE FUNDING CAN BE GIVEN Preference for Sheffield and Lincoln including the following areas: north Nottinghamshire, north Derbyshire and South Yorkshire.

WHO CAN BENEFIT Organisations benefiting carers, disabled people and people disadvantaged by poverty.

WHAT IS FUNDED Convalescent homes, travelling expenses of convalescent poor people, respite care for carers, people in need through illness, and community medicine.

WHAT IS NOT FUNDED No grants to individuals.

TYPE OF GRANT Recurring costs; up to two years.

RANGE OF GRANTS £500–£4,000.

SAMPLE GRANTS Sheffield Family Holiday Fund (£4,000); Sheffield Churches Council for Community Care (£3,500); Multiple Sclerosis Centre (North Yorkshire) (£3,000); Marie Curie Cancer Care (Lincoln) (£2,000); Sheffield Hospitals Charitable Trust and St Luke's Hospice (£1,000 each) and The Sick Children's Hospital Trust £500).

FINANCES *Year* 2010 *Income* £36,086 *Grants* £32,880 *Assets* £943,459

TRUSTEES G Connell; M G S Frampton; N J A Hutton; Mrs P M Perriam; Mrs J Mason; Dr B Sharrack; B Evans; R Hague; G Rylands; Dr J Burton.

HOW TO APPLY In writing to the correspondent, by the middle of March or September.

WHO TO APPLY TO Godfrey J Smallman, Secretary, Wrigleys Solicitors LLP, Fountain Precinct, Balm Green, Sheffield S1 2JA *Tel* 0114 2675 594 *Fax* 0114 2763176

■ The Tony Metherell Charitable Trust

CC NO 1046899   **ESTABLISHED** 1992

WHERE FUNDING CAN BE GIVEN UK, especially Hertfordshire and Worcestershire.

WHO CAN BENEFIT Particularly older people and people who have cancer or disabilities.

WHAT IS FUNDED General charitable purposes, including hospices, cancer charities and the care and welfare of people who are elderly or have disabilities.

WHAT IS NOT FUNDED No grants to overseas causes.

RANGE OF GRANTS Up to £5,000.

SAMPLE GRANTS H Hospice (£2,800).

FINANCES *Year* 2009–10 *Income* £13,775 *Grants* £50,000

TRUSTEES Jemma Eadie; Kate Cooper.

HOW TO APPLY In writing to the correspondent.

WHO TO APPLY TO Jemma Eadie, Trustee, 50 Lillishall Road, London SW4 0LP

■ The Metropolitan Drinking Fountain and Cattle Trough Association

CC NO 207743   **ESTABLISHED** 1960

WHERE FUNDING CAN BE GIVEN UK, mainly London; overseas.

WHO CAN BENEFIT Charitable organisations.

WHAT IS FUNDED Projects working to provide clean water supplies in developing countries, the provision of drinking fountains in schools and the restoration of disused drinking fountains. The preservation of the association's archive materials, artefacts, drinking fountains, cattle troughs and other installations.

SAMPLE GRANTS Appropriate Technology (£2,500); Dhaka Ahsania Mission, Resolve and The Spiti Project (£2,000 each); The Salvation Army (£1,500); and TescoSpana (£1,400).

FINANCES *Year* 2009–10 *Income* £29,390 *Grants* £35,095 *Assets* £590,294

TRUSTEES J E Mills, Chair; R P Baber; Mrs S Fuller; Sir J Smith; M W Elliott; M Nation; A King; M Bear; Mrs L Erith.

PUBLICATIONS The Drinking Fountain Association.

HOW TO APPLY In writing to the correspondent. In addition, in considering an application for a grant, trustees also require the following information: A copy of the most recent audited accounts; How has the cost of the project been ascertained, e.g. qualified surveyor?; How many people/animals is it estimated would use the fountain/trough in a day?; Will the charity supervise the project, if not who would?; Where is it anticipated the remainder of the funds to complete the project will come from?

WHO TO APPLY TO R P Baber, Secretary, Oaklands, 5 Queenborough Gardens, Chislehurst, Kent BR7 6NP *Tel* 020 8467 1261 *email* ralph. baber@tesco.net *Website* www. drinkingfountains.org

■ The Metropolitan Masonic Charity (formerly The London Masonic Charitable Trust)

CC NO 1081205   **ESTABLISHED** 2000

WHERE FUNDING CAN BE GIVEN Particular but not exclusive focus on London.

WHO CAN BENEFIT Registered charities.

WHAT IS FUNDED General charitable purposes. The trust coordinates donations to selected charities.

SAMPLE GRANTS Arrow riding for the disabled (£500); Barons Court project (£1,300); British School of Osteopathy (£5,000); Friendship Works (£5,000); St John's Youth Centre (£2,500); War Memorial Trust (£2,500); Thamesmead YMCA Activity Centre.

FINANCES *Year* 2009–10 *Income* £185,869 *Grants* £55,743 *Assets* £474,670

TRUSTEES Russell Race, Chair; Michael Birkett; Andrew Henderson; Rex Thorne; Robert Corp-Reader; Brian de Neut.

HOW TO APPLY In writing to the correspondent. 'The Metropolitan Grand Lodge of London, from time to time selects charities where relatively small amounts of money applied to specific projects will produce significant results.'

WHO TO APPLY TO Michael Birkett, Trustee, 60 Great Queen Street, PO Box 29055, London WC2B 5UN *Website* www.metgl.com

---

■ T and J Meyer Family Foundation Limited

CC NO 1087507   **ESTABLISHED** 2001

WHERE FUNDING CAN BE GIVEN UK and overseas.

WHO CAN BENEFIT Charitable organisations.

WHAT IS FUNDED The primary focus of the foundation is on education, healthcare and the environment. The criteria for charities are: organisations which alleviate the suffering of humanity through health, education and environment; organisations with extremely high correlation between what is gifted and what the beneficiary receives; organisations who struggle to raise funds either because either they are new, their size or their access to funds is constrained; organisations who promote long-term effective sustainable solutions.

SAMPLE GRANTS Sisters of Sacred Heart of J & M (£63,000); Living Heart, Peru (£4,700); Room to Read (£50,000); Barefoot College (£6,300); Trees Water People (£12,500); Friends without Borders (£31,000); Partners in Health (£63,000); Village Health Workers (£16,000); Angels Choir (£7,700); Bowel Cancer UK (£7,300); Hope and Homes for Children (£39,000); Royal Marsden Cancer Trust (£68,000); Samantha Dixon Brain Tumour (£15,000).

FINANCES *Year* 2010 *Income* £297,726 *Grants* £533,841 *Assets* £16,243,965

TRUSTEES A C Meyer; J D Meyer; Q H Meyer; I T Meyer; M M Meyer.

HOW TO APPLY No grants to unsolicited applications. Trustees meet four times a year

WHO TO APPLY TO T H Meyer, 3 Kendrick Mews, London SW7 3HG *email* info@tjmff.org

---

■ Mi Yu Foundation

CC NO 1136451   **ESTABLISHED** 2010

WHERE FUNDING CAN BE GIVEN Worldwide.

WHO CAN BENEFIT Organisations and individuals.

WHAT IS FUNDED The advancement of education of children and young people, in particular those who are orphaned, abandoned or disadvantaged in any part of the world. The relief of poverty, sickness and distress and any other charitable purposes.

TRUSTEES Jeffrey Lermer; Michelle Ambalo; Yudo Ambalo.

HOW TO APPLY In writing to the correspondent.

WHO TO APPLY TO J K Lermer, Trustee, 42 Lytton Road, Barnet EN5 5BY *Tel* 020 8441 1140 *email* info@lermer.co.uk

---

■ Mickleham Charitable Trust

CC NO 1048337   **ESTABLISHED** 1995

WHERE FUNDING CAN BE GIVEN UK, with a preference for Norfolk.

WHO CAN BENEFIT Registered charities.

WHAT IS FUNDED Relief for the abused and disadvantaged, particularly young people, and the blind.

TYPE OF GRANT Mainly recurrent.

RANGE OF GRANT £500–£10,000.

SAMPLE GRANTS Orbis International (£12,000); Harvest Trust (£6,000); Deafness Research UK, Age Concern – Norwich and Motability – Norfolk (£5,000 each); NR5 Project (£2,000); Whizz Kids (£1,500); and St Dunstans, Rethink, Norwich Youth for Christ, Canine Partners, Norfolk Family Mediation Service, Elizabeth Fitzroy Support, Musical Keys and Parkinson's Disease Society (£1,000 each).

FINANCES *Year* 2009–10 *Income* £126,040 *Grants* £144,000 *Assets* £3,086,893

TRUSTEES Philip Norton; Revd Sheila Nunney; Anne Richardson.

HOW TO APPLY In writing to the correspondent.

WHO TO APPLY TO Philip Norton, Trustee, c/o Hansells, 13–14 The Close, Norwich NR1 4DS *Tel* 01603 615731 *email* philipnorton@hansells.co.uk

---

■ Gerald Micklem Charitable Trust

CC NO 802583   **ESTABLISHED** 1988

WHERE FUNDING CAN BE GIVEN UK.

WHO CAN BENEFIT Registered charities benefiting at risk groups and people who are disadvantaged by poverty or socially isolated.

WHAT IS FUNDED Medicine and health, welfare and general charitable purposes.

WHAT IS NOT FUNDED The trust does not make grants to individuals, does not enter into sponsorship arrangements with individuals and does not make grants to organisations that are not UK-registered charities. The areas of charitable activity that fall outside the trust's current funding priorities are: drug/alcohol abuse and counselling; museums, galleries and heritage; performing arts and cultural organisations; churches; and overseas aid.

TYPE OF GRANT One-off and recurrent.

RANGE OF GRANTS £1,000–£6,000.

SAMPLE GRANTS Self Unlimited (£6,000); Support for Living, Osteopathic Centre for Children, The Rosemary Foundation, Whizz-Kidz (£4,000 each); The Bendrigg Trust; St Wilfrid's Ribchester PCC, Hampshire Deaf Association, Refuge, Diabetes UK (£3,000 each); Bhola's Children, The Royal Forestry Society and St Mary's Convent & Nursing Home – Chiswick (£2,000 each).

FINANCES *Year* 2010 *Income* £440,018 *Grants* £127,000 *Assets* £977,336

TRUSTEES Susan J Shone; Joanna L Scott-Dalgleish; Helen Ratcliffe.

HOW TO APPLY In writing to the correspondent. Interested applicants should note that the organisations which have received grants in the past should not be taken as indicative of a geographical or other bias.

WHO TO APPLY TO Mrs S J Shone, Trustee, Bolinge Hill Farm, Buriton, Petersfield, Hampshire GU31 4NN *Tel* 01730 264207 *email* mail@geraldmicklemct.org.uk *Website* www.geraldmicklemct.org.uk

---

■ The Masonic Province of Middlesex Charitable Trust

CC NO 1064406   **ESTABLISHED** 1997
WHERE FUNDING CAN BE GIVEN Middlesex.
WHO CAN BENEFIT Masons and others.
WHAT IS FUNDED Masonic charities and non-Masonic charities.
RANGE OF GRANTS £100–£5,500.
SAMPLE GRANTS Beneficiaries included: 13th Southall Sikh Scouts Group (£11,225); Breast Cancer Haven, Hanworth Park Preservation Trust and 3rd Hanworth Scout Group (£5,000 each); Dreamflight (£3,000); 5th Hayes Scout Group (£1,800); Catholic Children's Society, Harrow Citizens Advice Centre and Strongrove Playscheme (£1,000 each); Gothic Lodge Charitable Association (£750); and Spelthorne District Scouts Council (£500).
FINANCES *Year* 2009–10 *Income* £58,125 *Grants* £39,193 *Assets* £1,711,946
TRUSTEES Peter Richard Alleyne Baker; David Ian Allan; Jonathan Markham Gollow; Adrian John Howorth; Peter Gledhill.
HOW TO APPLY On a form is available from the correspondent or the Provincial Office.
WHO TO APPLY TO Peter Gledhill, Secretary, 85 Fakenham Way, Owlsmoor, Sandhurst, Berkshire GU47 0YS *Tel* 01344 777077 *email* peter.gledhill@btinternet.com

---

■ Midhurst Pensions Trust

CC NO 245230   **ESTABLISHED** 1965
WHERE FUNDING CAN BE GIVEN UK and overseas.
WHO CAN BENEFIT Registered charities and individuals.
WHAT IS FUNDED General charitable purposes and pensions to older people in need in Midhurst – West Sussex.
WHAT IS NOT FUNDED No grants to individuals who do not have a connection to the Cowdray Estate.
SAMPLE GRANTS The Birthday House Trust (£95,000).
FINANCES *Year* 2009–10 *Income* £102,749 *Grants* £95,000 *Assets* £4,029,816
TRUSTEES The Cowdray Trust Limited and Rathbone Trust Company Ltd.
HOW TO APPLY In writing to the correspondent. Acknowledgements will be sent to unsuccessful applicants if an sae is enclosed with the application.
WHO TO APPLY TO Laura Gosling, c/o Millbank Financial Services LtdPollen House, 10–12 Cork Street, London W1S 3LW *Tel* 020 7439 9061 *email* charity@mfs.co.uk

---

■ The Migraine Trust

CC NO 1081300   **ESTABLISHED** 1965
WHERE FUNDING CAN BE GIVEN UK and overseas.
WHO CAN BENEFIT Organisations benefiting people suffering from migraines, medical professionals, research workers and scientists.
WHAT IS FUNDED Research grants, fellowships and studentships (studentships are applied for by host institution only) for the study of migraine. Funds provide for research into migraine at recognised institutions, e.g. hospitals and universities.
FINANCES *Year* 2009–10 *Income* £583,449 *Grants* £72,578 *Assets* £388,406
TRUSTEES Andrew Jordan; J P S Wolff-Ingham; Prof. P J Goadsby; Ms S Hammond; Dr H McGregor; Dr Anne McGregor; Mrs Jennifer Mills; Dr Mark Wetherall; Dr Brendan Davies; Ian Watmore; Mrs Suzanne Marriot.
PUBLICATIONS Migraine News, Migraine: Understanding and coping with migraine.
OTHER INFORMATION The trust holds the Migraine Trust International Symposia, funds research into migraine, and has a full sufferer service.
HOW TO APPLY By application form available from trust. Applications will be acknowledged.
WHO TO APPLY TO Adam Speller, 2nd Floor, 55–56 Russell Square, London WC1B 4HP *Tel* 020 7462 6604 *email* info@migrainetrust.org *Website* www.migrainetrust.org

---

■ Miles Trust for the Putney and Roehampton Community

CC NO 246784   **ESTABLISHED** 1967
WHERE FUNDING CAN BE GIVEN The borough of Wandsworth.
WHO CAN BENEFIT Organisations benefiting people of all ages, people disadvantaged by poverty and homeless people.
WHAT IS FUNDED Schools, churches, youth organisations, and social welfare organisations caring for people who are poor, homeless, elderly or sick.
WHAT IS NOT FUNDED No grants to individuals.
TYPE OF GRANT Some recurring, but new grants may be one-off.
RANGE OF GRANTS £100–£5,000 with occasional larger special grants.
SAMPLE GRANTS 4th Putney Scouts (£6,400); Wandsworth Bereavement Service (£3,000); Putney Poor Relief Committee (£2,500); Wandsworth Mind (£2,000); St Mary's Church of England School (£1,500); and Children's Health Centre Samaritan Fund and Heathside Resource Centre (£1,000 each).
FINANCES *Year* 2010 *Income* £21,514 *Grants* £26,700
TRUSTEES A R Collender, Chair; Mrs A Raikes; R J G Holman; P Kitchen; Mrs a Stevens; Mrs L Moir; Mrs J Walters; Mrs C V M Davey; Mrs Kate Caseley.
HOW TO APPLY In writing to the correspondent. Applications are considered first by a sub-committee of trustees with specialist knowledge of the particular area to which the request for funds relates (church, youth or community); recommendations are then put before full meetings of the Trustees, which are held bi-annually.
WHO TO APPLY TO Mrs Angela Holman, Secretary & Administrator, 11 Genoa Avenue, Putney, London SW15 6DY *Tel* 020 8789 0953 *email* angelaholman@virgin.net

---

■ Millennium Stadium Charitable Trust

CC NO 1086596   **ESTABLISHED** 2001
WHERE FUNDING CAN BE GIVEN Wales.
WHO CAN BENEFIT The trust supports: not-for-profit organisations; properly constituted voluntary organisations; charitable organisations; voluntary groups working with local authorities (applicant cannot be the local authority);

applications from groups of any age (not just youth projects). Priority is given to organisations serving groups and communities suffering from the greatest disadvantage.

WHAT IS FUNDED Through its grant funding the trust aims to improve the quality of life of people who live and work in Wales. In particular the trust aims to promote education, history, language and culture, particularly for those who face disadvantage or discrimination. The trust makes grants in four programme areas: (1) sport; (2) the arts; (3) the environment; (4) the community. Wales is a country rich in culture, history, language and sporting successes. In today's era of globalisation people often forget what is in their locality. As a result the trust is keen to help young people learn more about their country via exchange programmes and has made provision to support youth exchange programmes which fall in to any of the funding categories of the trust.

WHAT IS NOT FUNDED The trust does not support: projects outside of Wales; day-to-day running costs; projects that seek to redistribute grant funds for the benefit of third party organisations; payments of debts/overdrafts; retrospective requests; requests from individuals; payment to profit making organisations; applications made solely in the name of a local authority. (N.B. In addition to the above, successful applicants may not-reapply to the trust until a three year period from the date of grant offer has elapsed. The grant offer letter will advise applicants of the date when they will be eligible to re-apply.).

RANGE OF GRANTS The trust issues funding according to the size of geographical area that an organisation has a remit to cover. National (Wales-wide) – up to £12,500; regional – up to £7,500; local – up to £2,500.

FINANCES *Year* 2009–10 *Income* £392,865 *Grants* £344,245 *Assets* £675,884

TRUSTEES Russell Goodway, Chair; Louise Casella; Ian Davies; Gerald Davies; Paul Glaze; Gerallt Hughes; Peredur Jenkins; Mike John; John Lloyd-Jones; Linda Pepper; Louise Prynne; Simon Wakefield; Wendy Williams.

HOW TO APPLY The trust holds three rounds a year one for each type of application – national, regional and local. Deadline dates can be found on the trust's website, along with full guidelines and application forms.

WHO TO APPLY TO The Trust Officer, c/o Fusion, Loft 2, Ocean House, Clarence Road, Cardiff Bay CF10 5FR *Tel* 029 2049 4963 *Fax* 029 2049 4964 *email* msct@fusionuk.org.uk *Website* www.millenniumstadiumtrust.co.uk

■ The Hugh and Mary Miller Bequest Trust

SC NO SC014950 **ESTABLISHED** 1976
WHERE FUNDING CAN BE GIVEN Mainly Scotland.
WHO CAN BENEFIT Registered charities. The trust supports disability causes, with the same 18 organisations receiving the majority of funding each year.
WHAT IS FUNDED Healthcare and disability.
WHAT IS NOT FUNDED Only registered charities are supported. No grants to individuals.
TYPE OF GRANT Capital including buildings, core costs, project, research, recurring costs, running costs and salaries. Funding is available for more than three years.
FINANCES *Year* 2009–10 *Grants* £86,638
TRUSTEES G R G Graham; H C Davidson.

OTHER INFORMATION No recent financial information was available, although previous research indicates that grants are made to regular beneficiaries totalling around £90,000 each year.
HOW TO APPLY The trust states that its funds are fully committed.
WHO TO APPLY TO Andrew S Biggart, Secretary, c/o Maclay Murray and Spens Solicitors, 151 St Vincent Street, Glasgow G2 5NJ *Tel* 0141 248 5011 *Fax* 0141 271 5319 *email* andrew.biggart@mms.co.uk

■ The Miller Foundation

SC NO SC008798 **ESTABLISHED** 1979
WHERE FUNDING CAN BE GIVEN Scotland and other parts of the UK.
WHO CAN BENEFIT Charities benefiting children and young adults; students; at risk groups; disabled groups; those disadvantaged by poverty; and socially isolated people.
WHAT IS FUNDED Grants are given to educational projects, especially at tertiary level. Organisations working for the welfare of humans and animals are also supported, as are schemes working with people who are disabled.
WHAT IS NOT FUNDED No grants to individuals.
RANGE OF GRANTS £1,000–£2,000.
FINANCES *Year* 2009–10 *Income* £158,497 *Grants* £150,000
TRUSTEES C Fleming-Brown; G R G Graham; J Simpson; G F R Fleming-Brown.
HOW TO APPLY In writing to the correspondent.
WHO TO APPLY TO The Secretary, Maclay Murray and Spens, 151 St Vincent Street, Glasgow G2 5NJ

■ The Millfield House Foundation

CC NO 271180 **ESTABLISHED** 1976
WHERE FUNDING CAN BE GIVEN North east England particularly Tyne and Wear.
WHO CAN BENEFIT Voluntary agencies and other bodies with charitable objectives working with socially and economically disadvantaged people. Bodies undertaking policy research and advocacy should have close links with or voluntary or community organisations in the region. The foundation will support national as well as local bodies, provided that projects are based in the North East of England (includes regional and sub-regional projects; projects which are locally based may be considered so long as they are of wider benefit).
WHAT IS FUNDED Projects supported might for example seek to: give a voice to excluded groups; bring firsthand experience of poverty to opinion formers and policy makers; promote social policy discussion in the region; campaign on local social issues. The financial resources of MHF are a tiny fraction of the total available for charitable activity in the North East. The trustees therefore wish to concentrate their resources on projects which most other funding bodies cannot or will not support. As a charity, the foundation must confine its grants to purposes accepted in law as charitable. However, official guidance makes it clear that charities may include a variety of political and campaigning activities to further their purposes. [See 'Speaking Out – Guidance on Political Activity and Campaigning by Charities' published by the Charity Commission].
WHAT IS NOT FUNDED The foundation 'will not fund straightforward service provision, or mainline

university research, or the wide range of other projects that are eligible for support elsewhere'.

TYPE OF GRANT MHF aims to provide, alone or in partnership with other funders, significant and medium-term support to a small number of carefully selected projects or organisations. It is unlikely to have more than about 6 to 12 grants in payment at the same time and can therefore approve only a small number of new grants in any one year. One-off grants may be between £5,000 and £50,000. Grants for more than one year could be between £20,000 and £30,000 per annum for two or three years.

RANGE OF GRANTS Between £5,000 and £50,000.

SAMPLE GRANTS Institute for Public Policy Research (£40,000); Gateshead Carers Association (£34,000); Regional Refugee Forum North East (£32,000); Age Concern and Shelter (£30,000 each); Barnardo's (£24,000); Mental Health North East (£23,000); Living Streets (£15,000); Compass (£10,000); Voluntary Organisations Network North East (£500).

FINANCES *Year* 2009–10 *Income* £144,033 *Grants* £238,296 *Assets* £5,628,668

TRUSTEES Rosemary Chubb; Grigor McClelland; Jen McClelland; Stephen McClelland; Sheila Spencer; Jane Streather; Rhiannon Bearne; Toby Lowe; Robert Williamson.

PUBLICATIONS Guidelines for Applicants. Reports on Grant-making: 1984–89 and 1989–96. Report: 'Funding Policy Change for a Better Society in the North East of England', 1996–2004, available in PDF version.

HOW TO APPLY Initial outline proposals should be made in writing to the correspondent. If the application meets the stated guidelines the administrator may request further information or arrange a meeting. Applications unconnected with Tyne and Wear are not acknowledged. The trustees meet twice a year, in May and November and the deadlines for these meetings are mid April and mid October. The administrator is willing to provide guidance for the preparation of final applications, but not without first receiving an outline proposal. Applications should include: (i) Full contact details, including email address if available. A covering letter containing a brief summary of the purpose of the project and the amount sought from MHF, and a substantive paper of no more than 4 pages. All other information should be provided as Appendices. (ii) A description of the project including its aims and intended outcomes, with specific reference to possible policy implications, an action programme and proposed timescale for delivery. (iii) A budget for the project giving a breakdown of total expenditure and of sources of anticipated income. (iv) A copy of the most recent annual report and audited accounts for the project and/or the sponsoring body. (v) The constitution of the responsible body. (vi) Details of the organisation's policy and procedures for equal opportunities and diversity. (vii) If appropriate, plans for dissemination of the results of the project. (Research reports should be summarised in a format similar to that of the 'Findings' series produced by the Joseph Rowntree Foundation). (viii) Details of arrangements for monitoring and evaluation. (ix) If funding is sought towards the costs of a salaried post, a job description. (x) The names of two independent referees (references may not be taken up in every case). For further information potential applicants are strongly advised to visit the trust's website.

WHO TO APPLY TO Terence Finley, Administrator, 19 The Crescent, Benton Lodge, Newcastle upon Tyne NE7 7ST *Tel* 0191 266 9429 *email* finley@lineone.net *Website* www.mhfdn.org.uk

---

■ **The Millfield Trust**

CC NO 262406   **ESTABLISHED** 1971

WHERE FUNDING CAN BE GIVEN UK and worldwide.

WHO CAN BENEFIT Individuals and organisations benefiting elderly people, Christians, and people in need.

WHAT IS FUNDED Support of religious or other charitable institutions or work. Advancement of the Protestant and Evangelical tenets of the Christian faith and encouragement of missionary activity. Relief of need. Preference to charities of which the trust has special interest, knowledge or association. Funds fully allocated or committed.

TYPE OF GRANT Unrestricted.

RANGE OF GRANTS £100–£12,500.

SAMPLE GRANTS Gideon's International (£12,500); Gospel Mission to South America (£8,500); Mark Gillingham Charitable Trust (£4,200); Ashbury Evangelical Free Church (£3,500); Mission to Europe (£3,000); Bible lands (£2,500); and Send a Cow and TEAR Fund (£1,100 each).

FINANCES *Year* 2009–10 *Income* £71,026 *Grants* £68,450 *Assets* £137,688

TRUSTEES D Bunce; P W Bunce; S D Bunce; A C Bunce; Mrs. Rita Bunce.

HOW TO APPLY No replies to unsolicited applications.

WHO TO APPLY TO D Bunce, Trustee, Millfield House, Bell Lane, Liddington, Swindon, Wiltshire SN4 0HE *Tel* 01793 790181

■ **The Millhouses Charitable Trust**

CC NO 327773   **ESTABLISHED** 1988

WHERE FUNDING CAN BE GIVEN UK and overseas.

WHO CAN BENEFIT Registered charities benefiting Christians, at risk groups, people disadvantaged by poverty, socially isolated people, victims of famine, disasters and war.

WHAT IS FUNDED Overseas aid, social welfare and community services (with a Christian emphasis). A preference is shown for Baptist charities.

WHAT IS NOT FUNDED Grants are made to registered charities only; no grants to individuals.

TYPE OF GRANT Mostly recurrent.

RANGE OF GRANTS £250–£12,000.

SAMPLE GRANTS NSPCC and Christian Solidarity (£5,000 each); Release International and Barnabus Fund (£2,500 each); Children's Society, Crisis and Oasis (£1,000 each); Rehab UK and Medical foundation (£500 each); and Mercy Ships, Operation Mobilisation and Smile (£250 each).

FINANCES *Year* 2009–10 *Income* £19,839 *Grants* £17,911

TRUSTEES Revd Jeanetta S Harcus; Dr A W Harcus; Dr J L S Alexander; Ms Penelope A Thornton; Mrs Fiona J van Nieuwkerk.

HOW TO APPLY In writing to the correspondent, but note that most of the grants given by this trust are recurrent. If new grants are made, they are usually to organisations known to the trustees.

WHO TO APPLY TO Paul Charles Kurthausen, c/o MacFarlane and Co., Cunard Building, Water Street, Liverpool L3 1DS *Tel* 0151 236 6161 *Fax* 0151 236 1095 *email* paulk@macca.co.uk

■ The Millichope Foundation

CC NO 282357   **ESTABLISHED** 1981
WHERE FUNDING CAN BE GIVEN UK, especially the West Midlands and Shropshire.
WHO CAN BENEFIT Registered charities, some grants to UK and international organisations; local applications limited to the West Midlands and Shropshire.
WHAT IS FUNDED General charitable purposes. Specific areas of interest are arts and culture, education, conservation, healthcare outside the NHS remit, respite care, environment and local historic buildings (such as churches). It also gives small donations to local community groups, usually in Shropshire, as well as one-off grants for disaster appeals or specific needs.
WHAT IS NOT FUNDED No grants to individuals or non-registered charities.
TYPE OF GRANT Normally an annual commitment for a period of five years.
RANGE OF GRANTS Usually £500–£5,000.
SAMPLE GRANTS Brazilian Atlantic Rainforest Forest (£15,000); Hope and Homes for Children (£10,000); Community Council of Shropshire and Megan Baker House (£5,000 each); Cambridge Foundation (£4,000); Teme Valley Youth Project and Galapagos Conservation Trust (£2,000 each); Birmingham City Mission and Sandwell MultiCare (£2,000 each); Age Concern – Birmingham, Juvenile Diabetes Research Foundation and Riding for the Disabled (£1,000 each); and Marches Family Network (£500).
FINANCES *Year* 2009–10 *Income* £398,226 *Grants* £271,687 *Assets* £5,964,719
TRUSTEES L C N Bury; Mrs S A Bury; Mrs B Marshall.
HOW TO APPLY In writing to the correspondent.
WHO TO APPLY TO Mrs S A Bury, Trustee, Millichope Park, Munslow, Craven Arms, Shropshire SY7 9HA *Tel* 01584 841234 *email* sarah@millichope.com

■ The Mills Charity

CC NO 207259   **ESTABLISHED** 1981
WHERE FUNDING CAN BE GIVEN Framlingham and surrounding district.
WHO CAN BENEFIT Charitable organisations and some individuals.
WHAT IS FUNDED General charitable purposes and social welfare.
SAMPLE GRANTS Grants were awarded to: The Thomas Mills High School (£30,000); The Mills Educational Foundation (£20,000); St Michaels Parish Church (£15,000); Framlingham Scout and Guide Group (£5,800); Dennington Bell Appeal (£5,000); Disability Advice Service (£1,700); Kettleborough Green Trust (£1,100); Royal British Legion (£500); and Optua (£100).
FINANCES *Year* 2009–10 *Income* £160,392 *Grants* £71,171 *Assets* £7,145,420
TRUSTEES H Wright, Chair; Mrs P C Booth; K W Musgrove; M J Kelleway; N Corke; Mrs K Hunt; Dr C Wright; Revd M Vipond.
OTHER INFORMATION £5,538 to individuals.
HOW TO APPLY In writing to the correspondent.
WHO TO APPLY TO R A Douglas, PO Box 1703, Framlingham, Woodbridge IP13 9WW *Tel* 01728 723188 *Fax* 01728 621321 *email* info@themillscharity.co.uk *Website* www.themillscharity.co.uk

■ The Millward Charitable Trust

CC NO 328564   **ESTABLISHED** 1989
WHERE FUNDING CAN BE GIVEN UK and overseas.
WHO CAN BENEFIT Charitable organisations.
WHAT IS FUNDED Social welfare, performing arts, medical research and animal welfare.
TYPE OF GRANT One-off grants.
SAMPLE GRANTS Birds Eye View (£36,000 in three grants); Music in the Round (£6,400); City of Birmingham Symphony Orchestra (£10,000 in two grants); CORD Sudan Appeal and Leamington Music RSPCA (£5,000 each); and Barnardo's, Christian Relief, Howard League for Penal Reform and RSPCA (1,000 each).
FINANCES *Year* 2009–10 *Income* £68,445 *Grants* £84,158 *Assets* £1,996,781
TRUSTEES Maurice Millward; Sheila Millward; John Hulse.
HOW TO APPLY In writing to the correspondent.
WHO TO APPLY TO John Hulse, Trustee, c/o Burgis & Bullock, 2 Chapel Court, Holly Walk, Leamington Spa, Warwickshire CV32 4YS *Tel* 01926 451000

■ The Clare Milne Trust

CC NO 1084733   **ESTABLISHED** 1999
WHERE FUNDING CAN BE GIVEN The south west of England, but Devon and Cornwall in practice.
WHO CAN BENEFIT Voluntary and community groups.
WHAT IS FUNDED Disability projects, especially those for adults in the south west of England, mainly in Devon and Cornwall. Preference is given to small and well-run local and regional charities with strong support from volunteers and with only modest expenditure on fundraising and administration.
WHAT IS NOT FUNDED No grants directly to or for individuals or to national charities.
TYPE OF GRANT Generally a partial contribution towards total cost of a project.
RANGE OF GRANTS Typically £1,000–£25,000.
SAMPLE GRANTS CEDA (£36,000); Dartmoor Pony Heritage Pony Trust (£28,000); Cornwall Multiple Sclerosis and Northam Lodge (£20,000 each); Echo (£16,000); Mobility Trust (£15,000); Stallcombe House, Broomhayes and Home Farm Trust (£10,000 each); Exeter Community Transport (£6,000); Barefoot (£5,000); Cornwall Disability Arts Group and The Sensory Trust (£2,000 each).
FINANCES *Year* 2009–10 *Income* £556,435 *Grants* £361,109 *Assets* £19,131,659
TRUSTEES Michael Brown, Chair; Lucie Nottingham; Tim Robinson; Margaret Rogers; Nigel Urwin.
HOW TO APPLY If you think your project meets the trust's criteria, you should write summarising your request on one side of an A4 sheet if possible, with minimal supporting literature; the trust will request a copy of your annual report and accounts later on if necessary. The trustees usually meet four times a year and to save unnecessary administration only applications which fit the trust's criteria will be responded to.
WHO TO APPLY TO Kim Lyons, Secretary, c/o Lee Bolton Monier-Williams Solicitors, 1 The Sanctuary, Westminster, London SW1P 3JT *Tel* 020 7404 0422 *email* milnetrust@hotmail.co.uk *Website* www.claremilnetrust.com

■ Milton Keynes Community Foundation

CC NO 295107 **ESTABLISHED** 1987

WHERE FUNDING CAN BE GIVEN Milton Keynes Unitary Authority.

WHO CAN BENEFIT Community groups, community interest companies, social enterprises, sports clubs, parish councils and local registered charities benefiting; people of all ages, at risk groups, carers, disabled people, those disadvantaged by poverty, homeless people, and victims of abuse, crime and domestic violence.

WHAT IS FUNDED The foundation's main priority is to help those in the Milton Keynes Council area who miss out because of poverty, ill health, disability or disadvantage. It also supports important initiatives in the spheres of the arts and leisure.

WHAT IS NOT FUNDED No grants are made to the following types of organisation: statutory organisations – including schools, hospitals and borough councils (applications from parish councils for community projects are accepted); political parties or groups affiliated to a political party; or individuals. Grants are normally not given for: sponsorship and fundraising events; contributions to major appeals; projects outside the beneficial area; political groups; projects connected with promoting a religious message of any kind; work which should be funded by health and local authorities or government grants aid; animal welfare; medical research or treatment; ongoing core costs not related to a particular service or activity; retrospective grants; nor grants to pay off deficits.

TYPE OF GRANT Small grants of up to £1,500; community grants up to £5,000 to cover equipment costs, projects and minor building work, training, publicity and one-off activity costs; arts grants awarded for artistic and cultural activities, particularly of high quality and originality; extraordinary grants for exceptional or urgent causes or for amounts of more than £5,000. The grants team must grant permission before extraordinary grants applications are made.

RANGE OF GRANTS Usually up to £5,000; possibility of more for extraordinary grants.

SAMPLE GRANTS Milton Keynes YMCA – towards a winter emergency accommodation service (£5,000 from the Koss Fund and Community Fund); Maybe Magazine – for a youth music project (£5,000 from the centre: mk Fund and NHBC Fund); Hanslope Village Hall Trust – towards repairs (£3,000 from the Brighton Acorn Fund); Scope – for an IT project for people with disabilities (£2,400 from the Margaret Powell Fund); and AKOTA – to fund a pilot project offering a Bengali language course to children (£1,000 from the Grassroots Fund.).

FINANCES *Year* 2010–11 *Income* £1,928,840 *Grants* £489,177 *Assets* £6,046,730

TRUSTEES Judith Hooper; Fola Komolafe; Francesca Skelton; Jane Matthews; Michael Murray; Peter Kara; Peter Selvey; Richard Brown; Roger Kitchen; Ruth Stone; Stephen Norrish.

PUBLICATIONS What is the Community Trust?, quarterly newsletter, Guide to Grants, annual report.

OTHER INFORMATION It is important to note that grant schemes can change frequently. For full details of the foundation's current grant programmes and their deadlines please consult the website.

HOW TO APPLY Application forms and guidelines are available on the website or can be requested by telephoning the office. The grants staff can be contacted to assist with any queries or help with applications. Deadlines for small grants programme is the last working Friday of each month and the community grants programme has five deadlines per year. Small grant applications are usually processed within 2 weeks and community grants, 5 weeks.

WHO TO APPLY TO Bart Gamber, Grants Director, Acorn House, 381 Midsummer Boulevard, Central Milton Keynes MK9 3HP *Tel* 01908 690276 *Fax* 01908 233635 *email* information@mkcommunityfoundation.co.uk *Website* www.mkcommunityfoundation.co.uk

■ The Edgar Milward Charity

CC NO 281018 **ESTABLISHED** 1980

WHERE FUNDING CAN BE GIVEN UK and overseas.

WHO CAN BENEFIT Causes known to the trustees, particularly those supported by the settlor.

WHAT IS FUNDED A limited number of Christian and humanitarian causes. The trustees currently have an established interest in a range of charities. Few new charities will be added to this list.

WHAT IS NOT FUNDED No new applications will be supported.

SAMPLE GRANTS The Bible Society and UCB (£2,000); Interserve (£1,500); and Africa Inland Mission, Greyfriars Missionary Trust, OSCAR and Urban Saints (£1,000 each).

FINANCES *Year* 2009–10 *Income* £49,072 *Grants* £30,250 *Assets* £1,186,216

TRUSTEES J S Milward, Chair; Mrs M V Roberts; G M Fogwill; S M W Fogwill; A S Fogwill; Mrs F Palethorpe; Mrs J C Austin.

HOW TO APPLY Unsolicited applications cannot be considered.

WHO TO APPLY TO A S Fogwill, Corresponding Secretary, 53 Brook Drive, Corsham, Wiltshire SN13 9AX

■ The Keith and Joan Mindelsohn Charitable Trust

CC NO 1075174 **ESTABLISHED** 1998

WHERE FUNDING CAN BE GIVEN Birmingham and West Midlands.

WHO CAN BENEFIT Charitable organisations, with a preference for smaller groups who lack the resources of national organisations and where the grant will make a more noticeable difference.

WHAT IS FUNDED General charitable purposes.

TYPE OF GRANT Project grants.

RANGE OF GRANTS £100–£500.

SAMPLE GRANTS Previous beneficiaries have included KIDS – West Midlands, Motor Neurone Disease, Whizz-Kidz, Heartlands Cystic Fibrosis, Birmingham Rathbone and Lady Hoare Trust.

FINANCES *Year* 2009–10 *Income* £12,665 *Grants* £30,042

TRUSTEES Jane Jaffa; Gillian Amiss; Gillian Hickman.

HOW TO APPLY In writing to the correspondent, preferably via email. The trustees meet three times a year.

WHO TO APPLY TO Richard Jaffa, Administrator, 32 Malcolmson Close, Edgbaston, Birmingham B15 3LS *Tel* 0121 454 6661 *Fax* 0121 605 4737 *email* rjaffa3266@aol.com

■ The Peter Minet Trust

CC NO 259963   **ESTABLISHED** 1969

WHERE FUNDING CAN BE GIVEN Mainly south east London boroughs, particularly Lambeth and Southwark.

WHO CAN BENEFIT Registered charities benefiting at risk groups, and people who have disabilities, are sick or disadvantaged by poverty.

WHAT IS FUNDED Registered charities (not individuals), particularly those working with young people, the sick, those with disabilities, disadvantaged people, the elderly, the arts and the environment.

WHAT IS NOT FUNDED The trust does not make grants for: individuals; national appeals by large charities; appeals outside the inner boroughs of South East London; appeals whose sole purpose is to make grants from collected funds; research.

TYPE OF GRANT Usually one-off for a specific project or part of a project.

RANGE OF GRANTS £50–£3,000.

SAMPLE GRANTS Bermondsey Arts Group, Southwark Playhouse Theatre Company, Putney Samaritans and The Young Vic (£3,000 each); Action Space London Events, Children with AIDS Charity, Live Music Now! and UK Sailing Academy (£2,000 each) and Bells Gardens Tenants and Residents Association, Southwark Homeless Information Project and The Food Chain (£1,000 each).

FINANCES *Year* 2009–10 *Income* £168,135 *Grants* £195,555 *Assets* £4,261,325

TRUSTEES J C B South, Chair; Ms P C Jones; R Luff; Revd Bruce Stokes; Mrs L Cleverly.

PUBLICATIONS Guidelines leaflet available.

OTHER INFORMATION Bruce Malcolm Stokes is also a trustee of First Fruit (Charity Commission no. 1066749); and Kick London (Charity Commission no. 1100072). Rodney Luff is also a trustee of The Simon Trust (Charity Commission no. 1029570); and The Will Charitable Trust (Charity Commission no. 801682).

HOW TO APPLY Application forms along with guidelines are available either, by post from the correspondent or, by downloading them from the trust's website. 'How to Apply for Main Grants and Small Grants: (i) please complete an application form that can be downloaded from www.peterminet.org.uk. We use the same form for Main Grants and Small Grants; (ii) this application form should be completed in Microsoft Word and emailed as a Word attachment (not a PDF) to info@peterminet.org.uk; (iii) please do not email brochures, letters or annual reports with your application. We only need an attachment of your application form. We do not need a copy of your latest signed audited accounts as we look at these on your Charity Commission's record on www.charity-commission.gov.uk; (iv) we prefer you to email us your application form, but if you cannot access the internet, please complete the form in black ink and send by post. Please do not use registered or recorded delivery as the office is not open full-time and this can delay your application.' If you have any questions about your application or how to send in your form, contact the office on 020 8772 3155 or info@peterminet.org.uk.

WHO TO APPLY TO The Administrator, 1a Taylors Yard, 67 Alderbrook Road, London SW12 8AD *Tel* 020 8772 3155 *email* info@peterminet. uk *Website* www.peterminet.org.uk

■ Minge's Gift and the Pooled Trusts

CC NO 266073   **ESTABLISHED** 1972

WHERE FUNDING CAN BE GIVEN UK, with some preference for the City of London.

WHO CAN BENEFIT Registered charities, schools, universities, hospitals and churches.

WHAT IS FUNDED General charitable purposes as directed by the Master and Wardens of the Cordwainers Company. The income of Minge's Gift is generally allocated for the long-term support of medical and educational establishments and towards disabled and/or disadvantaged young people. The Pooled Trusts mainly support individuals including scholars, the blind, deaf, clergy widows, spinsters of the Church of England, ex-servicemen and their widows and those who served in the merchant services.

WHAT IS NOT FUNDED Grants to individuals are only given through the Pooled Trusts.

TYPE OF GRANT Grants of up to, and in some cases over, three years for core costs, projects, research, and recurring costs; start-up costs are considered.

RANGE OF GRANTS £100–£16,000.

SAMPLE GRANTS Royal Society for the Blind (£16,000); University of Northampton (£15,000); and University of the Arts – London (£10,000). Other beneficiaries included: De Montfort University (£5,000); Footwear Friends (£3,000); Lord Mayors Fund (£2,000); Guildhall School of Music and Dance (£1,500); Museum of London (£1,000); St Olave's Church (£625); Queen Alexandra Hospital Home – Worthing (£500); Action for the Blind (£300); British Red Cross – City of London (£200); United Guilds Service (£125); and Shawe and Fisher Service (£110).

FINANCES *Year* 2009–10 *Income* £168,977 *Grants* £100,897 *Assets* £2,797,191

TRUSTEES The Master and Wardens of the Worshipful Company of Cordwainers.

OTHER INFORMATION In 2009–10, £15,400 was given in grants to individuals from the Pooled Trusts.

HOW TO APPLY In writing to the correspondent.

WHO TO APPLY TO John Miller, Company Clerk, The Worshipful Company of Cordwainers, Clothworkers Hall, Dunster Court, Mincing Lane, London EC3R 7AH *Tel* 020 7929 1121 *Fax* 020 7929 1124 *email* office@cordwain.org *Website* www.cordwainers.org

■ The Minos Trust

CC NO 265012   **ESTABLISHED** 1972

WHERE FUNDING CAN BE GIVEN UK and overseas.

WHO CAN BENEFIT Organisations.

WHAT IS FUNDED General charitable purposes, especially Christian causes.

RANGE OF GRANTS £25–£2,000, exceptionally higher.

SAMPLE GRANTS Previous beneficiaries include: Care Trust (£2,500), Tearfund (£2,000) and Ashburnham Christian Trust (£1,500), with £1,000 each to Bible Society, Friends of the Elderly and Youth with a Mission; Worldwide Fund for Nature (£450); Africa Christian Press (£400); Aid to Russian Christians (£300); Gideon's International (£100); Sussex Farming Wildlife Advisory Group and RSPB (£50 each).

FINANCES *Year* 2009–10 *Income* £7,361 *Grants* £25,030

TRUSTEES Revd K W Habershon; Mrs E M Habershon; Mrs D M Irwin-Clark.

HOW TO APPLY In writing to the correspondent, for consideration on an ongoing basis.
WHO TO APPLY TO The Trustees, Kleinwort Benson Trustees Ltd, 30 Gresham Street, London EC2V 7PG *Tel* 020 3207 7091

■ Minton Charitable Trust
CC NO 1112106   **ESTABLISHED** 2005
WHERE FUNDING CAN BE GIVEN UK.
WHO CAN BENEFIT Organisations and individuals.
WHAT IS FUNDED 'The advancement and promotion of the education of the public through the provision of, or assisting with, the provision of facilities, support, education, advice and financial assistance.'
RANGE OF GRANTS Up to £200,000.
SAMPLE GRANTS Swindon Academy (£200,000); and St Giles Trust (£125,000).
FINANCES *Year* 2009–10 *Income* £224,402 *Grants* £325,000 *Assets* £388,495
TRUSTEES Sir Anthony Armitage Greener; Richard Edmunds; Lady Audrey Greener.
HOW TO APPLY In writing to the correspondent.
WHO TO APPLY TO Sir Anthony Armitage Greener, Trustee, 26 Hamilton House, Vicarage Gate, London W8 4HL

■ The Mirfield Educational Charity
CC NO 529334   **ESTABLISHED** 1961
WHERE FUNDING CAN BE GIVEN The urban district of Mirfield.
WHO CAN BENEFIT Individuals and organisations.
WHAT IS FUNDED Schools; youth groups; and educational expenses for individuals.
RANGE OF GRANTS £500–£30,000.
SAMPLE GRANTS West Yorkshire Printworks (£2,260); Upper Hopton Cricket Club (£2,100); Mirfield Parish Cavaliers Cricket Club (£1,500); Church House Pre-school (£930); Gilder Hall Youth Foundation (£630); and Spen Valley School Football Association (£400).
FINANCES *Year* 2009–10 *Income* £49,404 *Grants* £8,675 *Assets* £1,346,141
TRUSTEES Dr H G Grason, Chair; D B Brook; B Nicholson; P A Morton; E A Speight; M Bolt; C Oldfield; G Jones; V Lees.
HOW TO APPLY In writing to the correspondent.
WHO TO APPLY TO Whitfield Hallam Goodall, 7 King Street, Mirfield WF14 8AW *Tel* 01924 499251 *email* mparkinson@whg.co.uk

■ The Mirianog Trust
CC NO 1091397   **ESTABLISHED** 2002
WHERE FUNDING CAN BE GIVEN UK.
WHO CAN BENEFIT Charitable organisations.
WHAT IS FUNDED General charitable purposes. Currently the trustees give preference to: the relief of poverty; overseas aid and famine relief; accommodation and housing; environment, conservation and heritage.
SAMPLE GRANTS Justice First (£8,000); Bwindi Hospital, Uganda, Oxfam and Women in Need (£6,000 each); Medical Foundation for the Victims of Torture (£4,000); Butterwick Hospice and Listening Books (£2,000 each); and Intercare (£1,000).
FINANCES *Year* 2009–10 *Income* £44,104 *Grants* £48,000 *Assets* £623,606
TRUSTEES Canon William Broad, Chair; Daphne Broad; Elizabeth Jeary.
HOW TO APPLY In writing to the correspondent. The trustees meet twice each year.

WHO TO APPLY TO Canon W E L Broad, Trustee, Moorcote, Thornley, Tow Law, Bishop Auckland DL13 4NU *Tel* 01388 731350

■ The Laurence Misener Charitable Trust
CC NO 283460   **ESTABLISHED** 1981
WHERE FUNDING CAN BE GIVEN UK.
WHO CAN BENEFIT There is a tendency to benefit those charities in which the settlor was interested.
WHAT IS FUNDED General charitable purposes, particularly Jewish organisations and medical causes.
RANGE OF GRANTS £4,000–£15,000.
SAMPLE GRANTS Jewish Association for the Physically Handicapped, Jewish Care and Nightingale House (£15,000 each); Jewish Temporary Shelter (£8,000); Blond McIndoe Centre, Cassel Hospital Families Centre Appeal, Elimination of Leukaemia Fund, Great Ormond Street Children's Hospital Fund, Seafarers UK, Sussex Stroke and Circulation Fund, Royal Marsden Hospital and World Jewish Relief (£7,000 each).
FINANCES *Year* 2009–10 *Income* £93,285 *Grants* £165,400 *Assets* £2,449,410
TRUSTEES Mrs J Legane; Capt. G F Swaine.
HOW TO APPLY In writing to the correspondent.
WHO TO APPLY TO David Lyons, c/o Leonard Jones & Co, 1 Printing Yard House, London E2 7PR *Tel* 020 7739 8790

■ The Mishcon Family Charitable Trust
CC NO 213165   **ESTABLISHED** 1961
WHERE FUNDING CAN BE GIVEN UK.
WHO CAN BENEFIT Registered charities, particularly Jewish organisations.
WHAT IS FUNDED General charitable purposes. Within the limited funds available each application is considered on its merits with preference given to applications for the relief of poverty from recognised organisations.
TYPE OF GRANT One-off.
RANGE OF GRANTS £20 upwards. Generally £5,000 or less.
SAMPLE GRANTS Jewish Israel Appeal (£37,000); Sick Children's Trust (£6,500); The Board of Deputies Charitable Trust (£6,000); Friends of Progressive Judaism (£5,000); Friends of Alyn (£2,000); The Lubavich Foundation and World Jewish Relief (£1,000 each); One World Action (£450); Jewish Book Council, Jewish Care, NSPCC and Rainbow Trust (£100 each); and The Stroke Association (£50).
FINANCES *Year* 2009–10 *Income* £57,160 *Grants* £88,037 *Assets* £1,839,710
TRUSTEES P A Mishcon; R O Mishcon; Mrs J Landau.
HOW TO APPLY In writing to the correspondent.
WHO TO APPLY TO The Trustees, Summit House, 12 Red Lion Square, London WC1R 4QD

■ The Misselbrook Trust
CC NO 327928   **ESTABLISHED** 1988
WHERE FUNDING CAN BE GIVEN UK with a preference for the Wessex area.
WHO CAN BENEFIT Registered charities.
WHAT IS FUNDED General charitable purposes.
TYPE OF GRANT One-off and recurrent.

RANGE OF GRANTS Up to £10,000, usually under £500.

SAMPLE GRANTS Cantell Maths and Computing College (£10,000); Marwell Preservation Trust (£1,500); AIDS Trust, Royal Star & Garter Home and Southampton Women's Aid (£1,000 each); and St John's Church, Alresford (£600).

FINANCES *Year* 2009–10 *Income* £337,190 *Grants* £31,700 *Assets* £1,032,672

TRUSTEES M Howson-Green; B M Baxendale; D A Hoare; Mrs M A Howson-Green.

HOW TO APPLY In writing to the correspondent

WHO TO APPLY TO M Howson-Green, Trustee, Ashton House, 12 The Central Precinct, Winchester Road, Chandlers Ford, Eastleigh, Hampshire, SO53 2GB *Tel* 023 8027 4555

■ The Brian Mitchell Charitable Settlement

CC NO 1003817   **ESTABLISHED** 1989

WHERE FUNDING CAN BE GIVEN UK.

WHO CAN BENEFIT Registered charities.

WHAT IS FUNDED General charitable purposes including education and the arts.

RANGE OF GRANTS Up to £20,000.

SAMPLE GRANTS Glyndebourne Festival Society (£20,000); The Skinners School (£10,000); and Canterbury Cathedral (£2,000). The remaining three beneficiaries received small grants totalling £600.

FINANCES *Year* 2009–10 *Income* £130,050 *Grants* £32,650 *Assets* £342,622

TRUSTEES Brian Mitchell; Hon. Michael Devonshire; Duncan Oakley; Andrew Buss; John Andrews.

HOW TO APPLY In writing to the correspondent, although please note that the charity has recently identified several regular beneficiaries.

WHO TO APPLY TO The Trustees, Round Oak, Old Station Road, Wadhurst, East Sussex TN5 6TZ *Tel* 01892 782072 *email* brnmitchell3@ googlemail.com

■ The Mitchell Charitable Trust

CC NO 290273   **ESTABLISHED** 1984

WHERE FUNDING CAN BE GIVEN UK and overseas.

WHO CAN BENEFIT Organisations benefiting: people of all ages; volunteers; Jews; at risk groups; people disadvantaged by poverty; and victims of abuse and domestic violence.

WHAT IS FUNDED Jewish organisations, social welfare, voluntary organisations.

WHAT IS NOT FUNDED No grants to individuals or for non-Jewish religious appeals. Applicants from small charities outside London are unlikely to be considered.

TYPE OF GRANT Some recurring.

RANGE OF GRANTS £50–£38,000.

SAMPLE GRANTS Hammersmith Clinical Research (£37,000); Ovarian Cancer Care (£34,500) and Prostate Cancer Research Foundation (£25,000); London School of Economics and Political Science (£5,750); Community Security Trust and Norwood (£5,000 each); National Council for Epilepsy (£500); and Kidney for Kids (£30).

FINANCES *Year* 2009–10 *Income* £43,423 *Grants* £116,364 *Assets* £1,149,718

TRUSTEES Ashley Mitchell; Elizabeth Mitchell; Antonia Mitchell; Keren Mitchell.

HOW TO APPLY In writing to the correspondent. Applications must include financial information. The trust does not reply to any applications unless they choose to support them. Trustees do not meet on a regular basis, thus applicants may not be advised of a grant for a considerable period.

WHO TO APPLY TO Ashley Mitchell, Trustee, 28 Heath Drive, London NW3 7SB *Tel* 020 7794 5668

■ The Esmé Mitchell Trust

IR NO XN48053   **ESTABLISHED** 1965

WHERE FUNDING CAN BE GIVEN Ireland, but mainly Northern Ireland.

WHO CAN BENEFIT Organisations, and individuals who are involved in the arts and cultural activities.

WHAT IS FUNDED General charitable purposes in Ireland as a whole but principally in Northern Ireland with a particular interest in cultural and artistic objects. Part of the trust fund is only available to assist certain heritage bodies as set out in Schedule 3 to the Capital Transfer Act 1984.

WHAT IS NOT FUNDED Grants are not usually given to individuals wishing to undertake voluntary service or further education.

TYPE OF GRANT No time limits have generally been set on grants. The trust has on occasions given grant assistance over a period of two to three years but in general tries not to become involved in commitments of a long-term nature.

FINANCES *Year* 2009–10 *Grants* £110,000

TRUSTEES P J Rankin; Mrs F Jay-O'Boyle; R P Blakiston-Houston.

OTHER INFORMATION In previous years the trust has had both an income of, and made grants totalling, around £110,000. Further information was not available.

HOW TO APPLY In writing to the correspondent. Applicants should submit three copies of the following: a concise description of the proposed project; a recent statement of accounts and balance sheet; a copy of the constitution; details of tax and legal or charitable status; a list of committee officers; information on other sources of finance; a contact address and telephone number.

WHO TO APPLY TO The Trustees, Cleaver Fulton Rankin Ltd. Solicitors, 50 Bedford Street, Belfast BT1 7FW *Tel* 028 9024 3141

■ Keren Mitzvah Trust

CC NO 1041948   **ESTABLISHED** 1994

WHERE FUNDING CAN BE GIVEN UK.

WHO CAN BENEFIT Jewish organisations; registered charities.

WHAT IS FUNDED General charitable purposes.

TYPE OF GRANT One-off and recurrent.

RANGE OF GRANTS Up to £32,000.

SAMPLE GRANTS Menorah High School for Girls (£32,000); Ezer Mizion (£22,000); Torah & Chessed, Kisharon (£20,000 each); Friends of Vishnas Mir (£16,000); Lezion Berina (£15,000); Achisomoch (£11,000); Side by Side (£10,000); CML (£8,000); The Shechita Defence Fund and UJIA (£5,000 each).

FINANCES *Year* 2010 *Income* £373,659 *Grants* £379,390 *Assets* £5,483

TRUSTEES Manny Weiss; Alan McCormack; Neil Bradley.

HOW TO APPLY The trust stated that the trustees support their own personal charities.

WHO TO APPLY TO Naomi Crowther, 53 Sugden Road, Thames Ditton, Surrey KT7 0AD *Tel* 020 3219 2600

Think carefully about every application. Is it justified?

745

■ The Mizpah Trust

cc no 287231   established 1983
where funding can be given UK and overseas.
who can benefit Registered charities.
what is funded General charitable purposes, especially Christian organisations.
type of grant One-off and recurrent.
range of grants £50 to £30,000.
sample grants The Vanessa Grant Trust (£30,000); The Warham Trust (£6,000); CURE International and Tearfund (£5,000 each); World Vision (£4,000); Friends of St Andrew's and The Christian Orphanage (£1,000 each); The Barnabus Trust (£150); and The Crosswinds Care Trust (£100).
finances *Year* 2009–10 *Income* £36,177 *Grants* £79,539 *Assets* £42,229
trustees A C O Bell; Mrs J E Bell.
other information £1,500 went in grants to individuals.
how to apply The trust has stated that 'no applications will be considered'.
who to apply to A C O Bell, Trustee, Foresters House, Humbly Grove, South Warnborough, Hook, Hampshire RG29 1RY

■ The Mobbs Memorial Trust Ltd

cc no 202478   established 1963
where funding can be given Stoke Poges and district within a 35-mile radius of St Giles' Church.
who can benefit Organisations benefiting: people of all ages; ex-service and service people; volunteers; unemployed; those in care, fostered and adopted; parents and children; at-risk groups; people with disabilities; those disadvantaged by poverty; ex-offenders and those at risk of offending; homeless people; those living in rural areas; socially isolated people; victims of abuse, crime and domestic violence.
what is funded St Giles' Church and other charitable purposes including: almshouses; sheltered accommodation; community development; support to voluntary and community organisations; combined arts; community arts and recreation; health; conservation and environment; schools and colleges; and community facilities and services.
type of grant Buildings and project. Funding is given for up to three years.
range of grants Up to £5,000.
sample grants British Red Cross (£5,000) BMX Track – Iver Heath (£4,400); Farnham Royal (£4,000); Action 4 Youth (£3,000); Stoke Poges Old People's Christmas Fund and Stoke Poges PCC Account (£2,000 each); Thames Hospice Care (£1,500).
finances *Year* 2009–10 *Income* £48,965 *Grants* £57,464 *Assets* £2,226,228
trustees M R Mobbs; Dr C N A Mobbs; C W Mobbs; Mrs S J Greenslade; A N P Mobbs.
other information A further £1,000 was given in grants to individuals.
how to apply In writing to the correspondent.
who to apply to Michael Mobbs, Chair, Gateside, Park Road, Stoke Poges, Slough SL2 4PG *Tel* 01753 642796

■ The Modiano Charitable Trust

cc no 328372   established 1989
where funding can be given UK and overseas.
who can benefit Charitable organisations, with some preference for Jewish groups.
what is funded Development work, arts and relief-in-need.
type of grant One-off and recurrent.
range of grants £50–£20,000.
sample grants Philharmonic Orchestra (£20,000); the Weiznam Institute Foundation (£10,000); and DEC Haiti Appeal, St. Paul's School and UJIA (£5,000 each); World Jewish Relief (£4,000); Life Action Trust (£3,500); CCJ and The Holocaust Educational Trust (£2,500 each); YMCA and the Reform Research Trust (1,000 each); and British Forces Association, Jewish Assoc. for the Mentally Ill (JAMI) and The St. John of Jerusalem Eye Hospital (£100 each).
finances *Year* 2009–10 *Income* £150,003 *Grants* £95,410 *Assets* £84,653
trustees G Modiano; Mrs B Modiano; L S Modiano; M Modiano.
how to apply In writing to the correspondent.
who to apply to G Modiano, Trustee, Broad Street House, 55 Old Broad Street, London EC2M 1RX *Tel* 020 7012 0000

■ The Moette Charitable Trust

cc no 1068886   established 1998
where funding can be given UK and overseas.
who can benefit People educationally disadvantaged through poverty.
what is funded 'The principal activity of the trust is the provision of support of the poor and needy for educational purposes.'
sample grants £15,000 to Finchley Road Synagogue; £2,500 each to King David Schools (Manchester) and Manchester Charitable Trust; £2,000 to The Purim Fund; £1,000 each to Yad Voezer and Yeshivas Lev Aryeh; £500 each to Hakalo and London School of Jewish Studies; £400 to Manchester Jewish Federation and £50 to Manchester Seminary for Girls.
finances *Year* 2009–10 *Income* £60,532 *Grants* £24,862 *Assets* £327,552
trustees Simon Lopian; Pearl Lopian.
how to apply In writing to the correspondent
who to apply to Simon Lopian, Trustee, 1 Holden Road, Salford M7 4NL *Tel* 0161 832 8721

■ The Mole Charitable Trust

cc no 281452   established 1980
where funding can be given UK, with a preference for Manchester.
who can benefit Individuals, registered charities and institutions benefiting children, young adults, Jews and people disadvantaged by poverty.
what is funded Jewish causes, educational institutions and organisations to relieve poverty.
range of grants £1,000–£60,000.
sample grants Three Pillars Charity (£60,000); Manchester Jewish Grammar School (£26,000); Chasdei Yoel Charitable Trust and United Talmudical Associates Limited (£20,000 each); Binoh of Manchester (£6,000); Beis Ruchel Girls' School (£3,000); Manchester Jewish Federation (£2,500); and Our Kids (£1,000).
finances *Year* 2009–10 *Income* £150,990 *Grants* £223,576 *Assets* £2,363,149
trustees M Gross; Mrs L P Gross.

HOW TO APPLY The following is taken from the trustees' report 2009–10: 'The trustees receive many applications for grants, mainly personal contact, but also verbally. Each application is considered against the criteria established by the charity. Although the charity does not advertise, it is well known within its community and there are many requests received for grants. Feedback received is used to monitor the quality of grants.'

WHO TO APPLY TO Martin Gross, Trustee, 2 Okeover Road, Salford M7 4JX *Tel* 0161 832 8721 *email* martin.gross@lopiangb.co.uk

■ The Monatrea Charitable Trust

CC NO 1131897　　**ESTABLISHED** 2009
WHERE FUNDING CAN BE GIVEN UK.
WHO CAN BENEFIT Registered charities.
WHAT IS FUNDED General charitable purposes.
SAMPLE GRANTS Capital Community Foundation; Prisoners' Advice Service; Roses Charitable Trust; Family Action; and South Central Youth.
FINANCES *Year* 2009–10 *Income* £49,877 *Grants* £44,237 *Assets* £119,666
TRUSTEES Patrick Stephen Vernon; Mary Vernon; Coutts & Co.
OTHER INFORMATION Grants ranged from £2,000 to £21,000.
HOW TO APPLY In writing to the correspondent.
WHO TO APPLY TO Coutts & Co, Trustee Dept, 440 Strand, London WC2R 0QS

■ The D C Moncrieff Charitable Trust

CC NO 203919　　**ESTABLISHED** 1965
WHERE FUNDING CAN BE GIVEN UK and worldwide, with a preference for Norfolk and Suffolk.
WHO CAN BENEFIT Registered charities only.
WHAT IS FUNDED General charitable purposes. Trustees already have a list of beneficiaries whose requirements outweigh the trustees' ability to help.
WHAT IS NOT FUNDED No grants for individuals.
RANGE OF GRANTS Usually £400–£2,000. Larger grants for larger one-off projects or certain regularly supported local charities.
SAMPLE GRANTS Previous grants have included those to: All Hallows Hospital, East Anglia's Children's Hospices, the Society for Lincolnshire History and Archaeology, Hemley Church PCC, Lowestoft Girl Guides Association and The Scouts Association, BREAK, Strongbones Children's Charitable Trust and East Anglian Air Ambulance Association.
FINANCES *Year* 2009–10 *Income* £42,542 *Grants* £32,500 *Assets* £1,888,299
TRUSTEES M I Willis; R E James; M F Dunne.
OTHER INFORMATION Accounts were available from the Charity Commission, but without a recent list of beneficiaries.
HOW TO APPLY In writing to the correspondent. The trust has previously stated that demand for funds exceeded available resources; therefore no further requests are currently invited.
WHO TO APPLY TO R E James, Trustee, 8 Quinnell Way, Lowestoft, Suffolk NR32 4WL

■ Monmouthshire County Council Welsh Church Act Fund

CC NO 507094　　**ESTABLISHED** 1996
WHERE FUNDING CAN BE GIVEN The administrative areas of Blaenau Gwent, Caerphilly, Monmouthshire, Torfaen and Newport.
WHO CAN BENEFIT Students, at risk groups, and people who are disadvantaged by poverty, socially isolated, disaster victims, or sick.
WHAT IS FUNDED Education, relief in sickness and need, people who are blind or elderly, medical and social research, probation, social and recreational, libraries, museums and art galleries and protection of historic buildings relating to Wales, places of worship and burial grounds, emergencies and disasters.
TYPE OF GRANT Mostly for provision, upkeep and repair of religious buildings and community halls.
RANGE OF GRANTS Up to £1,000.
SAMPLE GRANTS Previous beneficiaries include: Parish Church Llandogo, Parish Church Llangybi, Bridges Community Centre, St David's Foundation Hospice Care and North Wales Society for the Blind.
FINANCES *Year* 2009–10 *Income* £68,412 *Grants* £226,506 *Assets* £4,960,217
TRUSTEES Monmouthshire County Council.
HOW TO APPLY On a form available from the correspondent, this must be signed by a county councillor. They are considered in March, June, September and December.
WHO TO APPLY TO S K F Greenslade, Treasurer's Department, Monmouthshire County Council, County Hall, Croesyceiliog, Cwmbran NP44 2XH *Tel* 01633 644644 *Fax* 01633 644260

■ The Montague Thompson Coon Charitable Trust

CC NO 294096　　**ESTABLISHED** 1986
WHERE FUNDING CAN BE GIVEN UK.
WHO CAN BENEFIT Children with muscular diseases, medical research, environment.
WHAT IS FUNDED Relief of sickness in children with muscular dystrophy and/or other muscular diseases, carrying out and provide for research into infant diseases and advancing the education of the public in the study of ecology and wildlife.
WHAT IS NOT FUNDED No grants to individuals.
SAMPLE GRANTS Dogs for the Disabled (£11,500); Scope (£6,500); Muscular Dystrophy Campaign (£6,000); Action for Kids Charitable Trust (£5,000); The Jennifer Trust (£3,000); and Exmoor Calvert Trust (£2,000).
FINANCES *Year* 2009–10 *Income* £47,791 *Grants* £53,003 *Assets* £1,175,983
TRUSTEES P A Clarke, Chair; J P Lister; Mrs P Blake-Roberts.
HOW TO APPLY In writing to the correspondent.
WHO TO APPLY TO Mrs Philippa Blake-Roberts, Trustee, Old Rectory, Church Lane, Colton, Norwich NR9 5DE *Tel* 07766 072592

■ The Colin Montgomerie Charitable Foundation

CC NO 1072388　　**ESTABLISHED** 1998
WHERE FUNDING CAN BE GIVEN UK.
WHO CAN BENEFIT Charitable organisations.
WHAT IS FUNDED The relief of poverty, the advancement of education and religion, and general charitable purposes.

SAMPLE GRANTS Beneficiaries have included: British Lung Foundation, Cancer Vaccine Institute, NSPCC – Full Stop Campaign and University of Glasgow MR Scanner Fund.

FINANCES *Year* 2009 *Income* £1,630 *Grants* £40,000

TRUSTEES Colin Montgomerie; Guy Kinnings; Jonathan Dudman; Miss Donna Cooksley.

HOW TO APPLY In writing to the correspondent.

WHO TO APPLY TO Miss Donna Cooksley, Trustee, c/o Catella, Chiswick Gate, 3rd Floor, 598–608 Chiswick High Road, London W4 5RT

■ The Monument Trust

CC NO 242575 **ESTABLISHED** 1965

WHERE FUNDING CAN BE GIVEN Unrestricted, but UK and South Africa in practice.

WHO CAN BENEFIT Registered charities working in the fields outlined below.

WHAT IS FUNDED The arts, health and community care; AIDS; social development; general. Preference is given to new ideas or methods which can be replicated widely or become self-sustaining.

WHAT IS NOT FUNDED Grants are not normally made to individuals.

SAMPLE GRANTS Fitzwilliam Museum – Cambridge (£2.4 million), towards major exhibitions and selected other initiatives; The Great Steward of Scotland's Dumfries House Trust (£2 million), towards the further conservation and development of Dumfries House; Parkinson's Disease Society (£1.5 million), towards the research project 'Understanding the early pathological pathways in Parkinson's Disease' at the University of Oxford; Homerton University Hospital NHS Foundation Trust (£580,000), towards the building refurbishment and running costs of the Hospital's HIV care centre; Liverpool and Merseyside Theatres Trust Limited (£300,000), towards rebuilding the Everyman Theatre in Liverpool; Prison Radio Association (£200,000), towards the national syndication and programme production service; Bankside Open Spaces Trust (£180,000), to support development of community gardening in north Southwark and Lambeth; Corston Independent Funders' Coalition (£175,000), towards the Women's Diversionary Fund, a collaborative fund to help organisations to develop one-stop-shop services for women offenders; and Revolving Doors Agency (£150,000), towards core costs.

FINANCES *Year* 2009–10 *Income* £13,615,000 *Grants* £31,999,000 *Assets* £236,933,000

TRUSTEES Stewart Grimshaw; Linda Heathcoat-Amory; Sir Anthony Tennant.

OTHER INFORMATION The trust gives the following indication of its current particular area of interest: 'In the arts and heritage category [the trustees] particularly wish to be made aware of significant appeals.'

HOW TO APPLY 'See the guidance for applicants in the entry for the Sainsbury Family Charitable Trusts. A single application will be considered for support by all the trusts in the group. 'Proposals are generally invited by the trustees or initiated at their request. Unsolicited applications are not generally encouraged and are unlikely to succeed, unless they closely match the areas in which the trustees are interested.'

WHO TO APPLY TO Alan Bookbinder, Director, Allington House, 1st Floor, 150 Victoria Street, London SW1E 5AE *Tel* 020 7410 0330 *Fax* 020 7410 0332 *Website* www.sfct.org.uk

■ The Moonpig Foundation

CC NO 1136686 **ESTABLISHED** 2010

WHERE FUNDING CAN BE GIVEN Worldwide with maybe a preference for Uganda.

WHO CAN BENEFIT Organisations and individuals.

WHAT IS FUNDED General charitable purposes.

TRUSTEES Iain Stuart Marin; Paul James Lantsbury; Nicholas David Jenkins.

OTHER INFORMATION Nicholas Jenkins is also a trustee of The Nick Jenkins Foundation (Charity Commission no. 1135565).

HOW TO APPLY In writing to the correspondent.

WHO TO APPLY TO Nicholas David Jenkins, Trustee, Bapton Manor, Bapton, Warminster, Wiltshire BA12 0SB

■ George A Moore Foundation

CC NO 262107 **ESTABLISHED** 1970

WHERE FUNDING CAN BE GIVEN Principally Yorkshire and the Isle of Man.

WHO CAN BENEFIT Charitable and voluntary organisations.

WHAT IS FUNDED The trustees select causes and projects from the applications received during the year and also independently research and identify specific objectives where they wish to direct assistance. The type of grants made can vary quite widely from one year to another and care is taken to maintain a rough parity among the various fields covered so that one sphere of activity does not benefit unduly at the expense of another. Areas which are not or cannot be covered by official sources are favoured.

WHAT IS NOT FUNDED No assistance will be given to individuals, courses of study, expeditions, overseas travel, holidays, or for purposes outside the UK. Local appeals for UK charities will only be considered if in the area of interest. Because of present long-term commitments, the foundation is not prepared to consider appeals for religious property or institutions.

TYPE OF GRANT Grants are generally non-recurrent and the foundation is reluctant to contribute to revenue appeals.

RANGE OF GRANTS Mostly under £1,000.

SAMPLE GRANTS Henshaws Yorkshire (£35,000); Boston Charitable Foundation (£28,000); Marie Curie Cancer Care (£19,000); Caring for Life – Crag House Farm (£14,000); Saxton Village Pavilion (£10,000); Heart Research UK (£2,500); FEVA (£1,500); AbilityNet, Endeavour Training and Swaledale Festival (£1,000 each); Stroke Association (£600); Brain Tumour UK (£500); Knaresborough Horticultural Society (£250); and Sulby and District Rifle Club (£100).

FINANCES *Year* 2009–10 *Income* £260,647 *Grants* £149,274 *Assets* £5,638,838

TRUSTEES George Moore; Elizabeth Moore; Jonathan Moore; Paul Turner.

HOW TO APPLY In writing to the correspondent. No guidelines or application forms are issued. The trustees meet approximately four times a year, on variable dates, and an appropriate response is sent out after the relevant meeting. For large grants of over £5,000, the trust will normally hold a meeting with the applicant to determine how the money will be spent.

WHO TO APPLY TO Angela James, Chief Administrator, The Stables, Bilton Hall, Bilton-in-Ainsty, York YO26 7NP *Tel* 01423 359446 *Fax* 01423 359018 *email* info@gamf.org.uk *Website* www.gamf.org.uk

■ The Henry Moore Foundation

CC NO 271370   **ESTABLISHED** 1977

WHERE FUNDING CAN BE GIVEN UK and overseas.

WHO CAN BENEFIT Public visual art and educational bodies.

WHAT IS FUNDED Financial support is given to a broad range of institutions promoting the appreciation of the fine arts and in particular the works of Henry Moore through activities such as exhibitions, acquisitions, research and publishing.

WHAT IS NOT FUNDED The foundation does not give grants to individual applicants, for revenue expenditure. No grant (or any part of grant) may be used to pay any fee or to provide any other benefit to any individual who is a trustee of the foundation.

TYPE OF GRANT One-off.

RANGE OF GRANTS Up to £30,000 depending on grant category.

SAMPLE GRANTS The grant categories are: New projects; Collections; Fellowships for artists and post-doctoral research; Research and development; and Conferences, lectures and publications. Beneficiaries include: *Revealed: Turner Contemporary Opens*, Turner Contemporary, Margate (£20,000); Penrose Film Productions, Sussex for an Online collection database (£15,000); acquisition of Henry Moore, *Reclining Figure* for the Gropius House, Lincoln, Massachusetts (£7,000); *The Burlington Magazine*, London – sculpture coverage June 2010–July 2011 (£5,000); and artist's residencies Enschede, The Netherlands for Anthony Schrag (£3,000). For full details and further examples see the foundation's website.

FINANCES *Year* 2009–10 *Income* £1,775,283 *Grants* £857,371 *Assets* £97,403,944

TRUSTEES Marianne Brouwer; Greville Worthington; Dawn Ades; Simon Keswick; James Joll; Malcolm Baker; Duncan Robinson; Laure Genillard.

PUBLICATIONS The Henry Moore Foundation Review.

HOW TO APPLY Applicants should complete an application form which is available on the foundation's website. Applications must be posted to the grants administrator. Applications will be acknowledged by letter. The grants committee meets quarterly; consult the foundation's website for exact dates as the trust advises that applications received late will not be considered until after the meeting. It is advised to leave six months between the grants committee meeting and the project start date as funds cannot be paid for retrospective projects. Applicants should also advise the foundation whether it is envisaged that any trustee will have an interest in the project for which a grant is sought. Organisations may include supporting material with their application and this will be returned if requested.

WHO TO APPLY TO Charles M Joint, Grant Contact, Henry Moore Foundation, Dane Tree House, Perry Green, Much Hadham, Hertfordshire SG10 6EE *Tel* 01279 843333 *Fax* 01279 843 647 *email* admin@henry-moore.org *Website* www.henry-moore.org

■ The Nigel Moores Family Charitable Trust

CC NO 1002366   **ESTABLISHED** 1991

WHERE FUNDING CAN BE GIVEN UK, but mostly Wales and Liverpool.

WHO CAN BENEFIT Institutions benefiting children and young adults, actors and entertainment professionals, musicians, students and textile workers and designers.

WHAT IS FUNDED Principal objective should be the raising of the artistic taste of the public whether in relation to music, drama, opera, painting, sculpture or otherwise in connection with the fine arts, the promotion of education in the fine arts and academic education, the promotion of the environment, the provision of recreation and leisure facilities and the advancement of religion.

TYPE OF GRANT One-off and recurrent.

SAMPLE GRANTS A Foundation (£525,000); London Library (£20,000); Mostyn Gallery (£10,000); University of York (£6,750); Art School Palestine (£1,000); and Matts Gallery (£500).

FINANCES *Year* 2009–10 *Income* £16 *Grants* £1,800

TRUSTEES J C S Moores; Mrs P M Kennaway.

OTHER INFORMATION Unusually, in 2009–10 there were very low levels of income and expenditure.

HOW TO APPLY In writing to the correspondent.

WHO TO APPLY TO Paul Charles Kurthausen, c/o MacFarlane and Co., Cunard Building, Water Street, Liverpool L3 1DS *Tel* 0151 236 6161 *Fax* 0151 236 1095 *email* paulk@macca.co.uk

■ John Moores Foundation

CC NO 253481   **ESTABLISHED** 1963

WHERE FUNDING CAN BE GIVEN Primarily Merseyside (plus Skelmersdale, Ellesmere Port and Halton); Northern Ireland; and overseas.

WHO CAN BENEFIT Voluntary organisations and community groups in the UK benefiting people who are marginalised as a result of social, educational, physical, economic, cultural, geographical or other disadvantage. International relief organisations are also supported, but only organisations proactively selected by the trustees rather than applicants.

WHAT IS FUNDED Grass roots community groups; black and minority ethnic organisations; women including girls; second chance learning; advice and information to alleviate poverty; support and training for voluntary organisations. And, in Merseyside only: people with disabilities; carers; refugees; homeless people; child care; complementary therapies.

WHAT IS NOT FUNDED Generally the foundation does not fund: individuals; national organisations or groups based outside Merseyside even where some of the service users come from the area; statutory bodies or work previously done by them; mainstream education (schools, colleges, universities); faith-based projects exclusively for members of that faith, or for the promotion of religion; capital building costs – except to improve access for disabled people; festivals, carnivals and fêtes; medicine and health – except under the headings listed above; holidays, expeditions and outings; gifts, parties etc; sport; vehicles; animal charities; arts, crafts, heritage, or local history projects; conservation and environmental projects; employment and enterprise schemes; victims – except rape crisis and domestic violence projects; academic or medical research; uniformed groups (e.g. scouts, cadets, majorettes); sponsorship, advertising or fund-raising events. Unsolicited applications which fall outside the policy criteria are not considered. Unsolicited applications for the categories World Crises and One-off exceptional grants are not responded to.

TYPE OF GRANT One-off, revenue, project, equipment and start-up costs. Funding for up to three years. Volunteers' expenses and help towards education and training costs.

RANGE OF GRANTS £100–£50,000.

SAMPLE GRANTS Sefton Advocacy and St Joseph's Hospice Association (£9,000 each); Somali Umbrella Group (£5,400); West Lancashire Crossroads Caring for Carers and Tranmere Action Group (£5,000 each); Croxteth Child Development Service (£6,000); Norris Green Community Alliance (£7,000); Lyndale Knowsley Cancer Support Group (£8,000); Sefton Women & Children's Aid (£2,600); Step Forward (£1,200); Bread of Life Community Project (£4,500); One Vision Housing (£5,200); Kenyan Community Liverpool (£2,000); East Belfast Independent Advice Centre (£7,000); Polish Abroad; Northern Ireland Anti-Poverty Network; Ballybeen Women's Group (£5,000 each); Pennyburn Community Playgroup; Belfast Interface Project (£2,000 each); Shopmobility Lisburn (£1,000); Homeplus (£5,500); Lettershandoney & District Youth Project (£840); and UNICEF and Disasters Emergency Committee (£50,000 each).

FINANCES *Year* 2009–10 *Income* £875,893 *Grants* £738,150 *Assets* £24,363,180

TRUSTEES Barnaby Moores; Kevin Moores; Nicola Eastwood; Alison Navarro.

PUBLICATIONS Applying For a Grant.

OTHER INFORMATION The trust has a very comprehensive website that should be referred to.

HOW TO APPLY Please refer to the foundation's website and make sure your project falls within the criteria. If you are unsure, or if you would like to discuss your application before submitting it, please telephone the foundation staff who will be happy to advise you. Application should be made by letter (no more than four sides of A4) accompanied by a completed application form. Application forms and guidance notes can be obtained by letter, phone or email or from the foundation's website. Decisions about which projects to fund are made by the trustees who meet 5–6 times a year to consider Merseyside applications and 4 times a year to consider Northern Ireland applications. As a general rule, Merseyside applicants should allow 3–4 months for a decision to be made, and applicants from Northern Ireland should allow 4–5 months.

WHO TO APPLY TO Phil Godfrey, Grants Director, 7th Floor, Gostins Building, 32–36 Hanover Street, Liverpool L1 4LN *Tel* 0151 707 6077 *Fax* 0151 707 6066 *email* info@johnmooresfoundation.com *Website* www.jmf.org.uk

■ The Peter Moores Foundation

CC NO 258224   **ESTABLISHED** 1964

WHERE FUNDING CAN BE GIVEN UK and Barbados.

WHO CAN BENEFIT Organisations benefiting children and young adults, artists, actors, musicians, textile workers and designers, writers and poets, teachers, sportsmen and women and people who suffer from HIV/AIDs.

WHAT IS FUNDED The creation and staging of new operatic work in the UK; student singers and young artists to maintain college studies and projects to expand their professional experience; music organisations providing training and performance opportunities for young singers and conductors; Compton Verney House, the new museum-art gallery opened in 2004; health (especially AIDS), environmental,

education and youth projects in the UK and Barbados.

TYPE OF GRANT One-off or recurring, for buildings, revenue costs, capital costs and running costs.

RANGE OF GRANTS £100–£2 million.

SAMPLE GRANTS Compton Verney House Trust (£1.8 million); University of the West Indies (£52,000); ChildLine (£40,000); Opera Group (£44,000); Rossini in Wilbad (£16,000); Royal Opera House (£8,700); Compton Verney Collection Settlement (£15,000); National Opera Studio main scholarship (£17,000); Royal Philharmonic Society Main Scholarship (£14,000); Sunflowers Foundation (£15,000); and HIV/AIDs charities (£131,000).

FINANCES *Year* 2009–10 *Income* £4,247,736 *Grants* £2,370,109 *Assets* £592,334

TRUSTEES Michael Johnson, Chair; Eileen Ainscough; Ludmilla Andrew; Nicholas Payne; Kirsten Suenson-Taylor; Joanna Laing.

HOW TO APPLY In writing to the correspondent, but applicants should be aware that the foundation has previously stated that it 'will normally support projects which come to the attention of its patron or trustees through their interests or special knowledge. General applications for sponsorship are not encouraged and are unlikely to succeed.'

WHO TO APPLY TO Peter Saunders, Administrator, c/o Wallwork, Nelson and Johnson, Chandler House, 7 Ferry Road, Riversway, Preston PR2 2YH *Tel* 01772 430000 *Fax* 01772 430012 *email* moores@pmf.org.uk *Website* www.pmf.org.uk

■ The Morel Charitable Trust

CC NO 268943   **ESTABLISHED** 1972

WHERE FUNDING CAN BE GIVEN UK and the developing world.

WHO CAN BENEFIT Grants are normally made to projects of which the trustees have personal knowledge. Organisations benefiting people disadvantaged by poverty are prioritised, but those benefiting volunteers, people living in inner city areas and victims of famine will be considered.

WHAT IS FUNDED The arts, particularly drama; organisations working for improved race relations; inner city projects and developing world projects. Charities working in the fields of arts, culture and recreation; health; conservation and environment; education and training; and social care and development.

WHAT IS NOT FUNDED No grants to individuals.

TYPE OF GRANT Project.

RANGE OF GRANTS £500–£5,000.

SAMPLE GRANTS Health Unlimited (£5,000); Medical Aid for Palestine (£3,000); African Initiatives, Congo Children's Trust, Excellent Development, Kaloko Trust, Zambia, Nigeria Health Care Project and The Capricorn African Trust (£2,000 each); Ace Arts Community Exchange, and The Young Vic (£1,500 each); and Age UK and Soho Trust (£1,000 each).

FINANCES *Year* 2009–10 *Income* £54,017 *Grants* £65,100 *Assets* £1,303,322

TRUSTEES J M Gibbs, Chair; W M Gibbs; S E Gibbs; B M O Gibbs; Dr T Gibbs; Dr Emily Parry; Abigail Keane; Susanna Coan.

OTHER INFORMATION Projects supported are usually connected with places that the trustees have lived and worked, including the cities of Bristol, Leeds, Brecon and London and the countries of Ghana, Zambia, Malawi and the Solomon Islands.

HOW TO APPLY In writing to the correspondent. The trustees normally meet three times a year to consider applications.

WHO TO APPLY TO S E Gibbs, Trustee, 34 Durand Gardens, London SW9 0PP *Tel* 020 7582 6901

■ The Morgan Charitable Foundation

CC NO 283128 **ESTABLISHED** 1981
WHERE FUNDING CAN BE GIVEN UK.
WHO CAN BENEFIT Registered charities and institutions benefiting at risk groups and people who are disadvantaged by poverty or socially isolated.
WHAT IS FUNDED The trustees are primarily interested in social welfare causes.
WHAT IS NOT FUNDED No grants to individuals.
RANGE OF GRANTS £1,000–£8,000.
SAMPLE GRANTS Magen David Adom and World Jewish Relief (£6,000 each); Chai Cancer Care (£4,000); In Kind Direct Charity (£3,000); Jewish Care and Jewish Blind and Disabled (£2,000 each); and Afrikids, Aleh Charitable Foundation, Institute for Philanthropy, London Pro Arte Choir, Marie Curie Cancer Care, Ohel Sarah, Pears Foundation, and Royal National Lifeboat Institution (£1,000 each).
FINANCES *Year* 2010 *Income* £52,431 *Grants* £59,000 *Assets* £3,827,540
TRUSTEES The Morgan Charitable Foundation Trustees Ltd. (A Morgan; L Morgan; Mrs C Morgan).
HOW TO APPLY In writing to the correspondent. Applications will only be considered if accompanied by a copy of the charitable organisation's latest report and accounts. Trustees meet twice a year, usually in April and October. No telephone enquiries please.
WHO TO APPLY TO The Trustees, PO Box 57749, London Nw11 1FD *Tel* 07968 827709

■ The Mr and Mrs J T Morgan Foundation

CC NO 241835 **ESTABLISHED** 1965
WHERE FUNDING CAN BE GIVEN Mainly Wales.
WHO CAN BENEFIT Churches, national and local charities benefiting children, young people, students and Christians.
WHAT IS FUNDED Preference is given to the support of charities in Wales and to the promotion of education and religion in Wales.
WHAT IS NOT FUNDED No grants to individuals.
TYPE OF GRANT One-off.
RANGE OF GRANTS £100–£750.
SAMPLE GRANTS Previous beneficiaries have included: Taffs Well United Church (£500); An Open Door into Your Heart (£400); Whizz Kids (250); Motor Neurone Disease Association (£250); Special Needs Activity Club (£100); The Arthur Rank Centre (£500).
FINANCES *Year* 2010–11 *Income* £24,171 *Grants* £20,000
TRUSTEES Elaine Phillips; John Aylward; Richard Morean.
HOW TO APPLY In writing to the correspondent.
WHO TO APPLY TO J R Morgan, Calvert House, Calvert Terrace, Swansea SA1 6AP *Tel* 01792 655178

■ Diana and Allan Morgenthau Charitable Trust

CC NO 1062180 **ESTABLISHED** 1997
WHERE FUNDING CAN BE GIVEN Worldwide.
WHO CAN BENEFIT Charitable organisations, with an interest in Jewish groups.
WHAT IS FUNDED Jewish causes, overseas aid, arts, culture, health and education.
RANGE OF GRANTS £200–£35,000.
SAMPLE GRANTS British Friends of the Jaffa Institute (£35,000); Belsize Square Synagogue (£28,000); Central British Fund for World Jewish Relief (£8,500); London Jewish Cultural Centre and Jewish Care (£7,000 each); Brent Adolescent Centre (£5,000); Nightingale House (£3,500); Ben Uri Gallery (£2,000); Tricycle Theatre (£1,700); Marie Curie (£1,000); and Camphill Village Trust (£200).
FINANCES *Year* 2009–10 *Income* £95,112 *Grants* £114,700 *Assets* £7,277
TRUSTEES Allan Morgenthau; Diana Morgenthau.
OTHER INFORMATION A further £14,290 was given in grants to individuals.
HOW TO APPLY In writing to the correspondent.
WHO TO APPLY TO Allan Morgenthau, Trustee, Flat 27, Berkeley House, 15 Hay Hill, London W1J 8NS *Tel* 020 7493 1904

■ The Oliver Morland Charitable Trust

CC NO 1076213 **ESTABLISHED** 1999
WHERE FUNDING CAN BE GIVEN UK.
WHO CAN BENEFIT Registered charities usually chosen through personal knowledge of the trustees.
WHAT IS FUNDED Most of the funds are given to Quaker projects or Quaker-related projects.
WHAT IS NOT FUNDED No grants to individuals.
TYPE OF GRANT Grants are given for core, capital and project support for up to three years.
RANGE OF GRANTS Up to £30,000.
SAMPLE GRANTS Quaker Home Service – children and young people (£16,000); Refugee Council (£2,000); Leap Confronting Conflict, Living Again, Medical Aid for Palestine and Sightsavers International (£1,000 each); Come to God (£850); and Brooke Animal Hospital (£300).
FINANCES *Year* 2009–10 *Income* £82,071 *Grants* £96,861 *Assets* £1,510,637
TRUSTEES Priscilla Khan; Joseph Rutter; Jennifer Pittard; Kate Lovell; Charlotte Jones; Simon Pittard.
HOW TO APPLY 'Most of our grants are for continuing support of existing beneficiaries (approx 90%) so there is little left for responding to new appeals. We receive unsolicited applications at the rate of 6 or 7 each week, 99% are not even considered.'
WHO TO APPLY TO J M Rutter, Trustee, Thomas's House, Stower Row, Shaftesbury, Dorset SP7 0QW *Tel* 01747 853524

■ S C and M E Morland's Charitable Trust

CC NO 201645 **ESTABLISHED** 1957
WHERE FUNDING CAN BE GIVEN UK.
WHO CAN BENEFIT Quaker, local and UK charities which have a strong social bias and some UK-based international charities.
WHAT IS FUNDED Support to Quaker charities and others which the trustees have special interest in, knowledge of or association with, including

religious groups, relief of poverty and ill-health, promotion of peace and development overseas.

WHAT IS NOT FUNDED The trust does not usually give to animal welfare, individuals or medical research.

RANGE OF GRANTS Almost all less than £1,000 each.

SAMPLE GRANTS Britain Yearly Meeting (£7,500) and Oxfam (£1,000).

FINANCES *Year* 2009–10 *Income* £34,539 *Grants* £36,850 *Assets* £899,458

TRUSTEES Esther Boyd; Joseph Morland; Janet Morland; Howard Boyd; David Boyd.

HOW TO APPLY In writing to the correspondent. The trustees meet two times a year to make grants, in March and December. Applications should be submitted in the month before each meeting.

WHO TO APPLY TO Victoria Morland, Trustee, Gable House, Parbrook, Glastonbury, Somerset BA6 8PB *Tel* 01458 850804

■ The Morris Charitable Trust

CC NO 802290   **ESTABLISHED** 1989

WHERE FUNDING CAN BE GIVEN UK, with a preference for Islington; and overseas.

WHO CAN BENEFIT Supporting national, international and local community charities.

WHAT IS FUNDED General charitable purposes, placing particular emphasis on alleviating social hardship and deprivation. There is a preference for supporting causes within the borough of Islington.

WHAT IS NOT FUNDED No grants for individuals. No repeat donations are made within 12 months.

TYPE OF GRANT One-off grants for recurring costs for one year or less are priorities. Building and other capital grants, core costs, research grants, running costs, salaries and start-up costs are considered.

RANGE OF GRANTS £1–£7,500; average grant £575.

SAMPLE GRANTS Previously: £25,000 to Age Concern – Islington; £5,000 to The Bridge School – Islington; £1,000 to Islington Senior Citizens Fund.

FINANCES *Year* 2009–10 *Income* £125,213 *Grants* £143,501 *Assets* £152,158

TRUSTEES J A Morris, chair; P B Morris; A R Stenning; Gerald Morris; Dominic Jones.

PUBLICATIONS Information pamphlet.

HOW TO APPLY By application form available from the trust or downloadable from its website. The completed form should be returned complete with any supporting documentation and a copy of your latest report and accounts.

WHO TO APPLY TO Jack A Morris, Trustee, c/o Management Office, Business Design Centre, 52 Upper Street, London N1 0QH *Tel* 020 7359 3535 *Fax* 020 7226 0590 *email* info@ morrischaritabletrust.com *Website* www. morrischaritabletrust.com

■ The Bernard Morris Charitable Trust

CC NO 266532   **ESTABLISHED** 1973

WHERE FUNDING CAN BE GIVEN UK.

WHO CAN BENEFIT Charitable organisations and needy individuals.

WHAT IS FUNDED General charitable purposes.

SAMPLE GRANTS Previously: Oxford Synagogue (£16,000); Dragon School Trust (£12,000); One Voice (£2,500), OCJHS – Oxford Centre for Jewish and Hebrew Studies (£2,000), Soundabout (£1,000), the Story Museum (£500) and Centrepoint Homeless (£200).

FINANCES *Year* 2010–11 *Income* £23,083 *Grants* £80,323

TRUSTEES Simon Ryde; Judith Silver; Simon Fineman; Jessica Ryde.

HOW TO APPLY In writing to the correspondent.

WHO TO APPLY TO Simon Ryde, Trustee, 5 Wolvercote Green, Oxford OX2 8BD *Tel* 01865 516593

■ The Willie and Mabel Morris Charitable Trust

CC NO 280554   **ESTABLISHED** 1980

WHERE FUNDING CAN BE GIVEN UK.

WHO CAN BENEFIT Registered charities benefiting people who are ill, particularly with cancer, heart trouble, cerebral palsy, arthritis or rheumatism.

WHAT IS FUNDED Welfare and disability.

WHAT IS NOT FUNDED No grants for individuals or non-registered charities.

RANGE OF GRANTS £100–£15,000.

SAMPLE GRANTS St Thomas Lupus; PBC Foundation for Life; Marie Curie Cancer Care (£4,000 each); Strongbones Child Charitable Trust (£2,000); Stroke Association (£2,000); Salvation Army (£250) and English National Ballet (£100).

FINANCES *Year* 2009–10 *Income* £108,070 *Grants* £70,285 *Assets* £3,532,418

TRUSTEES Michael Macfadyen; Joyce Tether; Peter Tether; Andrew Tether; Angela Tether; Suzanne Marriott.

HOW TO APPLY The trustees 'formulate an independent grants policy at regular meetings so that funds are already committed'.

WHO TO APPLY TO Angela Tether, 41 Field Lane, Letchworth Garden City, Hertfordshire SG6 3LD *Tel* 01462 480583

■ The Peter Morrison Charitable Foundation

CC NO 277202   **ESTABLISHED** 1978

WHERE FUNDING CAN BE GIVEN UK.

WHO CAN BENEFIT Registered charities benefiting at risk groups and people who are disadvantaged by poverty and socially isolated.

WHAT IS FUNDED A wide range of social welfare causes.

RANGE OF GRANTS Up to £10,000.

SAMPLE GRANTS London Philharmonic Orchestra (£7,600); Kingston Theatres Trust St Giles Church ((£5,000); Grange Park Opera (£3,750); RNLI (£3,100); World Jewish Relief (£3,000); Barnfield Riding for the Disabled, Community Security Trust and RNIB (£2,500); and Comic Relief and The Donkey Sanctuary (£1,000 each); Alexander School PTA (£500); Life Line for the Old (£300); Mind (£200); The Woodland Trust (£100); and West London Synagogue Charitable Fund (£30).

FINANCES *Year* 2009–10 *Income* £28,579 *Grants* £54,507 *Assets* £901,347

TRUSTEES M Morrison; I R Morrison.

OTHER INFORMATION Ian Morrison is also a trustee of Kemis's Lectureship Charity (Charity Commission no. 1013259); and The Andover Charities (Charity Commission no. 206587).

HOW TO APPLY In writing to the correspondent.

WHO TO APPLY TO J Payne, Begbies Chettle Agar, Chartered Accountants, Epworth House, 25 City Road, London EC1Y 1AR *Tel* 020 7628 5801

■ G M Morrison Charitable Trust

CC NO 261380   **ESTABLISHED** 1970
WHERE FUNDING CAN BE GIVEN UK.
WHO CAN BENEFIT Registered charities only.
WHAT IS FUNDED A wide variety of activities in the social welfare, medical and education/training fields. The trustees give priority to those charities already supported. Very few charities are added to the list each year.
WHAT IS NOT FUNDED No support for individuals, charities not registered in the UK, schemes or activities which are generally regarded as the responsibility of statutory authorities, short-term projects or one-off capital grants (except for emergency appeals).
TYPE OF GRANT Mostly annual.
RANGE OF GRANTS £600 to £5,000, average £807.
SAMPLE GRANTS British Red Cross – Haiti Earthquake Appeal (£5,000); Oxfam – Emergency Response Horn of East Africa (£3,000); Royal College of Surgeons (£2,200); Royal Society of Arts Endowment Fund (£2,000); Help the Aged (£1,300); Enterprise Education Trust and University of Liverpool (£1,100 each); Child in Need – India and Refugee Council Day Centre (£1,000 each); Bath Institute of Medical Engineering (£900); Corporation for the Sons of the Clergy (£850); Family Holiday Association (£800); Fight for Sight (£750); Gastroenterology and Nutrition Research Trust (£700); Prisoners Abroad (£650); Canine Partners for Independence, the Tree Register and Victim Support – Sussex (£600 each).
FINANCES *Year* 2009–10 *Income* £168,978 *Grants* £177,600 *Assets* £7,464,445
TRUSTEES N W Smith, Chair; Miss E Morrison; A E Cornick; Mrs J Hunt.
HOW TO APPLY The trust's annual report states: 'Beneficiaries of grants are normally selected on the basis of the personal knowledge and recommendation of a trustee. The trust's grant making policy is however to support the recipient of grants on a long term recurring basis. The scope of its giving is determined only by the extent of its resources, and is not otherwise restricted. The trustees have decided that for the present, new applications for grants will only be considered in the most exceptional circumstances, any spare income will be allocated to increasing the grants made to charities currently receiving support. In the future this policy will of course be subject to periodic review. Applicants understanding this policy who nevertheless wish to apply for a grant should write to the [correspondent].' Monitoring is undertaken by assessment of annual reports and accounts which are required from all beneficiaries, and by occasional trustee visits. During the year 38 existing beneficiaries failed to submit their latest report and accounts and consequently lost their annual grant.
WHO TO APPLY TO A E Cornick, Trustee, Currey and Co, 21 Buckingham Gate, London SW1E 6LS *Tel* 020 7802 2700

■ The Stanley Morrison Charitable Trust

SC NO SC006610   **ESTABLISHED** 1989
WHERE FUNDING CAN BE GIVEN The west coast of Scotland, with a preference for Glasgow and Ayrshire.
WHO CAN BENEFIT Organisations benefiting young adults, and sportsmen and women.
WHAT IS FUNDED Sporting activities in Scotland, with particular emphasis on the encouragement of youth involvement; charities which have as their principal base of operation and benefit the west coast of Scotland, in particular the Glasgow and Ayrshire areas; charities whose funds arise from or whose assistance is provided to people having connection with the licensed trades and in particular the whisky industry; Scottish educational establishments.
TYPE OF GRANT Buildings, project and recurring costs. Grants and funding for up to and over three years will be considered.
RANGE OF GRANTS £100–£10,000.
SAMPLE GRANTS Previous beneficiaries include Scottish Cricket Union, Princess Royal Trust for Carers, Riding for the Disabled, Mark Scott Foundation, Glasgow University Sports Sponsorship, Grange Cricket Club – Youth Section, Cancer UK Scotland and Scottish Schools' Badminton Union.
FINANCES *Year* 2009–10 *Income* £45,837 *Grants* £30,000
TRUSTEES S W Morrison; J H McKean; Mrs M E Morrison; T F O'Connell; A S Dudgeon.
HOW TO APPLY In writing to the correspondent. Applicants should include details on the purpose of the grant, what funding has already been secured and the actual sum that they are looking for.
WHO TO APPLY TO The Trustees, c/o French Duncan, 375 West George Street, Glasgow G2 4LW

■ Moshal Charitable Trust

CC NO 284448   **ESTABLISHED** 1981
WHERE FUNDING CAN BE GIVEN UK.
WHO CAN BENEFIT Jewish causes.
WHAT IS FUNDED General charitable purposes.
SAMPLE GRANTS The trust's accounts are routinely basic, therefore no sample grants were available for 2010–11.
FINANCES *Year* 2010–11 *Income* £61,051 *Grants* £81,077 *Assets* £324,442
TRUSTEES D Halpern; L Halpern.
HOW TO APPLY In writing to the correspondent.
WHO TO APPLY TO The Trustees, c/o Sefton Yodaiken & Co., 40a Bury New Road, Prestwich, Manchester M25 0LD

■ Vyoel Moshe Charitable Trust

CC NO 327054   **ESTABLISHED** 1986
WHERE FUNDING CAN BE GIVEN UK and overseas.
WHO CAN BENEFIT Registered charities.
WHAT IS FUNDED Education and relief of poverty.
FINANCES *Year* 2007–08 *Income* £1,100,000 *Grants* £1,000,000 *Assets* £56,000,000
TRUSTEES Y Frankel; B Berger; S Seidenfeld.
OTHER INFORMATION The latest accounts available at the Charity Commission were for 2007/08.
HOW TO APPLY In writing to the correspondent.
WHO TO APPLY TO J Weinberger, Secretary, 2–4 Chardmore Road, London N16 6HX

■ The Moshulu Charitable Trust

CC NO 1071479   **ESTABLISHED** 1998
WHERE FUNDING CAN BE GIVEN UK.
WHO CAN BENEFIT Charitable organisations.
WHAT IS FUNDED 'Humanitarian' and evangelical causes.
SAMPLE GRANTS SWYM (£15,900); Christ Church (£11,700); Tear Fund (£5,400); Partnership UK (£3,000); Care for the Family (£2,400) and Seaway Trust (£1,600).

FINANCES *Year* 2009–10 *Income* £43,175
Grants £61,969 *Assets* £166,852

TRUSTEES H J Fulls; D M Fulls; G N Fulls; S M Fulls;
G F Symons.

OTHER INFORMATION Grants total figure includes
£2,700 in grants to individuals.

HOW TO APPLY In writing to the correspondent.

WHO TO APPLY TO H J Fulls, Trustee, Devonshire
Road, Heathpark, Honiton, Devon EX14 1SD
Tel 01404 540 770

■ Brian and Jill Moss Charitable Trust

CC NO 1084664 **ESTABLISHED** 2000

WHERE FUNDING CAN BE GIVEN Worldwide.

WHO CAN BENEFIT Registered charities only.

WHAT IS FUNDED Jewish causes and healthcare.

WHAT IS NOT FUNDED Donations are made to
registered charities only.

TYPE OF GRANT Capital projects and towards
'ordinary charity expenditure'.

SAMPLE GRANTS Previously: United Jewish Israel
Appeal (£43,000); Magen David Adom UK
(£31,000); Jewish Care (£16,000); World
Jewish Relief (£15,000); Chai Cancer Care
(£12,000); United Synagogue-Tribe (£11,000);
WIZO UK (£6,000); National Jewish Chaplaincy
Board (£5,500); Prostate Cancer Charitable
Trust (£5,000); Myeloma UK (£3,000); Israel
Folk Dance Institute (£500); and Jewish
Museum and Operation Wheelchairs (£250
each).

FINANCES *Year* 2009–10 *Income* £8,535
Grants £148,634

TRUSTEES Brian Peter Moss; Jill Moss; David Paul
Moss; Sarah Levy.

HOW TO APPLY In writing to the correspondent.
Appeals are considered as they are received
and the trustees will make donations throughout
the year.'

WHO TO APPLY TO Miss K Griffin, c/o Deloitte,
5 Callaghan Square, Cardiff CF10 5BT *Tel* 029
2046 0000

■ The Moss Charitable Trust

CC NO 258031 **ESTABLISHED** 1969

WHERE FUNDING CAN BE GIVEN UK and overseas, with
an interest in Dorset, Hampshire and Sussex.

WHO CAN BENEFIT Registered charities, especially
Christian.

WHAT IS FUNDED General charitable purposes,
specifically for the benefit of the community in
the county borough of Bournemouth, and
Hampshire, Dorset and Sussex; advancement of
religion either UK or overseas; advancement of
education; and relief of poverty, disease and
sickness.

TYPE OF GRANT Outright grant or interest-free loan.

RANGE OF GRANTS Up to £8,000, but mostly less
than £5,000.

SAMPLE GRANTS Christ Church – Westbourne
(£6,400); Great Wood Trust (£6,100); Slindon
PCC (£5,800 each); Scripture Union (£4,600);
Salvation Army (£2,000); and Worthing
Churches Homeless Trust (£1,000).

FINANCES *Year* 2009–10 *Income* £157,784
Grants £90,533 *Assets* £113,006

TRUSTEES J H Simmons; A F Simmons;
P L Simmons; D S Olby.

OTHER INFORMATION The grants total includes around
£8,500 given by the trust to individuals.

HOW TO APPLY No funds are available by direct
application. Because of the way in which this

trust operates it is not open to external
applications for grants.

WHO TO APPLY TO P D Malpas, 7 Church Road,
Parkstone, Poole, Dorset BH14 8UF *Tel* 01202
730002

■ The Robert and Margaret Moss Charitable Trust

CC NO 290760 **ESTABLISHED** 1984

WHERE FUNDING CAN BE GIVEN Oxfordshire, with a
preference for Oxford.

WHO CAN BENEFIT Charitable organisations.

WHAT IS FUNDED Research into human nutrition,
medical research, relief of poverty and
education.

RANGE OF GRANTS Usually £1,000.

SAMPLE GRANTS Fight for Sight (£5,000); Research
into Ageing, The Unicorn School and The
Listening Centre (£2,000 each); Elizabeth Finn
Care Centre, UCARE, Oxfordshire Playbus,
Windmill House Welfare Fund, Meningitis UK,
Pathway Workshop, Tandem, REACT and
Wellbeing of Women (£1,000 each).

FINANCES *Year* 2009–10 *Income* £40,446
Grants £37,325 *Assets* £1,400,237

TRUSTEES John Cole; Dr Tarrant Stein; Mrs Maggie
Perrin.

HOW TO APPLY In writing to the correspondent.

WHO TO APPLY TO Ms Helen Fanyinka, c/o Morgan
Cole, Buxton Court, 3 West Way, Oxford
OX2 0SZ *Tel* 01865 262600 *email* info@
morgan-cole.com

■ Moss Family Charitable Trust

CC NO 327529 **ESTABLISHED** 1987

WHERE FUNDING CAN BE GIVEN England.

WHO CAN BENEFIT Jewish organisations.

WHAT IS FUNDED Religious and welfare purposes.

WHAT IS NOT FUNDED Neither music nor the arts is
funded.

TYPE OF GRANT One-off.

RANGE OF GRANTS £100–£10,000.

SAMPLE GRANTS £10,000 to the Children's Charity;
£8,000 to West London Synagogue (WLS);
£5,000 to Jewish Child's Day; £4,000 each to
Norwood and the Presidents Club; £600 to
Hammerson House.

FINANCES *Year* 2009–10 *Income* £150,012
Grants £149,162 *Assets* £2,941

TRUSTEES S D Moss; R S Moss; Mrs V J Campus.

HOW TO APPLY In writing to the correspondent. The
trust is unlikely to respond to unsolicited
applications.

WHO TO APPLY TO K Sage, Administrator, 28 Bolton
Street, Mayfair, London W1J 8BP *Tel* 020 7491
5108

■ Mothercare Charitable Foundation

CC NO 1104386 **ESTABLISHED** 2004

WHERE FUNDING CAN BE GIVEN UK and worldwide.

WHO CAN BENEFIT Children and their mothers.

WHAT IS FUNDED Registered charities and research
organisations that promote the general wellbeing of children and their mothers; offering
them the very best chance of good health,
education, well-being and a secure start in life.
Specifically, the foundation welcomes
applications from registered charities and
research organisations associated with the
following criteria: ensuring the good health and

well-being of mums-to-be, new mums and their children; special baby-care needs and premature births; other parenting initiatives relating to family well-being.

WHAT IS NOT FUNDED No response to circular appeals. Support is not given to: animal welfare, appeals from individuals, the arts, elderly people, environment/heritage, religious appeals, political appeals, or sport.

SAMPLE GRANTS £36,000 to Wellbeing of Women; £15,000 each to Great Ormond Street Children's Charity and The Cambridge Foundation; £10,000 to Wellchild; £9,000 to Watchdog Ltd; £5,500 to Meningitis Research Foundation.

FINANCES *Year* 2009–10 *Income* £236,092 *Grants* £172,998 *Assets* £207,471

TRUSTEES Karren Brady; Ben Gordon; Ian Peacock; Clive Revett.

HOW TO APPLY In writing to the correspondent. Requests for donations will only be considered when made in writing on the application form that can be printed from the company's website. Applications are considered on a quarterly basis. Unsolicited appeals are unlikely to be successful.

WHO TO APPLY TO Simone Spencer-Ahmed, The Charity Administrator, Cherry Tree Road, Watford, Hertfordshire WD24 6SH *Tel* 01923 206077 *email* simone.spencer-ahmed@mothercare.co.uk *Website* www.mothercare.com

■ Moto in the Community Trust

CC NO 1111147 **ESTABLISHED** 2005
WHERE FUNDING CAN BE GIVEN Communities local to the 48 Moto service areas around the UK (details of stations can be found on its website).

WHO CAN BENEFIT Supports a wide variety of local charities and community projects.

WHAT IS FUNDED Projects that benefit the local community.

WHAT IS NOT FUNDED The trust does not consider applications that are for the promotion of religion or politics or from animal welfare charities.

SAMPLE GRANTS Breast Cancer Care (£61,000); Help for Heroes (£59,000); Wellbeing of Women (£10,000); RAF Wings (£2,000); Berkshire MS Therapy Centre and Flitwick Rotary Club (£1,000 each); St David's Primary School (£600); St Rocco's Hospice (£400) and Scottish Book Trust (£200).

FINANCES *Year* 2010 *Income* £261,608 *Grants* £147,161

TRUSTEES Brian Lotts, Chair; Suzanne Hollinshead; Christopher Rogers; Brian Larkin; Helen Budd; Ian Thomson; Heather Roberts; Sara Davies; Malcolm Plowes; Ashleigh Lewis; Ian Kernighan; Jon Shore; Peter Hazzard; Ellis Green.

HOW TO APPLY Application forms, guidelines and criteria are available on the Trust's website. Any questions can be directed to the Moto in the Community Trust Administrator (email: motocharity@talking360.com; tel.: 01525 714467 / 717303).

WHO TO APPLY TO Moto in the Community Trust Administrator, Freepost RLYC-BKXA-CJAA, 37 Beaumont Road, Flitwick, Bedfordshire MK45 1AL *Tel* 01525 714467 / 717303 *email* motocharity@talking360.com *Website* www.motointhecommunity.co.uk

■ J P Moulton Charitable Foundation

CC NO 1109891 **ESTABLISHED** 2005
WHERE FUNDING CAN BE GIVEN UK.
WHO CAN BENEFIT Research institutions, disadvantaged people.
WHAT IS FUNDED Medical research, education, training and counselling.
TYPE OF GRANT One-off and recurrent.
RANGE OF GRANTS £200–£258,000.
SAMPLE GRANTS University of Lancaster (£258,000); University College London (£65,000); University of Liverpool (£63,000); Meningitis Research Foundation (£57,000); University of Manchester (£49,000); University of Southampton (£48,000); Les Bourgs Hospice (£40,000); Imperial College (£33,000); CSV -'Summer of Service' initiative (£20,000); St Martin-in-the-Fields Development Trust (£10,000); Papworth Hospital (£5,000); and Sevenoaks Citizens Advice (£2,500).
FINANCES *Year* 2010 *Income* £1,300,944 *Grants* £684,313 *Assets* £6,077,798
TRUSTEES J P Moulton; Mrs P M Moulton; Sara Everett.
HOW TO APPLY In writing to the correspondent.
WHO TO APPLY TO J P Moulton, Trustee, c/o Better Capital LLP, 39–41 Charing Cross Road, London WC2H 0AR *Tel* 020 7440 0860

■ The Mount Everest Foundation

CC NO 208206 **ESTABLISHED** 1955
WHERE FUNDING CAN BE GIVEN Expeditions from Great Britain and New Zealand.
WHO CAN BENEFIT Organisations, young adults and older people.
WHAT IS FUNDED Support of expeditions for exploration and research in high mountain regions only.
WHAT IS NOT FUNDED Youth, training and commercial expeditions are not eligible.
TYPE OF GRANT Project.
RANGE OF GRANTS £600–£2,500.
FINANCES *Year* 2009–10 *Income* £37,847 *Grants* £33,100 *Assets* £1,017,400
TRUSTEES Sarah Tyacke, Chair; A Hodson; David Unwin; Paul Rose; Dr William Thurston; Martin Scott; Col. Henry Day.
PUBLICATIONS A map of Central Asia has been produced in collaboration with the Royal Geographical Society.
HOW TO APPLY On a form available from the correspondent. Deadlines for receipt of completed application forms are 31 August and 31 December for the following year's expeditions.
WHO TO APPLY TO R F Morgan, 23 Charlwood Road, London W15 1QA *Tel* 020 8788 6251 *email* bill.ruthven@btinternet.com *Website* www.mef.org.uk

■ The Edwina Mountbatten & Leonora Children's Foundation

CC NO 228166 **ESTABLISHED** 1960
WHERE FUNDING CAN BE GIVEN UK and overseas.
WHO CAN BENEFIT Medical organisations, particularly those benefiting children and nurses.
WHAT IS FUNDED Save the Children Fund (for children who are sick, distressed or in need), the promotion and improvement of the art and practice of nursing, St John Ambulance and charities for the relief of cancer sufferers.

WHAT IS NOT FUNDED No grants for research or to individual nurses working in the UK for further professional training.

TYPE OF GRANT Project grants.

RANGE OF GRANTS £2,000–£32,000.

SAMPLE GRANTS Save the Children and Rainbow Trust (£25,000 each); Cancer Research UK, St John Ambulance and St John Jerusalem Eye Hospital (£10,000 each); Help for Heroes (£5,000); Action Aid (£4,000); National Leprosy Fund (£3,000); The Fred Hollows Foundation (£3,400); and InterCare Medical Aid for Africa (£2,000).

FINANCES *Year* 2010 *Income* £120,903 *Grants* £97,400 *Assets* £4,926,752

TRUSTEES Countess Mountbatten of Burma, Chair; Hon. Alexandra Knatchbull; Lord Brabourne; Peter H T Mimpriss; Dame Mary Fagan; Lady Brabourne; Sir David Frost; Myrddin Rees; Sir Evelyn De Rothschild.

HOW TO APPLY In writing to the correspondent. The trustees meet once a year, generally in September/October.

WHO TO APPLY TO John Moss, Secretary, The Estate Office, Broadlands, Romsey, Hampshire SO51 9ZE *Tel* 01794 529750

■ Mountbatten Festival of Music

CC NO 1016088 **ESTABLISHED** 1993

WHERE FUNDING CAN BE GIVEN UK.

WHO CAN BENEFIT Registered charities benefiting (ex) servicemen/women.

WHAT IS FUNDED Charities connected with the Royal Marines and Royal Navy.

WHAT IS NOT FUNDED Charities or organisations unknown to the trustees.

TYPE OF GRANT One-off and recurrent.

SAMPLE GRANTS The Royal Marines website states that the proceeds of the festival go to the Royal Marines Charitable Trust Fund and CLIC Sargent. Previous beneficiaries have also included: Malcolm Sergeant Cancer Fund (£20,000); Metropolitan Police Benevolent Trust (14,000); RN Benevolent Fund; RNRMC and RM Museum (£10,000 each); Wrens Benevolent Trust, Seafarers UK, Royal British Legion, The 'Not Forgotten' Society, Queen Ann Hospital Home, and Scottish Veterans Residences (£1,000 each).

FINANCES *Year* 2009–10 *Income* £512,192 *Grants* £265,800 *Assets* £193,600

TRUSTEES Commandant General Royal Marines; Director of Royal Marines; Naval Personnel Team (RM) Team Leader.

HOW TO APPLY Unsolicited applications are not considered as the trust's income is dependent upon the running and success of various musical events. Any money raised is then disbursed to a set of regular beneficiaries.

WHO TO APPLY TO Lt Col I W Grant, Corps Secretary, The Corps Secretariat, Building 32, HMS Excellent, Whale Island, Portsmouth PO2 8ER *Tel* 02392 547 201 *email* royalmarines. charities@charity.vfree.com *Website* www. royalmarinesregimental.co.uk

■ The Mountbatten Memorial Trust

CC NO 278691 **ESTABLISHED** 1979

WHERE FUNDING CAN BE GIVEN Mainly UK, but some overseas.

WHO CAN BENEFIT Registered charities.

WHAT IS FUNDED Grants restricted to technological research in aid of disabilities.

WHAT IS NOT FUNDED No grants are made towards the purchase of technology to assist people with disabilities.

TYPE OF GRANT Technological research projects.

RANGE OF GRANTS £600–£45,000.

SAMPLE GRANTS Atlantic College (£45,000); Inspire Foundation (£1,150); The Naval Review, Royal National Institute for the Deaf and The Sequal Trust (£1,000 each) and Motivation Charitable Trust (£600).

FINANCES *Year* 2010 *Income* £47,075 *Grants* £50,450 *Assets* £521,035

TRUSTEES Countess Mountbatten of Burma; Lady Pamela Hicks; Ben Moorhead; Ashley Hicks; Hon. Michael John Knatchbull; Hon. Philip Knatchbull; William Fox and Kelly Knatchbull.

OTHER INFORMATION Grants were made totalling £50,000 of which £45,000 was awarded to Atlantic College.

HOW TO APPLY In writing to the correspondent, at any time.

WHO TO APPLY TO John Moss, Secretary, The Estate Office, Broadlands, Romsey, Hampshire SO51 9ZE *Tel* 01794 529750

■ The MSE Charity

CC NO 1121320 **ESTABLISHED** 2007

WHERE FUNDING CAN BE GIVEN UK.

WHO CAN BENEFIT Individuals and organisations aiming to eradicate financial illiteracy in the UK through education and innovative projects.

WHAT IS FUNDED Financial education; financial planning and advice services.

WHAT IS NOT FUNDED No funding for career development, vocational courses, undergraduate or postgraduate courses. No applications directly from persons under 18 years of age, such applicants will need a parent or guardian to apply on their behalf.

SAMPLE GRANTS Previous beneficiaries include: Bristol Debt Advice Centre; Tadley and District CAB; Cleanslate National CIC; Helping Hands for Refugees; Pen y Enfys; Nottingham Deaf Society; Bolton Lads' & Girls' Club; Stoke on Trent CAB; and The Holy Catholic School.

FINANCES *Year* 2010–11 *Income* £94,567 *Grants* £51,408 *Assets* £178,727

TRUSTEES Tony Tesciuba; John Hewison; Katie Birkett; Vanessa Bissessur.

HOW TO APPLY 'Applications must be made by a "constituted group". This roughly means an organisation with its own bank account and rules to make it accountable.' Applicants apply using the online application form on the trust's website. For up to date programme information, including closing dates, please consult the trust's website. **The trust tends to only open for applications for very short periods.** The trust welcomes queries from applicants who need help with the application process. The panel aim to make a decision on an application within six weeks of the deadline. Please note only the first 40 applications that meet the criteria will be considered by the panel. Groups whether successful or not may only submit one application in any two year period.

WHO TO APPLY TO Anthony Jeffrey, Administrator, Tesciuba, Tesciuba Ltd, The Chambers, 13 Police Street, Manchester M2 7LQ *Tel* 0161 834 9221 *email* stuart@msecharity.com *Website* www.msecharity.com

■ The Mugdock Children's Trust

SC NO SC006001   **ESTABLISHED** 1920
WHERE FUNDING CAN BE GIVEN Scotland.
WHO CAN BENEFIT Charities benefiting children up to the age of about 14 who are ill or disabled.
WHAT IS FUNDED 'Poor children from Glasgow or other districts of Scotland who are in need of convalescent treatment for sickness or any other disability; organisations of a charitable nature whose objects either consist of or include the provision in Scotland of rehabilitation, recreation or education for children convalescing or still suffering from the effects of illness, injury or disability; organisations of a charitable nature whose objects either consist of or include the provision in Scotland of accommodation or facilities for children who are in need of care or assistance.'
RANGE OF GRANTS £500–£6,000.
SAMPLE GRANTS Previous beneficiaries have included Abercorn School, Ark Trust, Barnardo's, Camphill Foundation, Cancer and Leukaemia in Childhood, Children First, Children's Heart Federation, Glasgow Children's Holiday Playscheme, Hopscotch Holidays Ltd, Sense, Sighthill Youth Centre, Stepping Stones for Families, Wanderers Youth Club and West Scotland Deaf Children's Society.
FINANCES *Year* 2009–10 *Income* £48,188 *Grants* £48,000
TRUSTEES Graham A Philips; Rosamund Blair; Moira Bruce; Dr Anne Cowan; Joyce Duguid; Avril Meighan; Alastair J Struthers; Christine Brown; James Morris.
HOW TO APPLY On a form available from the correspondent. Trustees meet in March and November.
WHO TO APPLY TO Mrs J Simpson, Secretary, Wylie and Bisset Accountants, 168 Bath Street, Glasgow G2 4TP *Tel* 0141 566 7000 *Fax* 0141 566 7001

■ The Mulberry Trust

CC NO 263296   **ESTABLISHED** 1971
WHERE FUNDING CAN BE GIVEN UK, with an interest in Harlow, Essex and surrounding areas, including London.
WHO CAN BENEFIT Charitable organisations.
WHAT IS FUNDED General charitable purposes.
RANGE OF GRANTS £1,000–£50,000.
SAMPLE GRANTS The Cambridge Foundation and the Foundation for Church Leadership (£100,000 each); Prison Dialogue (£30,000); Calm Centre Ltd (£25,000); NSPCC (£20,000); Stewardship (£15,000); Parents Like Us (£11,000); Credit Action and the Royal National Theatre (£10,000); Home Start Witham (£9,000); Boston Stump Restoration Development Trust, Church Housing Trust and Victim Support Essex (£5,000 each); Royal Academy of Arts (£3,000); and the Williams Syndrome Foundation (£1,000).
FINANCES *Year* 2009–10 *Income* £186,059 *Grants* £603,272 *Assets* £6,696,260
TRUSTEES John G Marks; Mrs Ann M Marks; Charles F Woodhouse; Timothy J Marks.
HOW TO APPLY The trust has stated that it 'will not, as a matter of policy, consider applications which are unsolicited'.
WHO TO APPLY TO Ms Cheryl Boyce, Farrer and Co, 66 Lincoln's Inn Fields, London WC2A 3LH *Tel* 020 7242 2022

■ The Edith Murphy Foundation

CC NO 1026062   **ESTABLISHED** 1993
WHERE FUNDING CAN BE GIVEN UK with some preference for Leicestershire.
WHO CAN BENEFIT Organisations benefiting people in need, animals, children and the disabled.
WHAT IS FUNDED Relief for people suffering hardship/distress due to their age, youth, infirmity, disability, poverty or social and economic circumstances. Relief of suffering of animals and provision for the care of unwanted or sick animals. Other general charitable purposes.
TYPE OF GRANT One-off and recurrent.
RANGE OF GRANTS Up to £375,000.
SAMPLE GRANTS University of Leicester (£375,000); Parish of Dromintee (£100,000); De Montford University (£50,000); Vitalise (£47,000); University of Leicester (£46,000); The Stroke Association (£30,000); Motor Neurone Disease Association (£20,000); PDSA (£15,000); Rainbow Children's Hospice, Launde Abbey, Leicester Charity Link and RSPCA (£10,000 each).
FINANCES *Year* 2009–10 *Income* £682,856 *Grants* £1,208,770 *Assets* £30,860,205
TRUSTEES David L Tams; Pamela M Breakwell; Christopher P Blakesley; Richard F Adkinson.
HOW TO APPLY In writing to the correspondent.
WHO TO APPLY TO David L Tams, Trustee, c/o Crane and Walton, 113–117 London Road, Leicester LE2 0RG *Tel* 0116 2551901

■ Murphy-Neumann Charity Company Limited

CC NO 229555   **ESTABLISHED** 1963
WHERE FUNDING CAN BE GIVEN UK.
WHO CAN BENEFIT Registered charities only.
WHAT IS FUNDED The trust has three main objects: to support projects aimed at helping those in society who suffer economic or social disadvantages or hardship arising from disability and/or social exclusion; to assist those working to alleviate chronic illness and disabling disease; to help fund research into medical conditions (particularly among the very young and the elderly) for which there is not yet a cure.
WHAT IS NOT FUNDED No grants to individuals, or non-registered charities.
TYPE OF GRANT One-off and recurrent grants for general costs (large charities) and specific projects (smaller organisations).
RANGE OF GRANTS £500–£2,500.
SAMPLE GRANTS Contact the Elderly and Evening Argus Christmas Appeal (£2,500 each); Haemophilia Society, Hebron Trust and Beacon House (£1,800 each); Acorn Villages, SE Cancer Help Centre and Hospice in the Weald (£1,500 each); Prostate Cancer Charity, Dementia Care Trust and RUKBA (£1,300 each); RNIB Sunshine House Nursery School, Chicks Camping Holidays, Bowel Disease Research Foundation and Tourettes Action (£1,000 each); REACT, Jesse May Trust and Hamlet Centre Trust (£750 each); and Tuberous Sclerosis Association (£500).
FINANCES *Year* 2009–10 *Income* £68,601 *Grants* £70,000 *Assets* £1,436,089
TRUSTEES Mark J Lockett; Colette Safhill; Marcus Richman.
HOW TO APPLY In writing to the correspondent, in a letter outlining the purpose of the required charitable donation. Telephone calls are not welcome. There are no application forms,

Think carefully about every application. Is it justified?

757

guidelines or deadlines. No SAE required. Grants are usually given in November and December.

WHO TO APPLY TO Mark J Lockett, Trustee, Hayling Cottage, Upper Street, Stratford-St-Mary, Colchester, Essex CO7 6JW *Tel* 01206 323685 *email* mncc@keme.co.uk

■ The John R Murray Charitable Trust

CC NO 1100199   **ESTABLISHED** 2003
WHERE FUNDING CAN BE GIVEN UK.
WHO CAN BENEFIT Registered charities.
WHAT IS FUNDED 'Arts an literature (although not strictly limited to such areas) and where the award of a grant will have an immediate and tangible benefit to the recipient in question.'
SAMPLE GRANTS National Library of Scotland (£322,000); Abbotsford Trust (£61,500); Friends of Highgate Cemetery Trust (£50,000); Save (£48,000); British School at Rome (£39,000); Kew Foundation (£25,000); College of Arms (£20,000); Historic Chapels Trust (£15,000); Anglo Peruvian Society (£10,000); South East Prisoner Forum Project (£7,500); Royal Society of Literature (£6,000); Music Works (£5,000); and British Red Cross Haiti Appeal (£2,000).
FINANCES *Year* 2010 *Income* £783,669 *Grants* £1,240,000 *Assets* £25,123,069
TRUSTEES John R Murray; Virginia G Murray; Hallam J R G Murray; John O G Murray; Charles J G Murray.
HOW TO APPLY The trustees will not consider unsolicited applications for grants.
WHO TO APPLY TO The Trustees, 50 Albemarle Street, London W1S 4BD

■ Peter John Murray Trust

CC NO 1134976   **ESTABLISHED** 2010
WHERE FUNDING CAN BE GIVEN Developing countries, mainly in Africa and the Caribbean.
WHO CAN BENEFIT Established voluntary and community groups.
WHAT IS FUNDED Projects relating needs and wellbeing of pre-school and school aged children where their lives have been seriously affected by violent conflict, poverty, abuse, preventable ill health/incapacity, natural disaster or any other kind of misfortune.
TYPE OF GRANT Mostly recurrent.
TRUSTEES Recilda Murray; Edith Murray; Peter Murray.
OTHER INFORMATION Please note the following statement taken from the trust's website about its funding principles: 'Financial help and various other forms of assistance are provided through our partner organisations that are established voluntary groups and charities providing commendable services within local communities. And it is their local experience and professional practice that we seek to rely on as the leading route to meeting the acute needs and wellbeing of their beneficiaries – seriously affected children with wrecked lives. It is part of our overall objective, when possible and where appropriate, to foster long term relationships with our partners. We seek to be actively engaged in the promotion of our partners' respective causes and indeed enabling seriously affected, desperate children to access basic but essential living needs so they can exist and live a better life.' For more information

on becoming a partner organisation, please contact the trust directly.
HOW TO APPLY In writing to the correspondent.
WHO TO APPLY TO Peter Murray, Trustee, 78 York Street, London W1H 1DP *Tel* 020 7692 7007 *Fax* 020 7692 7008 *email* info@pjm-trust.org *Website* www.pjm-trust.org

■ The Mushroom Fund

CC NO 259954   **ESTABLISHED** 1969
WHERE FUNDING CAN BE GIVEN UK and overseas, with a preference for St Helens.
WHO CAN BENEFIT Registered charities. Donations are made only to charities known to the trustees.
WHAT IS FUNDED General charitable purposes.
WHAT IS NOT FUNDED No grants to individuals or to organisations that are not registered charities.
TYPE OF GRANT Unrestricted.
RANGE OF GRANTS Up to £3,000.
SAMPLE GRANTS Pilkington Glass Collection Trust (£7,000); St Patrick's Church, Patterdale (£5,250); Samantha Dickson Brain Trust (£5,000); Pegasus Child Care Centre (£2,500); and National Wildflower Centre, St Helen's Women's Aid and Southport Offshore Rescue Team (£1,000 each).
FINANCES *Year* 2009–10 *Income* £31,167 *Grants* £42,100 *Assets* £922,544
TRUSTEES Mrs Rosalind Christian; Guy Pilkington; James Pilkington; Harriet Christian; Liverpool Charity and Voluntary Services.
HOW TO APPLY The trust does not consider or respond to unsolicited applications.
WHO TO APPLY TO The Trustees, Liverpool Charity and Voluntary Services, 151 Dale Street, Liverpool L2 2AH *Tel* 0151 227 5177 *email* enquiries@charitycheques.org.uk

■ The Music Sales Charitable Trust

CC NO 1014942   **ESTABLISHED** 1992
WHERE FUNDING CAN BE GIVEN UK, but mostly Bury St Edmunds and London.
WHO CAN BENEFIT Registered charities benefiting children and young adults, musicians, disabled people and people disadvantaged by poverty.
WHAT IS FUNDED The trust supports the education of children attending schools in the UK, relief of need, and other charitable purposes. The trustees are particularly interested in helping to promote music and musical education for young people.
WHAT IS NOT FUNDED No grants to individuals.
RANGE OF GRANTS £1,000–£30,000.
SAMPLE GRANTS Purcell School (£30,000); Bury St Edmunds Bach Society (£10,000); The Worshipful Company of Musicians, St Nicholas Hospice Care (£6,000 each); Westminster Synagogue (£5,000); Witold Lutoslawski Society (£2,500); Ipswich Community Play Bus, Citizens Advice Bureau, Maidstone Symphony Orchestra and Combat Stress (£1,000 each).
FINANCES *Year* 2009 *Income* £87,500 *Grants* £88,881 *Assets* £3,588
TRUSTEES Mr Robert Wise; Mr T Wise; Mr Ian Morgan; Mr Christopher Butler; Mr David Rockberger; Mrs Mildred Wise; Mr A E Latham.
HOW TO APPLY In writing to the correspondent. The trustees meet quarterly, generally in March, June, September and December.
WHO TO APPLY TO Neville Wignall, Clerk, Music Sales Ltd, Dettingen Way, Bury St Edmunds, Suffolk

IP33 3YB *Tel* 01284 702600 *email* neville.
wignall@musicsales.co.uk

■ Muslim Hands

CC NO 1105056　　　**ESTABLISHED** 1993
WHERE FUNDING CAN BE GIVEN Overseas.
WHO CAN BENEFIT Organisations benefiting people disadvantaged by poverty and victims of man-made or natural disasters and war.
WHAT IS FUNDED The relief of poverty and sickness in the event of natural disasters and areas of war; help to people in need, particularly orphans; advancement of the Islamic faith and distribution of Islamic literature; provision of schools, training colleges, safe water schemes, medical centres, and orphan sponsorship schemes.
FINANCES *Year* 2010 *Income* £12,981,161
Grants £9,720,296 *Assets* £5,969,782
TRUSTEES Pir Mohammad Amin-ul Hasanat Shah; Syed Lakhte Hassanain; Dr Musharaf Hussain; Sahibzada Ghulam Jillani; Saffi Ullah.
HOW TO APPLY In writing to the correspondent.
WHO TO APPLY TO The Trustees, 148–164 Gregory Boulevard, Nottingham NG7 5JE *Tel* 0115 911 7222 *Fax* 0115 911 7220 *email* contact@ muslimhands.org.uk *Website* www. muslimhands.org

■ The Mutual Trust Group

CC NO 1039300　　　**ESTABLISHED** 1994
WHERE FUNDING CAN BE GIVEN UK.
WHO CAN BENEFIT Organisations benefiting Jewish people and people disadvantaged by poverty.
WHAT IS FUNDED General charitable purposes. In particular, for the relief of poverty and the advancement of orthodox Jewish religious education.
SAMPLE GRANTS Yeshivat Kesser Hatalmud (£175,000); Yeshivat Shar Hashamayim (£156,000); Congregation Beis Hamedrash (£6,500) and 'other' (£2,400).
FINANCES *Year* 2010 *Income* £316,384
Grants £339,798 *Assets* £156,630
TRUSTEES B Weitz; M Weitz; A Weisz.
HOW TO APPLY In writing to the correspondent.
WHO TO APPLY TO B Weitz, Trustee, 12 Dunstan Road, London NW11 8AA *Tel* 020 8458 7549

■ MW (CL) Foundation

CC NO 1134917　　　**ESTABLISHED** 2010
WHERE FUNDING CAN BE GIVEN Worldwide, with a preference for Manchester.
WHO CAN BENEFIT Charitable organisations and education providers.
WHAT IS FUNDED Projects which promote education, relief of poverty and the advancement of the Orthodox Jewish faith.
TRUSTEES Hilary Olsberg; Vivienne Lewin; Jacob Halpern.
OTHER INFORMATION The foundation is closely linked with the MW (RH) Foundation, MW (GK) Foundation and MW (HO) Foundation and shares the same charitable objectives.
HOW TO APPLY In writing to the correspondent.
WHO TO APPLY TO Jacob Halpern, Trustee, 2b Mather Avenue, Prestwich, Manchester M25 0LA

■ MW (GK) Foundation

CC NO 1134916　　　**ESTABLISHED** 2010
WHERE FUNDING CAN BE GIVEN Undefined, in practice Manchester.
WHO CAN BENEFIT Charitable organisations and education providers.
WHAT IS FUNDED Projects which promote education, relief of poverty and the advancement of the Orthodox Jewish faith.
TRUSTEES Jacob Halpern; Rosalyn Halpern; David Olsberg.
OTHER INFORMATION The foundation was initially known as the Weisz Children Foundation and is closely linked with the MW (CL) Foundation, MW (RH) Foundation and MW (HO) Foundation.
HOW TO APPLY In writing to the correspondent.
WHO TO APPLY TO Jacob Halpern, Trustee, 2b Mather Avenue, Prestwich, Manchester M25 0LA

■ MW (HO) Foundation

CC NO 1134919　　　**ESTABLISHED** 2010
WHERE FUNDING CAN BE GIVEN Worldwide, with a preference for Manchester.
WHO CAN BENEFIT Charitable organisations and education providers.
WHAT IS FUNDED Projects which promote education, relief of poverty and the advancement of the Orthodox Jewish faith.
TRUSTEES Hilary Olsberg; Rosalind Halpern; Jacob Halpern.
OTHER INFORMATION The foundation was initially known as the Meir Weisz Foundation and is closely linked with the MW (CL) Foundation, MW (GK) Foundation and MW (RH) Foundation.
HOW TO APPLY In writing to the correspondent.
WHO TO APPLY TO Jacob Halpern, Trustee, 2b Mather Avenue, Prestwich, Manchester M25 0LA

■ MW (RH) Foundation

CC NO 1134918　　　**ESTABLISHED** 2010
WHERE FUNDING CAN BE GIVEN Worldwide, with a preference for Manchester.
WHO CAN BENEFIT Charitable organisations and education providers.
WHAT IS FUNDED Projects which promote education, relief of poverty and the advancement of the Orthodox Jewish faith.
TRUSTEES Hilary Olsberg; Rosalind Halpern; David Olsberg.
OTHER INFORMATION This foundation was initially known as the Deborah Weisz Foundation and is closely linked with the MW (CL) Foundation, MW (GK) Foundation and MW (HO) Foundation.
HOW TO APPLY In writing to the correspondent.
WHO TO APPLY TO David Olsberg, Trustee, 2b Mather Avenue, Prestwich, Manchester M25 0LA

■ MYA Charitable Trust

CC NO 299642　　　**ESTABLISHED** 1987
WHERE FUNDING CAN BE GIVEN Worldwide.
WHO CAN BENEFIT Children, young adults and Jewish people.
WHAT IS FUNDED Advancement of orthodox Jewish religion and education.
SAMPLE GRANTS 2004/05: £3,500 to ZSV Trust; £3,300 to KZF; £2,500 each to Beis Rochel and Keren Zedoko Vochesed; £2,000 each to London Friends of Kamenitzer Yeshiva and Maos Yesomim Charitable Trust; £1,100 to Bikkur Cholim De Satmar; £1,000 each to

Keren Mitzva Trust and Wlodowa Charity Rehabilitation Trust.

FINANCES *Year* 2009–10 *Income* £104,333 *Grants* £125,515 *Assets* £840,680

TRUSTEES Myer Rothfeld; Eve Rothfeld; Hannah Schraiber; Joseph Pfeffer.

OTHER INFORMATION The grant total includes £103,930 given to institutions and £21,585 distributed to individuals. A list of beneficiaries was not provided in the accounts.

HOW TO APPLY In writing to the correspondent.

WHO TO APPLY TO Myer Rothfeld, Trustee, Medcar House, 149a Stamford Hill, London N16 5LL *Tel* 020 8800 3582

■ MYR Charitable Trust

CC NO 1104406   **ESTABLISHED** 2004

WHERE FUNDING CAN BE GIVEN Israel, USA and England.

WHO CAN BENEFIT Members of the Orthodox Jewish faith.

WHAT IS FUNDED Advancement of the Orthodox Jewish religion, relief of sickness and poverty of recognised members of said faith.

SAMPLE GRANTS 2006: Cong Beth Joseph (£26,000); HP Charitable Trust (£2,300); UTA (£2,200); Gateshead Jewish Boarding School (£2,000); Keren Eretz Yisorel (£1,800); SCT Sunderland (£1,400) and GJLC (£1,000).

FINANCES *Year* 2010 *Income* £78,024 *Grants* £49,259 *Assets* £1,122,122

TRUSTEES Z M Kaufman; S Kaufman; A A Zonszajn; J Kaufman.

HOW TO APPLY In writing to the correspondent.

WHO TO APPLY TO Z M Kaufman, Trustee, 50 Keswick Street, Gateshead, Tyne and Wear NE8 1TQ

■ The Kitty and Daniel Nabarro Charitable Trust

cc no 1002786   **ESTABLISHED** 1991
WHERE FUNDING CAN BE GIVEN UK.
WHO CAN BENEFIT Registered charities.
WHAT IS FUNDED Relief of poverty, advancement of medicine and advancement of education. This trust will consider funding: information technology and computers; support and self-help groups; environmental issues; IT training; literacy; training for work; vocational training; and crime prevention schemes.
WHAT IS NOT FUNDED No grants to individuals.
SAMPLE GRANTS Cambridge Foundation Discovery Fund (£5,000); OCD Action (£2,000); Other grants (£5,000).
FINANCES *Year* 2009–10 *Income* £27,495 *Grants* £12,066 *Assets* £715,471
TRUSTEES D J N Nabarro; Katherine Nabarro; Allan Watson.
HOW TO APPLY The trustees allocate grants on an annual basis to an existing list of charities. The trustees do not at this time envisage grants to charities which are not already on the list. **This trust states that it does not respond to unsolicited applications.**
WHO TO APPLY TO D J N Nabarro, Trustee, PO Box 7491, London N20 8LY *email* admin.nabarro. charity@gmail.com

■ The Nadezhda Charitable Trust

cc no 1007295   **ESTABLISHED** 1992
WHERE FUNDING CAN BE GIVEN UK and worldwide, particularly Zimbabwe.
WHO CAN BENEFIT Christian organisations.
WHAT IS FUNDED Advancement of Christianity in the UK and overseas, particularly Zimbabwe.
WHAT IS NOT FUNDED No grants to individuals.
SAMPLE GRANTS Mind the Gap Africa (£24,000); Friends of the Theological College of Zimbabwe in the USA (£23,000); Bulawayo Orphanage Zimbabwe (£16,000); Crosslinks (£11,000); George Whitefield College (£4,000); and Shaw Trust (£2,000).
FINANCES *Year* 2009–10 *Income* £83,507 *Grants* £94,284 *Assets* £37,501
TRUSTEES William M Kingston; Mrs Jill M Kingston; Anthony R Collins; Ian Conolly.
HOW TO APPLY The majority of funds are presently directed to supporting the Christian Church in Zimbabwe. The trust does not, therefore, respond to unsolicited applications.
WHO TO APPLY TO Mrs Jill Kingston, Trustee, c/o Ballard Dale Syree Watson LLP, Oakmore Court, Kingswood Road, Hampton Lovett, Droitwich Spa WR9 0QH

■ The Naggar Charitable Trust

cc no 265409   **ESTABLISHED** 1973
WHERE FUNDING CAN BE GIVEN UK and overseas.
WHO CAN BENEFIT Jews.
WHAT IS FUNDED Jewish organisations; medical; the arts.
TYPE OF GRANT Some recurrent.
RANGE OF GRANTS £80–£100,000.

SAMPLE GRANTS British Friends of the Art Museums of Israel (£15,000); Western Marble Arch Synagogue (£11,000); CST (£8,500); The Contemporary Arts Society and The Royal Parks Foundation (£5,000 each); Jewish Care and One Family UK (£2,500 each); Royal Academy of Arts (£1,000); and St John's Wood Society (£15).
FINANCES *Year* 2009–10 *Income* £141,936 *Grants* £60,736 *Assets* £131,821
TRUSTEES Guy Naggar; Hon. Marion Naggar; Marc Zilkha.
HOW TO APPLY In writing to the correspondent.
WHO TO APPLY TO G Naggar, Trustee, 61 Avenue Road, London NW8 6HR *Tel* 020 7034 1919

■ The Eleni Nakou Foundation

cc no 803753   **ESTABLISHED** 1990
WHERE FUNDING CAN BE GIVEN Worldwide, mostly Continental Europe.
WHO CAN BENEFIT Charitable organisations.
WHAT IS FUNDED Advancement of education of the peoples of Europe in each other's culture, history, literature, language, institutions, art, science, religion, music and folklore, and promotion of the exchange of knowledge about the cultures of northern and southern Europe in order to bridge the divide between these cultures and promote international understanding.
TYPE OF GRANT Recurrent and one-off.
RANGE OF GRANTS £1,000–£45,000.
SAMPLE GRANTS Previously: £45,000 to Danish Institute at Athens; £17,500 to Hellenic Foundation; £9,000 to Eleni Nakou Scholarship Athens; £1,100 to Scandinavian Society for Modern Greek Studies.
FINANCES *Year* 2009–10 *Income* £2,466 *Grants* £60,000
TRUSTEES Kleinwort Benson Trustees Ltd.
OTHER INFORMATION The foundation had a large expenditure of £104,000 (2009–10).
HOW TO APPLY In writing to the correspondent. Applications are considered periodically. However, the trustees' state: 'It is unusual to respond favourably to unsolicited appeals'.
WHO TO APPLY TO Chris Gilbert, Secretary, c/o Kleinwort Benson Trustees Ltd, 30 Gresham Street, London EC2V 7PG *email* chris.gilbert@ kbpb.co.uk

■ The Janet Nash Charitable Settlement

cc no 326880   **ESTABLISHED** 1985
WHERE FUNDING CAN BE GIVEN UK.
WHO CAN BENEFIT Institutions and individuals.
WHAT IS FUNDED General charitable purposes.
TYPE OF GRANT Recurrent.
SAMPLE GRANTS The Royal Air Force Museum and the Get-a-Head Charitable Trust (£15,000); Acorns (£10,000); Shirley Medical Centre (£4,000); and Vision Charity (£3,000).
FINANCES *Year* 2009–10 *Income* £375,025 *Grants* £419,954 *Assets* £72,217
TRUSTEES Ronald Gulliver; M S Jacobs; Mrs C E Coyle.
OTHER INFORMATION In 2009–10 grants were made to individuals totalling £359,034; including £314,983 (Medical) and £44,051 (Hardship).
HOW TO APPLY Absolutely no response to unsolicited applications. In 2007, the trustees stated: 'The charity does not, repeat not, ever, consider any applications for benefit from the public.' Furthermore, that: 'Our existing charitable

Think carefully about every application. Is it justified?

761

commitments more than use up our potential funds and were found personally by the trustees themselves, never as a result of applications from third parties.'

WHO TO APPLY TO R Gulliver, Trustee, Ron Gulliver and Co. Ltd, The Old Chapel, New Mill Lane, Eversley, Hampshire RG27 0RA *Tel* 0118 973 3194

■ Nathan Charitable Trust

CC NO 251781   **ESTABLISHED** 1967
WHERE FUNDING CAN BE GIVEN UK and overseas.
WHO CAN BENEFIT Christian organisations.
WHAT IS FUNDED Evangelical Christian work and mission.
TYPE OF GRANT Mainly recurrent.
SAMPLE GRANTS Previous beneficiaries include: Operation Mobilisation, Carrot Tops, Leprosy Mission, Mission Aviation Fellowship, Open Doors, African Inland Mission, Bridges for Peace, Open Air Campaigners, Rhema Theatre Company and Christian Friends of Israel.
FINANCES *Year* 2009–10 *Income* £86
  Grants £35,000
TRUSTEES Thomas R Worth; Paula J Worth; Glyn A Jones.
OTHER INFORMATION The trust has now distributed almost all of its capital and has stated that no further donations will be made in the forseeable future.
HOW TO APPLY Funds are fully committed to current beneficiaries. No donations to be made in the foreseeable future.
WHO TO APPLY TO T R Worth, Trustee, The Copse, Sheviock, Torpoint, Cornwall PL11 3DZ *Tel* 01503 230413

■ The National Art Collections Fund

CC NO 209174   **ESTABLISHED** 1903
WHERE FUNDING CAN BE GIVEN UK.
WHO CAN BENEFIT Any museum, gallery or other institution in the UK with a permanent art collection on public display, providing it is registered with the Museums, Libraries and Archives Council.
WHAT IS FUNDED The purchase of works of art of all kinds. It also: presents works of art, which it has received as gifts or bequests, to museums and galleries; works to promote greater awareness of the visual arts; and campaigns to safeguard public art collections.
WHAT IS NOT FUNDED Applications where the applicant has already purchased or made a commitment to purchase the object, or made a financial commitment; other costs associated with acquisitions such as the conservation and restoration of works, transport and storage costs, temporary or permanent exhibitions and digitisation projects; applications from individuals, artist's groups, commercial organisations, hospitals, places of worship, schools or higher education institutions; funding towards professional development, travel or research.
TYPE OF GRANT One-off grants.
RANGE OF GRANTS There is no fixed upper or lower limit to the size of grant the committee may offer.
SAMPLE GRANTS Birmingham Museum and Gallery, Potteries Museum & Art Gallery – Staffordshire Hoard (£1.4 million each); Warwickshire Museum (£500,000); Glasgow Gallery of

Modern Art (£425,000); Nostell Priory (National Trust) – Brueghel Appeal (£419,000); British Museum (£260,000); Cecil Higgins Art Gallery (£196,000); Dulwich Picture Gallery; (£90,000); National Media Museum (£49,000); Powis Castle (£25,000); Whitworth Art Gallery (£24,000); Nottingham Castle (£5,000); Paisley Art Gallery and Observatory (£3,300); Museum of Transport (£2,000); and Potteries Museum and Art Gallery (£310).
FINANCES *Year* 2010 *Income* £10,036,000
  Grants £6,585,000 *Assets* £34,174,000
TRUSTEES David Very; Paul Zuckerman; Dr Wendy Baron; Prof. Michael Craig-Martin; Christopher Lloyd; Jonathan Marsden; Charles Sebag-Montefiore; Timothy Stevens; Dr Deborah Swallow; Prof. William Vaughan; Sally Osman; James Lingwood; Richard Calvocoressi; Caroline Butler; Prof. Chris Gosden; Antony Griffiths; Lisa Tickner; Michael Wilson.
  William Vaughan; the Hon. Felicity Waley-Cohen; Sally Osman; James Lingwood; Richard Calvocoressi.
PUBLICATIONS Review, Art Quarterly, Information notes for grant applicants.
OTHER INFORMATION The fund has a very comprehensive website.
HOW TO APPLY Firstly discuss the application with a member of the programmes office then register on the website to access the online application form. The Art Fund 'actively encourages strong applications from national and designated museums for objects which will enrich their collections and supports their effort s to expand into new collecting areas when appropriate. The Art Fund considers applications for whatever amount is needed. Applicants are expected also to apply for any public funding for which they might be eligible, and to raise funds from other sources if they can. The Grants Office requires all applications to be made online. Please see our website for full details and contact the Grants team to discuss any potential application.'
WHO TO APPLY TO Johnathan Guy Cubitt, Millais House, 7 Cromwell Place, London SW7 2JN *Tel* 020 7225 4800 *Fax* 020 7225 4848 *email* grants@artfund.org *Website* www.artfund.org

■ The National Churches Trust (formerly the Historic Churches Preservation Trust with the Incorporated Church Building Society)

CC NO 1119845   **ESTABLISHED** 1953
WHERE FUNDING CAN BE GIVEN UK.
WHO CAN BENEFIT Christian churches of architectural or historical importance that are in need of repair. Churches should meet the following criteria: the building must be open for regular public worship – the trust does not currently have grants available for cathedrals, but any other Christian places of worship can apply if they meet the eligibility criteria; it must be sited in England, Northern Ireland, the Isle of Man, Scotland or Wales; the congregation must belong to a denomination that is a member or associated member of Churches Together in Britain and Ireland; and all projects must be overseen by an architect who is either ARB, RIBA or AABC accredited, or by a chartered surveyor who is RICS accredited.

WHAT IS FUNDED To assist, with grants and loans, the efforts of congregations to carry out of essential repairs to the fabric of historic churches and improve their general facilities e.g. accessible toilets, kitchens and meeting rooms. The trust has also been working with WREN (Waste Recycling Environmental Ltd) to administer grants on their behalf to churches sited within a 10 mile radius of a landfill site operated by Waste Recycling Group. Please contact the trust for further information.

WHAT IS NOT FUNDED Please be aware that the trust cannot make grants for certain purposes including: non-church buildings (such as church halls and vicarages); bell repairs; organ repairs; repairs to internal furnishings; redecoration, other than after structural repairs; clock repairs; monument repairs. Grantee congregations must be members or associated members of Churches Together in Britain and Ireland.

TYPE OF GRANT Capital costs.

RANGE OF GRANTS From £2,500.

SAMPLE GRANTS Saltaire United Reformed Church – Yorkshire (£40,000) for repairs; St Patrick – Glasgow (£20,000) for repair and conservation of the building fabric, including repairs to the roof and gutters; Zion Baptist Church – Cambridge (£10,000) for building work to develop a vestibule used as a homeless shelter; St Mary's Parish Church – Carmarthenshire, Wales (£10,000) for urgent repairs to the tower and spire and repainting work; and St Leonard – Herefordshire (£5,000) towards the cost of incorporating community amenities within the Church.

FINANCES *Year* 2010 *Income* £1,509,023 *Grants* £1,311,886 *Assets* £3,356,353

TRUSTEES Charlotte Cole; Richard Carr-Archer; Michael Hoare; Anthony Wedgwood; John Readman; John Drew; Revd Nicholas Holtam; Jennifer Page.

PUBLICATIONS *Keeping Churches Alive – a brief history of the Trust* available directly from the trust or to download from the website.

OTHER INFORMATION In 2008 the Charity Commission appointed the National Churches Trust (NCT) as the sole trustee of the Historic Churches Preservation Trust (HCPT) and also granted a 'uniting direction'. Consequently, the NCT and HCPT are treated as a single charity for administrative, accounting and regulatory purposes. They will however, remain legally distinct so that the HCPT will operate as restricted funds within the NCT. A similar process is envisaged for the Incorporated Church Building Society (ICBS), which has been managed by the HCPT since 1983.

HOW TO APPLY The trust is currently reviewing funding which will be available from 2012. Application details will be published on the trust's website from January 2012. Applicants are advised that each fund has different application procedures. In 2010–11 applications to the Partnership Grants Programme had to be made via local Church trusts, a list of which was made available in a funding guidance document available on the trust's website. Applications for the WREN scheme were made by contacting the trust via email, expressing interest.

WHO TO APPLY TO Miriam Campbell, 31 Newbury Street, London EC1A 7HU *Tel* 020 7600 6090 *Fax* 020 7796 2442 *email* info@ nationalchurchestrust.org *Website* www. nationalchurchestrust.org

■ The National Manuscripts Conservation Trust

CC NO 802796   **ESTABLISHED** 1990

WHERE FUNDING CAN BE GIVEN UK.

WHO CAN BENEFIT Grants are made to record offices, libraries, other similar publicly funded institutions including local authority, university and specialist record repositories, and owners of manuscript material which is conditionally exempt from capital taxation or owned by a charitable trust and where reasonable public access is allowed, suitable storage conditions are available, and there is a commitment to continuing good preservation practice.

WHAT IS FUNDED Conservation of manuscripts and archives.

WHAT IS NOT FUNDED The following are not eligible: public records within the meaning of the Public Records Act; official archives of the institution or authority applying except in the case of some older records; loan collections unless exempt from capital taxation or owned by a charitable trust; and photographic, audio-visual or printed materials.

TYPE OF GRANT The grants cover the cost of repair, binding and other preservation measures including reprography, but not cost of equipment. Funding is for up to three years.

RANGE OF GRANTS To match the applicant's contribution, up to 50% of the total estimated cost. Grants are not normally considered for projects costing less than £1,000 or greater than £50,000.
£2,500–£40,000 (2009–10).

SAMPLE GRANTS During the year six grants were approved amounting to £75,000. The smallest grant was for £2,500 which went to the University of Edinburgh and the largest was for £40,000 which was awarded to the Fitzwilliam Museum, Cambridge.
Other beneficiaries include: Great Britain Trust, towards the conservation of original ship's plans from the David McGregor collection (£10,000); University of Glasgow, towards the conservation of MS Hunter 83 (£8,000) and Peterhouse, Cambridge, towards the Peterhouse Partbooks Conservation Project (£5,000).

FINANCES *Year* 2010 *Income* £79,343 *Grants* £75,000 *Assets* £1,872,757

TRUSTEES Lord Egremont; B Naylor; C Sebag-Montefiore.

PUBLICATIONS Guide for Applicants.

OTHER INFORMATION Visit the trust's website for full details of how to apply.
www.nationalarchives.gov.uk/preservation/trust/

HOW TO APPLY Applicants must submit six copies of the application form including six copies of a detailed description of the project. The applicant should also submit one copy of their most recent annual reports and accounts and details of its constitution. Grants are awarded bi-annually, each June and December, for 50% of the cost of conservation of manuscripts held by any record office, library or by an owner of manuscript material that is exempt from capital taxation or owned by a charitable trust. The trustees take into account the significance of the manuscript or archive, the suitability of the storage conditions, the applicants' commitment to continuing good preservation practice, and the requirement for the public to have reasonable access to it.

WHO TO APPLY TO Dr Anna Bulow, Secretary to the Trustees, c/o The National Archives, Ruskin

Avenue, Kew, Surrey TW9 4DU *Tel* 020 8392 5218 *email* nmct@nationalarchives.gov.uk *Website* www.nationalarchives.gov.uk/ preservation/trust/default.htm

■ The Nationwide Foundation
CC NO 1065552   **ESTABLISHED** 1997
WHERE FUNDING CAN BE GIVEN UK.
WHO CAN BENEFIT Registered UK charities. Note: only those with an income of under £750,000 are eligible for the small grants programme.
WHAT IS FUNDED The foundation makes grants to registered UK charities (including those in Northern Ireland) which offer financial and/or housing related support to survivors of domestic abuse and older people.
WHAT IS NOT FUNDED The foundation will not fund the following – for older people: transport schemes; for survivors of domestic abuse: counselling for survivors of domestic abuse; refurbishing, equipping or running costs of refuges; help to find employment. Other exclusions which apply to all applications: charities with 'unrestricted reserves' which exceed 50% of annual expenditure, as shown in their accounts; charities which are in significant debt as shown in their accounts; promotion of religion or politics; charities which have been declined by the foundation within the last 12 months; applications which do not comply with the foundation's funding criteria/guidelines.
TYPE OF GRANT Project, capital and revenue costs.
RANGE OF GRANTS Between £500 and £5,000.
SAMPLE GRANTS Black Community Development Project – Scotland (£5,000), to help establish an outreach service and employ a caseworker for people aged 50yrs+ from black and minority ethnic groups, to assist them with advice, support and management of finances, debts and benefits; St Peter's Community Advice Centre – London (£5,000), for outreach housing support, advice and help for Bangladeshi women who have been affected by domestic abuse; and Independent Living North Lincolnshire (£5,000), to assist with salary costs for the Outreach Benefits Adviser who provides a home visiting service to older people in North Lincolnshire. This service enables older people to remain living independently in their own homes and maximise income entitlement.
FINANCES *Year* 2009–10 *Income* £2,179,866 *Grants* £1,548,644 *Assets* £3,326,053
TRUSTEES John Kingston, Chair; Richard Davies; Lucy Gampell; Simon Law; Karen McArthur; Dr Michael McCarthy; Chris Rhodes; Ben Stimson; Fiona Ellis; Graeme Hughes.
OTHER INFORMATION The Investor Programme is closed and was due to re-open in early 2012, however no further information was available on this status so potential applicants are advised to check the foundation's website or contact the foundation directly. Grants are only currently available through the small grants programme; grants from this programme amounted to £351,000 in 2009–10.
HOW TO APPLY On an application form available from the foundation's website. Applicants should expect to wait up to three months for a final decision.
WHO TO APPLY TO Jennifer Thompson, Grants Officer, Nationwide House, Pipers Way, Swindon SN38 2SN *Tel* 01793 655113 *Fax* 01793 652409 *email* enquiries@nationwidefoundation.org.uk *Website* www.nationwidefoundation.org.uk

■ Nazareth Trust Fund
CC NO 210503   **ESTABLISHED** 1956
WHERE FUNDING CAN BE GIVEN UK and developing countries.
WHO CAN BENEFIT Young adults, Christian missionaries and victims of famine, war, and man-made or natural disasters – both individually and through registered institutions.
WHAT IS FUNDED Churches, Christian missionaries, Christian youth work, and overseas aid. Grants are only made to people or causes known personally to the trustees.
WHAT IS NOT FUNDED No support for individuals not known to the trustees.
RANGE OF GRANTS £20–£17,000.
SAMPLE GRANTS Harnham FC Youth Club (£17,000 in two grants); Harnham Free Church (£8,400 in 12 grants); Durham Road Baptist Church (£5,600 in 15 grants); IREF (£3,300 in two grants); Urban Saints – previously 'Crusaders' (£4,000 in three grants); Northwood Hills Evangelical Church (£2,000); IREF – UK (£1,400 in three grants); London School of Theology (£800 in three grants); Scripture Union (£400 in two grants); Christian Viewpoint for Men (£250); and Faith Missions Trust (£30).
FINANCES *Year* 2009–10 *Income* £57,429 *Grants* £53,800 *Assets* £34,515
TRUSTEES Revd David R G Hunt; Eileen M Hunt; Dr Robert W G Hunt; Elma R L Hunt; Philip R W Hunt; Nicola M Hunt.
OTHER INFORMATION The grant total includes £2,750 given to individuals.
HOW TO APPLY In writing to the correspondent, although the trust tends to only support organisations it is directly involved with.
WHO TO APPLY TO Dr Robert W G Hunt, Trustee, Barrowpoint, 18 Millennium Close, Salisbury, Wiltshire SP2 8TB *Tel* 01722 349322

■ The Nchima Trust
CC NO 1072974   **ESTABLISHED** 1962
WHERE FUNDING CAN BE GIVEN Malawi.
WHO CAN BENEFIT Individuals and established local organisations benefiting children and young adults, at-risk groups, and people who are disadvantaged by poverty or living in rural areas.
WHAT IS FUNDED Initiation and help in schemes aimed at advancing education, health, welfare standards and the provision of clean water, with particular emphasis on self-help schemes and assisting people with disabilities.
FINANCES *Year* 2009–10 *Income* £29,514 *Grants* £36,000 *Assets* £615,636
TRUSTEES Ms M R Richards; S Gardiner; Mrs K P Legg; A Scarborough, Chair; Mrs J Quinn; Mrs B A Scarborough; Mrs S McAlpine.
OTHER INFORMATION The trust makes fixed grants of approximately £2,500 a year plus other discretionary grants.
HOW TO APPLY In writing to the correspondent.
WHO TO APPLY TO Mrs Josie Quinn, Hon. Secretary and Administrator, 3 Close House Cottages, Knock, Cumbria CA16 6DL *Tel* 017683 62380 *email* admin@nchimatrust.org *Website* www.nchimatrust.org

■ The NDL Foundation
CC NO 1133508   **ESTABLISHED** 2010
WHERE FUNDING CAN BE GIVEN Worldwide.
WHO CAN BENEFIT Charitable organisations.
WHAT IS FUNDED General; children; sickness; art and culture.

SAMPLE GRANTS My School Pulse (£5,000).
FINANCES Year 2010 Grants £5,000
TRUSTEES Mrs Sylviane Destribats; Miss Laura Destribats; Frank E Destribats.
HOW TO APPLY In writing to the correspondent.
WHO TO APPLY TO Mrs Sylviane Destribats, Trustee, 8 Bolton Gardens Mews, London SW10 9LW

■ Needham Market and Barking Welfare Charities

CC NO 217499   ESTABLISHED 1961
WHERE FUNDING CAN BE GIVEN The town of Needham Market and the parish of Barking.
WHO CAN BENEFIT Organisations that benefit people in need, hardship or distress.
WHAT IS FUNDED Projects that benefit the local community especially those in need, hardship or distress.
RANGE OF GRANTS Up to £20,000.
SAMPLE GRANTS Previous grants from the Town Lands Trust have included: Needham Market Town Council (£20,000); Barking Village Hall (£12,000); Needham Market Bowls Club and Hurstlea Kerridge Boxing Club (£10,000 each) and Needham Market Community Centre and Needham Market Internet Cafe (£5,000 each).
FINANCES Year 2009–10 Income £25,903 Grants £24,000
TRUSTEES A F Wilcox; G C Miller; J Annis; R P Darnell; Mrs S C Wright; Mrs S Marsh; Mrs M Brown; M Smith; M Ost; D Bishop; G Oxenham.
OTHER INFORMATION An extra £3,055 was given in grants to individuals.
HOW TO APPLY In writing to the correspondent with audited accounts. Trustees meet every two months. Individuals should apply on the form available from the correspondent.
WHO TO APPLY TO Mrs Louise Gooding, Clerk, 23 School Street, Needham Market, Ipswich IP6 8BB

■ The Worshipful Company of Needlemakers' Charitable Fund

CC NO 288646   ESTABLISHED 1952
WHERE FUNDING CAN BE GIVEN City of London.
WHO CAN BENEFIT Organisations associated with the needlemaking industry, the City of London or education, including the Lord Mayor's and the Master's chosen charities.
WHAT IS FUNDED Education, welfare, religion, general charitable purposes.
RANGE OF GRANTS £100 to £5,000.
SAMPLE GRANTS £5,000 to the Royal School of Needlework and the Royal College of Surgeons of England; £4,000 to St Paul's Cathedral Choir School; £2,000 to Guildhall School of Music and Drama; £1,000 each to City University and City and Guilds of London Institute; and £500 to Royal British Legion City Branch Poppy Appeal.
FINANCES Year 2009–10 Income £36,056 Grants £43,050 Assets £1,253,389
TRUSTEES Worshipful Company of Needlemakers.
HOW TO APPLY In writing to the correspondent, but the trust has stated that it tends to support the same charities each year, so unsolicited applications are unlikely to be successful.
WHO TO APPLY TO Philip R Grant, Clerk, Worshipful Company of Needlemakers, PO Box 3682, Windsor SL4 3WR Tel 01753 860690 email needlemakers.clerk@yahoo.com Website www.needlemakers.org.uk

■ The Neighbourly Charitable Trust

CC NO 258488   ESTABLISHED 1969
WHERE FUNDING CAN BE GIVEN Bedfordshire and Hertfordshire.
WHO CAN BENEFIT Organisations benefiting people with disabilities.
WHAT IS FUNDED General and leisure/adventure trips for people with disabilities.
WHAT IS NOT FUNDED No grants to national charities (except occasionally a local branch) or individuals.
RANGE OF GRANTS Usually £100–£1,000 with some larger grants.
SAMPLE GRANTS Reach Out Projects (£7,500); St Elizabeth's Centre (£1,500); The Towersey Foundation (£1,200); ActOne Arts Base, Contact a Family, Pace Centre and The Eyeless Trust (£1,000 each); and Spinal Injuries (£500).
FINANCES Year 2009–10 Income £59,281 Grants £33,191 Assets £2,320,059
TRUSTEES John Sell; Emma Simpson; Jane Wade.
HOW TO APPLY In writing to the correspondent, for consideration at trustees' meetings twice a year.
WHO TO APPLY TO Sharon Long, Secretary, Ashbrittle House, 2a Lower Dagnall Street, St Albans, Hertfordshire AL3 4PA Tel 01727 843603 Fax 01727 843663 email admin@iplltd.co.uk

■ The James Neill Trust Fund

CC NO 503203   ESTABLISHED 1974
WHERE FUNDING CAN BE GIVEN Within 20 miles of Sheffield Cathedral.
WHO CAN BENEFIT Voluntary organisations.
WHAT IS FUNDED Voluntary work for the benefit of people in the area specified above.
TYPE OF GRANT Ongoing support for established organisations and one-off grants to meet start-up costs or unexpected expenses.
RANGE OF GRANTS Up to £5,000.
SAMPLE GRANTS Friends of Millhouses Park – Splash Project (£5,000); Cavendish Cancer Care and the South Yorkshire Community Foundation (£2,000 each); South Yorkshire & Hallamshire Clubs for Young People and Voluntary Action Sheffield (£1,000 each); Cruse Bereavement Care – Rotherham Branch (£900); Bluebell Wood Children's Hospice (£750); Sheffield Conservation Volunteers and Cathedral Archer Project (£600 each); Safe@Last, St Wilfred's Centre, FareShare South Yorkshire, Barnados and Share Psychotherapy (£500 each); Sheffield University Children's Project (£350); and Street Life Support (£250).
FINANCES Year 2009–10 Income £44,421 Grants £38,009 Assets £1,137,227
TRUSTEES Sir Hugh Neill; G H N Peel; Lady Neill; Mrs N R Peel; A M C Staniforth.
OTHER INFORMATION During the year pensioners received Christmas hampers amounting to £11,500 in total.
HOW TO APPLY In writing to the correspondent in July for consideration in August/September.
WHO TO APPLY TO Sir Hugh Neill, Trustee, Barn Cottage, Lindrick Common, Worksop, Nottinghamshire S81 8BA Tel 01909 562806

■ Nemoral Ltd

CC NO 262270   ESTABLISHED 1971
WHERE FUNDING CAN BE GIVEN Worldwide.
WHO CAN BENEFIT Orthodox Jewish communities.
WHAT IS FUNDED General charitable purposes, in practice, religious, educational and other

Think carefully about every application. Is it justified?

765

charitable institutions serving orthodox Jewish communities.

TYPE OF GRANT One-off, recurring, capital and occasionally loans.

FINANCES *Year* 2010 *Income* £200,000 *Grants* £1,156,965 *Assets* £2,175,945

TRUSTEES Ellis Moore; Rifka Gross; Michael Saberski.

OTHER INFORMATION A list of grant beneficiaries was not included in the trust's accounts.

HOW TO APPLY In writing to the correspondent.

WHO TO APPLY TO Rifka Gross, Secretary, c/o Cohen Arnold and Co., New Burlington House, 1075 Finchley Road, London NW11 0PU *Tel* 020 8731 0777

■ Ner Foundation

CC NO 1104866   **ESTABLISHED** 2004

WHERE FUNDING CAN BE GIVEN UK and Israel.

WHO CAN BENEFIT People of the Jewish faith.

WHAT IS FUNDED Advancement of the Orthodox Jewish religion.

SAMPLE GRANTS Relief of poverty (£47,000); schools (£17,000); yeshivos and seminaries (£17,000); advancement of religion (£2,500); and grants under £1,000 each (£14,000).

FINANCES *Year* 2009–10 *Income* £95,589 *Grants* £98,051 *Assets* £323,276

TRUSTEES A Henry; N Neumann; Mrs E Henry.

HOW TO APPLY In writing to the correspondent.

WHO TO APPLY TO A Henry, Trustee, 309 Bury New Road, Salford, Manchester M7 2YN

■ Nesswall Ltd

CC NO 283600   **ESTABLISHED** 1981

WHERE FUNDING CAN BE GIVEN UK.

WHO CAN BENEFIT Orthodox Jewish organisations.

WHAT IS FUNDED Orthodox Jewish causes, including education and relief in need.

SAMPLE GRANTS Previous beneficiaries have included: Friends of Horim Establishments, Torah Vochesed L'Ezra Vesaad and Emunah Education Centre.

FINANCES *Year* 2009–10 *Income* £98,890 *Grants* £96,615 *Assets* £555,593

TRUSTEES I Teitelbaum, Chair; Mrs R Teitelbaum; I Chersky; Mrs H Wahrhaftig.

HOW TO APPLY In writing to the correspondent, at any time.

WHO TO APPLY TO Mrs R Teitelbaum, Secretary, 28 Overlea Road, London E5 9BG *Tel* 020 8806 2965

■ Network for Social Change

CC NO 295237   **ESTABLISHED** 1986

WHERE FUNDING CAN BE GIVEN UK and overseas.

WHO CAN BENEFIT Small projects in the UK and overseas which are likely to affect social change, either through research, public education, innovatory services and other charitable activities.

WHAT IS FUNDED The network is a group of givers who actively seek out projects that they want to fund, rather than responding to applications, in the areas of arts and education for change, economic justice, green planet, health and wholeness, human rights and peace.

TYPE OF GRANT Smaller projects.

RANGE OF GRANTS Up to £130,000.

SAMPLE GRANTS Peace Direct (£57,000); Climate Change (£58,000) One society (£86,000); New Economics Foundation (£106,000); The Joseph Rowntree Charitable Trust (£89,000); the Climate Movement (£59,000); War on Want (£30,000); Raw for Women and Girl survivors of War (£21,000); Citizens UK Charity and Medical Justice Network (£15,000 each); Traidcraft Exchange (£14,000); Friends of the Earth Trust Limited (£13,000); Life Mosaic (£11,000); and Partnership for Children and the International Security Information Service (£10,000 each).

FINANCES *Year* 2009–10 *Income* £877,058 *Grants* £833,149 *Assets* £71,575

TRUSTEES Sue Gillie; Bevis Gillett; Sam Clarke; Monica Marian Sanders; Sara Robin; Tom Bragg; Anthony Stoll.

OTHER INFORMATION See website.

HOW TO APPLY The network chooses the projects it wishes to support and does not solicit applications. Unsolicited applications cannot expect to receive a reply. However, the network is conscious that the policy of only accepting applications brought by its members could limit the range of worthwhile projects it could fund. To address this, the network has set up a 'Project Noticeboard' (accessed via the network's website) to allow outside organisations to post a summary of a project for which they are seeking funding. Members of the network can then access the noticeboard and, if interested, contact the organisation for further information with a view to future sponsorship. The network states that any posts will be available on the website for six to nine months.

WHO TO APPLY TO Tish McCrory, Administrator, BM 2063, London WC1N 3XX *Tel* 01647 61106 *email* thenetwork@gn.apc.org *Website* thenetworkforsocialchange.org.uk

---

■ The New Appeals Organisation for the City and County of Nottingham

CC NO 502196   **ESTABLISHED** 1973

WHERE FUNDING CAN BE GIVEN Nottinghamshire.

WHO CAN BENEFIT Individuals and organisations benefiting at-risk groups and people who are disabled, disadvantaged by poverty or socially isolated.

WHAT IS FUNDED Help that is not available from any other source.

WHAT IS NOT FUNDED Appeals to cover debts, arrears, building expenses or educational expenses are not normally considered.

TYPE OF GRANT One-off.

SAMPLE GRANTS £6,000 to Gillies Ward; £3,000 to Newstead Primary School; £2,500 to Nottingham City Hospital Charity Account; £1,400 to Glenbrook P&F School; £500 each to Ravenshead Community Transport and Sherwood United Reform Church; and £100 to Nottingham Central Women's Aid.

FINANCES *Year* 2009–10 *Income* £44,162 *Grants* £55,061 *Assets* £51,344

TRUSTEES Phillip Everett, Joint Chair; Mrs Carol Wilson, Joint Chair; L S Levin; Mrs E Litman; G Davis.

HOW TO APPLY In writing to the correspondent. An initial telephone call from the applicant is welcome.

WHO TO APPLY TO Philip Everett, The Joint Chair, c/o 4 Rise Court, Hamilton Road, Sherwood Rise, Nottingham NG5 1EU *Tel* 0115 960 9644 (answerphone) *email* enquiries@newappeals. org.uk *Website* www.newappeals.org.uk

■ New Court Charitable Trust

CC NO 209790   **ESTABLISHED** 1947
WHERE FUNDING CAN BE GIVEN UK.
WHO CAN BENEFIT Registered charities.
WHAT IS FUNDED General charitable purposes.
SAMPLE GRANTS Previous beneficiaries included:
Alone in London, Burma Star Association,
Drugscope, Electronic Aids for the Blind, Fight
for Sight, Hereford International Summer
School, Invalids at Home and Trinity College of
Music, New Bridge Motability, Streatham Youth
Centre, Universities Settlement in East London,
Queen Elizabeth's Foundation for Disabled
People and World Jewish Relief.
FINANCES *Year* 2009–10 *Income* £13,965
Grants £10,000
TRUSTEES Leopold de Rothschild; Bernard Myers;
Veronica Kennard.
HOW TO APPLY In writing to the correspondent
enclosing annual report and accounts.
WHO TO APPLY TO The Trustees, Rothschild Trust
Corp Ltd, New Court, St Swithins Lane, London
EC4P 4DU *Tel* 020 7280 5000

■ Newby Trust Limited

CC NO 227151   **ESTABLISHED** 1938
WHERE FUNDING CAN BE GIVEN UK.
WHO CAN BENEFIT Welfare organisations,
postgraduates and individuals in need.
WHAT IS FUNDED Within the general objects of the
trust (medical welfare, relief of poverty, training
and education) one category for special support
is selected each year. Recent themes have
been: projects and/or training that encourage
artisanal skills (2009–10) and supporting
families in poverty (2010–11). Funding years run
from 6 April to 5 April.
TYPE OF GRANT Usually one-off for part of a project.
Buildings, capital, core costs and salaries may
be considered.
RANGE OF GRANTS Normally £150–£10,000.
SAMPLE GRANTS Down Syndrome Education
International (£30,000 in three grants);
Ditchling Museum (£20,000); Chichester
College (£10,000); Bedales Grants Trust Fund
(£7,500); Greenhouse Schools Project
(£6,000); Weald and Downland Open Air
Museum (£5,500); Medical Foundation for the
Care of Victims of Torture and Academy of
Ancient Music Trust (£5,000 each); and Hope in
the Valley Riding Group (£1,000).
FINANCES *Year* 2009–10 *Income* £312,706
Grants £268,480 *Assets* £13,005,667
TRUSTEES Anna L Foxell; Anne S Reed; Jean
M Gooder; Ben Gooder; Dr Richard D Gooder;
Susan A Charlton; Evelyn F Bentley; Nigel
Callaghan.
OTHER INFORMATION Grants to individuals accounted
for around £107,000 of the total.
HOW TO APPLY The application procedure differs
between each category as follows: *Annual
special category* – unsolicited applications will
not be considered; *Education, training and
research* – since 2008 the trust has supported
education at the post-graduate or post-doctoral
level only by allocating funds to selected
universities or institutions in the United
Kingdom. These are: City University, London, the
London School of Economics and Political
Science, the University of Edinburgh and the
University of Manchester. Grants are awarded at
the discretion of these universities subject to
guidelines related to the purposes of the trust;
Medical welfare and *Relief of poverty* – Social
Services or similar organisations may apply only

online on behalf of individuals in need using the
pre-application screening form on the trust's
website.
WHO TO APPLY TO Wendy Gillam, Secretary, Hill Farm,
Froxfield, Petersfield, Hampshire GU32 1BQ
Tel 01730 827557 *email* info@newby-trust.org.
uk *Website* www.newby-trust.org.uk

■ The Newcomen Collett Foundation

CC NO 312804   **ESTABLISHED** 1988
WHERE FUNDING CAN BE GIVEN London borough of
Southwark.
WHO CAN BENEFIT Individuals and small local
projects benefiting children, young adults and
students under 25.
WHAT IS FUNDED Education of young people under
25 years of age, including community arts and
recreation, with priority for dance and ballet,
music and theatre.
WHAT IS NOT FUNDED The trust can only help young
people living in the London borough of
Southwark. People on courses of further
education should have lived in Southwark for at
least two years before starting their course.
TYPE OF GRANT One-off.
RANGE OF GRANTS Up to £3,000.
SAMPLE GRANTS £3,000 to Cathedral Primary
School; £1,900 to St Giles Trust; £1,500 each
to Goodrich Community School, Foundation for
Young Musicians and Oliver Goldsmith Primary
School; £1,000 each to Fairbridge in London,
Southwark Young Carers Project, Magic Lantern,
Futures Theatre Company, Oval House Summer
School and Waterloo Sports & Football Club.
FINANCES *Year* 2009–10 *Income* £230,314
Grants £77,268 *Assets* £2,760,382
TRUSTEES R Lovell, Chair; R V Ashdown;
E H C Bowman; J Spencer; R Edwards;
A G H Stocks; Mrs B S Lane; A Leiffheidt; Miss
H Cockerill; P Scott; A Covell; M Ibbot; Revd
Canon B Saunders.
HOW TO APPLY By application form, available by
writing to the clerk. The governors consider
requests four times a year.
WHO TO APPLY TO Richard Goatcher, Clerk, Marshall
House, 66 Newcomen Street, London Bridge,
London SE1 1YT *Tel* 020 7407 2967 *Fax* 020
7403 3969 *email* richard@marshalls.org.uk
Website www.newcomencollett.org.uk

■ Mr and Mrs F E F Newman Charitable Trust

CC NO 263831   **ESTABLISHED** 1972
WHERE FUNDING CAN BE GIVEN UK and overseas.
WHO CAN BENEFIT Registered charities and Christian
organisations.
WHAT IS FUNDED Primarily local religious purposes;
overseas development; welfare and education;
and other charitable purposes.
WHAT IS NOT FUNDED No grants to individuals.
RANGE OF GRANTS £50–£3,000.
SAMPLE GRANTS 'A' Fund: Save Launde Abbey
(£3,000); Christian Aid (£560 in three grants);
Thai Village Project (£400); Guildford
Samaritans (£200); Woking Hospice (£150 in
two donations); Royal British Legion (£115);
Amos Trust, Age Concern and Oxfam (£100
each); and St John Ambulance (£50). 'B' Fund:
Tear Fund and Bible Society (£2,000 each);
Acorn Christian Healing Foundation (£1,000);
Riding Lights Trust, Traidcraft Exchange and
Amnesty International (£600 each); TESS and

SOMA (£500 each); and Community of the Holy Cross (£50).

FINANCES *Year* 2009–10 *Income* £26,155 *Grants* £26,036 *Assets* £242,545

TRUSTEES Frederick Newman; Margaret Hayes; David Newman; Michael Newman; George Smith.

OTHER INFORMATION Donations from 'A' Fund totalled £6,236 and donations from 'B' Fund totalled £19,800.

HOW TO APPLY In writing to the correspondent. The trustees usually meet once a year to consider applications.

WHO TO APPLY TO David Quinn, Administrator, c/o David Quinn Associates, Southcroft, Caledon Road, Beaconsfield, Buckinghamshire HP9 2BX *Tel* 01494 674396

■ The Frances and Augustus Newman Foundation

CC NO 277964   **ESTABLISHED** 1978

WHERE FUNDING CAN BE GIVEN Worldwide, in practice mainly UK.

WHO CAN BENEFIT Mainly professors working in teaching hospitals and academic units.

WHAT IS FUNDED Mainly, but not exclusively, funding for medical research projects and equipment including fellowships of the Royal College of Surgeons.

WHAT IS NOT FUNDED Applications are not normally accepted from overseas. Requests from other charities seeking funds to supplement their own general funds to support medical research in a particular field are seldom supported.

TYPE OF GRANT One-off and recurring. Research and salaries will also be considered. Funding may be given for up to three years.

RANGE OF GRANTS £1,000–£100,000.

SAMPLE GRANTS University of Cambridge – Next Generation Fellowship (£100,000 in total); Royal College of Surgeons (£70,000 in total); Peterhouse and the Stroke Association (£50,000 each); UCL Cancer Institute and the Alzheimer's Research Trust (£20,000 each); National Centre for Young People with Epilepsy (£10,000); St Peter's Hospice (£6,000); Royal College of Physicians, Women and Medicine and the Puffin Appeal (£5,000 each); Trinity Hospice (£4,500); Nyumbani UK (£4,000); War Memorial Trust (£2,000); and Dream Makers (£1,000).

FINANCES *Year* 2009–10 *Income* £284,374 *Grants* £347,028 *Assets* £11,665,880

TRUSTEES Sir Rodney Sweetnam, Chair; Lord Rathcavan; John L Williams.

HOW TO APPLY Applications should include a detailed protocol and costing and be sent to the correspondent. They may then be peer-reviewed. The trustees meet in June and December each year and applications must be received by the latest by the end of April or October respectively. The foundation awards for surgical research fellowships should be addressed to the Royal College of Surgeons of England at 35–43 Lincoln's Inn Fields, London WC2A 3PE, which evaluates each application.

WHO TO APPLY TO Hazel Palfreyman, Administrator, c/o Baker Tilly, Chartered Accountants, Hartwell House, 55–61 Victoria Street, Bristol BS1 6AD *Tel* 0117 945 2000 *Fax* 0117 945 2001 *email* hazel.palfreyman@bakertilly.co.uk

■ Newpier Charity Ltd

CC NO 293686   **ESTABLISHED** 1985

WHERE FUNDING CAN BE GIVEN UK.

WHO CAN BENEFIT Jewish organisations.

WHAT IS FUNDED Advancement of the orthodox Jewish faith and the relief of poverty.

SAMPLE GRANTS Previous beneficiaries include: BML Benityashvut, Friends of Biala, Gateshead Yeshiva, KID, Mesdos Wiznitz and SOFT for redistribution to other charities.

FINANCES *Year* 2009–10 *Income* £1,023,311 *Grants* £578,635 *Assets* £3,776,115

TRUSTEES Charles Margulies; Helen Knopfler; Rachel Margulies.

HOW TO APPLY In writing to the correspondent.

WHO TO APPLY TO Charles Margulies, Trustee, 186 Lordship Road, London N16 5ES

■ Alderman Newton's Educational Foundation

CC NO 527881   **ESTABLISHED** 1983

WHERE FUNDING CAN BE GIVEN Diocese of Leicester.

WHO CAN BENEFIT Individuals and schools.

WHAT IS FUNDED Church of England education.

TYPE OF GRANT One-off and recurrent.

FINANCES *Year* 2009–10 *Income* £124,443 *Grants* £130,576 *Assets* £133,266

TRUSTEES Two ex-officio trustees; eight nominative trustees; three co-optative trustees.

HOW TO APPLY On a form available from the correspondent. Applications may be made at any time.

WHO TO APPLY TO The Clerk, Leicester Charity Link, 20a Millstone Lane, Leicester LE1 5JN *Tel* 0116 222 2200

■ The NFU Mutual Charitable Trust

CC NO 1073064   **ESTABLISHED** 1998

WHERE FUNDING CAN BE GIVEN UK.

WHO CAN BENEFIT Organisations.

WHAT IS FUNDED The objects of the trust are the 'promotion and support of charitable purposes in the areas of agriculture, rural development and insurance in the UK – including education, the relief of poverty, social welfare and research – and any other charitable purpose'.

SAMPLE GRANTS The Farming Help Partnership (£75,000); Farming and Countryside Education (£50,000); The National Federation of Young Farmers Clubs/ Wales Young Farmers Clubs (£38,000); Rural Support (£11,700); Shakespeare Hospice at Home Service (£7,500); Bangor University (£2,600); Harper Adams Uni College (£1,105).

FINANCES *Year* 2010 *Income* £478,461 *Grants* £278,272 *Assets* £478,461

TRUSTEES Sir D Curry; Mr E.S Bailey; Mr R.C Butler; Mr I.D Grant; Mr P.A Kendall; Mr N Miller; Mr C.R Percy; Mr L.N Sinclair; Mr J.A Thompson.

HOW TO APPLY In writing to the correspondent.

WHO TO APPLY TO J D Creechan, Secretary to the Trustees, Tiddington Road, Stratford-upon-Avon, Warwickshire CV37 7BJ *Tel* 01789 204211 *email* nfu_mutual_charitable_trust@nfumutual. co.uk *Website* www.nfumutual.co.uk

■ The Night Garden Charity

CC NO 1139577   **ESTABLISHED** 2010

WHERE FUNDING CAN BE GIVEN UK.

WHO CAN BENEFIT Registered charities.

WHAT IS FUNDED General charitable purposes.

TRUSTEES Matthew Hansell; Richard Perrin; Derek Shilvock.

HOW TO APPLY In writing to the correspondent.

WHO TO APPLY TO Matthew Hansell, Trustee, Mills & Reeve LLP, 78–84 Colmore Row, Birmingham B3 2AB *Tel* 0121 456 8297 *email* matthew.hansell@mills-reeve.com

---

■ The Chevras Ezras Nitzrochim Trust

CC NO 275352   **ESTABLISHED** 1978

WHERE FUNDING CAN BE GIVEN UK, with a preference for London.

WHO CAN BENEFIT Organisations benefiting Jewish people who are disadvantaged by poverty.

WHAT IS FUNDED Orthodox Jewish organisations set up to raise money to help the poor in Jewish communities.

RANGE OF GRANTS £10–£4,000.

SAMPLE GRANTS Previous beneficiaries included: Mesifta, Kupas Tzedoko Vochesed, Beis Chinuch Lenonos, Hachzokas Torah Vochesed Trust, Ezras Hakohol Trust, Woodstock Sinclair Trust, Side by Side, Yeshivas Panim Meiros, Yeahuas Chaim Synagogue, TYY Trust, Square Yeshiva and Stanislow.

FINANCES *Year* 2010 *Income* £203,948 *Grants* £198,238 *Assets* £3,441

TRUSTEES Kurt Stern; Hertz Kahan; Moshe Rottenberg.

OTHER INFORMATION £169,000 was distributed to individuals.

HOW TO APPLY In writing to the correspondent.

WHO TO APPLY TO Hertz Kahan, Trustee, 53 Heathland Road, London N16 5PQ *Tel* 020 8800 5187

■ NJD Charitable Trust

CC NO 1109146   **ESTABLISHED** 2005

WHERE FUNDING CAN BE GIVEN UK and Israel.

WHO CAN BENEFIT People of the Jewish faith.

WHAT IS FUNDED The relief of poverty and hardship of members of the Jewish faith; the advancement of Jewish religion through Jewish education.

SAMPLE GRANTS UJIA (£42,000); Jewish Care (£15,000); Hadassah Medical Relief Association UK (£10,000); Holocaust Educational Trust and Shaare Hayim Synagogue (£5,000 each).

FINANCES *Year* 2009–10 *Income* £100,191 *Grants* £92,269 *Assets* £115,071

TRUSTEES Nathalie Dwek; Jean Glaskie; Jacob Wolf; Alexander Dwek.

HOW TO APPLY In writing to the correspondent.

WHO TO APPLY TO Alan Dawson, Trust Administrator, Crowe Clark Whitehill, St Brides' House, 10 Salisbury Square, London EC4Y 8EH *Tel* 020 7842 7306 *email* info@igpinvest.com

---

■ Alice Noakes Memorial Charitable Trust

CC NO 1039663   **ESTABLISHED** 1994

WHERE FUNDING CAN BE GIVEN Unrestricted.

WHO CAN BENEFIT Organisations and individuals.

WHAT IS FUNDED Animal welfare.

RANGE OF GRANTS £500 to £20,000.

SAMPLE GRANTS University of Cambridge (£20,000); Animal Health Trust (£12,500); RSPCA – Danaher Animal Home for Essex (£10,000); Fauna and Flora International, Friends of the Ferals, SNIP International and IOSF (£1,000 each); the Barn Owl Trust, Greek Cat Welfare Society, the Twinkle Trust Animal Aid, Gambi Cats, Freshfield Animal Rescue, Catsnip and Stella's School Scheme (£500 each).

FINANCES *Year* 2009–10 *Income* £63,103 *Grants* £66,800 *Assets* £2,022,752

TRUSTEES D W G Whipps; Mrs J H Simpson; S N Bayer; J F Hulme.

HOW TO APPLY 'Applications for grants fitting the trust's objectives should be sent to the trustees at the charity's registered office.' The trustees meet twice a year.

WHO TO APPLY TO The Trustees, Grove Barn, Oxen End, Little Bardfield, Braintree CM7 4PX *Tel* 01376 320456

■ Nominet Charitable Foundation

CC NO 1125735   **ESTABLISHED** 2008

WHERE FUNDING CAN BE GIVEN UK and overseas.

WHO CAN BENEFIT UK-based initiatives that contribute to a safe, accessible Internet used to improve lives and communities. A small number of investments in international projects may also be made.

WHAT IS FUNDED Web access – providing people with the motivation, skills and tools to get online in a meaningful and sustained way; web safety – improving understanding about the risks of being online and reducing internet crime and abuse; web in society – imaginative applications of the internet to address specific social problems.

WHAT IS NOT FUNDED The foundation will not fund the following: hardware infrastructure projects, e.g. a project to equip a school with PCs, or to install Wi-fi for a community; website improvements where no new functional or service delivery innovations are delivered; website development unless the project and organisation delivers against one of the foundation's areas of focus and meets its funding guidelines; organisational running costs per se.

RANGE OF GRANTS Up to £500,000.

SAMPLE GRANTS UnLtd (£500,000); the e-Learning Foundation (£282,000); Age UK (£185,000); Beatbullying (£175,000); Channel 4 (£100,000); Gemin-i.org (£82,000); Alzheimer's Society (£69,000); Busymummy Ltd and AbilityNet (£60,000 each); ENABLE Scotland (£59,000); and the Internet Watch Foundation, Gateshead College, Oxford Internet Institute, Citizens Online, Action for M.E. and UK Internet Crime and Disorder Reduction Partnership (£50,000 each).

FINANCES *Year* 2009–10 *Income* £3,066,355 *Grants* £2,206,438 *Assets* £5,290,744

TRUSTEES Jonathan Welfare, Chair; Nora Nanayakkara; James Kemp; Vanessa Miner; Ian Ritchie; Dr Peter Gradwell.

HOW TO APPLY Potential applicants should first read the Self-Evaluation Checklist then, if appropriate, complete an initial Eligibility Questionnaire – both the checklist and the questionnaire are available through the 'How to Apply' section of the trust's website. Once submitted, the trust aims to respond by email within two weeks. If invited to make a full application, further details such as a project plan and budget will be required. Funding applications are reviewed quarterly.

WHO TO APPLY TO Annika Small, Director, Nominet, Minerva House, Edmund Halley Road, Oxford Science Park, Oxford OX4 4DQ *Tel* 01865 334000 *Fax* 01865 332314 *email* enquiries@nominettrust.org.uk *Website* www.nominettrust.org.uk

Think carefully about every application. Is it justified?

769

The Noon Foundation

cc no 1053654   ESTABLISHED 1995
WHERE FUNDING CAN BE GIVEN UK.
WHO CAN BENEFIT Charitable organisations.
WHAT IS FUNDED General charitable purposes including, education, relief of poverty, community relations and alleviation of racial discrimination.
RANGE OF GRANTS £50–£56,000.
SAMPLE GRANTS Marie Curie Cancer Care (£56,000); Birkbeck University of London, Breast Cancer Care (£50,000 each); Macmillan Cancer Support (£48,000); Co-existence Trust (£15,000); Horizon Medical (£10,000); Garsington Opera (£2,500); London School of Economics, Oxfam (£2,000 each); Muslim Aid and Wellbeing (£1,000 each).
FINANCES *Year* 2010 *Income* £46,652 *Grants* £244,530 *Assets* £1,942,793
TRUSTEES Lord Noon; Akbar Shirazi; Mrs Zeenat Harnal; A M Jepson; A D Robinson; Mrs Zarmin N Sekhon.
OTHER INFORMATION Grants of less than £1,000 amounted to £3,970.
HOW TO APPLY All applications and queries should be made by email to: grants@noongroup.co.uk
WHO TO APPLY TO The Trustees, 25 Queen Anne's Gate, St James' Park, London SW1H 9BU *Tel* 020 7654 1600 *email* grants@noongroup.co.uk

The Norda Trust

cc no 296418   ESTABLISHED 1960
WHERE FUNDING CAN BE GIVEN UK.
WHO CAN BENEFIT Registered charities only.
WHAT IS FUNDED The trustees allocate funds principally in support of those working for the rehabilitation of prisoners both before and after release and support for the partners and families of prisoners. A special interest is taken in charities and organisations that support immigration detainees and the welfare of young offenders. As funds permit, the trust can also support small local charities whose primary aim should be to improve the quality of life for the most severely disadvantaged communities or individuals. The trustees have a particular interest in helping to support new initiatives where there is a high level of volunteer involvement. When funds allow applications will be considered from charities and organisations that, by the nature of the work they undertake, do not attract popular support.
WHAT IS NOT FUNDED The following areas are not funded by the trust: medical causes; animal causes; individuals; school fees; proselytising.
TYPE OF GRANT Capital, revenue and full project funding. The majority of awards are made on a one off basis, with very few commitments made over two or more years.
RANGE OF GRANTS Up to £15,000.
SAMPLE GRANTS Dover Detainee Visitor Group (£6,400); NEPACS (£6,000); Asylum Welcome and Families/Friends of Prisoners (£5,000 each); Asylum Aid and Burnbake Trust (£3,000 each); A4e HMP Dorchester and Youth Empowerment Crime Diversion Scheme (£2,000 each); Solihull Churches (£1,000); and Samaritans South West (£600).
FINANCES *Year* 2009–10 *Income* £101,877 *Grants* £98,000 *Assets* £2,890,249
TRUSTEES J N Macpherson; P Gildener.
HOW TO APPLY Via letter or email, outlining the appeal. All applicants should leave at least a year before re-applying. Up to date financial information is required from all applicants. The trust will then make contact to request any further information they need.
WHO TO APPLY TO Martin Ward, Administrator, The Shieling, St Agnes, Cornwall TR5 0SS *Tel* 01871 553822 *email* enquiries@thenordatrust.org.uk *Website* www.thenordatrust.org.uk

Norie Charitable Trust

cc no 1073993   ESTABLISHED 1999
WHERE FUNDING CAN BE GIVEN UK.
WHO CAN BENEFIT Charitable organisations.
WHAT IS FUNDED General charitable purposes.
RANGE OF GRANTS Up to £6,000.
SAMPLE GRANTS Changing Tunes (£5,000), Bath Literary Festival (£3,000); Keynsham Arts and Somerset Crimebeat (£2,000 each); and Bath Film Festival, Pier Art Centre and The Harbour (£1,000 each).
FINANCES *Year* 2009–10 *Income* £19,824 *Grants* £18,000
TRUSTEES C H W Parish; Miss K Bernstein; Mrs A Wilson.
HOW TO APPLY In writing to the correspondent.
WHO TO APPLY TO The Trustees, Victoria House, 1–3 College Hill, London EC4R 2RA *Tel* 020 7489 8076

Normalyn Charitable Trust

cc no 1077985   ESTABLISHED 1999
WHERE FUNDING CAN BE GIVEN UK.
WHO CAN BENEFIT Jewish people.
WHAT IS FUNDED General charitable purposes.
SAMPLE GRANTS United Synagogue (£11,200); Finchley Jewish Primary School Trust (£11,000); City of London School Bursary Trust (£6,300); United Jewish Israel Appeal (£6,100); Community Security Trust (£5,300); and British ORT and Finchley Jewish Chaplaincy Board (£1,000 each).
FINANCES *Year* 2009–10 *Income* £74,102 *Grants* £63,195 *Assets* £36,992
TRUSTEES D I Dover; J S Newman; Mrs J Newman.
HOW TO APPLY The trust does not accept unsolicited applications.
WHO TO APPLY TO J S Newman, Trustee, c/o BDO LLP, 55 Baker Street, London W1U 7EU *Tel* 020 7486 5888

The Norman Family Charitable Trust

cc no 277616   ESTABLISHED 1979
WHERE FUNDING CAN BE GIVEN Primarily Cornwall, Devon and Somerset.
WHO CAN BENEFIT Registered charities only.
WHAT IS FUNDED Grants are made at the trustees' discretion, mostly in south west England.
WHAT IS NOT FUNDED No grants to individuals. No funding for religious buildings or to assist any organisations using animals for live experimental purposes or generally to fund overseas work.
TYPE OF GRANT One-off, interest-free loans, project, research and start-up costs will be considered. Funding may be given for up to one year.
RANGE OF GRANTS £1,000–£37,000.
SAMPLE GRANTS Children's Hospice South West (£30,000); Peninsular Medical School (£20,000); Kenn Parish Hall and Resthaven (£15,000 each); and Budleigh Youth Project

(£7,500); Exeter Cathedral, Firefighters Charity and Help for Heroes (£5,000 each); Prince's Trust (£4,000); Alzheimer's Society and Motor Neurone Disease Association (£2,500 each); and Blue Cross, Cats Protection League and Shelter (£2,000 each).

FINANCES *Year* 2009–10 *Income* £386,675 *Grants* £381,689 *Assets* £8,681,819

TRUSTEES R J Dawe, Chair; Mrs M H Evans; M B Saunders; Mrs M J Webb; Mrs C E Houghton.

HOW TO APPLY In writing to the correspondent. A subcommittee of trustees meet regularly to make grants of up to £5,000. Grants in excess of £5,000 are dealt with at one of the quarterly meetings of all the trustees.

WHO TO APPLY TO R J Dawe, Chair of the Trustees, 14 Fore Street, Budleigh Salterton, Devon EX9 6NG *Tel* 01395 446699 *Fax* 01395 446698 *email* enquiries@normanfct.plus.com *Website* www.nfct.org

■ The Duncan Norman Trust Fund

CC NO 250434   **ESTABLISHED** 1996

WHERE FUNDING CAN BE GIVEN UK, with a preference for Merseyside.

WHO CAN BENEFIT Registered charities that are known to the trustees.

WHAT IS FUNDED General charitable purposes.

WHAT IS NOT FUNDED No grants to individuals.

SAMPLE GRANTS The Campaign for Drawing (£5,000); PCC of St Gwenfaen Church, Rhoscolyn (£2,000); Army Benevolent Fund, Combat Stress and Royal Star and Garter Home (£1,500 each); Breast Cancer Haven – London, Help for Heroes and PCC of SS Peter & Paul Church – Swalcliffe (£1,000 each).

FINANCES *Year* 2009–10 *Income* £29,436 *Grants* £25,500 *Assets* £758,214

TRUSTEES R K Asser; Mrs C Chapman; Mrs V S Hilton; Mrs C E Lazar; W Stothart; C L Venner.

OTHER INFORMATION Grants of less than £1,000 each totalled £21,500.

HOW TO APPLY The trust states that it only makes grants to charities known to the settlor and unsolicited applications are not considered.

WHO TO APPLY TO The Trustees, Liverpool Charity and Voluntary Services, 151 Dale Street, Liverpool L2 2AH *Tel* 0151 227 5177 *email* enquiries@charitycheques.org.uk *Website* www.merseytrusts.org.uk

■ The Normanby Charitable Trust

CC NO 252102   **ESTABLISHED** 1966

WHERE FUNDING CAN BE GIVEN UK, with a special interest in North Yorkshire and north east England.

WHO CAN BENEFIT Registered charities.

WHAT IS FUNDED The trust concentrates its support on general charitable purposes, however previous research has suggested a preference for supporting social welfare, disability and the arts. The trust has occasionally considered giving grants for the preservation of religious and secular buildings of historical or architectural interest.

WHAT IS NOT FUNDED No grants to individuals, or to non-UK charities.

RANGE OF GRANTS £50–£228,000.

SAMPLE GRANTS Moyne Institute (£228,000); Lythe Village Hall (£100,000); Mulgrave Community Sports Association (£25,000); Keats/Shelley Memorial Association (£10,000); Order of the Holy Paraclete (£5,000); Churches Regional Commission for Yorkshire and the Humber North York Moors Chamber Music Festival (£3,500 each); Hinderwell Methodist Church and Inter Active Whitby and District (£2,000 each); St Mungo's, The Salvation Army and Tom Carpenter Centre (£1,000 each); and St Catherine's Hospice (£500).

FINANCES *Year* 2009–10 *Income* £292,575 *Grants* £405,222 *Assets* £8,857,878

TRUSTEES The Marquis of Normanby; The Dowager Marchioness of Normanby; Lady Lepel Kornicki; Lady Evelyn Buchan; Lady Peronel Phipps de Cruz; Lady Henrietta Burridge.

OTHER INFORMATION 'In accordance with the objectives under the trust deed the trustees do exceptionally make grants outside the preferred area and this has happened during the current year [2009–10] in respect of the grant paid to The Moyne Institute.'

HOW TO APPLY In writing to the correspondent. There are no regular dates for trustees' meetings. Please note, only successful applications will be acknowledged.

WHO TO APPLY TO The Trustees, 52 Tite Street, London Sw3 4JA

■ The North British Hotel Trust

CC NO 221335   **ESTABLISHED** 1903

WHERE FUNDING CAN BE GIVEN Scotland.

WHO CAN BENEFIT Mainly registered charities.

WHAT IS FUNDED General, mainly welfare, health, older people, people with disabilities.

WHAT IS NOT FUNDED No grants to individuals.

TYPE OF GRANT Capital, revenue and project funding.

SAMPLE GRANTS Euan MacDonald Centre of Motor Neurone Disease (£61,000); HIT Scotland (£25,000 in total); Scottish Outward Bound (£12,500); Circle (£10,000); the Prince's Trust (£7,500); Cosgrove Care Limited (£6,000); Stepping Stones and Pebbles Crèche, Autism Initiatives UK and the Teenage Cancer Trust (£5,000 each); Hearts & Minds Limited (£4,000); Parkinson's Disease Society (£2,000); and Age Concern Eastwood (£1,000).

FINANCES *Year* 2009–10 *Income* £528,505 *Grants* £348,636 *Assets* £9,550,642

TRUSTEES Ian C Fraser; Patrick Crerar; Graham Brown; Mrs Jeanette Crerar; Mike Still; James Barrack; John Williams.

HOW TO APPLY Application forms are available from the correspondent.

WHO TO APPLY TO Claire Smith, Clerk, 1 Queen Charlotte Lane, Edinburgh EH6 6BL *email* nbht@samuelston.com

■ The North West Cancer Research Fund

CC NO 223598   **ESTABLISHED** 1948

WHERE FUNDING CAN BE GIVEN North West England and North and Mid Wales.

WHO CAN BENEFIT Those undertaking fundamental cancer research approved by and under the direction of the North West Cancer Research Fund Scientific Committee.

WHAT IS FUNDED Fundamental research into the causes of cancer, including the cost of associated equipment.

WHAT IS NOT FUNDED Funding is not given for research whose primary aim is to develop new forms of treatment or evaluate existing ones, such as drug development, nor for clinical trials.

TYPE OF GRANT Project; research; running and start-up costs; and salaries. Usually for three-year periods subject to review.

RANGE OF GRANTS Average grant size is £35,000 per annum, awarded for three years.

FINANCES *Year* 2009–10 *Income* £780,428 *Grants* £1,250,000 *Assets* £4,034,233

TRUSTEES W M Barton; A P Farmer; J C Lewys-Lloyd; Mrs W E Hadwin; M S Potts; Mrs B J Smith; Col. J G Bryson; Mrs P Mann; A Renison; Mrs B Lloyd Powell; Mrs H E Dring; Mrs J Pettitt; Mrs S Gill; Mrs O Ley; Kate Cowie; Richard Skelton; Gordon Findlay.

HOW TO APPLY Applications to be submitted to Tracey Ricketts, North West Cancer Research Fund, 22 Oxford Street, Liverpool, L7 7BL. One original copy is required and, in addition, an email PDF copy should be sent to research@nwcrf.co.uk. Forms can be downloaded from the Fund's website. Applications must be limited to 2,000 words. Relevant papers in print or submitted should be included as an appendix. Applications must be submitted by 1 April or 1 October. They will be considered approximately eight weeks later. Late applications will be held over to the following meeting.

WHO TO APPLY TO Anne Jackson, 22 Oxford Street, Liverpool L7 7BL *Tel* 0151 709 2919 *email* research@nwcrf.co.uk *Website* www.nwcrf.co.uk

■ North West London Community Foundation

CC NO 1097648   **ESTABLISHED** 2002

WHERE FUNDING CAN BE GIVEN London boroughs of Barnet, Brent, Ealing, Enfield, Haringey, Harrow and Hillingdon.

WHO CAN BENEFIT Local community and voluntary organisations.

WHAT IS FUNDED Children and young people; community development; education; arts and the humanities; relief of suffering, disadvantage or poverty; health and special needs.

WHAT IS NOT FUNDED No grants to individuals; organisations outside the area of benefit or statutory bodies and their agencies.

TYPE OF GRANT Usually one-off.

RANGE OF GRANTS £100–£10,000.

SAMPLE GRANTS Previously: Barnet Elderly Asian's Group; Harrow Young Achievers (£5,000 each); St Mary's Acorns Parent and Toddler Group; Community Link Up (£4,000 each); The Kilburn Festival; The Special Yoga Centre (£1,100 each); Somali Women Enterprise and Employment Project (£1,500); and Harrow in Leaf (£900).

FINANCES *Year* 2009–10 *Income* £733,564 *Grants* £333,236 *Assets* £411,107

TRUSTEES Natalie Forbes, Chair; Kanti Nagda; David Wood; Tajinder Nijjar; Howard Bluston; Malcolm Churchill.

OTHER INFORMATION A grant list was not included in the trust's accounts.

HOW TO APPLY Application forms and further details are available from the correspondent or from the foundation's website. Different funds have different application processes and deadlines so please refer to the individual fund guidelines.

WHO TO APPLY TO Kath Sullivan, Grants Officer, Central Depot Unit 4, Forward Drive, Harrow, Middlesex HA3 8NT *Tel* 020 8909 2788 *Fax* 020 8909 2730 *email* kath.s@nwlondoncf.org.uk *Website* www.northwestlondoncommunityfoundation.org.uk

■ The Northampton Municipal Church Charities

CC NO 259593   **ESTABLISHED** 1969

WHERE FUNDING CAN BE GIVEN The borough of Northampton.

WHO CAN BENEFIT Organisations and individuals in need.

WHAT IS FUNDED Social welfare, disability, religion and education.

TYPE OF GRANT One-off and recurrent.

RANGE OF GRANTS Usually £1,000 for individuals and between £1,000 and £30,000 for organisations.

SAMPLE GRANTS Emmanuel Church (£12,300); St Giles PCC Streetchurch (£7,500); Mount Pleasant Baptist Church (£5,000); Diocese of Peterborough (£4,500); St Andrews Primary School (£4,150); Motor Neurone Disease (£2,500); Northampton Hope Centre (£2,000); and Northampton Volunteer Centre (£1,500).

FINANCES *Year* 2009–10 *Income* £233,338 *Grants* £101,912 *Assets* £4,256,869

TRUSTEES Keith Davidson; James Buckby; Mrs Jane Duncan; Ronald Gate; Mrs Ruth Hampson; Mrs Valerie Holmes; Mrs Jean Lineker; Colin Wain; Jonathan Church; Clive Fowler; Mrs Pauline Hoggarth; Brian May; Terrence O'Connor.

OTHER INFORMATION From the grants total £10,600 went to individuals, £40,500 went towards pensioners grants and £5,500 went towards Christmas vouchers.

HOW TO APPLY In writing to the correspondent.

WHO TO APPLY TO Clerk to the Trustees, Wilson Browne Solicitors, 4 Grange Park Court, Roman Way, Grange Park, Northampton NN4 5EA *Tel* 01604 876697 *email* jforsyth@wilsonbrowne.co.uk

■ The Northampton Queen's Institute Relief in Sickness Fund

CC NO 208583   **ESTABLISHED** 1971

WHERE FUNDING CAN BE GIVEN The borough of Northampton.

WHO CAN BENEFIT Organisations benefiting children and young adults, at risk groups, and people who are disadvantaged by poverty or socially isolated.

WHAT IS FUNDED Youth groups, welfare organisations, hospitals and health organisations.

TYPE OF GRANT One-off and recurrent.

RANGE OF GRANTS £500–£3,000.

SAMPLE GRANTS St John Ambulance (£3,000); Nazareth House, Northants Association for the Blind, Nicholas Rothwell House, Home-Start and Northampton Hope Centre (£2,000 each); Friends of Northampton Hospital and the Army Benevolent Fund (£1,500 each); Door to Door, Methodist Homestead, Age Concern, National Kidney Association (£1,000 each); Life Lights and Playtime (£500 each).

FINANCES *Year* 2009–10 *Income* £37,445 *Grants* £30,500 *Assets* £978,914

TRUSTEES D M Orton-Jones, Chair; C F N Pedley; Mrs J Bradshaw; J Mackaness; Dr R Marshall; Dr J McFarlane; David Hammer; Dr J Scrivener Birkhead; Dr Charles Fox.

HOW TO APPLY In writing to the correspondent. There are one or two main meetings where applications are considered during the year, although decisions can be made in between.

WHO TO APPLY TO Mrs Susan Peet, Clerk to the Charity, Shoosmiths, 5 The Lakes, Northampton NN4 7SH *Tel* 01604 543111

■ The Earl of Northampton's Charity

CC NO 210291   ESTABLISHED 2003
WHERE FUNDING CAN BE GIVEN England, with a preference for London and the South East.
WHO CAN BENEFIT Charitable organisations.
WHAT IS FUNDED Welfare causes.
RANGE OF GRANTS £250–£4,000.
SAMPLE GRANTS Trinity Hospital – Castle Rising (£10,000); Trinity Hospital – Clun (£4,000); Jubilee Trust Almshouses (£2,000); and St M Michael's Church Framlington (£250).
FINANCES *Year* 2009–10 *Income* £769,000 *Grants* £16,000 *Assets* £22,126,000
TRUSTEES The Mercers Company.
OTHER INFORMATION £22,000 to individuals.
HOW TO APPLY Please note: The trust is currently not accepting any applications. It is under the trusteeship of the Mercers' Company and one application to the Company is an application to all of its trusts including the Mercers' Charitable Foundation and the Charity of Sir Richard Whittington.
WHO TO APPLY TO M McGregor, Clerk to the Mercers' Company, Mercers' Company, Mercers' Hall, Ironmonger Lane, London EC2V 8HE *Tel* 020 7726 4991 *Fax* 020 7600 1158 *email* mail@mercers.co.uk *Website* www.mercers.co.uk

■ The Northcott Devon Foundation

CC NO 201277   ESTABLISHED 1960
WHERE FUNDING CAN BE GIVEN Devon.
WHO CAN BENEFIT 'The principal objects of the charity are to provide support for individuals in Devon and to assist registered charities which seek to improve the living conditions of disabled or disadvantaged persons resident in Devon.'
WHAT IS FUNDED (a) Individuals or families living in Devon who are experiencing distress and hardship deriving from disability, illness, injury, bereavement or exceptional disadvantage, in circumstances where such assistance offers long-term benefit. (b) Registered charities operating primarily within Devon, whose objects are broadly in sympathy with those of the foundation, and who seek to improve the living conditions or life experiences of people who are disabled or disadvantaged living in Devon. (c) Young people of limited means undertaking philanthropic activities that are not part of a formal education or training programme, and who live in Devon.
WHAT IS NOT FUNDED The foundation is unable to enter into longer-term financial commitments. Assistance will not be given to statutory agencies, including self-governing National Health Service Trusts, in the performance of their duties. Assistance will not be given to clear any debts owed to statutory agencies or to financial institutions. Other debts will not formally be considered unless agreement has been reached with the creditors for full and final settlement in a substantially reduced sum.
TYPE OF GRANT Usually one-off for a specific purpose or project. Research, capital and buildings will be considered. Core funding is not considered.
RANGE OF GRANTS Normally upwards of £200 to £10,000.

SAMPLE GRANTS Whizz kids (£700); West of England School for the Blind (£500). A further £5,700 was given in small grants to institutions.
FINANCES *Year* 2009–10 *Income* £189,734 *Grants* £191,467 *Assets* £5,037,742
TRUSTEES Mrs Patricia Lane; Maj. Gen. John Grey; Michael Pentreath.
OTHER INFORMATION Grants to 967 individuals totalled £184,600.
HOW TO APPLY Organisations should initially apply in writing to the correspondent who will supply an application form and statement of policy. Please enclose an sae.
Applications from individuals are primarily considered through the county social services department or a registered charity.
Assistance will not be given unless applicants or their sponsors have checked thoroughly that assistance or benefit is not available from the Department of Social Security or other public funds.
WHO TO APPLY TO Geoffrey Folland, Secretary, 1b Victoria Road, Exmouth, Devon EX8 1DL *Tel* 01395 269204

■ The Northcott Devon Medical Foundation

CC NO 204660   ESTABLISHED 1961
WHERE FUNDING CAN BE GIVEN Devon.
WHO CAN BENEFIT Academics, medical professionals, research workers and postgraduate students.
WHAT IS FUNDED Support of postgraduate, medical research and the improvement of medical practice. Provision of schools, research laboratories, libraries and so on for the promotion of medicine, surgery and other subjects.
WHAT IS NOT FUNDED Tuition fees for medical/nursing undergraduates and living expenses.
RANGE OF GRANTS £400 to £5,000.
SAMPLE GRANTS the Peninsula Medical School which received funding for 10 projects (£20,000).
FINANCES *Year* 2009–10 *Income* £27,141 *Grants* £20,097 *Assets* £1,142,384
TRUSTEES Dr C Gardner-Thorpe; Prof. D Partridge; Dr A P Warin; J Thompson.
HOW TO APPLY On an application form available from the correspondent.
WHO TO APPLY TO R E T Borton, Secretary, Bishop Fleming, Stratus House, Emperor Way, Exeter Business Park, Exeter EX1 3QS *Tel* 01392 448800 *email* tborton@bishopfleming.co.uk

■ The Community Foundation for Northern Ireland

IR NO XN45242   ESTABLISHED 1979
WHERE FUNDING CAN BE GIVEN Northern Ireland and the six border counties of the Republic of Ireland.
WHO CAN BENEFIT Community groups, self-help organisations and voluntary organisations.
WHAT IS FUNDED Priority areas: peace-building; community development; social justice; cross-border development; active citizenship; poverty, social inclusion.
WHAT IS NOT FUNDED The foundation will not fund: activities that duplicate existing services; retrospective funding; capital build projects or large equipment purchase; promotion of religion; dinners, fund-raising promotions or other ticketed events; party political activity; housing associations; individuals, unless a fund is specifically aimed at helping individuals;

Think carefully about every application. Is it justified?

773

replacement of statutory funding; projects where the foundation's contribution is a minor part of a larger funded initiative, except where it clearly contributes to the foundation's funding objectives; projects beginning within 12 weeks of application or organisations that did not comply with the reporting requirements of previous grant aid.

TYPE OF GRANT One-off and reoccurring.

RANGE OF GRANTS £100–£150,000.

SAMPLE GRANTS Teach Na Failte (£202,600); SEEDS (£10,000); Justices for Magdalene's (£5,000); Council for the Homeless NI (£3,000); Multi-Cultural Senior Citizens group (£2,500); St Patrick's Girls' FC (£2,000); Suffolk Lenadoon Interface Group; Lesbian Advisory services Initiative (LASI) (£1,500 each); Community Arts Forum; Village Focus Group (£1,000 each); Women 2 Gather (£900); Music Theatre for Youth (£500).

FINANCES *Year* 2010–11 *Income* £5,198,029 *Grants* £3,752,810 *Assets* £15,632,316

TRUSTEES Tony McCusker, Chair; Les Allamby; Mike Bamber; Barbary Cook; Sammy Douglas; Dr Jeremy Harbison; Noreen Kearney; Julie Knight; Dr Mike Morrissey; Dr Duncan Morrow; Stephanie Morrow; Conal McFeely; Tayra McKee; Anne McReynolds; Hilary Sidwell; Colin Stutt.

PUBLICATIONS Various policy briefs, funder's briefs and models of best practice available on the website.

OTHER INFORMATION Funding programmes are subject to open and close for applications throughout the year. New funds are also established and some end, therefore it is important to contact the foundation or check their comprehensive website for the most recent information.

HOW TO APPLY Applications to any of the funds are made through the same online process. The foundation will match the application with the most suitable fund. There are comprehensive guidelines available on the website for applications. A turnaround time of 12 weeks should be allowed for all applications. There are two parts to the application process: Part A – complete the short online form to answer the questions about the project, beneficiaries and budget and Part B – you will be given a unique link to your own application form in an email along with guidelines on completing it. This part must be printed off and signed by two members of the organisation. Both parts should then be posted to the foundation together with the following documentation: a copy of the governing document; a copy of the most recent accounts or income and expenditure statement; a list of the management committee members and their contact details; a recent original bank statement for the organisation's bank account. The foundation will normally only fund groups located in Northern Ireland however some funds will make grants in the Republic as well. Applicants should check the fund specifications. Applications are assessed by the foundation's staff and recommendations are considered by the trustee's grants sub-committee. Successful applicants will be required to submit both qualitative and quantitative monitoring information for the benefit of both the grant holder and the foundation.

WHO TO APPLY TO Avila Kilmurray, Director, Community House, Citylink Business Park, 6a Albert Street, Belfast BT12 4HQ *Tel* 028 9024 5927 *Fax* 028 9032 9839 *email* info@communityfoundationni.org *Website* www.communityfoundationni.org

························

■ The Northern Rock Foundation

CC NO 1063906   **ESTABLISHED** 1997

WHERE FUNDING CAN BE GIVEN Cumbria, Northumberland, Tyne and Wear, County Durham and the Tees Valley.

WHO CAN BENEFIT Organisations helping people who are disadvantaged.

WHAT IS FUNDED Current grant programmes are: Managing Money – helps people who are in debt or who have other financial problems and needs; Having a Home – helps vulnerable people who are homeless or at risk of becoming homeless; Enabling Independence and Choice – helps older people, people with mental health problems, people with learning disabilities and carers; Changing Lives – helps young offenders and young people within the criminal justice system, refugees, asylum seekers and migrant communities, and people who misuse alcohol and/or drugs; Safety and Justice for Victims of Abuse – supports people who experience domestic abuse, sexual violence and exploitation and child abuse; Fresh Ideas Fund – provides funding for early stage development of new business ideas to help the charities the foundation supports to grow in size, increase their impact and improve their long term sustainability.

WHAT IS NOT FUNDED If your organisation or your project falls into one of the categories below do not apply to the foundation for a grant: activities which are not recognised as charitable in law; applications for under £1,000; charities which appear to us to have excessive unrestricted or free reserves (up to 12 months' expenditure is normally acceptable), or are in serious deficit; national charities which do not have a regional office or other representation in North East England or Cumbria; grant-making bodies seeking to distribute grants on the foundation's behalf; open-ended funding agreements; general appeals, sponsorship and marketing appeals; corporate applications for founder membership of a charity; retrospective grants; replacement of statutory funding; activities primarily the responsibility of central or local government or health authorities; individuals and organisations that distribute funds to individuals; animal welfare; mainstream educational activity, schools and educational establishments; medical research, hospitals, hospices and medical centres; medical treatments and therapies including art therapy; fabric appeals for places of worship; promotion of religion; expeditions or overseas travel; minibuses, other vehicles and transport schemes except where they are a small and integral part of a larger scheme; holidays and outings; playgrounds and play equipment; private clubs or those with such restricted membership as to make them not charitable; capital bids purely towards compliance with the Disability Discrimination Act; amateur arts organisations; musical instruments; sports kit and equipment.

TYPE OF GRANT Capital, core or project funding and for up to three or more years (sometimes renewable after that).

RANGE OF GRANTS £1,000–£1.9 million. Typically £40,000–£250,000.

SAMPLE GRANTS Citizens Advice – Northern Area (£1.5 million); Mind (£200,000); Regional Refugee Forum North East (£150,000); North East Special Needs Network (£127,000); Equal Arts (£68,000); Homeless Link (£123,000); Barnardo's SECOS and ACE Projects (£270,000); Derwentside Domestic Abuse Service (£105,000); Gay Advice Darlington (£99,000); Rape Crisis England and Wales

(£60,000); University of Bristol (£48,000); and Tony Mullin (£4,000).

FINANCES *Year* 2010 *Income* £15,173,000 *Grants* £12,394,000 *Assets* £43,455,000

TRUSTEES Alastair Balls, Chair; David Chapman; David Faulkner; Jackie Fisher; Tony Henfrey; Chris Jobe; Lorna Moran; Frank Nicholson; Mo O'Toole; Julie Shipley.

PUBLICATIONS Grant Programmes – Guidance for Applicants; various reports.

OTHER INFORMATION In 2010, the publicly owned Northern Rock was spilt into 2 separate companies; Northern Rock (Asset Management) plc stated that it would not continue to support the Foundation. Northern Rock plc, the new retail bank, agreed to donate 1% of pre-tax profits for the next 2 years. In 2011 it was announced that Virgin Money would buy Northern Rock plc in 2012 and the agreement with the Northern Rock Foundation was extended to at least 2013 so the Foundation and Virgin could make a new agreement on how they could work together.

In the foundation's latest annual report (2010) there was major concern that following the end of the 1% agreement they would not receive any more significant funding and they therefore resolved to promote the value of the relationship with the foundation when Northern Rock returned to the private sector. At this point the trustees decided to use the capital over the next 5 years to make grants. Currently it remains to be seen whether Virgin, the new owners of Northern Rock, will sustain the funding to the foundation. If they do not, it is likely that the foundation will wind down. In this situation it is possible that Virgin Money Giving, the company's not for profit arm, would increase their giving or take on some of the aims of the Northern Rock Foundation.

HOW TO APPLY The foundation provides comprehensive guidelines for applications on their website. As they have made a shift in their grantmaking to focus on sustainability they will encourage work to consolidate organisations and to increase collaboration including reviewing organisational focus or restructuring. The focus will also be on organisations that they currently have a relationship with. If an applicant has not applied to the foundation previously it is advised that they get in contact before applying. Guidelines available include specific instructions for applicants applying for salary costs or those applying from universities. There are also separate forms for applications for under £20,000 and for those that are over. The foundation prefers online applications as they are quicker and easier but applications may still be submitted via post, providing they are on the correct forms.

WHO TO APPLY TO Penny Wilkinson, Chief Executive, The Old Chapel, Woodbine Road, Gosforth, Newcastle upon Tyne NE3 1DD *Tel* 0191 284 8412 *Fax* 0191 284 8413 *email* generaloffice@nr-foundation.org.uk *Website* www.nr-foundation.org.uk

■ The Northmoor Trust

CC NO 256818   **ESTABLISHED** 1968

WHERE FUNDING CAN BE GIVEN UK.

WHO CAN BENEFIT Local, regional and UK charitable organisations benefiting people who are disadvantaged.

WHAT IS FUNDED The direct or indirect relief of poverty, hardship or distress.

WHAT IS NOT FUNDED Grants are only made to organisations which one or more of the trustees

have direct personal knowledge. No grants to individuals, or organisations concerned with religion, medicine or the arts. Occasionally grants are made to educational charities where the guiding criteria are met. The trust does not respond to general appeals.

TYPE OF GRANT One-off and recurrent.

RANGE OF GRANTS £5,000–£40,000.

SAMPLE GRANTS Zimbabwe Benefit Foundation (£20,000); Tower Hamlets Friends and Neighbours (£11,000); and Family and Friends and National Aids Trust (£5,000 each).

FINANCES *Year* 2009–10 *Income* £52,065 *Grants* £41,000 *Assets* £1,526,168

TRUSTEES Viscount Runciman; Dame Ruth Runciman; Ms Frances Bennett; Ms Cathy Eastburn.

HOW TO APPLY In writing to the correspondent, including the latest accounts and annual report, a list of the main sources of funding and a budget for the current year including details of other grant applications made. For first time applicants, a general description of aims and achievements to date and an outline of plans for future development. Applications should arrive by mid February for preliminary consideration in March, decisions are made in May. Applicants may be visited or asked to provide additional information for the May meeting. The trustees may also visit applicants between the two meetings.

WHO TO APPLY TO Mrs Hilary Edwards, Secretary, 44 Clifton Hill, London NW8 0QG *Tel* 020 7372 0698

■ The Northumberland Village Homes Trust

CC NO 225429   **ESTABLISHED** 1880

WHERE FUNDING CAN BE GIVEN Tyne and Wear, Durham, Cleveland and Northumberland.

WHO CAN BENEFIT Individuals and youth organisations benefiting those under 21years of age who are disadvantaged by poverty.

WHAT IS FUNDED The relief of poverty distress and sickness among children and young persons under the age of 21 years, with a preference for those who are resident in Tyne and Wear, Durham, Cleveland and Northumberland.

WHAT IS NOT FUNDED No personal applications will be considered unless supported by a letter from a registered charity or local authority, or unless the applicant is personally known to one of the trustees. No applications will be considered for 'gap year' projects or for work relating to medical research or such matters.

RANGE OF GRANTS £1,000–£5,000.

SAMPLE GRANTS Hirst Welfare Centre (£5,000); Fairbridge (£4,000); Dene Valley Community Partnership and The Eyeless Trust (£3,000 each); The National Autistic Society and Skillforce (£2,000 each); Rainbow Trust (£1,500); Happy Days and Scouts (£1,000 each).

FINANCES *Year* 2009–10 *Income* £40,470 *Grants* £29,500 *Assets* £1,222,783

TRUSTEES D Welch, Chair; Lord Gisborough; Mrs E P Savage; Mrs D Barkes; Mr R L Savage.

HOW TO APPLY Applications should be made by 30 September for consideration in November. Applications should be in writing and state: whether the applicant is an individual, private charity or registered charity; the objects (if a charity); the amount required and what it is for; and any other sources of funding.

WHO TO APPLY TO Mrs Savage, Clerk to the Trustees, Savage Solicitors, Robson House, 4 Middle Street, Corbridge NE45 5AT *Tel* 01434 632505

■ The Northumbria Historic Churches Trust

CC NO 511314   ESTABLISHED 1980
WHERE FUNDING CAN BE GIVEN The dioceses of Durham and Newcastle.
WHO CAN BENEFIT Churches that are at least 100 years old.
WHAT IS FUNDED The restoration, preservation, repair, maintenance, reconstruction, improvement and beautification of churches, their contents and their churchyards.
WHAT IS NOT FUNDED 'The trust is unable to help with work on bells, organs, church halls, decoration (unless consequential), notice boards, publications, heating, re-orderings, new facilities or routine maintenance.'
TYPE OF GRANT One-off, feasibility studies and buildings. Funding is for one year or less.
RANGE OF GRANTS £500–£5,000.
SAMPLE GRANTS Gateshead, St James the Great – Darlington and All Saints – Stranton (£5,000 each); St Mary – Wooler, Sunderland Minster, St Andrew – Bothal and St Augustine – Alston (£4,000 each); St Thomas – Stanhope (£3,500); St Bartholomew – Kirkheaton and St Edmund – Edmundbyers (£2,500 each); St Edwin – High Coniscliffe (£1,000), and Durham Road Baptist – Gateshead (£500).
FINANCES *Year* 2009–10 *Income* £59,422 *Grants* £66,000 *Assets* £212,992
TRUSTEES G Bell, Chair; Mrs E Conran; C Downs; Ven. P Elliot; P Scrope; J B Kendall; Canon J E Ruscoe; Mrs G Walker; Mrs E Norris; Mrs I Ferguson, R C Norris; Revd T Hurst, P Ryder.
OTHER INFORMATION No grants to individuals.
HOW TO APPLY In writing to the correspondent requesting an application form and guidelines. Initial telephone calls to discuss applications are welcomed.
WHO TO APPLY TO Peter De Lange, Secretary, 20 Aykley Vale, Aykley Hands, Durham DH1 5WA *Tel* 0191 383 2704 *email* secretary@northumbriahct.org.uk *Website* www.northumbriahct.org.uk

■ The Northwood Charitable Trust

SC NO SC014487   ESTABLISHED 1972
WHERE FUNDING CAN BE GIVEN Scotland, especially Dundee and Tayside.
WHO CAN BENEFIT Registered charities.
WHAT IS FUNDED General charitable purposes. In the past, grants have been given to a university and to medical and educational projects.
TYPE OF GRANT One-off and recurring grants.
SAMPLE GRANTS Previous beneficiaries include: Tenovus Medical Projects; Tayside Orthopaedic and Rehabilitation Technology Centre; Macmillan Cancer Relief Scotland; Brittle Bone Society; Dundee Repertory Theatre; Dundee Samaritans; Dundee Age Concern; Couple Counselling Tayside; and Tayside Association for the Deaf.
FINANCES *Year* 2009–10 *Income* £2,000,000 *Grants* £1,500,000
TRUSTEES Brian Harold Thomson; Andrew Francis Thomson; Lewis Murray Thomson.
HOW TO APPLY The trust has previously stated that funds are fully committed and that no applications will be considered or acknowledged.

WHO TO APPLY TO Brian McKernie, Secretary, William Thomson and Sons, 22 Meadowside, Dundee DD1 1LN *Tel* 01382 201534 *Fax* 01382 227654 *email* bmckernie@wtandsons.co.uk

■ The Norton Foundation

CC NO 702638   ESTABLISHED 1990
WHERE FUNDING CAN BE GIVEN UK, with a preference for Birmingham, Coventry and the County of Warwick.
WHO CAN BENEFIT Young people under 25 years of age.
WHAT IS FUNDED The trust was created in 1990. Its objects are to help children and young people under 25 who are in 'need of care or rehabilitation or aid of any kind, particularly as a result of delinquency, deprivation, maltreatment or neglect or who are in danger of lapsing or relapsing into delinquency'.
WHAT IS NOT FUNDED No grants for the payment of debts that have already been incurred. Grants are not made for further education (except in very exceptional circumstances).
SAMPLE GRANTS South Birmingham Young Homeless Project (£11,000); Warwickshire County Council, Youth and Community Service (£9,000); React (£2,700); The Industrial Trust and Arthur Rank Centre (£2,500 each); Birmingham Battalion of the Boys' Brigade, Lifelites, The PCC of St Marks and Warwickshire Association of Youth Clubs (£2,000 each); and Birmingham Rathbone, Birmingham Royal Ballet, Coventry Boys' Club, Depaul Trust, Dyslexia Association of Birmingham, Guy's Gift, Happy Days Children's Charity, The National Deaf Children's Society, Warwick Corps of Drums and Whizz Kids (£1,000 each).
FINANCES *Year* 2009–10 *Income* £233,252 *Grants* £105,538 *Assets* £4,100,252
TRUSTEES R H Graham, Suggett Chair; Alan Bailey; Michael R Bailey; Parminder Singh Birdi; Mrs Jane Gaynor; Mrs Sarah V Henderson; Richard G D Hurley; Brian W Lewis; Robert K Meacham; Richard C Perkins; Mrs Louise Sewell.
OTHER INFORMATION A total of £12,310 was given in grants to individuals.
HOW TO APPLY By letter which should contain all the information required as detailed in the guidance notes for applicants. Guidance notes are available from the correspondent or from the foundation's website.
WHO TO APPLY TO Richard C Perkins, Richard Perkins & Co, 50 Brookfield Close, Hunt End, Redditch B97 5LL *Tel* 01527 544446 *email* correspondent@nortonfoundation.org *Website* www.nortonfoundation.org

■ The Norton Rose Charitable Foundation

CC NO 1102142   ESTABLISHED 2004
WHERE FUNDING CAN BE GIVEN Worldwide.
WHO CAN BENEFIT Registered charities and organisations conducting charitable activities worldwide.
WHAT IS FUNDED Education, social welfare, medical.
RANGE OF GRANTS Up to £200,000.
SAMPLE GRANTS The Capital Community Foundation (£175,000); and Barretstown (£80,000).
FINANCES *Year* 2009–10 *Income* £468,135 *Grants* £608,681 *Assets* £9,406
TRUSTEES Simon Cox; Patrick Farrell; Glenn Hall; Campbell Steedman.

HOW TO APPLY 'In many cases, the charities we support are those we have supported in the past, but new charities are considered at all the regular trustee meetings. The trustees also meet on an ad hoc basis to consider specific urgent requests such as the support of major disaster relief appeals.'

WHO TO APPLY TO Patrick Farrell, Secretary, 3 More London Riverside, London SE1 2AQ *Tel* 020 7283 6000 *Website* www.nortonrose.com

■ The Norwich Church of England Young Men's Society

CC NO 206425   **ESTABLISHED** 1892

WHERE FUNDING CAN BE GIVEN Mainly in the Norfolk area.

WHO CAN BENEFIT Churches and charitable organisations.

WHAT IS FUNDED Religious and youth related activities mainly local but also overseas.

RANGE OF GRANTS £100–£7,500.

SAMPLE GRANTS Previous beneficiaries have included: Swardeston Cricket Club – Youth Section (£7,500); Norwich Cathedral (£2,500); Ashcroft Project and East Norfolk Youth for Christ (£1,000 each); Nancy Oldfield Trust (£750); Norfolk Deaf Association, Hamlet Centre Trust and Nelsons Trust (£500 each); Sewell Community Group (£250); and Norfolk and Norwich Diabetes Trust (£100).

FINANCES *Year* 2010 *Income* £225,172 *Grants* £29,126 *Assets* £1,557,473

TRUSTEES J Pidgen; J Copeman; Canon D Sharp; M Preston; C Futter.

HOW TO APPLY In writing to the correspondent. Applications are considered quarterly and only successful ones are acknowledged.

WHO TO APPLY TO C J Free, Secretary, 3 Brigg Street, Norwich NR2 1QN *Tel* 01603 628572

■ The Norwich Historic Churches Trust Ltd

CC NO 266686   **ESTABLISHED** 1973

WHERE FUNDING CAN BE GIVEN Norwich.

WHO CAN BENEFIT Historic churches.

WHAT IS FUNDED The preservation, repair and maintenance of disused churches of all denominations that have particular architectural or historic value.

FINANCES *Year* 2009–10 *Income* £170,511 *Grants* £85,981 *Assets* £59,381

TRUSTEES R Quinn; S Munro; K Rowe; P Tolley; Mrs R Salt; Ms S Curran; J W Knight; Cllr. J D Brociek-Coulton; N Groves; Mr S Altman; D Bradford; D MacGarry; N Williams; Ms F Hartley.

HOW TO APPLY The trust does not give grants to unsolicited applications, as all their monies are donated to the 17 churches the funds are already committed to.

WHO TO APPLY TO Lucy Santos, Secretary, PO Box 3408, Norwich NR3 3WE *email* lucy.santos@norwich-churches.org *Website* www.norwich-churches.org

■ The Norwich Town Close Estate Charity

CC NO 235678   **ESTABLISHED** 1892

WHERE FUNDING CAN BE GIVEN Within a 20-mile radius of the Guildhall of the city of Norwich.

WHO CAN BENEFIT Only charities based in the area specified and carrying out educational activities will be supported.

WHAT IS FUNDED Primarily Freemen of Norwich, for education, pensions, TV licences, and relief in need. Surplus monies may be used for grants to educational charities.

WHAT IS NOT FUNDED No grants to: individuals who are not Freemen (or dependants of Freemen) of the city of Norwich; charities more than 20 miles from Norwich; or charities which are not educational. Revenue funding for educational charities is not generally given.

TYPE OF GRANT Buildings, capital, one-off and project. Funding for up to one year will be considered.

SAMPLE GRANTS Central Norwich Hockey Consortium (£15,000); Eaton Primary School and Norfolk Homemakers Association (£10,000 each); Norfolk and Norwich Families House (£9,000); St Peter's Church Park Lane (£7,500); Hungate Medieval Art (£5,500); East Anglia Art Fund (£2,500); Wymondham Arts Forum (£2,000) and Magdelen Gates Pre-school (£300).

FINANCES *Year* 2009–10 *Income* £722,759 *Grants* £383,336 *Assets* £19,311,000

TRUSTEES David Fullman; John Rushmer; Michael Quinton; Brenda Ferris; Geoffrey Loades; Joyce Hopwood; Philip Blanchflower; Sally Barham; Anthony Hansell; Nigel Black; Richard Gurney; Jeanette Southgate; Robert Self.

HOW TO APPLY After a preliminary enquiry, in writing to the clerk. When submitting an application the following points should be borne in mind: brevity is a virtue – if too much written material is submitted there is a risk that it may not all be assimilated; the trustees like to have details of any other financial support secured; an indication should be given of the amount that is being sought and also how that figure is arrived at; the trustees will not reimburse expenditure already incurred; nor, generally speaking will the trustees pay running costs, e.g. salaries.

WHO TO APPLY TO David Walker, Clerk, Mr David Walker, 1 Woolgate Court, St Benedict's Street, Norwich NR2 4AP *Tel* 01603 621023 *email* david.walker@norwichcharitabletrusts.org.uk

■ Norwood and Newton Settlement

CC NO 234964   **ESTABLISHED** 1952

WHERE FUNDING CAN BE GIVEN England and Wales.

WHO CAN BENEFIT Methodist and other mainstream non-conformist churches. Church of England only in exceptional circumstances.

WHAT IS FUNDED New building work in Methodist and other Free Churches. Smaller national charities in which the Settlor expressed a particular interest and other charitable causes that commend themselves to the trustees.

WHAT IS NOT FUNDED Projects will not be considered where an application for National Lottery funding has been made or is contemplated. No grants to individuals, rarely to large UK charities and not for staff/running costs, equipment, repairs or general maintenance.

TYPE OF GRANT One-off capital grants.

RANGE OF GRANTS £1,000–£20,000.

Think carefully about every application. Is it justified?

777

SAMPLE GRANTS The largest grants made included those to: Colchester Baptist Church and Fulwood Methodist Church (£20,000 each); Whaddon Way Baptist/Cof E Church, Bletchley (£15,000); and Vine Baptist Church, Sevenoaks, The Mint Methodist Church and Fathers House Elim Church, Lancaster (£10,000 each).

Other grants made included those to: Red Lodge Community Church, Ely (£7,500); Ampthill Methodist Church, Bedfordshire and High Bentham Methodist Church, North Yorkshire (£5,000 each); Cheriton Baptist Church, Folkestone (£3,000); and Brailsford Methodist Church, Derby (£1,000).

FINANCES *Year* 2009–10 *Income* £324,312 *Grants* £308,500 *Assets* £6,928,451

TRUSTEES P Clarke; D M Holland; Mrs Stella Holland; R Lynch; Mrs Susan Newsom.

HOW TO APPLY In writing to the correspondent. In normal circumstances, the trustees' decision is communicated to the applicant within seven days (if a refusal), and if successful, immediately after the trustees' quarterly meetings.

WHO TO APPLY TO David M Holland, Trustee, 126 Beauly Way, Romford, Essex RM1 4XL *Tel* 01708 723 670

■ The Noswad Charity

CC NO 282080   **ESTABLISHED** 1981

WHERE FUNDING CAN BE GIVEN UK.

WHO CAN BENEFIT Emphasis is on charities that benefit the arts and people who are disabled, particularly ex-service people.

WHAT IS FUNDED The trustees continue to support those charitable bodies that they have hitherto supported.

WHAT IS NOT FUNDED No grants to individuals.

RANGE OF GRANTS £600–£2,600.

SAMPLE GRANTS Typically grants are made to Douglas Bader Foundation, Royal Air Force Benevolent Fund, BLESMA, RADAR, Macmillan Cancer Relief and National Arts Collections Fund. It also supports scholarships for postgraduate piano students at London music colleges.

FINANCES *Year* 2009–10 *Income* £21,677 *Grants* £25,000

TRUSTEES J A Mills; C N Bardswell; H E Bromley Davenport.

HOW TO APPLY In writing to the correspondent.

WHO TO APPLY TO C N Bardswell, Trustee, c/o Messrs Belmont and Lowe, Solicitors, Priory House, 18–25 St John's Lane, London EC1M 4HD *Tel* 020 7608 4600 *Fax* 020 7608 4601

■ The Notgrove Trust

CC NO 278692   **ESTABLISHED** 1979

WHERE FUNDING CAN BE GIVEN Generally in the Gloucestershire area.

WHO CAN BENEFIT Local or special interests of the trustees.

WHAT IS FUNDED Any local charities can be considered.

WHAT IS NOT FUNDED No grants available to support individuals or medical research.

TYPE OF GRANT Except in special circumstances, single donations only will be considered.

RANGE OF GRANTS £1,000 to £10,000.

SAMPLE GRANTS The Everyman Theatre, Cold Aston Primary School and Friends of the Moore Cottage Hospital (£10,000 each); Cheltenham Festivals, Everyman Theatre and Wheels Project Ltd (£5,000 each); Cheltenham Housing Aid Centre (£4,000); Army Benevolent Fund (£3,000); Windrush PCC (£2,000); and Stroud Valleys Project, Sportability and Guys Gift (£1,000 each).

FINANCES *Year* 2009–10 *Income* £142,766 *Grants* £129,800 *Assets* £5,404,524

TRUSTEES David Acland; Elizabeth Acland; Harry Acland.

HOW TO APPLY Applications are considered from Gloucestershire charities or from an organisation having an established connection with the trustees. Applicants should include a copy of their latest accounts. Speculative appeals from outside of Gloucestershire are strongly discouraged and unlikely to get a positive response. Past donations to charities outside Gloucestershire should not be taken as an indication of likely future support. The trust has stated telephone calls are unwelcome and due to a lack of clerical support, unsuccessful appeals will not be acknowledged.

WHO TO APPLY TO David Acland, Trustee, Elmbank Farmhouse, Cold Aston, Cheltenham, Gloucestershire GL54 3BJ *Tel* 01451 810652

■ The Nottingham General Dispensary

CC NO 228149   **ESTABLISHED** 1963

WHERE FUNDING CAN BE GIVEN Nottingham and Nottinghamshire.

WHO CAN BENEFIT Individuals or other organisations.

WHAT IS FUNDED The alleviation of need or aid in recovery through the provision of items and services not readily available from ordinary channels. Charities working in the fields of: respite; professional bodies; councils for voluntary service; and health will be considered.

TYPE OF GRANT One-off preferred. Capital, project, recurring costs. Funding for up to three years will be considered.

RANGE OF GRANTS £25–£4,000; mostly under £1,000.

SAMPLE GRANTS Vitalise Skylarks (£1,500); Transplant Sport UK, Spinal Injuries Association, Sign Help and Life Education Centres (£1,000 each); Listening Books (£900); Painful Bladder Group and Bilborough Carers Support Group (£800 each); CAKE Carers (£750); Rushcliffe Stroke Survivors Group (£710); Asian Fathers Special Needs Support Group (£645); Deafblind UK and Peter Le Marchant Trust (£500 each); Bereavement Keyworth (£350); and Heartline Association (£260).

FINANCES *Year* 2009–10 *Income* £43,515 *Grants* £32,377 *Assets* £1,200,194

TRUSTEES R Batterbury, Chair; D Levell; Dr I McLachlan; Mrs P Johnston; J Bendall; Dr S Harris; A Hopwood; Dr Angela Truman.

HOW TO APPLY In writing to the correspondent, supported by medical evidence.

WHO TO APPLY TO Anna Chander, Secretary, Cumberland Court, 80 Mount Street, Nottingham NG1 6HH *Tel* 0115 901 5562

■ The Nottingham Gordon Memorial Trust for Boys and Girls

CC NO 212536   **ESTABLISHED** 1976

WHERE FUNDING CAN BE GIVEN Nottingham and its immediate surrounding area.

WHO CAN BENEFIT Children and young people up to the age of 25.

WHAT IS FUNDED Relief in need, education and educational trips.

TYPE OF GRANT One off preferred.

RANGE OF GRANTS Up to £2,500.

SAMPLE GRANTS Previously: £2,500 to the Nottinghamshire Probation Service; £1,500 to the Nottingham Outward Bound Association.

FINANCES *Year* 2010 *Income* £41,638 *Grants* £35,266 *Assets* £1,126,203

TRUSTEES C N Cullen, Chair; J Tordoff; J Ramsden; D Lowe; P Hill; Revd P Watts; J Foxon; A King; W A Hammond; Revd I Wiseman.

HOW TO APPLY On a form available from the correspondent. Trustees meet twice yearly.

WHO TO APPLY TO Mrs Colleen Douglas, Clerk to the Trustees, Cumberland Court, 80 Mount Street, Nottingham NG1 6HH *Tel* 0115 901 5558

■ Nottinghamshire Community Foundation

CC NO 1069538   **ESTABLISHED** 1998

WHERE FUNDING CAN BE GIVEN Nottinghamshire.

WHO CAN BENEFIT Individuals, community groups and charities.

WHAT IS FUNDED The foundation states: 'We are committed to improving the quality of life of the people of Nottingham and Nottinghamshire by raising and managing funds for distribution in response to local needs. No matter where you live or work, there will be people living close by who suffer disadvantage – it may be through poverty, age, ill-health or disability. If, like us, you believe everyone deserves the chance to contribute and be valued as a member of the community, you can make a difference by helping us to support more local groups. We find, train and fund the smallest most inexperienced grass roots groups as well as working with small charities. Our aim is to find solutions that genuinely help those in need. For some people this can mean learning to read, for others, it is defeating the pervasive influence of drugs and gun crime; and for a few, it is about achieving excellence in a chosen field – sport, music or art.'

WHAT IS NOT FUNDED Please refer to the foundation's website for exclusions specific to each fund.

RANGE OF GRANTS Up to £5,000.

SAMPLE GRANTS Nottingham City NHS (£220,000); Grassroots City (£165,000); Nottinghamshire Robin Hood Fund (£135,000); Sports Relief (£50,000) and Real Help for Communities: Modernisation Fund (£16,000); Yoga Health Institute (£9,700); Rev & Go (£8,000); African Initiative Support and West Street Pre-school (£5,000 each); Friends of Trinity Show Band (£4,600); Mansfield Town Ladies (£4,400); Clipstone Welfare Ladies Football (£1,800); Activity Friends (£1,500) and Garden of Grace (£1,300).

FINANCES *Year* 2009–10 *Income* £2,950,683 *Grants* £1,841,957 *Assets* £1,749,897

TRUSTEES Christopher Hughes; Chris Hughes; Frances Walker; Philip Marsh; Paul Alfred McDuell; Alan Sutton; Charles Cannon; Alistair McDiarmid; Jeff Buck.

OTHER INFORMATION The following funds were available at the time of writing: RTC Fund; The Jones Trust Community Fund; Major Oak Fund; Boots Charitable Trust; Jessie Spencer Fund; Fair Share Trust Ashfield; Joan Oliver Fund; Danielle Beccan Memorial Fund and Experian Fund.

HOW TO APPLY Please refer to the foundation's website for full details of how to apply to the various programmes currently being administered.

WHO TO APPLY TO Ms Nina Dauban, Cedar House, Ransom Wood Business Park, Southwell Road West, Rainworth, Mansfield, Nottinghamshire *Tel* 01623 636202 *Fax* 01623 620204 *email* enquiries@nottscommunityfoundation.org. uk *Website* www.nottscf.org.uk

■ The Nottinghamshire Historic Churches Trust

CC NO 518335   **ESTABLISHED** 1985

WHERE FUNDING CAN BE GIVEN Nottinghamshire.

WHO CAN BENEFIT Churches and chapels.

WHAT IS FUNDED The trust gives grants for the preservation and repair of historic churches and chapels in Nottinghamshire and for the monuments, fittings and furniture and so on, of such churches.

WHAT IS NOT FUNDED Works of routine maintenance (such as repainting a door, non-specialist cleaning, etc.), new buildings, extensions, meeting rooms Coffee areas, sinks, new furniture, routine decoration (unless needing to use some specialist materials), routine electrical work (new switches, lights, cables for new installations), repair of modern furniture, fixtures, fittings, overhead projector screens, sound systems, new bells and bellframes, any work that has already started or been completed before application made.

RANGE OF GRANTS Up to £13,000.

SAMPLE GRANTS St Andrew's – Langor (£11,000); St Margaret's – Owthorpe (£7,500); St Helen's – Stapleford and St Wilfred's – Screveton (£5,000 each); St Peter's – East Drayton (£4,000); St Michael – Halam (£3,500); Holy Trinity – Kirton (£3,000); St. John the Baptist – Treswell (£2,500); St Nicholas – Hockerton (£2,000); All Souls – Radford (£1,500); St Helen's – Austerfield (£500); St Peter – Sibthorpe (£350).

FINANCES *Year* 2009–10 *Income* £84,855 *Grants* £116,350 *Assets* £258,162

TRUSTEES R Craven-Smith-Milnes; Mrs J Mellors – Chair; Dr C Brooke; Dr Jenny Alexander; D Atkins; Prof. J V Beckett; G Beaumont; G Renton; Richard Brackenbury; Robert Brackenbury; K Goodman; P Hoare; A Marriott; S Leigh Rix; Revd Canon K Turner; A Paris.

HOW TO APPLY Grant application forms along with guidance notes are available from the trust's website.

Alternatively, these can be obtained by ringing or writing to: Mrs L Francis, Grants Administrator, 15 Tattershall Drive, Beeston, Nottingham NG9 2GP. (Tel: 07757 800919; Email: linda.francis15@ntlworld.com).

WHO TO APPLY TO Keith Goodman, 59 Briar Gate, Long Eaton, Nottingham NG10 4BQ *Tel* 0115 972 6590 *email* nhct@keithgoodman.com *Website* www.nottshistoricchurchtrust.org.uk

■ The Nottinghamshire Miners' Welfare Trust Fund

CC NO 1001272   **ESTABLISHED** 1990
WHERE FUNDING CAN BE GIVEN Nottinghamshire.
WHO CAN BENEFIT Miners or ex-miners who are retired, redundant or unemployed.
WHAT IS FUNDED The trust supports miners or ex-miners in need living in Nottinghamshire, who are retired or redundant and still unemployed, and their dependants.
RANGE OF GRANTS £150–£9,000.
SAMPLE GRANTS Previous beneficiaries: CISWO – social worker funding (£8,800); CISWO – National Schemes of Benefit 2006 (£8,000); Edwinstowe Physiotherapy Clinic (£3,0000; North East Midlands Brass Band Association (£500); and Newstead Youth and Community Centre (£400).
FINANCES *Year* 2010 *Income* £92,024 *Grants* £88,313 *Assets* £2,499,094
TRUSTEES Mr Brookes; J C H Longden; M F Ball; J E Wood; M L Stevens.
OTHER INFORMATION Grants to individuals totalled £51,000.
HOW TO APPLY In writing to the correspondent at any time.
WHO TO APPLY TO D A Brooks, Secretary, Coal Industry Social Welfare Organisation, Berry Hill Lane, Mansfield NG18 4JR *Tel* 01623 625767 *Fax* 01623 626789

■ Novi Most International

CC NO 1043501   **ESTABLISHED** 1995
WHERE FUNDING CAN BE GIVEN Bosnia-Herzegovina.
WHO CAN BENEFIT Bosnians disadvantaged and displaced by war, especially children and young people.
WHAT IS FUNDED Christian youth-based ministry to meet physical, spiritual, emotional and social needs, with particular emphasis on long-term support of children and young people traumatised by war. Reconciliation and community development initiatives are also supported.
WHAT IS NOT FUNDED Grants seldom given to projects not connected with evangelical churches or where the trust's own staff or partners are not involved.
TYPE OF GRANT One-off and recurring.
FINANCES *Year* 2009–10 *Income* £232,204 *Grants* £46,269 *Assets* £95,885
TRUSTEES A Thomas; Revd D Stillman; S Evans; Christine Harris; A Silley.
PUBLICATIONS New Bridge and Bosnia Prayer Briefing.
HOW TO APPLY Funds fully committed for the foreseeable future. Unsolicited applications are not encouraged or acknowledged.
WHO TO APPLY TO Katie Flory, Secretary, Bushell House, 118–120 Broad Street, Chesham, Buckinghamshire HP5 3ED *Tel* 01494 793242 *Fax* 01494 793771 *email* chesham@novimost.org *Website* www.novimost.org

■ The Nuffield Foundation

CC NO 206601   **ESTABLISHED** 1943
WHERE FUNDING CAN BE GIVEN UK; southern and eastern Africa.
WHO CAN BENEFIT Charitable and voluntary organisations, and universities benefiting children, young adults and older people; research workers; students; legal professionals; those in care, fostered and adopted; parents and children; one-parent families; at risk groups; carers; disabled people; those disadvantaged by poverty; refugees; travellers; and people suffering from arthritis and rheumatism. Grants are not made to individuals except under the bursary and studentship schemes.
WHAT IS FUNDED Research, experiment or practical development in the fields of: child protection; family justice; access to justice; educational provision and children's needs; curriculum innovation; older people and their families; capacity development; miscellaneous.
WHAT IS NOT FUNDED The foundation normally makes grants only to UK organisations, and support work that will be mainly based in the UK, although the trustees welcome proposals for collaborative projects involving partners in European or Commonwealth countries. There are different exclusions for different programmes so please consult the full guidelines for each area before applying. There are a number of things that the foundation does not fund under any of its funding programmes, these include: general appeals; buildings or capital costs; applications solely for equipment – grants for equipment are allowed when they are part of a project that is otherwise acceptable; support or attend conferences or seminars; projects that could be considered by a government department, a Research Council or a more appropriate charity; the establishment of Chairs, or other permanent academic posts; grants for the production of films or videos, or for exhibitions; funding for school fees, a university course, or a gap year project; or requests for funding for financial help from or on behalf of individuals in distress.
TYPE OF GRANT One-off grants for projects.
RANGE OF GRANTS £5,000–£250,000.
SAMPLE GRANTS University College London (£371,000); University of Oxford (£304,000); London School of Economics (£273,000); Brunel University (£267,000); Gingerbread (£260,000); The Royal Statistical Society (£250,000); Department of Law, University of Sussex (£152,000); Liverpool School of Tropical Medicine (£118,000); Institute for Criminal Policy Research (£91,000); Council for Assisting Refugee Academics (£75,000); School of Education, Durham University (£50,000); British Association for Adoption and Fostering (£39,000); Refugee Council (£30,000); Law Centre Northern Ireland (£20,000); and School of Law, University of Edinburgh (£15,000).
FINANCES *Year* 2010 *Income* £4,692,000 *Grants* £5,710,000 *Assets* £232,429,000
TRUSTEES Prof. Genevra Richardson; Lord Krebs; Prof. Sir David Watson; Dr Peter Doyle; Prof. David Rhind; Mr Andrew Dilnot; Prof. Terrie Moffitt.
OTHER INFORMATION Many of the funding programmes have individual funding criteria and guidelines which are not listed here. Please consult the trust's excellent website before applying.
HOW TO APPLY The application process for all research and innovation grants is the same, regardless of whether you are applying for Law in Society, Children and Families, Education or Open Door. All applicants must first submit an outline application of *no more than* three pages. If your application is successful at this stage you will be invited to submit a full application of *no more* than 10 pages. The outline application should include: a general background needed to understand the application; issues to be addressed and research questions if relevant; what you will do to achieve your aims, including

an outline of the methodology if it is a research project, or of the activities you will undertake. This should be the largest section of the outline; the expected outcomes of the project, including identification of the relevant audiences and an explanation of how you will engage with them; an outline of the budget and the timetable. The budget should include a rough allocation between staffing, research assistance and direct costs; a short selected CV of the primary applicants. This should be no more than two pages in total, but it does not count towards the three page limit for the Outline; all outline and full applications need attach a front page summary sheet which can be downloaded from the foundation's website. The foundation welcomes cross-disciplinary collaborations or applications that straddle its own areas of interest. If your application meets the criteria of more than one programme, then submit the Outline to the most suitable category and note if you think there is an overlap. You do not need to submit it to more than one programme. The foundation currently operates several different grant programmes. Each programme publishes a comprehensive guide on its aims, policies and process for application, together with expectations for evaluation. All applications are reviewed by independent referees. Extensive guidance on the preparation of full applications is available from the foundation and is published in the foundation's funding guideline document available on the trust's excellent website where you will also find application timetables for project grants. The Oliver Bird Rheumatism PhD studentships are managed by the foundation's partner universities. Please contact the relevant university departments directly and not the foundation. Applicants considering the Africa programme should contact the programme head, Sarah Lock, first to obtain a preliminary view on your outline proposals eligibility. Applications requesting sums of £200,000 or more may take up to six months for a decision.

WHO TO APPLY TO Clerk to the Trustees, 28 Bedford Square, London WC1B 3JS *Tel* 020 7631 0566 *Fax* 020 7232 4877 *email* info@ nuffieldfoundation.org *Website* www. nuffieldfoundation.org

O

■ The Father O'Mahoney Memorial Trust

cc no 1039288   **established** 1993

WHERE FUNDING CAN BE GIVEN Developing countries.

WHO CAN BENEFIT Organisations benefiting 'impotent people and those disadvantaged by poverty'.

WHAT IS FUNDED The relief of 'impotent and poor' people in all parts of the world except the UK.

WHAT IS NOT FUNDED UK organisations; individual requests.

RANGE OF GRANTS Depends on finances; maximum usually £5,000.

SAMPLE GRANTS International Refugee Trust and Sacred Heart Fathers (£5,000 each); SPIMCA (£4,500); CAFOD – Honduras (£3,000); CAFOD – Haiti and ACAT (£2,000 each).

FINANCES *Year* 2009–10 *Income* £49,419 *Grants* £62,000 *Assets* £97,635

TRUSTEES C Carney-Smith; Ms C A Hearn; D M Maclean; M A Moran; Fr G Murray; A H Sanford; Mrs M Jennings; Mrs B Carney; H Smith.

HOW TO APPLY In writing to the correspondent. The trustees meet every two months to consider applications.

WHO TO APPLY TO Revd Gerry Murray, Our Lady of the Wayside Church, 566 Stratford Road, Shirley, Solihull, West Midlands B90 4AY *Tel* 0121 744 1967 *email* trust@olwayside.fsnet.co.uk

■ The Sir Peter O'Sullevan Charitable Trust

cc no 1078889   **established** 2000

WHERE FUNDING CAN BE GIVEN Worldwide.

WHO CAN BENEFIT Charitable organisations.

WHAT IS FUNDED Animal welfare.

TYPE OF GRANT Recurrent.

SAMPLE GRANTS £32,500 each to: Blue Cross, Brooke Hospital for Animals, Compassion in World Farming, World Horse (formerly International League for the Protection of Horses), the Racing Welfare Charities and the Thoroughbred Rehabilitation Centre.

FINANCES *Year* 2009–10 *Income* £318,337 *Grants* £195,000 *Assets* £74,904

TRUSTEES Christopher Spence; Lord Oaksey; Sir Peter O'Sullevan; Nigel Payne; Geoffrey Hughes; Bob McCreery; Michael Dillon.

HOW TO APPLY In writing to the correspondent.

WHO TO APPLY TO Nigel Payne, Trustee, The Old School, Bolventor, Launceston PL15 7TS *Tel* 01566 880292 *email* nigel@earthsummit. demon.co.uk *Website* www.thevoiceofracing. com

■ The Oak Trust

cc no 231456   **established** 1963

WHERE FUNDING CAN BE GIVEN UK.

WHO CAN BENEFIT Registered charities. Preference to charities that the trust has special interest in, knowledge of or association with, and with a turnover of below £1 million.

WHAT IS FUNDED General charitable purposes.

WHAT IS NOT FUNDED No support to individuals.

TYPE OF GRANT One-off and recurrent.

RANGE OF GRANTS £250–£4,000.

SAMPLE GRANTS The Cirdan Sailing Trust (£3,000); Christian Aid and Prader-Willi Syndrome Association UK (£2,000 each); Children's Overseas Relief Fund and Voice (£1,000 each); Cambridge Society for the Blind and Partially-sighted, Detention Advice Service, Practical Action – Darfor Appeal, The Swiften Charitable Trust and Westcott House (£500 each); Grace of God Church – Malawi and Maranatho Orphanage Ministries – Malawi (£250 each).

FINANCES *Year* 2009–10 *Income* £24,366 *Grants* £27,808

TRUSTEES Revd A C C Courtauld; J Courtauld; Dr Elizabeth Courtauld; Miss C M Hart.

HOW TO APPLY Written applications will no longer be accepted. Applications must be submitted via the online form on the trust's website. Details of the next submission date are included on the application form. Applicants will receive an acknowledgement of their application and notification of the outcome within 10 days of the review meeting by email.

WHO TO APPLY TO The Clerk to the Trustees, Essex House, 42 Crouch Street, Colchester CO3 3HH *Tel* 01206 217300 *email* bruce.ballard@birkettlong.co.uk *Website* www.oaktrust.org.uk

■ The Oakdale Trust

cc no 218827   **established** 1950

WHERE FUNDING CAN BE GIVEN UK, especially Wales and overseas.

WHO CAN BENEFIT Organisations doing social and medical work benefiting at risk groups, carers, disabled people, those disadvantaged by poverty, ex-offenders and those at risk of offending, homeless people, refugees, and victims of crime, famine and war.

WHAT IS FUNDED The trust gives preference to Welsh charities engaged in social work, medical support groups and medical research. Some support is given to UK charities working overseas and to conservation projects at home and abroad. Some arts and community arts activities, infrastructure support and development, community facilities and services, mediation, peace and disarmament will also be considered. The trust also supports Quaker activities.

WHAT IS NOT FUNDED No grants to individuals, holiday schemes, sport activities or expeditions.

TYPE OF GRANT Single outright grants. Buildings, capital, core costs, feasibility studies, one-off, project, research, recurring costs, salaries and start-up costs will be considered. Funding may be given for up to one year.

RANGE OF GRANTS Typical grant around £650.

SAMPLE GRANTS The Brandon Centre (£14,000) and Radnorshire Wildlife Trust (£9,600); Concern Universal (£7,000); F.P.W.P Hibiscus (£6,000); Friends of Swanirvar and Howard League for Penal Reform (£1,500 each); Institute of Orthopedics, MDF The Bipolar Organisation Cymru, Médecins Sans Frontières, Mid Wales Chamber Orchestra Ltd and Quaker Peace and Social Witness (£1,000 each); Pain Relief Foundation and Peace Direct (£500 each); and Pond Conservation Trust and River and Sea Sense (£250 each).

FINANCES *Year* 2009–10 *Income* £165,309 *Grants* £130,800 *Assets* £8,204,768

TRUSTEES Brandon Cadbury; Mrs Flavia Cadbury; Rupert Cadbury; Bruce Cadbury; Mrs Olivia Tatton-Brown; Dr Rebecca Cadbury.

HOW TO APPLY An official application form is available on request. However applicants are free to submit requests in any format so long as applications are clear and concise, covering aims, achievements, plans and needs supported by a budget. Applicants applying for grants in excess of £750 are asked to submit a copy of a recent set of audited annual accounts (which can be returned on request). The trustees meet twice a year in April and October to consider applications and to award grants. No grants are awarded between meetings. The deadline for the April meeting is 1 March and for the October meeting 1 September. The trust is administered by the trustees at no cost, and owing to a lack of secretarial help and in view of the numerous requests received, no applications are acknowledged even when accompanied by a stamped addressed envelope.

WHO TO APPLY TO Rupert Cadbury, Trustee, Tansor House, Tansor, Oundle, Peterborough PE8 5HS *Tel* 01832 226386 *email* oakdale@tanh. demon.co.uk

· ·
■ **The Oakley Charitable Trust**
cc no 233041   **ESTABLISHED** 1963
WHERE FUNDING CAN BE GIVEN UK, but with a strong preference for the Midlands and Channel Isles.
WHO CAN BENEFIT Registered charities.
WHAT IS FUNDED Predominantly welfare; health; education; arts; and conservation.
WHAT IS NOT FUNDED No grants to individuals can be considered. Grants are only made to registered charities.
TYPE OF GRANT One-off, core costs, project, research, recurring costs and buildings. Funding is available for one year or less.
RANGE OF GRANTS £50–£3,000.
SAMPLE GRANTS Norfolk Church Trust (£2,250); Jersey Hospice Care, Dyslexia Action the Royal British Legion and (£2,000 each); Alzheimer's Society (£1,100); Edgbaston Old Church, Midlands Arts Centre Appeal and Seafarers UK (£1,000 each); Starlight, Whizz-Kids and The Pen Room Museum (£500 each); Birmingham Music Festival (£250); The Emily Jordan Foundation, Extra Care Charitable Trust and Sense (£200); Link Community Development (£50).
FINANCES *Year* 2009–10 *Income* £49,441 *Grants* £58,710 *Assets* £193,020
TRUSTEES Mrs C M Airey; G M W Oakley; S M Sharp.
HOW TO APPLY In writing to the correspondent. Trustees usually meet in March, July and November.
WHO TO APPLY TO G M W Oakley, Trustee, 10 St Mary's Road, Harborne, Birmingham B17 0HA *Tel* 0121 427 7150

· ·
■ **The Oakmoor Charitable Trust**
cc no 258516   **ESTABLISHED** 1969
WHERE FUNDING CAN BE GIVEN UK.
WHO CAN BENEFIT Registered charities.
WHAT IS FUNDED General charitable purposes.
WHAT IS NOT FUNDED No grants to individuals.
RANGE OF GRANTS Up to £10,000.
SAMPLE GRANTS The London Library and Mary Rose Trust (£10,000 each); Save Britain's Heritage (£7,500); CAFOD (£5,000); Institute of Economic Affairs (£3,000); Downe House Trust (£2,000); Armed Forces Memorial, Elias Ashmole Group and Hampshire Country Learning (£1,000 each); Bembridge Harbour Trust and Convent of St Lucy – Chichester (£500 each);

Cancer Research (£250); and Friends of the Royal Opera House Foundation (£100).
FINANCES *Year* 2009–10 *Income* £21,593 *Grants* £52,291
TRUSTEES Rathbone Trust Company Ltd; P M H Andreae; Mrs R J Andreae.
HOW TO APPLY The trust states that it does not respond to unsolicited applications.
WHO TO APPLY TO The Administrator, Rathbone Trust Company Limited, 159 New Bond Street, London W1S 2UD *Tel* 020 7399 0807

· ·
■ **The Odin Charitable Trust**
cc no 1027521   **ESTABLISHED** 1993
WHERE FUNDING CAN BE GIVEN UK.
WHO CAN BENEFIT Registered charities.
WHAT IS FUNDED General charitable purposes with preference for: the arts; care for people who are disabled and disadvantaged people; hospices, homeless people, prisoners' families, refugees, gypsies and 'tribal groups' research into false memories and dyslexia.
WHAT IS NOT FUNDED Applications from individuals are not considered.
RANGE OF GRANTS £1,000–£3,000.
SAMPLE GRANTS British False Memory Society (£44,000); Helen Arkell Dyslexia Centre and The Dorothy House Foundation (£5,000 each); Julian House PACT and Survival International (£3,000 each); Jessie's Fund, Dressability and St. Pancras Thanet Street Trust (£2,000 each); and Kennet Furniture Recycling (£1,500).
FINANCES *Year* 2009–10 *Income* £354,113 *Grants* £230,059 *Assets* £4,840,320
TRUSTEES Mrs S G P Scotford; Mrs A H Palmer; Donna Kelly; Mrs P C Cherry.
HOW TO APPLY All appeals should be by letter containing the following: aims and objectives of the charity; nature of appeal; total target if for a specific project; contributions received against target; registered charity number; any other relevant factors. Letters should be accompanied by a set of the charitable organisation's latest report and full accounts and should be addressed to the correspondent.
WHO TO APPLY TO Mrs S G P Scotford, Trustee, PO Box 1898, Bradford-on-Avon, Wiltshire BA15 1YS *email* kelly.donna@virgin.net

· ·
■ **The Ofenheim Charitable Trust**
cc no 286525   **ESTABLISHED** 1983
WHERE FUNDING CAN BE GIVEN Worldwide, in practice UK with some preference for East Sussex.
WHO CAN BENEFIT Registered charities.
WHAT IS FUNDED General charitable purposes, in particular health, welfare, arts and the environment.
WHAT IS NOT FUNDED No grants to individuals.
TYPE OF GRANT Mainly recurring grants, but one-off donations are also made.
RANGE OF GRANTS Up to £20,000; mainly £5,000 or less.
SAMPLE GRANTS Trinity College of Music (£13,000); Save the Children Fund (£12,000); National Art Collections Fund, Marie Curie Cancer Care and St Mungo's (£9,000 each); British False Memory Society, Greater London Fund for the Blind, Glyndebourne Arts Trust and Canine Partners for Independence (£5,000 each); Universal Beneficent Association, Hospice Care Kenya, Alzheimer's Research Trust and Game Conservancy Trust (£3,000 each); and Home Start UK, Benslow Music Trust Instrument Loan

Scheme and Battersea Summer Scheme (£2,000 each).

FINANCES *Year* 2009–10 *Income* £343,437 *Grants* £318,470 *Assets* £11,402,974

TRUSTEES Roger Jackson Clark; Rory McLeod; Alexander Clark; Fiona Byrd.

HOW TO APPLY In writing to the correspondent. 'The trustees' policy has been to provide regular support for a number of charities and to respond to one-off appeals to bodies where they have some knowledge [. . .] They will consider all applications for grants and make awards as they see fit.'

WHO TO APPLY TO Geoffrey Wright, Baker Tilly, The Pinnacle, 170 Midsummer Boulevard, Milton Keynes MK9 1BP *Tel* 01908 687800 *email* geoff.wright@bakertilly.co.uk

■ Ogilvie Charities Deed No.2 (including the Charity of Mary Catherine Ford Smith)

CC NO 211778   **ESTABLISHED** 1890

WHERE FUNDING CAN BE GIVEN England and Wales, mainly, Suffolk, Essex and all London boroughs.

WHO CAN BENEFIT Organisations and individuals.

WHAT IS FUNDED Specific philanthropic work. Assistance to present or former governesses or female teachers in straitened circumstances. Country holidays for London children. Support of the charity's own homes and almshouses and residents living in them. Aid to other charitable institutions in the London boroughs, Essex and Suffolk or, if situated beyond, serving the needs of people living in those areas. Support may also be given to infrastructure and technical support and religious ancillary buildings.

WHAT IS NOT FUNDED No payment of debts.

TYPE OF GRANT One-off usually. Grants for individuals must be made through medical and other social workers. Funding may be given for up to one year.

SAMPLE GRANTS Previous beneficiaries included: Children's Country Holidays (£1,000); Governesses (£200); and Bedford Institute Association (£100).

FINANCES *Year* 2010 *Income* £53,823 *Grants* £30,000

TRUSTEES Felicity Lowe, Chair; Jean Goyder; Jolyon Hall; Margaret Smith; Dick Aynsley-Smith; Roger Brayshaw; Patrick Grieve; D Allan Howell; Simon Gibbs; Edward Wright; Belinda Grant.

OTHER INFORMATION Ogilvie Charities Deed No. 2 is primarily to benefit the Ogilvie Charities Deed No. 1. Any remaining income is applied to making grants to any charity for the benefit of people in Essex, Suffolk or London which are for specific fund raising projects. Charity of Mary Catherine Ford – Grants are given from this fund to other charities to help them with a specific project. The grant total was shared between individuals and organisations.

HOW TO APPLY In writing to the correspondent. Preliminary telephone enquiries are acceptable. Applicant organisations must send details of their project and copies of annual accounts. Grants are awarded for specific fund raising projects, not running costs and are allocated in October or November. Grants for individuals must be made through medical and other social workers.

WHO TO APPLY TO Mrs Gillian Galvan, General Manager, The Gate House, 9 Burkitt Road,

Woodbridge, Suffolk IP12 4JJ *Tel* 01394 388746 *Fax* 01394 388746 *email* ogilviecharities@btconnect.com *Website* www.theogilvietrust.org.uk

■ The Ogle Christian Trust

CC NO 1061458   **ESTABLISHED** 1938

WHERE FUNDING CAN BE GIVEN Worldwide.

WHO CAN BENEFIT Registered charities benefiting Bible students, pastors, Christians, evangelists and victims of famine.

WHAT IS FUNDED The trust's main concern is the promotion of Biblical Christianity. Currently it includes: new initiatives in evangelism; support for the publishing and distribution of scriptures and Christian literature; training of Bible students and pastors; and Christian social enterprise and famine relief.

WHAT IS NOT FUNDED Applications from individuals are discouraged; those granted require accreditation by a sponsoring organisation. Grants are rarely made for building projects. Funding will not be offered in response to general appeals from large national organisations.

TYPE OF GRANT Normally one-off or short-term commitments only. Salaries will not be funded.

RANGE OF GRANTS Up to £22,000.

SAMPLE GRANTS Operation Mobilisation (£21,000); Langham Partnership, Romans One Eleven Trust (£7,000 each); ELAM Ministries, OMF International, The Source (£5,000 each); ANCC, CCSM, Redcliffe College (£4,000 each); Lok Hospital, Oasis International, Starfish Asia (£3,000 each); France Mission Trust, Pakistan Fellowship of Evangelical Students (£2,000 each); Caring for Life, Enlighten, Keswick Ministries and Saltworkz (£1,000 each).

FINANCES *Year* 2009 *Income* £117,820 *Grants* £127,650 *Assets* £2,344,909

TRUSTEES Mrs F J Putley; R J Goodenough; S Proctor; Mrs L M Quanrud; Dr D Harley.

HOW TO APPLY In writing to the correspondent, accompanied by documentary support and an sae. Trustees meet in May and November, but applications can be made at any time.

WHO TO APPLY TO Mrs F J Putley, Trustee, 43 Woolstone Road, Forest Hill, London SE23 2TR *Tel* 020 8699 1036

■ Oglesby Charitable Trust

CC NO 1026669   **ESTABLISHED** 1992

WHERE FUNDING CAN BE GIVEN The North West of England.

WHO CAN BENEFIT Charitable organisations.

WHAT IS FUNDED Educational grants and building projects; environmental improvement projects; improving the life and welfare of the underprivileged, where possible, by the encouragement of self-help; and medical aid and research.

WHAT IS NOT FUNDED The trust will not support: non registered charities; those whose activities are for the purpose of collecting funds for redistribution to other charities; animal charities; charities whose principal operation area is outside the UK; church and all building fabric appeals; conferences; continuing running costs of an organisation; costs of employing fundraisers; expeditions; general sports, unless strongly associated with a disadvantaged group; holidays; individuals; loans or business finance; religion; routine staff training; sectarian religions; sponsorship and marketing appeals.

RANGE OF GRANTS Usually between £5,000–£20,000. Small grants of less than £1,000 are available.

SAMPLE GRANTS Previous beneficiaries include: Action for Kids, Alcohol Drug Abstinence Service, Centre for Alternative Technology, Cheadle Hulme School, Cheetham's School, Fairbridge – Family Contact Line, Halle Youth Orchestra, Manchester City Art Gallery, Manchester University Arts and Drama, Motor Neurone Disease, National Asthma Campaign, National Library For The Blind, Stroke Research and Whitworth Art Gallery.

FINANCES Year 2009–10 Income £835,238 Grants £764,774 Assets £846,809

TRUSTEES Jean Oglesby; Michael Oglesby; Robert Kitson; Kate Vokes; Jane Oglesby; Chris Oglesby; Peter Renshaw.

OTHER INFORMATION The trust also has a small grants programme, the Acorn Fund, which is administered by the Community Foundation for Greater Manchester, Beswick House, Beswick Row, Manchester M4 4LA; Tel: 0161 214 0940; website: www.communityfoundation.co.uk

HOW TO APPLY To enable the trustees to assess all applications from a similar basis, they ask that every applicant complete the Stage 1 Application Form. The trustees undertake to respond to this in 6 weeks. If this response is positive, then applicants will be required to complete a more detailed form under Stage 2. By Stage 2, wherever possible, the trustees will require a proper Financial Plan prepared by the applicant. This should contain clear and measurable goals, which will be reviewed at regular intervals by the parties. In cases where the applicant does not possess either the skills or the resources to prepare such a Plan, the Trust may be prepared to assist.

Finally, the trustees will want to interview the applicant(s) at their place of operation or project site, both prior to the granting of funds and during the lifetime of the project, to monitor its progress. In addition the trustees will expect regular communication from the applicant, either verbal or by letter, to keep them informed of how the project is moving forward.

WHO TO APPLY TO PO Box 336, Altrincham, Cheshire WA14 3XD email oglesbycharitabletrust@bruntwood.co.uk Website www.oglesbycharitabletrust.co.uk

....

■ **The Oikonomia Trust**

CC NO 273481   **ESTABLISHED** 1977

WHERE FUNDING CAN BE GIVEN UK and overseas.

WHO CAN BENEFIT Organisations benefiting evangelists.

WHAT IS FUNDED Evangelical work, famine and other relief through Christian agencies, particularly when accompanied with the offer of the Gospel. The trust is not looking for new outlets as those it has knowledge of are sufficient to absorb its available funds.

WHAT IS NOT FUNDED No grants made in response to general appeals from large national organisations.

RANGE OF GRANTS £500–£5,000.

SAMPLE GRANTS Barnabus Trust (£5,500); Slavic Gospel Association (£5,000); Bethel Church (£4,000); Asia Link, Association of Evangelists and Caring for Life (£3,000 each); Japan Mission (£2,500); Starbeck Mission (£2,000); People International (£1,000); and Carey Outreach Ministries (£500).

FINANCES Year 2009–10 Income £3,817 Grants £66,000

TRUSTEES D H Metcalfe; R H Metcalfe; S D Metcalfe; C Mountain; Revd R O Owens.

HOW TO APPLY In writing to the correspondent, although the trust has stated that most grants are made to the same organisations each year and as such new applications are unlikely to be successful. If an applicant desires an answer, an sae should be enclosed. Applications should arrive in January.

WHO TO APPLY TO Colin Mountain, Trustee, 98 White Lee Road, Batley, West Yorkshire WF17 8AF Tel 01924 502616 email c.mountain@ntlworld.com

....

■ **Oizer Charitable Trust**

CC NO 1014399   **ESTABLISHED** 1992

WHERE FUNDING CAN BE GIVEN UK with a preference for Greater Manchester.

WHO CAN BENEFIT Registered charities.

WHAT IS FUNDED Education and welfare.

SAMPLE GRANTS Manchester Talmudical College (£5,250); and Chasdei Yoel (£1,000).

FINANCES Year 2009–10 Income £502,621 Grants £411,502 Assets £1,426,376

TRUSTEES J Halpern; Mrs C Halpern.

HOW TO APPLY In writing to the correspondent.

WHO TO APPLY TO Joshua Halpern, Trustee, 46 Bury New Road, Prestwich, Manchester M25 0JU

....

■ **The Old Broad Street Charity Trust**

CC NO 231382   **ESTABLISHED** 1964

WHERE FUNDING CAN BE GIVEN UK and overseas.

WHO CAN BENEFIT Registered charities benefiting children, young adults, students, people working in a bank or financial institution, actors and entertainment professionals, musicians, textile workers and designers, and writers and poets.

WHAT IS FUNDED General charitable purposes with an emphasis on arts and education. Funding scholarships for people serving in a bank or financial institution in the UK to spend time in any seat of learning (principally INSEAD) to attain the highest level of executive management.

WHAT IS NOT FUNDED The trustees only support organisations of which they personally have some knowledge.

TYPE OF GRANT One-off and project grants for one year or less.

SAMPLE GRANTS Foundation Henri Cartier-Bresson (£58,000); Société Française le Lutte contre la Cécité et contre le Trachome (£13,000), Bezirksfursorge – Saanen (£12,000), The Mulberry Bush Organisation and Changing Faces (£10,000 each); Royal Marsden NHS Foundation (£7,500); International Menuhin Music Academy (£6,000), Royal Academy of Arts and St Mungo's (£2,500 each), The National Gallery Trust (£2,000), Whitechapel Gallery (£1,000) and Artangel (£750); and Tate Gallery Foundation (£600).

FINANCES Income £70,690 Grants £125,886 Assets £1,709,975

TRUSTEES Mrs Martine Cartier-Bresson; Adrian T J Stanford; Peter A Hetherington; Christopher J Sheridan; Clare Gough.

OTHER INFORMATION It was the wish of Louis Franck, the founder, that part of the income should be used to fund scholarships, preferably for UK citizens to reach the highest levels of executive management in banking and financial institutions. The trust makes provision for this each year by setting aside an annual amount and funding scholarships for people serving in a bank or financial institution in the UK to spend time in any seat of learning (principally INSEAD) to attain the highest level of executive management. £35,000 was given for this purpose in the financial year 2009–10.

HOW TO APPLY In writing to the correspondent. Unsolicited applications are not considered.

WHO TO APPLY TO Simon Jennings, Secretary to the Trustees, Rawlinson and Hunter, Eighth Floor, 6 New Street Square, London EC4A 3AQ *Tel* 020 7842 2000

■ The Old Enfield Charitable Trust

CC NO 207840   **ESTABLISHED** 1962

WHERE FUNDING CAN BE GIVEN The ancient parish of Enfield (old borough of Enfield).

WHO CAN BENEFIT Charities and individuals in need.

WHAT IS FUNDED Community projects and relief-in-need and educational grants to individuals.

SAMPLE GRANTS In 2009–10 £113,000 was donated to 127 individuals in relief-in-need and educational grants. Two grants were awarded to organisations: the Enfield Visually Impaired Bowls Club and Enfield Vision.

FINANCES *Year* 2009–10 *Income* £519,969 *Grants* £133,627 *Assets* £5,977,112

TRUSTEES Gordon Smith; Colin Griffiths; Audrey Thacker; Clive Parker; Horace Brown; Jim Eustance; Michael Braithwaite; Nicholas Taylor; Dr Patrick O'Mahony; Phyllis Oborn; Richard Cross; Susan Attwood; Chris Bond; Sam Bell; Bob Sander.

OTHER INFORMATION The 2009–10 financial accounts stated that: 'During the year due to the reduction in the grants budget a decision was taken at the beginning of the year to put Community Grants on hold until there was an economic turnaround'.

HOW TO APPLY In writing to the correspondent. Application forms and guidelines are available. Initial telephone calls are welcome. There is no deadline for applications.

WHO TO APPLY TO The Trust Administrator, The Old Vestry Office, 22 The Town, Enfield, Middlesex EN2 6LT *Tel* 020 8367 8941 *Fax* 020 8366 7708 *email* enquiries@toect.org.uk *Website* www.toect.org.uk

■ Old Possum's Practical Trust

CC NO 328558   **ESTABLISHED** 1990

WHERE FUNDING CAN BE GIVEN UK.

WHO CAN BENEFIT Registered charities and individuals of all ages.

WHAT IS FUNDED The increase of knowledge and appreciation of any matters of historic, artistic, architectural, aesthetic, literary, musical, theatrical or scientific interest; human and animal welfare.

WHAT IS NOT FUNDED The trust does not support the following: activities or projects already completed; capital building projects; personal training and education e.g. tuition or living costs for college or university; projects outside the UK; medical care or resources; feasibility studies; national charities having substantial amounts of potential funding likely from other sources.

RANGE OF GRANTS Mainly £500–£5,000.

SAMPLE GRANTS High Tide (£80,000); First Story (£20,000); Poetry Book Society (£14,000); Arete, Victoria and Albert Museum and Book Trade Benevolent Society (£10,000 each); Dogs

for the Disabled and the Times Stephen Spender Prize (£5,000 each); TS Elliot Festival (£4,000); Sue Coles School of Dance (£3,500); Garsington Opera, Animal Care Trust and London Children's Ballet (£3,000 each); Oxford CS Lewis Society (£2,000); and MK Snap (£1,000).

FINANCES *Year* 2009–10 *Income* £173,063 *Grants* £216,950 *Assets* £7,107,192

TRUSTEES Esme Eliot; Judith Hooper; Deidre Simpson; Clare Reihill.

OTHER INFORMATION One grant of £7,500 was given to an individual.

HOW TO APPLY Applications can only be made online through the trust's website. The trustees meet regularly to consider applications but state in the latest accounts that: 'the emphasis will be on continued support of those institutions and individuals who have received support in the past. Unfortunately we have to disappoint the great majority of applicants who nevertheless continue to send appeal letters.' To keep administration costs to a minimum the trust does not give reasons for unsuccessful applications or allow applicants to appeal a decision.

WHO TO APPLY TO The Trustees, PO Box 5701, Milton Keynes MK9 2WZ *email* generalenquiry@old-possums-practical-trust.org.uk *Website* www.old-possums-practical-trust.org.uk

■ The John Oldacre Foundation

CC NO 284960   **ESTABLISHED** 1981

WHERE FUNDING CAN BE GIVEN UK.

WHO CAN BENEFIT Universities, agricultural colleges and innovative projects benefiting students and research workers.

WHAT IS FUNDED Research and education in agricultural sciences.

WHAT IS NOT FUNDED No grants towards tuition fees.

TYPE OF GRANT One-off, recurrent, feasibility, project, research and funding of up to three years will be considered.

RANGE OF GRANTS Up to £55,000.

SAMPLE GRANTS University of Bristol (£51,000); Royal Agricultural College (£20,000), University of Wolverhampton (£17,000); Harper Adams University College (£15,000); Game & Wildlife Conservation Trust (£12,000).

FINANCES *Year* 2009–10 *Income* £111,399 *Grants* £182,500 *Assets* £7,708,165

TRUSTEES H B Shouler; S J Charnock; Ian Bonnett.

HOW TO APPLY In writing to the correspondent.

WHO TO APPLY TO Stephen J Charnock, Trustee, Bohicket, 35 Broadwater Close, Burwood Park, Walton on Thames, Surrey KT12 5DD

■ The Oldham Foundation

CC NO 269263   **ESTABLISHED** 1974

WHERE FUNDING CAN BE GIVEN The north west and south west of England.

WHO CAN BENEFIT Organisations benefiting children, young adults, ex-service and service people, Church of England and former employees of Oldham Batteries (employed before 1971). Funding is considered for people disadvantaged by poverty, victims of man-made or natural disasters, and people with cancer, HIV and AIDS and mental illness.

WHAT IS FUNDED Donations to former employees of Oldham Batteries (employed before 1971) and charitable activities where trustees give personal service or where they know people who do so. Charities working in the fields of arts,

786

Does the trust you have chosen match your needs? Haphazard applications waste postage and time

culture and recreation; conservation and environment; and churches will be considered. Support may also be given to hospices, nursing services, cancer research, libraries and museums, day centres, holidays and outings.

WHAT IS NOT FUNDED No grants for UK appeals or individuals.

TYPE OF GRANT Annual grant to former employees. Grants usually one-off. Does not provide core funding. General charitable grants with bias towards active participation by trustees.

RANGE OF GRANTS £50–£20,000; typical grant £250–£1,000.

SAMPLE GRANTS Cheltenham Music Festival (£11,000); Cheltenham Literature Festival (£10,400); Classic FM (£4,000); CABE (£3,000 each); St Peter's Church – Winchcombe (£2,000); Cheltenham Bach Choir, Merlin, the Kambia Appeal and International Red Cross (£1,000 each); Churches Conservation Trust (£500); Sense and Barnardo's (£250 each); Green Island Holiday Trust (£100); and Grandmothers United (£50).

FINANCES *Year* 2009–10 *Income* £62,825 *Grants* £67,755 *Assets* £1,201,818

TRUSTEES John Wetherherd Sharpe.

HOW TO APPLY In writing to the correspondent. Applications should include clear details of projects, budgets and/or accounts where appropriate. Telephone calls are not welcomed. The trustees meet annually but applications can be considered between meetings. Inappropriate appeals are not acknowledged.

WHO TO APPLY TO John Wetherherd Sharpe, Trustee, c/o Osborne Clarke Solicitors, 2 Temple Back East, Temple Quay, Bristol BS1 6EG *Tel* 0117 917 3022 *Fax* 0117 917 3033

■ The Olga Charitable Trust

CC NO 277925   **ESTABLISHED** 1979

WHERE FUNDING CAN BE GIVEN UK and overseas.

WHO CAN BENEFIT National organisations benefiting children, young adults, at risk groups, people disadvantaged by poverty, socially isolated people, and carers.

WHAT IS FUNDED Health and welfare, youth organisations, children's welfare, carers' organisations. All must be known to the trustees.

RANGE OF GRANTS £500–£12,000.

SAMPLE GRANTS Columba 1400 (£10,000); Holy Trinity Church, Haiti Earthquake Appeal and Kew Botanical Gardens (£5,000 each); CFAB (£3,000); The Exhuma Foundation (£2,000); Comfort Rwanda, New Bridge, PDSA and Queen Alexandra's Hospice Home (£1,000 each); and Perth YMCA (£500).

FINANCES *Year* 2009–10 *Income* £49,473 *Grants* £76,040 *Assets* £936,378

TRUSTEES HRH Princess Alexandra; James Robert Bruce Ogilvy.

HOW TO APPLY In writing to the correspondent, although the trust states that its funds are fully committed and applications made cannot be acknowledged.

WHO TO APPLY TO Adam Broke, Accountant, The Old Stables, Gracious Street, Selborne, Alton GU34 3JD *Tel* 020 7353 1597

■ The Onaway Trust

CC NO 268448   **ESTABLISHED** 1974

WHERE FUNDING CAN BE GIVEN UK, USA and worldwide.

WHO CAN BENEFIT Registered charities benefiting indigenous peoples, in the main, Native Americans, and animal welfare.

WHAT IS FUNDED Trustees like to provide seed funds for self-generating, self-sufficiency projects based upon indigenous traditional beliefs and practices. The trustees concentrate mainly on Native Americans. The Onaway Trust's wide remit is to relieve poverty and suffering. This is expressed in many areas: the environment, child and animal welfare, world refugees and human rights.

WHAT IS NOT FUNDED No grants for administration costs, travel expenses or projects considered unethical or detrimental to the struggle of indigenous people.

TYPE OF GRANT Small, start-up costs.

RANGE OF GRANTS £600–£9,000.

SAMPLE GRANTS Three grants were made to Plenty USA (£12,000); Institute for Development exchange (India) (£6,600); Centre of Sacred Studies, D.E.C Asia Quake Appeal(£5,000 each); Academy for Development of Science (India), Literates Welfare Association (India) (£4,000 each); Adaho Youth Environmental (Africa) (£2,500); and Tanzania Marginalised Are (£1,000).

FINANCES *Year* 2010 *Income* £133,316 *Grants* £47,348 *Assets* £4,366,064

TRUSTEES A Breslin; C Howles; Ms Annie Smith; Ms V A Worwood; D Watters.

HOW TO APPLY In writing to the correspondent, enclosing an sae.

WHO TO APPLY TO David Watters, Trust Administrator, Donavourd Farmhouse, Donavourd, Pitlochry PH16 5JS *Tel* 01796 470047 *email* david@onaway.org *Website* www.onaway.org

---

■ Open Gate

CC NO 1081701   **ESTABLISHED** 2000

WHERE FUNDING CAN BE GIVEN Derbyshire and surrounding areas; also developing countries.

WHO CAN BENEFIT Charitable organisations.

WHAT IS FUNDED Small-scale environmental, technological and educational projects in Derbyshire and the surrounding conurbations as well as in developing countries.

WHAT IS NOT FUNDED No grants to individuals.

TYPE OF GRANT Project grants for up to three years.

RANGE OF GRANTS £500–£5,000.

SAMPLE GRANTS CAFOD (£5,400); Highfield Happy Hens and Tools for Self Reliance (£5,000 each); Christian Aid, Harvest Help, Concern Worldwide and Tools for Self Reliance (£5,000 each); Practical Action and (£4,000); Fauna & Flora International and Book Aid International (£3,000 each); Hand in hand (£2,500); Africa Now (£2,000); Jeevika Trust (£1,500); Children in Crisis and African Initiatives (£1,000); The Children's Adventure Farm Trust (£600); and Ryder Cheshire Volunteers (£500).

FINANCES *Year* 2009–10 *Income* £118,946 *Grants* £198,055 *Assets* £1,467,550

TRUSTEES Tom Wiltshire, chair; Mary Wiltshire; John Wiltshire; Jane Methuen; Ned Wiltshire; Alice Wiltshire; Mrs Lesley Williamson.

HOW TO APPLY In writing to the correspondent. Quarterly meetings are held in the middle of January, April, July and October.

WHO TO APPLY TO Mary Wiltshire, Trustee, Brownhouse Cottage, Ashleyhay, Wirksworth,

Matlock, Derbyshire DE4 4AH *Tel* 01629
822018 *Website* www.opengatetrust.org.uk

■ The Ormsby Charitable Trust
cc no 1000599   **established** 1990
where funding can be given UK, London and the
South East.
who can benefit Registered charities.
what is funded Mainly organisations concerned
with people who are sick, older people and
young people.
what is not funded No grants to individuals,
animals or religious causes.
sample grants In Kind (£5,000); Newbury
Community Resource Centre (£4,500); Home
Farm Trust and Breast Cancer Haven Trust
(£3,800 each); Cornwall Air Ambulance
(£3,000); NSPCC (£2,000) and Ramsdell Village
Hall (£500).
finances *Year* 2009–10 *Income* £41,558
Grants £61,500 *Assets* £1,562,666
trustees Rosemary Ormsby David; Angela Ormsby
Chiswell; Katrina Ormsby McCrossan.
how to apply In writing to the correspondent.
who to apply to Mrs K McCrossan, Trustee, The
Red House, The Street, Aldermaston, Reading
RG7 4LN *Tel* 0118 971 0343

■ Orrin Charitable Trust
cc no 274599   **established** 1977
where funding can be given UK with a strong
preference for Scotland.
who can benefit Registered charities.
what is funded General charitable purposes
including conservation, disability and galleries.
what is not funded Grants are not given to
individuals.
range of grants Up to £10,000.
sample grants Help for Heroes (£10,000); National
Army Museum (£5,000); Art Academy, Atlantic
Salmon Conservation Trust and Wheeley Boat
Trust (£3,000 each); National Gallery of
Scotland (£2,000); and St Mary & All Souls
(£500).
finances *Year* 2009–10 *Income* £42,349
Grants £47,750 *Assets* £590,774
trustees Mrs E Y MacDonald-Buchanan;
H J MacDonald-Buchanan; A J MacDonald-
Buchanan.
how to apply The trust will not accept any
unsolicited appeals.
who to apply to Mary Kitto, c/o Hedley Foundation,
Victoria House, 1–3 College Hill, London
EC4R 2RA *Tel* 020 7489 8076

■ The O'Sullivan Family Charitable Trust
cc no 1123757   **established** 2008
where funding can be given Unrestricted, UK in
practice.
who can benefit Children and young people, care
homes, genetic research.
what is funded Organisations supporting the
advancement of health or relief for those in
need because of ill health, disability, financial
hardship or other disadvantage.
type of grant Grants to individuals and
organisations.
sample grants Previous grant beneficiaries include:
The Honeypot Charity (£10,000); and Canine
Partners (£5,000).

finances *Year* 2009–10 *Income* £71,352
Grants £185,236 *Assets* £3,818,447
trustees D. O'Sullivan; F. O'Sullivan; E. O'Sullivan;
S. O'Sullivan and T. O'Sullivan.
how to apply In writing to the correspondent.
who to apply to Diana O'Sullivan, Trustee, 36 Edge
Street, London W8 7PN

■ The Ouseley Trust
cc no 527519   **established** 1989
where funding can be given England, Wales and
Ireland.
who can benefit Cathedrals, choirs, parish
churches, and choir schools. Children who are
members of choirs of recognised choral
foundations. Funding is only given to individuals
through institutions.
what is funded Projects that promote and maintain
to a high standard the choral services of the
Church of England, the Church in Wales or the
Church of Ireland. These may include
contributions to endowment funds, courses,
fees, repairs of organs, and the purchase of
music.
what is not funded Grants will not be awarded to
help with the cost of fees for ex-choristers, for
chant books, hymnals or Psalters. Grants will
not be made for the purchase of new
instruments or for the installation of an
instrument from another place of worship where
this involves extensive reconstruction. Under
normal circumstances, grants will not be
awarded for buildings, cassettes, commissions,
compact discs, furniture, pianos, robes, tours or
visits. No grants are made towards new organs
or the installation of one which involves
extensive reconstruction.
range of grants Up to £50,000.
sample grants Previously: Hereford Cathedral
(£25,000); Carlisle Cathedral (£15,000); Abbey
School – Tewkesbury (£18,000 in two separate
grants); York Minster (£6,000 in two grants); St
Thomas the Apostle – Wigston (£5,000); St
James's School – Grimsby and Well Cathedral
School (£4,000 each); Bradford Cathedral
Salisbury Cathedral School and Oundle
International Organ Festival (£3,000 each); and
Christ Church Cathedral School, St Mary the
Virgin, Thomas Attwood Project and Wells
Cathedral School (£2,000 each).
finances *Year* 2010 *Income* £146,355
Grants £129,754 *Assets* £3,782,442
trustees Dr Christopher Robinson, Chair; Dr
J A Birch; Revd Canon Mark Boyling; Dr
S M Darlington; Mrs Gillian Perkins; Martin
Pickering; Adam Ridley; Dr John Rutter; Revd
A F Walters; Richard White; Timothy Byram-
Wigfield.
how to apply Applicants are strongly advised to
obtain a copy of the trust's guidelines (either
from the correspondent or their website,
currently under construction at the time of
writing) before drafting an application.
Applications must be submitted by an institution
on a form available from the correspondent.
Closing dates for applications are 31 January
for the March meeting and 30 June for the
October meeting.
who to apply to Martin Williams, Clerk, PO Box
281, Stamford, Lincolnshire PE9 9BU
Tel 01780 752266 *email* ouseleytrust@
btinternet.com *Website* www.ouseleytrust.org.uk

■ The Owen Family Trust

CC NO 251975   **ESTABLISHED** 1967

WHERE FUNDING CAN BE GIVEN UK, with a preference for West Midlands.

WHO CAN BENEFIT Schools (independent and church), Christian youth centres, churches, community associations, national organisations benefiting people of all ages, and people with Alzheimer's disease, cancer and strokes.

WHAT IS FUNDED Mainly support for projects known personally by the trustees. Christian outreach projects are supported, with consideration also given to the arts, conservation, cancer research, Christian education, church and related community buildings.

WHAT IS NOT FUNDED The trust states 'No grants to individuals unless part of a charitable organisation'.

TYPE OF GRANT Buildings, capital, and recurring costs will be considered. Funding may be given for more than three years.

RANGE OF GRANTS £100–£15,000.

SAMPLE GRANTS Oundle School Foundation (£15,000); Black Country Museum Development Trust, Lichfield Cathedral, The Feast and Frontier Youth Trust (£5,000 each); Acorns Children's Hospice and Lozells Project Trust (£3,000 each); The Friends of Whitchurch Heritage (£2,000); Cancer Support Centre, Sutton Coldfield, Lichfield Festival, St Chad's, Bagnall and The Extra Care Charitable Trust (£1,000 each); and Gloucester Cathedral (£255).

FINANCES *Year* 2009–10 *Income* £37,318 *Grants* £73,337 *Assets* £1,089,821

TRUSTEES Mrs H G Jenkins; A D Owen.

HOW TO APPLY In writing to the correspondent including annual report, budget for project and general information regarding the application. Organisations need to be a registered charity; however an 'umbrella' body which would hold funds would be acceptable. Only a small number of grants can be given each year and unsuccessful applications are not acknowledged unless an sae is enclosed. The trustees meet quarterly.

WHO TO APPLY TO A D Owen, Trustee, c/o Rubery Owen Holdings Limited, PO Box 10, Wednesbury WS10 8JD *Tel* 0121 526 3131

■ Oxfam (GB)

CC NO 202918   **ESTABLISHED** 1958

WHERE FUNDING CAN BE GIVEN Africa, Asia, Caribbean, Central America, Eastern Europe, countries of the former Soviet Union, Great Britain, Middle East, South America.

WHO CAN BENEFIT Organisations which benefit people of all ages who are disadvantaged by poverty, disabled or victims of famine, disasters or war.

WHAT IS FUNDED Organisations worldwide working for the relief of hunger, disease, exploitation and poverty. Organisations working in public education in the UK and Ireland.

WHAT IS NOT FUNDED Applications for individuals are not considered.

SAMPLE GRANTS LASOONA – Society for Human and Natural Resource Development (£2.2 million); Horn of Africa Voluntary Youth Committee (£1.4 million); Humanitarian Initiative Just Relief Fund (£1.2 million); Wajir South Development Association (£1 million); Save the Children UK (£762,000).

FINANCES *Year* 2010–11 *Income* £281,500,000 *Grants* £72,500,000 *Assets* £97,300,000

TRUSTEES John Gaventa; Vanessa Godfrey; Gareth Davies; Karen Brown; James Darcy; Maja Darawula; Sandra Dawson; Andy Friend; Rajiv Joshi; Matthew Martin; David Pitt-Watson; Majorie Scardino; Nkoyo Toyo; Tricia Zipfel.

HOW TO APPLY Applications should be made to the Regional Management Centre in the region concerned.

WHO TO APPLY TO Joss Saunders, Mr Joss Saunders, Oxfam GB, 2700 John Smith Drive, Oxford Business Park South, Oxford OX4 2JY *Tel* 0870 333 2444 *email* enquiries@oxfam.org.uk *Website* www.oxfam.org.uk

■ City of Oxford Charity

CC NO 239151   **ESTABLISHED** 2004

WHERE FUNDING CAN BE GIVEN The city of Oxford only.

WHO CAN BENEFIT Charitable organisations, schools and individuals.

WHAT IS FUNDED Educational needs, such as help with school uniforms, attending school trips and books and materials.

FINANCES *Year* 2009–10 *Income* £302,902 *Grants* £84,813 *Assets* £4,394,305

TRUSTEES 11 co-opted trustees; 6 nominated by the City Council; 2 nominated by the University of Oxford; 1 representing Oxfordshire Area Health Authority.

OTHER INFORMATION The charity also runs almshouses situated in St Clements – Oxford. The sum of £89,000 was spent on its upkeep in 2008.

HOW TO APPLY Application forms can be downloaded form the charity's website. Trustees meet to consider applications four times a year in March, June, September and December.

WHO TO APPLY TO David Wright, Clerk, 11 Davenant Road, Oxford OX2 8BT *Tel* 01865 247161 *email* enquiries@oxfordcitycharities.fsnet.co.uk *Website* www.oxfordcitycharities.org

■ The Oxfordshire Community Foundation

CC NO 1046432   **ESTABLISHED** 1995

WHERE FUNDING CAN BE GIVEN Oxfordshire.

WHO CAN BENEFIT Community-based non-profit organisations constituted in Oxfordshire. Beneficiaries of all ages, social circumstances, family situations and medical conditions will be considered, although the following are prioritised: parents and children; at risk groups; carers; disabled people; people disadvantaged by poverty; homeless people; immigrants; those living in rural areas; socially isolated people; victims of domestic violence; those with hearing loss, mental illness, and sight loss; and substance misusers.

WHAT IS FUNDED Specific projects up to one year with outputs related to poverty, unemployment, education and health promotion, including charities working in the fields of infrastructure and technical support, infrastructure development, charity or voluntary umbrella bodies, residential facilities and services, self-help groups, campaigning for health issues, health related volunteer schemes, equal opportunities and various community facilities and services.

WHAT IS NOT FUNDED Please refer to the foundation's website for exclusions specific to each fund.

TYPE OF GRANT One-off; capital. One-year start-up for projects, training and equipment.

RANGE OF GRANTS Up to £7,000.

SAMPLE GRANTS Previous grant beneficiaries: Abingdon Bridge, Chabad, Goring on Thames Sailing Club, Steeple Aston Youth Club, Sunflower Toddler Group, and UK Dads and the Potential Project (£7,000 each); Azad Hill FC (£6,900); Parasol Project (£6,800); Oxford Concert Party (£6,600); and Fusion £6,200).

FINANCES *Year* 2009–10 *Income* £514,945 *Grants* £441,153 *Assets* £1,617,190

TRUSTEES Anna Moon, Chair; Lady North DL, Vice chair; Colin Alexander; Mrs Glyn Benson; Ms Jane Mactaggert; Nigel Williams; Ian Lenagan; John Hemingway; Mrs Jane Wates; Prof. Ann Buchanan; Ms Shree Hindocha; Trevor French; Marie-Jane Barnett; David Astor CBE DL.

PUBLICATIONS *The Other Oxfordshire.*

HOW TO APPLY Please refer to the foundation's website for full details of how to apply to the various programmes currently being administered.

WHO TO APPLY TO Grants Manager, Oxfordshire Community Foundation, 3 Woodin's Way, Oxford OX1 1HD *Tel* 01865 798666 *Fax* 01865 245385 *email* grants@oxfordshire.org *Website* www.oxfordshire.org

■ The P F Charitable Trust

CC NO 220124   **ESTABLISHED** 1951
WHERE FUNDING CAN BE GIVEN Unrestricted. In practice UK with local interests in Oxfordshire and Scotland.
WHO CAN BENEFIT Voluntary organisations and charitable groups.
WHAT IS FUNDED General charitable purposes.
WHAT IS NOT FUNDED No grants to individuals or non-registered charities.
TYPE OF GRANT One-off and recurring, buildings, core costs, project, research and running costs. Funding may be given for up to three years.
RANGE OF GRANTS Mainly up to £50,000.
SAMPLE GRANTS St Martin-in-the Fields Development Trust (£300,000), towards redevelopment of the church; Eton Collage Appeal (£100,000), towards the establishment of an endowment fund; Great Ormond Street Hospital Children's Charity (£100,000), towards continued development; Charities Aid Foundation (£93,000), for onward distribution to other charities; and Soldiers of Oxfordshire Trust, British Heart Foundation, Cicely Saunders International, Scottish Community Foundation and Royal Shakespeare Company (£50,000).
FINANCES *Year* 2009–10 *Income* £1,742,757 *Grants* £2,305,550 *Assets* £92,209,277
TRUSTEES Robert Fleming; Philip Fleming; Rory D Fleming.
OTHER INFORMATION Grants of less than £50,000 each totalled almost £1.5 million.
HOW TO APPLY Applications to the correspondent in writing. Trustees usually meet monthly to consider applications and approve grants.
WHO TO APPLY TO The Secretary to the Trustees, Fleming Family & Partners, 15 Suffolk Street, London SW1Y 4HG *Tel* 020 7036 5685

■ The Doris Pacey Charitable Foundation

CC NO 1101724   **ESTABLISHED** 2004
WHERE FUNDING CAN BE GIVEN UK and Israel.
WHO CAN BENEFIT Charitable organisations.
WHAT IS FUNDED Jewish, medical, educational and social.
TYPE OF GRANT One-off and recurrent.
RANGE OF GRANTS £500–£138,000.
SAMPLE GRANTS OR Movement (£50,000); Jewish Chaplaincy and UJIA – Jewish Curriculum (£40,000 each); Magen David Adom (£20,000); Courtauld Institute of Art (£13,000); Norwood (£8,000); Surrey Opera (£4,000); National Deaf Children's Society (£1,000); the Noam Primary School (£250).
FINANCES *Year* 2009–10 *Income* £103,818 *Grants* £174,700 *Assets* £5,831,162
TRUSTEES J D Cohen; R Locke; L Powell.
HOW TO APPLY Unsolicited applications are not considered.
WHO TO APPLY TO J D Cohen, Trustee, 30 Old Burlington Street, London W1S 3NL *Tel* 020 7468 2600

■ Padwa Charitable Foundation

CC NO 1019274   **ESTABLISHED** 1992
WHERE FUNDING CAN BE GIVEN UK.
WHO CAN BENEFIT Organisations and individuals.
WHAT IS FUNDED The trust has the following aims: the relief of poverty; education; and charitable purposes beneficial to the community. Donations are given to both individuals and organisations.
RANGE OF GRANTS Up to £5,000.
SAMPLE GRANTS Previously: Headway – Tunbridge Wells; Richard House Trust; Fair Havens Hospice; Little Havens Children's Hospice; Starlight Children's Foundation; Universal Benevolent Society and Cancerkin (£5,000 each) Sense West (£4,250); Look (£3,500); Leonard Cheshire Disability (£3,300); Buckingham Emergency Food Appeal(£1,000) and three other grants of less than £1,000 each (£1,850).
FINANCES *Year* 2009–10 *Income* £19,519 *Grants* £12,000
TRUSTEES Neville R Evenden; Jeremy Randall; Alan C Goreham; Neil A Fulton.
HOW TO APPLY In writing to the correspondent.
WHO TO APPLY TO Stephen Bailey, Secretary, 1 Doughty Street, London WC1N 2PH *Tel* 020 7831 1872

■ The Pallant Charitable Trust

CC NO 265120   **ESTABLISHED** 1972
WHERE FUNDING CAN BE GIVEN UK, with a preference for areas within 50 miles of Chichester.
WHO CAN BENEFIT Church musicians and choristers.
WHAT IS FUNDED Chorister's scholarships and musician's salaries.
WHAT IS NOT FUNDED No grants to individuals, or for computer equipment or sponsorship for concerts.
SAMPLE GRANTS Chichester Cathedral Choristers Scholarships – Prebendal School Fees (£33,000 for four individuals); Friends of St Mary's Church – Stoughton (£7,000); Bosham PCC (£1,000); and RSCM Sussex area (£750).
FINANCES *Year* 2009–10 *Income* £40,924 *Grants* £26,442 *Assets* £1,036,416
TRUSTEES Dr A J Thurlow; Simon A E MacFarlane; C Smyth; C J Henville.
HOW TO APPLY In writing to the correspondent. Applications should be submitted by recognised organisations such as churches, schools, colleges or charities working in the field of church music.
WHO TO APPLY TO Simon MacFarlane, Trustee, c/o Thomas Eggar, The Corn Exchange, Baffins Lane, Chichester, West Sussex PO19 1GE *Tel* 01243 786111 *Fax* 01243 532 001

■ The Palmer Foundation

CC NO 278666   **ESTABLISHED** 1979
WHERE FUNDING CAN BE GIVEN Tower Hamlets.
WHO CAN BENEFIT Selected registered charities chosen by the trustees. Children and young adults at Coopers' Company and Coborn School and Strode's College will be considered.
WHAT IS FUNDED Grants and donations to charitable organisations and payments for educational scholarships, bursaries and prizes at Coopers' Company and Coborn School and Strode's College.
TYPE OF GRANT Recurrent grants for up to three years will be considered.

SAMPLE GRANTS Welfare (£375); educational (£7,200); City of London (£5,450); young people (£5,200); and 'other' (£150).
FINANCES *Year* 2009–10 *Income* £33,025 *Grants* £18,383 *Assets* £775,547
TRUSTEES The Coopers' Company.
HOW TO APPLY The trust conducts its own research and does not respond to unsolicited applications.
WHO TO APPLY TO Adrian Carroll, Clerk to the Trustees, Coopers' Hall, 13 Devonshire Square, London EC2M 4TH *Tel* 020 7247 9577 *email* clerk@coopers-hall.co.uk *Website* www.coopers-hall.co.uk

■ Eleanor Palmer Trust

CC NO 220857 **ESTABLISHED** 1558
WHERE FUNDING CAN BE GIVEN Former urban districts of Chipping Barnet and East Barnet.
WHO CAN BENEFIT Charities benefiting people disadvantaged by poverty, hardship or distress.
WHAT IS FUNDED Relief in need.
WHAT IS NOT FUNDED Anything other than relief-in-need is not considered.
TYPE OF GRANT One-off, project and capital. Funding for one year or less will be considered.
RANGE OF GRANTS £100–£5,000.
SAMPLE GRANTS Grants are broken down as follows: amenities for and grants for residents: £6,400; grants for relief in need: £18,100; lunch club for residents £1,900.
FINANCES *Year* 2009–10 *Income* £1,243,955 *Grants* £26,367 *Assets* £3,895,532
TRUSTEES Anthony Grimwade, Chair; Anthony Alderman; Helena Davis; Stephen G Lane; Catherine Older; Wendy Prentice; Revd Samuel Hall Speers; David Tait; Christopher Dallison; Amanda Wiles.
HOW TO APPLY In writing to the correspondent, providing details of your organisation's circumstances, the purpose of the grant and a copy of your latest accounts.
WHO TO APPLY TO Fred Park, Clerk to the Trustees, 106B Wood Street, Barnet, Hertfordshire EN5 4BY *Tel* 020 8441 3222 *email* info@eleanorpalmertrust.org.uk *Website* www.eleanorpalmertrust.org.uk

■ The Panacea Society

CC NO 227530 **ESTABLISHED** 1926
WHERE FUNDING CAN BE GIVEN UK, with a strong preference for Bedford and its immediate region.
WHO CAN BENEFIT Christian organisations that promote the religious aims of the Panacea Society.
WHAT IS FUNDED Advancement and promotion of the religious beliefs of the Society and the Christian religion generally; relief of sickness for the benefit of people living within the town of Bedford and its immediate region; and advancement of education generally and in the production, publication and dissemination of religious works. Grants awarded must be for charitable purposes and are made to UK-based organisations only. Priority will usually be given to grants that: will promote the religious aims of the Panacea Society; can benefit large numbers of people; will have a lasting impact; are of a capital nature; are to organisations rather than individuals; operate in Bedfordshire.
WHAT IS NOT FUNDED The society will not make grants: to political parties or political lobbying; to pressure groups; which support commercial ventures; or which could be paid out of central or local government funds.
SAMPLE GRANTS Pasque Charity – Keech Children's Hospice (£10,000); Bedford Open Door (£6,000); Beds and Northants MS Centre and Bedford MENCAP (£5,000 each); BeCHAR, Deafblind and Friendship Link & Action Group (£2,000 each); and Cruse Bedfordshire (£1,000).
FINANCES *Year* 2010 *Income* £488,811 *Grants* £337,389 *Assets* £24,204,463
TRUSTEES G Allan; L Aston; Revd Dr Jane Shaw; Prof. C Rowland; Dr J Meggitt.
HOW TO APPLY The trust has previously stated that it receives many applications that they are unable or unwilling to support. Please read the grant criteria carefully before submitting an application. Unsolicited applications are not responded to. Any organisation considering applying for funding support should make a formal application in writing to the correspondent. The application should set out the purpose for which the funding is required, and explain how it falls within the funding criteria and complies with their requirements. Full information on the work of the applicant body together with details of how the proposed funding will be applied should be given. The correspondent will acknowledge receipt of an application, and indicate if the application falls within their parameters. At this point the society may call for additional information, or indicate that it is unable to consider the application further. Most applications fail because they fall outside the criteria, however the society does not provide additional reasons why it is unable to support a particular application. When all relevant information has been received the application will be discussed at the next meeting of the society's trustees together with other valid applications. The trustees may at that meeting refuse or defer any application or request further information without giving reasons. Applicants will be advised in writing of the trustees' decision.
'At the end of 2010 and after much consideration, the Society decided that it would approach its Poverty and Sickness grant making in a different manner. Rather than invite organisations and groups to apply directly to the Society, for 2011 onwards funding would be provided to specialist funders working within the not for profit sector with the remit to then deal with all applications directly on behalf of the Society.'
'The Bedfordshire and Luton Community Foundation working in partnership with Community and Voluntary Service Mid and North Beds manage the Society's non-educational grant making activities within the local community.'
'Educational grants are still awarded and assessed directly by the Society.'
WHO TO APPLY TO David McLynn, Business Administrator, 14 Albany Road, Bedford MK40 3PH *Tel* 01234 359 737 *email* admin@panacea-society.org *Website* www.panacea-society.org

■ Panahpur

CC NO 1130367 **ESTABLISHED** 1911
WHERE FUNDING CAN BE GIVEN UK, overseas.
WHO CAN BENEFIT Christian charities and individuals, especially Christian missionary organisations.
WHAT IS FUNDED Scripture distribution/reading encouragement, relief work, missionary work, education and retreats.

RANGE OF GRANTS £500–£38,000.

SAMPLE GRANTS Oasis International (£38,000); Relationships Foundation (£10,000); Egypt Emerging Leadership – Xmedia (£9,000); CHGN – InterHealth Worldwide (£8,000); Ambassadors in Sport (£5,000); Redcliff College (£1,200); and Mena – Xmedia (£600).

FINANCES *Year* 2009–10 *Income* £62,150 *Grants* £71,732 *Assets* £0

TRUSTEES Paul East; Andrew Perry; Dorothy Haile; Andrew Matheson.

OTHER INFORMATION The activities of the Panahpur Charitable Trust (charity number: 214299) have recently been transferred to a new incorporated body, Panahpur (charity number: 1130367). In November 2009 the charitable trust moved its unrestricted net assets to Panahpur, while its restricted net assets were given to the Penhurst Church Trust (charity number: 1134097).

HOW TO APPLY The trustees do their own research and do not respond to unsolicited applications.

WHO TO APPLY TO Andrew Perry, Trustee, 84 High Street, Tonbridge, Kent TN9 1AP

■ The Panton Trust

CC NO 292910　　　**ESTABLISHED** 1983

WHERE FUNDING CAN BE GIVEN UK and overseas.

WHO CAN BENEFIT Worldwide organisations concerned with animal wildlife; UK: the environment.

WHAT IS FUNDED The trust states that it is 'concerned with any animal or animals or with wildlife in any part of the world, or with the environment of the UK or any part thereof. The trustees consider applications from a wide variety of sources and favour smaller charities which do not have the same capacity for large-scale fundraising as major charities in this field.'

TYPE OF GRANT Grants are made for strategic planning and project funding and can be for up to three years.

RANGE OF GRANTS Up to £5,000.

SAMPLE GRANTS St Tiggywinkles Wildlife Hospital, Whale and Dolphin Conservation Society, PDSA (£5,000 each); Flora and Fauna International (£4,000); Murray Edwards College (£3,500); Royal Botanic Garden – Kew (£3,000); Galapagos Conservation Trust (£2,000); and National Wood Recycling Project (£1,000).

FINANCES *Year* 2009–10 *Income* £52,429 *Grants* £55,525 *Assets* £181,568

TRUSTEES L M Slavin; R Craig.

OTHER INFORMATION Other grants of less than £1,000 totalled £11,000.

HOW TO APPLY In writing to the correspondent.

WHO TO APPLY TO Laurence Slavin, Trustee, Ramsay House, 18 Vera Avenue, Grange Park, London N12 1RA *Tel* 020 8370 7700

■ The James Pantyfedwen Foundation

CC NO 1069598　　　**ESTABLISHED** 1998

WHERE FUNDING CAN BE GIVEN Wales.

WHO CAN BENEFIT Welsh people; and organisations in Wales benefiting children, young adults, clergy, musicians, students, Christians, at risk groups, people disadvantaged by poverty and homeless people.

WHAT IS FUNDED Church buildings; religious purposes; students (mainly for postgraduate study); registered charities; local Eisteddfodau; and Sunday Schools. Charities working in the field of Christian education; religious umbrella bodies; infrastructure, support and development; cultural activity; academic research; and various community services and facilities will be considered.

WHAT IS NOT FUNDED No grants are made for revenue funding of any kind.

TYPE OF GRANT One-off.

RANGE OF GRANTS Up to a maximum of £15,000 in special cases; lower maximum in other cases.

SAMPLE GRANTS Grants were broken down as follows: Educational purposes (students) – £90,000; Religious buildings – £77,500; Eisteddfodau – £66,000; Registered charities – £13,000; Religious purposes – £36,500; Urdd Gobaith Cymru – £10,000; Special Projects – £39,000.

FINANCES *Year* 2009–10 *Income* £424,085 *Grants* £331,716 *Assets* £1,507,282

TRUSTEES E W Jones, Chair; Revd Dr R A Evans; Dr G T Hughes; I M Hughes; G R Jones; Miss G Pierce Jones; Revd J E Jones; D G Lewis; Most Revd Dr B C Morgan; Prof. D L Morgan; W J Phillips; K Richards; Revd I Roberts; R F Sharp; Revd P M Thomas; Dr P Elfed-Owens; Dr R Griffiths; Revd Canon E Morgan; Revd Dr G Tudur.

OTHER INFORMATION Organisations and individuals

HOW TO APPLY Applications should be made on a form available from the correspondent. Applications from churches and registered charities can be submitted at any time (trustees meet about five times a year in March, May, July, September and December); student applications should be submitted before 31 July in the academic year for which the application is being made. Applications to the special projects funds are considered twice a year and should be received by 15 June or 15 November for consideration in July or December respectively. All unsuccessful applicants receive a reply.

WHO TO APPLY TO Richard H Morgan, Executive Secretary, Pantyfedwen, 9 Market Street, Aberystwyth SY23 1DL *Tel* 01970 612806 *Fax* 01970 612806 *email* pantyfedwen@btinternet.com *Website* www.jamespantyfedwenfoundation.org.uk

■ The Paphitis Charitable Trust

CC NO 1112721　　　**ESTABLISHED** 2005

WHERE FUNDING CAN BE GIVEN UK and overseas.

WHO CAN BENEFIT Charitable organisations.

WHAT IS FUNDED General charitable purposes, particularly children's charities.

RANGE OF GRANTS £50 to £5,000.

SAMPLE GRANTS New Children's Hospital Appeal and Dyslexia Action (£5,000 each); Omonia Youth FC and Piggy Bank Kids (£2,500 each); Thrive, Child Care Action Trust, Caring for Life and Root Development Agency (£2,000 each); Forgotten Children and Police Community Clubs (£1,500 each); British Blind Sport (£1,400); REACT; Project Scotland and Cure Parkinson's Trust (£1,000 each); SAFE; Oxfam and Music Space (£500); and Marie Claire Cancer Care and Prospect Hospice (£250 each).

FINANCES *Year* 2009–10 *Income* £136,470 *Grants* £146,765 *Assets* £66,774

TRUSTEES Malcolm Cooke; Richard Towner; Kypros Kyprianou; Ann Mantz; Ian Childs.

OTHER INFORMATION This trust was set up by entrepreneur Theo Paphitis.

HOW TO APPLY In writing to the correspondent.

WHO TO APPLY TO The Trustees, 2nd Floor, 22–24 Worple Road, London SW19 4DD *Tel* 020 8971 9894

Think carefully about every application. Is it justified?

793

■ The Paragon Trust

CC NO 278348   **ESTABLISHED** 1979

WHERE FUNDING CAN BE GIVEN UK and overseas.

WHO CAN BENEFIT Charities and occasionally certain individuals but only those known to the trustees.

WHAT IS FUNDED A wide range of charitable bodies.

TYPE OF GRANT The majority of donations are standing orders.

RANGE OF GRANTS £500–£5,000.

SAMPLE GRANTS British Red Cross (£3,000); Canterbury Cathedral and Demelza House (£2,000 each); Amnesty International, Home Farm Trust, Medical Foundation (Victims of Torture), Send A Cow and Sightsavers (£1,000 each); Changing Faces, Leonard Cheshire Homes and Open Arms Malawi (£500 each).

FINANCES *Year* 2009–10 *Income* £80,830 *Grants* £95,515 *Assets* £1,676,684

TRUSTEES The Lord Wrenbury; Revd Canon R Coppin; Miss L J Whistler; P Cunningham; Dr Fiona Cornish.

OTHER INFORMATION Dr Fiona Cornish is also a trustee of Medical Support in Romania (Charity Commission no. 1058339) and Miss L Whistler is also a trustee of St Bede's School Trust, Sussex (Charity Commission no.278950).

HOW TO APPLY The trust states that it does not respond to unsolicited applications; all beneficiaries 'are known personally to the trustees and no attention is paid to appeal literature, which is discarded on receipt. Fundraisers are therefore urged to save resources by not sending literature.'

WHO TO APPLY TO Mrs Kathy Larter, Ref: 1211, c/o Thomson Snell and Passmore Solicitors, 3 Lonsdale Gardens, Tunbridge Wells, Kent TN1 1NX *Tel* 01892 701211

■ The Park Charitable Trust

CC NO 1095541   **ESTABLISHED** 2003

WHERE FUNDING CAN BE GIVEN UK.

WHO CAN BENEFIT Charitable organisations.

WHAT IS FUNDED 'The objects of the charity are the advancement of the Jewish Faith; the advancement of Jewish education; the relief of poverty amongst the Jewish community; the relief of patients suffering from cancer and heart conditions; giving financial support to hospitals and furthering such other charitable purposes as the trustees may from time to time determine in support of their charitable activities.'

SAMPLE GRANTS

Community projects	£46,000
Kollelim	£6,000
Relief of poverty	£151,000
Schools	£17,000
Yeshivot and seminaries	£49,000

FINANCES *Year* 2009–10 *Income* £1,346,536 *Grants* £294,513 *Assets* £3,733,874

TRUSTEES D Hammelburger; Mrs M Hammelburger; E Pine.

HOW TO APPLY In writing to the correspondent.

WHO TO APPLY TO E Pine, Trustee, 69 Singleton Road, Salford M7 4LX

■ The Park House Charitable Trust

CC NO 1077677   **ESTABLISHED** 1999

WHERE FUNDING CAN BE GIVEN UK and overseas, with a preference for the Midlands, particularly Coventry and Warwickshire.

WHO CAN BENEFIT Charitable organisations.

WHAT IS FUNDED General charitable purposes, with preference towards social welfare and Christian causes.

WHAT IS NOT FUNDED No grants to individuals.

TYPE OF GRANT Normally one-off for general funds.

RANGE OF GRANTS £2,000–£100,000.

SAMPLE GRANTS Scottish International Relief – Mary's Meals (£100,000); St Joseph and the Helpers Charity (£20,000); Diocese of Bijnor, Friends of the Holy Land (£15,000 each); CAAFOD, Good Rock Foundation (£10,000 each); Guys Gift (£5,000); Calcutta Rescue Fund (£3,000); Coventry Medjugorge Centre (£2,000); Maryvale Institute (£15,000); Community of Holy First (£5,000); and Tiny Tim's Children's Centre (£2,000).

FINANCES *Year* 2010 *Income* £180,606 *Grants* £247,000 *Assets* £1,435,572

TRUSTEES N P Bailey; Mrs M Bailey; P Bailey; Dr M F Whelan.

HOW TO APPLY In writing to the correspondent. The trust has stated that it does not expect to have surplus funds available to meet the majority of applications.

WHO TO APPLY TO Paul Varney, Dafferns LLP, One Eastwood, Harry Weston Road, Binley Business Park, Coventry CV3 2UB *Tel* 024 7622 1046

■ The Frank Parkinson Agricultural Trust

CC NO 209407   **ESTABLISHED** 1943

WHERE FUNDING CAN BE GIVEN UK.

WHO CAN BENEFIT Mainly corporate entities benefiting the improvement of agriculture and horticulture.

WHAT IS FUNDED The improvement and welfare of British agriculture, primarily to agricultural colleges and affiliated institutions.

WHAT IS NOT FUNDED Grants are given to corporate bodies and the trust is not able to assist with financial help to any individuals undertaking postgraduate studies or degree courses.

TYPE OF GRANT Short-term: two to four years preferred. One-off will also be considered.

RANGE OF GRANTS One-off at Chairman's discretion: smallest £200; largest over three years £100,000; typical grants (over two years) £40,000.

SAMPLE GRANTS Harper Adams University College (£75,000); Royal Agricultural Society of England and St George's House, Windsor Castle (£5,000 each) and AgriFood Charities Partnership (£500).

FINANCES *Year* 2010 *Income* £56,992 *Grants* £85,500 *Assets* £1,233,178

TRUSTEES C Bourchier; J S Sclanders; Prof. Paul Webster; D Gardner.

PUBLICATIONS A history of the trust since its inception in 1943, including an outline of projects previously funded, is available in a book entitled Tale of Two Trusts, which is available from the correspondent.

OTHER INFORMATION Grants were made to four organisations totalling £85,000.

HOW TO APPLY In writing to the correspondent. The trustees meet annually in April and applicants are expected to make an oral presentation. Further details of the whole application process can be found in the useful 'Guidelines for Grant Applications' which is available from the trust. Please note, however: 'The chairman has the authority to approve small grants between annual meetings, but these are only for minor sums and minor projects.'

WHO TO APPLY TO Miss Janet Smith, Secretary to the Trustees, 11 Alder Drive, Pudsey LS28 8RD *Tel* 0113 257 8613 *email* janetpudsey@live.co.uk

■ The Samuel and Freda Parkinson Charitable Trust

CC NO 327749   **ESTABLISHED** 1987

WHERE FUNDING CAN BE GIVEN UK.

WHO CAN BENEFIT Registered charities specified by the founder of the trust.

WHAT IS FUNDED General charitable purposes.

RANGE OF GRANTS £5,000–£25,000.

SAMPLE GRANTS Salvation Army; Leonard Cheshire Foundation (£24,000 each); Church Army (£15,000); RNLI (£14,500); RSPCA (£7,500); and Animal Concern, Animal Rescue and Animal Welfare (£5,000 each).

FINANCES *Year* 2009–10 *Income* £92,695 *Grants* £100,000 *Assets* £2,813,204

TRUSTEES D E G Roberts; Miss J A Todd; M J Fletcher.

OTHER INFORMATION The trust supports the same eight beneficiaries each year, although for varying amounts.

HOW TO APPLY The founder of this charity restricted the list of potential beneficiaries to named charities of his choice and accordingly the trustees do not have discretion to include further beneficiaries, although they do have complete discretion within the stated beneficiary list.

WHO TO APPLY TO Trust Administrator, Thomson Wilson Pattinson, Solicitors, Stonecliffe, Lake Road, Windermere, Cumbria *Tel* 01539 442233 *Fax* 01539 488 810

■ The Parthenon Trust

CC NO 1051467   **ESTABLISHED** 1995

WHERE FUNDING CAN BE GIVEN Unrestricted.

WHO CAN BENEFIT Charitable organisations.

WHAT IS FUNDED International aid, medical research, assistance to the disadvantaged including people with disabilities, culture and heritage, medical treatment and care, education, promotion of civil society and research on current affairs.

WHAT IS NOT FUNDED No grants for individuals, scientific/geographical expeditions or projects which promote religious beliefs.

TYPE OF GRANT Normally one-off grants for general purposes.

RANGE OF GRANTS £2,500–£400,000.

SAMPLE GRANTS Cancer Research UK (£400,000); Friends of Diva Opera (£150,000); Mont Blanc Foundation (£125,000); Ungureni Trust (£117,000); International Committee of the Red Cross, UNICEF UK (£100,000 each); Ashoka Africa (£84,000); Downside Up (£75,000); Cecily's Fund (£40,000); Andover Young Carers (£10,000); Basingstoke-Hoima Partnership for Health, Esther Benjamins Trust, Leprosy Mission, North Hampshire Medical Fund, Trinity Winchester, United Aid for Azerbaijan (£5,000 each); Feet First World Wide, Kariandusi School Trust and Langalanga Scholarship Fund (£2,500 each).

FINANCES *Year* 2010 *Income* £1,125,329 *Grants* £1,240,900 *Assets* £131,113

TRUSTEES Dr J M Darmady; J E E Whittaker; Mrs Y G Whittaker.

HOW TO APPLY In writing to the correspondent. Anyone proposing to submit an application should telephone the secretary beforehand. Unsolicited written applications are not normally acknowledged. Most grants are awarded at a trustees' meeting held early in the new year, although grants can be awarded at any time.

WHO TO APPLY TO J E E Whittaker, The Secretary, Saint-Nicolas 9, 2000 Neuchatel, Switzerland *Tel* 00 41 32 724 8130

■ Arthur James Paterson Charitable Trust

CC NO 278569   **ESTABLISHED** 1979

WHERE FUNDING CAN BE GIVEN UK.

WHO CAN BENEFIT Organisations benefiting children, older people, retired people, at risk groups, socially isolated people and those disadvantaged by poverty.

WHAT IS FUNDED Medical research, welfare of older people and children.

TYPE OF GRANT One-off.

RANGE OF GRANTS Under £5,000.

SAMPLE GRANTS Glenalmond College and Worcester College (£4,400 each); Over the Wall, St Giles Centre, Birmingham Royal Ballet, Guild Care, Make a Wish and University College London Hospitals (£3,300 each); Catch 22 and St Christopher Hospice (£900 each); and Friends of the Elderly, Home Start, National Society for Epilepsy and Prostate Cancer Charity (£875 each).

FINANCES *Year* 2009–10 *Income* £47,730 *Grants* £33,975 *Assets* £1,634,839

TRUSTEES Royal Bank of Canada Trust Corporation Ltd.

HOW TO APPLY There are no application forms. Send your application with a covering letter and include the latest set of report and accounts. Deadlines are February and August.

WHO TO APPLY TO Anita Carter, Trust Administrator, Royal Bank of Canada Trust Corporation Limited, 71 Queen Victoria Street, London EC4V 4DE *Tel* 020 7653 4756 *email* anita.carter@rbc.com

■ The Constance Paterson Charitable Trust

CC NO 249556   **ESTABLISHED** 1966

WHERE FUNDING CAN BE GIVEN UK.

WHO CAN BENEFIT Organisations benefiting children, older people, retired people, ex-service and service people, at risk groups, socially isolated people and those disadvantaged by poverty. Carers, disabled people, homeless people, victims of abuse, crime or domestic violence and people with dyslexia are also considered.

WHAT IS FUNDED Medical research, health care, welfare of older people and children (including accommodation and housing) and service people's welfare.

WHAT IS NOT FUNDED No grants to individuals.

TYPE OF GRANT One-off grants, which can be for capital costs (including buildings), core or running costs, project or research funding, or salaries.

RANGE OF GRANTS Up to £2,000.

SAMPLE GRANTS NDCS, Caring for Life and STEPS (£2,300 each); Down Syndrome Education and Independence at Home (£600 each); and the Genesis Appeal (£400).

FINANCES *Year* 2009–10 *Income* £33,163 *Grants* £14,660 *Assets* £1,133,095

TRUSTEES Royal Bank of Canada Trust Corporation Ltd.

HOW TO APPLY In writing to the correspondent, including covering letter and latest set of annual report and accounts. The trust does not have an application form. Deadlines for applications are June and December.

WHO TO APPLY TO Miss Anita Carter, Administrator, Royal Bank of Canada Trust Corporation Limited, 71 Queen Victoria Street, London EC4V 4DE *Tel* 020 7653 4756 *email* anita. carter@rbc.com

■ Miss M E Swinton Paterson's Charitable Trust

SC NO SC004835   **ESTABLISHED** 1989
WHERE FUNDING CAN BE GIVEN Scotland.
WHO CAN BENEFIT Organisations benefiting Christians and young people.
WHAT IS FUNDED Support to the Church of Scotland and other Christian groups in the maintenance of church buildings and in their work with young people.
WHAT IS NOT FUNDED No grants to individuals or students.
RANGE OF GRANTS £500–£1,000.
SAMPLE GRANTS Previous beneficiaries include: L'Arche Edinburgh Community, Livingstone Baptist Church, Lloyd Morris Congregational Church, Haddington West Parish Church, Acorn Christian Centre, Stranraer YMCA, Care for the Family, Boys' and Girls' Clubs of Scotland, Fresh Start, Friends of the Elms, Iona Community, Edinburgh Young Carers' Project, Epilepsy Scotland, Stoneykirk Parish Church, Scotland Yard Adventure Centre, Atholl Centre, Scottish Crusaders, Disablement Income Group Scotland and Artlink.
FINANCES *Year* 2010–11 *Income* £48,097 *Grants* £40,000
TRUSTEES Michael A Noble; J A W Somerville; C S Kennedy; R J Steel.
HOW TO APPLY In writing to the correspondent. Trustees meet once a year in July to consider grants.
WHO TO APPLY TO The Trustees, Lindsays' Solicitors, Caledonian Exchange, 19a Canning Street, Edinburgh EH3 8HE

■ The Patrick Charitable Trust

CC NO 213849   **ESTABLISHED** 1962
WHERE FUNDING CAN BE GIVEN UK, with a special interest in Cornwall and the West Midlands.
WHO CAN BENEFIT Registered charities.
WHAT IS FUNDED General charitable purposes.
WHAT IS NOT FUNDED No grants to individuals.
TYPE OF GRANT One-off or recurrent.
RANGE OF GRANTS £200 to £100,000. Usually below £10,000.
SAMPLE GRANTS Black Country Museum (£103,000); Royal Shakespeare Company (£40,000); Birmingham Royal Ballet (£20,500); Royal Orthopaedic Hospital (£15,000); Elmhurst School for Dance (£10,000); Performances Birmingham Limited (£6,400); the Princess Royal Trust for Carers (£6,000); Birmingham Hippodrome Theatre and Hall for Cornwall (£5,000 each); the Peckwood Centre (£3,000); Muscular Dystrophy Campaign and the Willow Trust (£2,000 each); the Princess Royal Trust for Carers (£1,200); Troop Aid and Earth Restoration Service (£1,000 each); Cornwall Community Foundation (£300).
FINANCES *Year* 2009–10 *Income* £130,309 *Grants* £147,578 *Assets* £6,231,104

TRUSTEES J A Patrick, Chair; M V Patrick; Mrs H P Cole; W Bond-Williams; N C Duckitt; G Wem.
HOW TO APPLY In writing to the correspondent at any time. The trust endeavours to reply to all applications with a decision.
WHO TO APPLY TO J A Patrick, Chair, The Lakeside Centre, 180 Lifford Lane, Birmingham B30 3NU *Tel* 0121 486 3399

■ The Jack Patston Charitable Trust

CC NO 701658   **ESTABLISHED** 1989
WHERE FUNDING CAN BE GIVEN Preferably Leicestershire and Cambridgeshire.
WHO CAN BENEFIT Charitable organisations, including rural churches.
WHAT IS FUNDED Preservation of wildlife and the environment, advancement of religion and preservation of rural church fabric.
WHAT IS NOT FUNDED No grants to individuals.
TYPE OF GRANT Single payments.
RANGE OF GRANTS Up to £5,000.
SAMPLE GRANTS Save Launde Abbey Appeal (£5,000); the Train a Priest Fund and Sue Ryder Care (£4,000 each); St Peter's Church – Wymondham, St Mary's Church – Freeby and St Helen's Church – Gumley (£3,500 each); RSPB (£3,000); the Woodland Trust, the Fenland Archaeological Trust and East Anglia Children's Hospices (£2,500 each); the Grasslands Trust, Butterfly Conservation and Deafblind UK (£2,000 each); Plantlife (£1,500); and the Red Squirrel Survival Trust and Happy Days Children's Trust (£1,000 each).
FINANCES *Year* 2009–10 *Income* £79,394 *Grants* £94,000 *Assets* £2,462,148
TRUSTEES Allan A Veasey; Charles J U Applegate.
HOW TO APPLY In writing to the correspondent.
WHO TO APPLY TO Charles J U Applegate, Trustee, Buckles Solicitors LLP, Grant House, 101 Bourges Boulevard, Peterborough PE1 1NG *Tel* 01733 888888 *Fax* 01733 888800 *email* www.buckles-law.co.uk

■ Ambika Paul Foundation

CC NO 276127   **ESTABLISHED** 1978
WHERE FUNDING CAN BE GIVEN Mainly UK and India.
WHO CAN BENEFIT Large organisations, registered charities, colleges and universities benefiting children, young adults and students.
WHAT IS FUNDED Main areas of interest are young people and education.
WHAT IS NOT FUNDED Applications from individuals, including students, are mainly ineligible. Funding for scholarships is made directly to colleges/ universities, not to individuals. No expeditions.
RANGE OF GRANTS Usually £100–£3,000.
SAMPLE GRANTS MIT Sloan School of Management (£657,000); University of Wolverhampton (£200,000); Great Ormond Street Hospital Children's Charity (£21,000); Magic Bus (£20,000); Zoological Society of London (£14,000); PiggyBankKids (£8,000); the Shela Dispensary (£3,000); Bhavan (£1,000); CST – Protecting Jewish Community (£500); and Anthony Nolan Trust and Mary Seacole Appeal (£100 each).
FINANCES *Year* 2009–10 *Income* £370,213 *Grants* £930,425 *Assets* £6,876,059
TRUSTEES Lord Paul of Marylebone; Lady Aruna Paul; Hon. Angad Paul; Hon. Anjli Paul; Hon. Ambar Paul; Hon. Akash Paul.

HOW TO APPLY In writing to the trustees at the correspondence address. Acknowledgements are sent if an sae is enclosed. However, the trust has no paid employees and the enormous number of requests it receives creates administrative difficulties.

WHO TO APPLY TO Lord Paul of Marylebone, Trustee, Caparo House, 103 Baker Street, London W1U 6LN *Tel* 020 7486 1417

■ Paycare Charity Trust (previously known as Patients' Aid Association Hospital and Medical Charities Trust)

CC NO 240378   **ESTABLISHED** 1964

WHERE FUNDING CAN BE GIVEN Generally in the East and West Midlands, Staffordshire and Shropshire and other areas where the association operates.

WHO CAN BENEFIT Mainly NHS hospitals and registered, medically related charities benefiting: children; young adults; older people; ex-service and service people; medical professionals, nurses and doctors; research workers; volunteers; people in care; at risk groups; carers; disabled people; those disadvantaged by poverty; homeless people; victims of abuse and domestic violence.

WHAT IS FUNDED Provision of equipment and patient amenities to NHS hospitals, hospices, convalescent homes and other medically related charities in the area where the parent association operates. These include: support to volunteers; health professional bodies; councils for voluntary service; advancement of respite; sheltered accommodation; health; special schools; speech therapy; special needs education; scholarships; medical research; specialist research; and community services.

WHAT IS NOT FUNDED Appeals must be from officials of the appealing body and submitted on official stationery. Appeals are not accepted from, or on behalf of, individuals or for provision of vehicles or general running costs.

TYPE OF GRANT Mainly medical equipment. Grants are not made towards running costs or administration.

RANGE OF GRANTS £100–£1,000.

SAMPLE GRANTS Happy Days Children's Charity (£1,200); The Children's Trust (£1,000); The Extra Care Trust (£950); Willen Hospice and St Mary's Hospice (£800 each); Handicapped Children's Action Group (£700); Listening Books (£600); Midlands Air Ambulance, Children's Heart Federation and Fight for Sight (£500 each); British Skin Foundation (£450); Springdale Methodist Church (£300); and Walsall Carer's Week and Age Concern (£200 each).

FINANCES *Year* 2010 *Income* £35,087 *Grants* £22,231 *Assets* £46,634

TRUSTEES E P Booth; G F Lewis; Mrs H Lisle; D Clegg, Chair; Patricia Stokes.

HOW TO APPLY Application forms are available from the correspondent. Any hospital or registered charity may apply for a grant and all such applications are considered by the trustees who meet four times a year. '[The] reason for the rejection of appeals is due usually to an excessive amount involved.' Each application is considered on merit.

WHO TO APPLY TO Janet Wrighton, Secretary, Paycare House, George Street, Wolverhampton WV2 4DX *Tel* 01902 371007 *Fax* 01902 371030 *email* enquiries@paycare.org

■ The Payne Charitable Trust

CC NO 241816   **ESTABLISHED** 1965

WHERE FUNDING CAN BE GIVEN Christian in Wales, West Midlands, Cumbria and India.

WHO CAN BENEFIT Missionaries, churches, and people engaged in the propagation of the Christian gospel.

WHAT IS FUNDED To support religious and charitable objects. The main area of interest is the support of evangelical Christians in the promotion and proclamation of the Christian gospel.

WHAT IS NOT FUNDED No grants for repairs to church buildings or towards education.

TYPE OF GRANT One-off grants and loans; capital support.

RANGE OF GRANTS Up to £30,000.

SAMPLE GRANTS Dayspring Trust for India (£30,000); Andrew League Trust (£28,500); Crusaders (£6,000); SASRA (£2,250); Nate & Ali Ussery – missionaries (£1,500); Armed Forces Christian Union and Heart Cry for Wales (£1,000 each); OAC West Midlands (£500); and Keith & Dorothy Ward – missionaries (£100).

FINANCES *Year* 2009–10 *Income* £17,015 *Grants* £38,000

TRUSTEES John Payne; Eric Payne.

OTHER INFORMATION Due to the large number of applications, some considerable time can elapse before communication can be sent.

HOW TO APPLY In writing to the correspondent. Applications should be submitted between 1 January and 21 March only, for grants made from the following 1 May. The trustees regret that they cannot support many of the deserving organisations that apply for a grant. Due to the large number of applications, some considerable time can elapse before communication can be sent.

WHO TO APPLY TO John Payne, Trustee, Fourwinds, Copthorn Road, Colwyn Bay LL28 5YP *Tel* 01492 532393 *email* john@ copthornehouse.com

■ The Harry Payne Trust

CC NO 231063   **ESTABLISHED** 1939

WHERE FUNDING CAN BE GIVEN Birmingham and the immediately surrounding areas of the West Midlands.

WHO CAN BENEFIT Voluntary organisations and charitable groups only. Support will be considered for a wide variety of medical conditions, but particularly where there is evidence of social disadvantage. The trust operates a non-discriminatory policy as regards religion.

WHAT IS FUNDED Priority is given to charitable work in Birmingham, where the trust was founded. Funding may be given to churches and religious ancillary buildings; family planning and Well Women clinics; hospices and hospitals; pre-school and special needs education; advice centres and community services and other charitable organisations.

WHAT IS NOT FUNDED No grants to individuals or organisations outside the beneficial area.

TYPE OF GRANT Capital (including buildings), one-off, research, running costs (including salaries), recurring costs and start-up costs will be considered. Funding may be given for up to three years.

RANGE OF GRANTS £100–£6,000, typical grant £250.

SAMPLE GRANTS Balsall Heath Church Centre (£4,000); Karis Neighbour Scheme and Birmingham Settlement (£2,000 each); Selly Oak Nursery School (£1,000); ExtraCare

Think carefully about every application. Is it justified?

797

Charitable Trust (£850); the Jericho Foundation, Family holiday Association and Changing Our Lives (£500 each); and Bag Books, Sudden Productions and RAF Association (£300 each).

FINANCES *Year* 2009–10 *Income* £57,943 *Grants* £52,812 *Assets* £1,280,977

TRUSTEES D J Cadbury; R C King; Mrs F M Adams; Mrs V C Dub; S S King; D A Payne; R I Payne.

HOW TO APPLY On a form available from the trust's website (or from the correspondent). Applications should include the organisation's most recent set of audited accounts and must be submitted by the end of May for the summer meeting and the end of November for the winter meeting. Successful applications will be acknowledged as soon as possible after the meeting at which they are considered.

WHO TO APPLY TO Robert C King, Secretary, 1 Matthews Close, Rushton, Kettering, Northamptonshire NN14 1QJ *Tel* 01536 418905 *email* robcking@aol.com *Website* www.harrypaynetrust.org.uk

■ The Peacock Charitable Trust

CC NO 257655   **ESTABLISHED** 1968

WHERE FUNDING CAN BE GIVEN UK with a possible preference for London and the south of England.

WHO CAN BENEFIT Registered charities benefiting children and young adults, ex-service and service people, disabled people, ex-offenders, at risk groups and carers. Also people with Alzheimer's disease, arthritis and rheumatism, cancer, hearing loss, heart disease, mental illness, multiple sclerosis, and substance abuse.

WHAT IS FUNDED Charities which the trustees have special knowledge of, interest in, or association with, in the fields of medical research, disability, and some youth work.

WHAT IS NOT FUNDED No donations are made to individuals and only in rare cases are additions made to the list of charities already being supported.

TYPE OF GRANT Capital, project and some recurring.

RANGE OF GRANTS £1,500–£105,000.

SAMPLE GRANTS Cancer Research UK (£105,000); Macmillan Cancer Support (£103,000); Fairbridge (£100,000); Marie Curie Cancer Care (£82,000); Neuro Disability Research Trust (£70,000); Brain Research Trust and the Jubilee Sailing Trust (£50,000 each); St Wilfred's Hospice (£47,000); British Eye Research Foundation (£32,000); Mental Health Foundation (£30,000); Action for ME and the Parkinson's Disease Society of the UK (£25,000 each); Addaction (£20,000); Arthritis Care (£16,000); Listening Books and Motivation (£15,000 each); Combat Stress and the Salvation Army (£10,000 each); Not Forgotten Association (£8,000); Marine Conservation Society, RNLI and the Straight Talking Project (£5,000 each); the Endeavour Club and REMAP (£3,000 each); and the St Helier Kidney Patients' Association (£1,500).

FINANCES *Year* 2009–10 *Income* £2,904,099 *Grants* £1,673,600 *Assets* £40,685,958

TRUSTEES Charles Peacock; Kenneth Burgin; Bettine Bond; Dr Clare Sellors.

HOW TO APPLY In writing to the correspondent.

WHO TO APPLY TO The Administrator, c/o Charities Aid Foundation, Kings Hill, West Malling, Kent ME19 4TA *Tel* 01732 520081 *Fax* 01732 520001

■ The Susanna Peake Charitable Trust

CC NO 283462   **ESTABLISHED** 1981

WHERE FUNDING CAN BE GIVEN UK, with a preference for the South West of England, particularly Gloucestershire.

WHO CAN BENEFIT Registered charities.

WHAT IS FUNDED General charitable purposes.

WHAT IS NOT FUNDED No grants to individuals.

TYPE OF GRANT Usually one-off grants.

RANGE OF GRANTS Usually £500–£5,000.

SAMPLE GRANTS Auditory Verbal UK (£10,000); ATP Enterprise, Chipping Norton Theatre Trust and Loughborough School PTA (£5,000 each); Cotswold Care Hospice and Crime Diversion Scheme (£4,000); Cheltenham Housing Aid Centre and Interact Wildlife (£3,000 each); Royal Blind Society and WaterAid (£2,000 each); Fine Cell Work (£1,000); and Christian Aid (£100).

FINANCES *Year* 2009–10 *Income* £152,889 *Grants* £156,450 *Assets* £5,202,575

TRUSTEES Susanna Peake; David Peake.

HOW TO APPLY In writing to the correspondent. 'The trustees meet on an ad hoc basis to review applications for funding, and a full review is undertaken annually when the financial statements are available. Only successful applications are notified of the trustees' decision.'

WHO TO APPLY TO The Administrator, Rathbone Trust Company Limited, 159 New Bond Street, London W1S 2UD *Tel* 020 7399 0811

■ The David Pearlman Charitable Foundation

CC NO 287009   **ESTABLISHED** 1983

WHERE FUNDING CAN BE GIVEN UK.

WHO CAN BENEFIT Jewish people.

WHAT IS FUNDED General charitable purposes.

SAMPLE GRANTS Previous beneficiaries included: British Friends of Igud Hakolelim B'Yerushalayim (£60,000); Lolev Charitable Trust (£30,000); Jewish Care (£16,000); Chevras Mo'oz Ladol (£15,000); Norwood (£12,000); the Duke of Edinburgh Trust (£7,000); Community Security Trust (£6,000); Life's 4 Living Trust Ltd (£6,400); Children Number One Foundation (£3,750); the Variety Club Children's Charity (£2,750); London Academy of Jewish Studies (£1,500); Jewish Music Institute and United Jewish Israel Appeal (£1,000).

FINANCES *Year* 2009–10 *Income* £195,583 *Grants* £72,220 *Assets* £1,735,856

TRUSTEES D A Pearlman; M R Goldberger; S Appleman; J Hager.

HOW TO APPLY In writing to the correspondent.

WHO TO APPLY TO Mr D Goldberger, Trustee, New Burlington House, 1075 Finchley Road, London NW11 0PU *Tel* 020 8731 0777

■ Pears Foundation

CC NO 1009195   **ESTABLISHED** 1991

WHERE FUNDING CAN BE GIVEN Worldwide.

WHO CAN BENEFIT Charitable organisations.

WHAT IS FUNDED 'The Pears Foundation invests in five main areas – (1) Community and young people: Shared Society – we aim to promote respect and understanding between people of different backgrounds and to enable individuals to participate in society based on a strong sense of personal identity and responsibility.

Faith and Social Justice – we aim to support faith communities to take a more central role in building a society based around the values of social justice. Empowering Vulnerable Groups – we aim to support vulnerable groups in society and enable them to campaign effectively on their own behalf. (2) Genocide prevention: Holocaust Education – we aim to improve the quality and geographic reach of education about the Holocaust, including its causes, its effects, its place in history and its role in our understanding about ideas of citizenship. Genocide Education and Campaigns – we aim to promote education about the causes and consequences of genocide and also support campaigns to prevent genocide today. (3) International development: Rights-based Development – we aim to make a contribution to a rights-based approach to international development. Faith-based Development – we aim to support Jewish engagement in international development and research about the contribution that faith communities can make. (4) Israel: Promoting Israel's Academic Expertise – we aim to support the application of Israel's academic expertise to the challenges of the world. Civil Society – we aim to support universal rights for all of Israel's citizens. Israeli Arabs – we aim to increase engagement and understanding about the issues facing Israel's Arab citizens. (5) Philanthropy: we aim to work with other philanthropic organisations committed to thinking about and advancing the role of philanthropy in society.'

TYPE OF GRANT Core, project and capital.

SAMPLE GRANTS Grants were broken down as follows: Community and young people (£3.2 million); Israel projects (£1.2 million); Genocide prevention (£2.3 million); International development (£347,000); Discretionary donations (£391,000).

FINANCES *Year* 2009–10 *Income* £7,703,633 *Grants* £7,235,534 *Assets* £14,540,171

TRUSTEES Trevor S Pears, Chair; Mark Pears; David Pears; Michael Keidan.

HOW TO APPLY 'Please note that we do not accept unsolicited applications. The foundation has a full time staff, and specialist consultants, who proactively research areas of interest, creating strategic plans and partnerships with organisations seeking to effect sustainable change. The trustees meet quarterly to review the strategic direction of the foundation and to consider major proposals.'

WHO TO APPLY TO The Trustees, 2 Old Brewery Mews, Hampstead, London NW3 1PZ *Tel* 020 7433 3333 *email* contact@pearsfoundation.org.uk *Website* www.pearsfoundation.org.uk

------

■ The Pedmore Sporting Club Trust Fund

CC NO 263907   **ESTABLISHED** 1973
WHERE FUNDING CAN BE GIVEN West Midlands.
WHO CAN BENEFIT Registered charities and individuals.
WHAT IS FUNDED General charitable purposes.
WHAT IS NOT FUNDED No grants towards running costs or salaries.
TYPE OF GRANT Recurrent.
RANGE OF GRANTS £300–£19,000.
SAMPLE GRANTS Belbroughton Scythe Fund – Help for Heroes (£1,500); Children's Heart Fund (£700); Dodford Children's Farm (£400); Brierly Hill Project (£300); Christmas Hampers – senior citizens (£1,500); Easter baskets – senior citizens (£1,000).
FINANCES *Year* 2010 *Income* £41,926 *Grants* £32,414 *Assets* £281,045
TRUSTEES N A Hickman; R Herman-Smith; R Williams; T J Hickman; J M Price.
HOW TO APPLY In writing to the correspondent or by email. The trustees meet to consider grants in January, May, September and November and typically will consider 30–40 applications.
WHO TO APPLY TO Alan Nicklin, Secretary, Pedmore Sporting Club Trust, Nicklin & Co, Church Court, Stourbridge Road, Halesowen B63 3TT *Tel* 07791 500449 *email* psclub@pedmorehouse.co.uk *Website* www.pedmoresportingclub.co.uk

------

■ The Dowager Countess Eleanor Peel Trust

CC NO 214684   **ESTABLISHED** 1951
WHERE FUNDING CAN BE GIVEN Worldwide in practice UK, with a preference for Lancashire (especially Lancaster and District), Cumbria, Greater Manchester, Cheshire and Merseyside.
WHO CAN BENEFIT Registered charities and universities.
WHAT IS FUNDED General charitable purposes, particularly medical charities, charities for the elderly and socially disadvantaged people.
WHAT IS NOT FUNDED Grants are not made to charities substantially under the control of central or local government or charities primarily devoted to children. Due to the number of applications received, the trust is usually unable to support small local charities with a gross annual income of less than £50,000, or those with substantial surpluses. Applications from individuals are not considered.
TYPE OF GRANT The trust prefers to support projects rather than running costs.
RANGE OF GRANTS Mostly between £1,000 and £5,000.
SAMPLE GRANTS Peel Studentship Trust – University of Lancaster (£30,000); Motivation Charitable Trust (£15,000); British Skin Foundation, British Red Cross and the Progressive Supranuclear Palsy Association (£10,000 each); University College London – Centre for Gastroenterology & Nutrition (£9,500); the Space Centre Preston Limited (£7,500); Acre Housing, British Liver Trust, Cued Speech Association UK and Tower Hamlets Mission (£5,000 each); Calibre Audio Library (£2,500); Spadework Ltd (£2,000); and Back Care and Disability North (£1,000 each).
FINANCES *Year* 2010–11 *Income* £522,324 *Grants* £273,345 *Assets* £15,466,955
TRUSTEES Sir Robert Boyd; John W Parkinson; Michael Parkinson; Prof. Richard Ramsden; Prof. Margaret Pearson; Julius Manduell.
HOW TO APPLY The trustees apply the following criteria in making grants: there is no geographical limitation on applications, however applications from charities in the 'preferred Locations' of Lancashire (especially Lancaster and District), Cumbria, Greater Manchester, Cheshire and Merseyside will receive preference over applications from other geographical areas; the trustees focus on small to medium sized charities where grants will make a difference. Applications from large well-funded charities (with income in excess of £2.5 million per annum) will normally be rejected, unless the project is a capital project; the trustees aim to support fewer charities with larger average grants (£5,000 or more); the trustees'

preference is to support capital projects or project driven applications and not running costs, although the trustees are flexible to take account of the needs of smaller charities; the trustees do make grants to disaster appeals which are considered on a case by case basis. The trustees feel it is important to know the charities to which grants are or may be awarded. They will therefore from time to time arrange to visit the charity and/or arrange for the charity to make a presentation to a trustees meeting. The following information is required in an application: a general outline of the reasons for the application; the amount of grant applied for; the latest annual report and audited accounts; if the application is for a major capital project, details of the cost of the project together with information regarding funds already in hand or pledged. A grant application form can be downloaded from the trust's website – print it out before filling it in and enclosing it with any other information that you may feel is relevant. *Applications for Medical Research Grants* – Applications for medical research grants will be categorised as appropriate for a 'minor grant' (£10,000 or less) or a 'major grant' (greater than £10,000 per annum for a defined research project for 1–3 years). Applications to be considered for a major grant will be assessed en-block annually at the trustee's March meeting. Applications will be competitive and will be met from funds set aside for this purpose. The following additional information is required: aims, objectives and direction of the research project; the institution where the research will be carried out and by whom (principal researchers); an outline of costs and of funding required for the project and details of any funds already in hand. A brief (but not too technical) annual report on the progress of projects receiving major grants will be requested from the research team.

WHO TO APPLY TO Allan J Twitchett, Secretary, Trowers & Hamlins LLP, Sceptre Court, 40 Tower Hill, London EC3N 4DX *Tel* 020 7423 8000 *Fax* 020 7423 8001 *email* secretary@peeltrust.com *Website* www.peeltrust.com

■ Pegasus (Stanley) Trust

CC NO 1108684 **ESTABLISHED** 2005
WHERE FUNDING CAN BE GIVEN Mainly Shropshire.
WHO CAN BENEFIT Organisations and individuals.
WHAT IS FUNDED The main object of the trust is relief in need for people who have had cancer and/or strokes, grants are also given to other charities.
RANGE OF GRANTS £500–£25,000.
SAMPLE GRANTS Zimbabwe Farmers Trust (£25,000); Help for Heroes (£20,000); County Air Ambulance (£15,000); Kanegoni (£13,000); Severn Hospice, Marie Curie (£10,000 each); Kenyan Rainbow School (£5,000); St John Ambulance (£3,000); and Globalteer (£1,5000).
FINANCES *Year* 2008–09 *Income* £656,455 *Grants* £105,120 *Assets* £105
TRUSTEES H R Gabb; H Carpenter; F Bury; C Gabb.
OTHER INFORMATION The trust organises an annual event in May at Stanley Hall, in Shropshire, to raise funds.
HOW TO APPLY In writing to the correspondent.
WHO TO APPLY TO The Trustees, 84 Faroe Road, London W14 0EP *email* ACSULW@aol.com *Website* www.pegasustrust.org

■ The Pell Charitable Trust

CC NO 1135398 **ESTABLISHED** 2010
WHERE FUNDING CAN BE GIVEN UK.
WHO CAN BENEFIT Registered charities.
WHAT IS FUNDED General charitable purposes, with a possible preference for the arts, particularly music.
TRUSTEES Marian Pell; Gordon Pell; Nicholas Pell.
HOW TO APPLY In writing to the correspondent.
WHO TO APPLY TO Coutts & Co, Trustee Dept, 440 Strand, London WC2R 0QS *Tel* 020 7663 6838

■ Peltz Trust

CC NO 1002302 **ESTABLISHED** 1991
WHERE FUNDING CAN BE GIVEN UK and Israel.
WHO CAN BENEFIT Charitable organisations.
WHAT IS FUNDED Arts, cultural and educational initiatives; health and welfare projects; religion.
WHAT IS NOT FUNDED No grants to individuals for research or educational awards.
RANGE OF GRANTS £1,000–£20,000.
SAMPLE GRANTS Oxford Centre for Hebrew and Jewish Studies (£33,000 in two grants); British Technion Society (£30,000); Facing History and Ourselves (£19,000 in two grants); Norwood Children and Families Trust (£11,000); Tate Gallery and ICSR Kings College (£10,000 each); Artichoke, One Family, St Stephen's Trust and UK Friends of Mogen David Adom (£5,000 each); Presidents Club Charitable Trust (£2,500); War Memorials Trust (£1,500); United Synagogue (£1,200); Royal Opera House Foundation, Jaffa Institute and Lifeline for the Old (£1,000 each); DALAID and Mousetrap Theatre Projects (£500 each); and the Rehabilitation Trust (£250).
FINANCES *Year* 2009–10 *Income* £171,007 *Grants* £186,100 *Assets* £36,092
TRUSTEES Martin Paisner; Daniel Peltz; Hon. Elizabeth Wolfson Peltz.
HOW TO APPLY In writing to the correspondent. The trustees meet at irregular intervals during the year to consider appeals from appropriate organisations.
WHO TO APPLY TO Martin D Paisner, Trustee, c/o Berwin Leighton Paisner, Adelaide House, London Bridge, London EC4R 9HA *Tel* 020 7760 1000 *Fax* 020 7760 1111

■ Pendragon Charitable Trust

CC NO 1139718 **ESTABLISHED** 2011
WHERE FUNDING CAN BE GIVEN UK and overseas.
WHO CAN BENEFIT Registered charities.
WHAT IS FUNDED 'We are set up to support exclusively charitable projects, with a focus in the following 3 areas: to advance the education of the public in the life sciences and to promote medical research with the aim of improving human health by supporting research, training, public engagement and dissemination of knowledge; to advance the Catholic values for the public benefit; and to relieve of those in need by reason of youth, age, ill-health, disability, financial hardship or other disadvantage. We intend to focus within these three areas on the major barriers and challenges experienced by those in need or experiencing disadvantage or hardship. The Pendragon Charitable Trust intends to support and work closely with organisations in the UK or abroad, that share its vision to provide practical solutions in the areas above.'

TRUSTEES Cadogan Trustees Limited.

HOW TO APPLY Applications can be made online using the form on the trust's website. Applications can also be made in writing to the trust via email, and must include full contact information and funding proposal fully describing the project.

'When describing the project, all applicants should include information about the organisation(s) running the project, the need the project is seeking to address, the activities that will be undertaken, and a project budget. We may contact you to request additional information or documentation needed to assess your application and the eligibility of the project under the law of England and Wales. Applications will be considered for decision at scheduled intervals throughout the year. In exceptional circumstances, it may be possible to assess an application on a more flexible basis to meet project timetables so please indicate any timing requirements clearly in your application. If your application is successful, you will be notified as soon as possible after the decision has been made on the contact details you provide.'

WHO TO APPLY TO Cadogan Trustees Limited, Cadogan Trustees Limited, Royalty House, 32 Sackville Street, London W1S 3EA *Tel* 020 74345 6068 *Fax* 020 74345 6001 *email* admin@pendragoncharitabletrust.co.uk *Website* www.pendragoncharitabletrust.co.uk

■ The Pennycress Trust

CC NO 261536　　　**ESTABLISHED** 1970

WHERE FUNDING CAN BE GIVEN UK and worldwide, with a preference for Cheshire and Norfolk.

WHO CAN BENEFIT Voluntary organisations and charitable groups only.

WHAT IS FUNDED General charitable purposes. Support is given to a restricted list of registered charities only, principally in Cheshire and Norfolk, in the fields of: arts and cultural heritage; education; infrastructure, support and development; science and technology; community facilities; campaigning on health and social issues; health care and advocacy; medical studies and research; and animal welfare.

WHAT IS NOT FUNDED No support for individuals.

TYPE OF GRANT Recurrent and one-off.

RANGE OF GRANTS Usually £100–£500.

SAMPLE GRANTS Previous beneficiaries have included All Saints' Church – Beeston Regis, Brain Research Trust, Brighton and Hove Parents' and Children's Group, British Red Cross, Crusaid, Depaul Trust, Elimination of Leukaemia Fund, Eyeless Trust, Genesis Appeal, Help the Aged, Matthew Project, RUKBA, St Peter's – Eaton Square Appeal, Salvation Army, Tibet Relief Fund, West Suffolk Headway, Women's Link and Youth Federation.

FINANCES *Year* 2009–10 *Income* £67,421 *Grants* £50,900 *Assets* £1,953,720

TRUSTEES Lady Aline Cholmondeley; Anthony J M Baker; C G Cholmondeley; Miss Sybil Sassoon.

HOW TO APPLY In writing to the correspondent. 'No telephone applications please.' Trustees meet regularly. They do not have an application form as a simple letter will be sufficient.

WHO TO APPLY TO Mrs Doreen Howells, Secretary to the Trustees, Flat D, 15 Millman Street, London WC1N 3EP *Tel* 020 7404 0145

■ The Performing Right Society Foundation

CC NO 1080837　　　**ESTABLISHED** 2000

WHERE FUNDING CAN BE GIVEN UK.

WHO CAN BENEFIT Music creators, performers and promoters who are involved in creatively adventurous or pioneering musical activity.

WHAT IS FUNDED A huge range of new music activity, for example, unsigned band showcases, festivals, residencies for composers, ground breaking commissions, live electronica, training of music producers, cross art form commissioning and special projects.

WHAT IS NOT FUNDED The foundation will not offer funding for: recordings/demos; college fees; musical equipment or instruments.

TYPE OF GRANT Usually one year funding for revenue costs.

SAMPLE GRANTS London Sinfonietta, Way out West, Jazz North East, SXSW, Camden Crawl, Flavour Magazine, Punch Records, The Irene Taylor Trust, NU Century Arts, Youth Music Theatre: UK, The Opera Group, The Late Music Festival, Chimera Productions and Oh Yeah Music Centre. Bands and artists supported include: James Blake, Jessica Curry, The Scottish Flute Trio, Matthew Bourne, Aaron Cassidy, Shiva Feshareki, Imogen Heap and Fuzzy Lights.

FINANCES *Year* 2010 *Income* £1,875,905 *Grants* £1,571,390 *Assets* £439,782

TRUSTEES Prof. Edward Gregson; Simon Platz; Michael Noonan; Baroness Morris of Yardley; Sally Millest; Paulette Long; Mick Leeson; Stephen McNeff; Lesley Douglas; Simon Darlow.

OTHER INFORMATION A list of grant recipients was not included in the accounts. However, details of previously funded projects are available on the foundation's website, though without information on the individual grant awards.

HOW TO APPLY Apply via the trust's website. The application forms for each programme also include full guidelines for applicants. Only one scheme per calendar year can be applied for. Deadlines for applications vary from programme to programme. Contact the foundation or go to the website for further information. The foundation stresses that it funds NEW music.

WHO TO APPLY TO Fiona Harvey, Applications Manager, 29–33 Berners Street, London W1T 3AB *Tel* 020 7306 4233 *Fax* 020 7306 4814 *email* info@prsformusicfoundation.com *Website* www.prsformusicfoundation.com

■ B E Perl Charitable Trust

CC NO 282847　　　**ESTABLISHED** 1981

WHERE FUNDING CAN BE GIVEN UK.

WHO CAN BENEFIT Orthodox Jewish organisations, particularly schools.

WHAT IS FUNDED The advancement of education in, and the religion of, the Orthodox Jewish faith and other general charitable purposes.

SAMPLE GRANTS Torah (5759) Limited, Shaare Zedek, Society of Friends of the Torah, Torah Temimah Primary School, WJR and Hendon Adath Yisroel Congregation. No details of grant amounts were available.

FINANCES *Year* 2009–10 *Income* £1,571,356 *Grants* £57,517 *Assets* £12,705,880

TRUSTEES Benjamin Perl, Chair; Dr Shoshanna Perl; Jonathan Perl; Joseph Perl; Naomi Sorotzkin; Rachel Jeidal.

OTHER INFORMATION Please note the following statement taken from the trust's 2009–10 annual report and accounts: 'The trustees have considered and approved plans for the

Think carefully about every application. Is it justified?

801

establishment of a major educational project in the UK. It is anticipated that the cost of this project will be in the order of £5 million and it is the intentions of the trustees to accumulate this amount over the next ten years. During the period an amount of £500,000 (2009–£500,000) was transferred to the Educational Reserve in order to fund this project. The Educational Reserve for this purpose stands at £2 million as at the balance sheet date. The trustees are pleased to report that by the balance sheet date they had paid a total amount of £825,000 for the purchase of a freehold property to be utilised as an advanced study centre for teenagers.'

HOW TO APPLY In writing to the correspondent.

WHO TO APPLY to Benjamin Perl, Chair, Foframe House, 35–37 Brent Street, Hendon, London NW4 2EF

■ The Persson Charitable Trust (formerly Highmoore Hall Charitable Trust)

CC NO 289027   **ESTABLISHED** 1984

WHERE FUNDING CAN BE GIVEN UK and overseas.

WHO CAN BENEFIT Registered charities benefiting: Christians; at risk groups; and victims of famine, man-made and natural disasters and war.

WHAT IS FUNDED Christian mission societies and relief agencies.

WHAT IS NOT FUNDED No grants to non-registered charities.

TYPE OF GRANT Mainly recurrent.

SAMPLE GRANTS Tearfund – Christian relief (£80,000); All Nations Christian College and Bible Reading Fellowship (£50,000 each), Alpha International (£40,000); Church Renewal Trust (£25,000); and Relationships Foundation (£10,000).

FINANCES Year 2009–10 *Income* £322,152 *Grants* £302,450 *Assets* £542,489

TRUSTEES P D Persson; Mrs A D Persson; J P G Persson; A S J Persson.

OTHER INFORMATION Smaller grants totalled £47,000.

HOW TO APPLY The trust states that it does not respond to unsolicited applications. Telephone calls are not welcome.

WHO TO APPLY TO P D Persson, Trustee, Long Meadow, Dark Lane, Chearsley, Aylesbury, Buckinghamshire HP18 0DA *Tel* 01844 201955

■ The Persula Foundation

CC NO 1044174   **ESTABLISHED** 1994

WHERE FUNDING CAN BE GIVEN Predominantly UK; overseas grants are given, but this is rare.

WHO CAN BENEFIT Mainly small registered charities benefiting at risk groups, people who are socially isolated, disadvantaged by poverty or homeless, people with cancer or disabilities, including visual impairment, deafness, spinal injuries and multiple sclerosis, and animals.

WHAT IS FUNDED Original and unique projects of national benefit in the areas of homelessness, disability, and human and animal welfare.

WHAT IS NOT FUNDED No grants to individuals, including sponsorship, for core costs, buildings/building work or to statutory bodies.

TYPE OF GRANT Up to two years.

SAMPLE GRANTS Tapesense (£30,000); Amnesty International UK (£20,000); and The Howard league for Penal Reform and Leagues Against Cruel Sports (£20,000 each). Previous beneficiaries have included Action for ME, African Children's Educational Trust, the Aids Trust, the Backup Trust, The Helen Bamber Foundation, Bullying Online, Disability Challengers, Dogs Trust, Emmaus, Humane Slaughter Association, Interact Worldwide, Kidscape, League Against Cruel Sports, The Mango Tree, the MicroLoan Foundation, National Deaf Children's Society, Practical Action, Prisoners Abroad, Prison Reform Trust, Respect for Animals, RNIB, RNID, St Mungo's, SOS Children, Stonewall, VIVA! And WSPA.

FINANCES Year 2009–10 *Income* £898,038 *Grants* £747,749 *Assets* £70,308

TRUSTEES Julian Richer; David Robinson; David Highton; Mrs R Richer; Mrs H Oppenheim.

PUBLICATIONS Guidelines available from the foundation's website.

HOW TO APPLY In writing to the correspondent.

WHO TO APPLY TO Fiona Brown, Chief Executive, Richer House, Hankey Place, London SE1 4BB *Tel* 020 7357 9298 *Fax* 020 7357 8685 *email* fiona@persula.org *Website* www.persula. org

---

■ The Pervez Musharraf Foundation

CC NO 1137685   **ESTABLISHED** 2010

WHERE FUNDING CAN BE GIVEN South Asia, in particular Pakistan.

WHO CAN BENEFIT The foundation gives grants to organisations which support children and young people, the elderly, people with disabilities and the general public/mankind.

WHAT IS FUNDED The advancement of education and training; disaster relief; relief of poverty, sickness and distress; promotion of good health; and the provision of recreational facilities.

TRUSTEES Mr A A Zar; Mr P Musharraf.

HOW TO APPLY In writing to the correspondent.

WHO TO APPLY TO Mr A A Zar, Trustee, Rifsons Ltd, 63–64 Charles Lane, London NW8 7SB *Tel* 020 7586 7032

■ The Jack Petchey Foundation

CC NO 1076886   **ESTABLISHED** 1999

WHERE FUNDING CAN BE GIVEN London boroughs, Essex and the Algarve, Portugal.

WHO CAN BENEFIT Registered charities and organisations supporting young people aged between 11 and 25.

WHAT IS FUNDED Support for young people through different programmes including: Achievement Award Scheme and the Individual Grants for Volunteering scheme. The foundation also runs the Petchey Academy, Jack Petchey's Speak Out Challenge!; Step Into Dance; Panathlon Challenge and TS Jack Petchey. For details of all these programmes please visit the foundation's website.

WHAT IS NOT FUNDED The foundation will not accept applications: that directly replace statutory funding; from individuals or for the benefit of one individual (unless under the Individual Grants for Volunteering); for work that has already taken place; which do not directly benefit people in the UK; for medical research; for animal welfare; for endowment funds; that are part of general appeals or circulars. The foundation is also unlikely to support: building or major refurbishment projects;

conferences and seminars; projects where the main purpose is to promote religious beliefs. The foundation only contributes to building or major refurbishment projects in exceptional circumstances.

SAMPLE GRANTS SpeakersBank Limited (£546,000); Royal Academy of Dance RAD (£440,000); School Planners (£80,000); ETTA (£70,500); Army Cadet Force (£67,000); Panathlon Challenge (£42,500); Boys' Brigade and Community Links (£19,000 each); YMCA and STEMNET (£10,000 each).

FINANCES *Year* 2009–10 *Income* £5,038,805 *Grants* £4,073,487 *Assets* £54,699

TRUSTEES Jack Petchey Foundation Company.

HOW TO APPLY Application forms for each of the grant schemes can be downloaded from the foundation's website. There are no deadlines for applications but they should be made in 'good time' before the money is needed. The foundation holds monthly management meetings and aims to give a decision within six weeks.

WHO TO APPLY TO Trudy Kilcullen, Chief Operating Officer, Exchange House, 13–14 Clements Court, Clements Lane, Ilford, Essex IG1 2QY *Tel* 020 8252 8000 *Fax* 020 8477 1088 *email* mail@jackpetcheyfoundation.org.uk *Website* www.jackpetcheyfoundation.org.uk

■ The Petplan Charitable Trust

CC NO 1032907   **ESTABLISHED** 1994

WHERE FUNDING CAN BE GIVEN UK.

WHO CAN BENEFIT Animal charities and organisations benefiting students, research workers and veterinarians.

WHAT IS FUNDED Veterinary research, animal welfare, education in animal welfare, and other charitable purposes. Help is limited to dogs, cats and horses only, those being the animals insured by Pet Plan. Rabbits will be considered.

WHAT IS NOT FUNDED No grants to individuals or non-registered charities. The trust does not support or condone invasive procedures, vivisection or experimentation of any kind.

RANGE OF GRANTS Scientific grants: £4,000–£99,000. Welfare and education grants: £200–£7,000.

SAMPLE GRANTS University of Edinburgh (£99,000); Royal Veterinary College (£30,000); University College London, University of Liverpool (£10,000 each); Animal Health Trust (£8,000); Brooke Hospital for Animals (£7,000); Blue Cross, Stokechurch Dog Rescue (£5,000 each); Three Counties Dog Rescue (£3,000); Jerry Green Foundation Trust (£2,500); Veterinary Fees (£2,000) and Greek Animal Welfare Fund (£1,000).

FINANCES *Year* 2009 *Income* £531,199 *Grants* £244,508 *Assets* £483,129

TRUSTEES David Simpson, Chair; Clarissa Baldwin; Patsy Bloom; John Bower; Ted Chandler; George Stratford; Neil Brettell.

HOW TO APPLY Closing dates for scientific and welfare applications vary so please check the trust's website first. Grant guidelines and application forms can also be downloaded from the trust's website.

WHO TO APPLY TO Catherine Bourg, Administrator, Great West House GW2, Great West Road, Brentford, Middlesex TW8 9EG *Tel* 020 8580 8013 *Fax* 020 8580 8186 *email* catherine. bourg@allianz.co.uk *Website* www.petplantrust. org

■ The Pharsalia Charitable Trust

CC NO 1120402   **ESTABLISHED** 2007

WHERE FUNDING CAN BE GIVEN Unrestricted, with a particular interest in Oxford.

WHAT IS FUNDED General charitable purposes.

RANGE OF GRANTS £100–£60,000.

SAMPLE GRANTS The major beneficiary during the year was Oxford Radcliffe Hospital Charitable Funds, which received over £60,000. Other grant beneficiaries included: St Edmund Hall (£50,000); Macmillan Cancer Support (£20,000); Help for Heroes (£8,000); Vincent's Club, Oxford University (£6,000); Royal British Legion and Age Concern, Oxford (£4,000 each); Helen & Douglas House (£3,000); Cancer Research UK (£2,000); Motability (£1,000); Canine Partners (£750) and SWGC Captains Charity (£500).

FINANCES *Year* 2009–10 *Income* £328,063 *Grants* £185,170 *Assets* £2,158,321

TRUSTEES Nigel Stirling Blackwell; Christina Blackwell; Trudy Sainsbury.

HOW TO APPLY In writing to the correspondent.

WHO TO APPLY TO Trudy Sainsbury, Trustee, 14 Hyde Place, Oxford OX2 7JB *Tel* 01367 870962

■ The Phillips and Rubens Charitable Trust

CC NO 260378   **ESTABLISHED** 1970

WHERE FUNDING CAN BE GIVEN UK.

WHO CAN BENEFIT Registered charities, especially Jewish causes.

WHAT IS FUNDED Jewish organisations, especially those in the fields of education, children's charities, the arts, and medical groups.

WHAT IS NOT FUNDED No grants are made to individuals.

TYPE OF GRANT Recurrent and one-off.

SAMPLE GRANTS £80,000 donated to the connected Phillips Family Charitable Trust; Jewish Israel Appeal (£52,000); Community Security Trust (£25,000); Jewish Community Secondary School (£21,000); Royal Opera House Foundation (£12,000); British ORT (£8,000); Charities Aid Foundation (£5,000); World Jewish Relief (£3,000); and The Michael Palin Centre for Stammering Children (£2,500).

FINANCES *Year* 2009–10 *Income* £255,588 *Grants* £280,093 *Assets* £9,401,166

TRUSTEES Michael L Philips; Mrs Ruth Philips; Martin D Paisner; Paul Philips; Gary Philips; Carolyn Mishon.

OTHER INFORMATION Grants to organisations of less than £1,000 each totalled £5,400.

HOW TO APPLY In writing to the correspondent at any time.

WHO TO APPLY TO M L Phillips, Trustee, Fifth Floor, Berkeley Square House, Berkeley Square, London W1J 6BY *Tel* 020 7491 3763 *Fax* 020 7491 0818

■ The Phillips Charitable Trust

CC NO 1057019   **ESTABLISHED** 1995

WHERE FUNDING CAN BE GIVEN UK, with a preference for the Midlands, particularly Northamptonshire.

WHO CAN BENEFIT Seafarer organisations, animal welfare organisations, the National Trust and English Heritage, and smaller one-off grants for national or local projects.

WHAT IS FUNDED Seafaring and animal welfare.

TYPE OF GRANT Recurrent.

RANGE OF GRANTS £500–£10,000.

SAMPLE GRANTS Northamptonshire Association of Youth Clubs (£10,000); Sportsaid Eastern (£7,500); Northamptonshire Museum, Royal Anglican Regiment Museum and Combat Stress (£5,000 each); Prince's Trust and the Army Benevolent Fund (£2,500); Northampton Hope Centre (£2,000); Martin Sailing Project (£1,500); Childhood First, Sailors Society and WYCA (£1,000); and Support Dogs (£500).

FINANCES *Year* 2009–10 *Income* £55,658 *Grants* £58,000 *Assets* £2,533,451

TRUSTEES M J Ford; M J Percival; Mrs A M Marrum; P R Saunderson; S G Schanschieff.

HOW TO APPLY In writing to the correspondent.

WHO TO APPLY TO Mrs G Evans, Clerk, c/o Hewitsons, 7 Spencer Parade, Northampton NN1 5AB *Tel* 01604 230400 *Fax* 01604 604164

■ The Phillips Family Charitable Trust

CC NO 279120   **ESTABLISHED** 1979

WHERE FUNDING CAN BE GIVEN UK.

WHO CAN BENEFIT Registered charities only.

WHAT IS FUNDED General charitable purposes, mainly Jewish organisations, and those concerned with older people, children, refugees and education.

WHAT IS NOT FUNDED No grants to individuals.

TYPE OF GRANT Grants are given for core, capital and project support.

RANGE OF GRANTS Up to £15,000, but mostly £5,000 or less.

SAMPLE GRANTS Community Security Trust (£5,500 in two grants); Chief Rabbinate Trust and Friends of Ohr Someach (£5,000 each); Jews' College (£3,000); Beth Shalom Ltd, Dalaid, My Israel and Sylvella Charity Ltd (£1,000 each).

FINANCES *Year* 2009–10 *Income* £60,000 *Grants* £80,054 *Assets* £4,741

TRUSTEES Michael L Phillips; Mrs Ruth Phillips; Martin D Paisner; Paul S Phillips; Gary M Phillips.

HOW TO APPLY In writing to the correspondent. Please note, the trust informed us that there is not much scope for new beneficiaries.

WHO TO APPLY TO Paul S Phillips, Trustee, Berkeley Square House, Berkeley Square, London W1J 6BY *Tel* 020 7491 3763

■ Philological Foundation

CC NO 312692   **ESTABLISHED** 1982

WHERE FUNDING CAN BE GIVEN City of Westminster and London borough of Camden.

WHO CAN BENEFIT Schools in the City of Westminster and the London borough of Camden, and their pupils and ex-pupils under 25 years of age.

WHAT IS FUNDED Individuals may receive grants for educational expenses and tuition fees; schools in the area may benefit over a wide range of purposes.

WHAT IS NOT FUNDED No support for schools not in Westminster or Camden and individuals who did not attend school in the City of Westminster or London borough of Camden. The foundation does not give bursaries, scholarships or loans.

RANGE OF GRANTS £200–£2,000.

FINANCES *Year* 2009–10 *Income* £89,286 *Grants* £56,382 *Assets* £853,116

TRUSTEES P E Sayers; Mrs S Standing; Cllr Mrs G Hampson; Mrs M Hall; Mrs J Keen; D Jones; G Margolis; R P Rea.

OTHER INFORMATION In 2009–10 the foundation gave grants to schools totalling £28,700 and grants to individuals totalling £27,700.

HOW TO APPLY There is an application form available for schools which may be obtained from the foundation. Individuals should apply in writing to the clerk. Trustees meet typically in January, March, June, September and December. Applications should be submitted several weeks before the relevant meeting. Successful applicants may reapply after one year.

WHO TO APPLY TO Mrs Audrey Millar, Clerk, Flat 15, Fitzwarren House, Hornsey Lane, Highgate, London N6 5LX *Tel* 020 7281 7439 *email* audreymillar@btinternet.com

---

■ The David Pickford Charitable Foundation

CC NO 243437   **ESTABLISHED** 1965

WHERE FUNDING CAN BE GIVEN UK (with a preference for Kent and London) and overseas.

WHO CAN BENEFIT Mainly, but not solely, young people particularly young people with special needs, and Christian evangelism.

WHAT IS FUNDED Support of a residential Christian youth centre in Kent for those in the 15 to 25 age group and other similar activities, mainly Christian youth work.

WHAT IS NOT FUNDED No grants to individuals. No building projects.

TYPE OF GRANT One-off and recurrent.

RANGE OF GRANTS £250–5,000.

SAMPLE GRANTS CARE (£5,000); Chaucer Trust (£4,000); Oasis Trust (£2,500); Brighter Future and Pastor Training international (£1,000 each); Toybox (£750); Alpha International, Flow Romania and Mersham Parish Church (£500 each); Compassion (£300); Samaritans (£250); and Lionhart (£15).

FINANCES *Year* 2009–10 *Income* £28,861 *Grants* £61,035 *Assets* £1,135,088

TRUSTEES C J Pickford; E J Pettersen.

HOW TO APPLY In writing to the correspondent. Trustees meet every other month from January. Applications will not be acknowledged. The correspondent states: 'It is our general policy only to give to charities to whom we are personally known.' Those falling outside the criteria mentioned above will be ignored.

WHO TO APPLY TO E J Pettersen, Trustee, Benover House, Rectory Lane, Saltwood, Hythe, Kent CT21 4QA *Tel* 01303 268322 *Fax* 01233 720 522

■ The Bernard Piggott Trust

CC NO 260347   **ESTABLISHED** 1970

WHERE FUNDING CAN BE GIVEN North Wales and Birmingham.

WHO CAN BENEFIT Organisations benefiting children, young adults, medical, actors and entertainment professionals, and Church of England and Wales.

WHAT IS FUNDED Church of England; Church of Wales; education; medical charities, both care and research; drama and the theatre; youth and children.

WHAT IS NOT FUNDED No grants to individuals.

TYPE OF GRANT Usually one-off capital. No further grants within two years.

RANGE OF GRANTS £250–£5,000. Average about £1,000.

SAMPLE GRANTS Birmingham Clubs for Young People and St Gwenfaen's, Rhoscolyn (£3,000 each);

Castle Bromwich Hall Gardens and DebRA (£2,000 each); Birmingham Boys' & Girls' Union, Cornerstone, Marie Curie, Oesphagael Patients Association, Headway, Queen Alexandra College, The Ackers and The Dystonia Society (£1,000 each); and Sea Ranger Association (£500).

FINANCES *Year* 2009–10 *Income* £103,727 *Grants* £68,375 *Assets* £1,354,540

TRUSTEES D M P Lea; N J L Lea; R J Easton; Venerable Meurig Llwyd Williams; Mark Painter.

HOW TO APPLY The trustees meet in May/June and November. Applications should be in writing to the secretary including annual accounts and details of the specific project including running costs and so on. General policy is not to consider any further grant to the same institution within the next two years.

WHO TO APPLY TO J P Whitworth, Jenny Whitworth, 4 Streetsbrook Road, Shirley, Solihull, West Midlands B90 3PL *Tel* 0121 744 1695 *Fax* 0121 744 1695

■ The Pilgrim Trust

CC NO 206602   **ESTABLISHED** 1930

WHERE FUNDING CAN BE GIVEN UK, but not the Channel Islands and the Isle of Man.

WHO CAN BENEFIT Local and UK charities and recognised public bodies.

WHAT IS FUNDED Preservation (covering ecclesiastical buildings, secular buildings), learning and social welfare.

WHAT IS NOT FUNDED Grants are not made to: individuals; non UK registered charities or charities registered in the Channel Islands or the Isle of Man; projects based outside the United Kingdom; projects where the work has already been completed or where contracts have already been awarded; organisations that have had a grant awarded by us within the past two years. Note: this does not refer to payments made within that timeframe; projects with a capital cost of over £1 million pounds where partnership funding is required; projects where the activities are considered to be primarily the responsibility of central or local government; general appeals or circulars; projects for the commissioning of new works of art; organisations seeking publishing production costs; projects seeking to develop new facilities within a church or the re-ordering of churches or places of worship for wider community use; any social welfare project that falls outside the trustees' current priorities; arts and drama projects – unless they can demonstrate that they are linked to clear educational goals for prisoners or those with drug or alcohol problems; drop in centres – unless the specific work within the centre falls within one of the trustees' current priority areas; youth or sports clubs, travel or adventure projects, community centres or children's play groups; organisations seeking funding for trips abroad; organisations seeking educational funding, e.g. assistance to individuals for degree or post-degree work or school, university or college development programmes; one-off events such as exhibitions, festivals, seminars, conferences or theatrical and musical productions.

TYPE OF GRANT Infrastructure costs for specific projects (salary and running costs up to a maximum of three years), capital grants. Also buildings, one-off, research and start-up costs.

SAMPLE GRANTS Toynbee Hall (£45,000); Prisoners' Advice Service (£30,000); The Paddocks Riding for All (£20,500); The Wallace Collection and the Jewish Museum (£15,000 each); and the Belfast Preservation Trust (£10,000).

FINANCES *Year* 2010 *Income* £1,225,040 *Grants* £2,398,167 *Assets* £56,609,953

TRUSTEES Lady Jay of Ewelme; Tim Knox; Paul Richards; Sir Mark Jones; Sir Alan Moses; John Podmore; James Fergusson; David Verey; Prof. Colin Blakemore; Lady Riddell; Sarah Staniforth; Michael Baughn.

HOW TO APPLY 'Main Grant Fund: As our primary grant outlet, this fund distributes approximately 90% of our annual grant budget. If the project fits our programme criteria, organisations can apply under this scheme for sums above £5,000. Small Grant Fund: This fund is reserved for requests of £5,000 or less. Applications to this fund normally require less detailed assessment (though a visit or meeting may be required) but applicants should include the names of two referees from organisations with whom they work.' Full funding guidelines are available from the trust's website. Applications can also be made online or a form can be requested from the correspondent. The trustees meet quarterly.

WHO TO APPLY TO Georgina Nayler, Director, Clutha House, 10 Storeys Gate, London SW1P 3AY *Tel* 020 7222 4723 *Fax* 020 7976 0461 *email* info@thepilgrimtrust.org.uk *Website* www.thepilgrimtrust.org.uk

■ The Cecil Pilkington Charitable Trust

CC NO 249997   **ESTABLISHED** 1966

WHERE FUNDING CAN BE GIVEN UK, particularly Sunningwell in Oxfordshire and St Helens.

WHO CAN BENEFIT Registered charities only.

WHAT IS FUNDED This trust supports conservation and medical research causes across the UK. It also has general charitable purposes.

WHAT IS NOT FUNDED No grants to individuals or non-registered charities.

RANGE OF GRANTS £500–£60,000.

SAMPLE GRANTS Psychiatry Research Trust (£50,000); Peninsular Medical School Foundation (£20,000); St Leonard's Church Restoration and SANE (£5,000 each); Wildfowl and Wetlands Trust (£2,000); and Sunningwell School of Art (£1,000).

FINANCES *Year* 2008–09 *Income* £197,510 *Grants* £136,500 *Assets* £7,558,677

TRUSTEES A P Pilkington; R F Carter Jonas; M R Feeny.

HOW TO APPLY The trust does not respond to unsolicited appeals.

WHO TO APPLY TO The Administrator, Duncan Sheard Glass, Castle Chambers, 43 Castle Street, Liverpool L2 9TL

■ The Elise Pilkington Charitable Trust

CC NO 278332   **ESTABLISHED** 1979

WHERE FUNDING CAN BE GIVEN UK.

WHO CAN BENEFIT Organisations benefiting equines and older people in need.

WHAT IS FUNDED Welfare and relief work as well as prevention of cruelty.

FINANCES *Year* 2009–10 *Income* £79,999 *Grants* £160,500 *Assets* £2,798,678

TRUSTEES Caroline Doulton, Chair; Tara Economakis; Revd Rob Merchant; Helen Timpany.

OTHER INFORMATION £95,000 in 10 grants was given to prevent cruelty to equine animals and £66,000 in 12 grants to provide help for the aged, infirm or poor.

HOW TO APPLY In writing to the correspondent.

WHO TO APPLY TO Kenton Lawton, Trust Administrator, Ridgecot, Lewes Road, Horsted Keynes, Haywards Heath, West Sussex RH17 7DY *Tel* 01825 790304

■ The Pilkington Charities Fund

CC NO 225911   **ESTABLISHED** 1964

WHERE FUNDING CAN BE GIVEN Worldwide, in practice mainly UK with a preference for Merseyside.

WHO CAN BENEFIT Registered charities.

WHAT IS FUNDED Health, social welfare, people with disabilities, older people and victims of natural disaster or war.

WHAT IS NOT FUNDED Applications from unregistered organisations and individuals are not considered.

TYPE OF GRANT Capital (including buildings), core costs, one-off, project, research, recurring costs. Funding for more than three years will be considered.

RANGE OF GRANTS Up to £10,000, although exceptional large grants are made.

SAMPLE GRANTS C & A Pilkington Trust Fund (£66,000). The more general distributions were for less than £5,000 each with the exception of: Cancer Research UK and the Willowbrook Hospice – St Helens (£10,000 each); Home Farm Trust (£8,000); Shelter (£7,000); and Team Oasis (£6,000). Other beneficiaries of £5,000 or less included: Alzheimer's Research Trust; Changing Faces; Foundation for the Study of Infant Death; Kidney Research UK; Missing People; Parents Against Drug Abuse; Somali Umbrella Group; Toxteth Town Hall Community Resource Centre; and Wirral Autistic Society.

FINANCES *Year* 2009–10 *Income* £444,057 *Grants* £350,500 *Assets* £17,414,256

TRUSTEES Neil Pilkington Jones; Mrs Jennifer Jones; Arnold Philip Pilkington.

HOW TO APPLY In writing to the correspondent. Applications should include charity registration number, a copy of the latest accounts and details of the project for which support is sought. Grants are awarded twice a year, in November and April.

WHO TO APPLY TO Sarah Nicklin, Trust Administrator, Rathbones, Port of Liverpool Building, Pier Head, Liverpool L3 1NW *Tel* 0151 236 6666 *Fax* 0151 243 7003 *email* sarah.nicklin@ rathbones.com

■ The Austin and Hope Pilkington Trust

CC NO 255274   **ESTABLISHED** 1967

WHERE FUNDING CAN BE GIVEN Unrestricted, but see Exclusions field.

WHO CAN BENEFIT Registered charities only. National projects are preferred to those with a local remit.

WHAT IS FUNDED The trust has a three-year cycle of funding. (2012 – community, medical; 2013 – children, youth; 2014 – music and the arts, elderly.) These categories are then repeated in a three-year rotation. .

WHAT IS NOT FUNDED Grants only to registered charities. No grants to individuals, including individuals embarking on a trip overseas with an umbrella organisation. Overseas projects are no longer supported. National organisations are more likely to be supported than purely local organisations. Charities working in the following areas are not supported: religion (including repair of Church fabric); animals (welfare and conservation); scouts, guides, cubs, brownies; village halls; individual hospices (national organisations can apply); capital appeals; schools; and minibuses.

TYPE OF GRANT Grants are usually awarded for one year only.

RANGE OF GRANTS Grants are usually between £1,000 and £3,000, with the majority being £1,000. Exceptionally, grants of up to £10,000 are made, but these are usually for medical research projects.

SAMPLE GRANTS The priorities for the charity in 2009 were community and disability. Beneficiaries included: The Connection at St Martin in the Fields (£5,000); Resources for Autism, Enterprise Education Trust, Action Space, Parentline Plus (£3,000 each); Get Hooked on Fishing, Blind in Business, ASGMA, Crime Diversion Scheme, Women in Prison, Hope Centre Ballymena, YWCA, Vassall Centre trust, Spadework, Multiple Sclerosis Trust and Normandy Community Therapy Garden (£1,000 each).

FINANCES *Year* 2009 *Income* £216,756 *Grants* £209,972 *Assets* £8,877,887

TRUSTEES Jennifer Jones; Deborah Nelson; Penny Shankar.

OTHER INFORMATION 2011 was the last year grants when grants were made to overseas projects.

HOW TO APPLY Applicants are strongly advised to visit the trust's website as projects supported and eligibility criteria change from year to year. Grants are made twice a year, with deadlines for applications being 1 June and 1 November. Applications should be made in writing to the correspondent – do not use signed for or courier. To apply for a grant, please submit *only* the following: A letter summarising the application, including acknowledgement of any previous grants awarded from the trust; a maximum of two sides of A4 (including photographs) summarising the project; a detailed budget for the project; a maximum of two sides of A4 (including photographs) summarising the charity's general activities; the most recent accounts and annual report. 'Please do not send CDs, DVDs, or any other additional information. If we require further details, we will contact the charity directly. Charities are therefore advised to send in applications with sufficient time before the June or November deadlines to allow for such enquiries.' With the increased level of applications, the trust has stated that all successful applicants will in future be listed on their website on the 'recent awards' after each trustee meeting. All applicants will still be contacted by letter in due course. Early applications are strongly encouraged.

WHO TO APPLY TO Karen Frank, Administrator, PO Box 124, Stroud, Gloucestershire GL6 7YN *email* admin@austin-hope-pilkington.org.uk *Website* www.austin-hope-pilkington.org.uk

■ The Sir Harry Pilkington Trust

CC NO 206740   **ESTABLISHED** 1962

WHERE FUNDING CAN BE GIVEN UK, with a preference for Merseyside.

WHO CAN BENEFIT Charitable organisations.

WHAT IS FUNDED General charitable purposes.

806

Does the trust you have chosen match your needs? Haphazard applications waste postage and time

SAMPLE GRANTS Liverpool Charity and Voluntary Services (£40,000); The Basement Night Drop-in Centre (£4,000); Albion Youth Club, Barnstondale Centre and Disability and Deaf Arts(£3,000 each); Dovecot Multi Activity Centre (£2,800); Healthy Energy Advice Team, Hetherlow Community Centre Association, Merseyside Caribbean Council and Pre School Equipment and Resource Centre (£2,000 each); and Woodlands Residents Association and Writing On the Wall (£1,000 each).

FINANCES *Year* 2009–10 *Income* £169,327 *Grants* £187,239 *Assets* £4,764,796

TRUSTEES Liverpool Charity and Voluntary Services.

HOW TO APPLY In writing to the correspondent. The trust welcomes an initial phone call to discuss the proposal.

WHO TO APPLY TO The Trustees, Liverpool Charity and Voluntary Services, 151 Dale Street, Liverpool L2 2AH *Tel* 0151 227 5177 *Website* www.merseytrusts.org.uk

---

■ The Col W W Pilkington Will Trusts – The General Charity Fund

CC NO 234710   **ESTABLISHED** 1964

WHERE FUNDING CAN BE GIVEN UK, with a preference for Merseyside.

WHO CAN BENEFIT Registered charities only.

WHAT IS FUNDED Medical, arts, social welfare, drugs misuse, international and environmental charities.

WHAT IS NOT FUNDED No support for non-registered charities, building projects, animal charities or individuals.

TYPE OF GRANT Generally annual.

SAMPLE GRANTS Halle Concerts Society, the New Works, Narconon, No Panic, Mary Seacole House, Buglife, Wildlife Trust for Lancs, Manchester and North Merseyside and Minority Rights Group International (£1,500 each).

FINANCES *Year* 2009–10 *Income* £55,805 *Grants* £46,000 *Assets* £1,479,387

TRUSTEES Arnold Pilkington; Hon. Mrs Jennifer Jones; Neil Pilkington Jones.

HOW TO APPLY In writing to the correspondent.

WHO TO APPLY TO The Clerk, PO Box 8162, London W2 1GF

■ Miss A M Pilkington's Charitable Trust

SC NO SC000282   **ESTABLISHED** 1972

WHERE FUNDING CAN BE GIVEN UK, with a preference for Scotland.

WHO CAN BENEFIT Registered charities.

WHAT IS FUNDED General charitable purposes, including conservation/environment, health and social welfare.

WHAT IS NOT FUNDED Grants are not given to overseas projects or political appeals.

FINANCES *Year* 2009–10 *Income* £136,298

HOW TO APPLY The trustees state that, regrettably, they are unable to make grants to new applicants since they already have 'more than enough causes to support'.

WHO TO APPLY TO The Clerk, Carters Chartered Accountants, Pentland House, Saltire Centre, Glenrothes, Fife KY6 2AH

■ The DLA Piper Charitable Trust

CC NO 327280   **ESTABLISHED** 1986

WHERE FUNDING CAN BE GIVEN UK.

WHO CAN BENEFIT Charitable organisations.

WHAT IS FUNDED General charitable purposes.

WHAT IS NOT FUNDED No grants to individuals.

TYPE OF GRANT Mainly single donations.

RANGE OF GRANTS £1,000–£10,000.

SAMPLE GRANTS Previously: the Cutty Sark Trust (£10,000); Solicitors' Benevolent Association (£8,500); Christie's Hospital, Green Belt Movement International and The Prince's Trust (£5,000 each); Yorkshire Air Ambulance and South Yorkshire Community Foundation Flood Disaster Relief Fund, The University of Michigan Law School (£51,000).

FINANCES *Year* 2009–10 *Income* £500 *Grants* £50,000

TRUSTEES N G Knowles; P Rooney.

OTHER INFORMATION Accounts were received at the Charity Commission but unable to view. Information was obtained from the Charity Commission website.

HOW TO APPLY In writing to the correspondent, for consideration every three months.

WHO TO APPLY TO G J Smallman, Secretary, Wrigleys Solicitors LLP, Fountain Precinct, Balm Green, Sheffield S1 2JA *Tel* 0114 267 5594 *email* godfrey.smallman@wrigleys.co.uk

---

■ The Plaisterers' Company Charitable Trust

CC NO 281035   **ESTABLISHED** 1980

WHERE FUNDING CAN BE GIVEN England and the City of London.

WHO CAN BENEFIT Former freemen and liverymen of the company; students and competitions in colleges related to the plastering trade; and selected City of London charities, in particular the Lord Mayor's Appeal. Individuals and organisations. General charitable grants with a focus primarily on charities and worthy good causes with a plastering emphasis; London/ City charities with a 'people' focus towards the disabled and disadvantaged; charities connected with HM Forces.

WHAT IS FUNDED Grants for relief in need, general charitable purposes and training promotion.

SAMPLE GRANTS The Bluecoat Foundation (£8,900); The Lord Mayor's Appeal (£6,300); St Paul's Cathedral (£4,300); Guildhall School of Music and Drama (£2,700); South Lanarkshire College (£1,300); Accrington & Rosendale College (£500).

FINANCES *Year* 2010–11 *Income* £81,047 *Grants* £37,020 *Assets* £799,408

TRUSTEES Mr R P Doran; Mr M J A Lepper; Sir R Ross; Mr R K Walker; Prof. J H Lacey; Mr N C C Bamping; Mr R E Dalrymple.

OTHER INFORMATION £425 to individuals

HOW TO APPLY The trust has previously stated that unsolicited applications are not accepted.

WHO TO APPLY TO R P Doran, Trustee, Westcroft, 3 Limes Road, Egham, Surrey TW20 9QT *Tel* 01784 435301 *Fax* 01784 748021

■ The Platinum Trust

CC NO 328570   **ESTABLISHED** 1990

WHERE FUNDING CAN BE GIVEN UK.

WHO CAN BENEFIT Charities benefiting people with disabilities.

WHAT IS FUNDED The relief of children with special needs and adults with mental or physical disabilities 'requiring special attention'.

WHAT IS NOT FUNDED No grants for services run by statutory or public bodies, or from mental-health organisations. No grants for: medical research/ treatment or equipment; mobility aids/ wheelchairs; community transport/disabled transport schemes; holidays/exchanges/holiday playschemes; special-needs playgroups; toy and leisure libraries; special Olympic and Paralympics groups; sports and recreation clubs for people with disabilities; residential care/ sheltered housing/respite care; carers; conservation schemes/city farms/horticultural therapy; sheltered or supported employment/ community business/social firms; purchase/ construction/repair of buildings; and conductive education/other special educational programmes.

RANGE OF GRANTS Usually £5,000–£45,000.

SAMPLE GRANTS Goss Michael Foundation – restricted funds (£353,000); Disability, Pregnancy and Parenthood International (£45,000); Centre for Studies on Inclusive Education (£30,000); Alliance for Inclusive Education (£20,000); Parents for Inclusion (£20,000); Independent Panel for Special Education Advice (£15,000); Disabled Parents Network (£10,000); DEMAND (£5,000); and Clear Vision (£300).

FINANCES *Year* 2009–10 *Income* £687,275 *Grants* £558,677 *Assets* £282,322

TRUSTEES Georgios K Panayiotou; Stephen Marks; C D Organ.

OTHER INFORMATION All the trustees are also trustees of Platinum Overseas Trust (Charity Commission no. 1004176) and Stephen Marks is also a trustee of The Mill Charitable Trust (Charity Commission no. 1128056). The trust was established by Georgios Panayiotou, AKA the singer George Michael.

HOW TO APPLY The trust does not accept unsolicited applications; all future grants will be allocated by the trustees to groups they have already made links with.

WHO TO APPLY TO The Secretary, Sedley Richard Laurence Voulters, 89 New Bond Street, London W1S 1DA *Tel* 020 7079 8814

■ G S Plaut Charitable Trust Limited

CC NO 261469   **ESTABLISHED** 1970

WHERE FUNDING CAN BE GIVEN Predominantly UK.

WHO CAN BENEFIT Voluntary organisations and charitable groups only.

WHAT IS FUNDED Sickness, disability, Jewish, elderly and general charitable purposes.

WHAT IS NOT FUNDED No grants to individuals or for repeat applications.

RANGE OF GRANTS £1,000–£3,000.

SAMPLE GRANTS Dogs for the Disabled, Magen David Adom UK and Children In Touch – 1978 (£3,000 each); Médecins Sans Frontières (£2,500); Toybox Charity, Tear Fund, Carers UK and Anglo Jewish Association (£2,000 each); Ex-Services Mental Welfare Society – Combat Stress (£1,500); and Sight Savers International, the Sobriety Project and British Retinitis Pigmentosa Society (£1,000 each).

FINANCES *Year* 2009–10 *Income* £49,189 *Grants* £47,000 *Assets* £1,167,559

TRUSTEES Mrs A D Wrapson; Miss T A Warburg; Mr W E Murfett; Mrs B A Sprinz; Miss R E Liebeschuetz.

HOW TO APPLY In writing to the correspondent. Applications are reviewed twice a year. An sae should be enclosed. Applications will not be acknowledged.

WHO TO APPLY TO Dr R A Speirs, Secretary, 39 Bay Road, Wormit, Newport-on-Tay, Fife DD6 8LW

■ Polden-Puckham Charitable Foundation

CC NO 1003024   **ESTABLISHED** 1970

WHERE FUNDING CAN BE GIVEN UK and overseas.

WHO CAN BENEFIT Registered charities only.

WHAT IS FUNDED 'In the limited areas described [here] we support projects that seek to influence values and attitudes, promote equity and social justice, and develop radical alternatives to current economic and social structures. **Peace and Sustainable Security:** We support the development of ways of resolving violent conflicts peacefully, and of addressing their underlying causes. **Environmental Sustainability:** We support work that addresses the pressures and conditions leading towards global environmental breakdown; particularly national initiatives in UK which promote sustainable living.'

WHAT IS NOT FUNDED The foundation does not fund: organisations that are large; organisations that are outside UK (unless they are linked with a UK registered charity and doing work of international focus); work outside the UK (unless it is of international focus); grants to individuals; travel bursaries (including overseas placements and expeditions); study; academic research; capital projects (e.g. building projects or purchase of nature reserves); community or local practical projects (except innovative projects for widespread application); environmental/ ecological conservation; international agencies and overseas appeals; general appeals; human rights work (except where it relates to peace and environmental sustainability).

TYPE OF GRANT Core costs and project funding for up to three years.

RANGE OF GRANTS Normally £5,000 to £15,000.

SAMPLE GRANTS British American Security Information Council (£15,000); Climate Outreach Information Network and Scientists for Global Responsibility (MEDACT*) (£11,000 each); British Pugwash Trust, International Coalition to ban Uranium Weapons (Manchester Environmental Research Centre Initiative*), Peace and Security Liaison Group (Lansbury House Trust Fund*) and Oxford Research Group (£10,000 each); Crisis Action UK (MEDACT*) (£9,000); Public Interest Research Centre and the Transition Network (£8,000 each); Apollo Gaia Project (Unit for Research into Changing Institutions*) (£7,000); Conflicts Forum (Street Theatre Workshop Trust*) and Oil Depletion Analysis Centre (£6,000 each); Airport Watch (Airfields Environment Trust*) and the UK Social Investment Forum (£5,000 each); Quaker Council for European Affairs British Committee (£4,000); Solar Aid and Women's International League for Peace and Freedom (MEDACT*) (£3,000 each); Be the Change (Gaia Foundation*) (£2,000); and World Court Project (Institute of Law and Peace*) (£1,400). *The names in brackets are charitable organisations receiving the grants on behalf of campaign organisations for their educational and research work.

FINANCES *Year* 2009–10 *Income* £459,334 *Grants* £333,000 *Assets* £12,678,780

TRUSTEES Harriet Gillett; Linda Patten; Daniel Barlow; Bevis Gillett; Val Ferguson; Ben Gillett; Suzy Gillett; Jean Barlow.

HOW TO APPLY The trustees meet twice a year in spring and autumn. Application forms and guidance notes can be downloaded from the foundation's website and must be submitted via email. Applicants are also asked to submit their latest set of audited accounts and an annual report, preferably via email. Please note: the foundation is happy to provide brief feedback on applications one week after the trustees have made a decision.

WHO TO APPLY TO Bryn Higgs, Secretary, BM PPCF, London WC1N 3XX *email* ppcf@polden-puckham.org.uk *Website* www.polden-puckham.org.uk

■ The Polehanger Trust

CC NO 1076447   **ESTABLISHED** 1999

WHERE FUNDING CAN BE GIVEN Worldwide.

WHO CAN BENEFIT Christian organisations.

WHAT IS FUNDED Christian causes.

SAMPLE GRANTS Stopsley Baptist Church – Global Sunday Appeal and Tear Fund (£5,000 each); Luton Christian Educational Trust (£2,000); Oasis Charitable Trust (£1,500); and Bedfordshire Festival of Music, Speech and Drama (£100).

FINANCES *Year* 2009–10 *Income* £5,616 *Grants* £15,000

TRUSTEES C S Foster; Mrs C J Foster.

HOW TO APPLY No grants to unsolicited applications.

WHO TO APPLY TO C S Foster, Trustee, Polehanger Farm, Shefford Road, Meppershall, Shefford, Bedfordshire SG17 5LH *Tel* 01462 813310

■ The Poling Charitable Trust

CC NO 240066   **ESTABLISHED** 1964

WHERE FUNDING CAN BE GIVEN Mainly Sussex.

WHO CAN BENEFIT Organisations.

WHAT IS FUNDED General charitable purposes.

WHAT IS NOT FUNDED No support for individuals or medical causes. No new proposals.

RANGE OF GRANTS £25–£5,600.

SAMPLE GRANTS Previous beneficiaries have included Arundel Festival, Chichester Cathedral Development Trust, City Music Society, Friends of Covent Garden, Parochial Church Council of St Nicholas, RAF Escapers, Royal Academy of Music, Sherborne Abbey, Sussex Association for Rehabilitation of Offenders, Sussex Association for the Deaf, Sussex Trust for Nature Conservation, Wave Heritage Trust, Pallant House Gallery and West Dean Foundation.

FINANCES *Year* 2009–10 *Income* £58,023

TRUSTEES A Hopkinson; Mrs P Hopkinson.

HOW TO APPLY In writing to the correspondent, however the trust stated that it has no spare income, as it is all fully committed.

WHO TO APPLY TO D H L Hopkinson, St John's Priory, Poling Street, Poling, Arundel, West Sussex BN18 9PS *Tel* 01903 882393

■ The George and Esme Pollitzer Charitable Settlement

CC NO 212631   **ESTABLISHED** 1960

WHERE FUNDING CAN BE GIVEN UK.

WHO CAN BENEFIT Registered charities, particularly Jewish organisations.

WHAT IS FUNDED General charitable purposes and Jewish causes.

SAMPLE GRANTS Jewish Museum (£10,000); Norwood Children and Families First and The Royal College of Surgeons (£2,000 each); Alexandra Rose Day, Anthony Nolan Trust, The Big Issue, Cove Park, Deafblind UK, Fields in Trust, Foundation for Conductive Education, Sense, Swinfen Charitable Trust, The Weiner Library and Who Cares Trust (£1,500 each); and Jewish Council for Racial Equality and Target Ovarian Cancer (£1,000 each).

FINANCES *Year* 2009–10 *Income* £95,117 *Grants* £79,500 *Assets* £2,815,146

TRUSTEES J Barnes; Catherine Alexander Charles; R F C Pollitzer.

HOW TO APPLY In writing to the correspondent.

WHO TO APPLY TO Miss L E Parrock, Saffery Champness, Beaufort House, 2 Beaufort Road, Clifton, Bristol B58 2AE *Tel* 01179 151617

■ The J S F Pollitzer Charitable Settlement

CC NO 210680   **ESTABLISHED** 1960

WHERE FUNDING CAN BE GIVEN UK and overseas.

WHO CAN BENEFIT Registered charities only.

WHAT IS FUNDED General charitable purposes.

WHAT IS NOT FUNDED No grants to individuals or students, i.e. those without charitable status.

TYPE OF GRANT One-off.

RANGE OF GRANTS Typically £1,000 each.

SAMPLE GRANTS Aidis Trust, Cruse Bereavement Care, Dyson Perrins Museum Trust, Education Uganda, Florence Nightingale Hospice Charity, Girls' Venture Corps Air Cadets, the Herpetological Conservation Trust, Highland Budokan Judo Club, Little Ouse Headwaters Project, MDF the Bipolar Association, the Memorial Arts Charity and the Sequal Trust (£1,000 each).

FINANCES *Year* 2009–10 *Income* £48,129 *Grants* £44,000 *Assets* £672,448

TRUSTEES R F C Pollitzer, Chair; Mrs E Pettit; Mrs S C O'Farrell.

HOW TO APPLY In writing to the correspondent. Grants are distributed twice a year, usually around April/May and November/December.

WHO TO APPLY TO Trust Accountant, Mary Street House, Mary Street, Taunton, Somerset TA1 3NW *Tel* 01823 286096

■ The Pollywally Charitable Trust

CC NO 1107513   **ESTABLISHED** 2005

WHERE FUNDING CAN BE GIVEN UK.

WHO CAN BENEFIT Jewish institutions of primary, secondary and further education and those caring for the poor and sick.

WHAT IS FUNDED Jewish causes, education, and welfare.

RANGE OF GRANTS Up to £15,000.

SAMPLE GRANTS British Friends of Orchos Chaim (£10,600); Edgware Foundation (£8,000); Tashbar Foundation (£2,800); Sparqoute Limited (£2,600); Amud Hachesed Trust (£1,700). Grants of less than £1,000 each were made to 31 organisations.

Think carefully about every application. Is it justified?

809

FINANCES *Year* 2009–10 *Income* £35,002 *Assets* £12,714

TRUSTEES J H Pollins; Mrs S L Pollins; J Waller; Mrs S Waller.

OTHER INFORMATION Grants were also given to 4 individuals.

HOW TO APPLY In writing to the correspondent.

WHO TO APPLY TO Jeremy Waller, Trustee, c/o Waller Pollins, 8th Floor, Premier House, 112 Station Road, Edgware, Middlesex *Tel* 020 8238 5858

■ The Polonsky Foundation

CC NO 291143   **ESTABLISHED** 1985

WHERE FUNDING CAN BE GIVEN UK, Israel and the USA.

WHO CAN BENEFIT Educational establishments.

WHAT IS FUNDED 'To support higher education internationally, principally in the arts and social sciences, and programmes favouring the study and resolution of human conflict. Much of this work is part of ongoing programmes being undertaken in conjunction with various Departments of the Hebrew University of Jerusalem and the Bezalel Academy of Art and Design, as well as other organisations within the United States and the United Kingdom.'

RANGE OF GRANTS Up to £250,000.

SAMPLE GRANTS The Jewish Museum (£250,000); British Friend of Haifa University (£107,000); Royal Shakespeare Company (£81,000); Bezalel Academy of Art and Design (£60,500); New York University (£20,500); Yale University (£18,500); Port Regis School (£8,500); Lincoln College (£5,000); North Western Reform Synagogue (£2,000); and Whitechapel Foundation (£1,000).

FINANCES *Year* 2009–10 *Income* £1,077,861 *Grants* £742,675 *Assets* £46,182,875

TRUSTEES Dr Georgette Bennett; Dr Leonard Polonsky; Valarie Smith.

HOW TO APPLY In writing to the correspondent.

WHO TO APPLY TO The Trustees, 8 Park Crescent, London W1B 1PG

■ The Ponton House Trust

SC NO SC021716   **ESTABLISHED** 1993

WHERE FUNDING CAN BE GIVEN The Lothians.

WHO CAN BENEFIT Organisations benefiting disadvantaged groups, principally young and elderly people.

WHAT IS FUNDED Grants are given mainly to support small charities working with young people, elderly people and disadvantaged groups.

WHAT IS NOT FUNDED No grants to individuals or non-charitable organisations.

TYPE OF GRANT One-off.

RANGE OF GRANTS Up to £6,300.

SAMPLE GRANTS Previously: Edinburgh Voluntary Organisations Trust (£9,000), for onward distribution to individuals; Bethany Christian Trust and Lothian Autistic Society (£1,500 each); Garvald Training Centre, Venture Scotland, Circle, Children 1st and Partners for Advocacy (£1,000); Rock Trust (£900); Maggie's Cancer Caring Centres (£750); and Equal Futures.

FINANCES *Year* 2009–10 *Income* £45,764 *Grants* £30,000

TRUSTEES Revd John Munro, Chair; Shulah Allen; Patrick Edwardson; Julie Matthews; Ian Boardman; James Verth.

OTHER INFORMATION Accounts were previously provided by the trust. For 2010–11 information

was obtained from the Office of the Scottish Charity Regulator website.

HOW TO APPLY In writing to the correspondent, there are no specific application forms. Trustees usually meet in January, April, July and October. Applications should include a full explanation of the project for which funding is sought plus annual reports and accounts.

WHO TO APPLY TO David S Reith, Secretary, Lindsays WS, Caledonian Exchange, 19A Canning Street, Edinburgh EH3 8HE *Tel* 0131 229 1212 *Fax* 0131 229 5611 *email* dsr@lindsays.co.uk

■ The Mayor of Poole's Appeal Fund

CC NO 1027462   **ESTABLISHED** 1993

WHERE FUNDING CAN BE GIVEN Dorset, Poole.

WHO CAN BENEFIT Charitable organisations.

WHAT IS FUNDED Work of particular interest to the Mayor.

SAMPLE GRANTS Dorset County Scouts, Ray Smith Charity Carers of Poole, Lewis Manning Hospice, Parkstone Sports and Arts Centre and Poole East Division Guides (£4,330 each); Poole and Bournemouth branch of the Tall Ships Youth Trust and the Alzheimer's Society (£250 each).

FINANCES *Year* 2009–10 *Income* £35,161 *Grants* £22,150 *Assets* £25,036

TRUSTEES Joyce Lavender; John McBride; Christopher Bulteel; Charles Meachin.

HOW TO APPLY In writing to the correspondent, but note the comments in the general section. Applications should be made before February each year, but preferably several months before February.

WHO TO APPLY TO Josephine Clements, Mayor's Secretary, Mayor's Office, Borough of Poole, Civic Centre, Poole, Dorset BH15 2RU *Tel* 01202 633 200 *Fax* 01202 633 094 *email* j.clements@poole.gov.uk *Website* www.boroughofpoole.com

■ The Popocatepetl Trust

CC NO 1133690   **ESTABLISHED** 2010

WHERE FUNDING CAN BE GIVEN Worldwide, with a preference for the UK.

TRUSTEES Eleanor Broad; Ms Grania P C Bryceson; Mrs Elizabeth G M Delliere; Mrs Monique M Surridge; Mrs Monique M Surridge; David Williams.

HOW TO APPLY In writing to the correspondent.

WHO TO APPLY TO David Williams, 7 Rose Lane, Ripley, Woking, Surrey GU23 6NE

■ Edith and Ferdinand Porjes Charitable Trust

CC NO 274012   **ESTABLISHED** 1973

WHERE FUNDING CAN BE GIVEN UK and overseas.

WHO CAN BENEFIT Jewish organisations; registered charities.

WHAT IS FUNDED General charitable purposes, particularly Jewish causes.

SAMPLE GRANTS the Jewish Museum (£25,000); Jewish Book Council (£20,000); Yesodey Hatorah Grammar School (£7,500); British Friends of the Art Museums of Israel (£4,000); and British Friends of OHEL Sarah (£2,500).

FINANCES *Year* 2009–10 *Income* £48,055 *Grants* £57,100 *Assets* £1,449,136

TRUSTEES Martin D Paisner; A S Rosenfelder; H Stanton.

HOW TO APPLY In writing to the correspondent.
WHO TO APPLY TO Martin D Paisner, Trustee, c/o Berwin Leighton Paisner, Adelaide House, London Bridge, London EC4R 9HA *Tel* 020 7760 1000 *Fax* 020 7760 1111

■ The John Porter Charitable Trust

CC NO 267170   **ESTABLISHED** 1974
WHERE FUNDING CAN BE GIVEN Worldwide, but mainly UK and Israel.
WHO CAN BENEFIT Registered and exempt charities.
WHAT IS FUNDED Education, culture, environment, health and welfare.
WHAT IS NOT FUNDED No grants to individuals.
RANGE OF GRANTS Usually up to £25,000.
SAMPLE GRANTS Sourasky Tel Aviv Medical Centre (£216,000); the Foundation of the International School of Verbier (£12,000); Israel Philharmonic Orchestra Foundation (£10,000); University of Oxford and Maccabi GB (£5,000 each).
FINANCES *Year* 2009–10 *Income* £229,208 *Grants* £252,454 *Assets* £11,163,568
TRUSTEES John Porter; Baroness Greenfield; Robert Glatter.
HOW TO APPLY In writing to the correspondent.
WHO TO APPLY TO The Trustees, c/o Blink Rothenberg, 12 York Gate, London NW1 4QS *Tel* 020 7544 8863

■ The Porter Foundation

CC NO 261194   **ESTABLISHED** 1970
WHERE FUNDING CAN BE GIVEN Israel and the UK.
WHO CAN BENEFIT Registered charities and community organisations.
WHAT IS FUNDED Practical projects to enhance the quality of people's lives and environment. Priorities are health, education, the environment and culture.
WHAT IS NOT FUNDED The foundation makes grants only to registered charitable organisations or to organisations with charitable objects that are exempt from the requirement for charitable registration. Grants will not be made to: individuals; general appeals such as direct mail circulars; charities which redistribute funds to other charities; third-party organisations raising money on behalf of other charities; or cover general running costs.
TYPE OF GRANT Usually project-based and capital.
SAMPLE GRANTS Friends of Daniel for Rowing Association (£63,000); New Israel Fund (£42,000); Tel Aviv University Trust (£40,000); Friends of the Israeli Opera (£20,000); Oxford Centre of Hebrew and Jewish Studies (£9,500); Beit Issie Shapiro (£2,000); and Whitechapel Gallery (£1,000).
FINANCES *Year* 2009–10 *Income* £804,503 *Grants* £551,161 *Assets* £46,233,950
TRUSTEES David Brecher; Albert Castle; Dame Shirley Porter; Steven Porter; Sir Walter Bodmer; John Porter; Linda Streit.
OTHER INFORMATION During recent years the foundation has cut back on the number of beneficiaries supported and is making fewer, larger grants, mainly to the connected Porter School of Environmental Studies at Tel Aviv University, or the university itself, and to other causes in Israel. This has led to a temporary reduction in UK-based activity. A limited number of community awards continue to be given, though usually to organisations already known to the foundation.
HOW TO APPLY An initial letter summarising your application, together with basic costings and background details on your organisation, such as the annual report and accounts, should be sent to the director. Speculative approaches containing expensive publicity material are not encouraged. If your proposal falls within the foundation's current funding criteria you may be contacted for further information, including perhaps a visit from the foundation staff. There is no need to fill out an application form. Applications fulfilling the criteria will be considered by the trustees, who meet three times a year, usually in March, July and November. You will hear shortly after the meeting whether your application has been successful. Unfortunately, it is not possible to acknowledge all unsolicited applications (unless a stamped, addressed envelope is enclosed). If you do not hear from the foundation, you can assume that your application has been unsuccessful. Due to limits on funds available, some excellent projects may have to be refused a grant. In such a case the trustees may invite the applicant to re-apply in a future financial year, without giving a commitment to fund.
WHO TO APPLY TO Paul Williams, Executive Director, Blick Rothenburg, Trust Department, 12 York Gate, Regent's Park, London NW1 4QS *Tel* 020 7544 8863 *email* theporterfoundation@btinternet.com

---

■ Porticus UK

CC NO 1069245   **ESTABLISHED** 1998
WHERE FUNDING CAN BE GIVEN UK.
WHO CAN BENEFIT Registered charities.
WHAT IS FUNDED The charity's four areas of interest are: strengthening family relationships; enriching education; transformation through faith; and ethics in practice.
WHAT IS NOT FUNDED No grants to non-registered charities. Applications for the following will not be considered: high profile appeals; major capital projects or restoration of buildings; grants to individuals; endowment appeals; overseas projects (including travel).
RANGE OF GRANTS £10,000 to £25,000.
FINANCES *Year* 2010 *Grants* £4,000,000
TRUSTEES Louise A Adams; Mark C L Brenninkmeyer; Stephen R M Brenninkmeyer.
OTHER INFORMATION Porticus UK is not in itself a grantmaker – it advises and assesses grants on behalf of several foundations in the Netherlands, including Stichting Porticus. In 2010 the charity assessed 488 applications which resulted in 129 new grants being made.
HOW TO APPLY On an application form available from the charity's website. Applications can be submitted at any time. The charity also says that: 'if you are unsure whether your project/organisation fits in with our guidelines, you are welcome to submit an initial brief outline of your organisation and funding requirements.'
WHO TO APPLY TO Nathan Koblintz, 4th Floor, Eagle House, 108–110 Jermyn Street, London SW1Y 6EE *Tel* 020 7024 3503 *Fax* 020 7024 3501 *email* porticusuk@porticus.com *Website* www.porticusuk.com

---

■ The Portishead Nautical Trust

CC NO 228876   **ESTABLISHED** 1964
WHERE FUNDING CAN BE GIVEN Bristol and North Somerset.
WHO CAN BENEFIT People under 25 years of age who are disadvantaged or at risk; voluntary and

---

charitable groups working with such people, with young offenders and with people with addictions.

WHAT IS FUNDED Projects with young people who are disadvantaged; educational support for such people; counselling services; and youth groups.

WHAT IS NOT FUNDED No grants for further education costs of non-disadvantaged people.

TYPE OF GRANT One-off, project, recurring costs and running costs will be considered. Funding may be given for up to three years.

RANGE OF GRANTS Usually £100–£5,000.

SAMPLE GRANTS Parkway Parent and Child Project (£1,900); Avon Outward Bound (£1,600); Bristol Children's Help Society and Happy Days Children's Charity (£1,500 each); Addiction Recovery Agency (£1,400); Relate Avon Family Counselling Service (£1,300); Hop, Skip and Jump South West and YMCA Clevedon (£1,200 each); and Handicapped Children's Action Group and the Spaniorium Trust (£750 each).

FINANCES *Year* 2009–10 *Income* £71,414 *Grants* £43,080 *Assets* £1,612,000

TRUSTEES Miss S Belk; G Russ; Dr G Owen; Mrs M Hoskins; Mrs I Perry; Mrs T J F Kirby; Mrs A F Kay; S P Gillingham; M R Cruse; C Crossman; Mrs W Bryant.

OTHER INFORMATION In 2009–10 grants totalling £2,150 were given to individuals.

HOW TO APPLY In writing to the correspondent.

WHO TO APPLY TO Brian Ruse, Secretary, c/o Dingley-Brown, 108 High Street, Portishead, Bristol BS20 6AJ *Tel* 01275 847463 *Fax* 01275 818 871

■ The Portrack Charitable Trust

CC NO 266120   **ESTABLISHED** 1973

WHERE FUNDING CAN BE GIVEN Some preference for Scotland.

WHO CAN BENEFIT Charitable organisations.

WHAT IS FUNDED General charitable organisations.

WHAT IS NOT FUNDED Grants are not given to individuals.

SAMPLE GRANTS Maggie's Cancer Caring Centres (£30,000); Yale University Press (£10,000); Medical Aid for Palestinians (£2,000); Carers UK, Listening Books, National Museums Scotland and Princess Royal Trust for Carers (£1,000 each); and St Andrew's Youth Club and University of Glasgow (£500 each).

FINANCES *Year* 2009–10 *Income* £70,457 *Grants* £69,500 *Assets* £3,210,883

TRUSTEES Charles Jencks; Keith Galloway; John Jencks.

OTHER INFORMATION Charles Alexander Jencks is also a trustee of the Keswick Foundation Limited (Charity Commission no. 278449); and Keith Galloway is also a trustee of Rockliffe Charitable Trust (Charity Commission no. 274117).

HOW TO APPLY In writing to the correspondent.

WHO TO APPLY TO The Trustees, Butterfield Bank, 99 Gresham Street, London EC2V 7NG *Tel* 020 7776 6700

■ The J E Posnansky Charitable Trust

CC NO 210416   **ESTABLISHED** 1962

WHERE FUNDING CAN BE GIVEN Worldwide, in practice mainly UK.

WHO CAN BENEFIT Charitable organisations.

WHAT IS FUNDED Jewish charities, health, social welfare, humanitarian.

WHAT IS NOT FUNDED No grants to individuals.

TYPE OF GRANT One-off.

RANGE OF GRANTS Typically £500–£30,000.

SAMPLE GRANTS Magen David Adom UK (£20,000); Friends of Alyn (£15,000); Jewish Care (£7,500); Norwood (£5,000); Terence Higgins Trust (£2,000); Tay Sachs Screening Programme (£1,000); and the Sue Ryder Foundation (£500).

FINANCES *Year* 2009–10 *Income* £79,538 *Grants* £138,500 *Assets* £3,813,056

TRUSTEES Mrs G Raffles; A Posnansky; P A Mishcon; Mrs E J Feather; N S Posnansky.

HOW TO APPLY Unsolicited applications will not be considered.

WHO TO APPLY TO Mr N S Posnansky, Trustee, Sobell Rhodes, Monument House, 215 Marsh Road, Pinner, London WA5 5NE *Tel* 020 7431 0909 *Fax* 020 7435 1516

■ The Mary Potter Convent Hospital Trust

CC NO 1078525   **ESTABLISHED** 1999

WHERE FUNDING CAN BE GIVEN Nottinghamshire.

WHO CAN BENEFIT Organisations and individuals.

WHAT IS FUNDED Relief of medical and health problems.

WHAT IS NOT FUNDED No grants to non-registered charities, or for capital/building costs.

TYPE OF GRANT Mainly one-off grants, but payments over two or three years may be considered.

SAMPLE GRANTS Rainbows Hospice (£6,000); Haywood House, Motor Neurone Disease and RELATE (£5,000 each); and Friary Drop in and Deaf/Blind (£4,000 each).

FINANCES *Year* 2009–10 *Income* £87,343 *Grants* £74,076 *Assets* £2,443,701

TRUSTEES Rupert A L Roberts, Chair; C N Bain; Sister Ann Haugh; Dr J P Curran; Mrs Jennifer M Farr; Christopher J Howell; Michael F Mason; Frederick T C Pell; Ms Jo Stevenson; Sister Margaret Watson.

HOW TO APPLY In writing to the correspondent. Unsuccessful applicants will not be notified.

WHO TO APPLY TO Michael F Mason, Administrator, Massers Solicitors, 15 Victoria Street, Nottingham NG1 2JZ *Tel* 0115 851 1666 *Fax* 0115 851 1673 *email* michaelm@massers.co.uk

---

■ The David and Elaine Potter Foundation

CC NO 1078217   **ESTABLISHED** 1999

WHERE FUNDING CAN BE GIVEN UK and other countries with particular emphasis on the developing world.

WHO CAN BENEFIT Charitable organisations working in the areas of education, science, human rights, and the general strengthening of civil society.

WHAT IS FUNDED Advancement of education and scientific research. Most grants are made for scholarships and other related activities that will improve understanding, governance and the promotion of a civil society; research through the creation of institutions and other means; human rights activism; initiatives that support democratic governance; and agencies and charities carrying out development, research and educational projects. Limited grants are also made for the arts.

WHAT IS NOT FUNDED No grants to individuals, animal welfare charities or humanitarian aid. Requests for endowment, capital campaigns, construction, equipment purchases and debt reduction will not be considered.

TYPE OF GRANT Capital, revenue, project funding over multiple years.

RANGE OF GRANTS £500–£150,000.

SAMPLE GRANTS Bureau of Investigative Journalism (£2 million); CIDA – UK Foundation, Independent Diplomat and the Royal Society (£150,000 each); Business Bridge Initiative (£90,000); Reprieve (£60,000); Room to Read (£31,000); Performa (£25,000); UCL Development Fund (£10,000); Royal Court Theatre (£5,000); and Global Dialogue – ARIADNE (£2,500).

FINANCES *Year* 2009 *Income* £1,570,481 *Grants* £3,216,721 *Assets* £20,633,626

TRUSTEES Michael S Polonsky; Michael Langley; Dr David Potter; Elaine Potter; Samuel Potter.

HOW TO APPLY The following details on how to apply to the foundation are taken from its website: 'The grant application process is divided into two stages: a letter of enquiry and an application. An applicant is invited to submit a full proposal only if their letter of enquiry has been accepted. There are no deadlines for letters of enquiry, as the foundation reviews these requests regularly. The members of the board of trustees request that correspondence be submitted to the foundation office in place of personal or written contact with individual board members. **Stage 1 – Letter of Enquiry** In order to initiate a proposal to the David and Elaine Potter Foundation, please submit a one to two-page letter of enquiry. Your letter should include the following information: contact name; contact telephone numbers/fax number; contact email; organisation background and brief description of activities; total income of the organisation in the last complete financial year; brief project synopsis, time frame, and anticipated outcome; grant amount requested and total project cost; charity status, charity registration number if applicable. Once the foundation director has reviewed your letter, we will contact you via email to acknowledge receipt. The contact information listed on your letter of enquiry is where all correspondence will be sent. If you do not receive email notification within two weeks, please contact us. Following up on a letter of enquiry is the organisation's responsibility. **Stage 2 – Application** Should the foundation approve your letter of enquiry, you may then complete and submit a formal application. Your formal application must include all information originally provided in the letter of enquiry and expand on details appropriately and as suggested by the foundation trustees. In assessing applications, the trustees consider the following information: whether the aims of the organisation meet the foundation priorities; a copy of the most recent report and audited accounts; a full description of the project requiring funding, with details of who will benefit; a complete budget for the project, with amount requested from the foundation; a description of how the project/programme will be evaluated and outcomes measured. **What happens next** The foundation director screens letters of enquiry and applications to establish whether sufficient information has been submitted. Additional details are sometimes requested before any further action is taken. At any point, a visit might also be arranged in order to gain greater insight into an organisation. All letters of enquiry and applications are considered on an individual basis by the trustees. Applicants are notified of the outcome of each stage by letter. **Evaluation** The foundation requires evaluation information

about the expenditure of grants and/or programme outcomes every six months after grant monies are received and until the funds have been expended. A final report on the grant will be required within three months of completion of the project/programme. If relevant to the grant evaluation process or to consider future funding, a site visit may be arranged at this time.'

WHO TO APPLY TO Mrs Angela Seay, Director, 10 Park Crescent, London W1B 1PQ *Tel* 020 7291 3993 *Fax* 020 7291 3991 *email* info@ potterfoundation.com *Website* www. potterfoundation.com

··

■ The Powell Foundation

CC NO 1012786 **ESTABLISHED** 1992

WHERE FUNDING CAN BE GIVEN Within the Milton Keynes Unitary Council area.

WHO CAN BENEFIT Individuals and local organisations benefiting older people and people of any age with disabilities.

WHAT IS FUNDED Grants for the benefit of older people and mentally and physically disabled people. Localised charities working in the fields of community development including supporting voluntary organisations, community arts and recreation, community facilities and services for people with disabilities, healthcare and special needs education.

SAMPLE GRANTS Milton Keynes Community Foundation (£95,000); the Pace Centre (£21,500).

FINANCES *Year* 2009–10 *Income* £137,478 *Grants* £116,719 *Assets* £3,829,470

TRUSTEES R W Norman; R Hill; P Smith.

OTHER INFORMATION Each year a large grant of up to £100,000 is awarded to Milton Keynes Community Foundation.

HOW TO APPLY Please visit the trust's website for full guidelines and details of how to apply. Application forms are available on request from the grants team who can either post or email the forms.

WHO TO APPLY TO Julia Upton, Chief Executive, c/o Milton Keynes Community Foundation, Acorn House, 381 Midsummer Boulevard, Central Milton Keynes MK9 3HP *Tel* 01908 690276 *Fax* 01908 233635 *email* information@ mkcommunityfoundation.co.uk *Website* www. mkcommunityfoundation.co.uk

··

■ The Praebendo Charitable Foundation

CC NO 1137426 **ESTABLISHED** 2010

WHERE FUNDING CAN BE GIVEN England, Scotland and Wales.

WHO CAN BENEFIT Organisations supporting children and young people; elderly people; people with disabilities, other charities and the general public/mankind and individuals.

WHAT IS FUNDED Education/training; advancement of health or saving of lives; people with disabilities; the prevention or relief of poverty; and religious activities.

TRUSTEES Susan Christmas; Helen Leech.

HOW TO APPLY In writing to the correspondent.

WHO TO APPLY TO Helen Leech, Trustee, Drift House, First Drift, Wothorpe, Stamford, Lincolnshire PE9 3JL *Tel* 01780 489082

Think carefully about every application. Is it justified?

········

813

■ Prairie Trust

CC NO 296019 **ESTABLISHED** 1987

WHERE FUNDING CAN BE GIVEN Worldwide.

WHO CAN BENEFIT Charitable organisations.

WHAT IS FUNDED A small number of organisations working on issues of third world development, climate change and conflict prevention, and particularly to support policy and advocacy work in these areas. The trustees are also interested in supporting innovative and entrepreneurial approaches to traditional problems.

WHAT IS NOT FUNDED No grants to individuals or for expeditions.

TYPE OF GRANT One-off and recurrent grants of up to two years.

RANGE OF GRANTS £100–£69,000.

SAMPLE GRANTS Not Stupid (£69,000 in 4 grants); the Funding Network (£60,000 in 16 grants across a number of groups); P8 (£30,000); Landmatters (£14,000); Institute of Fundraising (£3,100); Women in Need (£2,500); British Museum and Olivia Hodson Cancer Fund (£1,000 each); Royal Opera House Foundation (£320); and Ashmolean Museum (£100).

FINANCES *Year* 2009–10 *Income* £24,032 *Grants* £253,866 *Assets* £1,080,000

TRUSTEES Dr Frederick Mulder; Hannah Mulder.

OTHER INFORMATION At the end of the year investments stood at £449,000 and the trust transferred a further £631,000 into its CAF Gold account during the year.

HOW TO APPLY The trust states: 'As we are a proactive trust with limited funds and administrative help, we are unable to consider unsolicited applications'.

WHO TO APPLY TO The Administrator, 83 Belsize Park Gardens, London NW3 4NJ *email* info@ frederickmulder.com

■ The W L Pratt Charitable Trust

CC NO 256907 **ESTABLISHED** 1968

WHERE FUNDING CAN BE GIVEN UK, particularly York, and overseas.

WHO CAN BENEFIT Charitable organisations.

WHAT IS FUNDED In the UK: to support religious and social objectives with priority for York and district, including health and community services. Overseas: to help the developing world by assisting in food production and relief of famine and disease.

WHAT IS NOT FUNDED No grants to individuals. No grants for buildings or for upkeep and preservation of places of worship.

SAMPLE GRANTS York Diocesan Board of Finance and York Minister Development Campaign (£5,000 each); Christian Aid, Sightsavers International and Wilberforce Trust (£2,000); Oxfam and Save the Children (£1,000 each); and Action Research, Age Concern, Camphill Village Trust (Croft Community), Live Music Now, Mercy Ships, NSPCC, Shelter and Yorkshire Young Musicians (£500 each).

FINANCES *Year* 2009–10 *Income* £47,115 *Grants* £59,400 *Assets* £1,651,661

TRUSTEES J L C Pratt; C M Tetley; C C Goodway.

HOW TO APPLY In writing to the correspondent. Applications will not be acknowledged unless an sae is supplied. Telephone applications are not accepted.

WHO TO APPLY TO C C Goodway, Trustee, Grays, Duncombe Place, York YO1 7DY *Tel* 01904 634771 *email* christophergoodway@ grayssolicitors.co.uk

■ The Premier League Charitable Fund

CC NO 1137208 **ESTABLISHED** 2010

WHERE FUNDING CAN BE GIVEN England and Wales.

WHO CAN BENEFIT Organisations.

WHAT IS FUNDED general charitable purposes; education/training; the advancement of health or saving of lives; people with disabilities; the prevention or relief of poverty; sport and recreation and economic/community development.

TRUSTEES William Bush; R Scudamore.

HOW TO APPLY In writing to the correspondent.

WHO TO APPLY TO Monica Golding, 30 Gloucester Place, London W1U 8PL *Tel* 020 7864 9000 *email* creatingchances@premierleague.com *Website* www.premierleague.com

■ Premierquote Ltd

CC NO 801957 **ESTABLISHED** 1985

WHERE FUNDING CAN BE GIVEN Worldwide.

WHO CAN BENEFIT People of the Jewish faith.

WHAT IS FUNDED Jewish charitable purposes, relief of poverty, general charitable purposes.

SAMPLE GRANTS Previous beneficiaries have included Achisomoch, Belz Yeshiva Trust, Beth Jacob Grammar School for Girls Ltd, British Friends of Shuvu, Friends of Ohel Moshe, Friends of Senet Wiznitz, Friends of the United Institutions of Arad, Kehal Chasidel Bobov, Meadowgold Limited, Menorah Primary School, North West London Communal Mikvah and Torah Vedaas Primary School.

FINANCES *Year* 2009–10 *Income* £896,790 *Grants* £559,713 *Assets* £6,956,730

TRUSTEES D Last; Mrs L Last; H Last; M Weisenfeld.

HOW TO APPLY In writing to the correspondent.

WHO TO APPLY TO D Last, Trustee, 18 Green Walk, London NW4 2AJ *Tel* 020 7247 8376

■ Premishlaner Charitable Trust

CC NO 1046945 **ESTABLISHED** 1995

WHERE FUNDING CAN BE GIVEN UK and worldwide.

WHO CAN BENEFIT Jewish people and people disadvantaged by poverty.

WHAT IS FUNDED To advance orthodox Jewish education; to advance the religion of the Jewish faith in accordance with the orthodox practice; to relieve poverty; other general charitable purposes.

SAMPLE GRANTS Chen Vochessed Vrachamim (£19,000); Tchabe Kollel (£18,000); Marcaz Hayahalom (£12,000); Beis Rochel (£10,000); Yeshiva and Cong Machizikei (£7,000); and CMZ (£5,000).

FINANCES *Year* 2009–10 *Income* £126,204 *Grants* £118,990 *Assets* £421,712

TRUSTEES C Freudenberger; C M Margulies.

OTHER INFORMATION Other donations under £5,000 each totalled £47,000.

HOW TO APPLY In writing to the correspondent.

WHO TO APPLY TO C M Margulies, Trustee, 186 Lordship Road, London N16 5ES *Tel* 020 8802 4449

■ The Tom Press Charitable Foundation

CC NO 1136548 **ESTABLISHED** 2010
WHERE FUNDING CAN BE GIVEN Worldwide.
WHO CAN BENEFIT Individuals and organisations benefiting children and young people.
WHAT IS FUNDED Advancement of health, providing relief to children who are suffering from life-threatening illness; promotion of medical research into childhood illness and advancing the education of children with learning difficulties and those undergoing treatment in hospital. The foundation also aims to improve learning facilities in schools including the provision of libraries, language or IT facilities and equipment.
TRUSTEES Sue Press; Matthew Press; Mark Vines; Andy Press.
HOW TO APPLY In writing to the correspondent.
WHO TO APPLY TO Andy Press, Trustee, Maybrook, 19 Valley Way, Gerrards Cross, Buckinghamshire SL9 7PL *Tel* 01753 887921 *email* info@tompressfoundation.com *Website* www.tompressfoundation.com

■ The Douglas Prestwich Charitable Trust

CC NO 1017597 **ESTABLISHED** 1993
WHERE FUNDING CAN BE GIVEN UK, with a possible preference for the south of England.
WHO CAN BENEFIT Hospices and other organisations benefiting older people and people with disabilities.
WHAT IS FUNDED Help to older people, especially through hospices, and help for people with disabilities, especially through mechanical and other aids.
RANGE OF GRANTS Income grants usually £5,0000; capital grants up to £50,000.
SAMPLE GRANTS Previous beneficiaries include: Douglas Prestwich Award, Compaid, Disabled Living Foundation, Motability and the Mobility Trust.
FINANCES *Year* 2009–10 *Income* £5,267 *Grants* £70,000
TRUSTEES Margaret Prestwich; Olivia Meekin; David Monro.
HOW TO APPLY In writing to the correspondent; however, please note the trust stated that its 'present policy [] is only to consider grants to institutions which it has already assisted and where the need continues to be shown'.
WHO TO APPLY TO David Monro, 8 Great James Street, London WC1N 3DF *Tel* 020 7404 7001 *email* ddcm@monro-fisher.com

■ The William Price Charitable Trust

CC NO 307319 **ESTABLISHED** 1989
WHERE FUNDING CAN BE GIVEN Fareham's town parishes of St Peter and St Paul, Holy Trinity with St Columba and St John the Evangelist. Please note this area is that of the Fareham town parishes and not the borough of Fareham.
WHO CAN BENEFIT Schools and individuals under the age of 25 in the parishes.
WHAT IS FUNDED Schools for educational benefits not normally provided by the local education authority, and individuals for help with fees, travel, outfits, clothing, books and so on. Also promoting education in the doctrines of the Church of England.

WHAT IS NOT FUNDED Grants cannot be given to persons who live outside the area of the Fareham town parishes or to any organisation or establishment other than those outlined in this entry.
TYPE OF GRANT One-off.
SAMPLE GRANTS Schools and colleges (£106,400); churches (£7,500); individual hardship grants (£13,000); other individual grants (£3,300); and Fareham Welfare Trust (£11,000).
FINANCES *Year* 2009–10 *Income* £174,064 *Grants* £140,944 *Assets* £6,066,212
TRUSTEES William Price Trust Company.
HOW TO APPLY On a form available from the correspondent. 'Whenever possible applications should be made through the establishment concerned. Application forms are available on request. Larger grants are considered by trustees on a six-monthly basis with closing dates for applications of 1 March and 1 September. Smaller grants for individuals are considered quickly and normally in less than one month.'
WHO TO APPLY TO Dr C D Thomas, Clerk, 24 Cuckoo Lane, Stubbington, Fareham, Hampshire PO14 3PF *Tel* 01329 663685 *email* mazchris@tiscali.co.uk

■ The Lucy Price Relief-in-Need Charity

CC NO 516967 **ESTABLISHED** 1982
WHERE FUNDING CAN BE GIVEN The parish of Baginton in Warwickshire only.
WHO CAN BENEFIT Individuals up to the age of 25 and organisations benefiting such people.
WHAT IS FUNDED Education, sports and youth work.
SAMPLE GRANTS No grants list available.
FINANCES *Year* 2009 *Income* £6,171 *Grants* £23,000
TRUSTEES Mrs J E Fawcett; G R Yates; A J Brown; Nigel Thomas; S Williams; Mrs L Given.
HOW TO APPLY On a form available from the correspondent, or any of the trustees.
WHO TO APPLY TO Mrs Della Thomas, 19 Holly Walk, Baginton, Coventry CV8 3AE *Tel* 07884 182904

■ Sir John Priestman Charity Trust

CC NO 209397 **ESTABLISHED** 1931
WHERE FUNDING CAN BE GIVEN County borough of Sunderland and historic counties of Durham and York.
WHO CAN BENEFIT Local organisations benefiting children and older people, clergy, people of the Church of England and people disadvantaged by poverty.
WHAT IS FUNDED The trust includes a clothing fund to provide clothing for poor children resident in Sunderland who attend churches and Sunday school; and a general fund to provide for the relief of people who are poor, elderly or infirm. Also the establishment of hospitals and convalescent homes; the advancement of education of candidates for Holy Orders who after ordination will work in Durham for not less than six years; the benefit of the Church of England.
Grants are awarded to churches for building, restoring, altering, enlarging, maintaining and furnishing.
TYPE OF GRANT 'The trustees support a number of charities by way of regular annual grants, but otherwise the trustees' aim where possible to

award grants for specific projects as opposed to general running costs.

'The trustees generally award modest grants to a relatively large number of bodies rather than a few large grants.'

RANGE OF GRANTS £400–£12,000.

SAMPLE GRANTS Ripon Cathedral Development (£12,000); All Saints Church, Boldon Lane, St John's Church, Seaham (£10,000 each); Outward Bound Trust (£8,700); Durham Association of Clubs for Young People (£5,000); Independence at Home (£4,000); Motor Neurone Disease Association Durham, Governors of Durham School, Butterwick Hospice Care Teesdale (£3,000 each); Royal British Legion Poppy Appeal, RNIB, Listening Books (£2,000 each); British Polio Fellowship Sunderland, Corporation of the Sons of the Clergy (£1,000 each).

FINANCES *Year* 2010 *Income* £289,988 *Grants* £286,341 *Assets* £9,615,003

TRUSTEES Mr Peter Taylor; Mr Richard Farr; Mr Timothy Norton; Mr Anthony Coates; Mr Thomas Greenwell.

OTHER INFORMATION 'The trustees' policy is generally to award modest grants to a relatively large number of bodies rather than a few large grants. The charities supported cover a wide range of activities. In this way the trustees aim to provide for a wide variety of needs of persons resident in the geographical area of the trust.'

HOW TO APPLY In writing to the correspondent. The trustees meet in January, April, July and October. Applications should include clear details of the need the project is designed to meet plus estimates, where appropriate, and details of amounts subscribed to date.

WHO TO APPLY TO The Trustees, McKenzie Bell, 19 John Street, Sunderland SR1 1JG *Tel* 0191 567 4857

....

■ The Primrose Trust

CC NO 800049　　　　**ESTABLISHED** 1986
WHERE FUNDING CAN BE GIVEN UK.
WHO CAN BENEFIT Registered charities.
WHAT IS FUNDED General charitable purposes.
WHAT IS NOT FUNDED Grants are given to registered charities only.
SAMPLE GRANTS Badger Trust (£20,000); Animal Health Trust (£15,000); Langford Trust and Sea Shepherd (£10,000 each); and Barn Owl Trust, Community of the Holy Fire Loving Caring Members, Scottish Badgers and Vale Wildlife Hospital (£5,000 each).
FINANCES *Year* 2009–10 *Income* £120,802 *Grants* £75,000 *Assets* £3,500,845
TRUSTEES M G Clark; Susan Boyes-Korkis.
HOW TO APPLY In writing to the correspondent, including a copy of the most recent accounts. The trust does not wish to receive telephone calls.
WHO TO APPLY TO Steven Allan, 5 Callaghan Square, Cardiff CF10 5BT *Tel* 029 2026 4394

....

■ The Prince of Wales's Charitable Foundation

CC NO 1127255　　　　**ESTABLISHED** 1979
WHERE FUNDING CAN BE GIVEN Unrestricted.
WHO CAN BENEFIT Registered charities mainly in which the Prince of Wales has a particular interest.

WHAT IS FUNDED Culture, the environment, medical welfare, education, children and youth and overseas aid.

WHAT IS NOT FUNDED No grants to individuals.

TYPE OF GRANT One-off grants for capital or core expenditure.

RANGE OF GRANTS Typically up to £10,000; large grants are also made.

SAMPLE GRANTS The Great Stewart of Scotland's Dumfries House Trust (£975,000); The Prince's Foundation for Integrated Health (£186,000); Mihai Eminescu Trust (£158,000); The Prince's School of Traditional Arts (£85,000); Wells for India (£52,500); Leprosy Mission England and Wales and English National Opera (£46,000 each); Great Ormond Street Children's Hospital (£39,000); Music in Country Churches (£20,000); and Peak Choice Ltd (£10,000).

FINANCES *Year* 2009–10 *Income* £4,859,725 *Grants* £6,769,895 *Assets* £14,544,767

TRUSTEES Sir Michael Rake; Lord Rothschild; Leslie Jane Ferrar; Dame Amelia Fawcett.

OTHER INFORMATION The foundation makes small grants of up to £10,000 and 'major grants' – new guidance on how to apply for major grants was not available at the time of writing but will be available on the foundation's website from early 2012.

HOW TO APPLY In writing to the correspondent: 'write a letter setting out brief details of the project for which you are seeking support and how it fits the foundation's criteria. You should include details of your beneficiaries, where you work and any other charities or agencies that work with you; include the latest audited accounts for your charity and a note from your treasurer of your current financial position and how this award will help.'

WHO TO APPLY TO David Hutson, The Prince of Wales's Office, Clarence House, St James's, London SW1A 1BA *Tel* 020 7930 4832 ext 4788 *Fax* 020 7930 0119 *Website* princeofwales.gov.uk

....

■ The Foundation of Prince William and Prince Harry

CC NO 1132048　　　　**ESTABLISHED** 2009
WHERE FUNDING CAN BE GIVEN UK and overseas.
WHO CAN BENEFIT Registered charities.
WHAT IS FUNDED Young people – particularly those of [the Princes'] age and younger who are disadvantaged or in need of guidance and support at a crucial time in their lives; sustainable development – particularly to build on the growing awareness of the need to find better, more sustainable, models to balance development and the conservation of resources and the natural environment; Armed Forces – for the welfare of those who serve their country in the Armed Forces. Particularly looking after those who return broken in body or mind – or not at all – and their families.
FINANCES *Year* 2010 *Income* £629,141 *Assets* £465,145
TRUSTEES Anthony James Lowther-Pinkerton; Guy Monson; Sir David Manning; Edward Harley; Lord Janvrin; Fiona Shackleton.
OTHER INFORMATION All of the money spent by the foundation (£163,996) went on governance, staff and recruitment costs associated with the getting the foundation operational. It is anticipated that the foundation will begin making grants in 2012.
HOW TO APPLY The foundation is not currently seeking unsolicited applications (December

2011). Check the foundation's website for up-to-date information.

WHO TO APPLY TO Nick Booth, Chief Executive, St James's Palace, London SW1A 1BS *Tel* 020 7024 5694 *Website* www.princeofwales.gov.uk/newsandgallery/focus/the_foundation_of_prince_william_and_prince_harry_570302665.html

■ Princess Anne's Charities

CC NO 277814   **ESTABLISHED** 1979

WHERE FUNDING CAN BE GIVEN UK.

WHO CAN BENEFIT Registered charities, especially charities in which Princess Anne has a particular interest.

WHAT IS FUNDED Social welfare; medical research; children and youth; environment and wildlife; armed forces; and general charitable purposes.

WHAT IS NOT FUNDED No grants to individuals.

TYPE OF GRANT Project, capital and revenue funding. Loans and contracts may also be issued.

SAMPLE GRANTS Previous beneficiaries have included: Butler Trust, the Canal Museum Trust Cranfield Trust, Dogs Trust, Dorothy House Foundation, Durrell Wildlife Conservation Trust, the Evelina Children's Hospital Appeal, Farms for City Children, Farrer and Co Charitable Trust, Fire Services National Benevolent Fund, the Home Farm Trust, Intensive Care Society, International League for the Protection of Horses, King Edward VIII Hospital-Sister Agnes, National Autistic Society, Minchinhampton Centre for the Elderly, Mission to Seafarers, Princess Royal Trust for Carers, REDR, RYA Sailability, Save the Children Fund, Scottish Field Studies Association, Scottish Motor Neurone Disease Association, Sense, Spinal Injuries Association, Strathcarron Hospice, Transaid, London Bombing Relief Charitable Fund, Victim Support, VSO and Women's Royal Navy Benevolent Trust.

FINANCES *Year* 2009–10 *Income* £133,462 *Grants* £106,525 *Assets* £4,858,793

TRUSTEES Hon. M T Bridges; Rear Admiral T J H Laurence; B Hammond.

HOW TO APPLY 'The trustees are not anxious to receive unsolicited general applications as these are unlikely to be successful and only increase the cost of administration of the charity.'

WHO TO APPLY TO Capt. N Wright, Buckingham Palace, London SW1A 1AA

■ The Priory Foundation

CC NO 295919   **ESTABLISHED** 1986

WHERE FUNDING CAN BE GIVEN UK.

WHO CAN BENEFIT Registered charities, especially those benefiting children.

WHAT IS FUNDED General charitable purposes.

SAMPLE GRANTS Saracens Foundation (£34,000); Infer Trust and Ovarian Cancer Action (£30,000 each); London Borough of Barnet (£29,000); Wellbeing (£25,000); Arundel Castle Cricket Foundation (£24,000); Watford Palace Theatre (£21,000); Get-A-Head Appeal (£19,000); Barnet CAB (£6,500); Barnet Primary Care NHS Trust (£3,400); Children for Peace (£2,500); Disability Aid Fund (£1,000); Tim Parry Jonathan Ball Foundation for Peace and Dame Vera Lynn Trust (£2,500 each); and Mill Hill School (£1,000).

TRUSTEES N W Wray; L E Wray; T W Bunyard; D Poutney.

OTHER INFORMATION No accounts available since 2007.

HOW TO APPLY In writing to the correspondent.

WHO TO APPLY TO The Trustees, c/o Cavendish House, 18 Cavendish Square, London W1G 0PJ

■ Prison Service Charity Fund

CC NO 801678   **ESTABLISHED** 1989

WHERE FUNDING CAN BE GIVEN UK.

WHO CAN BENEFIT Charitable organisations.

WHAT IS FUNDED The trust does not accept outside applications – the applicant must be a member of staff.

RANGE OF GRANTS Up to £2,000, most grants are for less than £1,000.

SAMPLE GRANTS Motor Neuron Association and British Disabled (£2,000) Velindre Hospital Cancer Centre (£1,600); Legacy Rainbow House, Cancer Research UK, Villa Real Special School (£1,000 each); Anthony Nolan Appeal (£800); Rainbow Children's Hospice (£700); Robbie Jones Appeal (£630); Macmillan Cancer Support, Help for Heroes and Scope (£500 each); M.I.N.D (£350) and Rowan Park Special School (£150).

FINANCES *Year* 2010 *Income* £182,089 *Grants* £110,890 *Assets* £643,435

TRUSTEES A N Joseph, Chair; P Ashes; J Goldsworthy; P McFall; C F Smith; K Wingfield; J White.

HOW TO APPLY The trust does not accept outside applications – the person making the application has to be a member of staff.

WHO TO APPLY TO The Trustees, The Lodge, 8 Derby Road, Garstang, Preston PR3 1EU *Tel* 01995 604997 *email* bob@pscf.co.uk *Website* www.prisonservicecharityfund.co.uk

■ Private Equity Foundation

CC NO 1116139   **ESTABLISHED** 2006

WHERE FUNDING CAN BE GIVEN UK and Western Europe.

WHO CAN BENEFIT Registered charities.

WHAT IS FUNDED Children and young people, social welfare, education.

TYPE OF GRANT Core costs for up to 3 years.

SAMPLE GRANTS Place2Be (£160,000); Skill Force (£120,000); City Year (£25,000); Community Links (£21,500); and Cranfield Trust (£2,000).

FINANCES *Year* 2009–10 *Income* £3,973,667 *Grants* £328,265 *Assets* £3,414,447

TRUSTEES Johannes Huth, Chair; Ramez Sousou; David Barker; David Blitzer; Scott Collins; Todd Fisher; Carl Parker; Dwight Poler; Nikos Stathopoulos; Charlie Green; Tom Attwood; Sanjay Patel.

PUBLICATIONS The foundation also undertakes research, the findings from which are published on its website.

OTHER INFORMATION In 2008–09 the foundation made grants totalling £2.5 million.

HOW TO APPLY Charities must first complete a form (letter of inquiry) to express an interest in being selected for support from the foundation. The form and further details for applicants are available from the foundation's website.

WHO TO APPLY TO Hollie Montgomery, Events and Fundraising Manager, 2 Bath Place, Rivington Street, London EC2A 3DR *Tel* 020 7749 5129 *email* info@privateequityfoundation.org *Website* www.privateequityfoundation.org

■ The Privy Purse Charitable Trust

cc no 296079   established 1987

where funding can be given UK.

who can benefit Registered charities.

what is funded General charitable purposes. 'The main aims of the trustees are to make grants to charities of which The Queen is patron and to support ecclesiastical establishments associated with The Queen.'

range of grants Most grants are usually up to £1,000.

sample grants Hampton Court Palace Royal Chapel (£82,000); St James' Palace Royal Chapel (£57,500); Sandringham Group of Parishes (£54,500); Sandringham Church Organ (£20,000); Windsor Great Park Royal Chapel (£16,000); Royal Chapel Appeal Fund (£15,000); and the British Red Cross (£10,000).

finances *Year* 2009–10 *Income* £532,207 *Grants* £488,942 *Assets* £2,332,382

trustees Ian McGregor; Sir Alan Reid; Christopher Geidt.

how to apply The trust makes donations to a wide variety of charities, but does not respond to unsolicited applications.

who to apply to Ian McGregor, Trustee, Buckingham Palace, London SW1A 1AA *Tel* 020 7930 4832 *email* ian.mcgregor@royal.gsx.gov.uk

■ The Proven Family Trust

cc no 1050877   established 1995

where funding can be given Cumbria, Halton, Knowsley, Liverpool, St Helens, Sefton, Warrington and Wirral.

who can benefit Organisations benefiting children and older people; those in care, fostered and adopted; and animals. Support may be given to at risk groups and people who are disabled, disadvantaged by poverty, homeless, victims of abuse or domestic violence or who have Alzheimer's disease, arthritis and rheumatism, asthma, cancer, motor neurone disease, multiple sclerosis, Parkinson's disease or sight loss.

what is funded Charities working in the fields of holiday and respite accommodation; volunteer bureaux; religious and historic buildings; health; community facilities and services; and animal welfare. Other charitable purposes will be considered.

what is not funded No grants to individuals.

type of grant One-off grants for up to three years. Research grants will be considered.

range of grants Up to £1,000.

sample grants Previous beneficiaries included: Action for Kids, Cockermouth Youth Action Limited, Cumbria Cerebral Palsy, Cumbria County Scout Council, Harvest Trust, Kids First, Kingsway Christian Fellowship, Liverpool Blind and Deaf, Pain Research Institute, Parents Against Drugs, Penrith Methodist Church, Roundabout Centre, Shakespeare Centre Kendal, Student Partnership Worldwide and West Derby Community Association.

finances *Year* 2009–10 *Income* £28,705 *Grants* £27,799 *Assets* £639,932

trustees G R Quigley; M C Taxman; C J Worthington; S Griffiths; D S Kerr.

how to apply In writing to the correspondent for consideration twice a year.

who to apply to Colin Worthington, Trustee, 35 The Mount, Papcastle, Cockermouth, Cumbria CA13 0JY *Tel* 01900 823324

■ The Provincial Grand Charity of the Province of Derbyshire

cc no 701963   established 1989

where funding can be given Derbyshire.

who can benefit Masons and dependants; other charitable organisations.

what is funded Masonic charities and general charitable purposes.

sample grants Blythe House Hospice (£1,000); WORK, Derby Kids' Camp and Ryder-Cheshire Volunteers (£500 each); Brin's Cottage, Lennox Children's Cancer Fund and Ian Appeal (£300 each); and Guide Association Chesterfield HQ and 3rd Wingerworth Scout Group, Muscular Dystrophy Campaign and Nicholson Court Social Club (£250 each).

finances *Year* 2009–10 *Income* £87,290 *Grants* £31,052 *Assets* £1,366,980

trustees J G R Rudd; G M Sissons; Dr B Quartermain.

other information Grants were broken down as follows: Non-Masonic Charities £24,300; TLC Appeal – £3,800; Seasonal Relief – £1,750; and Albert Wilson Trust – £1,150.

how to apply In writing to the correspondent.

who to apply to Graham Sisson, Secretary, 21 Netherfield Road, Chapel-en-le-Frith, High Peak SK23 0PN *Tel* 01298 812801 *email* secretary@derbyshiremason.org *Website* www.derbyshiremason.org

■ PSA Peugeot Citroen Charity Trust

cc no 266182   established 1970

where funding can be given Coventry and Warwickshire.

who can benefit Local voluntary organisations and small charitable groups only.

what is funded General charitable purposes. Causes are often associated with the motor industry.

what is not funded No grants are given to individuals or outside the beneficial area. Sponsorships and charitable advertising are not considered.

type of grant One-off grants.

range of grants £50–£1,500; average £200–£300.

sample grants Previously: PT Charitable Fund for Employees (£1,500); Peugeot Seven (£400); Allesley Park Community Centre, Mercia MS Therapy Centre, Cancer Research UK and the Sycamore Tree Counselling Service (£300 each); Coventry Sphinx FC and GA Sports FC (£250 each); Tiny Tim's Children's Centre and Rugby CVS (£200 each); Warwickshire & Northamptonshire Air Ambulance and Bell House Rugby (£100 each); and Walsgrave Amateur Riding Club (£50).

finances *Year* 2009–10 *Income* £160 *Grants* £19,600

trustees M Barnes; R Lewis; M J Lynch; C Lees; P Bourke; A Didlick.

how to apply In writing to the correspondent.

who to apply to Catherine Ann Mulkern, The Old Stores, Church Street, Churchover, Rugby CV23 0EW *Tel* 024 7688 4106 *email* info@heartofenglandcf.co.uk

■ The Puebla Charitable Trust

CC NO 290055   **ESTABLISHED** 1984
WHERE FUNDING CAN BE GIVEN Worldwide.
WHO CAN BENEFIT Organisations benefiting people disadvantaged by poverty living in both urban and rural areas.
WHAT IS FUNDED 'At present, the council limits its support to charities which assist the poorest sections of the population and community development work – either of these may be in urban or rural areas, both in the UK and overseas.'
WHAT IS NOT FUNDED No grants for capital projects, religious institutions, research or institutions for people who are disabled. Individuals are not supported and no scholarships are given.
TYPE OF GRANT Up to three years.
SAMPLE GRANTS Child Poverty Action Group, Family Action Group, Shelter and South West London Law Centres (£60,000 each); Action on Disability and Development and Mines Advisory Group (£45,000 each); SOS Sahel and Donald Woods Trust (£20,000 each); and Chikupira (£1,000).
FINANCES *Year* 2009–10 *Income* £102,322 *Grants* £371,000 *Assets* £2,122,401
TRUSTEES J Phipps; M A Strutt.
HOW TO APPLY In writing to the correspondent. The trustees meet in July. The trust is unable to acknowledge applications.
WHO TO APPLY TO The Clerk, Ensors, Cardinal House, 46 St Nicholas Street, Ipswich IP1 1TT *Tel* 01473 220022

■ The Richard and Christine Purchas Charitable Trust

CC NO 1083126   **ESTABLISHED** 2000
WHERE FUNDING CAN BE GIVEN UK.
WHO CAN BENEFIT Medical organisations.
WHAT IS FUNDED Medical research, medical education and patient care.
FINANCES *Year* 2009–10 *Income* £8,877 *Grants* £8,860
TRUSTEES Daniel Auerbach; Mrs Pauline Auerbach; Dr Douglas Rossdale; Robert Auerbach.
OTHER INFORMATION Previously the trust has part-funded the post of Consultant Speech Therapist at the Charing Cross Hospital in association with Macmillan Cancer Relief.
HOW TO APPLY In writing to the correspondent.
WHO TO APPLY TO Daniel Auerbach, Trustee, 46 Hyde Park Gardens Mews, London W2 2NX *Tel* 020 7580 2448

■ The Puri Foundation

CC NO 327854   **ESTABLISHED** 1988
WHERE FUNDING CAN BE GIVEN Nottinghamshire, India (particularly the towns of Mullan Pur near Chandigarh and Ambala).
WHO CAN BENEFIT Organisations benefiting: children; young adults; students; older people; Hindus; the disabled; at risk groups; those disadvantaged by poverty; and socially isolated people.
WHAT IS FUNDED Welfare and community centres. The trust aims to: relieve those in conditions of need, hardship or distress; advance education; provide facilities for recreation; and relieve and rehabilitate young unemployed people in the Nottinghamshire area.
WHAT IS NOT FUNDED No grants are given for holidays.
RANGE OF GRANTS Minimum of £50.

SAMPLE GRANTS The Puri Foundation for Education in India (£100,000); Nottingham City Council (£18,600); National Hindu Student Forum (£15,000); Inspire and Achieve (£5,000); Hindu Forum of Britain (£1,000).
FINANCES *Year* 2009–10 *Income* £368,098 *Grants* £152,988 *Assets* £3,292,633
TRUSTEES N R Puri; A Puri; Miss M K McGowan.
HOW TO APPLY In writing to the correspondent.
WHO TO APPLY TO N R Puri, Trustee, Environment House, 6 Union Road, Nottingham NG3 1FH *Tel* 0115 901 3000 *Fax* 0115 901 3100

■ Mr and Mrs J A Pye's Charitable Settlement

CC NO 242677   **ESTABLISHED** 1965
WHERE FUNDING CAN BE GIVEN UK, with a special interest in the Oxfordshire region and, to a lesser extent, in Reading, Cheltenham and Bristol.
WHO CAN BENEFIT Organisations benefiting children and young adults are given priority, although those benefiting older people will also be funded.
WHAT IS FUNDED General charitable purposes at the trustees' discretion. Of particular interest are: environmental – this subject particularly deals with organic farming matters, conservation generally and health related matters such as pollution research and some wildlife protection; adult health and care – especially causes supporting: post natal depression, schizophrenia, mental health generally and research into the main causes of early death; children's health and care – for physical, mental and learning disabilities, respite breaks and so on; youth organisations – particularly projects encouraging self reliance or dealing with social deprivation; education – nursery, primary, secondary or higher/institutions (not individuals); regional causes around Oxford, Reading, Cheltenham and Bristol – under this category the trustees will consider academic and arts projects.
WHAT IS NOT FUNDED No grants for: organisations that are not recognised charities; activities which are primarily the responsibility of government or some other responsible body; activities which collect funds for subsequent re-distribution to other charities; corporate affiliation or membership of charities; endowment funds; expeditions or overseas charities; fabric appeals for places of worship, other than in geographical locations indicated above; fundraising events or activities; hospitals or medical centres (except for projects that are clearly additional to statutory responsibilities); individual, including students; overseas appeals; promotion of religion.
TYPE OF GRANT One-off, core costs, projects, research, recurring, running and start-up costs, and salaries. Capital costs may be considered. Funding may be given for up to or more than three years. Also interest-free loans.
RANGE OF GRANTS £250–£135,000.
SAMPLE GRANTS Organic Research Centre (£135,000); Music@Oxford (£75,000); University College Oxford (£50,000); Harris Manchester College and Magdalen College School (£30,000 each); Association for Post Natal Illness and Oxford Brookes University (£20,000 each); BTCV (£15,000); Headington School and ORH Children's Hospital Fund (£10,000 each); Mansfield College (£6,000); Oxford University Tennis Foundation (£3,000);

The Brain Research Trust (£2,000); and the Ashmolean Museum and the Dipex Charity (£1,000 each).

FINANCES *Year* 2010 *Income* £620,170 *Grants* £486,250 *Assets* £10,592,645

TRUSTEES Simon Stubbings; David S Tallon; Patrick Mulcare.

OTHER INFORMATION The majority of the trust's grants were for less than £1,000.

HOW TO APPLY All applications should be sent to the administrative office (and not to individual trustees). These are reviewed on a continual basis and the trustees meet quarterly to make their decisions. Any decision can therefore take up to four months before it is finally taken. However, all applicants are informed of the outcome of their applications and all applications are acknowledged. Telephone contact will usually be counter-productive. There are no application forms but the following information is essential: the registered charity number or evidence of an organisation's tax exempt status; brief description of the activities of the charity; the names of the trustees and chief officers [NB more important than patrons]; details of the purpose of the application and where funds will be put to use; details of the funds already raised and the proposals for how remaining funds are to be raised; the latest trustees report and full audited or independently examined accounts (which **must** comply with Charity Commission guidelines and requirements); details of full name of the bank account, sort code, and number into which any grant should be paid; the charity's email address.

WHO TO APPLY TO David S Tallon, Trustee, c/o Mercer and Hole Chartered Accountants, Gloucester House, 72 London Road, St Albans, Hertfordshire AL1 1NS *Tel* 01727 869141 *Fax* 01727 869149 *email* pyecharitablesettlement@mercerhole.co.uk *Website* www.pyecharitablesettlement.org

··

■ The Pyne Charitable Trust

CC NO 1105357   **ESTABLISHED** 2004

WHERE FUNDING CAN BE GIVEN UK and overseas, particularly Malawi, Moldova, Slovakia and Ukraine.

WHO CAN BENEFIT Organisations and individuals.

WHAT IS FUNDED Christian and health causes.

SAMPLE GRANTS Good Shepherd Mission (£60,000); Affordable Christian Housing Association (£21,000); Disasters Emergency Appeal (Haiti) (£20,000); Great Ormond Street Children's Hospital (£15,000); NSPCC (£10,000); Teen challenge London (£7,000); and Crossroads Christian Housing Association (£1,000).

FINANCES *Year* 2010 *Income* £153,850 *Grants* £135,380 *Assets* £34,784

TRUSTEES Michael Brennan; Pauline Brennan; Mike Mitchell.

HOW TO APPLY Ongoing support appears to be given to projects selected by the trustees.

WHO TO APPLY TO Pauline Brennan, Secretary, 26 Tredegar Square, London E3 5AG *Tel* 020 8980 4853

■ Quartet Community Foundation (formerly the Greater Bristol Foundation)

CC NO 1080418   **ESTABLISHED** 1987

WHERE FUNDING CAN BE GIVEN West England – Bristol, North Somerset, South Gloucestershire, Bath and North East Somerset.

WHO CAN BENEFIT Any charity aimed at increasing opportunities and enhancing the quality of life in the area; particularly smaller, low-profile community groups and people at a particular disadvantage through discrimination.

WHAT IS FUNDED There are a number of specific schemes which support the four geographical beneficial areas, aiming to help local communities. Grants are made for a wide range of charitable purposes including: education, the protection of good health, relief of poverty and sickness, social welfare and the environment. For further information on types of grants and guidance towards the most appropriate fund(s) for your organisation contact the foundation or visit their website.

WHAT IS NOT FUNDED The foundation does not give grants to: individuals; general appeals; statutory organisations or the direct replacement of statutory funding; political groups or activities promoting political beliefs; religious groups promoting religious beliefs; arts projects with no community or charitable element; sports projects with no community or charitable element; medical research, equipment or treatment; animal welfare; or projects that take place before an application can be processed.

SAMPLE GRANTS Voluntary Action North Somerset (£64,000); Amos Vale Cemetery Trust (£50,000); Society of Merchant Venturers (£42,000); Easton Community Children's Centre (£40,000); Big Issue Foundation (£27,000); Bristol Refugee Rights (£20,000); Restore Ltd (£15,000); L'Dub Race Club (£14,000); Epsom Riding for the Disabled (£10,000); St Margaret's Hospice Somerset (£9,000); Bath City Farm (£7,600); Dorset Blind Association (£7,400); and Pre-primary Education Centres in West Bengal (£5,100).

FINANCES *Year* 2009–10 *Income* £3,219,623 *Grants* £2,952,692 *Assets* £15,968,292

TRUSTEES John Kane; Alexander Hore-Ruthven; Mary Prior; Peter Rilett; Alison Reed; Tim Ross; Anna Schiff; Gail Bragg; Prof. Murray Stewart; Cedric Clapp; William Lee; Gill Stobart; Richard Hall; Lin Whitfield.

PUBLICATIONS Various research papers available online.

OTHER INFORMATION Full information on all grants programmes and how to apply can be found on the fund's website.

HOW TO APPLY Before you apply to the community foundation check that your group or project meets the following requirements: you must be a small charity, community group or local voluntary organisation operating in the West of England i.e. Bath and North East Somerset, Bristol, North Somerset or South Gloucestershire; you do not need to be a registered charity but you must be able to provide a copy of your group's constitution or set of rules; your group must be managed by a board of trustees or management committee; you must be able to provide the foundation with up-to-date financial information for your group. Applicants should refer to the fund's website for details on how to apply to each grants programme. The funding team can be contacted for any help or advice concerning grants applications.

WHO TO APPLY TO Helen Moss, Royal Oak House, Royal Oak Avenue, Bristol BS1 4GB *Tel* 0117 989 7700 *Fax* 0117 989 7701 *email* info@ quartetcf.org.uk *Website* www.quartetcf.org.uk

■ The Queen Anne's Gate Foundation

CC NO 1108903   **ESTABLISHED** 2005

WHERE FUNDING CAN BE GIVEN UK and overseas.

WHO CAN BENEFIT Charitable organisations.

WHAT IS FUNDED 'The foundation seeks to support projects and charities within the following broad criteria. It seeks to make a contribution that is meaningful in the context of the project/charity with which it is working. It tries to focus in particular on projects which might be said to make potentially unproductive lives productive. This tends to mean a bias towards educational, medical and rehabilitative charities and those that work with underprivileged areas of society. There is an attempt to focus a significant proportion of donations on Asia, Malawi and the UK.'

SAMPLE GRANTS Merlin (£80,000); St Mungo's (£50,000); English National Opera (£35,000); Policy Exchange and Families for Children (adoption) (each £30,000); World Medical Fund and Udanum Karangal (orphanage) (each £25,000); Blue Sky (£12,000); and Hackney Music Development Trust (£10,000).

FINANCES *Year* 2009–10 *Income* £184,916 *Grants* £809,217 *Assets* £3,601,222

TRUSTEES N T Allan; J M E Boyer; I G Lewis.

HOW TO APPLY In writing to the correspondent.

WHO TO APPLY TO The Trustees, WillcoxLewis LLP, The Old Coach House, Bergh Apton, Norwich, Norfolk NR15 1DD

■ Queen Mary's Roehampton Trust

CC NO 211715   **ESTABLISHED** 1928

WHERE FUNDING CAN BE GIVEN UK.

WHO CAN BENEFIT Ex-servicemen or women who were disabled in service and their dependants.

WHAT IS FUNDED Grants are made to charities supporting ex-service personnel who suffered disability while in service that provide welfare services, residential or nursing homes and their widows/widowers and dependants.

WHAT IS NOT FUNDED Grants are not made directly to individuals.

TYPE OF GRANT Annual recurring, one-off. Also capital and project. Funding may be given for up to two years.

RANGE OF GRANTS Usually £1,000–£50,000.

SAMPLE GRANTS The Soldiers' Charity (£35,000), for welfare grants; Royal Naval Benevolent Trust (£30,000), for welfare grants; Combat Stress (£25,000); Scottish Veterans' Garden City Association (£20,000), to refurbish properties; Queen Alexandra Hospital Home (£15,000), towards core costs; British Ex-Services Wheelchair Sports Association (£13,000), Gurkha Welfare Trust (£10,500), towards pensions; Royal Alfred Seafarers' Society (£7,000), towards core costs; Council of British

Think carefully about every application. Is it justified?

821

Service and Ex-Service Organisations (£5,000), towards administration costs; and Holidays for Heroes Jersey (£1,000).

FINANCES *Year* 2010–11 *Income* £481,609 *Grants* £428,000 *Assets* £11,549,764

TRUSTEES Maj Gen Peter Craig, Chair; Lt Col Simon Brewis; Cathy Walker; James Macnamara; Dr Gordon Paterson; Colin Green; Col Paul Cummings; Ray Greenwood; Com Stephen Farringdon; Beverley Davies; Debbie Bowles; Stephen Coltman; Sir Barry Thornton.

HOW TO APPLY On a standard application form available from the correspondent. Representatives of the trust may visit beneficiary organisations.

WHO TO APPLY TO Col Stephen Rowland-Jones, Clerk to the Trustees, 2 Sovereign Close, Quidhampton, Salisbury, Wiltshire SP2 9ES *Tel* 01722 501413 *email* qmrt@hotmail.co.uk

■ The Queen's Silver Jubilee Trust

CC NO 272373   **ESTABLISHED** 1976

WHERE FUNDING CAN BE GIVEN UK, the Channel Islands, Isle of Man and the Commonwealth.

WHO CAN BENEFIT Registered charities.

WHAT IS FUNDED Organisations working with young people, aged 14–30, across the UK, Commonwealth, Channel Islands and the Isle of Man, particularly those that support disadvantaged young people or those that enable young people to volunteer in their local community, broadly defined.

WHAT IS NOT FUNDED Grants are only made to registered charities. No grants to individuals.

TYPE OF GRANT One-off and recurring.

RANGE OF GRANTS Up to £10,000.

SAMPLE GRANTS The Prince's Trust (£1.2 million); HMP Coldingley, Nightstop Teeside, Llynfi Valley Project, The Bridge Mentoring Scheme and Read International (£10,000 each); Surf Life Saving GB and Aberlour Children's Trust (£8,000 each); Warwickshire Clubs For Young People and Commonwealth Youth Exchange Council (£5,000 each); Young and Free (£4,000); Oxford Wheels and Clock Tower Sanctuary (£3,000 each); and Wester Hailes Youth Agency and Blue Horizon (£2,000 each).

FINANCES *Year* 2009–10 *Income* £465,000 *Grants* £1,285,000 *Assets* £35,523,000

TRUSTEES Rt Hon Christopher Geidt; Sir Fred Goodwin; Stephen Hall; Sir Alan Reid; Peter Mimpriss; Michael Marks.

OTHER INFORMATION At the time of writing (October 2011), specific details of the trust's grant programme for 2012 and beyond were unavailable. Please check the trust's website for up-to-date information.

HOW TO APPLY Potential applicants are advised to email the contact before making a formal application. Applicants must ensure that: their organisation is eligible; they have read the Terms and Conditions and other guidance notes; they enclose their most recent annual report and accounts, or financial projections and previous income expenditure charts if the organisation is less than two years old; they enclose their most recent annual review or a brief summary of what their organisation does; retain a photocopy of all submitted materials. At the time of writing (October 2011), the trust was closed to new applications. Check the trust's website for current details of grants programmes for 2012 and beyond.

WHO TO APPLY TO Nicola Brentnall, 17–18 Park Square East, London NW1 4LH *Tel* 020 7543 1234 *Fax* 020 7543 1200 *email* nicola. brentnall@royal.gsx.gov.uk *Website* www. queenssilverjubileetrust.org.uk

■ Quercus Trust

CC NO 1039205   **ESTABLISHED** 1993

WHERE FUNDING CAN BE GIVEN UK.

WHO CAN BENEFIT Established organisations and registered charities.

WHAT IS FUNDED Mainly the arts, and other purposes which seek to further public knowledge, understanding and appreciation of any matters of artistic, aesthetic, scientific or historical interest.

WHAT IS NOT FUNDED No grants to individuals.

RANGE OF GRANTS £500–£70,000.

SAMPLE GRANTS Dance UK (£70,000); Royal National Theatre (£20,000); Royal Opera House Covent Garden and Kettle's Yard (£10,000 each); Royal Opera House Foundation (£7,500); Artichoke Trust (£5,000); British Friends of the Art Museums of Israel (£2,000); ORH Charitable Fund (£1,500); British Humanist Association, Donmar Warehouse Projects, Gala for Africa, Tate Foundation and Young Vic Theatre Company (£1,000 each); and Hofesh Shechter Company (£500).

FINANCES *Year* 2009–10 *Income* £128,184 *Grants* £131,495 *Assets* £5,243,857

TRUSTEES Lady Angela Bernstein; Kate E Bernstein.

HOW TO APPLY In writing to the correspondent, but please note, the trust has previously stated: 'All of the trust's funds are currently earmarked for existing projects.' In order to keep administrative costs to a minimum, the trust does not reply to any unsuccessful applicants.

WHO TO APPLY TO Chris Jones, Trust Administrator, Chantrey Vellacott DFK, Russell Square House, 10–12 Russell Square, London WC1B 5LF *Tel* 020 7509 9000

■ Quothquan Trust

CC NO 1110647   **ESTABLISHED** 2005

WHERE FUNDING CAN BE GIVEN Birmingham and the West Midlands.

WHO CAN BENEFIT Projects known to the trustees, usually Christian organisations benefiting the community.

WHAT IS FUNDED Usually local Christian projects. Any project outside the West Midlands must be known to the trustees, whether in the UK or abroad.

WHAT IS NOT FUNDED No grants are given towards: anything that does not have the promotion of Christianity as part of its ethos; activities that are the primary responsibility of central or local government; animal welfare; church buildings for restorations, improvements, renovations or new building; environmental projects such as conservation and protection of wildlife and landscape; expeditions and overseas trips; hospitals and health centres; individuals are not normally supported; large national charities are not normally supported, even for local projects; loans and business finance; medical research projects; overseas appeals, unless there is a recommendation from someone known personally to the trustees; promotion of any non-Christian religion; schools, universities and colleges.

SAMPLE GRANTS Churches (£252,000); Christian centres (£120,900); evangelism, bibles and education (£9,600); overseas missions and workers (£51,900); full-time Christian worker (£38,000); promotion of prayer (£15,000); low income or lone parent families (£17,000); students (£9,400).

FINANCES *Year* 2009 *Income* £117,071 *Grants* £286,991 *Assets* £1,842,545

TRUSTEES Archie Gilmour; Mrs J A Gilmour.

OTHER INFORMATION Grants totalling £73,500 were made to 42 individuals.

HOW TO APPLY In writing to the correspondent.

WHO TO APPLY TO Archie Gilmour, Trustee, Dale Farm, Worcester Lane, Four Oaks, Sutton Coldfield, West Midlands B75 5PR *Tel* 0121 323 3236 *Fax* 0121 323 3237 *email* appeals@quothquan.org

■ R J M Charitable Trust

cc no 288336   **ESTABLISHED** 1983
WHERE FUNDING CAN BE GIVEN UK and worldwide.
WHO CAN BENEFIT Jewish organisations.
WHAT IS FUNDED Jewish charitable purposes.
RANGE OF GRANTS £50–£100,000.
SAMPLE GRANTS UJIA (£100,000); KD AD Min
(£19,000); CRT (£10,000); CST and Aish
Hatorah (£5,000 each); North Salford
Synagogue (£3,300); Broughton Park Primary
School (£2,500); Policy Exchange (£2,000);
Henry Jackson Society, Central Region
Chaplaincy Board and Friends of Bnei Akiva
(£1,000 each); Sterecourt (£704); Reshet
(£300); Manchester Jewish Museum (£150);
Jerusalem Educational Trust (£100); and
Yeshiva (£50).
FINANCES *Year* 2009–10 *Income* £201,000
Grants £217,959 *Assets* £101,750
TRUSTEES Joshua Rowe; Michelle Rowe.
HOW TO APPLY In writing to the correspondent.
WHO TO APPLY TO Joshua Rowe, Trustee, 84 Upper
Park Road, Salford M7 4JA *Tel* 0161 720 8787
email joshua@broomwell.com

■ R S Charitable Trust

cc no 1053660   **ESTABLISHED** 1996
WHERE FUNDING CAN BE GIVEN UK.
WHO CAN BENEFIT Registered charities.
WHAT IS FUNDED Jewish causes and the relief of
poverty.
SAMPLE GRANTS Previous beneficiaries have included
British Friends of Tshernobil, Forty Ltd, NRST,
Society of Friends of the Torah, Talmud
Hochschule, Viznitz, Yeshiva Horomo and
Yeshivas Luzern.
FINANCES *Year* 2009–10 *Income* £611,448
Grants £279,577 *Assets* £1,776,968
TRUSTEES Harvey Freudenberger; Michelle
Freudenberger; Stuart Freudenberger; Max
Freudenberger.
HOW TO APPLY In writing to the correspondent.
WHO TO APPLY TO Max Freudenberger, Trustee,
138 Stamford Hill, London N16 6QT

■ The R V W Trust

cc no 1066977   **ESTABLISHED** 1958
WHERE FUNDING CAN BE GIVEN UK.
WHO CAN BENEFIT Organisations and individuals,
particularly composers, musicians and music
students.
WHAT IS FUNDED The trust's current grant-making
policies are as follows: (1) To give assistance to
British composers who have not yet achieved a
national reputation. (2) To give assistance
towards the performance and recording of music
by neglected or currently unfashionable 20th
century British composers, including
performances by societies and at festivals
which include works by such composers in their
programmes. (3) To assist UK organisations
that promote public knowledge and appreciation
of 20th and 21st century British music. (4) To
assist education projects in the field of music.
(5) To support post-graduate students of

composition taking first masters degrees at
British universities and conservatoires.
WHAT IS NOT FUNDED No grants for local authority or
other government-funded bodies, nor degree
courses, except first Masters' degrees in
musical composition. No support for dance or
drama courses. No grants for workshops without
public performance, private vocal or
instrumental tuition or the purchase or repair of
musical instruments. No grants for concerts that
do not include music by 20th and 21st century
composers or for musicals, rock, pop, ethnic,
jazz or dance music. No grants for the
construction or restoration of buildings. The
trust is not able to make grants towards the
music of Ralph Vaughan Williams.
RANGE OF GRANTS £2,000–£25,000.
SAMPLE GRANTS Vaughan Williams Memorial Library/
English Folk Dance & Song Society (£25,000);
Park Lane Group (£15,000); Huddersfield
Contemporary Music Festival (£12,000); Royal
Philharmonic Society Composition Prize
(£7,500); Scottish Opera, NMC, New London
Orchestra and English Touring Opera (£5,000
each); Artisan Trio, Sound and Buxton Festival
(£2,500 each).
FINANCES *Year* 2010 *Income* £386,465
Grants £331,220 *Assets* £1,491,308
TRUSTEES Hugh Cobbe, Chair; Dr Michael Kennedy;
The Lord Armstrong of Ilminster; Andrew Hunter
Johnston; Sir John Manduell; Jeremy Dale
Roberts; John Axon – Musicians Benevolent
Fund.
OTHER INFORMATION During 2010, 127 grants were
made totalling £330,000.
HOW TO APPLY All potential applicants should
contact the trust for further details of current
grant-making policy and details of how to apply
by emailing the secretary. The trust holds three
main grant-making meetings a year. Closing
dates for applications are 2 January, 1 May and
1 September. Applicants are notified of the
results approximately 8 weeks after these
dates.
WHO TO APPLY TO Ms Helen Faulkner, Administrator,
7–11 Britannia Street, London WC1X 9JS
email helen@rvwtrust.org.uk *Website* www.
rvwtrust.org.uk

■ The Monica Rabagliati Charitable Trust

cc no 1086368   **ESTABLISHED** 2001
WHERE FUNDING CAN BE GIVEN UK.
WHO CAN BENEFIT Charitable organisations. 'The
trustees have decided to prioritise small/
medium sized organisations where possible.'
WHAT IS FUNDED Mostly support for 'organisations
that focus on the alleviation of child suffering
and deprivation'. The trust also supports
humanitarian and medical causes.
SAMPLE GRANTS Rwanda Aid and St Joseph Priestly
Scholarships (£10,000 each); The Africa
Foundation and U Turn (£5,000 each);
International Childcare Trust (£3,000); Hereford
Cathedral (£2,500); Dream Makers, Down
Syndrome International Swimming Organisation
and Everychild (£2,000 each); FORWARD
(£1,000); and The Warfield Churches for the
Bethany Project (£500).
FINANCES *Year* 2009–10 *Income* £44,512
Grants £52,000 *Assets* £1,877,776
TRUSTEES S G Hambros Trust Company Limited;
R L McLean.
HOW TO APPLY The trustees report for 2009–10
states: 'The charity does not solicit applications

but considers all relevant applications and the trustees give any such applications fair consideration.'

WHO TO APPLY TO Shirley Baines, Administrator, S G Hambros Bank Limited, Norfolk House, 31 St. James's Square, London SW1Y 4JR *Tel* 020 7597 3060 *Fax* 020 7702 9263 *Website* www. rabagliati.org.uk

■ Rachel Charitable Trust

CC NO 276441   **ESTABLISHED** 1978

WHERE FUNDING CAN BE GIVEN Unrestricted.

WHO CAN BENEFIT Charitable organisations, mostly Jewish groups.

WHAT IS FUNDED General charitable purposes, in practice, mainly Jewish organisations.

SAMPLE GRANTS Previous beneficiaries include: British Friends of Shuut Ami, Children's Hospital Trust Fund, Cometville Limited, Encounter – Jewish Outreach Network, Chosen Mishpat Centre, Gertner Charitable Trust, Hertsmere Jewish Primary School, Jewish Learning Exchange, London Millennium Bikeathon, Manchester Jewish Grammar School, Project Seed, Shaarei Zedek Hospital, Shomrei Hachomot Jerusalem, Yeshiva Ohel Shimon Trust, Yeshiva Shaarei Torah Manchester.

FINANCES *Year* 2009–10 *Income* £4,327,142 *Grants* £3,098,177 *Assets* £26,202,573

TRUSTEES Leopold Noe; Susan Noe; Simon Kanter.

OTHER INFORMATION A separate list of donations made during the year was available from the trustees for £25.

HOW TO APPLY In writing to the correspondent.

WHO TO APPLY TO Robert Chalk, Secretary, F & C Reit Asset Management, 5 Wigmore Street, London W1U 1PB *Tel* 020 7016 3549

■ The Mr and Mrs Philip Rackham Charitable Trust

CC NO 1013844   **ESTABLISHED** 1992

WHERE FUNDING CAN BE GIVEN Norfolk.

WHO CAN BENEFIT Registered charities.

WHAT IS FUNDED General charitable purposes, although there is some preference for asthma charities and Samaritans.

WHAT IS NOT FUNDED No grants to individuals.

RANGE OF GRANTS Up to £4,000 (2009–10).

SAMPLE GRANTS Samaritans (£4,000); The Hamlet Centre Trust and YMCA Norfolk (£2,500 each); EACH and National Rheumatoid Arthritis Society (NRAS) (£2,000 each); The Prince's Trust, Mid Norfolk Group of Riding for the Disabled, Marie Curie Cancer Care and BUILD (£1,000 each); Samaritans – Great Yarmouth, Norfolk Family Mediation Service and BREAK (£500 each).

FINANCES *Year* 2009–10 *Income* £39,099 *Grants* £30,595 *Assets* £1,109,734

TRUSTEES Neil G Sparrow; C W L Barratt; Ann E S Rush.

HOW TO APPLY In writing to the correspondent.

WHO TO APPLY TO Neil G Sparrow, Clerk, Mr N G Sparrow, Kingfisher House, 1 Gilders Way, Norwich NR3 1UB *Tel* 01603 232300 *Fax* 01603 230533

■ Richard Radcliffe Charitable Trust

CC NO 1068930   **ESTABLISHED** 1998

WHERE FUNDING CAN BE GIVEN UK.

WHO CAN BENEFIT Charitable organisations.

WHAT IS FUNDED The trust stated its policy as being to support, through making grants to other organisations, the following charitable activities: to assist physically disabled people; to provide technical training to give young people a start in life; to support hospice care for people who are terminally ill; to provide help for people who are severely deaf and/or blind.

TYPE OF GRANT Mainly recurrent.

RANGE OF GRANTS Up to £4,000.

SAMPLE GRANTS Martlets Hospice (£5,000); St Barnabas Hospice, and RNIB (£2,500 each); Orbis, 4 Sight and Sight Savers (£1,875 each); and St Peters and St James Hospice, Macmillan Cancer Relief, Independent Age and Harvest Trust (£1,250 each).

FINANCES *Year* 2009–10 *Income* £49,231 *Grants* £40,362 *Assets* £1,487,982

TRUSTEES Dr P A Radcliffe; Miss M Radcliffe; Miss P Radcliffe; A M Bell.

HOW TO APPLY In writing to the correspondent.

WHO TO APPLY TO Dr Paul A Radcliffe, Boycott House, Welsh Lane, Stowe, Buckingham MK18 5DJ *Tel* 01280 813352

■ The Radcliffe Trust

CC NO 209212   **ESTABLISHED** 1714

WHERE FUNDING CAN BE GIVEN UK.

WHO CAN BENEFIT Registered or exempt charities. Organisations and schemes benefiting musicians and those involved in the crafts.

WHAT IS FUNDED (1) Music: 'The Radcliffe Trust supports classical music performance and training especially chamber music, composition and music education. Particular interests within music education are music for children and adults with special needs, youth orchestras and projects at secondary and higher levels, including academic research. (2) Craft: The Radcliffe Trust supports the development of the skills, knowledge and experience that underpin the UK's traditional cultural heritage and crafts sectors. This includes support for craft and conservation training, for practical projects and for strategic projects which demonstrate clear benefits to individuals and to the sector. However, the Trust remains committed to flexible, open and inclusive grant-giving and will consider other projects, should they fall broadly within its remit. The Radcliffe Trust wishes to promote standards of excellence through all its support.'

WHAT IS NOT FUNDED No grants to individual applicants. No retrospective grants are made, nor for deficit funding, core costs, general appeals or endowment funds. No new building appeals.

RANGE OF GRANTS Mostly £1,000–£5,000.

SAMPLE GRANTS The Allegri String Quartet (£22,000); Monastery of St Francis & Gorton Trust and National Library of Scotland (£15,000 each); Edward Barnsley Education Trust (£12,500 University of Oxford Bodleian Library (£12,000); Scottish Lime Centre (£10,000); The Bronte Society (£9,000); Clerkenwell Green Association (£8,000); Weald and Downland Open Air Museum and Church Buildings Council (£7,500 each); University of Nottingham (£6,000); English National Opera, Guideposts Trust, Halle Concerts Society, Kettles Yard and

Music in Country Churches (£5,000 each); Lake District Summer Music and Leicestershire Chorale (£2,000 each); Dante Quartet (£1,000); and St Bartholomew's Hospital (£600).

FINANCES *Year* 2009–10 *Income* £405,940 *Grants* £333,970 *Assets* £13,725,702

TRUSTEES Felix Warnock, Chair; Sir Henry Aubrey-Fletcher; Lord Balfour of Burleigh; Christopher Butcher; Mary Ann Sieghart.

HOW TO APPLY The trustees meet twice yearly to oversee the charity's activities and to make decisions on grants. The trust works with specialist advisers in each of its main sectors of activity: Mrs Sally Carter, Music Adviser and Ms Carole Milner, Heritage & Crafts Adviser. There is also a Music Panel and a Heritage & Crafts Committee which each meet twice a year to consider applications. The day-to-day running of the trust's financial and administrative affairs and processing of grant applications is undertaken by The Trust Partnership.

How to Apply
Please note that it is advisable to submit an application well in advance of the deadline. **Music Deadline:** January 31 for the June Trustee meeting; August 31 for the December Trustee meeting; **Heritage & Crafts Deadline:** February 28 for the June Trustee meeting; August 31 for the December Trustee meeting. All applications must include: a cover letter, which should include official address, telephone number, email address and charity registration number. The letter should be headed with the project title and the applicant should make clear his/her position in the charity. Please note that this letter should NOT include information on the project itself as this should be within the grant request; no more than three pages outlining the proposal and the specific request to the Trust. This should be structured as follows: the project title; a summary of the request in no more than 40 words; the timing of the project; the project background and description; a budget including a financial breakdown and total cost of the project as well as other income secured or requested and from what sources; the amount requested either as a one-off or recurrent grant; – an indication of past grants from the Radcliffe Trust (year, amount and purpose) other relevant supporting information, although applicants should be aware that this may not be circulated to Trustees. The cover letter and grant request should be emailed to the Administrator as Word or Excel documents and a hard copy also sent by post.

WHO TO APPLY TO Belinda Hunt, 6 Trull Farm Buildings, Tetbury, Gloucestershire GL8 8SQ *Tel* 01285 841900 *email* radcliffe@ thetrustpartnership.com *Website* www. theradcliffetrust.org

■ The Bishop Radford Trust

CC NO 1113562   **ESTABLISHED** 2006
WHERE FUNDING CAN BE GIVEN UK.
WHO CAN BENEFIT Christian organisations, including churches.
WHAT IS FUNDED The promotion of 'the work of the Christian church in a manner consistent with the doctrines and principles of the Church of England'. This includes the renovation, construction and maintenance of churches, the education of church workers and church ministry.
SAMPLE GRANTS Anglican Investment Agency Trust (£130,000); Diocese of Liverpool (£45,000); International Needs (£40,000); Save the

Children (£33,000); Diocese of London (£20,000); and Cambourne Parish (£5,000).
FINANCES *Year* 2009–10 *Income* £812,254 *Grants* £319,500 *Assets* £4,333,828
TRUSTEES Stephen Green; Janian Green; Suzannah O'Brien; Ruth Dare.
HOW TO APPLY In writing to the correspondent.
WHO TO APPLY TO The Secretary, Devonshire House, 1 Devonshire Street, London W1W 5DR

■ The Ragdoll Foundation

CC NO 1078998   **ESTABLISHED** 2000
WHERE FUNDING CAN BE GIVEN UK and worldwide.
WHO CAN BENEFIT Projects that involve children during their early years, although appropriate projects for older children will be considered.
WHAT IS FUNDED Arts projects with children which: promote the development of children through children's imaginative thinking; encourage innovation and innovative thinking and influence good practice elsewhere; offer creative solutions that deal with the causes of problems in childhood; ensures effective evaluation of projects to promote sharing and learning; or above all demonstrate how the voices of children can be heard.
WHAT IS NOT FUNDED Grants are not given for: replacement of statutory funding; work that has already started or will have been completed whilst the application is being considered; promotion of religion; animal welfare charities; vehicles, emergency relief work; general fundraising or marketing appeals; open ended funding arrangements; loans or business advice; charities which are in serious deficit; holidays; any large capital; endowment or widely distributed appeal; specialist schools; school fees for people over 17 years of age; and gap year funds.
RANGE OF GRANTS Typically £500–£20,000, although large-scale grants will be considered.
FINANCES *Year* 2009–10 *Income* £83,420 *Grants* £92,722 *Assets* £61,036
TRUSTEES Katherine Wood; Peter Hollingsworth; Peter Thornton; Anne Wood; Carole Thomson.
OTHER INFORMATION 'The Ragdoll Foundation is dedicated to developing the power of imaginative responses in children through the arts. It owns 15% of its parent company and springs from the same philosophical roots. This can be summed up by the quotation from Sylvia Ashton-Warner in her book *Teacher*, which has greatly influenced Anne's work: *I see the mind of a five year old as a volcano with two vents; destructiveness and creativeness. And I can see that to the extent that we widen the creative channel, we atrophy the destructive one.*'
HOW TO APPLY To register interest in future funding schemes please email the foundation. The email should contain the following details – your name, organisation, title of the proposed project and indicative project timescale.
WHO TO APPLY TO Karen Newell, Development Co-ordinator, Timothy's Bridge Road, Stratford upon Avon, Warwickshire CV37 9NQ *Tel* 01789 404100 *Fax* 1789404136 *email* info@ ragdollfoundation.org.uk *Website* www. ragdollfoundation.org.uk

826

Does the trust you have chosen match your needs? Haphazard applications waste postage and time

■ The Rainford Trust

CC NO 266157   **ESTABLISHED** 1973

WHERE FUNDING CAN BE GIVEN Worldwide, with a preference for areas in which Pilkington plc have works and offices, especially St Helens and Merseyside.

WHO CAN BENEFIT Individuals and charitable and voluntary organisations.

WHAT IS FUNDED The trust's accounts stated that its objectives are to: 'apply money for charitable purposes and to charitable institutions within the St Helens MBC area, and other places in the UK or overseas where Pilkington has employees. This does not prejudice the trustees' discretion to help charities that operate outside those areas.' Further to this the trust's charitable purposes are to support: 'the relief of poverty, the aged, the sick, helpless and disabled, and the unemployed' and 'the advancement of education including the arts, and other purposes with wide benefit for the community such as environmental and conservation projects'.

WHAT IS NOT FUNDED Funding for the arts is restricted to St Helens only. Applications from individuals for grants for educational purposes will be considered only from applicants who are normally resident in St Helens.

SAMPLE GRANTS The Citadel Arts Centre and Hope Academy (£20,000 each); Clonter Opera (£16,000); WASOT UK (£5,000); Hand in Hand (£2,500); National M E Centre (£2,000); The Arkwright Scholarship Trust and International Spinal Research Trust (£1,000 each); and Raynauds and Scleroderma Association (£500).

FINANCES *Year* 2009–10 *Income* £147,091 *Grants* £141,385 *Assets* £6,721,825

TRUSTEES Dr F Graham; Mrs A J Moseley; H Pilkington; Lady Pilkington; D C Pilkington; S D Pilkington; Mrs I Ratiu; Mrs L F Walker.

HOW TO APPLY On a form available from the correspondent. Applications should be accompanied by a copy of the latest accounts and cost data on projects for which funding is sought. Applicants may apply at any time. Only successful applications will be acknowledged.

WHO TO APPLY TO W H Simm, Secretary, c/o Pilkington plc, Prescot Road, St Helens, Merseyside WA10 3TT *Tel* 01744 20574 *email* rainfordtrust@btconnect.com

■ The Peggy Ramsay Foundation

CC NO 1015427   **ESTABLISHED** 1992

WHERE FUNDING CAN BE GIVEN British Isles.

WHO CAN BENEFIT Writers who have some writing experience who need time to write and cannot otherwise afford to do so; companies which might not otherwise be able to find, develop or use new work; and projects which may facilitate new writing for the stage.

WHAT IS FUNDED The advancement of education by the encouragement of the art of writing and the relief of poverty amongst stage writers and their families.

WHAT IS NOT FUNDED No grants are made for productions or writing not for the theatre. Adaptations and plays intended primarily for younger audiences are accepted only in special circumstances which imply wider originality. Commissioning costs are often considered as part of production costs. Course fees are not considered. Aspiring writers without some production record are not usually considered.

TYPE OF GRANT Grants awarded for projects, recurring costs and salaries, for up to three years.

SAMPLE GRANTS Organisational beneficiaries: Clean Break Theatre (£5000); Definitely Theatre (£2,500); Society of authors (£1,500).

FINANCES *Year* 2010 *Income* £228,949 *Grants* £190,961 *Assets* £4,961,023

TRUSTEES G Laurence Harbottle; Simon P H Callow; Michael Codron; Sir David Hare; John Tydeman; Harriet Walter; Tamara C Harvey; Mr Neil Adleman; Mr Rupert J Rhymes.

OTHER INFORMATION Grants to individuals do not normally exceed £5,000.

HOW TO APPLY Applications should be made in writing, including: a short letter explaining the need, the amount hoped for and the way in which any grant would be spent; a full CV not limited to writing; separate sheet answers to these questions:- when and where was the first professional production of a play of yours; who produced the play which qualifies you for a grant; when and where was your qualifying play produced, what was its run and approximate playing time and has it been revived; for that production were the director and actors all professionals engaged with Equity contracts; did the audience pay to attend. Trustees meet quarterly, but applications are considered between meetings. Allow 6–8 weeks for a definitive answer. Urgent appeals can be considered at other times. All appeals are usually acknowledged.
Grants are considered at four or five meetings during the year, although urgent appeals can be considered at other times. All appeals are usually acknowledged.

WHO TO APPLY TO G Laurence Harbottle, Trustee, Harbottle and Lewis Solicitors, Hanover House, 14 Hanover Square, London W1S 1HP *Tel* 020 7667 5000 *Fax* 020 7667 5100 *email* laurence.harbottle@harbottle.com *Website* www.peggyramsayfoundation.org

■ The Joseph and Lena Randall Charitable Trust

CC NO 255035   **ESTABLISHED** 1967

WHERE FUNDING CAN BE GIVEN Worldwide.

WHO CAN BENEFIT Registered charities (mainly headquarters organisations) benefiting at risk groups and people who are disadvantaged by poverty or socially isolated.

WHAT IS FUNDED Regular support to a selection of charities, providing medical, educational and cultural facilities.

WHAT IS NOT FUNDED No grants to individuals.

SAMPLE GRANTS Previous beneficiaries have included: Cancer Research UK, Community Security Trust, Diabetes UK, Downe House 21st Century Appeal, Holocaust Educational Trust, Jewish Care, Jewish Deaf Association, LPO, LSE Foundation, Motor Neurone Disease Association, ROH Foundation and Transplant Trust.

FINANCES *Year* 2009–10 *Income* £103,441 *Grants* £95,666 *Assets* £1,991,552

TRUSTEES Rofrano Trustee Services Ltd.

HOW TO APPLY The trust has stated that funds are fully committed and that it was 'unable to respond to the many worthy appeals'.

WHO TO APPLY TO David Anthony Randall, Europa Residence, Place des Moulins, Monte-Carlo MC98 000 *Tel* 00377 9350 0382

■ The Rank Foundation

CC NO 276976   ESTABLISHED 1953
WHERE FUNDING CAN BE GIVEN UK.

WHO CAN BENEFIT Charities or churches working in the areas of promoting Christianity, promoting education and general charitable purposes.

WHAT IS FUNDED The promotion of Christian principles through film and other media; encouraging and developing leadership amongst young people; supporting disadvantaged young people and those frail or lonely through old age or disability.

WHAT IS NOT FUNDED Grants to registered charities only. Appeals from individuals or appeals from registered charities on behalf of named individuals will not be considered; neither will appeals from overseas or from UK-based organisations where the object of the appeal is overseas. In an endeavour to contain the calls made upon the foundation to a realistic level, the directors have continued with their policy of not, in general, making grants to projects involved with: agriculture and farming; cathedrals and churches (except where community facilities form an integral part); culture; university/school building and bursary funds; medical research.

TYPE OF GRANT Small grants are largely one-off. Major grants can be re-occurring.

RANGE OF GRANTS Mostly small grants up to £7,500.

SAMPLE GRANTS YMCA George Williams College (£179,000); Help the Hospices (£100,000); Belfast Community Sports Development Network and Hemlington Detached Youthwork (£30,000 each); Meningitis Trust and St Pauls Church (£25,000 each); Community Foundation for Lancashire (£22,000); Countryside Alliance Foundation and Women in Prison (£20,000 each); Christians Against Poverty (£15,000); Kings School of Worcester (£575); and Tall Ships Youth Trust (£14,000).

FINANCES *Year* 2010 *Income* £6,811,000 *Grants* £5,740,000 *Assets* £221,120,000

TRUSTEES Earl St Aldwyn; James Cave; Andrew Cowan; Mark Davies; Lindsay Fox; Joey Newton; Lucinda Onslow; Lord Shuttleworth; Hon. Caroline Twiston-Davies; Johanna Ropner; Rose Fitzpatrick; Daniel Simon; Nicholas Buxton; Jason Chaffer.

PUBLICATIONS *Journeying Together; History of The Rank Foundation.*

OTHER INFORMATION In general, the directors are active in identifying initiatives where they provide substantial support and the vast majority of unsolicited appeals, particularly for major grants, do not receive funding.

HOW TO APPLY If you are interested in a major grant (over £7,500) you should contact the respective executive director. If you would like to submit an application for a major grant, in either the Special Project or Community Care category, then you should email a one page outline to the respective executive, details of which can be found on the 'contact us' section of the website. This should contain the following information: organisation objectives, location and structure (staff numbers); outline of what you do and where; what you are seeking support for – details of the specific programme including costs; any evidence of partnership working or summary of existing evaluation. For small grants (under £7,500) complete the short eligibility quiz online to confirm your application is eligible. This takes you to a short online form to which you can attach supporting documentation. The following information is required: charity name and registration number; brief details about the project and the sum to be raised – please ensure you include a clear aim or list of objectives; details of the amount raised so far towards the target and if relevant, briefly mention how you intend to raise the rest; a copy of the last audited accounts and annual report. There are two committees: appeals and community care and education and youth which both meet quarterly. Please note: due to the overwhelming number of appeals, the foundation can only fund about 25% of current applications. If you are unsure whether your appeal is likely to succeed then please contact the grants administrator for further advice. Due to overwhelming demand, unsolicited appeals are extremely unlikely to attract a grant in connection with salaries, general running costs or major capital projects.

WHO TO APPLY TO Jan Carter, Grants Administrator, 12 Warwick Square, London SW1V 2AA *Tel* 020 7834 7731 *email* jan.carter@rankfoundation.co.uk *Website* www.rankfoundation.com

■ The Joseph Rank Trust

CC NO 1093844   ESTABLISHED 1929
WHERE FUNDING CAN BE GIVEN Unrestricted. In practice, UK.

WHO CAN BENEFIT Registered charities benefiting Methodists, children, young adults, older people, and people with disabilities.

WHAT IS FUNDED The building, maintenance or adaptation of Methodist church properties; support for Christian-based social work, categorised under youth projects, community service, religious education, people with disabilities, older people, health.

WHAT IS NOT FUNDED No grants to individuals, for charities on behalf of individuals, or for unregistered organisations.

TYPE OF GRANT One-off and recurring.

RANGE OF GRANTS £10,000–£325,000.

SAMPLE GRANTS Belfast Community Sports Dev. Network (£30,000); Volunteer Development East Lothian (£73,000); YMCA George Williams College (£179,000); Ocean Youth Trust (£11,000); Rugby School (bursary) (£4,000); Community Action Placement (£17,000); Outward Bound (£17,000); Gap Year Project (£325,000); Winchester Young Carers Project (£20,000); Cornwall Music Therapy Trust (£20,000); Help the Hospices (£100,000); Liverpool Community Spirit (£20,000); Mentoring Mediation and Communication (£65,000); Cricket Foundation (£10,000); Forgiveness (£25,000); Smartmove Exeter (£12,000); Christians Against Poverty (£15,000).

FINANCES *Year* 2009–10 *Income* £6,811,000 *Grants* £6,585,289 *Assets* £225,210,000

TRUSTEES Lindsay Fox, chair; Joey Newton; Nicholas Buxton; James Cave; Jason Chaffer; Andrew Cowen; Mark Davies; Rose Fitzpatrick; Lucinda Onslow; Johanna Ropner; Lord Shuttleworth; Daniel Simon; Earl St Aldwyn; Hon Caroline Twiston-Davies.

PUBLICATIONS The Agency Handbook 2010–11; The Volunteers' Handbook 2010–11. Available on the trust's website.

HOW TO APPLY If applicants consider that their work might fall within the areas of interest of the trust the following basic information is required: charity name and charity registration number; an outline of the project for which funding is sought; details of the total amount required to fund the project in its entirety; details of the amount already raised, or irrevocably committed, towards the target; a copy of the most recent annual report and audited accounts. Applicants should endeavour to set out the essential details of a project on no more than two sides of A4 paper, with more detailed information being presented in the form of appendices. Applications should be in hard copy. In normal circumstances, papers received before the middle of February, May, August and November may be considered in March, June, September and December respectively. Visits to appeals may be made by the secretary and trustees. All appeals are acknowledged and the applicants advised that if they do not receive a reply by a specified date it has not been possible for the trustees to make a grant.

WHO TO APPLY TO D J Sanderson, CEO/ Director of grants and special projects, Worth Corner, Turners Hill Road, Crawley RH10 7SL *Tel* 01293 873947 *email* secretary@ranktrust. org *Website* www.ranktrust.org

··

■ **Ranworth Trust**

CC NO 292633　　　　**ESTABLISHED** 1985

WHERE FUNDING CAN BE GIVEN UK and developing countries, with a preference for East Norfolk.

WHO CAN BENEFIT Local registered charities in East Norfolk and international charities.

WHAT IS FUNDED General charitable purposes with a focus on care and education in the community in East Norfolk and providing technological initiative and support in developing countries.

WHAT IS NOT FUNDED No grants to non-registered charities.

RANGE OF GRANTS £1,000 to £350,000.

SAMPLE GRANTS Norfolk Community Foundation (£350,000); Practical Action and Water Aid (£20,000 each); Cancer Research UK (£15,000); Sightsavers, Médecins Sans Frontières and BREAK (£10,000 each); Reach Foundation and Hope and Homes for Children (£5,000 each); Fairhaven CE VA Primary School – South Walsham (£3,500); Samaritans – Norfolk Branch (£2,000); and Mango Tree and Canine Partners for Independence (£1,000 each).

FINANCES *Year* 2009–10 *Income* £168,346 *Grants* £514,500 *Assets* £3,983,846

TRUSTEES Hon. Jacquetta Cator; Charles Cator; Mark Cator.

OTHER INFORMATION The largest grant of £350,000 was given to Norfolk Community Foundation to establish 'The Ranworth Grassroots Fund'. The aim of the fund is to support a wide range of charitable, voluntary and community activities across Norfolk.

HOW TO APPLY The trust's website states that it will not be considering any new applications until 2012.

WHO TO APPLY TO Hon. Jacquetta Cator, Trustee, The Old House, Ranworth, Norwich NR13 6HS *Website* www.ranworthtrust.org.uk

··

■ **The Fanny Rapaport Charitable Settlement**

CC NO 229406　　　　**ESTABLISHED** 1963

WHERE FUNDING CAN BE GIVEN North west England.

WHO CAN BENEFIT Registered charities only.

WHAT IS FUNDED The trust supports mainly, but not exclusively, Jewish charities and health and welfare organisations.

WHAT IS NOT FUNDED No grants to individuals.

SAMPLE GRANTS Previous beneficiaries included Brookvale, Christie Hospital NHS Trust, Community Security Trust, Delamere Forest School, the Heathlands Village, King David Schools, Manchester Jewish Federation, South Manchester Synagogue, United Jewish Israel Appeal and World Jewish Relief.

FINANCES *Year* 2009–10 *Income* £22,354 *Grants* £20,000

TRUSTEES J S Fidler; N Marks.

HOW TO APPLY Trustees hold meetings twice a year in March/April and September/October with cheques for donations issued shortly thereafter. If the applicant does not receive a cheque by the end of April or October, the application will have been unsuccessful. No applications are acknowledged.

WHO TO APPLY TO J S Fidler, Trustee, Kuit Steinart Levy Solicitors, 3 St Mary's Parsonage, Manchester M3 2RD

··

■ **The Rashbass Family Trust**

CC NO 1135961　　　　**ESTABLISHED** 2010

WHERE FUNDING CAN BE GIVEN Undefined in practice the Barnet district of London.

WHO CAN BENEFIT Individuals and organisations supporting children and young people; older people; people with disabilities; those of a particular ethnic or racial origin; other charities and the general public.

WHAT IS FUNDED General charitable purposes; education/training; advancement of health or saving of lives; disability; prevention or relief of poverty; religious activities.

TRUSTEES Jacqueline Rashbass; Andrew Rashbass.

HOW TO APPLY In writing to the correspondent.

WHO TO APPLY TO Ms Jacqueline Rashbass, Trustee, 17 Wykeham Road, London NW4 2TB *Tel* 07974 151494

··

■ **The Ratcliff Foundation**

CC NO 222441　　　　**ESTABLISHED** 1959

WHERE FUNDING CAN BE GIVEN UK, with a preference for local charities in the Midlands, North Wales and Gloucestershire.

WHO CAN BENEFIT Any organisation that has charitable status for tax purposes.

WHAT IS FUNDED General charitable purposes.

WHAT IS NOT FUNDED No grants to individuals.

RANGE OF GRANTS £2,000–£12,000; most are for £5,000 or less.

SAMPLE GRANTS Avoncroft Museum of Historic Buildings and Multiple Births Foundation (£5,000 each); Harbury Village Hall (£4,000); Cottage and Rural Enterprises Ltd and White Ladies Aston PCC (£3,000 each); Focus Birmingham, Full House Furniture and Recycling Service Ltd and Gloucestershire Wildlife Trust (£2,000 each); and Colwyn Choral Society (£1,000).

FINANCES *Year* 2009–10 *Income* £192,952 *Grants* £170,000 *Assets* £3,275,405

TRUSTEES David M Ratcliff, Chair; Edward H Ratcliff; Carolyn M Ratcliff; Gillian Mary Thorpe; James M G Fea; Christopher J Gupwell.

OTHER INFORMATION 54 grants were for £2,000 or more in 2009–10.

HOW TO APPLY In writing to the correspondent.

WHO TO APPLY TO Christopher J Gupwell, Secretary and Trustee, Woodlands, Earls Common road, Stock Green, Redditch B96 6TB *Tel* 01386 792116 *email* chris.gupwell@btinternet.com

■ The Ratcliff Pension Charity

CC NO 234613 **ESTABLISHED** 1967

WHERE FUNDING CAN BE GIVEN The borough of Tower Hamlets, with a preference for the Stepney area.

WHO CAN BENEFIT Individuals and organisations benefiting older people, young people, at-risk groups, and people who are disadvantaged by poverty, socially isolated or in need.

WHAT IS FUNDED The welfare of older people, general welfare and community organisations.

SAMPLE GRANTS Individuals in need (£10,550); Community centres and churches (£4,850); young people charities (£3,900); elderly, disabled and welfare charities (£12,500); contingency fund payments (£7,600); and shelters for the homeless (£1,750).

FINANCES Year 2009–10 *Income* £38,182 *Grants* £41,056 *Assets* £472,788

TRUSTEES The Coopers' Company.

OTHER INFORMATION The grants total includes payments to 22 elderly individuals and grants to 33 welfare and community organisations. In addition Contingency Fund payments were made through social services (Tower Hamlets) and Age Concern amounting to £7,600.

HOW TO APPLY In writing to the correspondent.

WHO TO APPLY TO A Carroll, Clerk, Coopers' Hall, 13 Devonshire Square, London EC2M 4TH *Tel* 020 7247 9577 *email* clerk@coopers-hall.co.uk *Website* coopers-hall.co.uk

■ The Ratcliffe Charitable Trust

CC NO 802320 **ESTABLISHED** 1989

WHERE FUNDING CAN BE GIVEN UK.

WHO CAN BENEFIT Registered charities.

WHAT IS FUNDED General charitable purposes.

SAMPLE GRANTS Previous beneficiaries included Barnardo's, Family Holiday Association, New Martin Community Youth Trust, Motor Neurone Disease Association, Orchdale Vale Trust Limited, VSO, Cancer Care Dorset, GUTS, British Council for the Prevention of Blindness, British Laser Appeal, Save the Children, Brainwave, Compaid Trust, Chicks (camping for inner city kids) and South West Thames Kidney Fund.

FINANCES Year 2009–10 *Income* £28,294 *Grants* £28,500 *Assets* £1,030,415

TRUSTEES Timothy Christopher James Adams; David Robbins; George Vellam.

HOW TO APPLY In writing to the correspondent.

WHO TO APPLY TO The Trustees, c/o Barlow Robbins LLP, 55 Quarry Street, Guildford, Surrey GU1 3UE *Tel* 01483 543200

■ The E L Rathbone Charitable Trust

CC NO 233240 **ESTABLISHED** 1921

WHERE FUNDING CAN BE GIVEN UK, with a strong preference for Merseyside.

WHO CAN BENEFIT Registered charities.

WHAT IS FUNDED General charitable purposes, especially social work charities. Preference to charities that the trust has special interest in, knowledge of, or association with.

WHAT IS NOT FUNDED No grants to individuals seeking support for second degrees.

RANGE OF GRANTS £250–£5,000.

SAMPLE GRANTS Sheila Kay Fund (£5,000); St Aidens Catholic Primary and YKIDS (£3,000 each); Wirral Community Narrow Boat Trust (£2,000); Liverpool Cathedral Girls' Choir and Sanctuary Family Support (£1,500 each);

Fairbridge in Merseyside and Friends of the Elderly (£1,000 each); and Hope Centre (£500).

FINANCES Year 2009–10 *Income* £70,994 *Grants* £75,900 *Assets* £1,898,351

TRUSTEES J B Rathbone; Mrs S K Rathbone; Mrs V P Rathbone; R S Rathbone.

HOW TO APPLY In writing to the correspondent.

WHO TO APPLY TO The Secretary, Rathbone Investment Management Ltd, Port of Liverpool Building, Pier Head, Liverpool L3 1NW *Tel* 0151 236 6666

■ The Eleanor Rathbone Charitable Trust

CC NO 233241 **ESTABLISHED** 1947

WHERE FUNDING CAN BE GIVEN UK, with the major allocation for Merseyside; also international projects (Africa, the Indian Sub Continent, plus exceptionally Iraq and Palestine).

WHO CAN BENEFIT Organisations benefiting general charitable projects in Merseyside; women; and unpopular and neglected causes.

WHAT IS FUNDED The trust concentrates its support largely on the following: (1) charities and charitable projects focused on Merseyside; (2) charities benefiting women and unpopular and neglected causes but avoiding those with a sectarian interest; (3) charities with which any of the trustees have a particular knowledge or association or in which it is thought Eleanor Rathbone or her father William Rathbone VI would have had a special interest; (4) charities providing holidays for disadvantaged people from Merseyside. The trust also makes international grants which are governed by the following criteria: (1) The trust will only consider projects from Africa, the Indian Sub Continent, plus exceptionally Iraq and Palestine; (2) Applications will be considered only from small or medium sized charities; (3) Projects must be sponsored and monitored by a UK based charity. In addition, projects must meet one or more of the following criteria: (i) they will benefit women or orphan children; (ii) they will demonstrate local involvement in scoping and delivery, except where skills required are not currently available e.g. eye surgeons in remote rural areas; (iii) they will aim to repair the damage in countries recently ravaged by international or civil war; (iv) they will deliver clean water.

WHAT IS NOT FUNDED Grants are not made in support of: any activity which relieves a statutory authority of its obligations; individuals, unless (and only exceptionally) it is made through a charity and it also fulfils at least one of the other positive objects mentioned above; overseas organisations without a sponsoring charity based in the UK. The trust does not generally favour grants for running costs, but prefers to support specific projects, services or to contribute to specific developments.

TYPE OF GRANT Most donations are on a one-off basis, although requests for commitments over two or more years are considered.

RANGE OF GRANTS £100–£3,000 and exceptionally higher.

SAMPLE GRANTS Haven Project (£19,000); Queen's Nursing Institute (£15,000); Wirral Churches Arc Project (£5,000); Social Partnership and NMP Anti-racist trust (£3,000 each); St Gregory's Youth, Community Initiative and Somali Women's Group (£2,000 each); After Adoption and Zero Centre (£1,500 each); Wells For India, Volunteer Reading Help and Barnstondale

Does the trust you have chosen match your needs? Haphazard applications waste postage and time

Centre (£1,000 each); Sunseed Tanzania Trust (£900); LCVS (£500); and Mary Seacole House (£300).

FINANCES *Year* 2009–10 *Income* £267,197 *Grants* £215,965 *Assets* £7,381,370

TRUSTEES William Rathbone; Jenny Rathbone; Andrew Rathbone; Lady Morgan; Mark Rathbone.

HOW TO APPLY There is no application form. The trust asks for a brief proposal for funding including costings, accompanied by the latest available accounts and any relevant supporting material. It is useful to know who else is supporting the project. To keep administration costs to a minimum, receipt of applications is not usually acknowledged. Applicants requiring acknowledgement should enclose an sae. Trustees currently meet three times a year on varying dates (contact the Administrator for information on the latest deadlines).

WHO TO APPLY TO Mrs Liese Astbury, Administrator, 546 Warrington Road, Rainhill, Merseyside L35 4LZ *email* eleanor.rathbone.trust@ tinyworld.co.uk

■ The Sigrid Rausing Trust

CC NO 1046769   **ESTABLISHED** 1995

WHERE FUNDING CAN BE GIVEN Unrestricted.

WHO CAN BENEFIT Charitable or voluntary organisations.

WHAT IS FUNDED Human, women's and minority rights and social and environmental justice.

WHAT IS NOT FUNDED Individuals and faith based groups.

RANGE OF GRANTS Up to £750,000.

SAMPLE GRANTS Interights – UK (£750,000); The Global Witness Trust – UK (£600,000); International Lesbian and Gay Association European Region – Belgium (£555,000); BTselem – Israel (£450,000); European Roma Rights Centre – Hungary (£375,000); Sisters in Islam – Malaysia (£300,000); Legal Resources Centre – South Africa (£300,000); Mani Tese – Italy (£240,000); Journalists for Human Rights – Canada (£240,000); Memoria Abiert – Argentina (£180,000); NGO Platform on Shipbreaking (£150,000); and Zimbiala – UK (£100,000).

FINANCES *Income* £18,451,795 *Grants* £21,345,319 *Assets* £7,882,132

TRUSTEES Dr Sigrid Rausing; Joshua Mailman; Susan Hitch; Andrew Puddephatt; Geoff Budlender.

OTHER INFORMATION Many of the grants awarded in 2010 will be paid throughout 2011 and 2012 as part of multi-year commitments.

HOW TO APPLY The trust does not accept unsolicited applications for funding. From time to time, it may request proposals from organisations working in particular fields. Details of requests will be made available on the trust's website. If you have not been invited to apply, but wish to let the trust know about your work, you can send an email describing your organisation to research@srtrust.org. Programme staff review emails regularly, but are unlikely to be able to meet with you in person.

WHO TO APPLY TO Sheetal Patel, Administrator, 12 Penzance Place, London W11 4PA *Tel* 020 7313 7727 *Fax* 020 7908 9879 *email* info@ srtrust.org *Website* www.sigrid-rausing-trust.org

■ The Ravensdale Trust

CC NO 265165   **ESTABLISHED** 1973

WHERE FUNDING CAN BE GIVEN Merseyside, particularly St Helens.

WHO CAN BENEFIT Registered charities.

WHAT IS FUNDED General, health, welfare, children, young people, conservation, heritage and Christian causes.

WHAT IS NOT FUNDED No grants to individuals.

TYPE OF GRANT One-off and recurrent.

RANGE OF GRANTS Usually £100–£3,000.

SAMPLE GRANTS Rainhill Guide House (£19,600); Prescot Guide House and YWCA St Helens (£5,000 each); URC St Helens (£3,000); Liverpool Hope University – Music Department and The Hope Centre (£2,500 each); Arena and Willowbrook Hospice (£2,000 each); Victim Support (£1,500); Alderhey Imagine Appeal and Derbyshire Hill Family and Community Association (£1,000 each); and Home Start Liverpool (£500).

FINANCES *Year* 2009–10 *Income* £34,862 *Grants* £188,056 *Assets* £1,561,782

TRUSTEES Mrs J L Fagan; M R Feeny; Mrs C B Cudmore.

HOW TO APPLY In writing to the correspondent. No application form. No acknowledgement of applications are made. Grants are paid in May and October.

WHO TO APPLY TO Mrs J Fagan, Trustee, Brabners Chaffe Street, Horton House, Exchange Flags, Liverpool L2 3YL *Tel* 0151 600 3000 *Fax* 0151 600 3300

■ The Rayden Charitable Trust

CC NO 294446   **ESTABLISHED** 1985

WHERE FUNDING CAN BE GIVEN UK.

WHO CAN BENEFIT Jewish organisations.

WHAT IS FUNDED General charitable purposes.

SAMPLE GRANTS NWJDS (£7,000); Or Chadash (£6,500); Yesodey Hatorah (£3,000); Holocaust Education and Jewish Care (£2,500); and Central London Mikveh and CTN Jewish Life (£1,000 each).

FINANCES *Year* 2009–10 *Income* £46,100 *Grants* £44,687 *Assets* £12,658

TRUSTEES Shirley Rayden; Clive Rayden; Paul Rayden.

HOW TO APPLY In writing to the correspondent.

WHO TO APPLY TO The Trustees, c/o Beavis Morgan LLP, 82 St John Street, London EC1M 4JN *Tel* 020 7417 0417

■ The Roger Raymond Charitable Trust

CC NO 262217   **ESTABLISHED** 1971

WHERE FUNDING CAN BE GIVEN UK (and very occasionally large, well-known overseas organisations).

WHO CAN BENEFIT Mainly headquarters organisations. Overseas grants are only made to large, well-known organisations (such as Sight Savers International and UNICEF).

WHAT IS FUNDED Older people, education and medical causes.

WHAT IS NOT FUNDED Grants are rarely given to individuals.

TYPE OF GRANT One-off and recurrent.

SAMPLE GRANTS Bloxham School (£184,000); Alzheimer's Society (£3,000); and DEC Haiti and Garvald West Linton (£2,000 each).

FINANCES *Year* 2009–10 *Income* £251,996 *Grants* £208,787 *Assets* £11,640,695

TRUSTEES R W Pullen; M G Raymond.

OTHER INFORMATION Bloxham School is the principal beneficiary each year.

Grants (of under £2,000) totalling £18,000 were also made but not listed in the accounts.

HOW TO APPLY The trust stated that applications are considered throughout the year, although funds are not always available.

WHO TO APPLY TO R W Pullen, Trustee, Suttondene, 17 South Border, Purley, Surrey CR8 3LL *Tel* 020 8660 9133 *email* russell@pullen.cix.co.uk

The Rayne Foundation

CC NO 216291   **ESTABLISHED** 1962
WHERE FUNDING CAN BE GIVEN UK.
WHO CAN BENEFIT Registered charities.
WHAT IS FUNDED Medicine, education, social welfare and the arts. Under these four headings the foundation encourages applications which apply to its evolving list of areas of special interest: achieving learning outcomes through the work of artists and arts organisations; developing numeracy skills; and improved quality of life for older people. Excellent applications outside these areas are also welcomed. In 2009–10 over 65% of awards have been outside these areas.
WHAT IS NOT FUNDED Grants are not made: to individuals; to organisations working outside the UK; for work that has already taken place; for repayment of debts; for endowments; to those who have applied in the last twelve months. Please do not send 'round robin' or general appeals.
TYPE OF GRANT Salaries and all types of project costs plus a reasonable contribution to overheads (there is no fixed percentage); general running or core costs (normally for a maximum of three years); capital costs of buildings and equipment (unless specifically stated in certain sectors).
RANGE OF GRANTS Up to £50,000.
SAMPLE GRANTS London Borough of Tower Hamlets (£50,000); Institute for Voluntary Action Research (£40,000); Wigmore Hall (£30,000); Carers UK (£24,000); Tenovus – Youth Cancer Charity (£20,000); Bath Festivals and Watford Grammar School for Boys (£15,000); Dyslexia Action, Newlife Foundation for Disabled Children and Compassion in Dying (£10,000 each.).
FINANCES *Year* 2009–10 *Income* £1,362,875 *Grants* £1,072,919 *Assets* £58,585,478
TRUSTEES The Hon Robert Rayne, Chair; Lord Claus Moser; Lady Jane Rayne; Lady Hilary Browne-Wilkinson; Prof. Dame Margaret Turner-Warwick; Prof. Anthony Newman Taylor; The Hon Natasha Rayne; The Hon Nicholas Rayne; Sir Emyr Jones Parry.
HOW TO APPLY Applying for a grant is a two-stage process. First you must fill in the Stage One Application Form available from the foundation's website, which you can complete and email to applications@raynefoundation.org.uk or print out and post. If it is not possible for you to access the first stage application online you should call the trust on 020 7487 9650. 'If you can demonstrate that the Foundation's aims will be met, we will contact you to make a more detailed application. We aim to respond to all Stage One proposals within one month of receipt.' Continuation funding – if you have previously received a grant from the foundation, you must complete a satisfactory monitoring report before reapplying. Organisations can only hold one grant at a time. Please use the two-

stage process for all applications, even if you are asking the foundation to continue funding the same project.
WHO TO APPLY TO Morin Carew, Grants Administrator, Carlton House, 33 Robert Adam Street, London W1U 3HR *Tel* 020 7487 9650/9630 *email* info@raynefoundation.org.uk *Website* www.raynefoundation.org.uk

The Rayne Trust

CC NO 207392   **ESTABLISHED** 1958
WHERE FUNDING CAN BE GIVEN UK and Israel.
WHO CAN BENEFIT Registered charities.
WHAT IS FUNDED The trust's mandate, as determined by the trustees, is to understand and engage with the needs of UK and Israeli society. The trust is involved in social bridge building. Jewish organisations and charities supporting the arts and social welfare and benefiting children, older and young people, at risk groups and people disadvantaged by poverty or socially isolated are supported.
WHAT IS NOT FUNDED No grants to individuals or non-registered charities.
TYPE OF GRANT Capital expenditure and recurrent expenses.
SAMPLE GRANTS Language as a Cultural Bridge and Mirkam/Nasij (£42,000); The Jewish Joint Distribution Committee (£40,000); UK Task Force on Arab Citizens of Israel (£15,000); and North London Hospice (£10,000).
FINANCES *Year* 2009–10 *Income* £275,289 *Grants* £102,000 *Assets* £15,986,563
TRUSTEES Lady Jane Rayne; the Hon Robert A Rayne.
OTHER INFORMATION Grants of less than £10,000 totalled £8,000. Grants cancelled during the year totalled £13,000.
HOW TO APPLY If you are considering applying to the trust you should first discuss your proposal with the Grants Manager at The Rayne Foundation (tel. 020 7487 9630).
WHO TO APPLY TO Tim Joss, Director, Carlton House, 33 Robert Adam Street, London W1U 3HR

The John Rayner Charitable Trust

CC NO 802363   **ESTABLISHED** 1989
WHERE FUNDING CAN BE GIVEN England, with a preference for Merseyside and Wiltshire.
WHO CAN BENEFIT Registered charities. There is a preference for small charities in the UK to receive the largest donations.
WHAT IS FUNDED General charitable purposes.
WHAT IS NOT FUNDED No grants to individuals or non-registered charities.
TYPE OF GRANT One-off and recurrent grants. Funding may be given for up to three years.
RANGE OF GRANTS Up to £5,000.
SAMPLE GRANTS Beneficiaries were: Age UK, Marie Curie Cancer Care and Music in Hospitals (£4,000 each); ACIR Bowel Cancer Appeal, Blackheath Halls, Countryside Foundation for Education, Jubilee Sailing Trust, Theodora Children's Trust and Whizz-Kids (£3,000 each); Swindon Sea Cadet Unit (£2,000); and Gt Bedwyn School Association (£1,000).
FINANCES *Year* 2009–10 *Income* £29,208 *Grants* £33,000 *Assets* £791,122
TRUSTEES Mrs J Wilkinson; Dr J M H Rayner; Louise McNeilage.
HOW TO APPLY In writing to the correspondent by 31 January each year. Trustees meet to allocate

donations in February/March. Only successful applicants will be contacted. There are no application forms or guidelines.

WHO TO APPLY TO Mrs J Wilkinson, Trustee, Manor Farmhouse, Church Street, Great Bedwyn, Marlborough, Wiltshire SN8 3PE

···

■ The Sir James Reckitt Charity

CC NO 225356   **ESTABLISHED** 1921

WHERE FUNDING CAN BE GIVEN Hull and the East Riding of Yorkshire, UK and occasional support of Red Cross or Quaker work overseas.

WHO CAN BENEFIT Registered charities covering a wide range of causes, including Quaker causes and occasional relief for victims of overseas disasters.

WHAT IS FUNDED Charitable organisations submitting applications within the framework of the following priorities. General charitable purposes, with priority in descending order: the Society of Friends (Quakers) in all localities; Hull and the East Riding of Yorkshire, which excludes York; national and regional charities, particularly those concerned with current social issues and whose work extends to the Hull and East Yorkshire areas; local non-registered organisations in Hull provided they are known to the local Council for Voluntary Service through whom grants may be channelled; and international in special circumstances only, e.g. major disasters.

WHAT IS NOT FUNDED Grants are normally made only to registered charities. Local organisations outside the Hull area are not supported, unless their work has regional implications. Grants are not normally made to individuals other than Quakers and residents of Hull and the East Riding of Yorkshire. Support is not given to causes of a warlike or political nature. No replacement of statutory funding or activities which collect funds to be passed on to other organisations, charities or individuals.

TYPE OF GRANT One-off towards projects or running costs.

RANGE OF GRANTS Up to £64,000.

SAMPLE GRANTS Hull Pre-School Learning Alliance (£5,500); Barnardo's (£3,900); Children & Family Action in Withernsea (£2,000); The Mount School, York (£22,000); Friends School Saffron Walden (£19,000); Tweendykes Special Needs School (£5,000); Bricknall Live at Home Scheme (£6,500); Independent Age (£4,400); Age Concern East Riding (£2,200); Farm Africa (£3,000); Dove House Hospice (£30,000); North Humberside Hospice (£10,000); Migraine Trust (£2,000); Britain Yearly Meeting (£50,000); Pickering and Hull Monthly Meeting (£13,000); Quaker Social Action (£2,000); British Red Cross (£23,000); ZANE Zimbabwe National Emergency (£17,000); International Rescue Committee UK (£8,300); RAPT Rehabilitation for Addicted Prisoners (£6,000); Hull Homeless & Rootless Project (£3,800); Northern Ballet Theatre (£2,000); Cat ZERO (£15,000); Hull Sea Cadet Corps (£3,300); Tall Ships Youth Trust (£2,000).

FINANCES *Year* 2010 *Income* £896,291 *Grants* £924,811 *Assets* £27,663,432

TRUSTEES William Upton; James Harrison Holt; Caroline Jennings; Philip James Harrison Holt; Robin James Upton; Sarah Helen Craven; Martin Dickinson; Charles Maxsted; Simon J Upton; Simon E Upton; James Marshall; Edward Upton; Rebecca Holt; Dr Karina Mary Upton.

PUBLICATIONS A History of the Sir James Reckitt Charity 1921–1979 by B N Reckitt; A History of the Sir James Reckitt Charity 1921–1999 by G M Atherton. A leaflet detailing the charity's grant guidelines.

OTHER INFORMATION The grant total includes £40,000 given to individuals.

HOW TO APPLY In writing to the correspondent. The charity provides a checklist of information which should be included in any letter of application: the nature of your organisation, its structure and its relationship with other agencies and networks; the aims of your organisation and its mission statement; the purpose of the project, the need which has been identified and evidence of the need; exactly what the grant will be used for; the total cost of the project and how you intend to raise any balance; who will benefit from the project, the outcomes and how you will know if the project is successful; whether your organisation is a registered charity or, if a small local group, is it known to a local CVS; your bank account payee name to whom the cheque can be made payable; a set of the latest accounts or a record of income and expenditure which has been subject to independent scrutiny; your contact details, i.e. address, telephone number and email. Applications are measured against the charity's guidelines and decisions are taken at a twice-yearly meeting of trustees in May and October. Applications should be submitted by mid-April and mid-September respectively.

WHO TO APPLY TO James McGlashan, Administrator, 7 Derrymore Road, Willerby, East Yorkshire HU10 6ES *Tel* 01482 655861 *email* jim@derrymore.karoo.co.uk *Website* www.thesirjamesreckittcharity.org.uk

···

■ Eva Reckitt Trust Fund

CC NO 210563   **ESTABLISHED** 1940

WHERE FUNDING CAN BE GIVEN UK and overseas.

WHO CAN BENEFIT Charitable organisations.

WHAT IS FUNDED Welfare and relief-in-need; organisations supporting the extension and development of education and victims of war.

SAMPLE GRANTS Previous beneficiaries included: Children of the Andes, Christian Engineers in Development, Computer Aid International, Crisis, Medical Foundation for the Care of Victims of Torture, One World Action, Orbis, Prisoners of Conscience Appeal Fund, Send a Cow, St John of Jerusalem Eye Hospital, St Mungo's, Stephen Lawrence Charitable Trust, Traidcraft, Water and Sanitation for the Urban Poor and World Development Movement.

FINANCES *Year* 2009–10 *Income* £131,725 *Grants* £50,000

TRUSTEES Anna Bunney; Chris Whittaker; David Birch; Diana Holliday.

HOW TO APPLY In writing to the correspondent.

WHO TO APPLY TO David Birch, Trustee, 1 Somerford Road, Cirencester, Gloucestershire GL7 1TP *email* davidbirch50@googlemail.com

···

■ The Red Arrows Trust

CC NO 283461   **ESTABLISHED** 1981

WHERE FUNDING CAN BE GIVEN UK.

WHO CAN BENEFIT Royal Air Force and general charities.

WHAT IS FUNDED General charitable purposes.

SAMPLE GRANTS No information on beneficiaries was available.

FINANCES *Year* 2009–10 *Income* £53,448 *Grants* £30,826 *Assets* £35,876

TRUSTEES Roger Bowder; Keith Harkness; Mark Dunkley.

OTHER INFORMATION In 2009–10, £31,000 was given to 15 organisations.

HOW TO APPLY The trustees meet to consider grants in March and September and applications need to be received by February and August.

WHO TO APPLY TO K R Harkness, Trustee, Orchard House, 67 Ankle Road, Melton Mowbray LE13 0QJ *Tel* 01664 566844

■ Red Hill Charitable Trust

CC NO 307891   **ESTABLISHED** 1997

WHERE FUNDING CAN BE GIVEN South east England.

WHO CAN BENEFIT Charitable organisations.

WHAT IS FUNDED The promotion of education, including social and physical training, of individuals under the age of 25 who have emotional and/or behavioural difficulties and disorders.

WHAT IS NOT FUNDED No grants to individuals. Research projects are not normally considered.

TYPE OF GRANT The trustees prefer to make grants for a year at a time, and are reluctant to take on any open-ended commitments.

RANGE OF GRANTS Generally £1,000–£5,000.

SAMPLE GRANTS Heart of Kent Hospice (£10,000); Relateen (£7,000); Caldecott Foundation and Art Room (£5,000 each); St Joseph's School – Cranleigh (£4,200); RISB (£4,000 each); Company of Angels (£3,200); Foxhills Nurture Group (£2,500); Tall Ships and TRAX Buggies (£2,000 each); Goldwyn and Manor Junior School (£1,500 each); and Challenger Centre (£800).

FINANCES *Year* 2009–10 *Income* £75,480 *Grants* £97,071 *Assets* £2,636,559

TRUSTEES D E Wilson, Chair; A Bunting; J Hay; K Hall; W Mather; B Clifford; R Barton; B Head.

HOW TO APPLY On a form available from the correspondent by written request or email.

WHO TO APPLY TO The Clerk, 6 Clarendon Close, Bearsted, Maidstone ME14 4JD *Tel* 01622 739287 *Website* www.redhilltrust.org

■ The Red Rose Charitable Trust

CC NO 1038358   **ESTABLISHED** 1994

WHERE FUNDING CAN BE GIVEN UK with a preference for Lancashire and Merseyside.

WHO CAN BENEFIT Charities working with older people who or people who have physical or mental disabilities.

WHAT IS FUNDED Welfare causes and educational expenses for students.

SAMPLE GRANTS Liverpool Cathedral Centenary Fund (£5,000); and Brainwave, Clatterbridge Cancer Research Trust, Help the Aged, Make a Wish Foundation, Mango Tree, Sense and Sue Ryder Care (£1,000 each).

FINANCES *Year* 2009–10 *Income* £34,046 *Grants* £22,000 *Assets* £899,886

TRUSTEES James N L Packer; Jane L Fagan; Julian B Rathbone.

HOW TO APPLY In writing to the correspondent.

WHO TO APPLY TO J N L Packer, Trustee, c/o Rathbones, Port of Liverpool Building, Pier Head, Liverpool L3 1NW

■ The C A Redfern Charitable Foundation

CC NO 299918   **ESTABLISHED** 1989

WHERE FUNDING CAN BE GIVEN UK.

WHO CAN BENEFIT Registered UK charities.

WHAT IS FUNDED General charitable purposes, with some preference for those concerned with health and welfare.

WHAT IS NOT FUNDED No grants for building works or individuals.

TYPE OF GRANT Core costs, one-off, project and research. Funding is available for one year or less.

RANGE OF GRANTS £250–£50,000. The majority were between £250–£5,000.

SAMPLE GRANTS South Bucks Riding for the Disabled (£35,000); Saints and Sinners (£30,000); and White Ensign (£10,000); Live Music Now, Reed School Foundation Appeal and Special Yoga Centre (£5,000 each); the Royal College of Surgeons (£2,500); Whitefield Development Trust (£1,000); and Motor Neurone Disease Association and Thames Valley Hospice (£500 each); and The Camphill Family and the Pasque Charity (£250 each).

FINANCES *Year* 2009–10 *Income* £156,681 *Grants* £179,000 *Assets* £4,239,712

TRUSTEES Sir Robert Clark; William Maclaren; David Redfern; Terence Thornton; Simon Ward.

HOW TO APPLY The foundation does not accept unsolicited applications.

WHO TO APPLY TO The Trustees, PricewaterhouseCoopers, 9 Greyfriars Road, Reading, Berkshire RG1 1JG

■ The Reed Foundation

CC NO 264728   **ESTABLISHED** 1972

WHERE FUNDING CAN BE GIVEN UK and developing countries.

WHO CAN BENEFIT Charitable organisations.

WHAT IS FUNDED General charitable purposes, with an interest in the arts, education, women's causes and children and young people.

SAMPLE GRANTS World Wildlife Fund – UK (£83,000); Promoting Equality in African Schools (£28,000); The Prince's Trust (£25,000); Self Help Africa and the One Voice Movement (£20,000 each); Friends of the Earth (£15,000); In Kind Direct (£13,500); Activiteens, Refugee Council and British Youth Opera (£10,000 each); Dulwich Picture Gallery (£8,500); The Wildlife Trust for Lancashire, Manchester and North Merseyside (£5,000); and Camden Arts Centre (£1,000).

FINANCES *Year* 2010 *Income* £786,688 *Grants* £793,047 *Assets* £14,836,847

TRUSTEES Alec Reed; James A Reed; Richard A Reed; Mrs Alex M Chapman.

HOW TO APPLY In writing to the correspondent. The trust states that it does not respond to unsolicited applications.

WHO TO APPLY TO The Secretary, 6 Sloane Street, London SW1X 9LE *Tel* 020 7201 9980 *email* reed.foundation@reed.co.uk

■ Richard Reeve's Foundation

CC NO 1136337   **ESTABLISHED** 1928

WHERE FUNDING CAN BE GIVEN Camden, City of London and Islington.

WHO CAN BENEFIT Individuals up to the age of 25 (in certain circumstances up to the age of 40).

WHAT IS FUNDED Educational costs, uniforms, books, travel expenses, living costs, equipment and organisation projects that benefit a significant number of children at a time.

WHAT IS NOT FUNDED No grants for building costs, independent school fees, furniture/household goods, school meals, holidays, school outings or to replace statutory funding.

TYPE OF GRANT Normally cash – but uniforms bought from a recognised supplier.

RANGE OF GRANTS £350–£50,000.

SAMPLE GRANTS Christ's Hospital (£20,000); New Horizon Youth Centre (£10,000); St Luke's Parochial Trust (£9,000); Castlehaven Community Association, Volunteer Reading Help and Friendship Works (£5,000 each) and The Outward Bound Trust and Gospel Oak Primary School (£3,000 each).

FINANCES *Year* 2009–10 *Grants* £165,177 *Assets* £14,258,242

TRUSTEES Billy Dove; Sylvan Dewing; P Tickle; Cllr. Charlynne Pullen; Mrs M Hughesdon; M Jessett; Mr M Bennett; M Renshaw; S Bettley; S Farrington.

OTHER INFORMATION Grants are mainly made to individuals for educational purposes. In 2009–10 grants were paid to 83 individuals and 401 families totalling £102,000.

HOW TO APPLY Initially in writing to the correspondent outlining the request. Criteria and guidelines are available from the foundations website. Completed proposals should be returned by the middle of February, May, August or November for consideration by the end of the next calendar month.

WHO TO APPLY TO Cath Moffat, Grants Officer, 2 Cloth Court, London EC1A 7LS *Tel* 020 7726 4230 *email* clerk@richardreevesfoundation.org. uk *Website* www.richardreevesfoundation.org.uk

---

■ The Rehoboth Trust

CC NO 1114454   **ESTABLISHED** 2006

WHERE FUNDING CAN BE GIVEN UK and Israel.

WHO CAN BENEFIT Christians.

WHAT IS FUNDED Christian churches and ministers.

SAMPLE GRANTS Elm Church Kensington Temple (£17,000); 'Others' (£1,150).

FINANCES *Year* 2009 *Income* £35,275 *Grants* £26,269 *Assets* £3,987

TRUSTEES Shakti Sisodia, Chair; Andrea Sisodia; Lyndon Bowring; Jonathan Gwilt.

OTHER INFORMATION In 2009 £8,000 was awarded to individuals.

HOW TO APPLY In writing to the correspondent.

WHO TO APPLY TO Shakti Sisodia, Chair, 71 Rydal Gardens, Hounslow TW3 2JJ *Tel* 020 8893 3700

■ The Max Reinhardt Charitable Trust

CC NO 264741   **ESTABLISHED** 1973

WHERE FUNDING CAN BE GIVEN UK.

WHO CAN BENEFIT Charitable organisations.

WHAT IS FUNDED The trust supports organisations benefiting people who are deaf and fine arts promotion.

WHAT IS NOT FUNDED No grants to individuals.

SAMPLE GRANTS Paintings in Hospitals (£20,000); The Art Room (£6,000); Auditory Verbal UK and Modern Art Museum, Oxford (£1,000 each); Deafblind UK (£250); and Dogs Trust, Friends of the Earth, National Trust, Thrive, West London Homeless, Young and Free and Zane (£100 each).

FINANCES *Year* 2009–10 *Income* £38,827 *Grants* £31,654 *Assets* £731,697

TRUSTEES Joan Reinhardt; Veronica Reinhardt; Magdalen Wade.

HOW TO APPLY In writing to the correspondent.

WHO TO APPLY TO The Secretary to the Trustees, Flat 2, 43 Onslow Square, London SW7 3LR

■ Relief Fund for Romania Limited

CC NO 1046737   **ESTABLISHED** 1989

WHERE FUNDING CAN BE GIVEN Romania.

WHO CAN BENEFIT Romanian charities.

WHAT IS FUNDED Street children; work with people who are elderly, infirm or have disabilities; children in hospital; medical programmes to isolated rural areas; 'begging children' and the Roma community; children and adults with special needs in institutions; families at risk; people with tuberculosis; medical disability and the mental health arena; and children and adolescents with physical disabilities.

SAMPLE GRANTS Services for elderly people – Day Care Speranta-Bacau; Day Care Motoseni; Home Care Bacau and Home Care Villages. Services for children – Sticky Club Bacau, Panu and Godinest and Impart (children with handicap). Services for families – social support and mother and baby care.

FINANCES *Year* 2009–10 *Income* £704,894 *Grants* £117,569 *Assets* £12,302

TRUSTEES A Adams; N Ratiu.

HOW TO APPLY A brief, two-page proposal should be sent by post or email to the correspondent. Applicants who interest the trustees will then be asked to complete a second, more detailed proposal.

WHO TO APPLY TO E Parry, Secretary, 18 Fitzharding Street, London W1H 6EQ *Tel* 020 8761 2277 *Fax* 020 8761 0020 *email* mail@ relieffundforromania.co.uk *Website* www. relieffundforromania.co.uk

---

■ REMEDI

CC NO 1063359   **ESTABLISHED** 1973

WHERE FUNDING CAN BE GIVEN UK.

WHO CAN BENEFIT Charitable organisations, hospitals and universities.

WHAT IS FUNDED The support of pioneering research into all aspects of disability in the widest sense of the word, with special emphasis on disability and the way in which it limits the activities and lifestyle of all ages. Preference for applicants who wish to carry out innovative and original research and experience difficulty in attracting funding from the larger and better-known organisations. Collaboration with other charities working in the same field is encouraged.

WHAT IS NOT FUNDED Cancer and cancer-related diseases are not supported.

TYPE OF GRANT Grants are usually given for one year, occasionally for two and exceptionally for three years. Projects, equipment and therapy research are supported.

SAMPLE GRANTS Previous beneficiaries include: Dr Brona McDowell et al – Musgrave Park Hospital, Belfast; Professor Lalit Kalra – Kings College London; and Professor Nadina Lincoln – University of Nottingham.

FINANCES *Year* 2009–10 *Income* £129,562 *Grants* £106,637 *Assets* £213,001

TRUSTEES James Moseley; Brian Winterflood; Dr Anthony K Clarke; Jerry Hansford; Prof. Nick Bosanquet; Dr Adrian H M Heagerty; Michael

Hines; Colin Maynard; Karin Russell; Dr Anthony B Ward.

HOW TO APPLY Firstly, applicants should email a short summary (two pages of A4) of their project, including a breakdown of costs, proposed start date and length of the research programme. If the project is considered of interest to the trustees you will then be asked to complete a full application form. Full applications are peer reviewed and, if successful, passed on to the trustees for a final decision at their biannual meetings (usually in June and December). For full guidelines please visit the trust's website.

WHO TO APPLY TO Rosie Wait, Director, Elysium House, 126–128 New Kings Road, London SW6 4LZ *Tel* 020 7384 2929 *email* research@ remedi.org.uk *Website* www.remedi.org.uk

---

■ The Rest Harrow Trust

CC NO 238042   **ESTABLISHED** 1964
WHERE FUNDING CAN BE GIVEN UK.
WHO CAN BENEFIT Registered charities benefiting people who are in poor health, disabled, disadvantaged by poverty or homeless.
WHAT IS FUNDED Main areas of interest are older people, education, disability, housing, poverty, and youth. Particularly Jewish organisations.
WHAT IS NOT FUNDED No grants to non-registered charities or to individuals.
TYPE OF GRANT Occasionally one-off for part or all of a particular project.
RANGE OF GRANTS £100–£5,500. The majority were under £500 each.
SAMPLE GRANTS Nightingale House, Pinhas Rutenberg Educational Trust and Weizmann UK (£2,000 each); and British Friends of the Hebrew University, Jewish Care and World Jewish Relief (£1,000 each); Magen David Adorn UK (£700); Canon Collins Trust, Council of Christians & Jews and Friends of Israel Educational Foundation (£500 each); Sightsavers International, Spiro Ark, St Christopher's Hospice, Barnardo's, Bath Institute of Medical Engineering (BIME), Blond McIndoe Research Foundation, Book Aid International, Books Abroad, Bowel Disease Research Foundation, Brain Research Trust (£200 each); and Build Africa, Catch 22, Central & Cecil Housing Trust, Charity Search, ChildHope, Children's Adventure Farm Trust, Church Army and Church Housing Trust (£100 each).
FINANCES *Year* 2009–10 *Income* £58,145 *Grants* £45,494 *Assets* £857,678
TRUSTEES Mrs J B Bloch; Judith S Portrait; H O N and V Trustee Limited; Dominic B Flynn.
OTHER INFORMATION Grants are usually made to national bodies rather than local branches, or local groups.
HOW TO APPLY In writing to the correspondent. Applications are considered quarterly. Only submissions from eligible bodies are acknowledged.
WHO TO APPLY TO Judith S Portrait, c/o Portrait Solicitors, 1 Chancery Lane, London WC2A 1LF *Tel* 020 7092 6990

■ Reuben Brothers Foundation

CC NO 1094130   **ESTABLISHED** 2002
WHERE FUNDING CAN BE GIVEN UK and overseas.
WHO CAN BENEFIT Charitable organisations, with a possible preference for those operating in the UK, Israel, India and Iraq.
WHAT IS FUNDED Healthcare, education and general charitable purposes.
SAMPLE GRANTS Team London Project (£230,000); The Prince's Charities Foundation, Great Ormond Street Hospital's Tick Tock Club and the Community Security Trust (£25,000 each); and Jewish Care (£10,000).
FINANCES *Year* 2010 *Income* £2,995,907 *Grants* £970,034 *Assets* £66,278,281
TRUSTEES Richard Stone, Chair; Simon Reuben; David Reuben; Malcolm Turner; Michael Gubbay; Annie Benjamin; Patrick O'Driscoll; James Reuben; Dana Reuben; Debra Reuben.
OTHER INFORMATION Grants included £54,000 to 16 individuals.
HOW TO APPLY In writing to the correspondent, although the trust has stated that applications are by invitation only. Grant applications are processed with all requests for funds being put before the trustee meetings and the merits of each application being considered. Unsuccessful applicants are notified by post. Donations are sent out to the successful applicants having regard to the current reserves and the long-term policy of the foundation. Trustees meetings are held every month.
WHO TO APPLY TO Patrick O'Driscoll, Trustee, Millbank Tower, 21–24 Millbank, London SW1P 4PQ *Tel* 020 7802 5000 *Fax* 020 7802 5002 *email* contact@reubenfoundation.com *Website* www.reubenfoundation.com

---

■ The Joan K Reynell Charitable Trust

CC NO 1069397   **ESTABLISHED** 1997
WHERE FUNDING CAN BE GIVEN UK.
WHO CAN BENEFIT Registered charities.
WHAT IS FUNDED General charitable purposes.
RANGE OF GRANTS Up to £3,000.
SAMPLE GRANTS Save the Children; Compassion in World Farming, Hearing Dogs for Deaf People, Oxfam, RSPCA, the Cinnamon Trust, the Soil Association, the Woodland Trust, WWF-UK.
FINANCES *Year* 2009–10 *Income* £31,973 *Grants* £19,800 *Assets* £2,524
TRUSTEES Anthony Reynell; Michael Reynell.
HOW TO APPLY In writing to the correspondent.
WHO TO APPLY TO The Trustees, c/o HSBC Trust Co. Ltd, Norwich House, Nelson Gate, Southampton SO15 1GX *Tel* 023 8072 2210

■ The Nathaniel Reyner Trust Fund

CC NO 223619   **ESTABLISHED** 1965
WHERE FUNDING CAN BE GIVEN Merseyside area.
WHO CAN BENEFIT Registered charities and Christian organisations helping children, young adults, older people, clergy, Baptists, Church of England, Christians, evangelists and Methodists.
WHAT IS FUNDED The promotion of evangelical Christianity and also general charitable purposes, particularly the advancement of Christian religion and Christian religious buildings.
WHAT IS NOT FUNDED No grants to individuals, medical research, the arts or denominations other than URC or Baptist unless there is a clear and overriding ecumenical or community objective.
RANGE OF GRANTS Up to £5,000.
SAMPLE GRANTS Baptist Missionary Society Merseyside Auxiliary and North West Baptist Association (£3,500 each); Heswall United

Reformed Church, Parkgate & Neston United Reformed Church and The United Reformed Church Caradoc Mission (£2,500 each); Council for World Mission and Laird Street Baptist Church Family Support Centre (£1,000 each); Adelaide House, After Adoption, the Aspire Trust Ltd, BIRD, Contact the Elderly, Listening Ear, Shaftesbury Youth Club and Weston Spirit (£500 each).

FINANCES *Year* 2009–10 *Income* £23,058 *Grants* £36,000

TRUSTEES D E G Faragher, Chair; J R Watson; W B Howarth; Miss M Proven; F N Ward; D Craig; Miss J Hope.

HOW TO APPLY In writing to the correspondent. Trustees meet in April and November.

WHO TO APPLY TO Lawrence Downey, Secretary, Drury House, 19 Water Street, Liverpool L2 0RP *Tel* 0151 236 8989 *email* lawrence.downey@ maceandjones.co.uk

---

■ The Rhododendron Trust

CC NO 267192   **ESTABLISHED** 1974

WHERE FUNDING CAN BE GIVEN UK and overseas.

WHO CAN BENEFIT Registered charities.

WHAT IS FUNDED Overseas charities, UK social welfare charities and UK cultural charities.

WHAT IS NOT FUNDED The trust does not support medical research, individual projects, or local community projects in the UK.

TYPE OF GRANT Preferably project-based.

RANGE OF GRANTS £500 or £1,000 each.

SAMPLE GRANTS Cambodia Trust, Children in Crisis, Fauna and Flora International and Friends of Hlekweni (£1,000 each) and Beyond the Streets, Book Aid International, Brandon Centre, Contact the Elderly, Corrymeela, Crisis, Working with Massai, World Wildlife Fund and Zero Centre (£500 each).

FINANCES *Year* 2009–10 *Income* £103,765 *Grants* £50,000 *Assets* £1,429,382

TRUSTEES Peter Edward Healey; Dr Ralph Walker; Mrs Sarah Ray; Mrs Sarah Oliver.

HOW TO APPLY In writing to the correspondent at any time. The majority of donations are made in March. Applications are not acknowledged.

WHO TO APPLY TO P E Healey, Trustee, Cedar House, Sandbrook Business Park, Sandbrook Way, Rochdale OL11 1LQ

■ The Rhondda Cynon Taff Welsh Church Acts Fund

CC NO 506658   **ESTABLISHED** 1977

WHERE FUNDING CAN BE GIVEN Rhondda-Cynon-Taff, Bridgend and Merthyr Tydfil County Borough Councils, i.e. the former county of Mid Glamorgan, with the exception of Rhymney Valley which is now outside the area of benefit.

WHO CAN BENEFIT Churches, youth organisations and musical groups benefiting children, young adults, Christians, at risk groups, and people who are disadvantaged by poverty or socially isolated.

WHAT IS FUNDED Churches; youth activities; and welfare.

WHAT IS NOT FUNDED No grants to students, individuals, or projects of other local authorities. Grants are not given for running costs.

SAMPLE GRANTS Darren Las Environmental Group – Mountain Ash, Llanfair Uniting Church – Penrhys and Llwynypia Boys' and Girls' Club (£10,000 each); St Theodore's Church – Kenfig Hill (£9,000); Seion Welsh Baptist Church –

Cwmaman (£5,000); and Arts Factory – Maerdy and Cefn Coed Community Centre (£2,000 each).

FINANCES *Year* 2010–11 *Income* £358,900 *Grants* £184,442 *Assets* £10,319,000

TRUSTEES Rhondda Cynon Taff County Borough Council.

HOW TO APPLY The charity invites applications for funding of projects through advertising in the local press.

WHO TO APPLY TO George Sheldrick, Rhondda Cyon Taff Council, Accounts Section, Bronwydd House, Porth CF39 9DL *Tel* 01443 680373 *Fax* 01443 680592

■ Daisie Rich Trust

CC NO 236706   **ESTABLISHED** 1964

WHERE FUNDING CAN BE GIVEN UK, with a preference for the Isle of Wight.

WHO CAN BENEFIT Organisations and individuals.

WHAT IS FUNDED General charitable purposes.

TYPE OF GRANT Mostly recurrent.

RANGE OF GRANTS £250–£10,000.

SAMPLE GRANTS Earl Mountbatten Hospice (£10,000); Shanklin Voluntary Youth and Community Centre (£6,000); Isle of Wight RCC 'Helping Hands', Hampshire and Isle of Wight Air Ambulance and SSAFA Isle of Wight (£3,000 each); Isle of Wight Citizens Advice Bureau (£2,000); St Vincent's Care Home (£1,200); Macmillan Cancer Relief, Marie Curie Nurses and Parkinson's Disease Society (£1,000 each); Friends of Brading Roman Villa (£800); Fishbourne Sailability Club, Girls' Brigade 3rd Ryde Company and Challenge and Adventure (£500 each); and Isle of Wight Hospital Broadcasting Association (£250).

FINANCES *Year* 2009–10 *Income* £102,476 *Grants* £81,534 *Assets* £3,156,083

TRUSTEES Adrian H Medley, Chair; Ann C Medley; Maurice J Flux; David J Longford.

OTHER INFORMATION In 2009–10 grants to ex-employees of Upward and Rich Ltd, their dependants and other individuals totalled £32,434.

HOW TO APPLY In writing to the correspondent. The trustees hold regular meetings to decide on grant applications and are assisted by information gathered by the administrator.

WHO TO APPLY TO Mrs L Mitchell, Administrator, The Hawthorns, School Lane, Arreton, Newport, Isle of Wight PO30 3AD *Tel* 07866 449855 *email* daisierich@yahoo.co.uk

---

■ The Sir Cliff Richard Charitable Trust

CC NO 1096412   **ESTABLISHED** 1969

WHERE FUNDING CAN BE GIVEN UK and overseas.

WHO CAN BENEFIT Registered charities only, benefiting a broad spectrum, including: children, adults and young people; Baptists, Methodists, Anglicans and Evangelists; people who are disabled or have a medical condition.

WHAT IS FUNDED Smaller, grass-roots projects are often preferred, for general charitable purposes that reflect the support, Christian commitment and interest of Sir Cliff Richard, including: special schools, special needs education and vocational training; community centres, village halls, playgrounds and play schemes; care in the community and community transport; respite care and care for carers; cancer, MS and neurological research; Christian education and

Think carefully about every application. Is it justified?

837

outreach; missionaries and evangelicals; and animal homes and welfare.

WHAT IS NOT FUNDED Capital building projects, church repairs and renovations are all excluded. No support for individuals.

TYPE OF GRANT Usually small one-off sums for operational needs.

RANGE OF GRANTS Around £2,000 to £50,000.

SAMPLE GRANTS Tear Fund and Tennis Foundation (£5,000 each); Genesis Trust (£3,500); and the Arts Centre Group (£2,500).

FINANCES *Year* 2009–10 *Income* £235,754 *Grants* £85,780 *Assets* £344,887

TRUSTEES William Latham; Malcolm Smith; Sir Cliff Richard.

OTHER INFORMATION Smaller grants of less than £5,000 were made totalling £69,000.

HOW TO APPLY Applications should be from registered charities only, in writing, and for one-off needs. All applications are acknowledged. Grants are made quarterly in January, April, July and October.

WHO TO APPLY TO William Latham, Trustee, Harley House, 94 Hare Lane, Claygate, Esher, Surrey KT10 0RB *Tel* 01372 467752 *Fax* 01372 462352 *email* general@cliffrichard.org

■ C B Richard Ellis Charitable Trust

CC NO 299026   **ESTABLISHED** 1987

WHERE FUNDING CAN BE GIVEN Unrestricted.

WHO CAN BENEFIT Registered charities or recognised charitable causes, which have a strong link to C B Richard Ellis Ltd, for example, through client requests for support or staff fundraising activities.

WHAT IS FUNDED General charitable causes.

WHAT IS NOT FUNDED No grants to third parties, such as fundraising organisations or publication companies producing charity awareness materials.

RANGE OF GRANTS £20–£1,100.

SAMPLE GRANTS Breast Cancer Care (£1,100); Richard House Children's Hospice (£930); British Heart Foundation (£720); Macmillan Cancer Support (£627); Help for Heroes (£525); Shelter (£290); Yorkhill Children's Foundation (£200); Scottish Community Foundation, Suffolk Historic Churches Trust, Land Aid and National Woodland Trust (£150 each); UNICEF (£100); Oxfam (£75); Veterans Aid (£50); and Rainbow Trust (£20).

FINANCES *Year* 2009–10 *Income* £75,825 *Grants* £17,923 *Assets* £70,426

TRUSTEES Kevin Bramley; Matthew D Black; Michael J Prentice; Nick R Martel; Lena Patel; Nicholas E Compton.

HOW TO APPLY In writing to the correspondent. The trust stated that in recent years they have received as many as two hundred unsolicited requests for support that do not meet with the above donations criteria. Given the size of the trust, a response to such requests is not always possible.

WHO TO APPLY TO A C Naftis, Secretary to the Trustees, St Martin's Court, 10 Paternoster Row, London EC4M 7HP *Tel* 020 7182 3452

■ The Clive Richards Charity

CC NO 327155   **ESTABLISHED** 1986

WHERE FUNDING CAN BE GIVEN UK, with a preference for Herefordshire.

WHO CAN BENEFIT Individuals and registered charities benefiting children and older people, musicians, Roman Catholics, people who are disabled or disadvantaged by poverty and victims of crime.

WHAT IS FUNDED The assistance of education, people with disabilities, the arts, conservation and religion, mostly in the county of Herefordshire, especially in church schools.

TYPE OF GRANT One-off, project and buildings. Interest-free loans are considered. Grants may be for up to two years.

RANGE OF GRANTS From £1,000.

SAMPLE GRANTS The Hydosense Charitable Organisation – Hydosense Appeal (£123,000); Belmont Abbey General Fund (£22,000); the Mary Rose Appeal(£10,000); Welsh National Opera (£5,000); Royal National College for the Blind (£3,000); St Josephs Church – Bromyard (£2,500); and Bishop Vesey's Grammar School (£1,000).

FINANCES *Year* 2009–10 *Income* £310,965 *Grants* £208,293 *Assets* £50,787

TRUSTEES Peter Henry; Clive Richards; Sylvia Richards.

HOW TO APPLY In writing to the correspondent. The trustees meet monthly to consider applications. Please note, the trust has previously stated that due to its resources being almost fully committed it is extremely selective in accepting any requests for funding.

WHO TO APPLY TO Peter Henry, Trustee, Lower Hope, Ullingswick, Herefordshire HR1 3JF *Tel* 01432 820557 *Fax* 01432 820772

■ The Violet M Richards Charity

CC NO 273928   **ESTABLISHED** 1977

WHERE FUNDING CAN BE GIVEN UK, with a preference for East Sussex, particularly Crowborough.

WHO CAN BENEFIT Organisations benefiting: older people; medical professionals; researchers; medical students; and people with a medical condition.

WHAT IS FUNDED The trust's objects are the relief of age and ill health, through the advancement of medical research (particularly into geriatric problems), medical education, homes and other facilities for older people and those who are sick. The trustees are happy to commit themselves to funding a research project over a number of years, including 'seedcorn' projects.

WHAT IS NOT FUNDED No support for individuals.

TYPE OF GRANT Applications for grants of all types will be considered.

RANGE OF GRANTS £5,000–£55,000.

SAMPLE GRANTS Sole beneficiary for 2009–10: Brain Research Trust (£54,000).

FINANCES *Year* 2009–10 *Income* £62,933 *Grants* £53,749 *Assets* £1,952,486

TRUSTEES Mrs E H Hill; G R Andersen; C A Hicks; Mrs M Burt; Dr J Clements.

HOW TO APPLY In writing to the correspondent, however the trust states in its accounts that the trustees 'prefer to be proactive with charities of their own choice, rather than reactive to external applications'. The trustees generally meet to consider grants twice a year in the spring and the autumn. There is no set format for applying and only successful applications are acknowledged. Due to the change of grant policy to focus on a smaller number of projects, external applications are unlikely to be successful and are therefore discouraged.

WHO TO APPLY TO Charles Hicks, Secretary, c/o Wedlake Bell, 52 Bedford Row, London WC1R 4LR *Tel* 020 7395 3155 *Fax* 020 7395 3100 *email* chicks@wedlakebell.com

....

■ The Richmond Parish Lands Charity

CC NO 200069   **ESTABLISHED** 1786

WHERE FUNDING CAN BE GIVEN Richmond, Kew, North Sheen, East Sheen, Ham, Petersham and Mortlake.

WHO CAN BENEFIT Charitable organisations and individuals.

WHAT IS FUNDED The charity's objects are: the relief of poverty in the London Borough of Richmond upon Thames; the relief of sickness and distress in the borough; the provision and support of leisure and recreational facilities in the charity's beneficial area; the provision educational facilities and support for people in Richmond wishing to undertake courses; any other charitable purpose for the benefit of the inhabitants of Richmond. Strategic priorities are reviewed periodically – from July 2011 the charity's priority for strategic funding was social inclusion. Check the charity's website for current priorities.

WHAT IS NOT FUNDED Projects and organisations located outside the benefit area, unless it can be demonstrated that a substantial number of residents from the benefit area will gain from their work. UK charities (even if based in the benefit area), except for that part of their work which caters specifically for the area.

TYPE OF GRANT One-off and recurring; core costs.

RANGE OF GRANTS Up to around £50,000; small grants of £500 or less are considered separately.

SAMPLE GRANTS Beneficiaries included: RB Mind – Vineyard Project (£53,000 in total); Cambrian Community Centre (£40,000); MiD Mediation and Counselling (£21,000 in total); Brentford Football Community Sports (£20,000); Age Concern (£19,500); Richmond Youth Partnership (£18,000); Richmond Music Trust (£15,000); Latchmere House (£11,000); Ham Youth Centre (£9,000); Off The Record (£7,500); Environment Trust Richmond (£6,000); Furniture Scheme (£5,000); FiSH Neighbourhood Scheme (£4,500); Royal Hospital for Neuro-Disability (£3,000); Crossway Pregnancy Crisis Centre (£2,000); Young Science Events Richmond (£1,000); Greycourt School (£500).

FINANCES *Year* 2009–10 *Income* £1,419,700 *Grants* £861,927 *Assets* £59,609,209

TRUSTEES Colin Craib, Chair; Ashley Casson; David Marlow; Janet Kingston; Jeffery Harris; John Wylie; Margaret Marshall; Margaret Saunders; Niall Cairns; Rita Biddulph; Robert Guy; Sue Jones; Susan Goddard; Vivienne Press.

OTHER INFORMATION During the year £663,555 was given to organisations; £198,372 was given to individuals.

HOW TO APPLY Organisations receiving core grants from the charity must apply by the deadlines given on the charity's website. If you are applying for a grant that is new or a one-off application, and it does not fall within the charity's recent strategic priorities your application will not be considered until January each year. If you would like some clarification on whether your organisation would qualify for a

grant, please contact the charity on 020 8948 5701 for guidance. Application forms for small and larger grants can be downloaded from the charity's website. Please be sure that you have filled in all sections and that you have enclosed all the documents requested. When your application is received, it will be evaluated and any queries arising from it will be followed up. You may be assured that all eligible applications will be put before the trustees. There are currently 15 trustees all of whom live within the benefit area. three of them are nominated by the borough council, five are nominated by local voluntary organisations and the remainder are co-opted from the community. the mayor is an ex officio member of the board of trustees. Eligible applications must be received at least ten working days before the meeting at which they will be considered – check the charity's website for upcoming deadlines. You will be advised by letter within fourteen days of the meeting whether or not your application has been successful. Following agreement for a grant you will be sent a conditions of grant form setting out the terms and conditions of the grant. payment will be arranged on receipt of a signed agreement. A monitoring and evaluation form will also be required on completion of your next application form.

WHO TO APPLY TO Jonathan Monckton, Director, The Vestry House, 21 Paradise Road, Richmond, Surrey TW9 1SA *Tel* 020 8948 5701 *Fax* 020 8332 6792 *Website* www.rplc.org.uk

....

■ Ridgesave Limited

CC NO 288020   **ESTABLISHED** 1983

WHERE FUNDING CAN BE GIVEN UK and overseas.

WHO CAN BENEFIT Individuals and organisations benefiting Jews and people disadvantaged by poverty.

WHAT IS FUNDED The advancement of religion in accordance with the orthodox Jewish faith; the relief of poverty; education and other charitable purposes.

RANGE OF GRANTS Previously £40–£170,000.

SAMPLE GRANTS Previous beneficiaries include: Keren Associates Ltd, BAT, UTA, CM L, TYY, Square Foundation Ltd, Ateres Yeshua Charitable Trust, Side by Side, My Dream Time, British Friends of Rinat Aharon, Chanoch Lenaar, and All in Together Girls.

FINANCES *Year* 2009–10 *Income* £1,977,398 *Grants* £1,508,101 *Assets* £3,785,287

TRUSTEES Joseph Weiss; Zelda Weiss; E Englander.

OTHER INFORMATION No grants list was available.

HOW TO APPLY In writing to the correspondent.

WHO TO APPLY TO Zelda Weiss, Trustee, 141b Upper Clapton Road, London E5 9DB

....

■ The Ripple Effect Foundation

CC NO 802327   **ESTABLISHED** 1989

WHERE FUNDING CAN BE GIVEN UK.

WHO CAN BENEFIT Registered charities.

WHAT IS FUNDED General charitable purposes, particularly the broad fields of environmental work, empowering young people in the UK and third world development.

WHAT IS NOT FUNDED No grants made to individuals.

TYPE OF GRANT Multiple year funding available.

SAMPLE GRANTS Previously: Devon Community Foundation (£50,000); Network for Social Change (£11,000); and Homestart UK (£5,000).

FINANCES *Year* 2009–10 *Income* £24,677 *Grants* £200,000

TRUSTEES Caroline D Marks; I R Marks; I S Wesley.

HOW TO APPLY The trust states that it does not respond to unsolicited applications.

WHO TO APPLY TO Caroline D Marks, Trustee, Marlborough Investment Consultants Ltd, Wessex House, Oxford Road, Newbury, Berkshire RG14 1PA *Tel* 01635 814470

■ The Sir John Ritblat Family Foundation

CC NO 262463   ESTABLISHED 1971

WHERE FUNDING CAN BE GIVEN UK.

WHO CAN BENEFIT Charitable organisations, with some preference for Jewish groups.

WHAT IS FUNDED General charitable purposes.

WHAT IS NOT FUNDED No grants to individuals.

SAMPLE GRANTS Weizman UK (£60,000); Eton College (£50,000); The Wallace Collection (£45,000); London Business School (£13,000); The Royal Opera House Foundation (£9,000); Tate Foundation (£6,000); International Students House (£5,000); Tzedek (£500); and Venice in Peril (£200).

FINANCES *Year* 2009–10 *Income* £56,499 *Grants* £270,450 *Assets* £715,996

TRUSTEES Sir John Ritblat; N S J Ritblat; C B Wagman; J W J Ritblat.

HOW TO APPLY The trust has previously stated that its funds are fully committed.

WHO TO APPLY TO The Clerk, Baker Tilly, 1st Floor, 46 Clarendon Road, Watford WD17 1JJ *Tel* 01923 816400

■ The River Farm Foundation

CC NO 1113109   ESTABLISHED 2006

WHERE FUNDING CAN BE GIVEN UK and overseas.

WHO CAN BENEFIT Charitable organisations working in the UK and overseas.

WHAT IS FUNDED General charitable purposes.

SAMPLE GRANTS Busoga Trust (£10,000).

FINANCES *Year* 2009–10 *Income* £28,636,125 *Grants* £10,000 *Assets* £32,021,132

TRUSTEES Mark Haworth; Nigel Jeremy Langstaff; Michael David Willcox.

OTHER INFORMATION The trustees annual report for 2009–10 states: 'One of the trustees, Michael Willcox is a Principal Member of WillcoxLewis LLP, a firm of solicitors which raises invoices to the Foundation for legal and administrative services rendered. Michael Willcox is also a beneficiary of the trust which owns 100% of the shares in OCH Services Limited, an accountancy firm which raises invoices to the Foundation for services rendered. Payment of these invoices is authorised by the other trustees No trustees expenses have been reimbursed during the year.'

Due to the receipt of the £28.6 million received by the trustees during the year, we would expect grant-making to increase significantly from now on.

HOW TO APPLY 'The trustees decide on the grants to be made after careful review of the applications received. This strategy will continue to be implemented for as long as the number of applications remains relatively small. As the activities of the foundation expand in the future, it is envisaged that a more refined administrative process of assessment will be put in place.'

WHO TO APPLY TO M D Willcox, Trustee, Old Coach House, Sunnyside, Bergh Apton, Norwich NR15 1DD *Tel* 01508 480100 *email* info@ willcoxlewis.co.uk

■ The River Trust

CC NO 275843   ESTABLISHED 1977

WHERE FUNDING CAN BE GIVEN UK, with a preference for Sussex.

WHO CAN BENEFIT Organisations benefiting Christians.

WHAT IS FUNDED Evangelical Christian charities.

WHAT IS NOT FUNDED No grants to individuals. The trust does not support 'repairs of the fabric of the church' nor does it give grants for capital expenditure.

TYPE OF GRANT Certain charities are supported for more than one year.

RANGE OF GRANTS £500–£13,000.

SAMPLE GRANTS Youth with a Mission (£20,500); Barcombe PCC (£8,000); The Genesis Arts Trust (£5,000); Care for the Family (£4,000); Society of Mary and Martha (£3,000); and African Enterprise and Release International (£1,000 each).

FINANCES *Year* 2009–10 *Income* £157,327 *Grants* £105,945 *Assets* £639,321

TRUSTEES Kleinwort Benson Trustees Ltd.

HOW TO APPLY In writing to the correspondent. It is unusual for unsolicited appeals to be successful. Only successful applicants are notified of the trustees' decision. Some charities are supported for more than one year, although no commitment is usually given to the recipients.

WHO TO APPLY TO The Trustees, c/o Kleinwort Benson Trustees Ltd, PO Box 57005, 30 Gresham Street, London EC2V 7PG *Tel* 020 3207 7337 *Fax* 020 3207 7665

■ The Rivers Charitable Trust

CC NO 1078545   ESTABLISHED 1999

WHERE FUNDING CAN BE GIVEN UK and overseas.

WHO CAN BENEFIT Charitable organisations.

WHAT IS FUNDED The trust supports educational projects in the UK and abroad whether it is in terms of actual buildings, educational materials or paying for children's education. The trust seeks welfare projects to support via small charities with well-targeted schemes.

TYPE OF GRANT One-off grants. Recurring costs and running costs.

RANGE OF GRANTS £200–£20,000.

SAMPLE GRANTS Operation Smile (£10,000); Switchback (£5,000); Mathari Children's Foundation (£9,400); Chance (£4,000); Mathari UK visit sponsorship (£983); SOS (£400); CNCF Sponsor a Child (£240); and Harrodian School (£200).

FINANCES *Year* 2008–09 *Income* £89,000 *Grants* £30,000 *Assets* £680,000

TRUSTEES A J Rivers; K Constable; Mrs C J Bolton.

HOW TO APPLY In writing to the correspondent.

WHO TO APPLY TO Trustees, Basement, 108 Ledbury Road, London W11 2AH *Tel* 020 7792 1234 *email* ajrultra@btopenworld.com

■ Riverside Charitable Trust Limited

cc no 264015   **ESTABLISHED** 1972

WHERE FUNDING CAN BE GIVEN Mainly Rossendale, Lancashire.

WHO CAN BENEFIT Individuals and organisations benefiting people disadvantaged by poverty and illness, older people, and people employed or formerly employed in the shoe trade.

WHAT IS FUNDED Relief of need, education, healthcare, and other charitable purposes.

WHAT IS NOT FUNDED No grants for political causes.

TYPE OF GRANT Recurring costs.

SAMPLE GRANTS Grants were made to the following causes: Relief for sickness, infirmity and for the elderly – 23 grants totalling £42,000; General charitable public benefits – 74 grants totalling £60,000; Relief of poverty – 60 grants totalling £44,000; Death grants – 20 grants totalling £2,300.

FINANCES *Year* 2009–10 *Income* £60,470 *Grants* £148,613 *Assets* £2,170,915

TRUSTEES Leslie Clegg; Annie Higginson; Barry John Lynch; Frederick Drew; Gilbert Maden; Harry Francis; Ian Barrie Dearing; Jacqueline Davidson; Brian Terry; Angela O'Gorman; Mark Butterworth.

HOW TO APPLY In writing to the correspondent.

WHO TO APPLY TO Brian Terry, Trustee, E Sutton and Sons Ltd, PO Box 2, Bacup OL13 0DT *Tel* 01706 874 961

■ Rix-Thompson-Rothenberg Foundation

cc no 285368   **ESTABLISHED** 1982

WHERE FUNDING CAN BE GIVEN UK.

WHO CAN BENEFIT People with a learning disability.

WHAT IS FUNDED Projects connected with the care, education, training, development and leisure activities of people with a learning disability, particularly those that will enhance opportunity and lifestyle.

WHAT IS NOT FUNDED Applications for specific learning details are not supported.

RANGE OF GRANTS £1,000–£6,000 (2010).

SAMPLE GRANTS Llandovery Theatre (£6,000); Magpie Dance (£5,000); FAIR, Birmingham Royal Ballet and Avon North Mencap Ltd. (£4,000 each); Crossroads and SMILE (£3,000 each) and Sunflower Music Hall Ltd. (£1,200).

FINANCES *Year* 2010 *Income* £126,657 *Grants* £118,287 *Assets* £1,347,074

TRUSTEES Lord Rix; Walter Rothenberg; Loretto Lambe; Fred Heddell; Barrie Davis; Jonathan Rix; Brian Baldock; Suzanne J. Marriott.

OTHER INFORMATION 'The foundation maintains a close relationship with the Baily Thomas Charitable Fund which gives it substantial donations towards the annual grant-making activity.'

HOW TO APPLY In the first instance contact should be made through the RTR Administration office, at least 2 months prior to the next relevant meeting, contact details below. Once successfully through the application process, submissions are considered by the Board of Governors at their twice yearly meetings held in June and December and a decision made. *No unsolicited applications are considered*. The foundation does not support specific learning difficulties initiatives/projects.

WHO TO APPLY TO The Administrator, RTR Administrative Office, White Top Research Unit, Springfield House, 15/16 Springfield, Dundee DD1 4JE *Tel* 01382 384654 *email* P-RTR@dundee.ac.uk

■ Thomas Roberts Trust

cc no 1067235   **ESTABLISHED** 1997

WHERE FUNDING CAN BE GIVEN UK.

WHO CAN BENEFIT Organisations benefiting people with a disability or illness.

WHAT IS FUNDED The trust mainly makes grants to medical (particularly cancer support and research), disability and welfare organisations. It also considers applications from employees and former employees of the Thomas Roberts Group Companies.

RANGE OF GRANTS From £100 to £6,000.

SAMPLE GRANTS Cancer Research UK; Macmillan Cancer Relief; Marie Curie Cancer Care; Age Concern; Winchester Churches Nightshelter; Diabetes UK; Riding for the Disabled; Parkinson's Disease Society and Breast Cancer Campaign.

FINANCES *Year* 2009–10 *Income* £23,744 *Grants* £45,000

TRUSTEES R E Gammage; J Roberts; Mrs G Hemmings.

OTHER INFORMATION Information about grant amounts was not available.

HOW TO APPLY In writing to the correspondent. Applicants are required to provide a summary of their proposals to the trustees, explaining how the funds would be used and what would be achieved.

WHO TO APPLY TO James Roberts, Trustee, 5–6 The Square, Winchester, Hampshire SO23 9WE *Tel* 01962 843211 *Fax* 01962 843223 *email* trtrust@thomasroberts.co.uk

■ The Robertson Trust

sc no SC002970   **ESTABLISHED** 1961

WHERE FUNDING CAN BE GIVEN Scotland.

WHO CAN BENEFIT Registered charities only.

WHAT IS FUNDED Priority areas: health, care, education and training and community arts and sport. Other areas supported: work with children, young people and families; preservation of the environment; the strengthening of local communities; the development of culture, heritage and science; animal welfare; and the saving of lives.

WHAT IS NOT FUNDED The trust does not support: individuals or organisations which are not recognised as charities by the Office of the Scottish Charity Regulator (OSCR); general appeals or circulars, including contributions to endowment funds; local charities whose work takes place outside Scotland; generic employment or training projects; community projects where the applicant is a housing association; core revenue costs for playgroups, nurseries, after school groups etc; projects which are exclusively or primarily intended to promote political beliefs; students or organisations for personal study, travel or for expeditions whether in the United Kingdom or abroad; medical research; organisations and projects whose primary object is to provide a counselling, advocacy, advice and/or information service. The trust is unlikely to support: charities which collect funds for onward distribution to others; umbrella groups which do not provide a direct service to individuals e.g. CVS; feasibility studies and other research; charities already in receipt of a current donation from the trust.

Think carefully about every application. Is it justified?

841

TYPE OF GRANT One-off, annual, pledges (to give grants if a target figure is raised), and recurring.

SAMPLE GRANTS FARE – new centre for families (£170,000); Marie Curie Cancer Care – new hospice in Stobhill Hospital (£150,000); Girvan Youth Trust (£45,000 over 3 years); Community Connections – developing entrepreneurial skills and business practices in young people; Bobath Scotland – support of children with Cerebral Palsy (both £42,000 over 3 years); Edinburgh Community Food initiative – community food co-ops (£36,000 over 3 years); Royal Caledonian Curling Club – National Disability Officer (£33,000 over 3 years); The Accord Hospice – palliative care and support; Breast Cancer Care (£30,000 over 3 years); Independent Living Support – vulnerable individuals affected by homelessness and associated problems (£26,000 over 3 years); TechFest, Set Point – promotion of science, technology, engineering and mathematics, annual festival (£3,000); Action for Children – supporting young offenders; Outward Bound Metro – outdoor education for inner city young people; Mentor UK – alternatives to drinking; Alcohol Focus Scotland.

FINANCES *Year* 2009–10 *Income* £18,625,000 *Grants* £9,700,000 *Assets* £364,130,000

TRUSTEES Sir Ian Good, Chair; Richard Hunter; Dame Barbara Kelly; Shonaig Macpherson; David Stevenson; Ian B Curle; Fiona McBain.

OTHER INFORMATION Applicants should refer to the trust's excellent website.

HOW TO APPLY Applicants are advised to read the guidelines available to download on the trust's website. There are two ways to apply: By application form which is available on the trust's website, to be returned with the supporting documents, or by letter which should include the following details: a brief description of the organisation, including past developments and successes; a description of the project – what you want to do, who will be involved, where will it take place and how it will be managed; how you have identified the need for this work; what you hope will be the outputs and outcomes of this work and the key targets you have set; how you intend to monitor and evaluate the work so that you know whether or not you have been successful; the income and expenditure budget for this piece of work; how you propose to fund the work, including details of funds already raised or applied for; the proposed timetable. In addition the trust will also require three supporting documents. These are: a completed copy of the Organisation Information Sheet, which is available from the trust's website or the trust office; a copy of your most recent annual report and accounts. These should have been independently examined or audited; a job description, if you are applying for salary costs for a specified worker. The trust requests that applicants do not send a constitution or memorandum and articles. If there is any other bulky information which you feel may be relevant, such as a feasibility study, business plan or evaluation, then you should refer to it in your application, so that the assessment team can request it if required. Small and main donations form the bulk of the donations made by the trust and are assessed on a rolling programme with recommendations made to the trustees six times a year. Applications for major capital donations are considered three times a year in January, May and September.

WHO TO APPLY TO Lesley Macdonald, Assessment Manager, 85 Berkeley Street, Glasgow G3 7DX *Tel* 0141 221 3151 *Fax* 0141 221 0744 *email* enquires@therobertsontrust.org.uk *Website* www.therobertsontrust.org.uk

---

■ Edwin George Robinson Charitable Trust

CC NO 1068763   **ESTABLISHED** 1998

WHERE FUNDING CAN BE GIVEN UK.

WHO CAN BENEFIT Medical research organisations.

WHAT IS FUNDED The trustees favour applications from smaller organisations for specific research projects.

WHAT IS NOT FUNDED No grants to individuals or for general running costs for small local organisations.

RANGE OF GRANTS Mostly £500–£6,500.

SAMPLE GRANTS Previous beneficiaries include: Marie Curie Cancer Care, Diabetes UK, Bath Institute of Medical Engineering, Deafness Research, Brainwave, Action for Medical Research, Ness Foundation, Cure Parkinson's, Holly Lodge Centre and Salvation Army.

FINANCES *Year* 2009–10 *Income* £8,100 *Grants* £35,000

TRUSTEES E C Robinson; Mrs S C Robinson.

OTHER INFORMATION Accounts were received by the Charity Commission but were not available to view.

HOW TO APPLY In writing to the correspondent.

WHO TO APPLY TO E C Robinson, Trustee, 71 Manor Road South, Esher, Surrey KT10 0QB *Tel* 020 8398 6845

■ Robyn Charitable Trust

CC NO 327745   **ESTABLISHED** 1988

WHERE FUNDING CAN BE GIVEN UK and overseas.

WHO CAN BENEFIT Organisations benefiting children and young people.

WHAT IS FUNDED Education and social welfare for children in any part of the world.

WHAT IS NOT FUNDED No grants to individuals.

SAMPLE GRANTS Previous beneficiaries have included: One to One Children's Fund, The Purcell School, Variety Club, The Honeypot Charity, Malawi Against Aids and Teenage Cancer Trust.

FINANCES *Year* 2009–10 *Income* £709 *Grants* £30,000

TRUSTEES Malcolm Webber; Mark Knopfler; Ronnie Harris.

OTHER INFORMATION Accounts were received at the Charity Commission but were unavailable to view. Grants totalled around £30,000.

HOW TO APPLY In writing to the correspondent.

WHO TO APPLY TO The Trustees, c/o Harris and Trotter, 65 New Cavendish Street, London W1G 7LS *Tel* 020 7467 6300

■ The Rochester Bridge Trust

CC NO 207100   **ESTABLISHED** 1399

WHERE FUNDING CAN BE GIVEN Kent.

WHO CAN BENEFIT Charitable bodies.

WHAT IS FUNDED The maintenance and reconstruction of the Rochester bridges, Medway tunnel and any other crossings of the River Medway. After this has been achieved, grants can be made for other general charitable purposes. Around £100,000 is available for charities each year.

WHAT IS NOT FUNDED No grants to individuals. No funding for revenue. No grants for pet-care charities or general animal charities. Grants will not be made for the purchase of vehicles or trailers (apart from heritage vehicles) nor for office equipment, including IT equipment and furniture, that supports the running of an organisation rather than being available directly for the beneficiaries of a charity or contributing directly to a charity's objectives. Grants will not be made towards construction, improvement, refurbishment or other projects associated with community centres, village halls, parish halls, club or association buildings, sports pitches or mainstream schools or colleges. Grants are not made to individual mainstream schools and colleges, whether funded by the private, state, faith or charitable sectors, except for projects aimed at promoting interest and learning in the fields of civil engineering, history of Rochester, history of the River Medway, or agriculture. These projects are actively encouraged. Grants will not be made to nursing or care homes and childcare nurseries, except those providing support to severely disabled people and/or seriously disadvantaged children. The Trust will not fund routine maintenance work to any type of building. The Trust will not make general grants to major projects where its contribution would be a very small proportion of the total required (e.g. less than 10%).

TYPE OF GRANT Capital including equipment, buildings and one-off.

RANGE OF GRANTS Up to £100,000.

SAMPLE GRANTS Previous beneficiaries include: Maidstone Museum (£7,000); Friends of Bower Grove School (£6,000); Royal Aeronautical Society, Medway Branch (£4,000); Arkwright Trust (£3,900); Thanet Kidz Club, Ramsgate (£2,000); 457th Bomb Group Association – Connington (£1,500); Holy Trinity Church – East Peckham (£1,000); Gravesend and Rochester Agricultural Association (£350).

FINANCES *Year* 2009–10 *Income* £2,356,936 *Grants* £28,993 *Assets* £68,038,762

TRUSTEES Rodney B Gibson; Frank Chambers; Paul E J Harriot; Dr Anne F H Logan; Paul E Oldham; Russell J Race; Russell G Cooper; John A Spence; Richard G Thornby; Cllr Anthony R Goulden; Alan L Jarrett; Michael V Snelling.

HOW TO APPLY New applicants are directed to the trust's website, where the trust's criteria, guidelines and application process are posted.

WHO TO APPLY TO Mrs Threader, Bridge Clerk, The Bridge Chamber, 5 Esplanade, Rochester, Kent ME1 1QE *Tel* 01634 846706 *Fax* 01634 840125 *email* bridgeclerk@rbt.org.uk *Website* www.rbt.org.uk

■ The Rock Foundation

CC NO 294775   **ESTABLISHED** 1986

WHERE FUNDING CAN BE GIVEN Worldwide.

WHO CAN BENEFIT Charitable organisations, especially those which are built upon a clear biblical basis and which, in most instances, receive little or no publicity.

WHAT IS FUNDED Christian ministries and other charitable work.

SAMPLE GRANTS Proclamation Trust (£17,000); Carter (£14,000); Bible College of Victoria (£10,000); Relite Africa Trust (£6,000); and Soweto Church (£1,000).

FINANCES *Year* 2009–10 *Income* £790,567 *Grants* £176,062 *Assets* £572,966

TRUSTEES Richard Borgonon; Andrew Green; Kevin Locock; Jane Borgonon; Colin Spreckley; Peter Butler.

HOW TO APPLY The trust has previously stated: 'the trust identifies its beneficiaries through its own networks, choosing to support organisations it has a working relationship with. This allows the trust to verify that the organisation is doing excellent work in a sensible manner in a way which cannot be conveyed from a written application. As such, all appeals from charities the foundation do not find through their own research are simply thrown in the bin. If an sae is included in an application, it will merely end up in the foundation's waste-paper bin rather than a post box.'

WHO TO APPLY TO The Trustees, Park Green Cottage, Barhatch Road, Cranleigh, Surrey GU6 7DJ *Tel* 01483 274556

■ The Rock Solid Trust

CC NO 1077669   **ESTABLISHED** 1999

WHERE FUNDING CAN BE GIVEN Worldwide.

WHO CAN BENEFIT Christian charities and Christian projects.

WHAT IS FUNDED The advancement of the Christian religion; the maintenance, restoration and repair of the fabric of Christian church; the education and training of individuals; relief of need.

RANGE OF GRANTS £100–£20,000.

SAMPLE GRANTS Previously beneficiaries have included: Christchurch Clifton and Sherborne School Foundation (£20,000 each); Bristol University (£5,000); Chain of Hope and London School of Theology (£500 each); and RNLI (£100).

FINANCES *Year* 2009–10 *Income* £13,496 *Grants* £18,820

TRUSTEES J D W Pocock; T P Wicks; T G Bretell.

HOW TO APPLY In writing to the correspondent.

WHO TO APPLY TO J D W Pocock, Trustee, 8 Cupar Road, London SW11 4JW

■ The Roddick Foundation

CC NO 1061372   **ESTABLISHED** 1997

WHERE FUNDING CAN BE GIVEN Worldwide.

WHO CAN BENEFIT Charitable organisations.

WHAT IS FUNDED Arts, education, environmental, human rights, humanitarian, medical, poverty, social justice.

WHAT IS NOT FUNDED The trust states that it is 'particularly not interested in the following: funding anything related to sport; funding fundraising events or conferences; and sponsorship of any kind'.

RANGE OF GRANTS Up to £300,000.

SAMPLE GRANTS Mother Jones Anita Fund: A Global Justice Journalism Project (£267,500); Body & Soul (£100,000); Organic Marketing (£99,000); Helen Bamber Foundation (£70,000); New Economic Foundation, World Development Movement and Reprieve (£50,000 each); David Suzuki Foundation (£30,000); Chichester Festival Theatre, Foundation Rwanda and Protect Local Globally (£25,000 each); Crisis Action (£13,000); and Iasis (£10,000).

FINANCES *Year* 2009–10 *Income* £487,955 *Grants* £1,445,914 *Assets* £23,854,027

TRUSTEES Justine Roddick; Samantha Roddick; Gordon Roddick; Christina Schlieske.

HOW TO APPLY The foundation does not accept or respond to unsolicited applications. 'Grants made by the foundation are at the discretion of the board of trustees. The board considers making a grant and, if approved, notifies the intended recipient.'

WHO TO APPLY Karen Smith, PO Box 112, Slindon Common, Arundel, West Sussex BN18 8AS *Tel* 01243 814788 *email* karen@ theroddickfoundation.org *Website* www. theroddickfoundation.org

■ The Rofeh Trust

CC NO 1077682   **ESTABLISHED** 1999
WHERE FUNDING CAN BE GIVEN UK.
WHO CAN BENEFIT Charitable organisations.
WHAT IS FUNDED General charitable purposes, with a possible preference for Jewish causes.
FINANCES *Year* 2009–10 *Income* £50,000 *Grants* £57,000
TRUSTEES Martin Dunitz; Ruth Dunitz; Vivian Wineman; Henry Eder.
OTHER INFORMATION An annual report was available from the Charity Commission but there were no accounts to view.
HOW TO APPLY In writing to the correspondent.
WHO TO APPLY TO The Trustees, 44 Southway, London NW11 6SA *Tel* 020 8458 7382

■ Richard Rogers Charitable Settlement

CC NO 283252   **ESTABLISHED** 1981
WHERE FUNDING CAN BE GIVEN UK.
WHO CAN BENEFIT Charitable organisations.
WHAT IS FUNDED General purposes.
RANGE OF GRANTS £50–£50,000.
SAMPLE GRANTS National Communities Research Centre (£50,000); the Constant Gardener Trust and the National Community Resource Ltd (£13,000 each); Serpentine Gallery (£11,000); Refuge (£10,000); Tree House (£6,400); Crisis (£1,000); Trafford Hall (£900); British Heart Foundation (£500); Scientists for Global Responsibility (£330); Walk the Walk Worldwide (£300); and The RSA (£95).
FINANCES *Year* 2007–08 *Income* £80,331 *Grants* £127,410 *Assets* £992,305
TRUSTEES Lord R G Rogers; Lady R Rogers.
HOW TO APPLY In writing to the correspondent.
WHO TO APPLY TO K A Hawkins, Lee Associates, 5 Southampton Place, London WC1A 2DA *Tel* 020 7025 4600

■ Rokach Family Charitable Trust

CC NO 284007   **ESTABLISHED** 1981
WHERE FUNDING CAN BE GIVEN UK.
WHO CAN BENEFIT Jewish organisations; registered charities.
WHAT IS FUNDED Advancement of the Jewish religion; general charitable purposes.
SAMPLE GRANTS Beneficiaries were: Cosmon Belz Limited (£110,000); Moreshet Hatorah Ltd (£26,000); Belz Israel (£23,000); Friends of Wiznitz (£5,000); L & N Brenig Family Trust (£4,000); Society of Friends of the Torah (£3,000); and Lolev (£2,000).
FINANCES *Year* 2008–09 *Income* £434,210 *Grants* £185,182 *Assets* £2,132,615
TRUSTEES N Rokach; Mrs H Rokach; Mrs E Hoffman; Mrs M Feingold; Mrs A Gefilhaus; Mrs N Brenig.
OTHER INFORMATION Accounts are consistently late when submitted to the Charity Commission. We have used the latest available at the time of writing (December 2011).
HOW TO APPLY In writing to the correspondent.

WHO TO APPLY TO Norman Rokach, Trustee, 20 Middleton Road, London NW11 7NS *Tel* 020 8455 6359

■ The Helen Roll Charitable Trust

CC NO 299108   **ESTABLISHED** 1988
WHERE FUNDING CAN BE GIVEN UK.
WHO CAN BENEFIT Registered charities only, including universities, schools, colleges, research institutions, groups helping disadvantaged people, theatres, animal welfare charities, and environmental and wildlife organisations.
WHAT IS FUNDED General charitable purposes, particularly: education, especially higher education; libraries and museums; the arts; health and animal welfare.
WHAT IS NOT FUNDED No support for individuals or non-registered charities.
TYPE OF GRANT Generally one-off for specific projects, but within a framework of charities whose work is known to the trustees.
RANGE OF GRANTS £600–£13,000.
SAMPLE GRANTS Home Farm Trust (£12,000); Trinity College of Music (£6,000); Alzheimer's Research Trust (£5,000); Dartington International Summer School (£4,000); Friends of Animal League (£3,000); Oxfordshire Association for the Blind, Oxfordshire Family Mediation and Perthes Association (£2,000 each); Compassionate Friends (£1,500); and Barn Owl Trust (£1,000).
FINANCES *Year* 2009–10 *Income* £49,967 *Grants* £121,896 *Assets* £1,502,947
TRUSTEES Christine Chapman; Christine Reid; Patrick J R Stopford; Paul Strang; Frank R Williamson; Jennifer C Williamson; Peter R Williamson; Stephen G Williamson.
HOW TO APPLY In writing to the correspondent during the first fortnight in February. Applications should be kept short, ideally on one sheet of A4. Further material will then be requested from those who are short-listed. The trustees normally make their distributions in March.
WHO TO APPLY TO F R Williamson, Trustee, 30 St Giles, Oxford OX1 3LE *Tel* 01865 559 900

■ The Sir James Roll Charitable Trust

CC NO 1064963   **ESTABLISHED** 1997
WHERE FUNDING CAN BE GIVEN UK.
WHO CAN BENEFIT Registered charities.
WHAT IS FUNDED Mainly the promotion of mutual tolerance, commonality and cordiality in major world religions; promotion of improved access to computer technology in community-based projects other than political parties or local government; funding of projects aimed at early identification of specific learning disorders; and any other charitable projects as the trustees see fit.
RANGE OF GRANTS £1,000–£10,000, although mostly £1,000.
SAMPLE GRANTS DEC Haiti Earthquake Appeal (£10,000); CRISIS and DEC Indonesia Philippines & Vietnam (£5,000 each); Action Medical Research, Africa Equipment for Schools, Appropriate Technology Asia, Bowel Disease Research Foundation, Crime Diversion Scheme, Jessie May Trust, Link Community Development, Manna Society, Tall Ships Youth Trust Treehouse Trust and Whizz-Kidz (£1,250 each); and Crossroads Association, Konnect 9 Worldwide, Respite Association, Strongbones

Children's Foundation and Young Minds (£700 each).

FINANCES *Year* 2009–10 *Income* £190,835 *Grants* £145,000 *Assets* £3,955,809

TRUSTEES N T Wharton; B W Elvy; J M Liddiard.

HOW TO APPLY In writing to the correspondent.

WHO TO APPLY TO N T Wharton, Trustee, 5 New Road Avenue, Chatham, Kent ME4 6AR *Tel* 01634 830111

■ The Roman Research Trust

CC NO 800983   **ESTABLISHED** 1990

WHERE FUNDING CAN BE GIVEN UK, but preference given to Wiltshire and neighbouring counties to the west.

WHO CAN BENEFIT Individuals and organisations benefiting postgraduate students, professional archaeologists and non-professionals of equivalent standing.

WHAT IS FUNDED Excavation, recording, analysis and publication of Romano-British archaeological research not otherwise funded or for which existing funds are insufficient. Romano-British archaeological exhibitions in museums and other places accessible to the public; educational programmes related to Roman Britain.

WHAT IS NOT FUNDED Undergraduate or postgraduate courses.

TYPE OF GRANT Project and research. Funding is for one year or less.

RANGE OF GRANTS £200–£10,000. Typical grant £2,000.

SAMPLE GRANTS Previously: £5,000 each to University of Oxford for excavation of the amphitheatre at Frilford, and Wiltshire Archaeology and Natural History Society for work on the Littlecoat excavation archive; £2,000 to University of Sheffield for excavation and geophysical survey at Chedworth Villa; £1,500 to Primary Latin Project for illustrations for 'Minimus 2' £1,000 to Liverpool Museum for analysis of Roman artefacts from the Wirral; £500 to Yorkshire Archaeological Society for publication of excavations at Newton Kyme.

FINANCES *Year* 2009–10 *Income* £44,760 *Grants* £29,870 *Assets* £1,298,489

TRUSTEES Prof. Michael Fulford, Chair; Dr Janet Delaine; Robin Birch; Dr Ralph Jackson; Ms Amanda Claridge; Paul Booth; Mrs Jenny Hall.

OTHER INFORMATION No organisations were granted awards during 2009–10. The grant total was dispersed between 10 individual applicants as follows: £29,000 for general archaeological purposes. There were no bursary awards.

HOW TO APPLY By 15 November and 15 April annually. Application forms and guidelines available from the correspondent or the Roman Research website.

WHO TO APPLY TO Dr Ellen Swift, Honorary Secretary, SECL, Cornwallis Building, University of Kent, Canterbury, Kent CT2 7NF *Tel* 01227 827 159 *email* E.V.Swift@kent.ac.uk *Website* rrt.classics. ox.ac.uk

---

■ Romeera Foundation

CC NO 1076325   **ESTABLISHED** 1999

WHERE FUNDING CAN BE GIVEN Worldwide.

WHO CAN BENEFIT Charitable organisations.

WHAT IS FUNDED General charitable purposes.

SAMPLE GRANTS Arthur Rank Hospice (£2,500); British Heart Foundation (£1,650); Shri Kathiawar Nirashrit Balashram (£1,170); John

Grooms (£330); and Breakthrough Breast Cancer (£250).

FINANCES *Year* 2009–10 *Income* £17,763 *Grants* £15,300 *Assets* £2,174,667

TRUSTEES Madoo Mehta; Meenal Mehta.

HOW TO APPLY In writing to the correspondent.

WHO TO APPLY TO The Trustees, 16 Heathgate, London NW11 7AN *Tel* 020 8458 5864

■ The Gerald Ronson Foundation

CC NO 1111728   **ESTABLISHED** 2005

WHERE FUNDING CAN BE GIVEN UK and overseas.

WHO CAN BENEFIT Registered charities.

WHAT IS FUNDED General charitable activities with a preference for Jewish causes.

RANGE OF GRANTS Up to £200,000.

SAMPLE GRANTS Jewish Care (£202,000); The Jewish Community Secondary School Trust (£200,000); United Jewish Israel Appeal (£155,000); The Community Security Trust (£105,000); Great Ormond Street Hospital Children's Charity (£50,000); Roundhouse Trust (£33,500); and the Royal Opera House (£28,500).

FINANCES *Year* 2009–10 *Income* £150,075 *Grants* £1,033,738 *Assets* £11,738,595

TRUSTEES Gerald Maurice Ronson, Chair; Dame Gail Ronson; Alan Irving Goldman; Jonathan Simon Goldstein; Lisa Debra Ronson; Nicole Julia Ronson Allalouf; Hayley Victoria Goldenberg.

HOW TO APPLY In writing to the correspondent. 'The trust generally makes donations on a quarterly basis in June, September, December and March. In the interim periods, the Chairman's Action Committee deals with urgent requests for donations which are approved by the trustees at the quarterly meetings.'

WHO TO APPLY TO Jeremy Trent, Secretary, H W Fisher & Company, Acre House, 11–15 William Road, London NW1 3ER *Tel* 020 7388 7000 *email* jtrent@hwfisher.co.uk

---

■ The C A Rookes Charitable Trust

CC NO 512437   **ESTABLISHED** 1980

WHERE FUNDING CAN BE GIVEN South Warwickshire, especially Stratford-upon-Avon.

WHO CAN BENEFIT Small local projects, innovative projects and UK organisations benefiting older people in particular.

WHAT IS FUNDED Older people, general charitable purposes.

WHAT IS NOT FUNDED No grants to individuals for educational purposes.

TYPE OF GRANT One-off and recurrent.

RANGE OF GRANTS Up to £3,000.

SAMPLE GRANTS Christmas charity Donations to the Elderly (£2,000); Good Companions Club (£1,750; Stratford-upon-Avon Music Festival; Marie Curie Cancer Care (£1,000 each); Guide Dogs for the Blind; Stratford-upon-Avon Society; The Myton Hospices; Apprentices are M.A.D; Warwickshire Clubs for Young People (£500 each); Guy's Gift; British Forces Foundation; Coundon Care Centre Charity; Armonico Consort (£250 each).

FINANCES *Year* 2009–10 *Income* £205,357 *Grants* £11,560 *Assets* £1,398,322

TRUSTEES Christopher Ironmonger.

HOW TO APPLY In writing to the correspondent at any time including an sae.

WHO TO APPLY TO Mr Christopher Ironmonger, The Old School, Tiddington, Stratford-upon-Avon, Warwickshire CV37 7AW *Tel* 01789 269415

■ Mrs L D Rope Third Charitable Settlement

CC NO 290533   **ESTABLISHED** 1984

WHERE FUNDING CAN BE GIVEN UK and overseas, with a particular interest in Suffolk.

WHO CAN BENEFIT For unsolicited applications, charities who work at grassroots level within their community, generally small in size, that are little catered for from other sources, or those that are based in particularly deprived areas. Charities with a large and committed volunteer base and those that have relatively low administration costs, in terms of staff salaries.

WHAT IS FUNDED Relief of poverty, advancement of education, advancement of religion and other charitable purposes.

WHAT IS NOT FUNDED The following categories of unsolicited applications will not be successful: overseas projects; national charities; requests for core funding; buildings; medical research/ health care (outside of the beneficial area); students (a very limited amount is available for foreign students); schools (outside of the beneficial area); environmental charities and animal welfare; the arts; matched funding; repayment of debts for individuals.

TYPE OF GRANT For unsolicited requests, grants are usually one-off and small scale. Funding is given for one year or less.

RANGE OF GRANTS Generally £100–£1,000.

SAMPLE GRANTS EACH (East Anglian Children's Hospices) (£251,000); Worth Abbey (£175,000); International Refugee Trust (£90,000); Mrs L D Rope Second Charitable Settlement (£72,000); Norfolk Venda Project (£65,000); Medical Missionary Sisters (£40,000); New Dawn India (£37,000); St Albans RC High School – Ipswich (£10,500); RC Parish of St Joseph (£10,000); Cafod – Haiti Appeal (£10,000); IHAG (Ipswich Housing Action Group) (£7,500); and Disability Advice Service – East Suffolk (£5,000).

FINANCES *Year* 2009–10 *Income* £1,831,889 *Grants* £1,102,786 *Assets* £49,141,201

TRUSTEES Crispin Rope; Jeremy Heal; Anne Walker; Ellen Jolly; John Wilkins; Catherine Scott; Paul Jolly.

OTHER INFORMATION Grants to organisations totalled £998,000 and to individuals totalled £102,000. Of total grants made £323,000 was granted in response to unsolicited applications.

HOW TO APPLY Please send a concise letter (preferably one side of A4) explaining the main details of your request. Please always send your most recent accounts and a budgeted breakdown of the sum you are looking to raise. The trust will also need to know whether you have applied to other funding sources and whether you have been successful elsewhere. Your application should say who your trustees are and include a daytime telephone number.

WHO TO APPLY TO Crispin Rope, Trustee, Crag Farm, Boyton, Near Woodbridge, Suffolk IP12 3LH *Tel* 01473 333288

■ Rosa – the UK fund for women and girls

CC NO 1124856   **ESTABLISHED** 2008

WHERE FUNDING CAN BE GIVEN UK.

WHO CAN BENEFIT Charitable organisations.

WHAT IS FUNDED Women's organisations and projects supporting women.

WHAT IS NOT FUNDED Religious causes or political parties.

RANGE OF GRANTS £2,000–£29,000.

SAMPLE GRANTS Funding initiative against Female Genital Mutilation (£29,000); Lankelly Chase Foundation (£25,000); Body Image (£24,500); Sheila McKennie Foundation's 'Women Creating Change' award (£15,000).

FINANCES *Year* 2009–10 *Income* £131,437 *Grants* £96,528 *Assets* £46,739

TRUSTEES Mrs Marilyn List; Ms Maggie Baxter; Ms Gillian Egan; Ms Lindsay Driscoll; Ms Natalie Szeszkowski; Ms Aisha Gill; Ms Tania Bronstein; Ms Ruth Pearson.

OTHER INFORMATION Details can be found on the organisations website.

HOW TO APPLY Full guidelines can be downloaded at the Rosa website.

WHO TO APPLY TO Anya Stern, c/o Women's Resource Centre, Ground Floor East, 33–41 Dallington Street, London EC1V 0BB *Tel* 020 7324 3044 *email* info@rosauk.org *Website* www.rosauk.org

■ The Rosca Trust

CC NO 259907   **ESTABLISHED** 1966

WHERE FUNDING CAN BE GIVEN The boroughs of Southend-on-Sea, Castle Point and Rochford District Council only.

WHO CAN BENEFIT Registered charities.

WHAT IS FUNDED The trust supports registered health and welfare charities particularly those working with young and older people in its beneficial area.

WHAT IS NOT FUNDED Grants are not given outside the beneficial area or to individuals.

RANGE OF GRANTS Usually £250–£5,000.

SAMPLE GRANTS Essex Association of Boys' Clubs (£4,000); The Peaceful Placeday Centre, Shoebury (£3,000); Southend Mencap and Link Radio Castle Point and Rochford (£2,500 each); Headway; H.A.R.P (Homeless Action Resource Project); Southend Carers Forum; Brentwood Catholic Children's Society; Whizz Kids; Southend Christian Fellowship and Southend Community in Harmony Partnership (£2,000 each); St. Martins Residential Care Limited (£1,800); Southend Talking Newspaper (£1,650); Southend Vineyard; Milton Community Partnership; Trinity Family Network – Westcliff and React (£1,500); Soundabout and Friends of the Elderly (£500 each); 1st Rayleigh (St. Michael and All Angels) Scout Group (£250).

FINANCES *Year* 2009–10 *Income* £113,568 *Grants* £51,050 *Assets* £628,134

TRUSTEES K J Crowe; Mrs C Higgins; Mr C Bailey; Mrs D A Powell; Mrs M Sarling.

HOW TO APPLY In writing to the correspondent. Applications are reviewed in January, April and September. An sae is appreciated. Preliminary telephone calls are considered unnecessary.

WHO TO APPLY TO K J Crowe, Trustee, 19 Avenue Terrace, Westcliff-on-Sea, Essex SS0 7PL *Tel* 01702 307840 *email* kenbarcrowe@ blueyonder.co.uk

■ Alexandra Rose Charities

CC NO 211535   **ESTABLISHED** 1912

WHERE FUNDING CAN BE GIVEN England and Wales.

WHO CAN BENEFIT Registered charities that are involved in caring for people.

WHAT IS FUNDED Grants to registered charities only, who take part in the Alexandra Rose Day collections or Rose Raffle.

TYPE OF GRANT Alexandra Rose Day makes an immediate grant to the partner equivalent to

90% of its gross collection. For raffles, Alexandra Rose Day organises the prizes and prints the tickets, which the partner charity sells and receives 80% of all gross sales. The charity organises its own fundraising events including the Rose Ball and donates any surplus through its Special Appeal Fund, an annual programme of grants designed to bring immediate, practical benefits to people-caring charities and voluntary groups.

SAMPLE GRANTS Manor Farm Boys' Club (£3,200); Royal Naval Association Cardiff (£2,500); St Vincent de Paul Society (£1,700); It's Fun to Dance (£1,600) RNA – Dorchester (£1,300); and Blue Badge Network (£1,100).

FINANCES *Year* 2010 *Income* £281,535 *Grants* £103,406 *Assets* £628,516

TRUSTEES Andrew Mitchell MP; Lady Kathleen Grade; Iain Matthewson; Angela Anderson; Sonja Miller; Lady Marianna Falconer of Thoroton; Roger Lomax; Mike Morris; Lord Anthony St John of Bletso; Sophia Tayler; Dominic Tayler; Alan Kirby; Elizabeth Keir; Michael Mackenzie.

HOW TO APPLY Only charities participating in Rose Days or the Rose Raffle are eligible to apply. Please see the website for further information on how to get involved.

WHO TO APPLY TO The National Director, 5 Mead Lane, Farmhan, Surrey GU9 7DY *Tel* 01252 726171 *Fax* 01252 727559 *email* enquiries@ alexandrarose.org.uk *Website* www. alexandrarosecharities.org.uk

■ The Rose Foundation

CC NO 274875   **ESTABLISHED** 1977
WHERE FUNDING CAN BE GIVEN In and around London.
WHO CAN BENEFIT Registered charities.
WHAT IS FUNDED The main emphasis is on financing building projects for other charities, where the cost is less than £200,000. A policy of seeking small self-contained projects usually in London or the Home Counties has been adopted. The trustees' policy is to offer assistance where needed with the design and construction process, ensuring wherever possible that costs are minimised and the participation of other contributing bodies can be utilised to maximum benefit.
WHAT IS NOT FUNDED The foundation can support any type of building project (decoration, construction, repairs, extensions, adaptations) but not the provision of equipment (such as computers, transportation and so on). Items connected with the finishes, such as carpets, curtains, wallpaper and so on, should ideally comprise a part of the project not financed by the foundation. Funding will not be given for the purchase of a building or a site or for the seed money needed to draw up plans.
TYPE OF GRANT Part-funding building projects.
RANGE OF GRANTS Typically £5,000–£10,000.
SAMPLE GRANTS St John Ambulance (£555,000); New Amsterdam Charitable Foundation (£104,000); Fred Hollows Foundation (£46,000); Qazi Foundation (£15,000); Central Synagogue General Charities Fund (£12,000); Friends of St Mary's Association (£10,000); Old Vic Theatre (£7,000); Training Ship Broadsword (£6,000); Community Links (£5,000); Massey Shaw and Marine Vessels Preservation Society (£4,000); Help the Hospices (£3,500); and Hampstead Theatre (£1,200).
FINANCES *Year* 2009–10 *Income* £358,395 *Grants* £1,008,660 *Assets* £21,326,724

TRUSTEES Martin Rose; Alan Rose; John Rose; Paul Rose.
HOW TO APPLY In writing to the correspondent including details of the organisation and the registered charity number, together with the nature and probable approximate cost of the scheme and its anticipated start and completion dates. Applications can be submitted anytime between 1 July and 31 March (the following year). The foundation hopes to inform applicants of its decision by the second week in July.
WHO TO APPLY TO Martin Rose, Trustee, 28 Crawford Street, London W1H 1LN *Tel* 020 7262 1155 *Website* www.rosefoundation.co.uk

■ The Cecil Rosen Foundation

CC NO 247425   **ESTABLISHED** 1966
WHERE FUNDING CAN BE GIVEN UK.
WHO CAN BENEFIT Organisations benefiting people who are disabled or have diabetes, hearing and sight loss, heart disease or mental illness. Medical professionals and research workers are also considered.
WHAT IS FUNDED General charitable purposes especially to assist people who are blind, deaf, physically or mentally disabled; also for research into causes of heart disease, diabetes and mental illness.
WHAT IS NOT FUNDED No grants to individuals.
TYPE OF GRANT Research is considered.
SAMPLE GRANTS The Jewish Blind and Physically Handicapped Society (£75,000).
FINANCES *Year* 2009–10 *Income* £410,167 *Grants* £218,250 *Assets* £5,721,256
TRUSTEES M J Ozin; J A Hart; P H Silverman.
HOW TO APPLY The correspondent has previously stated that 'no new applications can be considered'. Unsuccessful applications are not acknowledged.
WHO TO APPLY TO M J Ozin, Trustee, 22 Lisson Grove, London NW1 6TT

■ Rosetrees Trust

CC NO 298582   **ESTABLISHED** 1987
WHERE FUNDING CAN BE GIVEN Worldwide, in practice, UK.
WHO CAN BENEFIT Independent vetted medical research projects, especially if departmentally backed and peer reviewed. The vast majority of grants are made through university and medical schools.
WHAT IS FUNDED Medical research only.
WHAT IS NOT FUNDED No support for individuals, or for non-medical research.
TYPE OF GRANT Project and research funding for up to three years will be considered. Seed corn funding for a preliminary or pilot report is also available.
RANGE OF GRANTS About £200–£300,000.
SAMPLE GRANTS Institutions including: University College London; Hebrew University; Kings College; Imperial College London; Institute of Cancer Research; Oxford University; Cardiff University; Southampton University; Manchester University; and Newcastle University.
FINANCES *Year* 2009–10 *Income* £32,370,336 *Grants* £675,631 *Assets* £32,158,303
TRUSTEES R A Ross; Lee Portnoi; Clive Winkler.
PUBLICATIONS A brochure, which outlines the trust's approach to the 100 projects it helps fund and its future plans, is available.
OTHER INFORMATION Note: the trust is very keen to share the expertise it has developed over 20 years, which is available to co-donors at no

cost. Organisations interested in sharing this knowledge should contact the trust directly. Six-monthly progress reports in layman's terms are a condition of any grant made. These should give the trustees a clear and concise picture of whether anticipated targets have been achieved. Peer review and endorsement are required.

HOW TO APPLY In writing to the correspondent. Applicants must complete a simple pro forma which sets out briefly in clear layman's terms the reason for the project, the nature of the research, its cost, its anticipated benefit and how and when people will be able to benefit. Proper reports in this form will be required at least six-monthly and continuing funding will be conditional on these being satisfactory.

The trust has previously stated: 'The trustees are not medical experts and require short clear statements in plain English setting out the particular subject to be researched, the objects and likely benefits, the cost and the time-scale. Unless a charity will undertake to provide two concise progress reports each year, they should not apply as this is a vital requirement. It is essential that the trustees are able to follow the progress and effectiveness of the research they support.'

WHO TO APPLY TO Richard Ross, Chief Executive and Trustee, Russell House, 140 High Street, Edgware, Middlesex HA8 7LW *Tel* 020 8952 1414 *email* richard@rosetreestrust.co.uk *Website* www.rosetreestrust.co.uk

■ The Rothera Charitable Settlement

CC NO 283950   **ESTABLISHED** 1982
WHERE FUNDING CAN BE GIVEN UK.
WHO CAN BENEFIT Registered charities.
WHAT IS FUNDED Welfare, animals, overseas aid, medical.
RANGE OF GRANTS £300–£1,000.
SAMPLE GRANTS Alzheimer's Society (£1,000); NSPCC (£650); Médecins Sans Frontières and Children's Brain Tumour Research (£550 each); Christian Aid; Malt Cross Trust; Special Care Baby Unit Fundraising Society and Water Aid (£500); RNLI and National Eye Research Centre (£450 each); NORSACA and The Abbeyfield Society (£300 each).
FINANCES *Year* 2010 *Income* £36,329 *Grants* £44,250 *Assets* £2,652
TRUSTEES Mrs C A Rothera; Mrs S E Rothera.
HOW TO APPLY Charities are selected at the discretion of the trustees.
WHO TO APPLY TO Mrs C A Rothera, Trustee, The Dumbles, Lowdham Road, Epperstone, Nottingham NG14 6BB *Tel* 0115 966 3005 *email* crothera@aol.com

■ The Rothermere Foundation

CC NO 314125   **ESTABLISHED** 1964
WHERE FUNDING CAN BE GIVEN UK.
WHO CAN BENEFIT Registered charities and individual graduates of the Memorial University of Newfoundland.
WHAT IS FUNDED Establishment and maintenance of 'Rothermere Scholarships' to be awarded to graduates of the Memorial University of Newfoundland to enable them to undertake further periods of study in the UK; and general charitable causes.
TYPE OF GRANT Fellowship grants, scholarships, other educational grants.

SAMPLE GRANTS Sandroyd School (£90,000); Tick Tock Club (£75,000); Kings Rifles & East African Forces Association and Museum of Garden History (£10,000 each); Help for Heroes (£5,000) and Southbank Centre (£1,000).
FINANCES *Year* 2009–10 *Income* £733,088 *Grants* £206,206 *Assets* £27,390,135
TRUSTEES Rt Hon. Viscount Rothermere; Viscountess Rothermere; V P W Harmsworth; J G Hemingway.
OTHER INFORMATION Three fellowship grants were awarded totalling £57,000.
HOW TO APPLY In writing to the correspondent.
WHO TO APPLY TO V P W Harmsworth, Secretary, Beech Court, Canterbury Road, Challock, Ashford, Kent TN25 4DJ *Tel* 01233 740 641

■ The Rotherwick Foundation

CC NO 1058900   **ESTABLISHED** 1996
WHERE FUNDING CAN BE GIVEN Within a 20-mile radius of either Ashdown Park Hotel, Wych Cross, East Sussex; Grand Hotel, Eastbourne, East Sussex; or Tylney Hall Hotel, Rotherwick, Hampshire.
WHO CAN BENEFIT Individuals and organisations benefiting students and Protestant Christians.
WHAT IS FUNDED The provision of scholarships, bursaries and maintenance allowances and educational grants tenable at any school, university or other educational establishment to people under 25 who, or whose parents or guardians, are resident in the specified localities or have for not less than five years attended a school or other educational establishment within those localities; the provision of financial assistance, equipment, books and clothing to such people on leaving school, university or other educational establishment for entry into a trade or profession; the provision of amenities and facilities including public recreation and sports grounds for public benefit; the advancement of religion and other charitable works of, and the maintenance of, Protestant churches; the provision, maintenance, improvement and equipment of hospitals, nursing homes, hospices and clinics; and such other charitable purposes as the trustees in their absolute discretion think fit to support or establish.
TYPE OF GRANT Funding is available for over to two years.
SAMPLE GRANTS Previous beneficiaries include: Brighton & Sussex Medical School, Lord Wandsworth College and Plumpton College (£20,000 each); St Peter and St James Hospice – Lewes and University of Sussex (£16,000 each); Beacon Community College – Crowborough and Marie Curie Cancer Care (£15,000); Hospice in the Weald, and Eastbourne Multiple Sclerosis Society (£10,000 each).
FINANCES *Year* 2009–10 *Income* £12,500
TRUSTEES T E Mugleston; G C Bateman; A H W Dixon.
OTHER INFORMATION Due to the trust's low income in 2009–10, only basic financial information was available from the Charity Commission.
HOW TO APPLY In writing to the correspondent.
WHO TO APPLY TO G C Bateman, Trustee and General Manager, Ashdown Park, Wych Cross, Forest Row, East Sussex RH18 5JR *Tel* 01342 820 227 *Fax* 01342 820222 *email* rotherwickfoundation@ashdownpark.com *Website* www.rotherwickfoundation.org

■ The Rothley Trust

CC NO 219849   **ESTABLISHED** 1959

WHERE FUNDING CAN BE GIVEN Northumberland, North and South Tyneside, Newcastle upon Tyne, Gateshead and the former counties of Cleveland and Durham (including Darlington) and Cleveland.

WHO CAN BENEFIT Registered charities only.

WHAT IS FUNDED Children, community, education, disability, medical, third world and youth. Apart from a few charities with which the trust has been associated for many years, its activities are now directed exclusively towards north east England (Northumberland to Cleveland inclusive). Developing world appeals, arising from this area only, will be considered.

WHAT IS NOT FUNDED No grants for further education, the repair of buildings used solely for worship, the advancement of religion, advancement in the arts, heritage or science, advancement of amateur sport (unless it has the means of alleviating the problems within the trust's approved categories above), advancement of human rights, conflict resolution or reconciliation (except family mediation), advancement of environmental protection or improvement, advancement of animal welfare and organisations focused on the elderly.

TYPE OF GRANT Mainly one-off donations towards specific projects and not running costs. Start-up costs, buildings, equipment, resources and capital grants will be considered.

RANGE OF GRANTS Typical grant £300.

SAMPLE GRANTS Maggie's (Newcastle and the North East) – Edinburgh (£5,000); Durham Association of Clubs for Young People and Consett Churches Detached Youth Project (£3,000 each); Brathay Hall Trust – Cumbria and YMCA North Shields (£2,000 each).
Grants of less than £1,500 each to organisations totalled £86,000.
In addition grants to individuals totalled £12,000.

FINANCES *Year* 2009–10 *Income* £175,032 *Grants* £126,327 *Assets* £6,401,495

TRUSTEES Dr H A Armstrong, Chair; A Brunton; Mrs J Brown; C Bucknall; Mrs A Galbraith; M Bridgeman; G Salvin; H Hargreave; D Holborn.

OTHER INFORMATION Grants to individuals totalled £12,000.

HOW TO APPLY Write to the correspondent including a copy of latest accounts/annual reports. An sae is appreciated. Full details can be found at the trust's website where criteria, guidelines and application process are posted.

WHO TO APPLY TO Diane Lennon, Secretary, Mea House, Ellison Place, Newcastle upon Tyne NE1 8XS *Tel* 0191 232 7783 *Fax* 0191 232 7783 *Website* www.rothleytrust.org.uk

■ The Roughley Charitable Trust

CC NO 264037   **ESTABLISHED** 1972

WHERE FUNDING CAN BE GIVEN Birmingham area (excluding Wolverhampton, Coventry, Worcester and the Black Country towns).

WHO CAN BENEFIT Registered charities; some UK and international projects supported but only where the trustees have a special interest.

WHAT IS FUNDED General charitable purposes. Funds are mostly committed to projects known to the trustees.

WHAT IS NOT FUNDED No support for animal charities, for individuals, for unsolicited projects outside of the Birmingham area or for Birmingham branches of national charities.

RANGE OF GRANTS Mostly £500 to £3,000. Larger grants to projects where trustees have special knowledge.

SAMPLE GRANTS Hope Destitution Fund (£28,000); Mac (£15,000); Birmingham Settlement (£10,000); Birmingham Centre for Arts Therapies (£5,000); Birmingham Children's Community Venture (£4,000); Quaker Peace Education Project (£2,500); Royal Birmingham Society of Artists and Adoption Support (£3,000 each); Piers Rd New Communities Centre Association and Birmingham Clubs for Young People (£2,500 each); The Birmingham Civic Society and Life Education Centres: Drug Prevention Education (£1,000 each); RSPB Sandwell and One Aim Mix Community Education (£500 each).

FINANCES *Year* 2009–10 *Income* £165,481 *Grants* £167,400 *Assets* £3,452,590

TRUSTEES Mrs D M Newton; J R L Smith; M C G Smith; V A Thomas.

HOW TO APPLY The trust has an annual meeting in September to consider written applications with report and accounts from Birmingham charities only for grants of up to £3,000. Larger grants are only made to Birmingham area projects in which trustees have a special interest. Full details can be obtained from the trust's website.

WHO TO APPLY TO J R L Smith, Trustee, 90 Somerset Road, Edgbaston, Birmingham B15 2PP *Tel* 0121 454 6833 *email* correspondent@roughleytrust.org.uk *Website* www.roughleytrust.org.uk

■ Mrs Gladys Row Fogo Charitable Trust

SC NO SC009685   **ESTABLISHED** 1970

WHERE FUNDING CAN BE GIVEN Edinburgh, Lothians and Dunblane.

WHO CAN BENEFIT Research workers and people with neurological diseases, but other medical research and charitable purposes are considered.

WHAT IS FUNDED Medical research, particularly in the field of neuroscience; also to local charity projects and to small charities mostly in Central Scotland.

WHAT IS NOT FUNDED No grants to individuals.

TYPE OF GRANT One-off.

RANGE OF GRANTS £1,000 to £5,000.

SAMPLE GRANTS Previous beneficiaries have been: £187,000 to SHEFC Brain Imaging Research Centre; £8,000 to Macmillan Cancer Relief; £6,000 to RNLI; £5,000 each to Alzheimer Scotland Action on Dementia, Age Concern and Salvation Army; £4,500 each to Multiple Sclerosis Society, Muscular Dystrophy Campaign and The Wishbone Trust; £4,000 each to Drum Riding for the Disabled, Invalids at Home and Stobhill Kidney Patient's Association; £3,500 to The Sandpiper Trust; £3,000 each to Erskine Hospital and Tak Tent.

FINANCES *Year* 2009–10 *Income* £126,578 *Grants* £150,000

TRUSTEES E J Cuthbertson; A W Waddell; Dr C Brough.

HOW TO APPLY In writing to the trustees. Trustees meet once a year to consider applications, usually in September.

WHO TO APPLY TO The Trustees, Brodies LLP Solicitors, 15 Atholl Crescent, Edinburgh EH3 8HA *Tel* 0131 228 3777 *Fax* 0131 228 3878 *email* Mailbox@brodies.co.uk

■ Rowanville Ltd

cc no 267278   established 1973
where funding can be given UK and Israel.
who can benefit Jewish organisations.
what is funded Established organisations for the advancement of religion in accordance with the orthodox Jewish faith.
range of grants Up to £50,000.
sample grants Chevras Mo'oz Ladol (£35,500); Yeshivas Shaarei Torah (£27,000); Friends of Beis Yisroel Trust (£20,500); Telz Academy Trust (£15,000); Union of Orthodox Hebrew Congregation (£10,000); Project Seed (£7,000); Pinto Talmudical College (£5,000); Akiva School Foundation (£3,000); and Made in Heaven (£1,000).
finances *Year* 2009–10 *Income* £1,140,888 *Grants* £692,645 *Assets* £6,045,846
trustees Joseph Pearlman; Ruth Pearlman; Michael Neuberger.
how to apply The trust has previously stated that applications are unlikely to be successful unless one of the trustees has prior personal knowledge of the cause, as this charity's funds are already very heavily committed.
who to apply to Ruth Pearlman, Secretary, 8 Highfield Gardens, London NW11 9HB *Tel* 020 8458 9266

■ The Christopher Rowbotham Charitable Trust

cc no 261991   established 1970
where funding can be given Bolton, Cheshire, Gateshead, Lancashire, Newcastle upon Tyne, North Tyneside and Northumberland.
who can benefit Registered charities.
what is funded 'The trustees prefer to give regular grants and are especially interested in: (i) People with physical or mental handicaps – improving their quality of life through equipment, activities and holidays. (ii) The young – with particular emphasis on improving prospects of employment by education and meaningful activities. (iii) Health – improving the quality of life of the ill, their carers and the old either at home or in hospital.' There is a preference for small local groups with low overheads.
what is not funded Grants are only given to registered charities. No grants to individuals or overseas charities and no grants for capital building costs. The trust prefers to give regular grants but does not fund salaries.
range of grants Up to £3,500.
sample grants Shiplake College (£3,500); Calvert Trust – Keilder and Bath Institute of Medical Engineering (£1,250 each); Coombe Trust Fund; Lionheart; Fairbridge in Tyne and Wear; Jubilee Sailing Trust; Music and the Deaf (£1,000 each).
finances *Year* 2009–10 *Income* £31,289 *Grants* £26,000 *Assets* £987,275
trustees Mrs C A Jackson, Chair; Mrs E J Wilkinson; R M Jackson.
how to apply In writing to the correspondent. There are no application forms, guidelines or deadlines. Telephone calls are not welcome. No SAE is required; applications are not acknowledged. Trustees meet annually in the autumn. Applications can be sent at any time.
who to apply to Mrs C A Jackson, Chair, 18 Northumberland Square, North Shields, Tyne and Wear NE30 1PX

■ The Rowing Foundation

cc no 281688   established 1981
where funding can be given UK.
who can benefit Organisations and clubs whose requirements may be too small or who may be otherwise ineligible for an approach to the National Lottery or other similar sources of funds.
what is funded The aid and support of young people (those under 18 or 23 if still in full-time education) and people who are disabled of all ages, through their participation in water sports, particularly rowing. Grants have also been made towards the purchase of buoyancy aids, splash suits, canoes and the promotion of taster rowing courses for youth clubs, sailing and other water sports clubs.
what is not funded The foundation does not give grants to individuals, only to clubs and organisations, and for a specific purpose, not as a contribution to general funds.
type of grant Pump-priming.
range of grants £500–£2,000.
sample grants Previous beneficiaries have included: Headway (£4,800); London Youth (£3,000); Cranmore School RC (£2,000); University of Derby and OarSport (£1,200 each); and Back Up Trust (£900).
finances *Year* 2010 *Income* £22,883 *Grants* £28,642
trustees John Buchan; Simon Goodey; Philip J Phillips; Iain Reid; Roger S Smith; John Chick; Christopher Sprague.
how to apply Applications should be made on a form, available to download from the Amateur Rowing Association website.
who to apply to Pauline Churcher, Secretary, 6 Lower Mall, Hammersmith, London W6 9DJ *Tel* 020 8878 3723 *Fax* 020 8878 6298 *email* p.churcher@sky.com *Website* www.ara-rowing.org/rowing-foundation

■ The Rowland Family Foundation

cc no 1111177   established 2005
where funding can be given UK and overseas.
who can benefit Charitable organisations.
what is funded Principal objectives include the relief of poverty, the advancement of education and religion and other purposes beneficial for the community.
range of grants From £2,000.
sample grants Hope and Homes for Children (£195,000); Chailey Heritage School (£142,000); Child Welfare Scheme (£40,000 each); and Royal Marsden Hospital (£2,000).
finances *Year* 2009–10 *Income* £620,926 *Grants* £379,000 *Assets* £5,199,744
trustees Mrs A M Rowland; N G Rowland.
how to apply In writing to the correspondent.
who to apply to Lucy Gibson, Harcus Sinclair, 3 Lincoln's Inn Fields, London WC2A 3AA *Tel* 020 7242 9700 *email* lucy.gibson@harcus-sinclair.co.uk

■ The Rowlands Trust

cc no 1062148   established 1997
where funding can be given West and South Midlands, including Hereford and Worcester, Gloucester, South Shropshire and Birmingham.
who can benefit Organisations benefiting people of all ages, research workers, disabled people and those disadvantaged by poverty.

WHAT IS FUNDED Medical and scientific research; the welfare of elderly, infirm, poor and disabled people; support for music and the arts; the environment; the encouragement of education and training for individuals to better themselves.

WHAT IS NOT FUNDED No support for individuals or to animal charities. No support is given for revenue funding.

TYPE OF GRANT One-off, capital including buildings, project and research.

RANGE OF GRANTS £500–£25,000.

SAMPLE GRANTS CTC Kinghurst Academy (£15,000); Baverstock School (£13,000); Longmynd Adventure Camp and New College, Worcester (£10,000); Carpet Museum Trust, Creation Skatepark and Walsall Hospice (£5,000 each); Cerebral Palsy Midlands (£3,000); Pentabus Arts Ltd – Ludlow, Warwickshire & Northamptonshire Air Ambulance (£2,000 each); and Birmingham Hippodrome Theatre Development Trust, Birmingham Symphonic Winds, Camp XL – Whitbourne, Warley Woods Community Trust Ltd and Wellington Cottage Care Trust (£1,000 each); and Worcestershire Wildlife Trust (£750).

FINANCES *Year* 2010 *Income* £169,657 *Grants* £482,424 *Assets* £5,365,306

TRUSTEES A C S Hordern, Chair; Mrs F J Burman; Mrs A M I Harris; G Barber; T Jessop.

HOW TO APPLY Applications forms are available from the correspondent and are the preferred means by which to apply. Completed forms should be returned with a copy of the most recent accounts. The trustees meet to consider grants four times a year.

WHO TO APPLY TO Ms N Fenn, Clerk to the Trustees, c/o Mills and Reeve, 78–84 Colmore Row, Birmingham B3 2AB *Tel* 0121 456 8341 *Fax* 0121 200 3028 *email* nicola.fenn@mills-reeve.com

....

■ The Joseph Rowntree Charitable Trust

CC NO 210037   **ESTABLISHED** 1904

WHERE FUNDING CAN BE GIVEN Unrestricted, in practice mainly UK, Republic of Ireland and Europe.

WHO CAN BENEFIT Registered charities, voluntary organisations and charitable groups.

WHAT IS FUNDED The trust generally funds work under the following five programmes: peace, racial justice, power and responsibility, Quaker issues and Ireland and Northern Ireland (promoting a peaceful society).

WHAT IS NOT FUNDED Generally, the trust does not make grants for: the personal support of individuals in need; educational bursaries; travel or adventure projects; medical research; building, buying or repairing buildings; business development or job creation; general appeals; providing care for elderly people, children, people with learning difficulties, people with physical disabilities, or people using mental health services; work which has already been done; work in larger, older national charities which have an established constituency of supporters; work in mainstream education; academic research, except as an integral part of policy and campaigning work that is central to the trust's areas of interest; work on housing and homelessness; the arts, except where a project is specifically concerned with issues of interest to the trust; work which the trust believes should be funded from statutory sources, or which has been in the recent past;

work which tries to make a problem easier to live with, rather than getting to the root of it; local work in Britain (except racial justice work in West Yorkshire); work outside the UK, Ireland and South Africa (except for groups working elsewhere within Europe at a European level). Further specific exclusions are included for individual programmes and information on these can be found on the trust's website. Within its areas of interest, the trust makes grants to a range of organisations and to individuals. It is not necessary to be a registered charity to apply to the trust. However, it can only support work which is legally charitable.

TYPE OF GRANT Single and multi-year funding for core and project costs.

RANGE OF GRANTS Up to £200,000.

SAMPLE GRANTS JUST – West Yorkshire (£200,000 over 3 years), towards core costs; Community Foundation for Northern Ireland (£203,000 over 3 years), towards a Transitional Support Co-ordinator for the Dialogue Programme; British American Security Information Council (£180,000 over 2 years), towards 'Getting to Zero' and 'Trident Commission' British Institute of Human Rights (£120,000 over 3 years), towards core costs; Compass (£100,000), toward the High Pay Commission; Campaign for Freedom of Information (£80,000 over 2 years), towards core costs; Black Training and Enterprise Group (£75,000 over 3 years), towards core costs; Envision (£54,500 over 3 years), towards 'Building on Success', which promotes community participation for more racially disadvantaged young people; Foundation for Democracy and Sustainable Development (£45,000 over 3 years), towards core costs; Moyallon Centre Management Committee (£28,500 over 3 years), towards a Vision and Outreach worker; Travellers Aid Trust (£16,500), towards a panel review of government policy on Gypsies and Travellers; Bradford Muslim Women's Council (£10,000), towards development costs; and 38 Degrees (£1,500), towards engaging with the Iraq war enquiry.

FINANCES *Year* 2010 *Income* £4,375,000 *Grants* £5,810,000 *Assets* £166,196,000

TRUSTEES Beverley Meeson; Christine Davis; Emily Miles; Margaret Bryan; Marion McNaughton; Peter Coltman; Susan Seymour; Helen Carmichael; Imran Tyabi; Stan Lee; Michael Eccles.

OTHER INFORMATION The Joseph Rowntree Charitable Trust is a Quaker trust and the value base of the trustees, as of the founder Joseph Rowntree (1836–1925), reflects the religious convictions of the Society of Friends.

HOW TO APPLY The trust expects all applicants to have made themselves familiar with the relevant funding programmes, summarised here but set out in full on the website and available in leaflet form. They then require an application letter (including budget, accounts and equal opportunities policy) and a completed registration form. The details expected in the letter are set out in detail on the website and in the leaflet. Applications can be submitted either online or by post. Organisations submitting an application by post can download a registration form from the website to complete. For those submitting their applications online, the registration details are included in the initial steps. There is a deadline for receipt of applications of around ten weeks before the meeting of trustees. It is very helpful if applications arrive well before the deadline. The period immediately after the deadline is the trust's busiest time, so it cannot normally consider applications that arrive late until the following funding round. The trust has three grant-making rounds each year. Contact the trust or go to the website for the latest information on deadlines.

WHO TO APPLY TO Stephen Pittam, Trust Secretary, The Garden House, Water End, York YO30 6WQ *Tel* 01904 627810 *Fax* 01904 651990 *email* jrct@jrct.org.uk *Website* www.jrct.org.uk

■ The Joseph Rowntree Foundation

CC NO 210169   **ESTABLISHED** 1904
WHERE FUNDING CAN BE GIVEN UK, with some preference for York and Bradford.
WHO CAN BENEFIT Organisations carrying out social science research.
WHAT IS FUNDED This is not a conventional grantmaking foundation. It supports research, of a rigorous kind, usually carried out in universities or research institutes, but also has a wide range of other activities not necessarily involving grants of any kind. The foundation initiates, manages and pays for an extensive social research programme. It does not normally respond to unsolicited applications and many of its programmes issue formal and detailed requests for proposals. However modest proposals for minor gap-filling pieces of work in the foundation's fields of interest may sometimes be handled less formally and more rapidly. For 2009–2011 the foundation's strategic objectives are research into 'Poverty', 'Place' and 'Empowerment'. The foundation does run a grants program for the City of York called the York Committee.
WHAT IS NOT FUNDED With the exception of funds for particular projects in York and the surrounding area, the foundation does not generally support: projects outside the topics within its current priorities; development projects which are not innovative; development projects from which no general lessons can be drawn; general appeals, for example from national charities; conferences and other events, websites or publications, unless they are linked with work which the foundation is already supporting; grants to replace withdrawn or expired statutory funding, or to make up deficits already incurred; educational bursaries or sponsorship for individuals for research or further education and training courses; grants or sponsorship for individuals in need. Grants from the York Committee are not given to: animal welfare groups; archaeological work; individuals; routine maintenance or construction of buildings; medical research; overseas visits or overseas holidays.
TYPE OF GRANT Project and research. Funding can be given for up to two years.
RANGE OF GRANTS Up to £100,000.
SAMPLE GRANTS Spending cuts: mitigating risks for Scotland's disadvantaged communities – Glasgow Caledonian University (£97,000); Designing carbon taxation to protect low income households – Policy Studies Institute (£95,000); How can Universities support disadvantaged communities – Durham University (£88,000); Building a sustainable quality part-time recruitment market – Women Like Us; Development Manager post – York Young Peoples Trust (£60,000); Modelling poverty – Institute for Fiscal Studies (£28,000); and Funding of the Rowntree Society (£25,000).

FINANCES *Year* 2010 *Income* £6,918,000 *Grants* £4,738,000 *Assets* £260,118,000
TRUSTEES Don Brand; Debby Ounsted; Ashok Jashapara; Bharat Mehta; Tony Stoller; Dame Mavis McDonald; Steven Burkeman; Graham Millar; Prof. Dianne Willcocks; Tony Stoller.
PUBLICATIONS Findings – short briefing papers summarising the main findings of projects in the Research and Development Programme; Special Reports designed to present research results with clarity and impact.
HOW TO APPLY The foundation does not respond to unsolicited applications. Instead, it issues 'calls for proposals' and invites submissions to them. Detailed information, including guidance and a proposal registration form, is available from the foundation's website. The York Committee has its own application guidelines and form, available on the foundations website. Meetings to decide grants are held four times a year, usually February, May, August and November.
WHO TO APPLY TO Julia Unwin, Chief Executive, The Homestead, 40 Water End, York YO30 6WP *Tel* 01904 629241 *Fax* 01904 620072 *Minicom* 01904 615910 *email* info@jrf.org.uk *Website* www.jrf.org.uk

■ Joseph Rowntree Reform Trust Limited

          ESTABLISHED 1904
WHERE FUNDING CAN BE GIVEN UK.
WHO CAN BENEFIT Campaigning organisations and individuals who have reform as their objective and are ineligible for charitable support.
WHAT IS FUNDED The promotion of political and democratic reform and the defence of civil liberties. The trust's main aims are to: correct imbalances of power; strengthen the hand of individuals, groups and organisations who are striving for reform; foster democratic reform, civil liberties and social justice.
WHAT IS NOT FUNDED The trust is not a registered charity and provides grants for non-charitable political and campaigning activities. Examples of work for which the trust does not make grants are: the personal support of individuals in need; educational bursaries; travel and adventure projects; building, buying or repairing properties; business development or job creation; general appeals; academic research; work which the trust believes should be funded from statutory sources, or which has been in the recent past; administrative or other core costs of party organisations.
TYPE OF GRANT Salaries; full project funding.
SAMPLE GRANTS Yes To Fairer Votes (£500,000), towards the campaign for a Yes vote in the AV Referendum; Liberal Democrats (£350,000), towards the cost of campaigning in target seats; Institute for Government (£50,000 over 2 years), towards their 'Methods of Selection of Candidates' project; Hope Not Hate Yorkshire (£40,000), to campaign against far right groups over 1 year; Action on Rights for Children (£33,000), to continue to campaign on children's rights issues; Compass (£23,000), to campaign for economic and banking reforms; Operation Black Vote (£10,000), towards their General Election campaign; and Alliance for Choice Northern Ireland (£5,000), to raise awareness amongst women of existing abortion law in Northern Ireland and begin the process of redressing both the misinformation and the fear among women in talking about abortion.

FINANCES *Year* 2010 *Grants* £1,000,000
Assets £30,000,000

TRUSTEES Dr Christopher Greenfield, Chair; Tina Day; Mandy Cormack; Dr Peadar Cremin; Archy Kirkwood; Andrew Neal.

PUBLICATIONS The trust produces a range of reports, all of which are available on its website.

OTHER INFORMATION The trust is not a charity and therefore pays tax on its income. Very little financial information was available; the trust budgets £1 million each year for grants.

HOW TO APPLY Applicants should email a one page outline to the correspondent before making a formal application. If accepted, a full application can then be made. The trust does not have a standard form, but any application should include: an Application Registration Form (available to download from the website); up to four pages setting out the proposal; a full budget for the project; the most recent audited accounts; a CV, if applying as an individual. Trust staff make an initial assessment of applications and are authorised to reject those that are clearly inappropriate. All staff rejections are reported to the directors at their next meeting, when they consider all remaining applications. The meetings take place at quarterly intervals in March, July, October and December and the deadline for applications is approximately four or five weeks prior to the trust meeting. Applications for small grants of up to £5,000 can, however, be considered at any time and applicants should hear of the decision within two weeks.

WHO TO APPLY TO Tina Walker, Trust Secretary, The Garden House, Water End, York YO30 6WQ *Tel* 01904 625744 *Fax* 01904 651502 *email* info@jrrt.org.uk *Website* www.jrrt.org.uk

······································

■ Royal Artillery Charitable Fund

CC NO 210202   **ESTABLISHED** 1964
WHERE FUNDING CAN BE GIVEN UK and overseas.
WHO CAN BENEFIT Service charities.
WHAT IS FUNDED Welfare of service and ex-service personnel.
RANGE OF GRANTS £1,000–£55,000.
SAMPLE GRANTS Army Benevolent Fund (£55,000); Regiment and Batteries (£51,500); Royal Artillery Institution (£35,000); Gunner Magazine (£20,000); King Edward VII Hospital (£2,800); and Erskine Homes (£1,000).
FINANCES *Year* 2010 *Income* £937,458 *Grants* £978,329 *Assets* £14,160,761
TRUSTEES Maj. Gen. J Milne; Brig. A Gordon; Col. G Gilchrist; Col. A Jolley; Col. C Fletcher-Wood; Maj. ATG Richards; Maj. AJ Dines; Brig. D E Radcliffe; Brig. R Haldenby; Brig. W J F Bramble; Col. M J Thornhill; Col. B W Jenkins; Col. IA Vere Nicoll.
OTHER INFORMATION Included in the grants total were grants to individuals amounting to £776,481.
HOW TO APPLY In writing to the correspondent.
WHO TO APPLY TO The Welfare Secretary, Artillery House, Artillery Centre, Larkhill, Wiltshire SP4 8QT *Tel* 01980 845698 *email* AC-RHQRA-RACF-WelfareClk2@mod.uk *Website* www.theraa.co.uk

······································

■ Royal British Legion

CC NO 219279   **ESTABLISHED** 1921
WHERE FUNDING CAN BE GIVEN UK, excluding Scotland.
WHO CAN BENEFIT People who have served in the Armed Forces, their widow(er)s and dependants, and those organisations which help them. Beneficiaries include those who have served in a hostile area with bodies such as the Mercantile Marines, the Allied Civil Police forces, the Home Guard, the Voluntary Aid Society and the Polish Resettlement Corps.
WHAT IS FUNDED The welfare of men and women who have served in the armed forces.
WHAT IS NOT FUNDED Memorials, commercial ventures, or any potential commercial ventures, for example clubs. Grants are not normally given for core costs, for example, administration or running costs of an organisation that is supporting ex-Service personnel. However, there may be exceptions to this, and the Royal British Legion aims to respond flexibly to applications, and is prepared to negotiate if there are special circumstances, for example, if the withholding of grant would harm the interests of ex-Service personnel.
TYPE OF GRANT One-off and recurring costs.
SAMPLE GRANTS St Dunstan's (£2.6 million); The Officers' Association (£1.6 million); SPEAR Housing Association Ltd (£239,000); English Churches Housing Group (£150,000); Poppyscotland (£112,000); Veterans Aid (£60,000); Skill Force (£40,000); and Gardening Leave (£25,000).
FINANCES *Year* 2009–10 *Income* £115,235,000 *Grants* £5,613,000 *Assets* £292,066,000
TRUSTEES John Farmer, Chair; John Crisford; Una Cleminson; Dennis Compton; Eddy Dixon; Noel Duston; Denise Edgar; John Fisher; Eddie Hefferman; Bill Parkin; Keith Prichard; Martyn Tighe; Peter Twidle; Terry Whittles; Adrian Burn; Dr Diana Henderson; Ian Lindsay; Anthony Macauley; Jenny Rowe; Revd Mike Williams; Wendy Bromwich.
PUBLICATIONS *The Legion* magazine.
OTHER INFORMATION A further £19.6 million was given to individuals. For further information, see *A Guide to Grants for Individuals in Need* also published by the Directory of Social Change.
HOW TO APPLY In the first instance you should contact Scarlet Harris, External Grants Officer (Tel. 020 3207 2138 or Email: externalgrants@britishlegion.org.uk) in order to explore whether you may be eligible for a grant, and at what level, so that you can be advised further on the detailed requirements. Following this, you will be sent an application form which will explain on it the information you need to send in depending on the size of grant you are asking for. Successful applicants, depending on the level of grant applied for, can expect to receive an award in between two and six months of sending in a correctly completed application form.
WHO TO APPLY TO External Grants Officer, Haig House, 199 Borough High Street, London SE1 1AA *Tel* 0845 772 5725 *Fax* 020 3207 2218 *email* info@britishlegion.org.uk *Website* www.britishlegion.org.uk

······································

■ Royal Docks Trust (London)

CC NO 1045057   **ESTABLISHED** 1995
WHERE FUNDING CAN BE GIVEN Part of the London Borough of Newham.
WHO CAN BENEFIT The trust supports the community in that part of the London borough of Newham that lies to the south of the London – Tilbury Trunk Road (A13) known as Newham Way.
WHAT IS FUNDED General charitable purposes. Areas of specific interest are: educational and vocational training; recreational and leisure-time pursuits; advancement of public education in

the arts; general improvement of the physical and social environment; relief of poverty and sickness; housing for people with disabilities or are otherwise in need; and preservation of buildings of historical or architectural significance.

WHAT IS NOT FUNDED No grants to individuals. It does not give revenue, top-up or retrospective funding.

RANGE OF GRANTS Up to £30,000.

SAMPLE GRANTS Ascension Eagles Cheerleaders and St John's Community Centre (£30,000 each); Community Links – Britannia Village (£20,000); Ascension Community Trust and Groundwork East London – Future Footprints (£16,500 each); Community Links – ASTA Centre (£15,000); West Silverton Village Community Foundation (£13,000); Newham Music Trust – Learning Through Music and Seeds for Life (£12,000 each); Iroko Theatre Company (£10,000).

FINANCES *Year* 2009–10 *Income* £186,917 *Grants* £189,526 *Assets* £6,585,583

TRUSTEES Eric Sorenson, Chair; Steve Nicholas; Sid Keys; Richard Gooding; Cllr Patrick Murphy; Cllr Paul Schafer; Alan Taylor.

OTHER INFORMATION Minor Community Grants amounted to £15,000.

HOW TO APPLY The trust operates an annual joint grants programme with the London Borough of Newham and applications are invited in the autumn for grants from the following year's programme. For an application form or for more information please contact Stephen Collins at: Community Support Unit, Culture and Community Department, London Borough of Newham, 292 Barking Road, East Ham, London, E6 3BA; Tel: 020 8430 2433; email: Stephen.Collins@newham.gov.uk. Further information and application forms for minor grants can also be obtained from the trust's website.

WHO TO APPLY TO Stephen Collins, Administrator, Community Support Unit, London Borough of Newham, Building 1000, Dockside Road, London E16 2QU *Tel* 020 8430 2433 *email* stephen.collins@newham.gov.uk *Website* www.royaldockstrust.org.uk

....

■ Royal Masonic Trust for Girls and Boys

CC NO 285836   **ESTABLISHED** 1982

WHERE FUNDING CAN BE GIVEN UK.

WHO CAN BENEFIT Charities and individual children of Freemasons.

WHAT IS FUNDED This trust predominantly makes grants to individual children of Freemasons who are in need. However grants are also made to UK organisations working with children and young people; it also supports bursaries at cathedrals and collegiate chapels.

SAMPLE GRANTS Previously: Non-Masonic grants went to Choral Bursaries (£204,000) and Ripon Cathedral Development (£14,000). The trust stated in its annual accounts that in 2007 it, 'continued to limit its non-Masonic activities to its existing Choral Bursary project, as there were insufficient funds available to make donations to other charities'.

FINANCES *Year* 2010 *Income* £5,291,000 *Grants* £219,000 *Assets* £125,694,000

TRUSTEES Council members appointed by a resolution of a General Court.

OTHER INFORMATION The grant total shown in this entry only refers to the funds distributed to non-

masonic charities. A further £5 million went to masonic beneficiaries.

HOW TO APPLY In writing to the correspondent. Please note: the trust states on its website that, 'at present, the trust's resources are sufficient only to support its primary beneficiaries and its existing projects. It is not able to consider applications for new non-Masonic grants at this time'. Any change to this policy will be noted on the trust's website.

WHO TO APPLY TO Leslie Hutchinson, Chief Executive, Freemasons' Hall, 60 Great Queen Street, London WC2B 5AZ *Tel* 020 7405 2644 *Fax* 020 7831 4094 *email* info@rmtgb.org *Website* www.rmtgb.org

....

■ The Royal Scots Benevolent Society

SC NO SC011397   **ESTABLISHED** 1960

WHERE FUNDING CAN BE GIVEN UK.

WHO CAN BENEFIT Soldiers and former soldiers, and their dependants, of the Royal Scots (The Royal Regiment) who are in need.

WHAT IS FUNDED Service welfare causes.

FINANCES *Year* 2009–10 *Income* £35,430 *Grants* £50,000

TRUSTEES J V Dent, Chair; M F Gibson; J W Blythe.

HOW TO APPLY Applications should be addressed to the SSAFA Forces Help branch/Division nearest to the applicant's home. If in difficulty the nearest British Legion office or Department of Social Security office will assist.

WHO TO APPLY TO Captain J Springthorpe, c/o HHQ RS, The Castle, Edinburgh EH1 2YT *Tel* 0131 310 5016 *email* rhqrs@btconnect.com *Website* www.theroyalscots.co.uk

....

■ The RRAF Charitable Trust

CC NO 1103662   **ESTABLISHED** 2004

WHERE FUNDING CAN BE GIVEN UK and the developing world.

WHO CAN BENEFIT Charitable organisations.

WHAT IS FUNDED General, medical research, children who are disadvantaged, religious organisations, aid for the developing world and support for the elderly.

RANGE OF GRANTS £500–£50,000.

SAMPLE GRANTS Refugee Support Network (£14,000); Dove Association and Kids Company (£7,000 each); Reaching Orphans for Care (£5,800); Hamlin Fistula (£5,000); Blues in Schools (£3,000); and Living Links (£1,500).

FINANCES *Year* 2009–10 *Income* £25,685 *Grants* £43,300 *Assets* £628,073

TRUSTEES Rathbone Trust Company Limited; Claire Tufnell; Emilie Astley-Arlington; Joanne Mcarthy; Rosemary Mcarthy; Elizabeth Astley-Arlington.

HOW TO APPLY In writing to the correspondent. Only successful applicants are notified of the trustees' decision.

WHO TO APPLY TO The Administrator, Rathbone Trust Company Limited, 159 New Bond Street, London W1S 2UD *Tel* 020 7399 0807

■ The Alfred and Frances Rubens Charitable Trust

CC NO 264430   ESTABLISHED 1972
WHERE FUNDING CAN BE GIVEN UK.
WHO CAN BENEFIT Registered charities only.
WHAT IS FUNDED General charitable purposes and Jewish causes.
WHAT IS NOT FUNDED No grants for national appeals.
TYPE OF GRANT Recurrent.
RANGE OF GRANTS £25–£2,000.
SAMPLE GRANTS Friends of the Jewish Museum, Jewish Care and Norwood Ravenswood (£2,000 each); Beth Shalom (£1,000); Chai Lifeline, Delamere Forest School, Wiener Library Endowment Trust and World Jewish Relief (£500 each); Friends of the Victoria and Albert Museum (£250); Institute of Jewish Affairs and Samaritans (£100 each); World Wildlife Fund (£50); and Society of Jewish Study (£25).
FINANCES Year 2009–10 Income £26,550 Grants £16,829 Assets £671,745
TRUSTEES Mrs J F Millan; Mrs A E Gutwin; Mrs W C Lambros.
HOW TO APPLY The trust states that it does not respond to unsolicited applications.
WHO TO APPLY TO Mrs J F Millan, Trustee, 4 Court Close, St John's Wood Park, London NW8 6NN

■ The Rubin Foundation

CC NO 327062   ESTABLISHED 1986
WHERE FUNDING CAN BE GIVEN UK and overseas.
WHO CAN BENEFIT Organisations benefiting Jewish people, students and people who are sick.
WHAT IS FUNDED Primarily, but not exclusively, Jewish charities. Also, medical charities, arts organisations and universities.
RANGE OF GRANTS Mostly up to £25,000; exceptionally up to £400,000.
SAMPLE GRANTS Previous beneficiaries included ULIA; Jewish Community Secondary School Trust; Jewish Museum; Civitas; Peace and Sport; Weidenfeld Institute for Strategic Dialogue; South Bank Centre; Board of Deputies of British Jews; Royal Opera House Foundation; the Roundhouse; Cancer Backup; and Maccabiah Football Bursaries.
FINANCES Year 2009–10 Income £21,018 Grants £400,000
TRUSTEES Alison Mosheim; Angela Rubin; R Stephen Rubin; Andrew Rubin; Carolyn Rubin.
OTHER INFORMATION Unfortunately, due the low income of the foundation during the year accounts are not required by the Charity Commission.
HOW TO APPLY The foundation has previously stated that 'grants are only given to people related to our business', such as charities known to members of the Rubin family and those associated with Pentland Group Ltd. Unsolicited applications are very unlikely to succeed.
WHO TO APPLY TO Allison McMillan, Secretary, The Pentland Centre, Lakeside House, Squires Lane, Finchley, London N3 2QL Tel 020 8346 2600 email amcmillan@pentland.com

■ William Arthur Rudd Memorial Trust

CC NO 326495   ESTABLISHED 1983
WHERE FUNDING CAN BE GIVEN In practice UK and Spain.
WHO CAN BENEFIT UK and certain Spanish charities.
WHAT IS FUNDED General charitable purposes.
FINANCES Year 2009 Income £56,158 Grants £50,500 Assets £863,656
TRUSTEES Miss A A Sarkis; D H Smyth; R G Maples.
OTHER INFORMATION The trust's accounts state that donations were made to registered charities in the UK and to certain Spanish charities; however, no grants list was provided.
HOW TO APPLY 'As the objects of the charity are not linked to any specific areas of charitable activity, the trustees receive a large number of applications for donations. They review the applications received and any wishes expressed by the settlor at their annual meeting and make their awards.'
WHO TO APPLY TO A A Sarkis, Trustee, 12 South Square, Gray's Inn, London WC1R 5HH Tel 020 7405 8932 email mail@mmandm.co.uk

■ The Rufford Foundation

CC NO 326163   ESTABLISHED 1982
WHERE FUNDING CAN BE GIVEN Developing countries, UK.
WHO CAN BENEFIT UK registered charities only, mainly in developing countries.
WHAT IS FUNDED The focus is on conservation, environmental and sustainable development projects in developing countries. UK organisations supporting social welfare or health may also receive support.
WHAT IS NOT FUNDED The foundation will not generally fund the following: building or construction projects; donations to individuals or projects that directly benefit one individual; UK projects with a local or regional focus; loans; endowment funds; student/gap year conservation expeditions; general appeals or circulars.
TYPE OF GRANT One-off and recurring.
RANGE OF GRANTS Up to £350,000.
SAMPLE GRANTS University of Southampton (£115,000); EIA Charitable Trust; Zoological Society of London (£100,000 each); RSPB (£75,000); Whitley Fund for Nature; Environmental Justice Foundation (£50,000 each); Wildlife Protection Society of India (£40,000); International Animal Rescue; Wildlife Conservation Nepal (£25,000); Botanic Gardens Conservation International; Ocean Youth Trust South (£20,000 each); St Albans High School for Girls (£13,000); Bat Conservation Trust; Samaritans (£10,000 each); Canine Partners for Independence; Farm Africa; University of Surrey (£5,000 each); British Council for the Prevention of Blindness; 3H Fund – Help the Handicapped Holiday Fund (£3,000 each); Dogs for the Disabled; International Childcare Trust (£2,500 each); Wells for India (£2,000).
FINANCES Year 2009–10 Income £2,716,452 Grants £2,594,510 Assets £63,364,422
TRUSTEES Charles Barbour; Anthony Johnson; John Laing; Col. Iain Smailes; Robert Reilly.
OTHER INFORMATION The Rufford Small Grants Foundation was established in 2007 due to the success of the Rufford Small Grants facility, to award the Rufford Small Grants in perpetuity. More information on RSGF can be found in its separate entry.
The sharp drop in grants paid during the year was due to the implementation of the trust's new grant giving policy which aims to ensure the future sustainability of the Rufford Foundation and the Rufford Small Grants Foundation and ensure that future capital is not used for grant giving. A grant of £5 million has been allocated to WWF-UK for its new headquarters.

HOW TO APPLY The trust considers all applications which meet its criteria but states that 'with limited funds available it is neither possible to give detailed reasons why applications are not successful nor to enter into any dialogue or correspondence regarding projects which have been refused funding. In all cases, organisations are only able to make a single application for funding from the foundation during any one-year period.' All applications must be received by post [addressed to the correspondent]. All new applicants must be charities registered in the UK.

There is no set form but applications must include: a covering letter with contact details; a comprehensive plan outlining the project for which funding is being sought, including measurable objectives (4–6 pages max); a full budget – with details of funding secured to date, other funding applications being made and the amount being requested from the foundation; a copy of the charity's most recent accounts; a copy of the latest annual report (if available). Please note, the foundation does not accept applications for funding by email and is unable to discuss the suitability of an application by telephone. Applications are accepted throughout the year. The foundation strives to respond to all applications within 4 weeks of receipt and asks that applicants do not telephone to check on their application, as they will be contacted in due course.

WHO TO APPLY TO Simon Mickleburgh, Grants Manager, 6th Floor, 248 Tottenham Court Road, London W1T 7QZ *Tel* 020 7436 8604 *email* simon@rufford.org *Website* www.rufford.org

■ The Rufford Small Grants Foundation

CC NO 1117270   **ESTABLISHED** 2006
WHERE FUNDING CAN BE GIVEN Worldwide.
WHO CAN BENEFIT Individuals and small groups outside of the developed world.
WHAT IS FUNDED Conservation of threatened animals, habitats and organisms.
WHAT IS NOT FUNDED The following is generally not eligible for funding: projects in first world countries; pure research; expeditions; a conference or seminar.
RANGE OF GRANTS Up to £25,000.
SAMPLE GRANTS Lenin Oviedo – Venezuela; Catalina Molina – Costa Rica; Gathuru Mburu – Kenya; Anh Le Doan – Vietnam and Andrew Kizito – Uganda (£6,000 each); Olga Filatova – Russia (£10,000); Peter Smetacek – India and Meng Xiuxiang – China (£12,000each); Colleen Begg – Mozambique (£20,000) and Abdul Wakid – India (£25,000).
FINANCES *Year* 2009–10 *Income* £1,977,536 *Grants* £1,848,103 *Assets* £25,187,666
TRUSTEES John H Laing; Col. M.I.T Smailes; Sarah Brunwin; Ben Edwards; Sarah M E Barbour.
OTHER INFORMATION A detailed breakdown, including project summaries, of recent grant recipients is available on the trust's website.
HOW TO APPLY Application forms can be downloaded from the foundation's website. They must be submitted as an email attachment and sent to the Rufford Small Grants Director care of: jane@rufford.org. Applications are considered on a rolling basis, there is no deadline.

WHO TO APPLY TO Josh Cole, Grants Director, 6th Floor, 248 Tottenham Court Road, London W1T 7QZ *Tel* 020 7436 8604 *email* josh@rufford.org *Website* www.ruffordsmallgrants.org/rsg

■ The Rugby Group Benevolent Fund Limited

CC NO 265669   **ESTABLISHED** 1973
WHERE FUNDING CAN BE GIVEN The Midlands.
WHO CAN BENEFIT Employees and ex-employees of the Rugby Group Limited; young people; older people; charitable organisations.
WHAT IS FUNDED Relief-in-need; general charitable purposes.
SAMPLE GRANTS Friends of Stockton School (£30,000); Friends of Wisdom Hospice and Harston Parish Church (£15,000 each); Warwickshire CAVA (£12,500); Overslade Community Association (£10,000); Long Itchington Congregational Church and St Peter and St James Hospice (£5,000 each); Winteringham Under Fives and Rugby and Northamptonshire Athletic Club (£1,000 each).
FINANCES *Year* 2009 *Income* £47,769 *Grants* £146,981 *Assets* £2,863,657
TRUSTEES G T Fuller; R J Millard; I M Southcott; C J Coates; C N Jones; N Appleyard; J D Wootten; G D L Thomas.
OTHER INFORMATION Around £37,000 was donated to individuals in the form of cash, fuel and Christmas hampers.
HOW TO APPLY In writing to the correspondent.
WHO TO APPLY TO Daphne Murray, Cemex House, Coldharbour Lane, Thorpe, Egham, Surrey TW20 8TD *Tel* 01932 583181

■ The Russell Trust

SC NO SC004424   **ESTABLISHED** 1985
WHERE FUNDING CAN BE GIVEN UK, especially Scotland.
WHO CAN BENEFIT Registered charities.
WHAT IS FUNDED General charitable purposes.
WHAT IS NOT FUNDED Only registered charities or organisations with charitable status are supported.
TYPE OF GRANT One-off, unrestricted grants, particularly to pump-prime new projects.
RANGE OF GRANTS Usually in the range of £250–£2,000. Three or four larger grants of £20,000 may be awarded annually.
SAMPLE GRANTS No grants list was available, but donations were broken down as follows: Youth work – £55,000; Health and welfare – £47,000; Education – £36,000; Local – £26,000; St Andrew's University – £25,500; Music and the Arts – £23,000; Church – £18,000; Preservation/Conservation – £12,000; Archaeology – £9,500.
FINANCES *Year* 2009–10 *Income* £261,665 *Grants* £251,850 *Assets* £9,393,381
TRUSTEES Fred Bowden; Mrs Cecilia Croal; Graeme Crombie; David Erdal; Don Munro; Ms Iona Russell; Alan Scott; C A G Parr.
HOW TO APPLY On a form available from the correspondent. A statement of accounts must be supplied. Trustees meet quarterly, although decisions on the allocation of grants are made more regularly.
WHO TO APPLY TO Iona Russell, Administrator and Trustee, Markinch, Glenrothes, Fife KY7 6PB *Tel* 01592 753311 *email* russelltrust@trg.co.uk

■ Ryklow Charitable Trust 1992

CC NO 1010122   **ESTABLISHED** 1992

WHERE FUNDING CAN BE GIVEN UK and overseas, with a preference for the East Midlands.

WHO CAN BENEFIT Organisations, generally to small or start up charities, and individuals.

WHAT IS FUNDED Projects in the developing world, especially those which are intended to be self sustaining or concerned with education; help for vulnerable families, minorities and the prevention of abuse or exploitation of children and young persons; and conservation of natural species, landscape and resources.

WHAT IS NOT FUNDED Only organisations which are UK registered, have a UK sponsor, or are affiliated to a UK registered charity will be considered.

RANGE OF GRANTS £500 to £3,000.

SAMPLE GRANTS Safe and Sound (£6,300) and Field Row Unitarian Chapel Belper (£5,000).

FINANCES *Year* 2009–10 *Income* £69,413 *Grants* £107,890 *Assets* £1,850,776

TRUSTEES Andrew Williamson; Ernest J S Cannings; Philip W Hanson; Sheila Taylor.

OTHER INFORMATION The grant total includes one award of £4,000 made to an individual.

HOW TO APPLY On a form available from the correspondent or to download from the trust's website. Applications should be brief and include an audited financial report (or at least a statement of finances). Forms should be submitted between 1 September and 31 December. The trustees usually make a decision once a year in March, with grants being award by the end of the month. Only in cases of real emergency will applications be considered at other times. Only successful applicants will be notified.

WHO TO APPLY TO Stephen Marshall, c/o Robinsons Solicitors, 10–11 St James Court, Friar Gate, Derby DE1 1BT *Tel* 01332 254157 *Fax* 01332 254 142 *email* ryklow@robinsons-solicitors.co.uk *Website* ryklowcharitabletrust.org

■ The J S and E C Rymer Charitable Trust

CC NO 267493   **ESTABLISHED** 1974

WHERE FUNDING CAN BE GIVEN East Yorkshire.

WHO CAN BENEFIT People who have retired from rural industry or agriculture.

WHAT IS FUNDED Housing for retired people who have spent the major part of their working lives in rural industry or agriculture; general charitable purposes in the specified area.

WHAT IS NOT FUNDED No grants to charities outside East Yorkshire.

RANGE OF GRANTS £10–£1,000.

SAMPLE GRANTS Recipients included local churches, community healthcare and NSPCC (regional branch).

FINANCES *Year* 2009–10 *Income* £34,113 *Grants* £56,644

TRUSTEES Mrs E C Rymer; T S Rymer; G H Brand.

HOW TO APPLY In writing to the correspondent.

WHO TO APPLY TO D Milburn, Southburn Offices, Southburn, Driffield, East Yorkshire YO25 9ED *Tel* 01377 227764 *Fax* 01377 227802 *email* charitable.trust@jsr.co.uk

■ S F Foundation

CC NO 1105843   **ESTABLISHED** 2004
WHERE FUNDING CAN BE GIVEN Worldwide.
WHO CAN BENEFIT Jewish organisations.
WHAT IS FUNDED The trust gives grants towards the 'advancement and furtherance of the Jewish religion and Jewish religious education and the alleviation of poverty amongst the Jewish community throughout the world.'
FINANCES *Year* 2009–10 *Income* £3,662,341 *Grants* £1,194,613 *Assets* £15,154,144
TRUSTEES Hannah Jacob; Rivka Niederman; Miriam Schrieber.
HOW TO APPLY 'The charity accepts applications for grants from representatives of various charities, which are reviewed by the trustees on a regular basis.'
WHO TO APPLY TO Rivka Niederman, Secretary, 143 Upper Clapton Road, London E5 9DB *Tel* 020 8802 5492

■ S O Charitable Trust

CC NO 326314   **ESTABLISHED** 1982
WHERE FUNDING CAN BE GIVEN Gateshead.
WHO CAN BENEFIT Jewish people.
WHAT IS FUNDED Jewish causes.
SAMPLE GRANTS Ber Er Hatorah (£18,000); Beis Soroh Schneirer and Beis Hamdrash (£9,000 each); 'Unknown' (£8,000); Letora Ve Horda (£6,000); and Gateshead Foundation for Torah (£5,000).
TRUSTEES Rabbi Simon Ohayon; N Ohayon; Mrs S Ohayon; A Ohayon.
PUBLICATIONS Accounts for 2009 are 641 days overdue. Accounts for 2010 are 153 days overdue.
OTHER INFORMATION Accounts for 2009 are 641 days overdue. Accounts for 2010 are 153 days overdue.
HOW TO APPLY In writing to the correspondent.
WHO TO APPLY TO Rabbi Simon Ohayon, Trustee, 19 Oxford Terrace, Gateshead, Tyne and Wear NE8 1RQ *Tel* 0191 477 0408

■ The Jeremy and John Sacher Charitable Trust

CC NO 206321   **ESTABLISHED** 1957
WHERE FUNDING CAN BE GIVEN UK and Israel.
WHO CAN BENEFIT Charitable organisations, with a preference for Jewish organisations.
WHAT IS FUNDED General, including arts, culture and heritage; medical and disability; community and welfare; education, science and technology; children and youth; and religion.
RANGE OF GRANTS £100–£30,000.
SAMPLE GRANTS Community Security Trust and Kings College London (£20,000 each); The National Gallery (£11,000); Royal Opera House Foundation (£6,800); New Israel Fund (£4,000); Beaminster Festival (£2,000); Army Benevolent Fund (£1,000); and Dorset Children's Hospice (£150).
FINANCES *Year* 2009–10 *Income* £123,691 *Grants* £97,072 *Assets* £4,399,972

TRUSTEES Simon John Sacher; Jeremy Michael Sacher; Hon. Mrs Rosalind E C Sacher; Mrs Elisabeth J Sacher.
HOW TO APPLY In writing to the correspondent at any time.
WHO TO APPLY TO The Trustees, c/o H W Fisher & Co, Chartered Accountants, Acre House, 11–15 William Road, London NW1 3ER *Tel* 020 7388 7000

■ The Michael Harry Sacher Trust

CC NO 288973   **ESTABLISHED** 1984
WHERE FUNDING CAN BE GIVEN UK and overseas.
WHO CAN BENEFIT Registered charities.
WHAT IS FUNDED General charitable purposes with a preference for arts, education, animal welfare, Jewish organisations and health. Requests are generally only considered if they are from organisations that are personally known to the trustees.
WHAT IS NOT FUNDED No grants to individuals or organisations which are not registered charities.
RANGE OF GRANTS £250–£30,000.
SAMPLE GRANTS British Friends of the Art Museums of Israel (£18,500); National Gallery Trust (£10,000); Jewish Care and Nightingale House (£5,000 each); Jeremy and John Sacher Charitable Trust (£3,400); Whale and Dolphin Conservation Society (£3,300); and The Mariinsky Theatre Trust (£375).
FINANCES *Year* 2009–10 *Income* £64,603 *Grants* £75,732 *Assets* £2,189,884
TRUSTEES Nicola Shelley Sacher; Michael Harry Sacher.
HOW TO APPLY In writing to the correspondent.
WHO TO APPLY TO The Trustees, c/o H W Fisher & Co, Chartered Accountants, Acre House, 11–15 William Road, London NW1 3ER *Tel* 020 7388 7000

■ The Raymond and Beverley Sackler Foundation

CC NO 327864   **ESTABLISHED** 1988
WHERE FUNDING CAN BE GIVEN UK and overseas.
WHO CAN BENEFIT The trust has a list of regular beneficiaries.
WHAT IS FUNDED Grants are given to the arts, sciences and medical research.
TYPE OF GRANT Annual grants.
SAMPLE GRANTS Yale University (£1.2 million); Weill Cornell Medical College (£820,000); and University College London – Cancer Centre (£75,000).
FINANCES *Year* 2009 *Income* £2,685,460 *Grants* £2,180,748 *Assets* £2,921,757
TRUSTEES C B Mitchell; Dr R R Sackler; J D Sackler; R M Smith; Dr R S Sackler; A Wikstrom; A Mattessich.
HOW TO APPLY Grants are not open to application.
WHO TO APPLY TO C B Mitchell, Trustee, New Zealand House, 9th Floor, 80 Haymarket, London SW1Y 4TQ *Tel* 020 7930 4944

■ The Sackler Trust (Formerly Dr Mortimer and Theresa Sackler Foundation)

CC NO 1132097   **ESTABLISHED** 1988
WHERE FUNDING CAN BE GIVEN UK.
WHO CAN BENEFIT Large institutions benefiting, arts and culture or medical research or actors and

entertainment professionals, musicians, textile workers and designers, and writers and poets.

WHAT IS FUNDED Arts and culture, science and medical research generally.

TYPE OF GRANT Some recurring; others one-off.

RANGE OF GRANTS Up to £500,000.

SAMPLE GRANTS Turquoise Mountain Trust (£150,000); Glyndebourne Arts Trust (£25,000); Southbank Centre (£10,000).

FINANCES *Year* 2010 *Income* £26,273,547 *Grants* £203,000 *Assets* £26,069,792

TRUSTEES Theresa Sackler; Christopher Mitchell; Raymond Smith; Marissa Sackler; Peter Stormonth Darling; Sophie Sackler Dalrypmle; Michael Sackler; Marianne Mitchell.

OTHER INFORMATION In 2009 the trust underwent restructuring meaning that the original trust's (Dr Mortimer and Theresa Sackler Foundation) assets were transferred to the new trust (The Sackler Trust). The previous trust still exists but its income and expenditure are insignificant (£8,000 and £4,000 respectively).

HOW TO APPLY In writing to the correspondent.

WHO TO APPLY TO Christopher B Mitchell, Trustee, 9th Floor, New Zealand House, 80 Haymarket, London SW1Y 4TQ *Tel* 020 7930 4944

■ The Ruzin Sadagora Trust

CC NO 285475　　　**ESTABLISHED** 1982

WHERE FUNDING CAN BE GIVEN UK and Israel.

WHO CAN BENEFIT Charities benefiting Jewish people.

WHAT IS FUNDED Preference for Jewish charities.

SAMPLE GRANTS Beth Israel Ruzin Sadagora (£196,000); Friends of Ruzin Sadagora (£180,000);, Beth Kaknesset Ohr Yisroel (£91,600); Mosdos Sadigur (£40,000); Yeshivas Torah Temimah (£9,000); Chevras Moaz Lodol (£6,500); Pardes House (£2,000).

FINANCES *Year* 2009–10 *Income* £252,048 *Grants* £260,640 *Assets* £494,472

TRUSTEES Rabbi I M Friedman; Mrs S Friedman.

HOW TO APPLY In writing to the correspondent.

WHO TO APPLY TO Rabbi I M Friedman, Trustee, Israel Moshe Friedman, 269 Golders Green Road, London NW11 9JJ *Tel* 020 8806 9514

■ The Saddlers' Company Charitable Fund

CC NO 261962　　　**ESTABLISHED** 1970

WHERE FUNDING CAN BE GIVEN UK.

WHO CAN BENEFIT Registered charities and institutions.

WHAT IS FUNDED Grants are made by the company in the following categories: City of London; saddlery trade; equestrian; education; disability charities, service charities and general charitable purposes.

WHAT IS NOT FUNDED No grants to individuals.

TYPE OF GRANT Usually one-off for one year.

RANGE OF GRANTS Up to £37,000.

SAMPLE GRANTS Alleyn's School – Saddlers' scholarships and bursaries (£130,000); Riding for the Disabled Association (£28,000); British Horse Society (£22,000); The Royal British Legion – Pedal to Paris (£7,300); Lord Mayor's Appeal; Birmingham Cathedral; Mansion House Scholarship Appeal (£5,000 each); Royal Veterinary College; Leathercraft Conservation Centre (£4,000 each); University of Liverpool (£3,900); Salisbury Cathedral (£3,000); Army Cadet Force – Middlesex and North West London; the Museum of Leathercraft (£2,000 each); St Christopher's Hospice (£1,800); City

of London Police Widows & Orphans Fund (£1,500); Autism Sussex; RoRo Sailing Project (£1,400 each); British Equestrian Vaulting; City of London Corporation – literacy project (£1,300 each); Royal Navy Officers Charity; The Firefighters Charity; Walsall Leather Museum; St Paul's Cathedral (£1,000 each).

FINANCES *Year* 2010–11 *Income* £393,389 *Grants* £350,935 *Assets* £9,261,898

TRUSTEES Campbell Pulley; D J Serrell-Wattes; David Hardy; David Snowden; Edward Pearson; Hugh Dyson-Laurie; Iain Pulley; John Vant; Jonathan Godrich; Michael Bullen; Michael Laurie; Peter Laurie; Peter Lewis; Tim Satchell; William Dyson-Laurie; Mark Farmar; David Chandler; Paul Farmar; Petronella Jameson; Charles Barclay; John Robinson; Hugh Thomas; James Welch.

HOW TO APPLY In writing to the correspondent. Grants are made in January and July, following trustees' meetings. Charities are asked to submit reports at the end of the following year on their continuing activities and the use of any grant received.

WHO TO APPLY TO Nigel Lithgow, Clerk to the Company, Saddlers' Hall, 40 Gutter Lane, London EC2V 6BR *Tel* 020 7726 8661/6 *Fax* 020 7600 0386 *email* clerk@saddlersco.co.uk *Website* www.saddlersco.co.uk

---

■ Erach and Roshan Sadri Foundation

CC NO 1110736　　　**ESTABLISHED** 2005

WHERE FUNDING CAN BE GIVEN Worldwide.

WHO CAN BENEFIT Registered charities, community groups and religious institutions.

WHAT IS FUNDED The main objects of the foundation are: providing financial assistance for education and welfare purposes; relieving poverty by alleviating homelessness; and assisting members of the Zoroastrian religious faith.

WHAT IS NOT FUNDED Applications are unlikely to be successful if they: involve animal welfare or heritage; are a general appeal from large UK organisations.

TYPE OF GRANT One-off grants for project costs.

RANGE OF GRANTS Up to around £25,000.

SAMPLE GRANTS The British Forces Foundation (£25,000); On Course (£22,000); Honeypot (£18,000); World Federation (£12,500); Bobby Van Trust (£10,000); Manthan (£9,000); The Passage (£5,000); Calcutta Rescue (£3,500); and Charlie's Charity (£1,500).

FINANCES *Year* 2010–11 *Income* £109,514 *Grants* £579,333 *Assets* £4,161,153

TRUSTEES Margaret Lynch; Shabbir Merali; Darius Sarosh; Jehangir Sarosh; Sammy Bhiwandiwalla.

HOW TO APPLY On a form which can be downloaded from the foundation's website, along with full and detailed guidelines. Forms can be returned by post or email. Meetings are held four times a year. Please note: 'Unsolicited material sent in addition to the clear and concise requirements of the application form is very likely to prove detrimental to your application. The trustees insist that additional items such as annual reports, glossy brochures, Christmas cards and accounts are not sent unless specifically requested.'

WHO TO APPLY TO Mark Cann, Administrator, 10a High Street, Pewsey, Wiltshire SN9 5AQ *email* markcann@ersf.org.uk *Website* www.ersf.org.uk

■ Saga Charitable Trust

CC NO 291991 **ESTABLISHED** 1985
WHERE FUNDING CAN BE GIVEN Developing countries.
WHO CAN BENEFIT Charitable organisations and projects.
WHAT IS FUNDED The prime objective is to benefit under-privileged communities at destinations in developing countries that host Saga Holidaymakers. It aims not just to donate money, but to invest in projects that will 'empower and support' local communities, provide practical help to those in need, and offer increased opportunities for disadvantaged groups to benefit from tourism.
WHAT IS NOT FUNDED No grants to individuals.
SAMPLE GRANTS Calabash Trust – South Africa (£32,000); Prayas Railway Children Project – India (£25,000); Meisori Primary School – Kenya (£15,000); The Butterfly Tree – Zambia (£12,000); Deafway – Nepal (£9,500); Kok Kreul School – Cambodia (£1,200) and Top Kids Kindergarten – Namibia (£200).
FINANCES *Year* 2009–10 *Income* £415,901 *Grants* £182,889 *Assets* £199,138
TRUSTEES Ms Susan Hopper; The Hon. Emma Soames; Mrs Makala Thomas; John Goodsell; Toby Hughes; Miss Aynsley Jardin; James Duguid.
HOW TO APPLY In writing to the correspondent at any time. 'Project funding is agreed by our Board of Trustees, who take care to ensure there is a reliable local sponsor to account for all expenditure.'
WHO TO APPLY TO Janice Lee, Director, The Saga Building, Enbrook Park, Folkestone, Kent CT20 3SE *Tel* 01303 771766 *Fax* 01303 776358 *email* contact@sagacharitabletrust.org *Website* www.sagacharitabletrust.org

■ The Jean Sainsbury Animal Welfare Trust

CC NO 326358 **ESTABLISHED** 1982
WHERE FUNDING CAN BE GIVEN UK and overseas.
WHO CAN BENEFIT UK registered national and international animal welfare charities.
WHAT IS FUNDED Projects concerned with animal welfare and wildlife.
WHAT IS NOT FUNDED No grants are given to charities which: are mainly engaged with the preservation of specific species of wild animals; have available reserves equal to more than one year's running costs (unless it can be demonstrated that reserves are being held for a designated project); are offering sanctuary to animals, with no effort to re-home, foster or rehabilitate; do not have a realistic policy for animals that cannot be given a reasonable quality of life; are involved with assistance animals e.g. Hearing Dogs for the Deaf, Riding for the Disabled etc; spend more than a reasonable proportion of their income on administration or cannot justify their costs per animal helped; are registered outside the UK. No support is given to veterinary schools (unless the money can be seen to be directly benefiting the type of animals the Trust would want to support). No individuals are supported.
TYPE OF GRANT Capital, buildings, campaigning, core costs, project, running costs and recurring costs. Funding for up to one year is available.
RANGE OF GRANTS £100–£12,000.
SAMPLE GRANTS Folly Wildlife Rescue (£35,000); North Clwyd Animal Rescue (£12,500); Doris Banham Sanctuary, RSPCA Norfolk West and Retired Greyhound Trust (£10,000 each); Boxer Welfare Scotland, Exotic Pet Refuge, Oldies Club and Twinkle Trust Animal Aid (£5,000 each); Cat and Rabbit Rescue and Labrador Welfare (£2,000 each); Friends of the Strays of Greece and Safe Haven for Donkeys in the Holy Land (£1,000 each) and Compassion in World Farming (£300).
FINANCES *Year* 2010 *Income* £419,724 *Grants* £315,300 *Assets* £12,566,347
TRUSTEES Colin Russell; Gillian Tarlington; James Keliher; Mark Spurdens; Adele Sparrow; Valerie Pike; Michelle Francine Allen.
HOW TO APPLY On a form available from the correspondent or to download from the trust's website. Applicants should complete and return seven copies of the form, their latest set of audited accounts and any other information which may be relevant to the application. Please note: the trust requests that you do not send originals as these cannot be returned. There are three trustees' meetings every year, usually in March, July and November and applications should be submitted by 1 February, 1 June and 1 October respectively. Further application information and policy guidelines are available by visiting the trust's website.
WHO TO APPLY TO Madeleine Orchard, Administrator, PO Box 469, London W14 8PJ *Tel* 020 7602 7948 *Website* jeansainsburyanimalwelfare.org. uk

■ The Alan and Babette Sainsbury Charitable Fund

CC NO 292930 **ESTABLISHED** 1953
WHERE FUNDING CAN BE GIVEN Worldwide.
WHO CAN BENEFIT Registered charities.
WHAT IS FUNDED Projects in the following fields: civil liberties, scientific and medical research, youth work, overseas projects and general charitable purposes.
WHAT IS NOT FUNDED Grants are not normally made to individuals.
TYPE OF GRANT One-off and on-going, core costs, capital, project and running costs.
RANGE OF GRANTS £1,000–£50,000.
SAMPLE GRANTS Juvenile Diabetes Research Foundation (£50,000); Canon Collins Educational Trust for South Africa (£40,000); Citizen Organising Foundation, Jewish Association of Business Ethics and Blue Elephant Theatre (£30,000 each); Cubitt (£20,000); Female Prisoners Welfare Project Hibiscus and Refugees Into Jobs (£15,000); Islington Music Centre (£14,000); King's College London, Minority Rights Group, Anglo-Israel Association and Arab-Jewish Center for Equality, Empowerment & Cooperation (£10,000 each); Council of Christians & Jews, World Jewish Relief, Lion Ballroom Ltd and Theatre Peckham (£5,000 each); The Sainsbury Archive and Toppesfield Community Village Shop Association Ltd (£4,300 each); Get Sorted Academy of Music (£3,000); and Vernon House School (£1,000).
FINANCES *Year* 2009–10 *Income* £411,263 *Grants* £316,500 *Assets* £12,871,921
TRUSTEES The Hon. Sir Timothy Sainsbury; Judith Portrait; John Julian Sainsbury; Miss L M H Anderson.
HOW TO APPLY The trust states that: 'proposals are likely to be invited by the trustees or initiated at their request. Unsolicited applications will only be successful if they fall precisely within an area in which the trustees are interested.' A single

application will be considered for support by all the trusts in the Sainsbury family group.

who to apply to Alan Bookbinder, Director, Allington House, 1st Floor, 150 Victoria Street, London SW1E 5AE *Tel* 020 7410 0330 *Fax* 020 7410 0332 *Website* www.sfct.org.uk

■ The Sainsbury Family Charitable Trusts

where funding can be given See individual trusts.
who can benefit Registered charities and institutions.
what is funded See the entries for the individuals trusts.
what is not funded No grants are normally given to individuals by many of the trusts (though a number of them fund bursary schemes and the like operated by other organisations). Grants are not made for educational fees or expeditions.
finances *Year* 2009–10 *Grants* £89,600,000
other information The trusts are: Gatsby Charitable Foundation; Linbury Trust; Monument Trust; True Colours Trust; Jerusalem Trust; Headley Trust; Kay Kendal Leukaemia Fund; Ashden Trust; Staples Trust; J J Charitable Trust; Alan and Babette Sainsbury Trust; Three Guineas Trust; Glass-House Trust; Woodward Charitable Trust; Mark Leonard Trust; Tedworth Trust; and the Indigo Trust.
how to apply 'Please do not send more than one application. It will be considered by all relevant trusts. The trusts only fund registered charities or activities with clearly defined charitable purposes. The trustees take an active role in their grant-making, employing a range of specialist staff and advisers to research their areas of interest and bring forward suitable proposals. Many of the trusts work closely with their chosen beneficiaries over a long period to achieve particular objectives. It should therefore be understood that the majority of unsolicited proposals we receive will be unsuccessful. As a rule the Gatsby, Glass-House, Linbury, Staples and Tedworth trusts do not consider unsolicited proposals. The other trusts will consider exceptional proposals which fit closely their specific areas of interest. There are no application forms, except in a small number of clearly defined areas: the Woodward Charitable Trust; the Kay Kendall Leukaemia Fund; the Headley Museums Archaeological Acquisition Fund. Applications to all other trusts should be sent by post, with a description (strictly no more than two pages please, as any more is unlikely to be read) of the proposed project, covering: the organisation – explaining its charitable aims and objectives, and giving its most recent annual income and expenditure, and current financial position – please do not send a full set of accounts; the project requiring funding – why it is needed, who will benefit and in what way; the funding – breakdown of costs, any money raised so far, and how the balance will be raised. At this stage please do not send supporting books, brochures, DVDs, annual reports or accounts. All applications will receive our standard acknowledgement letter. If your proposal is a candidate for support from one of the trusts, you will hear from us within 8 weeks of the acknowledgement. Applicants who do not hear from us within this time must assume they have been unsuccessful.'

who to apply to Alan Bookbinder, Director, Allington House, 1st Floor, 150 Victoria Street, London SW1E 5AE *Tel* 020 7410 0330 *Fax* 020 7410 0332 *Website* www.sfct.org.uk

■ St Andrew's Conservation Trust

cc no 282157　　**established** 1980
where funding can be given Preference for the South West of England and South West Wales.
who can benefit Charitable organisations.
what is funded The conservation, restoration and preservation of monuments, sculptures and artefacts of historic or public interest which are upon or attached to property owned by any charitable organisation. The trust also makes grants for the training of conservators and facilities.
Aid is granted to 'conservation projects involving decorative or artistic features in parish churches, abbeys and cathedrals in the South West of England and in South Wales'.
what is not funded No support is given for conservation or restoration of churchyard table tombs except in very restricted circumstances.
range of grants £100–£10,000.
sample grants Hinton St. George, Somerset: C16 monuments (Poulett Memorial Chapel) (£5,000); Mells, Somerset: Wall memorials, Cornworthy, Devon: Wall Monument (£2,000 each); Townstal, Devon: C14 Effigy (£500).
finances *Year* 2009 *Income* £32,355 *Grants* £29,765 *Assets* £542,265
trustees Gerard M Leighton; Hugh GL Playfair; Simon RV Pomeroy; Alan WG Thomas; Mrs Elsa van der Zee; John Bucknall; SJC Tudway Quilter; Ven John Peter Cyril Reed.
publications Accounts from 2009 available from the Charity Commission website. Accounts for 2010 were overdue.
other information Accounts from 2009 available from the Charity Commission website. Accounts for 2010 were overdue.
how to apply The trustees meet twice a year to discuss applications.
who to apply to Simon R V Pomeroy, Trustee, Duddle Farm, Nr Bockhampton, Dorchester, Dorset DT2 8QL *Tel* 01305 264516

■ St Christopher's College Educational Trust

cc no 313864　　**established** 1971
where funding can be given UK.
who can benefit Organisations and individuals connected to the Church of England.
what is funded Education and the support of children and youth organisations.
type of grant Small grants, usually one-off but can be for up to three years. Some part-funded projects.
range of grants Up to £15,000.
sample grants National Society (£15,000); Bradford and Ripon & Leeds Diocesan Board of Education (£3,500); Cliffe College (£2,500); St John's College Nottingham (£2,000); and Faith and Football (£750).
finances *Year* 2010 *Income* £155,521 *Grants* £27,250 *Assets* £983,991
trustees Dr D Sellick; Revd Prof. L Francis; Mrs B Harvey; Revd Canon D Isaac; J Swallow; Miss M Code; Ven. P Wheatley; M Hawes; Revd Canon Dr K Denison; John Bull.
other information Funds organisations & individuals.

HOW TO APPLY In writing to the correspondent.
WHO TO APPLY TO Dr David Sellick, 23 Robin's Hill, St John's Road, Hitchin SG4 9FE *Tel* 01462 440518 *email* davidsellick@uk7.net

....

■ St Francis's Leprosy Guild

CC NO 208741   **ESTABLISHED** 1895
WHERE FUNDING CAN BE GIVEN Developing countries.
WHO CAN BENEFIT People with leprosy or affected by leprosy, leprosy workers and medical staff.
WHAT IS FUNDED Leprosy treatment and care programmes, social, economic and physical rehabilitation, leprosy training and education, medical elective projects related to leprosy.
WHAT IS NOT FUNDED Centres not run by Catholic missionaries or not approved by the local bishop.
TYPE OF GRANT Money for running costs or for specific projects. Capital grants.
RANGE OF GRANTS Average grant: £3,000.
SAMPLE GRANTS India, Koviloor – Construction of new kitchen (£13,000); Brazil, Manaus – Leprosy Survey (£10,000) and India – Water project (£9,000).
FINANCES *Year* 2009–10 *Income* £452,606 *Grants* £380,622 *Assets* £562,355
TRUSTEES Dr Gosia Brykczynska; Ms Margaret Hood; Ms Veronica Melia; Revd Francis Wahle; Very Revd Fr Michael Copps; Mrs Gwen Sankey; Timothy Lawrence.
OTHER INFORMATION £307,000 in maintenance grants, £68,000 for 'special projects' and £5,300 for educational purposes.
HOW TO APPLY In writing for an application form to Honorary Secretary. Applications must be supported by expenditure details, the total cost and anticipated start date. In all cases charity registration title and number must be given. The committee regrets that applications cannot be acknowledged.
WHO TO APPLY TO Eric Williams, Trust Administrator, St. Francis Leprosy Guild, 73 St Charles Square, London W10 6EJ *Tel* 020 8969 1345 *Fax* 020 8969 3272 *email* enquiries@stfrancisleprosy.org *Website* www.stfrancisleprosy.org

....

■ St Gabriel's Trust

CC NO 312933   **ESTABLISHED** 1977
WHERE FUNDING CAN BE GIVEN Mainly in the UK.
WHO CAN BENEFIT Institutions engaged in higher or further religious education, with a view to training school RE teachers. Young adults and members of the Church of England may benefit.
WHAT IS FUNDED Higher and further religious education with the purpose of training RE teachers and encouraging good practice in RE.
WHAT IS NOT FUNDED Grants are not normally available for: any project for which local authority money is available, or which ought primarily to be funded by the church – theological study, parish or missionary work – unless school RE is involved; and research projects where it will be a long time before any benefit can filter down into RE teaching. No grants are made to schools as such; higher and further education must be involved.
TYPE OF GRANT Recurring, one-off, project, research and start-up will be considered.
SAMPLE GRANTS ACCT Virtual RE Centre, RE Council DFE think tank and RE Festival (£20,000 each); All Faiths and None (£12,500); Bible Reading Fellowship (£10,000); Spinnaker Trust (£7,000); and National Society – Bicentenary 2011 (£5,000).

FINANCES *Year* 2010 *Income* £304,919 *Grants* £258,621 *Assets* £6,648,216
TRUSTEES Dr Priscilla Chadwick, Chair; James Cowen; Revd Janina Ainsworth; John Keast; Jessica Giles; Barbara Lane; Mary Halvorson; Deborah Weston; Bruce Gill; Prof. Liam Gearon; Rosemary Walters.
OTHER INFORMATION Included in the grants total figure, is £113,648 spent on the St Gabriel's programme, an ongoing venture that has been run jointly with the Culham Institute. Also included are grants to 9 individuals totalling £7,109.
HOW TO APPLY In writing to the correspondent with an sae. Applicants are asked to describe their religious allegiance and to provide a reference from their minister of religion. Applications need to be received by the beginning of January, April or September as trustees meet in February, May and October.
WHO TO APPLY TO Peter Duffell, Clerk, Ladykirk, 32 The Ridgeway, Enfield, Middlesex EN2 8QH *Tel* 020 8363 6474

....

■ The St Hilda's Trust

CC NO 500962   **ESTABLISHED** 1904
WHERE FUNDING CAN BE GIVEN The diocese of Newcastle (Newcastle upon Tyne, North Tyneside and Northumberland).
WHO CAN BENEFIT Young people, generally and in particular today's equivalent of the original clientele of St Hilda's School (an approved school and community home); and people whose needs are not met by state social welfare provisions.
WHAT IS FUNDED Organisations working with young people and people in need (as specified above). Also considered are community businesses and development, support to voluntary and community groups, training for work, community centres and village halls, and community services.
TYPE OF GRANT Wide-ranging; sometimes recurring. The trustees prefer to support projects involving the employment of staff qualified to provide care and support to those in need rather than to provide buildings, equipment or motor vehicles.
RANGE OF GRANTS £100–£5,000.
FINANCES *Year* 2010 *Income* £78,033 *Grants* £57,925 *Assets* £1,520,735
TRUSTEES J Pinnegar; Revd Canon A S Craig; Mrs R Nicholson; Rt Revd M Wharton; Dr M Wilkinson; N Brockbank; D Welsh.
OTHER INFORMATION No published list of beneficiaries.
HOW TO APPLY Application forms will be sent on request. Completed forms should be returned by the last day of March, June, September and December.
WHO TO APPLY TO Mrs Josie Pinnegar, Church House, St John's Terrace, North Shields NE29 6HS *Tel* 0191 270 4100 *Fax* 0191 270 4101 *email* j.pinnegar@newcastle.anglican.org

....

■ St James' Trust Settlement

CC NO 280455   **ESTABLISHED** 1980
WHERE FUNDING CAN BE GIVEN Worldwide, with a preference for the UK and USA.
WHO CAN BENEFIT Registered charities.
WHAT IS FUNDED Projects in the areas of health, education and social justice.
WHAT IS NOT FUNDED No grants to individuals.

TYPE OF GRANT Core costs, one-off, project, research, recurring costs, salaries and start-up costs. Funding is for up to three years.

SAMPLE GRANTS Highbury Vale Blackstock Trust (£12,000); Prisoners Abroad (£10,000); CARIS, and Rainforest Foundation (£5,000 each); and World Children Unite (£2,500).

FINANCES *Year* 2009–10 *Income* £91,215 *Grants* £99,857 *Assets* £3,530,203

TRUSTEES Jane Wells; Cathy Ingram; Simon Taffler.

HOW TO APPLY The trust states that it 'does not seek unsolicited applications for grants and, without paid staff, are unable to respond to such applications'.

WHO TO APPLY TO The Trustees, Epworth House, 25 City Road, London EC1Y 1AR *Tel* 020 7628 5801

....

■ St James's Place Foundation

CC NO 1031456   **ESTABLISHED** 1994

WHERE FUNDING CAN BE GIVEN In practice mainly UK.

WHO CAN BENEFIT Registered charities supporting children and young people (up to the age of 25) with mental or physical conditions, life threatening or degenerative illnesses. Hospices are also supported, regardless of the ages of their clients.

WHAT IS FUNDED The small grants programme gives grants of up to £10,000 to organisations with a turnover of less than £200,000 a year. The major grants programme gives up to £25,000 for a maximum of two years to organisations with a turnover of less than £2 million. These turnover limitations do not apply to hospices.

WHAT IS NOT FUNDED The foundation has a policy of not considering an application from any charity within two years of receiving a previous application. The foundation does not provide support for: charities with reserves of over 50% of income; administrative costs; activities primarily the responsibility of statutory agencies; replacement of lost statutory funding; research; events; advertising; holidays; sponsorship; contributions to large capital appeals; single faith charities; social and economic deprivation; charities that are raising funds on behalf of another charity.

TYPE OF GRANT One-off.

RANGE OF GRANTS Mainly between £500–£10,000; but up to £96,000.

SAMPLE GRANTS New Horizon Youth Centre (London) – to fund an ICT Life Skills Project (£96,000 over three years); Fairbridge Scotland – towards a youth employability programme (£95,000); Philippine Community Fund – who work to alleviate poverty in the Philippines (£75,000); Volunteer Reading Help – to fund the cost of volunteers to offer support to disadvantaged children who are behind with reading skills (£60,000 over three years); Cerebral Palsy Sport – to fund the salary of a specialist athletics coach (£39,000); St Cuthbert's Hospice – to fund a specialist bereavement service for young people (£30,000); and The Orpheus Centre (Surrey) – towards refurbishment of the kitchen in this college for adults with disabilities (£27,500).

FINANCES *Year* 2010 *Income* £2,888,974 *Grants* £3,341,632 *Assets* £602,744

TRUSTEES Malcolm Cooper-Smith, Chair; David Bellamy; Mike Wilson; Andrew Croft; Hugh Gladman; David Lamb.

OTHER INFORMATION The foundation is not currently accepting new applications for the major grants programme. Please check the trust's website for updates on this grant scheme.

HOW TO APPLY Application forms are available from the foundation website and can be returned by email or post. Applications will only be considered if accompanied by a signed copy of the most recent audited accounts and annual report. An initial enquiry should be made before applying for a major grant. Applications will be assessed against a number of criteria, including user involvement, sustainability, maximum benefit and volunteer involvement. Assessment visits will normally be made and applications for major grants will either receive a visit or be invited to present to the foundation committee. The whole procedure can take between three to six months (sometimes longer if many applications are received) so it is advisable to apply in good time if funds are required for a certain date. There must normally be a two year gap between applications.

WHO TO APPLY TO Mark Longbottom, 1 Tetbury Road, Cirencester, Gloucestershire GL7 1FP *Tel* 01285 878562 *email* sjp.foundation@sjp.co.uk *Website* www.sjp.co.uk/foundation

....

■ Sir Walter St John's Educational Charity

CC NO 312690   **ESTABLISHED** 1992

WHERE FUNDING CAN BE GIVEN The boroughs of Wandsworth and Lambeth, with a preference for Battersea.

WHO CAN BENEFIT Young people under 25 who are resident in Wandsworth and Lambeth and who are in financial need. Grants are awarded both to individuals and local schools, colleges, youth clubs, and voluntary and community organisations. Special consideration is given to meeting the educational needs of young people who are disabled.

WHAT IS FUNDED The education of young people under 25 who are resident in Wandsworth and Lambeth. The charity has a special interest in the education of young people excluded from school, in early years education, and in young refugees and asylum seekers. The charity also supports the development of new educational initiatives and projects, curriculum enrichment programmes, and play scheme holiday projects. Student grants are made only to individuals on approved or recognised courses.

WHAT IS NOT FUNDED The charity does not normally fund expenditure involving ongoing salary or premises costs or donations to general fund-raising appeals. School pupils under 16, full-time students on postgraduate courses or gap-year travel are not normally supported.

TYPE OF GRANT One-off, buildings, capital, projects and start-up costs. Funding is for up to three years. Student grants are normally awarded yearly to meet the cost of books and equipment, travel to college, and childcare.

RANGE OF GRANTS £200–£50,000; typically less than £5,000. Most student grants are in the range £350–£600.

SAMPLE GRANTS Klevis Kola Foundation (£10,000); Homestart Wandsworth Ltd and South Thames College (£5,000 each); Family Friends (£4,800); Tara Arts (£2,400); Hurley Pre-school (£2,000); Grove Adventure Playground (£1,800); Arts Community Exchange (£1,500).

FINANCES *Year* 2009–10 *Income* £128,937 *Assets* £2,718,720

TRUSTEES A Tuck, chair; C Blackwood; Ms D Daytes; P Dyson; Revd. P Kennington; J O Malley; Ms S Rackham; J Radcliffe; Ms J Scribbins; Cllr

S Wilkie; Cllr K Abrams; B Fairbank; G Allen; Cllr P Dawson.

OTHER INFORMATION In 2007–08, £8,600 was given in grants to individuals.

HOW TO APPLY *Organisations:* Applicants will be asked to complete an application form and submit a two-page supporting letter. Organisations and individuals who wish to apply for grants are welcome to contact the charity's office by letter, email or telephone for further information and advice.

WHO TO APPLY TO Melanie Griffiths, Manager, Unit 11, Culvert House, Culvert Road, London SW11 5DH *Tel* 020 7498 8878 *email* manager@swsjcharity.org.uk *Website* www.swsjcharity.org.uk

■ St Katharine and Shadwell Trust

CC NO 1001047   **ESTABLISHED** 1990

WHERE FUNDING CAN BE GIVEN The London boroughs of Tower Hamlets, Hackney and City of London.

WHO CAN BENEFIT Grants are available to voluntary and community organisations. Some grants may be made to statutory organisations such as schools.

WHAT IS FUNDED 'We give grants and run projects to improve the quality of life in the local area. We work in the London Boroughs of Tower Hamlets Hackney and the City of London.'

WHAT IS NOT FUNDED The trust is unable to make grants either to or for individuals.

TYPE OF GRANT Capital, revenue and full project funding.

RANGE OF GRANTS £250–£10,000.

SAMPLE GRANTS Common Ground East, Futureversity, Shadwell Basin Outdoor Activity Centre and Tower Hamlets Education Business Partnership (£10,000 each); London Borough of Tower Hamlets (summer holiday programme) (£8,500); Summer Holiday Programme for Pensioners (£7,000); Wellington Way Sports Project, Somali Development Association, Kudu Arts Project, Banglatown Association (£5,000 each); ADEEG Community Centre (£4,000); Providence Row (£2,000); Vital Arts (£1,500) and Science in Schools – Hermitage Primary School and Mulberry School for Girls (£1,000 each).

FINANCES *Year* 2010 *Income* £1,139,814 *Grants* £734,316 *Assets* £9,215,706

TRUSTEES Eric Sorensen; Revd P David Paton; Cllr Denise Jones; Angela Orphanou; Dan Jones; David Hardy; Mark Gibson; Rosemary Ryde; Ian Fisher; Dr Tobias Jung; Christopher Martin; Jonathan Norbury.

OTHER INFORMATION 'We are a Community Foundation, raising funds and awarding grants to run and support a wide range of projects in East London. We have been actively working in Tower Hamlets for 18 years and in 2006 extended our work into Hackney, Newham and the City of London. Our knowledge of the area and the relationships we have developed enable us to support and sustain positive change. Our aim is to ensure that the ideas and aspirations of local people for improving their area can be realised.'

HOW TO APPLY Please see the trust's website for details of up-to-date schemes.

WHO TO APPLY TO The Director, 11–29 Fashion Street, London E1 6PX *Tel* 020 7782 6962 *email* enquiries@skst.org *Website* www.skst.org

■ The St Laurence Relief In Need Trust

CC NO 205043   **ESTABLISHED** 1962

WHERE FUNDING CAN BE GIVEN The ancient parish of St Laurence, then the borough of Reading.

WHO CAN BENEFIT Persons resident generally, or individually, in the area of the ancient parish of St Laurence in Reading and, thereafter, persons resident generally, or individually, in the county borough of Reading.

WHAT IS FUNDED Persons, generally or individually, who are in conditions of need, hardship or distress.

WHAT IS NOT FUNDED No grants to individuals outside the ancient parish of St Laurence, Reading or the county borough of Reading, even when supported by social services or similar agencies.

TYPE OF GRANT One-off or annual.

RANGE OF GRANTS £1,000 annual to £10,000 one-off.

SAMPLE GRANTS No specific information of grants awarded in 2010.

FINANCES *Year* 2010 *Income* £136,954 *Grants* £64,875 *Assets* £136,954

TRUSTEES Patricia Thomas; Revd Canon Brian Shenton; Cllr. Rosemary Williams; Revd Christopher Russell; MG Burges; S Hotston; LC Joslin.

OTHER INFORMATION Grants awarded to institutions in 2010 totalled £63,675. Grants awarded to individuals in 2010 amounted to £1,200.

HOW TO APPLY In writing to the correspondent, supplying latest accounts or details of bank balances and so on, together with reason for application. The trustees meet twice a year in April and November.

WHO TO APPLY TO John M James, Vale and West, Victoria House, 26 Queen Victoria Street, Reading RG1 1TG *Tel* 0118 957 3238

■ Saint Luke's College Foundation

CC NO 306606   **ESTABLISHED** 1977

WHERE FUNDING CAN BE GIVEN UK and overseas, with some preference for Exeter and Truro.

WHO CAN BENEFIT Individuals and universities, colleges and other agencies operating at university level.

WHAT IS FUNDED *Corporate awards* are made to departments of theology and RE in universities, colleges and other agencies operating at university level, to enhance their capacity to provide theological and religious education. The awards are usually small and short-term and, consequently, priority is given to pump-priming initiatives, and other such situations where, if the initiative proves itself, it may enable the grant-holder to demonstrate success to bodies which engage in longer-term funding. *Personal awards* are made to support individuals who are studying Theology or RE; or who are undertaking research leading to a Masters' degree or PhD in these fields.

WHAT IS NOT FUNDED Funding is not available for building work or to provide bursaries for institutions to administer. Schools are not supported directly (although support is given to teachers who are taking eligible studies). Grants are not normally made for periods in excess of three years.

TYPE OF GRANT Normally for a specific project or part of a project, or for a specific course or piece of research. Grants can be made for periods of up to three years.

SAMPLE GRANTS Grants were broken down into following categories: Personal and corporate grants: £62,000; Chapel and chaplaincy: £44,000; University of Exeter – Department of Theology: £31,000.

FINANCES *Year* 2009–10 *Income* £174,893 *Grants* £137,020 *Assets* £3,675,009

TRUSTEES Prof. Mark Overton; The Bishop Of Exeter; Prof. Grace Davie; Very Reverend Cyril Jonathan Meyrick; Dr Barbara Wintersgill; Dr Michael Wykes; Alyson Sheldrake; David Cain; Alice Hutchings; Dick Powell; The Revd Dr David Rake.

OTHER INFORMATION The trust's scheme requires that the first charge on the foundation's income is the maintenance of a chapel and a chaplaincy: grants can be made from the residue.

HOW TO APPLY From 1st January each year, applicants can request an application pack from the correspondent. Applications are considered once a year and should be received by 1 May for grants starting in September.

WHO TO APPLY TO Dr David Benzie, Director, 15 St Maryhaye, Tavistock, Devon PL19 8LR *Tel* 01822 613143 *email* director@st-lukes-foundation.org.uk *Website* www.st-lukes-foundation.org.uk

■ St Michael's and All Saints' Charities

CC NO 202750   **ESTABLISHED** 1980
WHERE FUNDING CAN BE GIVEN City of Oxford.
WHO CAN BENEFIT Charitable organisations, with an interest in Christian groups.
WHAT IS FUNDED Health and welfare.
WHAT IS NOT FUNDED Individuals are very rarely supported.
SAMPLE GRANTS Abbeyfield and Leys Youth Programme (£10,000 each); Oxford Homeless Pathways (£8,000); Donnington Doorstep Family Centre (£6,000); Oxford Sexual Abuse & Rape Crisis Line (£5,000); Seesaw (£3,000); and Soup Kitchen (£2,000).
FINANCES *Year* 2010 *Income* £112,605 *Grants* £100,300 *Assets* £1,436,560
TRUSTEES P Beavis; The Very Revd. R Wilkes; Prof. P Langford; M Lear; Lord Krebs; The Ven J Hubbard; Ruth Loseby; R Earl; P Dailey; S Shibli.
HOW TO APPLY In writing to the correspondent.
WHO TO APPLY TO Robert J Spencer Hawes, St Michael's Church Centre, St Michael at the North Gate, Cornmarket Street, Oxford OX1 3EY *Tel* 01865 240940 *email* robert.hawes@smng.org.uk

■ St Monica Trust Community Fund

CC NO 202151   **ESTABLISHED** 1962
WHERE FUNDING CAN BE GIVEN Preference for the south west of England, particularly Bristol and the surrounding area.
WHO CAN BENEFIT People with a physical or long-term physical health problem.
WHAT IS FUNDED To be considered, organisations must meet all of the following criteria: (i) Benefit people (over 16 years old) who have a physical disability or long-term physical health problem, including those with infirmities due to old age. (ii) Benefit people living in Bristol or the surrounding area (North Somerset, Somerset, South Gloucestershire, Gloucestershire, Bath

and North East Somerset and Wiltshire). (iii) Make a real difference to people's daily lives. (iv) Be both properly constituted and a not-for-profit organisation. (v) Fit in with the fund's current theme. Each year has a different theme – previously the grants scheme was open to organisations working with older people living with a long-term physical disability, impairment or physical health problem where substance misuse has been a contributing factor. Please see the fund's website for up-to-date information.

WHAT IS NOT FUNDED No grants to fund buildings, adaptations to buildings or minibus purchases.
TYPE OF GRANT Capital items, running costs.
RANGE OF GRANTS Grants of up to £10,000 each are available to organisations.
SAMPLE GRANTS Previously: Citizen's Advice Bureau (£9,800); St Peter's Hospice, Headway Bristol and Motor Neurone Disease Association (£7,500 each); IT Help@Home (£5,000); the New Place (£3,900); Bristol and Avon Chinese Women's Group (£2,000); Bath Institute of Medical Engineering (£1,500); and Western Active Stroke Group (£1,000).
FINANCES *Year* 2010 *Income* £20,758,000 *Grants* £139,194 *Assets* £205,410,000
TRUSTEES Revd Ian Gobey; Jane Edwards Cork; Trevor Smallwood; John Laycock; Gillian Camm; Charles Hunter; Dr. Pippa Marsh; Ms H E Evans; C A Griffiths; M D Lea; P J Rilett; Dr R Slinn; Lady Wills; S A Burnett; R T Wynn-Jones.
OTHER INFORMATION This trust has provided accommodation, care and support for older and disabled people for over 85 years. Grants are also made to individuals.
HOW TO APPLY On a form available from the correspondent, or to download from the fund's website. All applicants must submit a form together with additional information that is requested, for example, an annual report. Applications are considered once a year; please see the fund's website for deadline dates. All applications will be considered by the Community Fund Committee of the trust. Notification of the outcome will be made in writing. The fund states: 'we receive many more requests than we have funds available. For example, in 2009 we received 35 applications with requests totalling over £318,000: well above the £110,000 we had available. In practice this means that we do not give grants to organisations which do not fully meet our criteria.'
WHO TO APPLY TO Kate Stobie, Community Fund Manager, Cote Lane, Westbury-on-Trym, Bristol BS9 3UN *Tel* 0117 949 4003 *Fax* 0117 949 4044 *email* kate.stobie@stmonicatrust.org.uk *Website* www.stmonicatrust.org.uk

■ The Late St Patrick White Charitable Trust

CC NO 1056520   **ESTABLISHED** 1995
WHERE FUNDING CAN BE GIVEN UK, with a possible preference for Hampshire.
WHO CAN BENEFIT Registered charities.
WHAT IS FUNDED Large UK charities catering for people who are elderly or who have disabilities, and local groups in Hampshire. The trust has a list of regular beneficiaries, although grants are available to other organisations.
RANGE OF GRANTS Between £1,000 and £5,000.
SAMPLE GRANTS Age Concern, Arthritis Care, Barnardo's, Guide Dogs for the Blind Association and The Salvation Army (£5,000

each); Help the Aged (£3,000); and Prostrate Cancer Charity and the Foundation for Prevention of Blindness (£2,000 each).

FINANCES *Year* 2009–10 *Income* £44,438 *Grants* £47,000 *Assets* £1,943,618

TRUSTEES HSBC Trusts Co. (UK) Ltd.

HOW TO APPLY In writing to the correspondent. Applications are considered in February, May, August and November.

WHO TO APPLY TO Lee Topp, Trust Manager, HSBC Trust Co UK Ltd, Norwich House, Nelson Gate, Commercial Road, Southampton SO15 1GX *Tel* 023 8072 2240

■ Saint Sarkis Charity Trust

CC NO 215352 **ESTABLISHED** 1954

WHERE FUNDING CAN BE GIVEN UK and overseas.

WHO CAN BENEFIT Smaller registered charities benefiting Armenians and offenders.

WHAT IS FUNDED Primarily charitable objectives with an Armenian connection including Armenian religious buildings; and other small charities developing innovative projects to support prisoners in the UK.

WHAT IS NOT FUNDED The trust does not give grants to: individual applicants; organisations that are not registered charities; and registered charities outside the UK, unless the project benefits the Armenian community in the UK and/or overseas. The trust does not fund: general appeals; core costs or salaries (as opposed to project costs); projects concerning substance abuse; or medical research.

TYPE OF GRANT Mainly confined to one-off project grants.

RANGE OF GRANTS £1,600–£71,000.

SAMPLE GRANTS Armenian Church of Saint Sarkis (£71,000); Armenian Patriarchate (£29,000); Oxfam (£25,000); Friends of Armenia (£15,000); Terre et Culture (£12,000); Tate Gallery (£10,000); London Armenian Poor Relief (£8,500); Relate (£5,800); Worldwide Volunteering (£5,000); Anahid Association (£3,000); and University of London (£1,600).

FINANCES *Year* 2009–10 *Income* £266,019 *Grants* £203,965 *Assets* £7,378,487

TRUSTEES Martin Sarkis Essayan; Boghos Parsegh (Paul) Gulbenkian; Rita Vartoukian; Robert Brian Todd.

HOW TO APPLY In writing to the correspondent. There is no standard application form so applicants should write a covering letter including: an explanation of the exact purpose of the grant; how much is needed, with details of how the budget has been arrived at; details of any other sources of income (firm commitments and those still being explored); the charity registration number; the latest annual report and audited accounts; and any plans for monitoring and evaluating the work.

WHO TO APPLY TO Louisa Hooper, Secretary to the Trustees, 50 Hoxton Square, London N1 6PB *Tel* 020 7012 1408 *email* info@saintsarkis.org. uk *Website* www.saintsarkis.org.uk

---

■ St Teilo's Trust

CC NO 1032405 **ESTABLISHED** 1993

WHERE FUNDING CAN BE GIVEN Wales.

WHO CAN BENEFIT Christian organisations.

WHAT IS FUNDED Evangelistic initiatives in parishes, for example, Alpha courses, evangelistic events and literature distribution.

SAMPLE GRANTS Examples of grant support are detailed on the trust's website. Previous

beneficiaries include: Llandeilo PC, Gobaith Gymru, St Michael's Aberyswyth, Cilcoed Christian Centre, Parish of Bargoed, Postal Bible School and St David's Diocesan Council.

FINANCES *Year* 2009–10 *Income* £5,404 *Grants* £41,786

TRUSTEES Revd P C A Mansel Lewis, Chair; Mrs C Mansel Lewis; Revd Canon S R Bell; Revd Dr W A Strange; Revd P A Bement; Revd Bob Capper.

OTHER INFORMATION No grants list was available.

HOW TO APPLY In writing to the correspondent. Trustees meet in February, May and September. Applications should be sent by January, April and August. Guidelines are available from the trust.

WHO TO APPLY TO Revd P Mansel Lewis, Stradey Estate Office, 53 New Road, Llanelli SA15 3DP *Tel* 01554 773059 *email* info@saintteilostrust. org.uk *Website* www.saintteilostrust.org.uk

---

■ The Saintbury Trust

CC NO 326790 **ESTABLISHED** 1985

WHERE FUNDING CAN BE GIVEN West Midlands and Warwickshire (which the trust considers to be post code areas B, CV, DY, WS and WV), Worcestershire, Herefordshire and Gloucestershire (post code areas WR, HR and GL).

WHO CAN BENEFIT Registered charities.

WHAT IS FUNDED General charitable purposes with a preference for: addiction; arts and leisure; care of the dying; childhood and youth; community work; disability; education; environment; health; heritage; homelessness; old age; other special needs; and prisons.

WHAT IS NOT FUNDED No grants to animal charities, individuals (including individuals seeking sponsorship for challenges in support of charities), 'cold-calling' national charities or local branches of national charities. The trust only gives grants to charities outside of its beneficial area if the charity is personally known to one or more of the trustees.

RANGE OF GRANTS £500–£90,000.

SAMPLE GRANTS Previously: Birmingham Children's Hospitals Charities (£20,000); Trinity Winchester (£10,000); Nelson Trust; UCE Birmingham Conservatoire; Pimlico Opera (£5,000 each); Myton Hamlet Hospice Trust (£4,000); Tettenhall Wood School Fund; Good Gardeners' Foundation; Kings Norton PCC Restoration; St Basil's (£2,000 each); Adoption Support; Blind Art; Age Concern Malvern; Hop Skip and Jump – Cotswold (£1,000 each).

FINANCES *Income* £142,418 *Grants* £150,000

TRUSTEES Victoria K Houghton; Anne R Thomas; Jane P Lewis; Amanda E Atkinson-Willes; Harry O Forrester.

HOW TO APPLY In writing to the correspondent. Applications are considered in twice a year, usually in April and November.

WHO TO APPLY TO Mrs J P Lewis, Trustee, P O Box 464, Abinger Hammer, Dorking, Surrey RH4 9AF *Tel* 01306 730119

■ The Saints and Sinners Trust

CC NO 200536 **ESTABLISHED** 1961

WHERE FUNDING CAN BE GIVEN Mostly UK.

WHO CAN BENEFIT Registered charities.

WHAT IS FUNDED General charitable purposes, mainly welfare and medical. Priority is given to requests for grants sponsored by members of Saints and Sinners.

WHAT IS NOT FUNDED No grants to individuals or non-registered charities.

RANGE OF GRANTS £500–£10,000 but generally in the range of £1,000–£3,000.

SAMPLE GRANTS Nordoff Robins Music Therapy, Royal Shakespeare Company and White Ensign Association Limited (£5,000 each); National Talking Newspapers and White Lodge Centre (£3,000 each); Oxford Children's Hospital Appeal and Police Rehabilitation Trust (£2,000 each); and Sandy Gall's Afghanistan Appeal, Sightsavers International and Society for Welfare of Horses and Ponies (£1,000 each).

FINANCES *Year* 2009–10 *Income* £88,331 *Grants* £94,550 *Assets* £265,464

TRUSTEES N W Benson; Sir Donald Gosling; David Edwards; I A N Irvine.

HOW TO APPLY Applications are not considered unless nominated by members of the club.

WHO TO APPLY TO N W Benson, Trustee, Lewis Golden and Co., 40 Queen Anne Street, London W1G 9EL *Tel* 020 7580 7313

■ The Salamander Charitable Trust

CC NO 273657   **ESTABLISHED** 1977

WHERE FUNDING CAN BE GIVEN Worldwide.

WHO CAN BENEFIT Registered charities benefiting children, young adults, people disadvantaged by poverty and people who have disabilities.

WHAT IS FUNDED The trust has a list of charities, in the fields of advancement of education and religion, and relief of poverty or physical disability, to which it gives on an annual basis. No other charities are funded.

WHAT IS NOT FUNDED No grants to individuals. Only registered charities are supported.

RANGE OF GRANTS £250–£2,000, generally £1,000 or less.

SAMPLE GRANTS SAT-7 Trust, All Nations Christian College, All Saints in Branksome Park, Birmingham Christian College, Christian Aid, Churches Commission on overseas students, FEBA Radio, International Christian College, London Bible College, Middle East Media, Moorland College, St James PCC in Poole, SAMS, Trinity College and Wycliffe Bible Translators.

FINANCES *Year* 2009–10 *Income* £63,829 *Grants* £73,000 *Assets* £1,476,431

TRUSTEES Sheila M Douglas; Alison Hardwick; Phillip Douglas.

OTHER INFORMATION Grants were made to 96 organisations.

HOW TO APPLY The trust's income is fully allocated each year, mainly to regular beneficiaries. The trustees do not wish to receive any further new requests.

WHO TO APPLY TO Sheila M Douglas, Trustee, Threave, 2 Brudenell Avenue, Canford Cliffs, Poole, Dorset BH13 7NW *Tel* 01202 706661

■ The Salt Foundation

CC NO 511978   **ESTABLISHED** 1981

WHERE FUNDING CAN BE GIVEN Saltaire and Shipley.

WHO CAN BENEFIT Individuals and schools benefiting children, young adults, older people and students. During the year the foundation concentrated on its commitment to maintain one of its properties, Victoria Hall, but hopes to resume normal grant making in the near future.

WHAT IS FUNDED Education.

WHAT IS NOT FUNDED No grants to replace statutory funding.

TYPE OF GRANT One-off grants (although applicants may reapply), capital, project and recurring costs for funding of one year or less.

SAMPLE GRANTS Saltaire Community Festival Ltd (£6,000).

FINANCES *Year* 2009–10 *Income* £314,383 *Grants* £6,000 *Assets* £419,661

TRUSTEES Alex McClelland; Geraldine Whelan; James Flood; Robert Sowman; Ted Watson; Norman Roper; John Briggs; John Carroll; Paula Truman.

OTHER INFORMATION The foundation stated in 2009 that it has not made grant awards for the past 3 years because of the need to repair property for which it has responsibility.

HOW TO APPLY In writing to the correspondent.

WHO TO APPLY TO Mrs M Davies, Clerk, 17 Springfield Road, Baildon, Shipley, Yorkshire BD17 5NA *Tel* 01274 591508 *email* marjoriedavies@tiscali.co.uk

----

■ The Salt Trust

CC NO 1062133   **ESTABLISHED** 1977

WHERE FUNDING CAN BE GIVEN UK.

WHO CAN BENEFIT Charitable organisations.

WHAT IS FUNDED General charitable purposes.

SAMPLE GRANTS The trust stated that it 'supported a crisis debt counselling centre, a church worker, a few young people undertaking training, an Arts Centre, a Christian education organisation, individuals suffering from financial hardship and various relief organisations in keeping with the purposes of the charity.'

FINANCES *Year* 2009–10 *Income* £49,951 *Grants* £34,600 *Assets* £10,757

TRUSTEES Norman Adams; Dianne Parsons; Robert Parsons; Stephen Williams; Mark Molden.

HOW TO APPLY The trust does not accept unsolicited applications.

WHO TO APPLY TO Jill Jameson, 10 Tarragon Way, Pontprennau, Cardiff CF23 8SN *Tel* 029 2073 3422

■ Salters' Charitable Foundation

CC NO 328258   **ESTABLISHED** 1989

WHERE FUNDING CAN BE GIVEN Greater London or UK.

WHO CAN BENEFIT Priority is given to funding small nationwide charities and organisations connected with the City of London, where the trust's contribution would make a 'real difference'. As a matter of general policy, the company supports those charities where Salters are involved.

WHAT IS FUNDED The trust makes donations for a wide range of charitable purposes including, children and young people, health, homelessness, the developing world, the environment and members of the armed forces.

WHAT IS NOT FUNDED Please see the foundation's guidelines for information on restrictions.

TYPE OF GRANT Project grants – three year grants of up to £20,000; General grants – a limited amount of small donations up to £3,000.

RANGE OF GRANTS £150–£9,000 but mostly under £2,000.

SAMPLE GRANTS United Nations Environment Programme – World Conservation Monitoring Centre (£9,000); Guildhall School Trust (£7,500); Arkwright Schools Scholarship (£5,400); Drapers' Charitable Fund – Olympics (£4,000); Home Farm Trust, Providence Row and Federation of London Youth Clubs (£3,000 each); City of London Migraine Clinic, London Sea Cadet Corps – District 5 NE, Diabetes UK,

City University London and Blind in Business (£2,000 each); Royal Naval Benevolent Trust (£1,500); Ulysses Trust (£1,000); Banana Tree Project (£500); and Royal British Legion – City of London Poppy Appeal (£150).

FINANCES *Year* 2009–10 *Income* £153,546 *Grants* £125,995 *Assets* £313,588

TRUSTEES The Salters' Company.

OTHER INFORMATION In June 2010 the foundation was amalgamated with the Salters' Company Charity for Relief of Need (charity number: 244092).

HOW TO APPLY Applicants must follow the relevant Guidelines ('Project Grant' or 'General Support') depending on the type of grant they are requesting: Project Grant applicants need to fill in an application form, available from the foundation's website when the programme is open; General Support applicants need to submit a covering letter, supporting document and annual report and accounts. Applications can be made via email or post. All supported organisations are regularly reviewed and visited by the Charities Development Manager, members of the Charity Committee and other interested parties within the Company.

WHO TO APPLY TO Vicky Chant, Charities Development Manager, The Salters' Company, Salters' Hall, 4 Fore Street, London EC2Y 5DE *Tel* 020 7588 5216 *Fax* 020 7638 3679 *email* charities@salters.co.uk *Website* www.salters.co.uk

■ The Andrew Salvesen Charitable Trust

SC NO SC008000 **ESTABLISHED** 1989

WHERE FUNDING CAN BE GIVEN UK, with a preference for Scotland.

WHO CAN BENEFIT Organisations benefiting children who are ill and people who are disabled or homeless.

WHAT IS FUNDED Grants are made to a variety of charitable organisations who work for sick children, people who are disabled, homeless people and a range of other causes.

WHAT IS NOT FUNDED No grants to individuals.

SAMPLE GRANTS Previous beneficiaries have included Bield Housing Trust, William Higgins Marathon Account, Multiple Sclerosis Society in Scotland, Royal Zoological Society of Scotland, Sail Training Association, Scottish Down's Syndrome Association and Sick Kids Appeal.

FINANCES *Year* 2009–10 *Income* £78,007 *Grants* £70,000

TRUSTEES A C Salvesen; Ms K Turner; V Lall.

HOW TO APPLY The trustees only support organisations known to them through their personal contacts. The trust has previously stated that all applications sent to them are 'thrown in the bin'.

WHO TO APPLY TO The Trustees, c/o Meston Reid and Co., 12 Carden Place, Aberdeen AB10 1UR *Tel* 01224 625554 *email* info@mestonreid.com

■ The Sammermar Trust

CC NO 800493 **ESTABLISHED** 1988

WHERE FUNDING CAN BE GIVEN UK and overseas.

WHO CAN BENEFIT Charitable organisations.

WHAT IS FUNDED General charitable purposes.

RANGE OF GRANTS £1,000–£125,000.

SAMPLE GRANTS Head and Neck Cancer Research Trust (£30,000); Maggie's (Oxford) (£15,000); The Mango Tree (£12,000); Family Friends

(£10,000); West Dean College (£15,000); Acre Housing; Chipping Norton Theatre; Internally Displaced Persons, Sri Lanka; Oxford Philomusica (£5,000 each); Wycombe Air Centre (£2,000); Cheltenham Festivals (£2,000).

FINANCES *Year* 2009 *Income* £264,659 *Grants* £231,576 *Assets* £10,921,268

TRUSTEES Lady Judith Swire; M Dunne; M B Swire; M.V.Allfrey.

OTHER INFORMATION Grants of less than £1,000 totalled £8,700.

HOW TO APPLY In writing to the correspondent. The trust states that: 'although the trustees make some grants with no formal applications, they normally require organisations to submit a request saying how the funds could be used and what would be achieved'. The trustees usually meet monthly.

WHO TO APPLY TO Mrs Yvonne Barnes, Swire House, 59 Buckingham Gate, London SW1E 6AJ *Tel* 020 7834 7717

■ Basil Samuel Charitable Trust

CC NO 206579 **ESTABLISHED** 1959

WHERE FUNDING CAN BE GIVEN UK and worldwide.

WHO CAN BENEFIT Registered charities.

WHAT IS FUNDED General charitable purposes but mainly, medical, socially supportive, educational and cultural charities.

WHAT IS NOT FUNDED Only applications from registered charities are considered.

TYPE OF GRANT 'One-off' and recurring.

RANGE OF GRANTS £1,000–£100,000.

SAMPLE GRANTS Macmillan Cancer Support (£60,000); Royal National Theatre (£20,000); Prince's Trust and the Victoria and Albert Museum (£10,000 each); Attingham Trust, London's Air Ambulance, Museum of London, NSPCC and the Cystic Fibrosis Trust (£5,000 each); Hammerson Home Charitable Trust (£2,000); and St John of Jerusalem Eye Hospital Group (£1,000).

FINANCES *Year* 2009–10 *Income* £371,615 *Grants* £261,000 *Assets* £10,203,749

TRUSTEES Coral Samuel; Richard M Peskin.

HOW TO APPLY In writing to the correspondent. The trustees meet on a formal basis annually and regularly on an informal basis to discuss proposals for individual donations.

WHO TO APPLY TO Mrs Coral Samuel, Trustee, Smith & Williamson, 25 Moorgate, London EC2R 6AY *Tel* 020 7131 4376

■ Coral Samuel Charitable Trust

CC NO 239677 **ESTABLISHED** 1962

WHERE FUNDING CAN BE GIVEN UK.

WHO CAN BENEFIT Registered charities only.

WHAT IS FUNDED General charitable purposes, including educational, cultural and socially supportive charities.

WHAT IS NOT FUNDED Grants are only made to registered charities.

RANGE OF GRANTS £350–£10,000.

SAMPLE GRANTS Royal National Theatre and Sir John Soane's Museum (£10,000 each); Glyndebourne Arts Trust (£6,000); Burlington Magazine Foundation, SAVE and Royal Geographic Society (£5,000 each); Child Bereavement Charity (£3,000); Winston's Wish (£2,600); Commonwealth Jewish Trust (£2,000); RVC Animal Care Trust (£1,500); Maccabi GB and the Art Fund (£1,000 each); Personal Support Trust (£500); and JMI (£350).

FINANCES *Year* 2009–10 *Income* £190,871 *Grants* £101,450 *Assets* £5,296,288
TRUSTEES Coral Samuel; Peter Fineman.
HOW TO APPLY In writing to the correspondent.
WHO TO APPLY TO Coral Samuel, Trustee, c/o Smith and Williamson, 25 Moorgate, London EC2R 6AY *Tel* 020 7131 4376

■ The Hon. M J Samuel Charitable Trust

CC NO 327013   ESTABLISHED 1985
WHERE FUNDING CAN BE GIVEN UK and overseas.
WHO CAN BENEFIT Charitable organisations.
WHAT IS FUNDED The trust supports a wide range of causes, many of them Jewish, environmental or to do with mental health.
WHAT IS NOT FUNDED No grants to individuals.
TYPE OF GRANT Core costs, project and research. Funding of up to two years will be considered.
SAMPLE GRANTS Oxfam (£32,000); Full Fact (£31,000); Child Bereavement Trust (£10,000); Chicken Shed Theatre Company (£2,500); ChildLine/Dyslexia Action, Hazara Charitable Trust and Oxford Radcliffe Children's Hospital (£2,000 each); Community Security Trust (£1,500); James Wentworth-Stanley Memorial Fund and National Hospital Development Foundation (£1,000 each).
FINANCES *Year* 2009–10 *Income* £90,255 *Grants* £105,763 *Assets* £3,371,198
TRUSTEES Hon. Michael Samuel; Hon. Mrs Julia A Samuel; Viscount Bearsted.
OTHER INFORMATION In addition 13 (2009:15) other donations were made to institutions of less than £1,000 each totalling just over £5,000.
HOW TO APPLY In writing to the correspondent.
WHO TO APPLY TO The Secretary, 35 Connaught Square, London W2 2HL

■ The Peter Samuel Charitable Trust

CC NO 269065   ESTABLISHED 1975
WHERE FUNDING CAN BE GIVEN UK, with some preference for local organisations in South Berkshire, Highlands of Scotland and East Somerset.
WHO CAN BENEFIT Registered charities benefiting medical professionals, scientists, at-risk groups and people disadvantaged by poverty.
WHAT IS FUNDED Medical sciences, the quality of life in local areas, heritage and land/forestry restoration.
WHAT IS NOT FUNDED No grants to purely local charities outside Berkshire or to individuals.
TYPE OF GRANT Single and annual donations.
RANGE OF GRANTS £200–£20,000.
SAMPLE GRANTS DEC Haiti Earthquake Appeal and Peter Samuel Royal Free Charitable Trust (£10,000 each); Campaign for the University of Oxford, Anna Freud Centre and Game and Wildlife Conservation Trust (£5,000 each); Jewish Care and Norwood Ravenswood (£2,500 each); Berkshire Community Foundation and the RNID (£1,000 each); Anne Frank and You, Isle of Man and Woodland Trust (£500 each); and SANE (£250).
FINANCES *Year* 2009–10 *Income* £109,955 *Grants* £89,950 *Assets* £3,599,544
TRUSTEES Hon. Viscount Bearsted; Hon. Michael Samuel.
OTHER INFORMATION The Hon Michael Samuel is also a trustee of: Col. Wilfred Horatio Micholls Deceased Charitable Trust Fund (Charity Commission no. 267472); The Hon. A G Samuel Charitable Trust (Charity Commission no. 1090481); The M J Samuel Charitable Trust (Charity Commission no. 327013); and The Peter Samuel Royal Free Fund (Charity Commission no. 200049).
HOW TO APPLY In writing to the correspondent. Trustees meet twice-yearly.
WHO TO APPLY TO Miss Emma Chapman, Trust Administrator, The Estate Office, Farley Hall, Castle Road, Farley Hill, Berkshire RG7 1UL *Tel* 0118 973 0047 *Fax* 0118 973 0385 *email* emma@farleyfarms.co.uk

■ The Camilla Samuel Fund

CC NO 235424   ESTABLISHED 1964
WHERE FUNDING CAN BE GIVEN UK.
WHO CAN BENEFIT Medical research projects in a discipline agreed by the trustees at their annual meetings. Funding may be given to medical professionals and research workers.
WHAT IS FUNDED The promotion, encouragement, assistance, support, conduct and accomplishment of any research or inquiry into any matters relating to the causes, prevention, diagnosis, incidence, treatment, cure or effects of any form of illness, injury or disability requiring medical or dental treatment.
WHAT IS NOT FUNDED Individuals, general appeals.
TYPE OF GRANT Agreed expenses of research only. Maximum period three years, subject to satisfactory annual report and review by trustees.
SAMPLE GRANTS Previous beneficiaries have included Imperial Cancer Research Fund and EORTC.
FINANCES *Year* 2009–10 *Income* £15,897 *Grants* £4,561
TRUSTEES Sir Ronald Grierson; Hon. Mrs Waley-Cohen; Dr Hon. J P H Hunt.
HOW TO APPLY The trustees will request written applications following the recommendation of a suitable project by the medical trustees. However, please note as all the money available, together with the fund's future income, has been earmarked for four years for an important research project, the fund will not be in a position to consider any applications for grants during this period.
WHO TO APPLY TO The Secretary to the Trustees, 40 Berkeley Square, London W1J 5AL *Tel* 020 7581 9099

■ The Samworth Foundation

CC NO 265647   ESTABLISHED 1973
WHERE FUNDING CAN BE GIVEN Derby, Leicestershire, Nottinghamshire and Africa.
WHO CAN BENEFIT Registered charities only.
WHAT IS FUNDED General charitable purposes.
WHAT IS NOT FUNDED No grants to individuals.
RANGE OF GRANTS Between £10 and £100,000.
SAMPLE GRANTS Villa Maninga (£50,000); Launde Abbey and The Mango Tree (£20,000 each); Médecins Sans Frontières (MSF) (£12,500); Snow-Camp (£11,000); Tear Fund (£10,000); Nottingham Outward Bound Association (£5,000); Belvoir Castle Cricket Trust (£4,000); Thorpe Satchville Village Hall (£2,000); St Peters Nottingham Organ appeal and Molly's Fund (£1,000 each).
FINANCES *Year* 2009–10 *Income* £6,047,590 *Grants* £139,998 *Assets* £11,265,381
TRUSTEES Bob Dowson; Mrs Clare Price; Mrs Viccy Stott.

Think carefully about every application. Is it justified?

869

OTHER INFORMATION Donations of less than £1,000 each totalled £3,415.

HOW TO APPLY In writing to the correspondent. The foundation's grantmaking policy is to support a limited number of causes known to the trustees. Unsolicited applications are not normally considered.

WHO TO APPLY TO Miss W A Bateman, c/o Samworth Brothers (Holdings) Ltd, Chetwode House, 1 Samworth Way, Melton Mowbray, Leicestershire LE13 1GA *Tel* 01664 414500 *Fax* 01664 414501

■ The Sandhu Charitable Foundation

CC NO 1114236   **ESTABLISHED** 2006
WHERE FUNDING CAN BE GIVEN Worldwide.
WHO CAN BENEFIT Charities and charitable causes.
WHAT IS FUNDED General charitable purposes.
SAMPLE GRANTS Magic Bus UK (£12,000); Dec Haiti Appeal and Young Enterprise South East of England (£10,000 each); Jubilee Boy Hill School (£9,000); Latymer Foundation (£4,000); and Joint Educational Trust (£3,000).
FINANCES *Year* 2009–10 *Income* £1,492,972 *Grants* £77,458 *Assets* £3,220,220
TRUSTEES B S Sandhu, Chair; S Carey.
OTHER INFORMATION Included in the total figure were 9 grants of less than £3,000 totalling over £13,000.
HOW TO APPLY 'The charity is to support individual charities or charitable causes, mainly on a single donation basis, which they themselves identify.'
WHO TO APPLY TO The Trustees, c/o The Stanton Group, 3rd Floor, Saunders House, 52–53 The Mall, Ealing SW1X 7LY *Tel* 020 3159 5071 *email* enquiries@santoncapital.com

■ The Sandra Charitable Trust

CC NO 327492   **ESTABLISHED** 1987
WHERE FUNDING CAN BE GIVEN Not defined, in practice UK with slight preference for south east England.
WHO CAN BENEFIT Organisations benefiting children and young people, hospices, education, people with disabilities, people disadvantaged by poverty, the arts, and individual grants for nurses.
WHAT IS FUNDED Animal welfare and research, environmental protection, social welfare, health and youth development.
WHAT IS NOT FUNDED No grants to individuals other than nurses.
TYPE OF GRANT One-off and recurring.
RANGE OF GRANTS Typically £5,000 or less.
SAMPLE GRANTS Kids (£40,000); The Florence Nightingale Foundation (£25,000); Leander Club (£15,000); Oxfordshire Victoria County History Trust (£11,000); River Thames Society (£10,500); the Royal Horticultural Society and Scope (£10,000 each); Barnardo's, Crisis, Mercy Ships and Wessex Heartbeat (£5,000 each); DEC Haiti Earthquake and Plantlife (£4,000 each); Alone in London and Deafness Research UK (£3,000 each); Friends of Shakespeare's Church and Thames Valley Air Ambulance (£2,000 each); and the 9th Chelsea Scout Group and Woodland Heritage (£1,000 each).
FINANCES *Year* 2009–10 *Income* £417,262 *Grants* £537,833 *Assets* £15,375,197
TRUSTEES Richard Moore; Michael Macfadyen.

OTHER INFORMATION £460,610 was donated to 121 organisations and just over £77,223 to 127 individuals.

HOW TO APPLY The trust states that 'unsolicited applications are not requested, as the trustees prefer to support charities whose work they have researched ... the trustees receives a very high number of grant applications which are mostly unsuccessful'.

WHO TO APPLY TO Keith Lawrence, Secretary, Moore Stephens, 150 Aldersgate Street, London EC1A 4AB *Tel* 020 7334 9191 *Fax* 020 7651 1953 *email* keith.lawrence@moorestephens.com

■ The Sands Family Trust

CC NO 1136909   **ESTABLISHED** 2010
WHERE FUNDING CAN BE GIVEN Undefined, in practice the UK and overseas.
WHO CAN BENEFIT Organisations and individuals.
WHAT IS FUNDED General charitable purposes.
TRUSTEES Cripps Trust Corporation Ltd; Betsy Tobin; Peter Sands.
HOW TO APPLY In writing to the correspondent.
WHO TO APPLY TO Heartwood Wealth Management, 77 Mount Ephraim, Tunbridge Wells, Kent TN4 8BS *Tel* 01892 701801 *email* info@heartwoodwealth.com

■ Santander UK Foundation Limited

CC NO 803655   **ESTABLISHED** 1990
WHERE FUNDING CAN BE GIVEN UK.
WHO CAN BENEFIT Registered, excepted or exempt charities. Industrial and Provident societies can only be supported if they are founded under charitable, not membership, rules.
WHAT IS FUNDED 'All of our funding must directly help disadvantaged people through one or both of these charitable priorities – education and training, or financial capability. Education and training: this could be any activity disadvantaged people undertake where they improve their confidence in a skill or their understanding of a subject This does not have to be formal training or lead to a qualification, although those activities would be eligible too. It could be any activity disadvantaged people undertake where they improve their confidence in a skill or their understanding of a subject. Examples could include independent living skills, anger management, or improving self esteem. Other examples could include reminiscence projects for older people, art and craft sessions as well as IT classes. These are just a few examples and should not be regarded as a definitive list. Financial capability: this priority covers activities which help disadvantaged people understand how to manage their money. It could include budgeting skills, accessing affordable credit as well as managing the challenges that arise from being a carer, unemployment, disability or relationship break up. Examples could be the costs of running a credit union, projects delivering financial advice and helping people to understand their benefit entitlement. Successful applications under this priority have included equipping a training kitchen for homeless people who learnt how to budget effectively for their food and then went on to apply these principals to other parts of their lives.'
WHAT IS NOT FUNDED Donations are not made for: statutory duties; part of a major capital appeal;

a specific individual (this includes Gap Year funding, overseas travel, medical treatment or holidays); lobbying or political parties; the benefit of a single religious or single ethnic group; causes outside the UK; gaining specialist school status; commercial sponsorship or for fundraising events, conferences or advertising.

TYPE OF GRANT All funding is for one off donations. Grants are available to buy tangible items such as equipment or training materials. Grants are also available to fund project costs such as sessional worker fees, salaries, room hire or other costs incurred in the delivery of the charitable priorities.

RANGE OF GRANTS Up to £10,000.

FINANCES *Year* 2010 *Income* £3,550,647 *Grants* £4,083,179 *Assets* £10,750,276

TRUSTEES Lord Burns; S Lloyd; J Thorpe; S Williams.

OTHER INFORMATION The foundation changed its name from the Abbey Charitable Trust in early 2010. In 2011 grants were capped at £10,000 for all charities in the UK, including those located in Community Partnership Group areas (London Borough of Camden; Milton Keynes covering Buckinghamshire, Northamptonshire and Bedfordshire; Leicestershire and Rutland; Sheffield covering South Yorkshire; Bradford covering West Yorkshire; Teesside covering the area from Redcar to Darlington and Sunderland; Merseyside; Greater Glasgow; and Northern Ireland).

HOW TO APPLY The following guidance on making an application is given on the foundation's website. 'We have made applying to us as straightforward as possible and do not use an application form. We operate a rolling programme, with no deadlines for applications. Download and print off the grant application cover sheet which you can use as a checklist as you put together your application [available from the foundation's website]. You need to write us a letter on the headed notepaper of your charity which should include your registered charity number or whatever is appropriate for your charitable status. The letter should include the following: how much you are asking for?; what will this pay for? Include a simple budget detailing the main costs; how will disadvantaged people directly benefit? Include an estimate of the long term difference this grant will make; how does this meet one or both of our charitable priorities?; if the funding is for an existing project, tell us how our funding fits your funding strategy and what the project has achieved so far; if the funding is for a new project, tell us how you identified the need for this piece of work; If you are asking for revenue funding for salaries or running costs tell us what your funding strategy is to replace this funding at the end of our grant; if applicable, which other funders are you applying to? Make sure the letter is signed by two people, one of whom must be a trustee of the charity. If it helps explain what your project will do, you may want to include a flyer, newsletter or other sample training material that is produced for the beneficiaries. Please do **not** include: annual reports and accounts; DVDs or CDs; business plan or constitution; any other bulky items, plastic binders or covers. If you want confirmation that we have received your application, please enclose a self-addressed postcard or envelope with your application letter. We will post this to you when we open your application. If you do not receive any other correspondence from us within six weeks then you should assume that your application has been unsuccessful. We regret that due to the very high volume of requests received, we do not notify unsuccessful applicants or offer feedback on why your application has not been successful. We regret that we cannot accept online or emailed applications.'

WHO TO APPLY TO Alan Eagle, Foundation Manager, Santander House, 201 Grafton Gate East, Milton Keynes MK9 1AN *Tel* 01908 343224 *email* grants@santander.co.uk *Website* www.santanderfoundation.org.uk

....

■ The Sants Charitable Trust

CC NO 1078555   **ESTABLISHED** 1999

WHERE FUNDING CAN BE GIVEN UK.

WHO CAN BENEFIT Organisations.

WHAT IS FUNDED General charitable purposes.

RANGE OF GRANTS £300–£60,000.

SAMPLE GRANTS St Paul's Theological Centre (£25,000); Radley Foundation (£22,000); Footsteps Foundation (£10,000); Ashmolean Museum and Garsington Opera (£5,000 each); and Trinity College (£300).

FINANCES *Year* 2009–10 *Income* £85,036 *Grants* £91,300 *Assets* £1,094,511

TRUSTEES Alexander Sants; Mrs Caroline Sants; Hector W H Sants; John H Ovens.

HOW TO APPLY In writing to the correspondent.

WHO TO APPLY TO The Trustees, 17 Bradmore Road, Oxford OX2 6QP *Tel* 01865 310813

....

■ Jimmy Savile Charitable Trust

CC NO 326970   **ESTABLISHED** 1984

WHERE FUNDING CAN BE GIVEN UK.

WHO CAN BENEFIT Registered charities, hospitals and educational institutions.

WHAT IS FUNDED General charitable purposes.

TYPE OF GRANT One-off grants.

RANGE OF GRANTS £100–£15,000.

SAMPLE GRANTS A.A.I. Scientific Cultural Services (£15,000); John Augar – Cardiac Research Software (£5,000); Apostleship of the Sea and Institute of Cancer Research (£1,000 each); The C Group (Royal Marines) (£2,000); Music in Hospitals (£430); Leeds Teaching Hospitals (£750); Cleft Palate Charity (£350); S.E.N.S.E (£500); Guide Dogs (£250).

FINANCES *Year* 2008–09 *Income* £158,990 *Grants* £34,720 *Assets* £3,656,854

TRUSTEES James Collier; Luke Lucas; Dr Roger Bodley.

HOW TO APPLY The trust does not respond to unsolicited applications.

WHO TO APPLY TO The Trustees, 22 Lake View Court, Leeds LS8 2TX

....

■ The Scarfe Charitable Trust

CC NO 275535   **ESTABLISHED** 1978

WHERE FUNDING CAN BE GIVEN UK, with an emphasis on Suffolk.

WHO CAN BENEFIT Individuals and organisations working in the fields of arts, music, medical research and the environment.

WHAT IS FUNDED This trust will consider funding: conservation; environmental interests; medical research; hospices; arts and arts facilities; churches; religious ancillary buildings; art galleries and cultural centres; libraries and museums; and theatres and opera houses.

TYPE OF GRANT Capital, core costs, one-off, project, research, recurring costs and running costs. Funding is normally for one year or less.

RANGE OF GRANTS £150–£19,000.

SAMPLE GRANTS Aldeburgh Music (£10,000); Aldeburgh Young Musicians (£2,500); Disability

Advice Service, High Tide, Liveability, St Andrews, Hasketon and St Augustine's, Ashen (£1,000 each); Trinity College of Music (£850.00); Marie Curie Cancer Care (£750); St Helen's, Ipswich, St Mary's, Bacton, St Mary's, Cratfield and St Peters, Westleton (£500 each); RNID (£350); and Ipswich Chamber Music (£100).

FINANCES *Year* 2009–10 *Income* £51,325 *Grants* £43,831 *Assets* £1,183,180

TRUSTEES Sean McTernan; E Maule; John McCarthy.

HOW TO APPLY In writing to the correspondent by post or email. The trustees meet quarterly to consider applications.

WHO TO APPLY TO Eric Maule, Trustee, Salix House, Falkenham, Ipswich, Suffolk IP10 0QY *Tel* 01394 448339 *email* ericmaule@hotmail.com

■ The Schapira Charitable Trust

CC NO 328435   **ESTABLISHED** 1989

WHERE FUNDING CAN BE GIVEN UK.

WHO CAN BENEFIT Organisations benefiting Jewish people.

WHAT IS FUNDED Jewish charitable purposes.

RANGE OF GRANTS £500–£136,000.

SAMPLE GRANTS Emuno Educational Centre Ltd (£143,000); Friends of Tashbar Chazon Ish (£134,000); The New Rachmistrivke Synagogue (£38,000); Friends of Mir (£16,000); British Friends of Ramoth Jerusalem (£9,000); Chevras Machzikel Mesifta (£8,000); Yesamach Levav (£3,500); BCDT Limited (£4,000); Before Trust (£1,000) and Torah (5759) Limited (£720).

FINANCES *Year* 2010 *Income* £201,688 *Grants* £551,772 *Assets* £6,382,135

TRUSTEES Issac Y Schapira; Michael Neuberger; Suzanne L Schapira.

HOW TO APPLY In writing to the correspondent.

WHO TO APPLY TO The Trustees, 2 Dancastle Court, 14 Arcadia Avenue, Finchley, London N3 2JU *Tel* 020 8371 0381 *email* londonoffice@istrad.com

■ The Annie Schiff Charitable Trust

CC NO 265401   **ESTABLISHED** 1973

WHERE FUNDING CAN BE GIVEN UK, overseas.

WHO CAN BENEFIT Orthodox Jewish institutions supporting religious, educational and relief of poverty aims.

WHAT IS FUNDED The relief of poverty generally and payment to needy individuals of the Jewish faith, for the advancement of education and religion.

WHAT IS NOT FUNDED No support for individuals and non-recognised institutions.

RANGE OF GRANTS £1,800–£22,000.

SAMPLE GRANTS Chevras Mo'oz Ladol (£22,000); Gevruth Ari Torah Academy Trust (£16,000); Yesamech Levav Trust and Friends of Beis Yisrael Trust (£10,000 each); United Torah Association (£8,000); Yeshivo Horomo Talmudical College (£6,500); Beth David Institute (£6,000); WST Charity Limited (£5,000); Friends of Yeshivat Meor Hatalmud (£3,000); Yesodey Hatorah Schools (£2,000); and Society of Friends of the Torah (£1,800).

FINANCES *Year* 2009–10 *Income* £73,689 *Grants* £101,300 *Assets* £234,249

TRUSTEES Joseph Pearlman; Ruth Pearlman.

HOW TO APPLY In writing to the correspondent. Grants are generally made only to registered charities.

WHO TO APPLY TO Joseph Pearlman, Trustee, 8 Highfield Gardens, London NW11 9HB *Tel* 020 8458 9266

■ The Schmidt-Bodner Charitable Trust

CC NO 283014   **ESTABLISHED** 1981

WHERE FUNDING CAN BE GIVEN UK and overseas.

WHO CAN BENEFIT Jewish organisations and other registered charities.

WHAT IS FUNDED Health, education and welfare.

RANGE OF GRANTS £250–£35,000.

SAMPLE GRANTS Lubavitch Foundation (£20,000); Jewish Care (£12,500); United Synagogue (£11,000); British Friends of Or Chadash (£5,000); Yesodey Hatorah School (£3,000); SEED and Simon Marks Junior Primary School Trust (£2,000 each); and British Friends of Ohel Sarah (£250).

FINANCES *Year* 2009–10 *Income* £1,022,951 *Grants* £67,550 *Assets* £2,143,932

TRUSTEES Harvey Rosenblatt; Daniel Dover; Martin Paisner.

HOW TO APPLY In writing to the correspondent.

WHO TO APPLY TO Harvey Rosenblatt, Trustee, 5 Fitzhardinge Street, London W1H 6ED *Tel* 020 7486 3111

■ The R H Scholes Charitable Trust

CC NO 267023   **ESTABLISHED** 1974

WHERE FUNDING CAN BE GIVEN England.

WHO CAN BENEFIT Registered charities, particularly those benefiting children and young adults, the Church of England, and people who are disabled or disadvantaged by poverty.

WHAT IS FUNDED Preference is given to charities that the trustees have a special interest in, knowledge of, or association with. If any new charities are to be supported it will be in the fields helping children and young people who are disadvantaged or disabled. Particularly charities working in the fields of: residential facilities; respite and sheltered accommodation; Anglican bodies; music and opera; special schools and special needs education; training for community development; care in the community; day centres; holidays and outings; play schemes; and research into medicine.

WHAT IS NOT FUNDED Grants only to registered charities. No grants to individuals, animal charities, expeditions or scholarships. The trust tries not to make grants to more than one charity operating in a particular field, and does not make grants to charities outside England.

TYPE OF GRANT Both recurrent and one-off grants are made depending upon the needs of the beneficiary. Core costs, project and research. Funding for more than three years will be considered.

RANGE OF GRANTS £100–£1,200.

SAMPLE GRANTS £1,200 each went to the Church of England Pensions Board, the Friends of Lancing Chapel, Historic Churches Preservation Trust.

FINANCES *Year* 2009–10 *Income* £155,249 *Grants* £34,340 *Assets* £554,089

TRUSTEES R H C Pattison; Mrs A J Pattison.

OTHER INFORMATION All other grants were between £100 and £1,010.

HOW TO APPLY Due to a lack of funds the trust is not currently accepting unsolicited applications from organisations it is not already supporting.

WHO TO APPLY TO R H C Pattison, Trustee, Danehurst Corner, Danehurst Crescent, Horsham, West Sussex RH13 5HS *Tel* 01403 263482 *email* roger@rogpat.plus.com

■ The Schreib Trust

CC NO 275240　　ESTABLISHED 1977
WHERE FUNDING CAN BE GIVEN UK.
WHO CAN BENEFIT Jewish people, especially those disadvantaged by poverty.
WHAT IS FUNDED Relief of poverty and advancement of religion and religious education.
RANGE OF GRANTS Around £500–£80,000.
SAMPLE GRANTS Previous beneficiaries have included: Lolev, Yad Eliezer, Ponovitz, Craven Walk Charity Trust, Shaar Hatalmud, Beis Rochel, Beth Jacob Building Fund, Toiras Chesed and Oneg Shabbos.
FINANCES *Year* 2009–10 *Income* £567,555 *Grants* £509,797 *Assets* £429,335
TRUSTEES A Green; Mrs R Niederman; D Schreiber; Mrs I Schreiber.
OTHER INFORMATION No grants list was available.
HOW TO APPLY In writing to the correspondent.
WHO TO APPLY TO Mrs R Niederman, Trustee, 147 Stamford Hill, London N16 5LG *Tel* 020 8802 5492

■ The Schreiber Charitable Trust

CC NO 264735　　ESTABLISHED 1972
WHERE FUNDING CAN BE GIVEN UK.
WHO CAN BENEFIT Registered charities benefiting Jewish people.
WHAT IS FUNDED Jewish with a preference for education, social welfare and medical causes.
RANGE OF GRANTS £100–£50,000.
SAMPLE GRANTS Friends of Rabbinical College Kol Tora, Jerusalem Foundation, SOFT, Gateshead Talmudical College, Dalaid Limited and Aish Hatorah UK Limited.
FINANCES *Year* 2009–10 *Income* £178,592 *Grants* £155,273 *Assets* £3,892,972
TRUSTEES Graham S Morris; David A Schreiber; Sara Schreiber.
OTHER INFORMATION Grants totalling £146,000 were made for education and £9,000 for social welfare.
HOW TO APPLY The trust states that the trustees 'regularly appraise new opportunities for direct charitable expenditure and actively seek suitable causes to reduce the unrestricted fund to the appropriate level'.
WHO TO APPLY TO G S Morris, Trustee, PO Box 35547, The Exchange, 4 Brent Cross Gardens, London NW4 3WH *Tel* 020 8457 6500 *email* graham@schreibers.com

■ Schroder Charity Trust

CC NO 214050　　ESTABLISHED 1944
WHERE FUNDING CAN BE GIVEN Worldwide, in practice mainly UK.
WHO CAN BENEFIT Preference for UK-registered charities with a proven track record and those in which the trust has a special interest.
WHAT IS FUNDED General charitable purposes, particularly: health and welfare, community, education, international relief and development, young people, arts, culture and heritage, the environment and rural issues.
WHAT IS NOT FUNDED No grants to individuals.
TYPE OF GRANT One-off and recurring.

RANGE OF GRANTS Mainly small grants from £200–£5,000.
SAMPLE GRANTS Tavistock Trust for Aphasia (£11,000); Catholic Trust for England and Wales – Mallinckrodt Foundation (£10,000); Atlantic Education Project (£5,000); Cirencester Parish Church (£4,500); Water Aid (£3,000); Tax Help for Older People and Africa Now (£2,500 each); Game Conservancy Trust, Queen Victoria School – Dunblane, Tree Aid and Moorfields Eye Hospital Trust (£2,000 each); Skillshare International and Amber Foundation (£1,500 each); Leukaemia Research Fund (£1,200); National Society for Epilepsy and Borealis Theatre (£1,000 each); Silversmiths and Jewellers Charity (£500); and Winston Churchill Foundation of the United States (£210).
FINANCES *Year* 2009–10 *Income* £173,033 *Grants* £165,354 *Assets* £6,891,550
TRUSTEES Claire Fitzalan Howard; Charmaine Mallinckrodt; Bruno Schroder; T B Schroder; Leonie Fane; Frederick Schroder.
HOW TO APPLY In writing to the correspondent. Applicants should briefly state their case and enclose a copy of their latest accounts or annual review. Requests will be acknowledged in writing. The trust does not have the capacity to correspond with organisations on the progress of their application. Therefore, if you have not heard from the trust after six months, you can assume that the application has not been successful.
WHO TO APPLY TO Sally Yates, Secretary, 81 Rivington Street, London EC2A 3AY

■ The Schroder Foundation

CC NO 1107479　　ESTABLISHED 2005
WHERE FUNDING CAN BE GIVEN Worldwide, in practice mainly UK.
WHO CAN BENEFIT Charitable causes with a previous track record and organisations in which the foundation has a special interest.
WHAT IS FUNDED General mainly within the areas of the environment, education, arts, culture and heritage, social welfare, the community and international relief and development.
SAMPLE GRANTS Household Cavalry Operational Casualties Fund (£75,000); Courtauld Institute of Art and Great Ormond Street Hospital Children's Charity (£50,000 each); Beat Bullying and Priors Court Foundation (£40,000 each); School Home Support (£35,000); London Youth Support Trust (£30,000); Ashden Awards for Sustainable Energy (£25,000); Melanoma Focus – National Melanoma Database (£20,000); Hertford College – Oxford (£15,000); University of Cape Town Trust (£10,000); and Cranleigh Foundation (£4,000).
FINANCES *Year* 2010–11 *Income* £476,772 *Grants* £1,367,838 *Assets* £11,955,519
TRUSTEES Bruno Schroder, Chair; Edward Mallinckrodt; Nicholas Ferguson; Charmaine Mallinckrodt; Leonie Fane; Claire Howard; Richard Robinson; Philip Mallinckrodt.
HOW TO APPLY This trust **does not** respond to unsolicited applications. 'The trustees identify projects and organisations they wish to support and the foundation does not make grants to people or organisations who apply speculatively.'
WHO TO APPLY TO Sally Yates, Secretary, 81 Rivington Street, London EC2A 3AY

■ The Scotshill Trust

CC NO 1113071   **ESTABLISHED** 2006
WHERE FUNDING CAN BE GIVEN UK and overseas.
WHO CAN BENEFIT Registered charities.
WHAT IS FUNDED General, particularly health, arts, conservation, education, social needs, animal welfare and conservation.
WHAT IS NOT FUNDED No grants to individuals.
RANGE OF GRANTS £250–£50,000.
SAMPLE GRANTS Oxfam (£50,000); UJIA (£30,000); Samaritans (£25,000); Crisis (£20,000); Amnesty International, Medical Foundation, Big Issue, Richmond Fellowship and Salvation Army (£10,000 each); CARE International, Demand and SNAP (£5,000 each); Nightstop (£2,500); Amber Trust (£1,500); the Horse Trust and Redwings Horse (£1,000); and ILPH and Pace Centre (£500).
FINANCES *Year* 2009–10 *Income* £150,461 *Grants* £1,058,900 *Assets* £6,013,994
TRUSTEES Amanda Claire Burton; Paul Howard Burton; Deborah Maureen Hazan; Jeremy John Burton.
HOW TO APPLY Appeals should be in writing only to the trust managers. Unsuccessful appeals will not necessarily be acknowledged.
WHO TO APPLY TO The Trust Manager, Trustee Management Limited, 19 Cookridge Street, Leeds LS2 3AG *Tel* 0113 243 6466

■ Scott (Eredine) Charitable Trust

CC NO 1002267   **ESTABLISHED** 1990
WHERE FUNDING CAN BE GIVEN Not defined.
WHO CAN BENEFIT Charitable organisations.
WHAT IS FUNDED Service and ex-service charities; and medical and welfare causes.
SAMPLE GRANTS Charitable Fund (£35,000); Scots Guards Charitable Funds (£10,000); Household Division Sailing Association (£7,000); Scottish Veterans Residences (£5,000); King Edward VII Hospital for Officers, national Star Centre, St Dunstan's and The Erskine Hospital (£4,000 each); Taste for Adventure Centre (£3,000); Starlight Children's Foundation, World Vision and ZANE (£2,000 each); The Asker Appeal and The Fire Fighters Charity (£1,000 each); and The League of Remembrance (£500).
FINANCES *Year* 2010 *Income* £185,658 *Grants* £189,000 *Assets* £203,882
TRUSTEES M B Scott; K J Bruce-Smith; A J Scott.
HOW TO APPLY In writing to the correspondent.
WHO TO APPLY TO Keith Bruce-Smith, Trustee, Harcus Sinclair, 3 Lincoln's Inn Fields, London WC2A 3AA *Tel* 020 7242 9700

■ The Francis C Scott Charitable Trust

CC NO 232131   **ESTABLISHED** 1963
WHERE FUNDING CAN BE GIVEN Cumbria and north Lancashire (comprising the towns of Lancaster, Morecambe, Heysham and Carnforth).
WHO CAN BENEFIT Mostly registered charities addressing the needs of 0–19 year olds in the most deprived communities of Cumbria and north Lancashire. Organisations who are pursuing charitable objectives and have not-for-profit aims/constitution may be considered. Applications from national organisations will only be considered if the beneficiaries and project workers are based within the beneficial area.
WHAT IS FUNDED There is an emphasis on community services, support and development

for youth organisations, family support services and community development projects.
WHAT IS NOT FUNDED The trust does not consider appeals: from individuals; from statutory organisations; from national charities without a local base/project; from charities with substantial unrestricted reserves; from medical/health establishments; from schools/educational establishments; from infrastructure organisations/second-tier bodies; for projects principally benefiting people outside Cumbria/north Lancashire; for retrospective funding; for expeditions or overseas travel; for the promotion of religion; for animal welfare.
TYPE OF GRANT Most grants are multi-year revenue grants (i.e. salaries and running costs); capital projects that make a tangible difference to a local community are also supported.
RANGE OF GRANTS Up to £275,000.
SAMPLE GRANTS Calvert Trust – Keswick (£100,000); Thomas Gane Estate (FST beneficiaries) (£40,000); Champ's Camp, Safety Net Advice & Support Centre – West Cumbria and Marsh Community Centre (£20,000 each); Barrow Dad's Group (£18,000); Self Harm Awareness for the Furness Area, Eden Community Outdoors, University of Cumbria and New Rainbow Pre-School (£15,000 each); Practical Alternatives to Custody, St Matthews Community Halls and South Cumbria Dyslexia Association (£10,000 each); Morecambe Brass Band Association and Centre for Complementary Care (shootings) (£5,000 each); and Christ Church Night Shelter (£2,000).
FINANCES *Year* 2010 *Income* £654,514 *Grants* £906,910 *Assets* £28,140,436
TRUSTEES Susan Bagot, Chair; Joanna Plumptre; Alexander Scott; Madeleine Scott; Don Shore; Clare Spedding; Peter Redhead; Melanie Wotherspoon.
OTHER INFORMATION Applicants should refer to the trust's website which is very comprehensive and covers all aspects of the grantmaking process.
HOW TO APPLY The trust is always pleased to hear from charities that need help. If an organisation thinks that it may come within the trust's criteria it is encouraged to contact the director for an informal discussion before making an application. Application forms are available to download from the trust's website or can be requested by phone, email or post. Applications should be completed and returned with the latest set of accounts (via email or post). Applications for over £4,000 should be submitted at least 4 weeks before the trustee's meetings in late February, June, October and November. Please check the website for the latest deadlines. Applications for grants of less than £4,000 will be considered at small grants meetings every 3–4 weeks.
WHO TO APPLY TO Chris Batten, Director, Suite 3, Sand Aire House, New Road, Kendal, Cumbria LA9 4UJ *Tel* 01539 741610 *Fax* 01539 741611 *email* info@fcsct.org.uk *Website* www.fcsct.org.uk

■ The Frieda Scott Charitable Trust

CC NO 221593   **ESTABLISHED** 1962
WHERE FUNDING CAN BE GIVEN Old county of Westmorland and the area covered by South Lakeland District Council.
WHO CAN BENEFIT Small local charities, parish halls, youth groups and occasionally locally based work of larger charities.

WHAT IS FUNDED A very wide range of registered charities concerned with social welfare, community projects, the upkeep of village halls and voluntary sector infrastructure support and development.

WHAT IS NOT FUNDED Applications are not considered if they are from outside the beneficial area. No grants to individuals. No grants for retrospective funding, parish councils, health establishments, schools or educational establishments, places of worship or promoting religion, environmental causes, multi-year grants (except for start ups), animal charities, wildlife or heritage causes, gardens or allotments (unless addressing disadvantage), property buying (other than in exceptional circumstances), sporting activity, museums and art galleries, national charities (with exceptions made for branches operating in the beneficial area).

TYPE OF GRANT Capital including building costs, core costs, one-off, project, research, recurring costs, running costs, salaries and start-up costs. The Trustees are unwilling to commit to funding more than 1 year at any one time.

RANGE OF GRANTS £200–£10,000 with some larger grants.

SAMPLE GRANTS South Lakes Foyer (£75,000); Growing Well (£15,000); Young Cumbria – South Lakes (£11,500); Ryan Smith Rising Sun Trust, South Lakeland Mind and Westmorland Music Council (£10,000 each); Feature Youth Club (£6,000); Citizens Advice South Lakeland (£7,000); Coniston Mountain Rescue Team (£5,000); Brigsteer Village Hall and Grizebeck Village Hall Committee (£3,500 each); Kendal Family Drop-in Centre (£2,000); Charities Aid Foundation (£1,000); Kirkby Lonsdale Choral Society (£800).

FINANCES Year 2010–11 Income £223,063 Grants £274,524 Assets £6,566,587

TRUSTEES Sally J H Barker; Richard Brownson; Stuart Fairclough; Claire Hensman; Philip V Hoyle; Margaret G Wilson.

OTHER INFORMATION Please note: the trust asks that charities do not apply to both the Frieda Scott and Francis C Scott Charitable Trusts at the same time. If unsure, contact the trust for further guidance.

HOW TO APPLY An application form is available from the correspondent, or from the trust's website, which should be returned by email or post with the latest set of audited accounts. Potential applicants are welcome to ring for an informal discussion before submitting an application. Applications are considered at meetings in March, June, September and December and should be sent to the Grants Coordinator at least a month beforehand. Grants of less than £3,500 are considered by the small grants committee in between main trustee meetings.

WHO TO APPLY TO Debra Jessett, Grants Coordinator, Suite 3, Sand Aire House, New Road, Kendal, Cumbria LA9 4UJ Tel 01539 741610 Fax 01539 741611 email info@fcsct.org.uk Website www.friedascott.org.uk

■ Sir Samuel Scott of Yews Trust

CC NO 220878   **ESTABLISHED** 1951

WHERE FUNDING CAN BE GIVEN UK.

WHO CAN BENEFIT Medical research bodies benefiting medical professionals and research workers.

WHAT IS FUNDED Medical research.

WHAT IS NOT FUNDED No grants for: core funding; purely clinical work; individuals (although research by an individual may be funded if sponsored by a registered charity through which

the application is made); research leading to higher degrees (unless the departmental head concerned certifies that the work is of real scientific importance); medical students' elective periods; or expeditions (unless involving an element of genuine medical research).

TYPE OF GRANT One-off, project.

RANGE OF GRANTS Usually £1,000–£10,000.

SAMPLE GRANTS University of Oxford – Gray Institute (£103,000); Royal College of Surgeons, Alzheimer's Research Trust and Bath Institute of Medical Engineering (£10,000 each); Bristol Eye Hospital – National Eye Research Centre, International Spinal Research, Wellbeing of Women and Joint Action (£5,000 each); Meningitis UK (£4,000); Brain Research Trust (£3,000); Deafness Research UK and Ovarian Cancer Action (£2,000 each); and Marfan Trust and University of London – School of Pharmacy (£1,000 each).

FINANCES Year 2009–10 Income £108,053 Grants £245,000 Assets £5,578,519

TRUSTEES Lady Phoebe Scott; Hermione Stanford; Edward Perks.

HOW TO APPLY In writing to the correspondent. Trustees hold their half-yearly meetings in April and October and applications have to be submitted two months before. There are no special forms, but applicants should give the following information: the nature and purpose of the research project or programme; the names, qualifications and present posts of the scientists involved; reference to any published results of their previous research; details of present funding; and if possible, the budget for the next 12 months or other convenient period. All applications are acknowledged and both successful and unsuccessful applicants are notified after each meeting of the trustees. No telephone calls.

WHO TO APPLY TO The Secretary, c/o Currey and Co, 21 Buckingham Gate, London SW1E 6LS Tel 020 7802 2700

■ The Sir James and Lady Scott Trust

CC NO 231324   **ESTABLISHED** 1907

WHERE FUNDING CAN BE GIVEN The borough and district of Bolton.

WHO CAN BENEFIT Only registered charities, or not-for-profit organisations that are in the process of becoming a charity, will be considered.

WHAT IS FUNDED The trustees give priority to projects which help disadvantaged people or communities in Bolton. These have included projects which help elderly people, people with disabilities, young people, children and ethnic minority groups.

WHAT IS NOT FUNDED The trust does not consider applications from individuals or for church restoration, medical causes, expeditions and scholarships.

TYPE OF GRANT Recurring costs; one-off; capital costs including buildings; core costs; endowment; feasibility studies; project research; running costs; salaries; and start-up costs. Funding is available for one year or less.

RANGE OF GRANTS Up to £3,000.

SAMPLE GRANTS Harmony Youth Project (£2,500); Volunteer Reading Help, Montrose YMCA and Daytrippers (Bolton) (£2,000 each); Firwood and Moorfield Estate Residents' Association and New Bolton Somali Community Association (£1,000 each); Guide Association – Bolton and The Well (£500 each).

FINANCES *Year* 2009–10 *Income* £47,799 *Grants* £34,831 *Assets* £2,444,648

TRUSTEES Christopher J Scott, Chair; Madeleine M Scott; William L G Swan.

OTHER INFORMATION Grants of £15,400 were made to individuals.

HOW TO APPLY On a form available from the correspondent, or from the trust's website, together with a latest set of audited accounts. An initial telephone call is welcomed.

WHO TO APPLY TO Chris Batten, Secretary, Suite 3, Sand Aire House, New Road, Kendal, Cumbria LA9 4UJ *Tel* 01539 741610 *Fax* 01539 741611 *email* info@fcsct.org.uk *Website* www.sjlst.org.uk

---

■ The Scott Trust Foundation

CC NO 1027893 **ESTABLISHED** 1993

WHERE FUNDING CAN BE GIVEN UK and overseas.

WHO CAN BENEFIT To benefit children, young adults, students and journalists.

WHAT IS FUNDED 'The Scott Trust Charitable Fund was established in March 2005 by the Scott Trust Foundation. Its purpose is to foster, promote and support one of the key objectives of the Scott Trust, namely 'promoting the causes of freedom of the press and liberal journalism both in Britain and elsewhere.' Proposals which answer the following criteria will be considered for support: independent journalism; media literacy; journalistic training; journalistic ethics.

WHAT IS NOT FUNDED As a rule the charitable trust will not fund: building projects; fellowships, internships, bursaries other than the trust's own unless there are exceptional circumstances; new lecture series other than those planned at Kings Place. Small community projects with limited impact will NOT be considered. However, projects such as these might well be considered by individual Guardian Media Group companies, a list of which can be made available on request.

TYPE OF GRANT One-off.

FINANCES *Year* 2009–10 *Income* £282,000 *Grants* £100,000 *Assets* £15,237

TRUSTEES Larry Elliott; Alan Rusbridger; Geraldine Proudler; Jonathan Scott; Liz Forgan; Will Hutton; Andrew Graham; Anthony Salz; Ms Maleiha Malik.

HOW TO APPLY All proposals should include: brief outline of what your organisation does, its constitution, articles, etc. (if appropriate) and a list of the key individuals involved; specifics of the project and who will benefit; how the money would be spent; timescales. Proposals should be emailed to Ashley.hanley@guardian.co.uk or by post to Ashley Hanley, Scott Trust Co-ordinator, Kings Place, 90 York Way, London, N1 9GU. Please kindly note that any offers of funding should be taken up within three months of notification.

WHO TO APPLY TO Ashley Hanley, Scott Trust Co-ordinator, Kings Place, 90 York Way, London N1 9GU. *email* Ashley.hanley@guardian.co.uk

---

■ The Storrow Scott Will Trust

CC NO 328391 **ESTABLISHED** 1989

WHERE FUNDING CAN BE GIVEN Preference for the north east of England.

WHO CAN BENEFIT Charitable organisations.

WHAT IS FUNDED General charitable purposes.

WHAT IS NOT FUNDED Grants for individuals and for the purchase of depreciating assets such as mini-buses will not be considered.

RANGE OF GRANTS Up to £10,000.

SAMPLE GRANTS The Anaphylaxis Campaign and Camphill Village Trust and St Oswald's Hospice (£6,000 each); Chance to Shine – (For the Northumberland Cricket Clubs) (£3,000); Percy Hedley Foundation and Songs Bird Survival (£2,000 each); Ocean Youth Trust North East and Sedburgh School Foundation (£1,000 each).

FINANCES *Year* 2009–10 *Income* £46,731 *Grants* £41,000 *Assets* £751,684

TRUSTEES G W Meikle; J S North Lewis.

HOW TO APPLY In writing to the correspondent. There are no formal application forms.

WHO TO APPLY TO G W Meikle, c/o Dickinson Dees, One Trinity Gardens, Broad Chare, Newcastle upon Tyne NE1 2HF *Tel* 0191 279 9000 *Fax* 0191 279 9100

■ The Scottish Arts Council

SC NO SC002835 **ESTABLISHED** 1967

WHERE FUNDING CAN BE GIVEN Scotland.

OTHER INFORMATION Creative Scotland assumed the responsibilities and function of the Scottish Arts Council in 2010 (www.creativescotland.com).

WHO TO APPLY TO 249 West George Street, Glasgow G2 4QE *Tel* 0845 603 6000 *email* enquiries@creativescotland.com *Website* www.creativescotland.com

---

■ Scottish Coal Industry Special Welfare Fund

SC NO SC001200 **ESTABLISHED** 1932

WHERE FUNDING CAN BE GIVEN Scotland.

WHO CAN BENEFIT Miners.

WHAT IS FUNDED The fund was set up to improve the conditions of people employed in the mining industry and their families. It supports individuals in need and also the provision of recreational facilities, youth clubs and courses.

FINANCES *Year* 2009–10 *Income* £54,519

TRUSTEES Keith Jones, Chair; William Menzies; Robert McGill.

OTHER INFORMATION In November 2005 we reported that the fund's website contained only basic information, and that potential applicants should check it for further details on recent beneficiaries and other information as it develops. Over five years later there have been no developments.

HOW TO APPLY 'If you feel you, your group or organisation would qualify for some financial assistance from the fund, please write to us to request a grant. Please include as much information as possible in your letter to avoid any delay caused by questions raised by the trustees prior to grant issue. It is also extremely important to highlight your link to the coal mining industry in your grant request. The trustees meet quarterly to consider grant requests.' In November 2005 the trust stated that it intended to have an application form available to download from its website – as at December 2009 this had still not happened.

WHO TO APPLY TO Ian McAlpine, Secretary, c/o CISWO, Second Floor, 50 Hopetoun Street, Bathgate, West Lothian EH48 4EU *Tel* 01506 635550 *Fax* 01506 631555 *email* ian.mcalpine@ciswo.org.uk *Website* www.sciswf.org.uk

■ The Scottish Community Foundation

SC NO SC022910 **ESTABLISHED** 1995
WHERE FUNDING CAN BE GIVEN Scotland.
WHO CAN BENEFIT Small organisations helping to build and sustain local communities.
WHAT IS FUNDED There are two broad programmes, under which there are a range of different funds.
Scotland-wide programmes – includes express grants (up to £2,000); grants for women's projects; and comic relief local communities grants.
Local grants programmes – there are a variety of programmes which benefit people in specific areas of Scotland. Each has different grant levels, deadline dates and decision making practices. A list of local programmes is available on the foundation's website.
WHAT IS NOT FUNDED The foundation does not usually fund: individuals or groups which do not have a constitution; groups other than not-for-profit groups; groups whose grant request is for the advancement of religion or a political party (this means the foundation won't fund grant requests to support the core activities of religious or political groups); the purchase of second hand vehicles; trips abroad; the repayment of loans, payment of debts, or other retrospective funding; payments towards areas generally understood to be the responsibility of statutory authorities; groups who will then distribute the funds as grants or bursaries; applications that are for the sole benefit to flora and fauna. Applicants are invited to demonstrate the direct benefit to the local community and/or service users in cases where the grant application is concerned with flora and fauna; projects which do not benefit people in Scotland. Please note different grant programmes may have additional restrictions.
TYPE OF GRANT Capital, revenue and full project funding.
RANGE OF GRANTS Usually between £250 and £5,000 – occasionally larger grants are made.
SAMPLE GRANTS LifeScan Scotland, Judy Russell Fund for Women, Fairshare trust, Evelyn Jamieson Memorial, Poles Apart Trust, Our Community Our future, Elizabeth Montgomerie Appeal, Eaga (Scotland-wide), Al Maktoum Institute, ABO Wind Lairg Community Benefit, Clary Jack and Edinburgh Arts Prize.
FINANCES *Year* 2010–11 *Income* £8,725,000 *Grants* £2,734,000 *Assets* £14,485,000
TRUSTEES Bob Benson; Gillian Donald; Beth Edberg; Colin Liddell; Ian McAteer; Jimmy McCulloch; John Naylor; Ella Simpson; Lady Emily Stair; Tom Ward.
OTHER INFORMATION Please note that grant schemes change frequently and potential applicants should consult the foundation's website for details of current programmes and their deadlines.
HOW TO APPLY The foundation has a comprehensive website with details of the grant schemes currently being administered. Organisations are welcome to contact the grants team to discuss their funding needs before making any application. Trustees meet at least four times a year.
WHO TO APPLY TO Alice Dansey-Wright, Programmes Administrator, Empire House, 131 West Nile Street, Glasgow G1 2RX *Tel* 0141 341 4960 *Fax* 0141 341 4972 *email* nick@scottishcf.org *Website* www.scottishcf.org

■ The Scottish International Education Trust

SC NO SC009207 **ESTABLISHED** 1970
WHERE FUNDING CAN BE GIVEN Scotland.
WHO CAN BENEFIT Scots (by birth or upbringing) taking advanced studies for which support from public funds is not available.
WHAT IS FUNDED Grants are given to organisations and individuals whose concerns lie in education, the arts or the areas of economic or social welfare.
WHAT IS NOT FUNDED No grants to commercial organisations, for capital work, general maintenance, or for courses (e.g. undergraduate study) for which there is support from statutory bodies/public funds.
TYPE OF GRANT Normally one-off.
RANGE OF GRANTS Usually £1,000 to £3,000.
SAMPLE GRANTS Previous beneficiaries include Royal Scottish Academy of Music and Drama, Scottish International Piano Competition, Scottish Schools Debating Council and Scotland Yard Adventure Centre.
FINANCES *Year* 2009–10 *Income* £6,194,700
TRUSTEES Andy Irvine, Chair; Joseph Campbell; Sir Menzies Campbell; Sir Sean Connery; Tom Fleming; Lady Gibson; Prof. Sir Alistair Macfarlane; Sir Jackie Stewart; John F McClellan; Gerda Stevenson; Alex Salmond; David Michie.
HOW TO APPLY In writing to the correspondent. Guidelines for applicants are also available from the correspondent.
WHO TO APPLY TO The Director, Turcan Connell, Princes Exchange, 1 Earl Grey Street, Edinburgh EH3 9EE *Tel* 0131 225 1113 *email* siet@ukonline.co.uk *Website* www.scotinted.org.uk

■ The Scouloudi Foundation

CC NO 205685 **ESTABLISHED** 1962
WHERE FUNDING CAN BE GIVEN UK charities working domestically or overseas.
WHO CAN BENEFIT (a) The Institute of Historical Research, University of London, for publications, research and fellowships ('Historical Awards'), (b) registered charities in the fields of elderly people; children and youth; environment; famine relief and overseas aid; disability; the humanities (archaeology, art, history, libraries, museums, records); medicine, health and hospices; social welfare; and welfare of armed forces and sailors.
WHAT IS FUNDED Candidates fulfilling the Institute of Historical Research's criteria may apply to the Institute for their research and publication costs to be funded. 'Special Donations' are made for extraordinary appeals and capital projects, and not day-to-day expenditure or staff costs. No applications for 'Regular Donations' are invited as these are normally specially selected.
WHAT IS NOT FUNDED Donations are not made to individuals, and are not normally made for welfare activities of a purely local nature. The trustees do not make loans or enter into deeds of covenant.
TYPE OF GRANT There are three categories of grant: an annual donation for historical research and fellowships to the Institute of Historical Research at the University of London; recurring grants to a regular list of charities; and 'special donations' which are one-off grants, usually in connection with capital projects.
RANGE OF GRANTS Typically £1,000–£2,000.
SAMPLE GRANTS University of London – Institute of Historical Research (£68,000); British Red

Cross Disaster Fund, Friends of Kew and Richard's House Children's Hospice (£5,000 each); Brain Research Trust, British Records Association, British & International Sailors Society, CORDA the Heart Charity, Macmillan Cancer Support, Marie Curie Cancer Care, Mental Health Foundation, National Society for Epilepsy, Samaritans and Voluntary Service Bureau (£1,250 each); and British Library (£1,000).

FINANCES *Year* 2009–10 *Income* £233,085 *Grants* £204,106 *Assets* £5,294,142

TRUSTEES Sarah Stowell; David Marnham; James Sewell.

PUBLICATIONS Notes for the guidance of applicants for 'Special Donations' and 'Historical Awards'.

HOW TO APPLY Only Historical grants are open to application. Copies of the regulations and application forms for 'Historical Awards' can be obtained from: The Secretary, The Scouloudi Foundation Historical Awards Committee, c/o Institute of Historical Research, University of London, Senate House, Malet Street, London WC1E 7HU.

WHO TO APPLY TO The Administrators, c/o Haysmacintyre, Fairfax House, 15 Fulwood Place, London WC1V 6AY *Tel* 020 7969 5500 *Fax* 020 7969 5600

....

■ Seafarers UK (King George's Fund for Sailors)

CC NO 226446   **ESTABLISHED** 1917

WHERE FUNDING CAN BE GIVEN UK and Commonwealth.

WHO CAN BENEFIT Organisations caring for seafarers whether these are officers or ratings, men or women, past or present of the Royal Navy, the Merchant Navy, the Fishing Fleets and their dependants.

WHAT IS FUNDED Registered nautical charities and other registered charities which assist seafarers and their dependants in distress, provide training for young people to become sailors, provide training for sailors and support for other institutions which promote safety at sea.

WHAT IS NOT FUNDED The fund does not make any grants directly to individuals except in exceptional cases but rather helps other organisations which do this. However, the fund may be able to advise in particular cases about a suitable organisation to approach. Full details of such organisations are to be found in A Guide to Grants for Individuals in Need, published by DSC.

TYPE OF GRANT Annual grants for general purposes; capital grants for specific projects such as new buildings, modernisations, conversions, etc.; and interim grants may be considered at any time. Core costs, feasibility studies, recurring and running costs will also be considered.

RANGE OF GRANTS up to £300,000.

SAMPLE GRANTS Shipwrecked Fishermen and Mariners' Royal Benevolent Society (£256,000); Royal Navy and Royal Marines Charity (£166,000); Royal Alfred Seafarers Society (£125,000); Royal National Mission to Deep Sea Fishermen and Ex-Services Mental Welfare Society – Combat Stress (£100,000 each); Nautilus Welfare Funds (£91,000); International Seafarers Assistance Network (£67,000); Maritime Charities Funding Group Seafarers Projects (£40,000); Centres for Seafarers and KIDS (£35,000 each); Apostleship of the Sea (£30,000); Douglas Haig Memorial Homes (£11,000); Handicapped Children's Pilgrimage Trust (£7,500); Felixstowe Sea Cadets Corps (£6,600); Peterhead & District Fisherman's Benevolent Fund and Spinal Injuries Association (£5,000 each); and Scottish Shipping Benevolent Association (£1,200).

FINANCES *Year* 2010 *Income* £3,026,000 *Grants* £2,476,000 *Assets* £41,299,000

TRUSTEES Frank Welsh; Barry Miller; Maj Patrick Dunn; Anthony Lydekker; Capt David Parsons; James Watson; Michael Acland; Peter Mamelok; Timothy Warren; John Thompson; Christine Gould; Christian Marr; Simon Rivet-Carnac; Vice Admiral Peter Wilkinson.

PUBLICATIONS 'Flagship' and the 'Nautical Welfare Guide'.

OTHER INFORMATION The trust has a very informative and useful website that should be referred to.

HOW TO APPLY Applicants to the main grants scheme should download the form available on the trust's website and use the guidance notes also available. There is a deadline for this scheme each year which is published on the website. Those to the Marine Society and Sea Cadets scheme should use the specific form and guidelines available on the website. Applications to the small grants scheme should download the small grants form and guidelines available on the website. There are no closing dates for the schemes which awards grants of up to £5,000. Only one application from an organisation can be considered in any 12 month period.

WHO TO APPLY TO Dennis Treleaven, Head of Grants, 8 Hatherley Street, London SW1P 2YY *Tel* 020 7932 5984 *Fax* 020 7932 0095 *email* dennis.treleaven@seafarers-uk.org *Website* www.seafarers-uk.org

....

■ Seamen's Hospital Society

CC NO 231724   **ESTABLISHED** 1999

WHERE FUNDING CAN BE GIVEN UK.

WHO CAN BENEFIT Medical, care and welfare organisations working with seafarers and to individual seafarers and their dependants.

WHAT IS FUNDED Welfare causes.

RANGE OF GRANTS £4,000–£128,000.

SAMPLE GRANTS Seafarers' Benefits Advice Line (£250,000); MCFG Development Programme (£40,000); Nautilus Welfare Fund – Mariners' Park (£30,000); Merchant Seamen's War Memorial Society (£17,500); Royal Alfred Seafarers' Society (£10,000); Royal National Mission to Deep Sea Fishermen (£7,500); Scottish Nautical Welfare Society (£3,000); Queen Victoria Seamen's Rest (£2,500); and Annual National Service for Seafarers (£100).

FINANCES *Year* 2010 *Income* £494,388 *Grants* £469,500 *Assets* £8,121,190

TRUSTEES Capt. D Glass; J C Jenkinson; P McEwan; R Chichester; A R Nairne; Capt. A J Speed; Capt. C Stewart; J Newton; Dr C Mendes da Costa; Mark Carden; Anthony Lydekker; Commander Frank Leonard; Max Gladwyn; Graham Lane.

OTHER INFORMATION The society also operates the Seafarers' Benefits Advice Line, which provides free confidential advice and information on welfare benefits, housing, consumer problems, legal matters, credit and debt, matrimonial and tax. £361,000 was distributed to organisations helping seafarers, with a further £108,500 going to individuals.

HOW TO APPLY On a form available from the correspondent. Grants are awarded in November of each year.

WHO TO APPLY TO Peter Coulson, General Secretary, 29 King William Walk, Greenwich, London SE10 9HX *Tel* 020 8858 3696 *Fax* 020 8293 9630 *email* admin@seahospital.org.uk *Website* www.seahospital.org.uk

■ The Searchlight Electric Charitable Trust

CC NO 801644   ESTABLISHED 1988
WHERE FUNDING CAN BE GIVEN UK, with a preference for Manchester.
WHO CAN BENEFIT Registered charities. In the past the trustees have stated that it is their policy to only support charities already on their existing list of beneficiaries, or those already known to them.
WHAT IS FUNDED General charitable purposes.
WHAT IS NOT FUNDED No grants for individuals.
SAMPLE GRANTS Previous beneficiaries have included: UJIA (£45,000); CST (£6,000); Bnei a Kivah Sefer Torah (£5,000); Guide Dogs for the Blind (£4,000); Young Israel Synagogue (£2,600); the Federation (£2,000); Langdon College (£1,500); Heathlands, Lubavitch Manchester and Manchester Eruv Committee (£1,000 each); Reshet and the Purim Fund (£750 each); and Sense, Nightingales and Chabad Vilna (£500 each).
FINANCES *Year* 2009–10 *Income* £13,938 *Grants* £71,572
TRUSTEES D M Hamburger, Chair; H E Hamburger; M E Hamburger.
OTHER INFORMATION Grants of less than £500 totalled £15,000.
HOW TO APPLY In writing to the correspondent, but please note that in the past the trustees have stated that it is their policy to only support charities already on their existing list of beneficiaries or those already known to them.
WHO TO APPLY TO H E Hamburger, Trustee, Searchlight Electric Ltd, 900 Oldham Road, Manchester M40 2BS *Tel* 0161 203 3300 *email* heh@slightdemon.co.uk

■ The Searle Charitable Trust

CC NO 288541   ESTABLISHED 1982
WHERE FUNDING CAN BE GIVEN UK.
WHO CAN BENEFIT Established youth organisations benefiting those disadvantaged by poverty.
WHAT IS FUNDED Projects/organisations connected with sailing for youth development.
WHAT IS NOT FUNDED No grants for individuals or for appeals not related to sailing.
TYPE OF GRANT One-off, recurring costs, project and core costs. Funding is available for up to three years.
SAMPLE GRANTS One grant of £88,000 to RONA Trust, also a major beneficiary in previous years.
FINANCES *Year* 2009–10 *Income* £80,677 *Grants* £88,076 *Assets* £3,647,945
TRUSTEES Andrew D Searle; Victoria C Searle.
OTHER INFORMATION The trust funds the 'Donald Searle' sail training yacht which is part of a fleet of vessels run and operated by the London Sailing Project based at Southampton. The main aim of the trust is youth development within a nautical environment.
HOW TO APPLY In writing to the correspondent.
WHO TO APPLY TO Sarah Sharkey, 30 Watling Street, St Albans AL1 2QB

■ The Helene Sebba Charitable Trust

CC NO 277245   ESTABLISHED 1978
WHERE FUNDING CAN BE GIVEN UK, Canada and Israel.
WHO CAN BENEFIT Organisations involved in welfare and health, including medical research, and those benefiting people with disabilities or people of the Jewish faith.
WHAT IS FUNDED Support for: welfare, health and medical research; people who are disabled; and people of the Jewish faith.
RANGE OF GRANTS £500–£40,000.
SAMPLE GRANTS Friends of Israel Sports Centre for the Disabled (£32,000); SAS Success after Stoke (£7,000); Ferring Country Centre (£5,000); the Prostrate Cancer Charity (£4,000); Friends of Morris Fienmann Homes (£3,000); Foundation Training Company (£2,000); North London Hospice (£1,000); National Jewish Chaplaincy (£500).
FINANCES *Year* 2009–10 *Income* £52,132 *Grants* £108,500 *Assets* £2,352,486
TRUSTEES Mrs N C Klein; Mrs J C Sebba; L Sebba.
HOW TO APPLY In writing to the correspondent.
WHO TO APPLY TO David L Hull, PO Box 326, Bedford MK40 3XU *Tel* 01234 266657

■ The Samuel Sebba Charitable Trust

CC NO 253351   ESTABLISHED 1967
WHERE FUNDING CAN BE GIVEN UK and Israel.
WHO CAN BENEFIT Charitable bodies with a preference for Jewish organisations.
WHAT IS FUNDED The trust focuses on the areas of education, community, children and youth, medical, hospice and older people, arts, interfaith, medical, people with disabilities, mental health, health, asylum seekers and preventative medicine. The trust hopes to expand on its present grant giving and from time to time respond to environmental concerns and international aid.
WHAT IS NOT FUNDED No grants to individuals.
RANGE OF GRANTS Up to £300,000.
SAMPLE GRANTS Sulam School – Jerusalem (£296,000); New Yeruham Fund (£67,000); Tel Aviv university Trust (£60,000); Medical Foundation for the Care of Victims of Torture (£45,000); Music of Remembrance (£33,000); Alzheimer's Association of Israel (£32,000); Association for Civil Rights in Israel (£30,000); North London Hospice and Union of Jewish Students Hillel (£25,000 each); JDC Israel and Reuth – Women's Social Services (£20,000 each); Elem – Youth in Distress (£19,000); and Deafblind UK, Cystic Fibrosis Trust, The Parents Club – Bereaved Families Forum and Jewish Association for Business Ethics (£15,000 each).
FINANCES *Year* 2009–10 *Income* £704,864 *Grants* £2,844,974 *Assets* £39,851,315
TRUSTEES Leigh Sebba; Stanley Sebba; Prof. Leslie Sebba; Victor Klein; Clive M Marks; Lady Winston; Sallie Tangir.
HOW TO APPLY Organisations applying must provide proof of need, they must forward the most recent audited accounts, a registered charity number, and most importantly a cash flow statement for the next 12 months. All applications should have a stamped addressed envelope enclosed. It is also important that the actual request for funds must be concise and preferably summarised on one side of A4. The trustees meet quarterly. However, because of

ongoing support to so many organisations already known to the trust, it is likely that unsolicited applications will, for the foreseeable future, be unsuccessful.

WHO TO APPLY TO David Lerner, Chief Executive, 25–26 Enford Street, London W1H 1DW *Tel* 020 7723 6028 *Fax* 020 7724 7412

■ The Seedfield Trust

CC NO 283463   **ESTABLISHED** 1981
WHERE FUNDING CAN BE GIVEN Worldwide.
WHO CAN BENEFIT Registered charities benefiting: Christians; evangelists; victims of famine, man-made and natural disasters, and war; people disadvantaged by poverty; retired clergy; and missionaries.
WHAT IS FUNDED To support the preaching and teaching of the Christian faith throughout the world, including publication and distribution of Scripture, Christian literature and audio-visual aids. To assist in the relief of hardship and poverty, including retired ministers and missionaries.
WHAT IS NOT FUNDED No grants to individuals.
TYPE OF GRANT The trust rarely makes grants towards core funding or for activities that may require funding over a number of years, preferring to make one-off project grants.
RANGE OF GRANTS Up to £15,000.
SAMPLE GRANTS Overseas Missionary Fellowship (£10,000); European Christian Mission (International) – (£6,000); Mullers (£5,000); Gideons International (£3,000); Capernwray Hall, Choices, Islington and Operation Mobilisation (£2,000 each); Leprosy Mission, Manchester Mission and MECO UK/Ireland (£1,000 each); and Acorn Christian Healing Foundation (£500).
FINANCES *Year* 2010 *Income* £105,251 *Grants* £80,000 *Assets* £2,482,443
TRUSTEES Paul Vipond; Keith Buckler; David Ryan; Janet Buckler; Valerie James.
HOW TO APPLY In writing to the correspondent, for consideration by the trustees who meet twice each year. Please enclose an sae for acknowledgement.
WHO TO APPLY TO The Trustees, 3 Woodland Vale, Lakeside, Ulverston, Cumbria LA12 8DR *Tel* 015395 30359

■ Leslie Sell Charitable Trust

CC NO 258699   **ESTABLISHED** 1969
WHERE FUNDING CAN BE GIVEN UK, with some preference for the Bedfordshire, Hertfordshire and Buckinghamshire area.
WHO CAN BENEFIT Scout and Guide associations and individuals.
WHAT IS FUNDED Assistance for Scout and Guide associations.
TYPE OF GRANT Usually one-off payments for a small project, such as building repair works, transport, trips or equipment.
RANGE OF GRANTS Up to £5,000.
FINANCES *Year* 2009–10 *Income* £117,713 *Grants* £85,616 *Assets* £2,906,237
TRUSTEES Mary Wiltshire; Adrian Sell; John Byrnes.
OTHER INFORMATION In 2011 the trust set up the Peter Sell Annual Award to provide a grant of up to £5,000 to a project aimed at widening engagement and involvement in scouting and guiding.
HOW TO APPLY In writing to the correspondent. Applications should include clear details of the project or purpose for which funds are required,

together with an estimate of total costs and details of any funds raised by the group or individual for the project. The trust states that: 'Applications are usually treated sympathetically provided they are connected to the Scouting or Guide movement.' Please see the website for full guidelines.
WHO TO APPLY TO Sharon Long, Secretary, Ashbrittle House, 2a Lower Dagnall Street, St Albans, Hertfordshire AL3 4PA *Tel* 01727 843603 *Fax* 01727 843663 *email* admin@iplltd.co.uk *Website* www.lesliesellct.org.uk

■ Sellata Ltd

CC NO 285429   **ESTABLISHED** 1980
WHERE FUNDING CAN BE GIVEN UK.
WHO CAN BENEFIT Charitable organisations.
WHAT IS FUNDED The advancement of religion and the relief of poverty.
FINANCES *Year* 2009–10 *Income* £219,991 *Grants* £102,833 *Assets* £310,893
TRUSTEES Eliezer Benedikt; Nechy Benedikt; Pinchas Benedikt; Joseph Stern.
HOW TO APPLY In writing to the correspondent.
WHO TO APPLY TO Eliezer Benedikt, Trustee, 29 Fontayne Road, London N16 7EA

■ SEM Charitable Trust

CC NO 265831   **ESTABLISHED** 1973
WHERE FUNDING CAN BE GIVEN Mainly South Africa, Israel and UK.
WHO CAN BENEFIT Mainly educational institutions benefiting disabled people, children and young adults.
WHAT IS FUNDED Mainly recommendations of the settlor, particularly charities working in the fields of the education of disadvantaged and disabled people; and the empowerment of grassroots people in developing countries.
WHAT IS NOT FUNDED No grants to individuals.
TYPE OF GRANT Recurring and one-off.
RANGE OF GRANTS Mostly under £2,000.
SAMPLE GRANTS Natal Society for Arts (£81,000); Jewish Aid Community (£4,500); Tiverton MKT (£3,000); Lotem (£2,500); Care Ltd and Nicky Alliance Day Centre (£2,000 each); SOS Children's Villages, Friends of the Elderly, Disabled on Line Ltd and the Valley Trust (£1,000 each); and Skillforce, CP Sport and Trustees of Snowden (£500 each).
FINANCES *Year* 2009–10 *Income* £88,726 *Grants* £120,014 *Assets* £1,123,535
TRUSTEES Sarah Radomir; Michael Radomir.
HOW TO APPLY In writing to the correspondent.
WHO TO APPLY TO The Trustees, Reeves and Co LLP, 37 St Margaret's Street, Canterbury, Kent CT1 2TU *Tel* 01227 768231 *email* info@semtrust.org.uk *Website* www.semcharitabletrust.org

■ The Seneca Trust

CC NO 1137147   **ESTABLISHED** 2010
WHERE FUNDING CAN BE GIVEN UK.
WHO CAN BENEFIT Charities or other voluntary bodies.
WHAT IS FUNDED Social welfare, education, children and young people.
TRUSTEES Tatjana May; Adam Sweidan; Colin Lehmann; Angela Beech.
OTHER INFORMATION The settlors of the trust are Kevin Gundle, co-founder of Aurum Funds Limited and also a trustee of Absolute Return

for Kids (ARK), and his wife Deborah, who amongst other things has been involved in publishing and film production – her most recent venture is NetBuddy, an online resource offering tips, help and advice for parents and carers of children with learning disabilities. No accounts available or due for this new trust.

HOW TO APPLY In writing to the correspondent.

WHO TO APPLY TO Colin Lehmann, Trustee, Blick Rothenberg, 12 York Gate, London NW1 4QS *Tel* 020 7486 0111 *email* colin.lehmann@ blickrothenberg.com

■ The Ayrton Senna Foundation

CC NO 1041759 **ESTABLISHED** 1994

WHERE FUNDING CAN BE GIVEN Worldwide.

WHO CAN BENEFIT Children's health and education charities.

WHAT IS FUNDED The relief of poverty and the advancement of education, religion and health, particularly the provision of education, healthcare and medical support for children.

WHAT IS NOT FUNDED No grants to individuals.

SAMPLE GRANTS Instituto Ayrton Senna (£2.8 million).

FINANCES *Year* 2009–10 *Income* £44,571 *Grants* £0 *Assets* £491,570

TRUSTEES Viviane Lalli; Milton Guerado Theodoro da Silva; Neyde Joanna Senna da Silva; Leonardo Senna da Silva; Christopher Bliss; Stephen Howard Ravenscroft.

OTHER INFORMATION Although the trust did not make any charitable donations in 2010, this was unusual. In 2009, for example, the trust had a grant expenditure of £2.8 million.

HOW TO APPLY In writing to the correspondent.

WHO TO APPLY TO Christopher Bliss, Trustee, 8th Floor, 6 New Street Square, London EC4A 3AQ *Tel* 020 7842 2000

■ The Seven Fifty Trust

CC NO 298886 **ESTABLISHED** 1988

WHERE FUNDING CAN BE GIVEN UK and worldwide.

WHO CAN BENEFIT Registered charities benefiting Christians.

WHAT IS FUNDED Trustees mainly give to causes they have supported for many years.

WHAT IS NOT FUNDED No support for unsolicited requests.

RANGE OF GRANTS Up to £15,000.

SAMPLE GRANTS All Saints Church – Crowborough (£21,000); Compassion (£700); and Universities and Colleges Christian Fellowship (£100).

FINANCES *Year* 2009–10 *Income* £65,339 *Grants* £21,715 *Assets* £1,893,286

TRUSTEES Revd Andrew C J Cornes; Katherine E Cornes; Peter N Collier; Revd Susan M Collier.

OTHER INFORMATION Grants are also made to individuals.

HOW TO APPLY Unsolicited applications will not be considered.

WHO TO APPLY TO Revd Andrew C J Cornes, Trustee, All Saints Vicarage, Church Road, Crowborough, East Sussex TN6 1ED *Tel* 01892 667384

■ The Severn Trent Water Charitable Trust Fund

CC NO 1108278 **ESTABLISHED** 1997

WHERE FUNDING CAN BE GIVEN The area covered by Severn Trent Water Ltd, which stretches from Wales to east Leicestershire and from the Humber estuary down to the Bristol Channel.

WHO CAN BENEFIT Individuals in hardship and/or financial difficulties. Organisations that support money advice and debt counselling services.

WHAT IS FUNDED Relief of poverty, money advice and debt counselling.

WHAT IS NOT FUNDED Only applications from organisations within the Severn Trent Trust Fund area will be considered. A map of this area can be found on the trust's website.

TYPE OF GRANT Revenue grants, capital grants of up to £1,500. Continuation funding is available.

SAMPLE GRANTS ASHA/ Worcester CASH; Birmingham Disability Resource Centre; CARES Sandwell; Castle Vale Tenants & Residents Alliance; Citizens Advice Leicester; Community Focus; Coventry CAB; Edas; Forest of Dean CAB; IMA; Ladywood Project; Life Matters; Sherwood Forest Community Church; South Birmingham Young Homeless Project; Telford & Wrekin CAB; Wood End Advice and Information Centre.

FINANCES *Year* 2009–10 *Income* £6,724,804 *Grants* £5,073,092 *Assets* £1,397,912

TRUSTEES Dr Derek Harris, Chair; Elizabeth Pusey; David Vaughan; Alexandra Gribbin; Lowri Williams.

OTHER INFORMATION Grants to individuals totalled £4.5 million. Grants to organisations totalled £500,000.

HOW TO APPLY If you would like to apply for a grant on behalf of your organisation you can email the trust at: office@sttf.org.uk. A reply within 48 hours can be expected. Alternatively, initial interest can be lodged by posting no more than two A4 sheets outlining your proposed project.

WHO TO APPLY TO Gay Hammett, Operations Manager, Auriga Services Limited, FREEPOST RLZE-EABT-SHSA, Sutton Coldfield B72 1TJ *Tel* 0121 355 7766 *email* office@sttf.org.uk *Website* www.sttf.org.uk

■ sfgroup Charitable Fund for Disabled People

CC NO 1104927 **ESTABLISHED** 2004

WHERE FUNDING CAN BE GIVEN East and west Midlands and parts of the north west of England.

WHO CAN BENEFIT Individuals, organisations and national and local charities.

WHAT IS FUNDED Disabled individuals and organisations that provide care for those with physical or mental disabilities.

TYPE OF GRANT Small, one-off grants.

RANGE OF GRANTS Up to a maximum of £5,000.

SAMPLE GRANTS Previously: £5,000 to Acorns Children's Hospice for part-funding for a specialist nurse; £4,100 to Green Acres Day Centre for a walking frame; £2,900 to Willow Wood Day Centre for a combined hoist.

TRUSTEES Mrs Warwick; R Yong; M Taylor.

HOW TO APPLY Initial applications can be made by filling in a short application form. This can be done online at the sfgroup website, or by completing the form attached to its information leaflet which can be request by phone or email. The Fund Manager will contact potential recipients within two weeks of receiving applications to discuss requests in more detail.

WHO TO APPLY TO Brenda Yong, Fund Manager, FREEPOST NAT13205, Nottingham NG8 6ZZ *Tel* 0115 942 5646 *email* brenda.yong@sfcharity.co.uk *Website* www.sfgroup.com

■ SFIA Educational Trust Limited

CC NO 270272   ESTABLISHED 1959
WHERE FUNDING CAN BE GIVEN UK.
WHO CAN BENEFIT Schools and educational organisations.
WHAT IS FUNDED Bursaries to cover part fees for pupils with special learning difficulties, who are disadvantaged, have emotional/behavioural difficulties or physical disabilities, are gifted in a specialist area or have a specific boarding need. Grants are also given towards educational projects, books, equipment and school trips to promote the advancement of learning. Grants will only be considered for specific projects.
WHAT IS NOT FUNDED No applications will be considered from individuals or from schools/organisations in respect of pupils/students over the age of 18.
TYPE OF GRANT Specific projects and bursary funds.
RANGE OF GRANTS £100–£35,000.
SAMPLE GRANTS Prince's Trust (£35,000); Emmott Foundation (£30,000); Royal Wolverhampton School and King Edward's School – Witley (£15,000 each); Wildfowl and Wetland Trust (£10,000); Arkwright Scholarships (£9,000); Choir Schools' Association (£8,000); Cardiff County Council and Stubbers Adventure Centre (£5,000 each); National Youth Orchestra (£2,800); Beverley School (£2,000); Musicworks (£1,000); and Rainbow Under 5's Playgroup (£100).
FINANCES *Year* 2009–10 *Income* £298,311 *Grants* £280,360 *Assets* £5,449,322
TRUSTEES Beatrice Roberts; Anthony Hastings; David Prince; John Rees; Hugh Monro.
HOW TO APPLY Application forms are available on the trust's website. All applications should be received by 31 January accompanied by the most recent set of audited accounts. Applications are considered in March/April each year. After the meeting, all applicants will be informed of the outcome as soon as possible.
WHO TO APPLY TO Anne Feek, Chief Executive, Tectonic Place, Holyport Road, Maidenhead, Berkshire SL6 2YE *Tel* 01628 502040 *Fax* 01628 502049 *email* trust@plans-ltd.co.uk *Website* www.plans-ltd.co.uk/trusts

■ Shaara Ezra – The Moses Foundation

CC NO 1134373   ESTABLISHED 2010
WHERE FUNDING CAN BE GIVEN Worldwide.
WHO CAN BENEFIT Registered charities.
WHAT IS FUNDED General charitable purposes with a preference for the advancement of education and the protection of health.
TRUSTEES Menasey Marc Moses; Daniel Ezra Moses; Mrs Dawn Tracey Moses.
HOW TO APPLY In writing to the correspondent.
WHO TO APPLY TO Menasey Marc Moses, Trustee, 16 Crespigny Road, London NW4 3DY *Tel* 020 8202 7221 *email* shaare.ezra@hotmail.com

■ The Cyril Shack Trust

CC NO 264270   ESTABLISHED 1972
WHERE FUNDING CAN BE GIVEN UK.
WHO CAN BENEFIT Voluntary organisations and charitable groups only.
WHAT IS FUNDED General charitable purposes, with a preference for Jewish organisations.
WHAT IS NOT FUNDED No grants for expeditions, travel bursaries, scholarships or to individuals.
TYPE OF GRANT Capital; recurring.
SAMPLE GRANTS No grants list was available. Previous beneficiaries have included Finchley Road Synagogue, Nightingale House and St John's Wood Synagogue.
FINANCES *Year* 2009–10 *Income* £99,266 *Grants* £150,014 *Assets* £680,830
TRUSTEES J Shack; C Shack.
HOW TO APPLY In writing to the correspondent.
WHO TO APPLY TO The Clerk, c/o Lubbock Fine, Chartered Accountants, Russell Bedford House, City Forum, 250 City Road, London EC1V 2QQ *Tel* 020 7490 7766

■ The Jean Shanks Foundation

CC NO 293108   ESTABLISHED 1985
WHERE FUNDING CAN BE GIVEN UK.
WHO CAN BENEFIT People involved in medical research, i.e. medical schools, medical Royal Colleges and similar bodies.
WHAT IS FUNDED Medical research and education, with a preference for the area of pathology.
WHAT IS NOT FUNDED No grants for capital items. No grants for research which is already supported by another grant giving body or for projects of the type normally dealt with by bodies such as the MRC or Wellcome Trust.
TYPE OF GRANT Scholarships, research – up to 3 years.
RANGE OF GRANTS £7,500–£50,000.
SAMPLE GRANTS Royal College of Pathologists (£53,000); University of Oxford (£24,000); University of Cambridge (£21,000); Academy of Medical Sciences (£20,000); and University of Southampton, University of Leicester, University of Manchester, University of Sheffield, University of Hull, University of Cardiff, University of Liverpool, Keele University, Brighton and Sussex Medical School and Queen's University Belfast (£7,500 each).
FINANCES *Year* 2009–10 *Income* £1,503,241 *Grants* £306,640 *Assets* £17,135,122
TRUSTEES Prof. Sir Dillwyn Williams; Dr Julian Axe; Alistair Jones; Eric Rothbarth; Prof. Dame Lesley Rees; Prof. Andrew Carr; Prof. Sir James Underwood; Prof. Sir Nicholas Wright.
HOW TO APPLY In writing to the correspondent. Please check the foundation's website for full grant guidelines.
WHO TO APPLY TO Mrs B Sears, Peppard Cottage, Peppard Common, Henley on Thames, Oxon RG9 5LB *email* barbara.sears@ukgateway.net *Website* jeanshanksfoundation.org/index.html

■ The Shanley Charitable Trust

CC NO 1103323   ESTABLISHED 2003
WHERE FUNDING CAN BE GIVEN Worldwide.
WHO CAN BENEFIT Charitable organisations.
WHAT IS FUNDED The relief of poverty.
SAMPLE GRANTS Children in Crisis, Red Cross, Save the Children and SOS Children (£40,000 each); DEC Haiti Appeal and Water Aid (£30,000); and DEC Philippine Appeal (£10,000).

FINANCES *Year* 2009–10 *Income* £769,854 *Grants* £230,000 *Assets* £2,079,680
TRUSTEES C A Shanley; R F Lander; S J Atkins.
HOW TO APPLY In writing to the correspondent.
WHO TO APPLY TO S J Atkins, Trustee, Knowles Benning Solicitors, 32 High Street, Shefford, Bedfordshire SG17 5DG *Tel* 01462 814824

■ The Shanti Charitable Trust

CC NO 1064813   **ESTABLISHED** 1997
WHERE FUNDING CAN BE GIVEN UK, with preference for West Yorkshire, and developing countries (especially Nepal).
WHO CAN BENEFIT Charitable organisations.
WHAT IS FUNDED General, Christian, international development.
WHAT IS NOT FUNDED No grants to gap year students, or political or animal welfare causes.
RANGE OF GRANTS £100–£100,000.
SAMPLE GRANTS Missionaries of Charity (£30,000); International Nepal Fellowship (£10,500); Protac/Theotac, Nepal (£8,000); The Joshua Project and Western Nepal Disability Trust (£5,000 each); EWI-UK (£1,000); and Christian Links in Keighley Schools and CMS (£500 each).
FINANCES *Year* 2009–10 *Income* £37,005 *Grants* £76,250 *Assets* £161,167
TRUSTEES Barbara Gill; Timothy Parr; Ross Hyett.
HOW TO APPLY In writing to the correspondent. Please note most beneficiaries are those the trustees already have contact with.
WHO TO APPLY TO Timothy Parr, Trustee, Baker Tilly, The Waterfront, Salts Mill Road, Saltaire, Shipley BD17 7EZ *Tel* 01274 536400

■ ShareGift (The Orr Mackintosh Foundation)

CC NO 1052686   **ESTABLISHED** 1995
WHERE FUNDING CAN BE GIVEN UK.
WHO CAN BENEFIT UK registered charities.
WHAT IS FUNDED General charitable purposes, guided by the wishes of the donors of shares, from where its income derives.
WHAT IS NOT FUNDED No grants to non-UK registered charities.
RANGE OF GRANTS £250–£37,500.
SAMPLE GRANTS Great Ormond Street Hospital Children's Charity (£37,500); Daily Telegraph Christmas Appeal (£30,000); British Heart Foundation (£23,000); Breast Cancer Campaign (£20,000); Alzheimer's Society and River & Rowing Museum Foundation (£15,000 each); Marie Curie Cancer Care (£10,000); Sense International (£7,500); The Prince's Foundation for Children & the Arts (£6,000); World in Need International (£5,000); Cats Protection (£1,000); and Essex Women's Advisory Group (£250).
FINANCES *Year* 2010–11 *Income* £1,073,900 *Grants* £722,500 *Assets* £343,225
TRUSTEES Matthew Orr; Stephen Scott; Baroness Goudie.
HOW TO APPLY Applications for funding are not accepted and no response will be made to charities that send inappropriate applications. ShareGift's trustees choose to support UK registered charities which reflect the broad range of charities which are of interest to the people and organisations that help to create the charity's income by donating their unwanted shares, or by supporting the charity's operation in other practical ways.

However, charities wishing to receive a donation from ShareGift's trustees can increase their chances of doing so by encouraging their supporters to donate unwanted shares to ShareGift and to make a note of their charitable interests when so doing, using the regular donation form provided by ShareGift. In addition, ShareGift is willing to use its extensive experience of share giving philanthropically to help charities which wish to start receiving gifts of shares themselves. Charities are, therefore, welcome to contact ShareGift to discuss this further. ShareGift advises that, as basic training on share giving is now available elsewhere, charities wishing to benefit from their advice should ensure that they have first researched share giving generally and put some thought into how their charity intends to initiate and run a share giving appeal or strategy. Further information on this and other issues is available on its website.
WHO TO APPLY TO Lady Mackintosh, 2nd Floor, 17 Carlton House Terrace, London SW1Y 5AH *Tel* 020 7930 3737 *Fax* 020 7839 2214 *email* help@sharegift.org.uk *Website* www.sharegift.org

■ The Linley Shaw Foundation

CC NO 1034051   **ESTABLISHED** 1993
WHERE FUNDING CAN BE GIVEN UK.
WHO CAN BENEFIT Registered charities in rural locations.
WHAT IS FUNDED The conservation, preservation and restoration of the natural beauty of the countryside of the UK for the public benefit. In particular, charities that organise voluntary workers to achieve these objectives.
WHAT IS NOT FUNDED No grants to non-charitable organisations, or to organisations whose aims or objects do not include conservation, preservation or restoration of the natural beauty of the UK countryside, even if the purpose of the grant would be eligible. No grants to individuals.
RANGE OF GRANTS £500–£16,000.
SAMPLE GRANTS Beneficiaries included: Devon Wildlife Trust, Essex Wildlife Trust; Gazen Salts Nature Reserve; The Barn Owl Trust, The National Trust Brecon Beacons, Trees for Life and Ty-Croeso Centre.
FINANCES *Year* 2009–10 *Income* £42,617 *Grants* £94,949
TRUSTEES National Westminster Bank plc.
HOW TO APPLY In writing to the correspondent. All material will be photocopied by the trust so please avoid sending 'bound' copies of reports and so on. Evidence of aims and objectives are needed, usually in the forms of accounts, annual reports or leaflets, which cannot be returned. Applications are considered in February/early March and should be received by December/early January.
WHO TO APPLY TO The Trust Section, NatWest Trust Services, 5th Floor, Trinity Quay 2, Avon Street, Bristol BS2 0PT *Tel* 0117 940 3283 *Fax* 0117 940 3275

■ The Sheepdrove Trust

CC NO 328369   **ESTABLISHED** 1989
WHERE FUNDING CAN BE GIVEN UK, but especially north Lambeth, London, where applicable.
WHO CAN BENEFIT Registered charities only.

WHAT IS FUNDED General charitable purposes, particularly sustainability, biodiversity, organic farming, educational research and spiritual care.
TYPE OF GRANT One-off and recurrent.
SAMPLE GRANTS Slow Food UK Trust (£472,000 in total over 5 years; City & Guild London Art School (£70,000 in total); British Trust for Ornithology (£57,000); Homoeopathy at Wellie Level (£30,000); Ibiza Preservation Fund (£20,000); Newbury Spring Festival (£17,000); New Economics Foundation and the Wildlife Conservation Partnership (£15,000 each); UK Pesticides Campaign (£10,000); Future of Farming (£7,500); Agrarian Renaissance (£6,000); King Alfred School – Five Court Building Appeal (£2,000); and Education Business Partnership (£1,200).
FINANCES *Year* 2010 *Income* £500,832 *Grants* £687,402 *Assets* £20,231,894
TRUSTEES Juliet E Kindersley; Peter D Kindersley; Harriet R Treuille; Barnabas G Kindersley.
HOW TO APPLY In writing to the correspondent.
WHO TO APPLY TO Juliet E Kindersley, Trustee, Sheepdrove Organic Farm, Lambourn, Berkshire RG17 7UN *Tel* 01488 674726

The Sheffield and District Hospital Services Charitable Fund

CC NO 246057   **ESTABLISHED** 1965
WHERE FUNDING CAN BE GIVEN Mostly South Yorkshire, also UK.
WHO CAN BENEFIT NHS hospitals and trusts; registered charities.
WHAT IS FUNDED Medical equipment and general charitable purposes.
RANGE OF GRANTS Up to £50,000.
SAMPLE GRANTS Sheffield Teaching Hospitals NHS Foundation Trust (£110,000); Age Concern (£45,000); Marie Curie (£10,000); Freeman College (£8,500); Sue Ryder Care (£6,000); Blind British Sport, British Cross (£5,000 each); Sheffield Mencap & Gateway (£4,000); Shopmobility (£3,600).
FINANCES *Year* 2009–10 *Income* £253,467 *Grants* £417,855 *Assets* £387,243
TRUSTEES G Moore, Chair; D J Whitney; Dr J D S Hammond; Dr C Ryan.
HOW TO APPLY In writing to the correspondent.
WHO TO APPLY TO K Miller, The Secretary, Mr Graham Moore, Westfield House, 87 Division Street, Sheffield S1 1HT *Tel* 0114 2502058 *email* jgill@westfieldhealth.com *Website* www.westfieldhealth.com

The Shekinah Legacy

CC NO 1137846   **ESTABLISHED** 2010
WHERE FUNDING CAN BE GIVEN UK, Israel and Romania.
WHO CAN BENEFIT Registered charities.
WHAT IS FUNDED Education and the relief of poverty.
TRUSTEES Kevin Byrne; Richard Spiceley; Neville Smith.
OTHER INFORMATION Unfortunately no further information was available at the time of writing (December 2011).
HOW TO APPLY In writing to the correspondent.
WHO TO APPLY TO Neville Smith, Trustee, Caladine Accountants, 1A The Avenue, Eastbourne, East Sussex BN21 3YA *Tel* 0845 621 6666 *email* info@caladine.co.uk

The Sheldon Trust

CC NO 242328   **ESTABLISHED** 1965
WHERE FUNDING CAN BE GIVEN West Midlands.
WHO CAN BENEFIT Registered charities.
WHAT IS FUNDED The relief of poverty and distress in society, concentrating on community projects. Aftercare, hospice at home, respite care, self-help and support groups, and rehabilitation centres are also considered. Facilities for people who are disadvantaged or disabled. Encouragement of local voluntary groups, recreational facilities, youth, community, rehabilitation for drugs, alcohol, and solvent abuse, religion, older people, mental health and learning difficulties.
WHAT IS NOT FUNDED The trust does not consider general appeals from national organisations and does not usually consider appeals in respect of the cost of buildings.
SAMPLE GRANTS Bethany Christian Fellowship, Birmingham Phab Camps, CF Dream Holidays and Farms for City Children, Mercia MS Therapy Centre, Signhealth and St George House Charity, St Martin's Social Care Project and Warwickshire Clubs for Young People.
FINANCES *Year* 2009–10 *Income* £180,312 *Grants* £116,733 *Assets* £3,860,709
TRUSTEES A Bidnell; Revd R S Bidnell; J K R England; R V Wiglesworth; Mrs R Beatton; Mrs R Gibbins; Paul K England.
HOW TO APPLY Application forms are available from the correspondent but the trust prefers applicants to complete and submit their application online. The trustees meet three times a year, in April, August and November. Application forms, including the most recent signed accounts, a project budget and a job description (if applying for a salary) should be received at least six weeks before the date of the next meeting.
Successful organisations will be sent a grant offer and any conditions. Unsuccessful applicants will have to wait two years before re-applying. Please note: a designated sum is set aside for the holiday grants programme and applications are considered in April each year. Applications should be submitted by the end of February.
WHO TO APPLY TO The Trust Administrator, White Horse Court, 25c North Street, Bishop's Stortford, Hertfordshire CM23 2LD *Tel* 01279 506421 *email* charities@pwwsolicitors.co.uk *Website* www.pwwsolicitors.co.uk/charitable-applications

P and D Shepherd Charitable Trust

CC NO 272948   **ESTABLISHED** 1973
WHERE FUNDING CAN BE GIVEN Worldwide but particularly the north of England.
WHO CAN BENEFIT Mainly local organisations – particularly those in the north of England.
WHAT IS FUNDED General charitable purposes. Local charities or charities with which the trustees have personal knowledge of, interest in or association with particularly those supporting young people.
TYPE OF GRANT Mainly one-off.
SAMPLE GRANTS Special Boat Service Association and York Air Museum (£10,000 each); Army Benevolent Fund and York Air Ambulance (£5,000 each); Help for Heroes (£5,000); and Survive (£1,000).
FINANCES *Year* 2009–10 *Income* £178,566 *Grants* £96,645 *Assets* £496,607

TRUSTEES Mrs P Shepherd; Mrs J L Robertson; Patrick M Shepherd; Annabel Robertson; I O Robertson; Mrs C M Shepherd; Michael James Shepherd; J O Shepherd; R O Robertson.

OTHER INFORMATION In 2009–10 the trust also gave £500 in grants to two individuals.

HOW TO APPLY In writing to the correspondent.

WHO TO APPLY TO The Trustees, 5 Cherry Lane, Dringhouses, York YO24 1QH

■ The Sylvia and Colin Shepherd Charitable Trust

CC NO 272788   **ESTABLISHED** 1973

WHERE FUNDING CAN BE GIVEN North east England, but mostly within a 25-mile radius of York.

WHO CAN BENEFIT Registered charities only, benefiting children and older people, retired people and people who are disabled.

WHAT IS FUNDED In the medium-term the policy is to build up the trust's capital base. Currently the main areas of interest are community initiatives, care of older people, childcare, people who are mentally or physically disabled, conservation, and medical support and equipment.

WHAT IS NOT FUNDED Applications from individuals will not be considered and support does not extend to organisations working outside the areas defined above and excludes overseas activities.

TYPE OF GRANT Usually for specific projects on an enabling basis. Core funding or ongoing support will not normally be provided.

RANGE OF GRANTS £100–£7,000, typically £100–£500.

SAMPLE GRANTS York City Knights Foundation (£5,000); St Peter's School Foundation (£2,000); Bowel Disease Research Foundation, Whizz Kidz, Yorkshire Air Ambulance and York Minster Development Fund (£1,000 each); Scarborough & District CAB and Vitalise (£600 each); Opera North, The Children's Trust and Combat Stress (£500 each); Home Start (£300); St Andrews Church, Bishopthorpe (£200); Donkey Sanctuary (£100); Woodland Trust (£40).

FINANCES *Year* 2009–10 *Income* £176,406 *Grants* £137,096 *Assets* £2,896,014

TRUSTEES Mrs Sara C Dickson; David Dickson; Mrs Sylvia Shepherd.

HOW TO APPLY In writing to the correspondent. The trustees meet frequently. Applications should include details of the need to be met, achievements and a copy of the latest accounts.

WHO TO APPLY TO Mrs Sara C Dickson, Trustee, Mrs Sara Caroline Dickson, 15 St Edward's Close, York YO24 1QB *Tel* 01904 702762

■ The Archie Sherman Cardiff Foundation

CC NO 272225   **ESTABLISHED** 1976

WHERE FUNDING CAN BE GIVEN UK, Canada, Australia, New Zealand, Pakistan, Sri Lanka, South Africa, India, Israel, USA and other parts of the British Commonwealth.

WHO CAN BENEFIT Charitable organisations.

WHAT IS FUNDED Health, education, training, overseas aid, community and Jewish causes.

WHAT IS NOT FUNDED No grants to individuals.

SAMPLE GRANTS Magen David Adom UK (£60,000); United Jewish Israel Appeal (£47,500); Merephdi Foundation (£39,000); and Friends of Bar Ilan University (£10,000).

FINANCES *Year* 2009–10 *Income* £108,260 *Grants* £156,643 *Assets* £2,372,486

TRUSTEES Rothschild Trust Corporation Ltd.

HOW TO APPLY In writing to the correspondent.

WHO TO APPLY TO The Trustees, Rothschild Trust Corp Ltd, New Court, St Swithins Lane, London EC4P 4DU *Tel* 020 7280 5000

■ The Archie Sherman Charitable Trust

CC NO 256893   **ESTABLISHED** 1967

WHERE FUNDING CAN BE GIVEN UK and Israel.

WHO CAN BENEFIT Charitable organisations.

WHAT IS FUNDED Most grants are to Jewish organisations. Other causes supported are the arts, education, health, welfare and overseas aid.

TYPE OF GRANT Capital, buildings and project. Funding may be given for more than three years.

SAMPLE GRANTS Yemin Orde Therapeutic Centre (£129,000); Jacqueline and Michael Gee Charitable Trust and the Rosalyn and Nicholas Springer Charitable Trust (£125,000 each); Neve Ilan Ashkelon (£117,500); Belsize Square Synagogue (£100,500); the Diana and Allan Morgenthau Charitable Trust (£95,000); Jewish Care (£37,500); Nightingale House (£30,000); Royal National Theatre (£25,000); The Tel Aviv Foundation (£20,000); Community Security Trust (£15,000); The London Jewish Cultural Centre (£10,000); Yad Vashem UK Foundation (£5,300); Combat Stress (£2,000); and Glyndebourne Arts Trust (£1,500).

FINANCES *Year* 2009–10 *Income* £1,337,317 *Grants* £974,230 *Assets* £21,845,529

TRUSTEES Michael J Gee; Allan H S Morgenthau; Eric A Charles.

HOW TO APPLY In writing to the correspondent. Trustees meet every month except August and December.

WHO TO APPLY TO Michael Gee, Trustee, 27 Berkeley House, 15 Hay Hill, London W1J 8NS *Tel* 020 7493 1904 *email* trust@sherman.co.uk

---

■ The R C Sherriff Trust

CC NO 272527   **ESTABLISHED** 1976

WHERE FUNDING CAN BE GIVEN The borough of Elmbridge.

WHO CAN BENEFIT Local individuals for art training bursaries (short courses only) and local amateur and professional organisations planning arts activities of a developmental nature.

WHAT IS FUNDED The trust is primarily concerned with arts development projects and funds charities, schools and constituted organisations working with one or more art form for the benefit of members of the local community, especially where a professional artist is involved. The trust has funded projects concerned with music, dance, drama, visual arts, crafts, literature, film and new media.

WHAT IS NOT FUNDED Any project taking place outside the borough cannot be supported unless the principal beneficiaries are Elmbridge residents. The trust does not give retrospective grants; it does not fund higher education courses or long-term vocational training; and it rarely agrees to be the sole funder of a project, applicants are expected to raise funds from a variety of sources.

TYPE OF GRANT Capital, one-off, event underwriting, project and school funds. Funding of up to three years will be considered.

RANGE OF GRANTS £180–£11,000; typical grant £1,000.

SAMPLE GRANTS Hotbuckle Productions (£3,000); Elmbridge Community Link and St George's Arts (£2,500 each) and Brooklands Radio, Walton and Weybridge Amateur Operatic and Walton District Girl Guides (£1,000 each).

FINANCES *Year* 2010 *Income* £180,748 *Grants* £52,421 *Assets* £3,596,929

TRUSTEES Cllr Nigel Cooper; Cllr Claire Gibbens; Mrs Penny Harris; Cllr S Kapadia; Mrs Ruth Lyon; Cllr Mrs Tannia Shipley – chair; Cllr James Vickers; Alison Clarke; Mr B Cheyne; Mrs E Cooper; Wendy Smithers.

OTHER INFORMATION Grants to individuals and schools are unlikely to exceed £500 and grants to organisations and venues are unlikely to exceed £3,000.

HOW TO APPLY On a form which can be downloaded from the website or obtained from the trust office. Application deadlines, grant decision dates and full grant guidelines are also available. Trustees meet four times a year to consider applications. Applicants are advised to discuss their proposals and check their eligibility, with the Director, in advance. The website will also give information on past and current projects and successful applications.

WHO TO APPLY TO Loretta Howells, Director, Case House, 85–89 High Street, Walton on Thames, Surrey KT12 1DZ *Tel* 01932 229996 *email* arts@rcsherrifftrust.org.uk *Website* www.rcsherrifftrust.org.uk

....

■ **The Shetland Charitable Trust**

SC NO SC027025   **ESTABLISHED** 1976
WHERE FUNDING CAN BE GIVEN Shetland only.
WHO CAN BENEFIT Self-help and voluntary organisations benefiting the inhabitants of Shetland.
WHAT IS FUNDED Social welfare; art and recreation; environment and amenity.
WHAT IS NOT FUNDED Funds can only be used to benefit the inhabitants of Shetland.
TYPE OF GRANT Project, one-off, capital, running and recurring costs, agricultural ten-year loan scheme.
RANGE OF GRANTS Up to £2.5 million.
SAMPLE GRANTS Funding for other trusts: Shetland Recreational Trust (£2.5 million); Shetland Amenity Trust (£1.1 million); and Shetland Arts Development Agency (£696,000). Other organisations and local projects receiving grants during the year included: Support to Rural Care Model (£2.5 million); Planned Maintenance Scheme (£1.3 million); Xmas grant scheme (£578,000); COPE Limited (£330,000); Shetland Youth Information Service (£189,000); Voluntary Action Shetland (£144,000); Citizens Advice Bureau (£132,000); Community Support Grants scheme (£73,000); Shetland Churches Council Trust (£54,000); Buses for Elderly and Disabled (£52,000); Shetland Link Up (£48,000); Festival Grants (£30,000); Sheltered Housing Heating scheme (£25,500); VAS – ICT replacement (£20,000); and Couple Counselling Shetland (£12,000).
FINANCES *Year* 2010–11 *Income* £9,196,000 *Grants* £10,319,254 *Assets* £219,750,000
TRUSTEES William Manson; James Henry; Leslie Angus; Laura Baisley; James Budge; Alexander Cluness; Alastair Cooper; Adam Doull; Allison Duncan; Elizabeth Fullerton; Florence Grains; Robert Henderson; Andrew Hughson; Caroline Miller; Richard Nickerson; Valerie Nicolson; Frank Robertson; Gary Robinson; Joseph

Simpson; John Scott; Cecil Smith; Jonathon Wills.

HOW TO APPLY Applications are only accepted from Shetland-based charities. The trustees meet every two months. The trust has different contact points for different categories of grant: Christmas grants – contact the trust on 01595 744994; arts grants, development grants, senior citizens club grants and support grants – contact Michael Duncan on 01595 743828; and social assistance grants – contact the duty social worker at duty@shetland.gov.uk

WHO TO APPLY TO Ann Black, General Manager, 22–24 North Road, Lerwick, Shetland ZE1 0NQ *Tel* 01595 744994 *Fax* 01595 744999 *email* mail@shetlandcharitabletrust.co.uk *Website* www.shetlandcharitabletrust.co.uk

....

■ **SHINE (Support and Help in Education)**

CC NO 1082777   **ESTABLISHED** 1999
WHERE FUNDING CAN BE GIVEN Greater London and Manchester.
WHO CAN BENEFIT Organisations working with underachieving 7 to 18 year olds living in disadvantaged areas.
WHAT IS FUNDED Educational programmes which give young people the extra support and attention they need to learn the basic but essential tools for life. SHINE also supports projects that help talented children from poor neighbourhoods to recognise and then realise their full potential. Projects include intensive one-to-one literacy and numeracy support, Saturday learning programmes, homework clubs and computer-assisted study projects.
WHAT IS NOT FUNDED SHINE will not fund: individuals; the direct replacement of statutory funding; schools or other educational establishments, except where funding is for activities which are clearly additional; short term programmes; programmes targeted at specific subject or beneficiary groups; parenting programmes, where the primary focus is the parent rather than the child; activities promoting particular political or religious beliefs; projects taking place outside Greater London, except projects that are part of SHINE's replication programme.
TYPE OF GRANT Start ups, pilots, core costs and development or replication of projects.
RANGE OF GRANTS Up to £592,000.
SAMPLE GRANTS Lift for Learning – DigiSmart (£592,000); SHINE @ Kingswood (£180,000); IntoUniversity (£120,000); Watford Grammar School (£112,000); Children's Discovery Centre (£70,000); Brunel University Urban Scholars (£33,000); Serious Fun Eltham (£30,000); and National Literacy Trust (£7,500).
FINANCES *Year* 2010–11 *Income* £3,322,793 *Grants* £1,919,764 *Assets* £6,148,591
TRUSTEES Jim O'Neill, Chair; David Blood; Gavin Boyle; Mark Heffernan; Mark Ferguson; Cameron Ogden; Krutika Pau; Richard Rothwell; Caroline Whalley.
HOW TO APPLY All potential applicants must initially speak to a member of the grants team by telephoning 020 8393 1880. The trustees meet about three times a year, but not at fixed intervals.
WHO TO APPLY TO Paul Carbury, Chief Executive, 1 Cheam Road, Ewell Village, Surrey KT17 1SP *Tel* 020 8393 1880 *email* info@shinetrust.org.uk *Website* www.shinetrust.org.uk

■ The Barnett and Sylvia Shine No 2 Charitable Trust

CC NO 281821   **ESTABLISHED** 1980
WHERE FUNDING CAN BE GIVEN UK and overseas.
WHO CAN BENEFIT Registered charities.
WHAT IS FUNDED General charitable purposes.
WHAT IS NOT FUNDED No grants to individuals.
TYPE OF GRANT Usually one-off.
SAMPLE GRANTS Médecins Sans Frontières (£10,000); Macmillan Cancer Support (£3,000); Lifeboats, the Samaritans, the Smile Train – UK, St Mungo's and Water Aid (£2,000 each); and Chernobyl Children's Project – UK, One-to-One Children's Fund, the Royal Parks Foundation, and Send a cow to Africa (£1,000).
FINANCES Year 2009–10 Income £43,817 Grants £41,000 Assets £1,257,973
TRUSTEES Martin D Paisner; Barbara J Grahame; Prof. R Grahame.
HOW TO APPLY In writing to the correspondent.
WHO TO APPLY TO Martin D Paisner, Trustee, c/o Berwin Leighton Paisner, Adelaide House, London Bridge, London EC4R 9HA *Tel* 020 7760 1000 *Fax* 020 7760 1111

■ The Bassil Shippam and Alsford Trust

CC NO 256996   **ESTABLISHED** 1967
WHERE FUNDING CAN BE GIVEN UK, with a preference for West Sussex.
WHO CAN BENEFIT Organisations benefiting young and older people, people with learning disabilities, Christians and health and educational purposes.
WHAT IS FUNDED General charitable purposes. Support is concentrated on local charities located in West Sussex rather than on UK appeals, with emphasis on Christian objects and youth.
TYPE OF GRANT Capital grants for up to three years.
RANGE OF GRANTS Mostly under £1,000.
SAMPLE GRANTS Donnington House and Fordwater School (£10,000 each); Christian Youth Enterprise Sailing Centre and St Wilfrid's Hospice (£5,000 each); Newell Centre Association (£3,500); Pailant House Gallery, Crime Diversion Scheme and TEAR Fund – Haiti Donation (£1,000 each); Careforce, Cancerwise and Petworth Festival(£500 each); Disability Awareness UK and St John Ambulance – Sussex (£350 each); Miracles, the Chichester Stroke Club and the Meningitis Trust (£250 each); Action Medical Research (£200); and the Honeypot Trust (£100).
FINANCES Year 2009–10 Income £142,425 Grants £115,790 Assets £3,626,312
TRUSTEES J H S Shippam; C W Doman; Simon A E MacFarlane; S W Young; Mrs M Hanwell; R Tayler; Mrs S Trayler.
HOW TO APPLY In writing to the correspondent, including a copy of the latest set of reports, accounts and forecasts. The trustees meet three times a year to consider applications.
WHO TO APPLY TO Simon MacFarlane, Trustee, c/o Thomas Eggar, The Corn Exchange, Baffins Lane, Chichester, West Sussex PO19 1GE *Tel* 01243 786111 *Fax* 01243 775640

■ The Shipwrights' Company Charitable Fund

CC NO 262043   **ESTABLISHED** 1971
WHERE FUNDING CAN BE GIVEN UK.
WHO CAN BENEFIT Individuals and organisations with a maritime connection. Emphasis is given to those benefiting young people, church work and the City.
WHAT IS FUNDED Maritime training, sailors' welfare and maritime heritage. Churches and Anglican bodies are also supported.
WHAT IS NOT FUNDED Any application without a clear maritime connection.
TYPE OF GRANT Annual donations, general donations and outdoor activity bursaries. Buildings, capital, core costs, one-off, project and start-up costs. Funding for one year or less will be considered.
RANGE OF GRANTS Mainly £500–£5,000. Larger grants can be made from unspent surpluses from previous years.
SAMPLE GRANTS Tall Ships Youth Trust (£20,000); Marine Society and Sea Cadets (£17,000); George Green's School (two grants totalling £10,500); Jubilee Training Trust and Tower Hamlets – Summer University (£5,000 each); City of London Unit, Sea Cadet Corps, HMS Belfast (£3,000); and Maritime Rescue Institute, Ocean Youth Trust South, Thames Shipwright and the Trinity Sailing Trust (£1,000 each).
FINANCES Year 2009–10 Income £179,137 Grants £87,430 Assets £2,547,317
TRUSTEES The Worshipful Company of Shipwrights; William D Everard; Simon Sherrard; Sir Jock Slater; M Simon Robinson; Graham Clarke.
HOW TO APPLY In writing to the correspondent. Applications and guidelines are available from the trust's website. Applications are considered in February, June and November.
WHO TO APPLY TO The Clerk, Ironmongers' Hall, Shaftesbury Place, Barbican, London EC2Y 8AA *Tel* 020 7606 2376 *Fax* 020 7600 8117 *email* clerk@shipwrights.co.uk *Website* www. shipwrights.co.uk

■ The Shirley Foundation

CC NO 1097135   **ESTABLISHED** 1996
WHERE FUNDING CAN BE GIVEN Unrestricted, in practice, mainly UK.
WHO CAN BENEFIT Registered charities.
WHAT IS FUNDED The main areas of interest are information technology and autism (not excluding Asperger's syndrome) which occasionally extend to learning disabilities in general. The foundation's mission is 'the facilitation and support of pioneering projects with strategic impact in the field of autism spectrum disorders, with particular emphasis on medical research'.
WHAT IS NOT FUNDED No grants to individuals, or for non autism-specific work. The foundation does not make political donations.
TYPE OF GRANT Capital and revenue grants and full project funding.
SAMPLE GRANTS Balliol College, Oxford (£1 million), for the Historic Collections Centre in St Cross Church, Holywell; The World Health Organisation (£100,000); Mental Health Foundation (£4,900), for research for an Autistic Spectrum Disorders report; and a publication on the history of autism (£3,400).
FINANCES Year 2009–10 Income £93,909 Grants £1,108,300 Assets £3,303,808

TRUSTEES Dame Stephanie Shirley, Chair; Prof. Eve Johnstone; Michael Robert Macfadyen; Anne McCartney Menzies.

OTHER INFORMATION The foundation's 2009–10 annual report stated that at the end of 2010 there were no major projects or grants under consideration at that time, and that the trustees will continue to review grant requests and possible future projects as they arise.

HOW TO APPLY 'Trustees meet twice yearly but applications for support are received throughout the year. Only those within the foundation's Mission are considered; applicants are reminded that projects should be innovative in nature with the potential to have a strategic impact in the field of Autism Spectrum Disorders. Research proposals should be aimed ultimately at determining causes of autism. Researchers should refer to the 'Guidance: Application for a medical research grant' downloadable [from the foundation's website]. In the first instance a simple letter with outline proposal should be sent to Dame Stephanie Shirley at the registered address or emailed.'

WHO TO APPLY TO Anne McCartney Menzies, Trustee, North Lea House, 66 Northfield End, Henley-on-Thames, Oxfordshire RG9 2BE *Tel* 01491 579004 *Fax* 01491 574995 *email* steve@steveshirley.com *Website* www.steveshirley.com/tsf

---

■ Shlomo Memorial Fund Limited

CC NO 278973　　　　**ESTABLISHED** 1980
WHERE FUNDING CAN BE GIVEN Unrestricted.
WHO CAN BENEFIT Organisations benefiting Jewish people.
WHAT IS FUNDED Jewish causes.
SAMPLE GRANTS Previous beneficiaries include: Amud Haolam, Nachlat Haleviim, Torah Umesorah, Beit Hillel, ZSV Charities, Layesharim Tehilla, British Friends of Tashbar Chazon Ish, Chazon Ish, Mei Menuchos, Mor Uketsio, Shoshanat Hoamakim, Millennium Trust, and Talmud Torah Zichron Meir.
FINANCES *Year* 2009–10 *Income* £6,372,221 *Grants* £2,057,305 *Assets* £36,435,973
TRUSTEES Amichai Toporowitz, Chair; Hezkel Toporowitz; Eliyah Kleineman; Channe Lopian; Chaim Y Kaufman.
OTHER INFORMATION A list of grant beneficiaries was not included in the trust's accounts.
HOW TO APPLY In writing to the correspondent.
WHO TO APPLY TO Channe Lopian, Secretary, Cohen Arnold and Co., New Burlington House, 1075 Finchley Road, London NW11 0PU *Tel* 020 8731 0777 *Fax* 020 8731 0778

■ The Shoe Zone Trust

CC NO 1112972　　　　**ESTABLISHED** 2005
WHERE FUNDING CAN BE GIVEN Preference for Leicestershire and Rutland and for certain charities operating in the Philippines and other countries.
WHO CAN BENEFIT Children and young people.
WHAT IS FUNDED The objects of the charity are to make grants and donations to other charities to relieve the financial hardship and poverty and/or advancement of education, mainly for children and young persons under the age of 18 particularly in Leicestershire and Rutland and for certain charities operating in the Philippines.
SAMPLE GRANTS Shepherd of the Hills – Philippines (£51,000); CORD (£50,000); Ministries without Borders (£15,800); Leicester Charity Link

(£10,000); Wishes For Kids (£5,000); Century Cycle Challenge (£3,400); Footwear Friends (£1,000); Teenage Cancer (£120).
FINANCES *Year* 2010 *Income* £163,869 *Grants* £170,705 *Assets* £91,312
TRUSTEES Michael Smith, Chair, Charles Smith; Anthony Smith.
HOW TO APPLY In writing to the correspondent.
WHO TO APPLY TO The Trustees, Haramead Business Centre, Humberstone Road, Leicester LE1 2LH *Tel* 0116 222 3007 *Website* www.shoezone.net/sztrust.html

---

■ The J A Shone Memorial Trust

CC NO 270104　　　　**ESTABLISHED** 1974
WHERE FUNDING CAN BE GIVEN Merseyside and overseas.
WHO CAN BENEFIT Registered charities known to the trustees.
WHAT IS FUNDED Christian and local causes in Merseyside and mission work overseas.
RANGE OF GRANTS Usually up to £10,000.
SAMPLE GRANTS Toxteth Tabernacle and Mission Aviation Fellowship (£5,000 each); Penshurst Retreat Centre (£2,500); Royal Liverpool Philharmonic Society, College of St Barnabas and Titus Trust (£2,000 each); Tearfund and Local Solutions (£1,000 each).
FINANCES *Year* 2009–10 *Income* £42,423 *Grants* £32,500 *Assets* £779,277
TRUSTEES Anthony W Shone; Mr J D W Stileman; Liverpool Charity and Voluntary Services.
HOW TO APPLY The trust does not respond to unsolicited applications.
WHO TO APPLY TO Anthony W Shone, Trustee, Liverpool Charity and Voluntary Services, 151 Dale Street, Liverpool L2 2AH *Tel* 0151 236 2226

■ The Barbara A Shuttleworth Memorial Trust

CC NO 1016117　　　　**ESTABLISHED** 1992
WHERE FUNDING CAN BE GIVEN UK, with a preference for West Yorkshire.
WHO CAN BENEFIT Organisations benefiting people with disabilities, particularly children.
WHAT IS FUNDED Charities working with children who are disabled and associated causes. Grants are given especially for equipment and premises, but holidays and outings, training courses, and other needs are also considered.
TYPE OF GRANT Capital grants.
SAMPLE GRANTS Past beneficiaries have included: National Deaf Children's Society (£2,300); Chapel Grange Special School and Children's Liver Disease Foundation (£2,000 each); Aidis Trust (£1,500); United Response – York and Sunny Days Children's Charity (£1,000 each); St James's Hospital for 'Chemo Ducks' (£900); Muscular Dystrophy Group (£600); Symbol Trust (£500); Rutland House School for Parents (£350); and British Diabetic Association (£250).
FINANCES *Year* 2009–10 *Income* £21,705 *Grants* £3,000
TRUSTEES John Alistair Baty, Chair; Barbara Anne Shuttleworth; John Christopher Joseph Eaton; William Fenton.
HOW TO APPLY In writing to the correspondent.
WHO TO APPLY TO John Baty, Chair, Baty Casson Long, Shear's Yard, 21 Wharf Street, The Calls, Leeds LS2 7EQ *Tel* 0113 242 5848 *Fax* 0013 247 0342 *email* baty@btinternet.com

■ The Sickle Foundation

CC NO 1139438   **ESTABLISHED** 2010
WHERE FUNDING CAN BE GIVEN UK and Ireland.
WHO CAN BENEFIT Registered charities and individuals.
WHAT IS FUNDED General charitable purposes, with a preference for education in music, the arts and heritage, but principally focused on music. The trust seeks to help young musicians achieve their full potential towards securing careers as performers. In the main, the income of the trust is used to support the cost of studies and/or maintenance of outstanding postgraduate or post-diploma students who merit further training based on ability and individual need. This is done through scholarships and awards.
TRUSTEES David Harden; Bettina Harden; Matilda Harden.
OTHER INFORMATION The Harden family, settlors of the trust, have owned and occupied the Nanhoron estate where the trust is based for 700 years.
HOW TO APPLY An initial enquiry should be made before an application is submitted, as unsolicited applications are rarely successful.
WHO TO APPLY TO David Harden, Trustee, Nanhoron, Pwllheli, Gwynedd LL53 8DL   *Tel* 01758 730610 *email* bettina.harden@farming.co.uk

■ The Mary Elizabeth Siebel Charity

CC NO 1001255   **ESTABLISHED** 1990
WHERE FUNDING CAN BE GIVEN Within a 12-mile radius of Newark Town Hall.
WHO CAN BENEFIT Individuals and organisations benefiting older people who are ill, have disabilities or who are disadvantaged by poverty, and their carers.
WHAT IS FUNDED Hospice at home, respite care for carers and care in the community. Preference is given to assisting people who wish to live independently in their own homes.
TYPE OF GRANT Flexible, but one-off grants preferred for buildings, capital and core costs.
SAMPLE GRANTS £16,000 to Crossroads Care.
FINANCES *Year* 2009–10 *Income* £114,742 *Grants* £100,321 *Assets* £2,474,180
TRUSTEES P Blatherwick; D McKenny; Mrs R White; Mrs A Austin; Mrs S Watson; Miss J Moore.
OTHER INFORMATION The grant total includes £85,000 given to individuals.
HOW TO APPLY In writing to the correspondent, requesting an application form. The trustees meet every couple of months to discuss applications.
WHO TO APPLY TO Mrs Frances C Kelly, Administrator, Tallents, 3 Middlegate, Newark, Nottinghamshire NG24 1AQ   *Tel* 01636 671881 *Fax* 01636 700148 *email* fck@tallents.co.uk

■ David and Jennifer Sieff Charitable Trust

CC NO 206329   **ESTABLISHED** 1970
WHERE FUNDING CAN BE GIVEN UK.
WHO CAN BENEFIT Registered charities.
WHAT IS FUNDED General charitable purposes.
WHAT IS NOT FUNDED No grants to individuals.
RANGE OF GRANTS £100 to £13,000.
SAMPLE GRANTS Community Security Trust (£13,000); Mentor Foundation UK (£10,000); The Jaffa Institute (£5,000); The Koelster Trust, Policy Exchange, Oxford Radcliffe Children's Fund and Royal Opera House (£1,000 each); Newbury Spring Festival (£650) and Royal College of Music (£350).
FINANCES *Year* 2009–10 *Income* £31,414 *Grants* £53,240 *Assets* £572,068
TRUSTEES Hon. Sir David Daniel Sieff; Lady Jennifer Riat Sieff; Lord Wolfson of Sunningdale.
HOW TO APPLY In writing to the correspondent.
WHO TO APPLY TO The Trustees, H W Fisher and Company, Acre House, 11–15 William Road, London NW1 3ER   *Tel* 020 7388 7000

■ The Julius Silman Charitable Trust

CC NO 263830   **ESTABLISHED** 1971
WHERE FUNDING CAN BE GIVEN UK.
WHO CAN BENEFIT Charitable organisations.
WHAT IS FUNDED Support of at risk groups and humanitarian causes, focussing on Jewish organisations.
WHAT IS NOT FUNDED No grants to individuals.
TYPE OF GRANT One-off and recurrent.
RANGE OF GRANTS Up to £3,000.
SAMPLE GRANTS Kids for Kids (£2,600); Neve Michael and New Israel Fund (£1,000 each); Anti-Slavery, Norwood, Motability and Heads Up (£500 each); World Jewish Relief, Friendship Way and Jewish Childs Day (£250 each); and Samaritans of Bath, Wiltshire Splash and Cancer Research (£100 each).
FINANCES *Year* 2009–10 *Income* £24,107 *Grants* £13,000
TRUSTEES S A Silman; Mrs C Smith; Mrs W Silman.
HOW TO APPLY In writing to the correspondent. The trustees meet about four times a year.
WHO TO APPLY TO Stephen Silman, Trustee, Roselands, 2 High Street, Steeple Ashton BA14 6EL   *Tel* 01380 870421

■ The Leslie Silver Charitable Trust

CC NO 1007599   **ESTABLISHED** 1991
WHERE FUNDING CAN BE GIVEN UK, but mostly West Yorkshire.
WHO CAN BENEFIT Small local projects, new organisations and established organisations primarily benefiting children, young adults and Jewish causes.
WHAT IS FUNDED Medicine and health; welfare; sciences and humanities; the advancement of the Jewish religion, synagogues, Jewish religious umbrella bodies; arts, culture and recreation; community facilities; and other charitable purposes.
WHAT IS NOT FUNDED No grants to individuals or students.
TYPE OF GRANT One-off grants.
RANGE OF GRANTS £500–£55,000.
SAMPLE GRANTS Donisthorpe Hall (£55,000); Leeds Centre for Deaf and Blind People (£16,000); Holocaust Centre and Variety Club Children's Charity (£10,000 each); UJIA and Jewish National Fund (£5,000 each); the Zone (£4,000); Children in Crisis and Lord Mayor's Charity Appeal (£2,000 each); Second World War Experience (£1,000); and Holocaust Educational Trust (£500).
FINANCES *Year* 2009–10 *Income* £11,087 *Grants* £208,074
TRUSTEES Leslie H Silver; Mark S Silver; Ian J Fraser.
OTHER INFORMATION Accounts received at the Charity Commission but unavailable to view.

HOW TO APPLY In writing to the correspondent following a specific format. Please note the trust has previously stated that, 'the recipients of donations are restricted almost exclusively to the concerns in which the trustees take a personal interest and that unsolicited requests from other sources, although considered by the trustees, are rejected almost invariably'.
WHO TO APPLY TO Ian J Fraser, Trustee, R S M Tennon Ltd, 2 Wellington Place, Leeds LS1 4AP *Tel* 0113 244 5451 *Fax* 0113 242 6308

■ The Simpson Education and Conservation Trust

CC NO 1069695   **ESTABLISHED** 1998
WHERE FUNDING CAN BE GIVEN UK and overseas, with a preference for the neotropics (South America).
WHO CAN BENEFIT Charitable organisations.
WHAT IS FUNDED Advancement of education, including medical and scientific research; the conservation and protection of the natural environment and endangered species of plants and animals with special emphasis on the protection of forests and endangered avifauna in the neotropics (South America).
WHAT IS NOT FUNDED No grants to individuals.
TYPE OF GRANT One-off or up to three years, for development or project funding.
RANGE OF GRANTS £1,000–£60,000.
SAMPLE GRANTS Jocotoco Foundation (£62,000); Lord Trealor Trust and Friends of RBG Kew – for Tanzania (£1,000 each).
FINANCES *Year* 2009–10 *Income* £33,317 *Grants* £43,306 *Assets* £43,952
TRUSTEES Nigel Simpson, Chair; Prof. D M Broom; Dr J M Lock; Prof. S Chang; Dr Katherine Simpson.
HOW TO APPLY In writing to the correspondent. The day-to-day activities of this trust are carried out by email, telephone and circulation of documents, since the trustees do not all live in the UK.
WHO TO APPLY TO N Simpson, Chair, Honeysuckle Cottage, Tidenham Chase, Chepstow, Gwent NP16 7JW *Tel* 01291 689423 *Fax* 01291 689803

■ The Simpson Foundation

CC NO 231030   **ESTABLISHED** 1961
WHERE FUNDING CAN BE GIVEN UK.
WHO CAN BENEFIT Registered charities only, particularly those benefiting Roman Catholics.
WHAT IS FUNDED The support of charities favoured by the founder in his lifetime and others with similar objects; mainly Catholic charities.
WHAT IS NOT FUNDED No grants to non-registered charities or individuals.
SAMPLE GRANTS Venerable Collegio Inglese, St Benedict's Abbey, Sisters of Charity of Jesus and Mary, The Access Partnership, Congregation of the Blessed Sacrament and Providence Row Night Refuge and Home.
FINANCES *Year* 2009–10 *Income* £15,647 *Grants* £28,993
TRUSTEES C E T Bellord; P J M Hawthorne; Patrick Herschan.
HOW TO APPLY In writing to the correspondent, at any time. No telephone applications will be considered.
WHO TO APPLY TO Patrick Herschan, c/o Pothecary Witham Weld Solicitors, 70 St George's Square, London SW1V 3RD *Tel* 020 7821 8211 *Fax* 020 7630 6484

■ The Huntly and Margery Sinclair Charitable Trust

CC NO 235939   **ESTABLISHED** 1964
WHERE FUNDING CAN BE GIVEN UK.
WHO CAN BENEFIT Generally to registered charities.
WHAT IS FUNDED Well-established charities in particular.
RANGE OF GRANTS Up to £10,000.
SAMPLE GRANTS King Edward VII Hospital (£5,000); Too Many Women (£3,000); Injured Jockey's Fund (£2,500); Cheltenham Festival (£2,000); St Rose's Special School (£1,000); and Tiger Awareness (£500).
FINANCES *Year* 2009–10 *Income* £47,829 *Grants* £42,000 *Assets* £1,327,081
TRUSTEES Mrs A M H Gibbs; Mrs M A H Windsor; Mrs J Floyd.
HOW TO APPLY Unsolicited applications are rarely successful and due to the high number such requests the trust is not able to respond to them or return any printed materials supplied.
WHO TO APPLY TO Wilfrid Vernor-Miles, Administrator, c/o Vernor-Miles and Noble Solicitors, 5 Raymond Buildings, Gray's Inn, London WC1R 5DD *Tel* 020 7242 8688 *Fax* 020 7242 3192 *email* wilfridvm@vmn.org.uk

■ Sino-British Fellowship Trust

CC NO 313669   **ESTABLISHED** 1948
WHERE FUNDING CAN BE GIVEN UK and China.
WHO CAN BENEFIT Institutions benefiting individual postgraduate students.
WHAT IS FUNDED Scholarships to Chinese citizens to enable them to pursue their studies in Britain. Grants to British citizens in China to educate/train Chinese citizens in any art, science or profession.
TYPE OF GRANT Fees; fares; and allowances.
RANGE OF GRANTS Up to £120,000.
SAMPLE GRANTS Royal Society (£120,000); China Scholarship Council (£26,000); British Academy (£22,000 in two grants); Great Britain China Educational Trust (£20,000); Chinese University of Hong Kong and Open University of Hong Kong (£16,500 each); and School of Oriental and African Studies (£10,000).
FINANCES *Year* 2010 *Income* £397,037 *Grants* £413,672 *Assets* £12,743,183
TRUSTEES Prof. H Baker; A Ely; P Ely; Prof. Sir Heap; Dr J Langton; L Thompson; Prof. Sir Todd; Lady Pamela Youde.
OTHER INFORMATION Of total grants made £334,000 went to organisations in the UK and China. The remainder was spent on individual scholarships for students.
HOW TO APPLY On a form available by writing to the correspondence address.
WHO TO APPLY TO Mrs Anne Ely, Flat 23 Bede House, Manor Fields, London SW15 3LT *Tel* 020 8788 6252

■ The Skelton Bounty

CC NO 219370   **ESTABLISHED** 1934
WHERE FUNDING CAN BE GIVEN Lancashire (as it existed in 1934).
WHO CAN BENEFIT Registered charities benefiting young, older and infirm people.
WHAT IS FUNDED Restricted to Lancashire charities (not national ones unless operating in Lancashire from a permanent establishment within the county predominantly for the benefit of residents from that county) assisting young, elderly and infirm people.

WHAT IS NOT FUNDED No grants to individuals, religious charities or medical or scientific research.

TYPE OF GRANT Capital expenditure preferred.

RANGE OF GRANTS Up to £5,000.

SAMPLE GRANTS Good Companions – Bolton (£5,000); Action Force Africa, Liverpool (£4,700); Bowland Pennine Mountain Rescue Team and St Cyril's Children and Youth Project – Liverpool (£3,000 each); Garston Adventure Playground – Liverpool (£2,800); Fleetwood Gym Club for Young People and Frontline Trust – Liverpool (£2,000); Halton Autistic Family Support Group – Widnes (£1,600); Fazakerley Community Association (£1,500); Home Start Southport and Formby (£850) and After Adoption – Preston (£770).

FINANCES *Year* 2009–10 *Income* £95,703 *Grants* £91,053 *Assets* £2,037,880

TRUSTEES Sidney R Fisher; William D Fulton; Lord Shuttleworth; Sir Alan Waterworth; David G Wilson; Patricia Wilson; Margo Crighton Pitt; Mr Dennis G Mendoros; Ms Jane Squire; Ms Jacqueline Ann Hughes Lundy; Dame Lorna Elizabeth Fox Muirhead DBE; Mrs Patricia Frances Wilson.

HOW TO APPLY On a form available from the correspondent. Requests for application forms should be made as soon as possible after 1 January each year. The completed form should be returned before 31 March immediately following. Applications received after this date will not be considered. The trustees meet annually in July, with successful applicants receiving their grant cheques in late July/early August. Applications should include the charitable registration number of the organisation, or, where appropriate, a letter confirming charitable status.

WHO TO APPLY TO The Trustees, Cockshott Peck Lewis, 24 Hoghton Street, Southport, Merseyside PR9 0PA *Tel* 01704 534034

■ The Charles Skey Charitable Trust

CC NO 277697   **ESTABLISHED** 1979

WHERE FUNDING CAN BE GIVEN UK.

WHO CAN BENEFIT Organisations which the trustees have come across from their own research.

WHAT IS FUNDED General charitable purposes.

TYPE OF GRANT Grants are given on a one-off and recurring basis for core and capital support.

RANGE OF GRANTS £500–£10,000.

SAMPLE GRANTS Arnold Foundation – Rugby School, Lloyds Patriotic Fund and Royal Fusiliers Museum Appeal (£10,000 each); Trinity Hospice (£7,500); Roses Charitable Trust (£5,000); Camphill Village Trust (£3,000); the Dagenham Gospel Trust (£2,000); and Heritage of London Trust (£1,000).

FINANCES *Year* 2009–10 *Income* £199,620 *Grants* £92,000 *Assets* £3,518,422

TRUSTEES C H A Skey, Chair; J M Leggett; C B Berkeley; Revd J H A Leggett.

HOW TO APPLY The trust has previously stated that no written or telephoned requests for support will be entertained.

WHO TO APPLY TO J M Leggett, Trustee, Flint House, Park Homer Road, Colehill, Wimborne, Dorset BH21 2SP

■ Skipton Building Society Charitable Foundation

CC NO 1079538   **ESTABLISHED** 2000

WHERE FUNDING CAN BE GIVEN England and Wales.

WHO CAN BENEFIT Charitable organisations, schools and other organisations.

WHAT IS FUNDED General charitable organisations.

WHAT IS NOT FUNDED The foundation will not consider donations: to non-registered charities or individuals; to activities which are primarily the responsibility of central or local government or other responsible bodies; towards running costs including rent or staff wages; towards restoration or upkeep of buildings; towards expeditions or overseas travel; towards fundraising events, sponsorship or marketing appeals; towards the cost or maintenance of vehicles; to large national charities; or from charities which have applied to the foundation within the previous 12 months.

RANGE OF GRANTS Up to £5,000.

SAMPLE GRANTS Trinity Hospice – London (£4,500); Autism Initiatives (£3,400); Children's Adventure Farm – Cheshire and Transplant Sport UK (£2,500); Deafway – Preston, Saint Michael's Hospice – Harrogate and Rainbow Community Playgroup – Londonderry (£2,000 each); The Olive Branch (Faith in Action) – Lancaster and Pathway Project – Lichfield (£1,600 each); Cumbria Cerebral Palsy – Carlisle and Relate – Keighley (£1,000 each); Strongbones Children's Charitable Trust (£890); Colchester Furniture Project – Colchester (£500) and Hope UK (£350).

FINANCES *Year* 2009–10 *Income* £121,156 *Grants* £138,733 *Assets* £87,902

TRUSTEES Diana Chambers; Richard Twigg; Bishop Hope; Richard Robinson; Mrs Ethne Bannister.

HOW TO APPLY In writing to the correspondent enclosing the application form available on the trust's website. 'Your completed form must be returned enclosing your latest 2 years' Annual Accounts and any supporting literature you feel will strengthen your chances of receiving a grant.'

WHO TO APPLY TO Gill Davidson, Secretary, The Bailey, Skipton, North Yorkshire BD23 1DN *Tel* 01756 705000 *Fax* 01756 705743 *email* gill.davidson@skipton.co.uk *Website* www. skiptoncharitablefoundation.co.uk

■ The John Slater Foundation

CC NO 231145   **ESTABLISHED** 1963

WHERE FUNDING CAN BE GIVEN UK, with a strong preference for the north west of England especially West Lancashire.

WHO CAN BENEFIT Registered charities.

WHAT IS FUNDED Welfare, including animal welfare, and general charitable purposes.

WHAT IS NOT FUNDED No grants to individuals.

RANGE OF GRANTS £500–£10,000.

SAMPLE GRANTS Beneficiaries included: The Wellspring – Stockport (£18,000); Macmillan and Trinity Hospice (£10,000 each); Blackpool Ladies Sick Poor Association, Superintendent Gerald Richardson Memorial and Addlington Community Centre (£8,000); St John's Church, Levens (£5,000); RSPCA, RSPB, RNLI (£4,000 each); PDSA, Asthma Relief, Conquest Art (£2,000 each); Blue Cross (£1,000).

FINANCES *Year* 2009–10 *Income* £453,825 *Grants* £168,600 *Assets* £3,943,009

TRUSTEES HSBC Trust Co. (UK) Ltd.

HOW TO APPLY In writing to the correspondent, including accounts. Applications are considered twice a year, in May and November.

WHO TO APPLY TO R Thompson, Trust Manager, HSBC Trust Services, 10th Floor, Norwich House, Nelson Gate, Commercial Road, Southampton *Tel* 023 8072 2231 *Fax* 023 8072 2250

■ Sloane Robinson Foundation

CC NO 1068286   **ESTABLISHED** 1998
WHERE FUNDING CAN BE GIVEN UK.
WHO CAN BENEFIT Educational establishments.
WHAT IS FUNDED 'The foundation's principal charitable purpose is the advancement of the education of the public [. . .] The foundation is developing long term relationships with a number of academic institutions, with the ultimate goal of establishing scholarships and bursary schemes for overseas students to study in the UK.'
RANGE OF GRANTS £5,000–£125,000.
SAMPLE GRANTS Oxford University (£123,000); Rugby School (£87,000); Keble College – Oxford (£41,000); Lincoln College – Oxford (£40,000) and School of Oriental & African Studies (£5,000).
FINANCES *Year* 2009–10 *Income* £836,991 *Grants* £357,773 *Assets* £18,910,252
TRUSTEES G E S Robinson; H P Sloane; M D Willcox.
OTHER INFORMATION The grant total for 2009–10 totalled £358,000 of which £296,000 was given to institutions and £62,000 to private individuals.
HOW TO APPLY In writing to the correspondent. 'The trustees are pleased to receive updates from successful applicants to keep the trustees updated on the effective use of those funds – usually this is done by receiving a newsletter or similar.'
WHO TO APPLY TO M D Willcox, Trustee, Old Coach House, Sunnyside, Bergh Apton, Norwich NR15 1DD *Tel* 01508 480100 *email* info@willcoxlewis.co.uk

■ Rita and David Slowe Charitable Trust

CC NO 1048209   **ESTABLISHED** 1995
WHERE FUNDING CAN BE GIVEN UK and overseas.
WHO CAN BENEFIT Registered charities.
WHAT IS FUNDED General charitable purposes.
WHAT IS NOT FUNDED No grants are made to individuals (including gap year students) or religious bodies.
RANGE OF GRANTS £5,000–£13,000.
SAMPLE GRANTS Shelter (£13,000); Computer Aid International, David Baum Foundation and Big Issue Foundation (£10,000 each); Wells for India, Action Aid, Books Abroad, Excellent Development and Send a Cow (£5,000 each).
FINANCES *Year* 2009–10 *Income* £82,035 *Grants* £67,500 *Assets* £659,714
TRUSTEES Elizabeth Slowe; Graham Weinberg; Jonathan Slowe.
HOW TO APPLY In writing to the correspondent.
WHO TO APPLY TO The Trustees, 32 Hampstead High Street, London NW3 1JQ *Tel* 020 7435 7800

■ Ruth Smart Foundation

CC NO 1080021   **ESTABLISHED** 2000
WHERE FUNDING CAN BE GIVEN Worldwide.
WHO CAN BENEFIT Registered charities and charitable organisations.
WHAT IS FUNDED Relief of animal suffering.
TYPE OF GRANT One-off.
RANGE OF GRANTS £250–£12,000.
SAMPLE GRANTS Fauna & Flora International Africa Programmes (£11,000); Mauritian Wildlife Foundation (£6,000); Durrell Wildlife Conservation (£5,000); Friends of Mauritian Wildlife (£4,000); San Francisco Zoological Society (£3,000); Tusk Trust (£1,000); Royal Society for the Protection of Birds (£500) and The Devon Wildlife Trust (£250).
FINANCES *Year* 2010 *Income* £11,061,838 *Grants* £7,561,275 *Assets* £391,016,430
TRUSTEES Wilfrid Edward Vernor-Miles; John Crosfield Vernor-Miles; Paul Williams.
HOW TO APPLY 'The trustees support a number of charities on a regular basis and in practice finds that their income is fully committed and there is little, if any, surplus income available for distribution in response to unsolicited appeals.'
WHO TO APPLY TO The Trustees, Hunters, 9 New Square, Lincoln's Inn, London WC2A 3QN *Tel* 020 7412 5105

■ The SMB Charitable Trust

CC NO 263814   **ESTABLISHED** 1962
WHERE FUNDING CAN BE GIVEN UK and overseas.
WHO CAN BENEFIT Organisations for the advancement of the Christian religion and the relief of need, hardship or distress.
WHAT IS FUNDED Christian and welfare organisations. Accommodation and housing, various community services, healthcare, health facilities and buildings, famine/emergency aid, medical studies and research, and environmental and wildlife projects and campaigning will also be considered.
WHAT IS NOT FUNDED Grants to individuals are not normally considered, unless the application is made through a registered charity which can receive the cheque.
TYPE OF GRANT One-off grants, project grants and grants for recurring costs are prioritised. Also considered are building and other capital grants, funding for core and running costs, funding for salaries and start-up costs.
RANGE OF GRANTS Up to £4,000.
SAMPLE GRANTS Pilgrim Homes (£4,000); British Red Cross and Salvation Army (£3,000 each); Baptist Missionary Society and Mission Aviation Fellowship (£2,500); Marie Curie Foundation and West Ham Central Mission (£2,000 each); Shaftesbury Society (£1,500); Share Jesus International (£1,000); and Sports Reach (£500).
FINANCES *Year* 2009–10 *Income* £323,392 *Grants* £212,250 *Assets* £8,249,518
TRUSTEES E D Anstead; P J Stanford; Barbara O'Driscoll; J A Anstead; Claire Swarbrick.
HOW TO APPLY In writing to the correspondent, including the aims and principal activities of the applicant, the current financial position and details of any special projects for which funding is sought. Application forms are not used. Trustees normally meet in March, June, September and December and applications should be received before the beginning of the month in which meetings are held. Because of the volume of appeals received, unsuccessful applicants will only receive a reply if they

enclose an sae. However, unsuccessful applicants are welcome to reapply.

WHO TO APPLY TO Mrs B M O'Driscoll, Trustee, 15 Wilman Rd, Tunbridge Wells, Kent TN4 9AJ *Tel* 01892 537301 *Fax* 01892 618202 *email* smbcharitabletrust@googlemail.com

---

■ The Mrs Smith and Mount Trust

CC NO 1009718   **ESTABLISHED** 1992

WHERE FUNDING CAN BE GIVEN London and south east England, i.e. Norfolk, Suffolk, Cambridgeshire, Hertfordshire, Essex, Kent and Surrey.

WHO CAN BENEFIT Organisations benefiting people with mental illness or learning disability, homelessness and family support. Counselling is also supported with these categories.

WHAT IS FUNDED The trust has three main areas of interest mental illness/learning difficulties, family support within other two areas and homelessness.

WHAT IS NOT FUNDED The trustees do not consider building costs, only refurbishment or alterations necessary to bring them up to health and safety/fire regulations. No grants to individuals.

TYPE OF GRANT One-off and continuing revenue grants are considered.

RANGE OF GRANTS £2,000 to £15,000.

SAMPLE GRANTS The Maypole Project (£15,000); Notting Hill Churches Homeless Concern (£10,000); St Christopher's Hospice (£6,000); Family Support Clacton, Action for Refugees in Lewisham (AFRIL), Caris Haringey and Open Door St Albans (£5,000 each); Caspari Foundation (£4,500); Radicle (£4,000); Cold Weather Shelter (£2,700) and Positive Parenting Publications & Programmes (£2,100).

FINANCES *Year* 2009–10 *Income* £189,777 *Grants* £212,920 *Assets* £5,534,526

TRUSTEES Mrs Gillian M Gorell Barnes; Richard S Fowler; Douglas J Mobsby; Lisa Weaks.

OTHER INFORMATION In 2009–10 grants were made to 41 organisations totalling £213,000. No grants to individuals.

HOW TO APPLY 'The trustees meet three times per year in March, July and November and application forms and supporting documentation must reach our offices by the end of January, May and September respectively. We prefer all applicants to submit their application online. Applicants may download the application questions and prepare their answers in advance. You will be able to begin your application and then save and return to it later if required.'

WHO TO APPLY TO Mrs Jayne Day, c/o Pothecary Witham Weld Solicitors, 70 St George's Square, London SW1V 3RD *Tel* 020 7821 8211 *email* charities@pwwsolicitors.co.uk *Website* www.pwwsolicitors.co.uk

---

■ The N Smith Charitable Settlement

CC NO 276660   **ESTABLISHED** 1978

WHERE FUNDING CAN BE GIVEN Worldwide.

WHO CAN BENEFIT Registered charities.

WHAT IS FUNDED General charitable purposes but mainly social work, medical research, education, environment/animals, arts and overseas aid.

WHAT IS NOT FUNDED Grants are only made to registered charities and not to individuals.

TYPE OF GRANT Appeals for capital equipment are preferred over salary costs.

RANGE OF GRANTS £500–£5,000.

SAMPLE GRANTS Migraine Trust (£2,000); Nepal Leprosy Trust and East Cheshire Hospice (£1,000 each); Animal Health Trust (£650); Action for Kids, Autism West Midlands, Eden Project, Listening Books, Opera North, Royal British Legion and Whoopsadaisy (£500 each).

FINANCES *Year* 2009–10 *Income* £140,534 *Grants* £116,961 *Assets* £4,090,496

TRUSTEES T R Kendal; Miss A E Merricks; J H Williams-Rigby; G Wardle.

HOW TO APPLY In writing to the correspondent. The trustees meet twice a year.

WHO TO APPLY TO Anne E Merricks, Linder Myers, Phoenix House, 45 Cross Street, Manchester M2 4JF *Tel* 0161 832 6972 *Fax* 0161 834 0718

■ The Smith Charitable Trust

CC NO 288570   **ESTABLISHED** 1983

WHERE FUNDING CAN BE GIVEN UK and overseas.

WHO CAN BENEFIT Registered charities, usually large, well-known UK organisations, which are on a list of regular beneficiaries.

WHAT IS FUNDED General charitable purposes.

WHAT IS NOT FUNDED No grants to animal charities or to individuals.

RANGE OF GRANTS £3,000–£12,000.

SAMPLE GRANTS Sue Ryder Care (£9,000); Research Institute for the Care of the Elderly, Macmillan Cancer Relief and RNLI (£6,000 each); St Nicholas' Hospice and Help the Heroes (£5,000 each); and the Marine Society and Sea Cadets, Mind, Sense and Scope (£3,000 each).

FINANCES *Year* 2009–10 *Income* £157,118 *Grants* £91,975 *Assets* £5,359,648

TRUSTEES A G F Fuller; Paul Sheils; R I Turner; R J Weetch.

HOW TO APPLY Unsolicited applications are not considered.

WHO TO APPLY TO Paul Shiels, c/o Moon Beaver Solicitors, 24–25 Bloomsbury Square, London WC1A 2PL *Tel* 020 7637 0661 *Fax* 020 7436 4663 *email* psheils@mail.com

---

■ The Amanda Smith Charitable Trust

CC NO 1052975   **ESTABLISHED** 1996

WHERE FUNDING CAN BE GIVEN UK.

WHO CAN BENEFIT Registered charities.

WHAT IS FUNDED General charitable purposes.

SAMPLE GRANTS Previous beneficiaries included Cedar School and Nordoff Robbins Music Therapy.

FINANCES *Year* 2010 *Income* £0 *Grants* £1,410

TRUSTEES C Smith, Chair; Ms A Smith.

OTHER INFORMATION In 2010 the trust had no income and a total expenditure of £1,410. Further information was not available, except that it remains on the Central Register of Charities and so has not been dissolved.

HOW TO APPLY In writing to the correspondent.

WHO TO APPLY TO Neil Bradley, 1 Manchester Square, London W1U 3AB *Tel* 020 3219 2600

■ The E H Smith Charitable Trust

CC NO 328313   **ESTABLISHED** 1989

WHERE FUNDING CAN BE GIVEN UK, some preference for the Midlands.

WHO CAN BENEFIT Local and national organisations.

WHAT IS FUNDED General charitable purposes.

WHAT IS NOT FUNDED No grants to political parties. Grants are not normally given to individuals.

RANGE OF GRANTS Up to around £5,000 each; average about £750.

SAMPLE GRANTS Previous beneficiaries included: Romania Challenge (£4,900); Betel (£2,500); Solihull Hall (£1,500); Cancer Research UK (£900); County Air Ambulance (£700); Smile Train UK (£600); and Crash Christmas Cards, NSPCC and Junior Heybridge Swifts FC (£500 each).

FINANCES *Year* 2009–10 *Income* £10,414 *Grants* £40,000

TRUSTEES K H A Smith; Mrs B M Hodgskin-Brown; D P Ensell.

HOW TO APPLY In writing to the correspondent at any time.

WHO TO APPLY TO K H A Smith, Trustee, Westhaven House, Arleston Way, Shipley, West Midlands B90 4LH *Tel* 0121 706 6100

··

■ The Henry Smith Charity

CC NO 230102   **ESTABLISHED** 1628

WHERE FUNDING CAN BE GIVEN UK. Specific local programmes in east and west Sussex, Hampshire, Kent, Gloucestershire, Leicestershire, Suffolk and Surrey.

WHO CAN BENEFIT Charitable organisations.

WHAT IS FUNDED The trustees use the following programme areas to classify their grants: Black, Asian and Minority Ethnic (BAME); Carers; Community Service; Disability; Domestic and Sexual Violence; Drugs, Alcohol and Substance Misuse; Ex-Service Men and Women; Family Services; Healthcare; Homelessness; Lesbian, Gay, Bisexual and Transgender; Mental Health; Older People; Prisoners and Ex-offenders; Prostitution and Trafficking; Refugees and Asylum Seekers; and Young People.

WHAT IS NOT FUNDED Grants are not made towards the following: local authorities and areas of work usually considered a statutory responsibility; state maintained schools, colleges, universities and friend/parent teacher associations, or independent schools not exclusively for students with special educational needs; organisations not providing direct services to clients such as umbrella, second tier or grant-making organisations; youth clubs, except those in areas of high deprivation; uniformed groups such as Scouts and Guides, except those in areas of high deprivation; community centres, except those in areas of high deprivation; community transport organisations or services; professional associations or projects for the training of professionals; start up costs or organisations unable to demonstrate a track record; individuals, or organisations and charities applying on their behalf; projects that promote a particular religion, or capital appeals for places of worship; arts projects, except those which can clearly demonstrate a therapeutic or rehabilitative benefit to disabled people, prisoners or young people who experience educational, social and economic disadvantage, including young people in, or leaving, care; education projects except those which can clearly demonstrate a rehabilitative benefit to disabled people, prisoners or young people who experience educational, social and economic disadvantage, including young people in, or leaving, care; leisure, recreation or play activities, except those exclusively for disabled people or those which can clearly demonstrate a significant rehabilitative benefit to people with mental health problems or that significantly

improve opportunities and maximise the potential of young people who experience educational, social and economic disadvantage; overseas trips; projects taking place or benefiting people outside the UK; residential holidays for young people (except those that qualify under the Holiday Grants scheme); counselling projects, except those in areas of high deprivation and with a clearly defined client group; environmental projects where the primary purpose is conservation of the environment; Citizens Advice Bureau or projects solely providing legal advice; core running costs of hospices; feasibility studies; social research; campaigning or lobbying projects; projects where website development or maintenance is the focus of the bid; IT equipment (unless as direct support costs for a funded staff member); capital projects to meet the requirements of the Disability Discrimination Act; applicants declined within the previous six months; Organisations that do not have charitable aims (e.g. companies limited by shares and commercial organisations are not eligible to apply); mailshots or general appeals.

TYPE OF GRANT Capital and revenue; one-off grants and recurrent grants for up to 3 years.

RANGE OF GRANTS Small grants: £500–£10,000; Large grants: over £10,000.

SAMPLE GRANTS Cripplegate Foundation – towards funding local community projects which target vulnerable and hard to reach groups in Islington (£300,000); Cool Recovery – towards running costs of support services for people in south Devon affected by mental health problems (£120,000); Bethel Community Church – towards three years' salary of a co-ordinator at a community cafe and night shelter in Newport (£94,500); Choir With No Name – towards running costs (£75,000); Dudley Christian Fellowship – towards running costs of a charity for homeless people and substance misusers (£70,500); Action Medical Research – towards the second and third year of a project to research Rett Syndrome (£70,000); Headway Belfast – towards three years' salary of a Neuro Physiotherapist for an exercise project for people affected by brain injury (£60,000); British Refugee Council – towards one year's running costs of the Therapeutic Casework Unit based in London (£50,000); Age Concern Cardiff and the Vale of Glamorgan – towards running costs (£45,000); Cutteslowe Community Association – towards one year's salary of two part-time community workers at a community centre in Oxford (£33,000); Mildmay Mission Hospital – towards continued funding of the running costs of an occupational therapy service in London for people with AIDS (£28,000); Gargaar Somali Welfare Association – towards running costs of a luncheon club for older people from London's Somali and East African community (£15,000); Powerful Partnerships – core costs of an advocacy service in Edinburgh for people with learning disabilities (£15,000); Suffolk Punch Trust – towards equipment purchase for a centre in Suffolk that provides training to young offenders (£2,500); and African Sub-Saharan Development Partnership – towards a trip to Butlins for 15 Congolese children from a refugee background in London (£1,400).

FINANCES *Year* 2010 *Income* £14,264,000 *Grants* £25,481,000 *Assets* £701,474,000

TRUSTEES Carola Goodman-Law; James Hambro; Anna McNair Scott; Merlyn Lowther; Noel Manns; Anne Allen; Rt Hon Claire Countes; Diana Barran; Marilyn Gallyer; Mark Newton;

Peter Smallridge; Tristan Millington Drake; Nicholas Acland; Miko Geidroyc; Vivian Hunt; Bridget Biddell; Patrick Maxwell; Sir Richard Thompson.

OTHER INFORMATION £24.9 million of the grant total went to organisations and a further £1 million was made in grants to individuals.

HOW TO APPLY 'Each of our grant programmes has a slightly different application and assessment process. You will find information about how to make your application in the guidelines for each type of grant. Some of our grants require you to fill in an application form. For others there is no application form; instead we provide guidance about to structure your application and what supporting documents you need to send us. Please ensure you send us all the supporting documents we ask you to include with your application. Incomplete applications will be returned unread. We strongly recommend that you download and read the guidelines of the relevant grant programme carefully before you start your application. It is important that you follow our guidance on how to apply.' Guidelines for each programme can be downloaded from the Grant Programmes section of the charity's website.

WHO TO APPLY TO Richard Hopgood, Director, 6th Floor, 65 Leadenhall Street, London EC3A 2AD *Tel* 020 7264 4970 *Fax* 020 7488 9097 *Website* www.henrysmithcharity.org.uk

---

■ The Leslie Smith Foundation

CC NO 250030   **ESTABLISHED** 1964
WHERE FUNDING CAN BE GIVEN UK with a preference for Wiltshire, Norfolk, Middlesex, London and Dorset.

WHO CAN BENEFIT Registered charities, with a preference for those benefiting children with illnesses, both terminal and non-terminal, in the UK (excluding respite care and research); orphans; and schools, specifically special needs schools based in the UK.

WHAT IS FUNDED Preference is given to charities which the trust has special interest in, knowledge of, or association with, but with an emphasis on: counselling services; children's and young persons' welfare; health and allied services; ex-servicemen's welfare; and other causes the trustees deem appropriate.

WHAT IS NOT FUNDED Grants are given to registered charities only. No grants for individuals.

TYPE OF GRANT Buildings, capital, one-off, research and recurring costs. Funding is available for up to one year.

RANGE OF GRANTS £500–£25,000.

SAMPLE GRANTS Comic relief (£43,000); Shakespeare Globe (£25,000); Gaddum Centre, Joseph Weld Hospice and Royal British Legion (£10,000 each); Shooting Star Children's Hospice and Prisoners Abroad (£5,000 each); The Community Foundation and Step by Step (£2,500 each); and Norfolk Accident Rescue Service (£2,000).

FINANCES *Year* 2009–10 *Income* £55,961 *Grants* £181,255 *Assets* £2,892,785

TRUSTEES M D Willcox; H L Young Jones.

HOW TO APPLY In writing to the correspondent, including a summary of the project and a copy of the latest accounts. Only successful applications are acknowledged.

WHO TO APPLY TO The Trustees, c/o Willcox & Lewis, The Old Coach House, Sunnyside, Bergh Apton, Norwich NR15 1DD *Tel* 01508 480100 *Fax* 01508 480001 *email* info@willcoxlewis.co.uk

---

■ The Martin Smith Foundation

CC NO 1072607   **ESTABLISHED** 1998
WHERE FUNDING CAN BE GIVEN UK.

WHO CAN BENEFIT Organisations and individuals.

WHAT IS FUNDED Projects supporting art, music, sports and education.

TYPE OF GRANT One-off and recurrent.

RANGE OF GRANTS £50–£750,000.

SAMPLE GRANTS National Museum of Science and Industry (£750,000); Orchestra of the Age of Enlightenment – Smith Challenge (£165,000); Royal Academy of Music (£106,000); Bath Mozartfest (£15,000); Tetbury Music Festival (£7,500); Royal Philharmonic Society (£5,900); International Musicians Seminar Prussia Cove (£2,800); Ashmolean Museum (£1,000); and Wellbeing of Women (£250).

FINANCES *Year* 2009–10 *Income* £78,001 *Grants* £154,250 *Assets* £95,433

TRUSTEES Martin G Smith, Chair; Elise Smith; Jeremy J G Smith; Katherine Wake; Elizabeth F C Buchanan; B Peerless.

OTHER INFORMATION Grants totalling £31,000 were also made to individuals.

HOW TO APPLY This trust does not consider unsolicited applications.

WHO TO APPLY TO Martin Smith, 4 Essex Villas, London W8 7BN *Tel* 020 7937 0027

■ Stanley Smith General Charitable Trust

CC NO 326226   **ESTABLISHED** 1982
WHERE FUNDING CAN BE GIVEN UK.

WHO CAN BENEFIT Any organisations or people who are in need.

WHAT IS FUNDED General charitable purposes.

RANGE OF GRANTS Up to £20,000.

SAMPLE GRANTS British Red Cross – Haiti Earthquake Appeal and Save the Children Fund (£20,000 each); For Site (£19,000); Royal College of Art and Whizz Kids (£10,000 each); Sparks, The Alzheimer's Disease Society, Lord Wandsworth Foundation and Hop, Skip and Jump South West (£5,000 each); Global Giving – UK (£3,000) and The Woodland Trust (£2,000).

FINANCES *Year* 2009–10 *Income* £103,757 *Grants* £157,078 *Assets* £2,323,618

TRUSTEES A de Brye; Mrs J de Brye; Phillip Sykes.

HOW TO APPLY In writing to the correspondent.

WHO TO APPLY TO George Georghiou, Mercer and Hole Trustees Ltd, 72 London Road, St Albans, Hertfordshire AL1 1NS *Tel* 01727 869141

■ The Stanley Smith UK Horticultural Trust

CC NO 261925   **ESTABLISHED** 1970
WHERE FUNDING CAN BE GIVEN UK and overseas.

WHO CAN BENEFIT Grants are made to individuals or to institutions benefiting botany and horticulture.

WHAT IS FUNDED Grants are made to individual projects which involve the advancement of amenity horticulture and horticultural education. In the past, assistance has been given to: the creation, preservation and development of gardens to which the public is admitted; the cultivation and wider distribution of plants derived by breeding or by collection from the wild, to research; and to the publication of books with a direct bearing on horticulture.

WHAT IS NOT FUNDED Grants are not made for projects in commercial horticulture (crop production) or agriculture, nor are they made to support students taking academic or diploma courses of any kind, although educational institutions are supported.

TYPE OF GRANT Capital (including buildings), core costs, feasibility studies, interest-free loans, one-off, research and start-up costs. Grants are normally made as a contribution to cover the costs of identified projects. In exceptional cases grants are made over a three-year period.

SAMPLE GRANTS The Belmont Trust, Unst, Shetland and WB School (£5,000 each); Bristol University Botanic Garden, GardenAfrica, HM Prison Shepton Mallet and Trees for Cities (£2,500); Castle Howard Arboretum Trust and Fokas-Cosmetatos Foundation, Cephalonia, Greece (£2,000 each); and Combe Reading Room, Combe, Oxfordshire, Jane Austen's House, Chawton, Hampshire, Plant Heritage (NCCPG) and The Garden Museum, Lambeth, London (£1,000 each).

FINANCES *Year* 2009–10 *Income* £134,989 *Grants* £121,577 *Assets* £3,237,742

TRUSTEES C D Brickell; Lady Renfrew; J B E Simmons; A De Brye; P R Sykes; Dr D A H Rae; E Reed.

HOW TO APPLY In writing to the correspondent. *Guidelines for Applicants* are available from the trust. The director is willing to give advice on how applications should be presented. Grants are awarded twice a year, in spring and autumn. To be considered in the spring allocation, applications should reach the director before 15 February of each year; for the autumn allocation the equivalent date is 15 August. Potential recipients are advised to get their applications in early.

WHO TO APPLY TO James Cullen, Director, Cory Lodge, PO Box 365, Cambridge CB2 1HR *Tel* 01223 336 299 *Fax* 01223 336 278

■ **Philip Smith's Charitable Trust**

CC NO 1003751   **ESTABLISHED** 1991

WHERE FUNDING CAN BE GIVEN UK with a preference for Gloucestershire.

WHO CAN BENEFIT Local and national registered charities.

WHAT IS FUNDED The trust makes grants mainly in the fields of welfare, the environment, older people, children and the armed forces.

RANGE OF GRANTS £100–£20,000.

SAMPLE GRANTS NSPCC (£20,000); Merlin (£13,000 in two grants); Save the Children (£10,000); Chipping Campden Playing Field and Recreation Ground (£7,000 in two grants); Game and Wildlife Conservation Trust (£5,000); St James PCC Chipping Campden (£3,500 in two grants); the Connection at St Martin's (£2,500); Wester Ross Fisheries Trust and Combat Stress (£2,000 each); Farms for City Children (£1,300); British Red Cross and Countryside Foundation for Education (£1,000 each); Independent Age (£750); Family Haven (£500); and Royal Green Jackets (£100).

FINANCES *Year* 2009–10 *Income* £56,897 *Grants* £96,900 *Assets* £1,107,735

TRUSTEES Hon. Philip R Smith; Mary Smith.

HOW TO APPLY In writing to the correspondent. The trustees meet regularly to consider grants. A lack of response can be taken to indicate that the trust does not wish to contribute to an appeal.

WHO TO APPLY TO Helen D'Monte, Bircham Dyson Bell, 50 Broadway, London SW1H 0BL *Tel* 020 7783 3685 *Fax* 020 7222 3480 *email* helendmonte@bdb-law.co.uk

■ **The R C Snelling Charitable Trust**

CC NO 1074776   **ESTABLISHED** 1999

WHERE FUNDING CAN BE GIVEN Within a 30 mile radius of the village of Blofield in Norfolk.

WHO CAN BENEFIT UK registered charities, children, young and older people.

WHAT IS FUNDED Medical, educational, religious, welfare or environmental resources.

WHAT IS NOT FUNDED The trust gave the following list of ineligible expenditures: salaries; sponsorship for less than one year; general appeals where the need could be met several times over by grantors; national appeals; continued assistance with running costs.

TYPE OF GRANT One-off.

RANGE OF GRANTS Usually £500–£5,000.

SAMPLE GRANTS Norfolk Community Foundation (£100,000); RAF Air Defence Radar Museum (£4,000); Norfolk Street Pastors (£3,500); Alysham Recreation Ground (£2,000); Norwich Vineyard (£1,500); Norfolk YMCA and Norwich Cathedral (£1,000) and Norwich District Carers Forum (£500).

FINANCES *Year* 2009–10 *Income* £88,598 *Grants* £138,136 *Assets* £1,203,556

TRUSTEES R C Snelling; P Buttinger; R A Cogman; T Wise; P Minns; J Drake; R Nash.

HOW TO APPLY An online application form can be completed from the company's website. The trust is happy to receive queries via email.

WHO TO APPLY TO The Trustees, R C Snelling Ltd, Lijas Field, Laundry Lane, Blofield Heath, Norwich NR13 4SQ *Tel* 01603 712202 *email* trust@snellings.co.uk *Website* www.snellings.co.uk/charitable-trust.aspx

■ **The Snowball Trust**

CC NO 702860   **ESTABLISHED** 1989

WHERE FUNDING CAN BE GIVEN Coventry and Warwickshire.

WHO CAN BENEFIT Individuals or institutions for the benefit of children up to 21 years of age who are disabled.

WHAT IS FUNDED The provision of moveable equipment for sick and disabled children.

WHAT IS NOT FUNDED Applications for administration and maintenance costs, salaries, fees, short-term respite care and holidays are rejected.

TYPE OF GRANT Capital and one-off.

RANGE OF GRANTS Generally £500–£5,000, although there are no upper or lower limits.

FINANCES *Year* 2009–10 *Income* £15,292 *Grants* £40,473 *Assets* £95,000

TRUSTEES Shaun Flaherty; Elaine Hancox; David Fisher; Dr Alan Rhodes; D Perkin and R J Norman.

OTHER INFORMATION Grants totalled £40,000 of which £9,000 went to institutions and £31,000 to individuals.

HOW TO APPLY On a form available from the correspondent.

WHO TO APPLY TO Shaun Flaherty, Trustee, Mr Shaun Vernon Flaherty, 80 Howes Lane, Coventry CV3 6PJ *Tel* 024 7641 5733

■ **The Sobell Foundation**

CC NO 274369   **ESTABLISHED** 1977

WHERE FUNDING CAN BE GIVEN Unrestricted, in practice, England and Wales, Israel and the Commonwealth of Independent States.

WHO CAN BENEFIT Small national or local registered charities or organisations registered with the Inland Revenue.

WHAT IS FUNDED Jewish charities; medical care and treatment; care and education for children and adults with physical and/or mental disabilities; homelessness; care and support for the elderly; care and support for children from disadvantaged backgrounds.

WHAT IS NOT FUNDED No grants to individuals.

TYPE OF GRANT One-off, capital, project, running costs, buildings, core costs and recurring costs. Funding may be given for up to and over three years.

RANGE OF GRANTS £450–£300,000.

SAMPLE GRANTS Jewish Care (£300,000), the second instalment of a 3-year grant towards the building a new day care centre at their Golders Green campus; and Leonard Cheshire Disability (£85,000), the first instalment of a 3-year grant to expand Sobell Lodge care home in Kent. Approximately 53% of grants made were to UK non-Jewish charities, 31% to Israeli charities and charities in the CIS, 15% to UK Jewish charities and 1% to other overseas charities.

FINANCES *Year* 2009–10 *Income* £5,540,631 *Grants* £3,407,786 *Assets* £62,680,920

TRUSTEES Susan Lacroix; Roger Lewis; Andrea Scouller.

HOW TO APPLY 'Due to the enormous number of appeals the trustees are now receiving they have had to limit their support within the UK to charities operating in England and Wales.' Applications should be made in writing to the administrator using the application form obtainable from the foundation or printable from its website. The application form should be accompanied by: current year's summary income and expenditure budget; most recent annual report; most recent full accounts; and Inland Revenue certificate of exemption (if required). It will generally be two to three months before applicants are notified of the trustees' decision. The trustees receive a large number of applications for funding from registered charities during the year and support as many as possible of those which fall within the foundation's objectives. They aim to deal with requests within three months of receipt and to respond to each application received, whether or not a grant is made. Trustees meet every three to four months and major grants are considered at these meetings. Requests for smaller amounts may be dealt with on a more frequent basis. Most applications are dealt with on an ongoing basis, and there are no deadlines for the receipt of applications. Organisations should wait 12 months before reapplying.

WHO TO APPLY TO Penny Newton, Administrator, PO Box 2137, Shepton Mallet, Somerset BA4 6YA *Tel* 01749 813135 *Fax* 01749 813136 *email* enquiries@sobellfoundation.org.uk *Website* www.sobellfoundation.org.uk

■ Social Business Trust (Scale-Up)

CC NO 1136151　　**ESTABLISHED** 2010

WHERE FUNDING CAN BE GIVEN Undefined, in practice the UK.

WHO CAN BENEFIT Organisations.

WHAT IS FUNDED General charitable purposes.

TRUSTEES Damon Marcus Buffini; Paul Richard Armstrong; Simon Milton; Jonathan Myers; Tim Curry.

OTHER INFORMATION The charity's working name is Scale-Up.

HOW TO APPLY In writing to the correspondent.

WHO TO APPLY TO Adele Blakebrough, 4 More London Riverside, London SE1 2AU *Tel* 020 3117 1901

■ Solev Co Ltd

CC NO 254623　　**ESTABLISHED** 1967

WHERE FUNDING CAN BE GIVEN UK.

WHO CAN BENEFIT Individuals and organisations benefiting Jewish people.

WHAT IS FUNDED Principally Jewish causes.

SAMPLE GRANTS Previous beneficiaries include: Dina Perelman Trust Ltd (£100,000); Songdale Ltd (£40,000); Society of Friends of the Torah (£3,900); Finchley Road Synagogue (£2,300); NW London Talmudical College (£1,500); Yesodey Hatorah School (£700); and Gateshead Talmudical College (£400).

FINANCES *Year* 2009–10 *Income* £704,359 *Grants* £435,390 *Assets* £3,720,368

TRUSTEES R Tager; S Tager; J Tager; C M Frommer.

OTHER INFORMATION No information on grant beneficiaries has been included in the charity's accounts in recent years.

HOW TO APPLY In writing to the correspondent.

WHO TO APPLY TO R Tager, Trustee, 1 Spaniards Park, Columbas Drive, London NW3 7JD

■ Solihull Community Foundation

CC NO 1063014　　**ESTABLISHED** 1997

WHERE FUNDING CAN BE GIVEN Borough of Solihull and the surrounding area.

WHO CAN BENEFIT Registered charities, community and voluntary groups working to help local people across Solihull.

WHAT IS FUNDED General charitable purposes. The foundation is currently managing the following funds: Grassroots Grants, Sport Relief and the European Social Fund Community Grants. Please note: grant schemes can change frequently and potential applicants are advised consult the foundation's website for details of open programmes and their deadlines.

RANGE OF GRANTS Usually £250–£5,000.

SAMPLE GRANTS ReCom (£12,000); Dorridge Scout Group, North Solihull Community Festival and Nine Acres Drop In (£5,000 each); Mowhawks Ice Racing Club (£4,000); Castle Bromwich Swim Club (£3,600); Seeds of Hope (£3,000); Marston Green Community Group and 50+ Women's Group (£1,500) and Shirley Baptist Club Youth Club Extra (£800).

FINANCES *Year* 2009–10 *Income* £191,075 *Grants* £119,947 *Assets* £162,513

TRUSTEES Eric Baptiste; John Powell; Maggie Throup; Denis Ellis; George Lester.

HOW TO APPLY The foundation's website has details of the grant schemes currently being administered.

WHO TO APPLY TO Sharon Pinnock, Manager, Block 80, Land Rover, Lode Lane, Solihull B92 8NW *Tel* 0121 700 3934 *Fax* 0121 700 9158 *email* director@solihullcf.org *Website* www.solihullcf.org

■ The Solo Charitable Settlement

CC NO 326444　　**ESTABLISHED** 1983

WHERE FUNDING CAN BE GIVEN UK and Israel.

WHO CAN BENEFIT Organisations benefiting Jewish people, people with disabilities, research workers and medical professionals.

WHAT IS FUNDED Jewish organisations, medical research, arts and disability.

RANGE OF GRANTS Between £100–£30,000.

SAMPLE GRANTS Norwood Ravenswood (£10,500); Nightingale House (£6,000); Dulwich College (£5,000); Beth Shalom Holocaust Centre (£2,500); UCLH Fund No 1051 and Yad Vashem UK Foundation (£1,000 each); Future Dreams Trust (£500); Langdon Foundation, British ORT and Cystic Fibrosis Charity (£250 each); One to One Children's Fund and Combat Stress (£200 each); and British WIZO, Royal Marsden Charity and One Family UK (£100 each).

FINANCES *Year* 2009–10 *Income* £231,677 *Grants* £34,345 *Assets* £537,869

TRUSTEES Peter D Goldstein; Edna A Goldstein; Paul Goldstein; Dean Goldstein; Jamie Goldstein; Tammy Ward.

HOW TO APPLY In writing to the correspondent.

WHO TO APPLY The Trustees, c/o Randall Greene, Parallel House, 32–34 London Road, Guildford, Surrey GU1 2AB *Tel* 01483 230440

■ Dr Richard Solomon's Charitable Trust

CC NO 277309   ESTABLISHED 1978
WHERE FUNDING CAN BE GIVEN Overseas.

WHO CAN BENEFIT Voluntary groups and charitable organisations only.

WHAT IS FUNDED General, international development. The trust has previously stated that it prefers to support 'ecologically sound democratic projects'.

WHAT IS NOT FUNDED Individuals are not supported.

RANGE OF GRANTS Up to £21,000.

SAMPLE GRANTS Previous beneficiaries included: INDEPO – Institute for Rural Development – Bolivia (£21,000); Tools for Self Reliance and Appropriate Technology Asia (£3,500 each); Tree Aid and Forest Peoples Project (£2,500 each); Civil Liberties Trust and Refugee Council (£1,500 each); and Computer Aid International and Microloan Foundation (£1,000 each).

FINANCES *Year* 2009–10 *Income* £19,718 *Grants* £20,000

TRUSTEES Richard Edgar Bethel Solomon; Stella Natasha Solomon; Diana Jean Huntingford; Alison Margaret Sepping.

HOW TO APPLY In writing to the correspondent.

WHO TO APPLY TO Dr Richard Solomons, Trustee, Fell Edge Farm, Moorside Lane, Addingham, Ilkley, West Yorkshire LS29 9JX *Tel* 01943 830841

■ David Solomons Charitable Trust

CC NO 297275   ESTABLISHED 1986
WHERE FUNDING CAN BE GIVEN UK.

WHO CAN BENEFIT UK and local charitable organisations benefiting people who have learning difficulties and their carers.

WHAT IS FUNDED Research into, or the treatment and care of, people with mental disabilities.

WHAT IS NOT FUNDED No grants to individuals.

TYPE OF GRANT One-off, project and salaries. Administrative expenses and large building projects are not usually funded, although grants can be made towards furnishing or equipping rooms.

RANGE OF GRANTS Mostly £1,000–£2,000.

SAMPLE GRANTS Down's Syndrome Association (£8,000); Autism Bedfordshire and Special Yoga Centre (£3,000 each); Sarum Orchestra (£2,300); Martha Trust (£2,000); Support for Living, Art and Power, Into Work, National Trust for Scotland and Bishopswood School Association (£1,000 each); Pathway Workshop (£750); SEN, Stallcombe House, Adventure

Farm Trust and Musical Keys (£500 each); and Swiss Cottage School (£375).

FINANCES *Year* 2009–10 *Income* £86,862 *Grants* £77,625 *Assets* £2,229,703

TRUSTEES J L Drewitt; J J Rutter; Dr R E B Solomons; M T Chamberlayne; Dr L B Cooke; D J Huntingford.

HOW TO APPLY The trustees conduct their own research into potential applicants.

WHO TO APPLY TO Graeme Crosby, Administrator, Jasmine Cottage, 11 Lower Road, Breachwood Green, Hitchin, Hertfordshire SG4 8NS *Tel* 01438 833254 *email* g.crosby@waitrose.com

■ Friends of Somerset Churches and Chapels

CC NO 1055840   ESTABLISHED 1996
WHERE FUNDING CAN BE GIVEN The historic county of Somerset.

WHO CAN BENEFIT Churches and chapels.

WHAT IS FUNDED The repair of churches and chapels, which are open for worship in Somerset.

WHAT IS NOT FUNDED No grants to individuals. No support for new work, reordering or repairs to moveable items.

RANGE OF GRANTS Up to £10,000.

SAMPLE GRANTS Church grants – Winsham and Blackford (£5,000 each); Claverham (£3,000); Charlecombe (£2,000); Clutton and Badgeworth (£1,500 each) and Glastonbury – St Patrick's Chapel (£1,000).

FINANCES *Year* 2009–10 *Income* £34,899 *Grants* £24,250 *Assets* £133,877

TRUSTEES Hugh Playfair; Gerard Leighton; John Wood; David Sisson; Dr Robert Dunning; Jennifer Beazley; Rear Admiral Roger Morris; Jane Venner-Pack; The Very Revd Abbot of Downside; Paul Heal.

PUBLICATIONS 'Somerset Churches – Building, Repair and Restoration' was published by the trust in June 2007.

HOW TO APPLY Application forms and guidelines are available from the correspondent or to download from the website. Trustees meet four times a year.

WHO TO APPLY TO Angela Dudley, Grants Secretary, Whynot Cottage, Wellow, Bath, Somerset BA2 8QA *Tel* 01225 837134 *email* chedburn@chedburn.com *Website* www.fscandc.org.uk

■ Songdale Ltd

CC NO 286075   ESTABLISHED 1961
WHERE FUNDING CAN BE GIVEN UK and Israel.

WHO CAN BENEFIT People of the Orthodox Jewish faith.

WHAT IS FUNDED Jewish general charitable purposes.

SAMPLE GRANTS Previous beneficiaries include: Cosmon Belz Ltd, Kollel Belz, BFOT, Ezras Yisroel, Forty Limited, Darkei Ovois, Germach Veholachto, Keren Nedunnia Lchasanim, Belz Nursery and Bais Chinuch.

FINANCES *Year* 2009–10 *Income* £237,317 *Grants* £259,785 *Assets* £2,445,824

TRUSTEES M Grosskopf; Mrs M Grosskopf; Y Grosskopf.

OTHER INFORMATION No grants list was available.

HOW TO APPLY In writing to the correspondent.

WHO TO APPLY TO Yechiel Grosskopf, Trustee, 6 Spring Hill, London E5 9BE *Tel* 020 8806 5010

■ The E C Sosnow Charitable Trust

CC NO 273578   **ESTABLISHED** 1977
WHERE FUNDING CAN BE GIVEN UK and overseas.
WHO CAN BENEFIT Cultural institutions; UK and international organisations benefiting children, young people, students, older people and people who are disadvantaged.
WHAT IS FUNDED Education; medical organisations; emergency overseas aid; disability; the arts; and disadvantage.
WHAT IS NOT FUNDED No grants are made to individuals.
TYPE OF GRANT One-off.
RANGE OF GRANTS £200–£5,500.
SAMPLE GRANTS LSE (£5,000); Weizmann UK (£4,000); School Bursary Trust (£3,000); Brent Adolescent Centre (£2,500); Chicken Shed (£2,000); Spanish and Portuguese Congregation (£1,000); and Woodstock Sinclair Trust (£500).
FINANCES *Year* 2009–10 *Income* £52,569 *Grants* £51,000 *Assets* £1,834,348
TRUSTEES E R Fattal; Mrs F J M Fattal.
HOW TO APPLY In writing to the correspondent.
WHO TO APPLY TO The Trustees, PO Box 13398, London SW3 6ZL

■ The Souter Charitable Trust

SC NO SC029998   **ESTABLISHED** 1991
WHERE FUNDING CAN BE GIVEN UK, but with a preference for Scotland; overseas.
WHO CAN BENEFIT Grants are given to a variety of organisations supporting people of all ages; people who are in care, fostered or adopted; Christians; evangelists; carers; people disadvantaged by poverty; refugees; or victims of famine, man-made or natural disasters or war.
WHAT IS FUNDED Relief of human suffering, particularly projects with a Christian emphasis.
WHAT IS NOT FUNDED Building projects, individuals, personal education grants and expeditions are not supported.
TYPE OF GRANT One-off and recurring grants.
RANGE OF GRANTS Mostly £1,000 or less.
SAMPLE GRANTS Previous beneficiaries include: Alpha International (an Anglican evangelical movement based in London), Highland Theological College, Operation Mobilisation, Prince's Trust – Scotland, Sargent Cancer Care, Scripture Union and Turning Point Scotland.
FINANCES *Year* 2009–10 *Income* £2,779,338 *Grants* £2,000,000
TRUSTEES Brian Souter; Betty Souter; Ann Allen.
OTHER INFORMATION Total grants figure is approximate.
HOW TO APPLY In writing to the correspondent. Please keep applications brief and no more than two sides of A4 paper: if appropriate, please send audited accounts, but do not send brochures, business plans, DVDs and so on. The trust states that it will request more information if necessary. The trustees meet every two months or so, and all applications will be acknowledged in due course, whether successful or not. A stamped addressed envelope would be appreciated. Subsequent applications should not be made within a year of the initial submission.
WHO TO APPLY TO Andy Macfie, Secretary, PO Box 7412, Perth PH1 5YX *Tel* 01738 450408 *email* enquiries@soutercharitabletrust.org.uk *Website* www.soutercharitabletrust.org.uk

■ The South Square Trust

CC NO 278960   **ESTABLISHED** 1979
WHERE FUNDING CAN BE GIVEN UK, with a preference for London and the Home Counties.
WHO CAN BENEFIT The trust assists in two areas with general donations to registered charities, and support of individual students undertaking full-time undergraduate or postgraduate courses connected with the fine and applied arts within the UK. Individuals are considered especially for courses related to goldsmithing, silversmithing, and metalwork but also for music, drama and dance. Preference is given to students commencing undergraduate studies – students must be at least 18 years old. The trust has established scholarships and bursaries with schools connected with the fine and applied arts and a full list of these schools can be obtained from the clerk to the trustees. Where a school is in receipt of a bursary, no further assistance will be given to individuals as the school will select candidates themselves.
WHAT IS FUNDED Annual income is allocated in awards to individuals for educational purposes, specifically help with tuition fees but living expenses will be considered for courses as specified above. Donations are also considered to registered charities working in fields of the elderly, medical research and equipment, support groups, community groups, horticulture, green issues and other projects connected with the fine and applied arts.
WHAT IS NOT FUNDED No support for building projects, salaries or individuals wishing to start up a business. No grants given to individuals under 18 or those seeking funding for expeditions, travel, courses outside UK, short courses or courses not connected with fine and applied arts.
TYPE OF GRANT Registered charities: single donations to assist with specific projects, one-off expenses, core costs and research. Individual students: funding may be given for the duration of a course, for up to three years, payable in three term instalments to help with tuition fees or living expenses.
RANGE OF GRANTS Individuals: £500–£1,500; charities: £300–£2,000.
SAMPLE GRANTS Byam Shaw School of Art (£26,000); St Paul's School (£23,000); Textile Conservation Foundation (£12,000); Bristol Old Vic Theatre School, Guildford School of Acting and RADA (£10,000 each); Royal College of Music (£10,000); The Cass, London Metropolitan University (£9,000); and Royal Northern College of Music and School of Jewellery, Birmingham (£8,000 each).
FINANCES *Year* 2009–10 *Income* £174,094 *Grants* £215,060 *Assets* £3,328,619
TRUSTEES Andrew Blessley; W P Harriman; C P Grimwade; D B Inglis; R S Baldock.
OTHER INFORMATION In 2009–10 grants were broken down as follows: bursaries and scholarships to schools/colleges – £149,000; general charitable donations – £48,000; directly aided students and single payment grants – £18,000.
HOW TO APPLY Registered charities: In writing to the correspondent with details about your charity and the reason for requesting funding. Applications are considered three times a year, in November, March and June, and should be submitted at least one month before the next meeting. It is advisable to telephone the correspondent for up-to-date information about the criteria for funding. Individuals: Standard application forms are available from the correspondent. Forms are sent out between

January and April only, to be returned by the end of April for consideration for the following academic year.

WHO TO APPLY TO Mrs Nicola Chrimes, Clerk to the Trustees, PO Box 169, Lewes, East Sussex BN7 9FB *Tel* 01825 872264 *Website* www.southsquaretrust.org.uk

---

■ The Stephen R and Philippa H Southall Charitable Trust

CC NO 223190   **ESTABLISHED** 1947

WHERE FUNDING CAN BE GIVEN UK, but mostly Herefordshire.

WHO CAN BENEFIT Registered charities.

WHAT IS FUNDED General charitable purposes, with a preference for promoting education and conservation of the natural environment and cultural heritage.

RANGE OF GRANTS Up to about £20,000.

SAMPLE GRANTS The Worgan Trust – Mount Pleasant School Farm (£75,000); Hereford Waterworks Museum Trust (£49,000); Clifford PCC and Tobacco Factory Arts Trust (£5,000 each); and BODS (£2,500).

FINANCES *Year* 2009–10 *Income* £145,509 *Grants* £143,550 *Assets* £2,973,166

TRUSTEES Stephen Readhead Southall; Philippa Helen Southall; Anna Catherine Southall; Candia Helen Compton.

OTHER INFORMATION The trust has previously stated that it uses its surplus income for world emergencies and the development of Hereford Waterworks Museum.

HOW TO APPLY The trust makes several repeat donations and has previously stated that: 'no applications can be considered or replied to'.

WHO TO APPLY TO Philippa Southall, Trustee, Porking Barn, Clifford, Hereford HR3 5HE *Tel* 01497 831243

■ The W F Southall Trust

CC NO 218371   **ESTABLISHED** 1937

WHERE FUNDING CAN BE GIVEN UK and overseas.

WHO CAN BENEFIT Registered charities, especially imaginative new grassroots initiatives and smaller charities where funding will make a significant difference.

WHAT IS FUNDED Work of the Society of Friends; peace-making and conflict resolution; alcohol, drug abuse and penal affairs; environmental action; homelessness; community action; and overseas development.

WHAT IS NOT FUNDED No grants to individuals or large national charities.

TYPE OF GRANT Normally one-off payments.

RANGE OF GRANTS Up to £55,000; usually £100–£5,000.

SAMPLE GRANTS Yearly Meeting – Society of Friends (£55,000); Woodbrooke Quaker Study Centre (£10,000); International Voluntary Services (£6,500); Centre for Alternative Technology and St Augustine's Centre (£5,000 each); British Friends of Neve Shalom Children in Crisis, Mend UK and Peace Direct (£3,000 each); and Refugee Council (£2,000).

FINANCES *Year* 2009–10 *Income* £273,315 *Grants* £286,367 *Assets* £7,394,626

TRUSTEES Donald Southall, Chair; Joanna Engelkamp; Claire Greaves; Mark Holtom; Daphne Maw; Annette Wallis.

OTHER INFORMATION Grants of less than £3,000 were made to 49 organisations totalling nearly £100,000.

HOW TO APPLY In writing to the correspondent (via post or email), requesting an application form. Applications are usually considered in February/March and November. Applications received between meetings are considered at the next meeting.

WHO TO APPLY TO The Secretary, c/o Rutters Solicitors, 2 Bimport, Shaftesbury, Dorset SP7 8AY *Tel* 01747 852377 *Fax* 01747 851989 *email* southall@rutterslaw.co.uk

---

■ The Southdown Trust

CC NO 235583   **ESTABLISHED** 1963

WHERE FUNDING CAN BE GIVEN UK.

WHO CAN BENEFIT Young people aged 17 to 26 years.

WHAT IS FUNDED Grants towards the education of the specified age group.

WHAT IS NOT FUNDED No grants towards courses in the following subjects: law, journalism, women's studies, counselling, veterinary studies, computer/IT studies and media studies.

RANGE OF GRANTS Up to £7,000 (2010).

SAMPLE GRANTS Christ Church Oxford (£6,000); Silcock Trust (£3,000); Joint Educational Trust (£2,000); Hope UK (£250).

FINANCES *Year* 2010 *Income* £78,938 *Grants* £39,910 *Assets* £840,421

TRUSTEES John Geoffrey Wyatt; Hugh Rowland Wyatt; Andrew Cartwright Pugh; John Rowland Blades McBeath.

HOW TO APPLY The trust does not respond to unsolicited applications.

WHO TO APPLY TO John Geoffrey Wyatt, Trustee, Holmbush, 64 High Street, Findon, Worthing, West Sussex BN14 0SY

■ R H Southern Trust

CC NO 1077509   **ESTABLISHED** 1999

WHERE FUNDING CAN BE GIVEN Worldwide.

WHO CAN BENEFIT Charitable organisations.

WHAT IS FUNDED Advancement of education (including medical and scientific research); relief of poverty; disability; and preservation, conservation and protection of the environment (especially climate change). The trust favours projects where the work is innovative, connected to other disciplines/bodies and has diverse application.

TYPE OF GRANT Mainly long term core funding and special projects.

RANGE OF GRANTS £3,000–£30,000.

SAMPLE GRANTS Feasta (£41,000 in five grants); Soil Association (£26,000 in five grants); Equal Adventure (£20,000); Motivation (£15,000); Accord – Just Change (£11,000); Action Village India, Corporate European Observatory and Friends of the Earth (£10,000 each); EI Rural Links – Tamwed (£8,500); Global Witness and Sustrans (£5,000 each); and Ragmans Lane Farm (£246).

FINANCES *Year* 2009–10 *Income* £127,721 *Grants* £240,346 *Assets* £3,237,089

TRUSTEES Marion Wells; Charles Wells; James Bruges; Colkin Trustee Company Limited.

OTHER INFORMATION The grant total includes one award of £15,000 to an individual working on the Soil Fertility Project (charcoal project).

HOW TO APPLY In writing to the correspondent, though at present the trust's funds are fully committed.

WHO TO APPLY TO The Trustees, 23 Sydenham Road, Cotham, Bristol BS6 5SJ *Tel* 0117 942 5834

■ The Southover Manor General Education Trust

CC NO 299593   **ESTABLISHED** 1988
WHERE FUNDING CAN BE GIVEN Sussex.
WHO CAN BENEFIT Schools, colleges and individuals under the age of 25.
WHAT IS FUNDED The trustees support the 'education of boys and girls under 25 by providing books and equipment, supporting provision of recreational and educational facilities, scholarships and awards'.
WHAT IS NOT FUNDED No grants for people over 25 years of age. Organisations and individuals outside Sussex are not supported.
TYPE OF GRANT Capital and projects.
RANGE OF GRANTS Up to £20,000.
SAMPLE GRANTS William Parker Sports College (£20,000); Chailey Heritage School (£15,000); East Hoathly CE School (£10,000); Northease Manor School (£8,000) and Downs Infant School (£4,000).
FINANCES *Year* 2009–10 *Income* £110,085 *Grants* £134,669 *Assets* £2,356,612
TRUSTEES B J Hanbury, Chair; Mrs R C Teacher; P E Cooper; Mrs J S Gordon-Lennox; Mrs C M Duffield; Mrs J A Hall; J W Wakely; J Farmer; Mrs W Bradley; Mrs J Peel.
OTHER INFORMATION A single grant of £500 was made to an individual during the year. All other grants were made to institutions.
HOW TO APPLY In writing to the correspondent.
WHO TO APPLY TO The Secretary to the Trustees, PO Box 159, Lewes, East Sussex BN7 9ER *Tel* 01273 472882 *email* southovermanor@btinternet.com

■ The Southwold Trust

CC NO 206480   **ESTABLISHED** 1962
WHERE FUNDING CAN BE GIVEN Southwold and Reydon.
WHO CAN BENEFIT Registered charities.
WHAT IS FUNDED General charitable purposes.
RANGE OF GRANTS £700–£5,000 (2009–10).
SAMPLE GRANTS Southwold Museum (£5,000); Sole Bay Team Ministry (£2,500); Waveney Hospice Care (£1,500) and 1st Southwold Guides (£700).
FINANCES *Year* 2009–10 *Income* £37,145 *Grants* £12,850 *Assets* £119,023
TRUSTEES B T Segrave-Daly; Mrs E Utting; G J Filby; J W Denny; R Lee; J French; H Fuller; Sir Richard Dales; Michael Mayhew.
HOW TO APPLY In writing to the correspondent.
WHO TO APPLY TO David Gaffney, Treasurer, The Southwold Trust, Margary and Miller, 73 High Street, Southwold, Suffolk IP18 6DS *Tel* 01502 723308

■ The Sovereign Health Care Charitable Trust

CC NO 1079024   **ESTABLISHED** 1955
WHERE FUNDING CAN BE GIVEN UK with a preference for Bradford.
WHO CAN BENEFIT Generally local organisations benefiting older people, at risk groups, and people with disabilities, disadvantaged by poverty or socially isolated.
WHAT IS FUNDED The provision of amenities for hospital patients and to make grants to charitable organisations 'for the relief and assistance of needy, sick and elderly persons'.
WHAT IS NOT FUNDED No grants to individuals.
TYPE OF GRANT Buildings, core costs, one-off or recurrent, project, research, running costs.
RANGE OF GRANTS Up to £35,000.
SAMPLE GRANTS Yorkshire Air Ambulance (£29,000); Hospital Heartbeat Appeal (£18,500); Bradford Soup Run and Heart Research UK (£15,000 each); Community Cougars Foundation and Positive Lifestyles (£10,000 each); Samaritans (£7,500); Christians Against Poverty (£5,000); Changing Faces (£4,000); Harrogate & District NHS Trust (£3,500); Kirkwood Hospice and Prostate UK (£2,000 each); Listening Books (£1,500); and the Firefighters Charity (£1,000).
FINANCES *Year* 2010 *Income* £510,016 *Grants* £488,835 *Assets* £23,578
TRUSTEES Mark Hudson, chair; Michael Austin; Dennis Child; Michael Bower; Russ Piper; Kate Robb-Webb; Robert Dugdale; Stewart Cummings.
HOW TO APPLY In writing to the correspondent.
WHO TO APPLY TO The Secretary, Royal Standard House, 26 Manningham Lane, Bradford, West Yorkshire BD1 3DN *Tel* 01274 729472 *Fax* 01274 722252 *email* cs@sovereignhealthcare.co.uk *Website* www.sovereignhealthcare.co.uk

■ Spar Charitable Fund

CC NO 236252   **ESTABLISHED** 1964
WHERE FUNDING CAN BE GIVEN UK.
WHO CAN BENEFIT Registered charities, mostly well-known national organisations.
WHAT IS FUNDED General charitable purposes, with some preference for projects benefiting young people.
SAMPLE GRANTS NSPCC (£91,000); Business in the Community (£12,000); Clubs for Young People (£6,000); Caravan – NGBF (£5,000); Scottish Grocers Benevolent Fund (£1,300); and Kenia (£450).
FINANCES *Year* 2009–10 *Income* £90,930 *Grants* £115,383 *Assets* £799,217
TRUSTEES The National Guild of Spar Ltd.
OTHER INFORMATION This trust tends to choose one main beneficiary, which receives most of its funds, with smaller grants being made to similar beneficiaries each year.
HOW TO APPLY In writing to the correspondent.
WHO TO APPLY TO Philip Marchant, Director and Company Secretary, Mezzanine Floor, Hygeia Building, 66 - 68 College Road, Harrow, Middlesex HA1 1BE *Tel* 020 8426 3700 *email* philip.marchant@spar.co.uk

■ Sparks Charity (Sport Aiding Medical Research For Kids)

CC NO 1003825   **ESTABLISHED** 1991
WHERE FUNDING CAN BE GIVEN UK.
WHO CAN BENEFIT Research units at UK hospitals and universities.
WHAT IS FUNDED Medical research to enable children to be born healthy and to stay healthy.
WHAT IS NOT FUNDED The charity is unable to consider: applications which are concurrently submitted to other funding bodies; grants for further education, for example, MSc/PhD course fees; grants towards service provision or audit studies; grants for work undertaken outside the UK; grants towards 'top up' funding for work supported by other funding bodies; or grants to other charities.

TYPE OF GRANT project grants up to the value of £200,000, Research Training Fellowships and Programme grants.

RANGE OF GRANTS £50,000–£150,000. Applications outside this range will be considered.

SAMPLE GRANTS St Michael's Hospital – Bristol (£229,500); University of Bristol (£200,000); The Institute of Cancer Research (£197,000); University of Birmingham (£149,000); University of Cambridge (£137,500); University College London – Institute of Child Health (£137,000 in total); Imperial College – London (£118,000); University College London Hospitals NHS Foundations Trust (£100,000); and Newcastle University Medical School (£69,500).

FINANCES *Year* 2010–11 *Income* £3,527,117 *Grants* £1,336,998 *Assets* £477,755

TRUSTEES Sir T Brooking; Hugh Edmeades; Michael Higgins; Roger Uttley; Simon Waugh; Julian Wilkinson; Floella Benjamin; Jonathon Britton; Victoria Glaysher; Guy Gregory; Gabby Logan; David Orr; Frank van den Bosch.

HOW TO APPLY Sparks funds project grants up to the value of £200,000, Research Training Fellowships and Programme grants. Prior to submitting a full application, all applicants are required to complete an outline proposal form which is available for download from the charity's website in Word format. Completed outlines and any queries should be sent to: Dr Kirti Patel, Medical Research Manager, email: Kirti@sparks.org.uk, direct Tel/Fax 020 7799 2111/020 7222 2701. Please refer to the Sparks website for outline closing dates. Applicants with suitable research projects will be sent an application form (by email in Word format) and a copy of the relating terms and conditions. Closing dates for full applications are generally March and October; please refer to the sparks website.

WHO TO APPLY TO Dr Kirti Patel, Medical Research Manager, Heron House, 10 Dean Farrer Street, London SW1H 0DX *Tel* 020 7799 2111 *Fax* 020 7222 2701 *email* kirti@sparks.org.uk *Website* www.sparks.org.uk

---

■ Sparquote Limited

CC NO 286232   **ESTABLISHED** 1982

WHERE FUNDING CAN BE GIVEN A preference for north and west London, including Edgware in Middlesex.

WHO CAN BENEFIT Jewish charities.

WHAT IS FUNDED Education and welfare.

RANGE OF GRANTS Up to £40,000.

SAMPLE GRANTS Previous grant beneficiaries include: The Wlodowa Charity and Rehabilitation Trust (£41,000); the Telz Academy Trust (£30,000); British Friends of Mosdos Tchernobyl (£20,000); the Society of Friends of the Torah (£19,000); the Gevurath Ari Torah Trust (£15,000); Beis Nadvorna Charitable Trust (£10,000); the Edgware Foundation and Penshurst Corporation Limited (£5,000 each); Gateshead Institute for Rabbinical Studies (£3,500); Dina Perelman Trust Limited (£1,800); and American Friends (£1,000).

FINANCES *Year* 2009–10 *Income* £560,850 *Grants* £129,975 *Assets* £3,995,959

TRUSTEES David Reichmann; Dov Reichmann; Mrs A M Reichmann.

HOW TO APPLY In writing to the correspondent.

WHO TO APPLY TO Anne-Mette Reichmann, Secretary, Grovesnor House, 1 High Street, Edgware, Middlesex, HA87TA *Tel* 020 8731 0777 *Fax* 020 8731 0778

■ The Spear Charitable Trust

CC NO 1041568   **ESTABLISHED** 1962

WHERE FUNDING CAN BE GIVEN UK.

WHO CAN BENEFIT Individuals and organisations, particularly employees and former employees of J W Spear and Sons plc, their families and dependants.

WHAT IS FUNDED Welfare of employees and former employees of J W Spear and Sons plc, their families and dependants; also general charitable purposes, with some preference for animal welfare, the environment and health.

WHAT IS NOT FUNDED Appeals from individuals are not considered.

SAMPLE GRANTS Nuremberg Toy Museum and RSPCA – Enfield (£8,000 each); Imagine (Mozambique) (£6,000); Barnet and Chase Farm NHS Trust, Tree Aid and The Woodland Trust (£5,000 each); Lake Malawi Projects and Marine Conservation Society (£2,500 each); Grasslands Trust and No Panic (£2,000 each); and Jewish Care, Mayhew International and Scottish Seabird Sanctuary (£1,000 each).

FINANCES *Year* 2010 *Income* £123,739 *Grants* £122,704 *Assets* £4,744,878

TRUSTEES P N Harris; F A Spear; H E Spear; N Gooch.

OTHER INFORMATION In addition in 2010 individuals connected with J W Spear and Sons plc received £11,103.

HOW TO APPLY In writing to the correspondent.

WHO TO APPLY TO Hazel E Spear, Secretary, Roughground House, Beggarmans Lane, Old Hall Green, Ware, Hertfordshire SG11 1HB *Tel* 01920 823071 *Fax* 01920 823071

■ Spears-Stutz Charitable Trust

CC NO 225491   **ESTABLISHED** 1964

WHERE FUNDING CAN BE GIVEN Worldwide.

WHO CAN BENEFIT Registered charities.

WHAT IS FUNDED General charitable purposes, relief of poverty, Jewish causes, museums and arts organisations.

RANGE OF GRANTS £250 to £30,000.

SAMPLE GRANTS Previous beneficiaries include: Cancer Macmillan Fund, Royal Academy Trust, Royal Academy of Arts, Wellbeing, King Edward Hospital, Help the Aged and Westminster Synagogue.

FINANCES *Year* 2009–10 *Income* £93,084 *Grants* £89,913 *Assets* £4,180,433

TRUSTEES Glenn Hurstfield; Jonathan Spears.

OTHER INFORMATION This trust was previously known as the Roama Spears Charitable Settlement.

HOW TO APPLY In writing to the correspondent.

WHO TO APPLY TO The Trustees, Berkeley Law, 4th Floor, 19 Berkeley Street, London W1J 8ED *Tel* 020 7399 0930

■ The Worshipful Company of Spectacle Makers' Charity

CC NO 1072172   **ESTABLISHED** 1998

WHERE FUNDING CAN BE GIVEN Worldwide.

WHO CAN BENEFIT Registered charities.

WHAT IS FUNDED Work concerned with visual impairments, with a preference for national rather than local causes.

WHAT IS NOT FUNDED No grants are made to individuals.

TYPE OF GRANT Specific projects, not general funds.

SAMPLE GRANTS Action for Blind People, Blind in Business, Childhood Eye Cancer Trust, Eyeless Trust, St John's Eye Hospital in Jerusalem,

Prison Fellowship, Optical Workers' Benevolent Fund, British Council for the Prevention of Blindness, Vision 2020UK, Livings Paintings Trust, Vision Aid Overseas, Macular Disease Society, British Blind Sport and the Talking Newspaper Association.

FINANCES *Year* 2009–10 *Income* £82,534 *Grants* £63,947 *Assets* £699,942

TRUSTEES Brian Mitchell; Christine Tomkins; Venerable John Morrison; Mrs Liz Shilling; Edward Middleton; James Osborne.

OTHER INFORMATION The charity's website listed a number of grant beneficiaries, without the grant amounts.

HOW TO APPLY In writing to the correspondent including details of how the grant will be used and a copy of the latest audited accounts. Please note: the trustees meet in early spring to decide on grants, meaning that applications received between June and March are unlikely to be addressed quickly.

WHO TO APPLY TO John Salmon, Clerk, Apothecaries Hall, Blackfriars Lane, London EC4V 6EL *Tel* 020 7236 2932 *email* clerk@spectaclemakers.com *Website* www.spectaclemakers.com

■ The Jessie Spencer Trust

CC NO 219289   **ESTABLISHED** 1962

WHERE FUNDING CAN BE GIVEN UK, with a preference for Nottinghamshire.

WHO CAN BENEFIT Registered charities, with a preference for those in Nottinghamshire.

WHAT IS FUNDED General charitable purposes.

WHAT IS NOT FUNDED Grants are rarely made for the repair of parish churches outside Nottinghamshire.

TYPE OF GRANT Grants are made towards both capital and revenue expenditure. They can be recurrent for up to 10 years.

RANGE OF GRANTS £100–£10,000.

SAMPLE GRANTS Nottinghamshire Community Foundation (£30,000); Core – Digestive Disorders Foundation (£5,000); Marie Curie Cancer Care (£3,000); SSAFA (£1,500); Binns Organ Trust, the Jonathan Young Memorial Trust, Not Shut Up and Rutland House School (£1,000 each); Enterprise Education Trust (£750); and ASBAH, the Rehearsal Orchestra, York Foundation for Conservation and Craftsmanship and the Woodland Trust (£500 each).

FINANCES *Year* 2009–10 *Income* £128,237 *Grants* £160,090 *Assets* £3,404,345

TRUSTEES V W Semmens; R S Hursthouse; Jennifer Galloway; Bethan Mitchell.

OTHER INFORMATION There were also grants made to individuals totalling £1,600.

HOW TO APPLY In writing to the correspondent, including the latest set of audited accounts, at least three weeks before the trustees' meetings in March, June, September and December. Unsuccessful applications will not be notified.

WHO TO APPLY TO The Trustees, Berryman Shacklock LLP, Park House, Friar Lane, Nottingham NG1 6DN *Tel* 0115 945 3700 *Fax* 0115 948 0234

■ The Spero Foundation

CC NO 1136810   **ESTABLISHED** 2010

WHERE FUNDING CAN BE GIVEN Undefined, in practice overseas.

WHO CAN BENEFIT Organisations and individuals.

WHAT IS FUNDED General; education and training; health; community development; sports and recreation; arts; and heritage.

TRUSTEES Andrew Peggie; Brian Padgett; Joanna Landau; Eden Landau; Jonathan Emmutt.

HOW TO APPLY In writing to the correspondent.

WHO TO APPLY TO Sarah Hunt, St James's House, 3rd Floor, 23 King Street, London SW1Y 6QY *Tel* 020 7839 5169

■ The Ralph and Irma Sperring Charity

CC NO 1048101   **ESTABLISHED** 1995

WHERE FUNDING CAN BE GIVEN The parishes situated within a five-mile radius of the church of St John the Baptist, Midsomer Norton.

WHO CAN BENEFIT Organisations and individuals in the beneficial area.

WHAT IS FUNDED Grants are given to: provide or assist with the provision of residential accommodation; for the relief of people who are elderly, disabled or in need; assist with the establishment of village halls, recreation grounds, charitable sports grounds and playing fields; further the religious or other charitable work of the Anglican churches in the parishes; support hospitals and their leagues of friends; and further education of children and young people at educational institutions.

FINANCES *Year* 2009–10 *Income* £201,473 *Grants* £117,260 *Assets* £5,767,268

TRUSTEES Revd C G Chiplin; E W L Hallam; Miss S Blanning; K G W Saunders; Mrs N E Busby; Dr P Haxell.

HOW TO APPLY In writing to the correspondent.

WHO TO APPLY TO E W L Hallam, Trustee, Thatcher & Hallam Solicitors, Island House, Midsomer Norton, Radstock BA3 2HJ *Tel* 01761 414646

■ The Moss Spiro Will Charitable Foundation

CC NO 1064249   **ESTABLISHED** 1997

WHERE FUNDING CAN BE GIVEN UK.

WHO CAN BENEFIT Jewish people.

WHAT IS FUNDED Grants are made towards Jewish welfare.

SAMPLE GRANTS Previous beneficiaries have included American Friends of Yershivas Birchas Ha Torah, Lubavitch Foundation, J T Tannenbaum Jewish Cultural Centre, Friends of Neve Shalom, Jewish Care and HGS Emunah.

FINANCES *Year* 2009–10 *Income* £45 *Grants* £13,971

TRUSTEES Trevor David Spiro; Melvin Clifford Kay.

HOW TO APPLY In writing to the correspondent.

WHO TO APPLY TO Trevor Spiro, Trustee, Crowndean House, 26 Bruton Lane, London W1J 6JH *Tel* 020 7491 9817 *Fax* 020 7499 6850 *email* trevor@assassin.co.uk

■ Split Infinitive Trust

CC NO 1110380   **ESTABLISHED** 2005

WHERE FUNDING CAN BE GIVEN UK, with a preference for Yorkshire.

WHO CAN BENEFIT Individuals and companies and organisations with charitable status.

WHAT IS FUNDED Arts, education and the alleviation of sickness, poverty, hardship and distress.

RANGE OF GRANTS Grants are generally made between £500 and £5,000.

SAMPLE GRANTS The National Student Drama Festival Limited and Paddington Arts (£5,000 each); NDCS (£2,500); Clothing Solutions and Buckle for Dust Limited (£1,000 each).

FINANCES *Year* 2009–10 *Income* £50,233 *Grants* £30,390 *Assets* £147,551

TRUSTEES Sir Alan Ayckbourn, Chair; Heather Stoney; Paul Allen; Neil Adleman; Elizabeth Bell.

OTHER INFORMATION The trust received 94 applications during 2009–10, of which 36 applicants were successful.

HOW TO APPLY 'Applicants are asked to supply a letter describing the project with budget and, if relevant, an indication of where other funds are coming from. In the case of a performing arts production, a basic but precise production budget is requested. As support given for a production is not considered an investment seeking a return, no box office figures are requested although feedback as to how a production has been received is helpful but not a requisite.'

WHO TO APPLY TO Heather Stoney, Trustee, PO BOX 409, Scarborough YO11 9AJ *email* splitinfin@pendon.eclipse.co.uk

■ The Spoore, Merry and Rixman Foundation

CC NO 309040   **ESTABLISHED** 1958

WHERE FUNDING CAN BE GIVEN The (pre-1974) borough of Maidenhead and the ancient parish of Bray, not the whole of Royal Borough of Windsor and Maidenhead.

WHO CAN BENEFIT People under the age of 25 living in the beneficial area.

WHAT IS FUNDED The trust was set up to benefit people 'who need financial assistance in way of scholarships, bursaries, maintenance allowances or other benefits' to further their education.

WHAT IS NOT FUNDED Deals only with the (pre-1974) borough of Maidenhead and the ancient parish of Bray.

SAMPLE GRANTS Norden Farm Centre for the Arts, The Bridge Trust (£10,000 each); Larchfield Primary and Nursery School (£7,820); Ellington Primary and Nursery School (£5,385).

FINANCES *Year* 2010 *Income* £293,313 *Grants* £284,766 *Assets* £9,129,739

TRUSTEES Mrs D Kemp; Mrs P Proctor; Mrs A Redgrave; I Thomas; L Walters; G Fisher; The Mayor – Royal Borough of Windsor and Maidenhead; E Richards; A Hill; A Majeed; B Wielchowski.

OTHER INFORMATION Grants to organisations totalled £208,723 with a further £76,043 given in grants to individuals.

HOW TO APPLY On a form available from the correspondent. Applications are considered in January, April, July and October.

WHO TO APPLY TO M J Tanner, Secretary, Mrs Helen Macdiarmid, PO Box 4229, Slough SL1 0QZ *email* clerk@smrfmaidenhead.org *Website* www.smrfmaidenhead.org.uk

■ Spring Harvest

CC NO 1014540   **ESTABLISHED** 1994

WHERE FUNDING CAN BE GIVEN UK and overseas.

WHO CAN BENEFIT Organisations and individuals.

WHAT IS FUNDED Christian evangelism and welfare.

WHAT IS NOT FUNDED Salaries.

RANGE OF GRANTS Mostly up to £5,000 but higher amounts are considered.

SAMPLE GRANTS Open Doors with Brother Andrew and XLP (£30,000 each); Jubilee Action and London City Mission (£8,000 each); The Message Trust and Redeeming Our Communities (£6,000 each); Children Worldwide (£5,200); The Bless Network and Scripture Union International (£4,000 each); Five Talents and Heart of the Father (£3,000 each). Grants of under £3,000 totalled £53,000 to 31 other institutions. The trust also makes sums available to individuals and families in receipt of state benefits to enable people on a low income to attend the Spring Harvest event. In 2010 £21,600 was spent in this way. It was anticipated that this fund would be extended in 2011.

FINANCES *Year* 2009–10 *Income* £9,292,744 *Grants* £199,249 *Assets* £2,359,500

TRUSTEES Pete Broadbent, Chair; Krish Kandiah; Ian White; Peter Martin; Wendy Beech-Ward; Russell Rook; Geoff Booker; Ruth Valerio; David Dorricott; Allistair Watson.

OTHER INFORMATION In 2009 the trust merged with ICC Media Group to form the new Memralife Group. Although Spring Harvest retains its own original identity the trust is wholly administered by the Memralife Group. The two bodies have a common board of trustees and Spring Harvest grants are distributed by Memralife.

HOW TO APPLY There is one round of funding applications per year, usually at the end of November/early December, for distribution the following year. An application form is made available on the trust's website in spring. Applications can be for any amount up £5,000. If your application requests substantially more, the trust will consider it, but it is unlikely to be able to offer the total amount needed. Applications from non-UK organisations can only be considered if you have a UK office or a UK contact that knows you well and is able to comment on your work. All applications must be submitted on the trust's application form. The trust has one funding round per year and looks particularly for applications with a Christian bias where there's a link to its annual theme. Consult the trust's website for the relevant annual theme. 'We can't commit to on-going funding, so we don't usually support salary costs unless it is clear that the project can be sustained in the long term.'

WHO TO APPLY TO Pete Broadbent, Chair, 14 Horsted Square, Bellbrook Industrial Estate, Uckfield, East Sussex TN22 1QG *Tel* 01825 769000 *Fax* 01825 748899 *email* offerings@springharvest.org *Website* www.springharvest.org

■ Rosalyn and Nicholas Springer Charitable Trust

CC NO 1062239   **ESTABLISHED** 1997

WHERE FUNDING CAN BE GIVEN UK.

WHO CAN BENEFIT Organisations, particularly those supporting Jewish people, and individuals.

WHAT IS FUNDED The promotion of welfare, education and personal development, particularly amongst the Jewish community. Grants are made in the following categories: medical, health and sickness; education and training; arts and culture; religious activities; relief of poverty; and general charitable purposes.

RANGE OF GRANTS £60–£20,000, but mostly £1,000 or less.

SAMPLE GRANTS UJIA (£20,000); Royal Opera House Foundation (£15,000); Chai-Lifeline Cancer Care (£10,000); MDA UK (£6,300); World Jewish

Relief (£4,200); Belsize Square Synagogue (£3,400); Norwood Ravenswood (£3,000); Holocaust Educational Trust (£2,000); Presidents Club Charitable Trust (£1,300); Cystic Fibrosis Trust (£800); London Arts Museum and Foundation of Nursing Studies (£500 each); Jewish Child's Day (£400); and Derby Toch Children Camp (£150).

FINANCES *Year* 2009–10 *Income* £156,266 *Grants* £119,924 *Assets* £48,481

TRUSTEES Rosalyn Springer; Nicholas Springer; Judith Joseph.

HOW TO APPLY The trust has previously stated that it only supports organisations it is already in contact with. 99% of unsolicited applications are unsuccessful and because of the volume it receives, the trust is unable to reply to such letters. It would therefore not seem appropriate to apply to this trust.

WHO TO APPLY TO Nicholas Springer, Trustee, 15 Park Village West, London NW1 4AE *Tel* 020 7253 7272

■ The Springfields Employees' Medical Research and Charity Trust Fund

CC NO 518005   **ESTABLISHED** 1985

WHERE FUNDING CAN BE GIVEN Preston and South Ribble, Blackpool, Wyre and Fylde Areas.

WHO CAN BENEFIT Organisations benefiting disabled people.

WHAT IS FUNDED Grants to hospitals and local medical and welfare charities for medical equipment.

WHAT IS NOT FUNDED Support is only provided for specific pieces of equipment therefore funding is not available for items such as projects and salaries. Grants will not be provided to applicants outside the area of benefit unless it can be demonstrated that the research will benefit residents from within the area.

TYPE OF GRANT One-off grants.

RANGE OF GRANTS Up to £4,000.

SAMPLE GRANTS Breast Cancer Campaign (£4000); Little Sisters of the Poor (£1900); Fight for Sight (£1,400), The Genesis Appeal (£1,250); Dolly Mops (£500); MedEquip4ids (£3,100); Galloway's Society for the Blind (£2,300); Lee Smith Foundation (£1,200); FSID Program (£800); Listening Books (£3,000); Fylde Citizens Advice Bureau (£37).

FINANCES *Year* 2010 *Income* £23,341 *Grants* £27,813

TRUSTEES Duncan Craig; Ian Driver; Jackie Humphreys.

HOW TO APPLY In writing to the correspondent.

WHO TO APPLY TO Ian R Driver, Welfare Officer and Trustee, Westing House, Springfields Fuels Limited, Springfields, Salwick, Preston PR4 0XJ *Tel* 01772 764578 *Fax* 01772 762929 *email* ian.r.driver@springfieldsfuels.com

---

■ Springrule Ltd

CC NO 802561   **ESTABLISHED** 1992

WHERE FUNDING CAN BE GIVEN UK.

WHO CAN BENEFIT Jewish organisations.

WHAT IS FUNDED Advancement of the Jewish faith and the relief of poverty.

SAMPLE GRANTS Previously: Beis Yaakov Institutions, Friends of Horim and Torah Vechesed (£25,000 each); an Yad Eliezer (£5,000).

FINANCES *Year* 2009–10 *Income* £38,118 *Grants* £850,583 *Assets* £1,678,673

TRUSTEES M Jacober; R Nevies; J Monderer; H R Monderer; Mrs R L Nevies.

HOW TO APPLY In writing to the correspondent.

WHO TO APPLY TO Mrs M Jacober, Secretary, 5 North End Road, London NW11 7RJ

■ The Spurrell Charitable Trust

CC NO 267287   **ESTABLISHED** 1960

WHERE FUNDING CAN BE GIVEN UK, with some preference for Norfolk.

WHO CAN BENEFIT Charities known personally to the trustees.

WHAT IS FUNDED General charitable purposes.

RANGE OF GRANTS Up to £7,500.

SAMPLE GRANTS Merlin (£10,000; East Anglian Air Ambulance (£7,000); Break (£5,000); Aylesbury High School (£3,000); Alzheimer's Research Trust, Brain & Spine Foundation, Camphill Village Trust and North Norfolk Multiple Sclerosis Society (£1,200 each); Norfolk Deaf Association, Norwich & Central Norfolk Mind, Wireless for the Bedridden and Woodlands Trust (£600 each) and Felbrigg Crusaders, Sheringham & Cromer Choral Society and Sustead Village Hall Fund (£300 each).

FINANCES *Year* 2009–10 *Income* £61,561 *Grants* £80,060 *Assets* £2,222,094

TRUSTEES Alan T How; Mrs Inge H Spurrell; Martyn R Spurrell.

HOW TO APPLY Unsolicited applications are not considered.

WHO TO APPLY TO A T How, Trustee, Apartment 7, 99 Warwick Park, Tunbridge Wells, Kent TN2 5FD *Tel* 01892 541565

■ The Geoff and Fiona Squire Foundation

CC NO 1085553   **ESTABLISHED** 2001

WHERE FUNDING CAN BE GIVEN UK.

WHO CAN BENEFIT Charitable organisations.

WHAT IS FUNDED General charitable purposes.

RANGE OF GRANTS £500–£230,000.

SAMPLE GRANTS Wessex Children's Hospice – Naomi House (£277,000); the Stars Appeal – Salisbury District Hospital (£200,000); Teenage Cancer Trust (£156,000); Changing Faces (£152,000); Information Technologists' Company (£100,000); Sense Holiday Fund (£83,000); Stable Family Home Trust (£50,000); the Children's Trust (£10,000); Music for Youth (£7,500); Friends of Shepherds Down School (£6,000); Canine Partners for Independence (£5,000); Strong Bones Children's Charitable Trust (£2,500); Three Choirs Festival (£1,500); and Dressability (£500).

FINANCES *Year* 2009–10 *Income* £598,594 *Grants* £1,246,542 *Assets* £11,583,996

TRUSTEES G W Squire; Fiona Squire; B P Peerless.

HOW TO APPLY The trust has previously stated: 'the trustees have in place a well-established donations policy and we do not therefore encourage unsolicited grant applications, not least because they take time and expense to deal with properly.'

WHO TO APPLY TO Fiona Squire, Trustee, The North Canonry, 60–61 The Close, Salisbury SP1 2EN

Think carefully about every application. Is it justified?

905

The Stafford Trust

SC NO SC018079 **ESTABLISHED** 1991

WHERE FUNDING CAN BE GIVEN UK, with a preference for Scotland.

WHO CAN BENEFIT Charities registered in the UK.

WHAT IS FUNDED Animal welfare, medical research, local community projects, relief in need, HM Services personnel, overseas appeals, environment and sea rescue.

WHAT IS NOT FUNDED The trust does not support: religious organisations; political organisations; retrospective grants; student travel or expeditions.

RANGE OF GRANTS Mostly £500–£10,000. Occasionally recurring grants of up to three years.

SAMPLE GRANTS Strathcarron Hospice (£25,000); Citizen's Advice Edinburgh and Orcadia Creative Learning Centre (£15,000 each*); Crossroads Clackmannon (£11,000); Alzheimer's Research Trust and Seafarers UK (£10,000 each); Independent Resource Centre (£9,000*); Kidney Kids Scotland (£8,000); Alman Dramatic Club, Eric Liddel Centre and SANDS Lothian (£5,000 each); Link Living (£3,000); Borders Forest Trust and Scotland Seabirds Centre (£2,000 each); Care & Learning Alliance (£1,500); and REACT and West of Scotland Football Club for the Disabled (£1,000 each). *Payable over more than one year.

FINANCES *Year* 2009–10 *Income* £362,186 *Grants* £369,250

TRUSTEES A Peter M Walls; Hamish N Buchan; Gordon M Wyllie; Angus Morgan.

OTHER INFORMATION 'The Stafford Trust was set up in 1991 by the late Mrs Gay Stafford of Sauchie Estate near Stirling. During her lifetime, Mrs Stafford made substantial gifts to the Trust and on her death in 2005, the residue of her estate was bequeathed to the trust.'

HOW TO APPLY The trust has a short application form which can be downloaded from its website. Applicants are invited to complete the form using their own words without the restrictions of completing set questions. Please also supply the following, where appropriate: a brief description of your charity; a copy of your most recent annual report and accounts; a description of the project/funding requirement – what do you want to achieve and how will it be managed (the trustees look for clear, realistic and attainable aims); what is the expenditure budget for the project and the anticipated timescale; what funds have already been raised and what other sources are being approached; the need for funding must be clearly demonstrated; what will be the benefits of the project and how do you propose to monitor and evaluate whether the project has been successful; if applicable, what plans do you have to fund the future running costs of the project?

WHO TO APPLY TO Margaret Kane or Craig Clinton, c/o Dickson Middleton CA, PO Box 14, 20 Barnton St, Stirling FK8 1NE *Tel* 01786 474718 *Fax* 01786 451392 *email* staffordtrust@dicksonmiddleton.co.uk *Website* www.staffordtrust.org.uk

The Stanley Foundation Ltd

CC NO 206866 **ESTABLISHED** 1962

WHERE FUNDING CAN BE GIVEN UK.

WHO CAN BENEFIT Charitable organisations.

WHAT IS FUNDED Older people, medical care and research, education and social welfare.

WHAT IS NOT FUNDED No grants to individuals.

RANGE OF GRANTS £1,000–£10,000.

SAMPLE GRANTS Royal Opera House (£19,000); Tusk (£15,000); Action Against Addiction, National Gallery and Sculpt the Future (£10,000 each); Churches Conservation Trust, Dyslexia Association and Honeypot (£5,000); Independent Age (£3,000); British Museum (£2,000); and Friends of Chievely Church, Hospice in the Weald, Kathmandu Arts Centre and Tate Patrons (£1,000 each).

FINANCES *Year* 2009–10 *Income* £114,044 *Grants* £269,172 *Assets* £3,289,086

TRUSTEES C Shale: Georgina Stanley; N Stanley, Chair; S R Stanley; Elodie Stanley; S H Hall.

HOW TO APPLY In writing to the correspondent.

WHO TO APPLY TO N Stanley, Secretary, Flat 3, 19 Holland Park, London W11 3TD *Tel* 020 7792 3854 *email* nick@meristan.com

The Stanton Ballard Charitable Trust

CC NO 294688 **ESTABLISHED** 1986

WHERE FUNDING CAN BE GIVEN City of Oxford and the immediate neighbourhood.

WHO CAN BENEFIT Individuals, charities, institutions and organisations.

WHAT IS FUNDED Residents of the City of Oxford who are in conditions of need, hardship or stress; voluntary organisations providing services and facilities for such people; provision of leisure services; and the promotion of education.

WHAT IS NOT FUNDED No grants towards buildings or salaries.

RANGE OF GRANTS £100–£6,000 (2009).

SAMPLE GRANTS No grants list was included in the accounts for 2009–10 however previous beneficiaries have included: Rose Hill & Donnington Advice Centre (£6,000); Oxfordshire County Council (£5,600); Connection (£5,000); Oxford Citizens Housing Association (£3,000); St Bartholomew's Health Centre (£2,000); Barton Information Centre (£1,000); Listening Books (£500); Oxford Family Mediation (£450); Universal Benefit Society (£250); and First Wednesday Lunch Club (£100).

FINANCES *Year* 2010 *Income* £110,085 *Grants* £45,631 *Assets* £2,616,050

TRUSTEES Rosamund Nicholson; June Kimberley; Mary Tate; John Martin; Keith Pawson; Tony Woodward; Martin Slade; Howard Minns; Dianna Marsh.

HOW TO APPLY On an application form available from the correspondent on receipt of an sae.

WHO TO APPLY TO Janet Minns, Secretary, PO Box 81, Oxfordshire OX4 4ZA *Tel* 0870 760 5032

The Staples Trust

CC NO 1010656 **ESTABLISHED** 1992

WHERE FUNDING CAN BE GIVEN Overseas, UK.

WHO CAN BENEFIT Charities working in the fields of international development, environment and women's issues organisations benefiting victims of abuse and domestic violence.

WHAT IS FUNDED Overseas development: projects which contribute to the empowerment of women, the rights of indigenous people, improved shelter and housing, income-generation in disadvantaged communities and sustainable agriculture and forestry. There is a particular interest in development projects which take account of environmental sustainability and, in many cases, the environmental and developments benefits of the project are of equal importance. Environment: support for projects in developing countries, Central and Eastern Europe and the UK. Grants for renewable energy technology, training and skills upgrading and, occasionally, research. In Central and Eastern Europe, particular interest is given to providing training opportunities for community/business leaders and policy makers, and in contributing to the process of skill-sharing and information exchange. In the UK, there is an interest in helping communities protect, maintain and improve areas of land and to support work aimed at informing rural conservation policy. Women's issues: the interest is in domestic violence issues. The priority is for innovative or strategic programmes of support with a national focus (particularly work to tackle domestic violence from the male perpetrator perspective), also smaller grants to assist local refuge services and women's self-help groups. General. Frankopan Scholarship Fund, established to assist exceptionally talented students from Croatia to further or complete their studies (in any discipline) in the UK.

WHAT IS NOT FUNDED Normally, no grants to individuals.

TYPE OF GRANT One off and recurring for up to three years.

SAMPLE GRANTS Gender Studies Institute – London School of Economics and Political Science (£250,000); St Paul's Girls' School (£50,000); Latin American Mining Monitoring Programme and the University of Oxford (£30,000 each); Victoria & Albert Museum (£20,000); Karuna Trust – India (£15,000); Oxford Centre for Byzantine Research (£10,000); Lifeline Network Association (£5,000); University of Cambridge Development Office (£3,000); and Survive (£1,000).

FINANCES *Year* 2009–10 *Income* £440,778 *Grants* £459,834 *Assets* £11,635,612

TRUSTEES Jessica Frankopan; Peter Frankopan; James Sainsbury; Alex Sainsbury; Judith Portrait.

OTHER INFORMATION The trust is one of the Sainsbury Family Charitable Trusts which share a common administration. New grants approved during the year totalled £166,000.

HOW TO APPLY See the guidance for applicants section in the entry for the Sainsbury Family Charitable Trusts. A single application will be considered for support by all the trusts in the group. However, for this, as for many of the family trusts, 'proposals are generally invited by the trustees or initiated at their request. Unsolicited applications are discouraged and are unlikely to be successful, even if they fall within an area in which the trustees are interested'.

WHO TO APPLY TO Alan Bookbinder, Director, Allington House, 1st Floor, 150 Victoria Street, London SW1E 5AE *Tel* 020 7410 0330 *Fax* 020 7410 0332 *Website* www.sfct.org.uk

....

■ The Star Charitable Trust

CC NO 266695   **ESTABLISHED** 1974

WHERE FUNDING CAN BE GIVEN UK.

WHO CAN BENEFIT Charitable organisations.

WHAT IS FUNDED General charitable purposes.

SAMPLE GRANTS A list of grants was not available.

FINANCES *Year* 2009–10 *Income* £21,838 *Grants* £23,076

TRUSTEES D D Fiszman; P I Propper; D A Rosen.

HOW TO APPLY In writing to the correspondent.

WHO TO APPLY TO The Trustees, 2nd Floor, 16–18 Hatton Garden, London EC1N 8AT *Tel* 020 7404 2222 *Fax* 020 7404 3333

....

■ The Peter Stebbings Memorial Charity

CC NO 274862   **ESTABLISHED** 1977

WHERE FUNDING CAN BE GIVEN UK and developing countries.

WHO CAN BENEFIT Registered charities.

WHAT IS FUNDED The objects of the trust are to fund, in particular, medical research and education, and the welfare of those who are poor, old or sick.

WHAT IS NOT FUNDED No grants to individuals, non-registered charities or for salaries.

TYPE OF GRANT One-off grants only, for capital other than buildings, core costs, projects and start-up costs.

RANGE OF GRANTS Up to £100,000.

SAMPLE GRANTS Liver Group and The Medical Foundation for Victims of Torture (£50,000 each); Bromley by Bow Centre (£42,000); The Maya Centre (£30,000); Berkeley Reafforestation Trust (£20,000); Bibic (£10,000); Mercy Ships and Tools for Self Reliance (£5,000 each); and Amnesty International (£1,000).

FINANCES *Year* 2009–10 *Income* £209,977 *Grants* £351,358 *Assets* £6,704,218

TRUSTEES A J F Stebbings; N F Cosin; Mrs J A Clifford.

HOW TO APPLY It is the trustees' policy to make more substantial grants to a limited number of charities. Please note: the trust has previously stated that it does not respond to unsolicited applications and that its funds are fully committed.

WHO TO APPLY TO Andrew Stebbings, Trustee, 45 Pont Street, London SW1X 0BX *Tel* 020 7591 3333

....

■ The Steel Charitable Trust

CC NO 272384   **ESTABLISHED** 1976

WHERE FUNDING CAN BE GIVEN Mainly UK with 30% of all grants made to organisations in the Luton and Bedfordshire areas.

WHO CAN BENEFIT Registered charities.

WHAT IS FUNDED General, including social welfare; culture; recreation; health; medical research; environment; and overseas aid.

WHAT IS NOT FUNDED Individuals, students and expeditions are not supported.

TYPE OF GRANT 'One-off' and recurring.

RANGE OF GRANTS £1,000–£50,000.

SAMPLE GRANTS The National Society for Epilepsy (£50,000); Keech Hospice Care (£40,000); SSAFA Forces Help and Moorfields Eye Hospital Development Fund (£25,000 each); Luton Town Centre Chaplaincy and Cancer Research UK (£20,000 each); Bournemouth University (£15,000); South London Fine Art Gallery and Library (£10,000); Polka Children's Theatre Limited (£9,500); Bournemouth Symphony Orchestra (£8,000); Bedfordshire African Community Centre Limited and Refresh Limited (£5,000 each); Family Tree – Wirral (£4,000); Worcester YMCA (£3,000); Blind in Business Trust (£2,000); and War Memorials Trust (£1,000).

FINANCES *Year* 2010–11 *Income* £1,017,674 *Grants* £988,050 *Assets* £21,886,918

TRUSTEES Nicholas E W Wright; John A Childs, Chair; John A Maddox; Anthony W Hawkins; Paul Stevenson; Wendy Bailey; Mary Briggs; Philip Lawford.

HOW TO APPLY All applicants must complete the online application form. Applications submitted by post will not be considered. There is no deadline for applications and all will be acknowledged. Trustees meet regularly during the year, usually in February, May, August and November. All successful applicants will be notified by email and will be required to provide written confirmation of the details of the project or work for which they are seeking a grant. Payment is then made in the following month. To comply with the Data Protection Act 1998, applicants are required to consent to the use of personal data supplied by them in the processing and review of their application. This includes transfer to and use by such individuals and organisations as the trust deems appropriate. The trust requires the assurance of the applicant that personal data about any other individual is supplied to the trust with his/her consent. At the point of submitting an online application, applicants are asked to confirm this consent and assurance.

WHO TO APPLY TO Carol Langston, Administrator, Holme Farm, Fore Street, Bradford, Holsworthy, Devon EX22 7AJ *Tel* 01409 281403 *email* administrator@steelcharitabletrust.org.uk *Website* www.steelcharitabletrust.org.uk

■ The Steinberg Family Charitable Trust

CC NO 1045231   **ESTABLISHED** 1995
WHERE FUNDING CAN BE GIVEN UK, with a preference for Greater Manchester.
WHO CAN BENEFIT Charitable organisations, with a preference for Jewish groups.
WHAT IS FUNDED General charitable purposes.
WHAT IS NOT FUNDED Registered charities only.
RANGE OF GRANTS £150–£20,000 average £2,800.
SAMPLE GRANTS Fed (£27,500) and Integrated Education Fund (£25,000); Aish; Centre for Torah Education Trust; Crimestoppers; Imperial War Museum North; Yeshiva Orchos Chaim (£10,000 each); Lubavitch South Manchester; Holocaust Centre (£7,500 each); Genesis Appeal (£5,000); Manchester Junior Girls' School; St John's Hospice (£2,500 each); and Royal British Legion (£1,000).
FINANCES *Year* 2008–09 *Income* £1,415,542 *Grants* £440,750 *Assets* £13,015,103
TRUSTEES Dominic Burke, Chairman; Beryl Steinberg; Jonathan Steinberg; Lynne Attias.
OTHER INFORMATION Over the last 5 years this charity has been on average well over a year late in submitting its accounts to the Charity Commission.
HOW TO APPLY In writing to the correspondent, including evidence of charitable status, the purpose to which the funds are to be put, evidence of other action taken to fund the project concerned, and the outcome of that action.
WHO TO APPLY TO Jonathan Steinberg, Lime Tree Cottage, Bollingway, Hale, Altrincham WA15 0NZ *Tel* 0161 903 8851 *email* admin@steinberg-trust.co.uk

■ The Hugh Stenhouse Foundation

SC NO SC015074   **ESTABLISHED** 1968
WHERE FUNDING CAN BE GIVEN Mainly Scotland, with an emphasis on the west coast.
WHO CAN BENEFIT Charities benefiting children; young adults; those in care, fostered and adopted; and people disadvantaged by poverty. The foundation had stated that it tends to support smaller charities.
WHAT IS FUNDED General charitable purposes, including welfare, young people, and nature reserves, woodlands and bird sanctuaries.
WHAT IS NOT FUNDED Grants are not given for political appeals or to individuals.
TYPE OF GRANT Recurring, one-off and core costs. Funding is available for more than three years.
SAMPLE GRANTS Previous beneficiaries include: Maxwelton Chapel Trust (£24,000); Glasgow City Mission and Hopscotch (£2,000 each); Salvation Army (£1,700); REACT and the Safety Zone (£1,600 each); Lilias Graham Trust (£1,000); Visibility (£800); and Erskine Hospital (£650).
FINANCES *Year* 2009–10 *Income* £5,272,200
TRUSTEES Mrs A D Irvine Robertson; M R L Stenhouse; R G T Stenhouse; Mrs R C L Stewart.
OTHER INFORMATION No grants to individuals.
HOW TO APPLY In writing to the correspondent. Trustees meet in March and September. Applications should be received by February and August respectively.
WHO TO APPLY TO The Secretary, c/o Bell Ingram Ltd, Durn, Isla Road, Perth PH2 7HF

■ C E K Stern Charitable Trust

CC NO 1049157   **ESTABLISHED** 1992
WHERE FUNDING CAN BE GIVEN UK and overseas.
WHO CAN BENEFIT Orthodox Jewish charities.
WHAT IS FUNDED Orthodox Jewish causes.
FINANCES *Year* 2009–10 *Income* £102,577 *Grants* £40,670 *Assets* £822,832
TRUSTEES Z M Kaufman; Mrs C E Stern; S Kaufman; Z Stern.
HOW TO APPLY In writing to the correspondent.
WHO TO APPLY TO Z M Kaufman, Trustee, 50 Keswick Street, Gateshead, Tyne and Wear NE8 1TQ

■ The Sigmund Sternberg Charitable Foundation

CC NO 257950   **ESTABLISHED** 1968
WHERE FUNDING CAN BE GIVEN Worldwide.
WHO CAN BENEFIT Registered charities.
WHAT IS FUNDED Interfaith activities to promote racial and religious harmony, in particular between Christian, Jewish and Muslim faiths, and the education in, and understanding of, their fundamental tenets and beliefs.
WHAT IS NOT FUNDED No grants to individuals.
TYPE OF GRANT One-off or recurring.
RANGE OF GRANTS Up to £80,000, although most grants are of £1,000 or less.
SAMPLE GRANTS Three Faiths Forum (£83,000); The Movement for Reform Judaism (£70,000); The Board of Deputies Charitable Foundation (£9,000); Leo Baeck College Centre for Jewish Education (£5,000); World Congress of Faiths (£3,000) and Jewish National Fund (£1,100). There were a further 104 grants of less than £1,000 each, totalling £13,000.
FINANCES *Year* 2009–10 *Income* £300,765 *Grants* £201,420 *Assets* £4,765,415

TRUSTEES Sir S Sternberg; V M Sternberg; Lady Sternberg; Revd M C Rossi Braybrooke; M A M Slowe; R Tamir; M D Paisner.

OTHER INFORMATION During the year, 145 grant applications were accepted. Grants ranged from £1,000–£80,000 although the majority of grants were for less than £1,000 each.

HOW TO APPLY In writing to the correspondent.

WHO TO APPLY TO Sir S Sternberg, Trustee, Star House, 104/108 Grafton Road, London NW5 4BA *Tel* 020 7431 4200

■ Stervon Ltd

CC NO 280958   **ESTABLISHED** 1980

WHERE FUNDING CAN BE GIVEN UK.

WHO CAN BENEFIT Jewish people.

WHAT IS FUNDED Jewish causes and general charitable purposes.

SAMPLE GRANTS Previous beneficiaries include: Eitz Chaim; Rehabilitation Trust; Chasdei Yoel; Beis Yoel; Friends of Horeinu; Beis Hamedrash Hachadash; Tashbar; Tov V' Chessed; Beth Sorah Schneirer; Asser Bishvil.

FINANCES *Year* 2009 *Income* £270,085 *Grants* £267,305 *Assets* £113,909

TRUSTEES A Reich; G Rothbart.

OTHER INFORMATION No grants list was available.

HOW TO APPLY In writing to the correspondent.

WHO TO APPLY TO A Reich, Secretary, c/o Stervon House, 1 Seaford Road, Salford, Greater Manchester M6 6AS *Tel* 0161 737 5000

■ The Stevenage Community Trust

CC NO 1000762   **ESTABLISHED** 1990

WHERE FUNDING CAN BE GIVEN The borough of Stevenage and the surrounding villages of Aston, Benington, Cromer, Datchworth, Graveley, Knebworth, Little Wymondley, Old Knebworth, Walkern, Watton-at-Stone, Weston, and Woolmer Green.

WHO CAN BENEFIT Organisations and individuals in need who are recommended by a third party agency.

WHAT IS FUNDED General charitable purposes including community projects, disability, older people, children and youth.

WHAT IS NOT FUNDED Religious, education and political appeals are not supported.

TYPE OF GRANT Maximum £2,000 through the grant committee, larger grant requests go the full Board of Trustees.

RANGE OF GRANTS £50–£2,000.

FINANCES *Year* 2009–10 *Income* £130,795 *Grants* £39,526 *Assets* £499,645

TRUSTEES Mr K Follett, Chair; Cllr R Henry; Mr M Addison, Secretary; Mr D M Isted; Mr M Hennessey, Treasurer; Ms B Joshi; Mr R Ball; Mr A Juggins; Cllr S Batson; Mrs C K Kang; Mr I Campbell; Mr A Lang; Mr G Clark; Mr I Morton; Ms J E Daniel; Mr M Phoenix; Mr F Donohue; Mr R J Stewart; Mr A R Fuller; Mrs J Thomas; Mr P Tutin and Mr B Harley.

HOW TO APPLY On a form available from the trust by post, email, telephone or from the website. Grants applications are considered quarterly, however, the trust states that it 'can and does react to individuals in need speedily. It does this with referrals from Third Party Agencies and is unique in that it can offer this service to those most in need.'

WHO TO APPLY TO June Oldroyd, c/o EADS Astrium, Gunnels Wood Road, Stevenage HertfordshireSG1 2AS *Tel* 01438 773368 *Fax* 01438 773 341 *email* info@sct.uk.net *Website* www.stevenagecommunitytrust.org

---

■ The June Stevens Foundation

CC NO 327829   **ESTABLISHED** 1988

WHERE FUNDING CAN BE GIVEN UK, but mostly Gloucestershire.

WHO CAN BENEFIT Charitable organisations mainly for older and young people and animals.

WHAT IS FUNDED General charitable purposes.

WHAT IS NOT FUNDED No grants to individuals.

RANGE OF GRANTS £200–£1,000.

SAMPLE GRANTS Previous beneficiaries have included: Greek Animal Welfare Fund (£2,000); Brooke Hospital for Animals and the Royal British Legion (£1,500 each); Gloucestershire Historic Churches Trust (£1,000); Cirencester House for Young People and Gloucestershire Playing Fields Association (£750 each); and Cotswold Care Hospice and Women's Holiday Fund (£500 each).

FINANCES *Year* 2009–10 *Income* £15,117 *Grants* £35,000

TRUSTEES Miss J D Stevens; A J Quinton; A R St C Tahourdin.

OTHER INFORMATION The grants total is based on previous research.

HOW TO APPLY In writing to the correspondent.

WHO TO APPLY TO A R St C Tahourdin, Trustee, Herrington and Carmichael, Unit 8 Waters Edge, Riverside Way, Camberley GU15 3YL *Tel* 01252 686222

■ Stevenson Family's Charitable Trust

CC NO 327148   **ESTABLISHED** 1986

WHERE FUNDING CAN BE GIVEN Worldwide, in practice mainly UK.

WHO CAN BENEFIT Registered charities.

WHAT IS FUNDED Culture and arts, conservation and heritage, education, health, overseas aid and general charitable purposes.

WHAT IS NOT FUNDED No grants to individuals.

TYPE OF GRANT One-off and recurring.

RANGE OF GRANTS £150–£50,000.

SAMPLE GRANTS Berkshire Community Foundation (£50,000); University of Cape Town Trust (£28,000); National Trust for Scotland (£25,000); St Michael and All Angels – Sunninghill (£15,000); Royal Chapel Appeal and St Mary's PCC (£10,000 each); Sick Children's Trust (£5,000); Charleston Trust (£2,000); British Museum Society (£1,500); Merlin (£1,000); Camphill Village Trust Appeals Fund (£500); Reed's School Foundation Appeal and Cancer Research (£250 each); and Glyndebourne Arts Trust (£150).

FINANCES *Year* 2009–10 *Income* £161,385 *Grants* £183,228 *Assets* £2,434,773

TRUSTEES Sir Hugh Stevenson; Lady Catherine Stevenson.

HOW TO APPLY 'No unsolicited applications can be considered as the charity's funds are required to support purposes chosen by the trustees.'

WHO TO APPLY TO Sir Hugh Stevenson, Trustee, Old Waterfield, Winkfield Road, Ascot SL5 7LJ

■ The Steventon Allotments and Relief-in-Need Charity

CC NO 203331   **ESTABLISHED** 1987
WHERE FUNDING CAN BE GIVEN Parish of Steventon only.
WHO CAN BENEFIT Residents and groups in the parish of Steventon.
WHAT IS FUNDED Projects benefiting the local community, impoverished individuals, churches, schools, older people and the maintenance of the allotments.
WHAT IS NOT FUNDED Parish of Steventon only.
RANGE OF GRANTS Up to £34,000.
SAMPLE GRANTS Steventon Pre-School Group (£33,500); St Michael's CE School (£20,000 in two grants); St. Michael's Church (£13,600); Steventon Sports and Social Club (£6,200); Assistance to Steventon Residents (£1,800).
FINANCES *Year* 2010 *Income* £126,260 *Grants* £106,108 *Assets* £2,469,286
TRUSTEES Diana Ruth Bowder; Anne Veronica Shrimpton; Robin Wilkinson; Steven Arthur Frederick Ward; Kevin Paul Curley.
OTHER INFORMATION Grants of £83,000 were awarded to organisations and grants of £23,500 to individuals.
HOW TO APPLY In writing to the correspondent. The trustees meet monthly.
WHO TO APPLY TO Mrs Patrina Effer, 19 Lime Grove, Southmoor, Abingdon, Oxfordshire OX13 5DN *Tel* 01865 821055 *email* sarinc@patrina.co.uk

■ The Stewards' Charitable Trust

CC NO 299597   **ESTABLISHED** 1988
WHERE FUNDING CAN BE GIVEN Principally the UK.
WHO CAN BENEFIT Organisations and clubs benefiting young sportsmen and women.
WHAT IS FUNDED Support of rowing at all levels, from grassroots upwards. Beneficiaries should be in full-time education or training.
WHAT IS NOT FUNDED No grants to individuals or for building or capital costs.
TYPE OF GRANT Preferably one-off and especially where there are matched funds raised elsewhere.
RANGE OF GRANTS £3,000–£194,000.
SAMPLE GRANTS British Rowing Scholarships (£204,000); London Youth Rowing (£37,500); Rowing Foundation (£15,000); Project Oarsome (£12,000); Upper Thames Rowing Club – Junior Development (£10,000); Ball Cup Regatta (£4,500); Junior Inter-Regional Regatta (£3,000); World University Rowing Championships (£1,000); and Regatta for the Disabled (£500).
FINANCES *Year* 2009–10 *Income* £301,588 *Grants* £288,388 *Assets* £5,602,964
TRUSTEES M A Sweeney; C G V Davidge; C L Baillieu; R C Lester; Sir S Redgrave.
HOW TO APPLY In writing to the correspondent. Applications are usually first vetted by Amateur Rowing Association.
WHO TO APPLY TO Daniel Grist, Secretary, Regatta Headquarters, Henley-on-Thames, Oxfordshire RG9 2LY *Tel* 01491 572153 *Fax* 01491 575509 *Website* www.hrr.co.uk

■ The Stewards' Company Limited (incorporating the J W Laing Trust and the J W Laing Biblical Scholarship Trust)

CC NO 234558   **ESTABLISHED** 1947
WHERE FUNDING CAN BE GIVEN Unrestricted.
WHO CAN BENEFIT Organisations involved with training people in religious education. About half the trust's funds are given for work overseas.
WHAT IS FUNDED Christian evangelism, especially but not exclusively that of Christian Brethren assemblies. Grants given overseas are made under the following categories: church buildings; scriptures and literature; education and orphanages; education of missionaries' children; national evangelists and missionaries' vehicles. Grants given in the UK are categorised under: church buildings; evangelistic associations; scriptures and literature; teachers and evangelists; and youth and children. Substantial funds are also transferred to the Beatrice Laing Trust (see separate entry).
TYPE OF GRANT Usually one-off.
RANGE OF GRANTS About £15,000–£1 million.
SAMPLE GRANTS Echoes of Service (£864,000); Beatrice Laing Trust (£465,500); UCCF (£435,500); Retired Missionary Aid Fund (£200,000); European Leadership Forum (£165,000); Interlink (£140,000); International Fellowship of Evangelical Students (£130,000); and Bright Hope World and Tearfund (£100,000 each).
FINANCES *Year* 2010–11 *Income* £4,340,000 *Grants* £4,570,000 *Assets* £128,000,000
TRUSTEES Brian Chapman; Alexander McIlhinney; Dr Alexander Scott; Douglas Spence; Paul Young; Dr John Burness; William Adams; Andrew Griffiths; Prof. Arthur Williamson; Philip Page; Denis Cooper; Alan Paterson; Glyn Davies; Ian Childs; James Crookes; John Gamble; Philip Symons; William Wood; Andrew Street; Keith Bintley; John Aitken.
HOW TO APPLY In writing to the correspondent.
WHO TO APPLY TO Brian Chapman, Secretary, 124 Wells Road, Bath BA2 3AH *Tel* 01225 427236 *Fax* 01225 427278 *email* stewardsco@stewards.co.uk

■ The Andy Stewart Charitable Foundation

CC NO 1114802   **ESTABLISHED** 2006
WHERE FUNDING CAN BE GIVEN Worldwide.
WHO CAN BENEFIT Charitable organisations.
WHAT IS FUNDED General charitable purposes.
RANGE OF GRANTS Up to £72,000 (2010).
SAMPLE GRANTS Spinal Research (£72,000); Sir Peter O'Sullivan Charitable Trust (£10,000); Spinal Injuries (£6,200); Moorcroft Trust (£4,350); Brompton Foundation (£2,500) and Racing Welfare (£1,100). Further donations of £1,000 or less totalled £7,000.
FINANCES *Year* 2010 *Income* £288,078 *Grants* £108,700 *Assets* £528,843
TRUSTEES Andy Stewart; Mark Stewart; Paul Stewart.
OTHER INFORMATION During the year there were no grants awarded to individuals, only organisations.
HOW TO APPLY In writing to the correspondent.
WHO TO APPLY TO The Trustees, 18 Curzon Street, London W1J 7TA *Tel* 020 7397 8900 *Website* www.cenkos.com

■ The Sir Halley Stewart Trust

CC NO 208491   **ESTABLISHED** 1924

WHERE FUNDING CAN BE GIVEN UK and some work in Africa.

WHO CAN BENEFIT Charitable organisations and researchers.

WHAT IS FUNDED Research, innovative projects, feasibility and pilot studies and development projects in medical, social, educational and religious fields.

WHAT IS NOT FUNDED The trust will be unable to help with funding for any of the following: general appeals of any kind; the purchase, erection or conversion of buildings; capital costs; university overhead charges; the completion of a project initiated by other bodies. The trust does not normally fund: projects put forward indirectly through other umbrella or large charities; educational or 'gap' year travel projects; running costs of established organisations; climate change issues; personal education fees or fees for taught courses-unless connected with research which falls within current priority areas. Applications for such research work are normally made by a senior researcher seeking support for a student, or if coming directly from the student it should have project supervisor's written support; the trust does not favour grantmaking to enable the completion of a project or PhD.

TYPE OF GRANT One-off and project grants. Feasibility studies, research and salaries will also be considered. Funding may be given for up to three years.

RANGE OF GRANTS Up to £57,000.

SAMPLE GRANTS UNSEEN UK (£57,000); Feltham Community Chaplaincy Trust (£50,000); St Ethelburga's Centre for Peace – London (£39,000); Health Action Leicester for Ethiopia (HALE) (£33,000); Medic to Medic (£30,000); RECOOP – Resettlement of older prisoners (£27,000); KORI Arts (£25,000); PLAN UK – Burkina Faso and Sightsavers (£24,000 each); Most Mira (£20,000); and Clapham Pottery (£14,000); and LICC (£10,000).

FINANCES *Year* 2010–11 *Income* £831,000 *Grants* £849,000 *Assets* £24,296,000

TRUSTEES Lord Stewartby, President; Prof. Philip Whitfield, Chair; Prof. John Lennard Jones; Dr Duncan Stewart; William P Kirkman; George Russell; Prof. Phyllida Parsloe; Barbara Clapham; Prof. John Wyatt; Michael Ross Collins; Joanna Womack; Revd Lord Griffiths; Dr Caroline Berry; Prof. Gordon Willcock; Caroline Thomas; Brian Allpress; Theresa Bartlett; Louisa Macantab; Amy Holcroft.

PUBLICATIONS The trust has a helpful website with clear guidelines for applicants.

OTHER INFORMATION Grants of less than £10,000 – including those to individuals – totalled £52,000.

HOW TO APPLY The following guidelines for applicants is taken from the trust's website: applications will not be accepted by fax or email; applicants should make sure that their project fits the trust's objects and falls within its current priority areas; telephone enquiries to the trust's office are welcomed to discuss the suitability of an application. Please note there is only one member of staff so please be patient and try again if there is no one in the office when you telephone. The trust does not have an application form. Applicants should write to the administrator always including a one-page lay 'executive' summary of the proposed work. The proposal should state clearly: what the aims of the project are and why it is believed to be innovative; what the overall budgeted cost of the project is and how much is being requested from the trust; what the grant will be used for and how long the project will take to have practical benefits; how the project/research results will be disseminated; personal medical applications should be accompanied by a letter of support from a senior colleague or research supervisor; development projects should indicate where they would hope to obtain future funding from; where appropriate it is helpful to include a CV; job description, set of audited signed accounts and annual report.

There are no set application deadlines. When the trust has received your application they will make contact (normally within two weeks) either to ask for further information; to tell you the application will be going forward to the next stage of assessment and what the timetable for a final decision will be; or to tell you that they are unable to help. The trust imposes terms and conditions on each award. Please note that the trust receives many applications for support, and although an application may fit the objects of the trust, it may not necessarily be able to help.

WHO TO APPLY TO Sue West, Administrator, 22 Earith Rd, Willingham, Cambridge, Cambridgeshire CB24 5LS *Tel* 01954 260707 *Fax* 01954 260707 *email* email@sirhalleystewart.org.uk *Website* www.sirhalleystewart.org.uk

■ The Stewarts Law Foundation

CC NO 1136714   **ESTABLISHED** 2010

WHERE FUNDING CAN BE GIVEN Undefined, in practice the UK.

WHO CAN BENEFIT Organisations and individuals.

WHAT IS FUNDED General charitable purposes.

TRUSTEES John Cahill; Stuart Dench; Paul Paxton; James Healy-Pratt; Stephen Foster; Julian Chamberlayne; Daniel James Herman; Andrew Dinsmore; Kevin Grealis.

HOW TO APPLY In writing to the correspondent.

WHO TO APPLY TO John Cahill, Trustee, 5 New Street Square, London EC4A 3BF *email* info@stewartslaw.com

■ The Leonard Laity Stoate Charitable Trust

CC NO 221325   **ESTABLISHED** 1950

WHERE FUNDING CAN BE GIVEN England and Wales with a preference for the southwest of England, Bristol, Cornwall, Devon, Dorset and Somerset (especially west Somerset).

WHO CAN BENEFIT Methodist organisations benefiting children and young adults, people who are disabled and people disadvantaged by poverty. Community organisation projects and small local innovatory projects with a strong emphasis on self-help are preferred.

WHAT IS FUNDED The broad categories the trust supported are: medical and disability; churches; youth and children; community projects; disadvantage; and environment.

WHAT IS NOT FUNDED No grants to: individuals unless supported by a registered charity; large projects (over £500,000 and/or with more than £250,000 still to raise); general appeals by national charities; the running expenses of a charity.

TYPE OF GRANT Usually one-off for a specific project or part of a project.

RANGE OF GRANTS Typically £500–£1,000.

SAMPLE GRANTS St Agnes Methodist Church – Cornwall; Troon Methodist Church – Cornwall; Dame Hannah Rogers Trust; Prospect Hospice – Swindon; Parkinson's Disease Society – London; National Autistic Society and Accessible Coach Holidays (£1,000 each). Grants above £1,000 include: Turntable Furniture Project – Exeter (£1,500) and New Room (Wesley Chapel)- Bristol (£8,000).

FINANCES *Year* 2009–10 *Income* £64,212 *Grants* £65,000 *Assets* £1,778,929

TRUSTEES Mrs Sarah J Boughton; Stephen R Duckworth; Mrs Susan Harnden; Dr Christopher Stoate; Philip J Stoate; Revd Ward Jones; Dr Pam Stoate.

OTHER INFORMATION Although the trust does not want to rule out anywhere in England and Wales, it is a comparatively small trust and is forced to be very selective. Therefore, the further an applicant is from the trust's core area the less likely they are to be successful.

HOW TO APPLY 'There is no special application form, but applications should be in writing; neither telephone nor email applications will be entertained. Please supply clear details of: the need the intended project is designed to meet; the amount raised so far, with a breakdown of how much has been raised from within the local community and how much from other grant making bodies or other sources. Please also supply where possible: your registered charity number or, for unregistered organisations, a copy of your constitution; accounts or budgets; an email address for follow-up correspondence or application acknowledgement. Whilst applications can be considered at any time, the bulk are decided at our half-yearly meetings in mid-March and September of each year. Thus December to February and June to August are probably the best times to submit applications.'

WHO TO APPLY TO Philip J Stoate, Secretary, 7 Sherwood Close, Bracknell, Berkshire RG12 2SB *Tel* 0871 284 7780 *email* charity@erminea.org.uk *Website* www.stoate-charity.org.uk

■ **The Stobart Newlands Charitable Trust**

CC NO 328464   **ESTABLISHED** 1989

WHERE FUNDING CAN BE GIVEN UK.

WHO CAN BENEFIT Registered charities.

WHAT IS FUNDED General charitable purposes at the discretion of the trustees; mainly Christian organisations and missionary societies.

WHAT IS NOT FUNDED No grants for individuals.

TYPE OF GRANT Mainly recurrent.

RANGE OF GRANTS Up to £250,000.

SAMPLE GRANTS World Vision (£250,000); and Operation Mobilisation (£175,000); Castle Sowerby Chapel (£70,000); Bible Society (£41,000); Tear Fund, Every Home Crusade (£35,000 each); London City Mission (£26,000); Keswick Convention (£25,000); Logos Ministries (£23,000); and Living Well Trust (£20,000); Release International, Spurgeons (£10,000 each); Way to Life (£8,000); Trinitarian Bible Society (£5,000); Caring for Life (£3,000); and Cancer Research UK (£2,000).

FINANCES *Year* 2010 *Income* £695,012 *Grants* £864,400 *Assets* £140,912

TRUSTEES Richard Stobart; Margaret Stobart; Ronnie Stobart; Peter Stobart; Linda Rigg.

OTHER INFORMATION Grants of £1,000 or less totalled £1,700.

HOW TO APPLY Unsolicited applications are most unlikely to be successful.

WHO TO APPLY TO Ronnie Stobart, Trustee, Mill Croft, Newlands, Hesket Newmarket, Wigton, Cumbria CA7 8HP *Tel* 01697 478531

■ **The Edward Stocks-Massey Bequest Fund**

CC NO 526516   **ESTABLISHED** 1910

WHERE FUNDING CAN BE GIVEN Burnley.

WHO CAN BENEFIT Charitable organisations.

WHAT IS FUNDED Education, music, arts, culture and recreation.

RANGE OF GRANTS £80–£6,000 (2009–10).

SAMPLE GRANTS Burnley Mechanics Institute Trust (£5,000); Public Art Restoration Grant (£2,850); Prince's Trust, Burnley Youth Theatre; The Weaver's Triangle Trust and St Peters Church Concerts (£1,000 each); Burnley Junior Alliance Band (£500); Townwley Hall Society (£375).

FINANCES *Year* 2009–10 *Income* £32,622 *Grants* £50,000 *Assets* £923,070

TRUSTEES A David Knagg; Neil Beecham.

OTHER INFORMATION Burnley Borough Council and Lancashire County Council received £15,500 each in grants. £8,000 went to organisation/individual grants and £6,000 in scholarship awards.

HOW TO APPLY On a form available from the correspondent.

WHO TO APPLY TO Saima Afzaal, Burnley Borough Council, Town Hall, Manchester Road, Burnley BB11 1JA *Tel* 01282 425011 *Fax* 01282 438772

■ **The Stokenchurch Educational Charity**

CC NO 297846   **ESTABLISHED** 1987

WHERE FUNDING CAN BE GIVEN The parish of Stokenchurch.

WHO CAN BENEFIT Local nursery, primary and middle schools; children, young adults and students under the age of 25 residing in the Parish of Stokenchurch. Community groups.

WHAT IS FUNDED Grants are given for educational purposes and to a lesser extent, to the community.

WHAT IS NOT FUNDED No grants to applicants from outside the Parish of Stokenchurch.

SAMPLE GRANTS Previous beneficiaries: Stokenchurch Primary School (£9,000); The Mary Towerton School (£450); Radnage C of E Infant School (£440); Ibstone C of E Infant School (£405); Stokenchurch Medical Centre (£300); Living Springs (£150); Studley Green Youth Club (£130); and Stokenchurch Village Fete (£100).

FINANCES *Year* 2010 *Income* £65,422 *Grants* £50,410 *Assets* £1,767,126

TRUSTEES Mrs M Shurrock, Chair; A Palmer; A Saunders; F Downes; Revd A France; Mrs C Baker.

HOW TO APPLY On a form available from the correspondent. The trustees place an annual advertisement in the local press and two public places in Stokenchurch inviting applications. Educational applications must be received by 30 November of each academic year, community grants by 30 September each year.

WHO TO APPLY TO P H Cannon, Kinda Cool, Wycombe Road, Stokenchurch, High Wycombe, Buckinghamshire HP14 3RR *Tel* 01494 450123 *email* canmoor@cannonmoorcroft.co.uk

■ The Stoller Charitable Trust

cc no 285415   **ESTABLISHED** 1982
WHERE FUNDING CAN BE GIVEN UK, with a preference for the Greater Manchester area.
WHO CAN BENEFIT Established UK charities and local causes benefiting children and young adults.
WHAT IS FUNDED Preference for medically related causes, though other charitable purposes will be considered.
WHAT IS NOT FUNDED No grants to individuals.
TYPE OF GRANT Buildings, capital, one-off, project, research, recurring costs and start-up costs will be considered. Funding may be given for up to three years.
SAMPLE GRANTS Bauern Helfen Baeurn (£25,000); Onside North West (£25,000); Broughton House (£20,000); Central Manchester Children's Hospitals and Live Music Now (£10,000 each); Christie Hospital, Greater Manchester Appeal, Imperial War Museum North and National Memorial Arboretum (£5,000 each); Cancer Research UK and Oldham Liaison of Ex-Services Associations and (£2,500); Church Housing Trust, Commandery of John of Gaunt and Mines Advisory Group (£1,000 each); Salvation Army Eden Project (£400); and Windermere Air Show (£250).
FINANCES *Year* 2009–10 *Income* £63,894 *Grants* £252,289 *Assets* £5,837,894
TRUSTEES Norman K Stoller, Chair; Roger Gould; Jan Fidler; Sheila M Stoller.
HOW TO APPLY In writing to the correspondent. Applications need to be received by February, May, August or November. The trustees usually meet in March, June, September and December.
WHO TO APPLY TO Alison M Ford, Secretary, PO Box 164, Middleton, Manchester M24 1XA *Tel* 0161 653 3849

■ The M J C Stone Charitable Trust

cc no 283920   **ESTABLISHED** 1981
WHERE FUNDING CAN BE GIVEN UK.
WHO CAN BENEFIT UK charities and smaller scale local organisations.
WHAT IS FUNDED General with a preference for education, medicine and health, conservation and religion.
RANGE OF GRANTS Up to £50,000.
SAMPLE GRANTS Previous beneficiaries have included: Westonbirt School (£50,000); Bradfield Foundation and Great North Air Ambulance (£26,000 each); Wotton Under Edge Community Sports Fund (£20,000); Maggie Keswick Jencks Cancer (£10,000); National Trust (£5,000); Zimbabwe Rhodesia Relief and Gloucestershire Society (£1,000 each) and CDTR – Peruvian Appeal, Royal British Legion and Tewkesbury Abbey Appeal Trust (£250 each).
FINANCES *Year* 2010 *Income* £884 *Grants* £93,120
TRUSTEES Michael Stone; Louisa Stone; Charles Stone; Andrew Stone; Nicola Farquhar.
HOW TO APPLY The trust does not accept unsolicited applications.
WHO TO APPLY TO Michael Stone, Trustee, Estate Office, Ozleworth Park, Wotton-under-Edge, Gloucestershire GL12 7QA *Tel* 01453 845591

■ The Stone Family Foundation

cc no 1108207   **ESTABLISHED** 2005
WHERE FUNDING CAN BE GIVEN Worldwide.
WHO CAN BENEFIT Charities and international aid organisations.
WHAT IS FUNDED Relief of need or hardship.
WHAT IS NOT FUNDED No grants to individuals.
RANGE OF GRANTS Up to £500,000.
SAMPLE GRANTS Opportunity International (£464,000); WaterAid (£398,000); Hope and Home for Children (£219,000); Aid India (£54,000); Zamcog (£50,000); Rainforest Saver Foundation (£41,000); LSCDPA (Laos) (£32,500); Maytree Respite Centre (£32,000); Cult Information Centre (£29,000); and University of Oxford Development Trust (£3,500).
FINANCES *Year* 2010 *Income* £2,234,805 *Grants* £1,525,256 *Assets* £47,134,842
TRUSTEES Coutts & Co; John Kyle Stone; Charles H Edwards; Sophie Edwards.
OTHER INFORMATION Loans are also available.
HOW TO APPLY 'Applicants for grants and loans must be in writing, and trustees seek the completion of formal terms and conditions.'
WHO TO APPLY TO The Clerk, Coutts & Co, 440 Strand, London WC2R 0QS *Tel* 020 7663 6825

■ The Stone-Mallabar Charitable Foundation

cc no 1013678   **ESTABLISHED** 1992
WHERE FUNDING CAN BE GIVEN UK.
WHO CAN BENEFIT Registered charities.
WHAT IS FUNDED Particularly medical charities but will occasionally give to the arts, religion, overseas appeals, welfare and education.
WHAT IS NOT FUNDED No grants to individuals.
RANGE OF GRANTS £0–£50,000.
SAMPLE GRANTS Sheffield Institute Foundation for Motor Neurone Disease £8,000; Bolshoi Ballet School; Sally Oakley Smith – Motor Neurone Disease Event (£4,000); Alzheimer's Concern Ealing (£3,000); The Hard Man Trust £2,500; Thalidomide at 50 (£2,500); West London Mission; Christian Concern Crewe; Dermatrust; Cini UK; Pearson Holiday Fund (£1,000 each).
FINANCES *Year* 2008–09 *Income* £39,247 *Grants* £37,165 *Assets* £520,684
TRUSTEES Jonathan Stone; Thalia Stone; Robin Paul; Graham Hutton.
OTHER INFORMATION Unlisted grants of less than £1,000 each totalled £5,600.
HOW TO APPLY In writing to the correspondent.
WHO TO APPLY TO Jonathan Stone, Trustee, 41 Orchard Court, Portman Square, London W1H 6LF *email* jmls@ymail.com

■ The Samuel Storey Family Charitable Trust

cc no 267684   **ESTABLISHED** 1974
WHERE FUNDING CAN BE GIVEN UK, with a preference for Yorkshire.
WHO CAN BENEFIT Registered charities.
WHAT IS FUNDED General charitable purposes.
WHAT IS NOT FUNDED The trust does not support non-registered charities or individuals.
RANGE OF GRANTS Generally £2–£5,000.
SAMPLE GRANTS Hope and Homes for Children (£29,000); York University (£20,000); Pebbles Project (£2,000); Molly's Fund and RLNI (£1,000 each); Sistema Scotland (£500); World

Monument Fund in Britain (£250); Smile Train UK (£200) and Woodland Trust (£65).

FINANCES *Year* 2009–10 *Income* £138,387 *Grants* £92,729 *Assets* £4,640,305

TRUSTEES Hon. Sir Richard Storey; Wren Hoskyns Abrahall; Kenelm Storey.

HOW TO APPLY In writing to the correspondent.

WHO TO APPLY TO Hon. Sir Richard Storey, Trustee, 21 Buckingham Gate, London SW1E 6LS *Tel* 020 7802 2700

■ Peter Stormonth Darling Charitable Trust

CC NO 1049946   **ESTABLISHED** 1995

WHERE FUNDING CAN BE GIVEN UK.

WHO CAN BENEFIT Organisations benefiting children, young adults, and sportsmen and women.

WHAT IS FUNDED Preference for heritage, education, healthcare and sports facilities.

WHAT IS NOT FUNDED No grants to individuals.

RANGE OF GRANTS Up to £12,000.

SAMPLE GRANTS Winchester College Wykeham Campaign (£50,000) and Friends of East Sussex Hospices (£10,000); Reed's School (£4,000); Cheltenham Festivals (£2,500); Canine Partners and Chelsea Physic Garden (£2,000 each); and Brittle Bone Society, Courtauld Institute of Art and Sussex Community Foundation (£1,000 each).

FINANCES *Year* 2010 *Income* £150,010 *Grants* £93,500 *Assets* £2,825,024

TRUSTEES Tom Colville; John Rodwell; Peter Stormonth Darling; Elizabeth Cobb; Arabella Johannes; Christa Taylor.

HOW TO APPLY This trust states that it does not respond to unsolicited applications.

WHO TO APPLY TO Peter Stormonth Darling, Soditic Ltd, 12 Charles II Street, London SW1Y 4QU

■ Peter Storrs Trust

CC NO 313804   **ESTABLISHED** 1970

WHERE FUNDING CAN BE GIVEN UK.

WHO CAN BENEFIT Registered charities.

WHAT IS FUNDED The advancement of education.

RANGE OF GRANTS £1,500–£5,400.

SAMPLE GRANTS Peter House (£5,400); RNIB and Eggington Memorial Trust (£5,000 each); Skillforce and British Schools Exploring Society – Next Generation Initiative (£3,000 each); Barnardo's, British Bible Society, African Medical, World Wildlife Fund, Dorothy Kerin Trust, British Aid to Refugees, Royal Academy of Arts, Voluntary Services Overseas, Oxford Mission and Bath Church Houses (£2,000 each); and Zebra Trust (£1,500).

FINANCES *Year* 2009–10 *Income* £101,670 *Grants* £85,850 *Assets* £2,285,359

TRUSTEES Geoffrey Adams; Arthur Curtis; Julie Easton.

HOW TO APPLY In writing to the correspondent. Applications are considered every three to six months. Please note the trust receives far more applications than it is able to support, many of which do not meet the criteria outlined above. This results in a heavy waste of time and expense for both applicants and the trust itself.

WHO TO APPLY TO The Trustees, c/o Smithfield Accountants, 117 Charterhouse Street, London EC1M 6AA *Tel* 020 7253 3757 *Fax* 020 7253 3761

■ The Strangward Trust

CC NO 1036494   **ESTABLISHED** 1993

WHERE FUNDING CAN BE GIVEN Eastern England and the East Midlands.

WHO CAN BENEFIT Small local organisations concerned with people with disabilities.

WHAT IS FUNDED Funding for care and treatment of people who are physically or mentally disabled, particularly charities working in the field of the nursing service, hospice in the home, special schools, and holidays and outings.

TYPE OF GRANT One-off, capital, core costs. Funding is for one year or less.

RANGE OF GRANTS £1,000–£10,000.

SAMPLE GRANTS Multiple Sclerosis Therapy Centre, Fenland Association for Community Transport and Fenland Area Community Enterprise Trust (£10,000 each); Leicester Charity Link, Northants Hope Centre, The Pasque Charity and Thomas' Fund (£5,000 each); The Corner Club, Special Needs Out of School Club and St Barnabus Learning Centre (£3,000); Strongbones Children's Charitable Trust, Rowangate Primary School and Cam Sight (£2,500).

FINANCES *Year* 2009–10 *Income* £123,381 *Grants* £116,095 *Assets* £3,190,024

TRUSTEES Mrs T A Strangward, Chair; R Jones; J Higham Mrs A Allured.

OTHER INFORMATION Grants were made to 35 organisations and totalled £116,000.

HOW TO APPLY In writing to the correspondent.

WHO TO APPLY TO Mrs L Davies, Administrator, Vincent Sykes and Higham, Montague House, Chancery Lane, Thrapston, Northamptonshire NN14 4LN *Tel* 01832 732161 *Fax* 01832 733701 *email* louise.davies@vshlaw.co.uk *Website* www.vshlaw.co.uk

■ The Strasser Foundation

CC NO 511703   **ESTABLISHED** 1978

WHERE FUNDING CAN BE GIVEN Staffordshire.

WHO CAN BENEFIT organisations and individuals.

WHAT IS FUNDED General charitable purposes.

RANGE OF GRANTS Up to £1,000.

SAMPLE GRANTS Donna Louise Trust, Children's Hospice, Douglas Macmillan Hospice – Stoke-on-Trent and Royal British Legion (£1,000 each); Vitalise – for work with the disabled in Staffordshire, Spinal Injuries Association and Newcastle-under-Lyme Music Festival for Music, Speech & Drama – contribution for new piano (£500 each); Sence – for work with Deafblind in Staffordshire (£350); Moorlands South Community Mental Health Team (£250); Educational grant to student (£150).

FINANCES *Year* 2009–10 *Grants* £2,548,800 *Assets* £63,373,679

TRUSTEES A F Booth; A P Bell.

OTHER INFORMATION Grants of up to £1,000 are made to organisations and individuals in need.

HOW TO APPLY In writing to the correspondent. The trustees meet quarterly. Applications are only acknowledged if an sae is sent.

WHO TO APPLY TO F Hayes, c/o Knight and Sons, The Brampton, Newcastle-under-Lyme, Staffordshire ST5 0QW *Tel* 01782 619225

■ Stratford upon Avon Town Trust

CC NO 1088521   **ESTABLISHED** 2001

WHERE FUNDING CAN BE GIVEN Stratford upon Avon.

WHO CAN BENEFIT Organisations benefiting people living in the Stratford-upon-Avon council area.

WHAT IS FUNDED Relief of need, hardship and distress; relief of sickness, disability, old age and infirmity; support of facilities for education, including the advancement of learning and knowledge; support for recreations and other leisure-time facilities; advancement of the Christian religion.

WHAT IS NOT FUNDED No grants to organisations outside Stratford upon Avon.

TYPE OF GRANT Capital and revenue grants for up to three years.

RANGE OF GRANTS Up to £50,000.

SAMPLE GRANTS Non-discretionary grants were awarded to King Edward IV Grammar School (£617,000); 24 almshouses (£30,500); and Holy Trinity Church (£7,000). Discretionary grants included those to: Shakespeare Hospice and VASA (£50,000 each); Warwickshire Police Authority – Community Support Officers (£42,000); CAB (£40,000); Stratford High School (£39,500); Stratford upon Avon College (£31,500); and Stratford upon Avon Christmas Lights Co. (£30,000).

FINANCES *Year* 2010 *Income* £3,267,594 *Grants* £1,396,501 *Assets* £51,577,434

TRUSTEES John Lancaster, Chair; Cllr Jenny Fradgley; Jean Holder; Rosemary Hyde; Cllr Juliet Short; Carole Taylor; Tim Wightman; Clarissa Roberts; Rob Townsend; Charles Bates; Cllr Ian Fradgley.

HOW TO APPLY Application forms can be completed online (www.stratfordtowntrust.co.uk). Awards are made on a quarterly basis. The latest application deadlines are listed on the trust's website.

WHO TO APPLY TO Richard Eggington, Chief Executive, 14 Rother Street, Stratford-upon-Avon, Warwickshire CV32 6LU *Tel* 01789 207111 *Fax* 01789 207119 *email* admin@stratfordtowntrust.co.uk *Website* www.stratfordtowntrust.co.uk

---

■ Strathclyde Police Benevolent Fund

SC NO SC009899   **ESTABLISHED** 1975

WHERE FUNDING CAN BE GIVEN Strathclyde.

WHO CAN BENEFIT organisations and members of Strathclyde police, retired members, and widows or other dependants who may be in need.

WHAT IS FUNDED General charitable purposes.

TYPE OF GRANT One off and recurrent grants according to need.

FINANCES *Year* 2009–10 *Income* £177,587

TRUSTEES G Carmichael, chair; A Gillies; Linda McCartney; J Foster; R Watterson.

HOW TO APPLY In writing to the correspondent. Applications to be received by the end of March for consideration in the annual meeting held in April.

WHO TO APPLY TO The Trustees, Strathclyde Police Federation, 151 Merrylee Road, Glasgow G44 3DL *Tel* 0141 633 2020 *Fax* 0141 633 0276

■ The Strawberry Charitable Trust

CC NO 1090173   **ESTABLISHED** 2000

WHERE FUNDING CAN BE GIVEN Not defined but with a preference for Manchester.

WHO CAN BENEFIT Registered charities.

WHAT IS FUNDED The relief of poverty and hardship mainly amongst Jewish people and the advancement of the Jewish religion.

RANGE OF GRANTS Up to £32,000.

SAMPLE GRANTS United Jewish Israel Appeal (£35,000); Community Security Trust (£15,000); The Fed (£10,000); Lubavitch South Manchester (£8,000); King David School (£6,000); World Jewish Relief (£5,000); Belz and St John's Wood Synagogue (£3,000); Action on Addiction and Mew Children's Hospital (£2,000 each); and Tickets for Troops (£1,000).

FINANCES *Year* 2009–10 *Income* £44,102 *Grants* £113,532 *Assets* £482,906

TRUSTEES Emma Myers; Laura Avigdori; Anthony Leon.

OTHER INFORMATION Smaller grants of less than £1,000 were not listed separately, but totalled £14,000.

HOW TO APPLY In writing to the correspondent.

WHO TO APPLY TO Anthony Leon, Trustee, 4 Westfields, Hale, Altrincham WA15 0LL *Tel* 0161 980 8484 *email* anthonysula@hotmail.com

---

■ The W O Street Charitable Foundation

CC NO 267127   **ESTABLISHED** 1973

WHERE FUNDING CAN BE GIVEN Worldwide. There is a preference for the North West of England and Jersey.

WHO CAN BENEFIT Registered charities.

WHAT IS FUNDED Support is given for education, relief of poverty, helping people in financial difficulties (particularly people who are elderly, blind or who have disabilities), the relief of sickness and social welfare generally.

WHAT IS NOT FUNDED No grants towards: schools, colleges or universities; running or core costs; religion or church buildings; medical research; animal welfare; hospices; overseas projects or charities; NHS trusts. Applications directly from individuals are not considered.

TYPE OF GRANT One-off and recurring grants.

RANGE OF GRANTS Generally £1,000 to £15,000.

SAMPLE GRANTS The museum of Science and Industry in Manchester (£10,000); W O Street Jersey Charitable Trust (£40,000); The Sailors Families Society (£1,400); Well Child (£3,500); SignHealth (£6,600); Stick n Step (£2,500); Nightstop in Stockport and Trafford (£8,000); Scottish Spina Bifida Association (£327); Bury Parish Church (£5,000); Caring Today (£3,500); Emmott Foundation (£30,000); Harmony Youth Project (£4,000).

FINANCES *Year* 2010 *Income* £382,030 *Grants* £313,659 *Assets* £16,411,171

TRUSTEES Barclays Bank Trust Co. Ltd.

HOW TO APPLY In writing to the correspondent. Applications are considered on a quarterly basis, at the end of January, April, July and October.

WHO TO APPLY TO The Trust Officer, c/o Barclays Bank Trust Company Ltd, PO Box 15, Osborne Court, Gadbrook Park, Northwich CW9 7UR *Tel* 01606 313417

■ The A B Strom and R Strom Charitable Trust

CC NO 268916   **ESTABLISHED** 1971

WHERE FUNDING CAN BE GIVEN UK.

WHO CAN BENEFIT Registered charities.

WHAT IS FUNDED A set list of charities working with older people, schools/colleges, hospitals and Christian causes.

SAMPLE GRANTS Previously, grants in excess of £1,000 each were made to Yeshivas Hanegev

(£10,000), JRRC (£10,000 in two grants) and Redcroft and Russian Immigrants (£5,000 each).

FINANCES *Year* 2009–10 *Income* £60,426 *Grants* £45,187 *Assets* £618,735

TRUSTEES Regina Strom; Debbie Weissbraun.

HOW TO APPLY In writing to the correspondent. Please note that the same organisations are supported each year.

WHO TO APPLY TO Regina Strom, Trustee, c/o 11 Gloucester Gardens, London NW11 9AB *Tel* 020 8455 5949 *email* m@michaelpasha. worldonline.co.uk

■ The Sudborough Foundation

CC NO 272323   **ESTABLISHED** 1976

WHERE FUNDING CAN BE GIVEN UK, with a preference for Northamptonshire.

WHO CAN BENEFIT Educational establishments and other charities.

WHAT IS FUNDED Students in need or for scholarships; general charitable purposes.

WHAT IS NOT FUNDED No grants for expeditions or drama and dance courses.

RANGE OF GRANTS Up to £5,000.

SAMPLE GRANTS Evelyn Hodgson Memorial Trust (£10,000); George Muller Homes, Rock UK and Spurgeon's College(£5,000 each); University of Northampton – Max Engel Memorial (£3,000); Parkinson's Disease Society (£2,500); Homestart Northampton (£2,100); Royal College of Music (£1,500); Royal College of Obstetricians & Gynaecologists (£1,250); Marie Curie Cancer Care, Northampton Volunteering Centre, Farm Crisis Network and NSPCC (£1,000); Brain and Spine Foundation (£500); World Jewish Relief (£350); Breast Cancer Care (£200) and Fight for Sight (£150).

FINANCES *Year* 2009–10 *Income* £56,104 *Grants* £80,834 *Assets* £1,321,412

TRUSTEES Mr R Engel, Chair; Sir J Lowther; Mrs E A Engel; W M Reason; Mrs S E Leatham; Simon J A Powis; Julian Woolfson and Miss R J Engel.

HOW TO APPLY The foundation does not respond to unsolicited applications.

WHO TO APPLY TO Richard Engel, Chair, Mr Richard Engel, 8 Hazelwood Road, Northampton NN1 1LP

■ Sueberry Ltd

CC NO 256566   **ESTABLISHED** 1968

WHERE FUNDING CAN BE GIVEN UK and overseas.

WHO CAN BENEFIT Jewish organisations; UK welfare and medical organisations benefiting children and young adults; at risk groups; people who are disadvantaged by poverty, or socially isolated people.

WHAT IS FUNDED General, medical, educational and religious activities.

TYPE OF GRANT Mostly recurrent.

FINANCES *Year* 2009–10 *Income* £123,419 *Grants* £172,388 *Assets* £51,049

TRUSTEES D S Davis, Chair; C Davis; Mrs H Davis; J Davis; Mrs M Davis; A D Davis; S M Davis; Y Davis.

HOW TO APPLY In writing to the correspondent.

WHO TO APPLY TO D S Davis, Trustee, 18 Clifton Gardens, London N15 6AP

■ The Suffolk Foundation

CC NO 1109453   **ESTABLISHED** 2005

WHERE FUNDING CAN BE GIVEN Suffolk.

WHO CAN BENEFIT Registered charities and community groups.

WHAT IS FUNDED The foundation has a range of different funds designed for small community and voluntary groups working to help local people across Suffolk. Each scheme tends to have a different application procedure and size of award. The foundation is currently managing the following grant programmes: grassroots grants; Suffolk single gateway fund; Suffolk voluntary sector training programme fund; somebody's daughter grant; healthy ambitions grant; comic relief; high sheriff grants and award. Please note: grant schemes can change frequently. Potential applicants are advised to consult the foundation's website for details of current programmes and their deadlines.

WHAT IS NOT FUNDED No funding for: projects not benefiting people living in Suffolk; individuals for their personal needs; direct replacement of statutory obligation and public funding; general large appeals; medical research and equipment; statutory work in educational institutions; promotion of religious or political causes; sponsored events; fundraising events; retrospective grants; animal welfare; overseas travel or expeditions for individuals and groups. Please note: different programmes may have further exclusions. Organisations are advised to read the guidelines carefully before making an application.

TYPE OF GRANT One-off grants for capital and revenue costs and full project funding.

RANGE OF GRANTS Small grants averaging around £2,000.

SAMPLE GRANTS Suffolk County Council (£554,000); Grassroots Grant Programme (£398,000); The Henry Smith Foundation (£377,000); Healthy Ambitions (£340,000); Comic Relief (£46,000).

FINANCES *Year* 2009–10 *Income* £2,795,663 *Grants* £1,393,823 *Assets* £2,088,226

TRUSTEES David Sheepshanks; David Barclay; Deborah Cadman; James Dinwiddy; The Countess of Euston; Stephen Fletcher; Revd Canon Graham Hedger; Claire Horsley; Lady Howes; Graeme Kalbraier; Fiona Mahony; Sir David Rowland; Nigel Smith; Gulshanbir Kayembe and Peter Bye.

HOW TO APPLY The foundation's website has details of the grant schemes currently being administered and how to apply.

WHO TO APPLY TO Enid Kimes, Grants Officer, Old Reading Rooms, The Green, Grundisburgh, Woodbridge, Suffolk IP13 6TA *Tel* 01473 734120 *Fax* 01473 734121 *email* info@ suffolkfoundation.org.uk *Website* www. suffolkfoundation.org.uk

■ The Suffolk Historic Churches Trust

CC NO 267047   **ESTABLISHED** 1973

WHERE FUNDING CAN BE GIVEN Suffolk.

WHO CAN BENEFIT Churches and chapels over 100 years old of all denominations.

WHAT IS FUNDED The preservation, repair, maintenance, restoration and improvement of churches in Suffolk.

WHAT IS NOT FUNDED The trust does normally make grants for: electrical work; furnishings and fittings; churchyard walls; brasses and bells; monuments; redecoration, unless needed as part of an eligible project; new buildings or extensions to existing buildings.

RANGE OF GRANTS £300–£10,000. Higher than the maximum is only given in exceptional circumstances.

SAMPLE GRANTS Ipswich & St Edmundsbury Diocesan Maintenance Scheme (£25,000); Rushmere, St Michael Stanstea and Campsea Ash (£10,000); Helmingham Church (£7,000); Denham St John (£5,000).

FINANCES Year 2009–10 Income £304,814 Grants £314,305 Assets £777,022

TRUSTEES Robert Rous, Chair; Sir Christopher Howes; The Venerable David Jenkins; Jonathan Penn; Martin Favell; Mrs Diana Hunt; Christopher Spicer; Robert Williams; Simon Tennent; Mrs Celia Stephens; Clive Paine; Patrick Grieve; The Hon Charles Boscawen; Edward Bland.

HOW TO APPLY Application forms can be downloaded from the trust's website. 'The Grants Committee normally meets in the second week of January, April, July and October. Applications received by the end of the month prior to the meeting are considered at the meeting.'

WHO TO APPLY TO The Secretary, Brinkleys, Hall Street, Long Melford, Suffolk CO10 9JR Tel 01787 883884 Website www.shct.org.uk

■ The Alan Sugar Foundation

CC NO 294880   **ESTABLISHED** 1986
WHERE FUNDING CAN BE GIVEN UK.
WHO CAN BENEFIT Registered charities.
WHAT IS FUNDED Grants are made to causes of current and ongoing interest to the trustees.
WHAT IS NOT FUNDED No grants for individuals or to non-registered charities.
TYPE OF GRANT One-off and recurring, capital and project.
RANGE OF GRANTS £500–£200,000.
SAMPLE GRANTS Jewish Care (£200,000); Sport Relief (£50,000); MacMillan Cancer (£25,000); Children in Need (£3,000); Prostate Cancer Charitable Fund and Cancer Research UK (£2,000 each); and St Michael's Hospice (£500).
FINANCES Year 2009–10 Income £927,091 Grants £282,500 Assets £1,143,606
TRUSTEES Lord Alan Sugar; Colin Sandy; Simon Sugar; Daniel Sugar; Louise Baron.
HOW TO APPLY **This trust states that it does not respond to unsolicited applications.** All projects are initiated by the trustees.
WHO TO APPLY TO Colin Sandy, Trustee, Sterling House, Langston Road, Loughton, Essex IG10 3TS Tel 020 3225 5560 email colin@amsprop.com

■ Sugarworld Trust

CC NO 1139646   **ESTABLISHED** 2011
WHERE FUNDING CAN BE GIVEN UK.
WHO CAN BENEFIT Registered charities.
WHAT IS FUNDED General charitable purposes, with a preference for the Christian faith.
TRUSTEES David Barratt; Revd William Lovatt; Brian Arnott.
OTHER INFORMATION This is the charitable trust of the Sugarworld company.
HOW TO APPLY In writing to the correspondent.
WHO TO APPLY TO David Barratt, Trustee, 1 The Avenue, Eastbourne, East Sussex BN21 3YA Tel 01323 470807 email david@sugarworld.eu

■ Summary Limited

CC NO 1102472   **ESTABLISHED** 2004
WHERE FUNDING CAN BE GIVEN UK, with a preference for Hertfordshire.
WHO CAN BENEFIT Charitable organisations.
WHAT IS FUNDED Education, religion and social welfare.
RANGE OF GRANTS Up to £50,000.
SAMPLE GRANTS Berkhamsted School (£75,000 in total); Purcell School of Music and Berkhamsted Raiders Community Football Club (£50,000 each); The Stroke Association to provide support services within Hertsmere District Council (£28,000); Radlett Music Club (£20,000); The Radlett Centre (£14,000); Aldenham Parish (£12,000); Walton & Frinton Yacht Club, Peace Hospice Watford, Shooting Stars Hospice, Milton Keynes Hospital and Aldenham School (£10,000 each); RAFT (£6,000); Radlett Centre Trust Art Society (£5,600); and St John's Church and Caister Lifeboat (£5,000 each).
FINANCES Year 2010 Income £4,510,706 Grants £320,807 Assets £8,048,223
TRUSTEES John Apthorp; Duncan Apthorp; Justin Apthorp; Kate Arnold.
OTHER INFORMATION In 2010 the charity received a donation to the value of £4.3 million from the Milly Apthorp Charitable Trust, which is in the process of spending out and shares two trustees from the Apthorp family. As a result of this, the grant-making capacity of this charity has increased significantly.
HOW TO APPLY In writing to the correspondent.
WHO TO APPLY TO John Apthorp, Trustee, The Field House Farm, 29 Newlands Avenue, Radlett, Hertfordshire WD7 8EJ Tel 01923 855727

■ The Summerfield Charitable Trust

CC NO 802493   **ESTABLISHED** 1989
WHERE FUNDING CAN BE GIVEN Gloucestershire.
WHO CAN BENEFIT Registered charities local to Gloucestershire.
WHAT IS FUNDED 'The trustees are particularly interested in helping the arts, museums and the built heritage; the environment and natural heritage; community work; education, sport and recreation; and vulnerable or disadvantaged sectors of society.'
The trustees are interested in hearing from those involved in helping older people, people in need and the arts. Viewed especially favourably are: the needs of people living in rural areas; ventures which make a point of using volunteers (and which train volunteers); applicants who show clear indications that they have assessed the impact of their project upon the environment; and joint appeals from groups working in similar areas, who wish to develop a partnership. The trustees particularly welcome innovative ideas from: small, voluntary groups; schemes that indicate planning for long-term self-sufficiency; and projects that demonstrate active involvement with the beneficiaries.
WHAT IS NOT FUNDED Donations are not given towards medical research, private education or animal welfare appeals. Applications from individuals are no longer accepted. Should an individual resident of Gloucestershire require financial support for educational needs, they are recommended to contact the Lumb's Education Trust. SCT awards an annual grant to Lumbs to enable it to support local residents on SCT's behalf. Write to: Mrs Margaret Wanless, Lumbs

Education Trust, 4 Manor View, Cold Pool Lane, Up Hatherley, Cheltenham, GL51 6HZ. Appeals from churches for renovation and repair will not be accepted in 2010. You are advised to contact Gloucestershire Historic Churches Trust.

TYPE OF GRANT Usually one-off. The trustees prefer to award one-off grants to help fund specific projects rather than to make payments for revenue items. The trustees will occasionally consider start-up costs and grants for up to three years.

RANGE OF GRANTS £500–£29,000.

SAMPLE GRANTS Previously: Cheltenham Arts Festivals Ltd (£29,000); Art Shape Limited and Brewery Arts (£20,000 each); Forest of Dean Music Makers (£15,000); Abbey Schools (£12,000); and Cotswold Players, Global Dimension Trust, Gloucester Emergency Accommodation Resource, Thomas Morley Trust and Uplands Care Service (£10,000 each).

FINANCES Year 2010 Income £279,739 Grants £442,415 Assets £9,396,609

TRUSTEES Mr Edward Gillespie (Chair); Mrs Jamila Gavin; Mrs Jan Urban-Smith; Mr Anthony McClaran; Mr James Millar.

OTHER INFORMATION For 2010, grants were broken down as follows: Disadvantaged and vulnerable sectors (£144,000 in 18 grants); Arts, museums and built heritage (£84,000 in 19 grants); Community work (£112,000 in 22 grants); Education, sport and recreation (£73,000 in 14 grants); Environment and natural heritage (£30,000 in 5 grants). Note: these figures include support costs.

HOW TO APPLY The trustees meet quarterly; usually in March, June, September and December (see the trust's website for deadline dates). 'You should write to Mrs Lavinia Sidgwick, Administrator, stating in your own words what is required and why, and enclose your completed grant application cover sheet with supporting information. It helps if you advise us which other trusts you are applying to as we may consult them, unless you specifically ask us not to.' Applicants must download a grant application cover sheet. When compiling their application, applicants are welcome to telephone the trust and discuss queries. One of the trust's independent advisors is often asked to visit organisations who apply.

WHO TO APPLY TO Mrs Lavinia Sidgwick, Administrator, PO Box 4, Winchcombe, Cheltenham, Gloucestershire GL54 5ZD Tel 01242 676774 Fax 01242 677120 email admin@summerfield.org.uk Website www.summerfield.org.uk

■ The Bernard Sunley Charitable Foundation

CC NO 1109099   **ESTABLISHED** 1960
WHERE FUNDING CAN BE GIVEN Unrestricted, but mainly southern England.
WHO CAN BENEFIT Registered charities.
WHAT IS FUNDED General charitable purposes; with grants categorised under: education; arts; religion; community; children and youth; elderly; health; social welfare; environment; animal welfare; amateur sport; emergency and armed services; and overseas.
WHAT IS NOT FUNDED 'We would reiterate that we do not make grants to individuals; we still receive several such applications each week. This bar on individuals applies equally to those people taking part in a project sponsored by a charity such as VSO, Duke of Edinburgh Award Scheme,

Trekforce, Scouts and Girl Guides, and so on, or in the case of the latter two to specific units of these youth movements.'
TYPE OF GRANT One-off, capital and recurring, for up to a maximum of three years.
RANGE OF GRANTS £100–£100,000; typical grant £5,000–£10,000.
SAMPLE GRANTS Godmersham and Crundale Recreation Hall – Kent (£150,000); Royal Parks Foundation (£100,000); Wye College (£75,000); Fynvola Foundation (£60,000); St Clements Church – Sandwich and Anchor House East London (£50,000); Alzheimer's Society (£30,000); Royal Geographical Society (£25,000); Fight for Sight, Childhood First, Imperial War Museum and St John Ambulance (£10,000 each); Animal Health Trust (£7,000); and Kids Company and Bowel Cancer UK (£5,000 each).
FINANCES Year 2009–10 Income £2,795,000 Grants £2,315,000 Assets £80,849,000
TRUSTEES Joan M Tice; Bella Sunley; Sir Donald Gosling; Brian W Martin; Anabel Knight; William Tice.
HOW TO APPLY Appeals are considered regularly, but we would emphasise that we are only able to make grants to registered charities and not to individuals. There is no application form, but the covering letter to the director should give details as to the points below, and should be accompanied by the latest approved report and accounts. The details requested are as follows: the purpose of the charity and its objectives; the need and purpose of the project, for which a grant is requested, and who will benefit and how; the cost of the project – a breakdown of costs is sometimes helpful; the amount of money already raised and from whom, and how it is planned to raise the shortfall; if applicable, how the running costs of the project will be met, once the project is established; any other documentation that the applicant feels will help to support or explain the appeal.
'Be precise and to the point – one person is dealing with up to 200 applications each month. Grant applications may be sent to the foundation at any time during the year, and you will be advised of the outcome of the application within a period of three to four months. Please do not reapply for at least twelve months, as it will not be accepted.'
WHO TO APPLY TO John Rimmington, Director, 20 Berkeley Square, London W1J 6LH Tel 020 7408 2198 Fax 020 7499 5859 email office@sunleyfoundation.com

■ Surrey Community Foundation

CC NO 1111600   **ESTABLISHED** 2005
WHERE FUNDING CAN BE GIVEN Surrey.
WHO CAN BENEFIT organisations and individuals.
WHAT IS FUNDED Strengthening communities in Surrey.
TYPE OF GRANT Surrey Community Foundation has an on-going grant programme consisting of a number of funds established by individuals, families, trusts and companies. The foundation also administers Grassroots Grants, a national programme (2008–11) to support small, voluntary led community groups to build stronger more active communities. Grants for running costs or capital items of between £250 and £5,000 are available for small groups with an average annual income of less than £20,000.
RANGE OF GRANTS £500 to £16,000 (2009–10).
FINANCES Year 2009–10 Income £2,095,711 Grants £668,232 Assets £3,594,217

918

Does the trust you have chosen match your needs? Haphazard applications waste postage and time

TRUSTEES Prof. Patrick Dowling, Chair; Mr Stephen Blunt, Secretary; Mr Matthew Bowcock, Vice Chairman; Mr Richard Edmondson; Dr. Helen Bowcock; Mr Peter Hampson; Revd Christopher Hill; Mr Gordon Lee-Steere DL; Mr Jim McAllister; Mrs Tracey Redding and Mr Andrew Wates.

OTHER INFORMATION Surrey Community Foundation is part of a national network of community foundations.

HOW TO APPLY To discuss your project, or apply for funding, please contact Liz Westwood – Grants Manager (tel.: 01483 555641 or email: liz@surreycommunityfoundation.org.uk).

WHO TO APPLY TO Wendy Varcoe, Director, 1 Bishops Wharf, Walnut Tree Close, Guildford, Surrey *Tel* 01483 409230 *email* info@ surreycommunityfoundation.org.uk *Website* www.surreycommunityfoundation.org.uk

■ The Surrey Historic Buildings Trust Ltd

CC NO 279240   ESTABLISHED 1979
WHERE FUNDING CAN BE GIVEN Surrey.
WHO CAN BENEFIT Individuals or groups.
WHAT IS FUNDED Preservation of the historical, architectural and constructional heritage existing in Surrey.
WHAT IS NOT FUNDED No support for local authority-owned buildings or the general upkeep of places of worship (although specific artifacts or architectural features may attract a grant).
RANGE OF GRANTS Up to £6,000; usually £1,000 to £3,000.
SAMPLE GRANTS 1 and 2 New Inn, Dunsfold, The Forge, Chiddingfold (£3,000); Basket Cottage, Dunsfold (£2,000) and Misselbrook Cottage, Chiddingfold (£1,000). An additional 6 projects were awarded grants totalling £2,600.
FINANCES *Year* 2009–10 *Income* £45,259 *Grants* £29,021 *Assets* £477,243
TRUSTEES Alan Black; John Davey; David Davis; Angela Fraser; Cllr Jennifer Powell; Mrs P Adamson; Dennis Turner; Mrs N Westbury; J H Jessup; Cllr John Garrett; Mr Stephen Cooksey; Denis Fuller; Mr Nick Skellett; Colin Taylor; Cllr Jean Smith.
OTHER INFORMATION No major grants were awarded during the year.
HOW TO APPLY On an application form available from the correspondent or the website. Applicants should, where possible, produce two detailed estimates. In the case of highly specialized work, a single estimate may be acceptable. The application cannot be considered unless photographs of the building accompany it and, where available, plans should also be submitted.
WHO TO APPLY TO Jacqui Hird, Assistant Honorary Secretary, Surrey Historical Buildings Trust, Room 122, County Hall, Penrhyn Road, Kingston-upon-Thames, Surrey *Tel* 020 8541 9006 *email* jacqui.hird@surreycc.gov.uk *Website* surreycc.gov.uk

■ Sussex Community Foundation

CC NO 1113226   ESTABLISHED 2006
WHERE FUNDING CAN BE GIVEN East Sussex, West Sussex or Brighton and Hove.
WHO CAN BENEFIT Charities and community groups whose work benefits people in East Sussex, West Sussex or Brighton and Hove. The foundation welcomes applications from established organisations as well as new groups and projects.
WHAT IS FUNDED The foundation is particularly interested in supporting smaller community based groups where a small grant can make a difference.
WHAT IS NOT FUNDED No support for: individuals; organisations that are part of central, local or regional government; major capital appeals; fundraising events; sponsorship.
RANGE OF GRANTS Mostly £1,000–£5,000.
SAMPLE GRANTS Danehill Memorial Hall (£5,000); Battle Town Band and Furnihelp Mid Sussex (£4,500 each); Age Concern Rye & District Day Centre (£4,000); Crawley Black History Foundation and The Biglove Association (£2,500 each); Friday Club at Concordia (£2,100); Bosham Youth Centre, Stumped and Hope G (£2,000 each); Kinderoo (£1,500); Brighton Pebbles (£890); and Earthy Women and Kids (£750).
FINANCES *Year* 2009–10 *Income* £2,488,637 *Grants* £983,276 *Assets* £2,362,400
TRUSTEES Trevor James; John Peel; Kathy Gore; Neil Hart; Steve Manwaring; Sharon Phillips; Lesley Wake; Mike Simpkin; Humphrey Price; Richard Pearson; Margaret Johnson; Michael Martin; Charles Drayson.
HOW TO APPLY Applicants must have a signed copy of their constitution or set of rules; signed accounts; a copy of a recent bank statement; estimates for proposed purchases (if applicable) and copies of relevant policies (child protection, vulnerable adults, health & safety, etc). Applicants have to be able to show that they are not-for-profit, but do not always have to be a charity. Each of the funds listed under 'General information' are open to applications. As the criteria and application form differs for each you are advised to refer to the foundation's website. Please note that you may only apply to one programme at a time.
WHO TO APPLY TO Kevin Richmond, Administrator, Suite B, Falcon Wharf, Railway Lane, Lewes BN7 2AQ *Tel* 01273 409440 *email* info@ sussxgiving.org.uk *Website* www.sussexgiving. org.uk

■ The Sussex Historic Churches Trust

CC NO 282159   ESTABLISHED 1981
WHERE FUNDING CAN BE GIVEN Sussex.
WHO CAN BENEFIT Churches of any denomination over 100 years old and of some architectural or historical significance.
WHAT IS FUNDED Preservation, repair, maintenance and restoration of churches in Sussex.
WHAT IS NOT FUNDED No grants for bells.
TYPE OF GRANT Interest-free loans and buildings will be considered.
RANGE OF GRANTS £1,000–£10,000, typical grant £5,000.
SAMPLE GRANTS Previous beneficiaries included: Saint John the Baptist – Kirdford (£15,000); Saint Peter – Westhampnett (£10,000); Saint Mary – Salehurst (£6,000); Saint Mary – Bepton and Southwick, C.C.C. (£5,000 each); Saint

Mary – Broadwater, Saint John the Baptist – Crawley, Saint Peter ad Vincula – Folkington and Saint Dunstan – Mayfield (£3,000 each).

FINANCES *Year* 2010 *Income* £125,726 *Grants* £64,800 *Assets* £978,829

TRUSTEES Countess De La Warr; the Archdeacon of Chichester; the Archdeacon of Horsham; Christopher Whittick; The Archdeacon of Lewes and Hastings; Philip Jones; Lady Pamela Wedgwood; Bishop of Chichester; John Barkshire.

HOW TO APPLY In writing to the correspondent giving an outline of the work to be done and some indication of the financial state of the parish or congregation. An application form will then be sent to you, if what you propose qualifies for help. Applications must be made before work is started.

WHO TO APPLY TO Patricia Farmer, The Secretary, Diocesan Church House, 211 New Church Road, Hove, East Sussex BN3 4ED *Tel* 01273 421 021 *email* pat.farmer@diochi.org.uk *Website* www.sussexhistoricchurches.org.uk

■ The Adrienne and Leslie Sussman Charitable Trust

CC NO 274955   **ESTABLISHED** 1977

WHERE FUNDING CAN BE GIVEN UK, in practice Greater London, particularly Barnet.

WHO CAN BENEFIT Registered charities.

WHAT IS FUNDED General, Jewish.

WHAT IS NOT FUNDED No grants to branches of UK charities outside Barnet, non-registered charities and individuals.

SAMPLE GRANTS Previous beneficiaries have included: BF Shvut Ami, Chai – Lifeline and B'nai B'rith Hillel Fund, Child Resettlement, Children and Youth Aliyah, Finchley Synagogue, Jewish Care, Nightingale House, Norwood Ravenswood and Sidney Sussex CLL.

FINANCES *Year* 2009–10 *Income* £65,193 *Grants* £57,332 *Assets* £1,820,973

TRUSTEES Adrienne Sussman; Leslie Sussman; Martin Paisner.

HOW TO APPLY In writing to the correspondent.

WHO TO APPLY TO Adrienne Sussman, Trustee, 25 Tillingbourne Gardens, London N3 3JJ

■ The Sutasoma Trust

CC NO 803301   **ESTABLISHED** 1990

WHERE FUNDING CAN BE GIVEN UK and overseas.

WHO CAN BENEFIT Individuals and organisations.

WHAT IS FUNDED Bursaries and support to institutions in the field of social sciences, humanities and humanitarian activities. General grants may also be made.

TYPE OF GRANT Mainly recurrent.

SAMPLE GRANTS Lucy Cavendish College Fellowship (£19,500); University of Bergen (£12,000); Amrita Performing Arts (£8,000); LACP Zambia (£7,000); Emslie Horniman Fund and School of Oriental and African Studies (£5,000 each); Merlin Medical Relief (£3,000); Corporation of Haverford and Practical Action (£2,000 each); Lewa Wildlife Conservation (£1,000); and Anti-Slavery International (£500).

FINANCES *Year* 2009–10 *Income* £100,652 *Grants* £100,342 *Assets* £2,567,395

TRUSTEES Dr Angela R Hobart; Marcel A Burgauer; Jane M Lichtenstein; Prof. Bruce Kapferer; Dr Sally Wolfe; Dr Piers Vitebsky.

HOW TO APPLY In writing to the correspondent.

WHO TO APPLY TO Jane M Lichtenstein, Trustee, PO Box 157, Haverhill, Suffolk CB9 1AH *Tel* 07768 245384 *email* sutasoma.trust@btinternet.com

■ Sutton Coldfield Municipal Charities

CC NO 218627   **ESTABLISHED** 1898

WHERE FUNDING CAN BE GIVEN The former borough of Sutton Coldfield, comprising three electoral wards: New Hall, Vesey and Four Oaks.

WHO CAN BENEFIT Individuals in need and organisations, without restriction, in Sutton Coldfield.

WHAT IS FUNDED The aims are: to help people who are aged, sick, have disabilities or living in poverty; to support facilities for recreational and leisure activities; to promote the arts and advance religion; the repair of historic buildings; and advancement of education through grants to schools for maintenance and equipment.

WHAT IS NOT FUNDED No awards are given to individuals or organisations outside the area of benefit, unless the organisations are providing essential services in the area.

TYPE OF GRANT The trustees will consider making grants for buildings, projects, research, start-up costs, and capital and running costs for up to three years or as one-off payments. No cash payments are made; payments are made via invoices or vouchers.

RANGE OF GRANTS Up to £75,000.

SAMPLE GRANTS Previous beneficiaries include: St Giles Hospice; John Willmott School; Boldmere Swimming Club; New Hall Ward Advisory Board; New Hall Primary School; Holy Trinity (CE) Parish Church; Boldmere Methodist Church; Victim Support; Walmley Women's Institute; and Sutton Coldfield Asian Society.

FINANCES *Year* 2009–10 *Income* £1,416,117 *Grants* £920,420 *Assets* £43,343,981

TRUSTEES Dr Freddie Gick, Chair; Rodney Kettel; Sue Bailey; John Gray; Cllr Susanna McCorry; Alfred David Owen; Jane Rothwell; Cllr David Roy; Michael Waltho; Cllr James Whorwood; Carole Hancox; Cllr Margaret Waddington; Dr Stephen C Martin; Cllr Malcolm Cornish; Neil Andrews; Linda Whitfield.

OTHER INFORMATION As well as providing grants, the charities maintain 46 almshouses and provide school clothing grants to individuals.

HOW TO APPLY To make a grant application: contact the charity, either by letter, or by telephoning: 0121 351 2262; outline your needs and request a copy of the charity's guidelines for applicants; if appropriate, seek a meeting with a member of staff in making your application; ensure that all relevant documents, including estimates and accounts, reach the charity by the requested dates. Receipt of applications is not normally acknowledged unless a stamped addressed envelope is sent with the application. Applications may be submitted at any time. The grants committee meets at least eight times a year. The board of trustees must approve requests for grants over £30,000. At all stages, staff at the charities will give assistance to those making applications. For example, projects and applications can be discussed, either at the charity's office or on site. Advice about deadlines for submitting applications can also be given. There are application forms for individuals, who must obtain them from the charity.

WHO TO APPLY TO Andrew MacFarlane, Clerk to the Trustees, Lingard House, Fox Hollies Road, Sutton Coldfield, West Midlands B76 2RJ *Tel* 0121 351 2262 *Fax* 0121 313 0651 *Website* www.suttoncoldfieldmunicipalcharities. com

....

■ The Sutton Trust

CC NO 1067197   **ESTABLISHED** 1998
WHERE FUNDING CAN BE GIVEN UK only.
WHO CAN BENEFIT Educational institutions, and other groups that organise formal education projects or undertake educational research.
WHAT IS FUNDED Providing educational opportunities for children and young people from non-privileged backgrounds. The trust's current priorities are as follows: parents as first educators – narrowing gaps in school readiness and boosting cognitive development for non-privileged children; free schools and equity; encouraging the most effective teachers to serve in the most challenging schools; boosting provision for gifted and talented students from non-privileged backgrounds; access to highly selective universities and courses and the professions; understanding the drivers of social mobility.
TYPE OF GRANT Core costs, feasibility studies, interest-free loans, one-off, project, research, recurring costs, running costs, salaries and start-up costs. Capital and equipment grants are not considered. Grants are usually provided for one to two years only, but can be extended up to a maximum of three years, and further in exceptional circumstances.
SAMPLE GRANTS Cambridge University (various projects); Imperial College Maths Summer Schools; Feltam Community College; Family Links Teach First; SHINE Trust; Peers Early Education Partnership; London School of Economics (research project); UCAS (research projects); and Durham University (research projects).
FINANCES *Year* 2010 *Income* £1,397,910 *Grants* £867,367 *Assets* £892,296
TRUSTEES Sir Peter Lampl; David Backinsell; Glyn Morris.
OTHER INFORMATION Individual grant amounts were not listed in the accounts.
HOW TO APPLY 'During the course of [2008] the trustees decided to move away from large scale initiatives and refocus on research and policy work – attempting to prompt wider change in the educational system by looking into an issue, proposing and testing a solution, and advocating evidence based reform. In keeping with this model, the trust will continue to fund small scale demonstration projects which will, as before, span the early years, school and college settings and into higher education and the professions.'
The trust provides recent further clarification: 'Research and practical projects funded by the trust are commissioned from partners within our existing network of contacts in universities, schools and voluntary organisations. We do not accept unsolicited grants, but if you have a project in line with our current priorities and approach please contact us to discuss whether it is likely to receive support. Please be aware that we can only fund a small number of projects each year, even when proposals are in line with our aims and current priority areas.'

WHO TO APPLY TO The Trust Administrator, 111 Upper Richmond Road, Putney, London SW15 2TJ *Tel* 020 8788 3223 *Fax* 020 8788 3993 *Website* www.suttontrust.com

....

■ The Suva Foundation Limited

CC NO 1077057   **ESTABLISHED** 1999
WHERE FUNDING CAN BE GIVEN Unrestricted with a preference for Henley-on-Thames.
WHO CAN BENEFIT Charitable organisations.
WHAT IS FUNDED General charitable purposes. The following was taken from the foundation's 2009–10 annual report: 'The charity's principal activity during the year was the support of charities through the payment of donations. The objects of the charity are to promote any charitable purpose or support any charity selected by the directors. It is expressly contemplated that The Langley Academy may be a beneficiary of the charity.'
SAMPLE GRANTS Great Ormond Street Hospital (£27,000); Chiltern Centre for Disabled Children, Lambrook School Trust and Natural History Museum (£5,000 each); CLIC Sargent (£2,500); ORH Charitable Funds (£1,000); Remenham PCC and The Royal Marsden Cancer Charity (£500 each); and Friends of Henley Festival Society (£250).
FINANCES *Year* 2009–10 *Income* £297,044 *Grants* £138,587 *Assets* £9,534,551
TRUSTEES A Nicoll; P Nicoll.
HOW TO APPLY This trust does not accept unsolicited applications.
WHO TO APPLY TO Philip Kent, The Old Rectory, 17 Thameside, Henley-on-Thames RG9 1BH *Tel* 01491 848876

....

■ Swan Mountain Trust

CC NO 275594   **ESTABLISHED** 1977
WHERE FUNDING CAN BE GIVEN UK.
WHO CAN BENEFIT Organisations benefiting mental health patients and prisoners, ex-offenders and potential offenders.
WHAT IS FUNDED Projects and activities.
WHAT IS NOT FUNDED No grants for annual holidays, debt repayment, large appeals or for causes outside the trust's two main areas of work.
TYPE OF GRANT One-off.
RANGE OF GRANTS £250–£1,500.
SAMPLE GRANTS Previous beneficiaries include: AVID – Association of Visitors to Immigrant Detainees, Sheffield Mind, Prison Advice and Care Trust – London, HMP Morton Hall, Community Action Halfway Home, Foundation for the Arts and Mental Health, Lifecraft – Cambridge, Corner House Resource Centre and Wigan and Leigh CVS – Freebirds Mental Health Group.
FINANCES *Year* 2009–10 *Income* £26,568 *Grants* £30,000
TRUSTEES Dodie Carter; Janet Hargreaves; Peter Kilgarriff; Calton Younger.
OTHER INFORMATION Only limited information was available from the Charity Commission website. The grant total of £30,000 is estimated.
HOW TO APPLY In writing to the correspondent, enclosing an up-to-date report on fundraising, and a copy of the most recent annual report and accounts (or any financial information available). The trustees meet in early February, June and October each year, but can occasionally reach decisions quickly in an emergency. Applications should be made at least four weeks before the trustees' next meeting. The trust tries to be as

......

Think carefully about every application. Is it justified?

921

responsive as it can be to appropriate applicants.

WHO TO APPLY TO Janet Hargreaves, Trustee, 7 Mount Vernon, London NW3 6QS *Tel* 020 7794 2486

■ **Swansea and Brecon Diocesan Board of Finance Limited**

CC NO 249810   **ESTABLISHED** 1968

WHERE FUNDING CAN BE GIVEN Diocese of Swansea and Brecon (Neath Port Talbot, Powys and Swansea).

WHO CAN BENEFIT Clergy and organisations.

WHAT IS FUNDED The majority portion of the board's expenditure is on clergy stipends, emoluments and housing, with the balance being spent on Diocesan activities, grants and administration.

WHAT IS NOT FUNDED 'Applications from organisations outside the diocese will not be considered.'

FINANCES *Year* 2010 *Income* £3,398,324 *Grants* £179,399

TRUSTEES Ven. Alfred Thomas; Gwyn Lewis; Rt Revd John Davies; Ven. Robert Williams; Clive Rees; Revd Canon Peter Williams; Mrs Gillian Knight; David Davies; Nicolas Paravicini; John Lloyd.

HOW TO APPLY The charity does not respond to unsolicited applications.

WHO TO APPLY TO Mrs Heather Price, Diocesan Centre, Cathedral Close, Brecon, Powys LD3 9DP *Tel* 01874 623716 *email* heatherprice@churchinwales.org.uk *Website* www.churchinwales.org.uk/swanbrec

■ **The John Swire (1989) Charitable Trust**

CC NO 802142   **ESTABLISHED** 1989

WHERE FUNDING CAN BE GIVEN UK.

WHO CAN BENEFIT Charitable organisations.

WHAT IS FUNDED General charitable purposes, especially arts, welfare, education, medicine and research.

RANGE OF GRANTS £1,000–£102,000.

SAMPLE GRANTS St John of Jerusalem Eye Hospital (£102,000); New Marlow Theatre Development Trust (£75,000); Breast Cancer Hope Charity (£30,000); British Cardiovascular Society (£25,000); Krishna Gurung (£23,000); St Anthony's College (£13,000); and Carers First (£10,000). Action for ME (£7,500); Canterbury Festival (£6,000); Crimestoppers, Faversham Society, St Mary the Virgin – Great Parndon (£5,000 each); St Clare Hospice (£3,000); Ataxia-Telangiectasia Society, Changing Faces (£2,500 each); Caldecott Foundation, Kent Scouts (£2,000 each); Age Concern and Citizens Advice Bureau in Swale (£1,000 each). Grants of less than £1,000 amounted to a total of £39,000.

FINANCES *Year* 2009 *Income* £5,436,107 *Grants* £476,913 *Assets* £16,385,122

TRUSTEES Sir John Swire; J S Swire; B N Swire; M C Robinson; Lady M C Swire.

HOW TO APPLY In writing to the correspondent.

WHO TO APPLY TO Michael Todhunter, Charities Administrator, Swire House, 59 Buckingham Gate, London SW1E 6AJ *Tel* 020 7834 7717

■ **The Swire Charitable Trust**

CC NO 270726   **ESTABLISHED** 1976

WHERE FUNDING CAN BE GIVEN UK.

WHO CAN BENEFIT Regional and UK organisations.

WHAT IS FUNDED Children, the arts and heritage, medical research, welfare, the environment and general charitable purposes.

RANGE OF GRANTS £1,000–£25,000.

SAMPLE GRANTS Help for Heroes, Marine Society & Sea Cadets (£25,000 each); Air League Educational Trust (£23,500); Breast Cancer Haven (£20,000) and Royal Air Force Benevolent Fund (£15,000); Internally Displaced Persons in Sri Lanka (£11,000); Autism Speaks, Brydges Centre, Royal National College for the Blind (£10,000 each); The Japan Society (£7,500); Child Bereavement Charity, Commonwealth War Graves Commission (£5,000 each); Cleft Lip and Palate Association (£3,000); Helping Uganda Schools, Heritage of London Trust (£2,500 each); and Living Paintings (£1,500).

FINANCES *Year* 2009 *Income* £525,809 *Grants* £490,158 *Assets* £57,324

TRUSTEES Sir J Swire; Sir Adrian Swire; B N Swire; J S Swire; M Swire; J W J Hughes-Hallett.

HOW TO APPLY In writing to the correspondent. Applications are considered throughout the year.

WHO TO APPLY TO Swire House, 59 Buckingham Gate, London SW1E 6AJ *Tel* 020 7834 7717

■ **The Hugh and Ruby Sykes Charitable Trust**

CC NO 327648   **ESTABLISHED** 1987

WHERE FUNDING CAN BE GIVEN Principally South Yorkshire, also Derbyshire.

WHO CAN BENEFIT Registered charities.

WHAT IS FUNDED Principally local charities but some major UK charities are supported. The trust has major commitments with several medical charities. It is the policy of the trust to distribute income and preserve capital.

WHAT IS NOT FUNDED No grants are made to individuals. Most grants are made to organisations which have a connection to one of the trustees.

FINANCES *Year* 2009–10 *Income* £88,068 *Grants* £136,475 *Assets* £1,945,644

TRUSTEES Sir Hugh Sykes; Lady Ruby Sykes.

OTHER INFORMATION A list of beneficiaries was not included in the accounts.

HOW TO APPLY Applications can only be accepted from registered charities and should be in writing to the correspondent. In order to save administration costs, replies are not sent to unsuccessful applicants. If the trustees are able to consider a request for support, they aim to express interest within one month.

WHO TO APPLY TO Brian Evans, Administrator, The Coach House, Brookfield Manor, Hathersage, Hope Valley, Derbyshire S32 1BR *Tel* 01433 651190 *email* info@brookfieldmanor.com

■ **The Charles and Elsie Sykes Trust**

CC NO 206926   **ESTABLISHED** 1954

WHERE FUNDING CAN BE GIVEN In practice, anywhere in the UK with a preference for Yorkshire.

WHO CAN BENEFIT Registered charities only.

WHAT IS FUNDED People who are blind or partially sighted; children and youth; cultural and environmental heritage; people who are deaf,

922

Does the trust you have chosen match your needs? Haphazard applications waste postage and time

hard of hearing or speech impaired; people with disabilities; education; hospices and hospitals; medical research; medical welfare; mental health and mental disability; welfare of older people; overseas aid; services and ex-services; social and moral welfare; trades and professions; and sundry.

WHAT IS NOT FUNDED Unregistered and overseas charities are not considered. Individuals, local organisations not in the north of England, and recently-established charities are unlikely to be successful.

TYPE OF GRANT One off and recurring.

RANGE OF GRANTS £2,000–£25,000.

SAMPLE GRANTS Alzheimer's Research Trust – Cambridge (£25,000); Age Concern – Leeds (£12,500); Sobriety Project – Goole (£9,000); Bowel Disease Research Foundation, Music and the Deaf – Huddersfield and Wakefield & District Carers' Association (£5,000 each); St John's Under 5's Pre-School – Bradford (£4,000); Harrogate Citizen's Advice Bureau and the Pain Relief Foundation – Liverpool (£3,000 each); and Clothing Solutions – Bradford and Kidney Research UK (£2,000 each).

FINANCES *Year* 2010 *Income* £424,178 *Grants* £341,280 *Assets* £12,804,273

TRUSTEES John Ward, Chair; Mrs Anne E Brownlie; Martin P Coultas; Michael G H Garnett; R Barry Kay; Dr Michael W McEvoy; Peter G Rous; Dr Rosemary Livingstone; Sarah Buchan.

HOW TO APPLY Only applications from registered charities are considered, with a preference for those in, or benefiting people in, Yorkshire. Application forms can be requested from the trust or downloaded from the trust's website. The form should then be sent to the trust along with a copy of the organisation's latest accounts, annual report and any other relevant information. It is more favourable for the application if the accounts are current. If a grant is required for a particular project, full details and costings should be provided. Applications from schools, playgroups, cadet forces, scouts, guides, and churches must be for outreach programmes, and not for maintenance projects. Successful applications will receive a donation which may or may not be subject to conditions.

WHO TO APPLY TO Mrs Judith M Long, Secretary, Barber Titleys Solicitors, 6 North Park Road, Harrogate, Yorkshire HG1 5PA *Tel* 01423 817238 *Fax* 01423 851112 *Website* www. charlesandelsiesykestrust.co.uk

---

■ The Sylvanus Charitable Trust

CC NO 259520   **ESTABLISHED** 1968

WHERE FUNDING CAN BE GIVEN Europe and North America.

WHO CAN BENEFIT Organisations benefiting Roman Catholics and animals.

WHAT IS FUNDED The traditional Catholic Church and animal welfare, including wildlife sanctuaries.

WHAT IS NOT FUNDED No grants for expeditions, scholarships or individuals.

TYPE OF GRANT One-off and recurring.

RANGE OF GRANTS £1,000–£5,000.

SAMPLE GRANTS Society of St Pius X (£5,000); FRAME (£3,000); Durrell Wildlife Conservation Trust and Fauna & Flora International (£2,000 each); and Animal Health Trust and Help in Suffering (£1,000 each).

FINANCES *Year* 2010 *Income* £67,823 *Grants* £27,000 *Assets* £2,016,021

TRUSTEES John C Vernor-Miles; Alexander D Gemmill; Wilfred E Vernor-Miles; Gloria Taviner.

OTHER INFORMATION This trust has a sterling section for European grants and a dollar section for USA grants. The financial information in this entry relates to the Sterling section.

HOW TO APPLY The trustees usually make grants to charities known personally to them but occasionally make grants in response to unsolicited appeals. W hen considering applications for funding the trustees take into account how many years' reserves are held by an applicant and the proportionate costs of administration and fund-raising. They also consider the degree to which the trustees have been informed of progress made since previous grants. The Trustees do not give grants to individuals. In writing to the correspondent. The trustees meet once a year.

WHO TO APPLY TO John C Vernor-Miles, Trustee, c/o Hunters, 9 New Square, Lincoln's Inn, London WC2A 3QN *Tel* 020 7412 0050

■ The Hugh Symons Charitable Trust

CC NO 1137778   **ESTABLISHED** 2010

WHERE FUNDING CAN BE GIVEN Not defined, but a possible preference for Poole, Bradford and Sidmouth where the companies offices are based.

WHO CAN BENEFIT Registered charities.

WHAT IS FUNDED General charitable purposes.

TRUSTEES Barry E Glazier; Geoffrey H Roper; Ms Katherine A Roper; Mrs. Pauline H Roper.

OTHER INFORMATION 'Hugh Symons Information Management is one of the UK's leading scanning and microfilming bureaux, processing millions of images per month. The company was established in 1974 and provides a full range of scanning and microfilming bureau services from our Records Management Centres in Poole (head office), Bradford (northern head office) and Sidmouth.'

HOW TO APPLY In writing to the correspondent.

WHO TO APPLY TO Geoffrey H Roper, Trustee, Stubhampton House, Stubhampton, Blandford Forum, Dorset DT11 8JU *Tel* 01258 830135

■ The Stella Symons Charitable Trust

CC NO 259638   **ESTABLISHED** 1968

WHERE FUNDING CAN BE GIVEN UK.

WHO CAN BENEFIT Registered charities.

WHAT IS FUNDED Residential facilities and services; infrastructure, support and development; the advancement of religion; arts, culture and recreation; health; conservation and environment; education and training; and social care and development will be considered.

WHAT IS NOT FUNDED The trustees do not normally favour projects which provide a substitute for the statutory obligations of the state or projects which in their opinion should be commercially viable operations. No grants to individuals or to politically biased organisations.

TYPE OF GRANT Outright gifts and larger sums on loan on beneficial terms. Buildings, capital, core costs, one-off, project, research, recurring and running costs, salaries, and start-up costs. Funding for up to and over three years will be considered.

RANGE OF GRANTS The majority of grants are for £250.

SAMPLE GRANTS Norgren Social Club (£5,000);
Helen & Douglas House, Shipson Home Nursing
and Teenage Cancer Trust (£500 each); PDSA;
River & Sea Sense; Down's Syndrome
Association; Lucie Blackman Trust; Unicef UK;
Dream Makers; The Ear Foundation; Woodland
Trust (£250 each) and Macmillian Cancer Relief
(£100).

FINANCES *Year* 2009–10 *Income* £44,250
Grants £71,350 *Assets* £1,452,003

TRUSTEES Jonathan S S Bosley; Mrs Mervyne
E Mitchell; Mrs Katherine A Willis.

HOW TO APPLY In writing to the correspondent.

WHO TO APPLY TO Jonathan S S Bosley, Mr Jonathan
Simon Sheldon, Bosley, 20 Mill Street,
Shipston-on-Stour, Warwickshire CV36 4AW

■ T and S Trust Fund

CC NO 1095939 **ESTABLISHED** 2002
WHERE FUNDING CAN BE GIVEN UK.
WHO CAN BENEFIT Jewish organisations and the Jewish community.
WHAT IS FUNDED 'The advancement of education according to the tenets of the Orthodox Jewish Faith, the advancement of the Orthodox Jewish Religion and the relief of poverty amongst the elderly or persons in need, hardship and distress in the Jewish Community.'
TYPE OF GRANT One-off and recurrent.
RANGE OF GRANTS £1,000–£59,000.
SAMPLE GRANTS Orphan children fund (£59,000); Centre for Advanced Rabbinics (£8,000); New Hall Charitable Trust (£7,000); Rozac Charitable Trust (£6,000); Etz Chaim School(£4,500); Yeshaya Adler Memorial Fund (£2,000) and Tashbar (£1,000).
FINANCES *Year* 2009–10 *Income* £124,750 *Grants* £109,661 *Assets* £522,549
TRUSTEES A T Sandler; Mrs S Sandler; E Salomon.
OTHER INFORMATION In addition to the above there were 'relief of poverty grants' (£4,000).
HOW TO APPLY In writing to the correspondent.
WHO TO APPLY TO A Sandler, Trustee, 96 Whitehall Road, Gateshead, Tyne And Wear NE8 4ET *Tel* 0191 482 5050

■ The Tabeel Trust

CC NO 266645 **ESTABLISHED** 1974
WHERE FUNDING CAN BE GIVEN Worldwide with a preference for Clacton.
WHO CAN BENEFIT Evangelical Christian organisations.
WHAT IS FUNDED Christian charitable purposes, where the trustees have an existing interest.
RANGE OF GRANTS Up to £30,000.
SAMPLE GRANTS Previously: St George's Crypt – Leeds (£30,000); Essex County Evangelists' – Accommodation Trust (£10,000); ZACS (£6,000); Radio Worldwide (£5,000); Barnabas Fund (£4,000); Viz a Viz (£3,000); Tabernacle Baptist Church – Penarth (£2,000); Christian Institute (£1,000); and Upesi (£500).
FINANCES *Year* 2009–10 *Income* £21,479 *Grants* £63,858
TRUSTEES Douglas K Brown; Pauline M Brown; Barbara J Carter; Dr Mary P Clark; Jean A Richardson; James Davey; Sarah Taylor; Nigel Davey.
HOW TO APPLY Only charities with which a trustee already has contact should apply. Grants are considered at trustees' meetings in May and November.
WHO TO APPLY TO Barbara Carter, Trustee, 3 Oak Park, West Byfleet, Surrey KT14 6AG *Tel* 01932 343808

■ Tadlus Limited

CC NO 1109982 **ESTABLISHED** 2005
WHERE FUNDING CAN BE GIVEN UK and Israel.
WHO CAN BENEFIT Institutions, organisations and individuals involved in the orthodox Jewish faith.
WHAT IS FUNDED The promotion of religious education and worship.
TYPE OF GRANT One off and recurrent.
FINANCES *Year* 2009–10 *Income* £45,717 *Grants* £0 *Assets* -£1,024,155
TRUSTEES Jacob Grosskopf; Myer Grosskopf; Chaim Grosskopf.
OTHER INFORMATION At year end the trust had a deficit of £1 million in its reserves. This was due to ongoing problems with both of its investment properties, which led to their devaluation. The trustees state that they are, 'actively monitoring the situation and seeking negotiations with their bankers and creditors'. As a result, no grants were made during the year. No details on when the issues might be resolved were given in the accounts.
HOW TO APPLY In writing to the correspondent.
WHO TO APPLY TO Jacob Grosskopf, Trustee, 6 Spring Hill, London E5 9BE

■ The Tajtelbaum Charitable Trust

CC NO 273184 **ESTABLISHED** 1974
WHERE FUNDING CAN BE GIVEN Mainly UK and Israel.
WHO CAN BENEFIT Jewish organisations benefiting children, young adults and students will be considered. Support may be given to older and sick people.
WHAT IS FUNDED Orthodox synagogues, education establishments, hospitals and homes for older people.
RANGE OF GRANTS £500–£150,000.
SAMPLE GRANTS Previous beneficiaries include: United Institutions Arad, Emuno Educational Centre, Ruzin Sadiger Trust, Gur Foundation, Before Trust, Beth Hassidei Gur, Comet Charities Limited, Delharville, Kupat Gemach Trust, Centre for Torah and Chesed, Friends of Nachlat David and Friends of Sanz Institute.
FINANCES *Year* 2009–10 *Income* £538,916 *Grants* £510,369 *Assets* £4,086,280
TRUSTEES Ilsa Tajtelbaum; Jacob Tajtelbaum; Emanuel Tajtelbaum; Eli Jaswon.
HOW TO APPLY In writing to the correspondent.
WHO TO APPLY TO Ilsa Tajtelbaum, Trustee, 17 Western Avenue, London NW11 9HE *Tel* 020 8202 3464

■ The Gay and Keith Talbot Trust

CC NO 1102192 **ESTABLISHED** 2004
WHERE FUNDING CAN BE GIVEN Worldwide.
WHO CAN BENEFIT Charities working in developing countries.
WHAT IS FUNDED General charitable purposes including research and development of Cystic Fibrosis, Fistula work and overseas aid.
TYPE OF GRANT One off and recurring. Capital costs, revenue costs and full project funding.
SAMPLE GRANTS Previously: CAFOD – Sudan, Cystic Fibrosis Trust, Door of Hope, Medical Missionaries of Mary – Uganda and Nigeria, Our Lady of Windermere and St Herbert, Rwanda Group Trust, SVP – Sudan, Impact Foundation – Bangladesh and Uganda Childbirth Injury Fund.
FINANCES *Year* 2009–10 *Income* £1,623 *Grants* £40,000
TRUSTEES Gay Talbot; Keith Talbot.
HOW TO APPLY In writing to the correspondent.
WHO TO APPLY TO Keith Talbot, Fold Howe, Kentmere, Kendal, Cumbria LA8 9JW

Think carefully about every application. Is it justified?

925

■ The Talbot Trusts

CC NO 221356 **ESTABLISHED** 1928
WHERE FUNDING CAN BE GIVEN Sheffield and immediate surrounding areas.
WHO CAN BENEFIT organisations directly benefiting people who are sick, convalescent, disabled or infirm.
WHAT IS FUNDED Items, services or facilities which are calculated to relieve suffering or assist recovery.
WHAT IS NOT FUNDED No grants are given towards the direct relief of rates, taxes or other public funds and no commitment can be made to repeat or renew grants. Grants are not normally given to: non-registered charities or other organisations; individuals; appeal requests, research or educational costs; or to finance fundraising initiatives.
TYPE OF GRANT One-off, capital, core costs, running costs, salaries and start-up costs. Funding may be given for up to one year.
RANGE OF GRANTS £1,000–£4,000.
SAMPLE GRANTS Happy Days (£4,100); Family Action (£4,000); Listening Books, Vitalise and Sheffield Hospitals Charitable Trust (£3,000 each); Ecclesall Live at Home Scheme; St Wilfrid's Drop in Centre and St Luke's Hospice (£2,500 each); Relatives of Drug Addicts (£1,500); Happy Outings, Social Services (Physical Disability) and Hospital Social Services Dept (£1,000 each).
FINANCES *Year* 2009–10 *Income* £79,145 *Grants* £73,871 *Assets* £1,999,167
TRUSTEES Dr Brenda P Jackson; Dr Lawrence C Kershaw; Godfrey Smallman; Revd Can. Paul Shackerley; Ronald Jones; Jo Frisby.
HOW TO APPLY On a form available from the correspondent, for consideration in July and December.
WHO TO APPLY TO Neil Charlesworth, Clerk, Mr Neil Charlesworth, 11 Russett Court, Maltby, Rotherham S66 8SP *Tel* 01709 769022

■ The Talbot Village Trust

CC NO 249349 **ESTABLISHED** 1867
WHERE FUNDING CAN BE GIVEN The boroughs of Bournemouth, Christchurch and Poole; the districts of east Dorset and Purbeck.
WHO CAN BENEFIT Community organisations (such as schools, churches, youth clubs, playgroups and so on).
WHAT IS FUNDED Youth, older people and church-related charities.
WHAT IS NOT FUNDED No grants for individuals.
TYPE OF GRANT Grants and loans. Mainly for capital costs.
RANGE OF GRANTS Up to £50,000.
SAMPLE GRANTS Cherry Tree Nursery (£75,000); The Beacon Church (£50,000); Deanery Youth Worker Project (£47,000); Diverse Abilities (£40,000); Colehill & Wimborne Youth & Community Centre (£30,000); Carter Community School (£25,000); Alderholt Chapel; Life Education Wessex; Wessex Autistic Society (£20,000 each); The Variety Club Children's Charity (£12,000); Motability; 1st Woodcutts Scout Group (£10,000 each); The Salvation Army (£9,000); and Broadstone United Reform Church (£4,000).
FINANCES *Year* 2010 *Income* £1,795,240 *Grants* £884,215 *Assets* £36,104,746
TRUSTEES Christopher Lees, Chair; James Fleming; Sir George Meyrick; Sir Thomas Salt; Russell Rowe; Earl of Shaftesbury.
HOW TO APPLY In writing to the correspondent.

WHO TO APPLY TO Gary S Cox, Clerk, Dickinson Manser, 5 Parkstone Road, Poole, Dorset BH15 2NL *Tel* 01202 673071 *email* garycox@dickinsonmanser.co.uk

■ Tallow Chandlers Benevolent Fund

CC NO 246255 **ESTABLISHED** 1966
WHERE FUNDING CAN BE GIVEN London, mostly City of London.
WHO CAN BENEFIT Charitable organisations, schools and universities.
WHAT IS FUNDED Medical research, care of people with disabilities and the encouragement of excellence at schools and universities. It also helps City of London-based charities and charities where a liveryman or freeman is actively involved. Youth clubs are particularly supported.
RANGE OF GRANTS Up to £20,000.
SAMPLE GRANTS London Youth (£20,000); Bart's & Royal London School of Medicine (£15,000); Fairbridge London Team (£12,500); St Christopher's Hospice (£10,000); Centrepoint, Reed's School and Guildhall School Trust (£5,000 each); Royal London Society for the Blind (£3,500); Prince's Trust (£2,500); Covent Garden Cancer Research Trust (£2,000); International Spinal Research and Mission to Seafarers (£1,000 each).
FINANCES *Year* 2009–10 *Income* £514,609 *Grants* £173,312 *Assets* £4,469,317
TRUSTEES C P Tootal; D Kirby Johnson; R A B Nicolle; D R Newnham.
OTHER INFORMATION Approximately 40 grants were made to organisations, totalling £170,000.
HOW TO APPLY In writing to the correspondent. 'Every request for assistance will be considered first by the clerk and the chairman and then shortlisted for consideration by the education and charity committee.'
WHO TO APPLY TO Brig. R M Wilde, Clerk to the Trustees, Ms Susan Bunn, Tallow Chandlers Hall, 4 Dowgate Hill, London EC4R 2SH *Tel* 020 7248 4726 *Fax* 020 7236 0844 *email* clerk@tallowchandlers.org *Website* www.tallowchandlers.org

■ Talteg Ltd

CC NO 283253 **ESTABLISHED** 1981
WHERE FUNDING CAN BE GIVEN UK, with a preference for Scotland.
WHO CAN BENEFIT Registered charities benefiting Jewish people, children, young adults and people disadvantaged by poverty.
WHAT IS FUNDED To support the advancement of religion, especially Jewish, and the relief of poverty. Educational and other charitable purposes are also supported.
SAMPLE GRANTS Previous beneficiaries include: British Friends of Laniado Hospital, Centre for Jewish Studies, Society of Friends of the Torah, Glasgow Jewish Community Trust, National Trust for Scotland, Ayrshire Hospice, Earl Haig Fund – Scotland and RSSPCC.
FINANCES *Year* 2010 *Income* £370,665 *Grants* £245,937 *Assets* £3,613,082
TRUSTEES Fred Berkley; Adam Berkley; Delia Lynn Berkley; Maxwell Berkley.
HOW TO APPLY In writing to the correspondent.
WHO TO APPLY TO Fred Berkley, Trustee, 90 Mitchell Street, Glasgow G1 3NQ *Tel* 0141 221 3353

■ The Tangent Charitable Trust

CC NO 289729　　　**ESTABLISHED** 1984
WHERE FUNDING CAN BE GIVEN UK.
WHO CAN BENEFIT Registered charities and voluntary organisations.
WHAT IS FUNDED General charitable purposes.
RANGE OF GRANTS £1,000–£15,000.
SAMPLE GRANTS JAMI (£15,000); UCS Centennial Trust (£10,000); Great Ormond Street Hospital Children's Charity; Parochial Church Council of Easton Grey for 2008; and for 2009; Marwar Foundation – Indian Head Injury Foundation (£2,000); The President's Club Charity Trust (£1,300); United Synagogue (£1,100); Wellbeing of Women; Jewish Community Centre for London (£1,000 each).
FINANCES *Year* 2009–10 *Income* £60,008 *Grants* £45,358 *Assets* £13,231
TRUSTEES M P Green; Mrs T M Green; R S Marks; C V Robinson.
HOW TO APPLY In writing to the correspondent.
WHO TO APPLY TO Beverley Matthews, 21 South Street, London W1 2XB *Tel* 020 7663 6402

■ The Lady Tangye Charitable Trust

CC NO 1044220　　　**ESTABLISHED** 1995
WHERE FUNDING CAN BE GIVEN UK and worldwide, with some preference for the Midlands.
WHO CAN BENEFIT Charitable organisations, with a preference for work in the Midlands or developing world.
WHAT IS FUNDED General charitable purposes, with Christian and environmental causes are well-represented in the grants list.
SAMPLE GRANTS West Midland Urban Wildlife Trust (£3,000); Spana, ChildLine – Midlands and Aid to the Church in Need (£2,000 each); Amnesty International, Priest Training Fund and Crew Trust (£1,500 each); St Saviour's Church, Walsall and District Samaritans, Life and European Children's Trust (£1,000 each); and Charity Ignite – Big Ideal (£500).
FINANCES *Year* 2009–10 *Income* £26,851 *Grants* £32,940
TRUSTEES Gitta Clarisse Gilzean Tangye; Colin Ferguson Smith.
HOW TO APPLY In writing to the correspondent.
WHO TO APPLY TO Colin Ferguson Smith, Trustee, 55 Warwick Crest, Arthur Road, Birmingham B15 2LH

■ The David Tannen Charitable Trust

CC NO 280392　　　**ESTABLISHED** 1974
WHERE FUNDING CAN BE GIVEN UK.
WHO CAN BENEFIT Jewish organisations.
WHAT IS FUNDED Advancement of the Jewish religion.
RANGE OF GRANTS About £1,000–£100,000.
SAMPLE GRANTS Previous beneficiaries included: Cosmon Beiz Academy, Gevurath Ari Trust, Telz Academy Trust, Friends of Ohr Elchonon, Beis Ahron Trust, Wlodowa Charity, Chai Cancer Care, Kollel Skver Trust, Centre for Torah Trust, Gateshead Talmudical College, Jewish Women's Aid Trust, Torah 5759 Ltd and YTAF.
FINANCES *Year* 2009–10 *Income* £2,296,640 *Grants* £134,150 *Assets* £23,578,236
TRUSTEES Jonathon Miller; Alan Rose; David Tannen.

OTHER INFORMATION A list of recent beneficiaries was not included in the trust's 2009–10 accounts.
HOW TO APPLY In writing to the correspondent.
WHO TO APPLY TO Jonathon Miller, c/o Sutherland House, 70–78 West Hendon Broadway, London NW9 7BT *Tel* 020 8202 1066

■ The Tanner Trust

CC NO 1021175　　　**ESTABLISHED** 1993
WHERE FUNDING CAN BE GIVEN UK, with a slight preference for the South of England, and overseas.
WHO CAN BENEFIT Foundations, schools, societies, charities and projects.
WHAT IS FUNDED General charitable purposes.
WHAT IS NOT FUNDED No grants to individuals.
RANGE OF GRANTS £300–£5,000; exceptionally higher.
SAMPLE GRANTS National Trust (£6,500); CRCC and Great Dixter Charitable Trust (£6,000 each); Berkshire Community Foundation, Falmouth and Penryn Sea Cadets Group and Helford River Children's Sailing Trust (£5,000 each); JOLT (£4,000); Industrial Trust and Mercy Ships (£3,000 each); Mango Tree and Plant Heritage (£2,000 each); and Oxford Deaf and Hard of Hearing Centre (£300).
FINANCES *Year* 2009–10 *Income* £629,183 *Grants* £396,300 *Assets* £7,419,695
TRUSTEES Alice P Williams; Lucie Nottingham.
HOW TO APPLY The trust states that unsolicited applications are, without exception, not considered. Support is only given to charities personally known to the trustees.
WHO TO APPLY TO Celine Lecomte, Trust Administrator, c/o Blake Lapthorn Tarlo Lyons, Harbour Court, Compass Road, Portsmouth PO6 4ST *Tel* 02392 221122 *Fax* 02392 221123

■ The Lili Tapper Charitable Foundation

CC NO 268523　　　**ESTABLISHED** 1974
WHERE FUNDING CAN BE GIVEN UK.
WHO CAN BENEFIT Organisations benefiting Jewish people.
WHAT IS FUNDED Preference to charitable purposes or institutions which are for the benefit of Jewish people.
WHAT IS NOT FUNDED No grants to individuals.
SAMPLE GRANTS Previous beneficiaries include: UJIA, CST, Manchester Jewish Foundation, Teenage Cancer Trust, Keshet Eilon, Israel Educational Foundation, Chicken Shed Theatre Company and Jewish Representation Council.
FINANCES *Year* 2009–10 *Income* £79,182 *Grants* £77,170 *Assets* £3,165,993
TRUSTEES Michael Webber; Dr Jonathan Webber.
OTHER INFORMATION No details of grant beneficiaries were available.
HOW TO APPLY The trust states that it does not respond to any unsolicited applications.
WHO TO APPLY TO Michael Webber, Trustee, Yew Tree Cottage, Artists Lane, Nether Alderley, Macclesfield SK10 4UA

■ The Mrs A Lacy Tate Trust

cc no 803596 **established** 1990
where funding can be given East Sussex.
who can benefit Individuals and organisations benefiting at risk groups and people who are disabled, disadvantaged by poverty or socially isolated.
what is funded Welfare, disability and medical charities.
type of grant Often recurrent.
range of grants £250–£5,000.
sample grants Queen Alexandra Cottage Homes (£3,000); Surviving Christmas and The East Sussex Association for the Blind and Partially Sighted (£2,000 each); Hastings West Hill Youth Club, Relate Family Counselling for Eastbourne and Plumpton College (£1,000 each); Brighton Dome & Festival Ltd – Open Minds Project, Buddy Scheme and Sussex Association for Spina Bifida and Hydrocephalus (£500 each); The BEAT Youth Sports Club and Playing Field (£300); Rockinghorse (£250) and Downs Farm Residents Association (£100).
finances *Year* 2009–10 *Income* £50,276
Grants £45,822
trustees Linda A Bursess; Lesley A Macey; Ian M A Stewart; June M Roberts.
other information Grants to organisations totalled £27,000. Grants to 106 individuals totalled £19,000.
how to apply In writing to the correspondent.
who to apply to Ian M A Stewart, Heringtons Solicitors, 39 Gildredge Road, Eastbourne, East Sussex BN21 4RY *Tel* 01323 411020 *Fax* 01323 411040

■ The Taurus Foundation

cc no 1128441 **established** 2009
where funding can be given UK.
who can benefit Registered charities.
what is funded General charitable purposes.
range of grants Up to £10,000.
sample grants Norwood Ravenswood, Jewish Care, Rainbow Trust, CLIC Sargent and Chance UK (£10,000 each); Camp Simcha, Child Welfare Scheme, Momentum, Aspire and Just for Kids Law (£5,000 each); and Almeida Theatre and Donmar Warehouse Projects (£1,000 each).
finances *Year* 2009–10 *Income* £770,424
Grants £77,000 *Assets* £698,750
trustees Denis Felsenstein; Michael Jacobs; Alan Fenton; Anthony Forwood; Priscilla Fenton.
how to apply No grants to unsolicited applications.
who to apply to Carole Cook, Forsters LLP, 31 Hill Street, London W1J 5LS *Tel* 020 7863 8333 *email* carole.cook@forsters.co.uk

■ The Tay Charitable Trust

sc no SC001004 **established** 1951
where funding can be given UK, with a preference for Scotland, particularly Dundee.
who can benefit Registered charities.
what is funded General charitable purposes.
what is not funded Grants are only given to charities recognised by the Inland Revenue. No grants to individuals.
type of grant One-off and recurring.
range of grants £250–£5,000.
sample grants Dundee Heritage Trust and RNLI (£5,000 each); Boarders Forest Trust, DermaTrust, Edinburgh World Heritage Trust, Maritime Volunteer Service and University of St Andrews – Low Scholarship (£3,000 each);

Bowel Cancer UK, High Blood Pressure Foundation, John Muir Trust and National Trust for Scotland (£2,000 each); Princess Royal Trust for Carers (£1,500); and Army Benevolent Fund, Changing Faces, Dundee Symphony Orchestra, Guide Dogs for the Blind, Lincoln Cathedral, Samaritans, Scottish Countryside Alliance Trust, Skillforce Development and Tayside Council on Alcohol (£1,000 each).
finances *Year* 2009–10 *Income* £188,043
Grants £180,000
trustees Mrs E A Mussen; Mrs Z C Martin; G C Bonar.
how to apply No standard form; applications in writing to the correspondent, including a financial statement. An sae is appreciated.
who to apply to Mrs E A Mussen, Trustee, 6 Douglas Terrace, Broughty Ferry, Dundee DD5 1EA

■ C B and H H Taylor 1984 Trust

cc no 291363 **established** 1946
where funding can be given West Midlands, Ireland and overseas.
who can benefit Approximately 60% of funds available are currently given to the work and concerns of the Religious Society of Friends. The remaining funds are allocated to those charities in which the trustees have a special interest, particularly in the West Midlands. Applications are encouraged from minority groups and woman-led initiatives.
what is funded The general areas of benefit are:
(i) The Religious Society of Friends (Quakers) and other religious denominations.
(ii) Healthcare projects. (iii) Social welfare: community groups; children and young people; older people; disadvantaged people; people with disabilities; homeless people; housing initiatives; counselling and mediation agencies.
(iv) Education: adult literacy schemes; employment training; youth work. (v) Penal affairs: work with offenders and ex-offenders; police projects. (vi) The environment and conservation work. (vii) The arts: museums and art galleries; music and drama. (viii) Ireland: cross-community health and social welfare projects. (ix) UK charities working overseas on long-term development projects.
what is not funded The trust does not fund: individuals (whether for research, expeditions, educational purposes and so on); local projects or groups outside the West Midlands; or projects concerned with travel or adventure.
type of grant Regular annual donations and some single donations to special appeals.
range of grants Mainly £500–£5,000.
sample grants Britain Yearly Meeting (£30,000); Central England Quakers (£9,500); Friends of Swanivar (£7,000); Cape Town Quaker Peace Centre (£6,000); Oxfam, UNICEF, Christian Aid and Merlin (£5,000 each); Birmingham Settlement (£4,000); Salvation Army (£3,500); Action Aid (£3,000); Ironbridge Gorge Museum (£2,000); Bournville Parish Church, Birmingham Boys'/Girls' Union, Concern Africa, Dalit Solidarity Network and Shelter (£1,000 each); Cornwall Quakers (£850); Kanga Project and Home from Hospital (£500 each); and Birmingham Botanical Gardens (£250).
finances *Year* 2009–10 *Income* £334,756
Grants £254,650 *Assets* £8,975,172
trustees James Taylor; Constance Penny; Elizabeth Birmingham; Clare Norton; John Taylor; Thomas Penny; Robert Birmingham; Simon Taylor.

HOW TO APPLY There is no formal application form. Applicants should write to the correspondent giving the charity's registration number, a brief description of the charity's activities, and details of the specific project for which the grant is being sought. Applicants should also include a budget of the proposed work, together with a copy of the charity's most recent accounts. Trustees will also wish to know what funds have already been raised for the project and how the shortfall will be met. The trust states that it receives more applications than it can support. Therefore, even if work falls within its policy it may not be able to help, particularly if the project is outside the West Midlands. Trustees meet twice each year, in May and November. Applications will be acknowledged if an sae is provided.

WHO TO APPLY TO Clare Norton, Trustee, 14 Chamberlain Road, Worcester WR2 4PR

■ Humphrey Richardson Taylor Charitable Trust

CC NO 1062836   **ESTABLISHED** 1997
WHERE FUNDING CAN BE GIVEN Surrey and South London Boroughs.
WHO CAN BENEFIT State schools, choirs, amateur orchestras and individuals.
'The advancement of public education in and appreciation of the art and science of music and allied performing arts. The Trust's aims are to encourage and support music education at state primary, secondary and tertiary levels and to seek the continuing performance of live music in society, particularly by amateur performers.'
WHAT IS FUNDED Tuition fees, purchasing of instruments, music building-projects and grants to musical societies.
WHAT IS NOT FUNDED Projects or causes that are not associated with music.
RANGE OF GRANTS £250–£24,000.
SAMPLE GRANTS Royal College of Music (£23,200); Sutton Music Service (£20,000); University of Surrey (£18,000); Glenthorne High School (£13,000); Southbank Sinfonia (£7,000); Carshalton Boys' Sports College (£5,200); Mole Valley Silver Band (£3,500); National Youth Orchestra (£1,400); Oakfield Junior School (£520).
FINANCES Year 2010 Income £550,985 Grants £158,245 Assets £7,162,600
TRUSTEES Mr W Malings; Mr M Palmer; Mrs R Cox; Mr C Edgerton; Mr I Catling; Mr M Wood.
HOW TO APPLY In writing to the correspondent.
WHO TO APPLY TO The Administrator, c/o Messrs Palmers, 28 Chipstead Station Parade, Chipstead, Coulsdon, Surrey CR5 3TF Tel 01737 557546 email hrtaylortrust@btconnect.com

■ The Connie and Albert Taylor Charitable Trust

CC NO 1074785   **ESTABLISHED** 1998
WHERE FUNDING CAN BE GIVEN West Midlands.
WHO CAN BENEFIT Organisations concerned with medical research, hospices, education and recreation, and preservation.
WHAT IS FUNDED The trust was established by the will of Constance Iris Taylor in 1998 for the benefit of the West Midlands with the following object research into the cure and causes of cancer, blindness and heart disease provision and maintenance of nursing homes for people

who are elderly or unable to look after themselves provision of maintenance of hospices for people with terminal illnesses facilities for the education and recreation of children and young people the preservation, protection and improvements of any amenity or land of beauty, scientific or of horticultural interest and any building of historical, architectural or artistic or scientific interest.
RANGE OF GRANTS Up to £100,000.
SAMPLE GRANTS National Star College, Cheltenham (£100,000); Birmingham Children's Hospital (£70,000); Compton Hospice, Wolverhampton (£60,000); St Vincent's and St George's Association (£50,000); Wellbeing of Women (£25,000); South Staffordshire Medical Foundation (£20,000); Katherine House Hospice (£13,000) and National Blind Children (£2,000).
FINANCES Year 2010 Income £286,310 Grants £446,500 Assets £4,947,039
TRUSTEES Alan Foster; Harry Grundy; Richard D Long.
HOW TO APPLY In writing to the correspondent. The trust may visit applicants/beneficiaries.
WHO TO APPLY TO Harry Grundy, Trustee, The Farmhouse, Darwin Park, Abnalls Lane, Lichfield, Staffordshire WS13 8BJ email applications@taylortrust.co.uk Website www.taylortrust.co.uk

■ The Cyril Taylor Charitable Trust

CC NO 1040179   **ESTABLISHED** 1994
WHERE FUNDING CAN BE GIVEN Generally in Greater London.
WHO CAN BENEFIT Organisations benefiting students.
WHAT IS FUNDED General charitable purposes; to advance the education of the students of Richmond College and the American International University in London.
RANGE OF GRANTS Usually between £500–£3,000.
SAMPLE GRANTS Richmond Foundation (£100,000); Institute of Economic Affairs (£6,000); the British Friends of Harvard Business School (£3,000); and Trinity Hall, Cambridge (£1,000).
FINANCES Year 2009–10 Income £211,032 Grants £124,206 Assets £249,237
TRUSTEES Sir Cyril Taylor, Chair; Clifford D Joseph; Robert W Maas; Peter A Tchereprine; Stephen Rasch; Christopher Lintott; Lady June Taylor; Michael Berry; William Gertz; Marcie Schneider.
HOW TO APPLY In writing to the correspondent.
WHO TO APPLY TO Christopher Lintott, Trustee, Penningtons, Abacus House, 33 Gutter Lane, London EC2V 8AR Tel 020 7457 3000 Fax 020 7457 3240 email chris.lintott@penningtons.co.uk

■ The Taylor Family Foundation

CC NO 1118032   **ESTABLISHED** 2007
WHERE FUNDING CAN BE GIVEN UK and overseas, with a preference for London and the south east.
WHO CAN BENEFIT Children and young people. 'The objectives of the Taylor Family Foundation are to help and support children and young people, particularly those from disadvantaged backgrounds, in the areas of education, health, recreation and the performing arts.'
WHAT IS FUNDED Registered charities and statutory bodies.
WHAT IS NOT FUNDED No grants to individuals.
RANGE OF GRANTS £500–£60,000.
SAMPLE GRANTS World Land Trust – Venezuela was a major beneficiary receiving a generous grant of £455,000. Other beneficiaries include Merton

Think carefully about every application. Is it justified?

929

College (£62,000); Royal Opera House Foundation (£52,000); Great Ormond Street, RSA City Academy, Lucy Faithful Foundation and Save the Children – Wilberforce school (£25,000 each); Jigsaw4u (£19,500); Rainbow House Trust (£17,500); Save the Children – Haiti (£10,000) and Durrell Wildlife (£5,000).

FINANCES *Year* 2009–10 *Income* £1,942,694 *Grants* £978,741 *Assets* £1,365,653

TRUSTEES Ian R Taylor; Cristina A Taylor; Neville P Shepherd.

OTHER INFORMATION Grants were given to 31 organisations totalling £979,000.

HOW TO APPLY In writing to the correspondent.

WHO TO APPLY TO Neville Shepherd, Trustee, MR Neville Philip Shephard, Hill Place House, 55a High Street, Wimbledon, London SW19 5BA *Tel* 020 8605 2622 *email* cathy@ thetaylorfamilyfoundation.co.uk *Website* www. thetaylorfamilyfoundation.co.uk

■ A P Taylor Trust

CC NO 260741   **ESTABLISHED** 1969

WHERE FUNDING CAN BE GIVEN The parishes of Hayes and Harlington (as they existed on 9 January 1953).

WHO CAN BENEFIT Charitable organisations.

WHAT IS FUNDED The provision of recreational and leisure activities.

RANGE OF GRANTS The majority of grants are for £500 or less.

SAMPLE GRANTS Previous beneficiaries have included: Harlington Locomotive Society, Hillingdon Table Tennis Club, Station Road Allotment Society, Broughton Pensioners, Immaculate Heart of Mary Senior Citizens' Club, Westcombe Lodge Club, Hayes Town Women's Institute and Royal British Legion Women's Section.

FINANCES *Year* 2009–10 *Income* £67,322 *Grants* £32,960 *Assets* £1,170,275

TRUSTEES T McCarthy; M J Fitzpatrick; A Woodhouse; K Tyrrell.

OTHER INFORMATION Grants were made to 69 organisations totalling £33,000.

HOW TO APPLY In writing to the correspondent.

WHO TO APPLY TO Sean Fitzpatrick, Homeleigh, 68 Vine Lane, Hillingdon, Middlesex UB10 0BD *Tel* 01895 812811 *email* enquiries@ aptaylortrust.org.uk *Website* www.aptaylortrust. org.uk

■ Rosanna Taylor's 1987 Charity Trust

CC NO 297210   **ESTABLISHED** 1987

WHERE FUNDING CAN BE GIVEN UK and overseas, with a preference for Oxfordshire and West Sussex.

WHO CAN BENEFIT Registered charities only.

WHAT IS FUNDED General charitable purposes, including support for medical, cancer, children's development and environmental charities.

WHAT IS NOT FUNDED No grants to individuals or non-registered charities.

RANGE OF GRANTS £500–£24,000.

SAMPLE GRANTS Charities Aid Foundation (£24,000); Pearson Taylor Trust (£10,000); Disaster Emergencies Committee – Haiti Appeal (£5,000); and Resonance FM (£500).

FINANCES *Year* 2009–10 *Income* £29,947 *Grants* £39,500 *Assets* £1,116,042

TRUSTEES The Cowdray Trust Limited.

HOW TO APPLY In writing to the correspondent. Acknowledgements are not sent to unsuccessful applicants.

WHO TO APPLY TO Laura Gosling, c/o Millbank Financial Services Ltd, Pollen House, 10– 12 Cork Street, London W1S 3LW *Tel* 020 7439 9061 *email* charity@mfs.co.uk

■ Tearfund

CC NO 265464   **ESTABLISHED** 1968

WHERE FUNDING CAN BE GIVEN Worldwide, but mainly in poorer countries.

WHO CAN BENEFIT Evangelical Christian organisations which benefit at risk groups; people who are disabled, disadvantaged by poverty or socially isolated; and victims of famine, man-made or natural disasters, and war.

WHAT IS FUNDED Evangelical Christian ministry to meet all needs – physical, mental, social and spiritual. Funding is given to partner organisations only.

WHAT IS NOT FUNDED Applications for individuals will not be considered.

TYPE OF GRANT Project/partner.

RANGE OF GRANTS Smallest £1,000; typical £15,000.

FINANCES *Year* 2009–10 *Income* £64,848,000 *Grants* £54,393,000 *Assets* £21,103,000

TRUSTEES Ms Anne de Leyser; Prof. Julian Evans; Kim Hurst; Revd John Smith; Revd Sarah Tillett; Prof. Andrew Tomkins; David Todd; Andy Hickford; Simon Laver; Robert Camp; Clive Mather.

PUBLICATIONS Tear Times.

HOW TO APPLY Initial approaches by potential partner organisations should be made in writing.

WHO TO APPLY TO Graham Fairbairn, Secretary, Mr Andrew John Slatter, Tearfund, 100 Church Road, Teddington, Middlesex TW11 8QE *Tel* 0845 355 8355 *email* enquiry@tearfund.org *Website* www.tearfund.org

■ The Tedworth Charitable Trust

CC NO 328524   **ESTABLISHED** 1990

WHERE FUNDING CAN BE GIVEN Unrestricted, but UK in practice.

WHO CAN BENEFIT Registered charities.

WHAT IS FUNDED Parenting, family welfare and child development; environment and the arts; general.

WHAT IS NOT FUNDED Grants are not normally made to individuals.

TYPE OF GRANT One-off and core costs.

RANGE OF GRANTS Up to £35,000.

SAMPLE GRANTS Ashden Awards (£55,000); Best Beginnings (£45,000); Resurgence Magazine (£35,000); Worcester College – Oxford (£25,000); Tipping Point (£20,000); House of Illustration and the CarbonSense Foundation (£10,000 each); Women's Environmental Network (£7,500); and Platform (£5,000).

FINANCES *Year* 2009–10 *Income* £379,311 *Grants* £380,354 *Assets* £10,542,667

TRUSTEES Alex J Sainsbury; Margaret Sainsbury; Jessica M Sainsbury; Timothy J Sainsbury; Judith S Portrait.

OTHER INFORMATION The trust is one of the Sainsbury Family Charitable Trusts which share a common administration. An application to one is taken as an application to all.

HOW TO APPLY 'Proposals are likely to be invited by the trustees or initiated at their request. Unsolicited applications are unlikely to be successful, even if they fall within an area in which the trustees are interested.' A single application will be considered for support by all the trusts in the Sainsbury family group.

WHO TO APPLY TO Alan Bookbinder, Director, Allington House, 1st Floor, 150 Victoria Street, London SW1E 5AE *Tel* 020 7410 0330 *Fax* 020 7410 0332 *Website* www.sfct.org.uk

■ Tees Valley Community Foundation

CC NO 1111222   **ESTABLISHED** 1988

WHERE FUNDING CAN BE GIVEN The former county of Cleveland, being the local authority areas of Hartlepool, Middlesbrough, Redcar and Cleveland and Stockton-on-Tees.

WHO CAN BENEFIT Registered charities and constituted community groups.

WHAT IS FUNDED General charitable purposes. The foundation makes grants from various different funds, each with its own criteria.

WHAT IS NOT FUNDED No grants for: major fundraising appeals; sponsored events; promotion of religion; retrospective funding; holidays or social outings; existing operating costs, e.g. salaries, rent, overheads; groups with excessive unrestricted or free reserves; groups in serious deficit; replacement of statutory funding; meeting any need which is the responsibility of central or local government; religious or political causes; fabric appeals; or animal welfare. Each fund has separate exclusions which are available on the foundation's website.

TYPE OF GRANT Capital or revenue.

RANGE OF GRANTS Mostly under £12,000.

SAMPLE GRANTS Tees Credit Union Limited and Blindvoice UK (£40,000 each); My Sister's Place Women's Advice Centre (£32,000); Elm Tree Community Association (£13,000); Cultures (CIC) (£7,500); Acklam Rugby Club and The Silhouettes Jazz Band (£5,000 each); Redcar Literary Institute (£4,000); Whale Hill Community Association (£3,600); Sir William Turner's Hospital (£3,100); and Pig Pen Festivals (£1,000).

FINANCES *Year* 2009–10 *Income* £1,899,716 *Grants* £1,086,821 *Assets* £9,818,260

TRUSTEES Alan Kitching; Peter Rowley; Christopher Hope; Pamela Taylor; Craig Monty; Rosemary Young; John Irwin; Marjory Houseman; Keith Robinson; Neil Kinley; John Harrison; Wendy Shepherd; Brian Beaumont.

PUBLICATIONS Periodic newsletter.

OTHER INFORMATION As with all community foundations grant schemes change frequently. Please contact the foundation or check their website for details of current programmes and their deadlines.

HOW TO APPLY Application forms are available on the foundation's website. Applicants can received a maximum of £5,000 in any 12 month period from one or a combination of funds.

WHO TO APPLY TO Hugh McGouran, Wallace house, Fallon Court, Preston Farm Industrial Estate, Stockton-on-Tees TS18 3TX *Tel* 01642 260860 *Fax* 01642 313700 *email* info@ teesvalleyfoundation.org *Website* www. teesvalleyfoundation.org

■ Tegham Limited

CC NO 283066   **ESTABLISHED** 1981

WHERE FUNDING CAN BE GIVEN UK.

WHO CAN BENEFIT Registered charities.

WHAT IS FUNDED Jewish Orthodox faith and the relief of poverty.

FINANCES *Year* 2009–10 *Income* £235,680 *Grants* £230,672 *Assets* £1,522,785

TRUSTEES Sylvia Fluss; Nizza Fluss.

HOW TO APPLY The trust has stated that it has enough causes to support and does not welcome other applications.

WHO TO APPLY TO Sylvia Fluss, Trustee, 22 Park Way, London NW11 0EX *email* admin@geraldkreditor. co.uk

■ The Templeton Goodwill Trust

SC NO SC004177   **ESTABLISHED** 1938

WHERE FUNDING CAN BE GIVEN Glasgow and the West of Scotland (the Glasgow postal area).

WHO CAN BENEFIT Scottish registered charities.

WHAT IS FUNDED General charitable purposes. It is interested in supporting organisations which help others. Types of beneficiaries include: youth organisations, medical research charities, churches, ex-services' organisations and other organisations concerned with social work and providing caring services for all age groups.

WHAT IS NOT FUNDED Support is given to Scottish registered charities only. Individuals are not supported and grants are generally not given to arts or cultural organisations.

TYPE OF GRANT Discretionary, both continuing annual sums and 'one-off' support grants.

RANGE OF GRANTS £450–£4,600.

SAMPLE GRANTS Previous beneficiaries include: Girl Guides Association (£6,500); SSAFA (£4,200); Salvation Army, Scout Association (£4,000 each); Scottish Furniture Trades Benevolent Association (£3,300); Cancer Research UK and Marie Curie Memorial Foundation (£2,800 each); Tenovus Scotland (£2,500); Scottish Bible Society (£1,900); Dyslexia Scotwest (£1,000); The Fishermen's Mission (£700); and Diabetes UK Scotland (£500).

FINANCES *Year* 2009–10 *Income* £15,599,300 *Grants* £100,000

TRUSTEES J H Millar, Chair; B Bannerman; W T P Barnstaple; C Barrowman.

HOW TO APPLY In writing to the correspondent, preferably including a copy of accounts. Applications should be received by April as the trustees meet once a year, at the end of April or in May. Initial telephone calls are welcome. An sae is required from applicants to receive a reply.

WHO TO APPLY TO W T P Barnstaple, Trustee and Administrator, 12 Doon Street, Motherwell ML1 2BN *Tel* 01698 262202

■ Tesco Charity Trust

CC NO 297126   **ESTABLISHED** 1987

WHERE FUNDING CAN BE GIVEN UK.

WHO CAN BENEFIT National and local charity appeals benefiting children's welfare and education, people who are elderly and people with disabilities.

WHAT IS FUNDED Main areas of interest are: local charities promoting welfare and education of children, people who are elderly and people who are disabled.

WHAT IS NOT FUNDED No grants to political organisations, individuals or towards new buildings. The trust will not make donations to other trusts or charities for onward transmission to other charitable organisations.

TYPE OF GRANT Generally one-off, or for one year or less.

RANGE OF GRANTS Up to £20,000.

SAMPLE GRANTS Grant beneficiaries and charitable expenditure included: Muscular Dystrophy Campaign (£3.1 million); Marie Curie Cancer Care (£995,000); General fundraising (£770,000); Children and youth causes (£400,000); Disabilities and health (£355,000); Causes for the elderly (£145,000); Army Benevolent Fund (£50,000); British Red Cross (£30,000); Barking Badgers (£27,000); The Zoological Society of London (£20,000); Dyslexia Action (£17,000) and Addington High School (£12,000).

FINANCES *Year* 2009–10 *Income* £5,931,000 *Grants* £6,914,000 *Assets* £606,000

TRUSTEES David Reid; Lucy Neville-Rolfe; Paul Smythe; Paul Dickens; Juliet Crisp; Christophe Roussel.

HOW TO APPLY **Community Awards Scheme:** Applications should be made via the charity's website. 'There are two categories of Community Awards: 1. Grants to support children's welfare and/or children's educations (including special needs schools); 2. Grants to support elderly people and/or adults and children with disabilities. There are two rounds of funding every year for each category, please see the timescales below. Applications made outside the timescales for your category cannot be accepted. Decisions will not be finalised for approximately 3 months after the closing date of each round. Please consider this when completing your application. *Grants for children's education and children's welfare:* applications should be made between 1 December and 31 January or 1 May and 30 June. *Grants for older people and adults and children with disabilities: applications should be made between:* 1 February and 31 March or 1 August and 30 September. NB: charities can only make one application per year. **Larger Grants (Trust Meeting Grant):** A certain amount of budget is available at each Tesco Charity Trust meeting. However the number of donation requests we receive always exceeds the funds available. Therefore some good applications, while meeting our criteria, may have to be refused.'

WHO TO APPLY TO Michelina Filocco, Secretary, Tesco Charity Trust, Tesco House, Delamare Road, Cheshunt, Hertfordshire EN8 9SL *Tel* 01992 644 143 *Fax* 01992 646794 *email* michelina.filocco@uk.tesco.com *Website* www.tescoplc.com/tescocharitytrust

■ Thackray Medical Research Trust

CC NO 702896　　**ESTABLISHED** 1990
WHERE FUNDING CAN BE GIVEN Worldwide.
WHO CAN BENEFIT Charitable organisations, university departments and individual researchers.
WHAT IS FUNDED Provision of medical supplies to the developing world and research into the history of medical procedures and products.

TYPE OF GRANT 'Pump-priming', start-up or organisational expenses where alternative funding is not available for medical supply organisations.

SAMPLE GRANTS Thackray Museum (£154,000); Paul Thackray Heritage Foundation (£5,000); BMA (£2,500); and the Liverpool School of Tropical Medicine (£1,400).

FINANCES *Year* 2009–10 *Income* £171,928 *Grants* £162,885 *Assets* £5,613,145

TRUSTEES William Kendall Mathie; Matthew Wrigley; Martin Schweiger; Christin Thackray; John Campbell.

OTHER INFORMATION The trust initiated and supported the establishment of the award-winning Thackray Museum in Leeds, one of the largest medical museums in the world, and continues to support the research resource there.

HOW TO APPLY Application forms and guidance notes are available from the website. Applications are usually considered in October and April but may be considered at other times. The closing date for applications is the last day of July and January respectively.

WHO TO APPLY TO The Chair of the Trustees, c/o Thackray Museum, Beckett Street, Leeds LS9 7LN *email* w.k.mathie@leeds.ac.uk *Website* www.tmrt.co.uk

■ The Thames Wharf Charity

CC NO 1000796　　**ESTABLISHED** 1990
WHERE FUNDING CAN BE GIVEN UK.
WHO CAN BENEFIT Charitable organisations.
WHAT IS FUNDED General charitable purposes.
WHAT IS NOT FUNDED No grants for the purchase of property, motor vehicles or holidays.

SAMPLE GRANTS Alzheimer's Society (£37,000); Cancer Research UK (£19,000); Ellenor Hospice Care (£13,000); Architectural Association, British Museum Friends and Schumacher College (£12,000); National Society for the Prevention of Cruelty to Children (£11,000); Friends of Vineyard School (£10,000); Age UK Age Concern (£6,000); British Heart Foundation and Practical Action (£5,000); Open City Architecture (£3,500); Nottingham Regional Society for Adults and Children with Autism (£2,000); Prisoners of Conscience Appeal Fund (£1,000); and West Suffolk Special Care Baby Unit (£275).

FINANCES *Year* 2009–10 *Income* £819,965 *Grants* £531,235 *Assets* £2,548,971

TRUSTEES Avtar Lotay; Patrick Burgess; Graham Stirk; Audrey Gale.

HOW TO APPLY In writing to the correspondent.

WHO TO APPLY TO Kenneth Hawkins, H W Lee Associates, New Derwent House, 69/73 Theobalds Road, London WC1X 8TA *Tel* 020 7025 4600

■ The Thistle Trust

CC NO 1091327　　**ESTABLISHED** 2002
WHERE FUNDING CAN BE GIVEN UK.
WHO CAN BENEFIT Charitable institutions or projects in the UK.
WHAT IS FUNDED The promotion of study and research in the arts; and furthering public knowledge and education of art.
WHAT IS NOT FUNDED No grants to individuals.
RANGE OF GRANTS £200–£8,000.

SAMPLE GRANTS Graeae, National Youth Theatre, Orchestra Europa Limited, Place and Royal School of Needlework (£2,000 each); Birmingham Royal Ballet, Bishopsgate Institute, City of Birmingham Symphony Orchestra and Corn Exchange Newbury (£1,000 each); Shakespeare Schools Festival (£900); and Dance Umbrella Ltd (£500).

FINANCES *Year* 2009–10 *Income* £32,784 *Grants* £30,700 *Assets* £1,133,032

TRUSTEES Madeleine, Lady Kleinwort; Catherine Trevelyan; Neil Morris; Donald McGilvray; Nicholas Kerr-Sheppard.

HOW TO APPLY In writing to the correspondent including most recent report and financial accounts. The trustees meet at least once a year with only successful applicants notified of the trustees' decision.

WHO TO APPLY TO Ran Amin, Kleinwort Benson, 30 Gresham Street, London EC2V 7PG

■ The Loke Wan Tho Memorial Foundation

CC NO 264273   **ESTABLISHED** 1972

WHERE FUNDING CAN BE GIVEN Worldwide.

WHO CAN BENEFIT Registered charities only.

WHAT IS FUNDED Medical studies and research; conservation and environment; and overseas aid.

TYPE OF GRANT One-off project and research grants.

SAMPLE GRANTS Durrell Wildlife Conservation (£9,400); and University of Adelaide (£5,500).

FINANCES *Year* 2009–10 *Income* £113,728 *Grants* £14,872 *Assets* £5,424,873

TRUSTEES Lady Y P McNeice; Mrs T S Tonkyn; A P Tonkyn.

HOW TO APPLY In writing to the correspondent.

WHO TO APPLY TO The Secretary, RBC Trust Company (International) Ltd, La Motte Chambers, St Helier, Jersey, Channel Islands JE1 1BJ *Tel* 01534 602000

■ The David Thomas Charitable Trust

CC NO 1083257   **ESTABLISHED** 2000

WHERE FUNDING CAN BE GIVEN UK, in particular Gloucester and surrounding districts.

WHO CAN BENEFIT Institutions and registered charities.

WHAT IS FUNDED Social welfare and general charitable purposes.

RANGE OF GRANTS Up to £10,000.

SAMPLE GRANTS Save the Children UK (£5,000); Cancer Research UK and Disasters Emergency Committee – Haiti Earthquake relief (£4,000 each).
Previous beneficiaries include: Oxfam (£9,000); UNICEF UK (£8,000); Save the Children UK (£5,000); Cancer Research UK (£4,000); British Red Cross, Elizabeth Finn Care, Help the Aged, Marie Curie Cancer Care, Multiple Sclerosis Society, NSPCC, the Salvation Army and Sense (£3,000 each); the Eve Appeal, Museum of Garden History, Royal British Legion, the Sandpiper Trust, Scots Guards Charitable Fund and St Mungo's Community Housing Association (£2,000 each); the Prostate Cancer Charity (£1,500); All Saints Church – Selsey, Cotswold Care Hospice, Gloucestershire Dance and James Hopkins Trust (£1,000 each); and Gloucestershire County Cricket Club (£500).

FINANCES *Year* 2009–10 *Income* £43,504 *Grants* £94,500 *Assets* £1,780,940

TRUSTEES David Thomas; Charles Clark; James Davidson; R F Trustee Co. Limited.

HOW TO APPLY In writing to the correspondent.

WHO TO APPLY TO The Trustees, c/o R F Trustee Co. Limited, Ely House, 37 Dover Street, London W1S 4NJ *Tel* 020 7036 5685

■ The Arthur and Margaret Thompson Charitable Trust

SC NO SC012103   **ESTABLISHED** 1973

WHERE FUNDING CAN BE GIVEN The towns or burghs of Kinross and Milnathort.

WHO CAN BENEFIT Registered charities in the beneficial area.

WHAT IS FUNDED General charitable purposes.

FINANCES *Year* 2009–10 *Income* £14,871,400

TRUSTEES Dr D P Anderson; Revd Dr J P L Munro; J Greig; D L Sands; A G Dorward; I D Donaldson.

OTHER INFORMATION The trust gives grants to individuals and organisations.

HOW TO APPLY The trustees meet to consider applications about every four months.

WHO TO APPLY TO The Trustees, Miller Hendry, 10 Blackfriars Street, Perth PH1 5NS

■ The Elspeth J Thompson Charitable Trust

CC NO 1135158   **ESTABLISHED** 2010

WHERE FUNDING CAN BE GIVEN Worldwide.

WHO CAN BENEFIT Registered charities.

WHAT IS FUNDED General charitable purposes.

TRUSTEES Elspeth Thompson; David Longton; Gary Rycroft.

HOW TO APPLY In writing to the correspondent.

WHO TO APPLY TO Gary Rycroft, Trustee, Joseph A Jones & Co Solicitors, 6 Fenton Street, Lancaster LA1 1TE *Tel* 01524 63371 *Fax* 01524 65818 *email* office@jajsolicitors.co.uk

■ The Maurice and Vivien Thompson Charitable Trust

CC NO 1085041   **ESTABLISHED** 2000

WHERE FUNDING CAN BE GIVEN UK.

WHO CAN BENEFIT UK registered charities.

WHAT IS FUNDED General charitable purposes.

SAMPLE GRANTS Leicestershire First (£107,000). Previous years' beneficiaries include: Beacon Fellowship Charitable Trust (£15,000); Martin Johnson Development Scholarship (£7,500); Pelican Cancer Foundation (£3,000); Leicester and Rutland Crimebeat (£1,800); Shackleton Foundation and Sight for Africa (£1,000 each); RIED (£200); and Bridge2Aid (£100).

FINANCES *Year* 2009–10 *Income* £48,532 *Grants* £107,240 *Assets* £1,187,779

TRUSTEES M N B Thompson; Mrs V Thomson; P Rhodes.

HOW TO APPLY In writing to the correspondent.

WHO TO APPLY TO M N B Thompson, Trustee, 2 The Orchard, London W4 1JX *Tel* 020 8995 1547

Think carefully about every application. Is it justified?

933

■ The Thompson Family Charitable Trust

cc no 326801 **established** 1985
WHERE FUNDING CAN BE GIVEN UK.
WHO CAN BENEFIT Registered charities only.
WHAT IS FUNDED General charitable purposes, although the trustees are mostly interested in educational, medical and veterinary organisations, particularly those concerned with horses and horseracing.
WHAT IS NOT FUNDED No grants to individuals.
TYPE OF GRANT The trust makes one-off grants, recurring grants and pledges.
RANGE OF GRANTS Generally £200–£5,000, occasionally larger.
SAMPLE GRANTS Home of Horseracing Trust (£500,000); English PEN (£30,000); BBC Children in Need (£20,000); Multiple Sclerosis Society (£15,000); Cambridge Women's Aid and the North London Hospice (£10,000 each); British Horseracing Education and Standards Trust and Headway (£5,000 each); Cancer Research UK (£3,000); Addenbrooke's Charitable Trust and the Richard Dunwoody 1,000 Mile Challenge Trust (£1,000 each); and Girlguiding UK and the Injured Jockey Fund (£500 each).
FINANCES *Year* 2009–10 *Income* £4,181,081 *Grants* £648,075 *Assets* £75,425,624
TRUSTEES David B Thompson; Patricia Thompson; Katherine P Woodward.
OTHER INFORMATION The trust regularly builds up its reserves to enable it to make large donations in the future, for example towards the construction of new medical or educational facilities. 'It is the policy of the charity to hold reserves which will enable [it] to make major donations for capital projects in the near future (for example, to fund the construction and endowment of new medical or educational facilities) and appropriate projects are currently being investigated. [. . .] In addition to such capital projects it is envisaged that grants to other charities will in future be made at a higher annual level than in recent years.'
HOW TO APPLY In writing to the correspondent.
WHO TO APPLY TO Katherine P Woodward, Hillsdown Court, 15 Totteridge Common, London N20 8LR

■ The Thompson6 Charitable Trust

cc no 1137853 **established** 2010
WHERE FUNDING CAN BE GIVEN UK.
WHO CAN BENEFIT Registered charities.
WHAT IS FUNDED General charitable purposes.
TRUSTEES Coutts & Co.
HOW TO APPLY In writing to the correspondent.
WHO TO APPLY TO Coutts & Co, Trustee Dept, 440 Strand, London WC2R 0QS *Tel* 020 7663 6812

■ The Len Thomson Charitable Trust

sc no SC000981 **established** 1989
WHERE FUNDING CAN BE GIVEN Scotland, with a preference for Midlothian, particularly Dalkeith.
WHO CAN BENEFIT Charitable organisations.
WHAT IS FUNDED The trust supports young people, local community organisations and medical research.
RANGE OF GRANTS £1,000–£5,000.
SAMPLE GRANTS Previous beneficiaries include: The Edinburgh Sick Kids Friends Foundation

(£5,000); Brass in the Park (£3,000); CHAS, Maggie's Centre and Mercy Ships (£2,000 each); and British Red Cross, Lothian Special Olympics, Newtongrange Children's Gala Day, the Princess Royal Trust for Carers and Save the Children Fund (£1,000 each).
FINANCES *Year* 2009–10 *Income* £1,682,400
TRUSTEES Douglas A Connell; Mrs Elizabeth Thomson.
OTHER INFORMATION No grants are made directly to individuals.
HOW TO APPLY The trust does not reply to unsolicited applications.
WHO TO APPLY TO Douglas A Connell, Trustee, Turcan Connell WS, Princes Exchange, 1 Earl Grey Street, Edinburgh EH3 9EE *Tel* 0131 228 8111 *email* dac@turcanconnell.com

■ The Sue Thomson Foundation

cc no 298808 **established** 1988
WHERE FUNDING CAN BE GIVEN UK, Sussex, London or Surrey.
WHO CAN BENEFIT Organisations.
WHAT IS FUNDED (i) Major grants – The majority of the funds went to Christ's Hospital, which received £82,000. The foundation nominates one new entrant each year from a needy background to the school, subject to the child meeting Christ's Hospital's own admissions criteria academically, socially and in terms of need. The foundation commits to contributing to the child's costs at a level agreed with Christ's Hospital for as long as each of them remains in the school. (ii) Regular grants – It is the policy of the trustees to provide up to 10% of the foundation's available income each year for grants in this category, subject to the foundation's commitments to Christ's Hospital having been satisfied. Charities eligible for consideration for grants at this level include: Charities related to Christ's Hospital including the sister school, King Edward's – Witley; UK booktrade charities, including the charities of the Worshipful Company of Stationers and Newspaper Makers; Suitable grantmaking charities selected in recognition of pro-bono professional work done for the foundation by its trustees or others; Special situations or other applications at the trustees' discretion. Grants in this category may be spread over a period of years. (iii) Special grants – It is the policy of the trustees to set aside a further 10% of available income each year for this programme, subject to its commitments in the major and medium categories and other financial needs having been met. Special grants are awarded to up to four small charities at any one time. They are confined to charities that support young and older people in need through no fault of their own, often via well run small self-help organisations. They are confined to charities in Sussex, Surrey or London.
WHAT IS NOT FUNDED No grants to large, national charities (except Christ's Hospital) or individuals, except as part of a specific scheme. No research projects, charities concerned with animals, birds, the environment, gardens or historic buildings.
TYPE OF GRANT Major grants which are above £5,000; regular grants which can be from £500 to £5,000; special grants which can be up to £3,000 per year.
RANGE OF GRANTS Major grants which can be above £3,000 in any one year; Medium grants which can be from £500 to £3,000 in any one year;

Special grants which can be up to £3,000 per year for periods of 1–3 years.

SAMPLE GRANTS The Leonard Sainer Legal Education Foundation and the Sussex Snowdrop – Chichester (£3,000 each); Book Trade Benevolent Society and The Bridewell Foundation (£2,000 each); the National Literacy Trust – London (£1,400); and The Publishing Training Centre and the Stationers' Foundation (£500 each).

FINANCES *Year* 2009–10 *Income* £154,155 *Grants* £107,941 *Assets* £2,418,631

TRUSTEES Susan M Mitchell, Chair; Timothy J Binnington; Charles L Corman; Kathleen Duncan; Susannah Holliman.

OTHER INFORMATION The grant total includes £7,000 paid to individual students.

HOW TO APPLY In writing to the correspondent, or preliminary telephone enquiry. Unsolicited applications are not acknowledged, unless accompanied by an sae or an email address. Grant-making policies are published in the annual report and accounts, available from the Charity Commission website, and in relevant charity sector publications when the trustees are able to do so free of charge. This statement of policies is provided to anyone on request.

WHO TO APPLY TO Susannah Holliman, Administrator, 3 Danehurst Street, London SW6 6SA *Tel* 07508 038632 *email* stfsusannah@aol.com

....

■ The Sir Jules Thorn Charitable Trust

CC NO 233838   **ESTABLISHED** 1964
WHERE FUNDING CAN BE GIVEN Unrestricted.
WHO CAN BENEFIT Registered charities engaged in medical research (universities/hospitals only); medically related work; and humanitarian work.
WHAT IS FUNDED Medical research with strong clinical relevance, medicine generally, and small grants for humanitarian appeals.
WHAT IS NOT FUNDED The trust does not fund: research which is considered unlikely to provide clinical benefit within five years; research which could reasonably be expected to be supported by a disease specific funder, unless there is a convincing reason why the trust has been approached; research into cancer or AIDS, for the sole reason that they are relatively well funded elsewhere; 'top up' grants for ongoing projects; research which will also involve other funders, apart from the institution itself; individuals – except in the context of a project undertaken by an approved institution which is in receipt of a grant from the trust; research or data collection overseas; research institutions which are not registered charities; third parties raising resources to fund research themselves.
TYPE OF GRANT Medical research projects usually covering a period of up to three years, plus one-off donations to other charities.
SAMPLE GRANTS Combat Stress (£759,000), over 3 years for a new Community Outreach team providing practical as well as therapeutic assistance for veterans suffering psychological injuries attributable to their military service; The Queen's University of Belfast – School of Medicine, Dentistry and Biomedical Sciences (£500,000), for 'Vascular stem cell therapy for ischaemic retionopathies' research project; The National Society for Epilepsy (£300,000), towards the cost of a new Epilepsy Research Centre to be built at the society's Chalfont campus; National Star College for Disabled Youth (£200,000), to assist with a new

Therapies Centre to enhance the facilities provided for young people aged 16 – 25 with severe or complex physical disabilities or acquired brain injuries; and the Children's Trust – Tadworth (£200,000), towards the charity's appeal for funding to create new facilities to extend residential education for those aged 19 – 25 with profound and multiple learning difficulties. Small grants of £1,000 included those to: Barnet and Chase Farm Hospitals NHS Trust; Children's Country Holiday Fund; Hampshire and Isle of Wight Air Ambulance; Hospice of the Valleys; Medical Foundation for the Care of Victims of Torture; NSF Scotland; Rainbow Trust; Royal Hospital for Neuro-disability; The Children's Foundation; The Police Rehabilitation Trust; Wessex Autistic Society; and the Variety Club.

FINANCES *Year* 2009–10 *Income* £2,408,739 *Grants* £2,835,825 *Assets* £106,381,040

TRUSTEES Mrs Elizabeth S Charal; Prof. Sir Ravinder N Maini; Sir Bruce McPhail; Nancy V Pearcey; Christopher Sporborg; William Sporborg; John Rhodes; Prof. David Russell-Jones.

HOW TO APPLY **Medically-related grants:** appeals are considered annually by the trustees, usually in November. There is no specific application form. Proposals should be submitted to the trust's director and should cover: the background to the appeal, including any brochures and feasibility assessment; information about the applicant, which must be an institution having charitable status. Applications from individuals cannot be considered; details of the appeal, including the total sum being raised, donations or pledges already received, and the plans for securing the remainder. Time scales for implementation should be given; the latest trustees' report and audited financial statements should be provided. Potential applicants who wish to establish whether their appeal would fit the criteria should contact the trust.
Small grants: on an application form available from the trust's website or by contacting the office. There are no specific dates for submitting applications. Appeals may be made at any time and will be considered by the trustees as soon as possible, depending on volumes.

WHO TO APPLY TO David H Richings, Director, 24 Manchester Square, London W1U 3TH *Tel* 020 7487 5851 *Fax* 020 7224 3976 *email* info@julesthorntrust.org.uk *Website* www.julesthorntrust.org.uk

....

■ The Thornton Foundation

CC NO 326383   **ESTABLISHED** 1983
WHERE FUNDING CAN BE GIVEN UK.
WHO CAN BENEFIT Charities which are personally known to the trustees.
WHAT IS FUNDED General charitable purposes.
SAMPLE GRANTS St Dunstan-in-the-West (£50,000); Institute of Cancer Research (£17,000); The Cirdan Sailing Trust and National Gallery (£10,000 each); The Healing Foundation (£7,500); Museum of London and Helen House (£6,000 each); Action for Blind People, Books Abroad, Keble College – Oxford and Wessex Children's Hospice (£5,000 each); the Tait Memorial Trust (£3,000); BREAK and Prisoners of Conscience (£2,000 each); the Handel Society (£1,000) and British Heart Foundation and Cancer Research UK (£500 each).
FINANCES *Year* 2009–10 *Income* £58,388 *Grants* £153,745 *Assets* £4,591,089

TRUSTEES R C Thornton, Chair; A H Isaacs; H D C Thornton; Mrs S J Thornton.

HOW TO APPLY The trust strongly emphasises that it does not accept unsolicited applications, and, as it states above, only organisations that are known to one of the trustees will be considered for support. Any unsolicited applications will not receive a reply.

WHO TO APPLY TO A H Isaacs, Stephenson Harwood, 1 St Paul's Churchyard, London EC4M 8SH *Tel* 020 7329 4422

■ The Thornton Trust

CC NO 205357   **ESTABLISHED** 1962
WHERE FUNDING CAN BE GIVEN UK and overseas.
WHO CAN BENEFIT Charitable organisations.
WHAT IS FUNDED 'Promoting and furthering education and the evangelical Christian faith and assisting in the relief of sickness, suffering and poverty.'
SAMPLE GRANTS Africa Inland Mission (£20,000); St Andrew's Church, Hertford (£15,000); Bible Society and Saffron Walden Baptist Church (£11,000 each); London City Mission (£10,000); Redcliffe Missionary College (£6,000); Mission Aviation Fellowship (£4,000); Young Life Hyt (£3,000); Urban Saints (£2,000); Practical Action (£1,000); and National Prayer Breakfast (£100).
FINANCES *Year* 2009–10 *Income* £66,603 *Grants* £151,740 *Assets* £970,736
TRUSTEES D H Thornton; Mrs B Y Thornton; J D Thornton.
HOW TO APPLY The trust states: 'Our funds are fully committed and we regret that we are unable to respond to the many unsolicited calls for assistance we are now receiving.'
WHO TO APPLY TO D H Thornton, Trustee, Hunters Cottage, Hunters Yard, Debden Road, Saffron Walden, Essex CB11 4AA *Tel* 01799 526712

■ The Three Guineas Trust

CC NO 1059652   **ESTABLISHED** 1996
WHERE FUNDING CAN BE GIVEN Worldwide, in practice mainly UK.
WHO CAN BENEFIT Currently, registered charities working with people suffering from autism and Asperger's Syndrome.
WHAT IS FUNDED Initiatives related to autism and Asperger's Syndrome. Climate change research projects.
WHAT IS NOT FUNDED No grants for individuals or for research (except where it has an immediate benefit).
TYPE OF GRANT One off and recurrent.
RANGE OF GRANTS Typically up to £100,000.
SAMPLE GRANTS University of Cambridge (£874,000), for a project to construct a new global economic model of a world free from dependence on carbon; Bexley and Bromley Advocacy (£105,000); Autism Concern (£90,000); Jigsaw Group – Staffordshire (£9,000); and Sheffield Autistic Society (£5,000).
FINANCES *Year* 2009–10 *Income* £291,386 *Grants* £1,273,591 *Assets* £12,127,418
TRUSTEES Clare Sainsbury; Bernard Willis; Judith Portrait.
OTHER INFORMATION The trust is one of the Sainsbury Family Charitable Trusts which share a common administration. An application to one is taken as an application to all.
HOW TO APPLY See the guidance for applicants in the entry for the Sainsbury Family Charitable Trusts. A single application will be considered for support by all the trusts in the group. 'The trustees do not at present wish to invite applications, except in the field of autism and Asperger's syndrome, where they will examine unsolicited proposals alongside those that result from their own research and contacts with expert individuals and organisations working in this field. The trustees prefer to support innovative schemes that can be successfully replicated or become self-sustaining. They are also keen that, wherever possible, schemes supporting adults and teenagers on the autistic spectrum should include clients/service users in decision-making.'
WHO TO APPLY TO Alan Bookbinder, Director, Allington House, 1st Floor, 150 Victoria Street, London SW1E 5AE *Tel* 020 7410 0330 *Fax* 020 7410 0332 *Website* www.sfct.org.uk

---

■ The Three Oaks Trust

CC NO 297079   **ESTABLISHED** 1987
WHERE FUNDING CAN BE GIVEN UK and overseas, with a preference for West Sussex.
WHO CAN BENEFIT Organisations that promote the welfare of individuals and families. Grants are also made to individuals via statutory authorities or voluntary agencies.
WHAT IS FUNDED The trust regularly supports the same welfare organisations in the UK and overseas each year.
WHAT IS NOT FUNDED No direct applications from individuals. Applications from students for gap year activities are not a priority and will not be funded.
SAMPLE GRANTS Crawley Open House and Dalesdown and Raynauds Association (£15,000 each); Family Foundation Trust (Dalesdown) and Sussex Probation (£10,000 each); Mind – Brighton and Hove and The Connection at St Martin-in-the-Fields (£5,000 each); and Dermatrust (£3,000).
FINANCES *Year* 2009–10 *Income* £207,819 *Grants* £189,000 *Assets* £5,947,549
TRUSTEES Dianne Margaret Ward; Polly Elizabeth Hobbs; Carol Vivian Foreman; Carol Johnson; Pam Wilkinson; Dr P Kane; Sarah A Kane; Giles Duncan Wilkinson; Three Oaks Family Trust Co Ltd.
OTHER INFORMATION Additionally, in 2009–10, donations were made to 340 individuals totalling £57,000. Overseas donations of cash and in-kind were made totalling £98,000.
HOW TO APPLY The following guidelines are taken from the 2009–10 annual accounts: 'Grants are made to organisations that promote the welfare of individuals and families. In general, the trustees intend to continue supporting the organisations that they have supported in the past. Periodically and generally annually the trustees review the list of registered charities and institutions to which grants have been given and consider additions and deletions from the list. To save on administration, the trustees do not respond to requests unless they are considering making a donation. Requests from organisations for donations in excess of £2,000 are considered by the trustees on a quarterly basis in meetings usually held in January, April, July and September.' For the full guidelines, please visit the trust's website.
WHO TO APPLY TO The Trustees, P O Box 893, Horsham, West Sussex RH12 9JD *email* contact@thethreeoakstrust.co.uk *Website* www.thethreeoakstrust.co.uk

■ The Thriplow Charitable Trust

CC NO 1025531   **ESTABLISHED** 1993

WHERE FUNDING CAN BE GIVEN Preference for British institutions.

WHO CAN BENEFIT Universities, university colleges and other places of learning benefiting young adults and older people, academics, research workers and students.

WHAT IS FUNDED Advancement of higher and further education, the promotion of research and the dissemination of the results of such research.

WHAT IS NOT FUNDED Grants can only be made to charitable bodies or component parts of charitable bodies. In no circumstances can grants be made to individuals.

TYPE OF GRANT Research study funds, research fellowships, certain academic training schemes, computer facilities and building projects related to research.

RANGE OF GRANTS £2,000–£8,000.

SAMPLE GRANTS Previous beneficiaries have included: Cambridge University Library, Centre of South Asian Studies, Computer Aid International, Fight for Sight, Fitzwilliam Museum, Foundation for Prevention of Blindness, Foundation of Research Students, Hearing Research Trust, Inspire Foundation, Loughborough University, Marie Curie Cancer Care, Royal Botanic Gardens, Royal College of Music, Transplant Trust and University of Reading.

FINANCES *Year* 2009–10 *Income* £453,543 *Grants* £79,276 *Assets* £3,242,627

TRUSTEES Sir Peter Swinnerton-Dyer, Chair; Dr Harriet Crawford; Prof. Christopher Bayly; Sir David Wallace; Dame Jean Thomas.

HOW TO APPLY There is no application form. A letter of application should specify the purpose for which funds are sought and the costings of the project. It should be indicated whether other applications for funds are pending and, if the funds are to be channelled to an individual or a small group, what degree of supervision over the quality of the work would be exercised by the institution. Trustee meetings are held twice a year – in spring and in autumn.

WHO TO APPLY TO The Trustees, PO Box 225, Royston SG8 1BG

■ Mrs R P Tindall's Charitable Trust

CC NO 250558   **ESTABLISHED** 1966

WHERE FUNDING CAN BE GIVEN Africa, Wiltshire, Dorset.

WHO CAN BENEFIT Charitable organisations, churches, students in need and members of the clergy.

WHAT IS FUNDED Relief of poverty, furtherance of the work of the Christian church and advancement of education. Grants are also made to students in need and for the welfare of the clergy and their dependants.

FINANCES *Year* 2010 *Income* £85,000 *Grants* £65,000 *Assets* £2,000,000

TRUSTEES M R F Newman; G Fletcher; Revd Canon A C Philp; S Herbert; Miss C Newman; Mrs N A Halls.

OTHER INFORMATION Grants to individuals totalled £4,000.

HOW TO APPLY In writing to the correspondent enclosing an sae.

WHO TO APPLY TO Mrs I Rider, Secretary, Appletree House, Wishford Road, Middle Woodford, Salisbury SP4 6NG *Tel* 01722 782329

■ The Tinsley Foundation

CC NO 1076537   **ESTABLISHED** 1999

WHERE FUNDING CAN BE GIVEN UK and overseas.

WHO CAN BENEFIT Charitable organisations.

WHAT IS FUNDED The foundation will support: charities which promote human rights and democratisation and/or which educate against racism, discrimination and oppression; charities which promote self-help in fighting poverty and homelessness; and charities which provide reproductive health education in underdeveloped countries, but specifically excluding charities whose policy is against abortion or birth control.

SAMPLE GRANTS Human Rights Watch Charitable Trust (£25,000); Article 1 Charitable Trust and Network for Africa (£15,000 each); Medact and Peace Brigades International (£10,000 each); One World Action (£5,000); Global Dialogue and The Big Issue Foundation (£2,500 each); and Africa Now, Computer Aid International, English National Opera, Gatwick Detainees Welfare Group, Medical Foundation, Release International, St Mungo's and The Cambodia Trust (£1,000 each).

FINANCES *Year* 2009–10 *Income* £151,941 *Grants* £120,000 *Assets* £2,687,783

TRUSTEES H C Tinsley; R C Tinsley; T A Jones.

HOW TO APPLY 'While the charity welcomes applications from eligible potential grantees, the trustees seek out organisations that will effectively fulfil our objectives.'

WHO TO APPLY TO Henry C Tinsley, Trustee, 14 St Mary's Street, Stamford, Lincolnshire PE9 2DF *Tel* 01780 762056 *Fax* 01780 767594 *email* hctinsley@aol.com

■ The Tisbury Telegraph Trust

CC NO 328595   **ESTABLISHED** 1990

WHERE FUNDING CAN BE GIVEN UK and overseas.

WHO CAN BENEFIT Registered charities and churches.

WHAT IS FUNDED Christian, overseas aid and general charitable purposes. Most distributions are to charities of which the trustees have personal knowledge. Other applications are unlikely to be successful.

WHAT IS NOT FUNDED No applications from individuals for expeditions or courses can be considered.

TYPE OF GRANT Core costs, one-off, project, research and running costs will be considered.

SAMPLE GRANTS World Vision (£77,000); Friends of Kiwoko Hospital (£20,000); All Saints Church (£15,500); St Mary's Building Fund (£15,000); Practical Action (£10,500); Helen and Douglas House and Romania Care (£10,000 each); Crisis (£2,000 each); and Habitat for Humanity and Salvation Army (£1,000 each).

FINANCES *Year* 2009–10 *Income* £191,692 *Grants* £217,180 *Assets* £127,927

TRUSTEES Alison Davidson; John Davidson; Eleanor Orr; Roger Orr; Sonia Phippard.

HOW TO APPLY In writing to the correspondent. However, it is extremely rare that unsolicited applications are successful and the trust does not respond to applicants unless an sae is included. No telephone applications please.

WHO TO APPLY TO Mrs E Orr, Trustee, 35 Kitto Road, Telegraph Hill, London SE14 5TW *Tel* 020 7732 6550

Think carefully about every application. Is it justified?

937

■ TJH Foundation

cc no 1077311   **established** 1999
where funding can be given England and Wales with some preference for organisations based in the North West of England.
who can benefit Charitable organisations.
what is funded Social welfare, medical causes and racing welfare.
type of grant Mostly one-off.
sample grants Kevin Gray Memorial Charity (£15,000); The Princess Royal Trust for Carers (£4,000); Marie Curie Cancer Care and R.N.L.I (£500 each); Well Being for Women (£250); Racing Welfare (£50).
finances Year 2009–10 Income £25,500 Grants £22,550 Assets £308,896
trustees T J Hemmings, Chair; Mrs P A Clare; J C Kay; Ms K Revitt.
how to apply In writing to the correspondent.
who to apply to J C Kay, Trustee, Gleadhill House, Dawbers Lane, Euxton, Chorley, Lancashire PR7 6EA

■ The Tobacco Pipe Makers and Tobacco Trade Benevolent Fund

cc no 1135646   **established** 1961
where funding can be given City of London, and Sevenoaks School.
who can benefit Educational establishments benefiting children, young adults, students, and people disadvantaged by poverty.
what is funded To assist in the education of those who would not otherwise be able to afford it. To support only those charities with which the company can have an active relationship.
what is not funded No grants to individuals.
type of grant Ongoing scholarships.
range of grants £500–£12,000.
sample grants Riding for the Disabled – Barrow Farm (£12,000); Oxford & Bermondsey Youth Club, Speech and Language Hearing Centre (£10,000 each); Sevenoaks School (£8,500); Guildhall School of Music Awards (£8,000); Arundel Castle Cricket Foundation (£5,000); Headway (£1,000) and Corporation of the Sons of the Clergy (£500).
finances Year 2010–11 Income £363,505 Grants £63,852 Assets £5,056,070
trustees Roger L H Merton; Stephen L Preedy; Fiona Adler; George Lankester; Derek C P Harris; Alan G F Henderson; Graham Blashill; David Glynn-Jones; Nigel M S Rich.
other information The trust also runs a welfare support scheme for individuals with links to the tobacco trade. See the trust's website for further information.
how to apply The trust prefers applications from small charities and organisations who have links, including geographically, to the city of London. Applications in writing to the secretary. The committee meets regularly during the year to review and approve grants.
who to apply to Simon G Orlik, Clerk, Simon G Orlik, 23 Downsview Gardens, Dorking, Surrey RH4 2DX Tel 01306 877753 email info@ tobaccocharity.org.uk Website www. tobaccocharity.org.uk

■ The Tolkien Trust

cc no 273615   **established** 1977
where funding can be given UK, with some preference for Oxfordshire, and overseas.
who can benefit Mainly registered charities.
what is funded General charitable purposes including charities and charitable causes supporting children, young people, families, older people, homeless people, socially disadvantaged people, organisations supporting overseas aid and development, refugees, medical aid, research, education, the arts and religion.
range of grants £3,000–£200,000.
sample grants Oxfam's East Africa Appeal (£1 million); Action Against Hunger, Médecins Sans Frontières and UNICEF, which received £200,000 each to support their work following the earthquake in Haiti; University of Manitoba – Canada (£180,000 in total); Rebuild Sri Lanka (£80,000); WaterAid (£50,000); Practical Action (£45,000); Breakthrough Breast Cancer (£35,000); Rochdale Special Needs Cycling Club and Ty Hafan Children's Hospice (£30,000 each); National Deaf Children's Society (£24,000); Trust for Research and Education on the Arms Trade and the City of Birmingham Symphony Orchestra (£20,000 each); Christian Peace Education Fund and West London Churches Homeless Concern (£15,000 each); British Red Cross, Friends of Cardigan Bay and Oxford Playhouse Trust (£10,000 each); Cancer Research UK, Lincoln Clinic and Centre for Psychotherapy and Woman for Women International UK (£5,000 each); and the Poetry Trust (£3,000).
finances Year 2009–10 Income £2,017,443 Grants £3,697,000 Assets £26,290,897
trustees Christopher Reuel Tolkien; Priscilla Mary Anne Reuel Tolkien; Michael Reuel Tolkien; Baillie Tolkien.
other information The significant increase in the trust's finances is due to an out-of-court settlement with New Line Cinema in September 2009 regarding the trust's entitlement to its share of the profits from the hugely successful Lord of the Rings trilogy of films.
how to apply In writing to the correspondent. The majority of donations are made to charities or causes selected by the trustees. There are no guidelines for applicants and the trust does not enter into correspondence with applicants in the interests of controlling administrative costs. Decisions about donations annually at the end of March/ beginning of April. Therefore, any applications should be timed to reach the trust by no later than 15 December in the preceding year.
who to apply to Cathleen Blackburn, Manches LLP, 9400 Garsington Road, Oxford Business Park North, Oxford OX4 2HN Tel 01865 722106 Fax 01865 201012 email cathleen.blackburn@ manches.com

■ Tollemache (Buckminster) Charitable Trust

cc no 271795   **established** 1976
where funding can be given UK.
who can benefit Voluntary organisations and charitable groups only.
what is funded General charitable purposes.
what is not funded No grants to individuals.
sample grants Previous beneficiaries have included: Alzheimer's Society, Bassingthorpe PCC, Brooke Hospital for Animals, Buckminster Primary School, Buckminster United Football Club, Cancer Research, Cats Protection League, Coldstream Guards Association, Coston PCC, Ex Services Mental Welfare, NSPCC, Oxfam, Parkinson's Disease Society, Rainbows, Royal

Hospital for Neuro-Disability, Royal Star & Garter Home, Rutland House School for Parents, Sight Savers, Society for the Protection of Animals Abroad, South Witham PCC, Springfield Rifle Club, St Peter's Church and WSPA.
FINANCES *Year* 2010–11 *Income* £24,566 *Grants* £22,000
TRUSTEES Richard Tollemache; William H G Wilks.
HOW TO APPLY In writing to the secretary. No acknowledgements sent.
WHO TO APPLY TO Roger Stafford, Estate Office, Buckminster, Grantham, Lincolnshire NG33 5SD *Tel* 01476 860471 *Fax* 01476 861235

■ **Tomchei Torah Charitable Trust**
CC NO 802125　　**ESTABLISHED** 1989
WHERE FUNDING CAN BE GIVEN UK.
WHO CAN BENEFIT Jewish people and organisations.
WHAT IS FUNDED Jewish causes.
RANGE OF GRANTS Average £5,000.
SAMPLE GRANTS Previously: Friends of Mir; MST College; Friends of Sanz Institutions; United Talmudical Associates; Ezer North West; Menorah Grammar School; Friends of Torah Ohr; Ruzin Sadagora Trust; Achisomoch Aid Co and Chesed Charity Trust.
FINANCES *Year* 2009–10 *Income* £7,330 *Grants* £247,476
TRUSTEES I J Kohn; S M Kohn; A Frei.
HOW TO APPLY In writing to the correspondent at any time.
WHO TO APPLY TO I J Kohn, 36 Cranbourne Gardens, London NW11 0HP *Tel* 020 8458 5706

■ **The Tompkins Foundation**
CC NO 281405　　**ESTABLISHED** 1980
WHERE FUNDING CAN BE GIVEN UK, with a stated preference for the parishes of Hampstead Norreys, Berkshire and West Grinstead, West Sussex.
WHO CAN BENEFIT Registered charities.
WHAT IS FUNDED Health, education, religion and community purposes.
WHAT IS NOT FUNDED Grants are not given to individuals.
TYPE OF GRANT One-off and recurring.
RANGE OF GRANTS £500–£50,000.
SAMPLE GRANTS The Foundation of Nursing Studies and the Hesperus Foundation (£50,000 each); Right to Play (£30,000); Chicken Shed Theatre, Great Ormond Street Hospital Children's Charity, St John's Hospice and the Passage (£25,000 each); Leonard Cheshire Foundation, Order of Malta Volunteers, The Place 2 Be and the Police Foundation (£20,000); Help for Heroes, Longview and Toynbee Hall (£10,000 each); CTBF Enterprises (£9,000); and the Anna Freud Centre, Gayfields Home of Rest, Maggie's Centre and Variety Club Children's Charity (£5,000 each).
FINANCES *Year* 2009–10 *Income* £409,211 *Grants* £394,000 *Assets* £10,689,363
TRUSTEES Elizabeth Tompkins; Peter Vaines.
HOW TO APPLY In writing to the correspondent. 'The trustees aim to respond to need and therefore consider that more specific plans [for the future] would be too restrictive.'
WHO TO APPLY TO Richard Geoffrey Morris, 7 Belgrave Square, London SW1X 8PH *Tel* 020 7235 9322 *Fax* 020 7259 5129

■ **Toni and Guy Charitable Foundation Limited**
CC NO 1095285　　**ESTABLISHED** 2002
WHERE FUNDING CAN BE GIVEN England and Wales.
WHO CAN BENEFIT Registered charities and hospitals and Toni and Guy employees.
WHAT IS FUNDED General charitable purposes.
RANGE OF GRANTS £1,000–£50,000.
SAMPLE GRANTS Variety Club (£50,000); Italian Church Charity (£4,000); Guy Mascolo Memorial (£4,000); Hair and Beauty Benevolent (£5,000); MacMillan (£8,000).
FINANCES *Year* 2009–10 *Income* £136,525 *Grants* £112,017 *Assets* £26,166
TRUSTEES Richard A M Freeman; Pauline R Mascolo; Rupert Berrow; James McDonnell; Toni Mascolo.
HOW TO APPLY In writing to the correspondent. The trustees meet regularly throughout the year to consider grants to be made.
WHO TO APPLY TO Emma Chapman, 58–60 Stamford Street, London SE1 9LX *Tel* 020 79219091 *email* charitablefoundation@toniandguy.co.uk *Website* www.toniandguy.com/pages/category/charity

■ **The Torah Temimah Trust**
CC NO 802390　　**ESTABLISHED** 1989
WHERE FUNDING CAN BE GIVEN UK.
WHO CAN BENEFIT Orthodox Jewish organisations.
WHAT IS FUNDED Orthodox Jewish religious education and religion.
FINANCES *Year* 2009–10 *Income* £61,554 *Grants* £52,750 *Assets* £115,108
TRUSTEES Mrs E Bernath; M Bernath; A Grunfeld.
HOW TO APPLY In writing to the correspondent.
WHO TO APPLY TO Mrs E Bernath, Trustee, 16 Reizel Close, Stamford Hill, London N16 5GY *Tel* 020 8800 3021

■ **Toras Chesed (London) Trust**
CC NO 1110653　　**ESTABLISHED** 2005
WHERE FUNDING CAN BE GIVEN Worldwide.
WHO CAN BENEFIT Jewish organisations.
WHAT IS FUNDED the objects of the charity are: the advancement of the Orthodox Jewish faith; the advancement of Orthodox Jewish religious education; the relief of poverty and infirmity among persons of the Jewish faith; to provide a safe and user friendly environment to share mutual problems and experiences; to encourage active parental participation in their children's education.
FINANCES *Year* 2009–10 *Income* £217,149 *Grants* £215,153 *Assets* -£4,310
TRUSTEES A Stenn; S Stern; A Langberg.
OTHER INFORMATION In their annual report the trustees stated that the charity was making various grant applications in order to eliminate the £4300 deficit in funds.
HOW TO APPLY 'Applications for grants are considered by the trustees and reviewed in depth for final approval.'
WHO TO APPLY TO A Langberg, Trustee, 14 Lampard Grove, London N16 6UZ *Tel* 020 8806 9589 *email* ari@toraschesed.co.uk

■ **The Tory Family Foundation**
CC NO 326584　　**ESTABLISHED** 1984
WHERE FUNDING CAN BE GIVEN Worldwide, but principally Folkestone.
WHO CAN BENEFIT Charitable organisations.

WHAT IS FUNDED 'The charity was formed to provide financial assistance to a wide range of charitable needs. It is currently supporting a wide range of causes both from a national perspective and an international perspective. These causes include educational, religious, social and medical subjects and the donees themselves are often registered charities.'

WHAT IS NOT FUNDED Priority is given to applications from Kent. No grants are given for further education.

TYPE OF GRANT The charity does not normally aim to fund the whole of any given project, and thus applicants are expected to demonstrate a degree of existing and regular support.

RANGE OF GRANTS Up to £10,000, mostly £1,000 or less.

SAMPLE GRANTS Previous beneficiaries have included: Ashford YMCA, Bletchley Park, Canterbury Cathedral, Concern Worldwide, Deal Festival, Disability Law Service, Folk Rainbow Club, Foresight, Friends of Birzett, Gurkha Welfare, Kent Cancer Trust, Royal British Legion, Uppingham Foundation and Youth Action Wiltshire.

FINANCES *Year* 2009–10 *Income* £82,903 *Grants* £84,860 *Assets* £3,185,266

TRUSTEES P N Tory; J N Tory; S A Tory.

OTHER INFORMATION Some beneficiaries receive more than one grant during the year and many have been supported in previous years.

HOW TO APPLY In writing to the correspondent. Applications are considered throughout the year. To keep costs down, unsuccessful applicants will not be notified.

WHO TO APPLY TO Paul N Tory, Trustee, The Estate Office, Etchinghill Golf Club, Folkestone, Kent CT18 8FA *Tel* 01303 862280

■ Tottenham Grammar School Foundation

CC NO 312634　　　**ESTABLISHED** 1989

WHERE FUNDING CAN BE GIVEN The borough of Haringey.

WHO CAN BENEFIT Individuals under 25 who are in education in the borough, schools and voluntary organisations.

WHAT IS FUNDED Equipment and activities not provided by local authorities. Activities supported include youth clubs, Saturday schools and sports promotion. Grants are also made to individuals under 25 who, or whose parents, normally live in the borough, or who have attended school in the borough.

WHAT IS NOT FUNDED The foundation cannot fund: the direct delivery of the National Curriculum; the employment of staff; the construction, adaptation, repair and maintenance of buildings; the repair and maintenance of equipment.

SAMPLE GRANTS Haringey Sports Development Trust (£23,800); Chaverim Youth organisation (£13,700); Haringey Council (£6,000); Park View Academy School (£4,000); Lubavich Youth Groups (£6,000); Tiverton Primary School (£3,700) and Twisting Stocking Theatre (£1,650).

FINANCES *Year* 2009–10 *Income* £481,541 *Grants* £522,876 *Assets* £19,536,743

TRUSTEES Keith V Brown; Terry J R Clarke; Paul Compton; Anthony G Fogg; Frederick Gruncell; Peter Jones; Michael J McLellan; Keith McGuinness; Ms Victoria Phillips; Andrew Krokou.

OTHER INFORMATION Grants were made totalling £522,000 of which £177,000 was paid to institutions and £346,000 was paid to individuals.

HOW TO APPLY On a form available from the correspondent, please see website for further details.

WHO TO APPLY TO Graham Chappell, Clerk, PO Box 34098, London N13 5XU *Tel* 020 8882 2999 *Fax* 020 8882 9724 *email* trustees@tgsf.org.uk *Website* www.tgsf.org.uk

■ The Tower Hill Trust

CC NO 206225　　　**ESTABLISHED** 1938

WHERE FUNDING CAN BE GIVEN Tower Hill and St Katherine's ward in Tower Hamlets.

WHO CAN BENEFIT Community-based organisations and appeals benefiting children and young adults, at risk groups, people disadvantaged by poverty and socially isolated people.

WHAT IS FUNDED organisations working for the relief of need or sickness, the provision of leisure and recreation facilities for social welfare and in support of education, and to provide and maintain gardens and open spaces.

WHAT IS NOT FUNDED No grants to individuals.

TYPE OF GRANT General and capital projects involving building renovation will be considered.

RANGE OF GRANTS Generally £300–£25,000.

SAMPLE GRANTS Furniture on the street (£9,700); FareShare (£8,000); Thames 21 (£7,100); Attlee Foundation (£7,000); Sir John Cass Primary School and SSAFA Forces Help (£5,000 each).

FINANCES *Year* 2009–10 *Income* £222,930 *Grants* £167,397 *Assets* £77,990

TRUSTEES Mrs Davina Walter, Chair; Maj. Gen. Christopher Tyler; John Polk; Comm. John Burton-Hall; Hamish Ritchie; Mrs Susan Wood.

HOW TO APPLY 'We have a two-stage application process. Stage One – Initial Proposal: Initially we ask you to send in a proposal (up to three pages) that covers the points below. We also ask for certain additional documents (see below). When we receive your proposal we will send you an acknowledgement and may ask you for further clarification. You may submit your proposal at any time. Every three months (February, May, August and November), Trustees will look at all of the initial proposals we have received and draw up a shortlist. All proposals that are not on the shortlist will be rejected. Stage Two – Further Information: If your proposal is successfully shortlisted, you move on to stage two of the process and will be asked for further information. You may also receive a visit from our Grant Officer. Your proposal will then be presented to a Trustees' meeting, which will make the final decision about your request. Not all shortlisted organisations will receive funding, as the Trust considers more proposals than we are able to support. Please note that the whole process (stage one and stage two) is likely to take up to four months.'

WHO TO APPLY TO Elaine Crush, Grants Officer, Attlee House, 28 Commercial Street, London E1 6LR *Tel* 020 7377 6614 *Fax* 020 7377 9822 *email* enquiries@towerhilltrust.org.uk *Website* www.towerhilltrust.org.uk

■ The Towry Law Charitable Trust

(also known as the Castle Educational Trust)

CC NO 278880   **ESTABLISHED** 1979

WHERE FUNDING CAN BE GIVEN UK, with a slight preference for the south of England.

WHO CAN BENEFIT Organisations benefiting people of all ages and disabled people.

WHAT IS FUNDED Education, medical research and social welfare.

WHAT IS NOT FUNDED No grants to individuals, bodies which are not UK-registered charities, local branches or associates of UK charities.

RANGE OF GRANTS £45–£100,000.

SAMPLE GRANTS Over £1,000: Cancer Research UK (£1,500); Headway (£1,900); The National Financial Services Skills Academy (£10,000); The Prince's Trust (£100,000).

Less than £1,000: Teenage Cancer Trust; Trinity Methodist Church; Woking Hospice; The Scottish Society for Autism (£150 each); The Rotary Club of Leatherhead Benevolent Fund (£600); Leeds Community Foundation (£100); Sport Relief (£750); Abreast £500; Children in Need (£660).

FINANCES *Year* 2010–11 *Income* £734 *Grants* £129,988 *Assets* £1,494,999

TRUSTEES Andrew Fisher; David Middleton; Ms Alex Rickard.

HOW TO APPLY The trust has stated that unsolicited applications are not considered. The trust currently states: 'The Towry Charitable Trust is a Silver Patron of The Prince's Trust and, as such, is committed to supporting The Prince's Trust for the next 3 years. Once grants have been paid to The Prince's Trust each year, the Towry Consultative Committee (an employee Consultative Committee) determines the appropriate charities to which remaining funds may be paid by way of grant and support is given to charitable causes supported by individual employees. The Towry Consultative Committee will also determine the duration of the grant, which may vary from a one-off grant to grants for longer periods. In view of this programme of activities, the Towry Charitable Trust does not tend to consider ad hoc requests for grants.'

WHO TO APPLY TO Jacqueline Gregory, FCIS DMS, Towry Group, 6 New Street Square, London EC4A 3BF *Tel* 020 7936 7236 *email* jacqui.gregory@towrylaw.com

■ The Toy Trust

CC NO 1001634   **ESTABLISHED** 1991

WHERE FUNDING CAN BE GIVEN UK.

WHO CAN BENEFIT Children's charities.

WHAT IS FUNDED Projects benefiting children.

SAMPLE GRANTS Great Ormond Street Hospital (£45,000); Samaritans Purse International (£35,000); Christian Resource Ministries and World in Need (£10,000 each); Action for Kids, Alton Castle Children's Retreat and Book Aid International (£5,000 each); and Concern Worldwide and Pathway Project (£4,000 each).

FINANCES *Year* 2009–10 *Income* £193,045 *Grants* £266,599 *Assets* £103,812

TRUSTEES The British Toy and Hobby Association Ltd; N Austin; Clive Jones; Christine Nicholls; Frank Martin.

OTHER INFORMATION This trust was registered in 1991 to centralise the giving of the British Toy and Hobby Association.

HOW TO APPLY In writing to the correspondent.

WHO TO APPLY TO Roland Earl, c/o British Toy and Hobby Association, 80 Camberwell Road, London SE5 0EG *Tel* 020 7701 7271 *email* admin@btha.co.uk *Website* www.btha.co.uk

■ The Mayor of Trafford's Charity Fund

CC NO 512299   **ESTABLISHED** 1982

WHERE FUNDING CAN BE GIVEN The borough of Trafford.

WHO CAN BENEFIT Voluntary organisations and charitable groups only.

WHAT IS FUNDED The mayor/mayoress chooses a single charity (occasionally two) to support the year before he/she takes office; the charity must benefit the inhabitants of the borough of Trafford.

TYPE OF GRANT Capital; one-off; one year or less.

SAMPLE GRANTS Previous beneficiaries include: Victim Support (£18,000); Intergen (£1,000) and 'Earthquake Appeal' (£500).

FINANCES *Year* 2010 *Income* £22,402 *Grants* £22,402

TRUSTEES Ian Duncan; Jane Baugh; Jane Le Fevre.

HOW TO APPLY As the recipient charity is selected before the mayor takes office, it is unlikely that applications to this trust will be successful.

WHO TO APPLY TO The Mayor's Office, Trafford Town Hall, Talbot Road, Stretford, Trafford, Manchester *Tel* 0161 912 4106 *Fax* 0161 912 1251 *email* mayors.office@trafford.gov.uk

■ Annie Tranmer Charitable Trust

CC NO 1044231   **ESTABLISHED** 1989

WHERE FUNDING CAN BE GIVEN UK, particularly Suffolk and adjacent counties.

WHO CAN BENEFIT Organisations and individuals.

WHAT IS FUNDED The objectives of the trust are to: make grants in the county of Suffolk and adjacent counties; make grants to national charities according to the wishes of Mrs Tranmer during her lifetime; advance education and historical research relating to the national monument known as the Sutton Hoo burial site and Sutton Hoo estate; protect and preserve the Sutton Hoo burial site; to further the education of children and young people in Suffolk; make grants for general charitable purposes.

RANGE OF GRANTS Up to £10,000.

SAMPLE GRANTS East Anglian Air Ambulance (£10,000); Cancer Research UK and Mid Essex Hospital Services NHS Trust – Burns Unit (£5,000 each); Independent Age and Motor Neurone Disease (£3,000 each); Salvation Army, Age Concern – Suffolk and Headstart 4 Babies (£2,000 each); Liveability, Level Two Youth Project, Suffolk Punch Trust and the British Association for Adoption and Fostering (£1,000 each); Listening Books (£600); Ipswich Furniture Project, Optua and the Nancy Oldfield Trust (£500 each); and Jubilee Opera (£200).

FINANCES *Year* 2009–10 *Income* £107,159 *Grants* £105,308 *Assets* £3,320,733

TRUSTEES J F F Miller; Mrs V A Lewis; N J Bonham-Carter.

OTHER INFORMATION The grant total in 2009–10 included £16,000 donated to 39 individuals.

HOW TO APPLY This trust does not accept unsolicited applications.

WHO TO APPLY TO Mrs M R Kirby, Clerk to the Trustees, 51 Bennett Road, Ipswich IP1 5HX

Think carefully about every application. Is it justified?

941

■ The Constance Travis Charitable Trust

CC NO 294540   **ESTABLISHED** 1986

WHERE FUNDING CAN BE GIVEN UK (national charities only); Northamptonshire (all sectors).

WHO CAN BENEFIT UK-wide organisations and local groups in Northamptonshire.

WHAT IS FUNDED General charitable purposes.

WHAT IS NOT FUNDED No grants to individuals or non-registered charities.

TYPE OF GRANT One-off grants for core, capital and project support.

RANGE OF GRANTS Up to £30,000.

SAMPLE GRANTS British Red Cross and Oxfam (£50,000 each); Royal Academy of Music (£47,500); Northants Association of Youth Clubs and Volunteer Reading Help (£15,000 each); Gateway School, The Institute of Cancer Research and National Tremor Foundation (£10,000 each); St Mary The Boltons (£7,500); Wootton Parish Church Council (£6,000); Royal National Institute of the Blind, Peoples Dispensary for Sick Animals and Prisoners Abroad (£5,000 each); Royal Marines Charitable Trust Fund (£3,000); Theatre Is and Northamptonshire Museum (£2,000 each); and Countryside Alliance (£1,500).

FINANCES *Year* 2010 *Income* £16,261,207 *Grants* £841,300 *Assets* £60,312,990

TRUSTEES Mrs Constance M Travis; Earnest R A Travis; Peta J Travis; Matthew Travis.

OTHER INFORMATION In 2010 the trust merged with another trust with similar charitable purposes, the Anthony Travis Charitable Trust.

HOW TO APPLY In writing to the correspondent. The trust's 2010 accounts note that though the trustees make grants with no formal application, they may invite organisations to submit a formal application.

WHO TO APPLY TO Earnest R A Travis, Trustee, Quinton Rising, Quinton, Northampton NN7 2EF *Tel* 01604 862296

■ The Treeside Trust

CC NO 1061586   **ESTABLISHED** 1997

WHERE FUNDING CAN BE GIVEN UK, but mainly in Oldham.

WHO CAN BENEFIT Mainly small local charities, as well as a few UK-wide charities which are supported on a regular basis.

WHAT IS FUNDED General charitable purposes.

RANGE OF GRANTS The trust states: 'In the main the trustees intend to make a limited number of substantial grants each year, rather than a larger number of smaller ones, in order to make significant contributions to some of the causes supported.'

SAMPLE GRANTS A list of beneficiaries was unavailable.

FINANCES *Year* 2009–10 *Income* £136,623 *Grants* £115,250 *Assets* £1,371,234

TRUSTEES C C Gould; J R B Gould; J R W Gould; D M Ives; R J Ives.

OTHER INFORMATION The majority of grants are made as a result of half-yearly reviews. Generally a limited number of substantial grants are made, none exceeding £15,000.

HOW TO APPLY The trust has stated that they 'do not welcome unsolicited applications'.

WHO TO APPLY TO J R Beresford, 4 The Park, Grasscroft, Oldham OL4 4ES *Tel* 01457 876422

■ The Tresillian Trust

CC NO 1105826   **ESTABLISHED** 2004

WHERE FUNDING CAN BE GIVEN Worldwide.

WHO CAN BENEFIT Charitable organisations.

WHAT IS FUNDED Overseas aid and welfare causes. In the UK, community based projects supporting the elderly and young people; in Africa, Asia and South America, projects supporting the education and health of women and children; and worldwide projects dealing with conflict and disaster areas and the environment.

SAMPLE GRANTS Habitat for Humanity (£10,000); Playpumps International (£9,000); Indraprasthra Medic (£6,000); Alive and Kicking UK, Book Aid International, Child Welfare Scheme, Contact the Elderly, Frishta Children's Village – India and Tools for Self Reliance (£1,000 each); and St John of Jerusalem Eye Hospital, TB Alert and Tree Africa (£500 each).

FINANCES *Year* 2009–10 *Income* £508,532 *Grants* £59,042 *Assets* £2,527,007

TRUSTEES G E S Robinson; P W Bate; M D Willcox.

HOW TO APPLY In writing to the correspondent. 'The trust is very selective in the grant making process and applications are reviewed by the trustees personally.'

WHO TO APPLY TO M D Willcox, Trustee, Old Coach House, Sunnyside, Bergh Apton, Norwich NR15 1DD *Tel* 01508 480100 *email* info@willcoxlewis.co.uk

■ The Triangle Trust (1949) Fund

CC NO 222860   **ESTABLISHED** 1949

WHERE FUNDING CAN BE GIVEN Worldwide, but in practice, the UK.

WHO CAN BENEFIT Individuals and organisations, mainly registered charities.

WHAT IS FUNDED Organisations supporting carers, people with disabilities, older people, disadvantaged people, integration and rehabilitation and community arts and education. Also individuals in need who are employed or who have been employed in the pharmaceutical industry, and their dependants.

WHAT IS NOT FUNDED Direct applications from individuals; overseas charities or projects outside the UK; charities for the promotion of religion; medical research; environmental, wildlife or heritage appeals; applications funded in the last two years, unless at the trustees invitation.

TYPE OF GRANT One-off, recurring, salaries and running costs.

RANGE OF GRANTS Usually up to £10,000; most grants are for between £1,000 and £5,000.

SAMPLE GRANTS Family Action Education (£45,000); Leicester Charity Link (£35,000); Mobility Trust (£20,000); Dundee City Council (£16,000); South Yorkshire Probation (£14,000); Aberdare Town Centre Project, Bristol Care & Repair and Leukaemia CARE (£10,000 each); Right Employment (£9,000); Asperger East Anglian (£8,000); The Trust Women's Project (£7,000); Relate Brighton & Hove (£6,000); National Youth Orchestra, Storybook Dads and Threshold Housing Advice (£5,000 each); Sudden Productions and St Wilfred's Centre (£3,000 each); St Luke's Family Centre – Belfast and Crossroads Care North Somerset (£2,000 each); and Carers' Forum Stirling (£1,000).

FINANCES *Year* 2009–10 *Income* £608,777 *Grants* £610,854 *Assets* £15,721,761

TRUSTEES Melanie Burfitt, Chair; Dr Robert Hale; Mark Powell; Bruce Newbigging; Kate Purcell; Jamie Dicks; Helen Evans; Andrew Pitt.

OTHER INFORMATION In addition to the figure given above, £43,000 was given in grants to individuals in need.

HOW TO APPLY Organisations should apply using the trust's application form, available from the website. Guidelines are also provided by the trust. Application hardcopies should be typed, and applicants should include their latest report and accounts with the application form (if submitting an online application, applicants should send their latest report and accounts separately as soon possible). The trustees meet quarterly in February, June, October and December to award grants. Applications should be submitted in the preceding month (January, May, September and November). Please note: applicants may be asked to present their project(s) to the trustees.

WHO TO APPLY TO Lesley Lilley, Secretary to the Trustees, 32 Bloomsbury Street, London WC1B 3QJ *Tel* 020 7299 4245 *email* lesleylilley@triangletrust.org *Website* www. thetriangletrust1949fund.org.uk

■ The True Colours Trust

CC NO 1089893   **ESTABLISHED** 2001
WHERE FUNDING CAN BE GIVEN UK and Africa.
WHO CAN BENEFIT Registered charities.
WHAT IS FUNDED Grant-making is focused in three areas: children and young people with complex disabilities in the UK; palliative care for children and young people in the UK; and palliative care in sub-Saharan Africa. The trust also makes small grants to local charities supporting disabled children, children with life-limiting conditions, their siblings and their families.
WHAT IS NOT FUNDED No grants to individuals.
TYPE OF GRANT One-off and recurring. Local grants tend to be one-off and for capital expenditure.
RANGE OF GRANTS Up to £250,000. Small grants up to £10,000.
SAMPLE GRANTS Great Ormond Street Hospital Children's Charity (£750,000 over 3 years), towards the True Colours Chair in Palliative Care for Children and Young People; African Palliative Care Association (£330,000 in total), most of which going towards the True Colours Trust African small grants programme for the period 2008–2013, which APCA administers; Palliative Care Association of Zambia (£231,000 over 2 years), towards the pilot of morphine in Zambia's hospices; Heart 'n' Soul (£150,000 over 3 years), towards its work with young people; Social Finance (£75,000), towards phase two of the Disabled Children's Credit Facility; and the Dance Art Foundation (£20,000), towards core costs. Small grants to UK organisations included those to: Hope House (£10,500), towards refurbishment works; Guy's Gift (£10,000), towards core costs; Birtenshaw Hall Children's Charitable Trust (£8,000), towards the costs of a sensory garden; Break All About Caring, towards its holiday programme, Demelza House Children's Hospice, towards its bereavement service, and Mosaic, towards core costs (£5,000 each); and Kent Kids (£4,000), towards refurbishment works.
FINANCES *Year* 2009–10 *Income* £2,014,519 *Grants* £1,663,411 *Assets* £8,459,411
TRUSTEES Lucy A Sainsbury; Dominic B Flynn; Bernard J C Willis; Tim Price.
HOW TO APPLY Programme Grants: The trust only funds registered charities or activities with clearly defined charitable purposes. The trustees take an active role in their grant-

making, employing a range of specialist staff and advisers to research their areas of interest and bring forward suitable proposals. The trust works closely with its chosen beneficiaries over a long period to achieve particular objectives. It should therefore be understood that the majority of unsolicited proposals the trust receives will be unsuccessful. Applications should be sent by post with a description (strictly no more than two pages please, as any more is unlikely to be read) of the proposed project, covering: the organisation – explaining its charitable aims and objectives, and giving its most recent annual income and expenditure, and current financial position (do not send a full set of accounts); the project requiring funding – why it is needed, who will benefit and in what way; the funding – breakdown of costs, any money raised so far, and how the balance will be raised. At this stage do not send supporting books, brochures, DVDs, annual reports or accounts. All applications will receive a standard acknowledgement letter. If your proposal is a candidate for support, you will hear within 8 weeks of the acknowledgement. Applicants who do not hear from the trust within this time must assume they have been unsuccessful.

Small Grants: The small grants programme is broken down into two categories: UK and Africa.

UK: The UK small grants programme is to fund local organisations and projects that support disabled children and their families. No direct support will be given for salaries and the grants are usually on a one-off basis. Key areas of particular interest to the trustees are: hydrotherapy pools; multi sensory rooms; mini buses; young carers projects; sibling projects; bereavement support. Applications for small grants should be made using our online application form [available from the trust's website].

Africa: The Africa small grants programme is administered by the African Palliative Care Association (APCA). This programme provides grants, of between £1,000–£2,500, to organisations offering palliative services across the continent. Trustees favour support for items which directly improve the patient experience and the standard of palliative care services. Priority is given to the following, in no particular order: equipment for patients (beds, wheelchairs etc); innovative projects for paediatric services (this could include purchasing toys); medicines; capital improvement costs (such as adapting buildings to improve the patient experience); developing small palliative care projects. Applications should be sent directly to APCA at TrueColoursSmallGrants@apca.co.ug.

See the guidance for applicants in the entry for the Sainsbury Family Charitable Trusts. A single application will be considered for support by all the trusts in the group. However, please see comments regarding the selection of beneficiaries.

WHO TO APPLY TO Alan Bookbinder, Director, The Sainsbury Family Charitable Trusts, Allington House, 1st Floor, 150 Victoria Street, London SW1E 5AE *Tel* 020 7410 0330 *Fax* 020 7410 0332 *email* truecolours@sfct.org.uk *Website* www.truecolourstrust.org.uk

Truedene Co. Ltd

CC NO 248268   **ESTABLISHED** 1966

WHERE FUNDING CAN BE GIVEN UK and overseas.

WHO CAN BENEFIT Organisations benefiting children, young adults, students and Jewish people.

WHAT IS FUNDED Educational, religious and other charitable institutions, principally Jewish.

RANGE OF GRANTS £1,000–£150,000.

SAMPLE GRANTS Previous beneficiaries have included: Beis Ruchel D'Satmar Girls' School Ltd, British Friends of Tchernobyl, Congregation Paile Yoetz, Cosmon Belz Limited, Friends of Mir, Kolel Shomrei Hachomoth, Mesifta Talmudical College, Mosdos Ramou, Orthodox Council of Jerusalem, Tevini Limited, United Talmudical Associates Limited, VMCT and Yeshivo Horomo Talmudical College.

FINANCES *Year* 2009–10 *Income* £1,297,024 *Grants* £956,173 *Assets* £4,083,235

TRUSTEES Sarah Klein, Chair; Samuel Berger; Solomon Laufer; Sije Berger; Zelda Sternlicht.

OTHER INFORMATION No list of grant beneficiaries was included in the accounts.

HOW TO APPLY In writing to the correspondent

WHO TO APPLY TO The Trustees, c/o Cohen Arnold, New Burlington House, 1075 Finchley Road, London NW11 0PU *Tel* 020 8731 0777

The Truemark Trust

CC NO 265855   **ESTABLISHED** 1973

WHERE FUNDING CAN BE GIVEN UK.

WHO CAN BENEFIT Registered charities with preference for small local charities, neighbourhood-based community projects and innovative work with less popular groups.

WHAT IS FUNDED 'The relief of all kinds of social distress and disadvantage.'

WHAT IS NOT FUNDED Grants are made to registered charities only. Applications from individuals, including students, are ineligible. No grants are made in response to general appeals from large national charities. Grants are seldom available for churches or church buildings or for scientific or medical research projects.

TYPE OF GRANT Usually one-off for a specific project or part of a project. Core funding and/or salaries rarely considered.

RANGE OF GRANTS Average grant £1,000.

SAMPLE GRANTS White Eagle Publishing Trust (£13,000); Quiet Mind Centre (£10,000); Bradford Family Support Network and Ellen Tinkham School – PTFA (£5,000 each); Lighthouse and MS Therapy Centre (£4,000 each); 1st Clanfield Scout Group and At Risk Teenagers (£3,000 each); Avon Riding Centre (£2,500); Disabled on Line and Longcause Community Special School (£2,000 each); Adoption Support and Evergreens (£1,500 each); and Latin American Disabled People's Project, Life Education Centre, Special Toys Educational Postal Service and Wand Mental Health (£1,000 each).

FINANCES *Year* 2009–10 *Income* £439,176 *Grants* £289,000 *Assets* £10,921,850

TRUSTEES Sir T Lucas; S Neil; Mrs W Collett; D Hawkins; Mrs J Hayward; Kate Hussey.

HOW TO APPLY In writing to the correspondent, including the most recent set of accounts, clear details of the need the project is designed to meet and an outline budget. Trustees meet four times a year. Only successful applicants receive a reply.

WHO TO APPLY TO The Trustees, PO Box 2, Liss, Hampshire GU33 6YP *Tel* 01730 894120

Truemart Limited

CC NO 1090586   **ESTABLISHED** 1984

WHERE FUNDING CAN BE GIVEN UK-wide and overseas, with a preference for Greater London.

WHO CAN BENEFIT Charitable organisations.

WHAT IS FUNDED The advancement of religion in accordance with the Orthodox Jewish faith, the relief of poverty and general charitable purposes.

FINANCES *Year* 2009–10 *Income* £191,305 *Grants* £91,900 *Assets* £82,238

TRUSTEES I Heitner; B Hoffman.

OTHER INFORMATION No list of grant beneficiaries was included in the accounts.

HOW TO APPLY In writing to the correspondent.

WHO TO APPLY TO Mrs S Heitner, Secretary, 34 The Ridgeway, London NW11 8QS *Tel* 020 8455 4456

Trumros Limited

CC NO 285533   **ESTABLISHED** 1982

WHERE FUNDING CAN BE GIVEN UK.

WHO CAN BENEFIT Jewish institutions.

WHAT IS FUNDED Jewish religious and educational institutions.

RANGE OF GRANTS £100–£20,000; typical grant under £1,000.

SAMPLE GRANTS Before Trust (£51,000); Beis Yosef Zvi (£36,000); Chevras Mo'oz Ladol (£28,780); Hamayon (£25,000); Yaldei Yisroel (£20,000); Kupas Tsedoko Vochessed £13,600; Achisomoch Aid Co (£12,720); London Academy of Jewish Studies (£11,250); Jewish Learning Exchange (£10,000).

FINANCES *Year* 2009 *Income* £879,686 *Grants* £384,398 *Assets* £7,265,313

TRUSTEES R S Hofbauer; H Hofbauer.

HOW TO APPLY In writing to the correspondent, but note that the trust states it is already inundated with applications.

WHO TO APPLY TO H Hofbauer, Trustee, 282 Finchley Road, London NW3 7AD *Tel* 020 7431 3282 *email* r.hofbauer@btconnect.com

The Trust for Education

CC NO 1000408   **ESTABLISHED** 1990

WHERE FUNDING CAN BE GIVEN UK and Africa with a preference for West Yorkshire.

WHO CAN BENEFIT Educational institutions and charities.

WHAT IS FUNDED 'The charity's objects are to advance education of the public, in particular, by the development of people's abilities to enter into post-compulsory education and the promotion and development of public knowledge and understanding about the institutions engaged in post-compulsory education and the range and diversity of their provision.'

WHAT IS NOT FUNDED 'The charity does not make grants to individuals for educational purposes, but only works through charities advancing education directly or indirectly.'

RANGE OF GRANTS £500–£150,000.

SAMPLE GRANTS Barnardo's (£150,000); Beat Bullying; First Housing (£5,000 each); Concern Universal (£500); Environmental Vision; Listening Books; Spitalfields Crypt; Starfish (£1,000); St Giles Trust (£16,000); UCLAN (£35,000).

FINANCES *Income* £86,112 *Grants* £214,767 *Assets* £1,776,596

TRUSTEES Francis J Griffiths, Chair; Derek J Betts; Richard Mansell; Thomas Riordan.

HOW TO APPLY In writing to the correspondent.
WHO TO APPLY TO Malcolm J Lynch, Secretary, 19 Cookridge Street, Leeds LS2 3AG email malcolm.lynch@wrigleys.co.uk

---

■ Trust Sixty Three

CC NO 1049136   **ESTABLISHED** 1995
WHERE FUNDING CAN BE GIVEN UK and overseas, with a preference for Bedfordshire and Hertfordshire.
WHO CAN BENEFIT Mostly disability causes, overseas aid and famine relief.
WHAT IS FUNDED General charitable purposes.
WHAT IS NOT FUNDED No grants to individuals.
SAMPLE GRANTS Previous beneficiaries include Brandles School, Bedfordshire County Council, Pasque Hospice, St Mary's Church, Home Start Hitchin, Mobility Trust, Scope, Clophill Churches Aid Appeal, Botton Village, North Hertfordshire Sanctuary, Bedfordshire Cargen Carers and Hertfordshire Community Foundation.
FINANCES *Year* 2009–10 *Income* £2,552 *Grants* £6,000
TRUSTEES Joanne Hobbs; Clive G Nott; Deborah Staines.
OTHER INFORMATION The grant total is an estimate based on previous research.
HOW TO APPLY The trust has previously stated that in the future it will be focussing solely on its existing grantees.
WHO TO APPLY TO Joanne Hobbs, Trustee, 16 John Bunyan Close, Maulden, Bedford MK45 2XA

■ The Trusthouse Charitable Foundation

CC NO 1063945   **ESTABLISHED** 1997
WHERE FUNDING CAN BE GIVEN Unrestricted, but mainly UK.
WHO CAN BENEFIT Registered charities and other not-for-profit organisations.
WHAT IS FUNDED Within the trust's overarching themes, there are three broad areas of funding: community support; disability and healthcare; arts, education and heritage.
WHAT IS NOT FUNDED The foundation will not normally consider supporting the following: animal welfare; applications for revenue funding for more than one year; capital appeals for places of worship; grant making organisations or umbrella groups; grants for individuals (including bursaries through a third party organisation); feasibility studies and evaluations; local authorities; Local Education Authority schools or their Parent Teachers Associations, except if those schools are solely for students with Special Needs; medical research projects; office IT equipment including software costs; organisations that have received a grant for three consecutive years from the foundation; projects involving the start-up or piloting of new services; projects where the primary objective is environmental or conservation; projects where the primary objective is the promotion of a particular religion; renovation or alteration projects to make a building compliant with the Disability & Discrimination Act; revenue funding for organisations with an income of over £300,000 per annum; services operated by the NHS; social research; training of professionals within the UK; universities. Under normal circumstances, the foundation is not currently funding projects which are for: the purchase of computers, other electronic equipment or software for delivery of the charity's work (e.g.

for an IT suite in a youth centre); PR or other awareness raising campaigns, including the publication of leaflets or events calendars, websites.
TYPE OF GRANT One-off for specific purposes.
RANGE OF GRANTS Generally up to £30,000.
SAMPLE GRANTS Hearing Dogs for Deaf People – Humberside & East Riding (£125,000); Cornwall Community Foundation (£50,000); HOPE Scotland Ltd and St Paul's Parish Centre – Spennymoor (£30,000 each); Parwich Memorial Hall – Derbyshire (£26,000); Federation of London Youth Clubs and St Michael's Hospice (£20,000 each); Grimsby Cleethorpes & District Mind (£15,000); Whitechapel Art Gallery (£13,000); Lifeline Project Ltd – Kirklees (£10,000); Bishop Ho Ming Wah Association (£7,000); Somali Employment & Training Project (£5,000); Readwrite (£4,500); and Braithwaite & Guardhouse Community Association (£1,000).
FINANCES *Year* 2009–10 *Income* £1,033,000 *Grants* £2,406,786 *Assets* £59,612,000
TRUSTEES Sir Jeremy Beecham; Baroness Sarah Hogg; The Duke of Marlborough; Anthony Peel; The Hon. Mrs Olga Polizzi; Sir Hugh Rossi; Lady Janet Balfour of Burleigh; Sir John Nutting; Mr Howell Harris-Hughes; Revd Rose Hudson-Wilkin; Lady Hamilton.
HOW TO APPLY On an application form available from the foundation's website, accessed following the completion of a brief eligibility questionnaire, which also identifies which type of grant may be most suitable. Details of additional information to be included with the application are given on the form. Applications must be made by post.
WHO TO APPLY TO Judith Leigh, Grants Manager, 6th Floor, 65 Leadenhall Street, London EC3A 2AD *Tel* 020 7264 4990 *Website* www.trusthousecharitablefoundation.org.uk

---

■ The James Tudor Foundation

CC NO 1105916   **ESTABLISHED** 2004
WHERE FUNDING CAN BE GIVEN UK and overseas.
WHO CAN BENEFIT Institutions and registered charities.
WHAT IS FUNDED The foundation's six programme areas are: palliative care; medical research; health education, awards and scholarship; the direct relief of sickness; the UK independent healthcare sector; the fulfilment of the foundation's charitable objects by other means.
WHAT IS NOT FUNDED Grants are not made: that directly replace, or negatively affect, statutory funding; for work that has already taken place; for endowment funds; for economic, community development or employment use; for adventure or residential courses, expeditions or overseas travel; for sport or recreation uses, including festivals; for environmental, conservation or heritage causes; for animal welfare; from applicants who have applied within the last 12 months.
TYPE OF GRANT Project funding, awards and scholarships, capital projects and equipment and staffing costs.
RANGE OF GRANTS Mostly up to £10,000.
SAMPLE GRANTS World Health Organisation (£50,000); University of Nottingham (£45,000); University of Bristol (£37,000); Help the Hospices (£17,000); Konnect9 (£16,500); Rainbow Hospice (£15,000); Anglo-French Medical Society (£12,000); Red Cross Appeal for Disaster Relief in Pakistan (£3,000).
FINANCES *Year* 2009–10 *Income* £724,700 *Grants* £749,068 *Assets* £25,083,467

Think carefully about every application. Is it justified?

945

TRUSTEES Martin G Wren, Chair; Richard R G Esler; Malcolm R Field; Roger K Jones; Cedric B Nash.

HOW TO APPLY On an application form available from the foundation's website. Comprehensive guidelines for applicant are also available from there.

WHO TO APPLY TO The Secretary, WestPoint, 78 Queens Road, Clifton, Bristol BS8 1QU *Tel* 0117 985 8715 *Fax* 0117 985 8716 *email* admin@jamestudor.org.uk *Website* www.jamestudor.org.uk

■ Tudor Rose Ltd

CC NO 800576   **ESTABLISHED** 1987

WHERE FUNDING CAN BE GIVEN UK.

WHO CAN BENEFIT Registered charities benefiting Jewish people and people disadvantaged by poverty.

WHAT IS FUNDED Advancement of religion (orthodox Jewish), relief of poverty and other charitable purposes.

SAMPLE GRANTS Lolev Charitable Trust; Woodlands Charity; KTV; Bell Synagogue; Hatzola; Lubavitch Centre; and TCT.

FINANCES Year 2009–10 Income £435,054 Grants £267,521 Assets £3,075,883

TRUSTEES M Lehrfield; S Taub; S L Taub.

OTHER INFORMATION A list of grant beneficiaries was not included in the accounts.

HOW TO APPLY In writing to the correspondent.

WHO TO APPLY TO Samuel Taub, Secretary, c/o Martin and Heller, 5 North End Road, London NW11 7RJ

■ The Tudor Trust

CC NO 1105580   **ESTABLISHED** 1955

WHERE FUNDING CAN BE GIVEN UK and sub-Saharan Africa.

WHO CAN BENEFIT Registered charities and other charitable organisations.

WHAT IS FUNDED Organisations working directly with people who are on the margins of society; A focus on building stronger communities by overcoming isolation and fragmentation and encouraging inclusion, connection and integration; Organisations which are embedded in and have developed out of their community – whether the local area or a 'community of interest' High levels of user involvement, and an emphasis on self-help where this is appropriate; Work which addresses complex and multistranded problems in unusual or imaginative ways; Organisations which are thoughtful in their use of resources and which foster community resilience in the face of environmental, economic or social change.

WHAT IS NOT FUNDED The trust supports work which addresses the needs of people at the margins of society. Applications will only be considered if they have a strong focus on supporting and empowering disadvantaged people and communities. They do not make grants to: Individuals, or organisations applying on behalf of individuals; Larger charities (both national and local) enjoying widespread support; Statutory bodies; Hospitals, health authorities or hospices; Medical care, medical equipment or medical research; Universities, colleges or schools; Academic research, scholarships or bursaries; Nurseries, playgroups or crèches; One-off holidays, residentials, trips, exhibitions, conferences, events etc; Animal charities; The promotion of religion; The restoration or conservation of buildings or habitats (where

there isn't a strong social welfare focus); Work outside the UK. The trust runs a targeted grants programme promoting sustainable agriculture in sub-Saharan Africa. They do not consider unsolicited proposals from groups working overseas; Endowment appeals; Work that has already taken place.

TYPE OF GRANT Capital and revenue grants, core funding.

RANGE OF GRANTS There is no minimum or maximum grant. Average grant in 2010–11 was £56,000.

SAMPLE GRANTS Family Centre Trust (£1.35 million), to finance the construction of a new family and visitors' centre at HMP Wormwood Scrubs; Bail for Immigration Detainees (£150,000 over 3 years), as continuation funding for this national advice and campaigning charity, based in East London, for people held in immigration detention centres; New Futures Corner House Ltd (£124,000 over 3 years), towards the salary of a therapeutic support worker to work in a new residential home for young women who are at risk of or who have experienced sexual exploitation; A Way Out (£90,000 over 3 years), towards the core running costs for working with vulnerable and hard to reach young people in Stockton on Tees and the Tees Valley; Outside Chance (£90,000 over 3 years), towards the core costs of an organisation working with young people at risk of offending across England; Doncaster CVS (£90,000 over 3 years), for the Give Us A Voice project for Gypsy/Traveller people; Salisbury Trust for the Homeless (£70,000), towards the conversion of a disused almshouse in Salisbury into 12 move-on flats for single homeless people; Centre for Complementary Care, Eskdale (£60,000 over 3 years), towards the running costs of an organisation in Cumbria which provides healing and complementary therapies for local people; Llynfi Valley 11–25 Project (£10,000), towards the running costs of a youth project in Maesteg; Sikh Resource and Community Development Centre (£2,500): as a development grant towards an external consultancy scoping exercise; Heads Together Productions Ltd (£2,100), as development funding to provide peer learning for staff and young volunteers; and Community Rehabilitation & Environmental Protection Programme (£270), to cover additional costs relating to a 2-day capacity building visit to SACDEP in Kenya.

FINANCES Year 2010–11 Income £7,588,000 Grants £18,950,000 Assets £239,796,000

TRUSTEES Mary Graves; Helen Dunwell; Desmond Graves; Penelope Buckler; Christopher Graves; Catherine Antcliff; Louise Collins; Elizabeth Crawshaw; Matt Dunwell; James Long; Ben Dunwell; Francis Runacres; Monica Barlow; Vanessa James.

OTHER INFORMATION Excellent annual report and accounts are available from the trust. The trust's website also includes full, clear guidelines for applicants.

HOW TO APPLY There is a two-stage application process which is explained in detail on the trust's website including forms and guidelines. Applicants are welcome to contact the trust regarding their application.

WHO TO APPLY TO The Trustees, 7 Ladbroke Grove, London W11 3BD *Tel* 020 7727 8522 *Fax* 020 7221 8522 *Website* www.tudortrust.org.uk

The Tufton Charitable Trust

cc no 801479   **established** 1989
WHERE FUNDING CAN BE GIVEN UK.
WHO CAN BENEFIT Individuals and organisations.
WHAT IS FUNDED Christian activity supporting evangelism.
WHAT IS NOT FUNDED No grants for repair or maintenance of buildings.
TYPE OF GRANT One-off and project-related.
SAMPLE GRANTS Emmaus UK (£75,000); Glyndebourne (£30,000); Caritas Foundation of Western Kansas (£29,000); the Arts Educational School (£27,000); Soul Survivor (£10,000); St John Ambulance (£7,000); and Institute of Economic Affairs, Catholic Evangelisation Services and The Turner Contemporary (£5,000 each).
FINANCES *Year* 2010 *Income* £448,656 *Grants* £363,120 *Assets* £588,856
TRUSTEES Sir Christopher Wates; Lady Wates; J R F Lulham; Wates Charitable Trustees Ltd.
HOW TO APPLY In writing to the correspondent, including an sae.
WHO TO APPLY TO The Trustees, Tufton Place, Ewhurst Place, Northiam, East Sussex TN31 6HL

The R D Turner Charitable Trust

cc no 263556   **established** 1971
WHERE FUNDING CAN BE GIVEN UK, with a preference for the Worcestershire area.
WHO CAN BENEFIT Registered charities only.
WHAT IS FUNDED General charitable purposes. The trustees have resolved that the following objectives be adopted: to support by means of grants and loans other registered charities, particularly in the Worcestershire area; to maintain and enhance the amenities of the villages of Arley and Upper Arley; and such other general charitable purposes in connection with the villages of Arley and Upper Arley as the trustees shall in their absolute discretion determine/decide.
WHAT IS NOT FUNDED No grants to non-registered charities or to individuals.
TYPE OF GRANT One-off and recurrent.
RANGE OF GRANTS £500–£15,000.
SAMPLE GRANTS St Richard's Hospice (£15,000); Worcestershire and Dudley Historic Churches Trust (£12,000); British Red Cross Hereford and Worcester (£10,000); ARCOS, Cobalt Appeal Fund and Motor Neurone Disease Association (£5,000 each); County Air Ambulance Trust and Relate Worcestershire (£3,000); Sunfield Children's Homes (£2,000); Listening Books (£1,000); and Talking Newspapers of the UK (£500).
FINANCES *Year* 2009–10 *Income* £975,512 *Grants* £162,500 *Assets* £27,057,994
TRUSTEES J M Del Mar, Chair; D P Pearson; S L Preedy; P J Millward; J M G Fea.
HOW TO APPLY The trust does not have a grant application form. Applicant Charities are requested to send a letter of no more than two pages describing their appeal, together with a copy of their latest accounts, to the Trust Administrator at the Grants Office.
WHO TO APPLY TO Timothy J Patrickson, Administrator, 3 Poplar Piece, Inkberrow, Worcester WR7 4JD *Tel* 01386 792014 *email* timpatrickson@hotmail.co.uk

The Douglas Turner Trust

cc no 227892   **established** 1964
WHERE FUNDING CAN BE GIVEN UK and overseas; however, in practice, there is a strong preference for Birmingham and the West Midlands.
WHO CAN BENEFIT Registered charities.
WHAT IS FUNDED Mainly local charities including charities supporting: youth and children; work in the community; health and people with disabilities; hospices; older people; international aid; environment and heritage; social support; the arts; and medical research.
WHAT IS NOT FUNDED No grants to individuals or unregistered charities.
TYPE OF GRANT Recurring and one-off donations, capital and core costs.
RANGE OF GRANTS £500–£20,000.
SAMPLE GRANTS St Mary's Hospice Ltd (£17,000); Birmingham Boys' & Girls' Union (£10,000); and Multiple Births Foundation (£5,000). Previous beneficiaries included: 870 House Youth Movement; Gingerbread; Listening Books; Dial Walsall; Compton Hospice; Gracewell Homes Foster Trust; Cotteridge Church Day Centre; Busoga Trust; Birmingham Botanical Gardens; Midlands Actors' Theatre; and Action Medical Research.
FINANCES *Year* 2009–10 *Income* £350,895 *Grants* £409,534 *Assets* £14,094,637
TRUSTEES John M Del Mar, Chair; James M G Fea; Peter J Millward; David P Pearson; Stephen L Preedy.
HOW TO APPLY In writing to the correspondent, 'on applicant letterhead, two pages or less, and preferably not stapled together', with a copy of the latest annual report and accounts. There are no application forms. The trustees usually meet in February, May, August and December to consider applications, which should be submitted in the month prior to each meeting. Telephone enquiries may be made before submitting an appeal.
WHO TO APPLY TO Tim J Patrickson, Trust Administrator, 3 Poplar Piece, Inkberrow, Worcester WR7 4JD *Tel* 01386 792014 *email* timpatrickson@hotmail.co.uk

The Florence Turner Trust

cc no 502721   **established** 1973
WHERE FUNDING CAN BE GIVEN UK, but with a strong preference for Leicestershire.
WHO CAN BENEFIT Smaller projects are favoured where donations will make a 'quantifiable difference to the recipients rather than favouring large national charities whose income is measured in millions rather than thousands'. Grants are made for the benefit of individuals through a referring agency such as social services, NHS trusts or similar responsible bodies.'
WHAT IS FUNDED 'It is usual practice to make grants for the benefit of individuals through a referring agency such as Social Services, NHS Trusts or similar responsible bodies.'
WHAT IS NOT FUNDED The trust does not support individuals for educational purposes.
SAMPLE GRANTS Leicester Charity Link (£12,000); Leicester Grammar School – Bursary (£10,000); Age Concern Leicester, Leicester and Leicestershire Historic Churches Preservation Trust and VISTA (£2,400 each); LOROS (£2,000); New Parks Club for Young People (£1,500); and Four Twelve Ministries and Help for Heroes (£1,000 each).

FINANCES *Year* 2009–10 *Income* £176,153 *Grants* £82,021 *Assets* £5,162,014
TRUSTEES Roger Bowder; Allan A Veasey; Caroline A Macpherson.
HOW TO APPLY In writing to the correspondent. Trustees meet every eight or nine weeks.
WHO TO APPLY TO The Trustees, c/o Harvey Ingram Owston, 20 New Walk, Leicester LE1 6TX

■ Miss S M Tutton Charitable Trust

CC NO 298774   **ESTABLISHED** 1988
WHERE FUNDING CAN BE GIVEN UK.
WHO CAN BENEFIT The trust provides financial support to young singers through the Sybil Tutton Awards. In addition it makes grants to selected music colleges and training opera companies.
WHAT IS FUNDED Awards and grants for postgraduate opera studies and grants to music colleges, charities and opera companies. The trust has some funds available for occasional discretionary grants, but they are very limited.
TYPE OF GRANT Scholarships and organisation grants.
SAMPLE GRANTS The annual report did not detail the support given to organisations but past beneficiaries have included: British Youth Opera, The Britten-Pears Young Artist Programme, Clonter Opera, The National Opera Studio and Young Concert Artists Trust.
FINANCES *Year* 2010 *Income* £55,414 *Grants* £48,902 *Assets* £2,976,322
TRUSTEES Musicians Benevolent Fund.
OTHER INFORMATION In 2010 £36,000 was distributed via the Sybil Tutton awards
HOW TO APPLY Awards are administered by the Musicians Benevolent Fund. The website states: 'We are no longer accepting applications from individuals. Candidates will be selected on a nominations only basis, by Heads of voice from the conservatoires, music colleges and National Opera Studio. Institutions will be fully informed of the nomination process.'
WHO TO APPLY TO Musicians Benevolent Fund, 7–11 Britannia Street, London W1U 7EU *Tel* 020 7239 9100 *email* awards@helpmusicians.org.uk *Website* www.helpmusicians.org.uk

■ The TUUT Charitable Trust

CC NO 258665   **ESTABLISHED** 1969
WHERE FUNDING CAN BE GIVEN Worldwide.
WHO CAN BENEFIT Small to medium-sized organisations, particularly those having close associations with trade unions.
WHAT IS FUNDED General at trustees' discretion, with an overriding priority to charities with strong trade union connections or interests.
WHAT IS NOT FUNDED No grants to individuals or to charities based overseas.
RANGE OF GRANTS Up to £40,000.
SAMPLE GRANTS Previously: NACRO (£40,000); Alma Hospital and PFA Centenary Fund (£5,000 each); Macmillan Cancer Relief (£3,000); Evelina Children's Hospital Appeal (£2,300); CCA, Concern Worldwide and Scrap Poverty in Africa (£2,000 each); UK Sports Association and Woking Hospice (£1,000 each); and World Development Movement Trust, Hope and Homes for Children, Cruse Bereavement Care and the Respite Association (£500 each).
FINANCES *Year* 2009–10 *Income* £10,678 *Grants* £64,810

TRUSTEES Lord Christopher; A Tuffin; M Walsh; M Bradley; B Barber; Lord Brookman; E Sweeney.
HOW TO APPLY 'To apply for a grant, charitable organisations should apply for a Form of Request and submit this, duly completed. The Trustees meet three times a year to consider requests received.'
WHO TO APPLY TO Ann Smith, Secretary, Congress House, Great Russell Street, London WC1B 3LQ *Tel* 020 7637 7116 *Fax* 020 7637 7087 *email* info@tufm.co.uk *Website* www.tufm.co.uk

■ TVML Foundation

CC NO 1135495   **ESTABLISHED** 2010
WHERE FUNDING CAN BE GIVEN UK and overseas, with a preference for Brazil, Israel and the USA.
WHO CAN BENEFIT Charities and community groups.
WHAT IS FUNDED 'Educational and lifehood initiatives'.
FINANCES *Year* 2010 *Income* £1,636,296 *Grants* £76,933
TRUSTEES Marcos Lederman; Vivian Lederman; Marcelo Steuer.
OTHER INFORMATION Grants are made to organisations and individuals. A list of grant beneficiaries was not included in the accounts.
HOW TO APPLY In writing to the correspondent.
WHO TO APPLY TO Marcos Lederman, Trustee, Spinnaker Capital Limited, 6 Grosvenor Street, London W1K 4DJ *Tel* 020 7903 2900 *Fax* 020 7903 2999 *email* marcos.lederman@spinnakercapital.com

■ Two Ridings Community Foundation

CC NO 1084043   **ESTABLISHED** 2000
WHERE FUNDING CAN BE GIVEN York and North Yorkshire.
WHO CAN BENEFIT Charities and community groups.
WHAT IS FUNDED Health and social welfare.
RANGE OF GRANTS Up to £20,000.
FINANCES *Year* 2009–10 *Income* £442,768 *Grants* £370,378 *Assets* £756,000
TRUSTEES Wendy Bundy, Chair; Colin Stroud; John Webster, treasurer; Christine Bainton; Hon. Michael Benson; Fred Brown; Geoffrey Brownlee; Michael Holford; Philip Ingham; Susan Winterburn.
OTHER INFORMATION Grant schemes change frequently. Please consult the foundation's website for details of current programmes.
HOW TO APPLY The foundation's website has details of the grant schemes currently being administered and how to apply.
WHO TO APPLY TO Jan Norton, Grants Manager, Primrose Hill, Buttercrambe Road, Stamford Bridge, York YO41 1AW *Tel* 01759 377400 *Fax* 01759 377401 *email* office@trcf.org.uk *Website* www.trcf.org.uk

■ Community Foundation Serving Tyne and Wear and Northumberland

CC NO 700510   **ESTABLISHED** 1988
WHERE FUNDING CAN BE GIVEN Tyne and Wear and Northumberland.
WHO CAN BENEFIT Voluntary organisations benefiting the local community. Individuals.
WHAT IS FUNDED The help of those in greatest need. The funds generally have a specific cause as

their individual funding priority, but overall the foundation has social welfare as its predominant cause to support. Projects that help communities and individuals who are disadvantaged because of poverty, poor health or disability are of particular interest. Some arts and environment work is funded, but only when it is of direct benefit to those in social need.

WHAT IS NOT FUNDED Grants are not normally given for: non charitable activities; sponsorship and fundraising events; small contributions to major appeals; large capital projects; endowments, loan repayments or for activities bought or ordered before the foundation makes a grant; grants which will be used to make grants to a third party; political activities; acts of religious worship; work which could be funded by health and local authorities or government grant aid; work which only benefits animals. Exceptions may be made to this at the request of the donors.

TYPE OF GRANT Mostly single grants, but some grants recurrent for up to three years. Will consider capital, core costs, recurring, running and start-up costs, as well as one-off, feasibility studies and salaries.

RANGE OF GRANTS Usually up to £5,000, exceptionally up to £100,000.

SAMPLE GRANTS Wear Rivers Trust – Environmental Education Officer (£15,000); Friends of Swanton Close Park (£5,000); The Society of Disabled Refugees and Asylum Seekers (£4,500); Youth Empowerment Across South Tyneside (£4,000); Sunderland Cardiac Support Group, Volunteers in Action Healthy Eating and Walking Club and Allen Valley Bowling Club (£3,000 each); Tyndale Stroke Club (£2,000); Indian Cultural Association (£800).

FINANCES *Year* 2010–11 *Income* £6,684,447 *Grants* £4,706,570 *Assets* £50,829,292

TRUSTEES Ashley Winter, Chair; Prof. Chris Drinkwater; Colin Seccombe; John Clough; Alastair Conn; Roger Kelly; Gev Pringle; Fiona Cruickshank; Betty Weallans; Kate Roe; Sue Winfield; Jamie Martin; Jo Curry; Charles Harvey; Dean T Huggins.

PUBLICATIONS Yearbooks and various reports.

HOW TO APPLY There is one application form for the general Community Foundation grants and generally, separate forms for the other rolling grants programmes and one-off funds. All of these plus application guidelines are available on the website under the 'apply' section. Some of the programmes have deadlines and some do not, also, new programmes begin and others finish therefore the trust's website should be checked for the most recent information. If a grant is approved, there are terms and conditions that must be adhered to and a project report to be submitted.

WHO TO APPLY TO The Grants Team, Cale Cross, 156 Pilgrim Street, Newcastle upon Tyne NE1 6SU *Tel* 0191 222 0945 *Fax* 0191 230 0689 *email* grants@communityfoundation.org.uk *Website* www.communityfoundation.org.uk

··

■ Trustees of Tzedakah

CC NO 251897   **ESTABLISHED** 1966

WHERE FUNDING CAN BE GIVEN Worldwide, in practice UK and Israel.

WHO CAN BENEFIT Mainly Jewish religious institutions and people disadvantaged by poverty.

WHAT IS FUNDED The relief of poverty; advancement of education; advancement of religion; and general charitable purposes.

WHAT IS NOT FUNDED Grants only to registered charities. No grants to individuals.

RANGE OF GRANTS £25–£35,000.

SAMPLE GRANTS Previous beneficiaries include: Hasmonean High School Charitable Trust; Gertner Charitable Trust; Society of Friends of the Torah; Hendon Adath Yisroel Synagogue; Medrash Shmuel Theological College; Torah Temimoh; Willow Foundation; Tifferes Girls' School; Sage Home for the Aged; Wizo; and Torah Movement of Great Britain.

FINANCES *Year* 2009–10 *Grants* £450,000

TRUSTEES Trustees of Tzedakah Ltd.

OTHER INFORMATION Up-to-date information is usually unavailable as accounts are consistently filed late with the Charity Commission.

HOW TO APPLY This trust states that it does not respond to unsolicited applications.

WHO TO APPLY TO Michael Lebrett, Brentmead House, Britannia Road, London N12 9RU *Tel* 020 8446 6767

■ UKI Charitable Foundation

CC NO 1071978   **ESTABLISHED** 1998
WHERE FUNDING CAN BE GIVEN UK.
WHO CAN BENEFIT Registered charities and individuals.
WHAT IS FUNDED General charitable purposes, education training, medical/health/sickness, disability, the relief of poverty and religious activities.
SAMPLE GRANTS The accounts stated that a list of donations paid could be obtained from the correspondent. Despite a request being made in writing, including an sae, no list was received.
FINANCES *Year* 2009–10 *Income* £654,327 *Assets* £3,696,325
TRUSTEES Jacob Schimmel; Vered Schimmel; Anna Schimmel.
OTHER INFORMATION During the year no grants were made to individuals.
HOW TO APPLY In writing to the correspondent.
WHO TO APPLY TO Abraham Schimmel, Trustee, Mr Jacob Schimmel, UKI International, 54–56 Euston Street, London NW1 2ES *Tel* 020 7387 0155

■ Ulster Garden Villages Ltd

ESTABLISHED 1946
WHERE FUNDING CAN BE GIVEN Northern Ireland.
WHO CAN BENEFIT Organisations and individuals.
WHAT IS FUNDED Financial assistance is given to aid housing for people who are disadvantaged, elderly or have disabilities as well as donations to assist improvements in quality of life for such people. There are also interests in helping youth organisations and movements, preservation of heritage and organisations seeking to improve health in the community.
WHAT IS NOT FUNDED Grants are not made to: individuals; organisations whose application is not charitable and with public benefit; activities which are primarily the responsibility of central and local government; sponsorship or marketing appeals; promotion of religion; expeditions or overseas travel; charities who collect funds for distribution to other charities.
RANGE OF GRANTS Usually £1,000 to £5,000; up to £250,000 is considered.
SAMPLE GRANTS Royal Victoria Hospital – Institute of Vision Science; Royal Victoria Hospital – Percutaneous Aortic Valve Replacement; Belfast City Hospital – the Garden Village Suite; the Northern Ireland Children's Hospice; QUB Foundation Great Hall; Belmont Tower; the Lyric Theatre, Camphill Communities in Northern Ireland; Croft Community; Disability Sport NI; Clifton Nursing Home; Habitat for Humanity Northern Ireland; the Scout Association; Ulster Waterways Group; Rams Island.
FINANCES *Grants* £1,000,000
TRUSTEES Tony Hopkins; Kevin Baird; Mrs Martie Boyd; Drew Crawford; Susan Crowe; Brian Garrett; Erskine Holmes; Sir Desmond Lorimer; William J Webb.
OTHER INFORMATION No current financial information was available. Previously grants have totalled around £1 million.

HOW TO APPLY On an application form available from the charity's website. Guidelines on how to apply are also on the website. Applications should be posted or delivered to the office which is normally attended on Tuesday, Wednesday and Thursday between 9am and 1pm.
WHO TO APPLY TO Mrs Martie Boyd, Executive Director, Forestview, Purdy's Lane, Newtonbreda, Belfast BT8 7AR *Tel* 028 9049 1111 *Fax* 028 9049 1007 *email* admin@ulstergardenvillages.co.uk *Website* www.ulstergardenvillages.co.uk

■ Ultach Trust

IR NO XN83581   **ESTABLISHED** 1989
WHERE FUNDING CAN BE GIVEN Northern Ireland only.
WHO CAN BENEFIT Generally voluntary Irish-language or cross-community groups based in Northern Ireland. Irish medium schools benefiting children and young adults.
WHAT IS FUNDED The trust normally funds new or established groups based in Northern Ireland involved in the promotion of the Irish language. Grants are normally aimed at specific projects and schemes rather than ongoing costs. Particular consideration is given to groups developing inter-community Irish-language activities. The trustees also, in exceptional cases, support projects aimed at improving the position of Irish people in the community and promoting knowledge of the language.
WHAT IS NOT FUNDED Generally the following are not supported: individuals, ongoing running costs, major capital programmes, to substitute cutbacks in statutory funding, travel expenses, publications or videos.
TYPE OF GRANT Except with regard to Irish-medium education, funding is generally restricted to starter finances and single projects.
FINANCES *Grants* £50,000
TRUSTEES Ruairí Ó Bléine; Bill Boyd; Réamonn Ó Ciaráin; Seán Ó Coinn; Déaglán Ó Doibhlín; Risteard Mac Gabhann; Joyce Gibson; Sue Pentel; Robin Glendinning; Barry Kinghan.
PUBLICATIONS Titles of publications and Irish courses available on request.
OTHER INFORMATION No financial information was available
HOW TO APPLY An application form and condition's of funding are available from the trust's website.
WHO TO APPLY TO Róise Ní-Bhaoill, Deputy Director, 6/10 William Street, Cathedral Quarter, Belfast BT1 1PR *Tel* 028 9023 0749 *Fax* 028 9023 1245 *email* eolas@ultach.org *Website* www.ultach.org

■ Ulting Overseas Trust

CC NO 294397   **ESTABLISHED** 1986
WHERE FUNDING CAN BE GIVEN The developing world (mostly, but not exclusively, Asia, Africa and South and Central America).
WHO CAN BENEFIT Christian workers in the developing world undergoing further training for Christian service.
WHAT IS FUNDED Bursaries, normally via grants to Christian theological training institutions or organisations with a training focus, for those in the developing world who wish to train for the Christian ministry, or for those who wish to improve their ministry skills. It gives priority to the training of students in their home countries or continents.

WHAT IS NOT FUNDED No grants are given for capital projects such as buildings or library stock, nor for training in subjects other than Biblical, theological and missionary studies. Grants are only made to institutions to pass on to their students; direct grants to individuals cannot be made.

RANGE OF GRANTS Up to £14,000.

SAMPLE GRANTS IFES (£16,500); Scripture Union international (£15,000); Langham Trust (£13,500); Oxford Centre for Mission Studies (£7,000); Pan African Christian College (£5,500); Asian Theological Seminary (£5000); Cornerstone Christian College (£2,000); and Arab World Ministries (£1000).

FINANCES *Year* 2009–10 *Income* £108,345 *Grants* £114,345 *Assets* £3,473,147

TRUSTEES A J Bale, Chair; Mrs M Brinkley; D Ford; J C Heyward; J Kapolyo; Dr J B A Kessler; R Pearce; K-S Tan; Timothy B Warren.

HOW TO APPLY The funds of the trust are already committed. Unsolicited applications cannot be supported.

WHO TO APPLY TO Timothy B Warren, Trustee c/o Pothecary Witham Weld Solicitors, 70 St George's Square, London SW1V 3RD

■ The Ulverscroft Foundation

CC NO 264873   **ESTABLISHED** 1972

WHERE FUNDING CAN BE GIVEN Worldwide.

WHO CAN BENEFIT Projects which will have a positive effect on the quality of life of visually impaired people (blind and partially sighted). Funding is channelled via recognised organisations which help the visually impaired, for example, libraries, hospitals, clinics, schools and colleges, and social and welfare organisations.

WHAT IS FUNDED To support sick and disabled people, particularly those with defective eyesight, and to promote or conduct medical research. Grants are given to hospitals for research, and to libraries and groups of visually impaired people for items such as computer equipment.

WHAT IS NOT FUNDED Applications from individuals are not encouraged. Generally, assistance towards salaries and general running costs are not given.

TYPE OF GRANT Annual for up to and more than three years. Buildings; capital; project and research; one-off and recurring grants.

SAMPLE GRANTS Calibre and Sight Savers International (£5,000 each); J S Smith French Eye Diseases (£4,000); Birmingham Talking Newspaper, Blind in Business and Sense International (£2,000 each); and Intercare, Listening Books, John Fawcett Foundation, St John of Jerusalem and York Blind & Partially Sighted Society (£1,000 each).

FINANCES *Year* 2009–10 *Income* £12,761,392 *Grants* £57,710 *Assets* £17,138,718

TRUSTEES A W Leach, Chair; P H F Carr; Pat Beech; D Owen; R Crooks.

OTHER INFORMATION The foundation controls a trading subsidiary which republishes books in a form accessible by people with partial sight.

HOW TO APPLY In writing to the correspondent including latest annual report and accounts. Applicants are advised to make their proposal as detailed as possible, to include details of the current service to people who are visually impaired, if any, and how the proposed project will be integrated or enhanced. If possible the trust asks for an estimate of how many people who are visually impaired use/will use the service, the amount of funding obtained to date,

if any, and the names of other organisations to which they have applied. The success of any appeal is dependent on the level of funding at the time of consideration. The trustees meet four times a year to consider applications.

WHO TO APPLY TO Joyce Sumner, Secretary, 1 The Green, Bradgate Road, Anstey, Leicester LE7 7FU *Tel* 0116 236 1595 *Fax* 0116 236 1594 *email* foundation@ulverscroft.co.uk *Website* www.foundation.ulverscroft.com

■ Ulverston Town Lands Charity

CC NO 215779   **ESTABLISHED** 1963

WHERE FUNDING CAN BE GIVEN The urban district of Ulverston.

WHO CAN BENEFIT Local organisations and schools.

WHAT IS FUNDED Youth, health, welfare, disability.

WHAT IS NOT FUNDED No grants outside the beneficial area. Grants are generally given to organisations and not to individuals. The trust prefers to support grants for specific items or equipment rather than running costs.

TYPE OF GRANT One-off grants for specific items or equipment.

RANGE OF GRANTS Up to £3,000.

SAMPLE GRANTS St Mary's Hospice, Prince's Trust and Cumbria Flood Recovery Fund (£3,000 each); Sandside Lodge School (£2,000); Sir John Barrow School Hardship Fund (£1,700); Rotary Club of Ulverston (£1,000); St Mary's Catholic Primary School, CADAS, Age Concern and Furness Youth Theatre (£500 each); WRVS for meals on wheels (£350); Churchwalk Infant School (£300); Ulverston Blind Class and Marsh House Amenities Fund (£200 each).

FINANCES *Year* 2009–10 *Income* £48,524 *Grants* £38,004 *Assets* £106,707

TRUSTEES Edwin Twentyman, Chair; Colin Hodgeson; Cllr J W Prosser; Cllr Janette Jenkinson; Anthony Edmondson; Colin Williams; Cynthia Earnshaw; Anthony Bryson; Janet Hancock.

HOW TO APPLY In writing to the correspondent. Trustees meet four or five times a year.

WHO TO APPLY TO J Going, Secretary to the Trustees, Messrs Hart Jackson and Sons, PO Box 2, 8 and 10 New Market Street, Ulverston, Cumbria LA12 7LW *Tel* 01229 583291 *Fax* 01229 581136

■ The Underwood Trust

CC NO 266164   **ESTABLISHED** 1973

WHERE FUNDING CAN BE GIVEN Worldwide. In practice UK with a preference for Scotland and Wiltshire.

WHO CAN BENEFIT Registered charities only, or bodies with equivalent status such as universities or churches.

WHAT IS FUNDED General charitable purposes, in particular, medicine and health, social welfare, education arts, environment and wildlife.

WHAT IS NOT FUNDED Individuals directly; political activities; commercial ventures or publications; the purchase of vehicles including minibuses; overseas travel or holidays; retrospective grants or loans; direct replacement of statutory funding or activities that are primarily the responsibility of central or local government; large capital, endowment or widely distributed appeals.

RANGE OF GRANTS Up to £100,000.

SAMPLE GRANTS University of West of England – Endowment of Chair in Speech & Language Therapy Research Unit (£1.2 million); Glyndebourne Arts Trust – New generation programme (£1 million); Royal Over-Seas League Golden Jubilee Trust (£500,000);

Shooting Star Children's Hospice (£100,000); Chamber Orchestra of Europe (£65,000 in total); Prisoners Abroad (£44,000); Prospect Foundation Limited (£15,000); and the Countryside Foundation for Education (£2,000).

FINANCES *Year* 2009–10 *Income* £586,262 *Grants* £4,720,240 *Assets* £32,234,452

TRUSTEES Robin Clark, Chair; Jack C Taylor; Briony Wilson.

HOW TO APPLY Please do not apply to the trust unless invited to do so. The trust's website states that: 'Due to the current economic situation and the reduction in interest rates our income has been greatly reduced. As such there are currently no free funds in the trust and therefore *the trust is unable to accept unsolicited applications.* This position is expected to continue for the foreseeable future, but any changes to this will be posted on [its] website at the time.' Please note: the trust is unable to deal with telephone or email enquiries about an application.

WHO TO APPLY TO Antony P Cox, Trust Manager, Fourth Floor South, 35 Portman Square, London W1H 6LR *Tel* 020 7486 0100 *Website* www.theunderwoodtrust.org.uk

■ The Union of Orthodox Hebrew Congregation

CC NO 249892   **ESTABLISHED** 1966
WHERE FUNDING CAN BE GIVEN UK.
WHO CAN BENEFIT Jewish organisations.
WHAT IS FUNDED To protect and to further in every way the interests of traditional Judaism in Great Britain and to establish and support such institutions as will serve this object.
SAMPLE GRANTS Previous beneficiaries have included: Addas Yisoroel Mikva Foundation, Achieve Trust, Atereth Shau, Beis Malka, Beis Shmuel, Belz Nursery, Bnos Yerushaim, Chesed Charity Trust, London Board of Schechita, Mutual Trust, Maoz Ladol, North West London Mikvah, Needy Families and Poor Families Pesach, Society of Friends of the Torah, Talmud Centre Trust and VMCT.
FINANCES *Year* 2009 *Income* £1,375,451 *Grants* £452,777 *Assets* £1,527,646
TRUSTEES B S F Freshwater; C Konig; Rabbi A Pinter.
OTHER INFORMATION £436,706 was given in grants to organisations and £16,000 to individuals.
HOW TO APPLY In writing to the correspondent.
WHO TO APPLY TO The Administrator, Landau Morley, Lanmor House, 370–386 High Road, Wembley HA9 6AX *Tel* 020 8903 5122

■ The United Society for the Propagation of the Gospel

CC NO 234518   **ESTABLISHED** 1701
WHERE FUNDING CAN BE GIVEN Mainly churches in Africa, West Indies, South Pacific, South America, Pakistan, India, Indian Ocean, Myanmar (Burma), Bangladesh, East Asia.
WHO CAN BENEFIT Overseas Anglican provinces and dioceses and churches in communion with the Anglican Church which benefit Christians and other disadvantaged groups.
WHAT IS FUNDED The promotion of the Christian religion and related charitable works.
WHAT IS NOT FUNDED Direct applications from individuals are not considered.
TYPE OF GRANT One-off grants; bursaries; loans.

FINANCES *Year* 2010 *Income* £4,209,310 *Grants* £1,221,850 *Assets* £37,419,376
TRUSTEES The Revd Roger Antell; Richard Barrett; Mrs Monica Bolley; The Rt Revd Purely Lyngdoh; Most Revd Mauricio Andrade; Revd Canon Christopher Chivers; Rt Revd Royden Screech; Rt Revd Joseph Seoka; Canon Linda Ali; Rt Revd Canon Richard Bartlett; Dr Hannah Batson; Rt Revd Alan Brookfield; Rt Revd Canon Christopher Burke; Rt Revd Michael Burrows; Revd Dr John Perumbalath; Nigel Wildfish.
HOW TO APPLY Applications must be submitted by Anglican Archbishops or Bishops to the Finance in Mission Officer.
WHO TO APPLY TO Finance in Mission Officer, Harling House, 47/51 Great Suffolk Street, London SE1 0BS *Tel* 020 7921 9200 *email* enquiries@uspg.org.uk *Website* www.uspg.org.uk

■ United Utilities Trust Fund

CC NO 1108296   **ESTABLISHED** 2005
WHERE FUNDING CAN BE GIVEN The area supplied by United Utilities Water Plc (predominantly the north west of England).
WHO CAN BENEFIT Mainly individuals, but also organisations.
WHAT IS FUNDED Social welfare and debt advice.
WHAT IS NOT FUNDED The trust will not fund: existing projects; charities which appear to us to have sufficient unrestricted or free reserves, or are in serious deficit; projects outside the geographical area; national charities that do not have the facility to accept the funding on a regional basis; grant making bodies seeking to distribute grants on UUTF's behalf; general appeals, sponsorship and marketing appeals; replacement of existing programmes or statutory funding.
TYPE OF GRANT Small one-off donations and larger grants for up to 2 years.
RANGE OF GRANTS Up to £30,000.
SAMPLE GRANTS Wythenshawe Law Centre (£30,000); Manchester Refugee Support Network (£29,000); Broad African Representative Council (£28,000); North Liverpool CAB (£27,000); MHIST (£21,000); Age Concern Blackburn and Darwen (£20,000); and Middleton/Brentwood Day Centre (£1,000).
FINANCES *Year* 2009–10 *Income* £5,030,994 *Grants* £4,829,968 *Assets* £115,030
TRUSTEES Deborah Moreton, Chair; Alan Manning; Alastair Richards; Nick Pearson; Simon Dewsnip; Allen Mackie; Carl Smith.
OTHER INFORMATION During the year £4.6 million was paid in grants to individuals. A further £230,000 was donated to 15 debt counselling organisations.
HOW TO APPLY On an application form available from the correspondent or the trust's website.
WHO TO APPLY TO The Secretary (Auriga Services Limited), United Utilities Trust Fund, Emmanuel Court, 12–14 Mill Street, West Midlands B72 1TJ *Tel* 0845 179 1791 *email* contact@uutf.org.uk *Website* www.uutf.org.uk

■ Unity Theatre Trust

CC NO 210387   **ESTABLISHED** 1964
WHERE FUNDING CAN BE GIVEN UK.
WHO CAN BENEFIT Registered charities and theatres.
WHAT IS FUNDED Drama and theatre related activities; performing arts.
WHAT IS NOT FUNDED The trust does not give grants for core funding, i.e. for annual running costs of an organisation, such as rent, telephone,

salaries, etc. The trust also prefers not to be the sole funder of a project but rather the junior partner in such funding.

TYPE OF GRANT Project funding and bursaries.

RANGE OF GRANTS £1,000 and £2,000.

FINANCES *Year* 2009–10 *Income* £38,933 *Grants* £28,070 *Assets* £791,632

TRUSTEES Ann Mitchell; Harry Landis; Clive Gehle; Jack Grossman; John Burgess; Kate O'Donoghue; Maureen Coman; Maggie McCarthy; Kayelle O'Donoghue.

OTHER INFORMATION A list of beneficiaries was not available.

HOW TO APPLY On an application form which can be downloaded from the trust's website. Full details are as follows: 'A grant request will only be considered on completion of an application form supplied by the trust. All successful applicants must keep detailed accounts in relation to the disbursement of the grant received and make these available to the trust for inspection at all reasonable times. Any unused grant must be returned, unless prior permission has been given by the trust for any other use. In their efforts to monitor the effectiveness of their grant strategy, the trustees expect all recipients of grant to inform the trust of the success or otherwise of the activities for which the grant was given. They also expect to be invited to the performance of plays or events the trust awards grants to. No grant may be used for any other purpose than that for which it was approved for without the prior permission of the trust. All applicants, by accepting receipt of any grant, agree not to contravene the charitable aims of the trust as summarised in the section of this website called 'The Theatre' and as restated in the guidance notes supplied with the application form. All successful applicants will be asked to confirm in writing their agreement as above before any grant is released. There will usually be FOUR decision dates in any one year, one in each of the following quarters, unless the trustees deem it necessary to meet outside these dates – 1st Quarter: January, February, March; 2nd Quarter: April, May, June; 3rd Quarter: July, August, September; 4th Quarter: October, November, December. Applications should be received 30 days prior to the planned trust meeting. The trustees will inform successful applicants how their grant will be administered but it will usually be done in one of the following ways: total grant in advance with invoices or accounts on request by the trustees; total grant after receipt of invoices or accounts; by instalments, with or without progress reports or account details of the preceding period; a progress report should be submitted to the trust by all successful projects.'

WHO TO APPLY TO Andreas Michaelides, Secretary, 37 Dunsmure Road, London N16 5PT *Tel* 020 8802 6437 *email* secretary@unitytheatre.org.uk *Website* www.unitytheatre.org.uk

---

■ UnLtd (Foundation for Social Entrepreneurs)

CC NO 1090393   **ESTABLISHED** 2001

WHERE FUNDING CAN BE GIVEN UK.

WHO CAN BENEFIT UnLtd awards are for people: over the age of 16; living in the UK; who are applying as an individual or informal group; who want to run projects that: benefit the public or a community in the UK, need an UnLtd award to ensure its success, offer a learning opportunity for the applicant(s), are a new initiative.

WHAT IS FUNDED Social enterprise.

TYPE OF GRANT Award winners receive a complete, tailored package of money, training and advice at every stage of their project.

FINANCES *Year* 2010–11 *Income* £8,764,035 *Grants* £3,762,985 *Assets* £2,258,460

TRUSTEES Rich Benton, Chair; John Brown; Norman Cumming; Anthony Freeling; Rodney Stares; Alastair Wilson; Martin Wyn Griffith; Richard Tyrie; Rajeeb Dey; Natalie Campbell; Andrew Croft; Dr Alison Fielding; Judith McNeill.

OTHER INFORMATION UnLtd is unique here in that it exists to make grants to individuals to undertake social initiatives. In effect it makes grants for the start-up costs of new organisations and community groups to enterprising individuals who need support to implement their ideas and projects for improving their communities.

HOW TO APPLY Applicants are advised to read the guidelines on the website carefully to check that they meet the criteria and then contact the nearest UnLtd office (see below) to discuss their ideas.

Regional offices
Head office/London office: 123 Whitecross Street, Islington, London EC1Y 8JJ. Telephone: 020 7566 1100; Fax: 020 7566 1101/1139; Email: info@unltd.org.uk. *Birmingham office*: Unit G2, The Ground Floor, The Arch, 48–52 Floodgate Street, Birmingham B5 5SL. Telephone: 0121 766 4570. *Bradford office*: 15 Halfield Road, Bradford BD1 3RP. Telephone: 01274 750630. *Northern Ireland office*: Room 55–57, Scottish Mutual Building, 16 Donegal Square South, Belfast BT1 5JG. Telephone: 028 9024 4007. *Scotland UnLtd office (Glasgow)*: Tobacco Merchants House, 42 Miller Street, Glasgow G1 1TD. Telephone: 0141 221 2322. *Scotland UnLtd office (Edinburgh)*: Cornerstone House, 2 Melville Street, Edinburgh EH3 7NS. Telephone: 0131 226 7333. *Wales office*: Fourth Floor, Baltic House, Mount Stuart Square, Cardiff CF10 5FH. Telephone: 029 2048 4811.

WHO TO APPLY TO Raymond Tran, Director of Finance, IT and Human Resources, 123 Whitecross Street, Islington, London EC1Y 8JJ *Tel* 020 7566 1100 *Fax* 020 7566 1101 *email* info@unltd.org.uk *Website* www.unltd.org.uk

---

■ The Michael Uren Foundation

CC NO 1094102   **ESTABLISHED** 2002

WHERE FUNDING CAN BE GIVEN UK and overseas.

WHO CAN BENEFIT Registered charities.

WHAT IS FUNDED General charitable purposes. 'The trustees are particularly keen on making grants for specific large projects. This could mean that, to satisfy this objective, no significant grants are paid in one year. With the resultant reserves retained a large grant could be made in the following year.'

TYPE OF GRANT Mainly large project grants.

RANGE OF GRANTS £500–£500,000.

SAMPLE GRANTS King Edward VII Hospital in Marylebone (£570,000) for the new Michael Uren Critical Care Unit; The City of London Royal Fusiliers Volunteers Trust (£125,000); UK Trust for Nature Conservation in Nepal (£75,000); International Animal Rescue (£50,000); Friends of St Mary's Kenardington (£30,000); Magdalen and Lasher Trust (£20,000); and Street Child of Sierra Leone (£10,000).

FINANCES *Year* 2009–10 *Income* £3,300,173 *Grants* £880,025 *Assets* £60,139,358

Think carefully about every application. Is it justified?

953

TRUSTEES Michael Uren; Anne Gregory-Jones; Janis Bennett; Alastair McDonald.

HOW TO APPLY In writing to the correspondent.

WHO TO APPLY TO Anne Gregory-Jones, Trustee, Haysmacintyre, Fairfax House, 15 Fulwood Place, London WC1V 6AY *email* agregory-jones@haysmacintyre.com

■ The David Uri Memorial Trust

CC NO 327810   **ESTABLISHED** 1988

WHERE FUNDING CAN BE GIVEN Worldwide.

WHO CAN BENEFIT Registered charities benefiting Jewish people, at risk groups and people who are disadvantaged by poverty or social isolation.

WHAT IS FUNDED Mainly Jewish organisations; also welfare and education charities.

WHAT IS NOT FUNDED No grants to individuals.

SAMPLE GRANTS Previous beneficiaries have included: National Jewish Chaplaincy Board, Age Concern, Crisis at Christmas, Jefferies Research Wing Trust, NSPCC and Yakar Education Foundation.

FINANCES *Year* 2009–10 *Income* £285,282 *Grants* £89,000 *Assets* £2,901,573

TRUSTEES Mrs S Blackman; Mrs B Roden; B Blackman.

HOW TO APPLY In writing to the correspondent.

WHO TO APPLY TO The Trustees, Suite 511, 19–21 Crawford Street, London W1H 1PJ

■ Uxbridge United Welfare Trust

CC NO 217066   **ESTABLISHED** 1991

WHERE FUNDING CAN BE GIVEN Former urban district of Uxbridge, includes Uxbridge, Hillingdon, Ickenham, Harefield and Cowley.

WHO CAN BENEFIT Local organisations benefiting children, young adults and people disadvantaged by poverty.

WHAT IS FUNDED Education, relief of poverty, including the provision of almshouses.

WHAT IS NOT FUNDED No grants are made outside the beneficial area.

SAMPLE GRANTS A list of beneficiaries was not available.

FINANCES *Year* 2010 *Income* £168,158 *Grants* £43,924 *Assets* £6,275,003

TRUSTEES John Childs; Pauline Crawley; Betty O'Rourke; David Routledge; Peter Ryerson; Gerda Driver; Elizabeth Jones; Raymond Graham; Michael Cater; Duncan Struthers; Susan James.

HOW TO APPLY In writing to the correspondent to obtain an application form. Applications are considered at the trustee's monthly meetings.

WHO TO APPLY TO Josie Duffy, Trustee, Woodbridge House, New Windsor Street, Uxbridge UB8 2TY *Tel* 01895 232976 *email* info@uuwt.org *Website* www.uuwt.org

954

Does the trust you have chosen match your needs? Haphazard applications waste postage and time

■ 'v'

CC NO 1113255   **ESTABLISHED** 2006
WHERE FUNDING CAN BE GIVEN England.
WHO CAN BENEFIT Young people aged between 16 and 25.
WHAT IS FUNDED 'v' is an independent charity set in 2006 up to inspire a new generation of young volunteers and enable lasting change in the quality, quantity and diversity of volunteering opportunities for 16 to 25 year olds in England. It aim is to implement the recommendations of the Russell Commission, looking to 'revolutionise youth volunteering in England and create a culture where it is natural for young people to volunteer and natural for organisations to support them in doing so, because the benefits of volunteering are widely understood and celebrated'. Its Advisory Board of young people – 'v20' – play a fundamental role in guiding the work of the charity. 'v' aims to inspire more investment in youth volunteering and supports cutting edge partnerships between the private and third sector. Through the 'v' Match Fund, 'v' can match up to 100% of new investment from private companies, individuals, foundations or charitable trusts. This could make you more attractive to a sponsor, as with double the budget, you could double the impact of their investment.
WHAT IS NOT FUNDED 'v' cannot match funds from public sector organisations, (for example: national and local government, EU funding or lottery funders).
TYPE OF GRANT Match funding.
SAMPLE GRANTS Beneficiaries of 'v' funds include Barnardo's, ChildLine, Prince's Trust, Oxfam, RNIB and Save the Children. A full list of grants is available upon request.
FINANCES *Year* 2009–10 *Income* £21,602,000 *Grants* £37,200,000 *Assets* £6,877,000
TRUSTEES Rod Aldridge (chair); Dame Tanni Grey Thomson DBE; Manny Amadi; Tim Smart; Joan Watson; Tricia Killen; Lorraine O'Reilly; Natalie Campbell; Mohammed Ahmed; Larissa Joy; Lucy Kerrigan; Vanessa Sanyauke; Rosina St James.
HOW TO APPLY Go to the charity's website and complete the online eligibility questionnaire. An application form and guidance notes will then be emailed to you.
WHO TO APPLY TO Jayne Colquhoun, Secretary, 5th Floor, Dean Bradley House, 52 Horseferry Road, London SW1P 2AF *Tel* 020 7960 7019 *Fax* 020 7960 7099 *Minicom* 020 7960 7099 *email* info@wearev.com *Website* www.vinspired.com

■ The Vail Foundation

CC NO 1089579   **ESTABLISHED** 2001
WHERE FUNDING CAN BE GIVEN UK and overseas.
WHO CAN BENEFIT Registered charities.
WHAT IS FUNDED Jewish causes.
RANGE OF GRANTS Up to £400,000.
SAMPLE GRANTS Jewish Care (£575,000 in 3 grants); KKL Charity Limited (£470,000 in 5 grants); United Jewish Israel Appeal (£150,000); London School of Jewish Studies (£125,000); Jewish Community Secondary School (£100,000); Project Seed (£50,000); Jewish Learning Exchange (£30,000); UNICEF UK (£25,000); Anne Frank Trust (£15,000); Jewish Leadership Council (£10,000); Langdon Foundation and the Old Vic Theatre Trust 2000 (£5,000 each); and the Roundhouse Trust and the Jewish Volunteering Network (£1,000 each).
FINANCES *Year* 2009–10 *Income* £282,423 *Grants* £1,994,800 *Assets* £9,162,417
TRUSTEES Michael S Bradfield; Paul Brett; Michael H Goldstein.
HOW TO APPLY In writing to the correspondent. 'The trustees consider all requests which they receive and make such donations as they feel appropriate.'
WHO TO APPLY TO Michael S Bradfield, Trustee, 5 Fitzhardinge Street, London W1H 6ED *Tel* 020 7317 3000

■ Vale of Glamorgan – Welsh Church Fund

CC NO 506628   **ESTABLISHED** 1996
WHERE FUNDING CAN BE GIVEN Vale of Glamorgan and City of Cardiff council areas.
WHO CAN BENEFIT Organisations benefiting children, young adults, students and local communities may all be considered.
WHAT IS FUNDED Restoration of churches and memorials; education and training, particularly vocational or religious; health; social welfare; arts and culture; recreation and sport; environment and animals; faith activities; science and technology; social sciences, policy and research; and philanthropy and the voluntary sector.
WHAT IS NOT FUNDED No grants to individuals.
TYPE OF GRANT One-off.
RANGE OF GRANTS 'Whilst no maximum/minimum grant levels are stipulated, awards are usually in the region of £1,500.'
SAMPLE GRANTS Holy Trinity Presbyterian Church, Barry (£10,000); The United Reform Church, Barry (£10,000); Bethel Baptist Church, Barry (£8,500); Elfred Avenue United Church, Penarth (£500).
FINANCES *Year* 2009–10 *Income* £48,000 *Grants* £32,500 *Assets* £3,730,000
TRUSTEES The Vale of Glamorgan County Borough Council.
HOW TO APPLY For organisations based in the Vale of Glamorgan, further information can be obtained from the correspondent. For organisations based in Cardiff, please contact R Anthony at Cardiff County Council (tel. 029 2087 2395). Applications are accepted throughout the year and meetings of the trustees convened to consider applications as and when required.
WHO TO APPLY TO A D Williams, Director of Finance, ICT and Property, The Vale of Glamorgan Council, Civic Offices, Holton Rd, Barry CF63 4RU *Tel* 01446 709250 *email* adwilliams@valeofglamorgan.gov.uk

■ The Valentine Charitable Trust

CC NO 1001782   **ESTABLISHED** 1990
WHERE FUNDING CAN BE GIVEN Unrestricted, but mainly Dorset. Developing countries.
WHO CAN BENEFIT Registered charities.
WHAT IS FUNDED Welfare, the environment and overseas aid.

WHAT IS NOT FUNDED No grants to individuals. The trust would not normally fund appeals for village halls or the fabric of church buildings.

TYPE OF GRANT Core, capital and project support is given as well as loan finance. One-off grants are preferred, but funding can be for longer periods.

RANGE OF GRANTS Up to £25,000.

SAMPLE GRANTS Special Boat Service Association (£25,000); Wessex Autistic Society (£20,000); Bournemouth Symphony Orchestra (£15,000); Disability & Development Partners (£11,000); Action on Addiction, Combat Stress and Victoria Education Centre & Sports College (£10,000 each); Rainbow Trust (£7,000); Brainwave Centre (£6,000); British Liver Trust, Dorset MS Therapy Centre and the Jubilee Sailing Trust (£5,000 each); Bournemouth Town Centre Detached Youth and Live Music Now (£4,000 each); Breakthrough Breast Cancer and MOVE Europe (£3,000 each); Donald Woods Foundation (£2,000); and Self Help Africa and Farming & Wildlife Advisory Group (£1,000 each).

FINANCES *Year* 2009–10 *Income* £829,869 *Grants* £806,868 *Assets* £25,138,535

TRUSTEES Douglas J E Neville-Jones; Roger A Gregory; Mrs Shiela F Cox; Mrs Susan Patterson; Mrs Patricia B N Walker; Peter Leatherdale; Mrs Diana Tory; Donald Jack.

HOW TO APPLY In writing to the correspondent. The trust provides the following insight into its application process in its annual report: 'All applications will be acknowledged with standard letters, even those that are not appropriate for receiving a grant. This responsibility is delegated to Douglas J E Neville-Jones who then provides a report to the next trustees' meeting. The following general comments summarise some of the considerations the trustees seek to apply when considering applications for funding. The trustees look for value for money. While this concept is difficult to apply in a voluntary sector it can certainly be used on a comparative basis and subjectively. If the trustees have competing applications they will usually decide to support just one of them as they believe that to concentrate the charity's donations is more beneficial than to dilute them. Regular contact with the charities to which donations are made is considered essential. Reports and accounts are also requested from charities which are supported and the trustees consider those at their meetings. The trustees take great comfort from the fact that they employ the policy of only making donations to other charities or similar bodies. However they are not complacent about the need to review all donations made and the objects to which those have been given. The trustees are conscious that, particularly with the smaller and local charities, the community of those working for and with the charity is an important consideration. The trustees regularly review the classifications to which donations have been made so that they can obtain an overview of the charity's donations and assess whether their policies are being implemented in practice. They are conscious that when dealing with individual donations it is easy to lose sight of the overall picture.'

WHO TO APPLY TO Douglas J E Neville-Jones, Trustee, Preston Redman LLP, Hinton House, Hinton Road, Bournemouth, Dorset BH1 2EN *Tel* 01202 292424 *Fax* 01202 552758 *email* valentine@prestonredman.co.uk

■ The Valiant Charitable Trust

CC NO 1135810   **ESTABLISHED** 2010

WHERE FUNDING CAN BE GIVEN UK.

WHO CAN BENEFIT Registered charities.

WHAT IS FUNDED General, older people, people with disabilities.

TRUSTEES Roger Woolfe; Lady Valarie Dixon; Paul Brenham.

OTHER INFORMATION The settlor of the trust is Lady Valerie Dixon, widow of the late Sir Ian Dixon, former chair of the Willmott Dixon construction group.

HOW TO APPLY In writing to the correspondent.

WHO TO APPLY TO Roger Woolfe, Trustee, Collyer Bristow Solicitors, 4 Bedford Row, London WC1R 4DF *Tel* 020 7242 7363 *email* roger.woolfe@collyerbristow.com

■ The Albert Van Den Bergh Charitable Trust

CC NO 296885   **ESTABLISHED** 1987

WHERE FUNDING CAN BE GIVEN UK and overseas.

WHO CAN BENEFIT Charitable organisations.

WHAT IS FUNDED Medical research, disability, community, care of the elderly, children and general charitable purposes.

SAMPLE GRANTS Previous beneficiaries have included: BLISS, Bishop of Guildford's Charity, British Heart Foundation, Counsel and Care for the Elderly, Leukaemia Research Trust, Multiple Sclerosis Society, Parentline Surrey, National Osteoporosis Society, RNID, Riding for the Disabled – Cranleigh Age Concern, SSAFA, St John Ambulance and United Charities Fund – Liberal Jewish Synagogue.

FINANCES *Year* 2009–10 *Income* £104,400 *Grants* £90,300 *Assets* £3,073,424

TRUSTEES Jane Hartley; Nicola Glover; Bruce Hopkins.

HOW TO APPLY In writing to the correspondent, including accounts and budgets.

WHO TO APPLY TO Jane Hartley, Trustee, Trevornick Farmhouse, Holywell Bay, Newquay, Cornwall TR8 5PW

■ John and Lucille van Geest Foundation

CC NO 1001279   **ESTABLISHED** 1990

WHERE FUNDING CAN BE GIVEN UK, with some interest in south Lincolnshire and adjoining areas; occasionally overseas.

WHO CAN BENEFIT Registered charities.

WHAT IS FUNDED Medical research in the following areas: brain damage e.g. Alzheimer's Disease, Huntington's Disease, Parkinson's Disease and strokes; cancer; heart disease; lung disease; sight and/or hearing loss. Healthcare for people in need through illness, infirmity or social circumstances and in particular the welfare of older people and of children resident in South Lincolnshire.

WHAT IS NOT FUNDED No grants to individuals.

TYPE OF GRANT Capital, revenue and full project funding. Primarily one-off, although any type of grant is considered.

RANGE OF GRANTS £2,000–£247,500.

SAMPLE GRANTS Nottingham Trent University (£4.9 million); Royal National Institute for Deaf People (£247,500); University of Leicester (£134,000); University of Cambridge Brain Repair Centre (£112,000); Lincolnshire & Nottinghamshire Air Ambulance (£24,000); East

Anglia Children's Hospice (£20,000); British Heart Foundation (£15,000); St Barnabas Hospice Trust (£12,000); Action For Children (£10,000); Headway Cambridgeshire (£5,000); and the Dystonia Society (£2,000).

FINANCES *Year* 2009–10 *Income* £831,095 *Grants* £5,702,211 *Assets* £31,479,981

TRUSTEES Hilary P Marlowe; Stuart R Coltman; Tonie Gibson.

HOW TO APPLY In writing to the correspondent. Please note that only charities engaged in areas of work to which the trust's policy extends are considered (and in the case of healthcare grants, only charities providing services in South Lincolnshire and adjoining area). Telephone calls are not welcome. The trustees meet two to three times a year to consider applications, but there are no set dates. Every applicant will receive a reply.

WHO TO APPLY TO Brenda Ruysen, Clerk to the Trustees, 108 Pinchbeck Road, Spalding, Lincolnshire PE11 1QL *email* trustees@johnandlucillevangeestfoundation.org *Website* johnandlucillevangeestfoundation.org

■ The Van Neste Foundation

CC NO 201951   **ESTABLISHED** 1959

WHERE FUNDING CAN BE GIVEN UK (especially the Bristol area) and overseas.

WHO CAN BENEFIT Registered charities.

WHAT IS FUNDED Currently the main areas of interest are: developing world; people who are disabled or elderly; advancement of religion; community and 'Christian family life' and 'respect for the sanctity and dignity of life'.

WHAT IS NOT FUNDED No grants to individuals or to large, well-known charities. Applications are only considered from registered charities.

TYPE OF GRANT Usually one-off for a specific project or part of a project. Core funding is rarely considered.

SAMPLE GRANTS Life (£30,000); CCS Adoption (£20,000); CAFOD in Bolivia (£15,000); Moquegua Project Peru and Windmill Hill City Farm (£10,000 each); Royal West of England Academy (£6,000); African Initiatives, Home Start, Prisoners Abroad and Rainbow Development Africa (£5,000 each); St Peter's Church Henleaze – Bristol (£1,000); Dolphin Society (£250).

FINANCES *Year* 2009–10 *Income* £227,304 *Grants* £215,500 *Assets* £6,474,401

TRUSTEES M T M Appleby, Chair; F J F Lyons; G J Walker; J F Lyons; B M Appleby; Michael Lyons; Tom Appleby.

HOW TO APPLY Applications should be in the form of a concise letter setting out the clear objectives to be obtained, which must be charitable. Information must be supplied concerning agreed funding from other sources together with a timetable for achieving the objectives of the appeal and a copy of the latest accounts. The foundation does not normally make grants on a continuing basis. To keep overheads to a minimum, only successful applications are acknowledged. Appeals are considered by the trustees at their meetings in January, June and October.

WHO TO APPLY TO Fergus Lyons, Secretary, 15 Alexandra Road, Clifton, Bristol BS8 2DD *Tel* 01179 735167

■ Mrs Maud Van Norden's Charitable Foundation

CC NO 210844   **ESTABLISHED** 1962

WHERE FUNDING CAN BE GIVEN UK.

WHO CAN BENEFIT Registered UK charities only.

WHAT IS FUNDED General charitable purposes, particularly aid to younger or older people. Also preservation of the environment and heritage, disability and animal welfare.

WHAT IS NOT FUNDED No grants to individuals, expeditions or scholarships. The trustees make donations to registered UK charities only.

TYPE OF GRANT One-off and research.

RANGE OF GRANTS All but one of grants made were for £1,500 each.

SAMPLE GRANTS Princess Royal Trust for Carers (£3,000); Royal Hospital for Neuro-disability (£2,500); Changing Faces, Church Urban Fund, Home Warmth for the Aged, Humane Slaughter Association, National Rheumatoid Arthritis Society, Police Community Clubs of Great Britain, and Vitalise (£1,500 each); Ellen Macarthur Cancer Trust (£500).

FINANCES *Year* 2010 *Income* £38,746 *Grants* £40,500 *Assets* £1,098,378

TRUSTEES Ena Dukler; John Gordon; Elizabeth Humphryes; Neil Wingerath.

HOW TO APPLY All appeals should be by letter containing the following: aims and objectives of the charity; nature of the appeal; total target, if for a specific project; contributions received against target; registered charity number; any other factors. Letters should be accompanied by a copy of the applicant's latest reports and accounts.

WHO TO APPLY TO The Trustees, BM Box 2367, London WC1N 3XX

■ The Vandervell Foundation

CC NO 255651   **ESTABLISHED** 1968

WHERE FUNDING CAN BE GIVEN UK.

WHO CAN BENEFIT Individuals and organisations.

WHAT IS FUNDED General charitable purposes.

RANGE OF GRANTS £1,000–£30,000.

SAMPLE GRANTS Big Issue (£30,000); Prisoners Educational Trust (£20,000); Oxford Medical School (£18,000); PMS Foundation; QMUL; King's College London School of Medicine (£15,000 each); Lucy Cavendish College; Weekend Arts College(£10,000 each); London Air Ambulance; and Royal National Theatre (£5,000 each).

FINANCES *Year* 2010 *Income* £258,060 *Grants* £391,286 *Assets* £6,655,160

TRUSTEES The Vandervell Foundation Limited Trustee Company.

HOW TO APPLY In writing to the correspondent. Trustees meet every two months to consider major grant applications; smaller grants are considered more frequently.

WHO TO APPLY TO Valerie Kaye, Administrator, Hampstead Town Hall Centre, 213 Haverstock Hill, London NW3 4QP *Tel* 020 7435 7546

■ The Vardy Foundation

CC NO 328415   **ESTABLISHED** 1987

WHERE FUNDING CAN BE GIVEN UK with a preference for North East England, overseas.

WHO CAN BENEFIT Registered charities, social enterprises and individuals.

WHAT IS FUNDED General charitable purposes, education in North East England, young people and social welfare.

WHAT IS NOT FUNDED The foundation will not fund: applications for more than a 3 year commitment; animal welfare projects; health related charities; projects normally provided by central or local government; individuals (including requests for educational support costs) (NB: the foundation does award grants to individuals, however these are likely to already be connected to the foundation or one of the educational institutions that receive funding from the foundation; projects that do not demonstrate an element of self funding or other funding; contribute to an organisation's healthy reserves or endowments.

TYPE OF GRANT One-off and recurrent for up to 3 years. Capital and revenue.

RANGE OF GRANTS Up to £200,000. Small grants for £5,000 or less.

SAMPLE GRANTS Thana Trust (£200,000); Youth for Christ (£144,000); Bede Academy (£140,000); The Message Trust (£112,500); and the University of Sunderland (£100,000).

FINANCES *Year* 2009–10 *Income* £907,177 *Grants* £1,649,339 *Assets* £22,003,011

TRUSTEES Sir Peter Vardy; Lady Margaret Barr Vardy; Peter D D Vardy; Richard Vardy.

OTHER INFORMATION Individual grants totalled £112,500.

HOW TO APPLY Please note that as of 1 July 2011 the foundation is undertaking an internal review of its activities and will not be accepting funding applications until further notice.

WHO TO APPLY TO Victoria Spencer, Venture House, Aykley Heads, Durham DH1 5TS *Tel* 0191 374 4727 *email* foundation@regvardy.com *Website* vardyfoundation.com

■ The Variety Club Children's Charity

CC NO 209259   **ESTABLISHED** 1949
WHERE FUNDING CAN BE GIVEN UK.

WHO CAN BENEFIT Hospitals, schools, charities and other organisations.

WHAT IS FUNDED The welfare of children up to the age of 19 who are disadvantaged or have disabilities.

WHAT IS NOT FUNDED For grants to organisations: trips abroad; medical treatment or research; administrative or salary costs; maintenance or ongoing costs; repayment of loans; distribution to other organisations; computers; education/ tuition fees; garden adaptions; basic cost of a family vehicle; hire, rental costs or down payments; and non-specific appeals.

TYPE OF GRANT One-off and recurring. Money and equipment, including coaches, to organisations. Individual children have received money, electric wheelchairs, toys and holidays.

RANGE OF GRANTS Up to £125,000.

SAMPLE GRANTS Leeds Teaching Hospitals NHS Trust (£125,000); Sports Aid (£108,000); Martin House, Amateur Swimming Association (Loughborough), King's College Hospital (£50,000 each); Stepping Stones (Lancashire), Charlie Chaplin Adventure Playground (London) (£37,000 each); Oakwood School (Manchester), Butterwick Hospice Care (Stockton-on-Tees) (£36,000 each); Heath Park Business & Enterprise Co. (Wolverhampton) (£26,000); East Muir School (Glasgow) (£24,000); Linden Lodge School (London) (£10,000); and Kenth Youth (Gillingham) (£5,000).

FINANCES *Year* 2010 *Income* £10,003,594 *Grants* £4,051,935 *Assets* £3,544,129

TRUSTEES Kenneth R Mustoe; Keith Andrews; John E Barnett; Gary Beckwith; Anthony Blackburn; Malcolm Brenner; Laurence Davis; Alan Fraser; Lionel Rosenblatt; John Sachs; Jonathan Shalit; Pamela Sinclair; Anne Wadsworth; Norman Kaphan; Russell Kahn; Ronnie Nathan; Anthony Harris; Stephen Crown; Jarvis Astaire; Tony Hatch; Nicholas Shattock; Ronald Sinclair; Richard Freeman; Grant Lewis; Lloyd Barr; Philip Burley; Robert Beecham; Stanley Salter; Joseph Williams.

OTHER INFORMATION A total of £45,000 was disbursed in grants of less than £5,000 to organisations.
A further £94,000 was made in grants to individuals.

HOW TO APPLY There are application forms for each programme, available – with application guidelines – from the charity or through its website.

WHO TO APPLY TO Stanley Salter, Variety Club House, 93 Bayham Street, London NW1 0AG *Tel* 020 7428 8100 *email* grants@varietyclub.org.uk *Website* www.varietyclub.org.uk

■ Veneziana Fund

CC NO 1061760   **ESTABLISHED** 1997
WHERE FUNDING CAN BE GIVEN Venice and the UK.

WHO CAN BENEFIT Charitable organisations working with old buildings or art.

WHAT IS FUNDED This trust gives half its grant total to the Venice in Peril Fund (amounting to £35,000 in 2009–10), and in the UK or the preservation, restoration, repair and maintenance of: buildings originally constructed before 1750; the fixtures and fittings of such buildings; and works of art made before 1750 (including the purchase of such items).

WHAT IS NOT FUNDED No grants are made towards heating systems or toilets.

TYPE OF GRANT One-off capital grants.

RANGE OF GRANTS Up to £2,000.

SAMPLE GRANTS Beneficiaries included: Venice in Peril (£35,000); Holburne Museum of Art (£2,000); All Saints Church Newland, Landmark Trust – Astley Castle, Friends of St Cuby's Church – Duloe, Fowey Parish Church (£1,500); St Chad's Church – Chad, St James Church – Stanstead (£1,250).

FINANCES *Year* 2009–10 *Income* £61,494 *Grants* £69,500 *Assets* £39,044

TRUSTEES Peter J Boizot; T B Warren; Jackie Freeman; Jane Botros.

HOW TO APPLY The trustee's consider appeals twice a year in spring and autumn. Applications should be submitted online via www.pwwsolicitors.co.uk. The trustees require applicants to have raised two thirds of the total required from other sources before applying to the fund.

WHO TO APPLY TO Jayne Day, Administrator, c/o Pothecary Witham Weld Solicitors, 25C North Street, Bishop's Stortford, Hertfordshire CM23 2LD *Tel* 020 7821 8211 *email* charities@pwwsolicitors.co.uk *Website* www.pwwsolicitors.co.uk

■ The William and Patricia Venton Charitable Trust

CC NO 1103884   **ESTABLISHED** 2004
WHERE FUNDING CAN BE GIVEN UK.

WHO CAN BENEFIT Older people, day centres, animal welfare.

WHAT IS FUNDED Relief in need for older people, particularly day centre provision and the prevention of cruelty and suffering among animals.

RANGE OF GRANTS £1,000–£18,000.

SAMPLE GRANTS Beneficiaries include: RSPCA Cornwall (£17,000); Cats Protection League (£7,000); Battersea Dogs and Cats Home, the Council for Music in Hospitals, SERVE and Abbey Field Bromley Society Ltd (£5,000 each); Age Concern Hampshire (£2,500) and British School of Osteopathy (£1,200).

FINANCES *Year* 2009–10 *Income* £113,111 *Grants* £52,611 *Assets* £221,093

TRUSTEES G B Hillman-Liggett; C C Saunby; G J Cudlipp.

HOW TO APPLY In writing to the correspondent.

WHO TO APPLY TO The Trustees, Laytons Solicitors, Carmelite, 50 Victoria Embankment, Blackfriars, London EC4Y 0LS *Tel* 01590 623818

■ The Verdon-Smith Family Charitable Settlement

CC NO 284919   **ESTABLISHED** 1983

WHERE FUNDING CAN BE GIVEN South-West England, and especially Somerset, Bristol, Wiltshire, South Gloucestershire and North Dorset.

WHO CAN BENEFIT Registered charities with emphasis on local activity and needs benefiting: people of all ages; ex-service and service people; seafarers and fishermen; musicians; widows and widowers; Church of England; disabled people; disaster victims; and homeless people.

WHAT IS FUNDED This trust will consider funding: almshouses and respite accommodation; architecture; music; visual arts; arts education; orchestras; cultural activities; religious buildings; acute health care; hospices and hospice at home; respite care for carers; cancer and MS research; conservation; animal welfare; church schools; independent schools; care in the community and day centres. There is a quarterly review of regular donations with occasional addition of new donations.

WHAT IS NOT FUNDED No grants to individuals, or for salaries or running costs. Grants to organisations with recognized charitable status only.

TYPE OF GRANT Recurrent, occasional one-off, buildings, capital, core costs, project and research. Funding is available for one year or less.

RANGE OF GRANTS £50–£500.

SAMPLE GRANTS Average grant of £150. Previous beneficiaries include: Corsham Festival; Devon Wildlife Trust; Gloucestershire Society; Salisbury Trust for the Homeless; Shaw Trust; Royal Hospital for Children – Bristol; Jubilee Sailing Trust; West Lavington Youth Club; Canine Partners for Independence; Motability for Somerset; Arthritis Research Campaign; Royal British Legion; Building of Bath Museum Appeal; Salisbury Cathedral Choral Foundation; Grateful Society; Genesis Trust; and Avon Outward Bound Association.

FINANCES *Year* 2009–10 *Income* £33,208 *Grants* £26,800 *Assets* £566,140

TRUSTEES William G Verdon-Smith, Chair; Mrs Elizabeth J White; Mrs Diana N Verdon-Smith.

HOW TO APPLY In writing to the correspondent. The trustees meet quarterly and applications will not be acknowledged unless successful.

WHO TO APPLY TO Mrs Elizabeth J White, Trustee, 5 Sydney Buildings, Bath, Somerset BA2 6BZ *Tel* 01225 426458

■ Roger Vere Foundation

CC NO 1077559   **ESTABLISHED** 1999

WHERE FUNDING CAN BE GIVEN UK and worldwide, with a special interest in High Wycombe.

WHO CAN BENEFIT Charitable organisations.

WHAT IS FUNDED The relief of financial hardship in and around, but not restricted to, High Wycombe; advancement of education; advancement of religion; advancement of scientific and medical research; conservation and protection of the natural environment and endangered plants and animals; relief of natural and civil disasters; and general charitable purposes.

RANGE OF GRANTS In 2009–10 no single grant exceeded £1,000.

SAMPLE GRANTS Previous beneficiaries include: Cord Blood Charity, the Leprosy Mission, Claire House Children's Hospice, Angels International, Signalong Group, Changing Faces, Women's Aid, St John Water Wing, UK Youth and Jubilee Plus.

FINANCES *Year* 2009–10 *Income* £144,674 *Grants* £243,770 *Assets* £3,516,966

TRUSTEES Rosemary Vere, Chair; Marion Lyon; Peter Allen.

HOW TO APPLY In writing to the correspondent. The trustees meet regularly to consider requests.

WHO TO APPLY TO Peter Allen, Trustee, 19 Berwick Road, Marlow, Buckinghamshire SL7 3AR

■ Victoria Homes Trust

IR NO XN45474   **ESTABLISHED** 1892

WHERE FUNDING CAN BE GIVEN Northern Ireland.

WHO CAN BENEFIT Registered charities benefiting children and young people.

WHAT IS FUNDED Voluntary projects in the fields of homelessness, alcohol and drug abuse and counselling.

WHAT IS NOT FUNDED Grants are not normally given to individuals.

FINANCES *Year* 2010 *Grants* £45,000

HOW TO APPLY On a form available from the correspondent or from the charity's website. A copy of the most recent audited accounts should be included. Applications should be typed or written in block capital letters using black ink. If the project requires work which involves planning permission, evidence that the permission has been granted should be enclosed. The trust asks that pamphlets or other printed matter should not be sent. Trustees meet in June and January. Applications should be submitted before 30 April and 30 November respectively.

WHO TO APPLY TO Derek H Catney, Secretary, 2 Tudor Court, Rochester Road, Belfast BT6 9LB *Tel* 028 9079 4306 *email* derek.catney@victoriahomestrust.org.uk *Website* www.victoriahomestrust.org.uk

---

■ The Nigel Vinson Charitable Trust

CC NO 265077   **ESTABLISHED** 1973

WHERE FUNDING CAN BE GIVEN UK, with a preference for north east England.

WHO CAN BENEFIT Individuals and organisations.

WHAT IS FUNDED Economic/community development and employment; and general charitable purposes.

TYPE OF GRANT Capital (including buildings), one-off, project and research. Funding is for one year or less.

SAMPLE GRANTS Institute for Policy Research (£28,000); Civitas (£17,000); Institute of Economic Affairs (£12,000); Hampden Trust (£10,000); Politics and Economics Research Trust (£5,000); Christian Institute (£4,000); Songbird Survival (£2,000); and Elizabeth Finn Care (£1,500).

FINANCES *Year* 2009–10 *Income* £104,038 *Grants* £105,355 *Assets* £4,201,379

TRUSTEES Hon. Rowena A Cowan; Rt Hon. Lord Vinson of Roddam Dene; Thomas O C Harris; Hon. Miss Bettina C Witheridge; Hon. Mrs Antonia C Bennett; Miss E Passey.

HOW TO APPLY In writing to the correspondent. The trustees meet periodically to consider applications for grants of £1,000 and above. All grants below £1,000 are decided by The Rt. Hon. Nigel Lord Vinson on behalf of the trustees.

WHO TO APPLY TO The Trustees, Hoare Trustees, 37 Fleet Street, London EC4P 4DQ *Tel* 020 7353 4522

■ The William and Ellen Vinten Trust

CC NO 285758   **ESTABLISHED** 1982

WHERE FUNDING CAN BE GIVEN UK, but mostly Bury St Edmunds.

WHO CAN BENEFIT Individuals, schools and colleges; and industrial firms and companies. There is a strong preference for Bury St Edmunds.

WHAT IS FUNDED The trustees' report states that: 'The principal activity of the trust during the year was continuing to pursue initiatives to increase the interest of schools and college students in the Bury St Edmunds' area in science and technology subjects, with a view to increasing the numbers who might consider careers related to the subjects and improving their attainment.'

SAMPLE GRANTS A list of beneficiaries was not available.

FINANCES *Year* 2009–10 *Income* £59,937 *Grants* £40,882 *Assets* £1,366,529

OTHER INFORMATION Grants given towards education (£25,000) and training (£16,000).

HOW TO APPLY The trust stated that as a proactive charity it does not seek unsolicited applications. Such applications are now so significant in number that the trust has decided not to respond to them, however discourteous this may seem.

WHO TO APPLY TO The Chair of the Trustees, 80 Guildhall Street, Bury St Edmunds, Suffolk IP33 1QB *Tel* 01359 234494

■ The Vintners' Company Charitable Foundation

CC NO 1015212   **ESTABLISHED** 1992

WHERE FUNDING CAN BE GIVEN Greater London only.

WHO CAN BENEFIT Schools and charitable organisations.

WHAT IS FUNDED Prevention of drug and alcohol abuse. Funding for schools can be for general purposes.

WHAT IS NOT FUNDED No grants to UK-wide or research charities.

TYPE OF GRANT One-off.

SAMPLE GRANTS Previous beneficiaries include: National Association of Children of Alcoholics (£30,000). Also, £12,000 to general charities and £5,000 in educational grants.

FINANCES *Year* 2009–10 *Income* £81,823 *Grants* £30,000 *Assets* £583,870

TRUSTEES Michael Cox; Sam Dow; Brigadier Michael Smythe; Martin Mason; Michael Turner.

HOW TO APPLY In writing to the correspondent.

WHO TO APPLY to Kate Marshall, Charities Secretary, Vintners' Company, Vintners' Hall, Upper Thames Street, London EC4V 3BG *Tel* 020 7236 1863 *Fax* 020 7236 8177 *email* catherine@vintnershall.co.uk *Website* www.vintnershall.co.uk

■ Vintners' Gifts Charity

CC NO 1091238   **ESTABLISHED** 1992

WHERE FUNDING CAN BE GIVEN Greater London.

WHO CAN BENEFIT Hospices, hospitals and organisations benefiting older people, people with disabilities, those who have experienced abuse or addiction, young people, the homeless and the disadvantaged.

WHAT IS FUNDED The Vintners' Company concentrates on different sections of charitable giving every six months. May 2010 – Disabilities, November 2010 – Hospices/hospitals, May 2011 – Youth/youth projects, November 2011 – Homeless & Disadvantaged.

WHAT IS NOT FUNDED No grants to national charities, research organisations or charities that help buildings (as opposed to people).

TYPE OF GRANT One-off.

RANGE OF GRANTS £500–£7,000.

SAMPLE GRANTS Beneficiaries include: Addiction Support & Care Agency (£7,000); Drug & Alcohol Service London (£6,200); Advocacy, Hoxton Health Group and Equinox Care (£5,000); In Depth Community Task Force (£3,000) and Hearing Dogs for the Deaf (£1,000).

In addition, a further £64,453 of grants were made for a wide range of causes including education (£23,300), support of the Company's pensioners (£6,270), The Benevolent Society's home at Eastbourne (£14,676), Vintners' Scholarships (£6,300) and The Lord Mayor's Appeal (£2,500).

Please note that the beneficiaries listed are not necessarily representative of future grant recipients due to the charity changing its focus every six months.

FINANCES *Year* 2009–10 *Income* £186,701 *Grants* £156,316 *Assets* £1,982,448

TRUSTEES The Master and Wardens of the Vintners' Company. Martin Mason; Sam Dow; Michael Cox; Brigadier Michael Smythe; Michael Turner.

HOW TO APPLY In writing to the correspondent, giving details of the charity and a brief description of the project, if applicable, together with a copy of the latest audited accounts. Applicants must be prepared to be visited by a member of The Vintners' Company. The Charities Committee Meetings are in May and November. Applications should be received by 14 February for May Meetings and 14 August for November Meetings.

WHO TO APPLY TO Mrs Kate Marshall, Charities Secretary, Vintners' Company, Vintners' Hall, Upper Thames Street, London EC4V 3BG *Tel* 020 7236 1863 *Fax* 020 7236 8177 *email* catherine@vintnershall.co.uk *Website* www.vintnershall.co.uk

■ Vision Charity

CC NO 1075630   **ESTABLISHED** 1976
WHERE FUNDING CAN BE GIVEN UK and overseas.
WHO CAN BENEFIT 'Registered institutional charities and other organisations and individuals involved in helping blind, dyslexic or visually impaired children.'
WHAT IS FUNDED Welfare of children with dyslexia or visual difficulties.
TYPE OF GRANT 'The monies raised are used expressly to purchase equipment, goods or specialist services. The Vision Charity will make cash donations only in very exceptional circumstances, as approved by its Board of Trustees.'
SAMPLE GRANTS Dyslexia Action (£25,000); London Society for the Blind – Dorton House School (£17,000); Blind in Business (£10,000); Autism Independent UK (£8,500); Royal Blind Society (£7,500); Moorfields Eye Hospital (£5,000).
FINANCES *Year* 2009–10 *Income* £643,827 *Grants* £115,860 *Assets* £377,947
TRUSTEES Herbert Brenninkmeijer, Chair; Bill Bohanna; W Vestey.
PUBLICATIONS *Vision Charity News* (published twice yearly).
OTHER INFORMATION 'Vision is keen to emphasize its increasing international focus, both in terms of its fundraising activities and in directing its donations.'
HOW TO APPLY A brief summary of the request should be sent to the correspondent. If the request is of interest to the trustees, further details will be requested. If the request has not been acknowledged within three months of submission, the applicant should assume that it has not been successful. The charity is interested to receive such applications but regrets that it is not able to acknowledge every unsuccessful submission.
WHO TO APPLY TO The Trustees, PO Box 553, Chatham ME4 9AN *Website* www.visioncharity.co.uk

■ Vivdale Ltd

CC NO 268505   **ESTABLISHED** 1974
WHERE FUNDING CAN BE GIVEN UK.
WHO CAN BENEFIT Jewish people.
WHAT IS FUNDED The advancement of religion in accordance with the orthodox Jewish faith and general charitable purposes.
SAMPLE GRANTS Previous beneficiaries have included: Achisomach Aid Company Ltd, Beis Soroh Schneirer, Beis Yaakov Town, Beis Yisroel Tel Aviv, Comet Charities Ltd, Friends of Harim Bnei Brak, Jewish Teachers Training College Gateshead, Mosdos Bnei Brak, Torah Vechesed Ashdod and Woodstock Sinclair Trust.
FINANCES *Year* 2009–10 *Income* £93,496 *Grants* £108,641 *Assets* £2,357,414
TRUSTEES D H Marks; L Marks; F Z Sinclair.
OTHER INFORMATION No list of grant beneficiaries was included in the accounts.
HOW TO APPLY In writing to the correspondent.
WHO TO APPLY TO D H Marks, Trustee, 17 Cheyne Walk, London NW4 3QH

■ The Viznitz Foundation

CC NO 326581   **ESTABLISHED** 1984
WHERE FUNDING CAN BE GIVEN UK and abroad.
WHO CAN BENEFIT Organisations, including schools and registered charities.
WHAT IS FUNDED 'The objects of the charity are to pay and apply and appropriate the whole of the trust fund to those purposes both in the UK and abroad recognised as charitable by English Law and in accordance with the trust deed and the wishes of the Grand Rabbi of Viznitz.'
FINANCES *Year* 2009–10 *Income* £217,898 *Grants* £0 *Assets* £1,928,634
TRUSTEES H Feldman; E Kahan.
OTHER INFORMATION No grants were made in this financial year. In 2008–09 grants totalling £146,000 were made.
HOW TO APPLY In writing to the correspondent.
WHO TO APPLY TO H Feldman, Trustee, 23 Overlea Road, London E5 9BG *Tel* 020 8557 9557

■ The Vodafone (Group) Foundation

CC NO 1089625   **ESTABLISHED** 2002
WHERE FUNDING CAN BE GIVEN Worldwide. In the UK: Banbury, Newark, Northern Ireland, Stoke, Trowbridge, Warrington, West Berkshire and where Vodafone stores are located.
WHO CAN BENEFIT Registered charities and community groups.
WHAT IS FUNDED organisations working with young people aged between 16 and 25. 'In the UK the Vodafone Foundation focuses on helping 16–25 year-olds facing exclusion from society, whether reaching a cross road in their lives, struggling with emotional well-being or having difficulty accessing the information that they need. It is committed to creating sustainable change and working collaboratively with its charity partners providing a range of resources in addition to financial support wherever possible. It also supports young people in local communities where Vodafone has significant physical presence, and Vodafone employees who are involved in community activities.'
WHAT IS NOT FUNDED No grant to individuals.
RANGE OF GRANTS £500–£2 million.
SAMPLE GRANTS Grant beneficiaries include: Red Dust Role Models (£625,000); Homeless World Cup Foundation (£250,000); Villages Greece (£120,000); Vodafone Foundation Ghana (£75,000); Hellenic Cerebral Palsy Society (£53,000); SOS Children's Tatra Voluntary Rescue Group (£21,000); United Nations Foundation (£12,000); William J. Clinton Foundation (£2,500).
The foundation also donated a significant amount in grants to the World Disaster Fund including £100,000 to Vodafone Turkey to help with the Istanbul floods, £90,000 to Vodafone Italy to help with the Abruzzo earthquake and £10,000 to Vodafone Portugal to help with Madeira floods. During the year, the foundation also supported many aid charities such as Humanitarian Aid Relief Trust, Build Africa and World of Difference (£25,000 each).
FINANCES *Year* 2009–10 *Income* £21,186,391 *Grants* £24,627,185 *Assets* £14,965,489
TRUSTEES Nick Land, Chair; Margherita Della Valle; Elizabeth Filkin; Ian Gray; Lord Hastings of Scarisbrick; Matthew Kirk; Guy Laurence; Frank Rovekamp; Ronald Schellekens; Tina Southall.
OTHER INFORMATION Almost all of the foundation's income comes from Vodafone Group Plc. This global foundation has taken over the function of the Vodafone UK Foundation, which ceased to exist in early 2009. Grants worldwide totalled £25 million.
No direct grants were awarded to individuals.

HOW TO APPLY On a form available to download from the foundation's website.

WHO TO APPLY TO Andrew Dunnett, Director, Vodafone Group PLC, Vodafone House, The Connection, Newbury, Berkshire RG14 2FN *email* groupfoundation@vodafone.com

■ The Volant Charitable Trust

SC NO SC030790   **ESTABLISHED** 2000

WHERE FUNDING CAN BE GIVEN UK, with a preference for Scotland, and overseas.

WHO CAN BENEFIT Organisations benefiting women, children, the relief of poverty, the alleviation of social deprivation and the provision of social benefit to the community.

WHAT IS FUNDED 'Research into the causes, treatment and possible cures of Multiple Sclerosis (the trust is not considering further applications for funding in this area at the present time); charities and projects, whether national or community-based, at home or abroad, that alleviate social deprivation, with a particular emphasis on women's and children's issues (at present the trustees consider the funding of major disaster appeals and this is the focus of the trust's international support; therefore, applications for other projects overseas are not being considered for the foreseeable future).'

WHAT IS NOT FUNDED No grants to individuals.

TYPE OF GRANT One-off and recurrent grants; core costs and project grants.

SAMPLE GRANTS Unicef – Ethiopia Children's Appeal (£1 million); British Red Cross Society – Darfur Appeal and DEC – Haiti Earthquake Appeal (£500,000 each); The Kids Company (£225,000); University of Edinburgh (£125,000); Royal Blind and Sacro (£90,000 each); and Young Enterprise (£82,500).

FINANCES *Year* 2009–10 *Income* £5,611,267 *Grants* £4,016,259 *Assets* £49,071,538

TRUSTEES J K Rowling; Dr N S Murray; G C Smith; R D Fulton.

HOW TO APPLY Applications for funding requests of up to and including £10,000 per annum, for those projects based in **Scotland** only, are dealt with by the appointed agents, the Scottish Community Foundation. All other requests for funding are dealt with via an application form available from the trust's website. Complete and return the application form, plus any supporting materials by post. Applications should not be hand delivered. If an application is hand delivered, management at Mail Boxes are not in a position to discuss applications and will not be expected to provide any form of receipt.

WHO TO APPLY TO Christine Collingwood, Administrator, PO Box 8, 196 Rose Street, Edinburgh EH2 4AT *email* admin@volanttrust.com *Website* www.volanttrust.com

■ Voluntary Action Fund

SC NO SC035037   **ESTABLISHED** 2003

WHERE FUNDING CAN BE GIVEN Scotland.

WHO CAN BENEFIT Registered charities and organisations with a constitution and activities that could be considered charitable.

WHAT IS FUNDED The fund currently runs three grantmaking programmes: Volunteering Scotland Grant Scheme; Equality Grants Programme; and Community Grants. All are linked by the common threads of social inclusion and support for organisations to become stronger. See the fund's website for up-to-date programme information.

WHAT IS NOT FUNDED Each programme has its own set of eligibility criteria. Please contact the fund directly or go to the website for full details.

TYPE OF GRANT Please check the individual scheme guidelines.

RANGE OF GRANTS Up to about £40,000 but mostly under £5,000.

SAMPLE GRANTS Abused Men in Scotland, African and Caribbean Network, The Arts and Crafts Group, Carrick Way Community Interest Company, Jeanfield Swifts Youth FC, Carluke Day Centre for the Elderly, and Neilston Toddler and Playgroup (£1,000 each); North Ayr Women's Complimentary Health Group (£960); Caledonia South Lanarkshire (£950); Walkerburn Out of School Club (£660); Stockaree Tenants Organisations (£650); and Drumbowie Environment Action Group (£300).

FINANCES *Year* 2009–10 *Income* £5,312,157 *Grants* £4,971,609 *Assets* £179,145

TRUSTEES Ron Daniel, Chair; Dorothy MacLauchlin; Michael Cunningham; Julie Hogg; Pam Judson; Caron Hughes; John McDonald; Douglas Guest.

PUBLICATIONS *Voluntary Action Fund: Ambition & Influence since 1982*

HOW TO APPLY Application forms and guidance notes for open programmes are available on the fund's website. The fund recommends that interested parties contact them to discuss the project before making any application. Funds may open and close so applicants should check the website for the most recent updates.

WHO TO APPLY TO Keith Wimbles, Chief Executive, Dunfermline Business Centre, Unit 14, Izatt Avenue, Dunfermline, Fife KY11 3BZ *Tel* 01383 620780 *Fax* 01383 626314 *email* info@ voluntaryactionfund.org.uk *Website* www. voluntaryactionfund.org.uk

■ Wade's Charity

CC NO 224939   **ESTABLISHED** 1530

WHERE FUNDING CAN BE GIVEN Leeds, within the pre-1974 boundary of the city (approximately LS1 to LS17 postcodes).

WHO CAN BENEFIT Charities benefiting people of all ages and those living in urban areas. Mainly youth organisations and community centres. (Grants are only a part of the charity's activities.).

WHAT IS FUNDED 'The provision of facilities for recreation, amusement, entertainment and general social intercourse for citizens of every age of areas of population in the City of Leeds occupied in the main by the working classes including in any such objects the establishment of what are commonly known as community centres and youth centres.' Please see the charity's website for full guidelines.

WHAT IS NOT FUNDED No grants given to: applications from outside the beneficial area, i.e. from outside the pre-1974 boundary of the city of Leeds covered roughly by postcodes LS1 to LS17; applications from non-charitable organisations; applications from individuals; applications for church repairs (unless there is proven significant community use); circulars or general appeals from high profile national charities; applications which do not offer benefit within the terms of the trust; applications for activities which are the responsibility of statutory or local authority funding, particularly within health or education; applications to fund salaries.

TYPE OF GRANT The majority of grants are given on a one-off basis.

RANGE OF GRANTS Average grant around £2,000.

SAMPLE GRANTS Leeds Parish Church Choir (£2000); Healthy Living Network Leeds (£2,400); The Hunslet Club (£10,000); Invlove/LTCC (£800); Age Concern Leeds (£3000); Seacroft Chance project (£1000); Radio Poplar (£600); Leeds Children's Charity (£5000); The Leeds Skatepark Co (£2000); Trees for Cities (£1,500).

FINANCES *Income* £179,581 *Grants* £135,699 *Assets* £5,297,185

TRUSTEES Bernard Atha; Peter Marshall; Susan Reddington; John Tinker; Revd Alan Taylor; Ann Chadwick; Revd Canon Anthony Bundock; Ann Blackburn; John Roberts; John Stoddart-Scott; Hilary Finnigan; Kenneth Jones; Bill Hyde; Bruce Smith; M Pullan; E Ziff.

OTHER INFORMATION A small grants programme has been operating through Voluntary Action Leeds for many years. This programme enables small community groups (with an annual income of less than £10,000) who may not be a registered charity to apply for funds of up to £100 to contribute towards their administrative costs.

HOW TO APPLY Main grants – In writing to the correspondent, including the following information: the name, address and telephone number of both the applicant and the organisations they are applying on behalf of; registered charity number; an outline of what the organisation does; an outline of the purpose for which the grant is being sought; a copy of the latest signed accounts. If an application potentially fulfils at least one of the charity's primary charitable objectives of the charity, an appointment will then be made for the Grants Adviser to visit the organisation to establish further relevant information about the application. The application will then be considered by the board of trustees at one of their grants meetings, these are usually held in April, July and November. The deadline for inclusion at any meeting is four weeks prior to the meeting date. The charity is happy to discuss ideas before a formal application is made. Applicants may only submit an application once per calendar year. Voluntary Action Leeds advertises the small grants programme in their newsletter at the start of each year.

WHO TO APPLY TO Kathryn Hodges, 5 Grimston Park Mews, Grimston Park, Tadcaster LS24 9DB *Tel* 01937 830295 *email* wadescharity@btinernet.com *Website* www.wadescharity.org

■ The Scurrah Wainwright Charity

CC NO 1002755   **ESTABLISHED** 1991

WHERE FUNDING CAN BE GIVEN Preference for Yorkshire, South Africa and Zimbabwe.

WHO CAN BENEFIT Charitable organisations.

WHAT IS FUNDED The charity 'looks for innovative work in the field of social reform, with a preference for 'root-cause' rather than palliative projects. It favours causes that are outside the mainstream, and unlikely to be funded by other charities'.

WHAT IS NOT FUNDED No support is given to: individuals; animal welfare; buildings; medical research or support for individual medical conditions; substitution for Government funding (e.g. in education and health); charities who send unsolicited general appeal letters.

TYPE OF GRANT Contributions to core costs.

RANGE OF GRANTS Typically £1,000–£5,000, but in 'cases of exceptional merit' larger grants may be awarded.

SAMPLE GRANTS Oxfam (£24,000); Fawcett Society (£10,000); CHAS Bradford (£5,000); Circle of Support and Accountability (£5,000); Food Aware (£3,000); Bar Human Rights (£2,500); Beatrix Campbell, Spinwatch, Stamp Out Poverty, Riders for Health and Forum for Discussion of Israel and Palestine (£2,000 each); and Essential Needs, Salvation Army, Million Women Rise and Robin Hood Project (£1,000 each).

FINANCES *Year* 2009–10 *Income* £57,453 *Grants* £96,910 *Assets* £1,740,163

TRUSTEES M S Wainwright, Chair; R R Bhaskar; H P I Scott; H A Wainwright; J M Wainwright; P Wainwright; T M Wainwright.

OTHER INFORMATION 'The Wainwright family runs two trusts, one charitable [The Scurrah Wainwright Charity], one non-charitable [The Andrew Wainwright Reform Trust Ltd]. The trusts are based on the family's traditions of liberal values and support for the socially disempowered. The trustees are all family members, based in West Yorkshire.'

HOW TO APPLY Please follow these preliminary steps: check that your aims meet the charity's criteria; check that the amount of money you need falls within the charity's limits; check deadlines: the trustees meet three times a year – in March, July and November – and applications must be submitted by 1 February, 1 June or 1 October respectively.

Write a succinct but complete application that should include: an opening section that gives the name and postal address of your organisation, details of a named contact for the application and where you heard about the Charity; background information about you and/or your organisation; the nature of the project you wish to pursue and what it seeks to achieve; your plans for practical implementation of the work and a budget; your most recent accounts and details of any additional sources of funding already secured or to be sought; whether you will accept a contribution to the amount requested.

If the above information (excluding your accounts) takes up more than two sides of A4, please include a summary of that information on no more than two sides of A4, using a font no smaller than 12-point.

Applicants may contact the administrator, preferably by email, for any clarification. If you have not heard from the administrator by the end of the month in which the trustees' meeting was held you must assume your application was not successful.

WHO TO APPLY TO Kerry McQuade, Administrator, 16 Blenheim Street, Hebden Bridge, West Yorkshire HX7 8BU *email* admin@ wainwrighttrusts.org.uk *Website* www. wainwrighttrusts.org.uk

···

■ The Wakefield and Tetley Trust

CC NO 1121779   **ESTABLISHED** 2008
WHERE FUNDING CAN BE GIVEN London boroughs of Tower Hamlets, Southwark and the City of London.
WHO CAN BENEFIT Community groups and charities.
WHAT IS FUNDED Social welfare and general charitable purposes.
WHAT IS NOT FUNDED The trust will not support: grants to individuals; work that has already taken place; applicants who have been rejected by the trust within the last six months; organisations with significant unrestricted reserves; organisations in serious financial deficit; the promotion of religion; animal charities; statutory bodies and work that is primarily the responsibility of central or local government; health trusts, health authorities and hospices (or any sort of medical equipment or medical research). The trust is unlikely to support: building restoration or conservation; uniformed youth groups; schools, supplementary schools or vocational training; environmental improvements.
TYPE OF GRANT Up to three years for project costs and core costs.
RANGE OF GRANTS Grants range from £500 to £65,000 over one year; the average grant awarded in 2009–10 was £7,000.
SAMPLE GRANTS Beneficiaries included: All Hallows by the Tower (£65,000), to support community, volunteering and education projects at the Church over a five year period. Newlon Fusion – John Scurr Centre (£35,000); Volunteer Centre Tower Hamlets (£18,000); Winant Clayton Volunteers (£14,000); South Bromley Forum (£5,000); London Gypsy Traveller Unit (£4,800); Set Fashion Free (£2,900); Pumphouse Educational Museum (£2,700); Southwark Churches Care (£2,000); Immigrants' Information Centre (£1,500); Alternative Arts (£1,000) and Charles Dickens Primary School (£500).

FINANCES *Year* 2009–10 *Income* £383,442 *Grants* £251,577 *Assets* £5,557,864
TRUSTEES The Venerable Peter Delaney (Chairman); William Almond; Ellen Carroll; Patrick Kelly; Aderonke Kokoruwe; Lady Judy Moody-Stuart; Stuart Morganstein; Clare Murphy; Kenneth Prideaux-Brune; Helal Rahman and Susan Reardon-Smith.
HOW TO APPLY You will need to demonstrate that your organisation: benefits people resident or working in Tower Hamlets and/or Southwark and/or the City of London; undertakes charitable work (however you do not have to be a registered charity); has a constitution or a set of rules which governs its activities; has its own bank or building society account where two or more named people (including one trustee or management committee member) have to sign all the cheques; can provide annual accounts for the previous year (if your organisation is new, copies of your most recent bank or building society statements will suffice).

The trust is likely to receive many more proposals than it is able to fund so the following funding priorities have been agreed. The trust particularly welcomes applications for: cross-cultural and intergenerational projects that help to bring people together, reduce barriers and support community cohesion; new initiatives that address emerging needs new methods of tackling existing problems.

The trust will prioritise: projects with local support and beneficiary involvement; projects that have a well-considered plan and demonstrate the difference that will be made; organisations with an annual turnover of less than £500,000; organisations with a relevant track record and experience. These priorities will be subject to regular review. The trust is happy to consider requests to fund project costs, relevant core costs and associated training. However, it is unlikely to support equipment or capital costs.

WHO TO APPLY TO Elaine Crush, Grants Officer, Attlee House, 28 Commercial Street, London E1 6LR *Tel* 020 7377 6614 *email* enquiries@ wakefieldtrust.org.uk *Website* www. wakefieldtrust.org.uk

···

■ Wakeham Trust

CC NO 267495   **ESTABLISHED** 1974
WHERE FUNDING CAN BE GIVEN UK.
WHO CAN BENEFIT Registered charities.
WHAT IS FUNDED 'We provide grants to help people rebuild their communities. We are particularly interested in neighbourhood projects, community arts projects, projects involving community service by young people, or projects set up by those who are socially excluded. 'We also support innovative projects to promote excellence in teaching (at any level, from primary schools to universities), though we never support individuals.'
WHAT IS NOT FUNDED No grants to individuals or large, well-established charities, or towards buildings and transport.
RANGE OF GRANTS Normally £75–£750.
SAMPLE GRANTS Archdiocese of Pondicherry (£5,000); ATD Fourth World (£1,000); Bridport Arts (£500); Bath Youth for Christ (£200); Chichester Family Church (£150).
FINANCES *Year* 2009–10 *Income* £29,587 *Grants* £60,963 *Assets* £1,511,011

TRUSTEES Harold Carter; Barnaby Newbolt; Tess Silkstone.

HOW TO APPLY By letter or by filling in the online form on the trust's website – the trust prefers online applications. Full guidelines are also available on the trust's website.

WHO TO APPLY TO The Trustees, Wakeham Lodge, Rogate, Petersfield, Hampshire GU31 5EJ *Tel* 01730 821748 *email* wakehamtrust@mac.com *Website* www.wakehamtrust.org

---

■ The Community Foundation in Wales

CC NO 1074655   ESTABLISHED 1999

WHERE FUNDING CAN BE GIVEN Wales.

WHO CAN BENEFIT Local charities, community groups and voluntary organisations that are engaged in tackling social need and economic disadvantage at a grass-roots level.

WHAT IS FUNDED The promotion of any charitable purposes for the benefit of communities within Wales. Projects providing worthwhile service to the community. The foundation manages a number of funds, many with their own individual criteria and some which relate to specific geographical areas of Wales. Community cohesion; the environment; older people; minority groups; young people; economic disadvantage; social exclusion; rural isolation; crime reduction; substance misuse and addiction; skills development and confidence-building; education and lifelong learning; and sport as a vehicle for social inclusion.

WHAT IS NOT FUNDED Political organisations and pressure groups; religious organisations, where the primary aim of the project is the promotion of faith; individuals, unless the specific focus of a fund; general appeals; sports organisations where no obvious charitable element exists; medical research; statutory bodies e.g. schools, local authorities and councils, although the foundation will consider applications from school PTAs if the intended project is non-statutory in nature; animal welfare; arts and heritage projects unless there exists a clear, demonstrable community benefit; large capital projects; retrospective applications for projects that have taken place.

RANGE OF GRANTS The majority of grants awarded are under £5,000.

FINANCES *Year* 2009–10 *Income* £3,682,052 *Grants* £1,600,802 *Assets* £6,257,242

TRUSTEES The Hon Anthony Lewis (Chair); Mr David Dudley; Mr Michael Westerman; Mr Julian Smith; Mr Frank Learner (Honorary treasurer); Ms Ilene Hoyle; Mr Drewe Lacey; Dr Caryl Cresswell; Mr Peter Davies; Mr Jonathan Hollins and Mr Henry Robertson.

OTHER INFORMATION 'The Community Foundation in Wales promotes the cause of philanthropy in Wales by creating and managing relationships between donors and those who are running life-enhancing initiatives. We are dedicated to strengthening local communities by providing a permanent source of funding, building endowment and *immediate impact* funds to link donors to local needs.'

HOW TO APPLY Please visit the 'current grants' page of its website. If an organisation is uncertain about whether it meets the criteria for any of its named funds a general application may be completed at any time during the year. The foundation aims to match proposals to available funding and make contact if further information is required.

WHO TO APPLY TO The Company Secretary, Ms Liza Kellett, 9 Coopers Yard, Curran Road, Cardiff CF10 5NB *Tel* 029 2052 0250 *email* mail@cfiw.org.uk *Website* www.cfiw.org.uk

---

■ Wales Council for Voluntary Action

CC NO 218093   ESTABLISHED 1963

WHERE FUNDING CAN BE GIVEN Wales.

WHO CAN BENEFIT Registered charities and voluntary organisations only.

WHAT IS FUNDED Grants schemes include the Communities First Trust Fund.

WHAT IS NOT FUNDED Grants are made to constituted voluntary organisations only. Check for specific exclusions for individual funds. For the Communities First Trust Fund, the following are not supported: applications for a project on behalf of another group/organisation/Communities First Partnership/statutory body/school; Communities First Partnerships; organisations whose annual income exceeds £150,000; national organisations – unless the group is a local branch with local management/accountability arrangements and its own bank account; political organisations; individuals– applications must come from a community organisation; private businesses; Communities First Trust Fund Referees – however the group the referee is associated with may apply provided they use a different nominated referee; town and community councils; schools; other statutory organisations, e.g. local authorities, local education authorities; local authority music services – the Friends of the Music Service may apply to the trust fund providing the costs are not revenue costs (e.g. staff costs & running costs). Groups are not eligible to apply if there is a previous CFTF project that has been 'deemed closed' because it has not been completed as per the terms and conditions of grant award. Groups are not eligible to apply to the CFTF if they have an outstanding End of Project report from a previous CFTF or Music Trust Fund grant. The previous grant award must be completed and accounted for before a new application is submitted.

TYPE OF GRANT Capital, core costs, one-off, project, recurring costs, running costs, start-up costs.

SAMPLE GRANTS Grants were made to 1,785 organisations.

FINANCES *Year* 2009–10 *Income* £30,749,169 *Grants* £14,836,856 *Assets* £12,412,726

TRUSTEES Win Griffiths, Chair; Louise Bennett; Nerys Haf Biddulph; Mike Denham; Walter Dickie; Eurwen Edwards; Paul Glaze; Simon Harris; Margaret Jervis; Efa Gruffudd Jones; Harri Jones; John R Jones; Liza Kellet; Joy Kent; Mike Lewis; Marcella Maxwell; Mark McLean; Judy Owen; Chad Patel; Martin Pollard; Jaswant Singh Jas; L Mair Stephens; Anne Stephenson; Hilary Stevens; Fran Targett; Nick Taylor; Alan Underwood; Mal Williams; Michael Williams; Catriona Williams; Wendy Williams; Victoria Winckler; Clive Wolfendale; Shirley Yendell; Pauline Young.

PUBLICATIONS Guidance notes for applicants available on request. Visit www.wcva.org.uk or call the Helpdesk on 0870 607 1666.

OTHER INFORMATION Contact WCVA directly for up-to-date information on open schemes.

HOW TO APPLY There are separate application forms for each scheme. Contact WCVA on 0870 607 1666, or visit its website, for further information.

WHO TO APPLY TO Helen Wilson, Grants Manager, Baltic House, Mount Stuart Square, Cardiff CF10 5FH *Tel* 0870 607 1666 *Fax* 029 2043 1701 *Minicom* 029 2043 1702 *email* help@wcva.org.uk *Website* www.wcva.org.uk

····································

■ Robert and Felicity Waley-Cohen Charitable Trust

CC NO 272126   ESTABLISHED 1976
WHERE FUNDING CAN BE GIVEN England and Wales, focus on Warwickshire and Oxfordshire.
WHO CAN BENEFIT Charitable organisations, schools and those of the Jewish faith.
WHAT IS FUNDED Jewish, children, education, fine arts, health.
WHAT IS NOT FUNDED No grants to individuals.
TYPE OF GRANT One off grant.
RANGE OF GRANTS £30–£16,500.
SAMPLE GRANTS Child Bereavement Charity (£2,500); Plan International (£900); Help the Heroes (£100); Liberal Jewish Synagogue (£1,250); Racing Welfare (£250); Tate Foundation (£5000); Oxford Radcliffe Hospitals Charitable Funds (£16,485); V & A Museum (£1,500); UKELA (£750); Book Link (£500); Cancer Research (£100).
FINANCES *Year* 2009–10 *Income* £115,832 *Grants* £49,544 *Assets* £1,721,477
TRUSTEES R Waley-Cohen; Hon F Waley-Cohen.
HOW TO APPLY In writing to the Correspondent.
WHO TO APPLY TO R Waley-Cohen, Trustee, 18 Gilston Road, London SW10 9SR *Tel* 020 7244 6022 *email* ccopeman@alliance.co.uk

····································

■ The Walker Trust

CC NO 215479   ESTABLISHED 1897
WHERE FUNDING CAN BE GIVEN Shropshire.
WHO CAN BENEFIT Individuals and organisations benefiting children and young adults who are in care, fostered and adopted.
WHAT IS FUNDED The establishment or towards maintenance of any hospital, infirmary, convalescent home or other institution having for its object the relief of sickness or promoting convalescence; the provision of medical or surgical aid or appliance; any institution for the maintenance and education of orphans.
WHAT IS NOT FUNDED No grants to individuals for second degrees or postgraduate courses. Appeals from outside Shropshire will not be considered or replied to.
TYPE OF GRANT One-off capital grants.
RANGE OF GRANTS Up to £20,000.
SAMPLE GRANTS Schools and other organisations: Shropshire Army Cadet Force Band and Bugles and Adams Grammar School Newport (£5,000); Albrighton Trust and Bridges Development Centre (£3,000); Holy Trinity Church Meole Brace (£1,500) and Whitchurch History & Archeology Group (£1,000).
Health and disability: Combat Stress Newport (£20,000); SVAP (£15,000); The Pioneer Centre (£5,000); RNIB (£2,500); Ludlow & District Riding for disabled (£1,000).
FINANCES *Year* 2009–10 *Income* £170,817 *Grants* £185,381 *Assets* £5,693,374
TRUSTEES A E H Herber-Percy JP, Chair; Nicholas Bishop; Mrs Caroline Paton-Smith; Joy Francis; Mr D G Lloyd and Mr M G Pate.
OTHER INFORMATION The grant total in 2009–10 included: £90,000 to organisations and £98,000 to individuals.

Grants to individuals include costs for university and college courses, music and drama and foreign travel.
HOW TO APPLY In writing to the correspondent. Details of other assistance applied for must be given and, in the case of organisations, the latest annual report and accounts. The trustees meet in January, April, July and October each year, but arrangements can be made for urgent applications to receive consideration between meetings. Applications must reach the clerk not less than one month before a decision is required.
WHO TO APPLY TO Edward Hewitt, Clerk, 2 Breidden Way, Bayston Hill, Shrewsbury SY3 0LN *Tel* 01743 873866

····································

■ The Thomas Wall Trust

CC NO 206121   ESTABLISHED 1920
WHERE FUNDING CAN BE GIVEN UK.
WHO CAN BENEFIT Individuals and registered charities. Small charities and small schemes are preferred to large national ones.
WHAT IS FUNDED 'The object must be in a broad sense educational and/or concerned with social service.'
WHAT IS NOT FUNDED Grants are not made: towards the erection, upkeep or renovation of buildings; to hospitals, almshouses or similar institutions; for objects which are purely medical; for projects outside of the UK.
TYPE OF GRANT 'The application should preferably be for some specific scheme or objective, but in some cases single grants will be considered towards general running costs.' Successful applicants will normally not receive recurrent funding and can only reapply after five years.
SAMPLE GRANTS Careers 'N' Kids (£2,000); Behind Closed Doors (£1,500); Just Different (£1,200); and Adventure Unlimited, Caboodle Theatre, Hackney Quest, Just 42, One in a Million and West London Churches Homeless Concern (£1,000 each).
FINANCES *Year* 2009–10 *Income* £112,164 *Grants* £27,570 *Assets* £2,609,346
TRUSTEES Dr G.M. Copland, Chair; Mrs M A Barrie; P Bellamy; C R Broomfield; Miss A S Kennedy; Miss A-M. Martin; Mrs A Mullins; Revd Dr R Waller.
OTHER INFORMATION An additional £40,529 was awarded to 43 individuals.
HOW TO APPLY There is no application form for charitable organisations to use except that all applicants must complete a cover sheet which can be downloaded from the trust's website. A copy of the latest available set of accounts for their charity should be included along with an sae, which will be used to acknowledge receipt of application. The trustees meet twice a year, in July and November. Applications for the July meeting must be received by mid-May and for the November meeting by end of September.
WHO TO APPLY TO Ms Sue Ellis, Charities Officer, Skinners' Hall, 8 Dowgate Hill, London EC4R 2SP *Tel* 020 7213 0564 *email* information@thomaswalltrust.org.uk *Website* www.thomaswalltrust.org.uk

■ Wallace and Gromit's Children's Foundation

CC NO 1096483   **ESTABLISHED** 2003
WHERE FUNDING CAN BE GIVEN UK.
WHO CAN BENEFIT Children's hospitals, hospices and healthcare organisations.
WHAT IS FUNDED Wallace & Gromit's Children's Foundation is a national charity raising funds to improve the quality of life for children in hospitals and hospices throughout the UK. The foundation provides funding to support projects such as: (i) Arts, music play and entertainment programmes to stimulate young minds and divert attention away from illness. (ii) Providing welcoming and accessible environments and surroundings, designed specifically for children in a fun and engaging way. (iii) Funding Education and Information Programmes to educate young people and recognising the importance of self help and health related issues. (iv) Helping to fund the acquisition of medical facilities, which can help to improve diagnosis and treatment of a wide range of conditions and illnesses in children. (v) Sustaining family relationships helping to keep families together during emotionally difficult times. (vi) Helping to meet the cost of care in a children's hospice where children and their families are cared for during good days, difficult days and last days. (vii) Supporting children with physical and emotional difficulties empowering and increasing confidence.
WHAT IS NOT FUNDED No support for; charities not supporting children's healthcare; organisations that do not have charitable status; animal, religious or international charities; retrospective funding; organisations that do not work within a hospital or hospice environment; organisations that provide excursions, holidays or away days; no grants will be made to individuals.
SAMPLE GRANTS Birmingham Children's Hospital (£10,000); SICK kids friends foundation (£8,000); Alder Hey IMAGINE Appeal (£5,000); CHASE Hospice care for children (£4,000).
FINANCES *Year* 2009–10 *Income* £198,900 *Grants* £125,472 *Assets* £27,363
TRUSTEES I Hannah, Chair; S Cooper; P Lord; J Moule; N Park; D Sproxton.
OTHER INFORMATION Wallace and Gromit's Wrong Trousers Day is the Foundations primary fundraising event which encourages the general public to wear the wrong trousers for the day and donate funds raised to the foundation.
HOW TO APPLY Grants are distributed on an annual basis. Application forms and guidelines are posted on the foundation's website from October and the closing date for applications is usually in December. All awards are made by the end of March.
WHO TO APPLY TO The Company Secretary, PO Box 2186, Bristol BS99 7NT *email* info@ wrongtrousersday.org *Website* www. wallaceandgromitfoundation.org

■ Wallington Missionary Mart and Auctions

CC NO 289030   **ESTABLISHED** 1965
WHERE FUNDING CAN BE GIVEN Overseas.
WHO CAN BENEFIT Missionary societies working overseas benefiting Christians.
WHAT IS FUNDED Christian education and outreach.
WHAT IS NOT FUNDED Only registered Christian charities may receive support. Applications from individuals are only considered if funds will go to a Christian missionary society or Christian charity.
TYPE OF GRANT Usually one-off grants for core costs. Fully committed for charities selected by the trustees.
RANGE OF GRANTS £1,500–£7,000.
SAMPLE GRANTS Beneficiaries included: Wycliffe Bible Translators (£6,800); Youth with a mission (£6,000); OMF International UK (£5,500); Operation Mobilisation (£3,800); SIM UK (£3,500); Tear Fund (£2,400); Limuru Children's Centre (£1,700); International Fellowship Evangelical Students (£1,500); London City Mission (£1,200).
FINANCES *Year* 2009–10 *Income* £170,379 *Grants* £68,124 *Assets* £179,077
TRUSTEES Stephen J Crawley; Brian E Chapman; Harry F Curwood; Geoffrey C Willey; Derek C Lewin; Mrs Sylvia M Symes; Pat Collett.
OTHER INFORMATION This trust receives its income through receiving donated goods from the public, which are sold at the auctions it stages four to six times a year. For further information on these auctions, please see its website.
HOW TO APPLY In writing to the correspondent, with an sae. The trustees meet to consider grants throughout the year.
WHO TO APPLY TO Brian E Chapman, Trustee, 99 Woodmansterne Road, Carshalton Beeches, Surrey SM5 4EG *Tel* 020 8643 3616 *email* enq@wmma.org.uk *Website* www. wallingtonmissionary.org.uk

■ The F J Wallis Charitable Settlement

CC NO 279273   **ESTABLISHED** 1979
WHERE FUNDING CAN BE GIVEN UK, with some interest in Hampshire and Surrey.
WHO CAN BENEFIT Charitable organisations, including both headquarters and branches of large UK charities.
WHAT IS FUNDED General charitable purposes. In 2005/06 the settlement introduced a criteria-based approach to grantmaking. The trustees intend to alternate the areas of charitable activity that will receive grants between disability, children charities and medical research/health and sickness in one year and animal charities, community charities and hospices in the next.
WHAT IS NOT FUNDED No grants to individuals or to local charities except those in Surrey or in Hampshire. The same organisation is not supported twice within a 24-month period.
TYPE OF GRANT Mostly one-off but there are some recurring grants.
RANGE OF GRANTS £500–£1,000.
SAMPLE GRANTS the PSP Association (£2,000); Abbeyfield, Carroll Centre, Conquest Art, Fields in Trust, QUIT, Slough Furniture Project, Target Ovarian Cancer and WWT London Wetland Centre (£1,000 each); Hampshire and Isle of Wight Wildlife Trust and St Luke's Church – Stoke Hammond (£500 each); and St Clare Hospice (£250).
FINANCES *Year* 2009–10 *Income* £45,128 *Grants* £36,750 *Assets* £1,170,021
TRUSTEES F H Hughes; A J Hills; Revd J J A Archer.
HOW TO APPLY In writing to the correspondent. No telephone calls. Applications are not acknowledged and unsuccessful applicants will only be contacted if an sae is provided. Trustees meet in March and September and applications need to be received the month prior to the trustees' meeting.

WHO TO APPLY TO F H Hughes, Trustee, c/o Bridge House, 11 Creek Road, Hampton Court, East Molesey, Surrey KT8 9BE

■ Walton on Thames Charity

CC NO 230652   **ESTABLISHED** 1984
WHERE FUNDING CAN BE GIVEN Ancient parish of Walton on Thames, Surrey.
WHO CAN BENEFIT Charitable and other community organisations, including schools and sports clubs.
WHAT IS FUNDED Social welfare.
SAMPLE GRANTS Previous beneficiaries include: Ashley School, Bell Farm School, Cardinal Newman RC School, Cleeves School, Citizens Advice, Painshill Park and Scout Groups.
FINANCES *Year* 2009–10 *Income* £1,671,770 *Grants* £20,000 *Assets* £18,680,453
TRUSTEES Chris Sadler; David Nash; Clare Warne; Barry Cheyne; Robert Freeman; Mary Trimble; Duncan Parkes; Valerie Saint; Mary Sheldon; Canon Charles Stewart; Ben White; Christine Cross; Christine Elmer.
OTHER INFORMATION Food vouchers and sundry grants were made totalling £19,000 and association grants totalled £1,000. The vast majority of the trust's funds are spent on its own work, therefore surplus funds are not always available to be given in grants.
HOW TO APPLY Application forms are available by telephone. The charity's accounts state that 'applications are received increasingly from referring agencies such as the local. Citizens Advice Bureau or Social Services and are assessed against specific criteria. Applicants are asked to provide supporting evidence for their application for funding.'
WHO TO APPLY TO Victor Cass, Mayfield, 74 Hersham Road, Walton on Thames KT12 5NU *Tel* 01932 220242 *Fax* 01932 252603 *email* vcass@waltoncharity.org.uk *Website* www.waltoncharity.org.uk

■ War on Want

CC NO 208724   **ESTABLISHED** 1959
WHERE FUNDING CAN BE GIVEN Developing countries only.
WHO CAN BENEFIT Typically, War on Want directly funds the work of labour organisations and NGOs in developing countries, usually trade unions or similar workers' organisations, and women's organisations.
WHAT IS FUNDED Overseas development projects that address the root causes of poverty, oppression and injustice in developing countries.
WHAT IS NOT FUNDED War on Want is an overseas development agency and does not make grants to organisations in the UK.
TYPE OF GRANT Continuous project funding.
SAMPLE GRANTS Sweatshops and Plantations (£418,000); Informal Economies (£101,000); Food Justice (£200,000); Economic Justice (£491,000); Global Justice (£162,000); Conflict Zones (£50,000).
FINANCES *Year* 2009–10 *Income* £1,879,648 *Grants* £1,422,806 *Assets* £1,752,609
TRUSTEES Martin Hughes; Sue Branford; James O'Nions; David Spooner; Polly Jones; David Hillman; Paul Moon; Mark Luetchford; Guillermo Rogel; Steve Preston; Gaynelle Samuel and Mansoor Mirza.
PUBLICATIONS Upfront (a regular newsletter); publications list – covering subjects such as

health, women, trade, aid, Asia, Latin America and Africa.
HOW TO APPLY Unsolicited applications are not accepted and will not be acknowledged.
WHO TO APPLY TO The Director, Development House, 56–64 Leonard Street, London EC2A 4LT *Tel* 020 7549 0563 *Fax* 0207 549 0556 *email* mailroom@waronwant.org *Website* www.waronwant.org

■ Sir Siegmund Warburg's Voluntary Settlement

CC NO 286719   **ESTABLISHED** 1983
WHERE FUNDING CAN BE GIVEN UK, especially London.
WHO CAN BENEFIT Registered charities only.
WHAT IS FUNDED The arts.
WHAT IS NOT FUNDED No grants to individuals.
TYPE OF GRANT Revenue funding and capital projects.
RANGE OF GRANTS Up to £150,000.
SAMPLE GRANTS Royal Shakespeare Company (£125,000); Academy of Ancient Music and the National Children's Orchestra (£100,000 each); Chickensled Theatre Company and the Royal Welsh College of Music and Drama (£50,000 each); Cheltenham Festivals (£40,000); Paintings in Hospitals (£30,000); British Youth Opera (£25,000); Jewish Book Week (£10,000); and Oxford Playhouse (£5,000).
FINANCES *Year* 2010–11 *Income* £233,812 *Grants* £1,672,000 *Assets* £10,566,247
TRUSTEES Hugh Stevenson; Doris Wasserman; Dr Michael Harding; Christopher Purvis.
OTHER INFORMATION Following the trustees decision to start planning for the eventual wind-down of the trust, they have begun withdrawing larger amounts from the invested portfolio and distributing this in grants.
HOW TO APPLY Organisations are invited to send applications by email to applications@sswvs.org. It is requested that initial applications should be no more than four sides and should be accompanied by the latest audited accounts. Applications sent by post will not be considered.
WHO TO APPLY TO The Secretary, 19 Norland Square, London W11 4PU *email* applications@sswvs.org

■ The Ward Blenkinsop Trust

CC NO 265449   **ESTABLISHED** 1972
WHERE FUNDING CAN BE GIVEN UK, with a special interest in Merseyside and surrounding counties.
WHO CAN BENEFIT Charitable organisations.
WHAT IS FUNDED General charitable purposes with emphasis on support for medical research, social welfare, arts and education.
WHAT IS NOT FUNDED No grants to individuals.
SAMPLE GRANTS Previous beneficiaries have included Action on Addiction, BID, Chase Children's Hospice, Clatterbridge Cancer Research, Clod Ensemble, Comic Relief, Depaul Trust, Fairley House, Give Youth a Break, Halton Autistic Family Support Group, Hope HIV, Infertility Network, George Martin Music Foundation, Royal Academy of Dance, St Joseph's Family Centre, Strongbones Children's Charitable Trust, Walk the Walk, Winchester Visitors Group and Wirral Holistic Care Services.
FINANCES *Year* 2009–10 *Income* £194,454 *Grants* £157,499 *Assets* £2,101,733

TRUSTEES A M Blenkinsop; Ms S J Blenkinsop; Ms C A Blenkinsop; Mrs F A Stormer; Mrs H E Millin.

HOW TO APPLY In writing to the correspondent.

WHO TO APPLY TO Charlotte Blenkinsop, Trustee, PO Box 28840, London SW13 0WZ *Tel* 020 8878 9975

■ The George Ward Charitable Trust

CC NO 516954   **ESTABLISHED** 1985

WHERE FUNDING CAN BE GIVEN The area covered by Hinckley and Bosworth Borough Council.

WHO CAN BENEFIT Organisations and former employees of George Ward (Barwell) Ltd and George Geary and Son Ltd, and their dependants.

WHAT IS FUNDED General charitable purposes.

RANGE OF GRANTS Usually up to £1,000.

SAMPLE GRANTS Beneficiaries included: DLRAA (formerly County Air Ambulance), St Mary's Church Barwell Minibus Appeal (£1,000 each); LOROS* (£750); The Trees Hinckley residential home for people with learning disabilities – Comforts Fund, Stoke Golding Village Hall – Refurbishment, William Bradford Community College (£500 each); TSUK Transplant Active (£450) and Meadow Road Community Centre, Barwell, Voluntary Action Hinckley & Bosworth (£350 each).

FINANCES *Year* 2009–10 *Income* £41,665 *Grants* £20,000 *Assets* £1,027,897

TRUSTEES D M Radford; J A Calow, Chair.

HOW TO APPLY In writing to the correspondent at any time.

WHO TO APPLY TO Mrs S Hiom, Secretary, Stephanie Hiom, Thomas May and Co., Allen House, Newarke Street, Leicester LE1 5SG *Tel* 0116 233 5959 *Fax* 0116 233 5958 *email* stephaniehiom@thomasmay.co.uk

■ The Barbara Ward Children's Foundation

CC NO 1089783   **ESTABLISHED** 2001

WHERE FUNDING CAN BE GIVEN England and Wales.

WHO CAN BENEFIT Registered charities and other institutions.

WHAT IS FUNDED Mostly work with children who are seriously or terminally ill, disadvantaged or otherwise.

TYPE OF GRANT Grants given range from one-off donations to project-related grants that run for two or three years.

SAMPLE GRANTS Rainbow Centre and MERU (£35,000 each); BIBIC (£29,000); Reedham Trust (£29,000); National Blind Children's Society and New College Worcester (£25,000 each); and WellChild (£22,000); The Bobath Centre, The Food Chain and Hop, Skip and Jump – South West (£12,000 each); Changing Faces and Disability Challengers (£10,000 each); Army Cadet Force Association, Arts for All, Asian Students Christian Trust, CHICKS, Child Care Action Trust, Dandelion Trust, Hopscotch, Over the Wall, Peter Pan Nursery, Suffolk School for Parents and Huntington's Disease Association (£5,000 each); Let Us Play and STEPS(£4,000 each); Pearson's Holiday Fund (£3,000); and the Elizabeth Svendsen Trust for Children and Donkeys (£2,000).

FINANCES *Year* 2010 *Income* £492,848 *Grants* £507,151 *Assets* £8,490,096

TRUSTEES Barbara Irene Ward, Chair; D C Bailey; J C Banks; A M Gardner; K R Parker; B M Walters.

HOW TO APPLY In writing to the correspondent including latest set of audited financial statements. The trustees usually meet quarterly.

WHO TO APPLY TO Christopher Banks, Trustee, Copyhold, Lock Lane, Partridge Green, Horsham RH13 8EF *Website* www.bwcf.org.uk

■ The John Warren Foundation

CC NO 201522   **ESTABLISHED** 1949

WHERE FUNDING CAN BE GIVEN Lincolnshire, then Bedfordshire, Northamptonshire and Nottinghamshire.

WHO CAN BENEFIT Churches.

WHAT IS FUNDED Church fabric repairs.

WHAT IS NOT FUNDED No support for major cathedral appeals.

TYPE OF GRANT One-off grants.

SAMPLE GRANTS 27 charitable donations principally relating to the upkeep, repair and improvement of churches and church buildings.

FINANCES *Year* 2009–10 *Income* £27,983 *Grants* £27,983 *Assets* £701,694

TRUSTEES J E Lamb; R H Lamb; B H Marshall.

HOW TO APPLY In writing to the correspondent.

WHO TO APPLY TO J E Lamb, Trustee, Lamb & Holmes Solicitors, West Street, Kettering, Northamptonshire NN16 0AZ *Tel* 01536 513195 *Fax* 01536 410191 *email* enquiries@ lamb-holmes.co.uk

■ The Waterloo Foundation

CC NO 1117535   **ESTABLISHED** 2007

WHERE FUNDING CAN BE GIVEN UK, with a preference for Wales, and overseas.

WHO CAN BENEFIT Organisations working on childhood development, in the developing world, the environment, and projects in Wales.

WHAT IS FUNDED 'We welcome applications from registered charities and organisations with projects that have a recognisable charitable purpose. Your project has to be allowed within the terms of your constitution or rules and, if you are not a registered charity, you will need to send us a copy of your constitution or set of rules. We make grants for all types of projects; start-up, initial stages and valuable ongoing funding. This can include running costs and overheads as well as posts; particularly under the World Development and Projects in Wales. We do not have any upper or lower limit on the amount of grant we offer but it is unlikely that we would offer a grant of more that £100,000.'

WHAT IS NOT FUNDED The foundation will not support applications for grants for work that has already taken place; applications for grants that replace or subsidise statutory funding. 'We will not consider applications for grants in the following areas: the arts and heritage, except in Wales; animal welfare; the promotion of religious or political causes; general appeals or circulars. We are unlikely to support projects in the following areas: from individuals; for the benefit of an individual; medical charities (except under certain aspects of our 'Child Development' programme, particularly mental health); festivals, sports and leisure activities; websites, publications, conferences or seminars, except under our 'Child Development' programme.'

TYPE OF GRANT Project and core costs; one-off and recurrent grants.

RANGE OF GRANTS Up to £100,000.

SAMPLE GRANTS WaterAid (£175,000); Link Community Development (£150,000); Microloan Foundation (£100,000); and The Fairtrade Foundation (£20,000). Other organisations awarded funding were listed without figures, these included: University of Bristol; Crossroads Care Mid & West Wales; The Forest Trust; Kids Company; Food and Behavioural Research; The Prince's Trust Wales; Blue Ventures and The National Autistic Society.

FINANCES *Year* 2010 *Income* £4,191,943 *Grants* £5,521,987 *Assets* £121,367,714

TRUSTEES Heather Stevens; David Stevens; Janet Alexander; Caroline Oakes.

HOW TO APPLY 'We hope to make applying for a grant fairly painless and fairly quick. However it will help us a great deal if you could follow the simple rules below when sending in an application (there are no application forms). Email applications to applications@waterloo foundation.org.uk (nowhere else please!). Include a BRIEF description (equivalent to 2 sides of A4) within your email, but NOT as an attachment, of your project or the purpose for which you want the funding, detailing: your charity's name, address and charity number; email, phone and name of a person to reply to; a link to your website; what it's for; who it benefits; how much you want and when; what happens if you don't get our help; the programme under which you are applying. Don't write long flowery sentences – we won't read them. Do be brief, honest, clear and direct. Use abbreviations if you like! Don't send attachments to your email – your website will give us an introduction to you so you don't need to cover that. **Who can apply?** We welcome applications from registered charities and organisations with projects that have a recognisable charitable purpose. Your project has to be allowed within the terms of your constitution or rules and, if you are not a registered charity, you will need to send us a copy of your constitution or set of rules. We make grants for all types of projects; start-up, initial stages and valuable ongoing funding. This can include running costs and overheads as well as posts; particularly under the World Development and Projects in Wales. We do not have any upper or lower limit on the amount of grant we offer but it is unlikely that we would offer a grant of more that £100,000. **Applicants outside the UK:** please consult the trust's website for special application guidance.'

WHO TO APPLY TO Janice Matthews, Finance Manager, c/o 46–48 Cardiff Road, Llandaff, Cardiff CF5 2DT *Tel* 029 2083 8980 *email* info@waterloofoundation.org.uk *Website* www.waterloofoundation.org.uk

■ G R Waters Charitable Trust 2000

CC NO 1091525   **ESTABLISHED** 2000

WHERE FUNDING CAN BE GIVEN UK, also North and Central America.

WHO CAN BENEFIT Registered charities.

WHAT IS FUNDED General charitable purposes.

RANGE OF GRANTS £100–£132,000.

SAMPLE GRANTS Fundacion Un Techo Para Chile (£132,000); Cinema Jenin Association – Palestine (£126,000); Nordoff Robbins Music Therapy, Mandeville School (£50,000 each); Cystic Fibrosis Dream Holidays, Dream Connection (£5,000 each); Royal British Legion

and Help for Heroes (£3,000); Rainbow for Conductive Education (£2,000); and Amnesty International (£1,000).

FINANCES *Year* 2009–10 *Income* £93,900 *Grants* £382,875 *Assets* £1,116,940

TRUSTEES M Fenwick; C Organ.

OTHER INFORMATION This trust was registered with the Charity Commission in 2002, replacing Roger Waters 1989 Charitable Trust (Charity Commission number 328574), which transferred its assets to this new trust. (The 2000 in the title refers to when the declaration of trust was made.) Like the former trust, it receives a share of the Pink Floyd's royalties as part of its annual income. It has general charitable purposes throughout the UK, as well as North and Central America. £8,000 in grants also made to two individuals.

HOW TO APPLY In writing to the correspondent.

WHO TO APPLY TO Michael Lewis, Finers Stephens Innocent, 179–185 Great Portland Street, London W1W 5LS *Tel* 020 7323 4000

■ The Waterways Trust

CC NO 1074541   **ESTABLISHED** 1999

WHERE FUNDING CAN BE GIVEN England and Wales.

WHO CAN BENEFIT Organisations, community groups or schools.

WHAT IS FUNDED Waterway related projects; projects providing lasting environmental enhancement; projects encouraging involvement in the waterways; and projects involving and benefiting the community.

TYPE OF GRANT Project funding.

RANGE OF GRANTS Up to £5,000.

FINANCES *Year* 2009–10 *Income* £2,271,892 *Grants* £2,429,068 *Assets* £413,922

TRUSTEES Francis Done, Chair; Helen Carey; Ian Valder; John Hume; S Dunlop; B Harvey; Richard Combes; Laurence Newman; Chris Coburn; D Organ; Judy Niner.

HOW TO APPLY The Small Grants Scheme application form is available from the trust's website.

WHO TO APPLY TO P C W Juniper, Secretary, The Trust House, Llanthony Warehouse, The Docks, Gloucester GL1 2EH *Tel* 01452 318220 *email* enquiries@thewaterwaystrust.org.uk *Website* www.thewaterwaystrust.org.uk

■ The Wates Foundation

CC NO 247941   **ESTABLISHED** 1966

WHERE FUNDING CAN BE GIVEN Berkshire; Bristol, Avon & Somerset; Buckinghamshire; Dorset; Gloucestershire; Middlesex; Nottinghamshire; Oxfordshire; Surrey; Sussex and the Greater London Metropolitan Area as defined by the M25 motorway.

WHO CAN BENEFIT Projects with charitable status. Practical projects involving people are preferred especially those benefiting young and disadvantaged people.

WHAT IS FUNDED The foundation aims to alleviate conditions of distress, deprivation and disadvantage that lead to social exclusion by funding charitable work across a broad range of social priorities that will bring about positive change. Current programmes are: Building Family Values; Community Health; Life Transitions; and Safer Communities.

WHAT IS NOT FUNDED See 'applications'.

TYPE OF GRANT Grants may be one-off and for salaries, although buildings, capital, project, research, start-up, core, running and recurring costs will also be considered.

RANGE OF GRANTS Normally up to £50,000.

SAMPLE GRANTS Cool2Care (£50,000); Jessie May Trust (£45,000); Home-Start, Bristol (£40,000); The Art Room and Oxfordshire Parent Infant Project (£30,000 each); Demos and Gardening Leave (£20,000 each); Advocacy First (£15,500); St George's (Hanworth) Youth Club (£10,000); Surrey Job Match (£6,000); Charlton Advice Centre (£5,000); and HMP/YOI Downview (£1,500).

FINANCES *Year* 2009–10 *Income* £159,622 *Grants* £2,870,393 *Assets* £20,417,670

TRUSTEES Annabelle Elliott; Christopher Agace; Richard Wates; Emily King; Kate Minch; William Wates.

OTHER INFORMATION The foundation regularly reviews its activities and programmes – please check the foundation's website for current information.

HOW TO APPLY Note the following statement from the foundation: 'The Wates Foundation reviewed its grant making policy in November 2011 in the light of a range of factors, including finance and levels of demand for support. As a result of this review, the foundation has adopted a wholly pro-active grant making strategy and will no longer take applications or bids for support from external organisations. Any unsolicited applications or bids will be rejected automatically. This strategy will be in place for three years until 31 March 2015.'

WHO TO APPLY TO Brian Wheelwright, Director, Wates House, Station Approach, Leatherhead, Surrey KT22 7SW *Tel* 01372 861000 *Fax* 01372 861252 *email* director@watesfoundation.org.uk *Website* www.watesfoundation.org.uk

---

■ Blyth Watson Charitable Trust

CC NO 1071390   **ESTABLISHED** 1997

WHERE FUNDING CAN BE GIVEN UK.

WHO CAN BENEFIT Charitable organisations.

WHAT IS FUNDED The trust dedicates its grant-giving policy in the area of humanitarian causes based in the UK.

TYPE OF GRANT Mainly one-off.

SAMPLE GRANTS Connection at St Martin's, Society for the Relief of Distress, Royal Academy of Music and Journey of a Lifetime. A number of hospices were also supported.

FINANCES *Year* 2009–10 *Income* £83,894 *Grants* £95,886 *Assets* £2,649,522

TRUSTEES Nicholas Brown; Ian McCulloch.

OTHER INFORMATION The grant total provided includes support costs.

HOW TO APPLY In writing to the correspondent. Trustees usually meet twice during the year in June and December.

WHO TO APPLY TO The Trustees, 50 Broadway, Westminster, London SW1H 0BL *Tel* 020 7227 7000

■ The Howard Watson Symington Memorial Charity

CC NO 512708   **ESTABLISHED** 1946

WHERE FUNDING CAN BE GIVEN The former urban district of Market Harborough.

WHO CAN BENEFIT Residents of Market Harborough.

WHAT IS FUNDED The trust has a particular interest towards relief of need, welfare, recreation, leisure and education.

RANGE OF GRANTS Up to £5,000.

SAMPLE GRANTS The majority of the charity's expenditure went towards the maintenance and repair of Brooklands Gardens (£208,000), with

£5,000 given in grants to a sole beneficiary Market Harborough C of E Primary School for the purpose of an art room extension. Previous beneficiaries have included: St Nicholas Church (£5,000); Marshall Court (£3,000); Arts Fresco (£1,500); Global Young Leaders Conference (£500) and Robert Smyth Cricket Festival (£100).

FINANCES *Year* 2009–10 *Income* £230,244 *Grants* £256,242 *Assets* £2,894,698

TRUSTEES Harborough District Council.

HOW TO APPLY In writing to the correspondent. Applications are considered in early autumn. 'The Charity has devised a standard form for applications for financial assistance and all applications are subjected to a validation process undertaken by the Clerk to the Trustee.'

WHO TO APPLY TO Anne Cowan, Events Co-ordinator, 17 Thatch Meadow Drive, Market Harborough, Leicestershire LE16 7XH *Tel* 01838 821291

■ John Watson's Trust

SC NO SC014004   **ESTABLISHED** 1984

WHERE FUNDING CAN BE GIVEN Scotland, with a strong preference for Lothian.

WHO CAN BENEFIT Individuals, charitable organisations, ad hoc groups, research bodies or individuals. Beneficiaries must be under 21 years of age. People in care, fostered or adopted; children of one-parent families; people with disabilities; and people disadvantaged by poverty will be considered.

WHAT IS FUNDED (a) Grants to children and young people under 21, physically or mentally disabled or socially disadvantaged, for education and training, equipment, travel, and educational, social, recreational and cultural activities. Grants can be made to charitable organisations and ad hoc groups in this field and to bodies and individuals for educational research. (b) Grants for boarding education to orphans and children subject to some other special family difficulty.

WHAT IS NOT FUNDED No general appeals. Grants are not given for running or capital costs.

TYPE OF GRANT Equipment, small capital expenditure, tuition, student support, personal equipment (such as special wheelchairs, special typewriters), projects and activities including travel. One year only, but can be extended.

RANGE OF GRANTS Up to £5,000.

SAMPLE GRANTS Previous beneficiaries included: Dunedin School (£5,000); Lothian Special Olympics (£3,500); Craigroyston High School, Nancy Ovens Trust and Scouts Scotland (£2,000 each); Gracemount Primary School and Multicultural Family Base (£1,500 each); and Cosgrove Care, Ferryhill Primary School and Sleep Scotland (£1,000 each).

FINANCES *Year* 2009–10 *Income* £22,151,500

TRUSTEES Six representatives of the Society of Writers to Her Majesty's Signet; two nominated by the City of Edinburgh Council; one nominated by the Lothian Association of Youth Clubs; one nominated by the Merchant Company Education Board; one co-opted trustee.

PUBLICATIONS Background notes and application forms available.

OTHER INFORMATION The 2008 grant total includes £58,582 distributed to individuals.

HOW TO APPLY On a form, available from the correspondent, or downloadable from the trust's website.

WHO TO APPLY TO Iola Wilson, Administrator, The Signet Library, Parliament Square, Edinburgh EH1 1RF *Tel* 0131 220 1640 *Fax* 0130 220 1640 *email* johnwatsons@onetel.com *Website* www.johnwatsons.com

■ Weatherley Charitable Trust

CC NO 1079267   ESTABLISHED 1999
WHERE FUNDING CAN BE GIVEN Unrestricted.
WHO CAN BENEFIT Grants to individuals and organisations.
WHAT IS FUNDED General charitable purposes.
FINANCES *Year* 2009–10 *Income* £0
Grants £75,131
TRUSTEES Christine Weatherley; Richard Weatherley; Neil Weatherley.
OTHER INFORMATION The trust had no income in 2009–10. No list of grant beneficiaries was included with the accounts.
HOW TO APPLY This trust does not accept unsolicited applications.
WHO TO APPLY TO Christine Weatherley, Trustee, Northampton Science Park Ltd, Newton House, Kings Park Road Moulton Park, Northampton NN3 6LG

■ The Weavers' Company Benevolent Fund

CC NO 266189   ESTABLISHED 1973
WHERE FUNDING CAN BE GIVEN UK.
WHO CAN BENEFIT Registered charities; preference to small, community-based groups, rather than larger, established charities. 'To be eligible for funding, local organisations such as those working in a village, estate or small town should normally have an income of less than about £100,000. Those working across the UK should normally have an income of not more than about £250,000.'
WHAT IS FUNDED Supporting work with: disadvantaged young people; and offenders and ex-offenders, particularly those under 30 years of age. 'We like to encourage new ideas and to fund projects that could inspire similar work in other areas of the country.'
WHAT IS NOT FUNDED Funding is not given for the following: '(i) Long-term support – We will not normally provide long-term support. (ii) General appeals – We will not support sponsorship, marketing or other fundraising activities. (iii) Endowment funds – We will not support endowment funds, nor bursaries or long-term capital projects. (iv) Grant-giving charities. (v) Retrospective funding – We will not make grants for work that has been completed or will be completed while the application is being considered. (vi) Replacement funding – We will not provide grants for work that should be covered by statutory funding. (vii) Building projects – We will not fund building work but may help with the cost of equipment or furnishings. (viii) Disability Discrimination Act – We will not fund capital projects to provide access in compliance with the DDA (ix) Personal appeals – We will not make grants to individuals. Applicants must be registered charities, in the process of registering, or qualified as charitable. (x) Umbrella bodies or large, established organisations – We will not normally support projects in which the charity is collaborating or working in partnership with umbrella bodies or large, established organisations. (xi) Overseas – We will not

support organisations outside the UK, nor overseas expeditions or travel. Funding is not usually given for the following: (i) Work with children under 5 years of age. (ii) Universities or colleges. (iii) Medical charities or those involved in medical care. (iv) Organisations of and for disabled people. (v) Environmental projects. (vi) Work in promotion of religious or political causes.'
TYPE OF GRANT Grants may be awarded for up to three years. The trust particularly welcomes applications for pump-priming grants from small community-based organisations where a grant would form a major element of the funding. It prefers to support projects where the grant will be used for an identified purpose. Applications for core funding will be considered, such as general administration and training that enable an organisation to develop and maintain expertise. The trust appreciates the importance of providing ongoing funding for successful projects, which have 'proved their worth'. Salaries are normally funded for up to three years but payment of the second and third year grants are subject to satisfactory progress reports. In exceptional circumstances, the trust may provide emergency or deficit funding for an established organisation. Applicants most likely to be granted emergency funding are charities which the company knows or has previously supported.
RANGE OF GRANTS Usually up to £15,000, but applications for smaller amounts from small or new organisations are welcomed.
SAMPLE GRANTS Cowpen Quay Association and Worldwide Volunteering (£15,000 each); Upper Room and Urban Hope (£13,000 each); Footprints and The Prison Reform Trust (£10,000 each); Youth Empowerment Crime Diversion Scheme (£8,000); Leys Youth Programme and The Premises Music Education (£5,000 each); CMO Productions and Guildhall School of Music and Drama (£3,000 each); The Evelina's Children's Hospital (£2,000); Cana Ethiopia and St Paul's Cathedral (£500 each); and City of London Festival and Movement of Peasant Workers, Guatemala (£250 each).
FINANCES *Year* 2009–10 *Income* £362,011
Grants £258,574 *Assets* £7,903,714
TRUSTEES The Worshipful Company of Weavers.
HOW TO APPLY Detailed *Guidelines for Applicants* are available from the Weaver's Company website. Application forms can be downloaded from the fund's website, or by post or email. The grants committee meets in February, June and October of each year, it may take up to four months for applications to be processed.
WHO TO APPLY TO John Snowdon, Clerk, The Worshipful Company of Weavers', Saddlers' House, Gutter Lane, London EC2V 6BR *Tel* 020 7606 1155 *Fax* 020 7606 1119 *email* clerk@weaversco.co.uk *Website* www.weavers.org.uk

■ Webb Memorial Trust

CC NO 313760   ESTABLISHED 1944
WHERE FUNDING CAN BE GIVEN UK and Eastern Europe.
WHO CAN BENEFIT Individuals, universities and other organisations.
WHAT IS FUNDED The trust is set up with the aims of the advancement of education and learning with respect to the history and problem of government and social policy (including socialism, trade unionism and co-operation) in Great Britain and elsewhere by: research; lectures, scholarships and educational grants;

such other educational means as the trustees may from time to time approve.

WHAT IS NOT FUNDED No grants in support of any political party.

SAMPLE GRANTS Ruskin College (£126,000) and the Fabian Society (£76,500).

FINANCES *Year* 2008–09 *Income* £71,427 *Grants* £202,484 *Assets* £1,643,137

TRUSTEES Richard Rawes, Chair; Mike Parker; Robert Lloyd-Davies; Dianne Hayter; Mike Gapes; Barry Knight.

OTHER INFORMATION The Webb Memorial Trust was established as a memorial to the socialist pioneer Beatrice Webb.

HOW TO APPLY See the trust's website for details of availability.

WHO TO APPLY TO Mike Parker, The Hon. Secretary, Mount Royal, Allendale Road, Hexham, Northumberland NE46 2NJ *Website* www. webbmemorialtrust.org.uk

■ The David Webster Charitable Trust

CC NO 1055111 **ESTABLISHED** 1995

WHERE FUNDING CAN BE GIVEN UK.

WHO CAN BENEFIT Charitable organisations.

WHAT IS FUNDED Ecological and broadly environmental projects.

SAMPLE GRANTS Bird Life International (£100,000); Wells Cathedral (£25,000); Herts & Middlesex Wildlife Trust, Rosslyn Chapel, Isabel Hospice, The Tank Museum, Royal Navy Submarine Museum (£10,000 each); National Trust, Beds & Cambs Wildlife Trust (£5,000 each); Bat Conservation Trust, Norfolk Wherry Trust (£2,000); and High Cross PCC (£1,000).

FINANCES *Year* 2009–10 *Income* £183,365 *Grants* £190,000 *Assets* £3,188,623

TRUSTEES T W D Webster; N Thompson.

HOW TO APPLY In writing to the correspondent.

WHO TO APPLY TO N Thompson, Marshalls, Marshalls Lane, High Cross, Ware, Hertfordshire SG11 1AJ *Tel* 01920 462001

■ The William Webster Charitable Trust

CC NO 259848 **ESTABLISHED** 1969

WHERE FUNDING CAN BE GIVEN North East England.

WHO CAN BENEFIT Registered charitable organisations in the north east of England, or for the benefit of branches in the north east of England.

WHAT IS FUNDED General charitable purposes.

WHAT IS NOT FUNDED No grants to individuals or to non-charitable organisations. Core/running costs are not funded.

TYPE OF GRANT One-off only, for capital projects.

SAMPLE GRANTS Previous beneficiaries include: Bubble Foundation and the Derwentside Hospice Care Foundation (£4,000 each), the National Rheumatoid Arthritis Society Richmond (£2,500), YMCA, St Columbus United Reformed Church (£2,000 each), Teesdale Disability Access Forum (£1,500), Different Strokes and Longframlington Memorial Hall (£1,000 each) and Aidis Trust (£500).

FINANCES *Year* 2009–10 *Income* £88,447 *Grants* £92,750 *Assets* £2,087,747

TRUSTEES Barclays Estates and Trusts.

HOW TO APPLY Applications should be submitted by the end of May for consideration in July; by the end of September for consideration in November; and by the end of January for consideration in March. They should include details of the costings of capital projects, of funding already raised, a set of the latest annual accounts and details of the current charity registration.

WHO TO APPLY TO Robin Taylor, Trust Officer, Barclays Bank Trust Company Ltd, Osborne Court, Gadbrook Park, Rudheath, Northwich, Cheshire *Tel* 01606 313179 *Fax* 01606 313005

■ The Weinberg Foundation

CC NO 273308 **ESTABLISHED** 1971

WHERE FUNDING CAN BE GIVEN UK and overseas.

WHO CAN BENEFIT Registered charities.

WHAT IS FUNDED General charitable purposes.

SAMPLE GRANTS Previous beneficiaries included: Natan Foundation; Friends of EORTC; Amnesty International; Community Security Trust; Ability Net; Philharmonia Orchestra; Royal Shakespeare Theatre; St James's Palace Foundation; University of Cambridge; UJIA Campaign; South Bank Foundation; and the Elton John AIDS Foundation.

FINANCES *Year* 2009–10 *Income* £2,138 *Grants* £85,000

TRUSTEES Sir Mark Weinberg; Joy Whitehouse.

HOW TO APPLY In writing to the correspondent.

WHO TO APPLY TO Nathan Steinberg, Munslows, 2nd Floor, Manfield House, 1 Southampton Street, London WC2R 0LR *Tel* 020 7845 7500

■ The Weinstein Foundation

CC NO 277779 **ESTABLISHED** 1979

WHERE FUNDING CAN BE GIVEN Worldwide.

WHO CAN BENEFIT Registered charities.

WHAT IS FUNDED Jewish, medical and welfare causes.

WHAT IS NOT FUNDED No grants to individuals.

TYPE OF GRANT Recurrent.

RANGE OF GRANTS Up to £20,000.

SAMPLE GRANTS Previous grants include: Chevras Evas Nitzrochim Trust (£8,000); Friends of Mir (£6,000); SOFT UK (£2,200); Chesed Charitable Trust and Hachnosas Torah Vechesed Charity (£1,500 each); and Youth Aliyah (£1,000).

FINANCES *Year* 2009–10 *Income* £44,968 *Grants* £67,599 *Assets* £1,467,649

TRUSTEES Stella Weinstein; Michael Weinstein; Philip Weinstein; Lennne Newman.

HOW TO APPLY In writing to the correspondent.

WHO TO APPLY TO M L Weinstein, Trustee, 32 Fairholme Gardens, Finchley, London N3 3EB *Tel* 020 8346 1257

■ The Weinstock Fund

CC NO 222376 **ESTABLISHED** 1962

WHERE FUNDING CAN BE GIVEN Unrestricted, but with some local interest in the Wiltshire and Newbury area.

WHO CAN BENEFIT Registered charities.

WHAT IS FUNDED 'The trustees support a wide range of charitable causes, particularly in the field of welfare, children, education, medicine and arts.'

WHAT IS NOT FUNDED No grants to individuals or unregistered organisations.

RANGE OF GRANTS £500–£25,000.

SAMPLE GRANTS St George's Hospital (£25,000); St Peter's College Oxford (£20,000); Canterbury Cathedral (£10,000); Newbury Spring Festival (£6,000); and the Philharmonia Orchestra,

Think carefully about every application. Is it justified?

973

Ashmolean Museum and Cambridge University (£5,000 each).

FINANCES *Year* 2009–10 *Income* £416,730 *Grants* £255,460 *Assets* £9,826,309

TRUSTEES Susan G Lacroix; Michael Lester; Laura H Weinstock.

HOW TO APPLY In writing to the correspondent. There are no printed details or applications forms. Previous information received stated 'Where nationwide charities are concerned, the trustees prefer to make donations centrally.' Donations can only be made to registered charities, and details of the registration number are required before any payment can be made.

WHO TO APPLY TO Miss Jacqueline Elstone, Trust Administrator, PO Box 17734, London SW18 3ZQ

■ The James Weir Foundation

CC NO 251764 **ESTABLISHED** 1967

WHERE FUNDING CAN BE GIVEN UK, with a preference for Ayrshire and Glasgow.

WHO CAN BENEFIT Recognised charities in the UK, mainly Scottish charities benefiting people who are sick.

WHAT IS FUNDED The foundation has general charitable purposes, giving priority to schools and educational institutions; Scottish organisations, especially local charities in Ayrshire and Glasgow; and charities with which either James Weir or the trustees are particularly associated.

WHAT IS NOT FUNDED Grants are given to recognised charities only. No grants to individuals.

TYPE OF GRANT One-off and recurrent.

RANGE OF GRANTS Mostly £1,000–£3,000.

SAMPLE GRANTS University of Strathclyde (£9,500); British Association for the Advancement of Science, National Trust for Scotland, RAF Benevolent Fund, Royal College of Surgeons and Royal College of Physicians (£5,000 each); Aberlour, Age Concern Scotland, Brainwave, Breast Cancer Campaign, Hopscotch, Jubilee Sailing Trust, Lee Smith Foundation and Youth Action Wiltshire (£3,000 each); ABF The Soldiers' Charity and Epilepsy Scotland (£2,000 each); and Bi Polar Scotland, Borderline and New Dimensions (£1,000 each).

FINANCES *Year* 2010 *Income* £190,009 *Grants* £202,738 *Assets* £6,812,721

TRUSTEES Simon Bonham; William Ducas; Elizabeth Bonham.

OTHER INFORMATION The following six charities are listed in the trust deed as potential beneficiaries: the Royal Society; the British Association for Advancement of Science; the RAF Benevolent Fund; the Royal College of Surgeons; the Royal College of Physicians; and the University of Strathclyde.

HOW TO APPLY In writing to the correspondent. Distributions are made twice-yearly in June and November when the trustees meet. Applications should be received by May or October.

WHO TO APPLY TO The Secretary, Mercer & Hole Trustees Ltd, Gloucester House, 72 London Road, St Albans, Herts AL1 1NS *Tel* 01727 869141

■ The Joir and Kato Weisz Foundation

CC NO 1134632 **ESTABLISHED** 2010

WHERE FUNDING CAN BE GIVEN Worldwide, with a preference for England, Wales, France, Hungary, Italy and Israel.

WHO CAN BENEFIT Registered charities.

WHAT IS FUNDED General charitable purposes.

TRUSTEES George Weisz; Gideon Wittenberg.

HOW TO APPLY In writing to the correspondent.

WHO TO APPLY TO Shirley Baines, Administrator, S G Hambros Bank Limited, Norfolk House, 31 St. James's Square, London SW1Y 4JR *Tel* 020 7597 3000 *Fax* 020 7702 9263

■ The Barbara Welby Trust

CC NO 252973 **ESTABLISHED** 1967

WHERE FUNDING CAN BE GIVEN UK, with a small preference for Lincolnshire.

WHO CAN BENEFIT Normally limited to established charitable foundations and institutions.

WHAT IS FUNDED General charitable purposes. Preference is given to charities of which the founder had special knowledge or those with objects with which she was specially associated.

WHAT IS NOT FUNDED Applications for individual assistance are not normally considered unless made through an established charitable organisation.

RANGE OF GRANTS £500–£7,500.

SAMPLE GRANTS Launde Abbey (£5,000); Lincolnshire Agricultural Society (£2,500); Be Your Best Foundation, The Connection at St Martin's, St Wulfram's Church and St Luke's Hospital for the Clergy (£1,000 each); and Elizabeth Finn Care, Grantham & District Phab, Strut in the Community and The Kings School New Trust (£500 each).

FINANCES *Year* 2009–10 *Income* £32,639 *Grants* £28,250 *Assets* £963,039

TRUSTEES N J Barker; C W H Welby; C N Robertson.

HOW TO APPLY In writing at any time to the above address, although the trustees usually meet to consider grants in March and October.

WHO TO APPLY TO The Trustees, Hunters, 9 New Square, Lincoln's Inn, London WC2A 3QN

■ The Weldon UK Charitable Trust

CC NO 327497 **ESTABLISHED** 1987

WHERE FUNDING CAN BE GIVEN UK and overseas.

WHO CAN BENEFIT Registered charities.

WHAT IS FUNDED The trust has previously had an interest in arts institutions, although this emphasis is decreasing in favour of social welfare and educational projects.

WHAT IS NOT FUNDED No grants to individuals.

TYPE OF GRANT Capital grants.

SAMPLE GRANTS Connection at St Martin's (£32,000); and Red Balloon (£10,000). Four other organisations received grants of less than £10,000 each totalling £16,700.

FINANCES *Year* 2009–10 *Income* £2,148 *Grants* £50,000

TRUSTEES Nabil Fattal; Anthony Weldon.

OTHER INFORMATION Income and expenditure have declined in recent years which indicate that the trust may be in the process of winding up.

HOW TO APPLY In writing to the correspondent, although the trust has previously stated that it is fully committed with existing projects.

974

Does the trust you have chosen match your needs? Haphazard applications waste postage and time

WHO TO APPLY TO Howard Long, 4 Grosvenor Place, London SW1X 7HJ *Tel* 020 7235 6146 *Fax* 020 7235 3081

■ The Wellcome Trust

CC NO 210183   **ESTABLISHED** 1936
WHERE FUNDING CAN BE GIVEN UK and overseas.
WHO CAN BENEFIT Academic researchers working in the fields of human and veterinary medicine, bio-ethics, public understanding of science and the history of medicine.
WHAT IS FUNDED The support of clinical and basic scientific research into human and veterinary medicine; support of research in tropical medicine; the social and ethical implications of medical advances; and the history of medicine. Grants to individuals are usually given via a university, although small grants for travel or developing public understanding of science may be given directly.
WHAT IS NOT FUNDED The trust does not normally consider support for the extension of professional education or experience, the care of patients or clinical trials. Contributions are not made towards overheads and not normally towards office expenses. The trust does not supplement support provided by other funding bodies, nor does it donate funds for other charities to use, nor does it respond to general appeals.
TYPE OF GRANT All types of grant including project grants, programme grants, fellowships, research expenses, travel grants, equipment and occasionally laboratory equipment for research in human and veterinary medicine and the history of medicine. Grants may last for more than three years.
SAMPLE GRANTS University of Oxford (£79.4 million); University of Cambridge (£51.7 million); University of Edinburgh (£28 million); Kenya Medical Research Institute (£24.1 million); University of Manchester (£13.7 million); University of Bristol (£12 million); Structural Genomics Consortium Ltd (£8 million); University of Liverpool (£6.2 million); Diamond Light Source Ltd (£5 million); University of Leicester (£3.3 million); and Keele University (£3.1 million).
FINANCES *Year* 2009–10 *Income* £230,300,000 *Grants* £551,500,000 *Assets* £12,740,500,000
TRUSTEES Sir William Castell; Prof. Dame Kay Davies; Prof. Christopher Fairburn; Prof. Richard Hynes; Roderick Kent; Baroness Eliza Manningham-Buller; Prof. Peter Rigby; Prof. Peter Smith; Prof. Anne Johnson; Peter Davies.
PUBLICATIONS The trust produces various reports and publications, all of which are available from its website.
OTHER INFORMATION The Wellcome Trust is one of the world's leading biomedical research charities and is the UK's largest non-governmental source of funds for biomedical research – it is also the UK's largest charity. The trust has a revised strategic plan for 2010–2020.
HOW TO APPLY **eGrants – online application:** The eGrants system enables applicants to apply for grants online. The system provides workflow to steer the application through head of department and university administration approval steps until final submission to the Wellcome Trust. Most applicants for Science Funding and Medical Humanities grants are required to submit their applications via the trust's eGrants system. However, Word forms

are still available for: preliminary applications; Public Engagement grants; Technology Transfer grants; and applicants who have limited/unreliable access to the internet – please email the eGrants helpdesk – ga-formsupport@wellcome.ac.uk – if this is the case.
If you haven't applied using eGrants before, here is what you need to do: make sure your institution (or the institution that would be administering the grant, if you are not already based there) is registered with the trust; access the eGrants page of the trust's website and fill in a home page for yourself (this will include your personal details that can be downloaded onto future application forms). Other people – such as coapplicants – will need to fill in details too.
The benefits of the eGrants system include: better functionality; clear sign off process through the host institution; reduced administration at the trust; helping us to capture management information (useful for the trust and the applicant).
How to register: You can register with eGrants through the log-in page on the trust's website. Further information on the registration process, help and guidance notes are available by accessing this page.
Registration status of institutions: If you wish to register with eGrants but are not sure whether your institution is registered, you can check the list of registered institutions on the trust's website. If your institution is not on this list you should contact your administration office directly for further information.
Frequently asked questions: A list of frequently asked questions for eGrants is available from the trust's website.
WHO TO APPLY TO Grants Information Officer, Gibbs Building, 215 Euston Road, London NW1 2BE *Tel* 020 7611 8888 *Fax* 020 7611 8545 *email* grantenquiries@wellcome.ac.uk *Website* www.wellcome.ac.uk

■ Welsh Church Fund – Dyfed area (Carmarthenshire, Ceredigion and Pembrokeshire)

CC NO 506583   **ESTABLISHED** 1977
WHERE FUNDING CAN BE GIVEN Carmarthenshire, Ceredigion and Pembrokeshire.
WHO CAN BENEFIT Individuals, churches, chapels, and registered charities, particularly those concerned with health and welfare.
WHAT IS FUNDED General charitable purposes, particularly religious work, health and welfare.
TYPE OF GRANT One-off and recurrent.
RANGE OF GRANTS Up to £10,000.
SAMPLE GRANTS Carmarthenshire-Eglwys Y Bedyddwyr Ramoth, Providence Chapel, Llandybie Public Memorial Hall (£3,000 each); Lluest Horse and Pony Trust (£2,000) and Dyslecsia Cymru (£1,100).
Pembrokeshire – St Michaels & All Angels Church Cosheston, St Mary's Church, Haverfordwest (£3,000 each); Blaenwen Baptist Chapel (£1,300).
Ceredigion-Cadwgan Building Preservation Trust (£10,000); Mentro Lluest (£6,000); Ceredigion Association for the Blind (£4,400).
FINANCES *Year* 2010–11 *Income* £63,075 *Grants* £104,806 *Assets* £5,278,575
TRUSTEES Selected members of Carmarthenshire, Ceredigion and Pembrokeshire County Councils.
HOW TO APPLY In writing to the correspondent.

WHO TO APPLY TO Anthony Parnell, Resources Department, Carmarthenshire County Council, County Hall, Carmarthen, Dyfed SA31 1JP *Tel* 01267 224180 *Fax* 01267 228638 *Website* www.carmarthenshire.gov.uk

---

■ The Welton Foundation

CC NO 245319   **ESTABLISHED** 1965
WHERE FUNDING CAN BE GIVEN UK and overseas.
WHO CAN BENEFIT Registered charities and voluntary organisations.
WHAT IS FUNDED Principally supports projects in the health and medical fields. Other charitable purposes considered include education, welfare and arts organisations.
WHAT IS NOT FUNDED Grants only to registered charities, and not in response to general appeals.
TYPE OF GRANT Some recurrent funding and several small and large donations.
SAMPLE GRANTS University of Cape Town (£150,000); Royal Marsden Cancer Campaign, Great Ormond Street Children's Charity and the Royal Academy (£100,000 each); Wellbeing of Women (£50,000); Combat Stress and the Speech, Language and Hearing Centre (£10,000 each); Elizabeth Finn Care and St Andrew's Club (£5,000 each); Court Based Personal Support (£3,000); One to One Children's Fund (£2,500); and Paintings in Hospitals (£2,000).
FINANCES *Year* 2009–10 *Income* £267,816 *Grants* £564,236 *Assets* £6,413,550
TRUSTEES D B Vaughan; H A Stevenson; Dr Michael Harding.
HOW TO APPLY The foundation has previously stated that 'due to the number of appeals received, the foundation only replies to those that are successful'. However the foundation now also states that grants are not made to unsolicited applicants.
WHO TO APPLY TO The Trustees, Old Waterfield, Winkfield Road, Ascot, Berkshire SL5 7LJ

■ The Wessex Youth Trust

CC NO 1076003   **ESTABLISHED** 1999
WHERE FUNDING CAN BE GIVEN Worldwide.
WHO CAN BENEFIT Registered charities with which the Earl and Countess have a personal interest.
WHAT IS FUNDED General charitable purposes. 'The charity is particularly, although not exclusively, interested in supporting projects which provide opportunities to help, support and advance young people.'
WHAT IS NOT FUNDED No grants are made to: non-registered charities or causes; individuals, including to people who are undertaking fundraising activities on behalf of a charity; organisations whose main objects are to fund or support other causes; organisations whose accounts disclose substantial financial resources and that have well-established and ample fundraising capabilities; fund research that can be supported by government funding or that is popular among trusts.
TYPE OF GRANT Mostly one-off grants. Substantial recurrent grants are also made.
SAMPLE GRANTS Beneficiaries included: Blind in Business, the Brainwave Centre, Cardboard Citizens, Caring for Life, Children's Adventure Farm Trust, Classworks Theatre, the Country Trust, Demelza Hospice Care for Children, East Reading Explorer Scouts, Happy Days Children's Charity, Kidscape, Project Scotland, Tolerance

International UK and the National Autistic Society.
FINANCES *Year* 2009–10 *Income* £281,401 *Grants* £147,041 *Assets* £508,277
TRUSTEES Mark Foster-Brown; Malcolm Cockren; Denise Poulton; Robert Clinton; Kate Cavelle; Richard Parry.
OTHER INFORMATION The accounts stated: 'The Charities [sic] Commission has been supplied with details of amounts given to each charity together with an explanation of the reasons for the non-disclosure of individual amounts in the financial statements.'
Non-disclosure of grants information should only be made where the information being made public may be potentially harmful to the trust or its recipients; failing to disclose information without providing an explanation in the public sphere may prompt unjustified speculation about the nature of grants made.
HOW TO APPLY In writing to the correspondent in the first instance. A response will be made within two weeks in the form of an application form and guidelines to eligible applicants or a letter of rejection if more appropriate. Completed forms, which are not acknowledged upon receipt, need to be submitted by 1 May or 1 November, for consideration by the end of the month. Clarity of presentation and provision of financial details are among the qualities which impress the trustees. Successful applicants will receive a letter stating that the acceptance of the funding is conditional on an update being received before the next meeting. The trust's criteria state other correspondence cannot be entered into, and organisations cannot reveal the size of any grants they receive.
WHO TO APPLY TO Jenny Cannon, Chelwood, Rectory Road, East Carleton, Norwich NR14 8HT *Tel* 01508 571230

■ The West Charitable Trust

CC NO 1138029   **ESTABLISHED** 2010
WHERE FUNDING CAN BE GIVEN England and Wales.
WHO CAN BENEFIT Registered charities.
WHAT IS FUNDED The advancement of Christian religion and providing support to organisations for general charitable purpose.
TRUSTEES P West; J Peperell; Mrs J L West.
HOW TO APPLY In writing to the correspondent.
WHO TO APPLY TO Peter West, Trustee, 80 Copperfields, High Wycombe, Buckinghamshire HP12 4AN

■ The West Derby Wastelands Charity

CC NO 223623   **ESTABLISHED** 1964
WHERE FUNDING CAN BE GIVEN The ancient township of West Derby in Liverpool.
WHO CAN BENEFIT Local organisations and local branches of national organisations benefiting volunteers; at-risk groups; carers; people disadvantaged by poverty; socially isolated people; and victims of abuse, crime or domestic violence.
WHAT IS FUNDED Health and welfare; carers organisations; education & training; victim support and volunteer organisations.
WHAT IS NOT FUNDED The trust has stated that 'education or maintenance during education is not funded'.
RANGE OF GRANTS £150–£5,000.

SAMPLE GRANTS Rhys Jones Appeal (£5,000); Elim Kensington Church (£3,500); Tuebrook Police Station (£3,500); Bradbury Fields (£2,000); Kinship Carers (£2,000); West Derby Methodist Church (£2,000); Holly Lodge Girl's College (£1,500); and RNIB (£1,000).

FINANCES *Year* 2010 *Income* £50,607 *Grants* £47,742 *Assets* £1,620,818

TRUSTEES Joan Driscoll; Barry Flynn; Dorothy Gavin; Jean Holmes; John F Kerr; Barbara Kerr; Peter H North; Barbara A Shacklady; Derek Corlett; Barbara Antrobus; Anthony R Heath.

OTHER INFORMATION The grant total includes £1,000 given to individuals.

HOW TO APPLY In writing to the correspondent.

WHO TO APPLY TO Lawrence Downey, Secretary, c/o Weightmans, Drury House, 19 Water Street, Liverpool L2 0RP *Tel* 0151 236 8989 *email* lawrence.downey@weightmans.com

---

■ West London Synagogue Charitable Fund

CC NO 209778   **ESTABLISHED** 1959

WHERE FUNDING CAN BE GIVEN UK.

WHO CAN BENEFIT Registered charities only.

WHAT IS FUNDED Grants are made to Jewish, Israeli, inter-faith and non-Jewish charities for general charitable purposes, at a national level and a local level within Westminster and Marylebone.

WHAT IS NOT FUNDED No grants to individuals.

RANGE OF GRANTS Up to £8,000.

SAMPLE GRANTS Admiral Nurses and the Psoriasis Association £4,000 each); Rabbi Freeman's Discretionary Fund (£1,000); Down's Syndrome Association and Save A Child's Heart (£500 each); Bet Shalom, Bobath Centre and Respite Carers (£300 each).

FINANCES *Year* 2010 *Income* £31,149 *Grants* £30,300 *Assets* £4,343

TRUSTEES Simon Raperport; Jane Cutter; Michael Cutter; Francine Epstein; Vivien Feather; Jacqui Green; Ruth Jacobs; Hermy Jankel; Monica Jankel; Phyllis Levy; Elaine Parry; Jean Regen; Vivien Rose; and four ex-officio trustees.

OTHER INFORMATION The fund prefers to be involved with charities which synagogue members are involved with or helped by.

HOW TO APPLY In writing to the correspondent.

WHO TO APPLY TO The Fund Coordinator, 33 Seymour Place, London W1H 5AU

■ The West Yorkshire Police Community Fund

CC NO 505514   **ESTABLISHED** 1996

WHERE FUNDING CAN BE GIVEN West Yorkshire.

WHO CAN BENEFIT Charitable organisations and serving and former members of the West Yorkshire Police Force.

WHAT IS FUNDED Awareness of crime prevention, promotion of road safety and education in all matters relating to drug, alcohol and other substance misuse.

RANGE OF GRANTS Up to £2,500.

SAMPLE GRANTS Previous beneficiaries include: Pitstop (£2,200); Bradford Street Angels (£2,000); Action for Black Community Development (£1,500); Big Swing Adventure Playground (£1,000); SAFE (£680); South Leeds Saints Football Club (£490); and Rothwell Town AFC (£360).

FINANCES *Year* 2009–10 *Income* £463,448 *Grants* £67,618 *Assets* £462,448

TRUSTEES Martin A Stubbs; Peter Scott; Mark Aspin; Jessica Wainwright; Andy Mitchell; Andrew Mitchell; Mick Murgatroyd; Alan Lees; Kerry Holden; Michael Downes; Chief Constable of West Yorkshire.

HOW TO APPLY Application forms, guidelines and grant round information is available on the fund's website.

WHO TO APPLY TO Martin A Stubbs, Trustee, Finance Department, West Yorkshire Police HQ, PO Box 9, Wakefield, West Yorkshire WF1 3QP *Tel* 01924 292229 *Fax* 01924 292229 *Website* www.westyorkshire.police.uk

---

■ Mrs S K West's Charitable Trust

CC NO 294755   **ESTABLISHED** 1986

WHERE FUNDING CAN BE GIVEN UK.

WHO CAN BENEFIT Registered charities.

WHAT IS FUNDED Charities are selected by the trustees. General charitable purposes.

RANGE OF GRANTS £2,000–£5,000.

SAMPLE GRANTS Spen Valley Faith in Schools Trust (£5,000); Go Africa (£4,000); OMF International (£2,500); and BLESMA and Turning Point (£2,000 each).

FINANCES *Year* 2009–10 *Income* £34,079 *Grants* £15,500 *Assets* £985,253

TRUSTEES Peter Schoon; Chris Blakeborough; Judith Grandage.

OTHER INFORMATION The trust owns a shop in St Annes, Lancashire, which provides most of its income.

HOW TO APPLY The trust states that it does not respond to unsolicited applications and would prefer not to receive any such applications asking for support.

WHO TO APPLY TO Peter Schoon, Trustee, 20 Beech Road, Garstang, Preston PR3 1FS

■ The Westcroft Trust

CC NO 212931   **ESTABLISHED** 1947

WHERE FUNDING CAN BE GIVEN Unrestricted, but with a special interest in Shropshire.

WHO CAN BENEFIT Registered charities only.

WHAT IS FUNDED Currently the trustees have five main areas of interest: international understanding, including conflict resolution and the material needs of the third world; religious causes, particularly of social outreach, usually of the Society of Friends (Quakers) but also for those originating in Shropshire; development of the voluntary sector in Shropshire; special needs of people with disabilities, primarily in Shropshire; development of community groups and reconciliation between different cultures in Northern Ireland. Woodlands and medical research into orthopaedics will be considered. Medical education is only helped by support for expeditions abroad which include pre-clinical students. Medical aid, education and relief work in developing countries are helped but mainly through UK agencies; international disasters may be helped in response to public appeals.

WHAT IS NOT FUNDED Grants are given to charities only. No grants to individuals or for medical electives, sport, the arts (unless specifically for people with disabilities in Shropshire) or armed forces charities. Requests for sponsorship are not supported. Annual grants are withheld if recent accounts are not available or do not satisfy the trustees as to continuing need.

TYPE OF GRANT Single or annual with or without specified time limit. Few grants for capital or endowment. One-off, research, recurring costs,

Think carefully about every application. Is it justified?

977

running costs and start-up costs. Funding for up to and over three years will be considered.

SAMPLE GRANTS Oxfam (£2,500); Liverpool School of Tropical Medicine (£900); Save the Children Fund (£850); Action Village India (£750); Macmillan Shropshire (£500); Telford Christian Council (£450) and Shropshire Playbus (£250).

FINANCES *Year* 2009–10 *Income* £93,526 *Grants* £92,420 *Assets* £2,202,730

TRUSTEES Mary C Cadbury; Richard G Cadbury; James E Cadbury; Erica R Cadbury.

HOW TO APPLY In writing to the correspondent. There is no application form or set format but applications should be restricted to a maximum of three sheets of paper, stating purpose, overall financial needs and resources together with previous years' accounts if appropriate. Printed letters signed by 'the great and good' and glossy literature do not impress the trustees, who prefer lower-cost applications. Applications are dealt with about every two months. No acknowledgement will be given. Replies to relevant but unsuccessful applicants will be sent only if a stamped-addressed envelope is enclosed. As some annual grants are made by Bank Telepay, details of bank name, branch, sort code, and account name and number should be sent in order to save time and correspondence.

WHO TO APPLY TO Mary Cadbury, Managing Trustee, 32 Hampton Road, Oswestry, Shropshire SY11 1SJ

■ The Westminster Foundation

CC NO 267618   **ESTABLISHED** 1974

WHERE FUNDING CAN BE GIVEN Unrestricted, mainly UK.

WHO CAN BENEFIT Registered charities.

WHAT IS FUNDED Social welfare, military charities, education, environment and conservation.

WHAT IS NOT FUNDED No grants to individuals, 'holiday' charities, student expeditions, or research projects.

TYPE OF GRANT Usually one-off, but any type is considered. Larger grants are awarded over several years.

SAMPLE GRANTS Combat Stress (£1 million over 4 years), for an initiative to develop and deliver a tailor made programme as part of the Enemy Within Appeal for veterans of the Territorial Army suffering from Post Traumatic Stress Disorder; Bray Fellowship (£1 million over 3 years), towards the capital costs over of major restoration work required at St George's Chapel – Windsor; North Highland Initiative (£300,000 over 3 years), towards the third phase of a project to bring together the farming community, local businesses and the tourism industry to try to address some of the challenges facing rural communities in the Scottish Highlands; St Mungo's (£117,000 over 3 years), for a salary and core project costs; Community Foundation for Merseyside (£105,000), towards the grants programme of the Duke of Westminster's Liverpool ONE Foundation; Land Aid Charitable Trust (£101,000 over 4 years), towards its grants programme; Radicle (£75,000 over 3 years), towards salaries and running costs; The Clink (£66,000), for the salary of the chief executive; Kidscape (£55,500 over 3 years), towards the charity's rent; Start-Up Online (£45,000 over 3 years), towards staffing and running costs; NSPCC (£30,000), towards the costs of recruitment and training for 15 volunteer counsellors for ChildLine North West; UK4U (£25,000), towards the cost of Christmas

boxes for armed services personnel serving overseas; and Macmillan Cancer Support (£20,000), towards the salary costs of a Macmillan Nurse Consultant at the Royal Marsden Hospital.

FINANCES *Year* 2010 *Income* £3,907,200 *Grants* £4,823,395 *Assets* £37,793,873

TRUSTEES The Duke of Westminster, Chair; Jeremy H M Newsum; Mark Loveday.

HOW TO APPLY In writing to the correspondent, 'as succinctly as possible and including only the most relevant details relating to the application'. The trustees meet four times a year. Details of current application deadlines are published on the foundation's website.

WHO TO APPLY TO Mrs J Sandars, Administrator, 70 Grosvenor Street, London W1K 3JP *Tel* 020 7408 0988 *Fax* 020 7312 6244 *email* westminster.foundation@grosvenor.com *Website* www.grosvenorestate.com/charity

■ The Garfield Weston Foundation

CC NO 230260   **ESTABLISHED** 1958

WHERE FUNDING CAN BE GIVEN UK.

WHO CAN BENEFIT UK registered charities, independent schools, housing corporations and churches.

WHAT IS FUNDED A broad range of activities in the fields of education, the arts, health (including research), welfare, environment, youth, religion and other areas of general benefit to the community.

WHAT IS NOT FUNDED The foundation cannot consider any funding request made within 12 months of the outcome of a previous application, whether a grant was received or not. It will only consider applications from UK registered charities and your registration number is required (unless you have exempt status as a church, educational establishment, hospital or housing corporation). Projects outside the UK, even if the organisation is a registered charity within Britain, are not typically funded. The foundation is not able to accept applications from individuals or for individual research or study. It does not support animal welfare charities. Typically the foundation does not fund one-off events, galas or festivals, even if for fundraising purposes. It does not fund specific salaries and positions (though it will consider contributing to the core operating costs of charitable organisations). Funding commitments over several years are not made – grants made are typically for a single year. It is unusual for the foundation to consider making a grant to organisations who cannot demonstrate significant progress with fundraising, so please bear this in mind when considering the timing of your application. In general, the trustees look for organisations to have raised the majority of funding through local or statutory sources before an approach is made. The foundation does not place limits on information sent, however it does ask that applications are concise and include only the most relevant details relating to the application.

TYPE OF GRANT Usually small contributions to a specific project or part of a project. Capital (including buildings), core costs, endowments, one-off, research, recurring costs, running costs and start-up costs. Salaries are rarely considered. Funding is given by means of a single cash donation.

RANGE OF GRANTS Up to £3 million.

SAMPLE GRANTS The British Museum (£3 million); English Heritage – Stonehenge and the Royal Marsden Cancer Campaign (£1 million each);

Cancer Research UK and the Royal Shakespeare Company (£500,000 each); Fields in Trust (£300,000); Bristol Old Vic Trust Limited (£250,000); York Museums Trust (£200,000); Norwich Cathedral Trust (£100,000); The Wordsworth Trust (£90,000); The Marine Stewardship Council (£80,000); The School of Pharmacy – University of London (£75,000); National Space Centre – Leicester (£50,000); The Basement – Liverpool (£20,000); Milford on Sea Community Centre (£10,000); Home-Start Sheffield (£5,000); and the Friends of Penn Hall School – Wolverhampton (£3,000).

FINANCES *Year* 2009–10 *Income* £60,052,000 *Grants* £34,225,000 *Assets* £4,085,787,000

TRUSTEES Camilla H W Dalglish; Catrina A Hobhouse; Jana R Khayat; Sophia M Mason; Eliza L Mitchell; W Galen Weston; George G Weston: Melissa Murdoch.

OTHER INFORMATION In 2009–10 the foundation made 1,529 grants.

HOW TO APPLY All applications are considered on an individual basis by a committee of trustees. From time to time, more information about a charity or a visit to the project might be requested. Trustees meet monthly and there is no deadline for applications, which are considered in order of receipt. It normally takes three or four months for an application to be processed. All applicants are notified of the outcome by letter. Grants are normally made by means of a single payment and the foundation does not normally commit to forward funding. In writing to the correspondent. A basic details form is available to download from the foundation's website and must be included with a letter of application. All applications are considered on an individual basis by a committee of trustees. From time to time, more information about a charity or a visit to the project might be requested. Trustees meet monthly and there is no deadline for applications, which are considered in order of receipt. It normally takes three or four months for an application to be processed. All applicants are notified of the outcome by letter. Grants are normally made by means of a single payment and the foundation does not normally commit to forward funding. All applications are asked to include the following information: the charity's registration number; a copy of the most recent report and audited accounts; an outline description of the charity's activities; a synopsis of the project requiring funding, with details of who will benefit; a financial plan; and details of current and proposed fundraising.

WHO TO APPLY TO Philippa Charles, Administrator, Weston Centre, 10 Grosvenor Street, London W1K 4QY *Tel* 020 7399 6565 *Website* www.garfieldweston.org

■ The Barbara Whatmore Charitable Trust

CC NO 283336   **ESTABLISHED** 1981
WHERE FUNDING CAN BE GIVEN UK.
WHO CAN BENEFIT Charitable organisations.
WHAT IS FUNDED The arts and music and the relief of poverty.
RANGE OF GRANTS Up to £3,500.
SAMPLE GRANTS National Youth Orchestra (£6,000); Campaign for Drawing (£3,500); Theatre 503 (£3,000); Royal School of Needlework and the Wallace Collection (£2,000); Wonderful Beast Theatre Company (£1,000); Cambridge

University Library (£500); and New Lanark Conservation (£250).

FINANCES *Year* 2009–10 *Income* £43,533 *Grants* £49,255 *Assets* £1,309,218

TRUSTEES Patricia Marion Cooke-Yarborough, Chair; David Eldridge; Denis Borrow; Gillian Lewis; Luke Alec Gardiner; Sally Carter; Stephen James Bate.

HOW TO APPLY In writing to the correspondent.

WHO TO APPLY TO Mrs P M Cooke-Yarborough, Chair, Spring House, Priors Way, Aldeburgh, Suffolk IP15 5EW *Tel* 01728 452885

■ The Whitaker Charitable Trust

CC NO 234491   **ESTABLISHED** 1964
WHERE FUNDING CAN BE GIVEN UK, but mostly East Midlands and Scotland.
WHO CAN BENEFIT UK-wide organisations and local organisations (registered charities only).
WHAT IS FUNDED The trust has general charitable objects, although with stated preferences in the following fields: local charities in Nottinghamshire and the east Midlands; music; agriculture and silviculture; countryside conservation; Scottish charities.
WHAT IS NOT FUNDED Support is given to registered charities only. No grants are given to individuals or for the repair or maintenance of individual churches.
SAMPLE GRANTS A substantial grant of £42,000 was made to Atlantic College. Other beneficiaries include: Leith School of Art £13,000; Nottingham University, Bristol University, Phoenix Foundation, Game and Wildlife Conservation Trust Scotland and Teaching Trees – £10,000 each; Live Music now £6,000; Heritage Trust of Lincolnshire £3,750; Bassetlaw Hospice £3,000.
FINANCES *Year* 2009–10 *Income* £206,372 *Grants* £185,250 *Assets* £7,274,403
TRUSTEES E R H Perks; D W J Price; Lady Elizabeth Whitaker.
HOW TO APPLY In writing to the correspondent. Applications should include clear details of the need the intended project is designed to meet plus a copy of the latest accounts available and an outline budget. If an acknowledgement of the application, or notification in the event of the application not being accepted is required, an sae should be enclosed. Trustees meet on a regular basis.
WHO TO APPLY TO The Trustees, c/o Currey and Co., 21 Buckingham Gate, London SW1E 6LS *Tel* 020 7802 2700

■ The Colonel W H Whitbread Charitable Trust

CC NO 210496   **ESTABLISHED** 1953
WHERE FUNDING CAN BE GIVEN UK, with an interest in Gloucestershire.
WHO CAN BENEFIT Charitable organisations.
WHAT IS FUNDED The promotion of education and in particular: (a) the provision of financial assistance towards the maintenance and development of Aldenham School, and (b) the creation of Colonel W H Whitbread scholarships or bursaries or prizes to be awarded to pupils at Aldenham School; charitable organisations within Gloucestershire; the preservation, protection and improvement for the public benefit of places of historic interest and natural beauty. The trustees make charitable distributions on an arbitrary basis, having

reviewed all applications and considered other charities that they wish to benefit.

RANGE OF GRANTS £1,000–£5,000; occasionally larger amounts are given. The trustees will only in exceptional circumstances consider grant applications for purposes which fall outside its stated areas of support. In these cases, the trustees will distribute a minimum of £500 per distribution.

SAMPLE GRANTS Previous beneficiaries have included: 1st Queen's Dragon Guards Regimental Trust, Abbey School Tewkesbury, Army Benevolent Fund, CLIC Sargent, DEC Tsunami Earthquake Appeal, Friends of Alderman Knights School, Gloucestershire Historic Churches Trust, Great Ormond Street Hospital Children's Charity, Household Cavalry Museum Appeal, Hunt Servants' Fund, Queen Mary's Clothing Guild, Royal Hospital Chelsea and St Richard's Hospice.

FINANCES *Year* 2010 *Income* £102,139 *Grants* £102,500 *Assets* £7,322,483

TRUSTEES H F Whitbread; J R Barkes; R T Foley.

HOW TO APPLY A brief summary (no more than one side of A4) in writing (by email if possible) to the correspondent. It is not necessary to send any accompanying paperwork at this stage. Should the trustees wish to consider any application further, then an application form would be sent out.

WHO TO APPLY TO Susan M Smith, Fir Tree Cottage, World's End, Sinton Green, Worcestershire WR2 6NN *Tel* 07812 454321 *email* whwhitbread.trust@googlemail.com

■ The Simon Whitbread Charitable Trust

CC NO 200412   **ESTABLISHED** 1961

WHERE FUNDING CAN BE GIVEN UK, with a preference for Bedfordshire.

WHO CAN BENEFIT Registered charities, or bodies with similar status.

WHAT IS FUNDED The trust supports general causes in Bedfordshire, and education, family welfare, medicine, medical research and preservation UK-wide. Preference is given to charities which the trustees have special interest in, knowledge of, or association with.

WHAT IS NOT FUNDED Generally no support for local projects outside Bedfordshire.

TYPE OF GRANT Usually one-off, but dependent on circumstances.

SAMPLE GRANTS Previous beneficiaries have included All Saints Church, Army Benevolent Fund, Arthritis Care, Bedfordshire Historical Records Society, Bedfordshire Music Trust, Chillingham Wild Cattle, Countryside Foundation for Education, Gravenhurst Parish Council, Mencap, National Association of Widows, St Luke's Hospital for the Clergy, Spurgeons Child Care, Royal Green Jackets, Retirement Education Centre Bedfordshire, RSPB, St Mungo's and Scope.

FINANCES *Year* 2009–10 *Income* £120,822 *Grants* £138,900 *Assets* £62,866

TRUSTEES Sir Samuel Charles Whitbread; E C A Martineau; Mrs E A Bennett.

HOW TO APPLY In writing to the correspondent. Acknowledgements are not given. Please do not telephone.

WHO TO APPLY TO E C A Martineau, Hunters, 9 New Square, Lincoln's Inn, London WC2A 3QN

■ The Melanie White Foundation Limited

CC NO 1077150   **ESTABLISHED** 1999

WHERE FUNDING CAN BE GIVEN Unrestricted.

WHO CAN BENEFIT Charitable organisations.

WHAT IS FUNDED General charitable purposes. 'The charity's principal activity during the year was the support of charities through the payments of donations. The objects of the charity are to promote any charitable purpose or support any charity selected by the directors. It is expressly contemplated that CLIC Sargent may be a beneficiary of the application of some or all funds or other benefits by the charity.'

SAMPLE GRANTS CLIC Sargent (£235,000); A Team Foundation (£2,500); Multiple Sclerosis Society (£2,000); The Guards Museum (£1,000); Alzheimer's Research Trust, Help for Heroes and Paul Laurie Foundation (£500 each); and Shooting Stars Children's Hospice (£250).

FINANCES *Year* 2009–10 *Income* £312,987 *Grants* £242,228 *Assets* £10,076,653

TRUSTEES Mrs. M White; A White.

HOW TO APPLY This trust does not accept unsolicited applications.

WHO TO APPLY TO The Trustees, Boodle Hatfield Secretarial Limited, 89 New Bond Street, London W1 S 1 DA

■ White Stuff Foundation

CC NO 1134754   **ESTABLISHED** 2010

WHERE FUNDING CAN BE GIVEN UK.

WHO CAN BENEFIT Registered charities, which are local to a White Stuff shop, office, warehouse or manufacturer (operating at county or local authority level, rather than nationally or internationally), and have an annual income of less than £1 million. Potential partners must not be political or religious or conflict with the foundation values.

WHAT IS FUNDED Projects supporting disadvantaged children and/or young people.

WHAT IS NOT FUNDED No grants are made to non-partner charities.

TRUSTEES Sally Bailey, Chair; Rebecca Kong; Sean Thomas; Victoria Hodges; David Abramson; Immanuel Mensik; Nigel Wreford-Brown.

OTHER INFORMATION The foundation runs a partnering scheme between White Stuff shops and small charities supporting disadvantaged children and young people. There are currently over 75 partner charities across the UK and one in India, which receive regular grants and support.

HOW TO APPLY In writing to the correspondent, including the following information: the charity's name, registration number and website (if applicable); the shop the charity would like to be partnered with (the foundation's website has an up-to-date list of shops looking for charity partners); an overview of the charity's activities; the geographical area of the charity's operations; the charity's annual income in the last financial year; what impact up to £5,000 of funding would have on the charity; any fundraising or volunteering opportunities that White Stuff could get involved in.

WHO TO APPLY TO Sally Buckley, Foundation Manager, Canterbury Court, 1–3 Brixton Road, London SW9 6DE *Tel* 020 7091 8501 *Fax* 020 7091 8599 *email* giving@whitestufffoundation.org *Website* www.whitestuff.com

■ The Whitecourt Charitable Trust

CC NO 1000012 **ESTABLISHED** 1990
WHERE FUNDING CAN BE GIVEN UK and overseas, with a preference for South Yorkshire.
WHO CAN BENEFIT Organisations benefiting Christians.
WHAT IS FUNDED General charitable purposes. Trustees prefer to support Christian projects, especially near Sheffield.
WHAT IS NOT FUNDED No support for animal or conservation organisations or for campaigning on social issues.
RANGE OF GRANTS £25–£10,000.
SAMPLE GRANTS Christ Church Fulwood (£9,750); Monkton Combe School Bursary Fund (£3,000); Oaks Building Appeal (£2,500); Christian Aid (£2,000); Church Missionary Society and South Yorkshire Community Foundation (£1,100 each); and St John's College, Nottingham and Whirlow Grange (£1,000 each).
FINANCES *Year* 2009–10 *Income* £47,401 *Grants* £50,490 *Assets* £504,003
TRUSTEES P W Lee; G W Lee; M P W Lee.
HOW TO APPLY In writing to the correspondent, at any time. However, the trust states very little money is available for unsolicited applications, due to advance commitments.
WHO TO APPLY TO Mrs G W Lee, Trustee, 48 Canterbury Avenue, Fulwood, Sheffield S10 3RU *Tel* 0114 230 5555

■ A H and B C Whiteley Charitable Trust

CC NO 1002220 **ESTABLISHED** 1990
WHERE FUNDING CAN BE GIVEN England, Scotland and Wales, with a special interest in Nottinghamshire.
WHO CAN BENEFIT Registered charities.
WHAT IS FUNDED General charitable purposes, particularly the arts and environment.
RANGE OF GRANTS Up to £10,000.
SAMPLE GRANTS National Trust and Collier Charity (£10,000 each); and Cats Protection League and Mansfield Choral Society (£5,000 each).
FINANCES *Year* 2009–10 *Income* £40,107 *Grants* £30,000 *Assets* £1,346,489
TRUSTEES E G Aspley; K E B Clayton.
HOW TO APPLY The trust does not seek applications.
WHO TO APPLY TO E G Aspley, Trustee, Marchants Solicitors, Regent Chambers, Regent Street, Mansfield, Nottinghamshire NG18 1SW *Tel* 01623 655111

■ The Norman Whiteley Trust

CC NO 226445 **ESTABLISHED** 1963
WHERE FUNDING CAN BE GIVEN Worldwide, although in practice mainly Cumbria.
WHO CAN BENEFIT Organisations benefiting Christians and evangelists.
WHAT IS FUNDED To help evangelical Christian causes primarily.
WHAT IS NOT FUNDED Whilst certain overseas organisations are supported, applications from outside of Cumbria are not accepted.
TYPE OF GRANT One-off, recurrent, capital, running costs.
SAMPLE GRANTS Kinder Und Jugendwerk (£9,000); South Lakes Youth for Christ and Kisi Kids – Kinder Machen (£6,000 each); Greenstones Christian Trust and Osterreichische Evangelische Allianz (£5,000 each); New Life Church (£4,000); Let TL Children Come and Scripture Union (£2,700); Richard Foster and

Step by Step (£1,000 each); and Harbour Light Church and The Olive Branch (£500 each).
FINANCES *Year* 2009–10 *Income* £146,649 *Grants* £84,662 *Assets* £2,594,532
TRUSTEES Miss P Whiteley; P Whiteley; D Dickson; J Ratcliff.
HOW TO APPLY In writing to the correspondent. Trustees meet to consider applications twice a year.
WHO TO APPLY TO The Trustees, High Barugh, Gaisgill, Penrith, Cumbria CAIO 3UD

■ The Whitley Animal Protection Trust

CC NO 236746 **ESTABLISHED** 1964
WHERE FUNDING CAN BE GIVEN UK and overseas, with a preference for Scotland.
WHO CAN BENEFIT Registered charities only.
WHAT IS FUNDED Prevention of cruelty to animals and the promotion of their conservation and environment.
WHAT IS NOT FUNDED No grants to non-registered charities.
TYPE OF GRANT Core and project grants, one-off or for several years.
RANGE OF GRANTS Generally £1,000–£20,000, although larger amounts are often given.
SAMPLE GRANTS Whitley Fund for Nature (£192,700); Fauna and Flora International Northern White Rhino (£50,000); Fauna and Flora International and River and Fisheries Trust, Scotland (£20,000 each); and Edinburgh Zoo (£5,000).
FINANCES *Year* 2009 *Income* £370,774 *Grants* £367,272 *Assets* £7,995,147
TRUSTEES E Whitley, Chair; Mrs P A Whitley; E J Whitley; J Whitley.
HOW TO APPLY The trust has previously stated that it 'honours existing commitments and initiates new ones through its own contacts rather than responding to unsolicited applications'.
WHO TO APPLY TO M T Gwynne, Secretary, Padmore House, Hall Court, Hall Park Way, Telford TF3 4LX *Tel* 01952 641651

■ The Whittlesey Charity

CC NO 1005069 **ESTABLISHED** 1990
WHERE FUNDING CAN BE GIVEN The parishes of Whittlesey Urban and Whittlesey Rural.
WHO CAN BENEFIT Charitable organisations within the beneficial area.
WHAT IS FUNDED General charitable purposes.
RANGE OF GRANTS £250–£5,000.
SAMPLE GRANTS St Andrew's Church and Friends of Holy Trinity Church (£5,000 each); St Mary's PCC (£2,300); Hospital at Home (£1,000); Coates Silver Lining Club (£500); Talking Newspaper (£350); and Whittlesey Community Car Scheme (£250).
FINANCES *Year* 2010 *Income* £68,686 *Grants* £29,609 *Assets* £1,747,286
TRUSTEES Mrs Pearl Beeby; Ralph Butcher; David W Green; Geoffrey Oldfield; Gordon Ryall; Revd Nigel A Whitehouse; David Wright; Philip Oldfield; Roger Brown; Gill Lawrence.
HOW TO APPLY Charities in the parishes of Whittlesey Urban and Whittlesey Rural should apply in writing for consideration in February, May or September (although urgent requests can be dealt with more quickly). Charities from outside these parishes should not apply as they will not receive any response.

WHO TO APPLY TO P S Gray, Secretary, 33 Bellamy Road, Oundle, Peterborough PE8 4NE
Tel 01832 273085 *Fax* 01832 273085

■ The Lionel Wigram Memorial Trust

CC NO 800533   ESTABLISHED 1988
WHERE FUNDING CAN BE GIVEN UK, with a preference for Greater London.
WHO CAN BENEFIT Registered charities and voluntary organisations.
WHAT IS FUNDED General charitable purposes. The trustees 'have particular regard to projects which will commemorate the life of Major Lionel Wigram who was killed in action in Italy in 1944'. The trust makes grants to a wide range of organisations, especially in the illness and disabilities sector.
TYPE OF GRANT One-off and recurrent.
RANGE OF GRANTS £50–£8,000.
SAMPLE GRANTS U Can Do IT (£32,000 in four grants); Newbury Spring Festival Society Limited (£3,500 in three grants); Dressability, Eyeless Trust, Marine Conservation Society, The Respite Association, Access to Art, The Manna Society, The Passage and War Memorials Trust (£500 each); Child Bereavement Charity and Royal Hospital Chelsea (£100 each); and Jo's Trust (£50).
FINANCES *Year* 2009–10 *Income* £68,706 *Grants* £53,850 *Assets* £684,796
TRUSTEES A F Wigram; Mrs S A Wigram.
HOW TO APPLY In writing to the correspondent.
WHO TO APPLY TO Tracy Pernice, PA to A F Wigram, Highfield House, 4 Woodfall Street, London SW3 4DJ *Tel* 020 7730 6820

■ The Richard Wilcox Welfare Charity

CC NO 1082586   ESTABLISHED 2000
WHERE FUNDING CAN BE GIVEN UK.
WHO CAN BENEFIT Registered charities.
WHAT IS FUNDED Prevention of cruelty and relief of suffering and distress of animals of any species who are in need of care, attention and protection; relief of sickness and protection and preservation of good health; promoting the research and advancement of the causes and treatment of diseases; relief of patients receiving treatment in hospital or on discharge; providing, maintaining and improving hospitals and other institutions providing medical treatment; assisting or promoting any charitable organisation or charitable purpose.
SAMPLE GRANTS Ian Rennie Hospice (£210,000); DNA (£100,000); Chiltern Air Ambulance (£48,000); Nyumbarni (£41,000); Tiggywinkles (£20,000); Fairbridge Tyne and Wear (£5,000); Vision Aid Overseas (£3,000); and Hike for Hope (£500).
FINANCES *Year* 2009–10 *Income* £165,787 *Grants* £669,000 *Assets* £1,493,916
TRUSTEES John Ingram; Nick Sargent; Roger Danks.
OTHER INFORMATION The 2009–10 trustees' annual report states: 'The trustees have decided to close the charity and plan to wind up the affairs during the next 12 months.'
HOW TO APPLY In writing to the correspondent. The trustees meet quarterly to assess grant applications.
WHO TO APPLY TO Richard Oury, Administrator, Herschel House, 58 Herschel Street, Slough SL1 1PG *Tel* 01753 551111

■ The Felicity Wilde Charitable Trust

CC NO 264404   ESTABLISHED 1972
WHERE FUNDING CAN BE GIVEN UK.
WHO CAN BENEFIT Registered charities only.
WHAT IS FUNDED Children's charities and medical research, particularly into asthma.
WHAT IS NOT FUNDED No grants to individuals or non-registered charities.
SAMPLE GRANTS Asthma UK (£30,000); James Hopkins Trust and Joint Action (£5,000 each); Kidney Research UK and West Scotland Deaf Children's Society (£3,000 each); Happy Days Children's Charity and Medic Alert (£2,000 each); Kidscan, Shared Care Network (£1,000 each); and Christian Lewis Trust (£500).
FINANCES *Year* 2009–10 *Income* £70,540 *Grants* £138,000 *Assets* £137,500
TRUSTEES Barclays Bank Trust Co Ltd.
HOW TO APPLY In writing to the correspondent at any time. Applications are usually considered quarterly.
WHO TO APPLY TO Sarah Buckley, Trust Officer, Barclays Bank Trust Company Ltd, Estates and Trusts, Osborne Court, Gadbrook Park, Northwich, Cheshire CW9 7UE

■ The Wilkinson Charitable Foundation

CC NO 276214   ESTABLISHED 1978
WHERE FUNDING CAN BE GIVEN UK.
WHO CAN BENEFIT Academic institutions.
WHAT IS FUNDED The trust was set up for the advancement of scientific knowledge and education at Imperial College – University of London. The trustees have continued their policy of supporting research and initiatives commenced in the founder's lifetime and encouraging work in similar fields to those he was interested in.
WHAT IS NOT FUNDED No grants to individuals.
RANGE OF GRANTS £500–£31,000.
SAMPLE GRANTS Wolfson College – Oxford (£31,000); University College – London and Lady Margaret Hall Development Fund – Oxford (£2,500 each); British Heart Foundation and and Alzheimer's Society (£500 each).
FINANCES *Year* 2009–10 *Income* £33,099 *Grants* £38,000 *Assets* £1,356,650
TRUSTEES B D S Lock; G C Hurstfield.
HOW TO APPLY In writing to the correspondent.
WHO TO APPLY TO B D S Lock, Trustee, c/o Lawrence Graham LLP, 4 More London Riverside, London SE1 2AU

■ The Will Charitable Trust

CC NO 801682   ESTABLISHED 1989
WHERE FUNDING CAN BE GIVEN Worldwide, in practice UK.
WHO CAN BENEFIT Registered or exempt charities with a proven record.
WHAT IS FUNDED Care of and services for blind people, and the prevention and cure of blindness; care of people with learning disabilities in a way that provides lifelong commitment, a family environment and the maximum choice of activities and lifestyle; care of and services for people suffering from cancer, and their families; conservation of the countryside in Britain, including its flora and fauna.

WHAT IS NOT FUNDED Grants are only given to registered or exempt charities. 'It is unlikely that applications relating to academic or research projects will be successful. The trustees recognise the importance of research, but lack the resources and expertise required to judge its relevance and value.'

TYPE OF GRANT One-off or recurring.

RANGE OF GRANTS £5,000–£20,000.

SAMPLE GRANTS Maggie's Cancer Caring Centres (£100,000 – exceptional grant); Sightsavers (£20,000); Lakelands Day Care Hospice and Aspire Living Limited (£15,000 each); Essex Wildlife Trust (£14,000); DGSM YourChoice (£13,000); Focus Birmingham (£12,000); South Lakes Society for the Blind (£10,000); Music in Hospitals (£7,000); Gwent Wildlife Trust (£6,000).

FINANCES *Year* 2009–10 *Income* £574,553 *Grants* £592,000 *Assets* £16,900,581

TRUSTEES Mrs Vanessa A Reburn; Alastair J McDonald; Ian C McIntosh; Rodney Luff.

HOW TO APPLY Applications in writing to the correspondent. There are no application forms – the trust offers the following advice on its website on how applications should be presented: 'We are not necessarily looking for glossy professional bids and understand that your application to us will vary according to the size of organisation you are, and the size of the proposed project. It can be a professionally prepared presentation pack, but can equally be a short letter with supporting information. Both will receive equal consideration. Whatever the presentation, the following is a guide to the main areas that we like to see covered. This is however intended only as a guide to assist you in preparing an application, it should *not* be seen as a prerequisite for applying for a grant – we understand that some small organisations will not have the sort of project(s) that need detailed treatment. Generally, we expect most applications will contain the following: an overview of your organisation. Please tell us in a nutshell who you are and what you do; tell us what you want a grant for/towards. Give us a full description of your project. For instance, what do you hope to achieve/who will benefit from the project and how?; costs. Tell us what your project is going to cost, giving details of the main items of expenditure. Tell us how you intend to fund it, and how much you have raised so far; a contingency plan. What will you do if you do not raise the funds you need?; a timetable. Tell us your timescale for raising funds and when you aim to have the project up and running; a copy of your latest audited Annual Accounts must be included. A copy of your Annual Review is also useful if you have one; other information. Please include any other information which you feel will assist us in judging your application. This could include for example a copy of any newsletter you produce, or short promotional/advertising leaflets. Such publications often help give a flavour of an organisation.'

Deadlines: *Blind people and learning disabilities* – applications should be submitted from November and by 31 January at the latest. Decisions are made in the following March and successful applicants will be notified by the end of the month; *Cancer care and conservation* – applications should be submitted from June and by 31 August at the latest. Decisions are made in the following November and successful applicants will be notified by the end of the month.

WHO TO APPLY TO Christine Dix, Grants Administrator, Grants Office, Sunbury International Business Centre, Brooklands Close, Sunbury on Thames, Middlesex TW16 7DX *Tel* 01932 724148 *email* admin@willcharitabletrust.org.uk *Website* willcharitabletrust.org.uk

■ The Kay Williams Charitable Foundation

CC NO 1047947   **ESTABLISHED** 1995

WHERE FUNDING CAN BE GIVEN UK.

WHO CAN BENEFIT Registered charities.

WHAT IS FUNDED General charitable purposes including medical research, disability causes and animal welfare.

FINANCES *Year* 2009–10 *Income* £12,270 *Grants* £39,000

TRUSTEES R M Cantor; Mrs M C Williams.

HOW TO APPLY In writing to the correspondent.

WHO TO APPLY TO R M Cantor, Trustee, BDO LLP, Kings Wharf, 20–30 Kings Road, Reading, Berkshire RG1 3EX *Tel* 0118 950 4013

■ The Williams Charitable Trust

CC NO 1086668   **ESTABLISHED** 2001

WHERE FUNDING CAN BE GIVEN UK.

WHO CAN BENEFIT Charitable organisations.

WHAT IS FUNDED 'The objects of the trust are to support education and training, the advancement of medicine and general charitable purposes.'

SAMPLE GRANTS Donmar Warehouse (£25,000); Young Disciples (£10,000); Wilton Music Hall Trust (£5,000); Myelomia UK and Help for Heroes (£2000 each).

FINANCES *Year* 2009–10 *Income* £41,564 *Grants* £60,010 *Assets* £2,473,513

TRUSTEES S K M Williams; H A Williams; J Riddick; A M Williams; M T M Williams.

HOW TO APPLY In writing to the correspondent.

WHO TO APPLY TO Stuart Williams, Trustee, 85 Capital Wharf, 50 Wapping High Street, London E1W 1LY

■ The Williams Family Charitable Trust

CC NO 255452   **ESTABLISHED** 1959

WHERE FUNDING CAN BE GIVEN Worldwide.

WHO CAN BENEFIT Jewish people.

WHAT IS FUNDED Organisations benefiting Jewish people.

RANGE OF GRANTS Generally less than £1,000.

SAMPLE GRANTS Previous beneficiaries have included: But Chabad, Friends of Mifalhtorah for Shiloh, Holon Association for Absorption of Immigrants, Ingun Yedidut, Israel Concern Society, Karen Denny Pincus, Mogdal Un, Yedidut Maabeh Eliahu and Yesodrey Hetorah Schools.

FINANCES *Year* 2010 *Income* £41,365 *Grants* £33,500 *Assets* £13,400

TRUSTEES Shimon Benison; Arnon Levy; Barry Landy.

HOW TO APPLY In writing to the correspondent.

WHO TO APPLY TO Barry Landy, Trustee, 192 Gilbert Road, Cambridge CB4 3PB *Tel* 01223 570417 *email* bl10@cam.ac.uk

■ Williams Serendipity Trust

CC NO 1114631 **ESTABLISHED** 2006
WHERE FUNDING CAN BE GIVEN UK, with a preference for Greater London.
WHO CAN BENEFIT Children, education, medical, general.
RANGE OF GRANTS £100–£500,000.
SAMPLE GRANTS Uppingham Foundation (£500,000); Sir George Williams YMCA College (£20,000); Conington Parish Church Council (£10,000); YMCA, Ashburnham Christian Church (£1,000 each); Jane Goodhall Institute (£500); St Andrews Ecumenical Trust and RNLI City of London (£100 each).
FINANCES *Year* 2009 *Income* £213,325 *Grants* £532,700 *Assets* £414,495
TRUSTEES Mr C C Williams; Mrs G B Williams; Mr A A Williams.
HOW TO APPLY In writing to the correspondent. Trustees' meetings are held at least twice each year.
WHO TO APPLY TO Colin Williams, Trustee, R M Walkden & Co Ltd, 14 Pensioner's Court, The Charterhouse, Charterhouse Square, London EC1M 6AU

■ The H D H Wills 1965 Charitable Trust

CC NO 1117747 **ESTABLISHED** 1965
WHERE FUNDING CAN BE GIVEN Mainly UK.
WHO CAN BENEFIT Registered or recognised charities only.
WHAT IS FUNDED General charitable purposes. The Martin Wills Fund gives particular favour to wildlife conservation projects in years three and four of its seven year funding priority cycle.
WHAT IS NOT FUNDED No grants to individuals or national charities.
TYPE OF GRANT One-off grants.
RANGE OF GRANTS The vast majority of grants from the General Fund total £1,000 or less.
FINANCES *Year* 2009–10 *Income* £2,580,294 *Grants* £698,552 *Assets* £53,515,389
TRUSTEES John Carson; The Lord Killearn; Lady E H Wills; Dr Catherine Wills; Liell Francklin; Martin Fiennes; Thomas Nelson.
OTHER INFORMATION The trust runs two separate funds: the General Fund and the Martin Wills Fund. The two funds operate in different areas of grantmaking and, in the case of the Martin Wills Fund, on a seven-year cycle.
HOW TO APPLY In writing to the correspondent. The trust considers small appeals monthly and large ones bi-annually from the Martin Wills Fund. Only one application from a given charity will be considered in any 18-month period.
WHO TO APPLY TO Wendy Cooper, Trust Secretary, Henley Knapp Barn, Fulwell, Chipping Norton, Oxfordshire OX7 4EN *Tel* 01608 678051 *email* hdhwills@btconnect.com *Website* www.hdhwills.org

■ Dame Violet Wills Charitable Trust

CC NO 219485 **ESTABLISHED** 1955
WHERE FUNDING CAN BE GIVEN UK and overseas, but there may be a preference for Bristol.
WHO CAN BENEFIT Registered evangelical Christian charities.
WHAT IS FUNDED Evangelical Christian activities.
WHAT IS NOT FUNDED Grants are not given to individuals.
TYPE OF GRANT One-off and recurrent.
RANGE OF GRANTS Mainly £100–£3,000.
SAMPLE GRANTS Evangelists Fund (£12,000); Bath Youth for Christ – Hope in our Schools and Echoes of Service – Bristol Missionaries (£2,000 each); Bristol International Student Centre (£1,200); Living Waters Radio Ministry (£500); and Langham Partnership – Hippo Project (£375).
FINANCES *Year* 2010 *Income* £72,631 *Grants* £62,127 *Assets* £1,639,121
TRUSTEES Julian Marsh; Margaret Lewis; Revd Dr Ernest Lucas; Revd Alexander Cooper; Revd Ray Lockhart; Derek Cleave; John Dean; Rosalind Peskett; Stuart Burton; Janet Persson; Rachel Daws; David Caporn; Mrs E Street.
HOW TO APPLY In writing to the correspondent. Trustees meet in March and in September.
WHO TO APPLY TO Julian Marsh, Treasurer, 3 Cedar Way, Portishead, Bristol BS20 6TT

■ The Dame Violet Wills Will Trust

CC NO 262251 **ESTABLISHED** 1965
WHERE FUNDING CAN BE GIVEN Bristol and south Devon areas.
WHO CAN BENEFIT Registered charities.
WHAT IS FUNDED The support of homes established privately by the late Dame Violet Wills and charities active in Bristol and south Devon.
TYPE OF GRANT Single donations.
SAMPLE GRANTS Previous beneficiaries include: Amos Vale, Bristol and the Colston Society, Bristol Cathedral Trust, Church of the Good Shepherd, Clifton Gateway Club, Guide Dogs for the Blind, Lord Mamhead Homes, RNLI, Rainbow Centre, Rowcroft Hospice, Samaritans, St Loye's Foundation and WRVS.
FINANCES *Year* 2009–10 *Income* £82,938 *Grants* £85,500 *Assets* £2,524,226
TRUSTEES H J Page; D P L Howe; T J Baines.
HOW TO APPLY In writing to the correspondent. The trustees meet four times per year to consider applications.
WHO TO APPLY TO D P L Howe, Trustee, 7 Christchurch Road, Clifton, Bristol BS8 4EE

■ The Wilmcote Charitrust

CC NO 503837 **ESTABLISHED** 1974
WHERE FUNDING CAN BE GIVEN Birmingham and Midlands.
WHO CAN BENEFIT Registered charities and voluntary organisations.
WHAT IS FUNDED General charitable purposes.
TYPE OF GRANT Mainly recurrent.
RANGE OF GRANTS £95–£2,500; mainly around £500.
SAMPLE GRANTS **Ex-Service charities** – ABF Birmingham, Royal Star & Garter Homes, SSAFA and British Forces Foundation (£500 each). **Medical charities** – Douglas House (£1500); Premier Cru (£700); British Red Cross, Alzheimer's Society, Shakespeare Hospice, University Hospital Birmingham (£500 each); Nurse Aid (£250). **Children's and Young Person's charities** – 1st Wilmcote Scout Group, Edward Russ Trust, CBSO Education Programme, National Youth Orchestra of Great Britain (£500 each); Butterfly Tree, Youth Aliyah (£250 each); Birmingham Children's Hospital(£100). **General charities** – Guide dogs for the Blind, Birmingham Music Festival, Cotswolds Canal Trust, Prisoners Education Trust (£500 each); Ed Weetman Charity Flat Race(£300); Food Lifeline (£250). **Religious**

charities – St James Church Manorbier (£2500); St David's Church Selly Oak, New Life Church Warwick, (£500 each); Jewish Childs Day (£250). **Aged charities** – BCOP, Coundon Care Centre, Lady Katherine Leveson Foundation (£500 each).

FINANCES *Year* 2010–11 *Income* £122,738 *Grants* £57,295 *Assets* £1,713,279

TRUSTEES G C Allman; B W Frost; Mrs A L M Murphy; Mrs R J S Whiteside; Mr G Beach.

HOW TO APPLY In writing to the correspondent.

WHO TO APPLY TO Carol Worrall, Trust Administrator, Mrs Carol Worrall, Warren Chase, Billesley Road, Wilmcote, Stratford-upon-Avon CV37 9XG *Tel* 01789 298472 *Fax* 01789 298472

■ Sumner Wilson Charitable Trust

CC NO 1018852   **ESTABLISHED** 1992

WHERE FUNDING CAN BE GIVEN UK.

WHO CAN BENEFIT Registered charities.

WHAT IS FUNDED General charitable purposes.

RANGE OF GRANTS Mostly under £2,000.

SAMPLE GRANTS St James's Place Foundation (£19,000); Prostate Cancer Charitable Trust (£2,800); Full Circle Fund (£2,500); Friends of Young Carers – Swindon (£2,000); St Edwards School (£1,100); and Relate, Ride High, Lewisham Theatre, Breakthrough Cancer, AMREF and Rushmoor Healthy Living (£1,000 each).

FINANCES *Year* 2009–10 *Income* £34,345 *Grants* £46,125 *Assets* £2,518,236

TRUSTEES Lord Joel G Joffe; Amanda W S Christie; Michael S Wilson.

HOW TO APPLY In writing to the correspondent, or to the trustees.

WHO TO APPLY TO N A Steinberg, Trust Administrator, Munslows Accountants, Mansfield House, 2nd Floor, 1 Southampton Street, London WC2R 0LR *Tel* 020 7845 7500 *email* mail@munslows.co.uk

■ David Wilson Foundation

CC NO 1049047   **ESTABLISHED** 1995

WHERE FUNDING CAN BE GIVEN UK with a strong preference for the Leicestershire and Rutland area.

WHO CAN BENEFIT Primarily organisations which benefit the Leicestershire and Rutland area.

WHAT IS FUNDED General charitable purposes.

RANGE OF GRANTS Up to £87,000.

SAMPLE GRANTS Leicester STRIDE (£87,000) and Leicester University (£50,000).

FINANCES *Year* 2009–10 *Income* £108,103 *Grants* £137,000 *Assets* £6,352,203

TRUSTEES James Wilson; Thomas Neiland; Laura Wilson; Richard Wilson.

OTHER INFORMATION No grants were made to individuals.

HOW TO APPLY In writing to the correspondent.

WHO TO APPLY TO John Gillions, Administrator, Mr John Andrew Gillions, Fisher Solicitors, 4–8 Kilwardby Street, Ashby de la Zouch, Leicestershire LE65 2FU *Tel* 01530 412167 *email* john.gillions@fisherslaw.co.uk

■ The Wilson Foundation

CC NO 1074414   **ESTABLISHED** 1999

WHERE FUNDING CAN BE GIVEN Northamptonshire.

WHO CAN BENEFIT Organisations working with people aged 10 to 21.

WHAT IS FUNDED Educational purposes, including activity-based courses/centres.

TYPE OF GRANT Recurrent project funding, one-off scholarships, running costs.

RANGE OF GRANTS Organisations: £150–£12,000.

SAMPLE GRANTS Beneficiary organisations included: Longtown Outdoor Education Centre (£12,000); Prince's Trust (£8,000); Northampton Hospital Paediatric Department (£6,400); Northamptonshire YMCA (£2,000); Macmillan Nurses (£1,000).

FINANCES *Year* 2009–10 *Income* £67,718 *Grants* £81,246 *Assets* £4,638,402

TRUSTEES A Hewitt; G Wilson; N Connolly Wilson; Mrs F Wilson; A Welch; Mrs P S Wilson.

HOW TO APPLY Individuals: Application form available on the trust website. Organisations: In writing to the trustees.

WHO TO APPLY TO Nick Wilson, Chairman, The Maltings, Tithe Farm, Moulton Road, Holcot, Northamptonshire NN6 9SH *Tel* 01604 782240 *Fax* 016 0478 2241 *email* info@thewilsonfoundation.co.uk *Website* www.thewilsonfoundation.co.uk

■ J and J R Wilson Trust

SC NO SC007411   **ESTABLISHED** 1989

WHERE FUNDING CAN BE GIVEN Mainly Scotland, particularly Glasgow and the west coast of Scotland.

WHO CAN BENEFIT Organisations benefiting older people and animals and birds.

WHAT IS FUNDED Grants are given to charitable bodies which are concerned with older people, or the care of both domestic and wild animals and birds.

WHAT IS NOT FUNDED No grants to individuals.

SAMPLE GRANTS Previous beneficiaries included: Royal Society for the Protection of Birds (£4,500); Cancer Bacup (£4,000); St Margaret's Hospice – Clydebank and SSPCA (£3,000 each); Maggie's Cancer Care – Glasgow and Marine Connection (£2,000 each); Accord Hospice – Paisley, Ardgowan Hospice – Greenock, British Red Cross, Princess Royal Trust for Carers, Royal National Institute of Blind People, Royal Zoological Society Scotland and Trees for Life (£1,000 each).

FINANCES *Year* 2010–11 *Income* £120,757

TRUSTEES H M K Hopkins; J G L Robinson; K H Mackenzie; R N C Douglas; G I M Chapman.

HOW TO APPLY In writing to the correspondent. The trustees meet at least once a year.

WHO TO APPLY TO Hugh Hopkins, Secretary and Trustee, BMK Wilson Solicitors, 90 St Vincent Street, Glasgow G2 5UB

■ The Community Foundation for Wiltshire and Swindon

CC NO 298936   **ESTABLISHED** 1991

WHERE FUNDING CAN BE GIVEN Wiltshire and Swindon only.

WHO CAN BENEFIT Local voluntary and community groups.

WHAT IS FUNDED The primary focus is on disadvantage including, supporting community care, tackling isolation and investing in young people. There are other funds, please see www.wscf.org.uk for details of up-to-date schemes.

WHAT IS NOT FUNDED The foundation will not fund: groups that have more than 12 months running costs in unrestricted (free) reserves; projects

Think carefully about every application. Is it justified?

985

operating outside the County of Wiltshire / Borough of Swindon; organisations delivering services in Wiltshire or Swindon who do not have a local management structure; sponsored events; general large appeals; the advancement of religion; medical research and equipment; animal welfare; party political activities.

TYPE OF GRANT Project, core costs and capital grants.

RANGE OF GRANTS Main grants: £500–£5,000 per year for three years. Small grants: £50–£500 on a one-off basis.

FINANCES *Year* 2009–10 *Income* £1,784,106 *Grants* £913,000 *Assets* £7,677,532

TRUSTEES Richard Handover, Chair; Elizabeth Webbe; Denise Bentley; Christopher Bromfield; Clare Evans; David Holder; Andrew Kerr; Angus Macpherson; Dame Elizabeth Neville; Tim Odoire; Alison Radevsky; John Rendell; Dr Fiona Richards; Ram Thiagarajah; Sarah Troughton; John Woodget; Simon Wright.

OTHER INFORMATION The foundation has a Main Grants and a Small Grants programme. Check the foundation's website for details of other current programmes.

HOW TO APPLY The foundation describes its application process as follows: '1. to ensure that you do not waste time unnecessarily, we strongly recommend that you read the [exclusions] carefully before you start your expression of interest form; 2. if after step 1, you feel that your project is eligible, fill in our expression of interest form [available from the foundation's website]. We will let you know if you are eligible and send you an application pack. We make our application forms as straightforward and as short as possible. If your project is not eligible to apply to one of our funds, we will aim to put you in touch with someone who can help you; 3. complete the form and return it, within the deadline shown on the front of the pack. If you have any problems completing it, call us for assistance; 4. a member of the Grants Team will assess your application and will either visit or telephone you. This meeting also provides the opportunity to discuss the application further and answer any questions; 5. your application and our assessment report go forward to the relevant Local Grants Committee. The committee then makes the decisions and these are ratified by our Trustees; 6. if we turn you down, you will get details in writing of the reason why. Contact us by telephone or email and we will let you know if you can re-apply; 7. if you are awarded a grant, you will be asked to report back to us on how the money is spent and has been achieved.'

WHO TO APPLY TO Chan Chitroda, Grants Officer, 48 New Park Street, Devizes, Wiltshire SN10 1DS *Tel* 01380 729284 *Fax* 01380 729772 *email* info@wscf.org.uk *Website* www.wscf.org.uk

■ The Benjamin Winegarten Charitable Trust

CC NO 271442   **ESTABLISHED** 1976

WHERE FUNDING CAN BE GIVEN UK.

WHO CAN BENEFIT Individuals and organisations benefiting Jewish people and people disadvantaged by poverty.

WHAT IS FUNDED Relief of poverty and the advancement of Jewish religion and religious education.

RANGE OF GRANTS £200–£5,000.

SAMPLE GRANTS Previous beneficiaries have included Hechal Hatovah Institute, the Jewish Educational Trust, the Mechinah School, Merkaz Lechinuch Torani Zichron Ya'akov, Ohr Someach Friends, Or Akiva Community Centre, Yeshivo Hovomo Talmudical College and ZSVT.

FINANCES *Year* 2009–10 *Income* £130,898 *Grants* £86,600 *Assets* £768,323

TRUSTEES B A Winegarten; E Winegarten.

OTHER INFORMATION The grant total in 2007–08 includes £4,000 donated to individuals.

HOW TO APPLY In writing to the correspondent.

WHO TO APPLY TO B A Winegarten, Trustee, 25 St Andrew's Grove, Stoke Newington, London N16 5NF

■ The Harold Hyam Wingate Foundation

CC NO 264114   **ESTABLISHED** 1960

WHERE FUNDING CAN BE GIVEN UK and developing world.

WHO CAN BENEFIT Registered charities and organisations working in developing countries.

WHAT IS FUNDED Jewish life and learning, performing arts, music, education and social exclusion, overseas development and medical research (travel costs).

WHAT IS NOT FUNDED No grants to individuals (the scholarship fund is administered separately). The foundation will not normally make grants to the general funds of large charitable bodies, wishing instead to focus support on specific projects.

TYPE OF GRANT Either one-off or recurrent for a limited period. Also capital projects on a highly selective basis.

RANGE OF GRANTS Generally £10,000 or less.

SAMPLE GRANTS Queen Mary & Westfield College (£142,000); Whitechapel Society for the Advancement of Knowledge of Gastroenterology (£79,500); World Ort Union (£28,000); Oxford Centre for Hebrew & Jewish Studies (£25,000); and the Soho Theatre (£18,000); London Sinfonietta and the Who Cares? Trust (£10,000 each); Childhood First (£9,000); Springboard for Children (£8,000); The Jewish Museum – London (£7,500); Brandon Centre and London Master Classes (£6,500 each); Bush Theatre, Dhaka Ahsania Mission and The Place2Be (£5,000 each); Cardboard Citizens and the Busoga Trust (£3,000 each); Young Concert Artists Trust (£2,500); and the London School of Medicine & Dentistry (£1,000).

FINANCES *Year* 2009–10 *Income* £378,196 *Grants* £1,199,789 *Assets* £9,990,449

TRUSTEES Roger Wingate; Tony Wingate; Prof. Robert Cassen; Prof. David Wingate; Prof. Jonathon Drori; Daphne Hyman; Emily Kasriel; Dr Richard Wingate.

OTHER INFORMATION The foundation also operates a scholarship scheme, under the name of Wingate Scholarships. Further details can be found at www.wingatescholarships.org.uk. In 2009–10 scholarships totalled £472,600.

HOW TO APPLY Applicants are advised to write to the trust administrator with full details, including the most recent financial accounts. Applications are only acknowledged if a stamped addressed envelope is enclosed or if the application is successful. The administrator of the foundation only deals with enquiries by post and it is hoped that the guidelines and examples of previous support for successful applicants, given on the foundation's website, provides sufficient information. There is no email address for the

986

Does the trust you have chosen match your needs? Haphazard applications waste postage and time

foundation. Trustee meetings are held quarterly and further information on upcoming deadlines can be found on the foundation's website.

WHO TO APPLY TO Karen Marshall, Trust Administrator, 2nd Floor, 20–22 Stukeley Street, London WC2B 5LR *Website* www. wingatefoundation.org.uk

■ The Francis Winham Foundation

CC NO 278092   **ESTABLISHED** 1979
WHERE FUNDING CAN BE GIVEN England.
WHO CAN BENEFIT Older people.
WHAT IS FUNDED Organisations, institutions and foundations benefiting older people.
SAMPLE GRANTS Pasque Charity – Keech Hospice Care (£50,000); SSAFA (£22,000 in 70 donations); Help the Hospices (£15,000); Home Warmth for the Aged (£10,000); and Independence at Home (£5,000).
FINANCES *Year* 2009–10 *Income* £80,839 *Grants* £216,211 *Assets* £2,430,130
TRUSTEES Francine Winham; Josephine Winham; Elsa Peters.
HOW TO APPLY In writing to the correspondent. The trust regrets it cannot send replies to applications outside its specific field of help for older people. Applications should be made through registered charities or social services departments only.
WHO TO APPLY TO Mrs J Winham, Trustee, 41 Langton Street, London SW10 0JL *Tel* 020 7795 1261 *email* francinetrust@btopenworld. com

■ Anona Winn Charitable Trust

CC NO 1044101   **ESTABLISHED** 1995
WHERE FUNDING CAN BE GIVEN UK.
WHO CAN BENEFIT Charitable organisations.
WHAT IS FUNDED Health, young people, people with disabilities, the arts and the armed forces.
WHAT IS NOT FUNDED No applications are considered from individuals.
RANGE OF GRANTS Mostly £1,000–£5,000.
SAMPLE GRANTS Charities Aid Foundation (£40,000); St Wilfrid's Hospice and Sussex Snowdrop Trust (£6,000 each); Ovarian Cancer Action and Help for Heroes (£5,000 each); Smile Train and Motor Neurone Disease Association (£4,000 each); Foundation for the Study of Infant Deaths (£3,000); Stonepillow and Beat (£2,000 each); and Racing Welfare (£1,000).
FINANCES *Year* 2009 *Income* £37,263 *Grants* £105,000 *Assets* £864,958
TRUSTEES Trefoil Trustees Ltd.
HOW TO APPLY Applications will only be considered if received in writing and accompanied by the organisation's latest report and full accounts. The trustees usually meet in February and July to decide on distributions.
WHO TO APPLY TO The Trustees, New Inn Cottage, Croft Lane, Winstone, Cirencester GL7 7LN

■ The Winton Charitable Foundation

CC NO 1110131   **ESTABLISHED** 2005
WHERE FUNDING CAN BE GIVEN National and overseas.
WHO CAN BENEFIT Academic institutions and other organisations.
WHAT IS FUNDED Academic, recreation, health and welfare.

SAMPLE GRANTS Afrikids (£21,000); The Helen & Douglas Trust (£18,000); Centraid of Great Montreal, UNICEF (£10,000 each).
FINANCES *Income* £200,134 *Grants* £113,858 *Assets* £263,772
TRUSTEES M J Hunt; D W Harding.
OTHER INFORMATION A 33% decline in donations has limited grant making capacity in the last year.
HOW TO APPLY In writing to the correspondent.
WHO TO APPLY TO M J Hunt, Trustee, 1–5 St Mary Abbot's Place, London W8 6LS *Tel* 020 7610 5350

■ Wirral Mayor's Charity

CC NO 518288   **ESTABLISHED** 1986
WHERE FUNDING CAN BE GIVEN Wirral; Overseas.
WHO CAN BENEFIT Local organisations, and local branches of UK organisations.
WHAT IS FUNDED A large variety of causes including welfare and medical charities, children and youth organisations, and disability groups. Many are community-based or local branches of UK charities.
RANGE OF GRANTS £100–£14,000.
SAMPLE GRANTS Wirral Autistic Society, Forsight Appeal (£14,300 each); Help for Heroes (£6,000); Wirral Resource Centre & Toy Library (£520); Bread of Life (£250); Wirral Breast Cancer Support (£200); Merseyside Police – Youth Diversionary Activities (£100).
FINANCES *Year* 2009–10 *Income* £2,944,360 *Grants* £5,046,577
TRUSTEES Cllr Alan Jennings; Mr J Wilkie; Mr I Coleman; Cllr Moira McLaughlin.
HOW TO APPLY In writing to the correspondent.
WHO TO APPLY TO The Mayor's Secretary, Wirral Borough Council, Town Hall, Brighton Street, Wallasey, Wirral CH44 8ED *Tel* 0151 691 8527 *Fax* 0151 691 8468 *email* mayor@wirral.gov.uk

■ The Witzenfeld Foundation

CC NO 1115034   **ESTABLISHED** 2006
WHERE FUNDING CAN BE GIVEN UK and Israel.
WHO CAN BENEFIT Charitable organisations.
WHAT IS FUNDED General charitable purposes.
FINANCES *Year* 2009–10 *Income* £85,587 *Grants* £100,005 *Assets* £4,960
TRUSTEES Alan Witzenfeld; Lyetta Witzenfeld; Emma Witzenfeld; Mark Witzenfeld.
HOW TO APPLY In writing to the correspondent.
WHO TO APPLY TO Alan Witzenfeld, Trustee, 9 Chadwick Road, Westcliff on Sea, Essex SS0 8LS

■ The Michael and Anna Wix Charitable Trust

CC NO 207863   **ESTABLISHED** 1955
WHERE FUNDING CAN BE GIVEN UK.
WHO CAN BENEFIT Registered charities (mainly UK) benefiting students, at risk groups, and people who are disabled, disadvantaged by poverty or socially isolated.
WHAT IS FUNDED Main areas of interest are older people, disability, education, medicine and health, poverty and welfare and Jewish.
WHAT IS NOT FUNDED Applications from individuals are not considered. Grants are to national bodies rather than local branches or local groups.
TYPE OF GRANT 'Modest semi-regular' donations. Also one-off for part or all of a specific project.

RANGE OF GRANTS Mostly for smaller amounts in the range of £100 and £500 each.

SAMPLE GRANTS British Friends of the Hebrew University, British Technion Society, Nightingale and Weizmann UK (£5,000 each); Jewish Care, Norwood and Pinhas Rutenberg Educational Trust (£2,000 each); World Jewish Relief (£1,000); Age Concern/Help the Aged, Alzheimer's Research Trust, Association of Jewish Refugees, British Friends of Neve Shalom, British Friends of Rambam Medical Centre, British ORT, Council of Christians and Jews, Friends of Alyn, Langdon Foundation, Shaare Zedek UK, UJIA and Wiener Library (£500 each); and Canine Partners, Care International UK, Magen David Adorn UK, Manchester Jewish Community Care and Medical Engineering Resource Unit (£200 each).

FINANCES *Year* 2009–10 *Income* £72,455 *Grants* £65,000 *Assets* £1,731,482

TRUSTEES Mrs J B Bloch; D B Flynn; Miss Judith Portrait.

HOW TO APPLY In writing to the trustees. Applications are considered half-yearly. Only applications from registered charities are acknowledged. Frequent applications by a single charity are not appreciated.

WHO TO APPLY TO Sarah Hovil, Portrait Solicitors, 1 Chancery Lane, London WC2A 1LF *Tel* 020 7092 6985

■ The Wixamtree Trust

CC NO 210089   **ESTABLISHED** 1949

WHERE FUNDING CAN BE GIVEN UK, in practice mainly Bedfordshire.

WHO CAN BENEFIT Local charities and a small number of national charities with a focus on family social issues. Applicants must be a registered charity or considered to be charitable in nature by the Inland Revenue.

WHAT IS FUNDED General. In particular, social welfare, environment and conservation, medicine and health, the arts, education, sports and leisure, international and training and employment.

WHAT IS NOT FUNDED No grants to non-registered charities or individuals.

TYPE OF GRANT One-off projects, capital, core costs and research. Single grants are usually given but successful applicants may reapply on an annual basis.

RANGE OF GRANTS On average £1,000–£5,000, although larger grants can be made.

SAMPLE GRANTS Beneficiaries were not listed in the accounts but could be viewed on the website: though individual grant awards were not included. Beneficiaries included: Bedfordshire & Northamptonshire Multiple Sclerosis Therapy Centre; Motor Neurone Disease Association; Prostate Research Campaign UK; Keech Hospice Care; Hospice at Home Volunteers Bedford; Leighton Linslade Homeless Service; British Association for Adoption and Fostering; Prince's Trust – Bedfordshire Programme; Help the Aged – Luton Your Money Matters Project; and Scope – Response Service in Bedfordshire.

FINANCES *Year* 2009–10 *Income* £746,607 *Grants* £651,891 *Assets* £22,517,006

TRUSTEES Sam C Whitbread; Mrs J M Whitbread; H F Whitbread; Charles E S Whitbread; Geoff McMullen; I A D Pilkington.

HOW TO APPLY Application forms can be downloaded from the website or requested via email or post. The trust prefers completed forms to be returned by email so that any amendments can be made before they are presented to the

trustees for consideration at their quarterly meetings. Future meeting dates and application deadlines are listed on the website. All requests for support should be accompanied by a current report and accounts.

WHO TO APPLY TO Paul Patten, Administrator, 148 The Grove, West Wickham, Kent BR4 9JZ *Tel* 020 8777 4140 *email* wixamtree@thetrustpartnership.com *Website* www.wixamtree.org

---

■ The Woburn 1986 Charitable Trust

CC NO 295525   **ESTABLISHED** 1986

WHERE FUNDING CAN BE GIVEN Primarily Woburn.

WHO CAN BENEFIT Primarily older people; also welfare and medical charities.

WHAT IS FUNDED The provision and maintenance of housing for Woburn estate pensioners in need; research into, and the provision of facilities for, the welfare of elephants.

TYPE OF GRANT Recurrent and single donations.

RANGE OF GRANTS Up to £23,000.

SAMPLE GRANTS Beneficiaries include: Bedfordshire and Luton Community Foundation (£23,000); St Francis Children's Society, All Saints Dunterton and Marie Curie Cancer Care (£1,000 each); Red Squirrel Survival Trust (£500); Action for Blind People, Addenbrooke's Charitable Trust and Mercy Corps, (£250 each); Woburn Sands Christmas Carnival (£100).

FINANCES *Year* 2009–10 *Income* £96,401 *Grants* £28,600 *Assets* £1,614,387

TRUSTEES The Duke of Bedford; D H Fox; P R W Pemberton.

HOW TO APPLY In writing to the correspondent.

WHO TO APPLY TO K Shurrock, Administrator, The Bedford Office, Woburn, Milton Keynes, Bedfordshire MK17 9WA *Tel* 01525 290333 *Fax* 01525 290731 *email* kshurrock@woburnabbey.co.uk

---

■ The Maurice Wohl Charitable Foundation

CC NO 244519   **ESTABLISHED** 1965

WHERE FUNDING CAN BE GIVEN UK and Israel.

WHO CAN BENEFIT In practice, Jewish groups and health, welfare and medical organisations.

WHAT IS FUNDED Support is given to organisations in the UK with particular emphasis on the following areas: the care, welfare and support of children (including education); the promotion of health, welfare and the advancement of medical services; the relief of poverty, indigence and distress; the care, welfare and support of the aged, infirm and disabled; the support of the arts.

WHAT IS NOT FUNDED The trustees do not in general entertain applications for grants for ongoing maintenance projects. The trustees do not administer any schemes for individual awards or scholarships and they do not, therefore, entertain any individual applications for grants.

SAMPLE GRANTS Birkbeck University of London (£950,000), towards building molecular biology laboratories; Jewish Museum London (£750,000), towards building a religion gallery; Chai Cancer Care (£500,000), towards building a new wing of the building; WST Charity Limited (£150,000), towards onward assistance for the relief of poverty; Community Security Trust (£75,000), towards their Streetwise Project;

Medical Aid Trust (£10,000); and the Jewish Volunteering Network (£5,000).

FINANCES *Year* 2009–10 *Income* £5,400,103 *Grants* £2,974,160 *Assets* £80,788,048

TRUSTEES Mrs Ella Latchman; Prof. David Latchman; Martin D Paisner; Daniel Dover; Sir Ian Gainsford.

HOW TO APPLY In writing to the correspondent. The trustees meet regularly throughout the year.

WHO TO APPLY TO Joseph Houri, Secretary, Fitzrovia House, 2nd Floor, 153 - 157 Cleveland Street, London W1T 6QW *Tel* 020 7383 5111 *email* josephhouri@wohl.co.uk

··

■ The Charles Wolfson Charitable Trust

CC NO 238043   **ESTABLISHED** 1960

WHERE FUNDING CAN BE GIVEN Unrestricted, mainly UK.

WHO CAN BENEFIT Registered charities, hospitals and schools. Particular, but not exclusive regard is given to the Jewish community.

WHAT IS FUNDED Medical and scientific research and facilities, education and welfare.

WHAT IS NOT FUNDED No grants to individuals.

TYPE OF GRANT Mostly capital or fixed term projects and the provision of rent-free premises. Grants may be made for up to three years.

RANGE OF GRANTS Up to £500,000.

SAMPLE GRANTS Previous beneficiaries included: Addenbrooke's Charitable Trust and Yavneh College Trust (£500,000 each); Jewish Care (£350,000); Cure Parkinson's Trust (£200,000); Huntingdon Foundation (£125,000); Royal Marsden Cancer Campaign (£50,000); Sir George Pinker Appeal (£30,000); Zoological Society of London (£25,000); Priors Court Foundation (£10,000); Tavistock Trust for Aphasia (£5,000); and the Roundhouse Trust (£1,000).

FINANCES *Year* 2009–10 *Income* £9,209,419 *Grants* £4,133,277 *Assets* £137,577,877

TRUSTEES Lord David Wolfson of Sunningdale; Hon. Simon Wolfson; Dr Sara Levene; Hon. Andrew Wolfson.

OTHER INFORMATION A recent list of grants was not available.

HOW TO APPLY In writing to the correspondent. Grants are made in response to applications, and while all applications will be considered, the trustees cannot undertake to notify all unsuccessful applicants because of the volume of appeals received.

WHO TO APPLY TO Cynthia Crawford, Administrator, 129 Battenhall Road, Worcester WR5 2BU

··

■ The Wolfson Family Charitable Trust

CC NO 228382   **ESTABLISHED** 1958

WHERE FUNDING CAN BE GIVEN UK; mostly Israel.

WHO CAN BENEFIT Particularly Jewish groups and Israeli institutions.

WHAT IS FUNDED Science, technology and medicine; education; medical research and care and welfare; arts and humanities.

WHAT IS NOT FUNDED Grants are not made to individuals.

TYPE OF GRANT One-off for capital costs and equipment.

RANGE OF GRANTS Up to £300,000.

SAMPLE GRANTS Weizmann Institute of Science – Israel (£265,000); Bar-Ilan University – Israel (£250,000); and Tel Aviv University – Israel

(£235,000). Other beneficiaries include: Rochdale Special Needs Cycle Club (£20,000); Jewish Lads' and Girls' Brigade – London (£5,000); Center for Blind and Deaf Persons (£3,500); and the Temple Music Foundation (£1,500).

FINANCES *Year* 2009–10 *Income* £1,199,000 *Grants* £4,933,000 *Assets* £31,179,000

TRUSTEES Sir Eric Ash; The Hon. Janet Wolfson de Botton; Lord Turnberg; Lord Wolfson of Marylebone; Martin D Paisner; Sir Bernard Rix; Lady Wolfson; Sir Ian Gainsford; The Hon. Laura Wolfson Townsley.

HOW TO APPLY The trust shares its application procedure with the Wolfson Foundation. However, as most grants are made in Israel the following information is particularly relevant: 'Our funding programmes in Israel are currently focussed on universities and hospitals. Awards for these organisations are normally made under the umbrella of designated programmes in which relevant organisations are invited to participate. Over the past few years, funding for universities has been for equipment supporting nationally co-ordinated programmes on important research themes including nanotechnology, desalination, quantum information and solar energy. Funding for hospitals in Israel is mainly for medical equipment. Awards are also made for cultural institutions with a national importance, as well as for smaller organisations working with people with special needs. In the first instance, all applications from Israel should be sent to the Advisory Committee: Professor Haim Ben-Shahar, WFCT Advisory Committee, The Eitan Berglas School of Economics, Tel Aviv University, Tel-Aviv 69978, Israel; Email: wfct@post.tau.ac.il'

WHO TO APPLY TO Paul Ramsbottom, Secretary, 8 Queen Anne Street, London W1G 9LD *Tel* 020 7323 5730 *Fax* 020 7323 3241 *Website* www.wolfson.org.uk

··

■ The Wolfson Foundation

CC NO 206495   **ESTABLISHED** 1955

WHERE FUNDING CAN BE GIVEN Mainly UK, but also Israel.

WHO CAN BENEFIT Registered charities and exempt charities (such as universities and schools), benefiting people of all ages, especially academics, scientists and terminally ill people.

WHAT IS FUNDED Renovation of historic buildings; libraries; museums; support for preventative medicine; science and technology; programmes for people with special needs, and education. Grants for university research are awarded through competitive programmes.

WHAT IS NOT FUNDED Grants are not made directly to individuals or conduit organisations. The following are also ineligible for funding: overheads, maintenance costs, VAT and professional fees; non-specific appeals (including circulars), and endowment funds; costs of meetings, exhibitions, concerts, expeditions, etc.; the purchase of land or existing buildings (including a building's freehold); film or website production; repayment of loans; projects that have already been completed or will be by the time of award.

TYPE OF GRANT Capital, equipment.

RANGE OF GRANTS £2,000–£3,000,000.

SAMPLE GRANTS Imperial College London – Robotic Assisted Microsurgery Laboratory (£3 million); University of Cambridge – New building for Department of Materials Science and Metallurgy (£2.2 million); Royal Society (£1.5 million), for the conversion of a coach house to create meeting rooms at Chicheley Hall, Buckinghamshire; University of Warwick – New Centre for Mechanochemical Cell Biology (£1 million); University of Dundee – Diabetes Research Centre (£500,000); Historic Royal Palaces (£200,000), for the refurbishment of Teck Saloon and North Drawing Room in redevelopment of Kensington Palace; Rainbows Children's Hospice – Loughborough (£150,000), towards refurbishment work and equipment; National Museum Wales (£100,000), towards the renovation of galleries; University of Birmingham (£70,000), towards a seminar room in the new Music Centre; National Autistic Society, Devon (£60,000), towards refurbishment work; Theatre Royal Bath (£50,000), towards refurbishment work; Southbank Centre (£30,000), towards the repair of the Pyramid Roof of the Hayward Gallery; and Maidstone Grammar School for Girls (£14,000), towards building work and equipment.

FINANCES *Year* 2009–10 *Income* £24,380,000 *Grants* £28,195,000 *Assets* £652,835,000

TRUSTEES Hon. Janet Wolfson de Botton, Chair; Hon. Laura Wolfson Townsley; Sir Eric Ash; Sir David Cannadine; Hon. Deborah Wolfson Davis; Prof. Hermione Lee; Lord McColl; Sir Michael Pepper; Lord Turnberg; Sir David Weatherall; Lady Wolfson of Marylebone.

HOW TO APPLY 'The Wolfson Foundation has a two stage application process. Please note that, under some funding programmes, applicants are asked to submit via partner organisations. The information below refers to applications submitted directly to the Wolfson Foundation. **Stage 1** In the first instance, please write with an outline of your project. As well as a brief description of the project, the outline should contain the total cost, the current funding shortfall and the proposed timetable. The letter need not be longer than 1–2 pages. It is important, however, that the initial application comes with the full backing of the institution and is therefore signed by the Chief Executive, Vice Chancellor or equivalent. Statutory accounts for the past two years should be submitted at this initial stage. Our Finance Officer may be in contact if there are any queries – so it is helpful to provide contact details for this purpose. The aim of the first stage is to determine whether a project is eligible. We respond to all enquiries, whether or not we are able to invite a further proposal. **Stage 2** Once an application has been invited, guidelines are issued for a full application. The deadlines this year for full, second stage, applications are 1 March and 1 September. Please note that Stage 1 applications can be submitted at any time but in any case not less than 6 weeks in advance of these deadline dates. All second stage applications are sent to expert reviewers and are also considered by a specialist panel, who make recommendations to the trustees. Details of panel membership are given here. If questions or queries are raised by expert reviewers or by the panel, applicants are given a chance to respond. Please note that match funding is generally expected to be in place before a Stage 2 application is submitted.'

Schools application process
'Please note this information does not apply to special schools, who should apply under the special needs programme. Some 50 applications are invited each year. They are considered first by the Schools Panel whose recommendations are then decided by trustees at their meetings in June and December. Members of the panel visit applicant schools. This means that the lead-in time from initial enquiry to an application being invited and considered is rather longer than for other programmes. It is also a popular programme which may mean an invitation to apply has to be deferred to the next meeting if the allocation for the first is already subscribed. The timetable leading to each meeting of Trustees is as follows: for the June meeting. Initial enquiries will have been received the year before and the schools put on a list for invitation. In about September letters of invitation are sent, enclosing a Method of Application guidance note. The deadline date for receipt of applications is 31 January the following year. Schools are visited between February and April, applications considered by the Education Panel in May and recommendations made to the June meeting of Trustees. For the December meeting. Following initial enquiries and listing, letters of invitation are sent early in the year. The deadline date for application is mid June and schools are visited at the end of the summer term or early in the autumn term. The Education Panel meets in late October/early November and its recommendations go forward to the December meeting of Trustees. **The following points may be relevant to making an initial enquiry:** *Excellence:* the main thrust of the schools programme has been to provide support to schools that already have a proven record of excellent performance. However, the trustees will also help schools which, whilst not yet in the upper reaches of the performance tables, have a clear record of continuing improvement. Schools should cite their place in The Financial Times list of the top 1000 schools; refer to a recent 'excellent' Ofsted/ISI report; or provide information on academic attainments (full results of GCSE examinations for the preceding academic year presented in the form required by the Department for Children, Schools and Families, together with summary results for the last five years). *Eligible projects:* these may be capital or equipment projects. A bid for both may be included in a single application. Grants are not made retrospectively so work on a project for which support is sought must be ongoing at the time of the trustees' meeting. Grants are made for the support of the teaching of science and technology for students taking A level or GCSE examinations. A music technology project may be considered on occasion, but the main focus of the schools programme is science and technology. *Ineligible projects:* examples of ineligible projects are those relating to performing or creative arts centres, dance studios, theatres, sports facilities, libraries and projects exclusively for junior pupils in the school. *Denominational schools:* in making application, schools are asked for confirmation of non-discriminatory entry policies in respect of religious allegiance. Schools that are predominantly denominational may be supported but assurance should be provided that a significant number of pupils of other faiths, or of none, are admitted and that the school sees such a group as a positive asset for all the pupils in the school. An indication of the relevant numbers of such pupils should be provided. *Independent schools:* only schools with a sixth form of at least 50 students may be invited. *Previous grant(s):* it is usual to allow some five years to elapse before another application from the same organisation may be considered.'

WHO TO APPLY TO Paul Ramsbottom, Secretary, 8 Queen Anne Street, London W1G 9LD *Tel* 020 7323 5730 *Fax* 020 7323 3241 *Website* www.wolfson.org.uk

■ The Wolseley Charitable Trust

CC NO 326607   **ESTABLISHED** 1984

WHERE FUNDING CAN BE GIVEN UK.

WHO CAN BENEFIT Grants are made to organisations and individuals situated locally to the businesses of Wolseley plc and its subsidiary companies, or for causes recommended by employees of such subsidiary companies.

WHAT IS FUNDED General charitable purposes that benefit the communities in which the business of Wolseley plc and its subsidiary companies operate.

RANGE OF GRANTS Up to £28,000.

SAMPLE GRANTS Previous beneficiaries have included: Helen and Douglas House, Ripon International Festival (£5,000 each); Acorns Children's Hospice (£3,000); Berkshire Community Foundation (£2,500); St Christopher's Hospice (£1,000); Against Breast Cancer, Birmingham Children's Hospital Charity, Chase, Meningitis Research Foundation and Rainbow Family Trust (£500 each).

FINANCES *Year* 2009–10 *Income* £1,737 *Grants* £120,300

TRUSTEES R Smith; S P Webster; M J White.

HOW TO APPLY In writing to the correspondent.

WHO TO APPLY TO The Trustees, Parkview 1220, Arlington Business Park, Theale, Reading RG7 4GA *Tel* 0118 929 8700

■ Women's World Day of Prayer

CC NO 233242   **ESTABLISHED** 1932

WHERE FUNDING CAN BE GIVEN UK and worldwide.

WHO CAN BENEFIT Christian literature societies.

WHAT IS FUNDED Promotion of the Christian faith through education, literature and audio-visual material.

WHAT IS NOT FUNDED No grants to individuals.

TYPE OF GRANT Annual, regular or one-off.

RANGE OF GRANTS £200–£21,000.

SAMPLE GRANTS United Society of Christian Literature, Feed the Minds, Bible Society (£18,000 each); World in Need, Christian Aid, Wycliffe UK Ltd (£10,000 each); Bible Reading Fellowship, International Bible Reading Association (£7,500 each); Royal National Institution for the Blind (£4,000).

FINANCES *Year* 2010 *Income* £538,075 *Grants* £228,457 *Assets* £363,530

TRUSTEES Mrs J Hackett; Mrs Emma Wilcock; Mrs M M Barton.

PUBLICATIONS Order of service for the Day of Prayer; children's service; Bible study notes on theme for year; annual booklet, Together in Prayer; meditation cards; prayer cards.

HOW TO APPLY In writing to the correspondent, before the end of June. Grants are made in November.

WHO TO APPLY TO Mrs Mary Judd, Administrator, Commercial Road, Tunbridge Wells, Kent TN1 2RR *Tel* 01892 541411 *Fax* 01892 541745 *email* office@wwdp-natcomm.org *Website* www.wwdp-natcomm.org

■ The James Wood Bequest Fund

SC NO SC000459   **ESTABLISHED** 1932

WHERE FUNDING CAN BE GIVEN Glasgow and the 'central belt of Scotland'.

WHO CAN BENEFIT Registered charities.

WHAT IS FUNDED General charitable purposes. Church of Scotland, historic buildings and other registered charities based in Scotland with preference being given to the central belt.

WHAT IS NOT FUNDED Registered charities only. Grants cannot be made to individuals.

TYPE OF GRANT Capital.

RANGE OF GRANTS £500–£4,000.

SAMPLE GRANTS Previous beneficiaries included: Society of Friends of Glasgow Cathedral, Scottish Brass Band Association, Shelter Scotland, Children 1st, Princess Royal Trust for Carers, Erskine Hospital and Scottish Spina Bifida Association; Glasgow and West of Scotland Society for the Blind, Mental Health Foundation, Aberlour Child Care Trust, RSPB Scotland, Hopscotch Theatre Company, Reality at Work in Scotland and Sense Scotland.

FINANCES *Year* 2009–10 *Income* £6,268,500

TRUSTEES Eric H Webster; David A R Ballantine; Alistair James Campbell.

HOW TO APPLY In writing to the correspondent, including if possible a copy of the latest accounts, a budget for the project, sources of funding received and other relevant financial information. Trustees meet in January, April, July and October. Applications should be received by the preceding month.

WHO TO APPLY TO David A R Ballantine, Trustee, Mitchells Roberton Solicitors, George House, 36 North Hanover Street, Glasgow G1 2AD *Tel* 0141 552 3422 *Fax* 0141 552 2935 *email* darb@mitchells-roberton.co.uk

■ The Wood Family Trust

SC NO SC037957   **ESTABLISHED** 2007

WHERE FUNDING CAN BE GIVEN UK, with a preference for Scotland; developing countries.

WHO CAN BENEFIT Organisations and individuals.

WHAT IS FUNDED The Wood Family Trust has three clear areas of investment focus: (1) Making Markets Work for the Poor Sub Saharan Africa (anticipated to be 75% of the overall investment); (2) Volunteering Overseas and Global Citizenship (anticipated to be 12.5% of the overall investment); (3) Developing Young People in Scotland(anticipated to be 12.5% of the overall investment).

SAMPLE GRANTS Grants were made totalling £949,000 of which £520,000 was designated to institutions with the purpose of 'making markets work for the poor', £84,000 was designated to overseas volunteering and £390,000 was designated to the cause 'developing young people in Scotland'. No grants were made to individuals.

FINANCES *Year* 2009–10 *Income* £953,800,000 *Grants* £949,000 *Assets* £33,537,000

TRUSTEES Sir Ian Wood, Chair; Lady Helen Wood; Garreth Wood; Graham Good.

OTHER INFORMATION This trust became operational in September 2007. During 2009–10 no grants were awarded to individuals.

HOW TO APPLY 'The trust is proactive by nature and will only accept applications through our Volunteering Overseas investment programme.' Please contact the trust for further information on how to make an application.

WHO TO APPLY TO Jo Mackie, Chief Executive, John Wood House, Greenwell Road, Aberdeen AB12 3AX *email* info@woodfamilytrust.org.uk *Website* www.woodfamilytrust.org.uk

■ The Woodcock Charitable Trust

cc no 1110896   **established** 2005
where funding can be given UK.
who can benefit Charitable organisations.
what is funded General charitable purposes and children's charities.
sample grants Egmont Trust (£90,000); RNIB (£11,000); George Adamson Wildlife Preservation Trust and Kids Company (£5,000 each); Walden Spoon (£4,500); Surrey Air Ambulance and Tusk Trust (£1,000 each); and Action on Addiction (£750).
finances *Year* 2010–11 *Income* £128,218 *Grants* £129,000 *Assets* £81,560
trustees M N Woodcock; S M Woodcock.
how to apply In writing to the correspondent.
who to apply to Lucy Gibson, Harcus Sinclair, 3 Lincoln's Inn Fields, London WC2A 3AA *Tel* 020 7242 9700

■ The F Glenister Woodger Trust

cc no 802642   **established** 1990
where funding can be given West Wittering.
who can benefit Charities and other community organisations.
what is funded General charitable purposes in West Wittering and surrounding areas.
range of grants £800–£299,000.
sample grants Beneficiaries include: West Wittering Cycle Route Construction (£299,000); Witterings Medical Centre (£248,000); West Wittering Flood Defence (£212,000); Chichester Counselling Services (£50,000); Chichester Harbour Conservancy (£35,000); Donnington House Care Home (£20,000); Lodge Hill Centre (£10,000). Smaller grants include: West Wittering Memorial Hall Committee (£6,000); Independent Age (£2,000); Dyslexia Action (£1,500).
finances *Year* 2010–11 *Income* £1,157,763 *Grants* £1,256,467 *Assets* £32,355,995
trustees R C Shrubb, Chair; Mrs R Champ; W H Craven; S F Dobbin; Miss M Thompson; Mrs T Thompson; Revd J B Williams.
how to apply In writing to the correspondent. Trustees meet quarterly.
who to apply to Mr Richard Shrubb, Chair, Wicks Farm Holiday Park, Redlands Lane, West Wittering, West Sussex PO20 8QE *Tel* 01243 513116

■ Woodlands Foundation Limited

cc no 1108132   **established** 2004
where funding can be given UK and Israel.
who can benefit Students studying in Jewish Talmudical colleges and relevant schools and institutions which teach the Orthodox Jewish religion.
what is funded Jewish education.
sample grants Previous beneficiaries have included Bais Menachem Charity, Chabud Community Centre, Labuvitch Community Centre, Lolev Charity and Parsha Ltd.
finances *Year* 2009 *Income* £8,900 *Grants* £118,000
trustees M Taub, Chair; R Klopmann; M C Lehrfeld.
how to apply In writing to the correspondent.
who to apply to The Trustees, Martin and Heller, 5 North End Road, Golders Green, London NW11 7RJ *Tel* 020 9455 6789

■ Woodlands Green Ltd

cc no 277299   **established** 1979
where funding can be given Worldwide.
who can benefit Organisations benefiting Jewish people.
what is funded Jewish charities performing educational projects.
what is not funded No grants to individuals, or for expeditions or scholarships.
sample grants Previous beneficiaries have included Achisomoch Aid Co, Beis Soro Schneirer, Friends of Beis Yisroel Trust, Friends of Mir, Friends of Seret Wiznitz, Friends of Toldos Avrohom Yitzchok, JET, Kahal Imrei Chaim, Oizer Dalim Trust, NWLCM, TYY Square and UTA.
finances *Year* 2009–10 *Income* £229,379 *Grants* £229,979 *Assets* £1,320,663
trustees A Ost; E Ost; D J A Ost; J A Ost; A Hepner.
other information In 2009–10, the trust gave grants to over 40 organisations. No list of grant beneficiaries was included in the accounts.
how to apply In writing to the correspondent.
who to apply to J A Ost, Secretary, 19 Green Walk, London NW4 2AL

■ Woodlands Trust

cc no 259569   **established** 1969
where funding can be given West Midlands, Warwickshire, London within the boundaries of the M25.
who can benefit Organisations benefiting young adults and older people; at risk groups; carers; disabled people; people disadvantaged by poverty; ex-offenders and those at risk of offending; homeless people; people living in rural and urban areas; socially isolated people; refugees; victims of abuse, crime or domestic violence.
what is funded Preference to charities which the trust has special interest in, knowledge of, or association with. Particularly charities working in the fields of hospice at home; respite care and care for carers; support and self-help groups; woodlands and horticulture.
what is not funded No grant for the cost of buildings. No grants to individuals.
type of grant Core costs, one-off, project, research, running costs, recurring costs, salaries and start-up costs. Funding of up to two years will be considered.
range of grants Mostly £1,000–£5,000.
sample grants Beneficiaries included: Dorothy Parks Centre (£6,000); Where Next Association and Cardinal Hume Centre (£5,000) Actions for kids charitable trust (£4,200); Space (£4,000) and Age Concern and Help the Aged (£1,600).
finances *Year* 2009–10 *Income* £67,544 *Grants* £78,804 *Assets* £1,772,909
trustees Miss J M Steele; Mrs R M Bagshaw; Mrs J N Houston; T R W Steele; Chairman; J C Barratt; Mr D J Bagshaw and Mrs E M Brennan.
how to apply On a form available from the correspondent. The trustees meet to consider applications in April and October each year, and applications should be submitted in January and July.
who to apply to Jayne Day, Administrator, c/o Pothecary Witham Weld Solicitors, 25C North Street, Bishop's Stortford, Hertfordshire CM23 2LD *Tel* 01279 506421 *email* charities@pwwsolicitors.co.uk *Website* www.pwwsolicitors.co.uk/charitable-applications

■ Woodroffe Benton Foundation

CC NO 1075272   **ESTABLISHED** 1988

WHERE FUNDING CAN BE GIVEN UK.

WHO CAN BENEFIT Registered charities only.

WHAT IS FUNDED Financial assistance in times of disaster on behalf of individuals in need within the UK through registered charitable bodies; accommodation and housing; promotion of education – especially through scholarships at Queen Elizabeth Grammar School in Ashbourne; conservation and environment; and community services and facilities.

WHAT IS NOT FUNDED Grants are not made outside the UK and are only made to registered charities. No grants to individuals. Branches of UK charities should not apply as grants, if made, would go to the charity's headquarters.

TYPE OF GRANT Starter finances, recurrent, research, project, one-off, core costs, feasibility studies and running costs. Funding is available for one year or less.

RANGE OF GRANTS Most grants are for less than £2,000 – the trust does not normally make more than one grant to the same charity in a 12 month period.

SAMPLE GRANTS Queen Elizabeth's Grammar School (£26,000); Community Links (£13,000); Ifield Park Care Home (£12,500); Furniture re-use network, Friendship Works, Young People's Trust for the Environment and Prisoners' Families and Friends (£5,000 each).

FINANCES *Year* 2009–10 *Income* £205,092 *Grants* £216,635 *Assets* £6,122,498

TRUSTEES J J Hope, Chair; P M Miles; C G Russell; Mrs Rita Drew; P Foster.

HOW TO APPLY On a form available from the correspondent. Full guidance notes on completing the form and procedures for processing applications are sent with the form. Trustees meet quarterly.

WHO TO APPLY TO Alan King, Secretary, 16 Fernleigh Court, Harrow, London HA2 6NA *Tel* 020 8421 4120 *email* alan.king3@which.net

■ The Woodward Charitable Trust

CC NO 299963   **ESTABLISHED** 1988

WHERE FUNDING CAN BE GIVEN Unrestricted.

WHO CAN BENEFIT Registered charities.

WHAT IS FUNDED Arts, community and social welfare (including children's summer holiday schemes), disability, health, education, environment. Priority to a few charitable causes of which the trustees have personal knowledge, and smaller-scale, locally based initiatives.

WHAT IS NOT FUNDED Trustees will not normally fund: charities whose annual turnover exceeds £250,000; construction projects such as playgrounds, village halls, and disabled accesses; general school appeals including out of hours provision; hospices; medical research; parish facilities; playgroups and pre-school groups; requests for vehicles. Trustees will definitely not support: individuals in any capacity; educational fees.

TYPE OF GRANT Usually one-off.

RANGE OF GRANTS Usually between £1,000–£5,000.

SAMPLE GRANTS Unlock – National Association of Reformed Offenders (£15,000); International Children's Trust (£10,000); Friends, Families and Travellers (£7,700); First Step Drop-in Centre (£5,000); Friends First (£4,000); Changing Tunes (£3,000); Behind Closed Doors (£2,500); East Cleveland Youth Housing Trust (£1,200) and Get Hooked on Fishing Midlands (£1,000).

Soundabout (£5,000); U Can Do It (£4,800); Oxford Parent-Infant Project (£3,000); Reach Inclusive Arts (£2,500) and Anglo-Egyptian Society (£1,000).

National Opera Studio (£5,000); Theatre Modo and Young Musicians Symphony Orchestra (£3,000).

The Ashden Awards (£5,000) and Wester Hailes Youth Agency (£2,000).

FINANCES *Year* 2009–10 *Income* £317,596 *Grants* £240,000 *Assets* £9,904,410

TRUSTEES Camilla Woodward; Rt Hon. Shaun A Woodward; Miss Judith Portrait.

OTHER INFORMATION The trust is one of the Sainsbury Family Charitable Trusts which share a common administration. An application to one is taken as an application to all.

HOW TO APPLY On simple application forms available from the trust, or via its website. Potential applicants are invited to telephone the administrator in advance to discuss the advisability of making an application. Main grants are allocated following trustees' meetings in January and July each year, with the exception of summer schemes, which are considered at the beginning of May each year. All application forms are assessed on arrival and if additional information is required you will be contacted further. Applicants must make sure the trust receives a project budget and audited accounts. The website has a useful diary of trustees' meetings and of the cut-off dates for applications.

WHO TO APPLY TO Karin Hooper, Administrator, Allington House, 1st Floor, 150 Victoria Street, London SW1E 5AE *Tel* 020 7410 0330 *Fax* 020 7410 0332 *email* contact@woodwardcharitabletrust.org.uk *Website* www.woodwardcharitabletrust.org.uk

■ The A and R Woolf Charitable Trust

CC NO 273079   **ESTABLISHED** 1977

WHERE FUNDING CAN BE GIVEN Worldwide; UK, mainly in Hertfordshire.

WHO CAN BENEFIT Registered charities and voluntary organisations only.

WHAT IS FUNDED The trust supports a range of causes, including Jewish organisations, animal welfare and conservation causes, children and health and welfare charities.

WHAT IS NOT FUNDED No grants to individuals or non-registered charities unless schools, hospices and so on.

RANGE OF GRANTS Mostly £100–£5,000.

SAMPLE GRANTS Previous beneficiaries include: Central British Fund for World Jewish Relief, the Peace Hospice, United Nations International Children's Emergency Fund, University of Hertfordshire Charitable Trust, Northwood Pinner Liberal Synagogue, RSPCA, WWF UK, the Multiple Sclerosis Society, Jewish Child's Day, Wellbeing for Women, National Schizophrenia Fellowship, International Primate Protection League UK, the Hertfordshire and Middlesex Wildlife Trust and Senahasa Trust.

FINANCES *Year* 2009–10 *Income* £49,712 *Grants* £27,553 *Assets* £2,562,848

TRUSTEES Andrew Rose; Dr Gillian Edmonds; Stephen Rose; Joyce Rose.

HOW TO APPLY Support is only given to projects/organisations/causes personally known to the trustees. The trust does not respond to unsolicited applications.

Think carefully about every application. Is it justified?

993

WHO TO APPLY TO The Trustees, c/o Griffiths Preston Accountants, Aldbury House, Dower Mews, 108 High Street, Berkhamsted, Hertfordshire HP4 2BL *Tel* 01442 870277

■ ME Woolfe Charitable Trust

CC NO 1135193 **ESTABLISHED** 2010
WHERE FUNDING CAN BE GIVEN Undefined, in practice national.
WHO CAN BENEFIT Charitable organisations.
WHAT IS FUNDED General charitable purposes, with a possible preference for projects involving education and training, the advancement of health or the saving of lives, people with disabilities and animal welfare.
TRUSTEES Carol Mason; Nicholas Pye.
HOW TO APPLY In writing to the correspondent.
WHO TO APPLY TO Carol Mason, Trustee, Hill Dickinson Solicitors, 1 St Paul's Square, Liverpool L3 9SJ *Tel* 0151 600 8395 *email* carol.mason@hilldickinson.com

■ Worcester Municipal Charities (incorporating Worcester Consolidated Municipal Charity and Worcester Municipal Exhibitions Foundation)

CC NO 205299 **ESTABLISHED** 1836
WHERE FUNDING CAN BE GIVEN The city of Worcester.
WHO CAN BENEFIT Poorer people, individually or generally, in Worcester City.
WHAT IS FUNDED Grants to relieve need. Purchase of household equipment, clothes, food and so on, help with bills. Donations to organisations that help poorer people. Grants to poorer students.
WHAT IS NOT FUNDED No grants to organisations of over 49% of their annual income. No grants to individuals unless all statutory sources have been exhausted. Requests for furniture (except bunk beds) are referred to the 'Armchair Project'. Requests for clothes are referred to the 'Lydia Project'.
TYPE OF GRANT Cheque or purchase of item.
RANGE OF GRANTS £1,000–£35,000 for running costs; £100–£100,000 for capital costs; £50–£1,000 for individuals.
SAMPLE GRANTS £80,000 to Worcester CAB and WHABAC; £60,000 to Black Pearl Credit Union; £13,000 to Maggs Day Centre; £11,000 each to Worcester Play Council and Ethnic Access Link Scheme.
FINANCES *Year* 2010 *Income* £866,956 *Grants* £348,346 *Assets* £13,724,207
TRUSTEES Paul Griffith, Chair; Philip Hytch; P Denham; Margaret Jones; Bob Kington; Stanley Markwell; G Hughes; Sue Osborne; Martyn Saunders; Brenda Sheridan; Dr David Tibbutt; Robert Peachey; R Berry; C Lord; Mrs C Panter; A Whitcher; J Whitehouse; Mrs J Holden; Miss M Kirk.
OTHER INFORMATION The grants total includes £95,500 given to individuals.
HOW TO APPLY In writing to the correspondent requesting an application form.
WHO TO APPLY TO Ian Pugh, Clerk to the Trustees, Hallmarks Solicitors, 3–5 Sansome Place, Worcester WR1 1UQ *Tel* 01905 726600 *Fax* 01905 743366 *email* mary.barker@hallmarkhulme.co.uk

■ The Worcestershire and Dudley Historic Churches Trust

CC NO 1035156 **ESTABLISHED** 1993
WHERE FUNDING CAN BE GIVEN The diocese and county of Worcester.
WHO CAN BENEFIT Christian churches.
WHAT IS FUNDED The trust gives grants for the preservation, repair and improvement of churches in the beneficial area and of the monuments, fittings and furniture etc., of such churches.
WHAT IS NOT FUNDED No grants for new building projects, organs or bells.
RANGE OF GRANTS £500–£5,000.
SAMPLE GRANTS St Mary RC, Harvington (£2,500); St Leonard, Newland (£5,000); St Kenelem, Clifton-upon-Teme (£5,800), St John the Baptist, Wickhamford (£3,000); St Peter, Astley (£3,500); Bewdley Methodist (£2,300); Holy Trinity, Malvern (£5,000); St Cassian, Chaddesley Corbett (£3,000); St John URC, Stourbridge (£1,200); St Michael, Dines Green (£2,000).
FINANCES *Year* 2010 *Income* £41,888 *Grants* £41,205 *Assets* £86,641
TRUSTEES Tim Bridges – Chairman; John Davies; Jean Crabbe; John Bailey; John Colley; Sam Driver White; Andrew Grant; Annette Leech; Richard Slawson; Michael Thomas.
HOW TO APPLY Requests for grants should be discussed with the secretary who will advise as to whether the project meets the criteria. An application form will then be sent. Decisions on grants are made at the trust's quarterly meetings and following a visit by a trustee.
WHO TO APPLY TO John Davies, Secretary, Yarrington's, Alfrick, Worcestershire WR6 5EX *Tel* 01886 884336 *email* flora.donald@virgin.net *Website* www.worcestershirechurches.blogspot.com

■ The Fred and Della Worms Charitable Trust

CC NO 200036 **ESTABLISHED** 1961
WHERE FUNDING CAN BE GIVEN UK.
WHO CAN BENEFIT Jewish organisations, education and the arts.
WHAT IS FUNDED General charitable purposes, but in practice almost all of the money goes to Jewish organisations.
WHAT IS NOT FUNDED No grants to individuals.
TYPE OF GRANT One-off grants.
SAMPLE GRANTS British Friends of Jerusalem Foundation (£50,000); UJIA (£10,000); Maccabi GB (£5,000); JNF Charitable Trust and Highgate Synagogue (£1,000).
FINANCES *Year* 2009–10 *Income* £81,044 *Grants* £78,693 *Assets* £1,923,909
TRUSTEES Mrs D Worms; M D Paisner; F S Worms; A D Harverd.
OTHER INFORMATION No grants to individuals.
HOW TO APPLY The trust has previously stated that its funds were fully committed.
WHO TO APPLY TO The Trustees, 35 King David Gardens, 27 King David Street, Jerusalem, 94101, Israel *Tel* 00 972 2 6246 993 *email* fredsimonworms@gmail.com

■ The Wragge and Co. Charitable Trust

CC NO 803009 **ESTABLISHED** 1990
WHERE FUNDING CAN BE GIVEN Mainly West Midlands.
WHO CAN BENEFIT Local and national charities operating in the area.
WHAT IS FUNDED General charitable purposes, with an interest in health.
WHAT IS NOT FUNDED No grants to individuals or to organisations which are not charities.
RANGE OF GRANTS Generally £100/£500 each.
SAMPLE GRANTS Beneficiaries included: KES Foundation (£8,800); British Heart Foundation (£2,700); Cure Leukaemia (£1,000); DebRA (£500); Cancer Research UK (£300); Help for Heroes (£150) and Joshua Orphan Care Trust (£150).
FINANCES Year 2009–10 Income £25,871 Grants £26,638 Assets £15,894
TRUSTEES Jeremy Q S Poole; Philip Clissitt; Lee Nuttall.
HOW TO APPLY In writing to the correspondent with a copy of the most recent accounts.
WHO TO APPLY TO Lee Nuttall, Trustee, Wragge and Co., 55 Colmore Row, Birmingham B3 2AS *Tel* 0121 233 1000 *Fax* 0870 904 1099

■ The Diana Edgson Wright Charitable Trust

CC NO 327737 **ESTABLISHED** 1987
WHERE FUNDING CAN BE GIVEN UK with some preference for Kent.
WHO CAN BENEFIT Registered charities.
WHAT IS FUNDED General charitable purposes and animal conservation and social welfare causes.
SAMPLE GRANTS Barbourne Church of England School (£5,000); Gurkha Welfare Trust (£3,000); Chernobyl Children's Lifeline (£2,000); Smeeth Parish Club (£1,500); Caledott Foundation, the Donkey Sanctuary and Kent Air Ambulance (£1,000 each); Camphill Family, Folkestone Rainbow Trust, Kent Minds and Mouth and Foot Painting Artists (£500 each).
FINANCES Year 2009 Income £45,946 Grants £54,300 Assets £1,264,050
TRUSTEES R H V Moorhead; P Edgson Wright; H C D Moorhead.
HOW TO APPLY In writing to the correspondent.
WHO TO APPLY TO R H V Moorhead, Trustee, c/o 2 Stade Street, Hythe, Kent CT21 6BD

■ The Matthews Wrightson Charity Trust

CC NO 262109 **ESTABLISHED** 1970
WHERE FUNDING CAN BE GIVEN UK and some overseas.
WHO CAN BENEFIT Smaller charities and individuals.
WHAT IS FUNDED General charitable purposes. The trustees favour smaller charitable projects seeking to raise under £25,000. Grants are given in the following categories 'youth', 'third world', 'disabled', 'Christian causes', 'rehabilitation', 'arts', 'poor and homeless', 'medical' and 'elderly'. In 2008 youth causes received significant support (£43,000 in 52 grants).
WHAT IS NOT FUNDED 'The trustees would not normally support the maintenance of the fabric of churches, schools and village halls, and do not make donations to animal charities.'

TYPE OF GRANT One-off cash grants, on annual basis. Core costs are preferred to projects.
RANGE OF GRANTS The standard 'unit' donation for 2008 was £500, with a few larger grants made to regular beneficiaries.
SAMPLE GRANTS Previously: Tools for Self-Reliance (£2,400); and the Butler Trust, Childhood First, the Daneford Trust, DEMAND, Live Music Now! New Bridge and Practical Action (£1,200 each). Most other donations, with a few exceptions, were for £400 or £500 each.
FINANCES Year 2009–10 Income £63,779 Grants £72,300 Assets £1,456,655
TRUSTEES Priscilla W Wrightson; Robert Partridge; Guy D G Wrightson; Isabelle S White; Maria de Broe Ferguson.
OTHER INFORMATION In addition to donations to charitable bodies, the trust also gives to trainee doctors for medical elective expenses and to individuals taking 'gaps' abroad for personal development. Awards totalling £10,000 were also made to support students at the Royal College of Art who find their grants and other income inadequate (hardship grants), and awards totalling £5,000 were made to students to further ideas for UK industrial production (starting your own business awards).
HOW TO APPLY In writing to the correspondent including a set of accounts. Applications received are considered by the trustees on a monthly basis. Applicants who wish to be advised of the outcome of their application must include an sae. Successful applicants are advised of the trustees' decision at the earliest opportunity.
WHO TO APPLY TO Jon Mills, Secretary and Administrator, The Old School House, Church Lane, Easton, Hampshire SO21 1 EH *Tel* 0845 241 2574

■ Miss E B Wrightson's Charitable Settlement

CC NO 1002147 **ESTABLISHED** 1990
WHERE FUNDING CAN BE GIVEN UK.
WHO CAN BENEFIT Organisations and individual young people with musical talent.
WHAT IS FUNDED The trust objects make provision for general charitable purposes including inshore rescue services; multiple sclerosis causes but particularly young people with musical talent. It primarily supports individuals, mostly between the ages 8–18 years of age, but applications can also be made by groups and charities seeking funding for the advancement of music education and recreational charitable objects and circumstances related to financial hardship and social deprivation receive preferential consideration.
WHAT IS NOT FUNDED No school fees, but can assist with other music education related activities. Will not usually offer more than three grants to one individual.
TYPE OF GRANT One off, recurring.
FINANCES Year 2009–10 Income £24,139 Grants £56,000
TRUSTEES Mr T Callard; Mrs E Clarke; P Dorking.
HOW TO APPLY In writing to the correspondent. Applicants are asked to provide the following: Completed application form; financial hardship supporting documentation; references (two); a brief musical CV for those over 12; reasons for applying; details of applications to other grant giving bodies.
Relevant forms and application guidance are available from the trust website. Trustees meet

regularly to consider applications and 'all properly completed applications are acknowledged'. Guidelines are provided by the trust for applications by individuals, but not organisations.

WHO TO APPLY TO Mrs N Hickman, Swangles Farm, Cold Christmas Lane, Thundridge, Ware SG12 7SP *email* info@wrightsontrust.co.uk *Website* www.wrightsontrust.co.uk

■ The Joan Wyatt Charitable Trust

CC NO 1136314   **ESTABLISHED** 2010
WHERE FUNDING CAN BE GIVEN Worldwide.
WHO CAN BENEFIT Registered charities.
WHAT IS FUNDED General charitable purposes.
TRUSTEES NatWest Trust Services.
HOW TO APPLY In writing to the correspondent.
WHO TO APPLY TO NatWest Trust Services, 5th Floor, Trinity Quay 2, Avon Street, Bristol BS2 0PT *Tel* 0117 940 3283

■ Wychdale Ltd

CC NO 267447   **ESTABLISHED** 1974
WHERE FUNDING CAN BE GIVEN UK and abroad.
WHO CAN BENEFIT Jewish people.
WHAT IS FUNDED Jewish educational institutions.
WHAT IS NOT FUNDED Non-Jewish organisations are not supported.
SAMPLE GRANTS Dajtrain Ltd (£28,000); United Ttalmudical Associates (£24,000); the Society of Friends of the Torah (£18,000); Chevras Mo'oz Ladol (£16,000); and Tomchei Sharei Zion (£10,000).
FINANCES *Year* 2009–10 *Income* £217,986 *Grants* £430,179 *Assets* £1,518,117
TRUSTEES C D Schlaff; J Schlaff; Mrs Z Schlaff.
HOW TO APPLY In writing to the correspondent.
WHO TO APPLY TO The Secretary, 89 Darenth Road, London N16 6EB

■ Wychville Ltd

CC NO 267584   **ESTABLISHED** 1973
WHERE FUNDING CAN BE GIVEN UK.
WHO CAN BENEFIT Organisations benefiting Jewish people.
WHAT IS FUNDED Jewish organisations and general charitable purposes.
FINANCES *Year* 2009–10 *Income* £622,007 *Grants* £600,000 *Assets* £105,310
TRUSTEES B Englander, Chair; Mrs S Englander; E Englander; Mrs B R Englander.
OTHER INFORMATION No list of grant beneficiaries was available.
HOW TO APPLY In writing to the correspondent.
WHO TO APPLY TO Mrs S Englander, Secretary, 44 Leweston Place, London N16 6RH

■ The Wyndham Charitable Trust

CC NO 259313   **ESTABLISHED** 1969
WHERE FUNDING CAN BE GIVEN UK and developing countries.
WHO CAN BENEFIT Charitable organisations.
WHAT IS FUNDED General charitable purposes.
WHAT IS NOT FUNDED No grants to organisations not known to the trustees, or to any individuals.
RANGE OF GRANTS Up to £10,500.
SAMPLE GRANTS Larger grants included those to: Anti-Slavery International (£10,500); The Royal College of Surgeons of England (£2,200); and Institute of cancer research (£1,200).

Other beneficiaries receiving less than £1,000 each included: Interact Worldwide; LEPRA; Multiple Sclerosis Society; Research into Ageing; Hope UK; New Forest Citizens Advice Bureau; Church Mission Society and Help for Heroes.
FINANCES *Income* £25,360 *Grants* £44,728
TRUSTEES John Gaselee; Juliet Gaselee; David John Gaselee and Sarah Persaphone Gaselee.
OTHER INFORMATION During the year, two new trustees were appointed 'to provide additional strength and continuity'.
HOW TO APPLY In writing to the correspondent. The trust stated that unsolicited applications are unlikely to be supported and they do not encourage requests.
WHO TO APPLY TO John Gaselee, Trustee, J Gaselee Esq, 34a Westfield Road, Lymington, Hampshire SO41 3QA *email* wyndham_ct@yahoo.co.uk *Website* www.wyndham-ct.org

■ The Wyseliot Charitable Trust

CC NO 257219   **ESTABLISHED** 1968
WHERE FUNDING CAN BE GIVEN UK.
WHO CAN BENEFIT Registered charities only.
WHAT IS FUNDED Medical, especially cancer research and care; welfare; arts organisations, including music, visual arts and literature.
WHAT IS NOT FUNDED Local charities are not supported. No support for individuals; grants are only made to registered charities.
RANGE OF GRANTS Up to £5,000.
SAMPLE GRANTS Alzheimer's Trust, Cystic Fibrosis Trust, Royal Marsden Cancer Fund, Mind, Royal college of Music, Trinity Hospice, Cancer Relief Macmillan Fund and St Mungo's Trust (£5,000 each); Notting Hill Foundation (£4,000); and Runnymede Trust (£2,000).
FINANCES *Year* 2009–10 *Income* £95,708 *Grants* £98,000 *Assets* £1,565,620
TRUSTEES Jonathan Rose; Emma Rose; Adam Raphael.
HOW TO APPLY In writing to the correspondent; however, note that the trust states that the same charities are supported each year, with perhaps one or two changes. It is unlikely new charities sending circular appeals will be supported and large UK charities are generally not supported.
WHO TO APPLY TO J H Rose, Trustee, 17 Chelsea Square, London SW3 6LF

■ The Xerox (UK) Trust

CC NO 284698   **ESTABLISHED** 1982

WHERE FUNDING CAN BE GIVEN UK.

WHO CAN BENEFIT Usually local or mid-sized organisations benefiting children, young adults, at risk groups, and people who are disabled, disadvantaged by poverty or socially isolated.

WHAT IS FUNDED The advancement of equality of opportunity, working with people who are disabled, disadvantaged or terminally ill; and young people.

WHAT IS NOT FUNDED No grants to individuals, religious or political organisations or national bodies.

TYPE OF GRANT One-off grants.

RANGE OF GRANTS £200–£8,000.

SAMPLE GRANTS Previous beneficiaries have included: Beating Bowel Cancer (£8,000); Ataxia-Telangiectasie Society and Disabled Online (£5,000 each); Hemel Hempstead Explorer Scouts and the Elizabeth Foundation (£1,000 each); Deafblind UK (£500); and MacMillan Cancer Support (£200).

FINANCES *Year* 2010 *Income* £3 *Grants* £24,000

TRUSTEES F J Mooney; J Edwards; J Hopwood.

HOW TO APPLY In writing to the correspondent, preferably supported by a Xerox employee. Applications are considered in April and October, for payment in June and December respectively.

WHO TO APPLY TO Cheryl Walsh, Trust Administrator, Xerox Ltd, Bridge House, Oxford Road, Uxbridge UB8 1HS *Tel* 01895 251133

■ Yankov Charitable Trust

CC NO 1106703   **ESTABLISHED** 2004
WHERE FUNDING CAN BE GIVEN Worldwide.
WHO CAN BENEFIT Jewish organisations.
WHAT IS FUNDED 'The advancement of the Jewish religion and culture among the Jewish community throughout the world.'
SAMPLE GRANTS Previous grant beneficiaries include: European Yarchei Kalloh (£53,000); Keren Machzikei Torah (£23,000); Kollel Tiferes Chaim (£21,000); Agudas Israel Housing Association (£12,000); Ponovez Hachnosos Kalloh (£7,600); Freiman Appeal (£7,200); Beth Jacob Grammar School (£4,000); British Friends of Tiferes Chaim (£3,000); Yeshiva Tzemach Yisroel (£2,000); British Friends of Rinat Ahsron (£1,500); and Yeshivat Givat Shaul (£1,000).
FINANCES *Year* 2009–10 *Income* £249,560 *Grants* £121,079 *Assets* £116,358
TRUSTEES J Schonberg; Mrs B S Schonberg.
HOW TO APPLY In writing to the correspondent.
WHO TO APPLY TO The Trustees, 40 Wellington Avenue, London N15 6AS *Tel* 020 3014 3974

■ The Yapp Charitable Trust

CC NO 1076803   **ESTABLISHED** 1999
WHERE FUNDING CAN BE GIVEN England and Wales.
WHO CAN BENEFIT It is the trustees' policy to focus their support on smaller charities (local rather than UK), and to offer grants only in situations where a small grant will make a significant difference. The trust therefore only considers applications from charities whose normal turnover is less than £60,000 in the year of application. Grants are only made to applicants who have charitable status. 'We concentrate on sustaining existing work rather than funding new work because many funders prefer new projects.'
WHAT IS FUNDED Older people; children and young people aged 5–25; people with disabilities or mental health problems; moral welfare, e.g. people trying to overcome life-limiting problems such as addiction, relationship difficulties, abuse or a history of offending; education and learning (including lifelong learning); and scientific or medical research. The trust gives priority to work that is unattractive to the general public or unpopular with other funders, particularly when it helps improve the lives of marginalised, disadvantaged or isolated people. Within these areas the trust gives preference to charities that can demonstrate the effective use of volunteers. Grant-making policies are kept under review – current priorities and exclusions are publicised on the trust's website.
WHAT IS NOT FUNDED 'We do not accept applications from: (i) Scotland and Northern Ireland – your charity must work in England or Wales; (ii) charities whose total annual expenditure is more than £60,000; (iii) charities that are not registered with the Charity Commission in England and Wales – you must have your own charity number or be excepted from registration (Industrial and Provident Societies and Community Interest Companies are not eligible to apply); (iv) branches of national charities – you must have your own charity number, not a shared national registration; (v) new organisations – you must have been operating as a fully constituted charity for at least 3 years, even though you may have registered as a charity more recently. We do not make grants for: (i) new work – we provide continuation funding to sustain existing work that has been happening for at least a year (we do not offer grants to launch new or additional activities nor to put on special events); (ii) we do not offer funding to create new paid posts even if the work is now being done by volunteers; (iii) capital-type expenditure – equipment, buildings, renovations, furnishings, minibuses. (iv) work with under-5s; (v) childcare; (vi) holidays and holiday centres; (vii) core funding of general community organisations such as community associations, community centres and general advice services, because some of their work is outside our charitable objects: (viii) bereavement support: (ix) debt advice; (x) community safety initiatives; (xi) charities raising money to give to another organisation, such as schools, hospitals or other voluntary groups (xii) individuals – including charities raising funds to purchase equipment for or make grants to individuals.'
TYPE OF GRANT Running costs and salaries.
RANGE OF GRANTS Grants are normally for a maximum of £3,000 per year. Most grants are for more than one year because priority is given to ongoing needs.
SAMPLE GRANTS Working together (£9,000); Disability Advice Service (East Suffolk) (£7,500); Hillingdon Asian Women Group (£6,000); Community Transport Helpline (£4,500); Carrs Lane Counselling Centre (£4,000) and Four Seasons Activity Group (£3,000).
FINANCES *Year* 2009–10 *Income* £207,412 *Grants* £293,030 *Assets* £5,256,038
TRUSTEES David Aeron-Thomas; Revd Timothy C Brooke; Annette Figueiredo; Ron Lis; Stephanie Willats.
OTHER INFORMATION The Yapp Welfare Trust (two-thirds share) and The Yapp Education and Research Trust (one-third share) merged in September 1999 to become The Yapp Charitable Trust.
HOW TO APPLY 'We have a simple application form which we ask you to send in by post, together with a copy of your most recent annual report and accounts and any other information you wish to send. Applications are processed continuously. When we receive your application we will be in touch, usually within two weeks: to ask for more information; or to tell you the application will be going forward to the next stage of assessment and give an idea of when you can expect a decision; or to let you know we can't help. The time it takes to process an application and make a grant is usually between two months and six months. We always write to let you know the decision. We will accept an application only once each year and you can have only one grant at a time from us. Current grant-holders may make a new application when their grant is coming to an end. If we refused your last application you must wait a year before applying again. The application form and guidelines can be downloaded in Word or PDF format from the trust's website. Alternatively they can be obtained from the trust's administrator.'

WHO TO APPLY TO Joanne Anderson, Administrator, 8 Leyburn Close, Ouston, Chester le Street DH2 1TD *Tel* 0191 492 2118 *email* info@yappcharitabletrust.org.uk *Website* www.yappcharitabletrust.org.uk

---

■ The Yardley Great Trust

CC NO 216082   **ESTABLISHED** 1355

WHERE FUNDING CAN BE GIVEN The ancient parish of Yardley now part of the County of West Midlands. This includes the wards of Yardley, Acocks Green, Fox Hollies, Billesley, Hall Green and parts of the wards of Hodge Hill, Shard End, Sheldon, Small Heath, Sparkhill, Moseley, Stechford, Sparkbrook and Brandwood. (A map is available on request.).

WHO CAN BENEFIT Individuals and organisations benefiting people of all ages in the ancient parish of Yardley in Birmingham.

WHAT IS FUNDED Individuals in need, hardship or distress. Projects which benefit the community, particularly charities working in the fields of support for voluntary and community organisations, community centres and village halls, community transport, day centres, holidays and outings, meals provision and play schemes.

TYPE OF GRANT Usually one-off. Buildings, capital, feasibility studies, project and start-up costs funded for one year or less will be considered.

RANGE OF GRANTS £250–£7,500.

SAMPLE GRANTS Birmingham and Solihull Women's Aid (£7,500); St Richard's Community Centre (£5,000); Greswold House £2,000); St Michaels Meals on Wheels & Day Centre, Ninestiles School/Westmidlands Police (1,500 each); Stay (£1,000); and Church of Ascension (£600).

FINANCES *Year* 2010 *Income* £1,627,262 *Grants* £54,931 *Assets* £6,301,547

TRUSTEES Mrs I Aylin, Chair; Revd A Bullock; Mrs J Hayes; Mrs J Holt; Cllr Mrs B Jackson; C James; Revd J Ray; Revd J Richards; K Rollins; Revd J Self; Revd D Senior; M Cox; W Sands; A Veitch; R Jones.

OTHER INFORMATION In 2010 grants were also made to individuals of less than £500 each amounting to £24,000. £2,400 was also distributed to residents as Christmas monies.

HOW TO APPLY On a form available from the correspondent. Applications from individuals should be via a third party. Applications are considered on the second Thursday of each month.

WHO TO APPLY TO Mrs K L Grice, Clerk to the Trustees, Old Brookside, Yardley Fields Road, Stechford, Birmingham B33 8QL *Tel* 0121 784 7889 *Fax* 0121 785 1386 *email* enquiries@ygtrust.org.uk *Website* www.yardley-great-trust.org.uk

---

■ The Dennis Alan Yardy Charitable Trust

CC NO 1039719   **ESTABLISHED** 1993

WHERE FUNDING CAN BE GIVEN Overseas and UK with a preference for the East Midlands.

WHO CAN BENEFIT Major UK and international charities.

WHAT IS FUNDED General charitable purposes.

WHAT IS NOT FUNDED No grants to individuals or non-registered charities.

FINANCES *Year* 2009–10 *Income* £23,996 *Grants* £27,750 *Assets* £511,968

TRUSTEES Dennis Alan Yardy, Chair; Mrs Christine Anne Yardy; Jeffrey Creek; Mrs Joanne Stoney.

OTHER INFORMATION A grants list was not included in the latest accounts.

HOW TO APPLY In writing to the correspondent.

WHO TO APPLY TO The Secretary, PO Box 5039, Spratton, Northampton NN6 8YH

■ The W Wing Yip and Brothers Foundation

CC NO 326999   **ESTABLISHED** 1986

WHERE FUNDING CAN BE GIVEN Birmingham, Manchester, Croydon and Cricklewood.

WHO CAN BENEFIT Chinese organisations benefiting children, young adults, students and people disadvantaged by poverty.

WHAT IS FUNDED Chinese organisations especially those concerned with education, relief of poverty, Chinese students, and education of Chinese children living in the above stated areas.

TYPE OF GRANT One-off, project and start-up costs. Funding for up to two years will be considered.

RANGE OF GRANTS Up to £100,000.

SAMPLE GRANTS Beneficiaries included: Bursaries to 76 students (£100,000); Churchill College Cambridge (£25,000); Meridan Chinese Studies (£2,000) and Chinese Educational Cultural Community Centre (£3,000).

FINANCES *Year* 2009–10 *Income* £202,580 *Grants* £152,400 *Assets* £1,304,597

TRUSTEES Robert A Brittain; Ms Jenny Loynton; Git Ying Yap; Hon Yuen Yap; Lee Sing Yap; Brian J Win Yip; Woon Wing Yip.

HOW TO APPLY In writing to the correspondent.

WHO TO APPLY TO Robert A Brittain, Trustee, MR Robert Alan Brittain, W Wing Yip PLC, The Wing Yip Centre, 375 Nechells Park Road, Nechells, Birmingham *Tel* 0121 327 6618 *Fax* 0121 327 6612

■ The York Children's Trust

CC NO 222279   **ESTABLISHED** 1976

WHERE FUNDING CAN BE GIVEN Within 20 miles of York City.

WHO CAN BENEFIT Individuals; group-based organisations; local groups and schools benefiting people under 25 years of age, parents and children; one-parent families; at risk groups; people with disabilities; people disadvantaged by poverty, and people fostering talents in music, drama and athletic activities.

WHAT IS FUNDED Voluntary groups helping in the care and development of young people through arts, culture and recreation, healthcare, education and community services; support of individuals with special needs.

WHAT IS NOT FUNDED The trust will not normally give grants for private education fees. Exceptions may be made where unforeseen circumstances, such as the death of a parent, would prevent a child completing the last year of a critical stage of education such as A-levels.

RANGE OF GRANTS £800–£8,000.

SAMPLE GRANTS City of York Council (£8,000); CFS York (£5,000); Calvert Carpets (£4,000); Heworth Green Nursery (£3,000); York City Knights Foundation, Child Development Centre (£2,000 each); Home Start York (£1,500); Market Weighton Scout & Guide HQ, LIPA and Peter Pan Nursery (£1,000 each).

FINANCES *Year* 2010 *Income* £78,560 *Grants* £75,978 *Assets* £2,085,620

TRUSTEES Colin Stroud; Mark Sessions; Lenore J Hill; Keith Hayton; Peter Watson; William Miers; Lynn Wagstaff; Alan D Ward; Anne Kelly; Percy Roberts; Rosalind F Fitter; Julie A Simpson; Dawn M Moores; Kathy Pickard; Kitty Lamb.

OTHER INFORMATION In addition, £40,000 was given in grants to 137 individuals.

HOW TO APPLY In writing to the correspondent.

WHO TO APPLY TO Margaret Brien, Secretary, 29 Whinney Lane, Harrogate, North Yorkshire HG2 9LS *Tel* 01423 524765 *email* yorkchildrenstrust@hotmail.co.uk

■ Yorkshire Agricultural Society

CC NO 513238   ESTABLISHED 1837

WHERE FUNDING CAN BE GIVEN Yorkshire and Humbershire; occasionally extending into Durham, Northumberland and the former county of Cleveland.

WHO CAN BENEFIT Primarily local activities and organisations, particularly those in farming and related industries, and those living in rural areas. Priority is given to charities in Yorkshire and former Cleveland, with some activities extending into Durham and Northumberland.

WHAT IS FUNDED (a) Promotion of agriculture and allied industries, related research and education. (b) Protection and safeguarding of the environment. (c) Holding of an annual agricultural show. (d) Appropriate charitable purposes. Environmental projects normally require relevance to agriculture to attract support. The trust will consider giving support to religious umbrella bodies, schools and colleges, and rural crime prevention schemes, all within the context of farming and the rural economy.

WHAT IS NOT FUNDED No support to students. Overseas projects are seldom supported.

TYPE OF GRANT Most usually once only or starter/pump priming finance. Buildings, capital, core costs, feasibility studies, projects, research, running costs, recurring costs and salaries will be considered. Funding may be given for up to three years.

RANGE OF GRANTS £200–£10,000, typical grant under £1,000.

SAMPLE GRANTS Beneficiaries included: Leeds University (£14,000); Nuffield Scholarship and East Yorkshire Young Farmers (£7,500); York University (£4,000) and National Pony Society (£1,000).

FINANCES *Year* 2009–10 *Income* £7,458,761 *Grants* £48,776 *Assets* £24,110,400

TRUSTEES Mrs C Bromet; R W Twiddle; W M Cowling; J J E Brennan; S F O Theakston; J D M Stoddart-Scott; G C N Lane-Fox.

PUBLICATIONS Quarterly newsletter.

OTHER INFORMATION No grants were made to individuals during the year.

HOW TO APPLY In writing to the correspondent, to be considered quarterly. Applications should include accounts, proposed budget, details of confirmed and anticipated funding and ongoing management and costs.

WHO TO APPLY TO N Pulling, Chief Executive, Regional Agricultural Centre, Great Yorkshire Showground, Railway Road, Harrogate HG2 8NZ *Tel* 01423 541000 *Fax* 01423 541414 *email* info@yas.co.uk *Website* www.yas.co.uk

■ Yorkshire Building Society Charitable Foundation

CC NO 1069082   ESTABLISHED 1998

WHERE FUNDING CAN BE GIVEN UK, with a preference for grant making in branch localities.

WHO CAN BENEFIT Charitable organisations/good causes meeting foundation criteria.

WHAT IS FUNDED General charitable purposes/specific items to maximum donation of £2,000.

WHAT IS NOT FUNDED 'We do not support any activity which is not carried out by a registered charity or which does not otherwise count as being a good cause. Additionally, there may be projects or activities that could be considered as registered charities or good causes but which do not fall within our priorities or meet other criteria. Examples of these are: applications for general ongoing funding/running costs; requests for administration costs, research funds, salaries and sponsorship of events; requests for any administration equipment such as telephones, security systems or computers, for a charity's own use; causes serving only a specific sector of the community selected on the basis of ethnic, racial or religious grounds; overseas travel, expeditions or educational expenses, including causes that would otherwise qualify for support but require funds for activities outside the UK; applications from individuals seeking assistance; support of political activities or the advancement of religion; support of activities in, or equipment for, mainstream schools and other local/government funded bodies; support for those who are not thought to be vulnerable e.g., Scouts/Girl Guides (unless for special needs groups); provision of mainstream sports clubs (other than those specifically targeted at our priority cases); any organisation considered to be illegal or which may act illegally, or where funds are raised from, or for immoral purposes; any fundraising or activity which would, or could benefit the organisers directly.'

TYPE OF GRANT Money for specific items.

RANGE OF GRANTS Usually around £2,000 but can be up to £108,000.

SAMPLE GRANTS British Heart Foundation (£108,000); St Ann's Hospice (£7,500); Ashgate Hospice (£3,500); Samaritans of Dumfermline (£2,000); Albrighton Trust (£1,900); Bay Search & Rescue (£1, 800) and Bowland Pennine Mountain Rescue Team (£1,600).

FINANCES *Year* 2009–10 *Income* £418,306 *Grants* £452,510 *Assets* £295,924

TRUSTEES Christopher J Faulkner; Sarah Wildon; Christopher Parrish; Andy Caton.

OTHER INFORMATION There were a further 2382 grants given throughout the year totalling £252,000.

HOW TO APPLY Please contact the branch closest to you who will be able to help with an initial assessment of your application. Alternatively, if there isn't a local branch near you, details can be sent direct to head office for consideration. Application forms can be downloaded from the society's website.

WHO TO APPLY TO Mrs Ann Fitzpatrick, Yorkshire Building Society, Yorkshire House, Yorkshire Drive, Bradford, West Yorkshire *Tel* 01274 472676 *Fax* 01274 472251 *email* charitable@ybs.co.uk *Website* www.ybs.co.uk/cf

■ The South Yorkshire Community Foundation

CC NO 517714   **ESTABLISHED** 1986

WHERE FUNDING CAN BE GIVEN South Yorkshire wide, with specific reference to Barnsley, Doncaster, Rotherham, Sheffield.

WHO CAN BENEFIT Community and voluntary organisations benefiting people disadvantaged by poverty children and young people.

WHAT IS FUNDED General charitable purposes, particularly social welfare.

WHAT IS NOT FUNDED Groups that have substantial unrestricted funds, national charities, activities promoting political or religious beliefs or where people are excluded on political or religious grounds, statutory bodies e.g. schools, local councils, colleges, projects outside of South Yorkshire, endowments, small contributions to large projects, projects for personal profit, minibuses or other vehicle purchases, projects that have already happened, animals, sponsorship and fundraising events.

TYPE OF GRANT The main grants programme is for amounts under £1,000. Capital and revenue costs. South Yorkshire Key Fund grants are for similar purposes for larger amounts.

RANGE OF GRANTS Generally up to £10,000.

SAMPLE GRANTS A wide range of organisations across all of the foundation's areas of operation were supported under various programmes, some of which may no longer be running. Many organisations received grants from more than one fund.

FINANCES *Year* 2009–10 *Income* £3,815,443 *Grants* £1,774,730 *Assets* £4,144,553

TRUSTEES Jonathan Hunt, Chair; David Moody; Sir Hugh Neill; Peter W Lee; Martin P W Lee; Peter Hollis; Isadora Aiken; Frank Carter; Jackie Drayton; Galen Ives; Christopher Jewitt; Michael Mallett; Sue Scholey; Maureen Shah; Allan Sherriff; Lady R Sykes; R J Giles Bloomer; Timothy M Greenacre; Allan Jackson; Jane Kemp; Jane Marshall.

HOW TO APPLY Applications are made by completing a simple form, available for download from the foundation's website.

WHO TO APPLY TO Sandra Mullins, Operations Manager, Unit 3 - G1 Building, 6 Leeds Road, Attercliffe, Sheffield S9 3TY   *Tel* 0114 242 4294   *Fax* 0114 242 4605   *email* grants@sycf.org.uk   *Website* www.sycf.org.uk

■ The Yorkshire Dales Millennium Trust

CC NO 1061687   **ESTABLISHED** 1996

WHERE FUNDING CAN BE GIVEN The Yorkshire Dales.

WHO CAN BENEFIT Voluntary organisations, community groups, farmers and other individuals, Yorkshire Dales National Park Authority, estates, National Trust, parish councils, district councils and English Nature.

WHAT IS FUNDED The conservation and regeneration of the natural and built heritage and community life of the Yorkshire Dales, for example, planting new and restoring old woods, the restoration of dry stone walls and field barns, conservation of historical features and community projects.

FINANCES *Year* 2009–10 *Income* £1,777,960 *Grants* £1,624,642 *Assets* £614,617

TRUSTEES Joseph Pearlman; Carl Lis; Colin Speakman; Dorothy Fairburn; Dorothy Fairburn; Hazel Cambers; David Sanders Rees-Jones; Jane Roberts; Peter Charlesworth; Stephen Macare; David Joy; Thomas Wheelwright;

Margaret Billing; Michael Ackrel; Andrew Campbell; David Shaw; Wendy Hull; Karen Cowley.

HOW TO APPLY In writing to the correspondent.

WHO TO APPLY TO Sue Musgrave, Finance & Administration Manager, The Old Post Office, Main Street, Clapham, Lancaster LA2 8DP   *Tel* 01524 251002   *Fax* 01524 251150   *email* info@ydmt.org   *Website* www.ydmt.org

■ The Yorkshire Historic Churches Trust

CC NO 700639   **ESTABLISHED** 1988

WHERE FUNDING CAN BE GIVEN Yorkshire (the historic county of Yorkshire before local government reorganisation in 1974).

WHO CAN BENEFIT All Christian churches.

WHAT IS FUNDED The repair, restoration, preservation and maintenance of churches in the area stated above.

WHAT IS NOT FUNDED No grants for the reordering of churches or any other new work including provision of disabled facilities.

TYPE OF GRANT Capital building grants. Funding of up to three years will be considered.

RANGE OF GRANTS £250–£5,000.

SAMPLE GRANTS St Mary – Watton (£4,500); St John the Baptist – Royston (£3,000); St Peter & St Paul – Leyburn (£2,000); Gracious Street Methodist – Knaresborough – (£1,000); St Mary – Hutton Magna (£500) and St Mary – Masham (£250).

FINANCES *Year* 2010 *Income* £109,696 *Grants* £85,500 *Assets* £877,952

TRUSTEES G Binfield; R J Carr-Archer; The Lord Crathorne; M Warburton; W Legard; J G H Mackrell; D Quick; R Wardroper; B Smith; W J A Smith; Revd C Witton; Miss S Weston; P M Johnston; Ms C Otton-Goulder; Revd A Holmes; A P Hesselwood; Dr J Whiston.

HOW TO APPLY Application forms and guidelines are available from the Trust's website.

WHO TO APPLY TO Mrs J V Fotheringham, c/o Ferrey and Mennim, 48 Goodramgate, York YO1 7LF   *Tel* 01904 620103   *Fax* 01904 626983   *email* YHCT@ferreyandmennim.co.uk   *Website* www.yhct.org.uk

■ The John Young Charitable Settlement

CC NO 283254   **ESTABLISHED** 1981

WHERE FUNDING CAN BE GIVEN UK and overseas.

WHO CAN BENEFIT Charitable organisations.

WHAT IS FUNDED General charitable purposes.

RANGE OF GRANTS £120–£10,000.

SAMPLE GRANTS Previously: Caius House (£13,000); the Boulase Smart, Médecins du Monde, Pancreatic Cancer Research Fund, RSBP and St Barnabas Hospice Trust (£5,000 each); Chichester Harbour Trust (£2,000); and Action Aid (£250).

FINANCES *Year* 2009–10 *Income* £0 *Grants* £47,072

TRUSTEES J M Young; D P H Burgess.

HOW TO APPLY In writing to the correspondent.

WHO TO APPLY TO Kenneth Hawkins, H W Lee Associates, New Derwent House, 69/73 Theobalds Road, London WC1X 8TA   *Tel* 020 7025 4600

Think carefully about every application. Is it justified?

1001

■ The William Allen Young Charitable Trust

CC NO 283102   **ESTABLISHED** 1978
WHERE FUNDING CAN BE GIVEN UK, with a preference for South London.
WHO CAN BENEFIT Registered charities.
WHAT IS FUNDED General charitable purposes, with a preference for health and social welfare.
SAMPLE GRANTS Anti Slavery International, the British Consular Age Concern Partnership Project and Gonville and Caius College, Cambridge (£20,000 each); British Benevolent Fund of Madrid and the Cardinal Hume Centre (£10,000 each); Somerset Otter Group (£8,000); Wimbledon Cricket Club (£5,000).
FINANCES *Year* 2009–10 *Income* £420,086 *Grants* £469,996 *Assets* £16,777,638
TRUSTEES T C Young; J G A Young; T F B Young.
HOW TO APPLY The trust has stressed that all funds are committed and consequently unsolicited applications will not be supported.
WHO TO APPLY TO Torquil Sligo-Young, Young & Co.'s Brewery PLC, Riverside House, 26 Osiers Road, London SW18 1NH *Tel* 020 8875 7000

■ The John K Young Endowment Fund

SC NO SC002264   **ESTABLISHED** 1992
WHERE FUNDING CAN BE GIVEN Edinburgh.
WHO CAN BENEFIT Registered charities.
WHAT IS FUNDED Grants are given to support medical and surgical research and research in chemistry as an aid to UK industry. Also to fund charities which are concerned with the physical wellbeing of the youth of Edinburgh or with restoring people who are sick to health.
WHAT IS NOT FUNDED No grants to individuals or non-registered charities.
TYPE OF GRANT One-off grants are awarded. Funding is available for up to one year.
RANGE OF GRANTS £500–£2,000.
SAMPLE GRANTS Previous beneficiaries have included: Alzheimer's Scotland, Kidney Kids Scotland and Tommy's (£2,000 each); Alzheimer's Research Trust, British Institute for Brian Injured Children, Capability Scotland, Maggie's Cancer Caring Centres and Lee Smith Foundation (£1,000 each); Bethany Christian Trust and Fairbridge in Scotland (£1,500 each); and Guide Dogs for the Blind Association, PBC Foundation and Youth Scotland (£500 each).
FINANCES *Year* 2009–10 *Income* £3,864,300
TRUSTEES A J R Ferguson; R J S Morton; Mrs S F J Judson; D J Hamilton.
HOW TO APPLY In writing to the correspondent. Trustees meet to consider grants in the autumn.
WHO TO APPLY TO The Trust Administrator, Quartermile Two, 2 Lister Square, Edinburgh EH3 9GL

■ Youth Music

CC NO 1075032   **ESTABLISHED** 1999
WHERE FUNDING CAN BE GIVEN England.
WHO CAN BENEFIT Music organisations, singing groups, nursery schools, nursery departments of large organisations, schools, after-school clubs, youth groups, recording studios, local authority departments and other organisations providing music-making opportunities to children and young people of any age up to 18.
WHAT IS FUNDED Funding programmes exist on a one-year cycle, targeting a specific element of youth music. Current programmes are: First Steps, which supports music-making activities for 0–5 year olds; Make It Sound, which focuses on music-making for 5–18 year olds who otherwise lack the chance to take part; and Vocalise!, which aims to encourage children and young people to sing, particularly those who would otherwise lack the chance to take part.
WHAT IS NOT FUNDED Funding is not available towards: instrument purchase; individual schools (although work between two or more schools can be supported); individuals; equipment purchases (unless as part of a project, in which case equipment purchases can constitute up to 5% of the grant); one-off events, including trips; projects lasting less than three months; or work which is a continuation of an existing project rather than new work or a new approach to work already undertaken.
SAMPLE GRANTS Beneficiaries included: Music for Youth (£179,000); Big About Music, Community Music East (CME), Pie Factory Music; Soundwave and North Music Trust (£120,000); Battersea Arts Centre (£75,000); Merseyside Youth Association Ltd (£60,000); Sound It Out Community Music (£50,000); Rhythmix (£45,000); Jessie's Fund (£17,000); CM Sounds (£10,000) and Loughborough University Development Trust (£6,000).
FINANCES *Year* 2009–10 *Income* £124,069 *Grants* £1,947,294 *Assets* £4,489,755
TRUSTEES Richard Stilgoe, Chair; David Carrington; Nicholas Cleoburyl; Menna McGregor; George Caird; Kathleen Duncan; Tolga Kashif; Sally Osman; Caragh Merrick; David Poole.
OTHER INFORMATION This trust is funded each year by a £10 million payment from the National Lottery, channelled through Arts Council England. Awards are made of between £5,000 and £30,000 to organisations running projects that meet the specific programme requirements.
HOW TO APPLY On a form available from the correspondent, or downloadable from the website. Decisions on whether an application is successful will be made within three months of application, although they must be received by 31 March each year as each programme only has a one-year life span (although they can be continued into the following year). New programmes come into effect on 1 July each year, with information on what can be funded announced on 29 April. The first decisions for each programme are announced on 1 October. It is recommended that potential applicants check the trust's website for up-to-date criteria, priorities and guidelines prior to application.
WHO TO APPLY TO Michael Jones, One America Street, London SE1 0NE *Tel* 020 7902 1060 *Fax* 020 7902 1061 *email* info@youthmusic.org.uk *Website* www.youthmusic.org.uk

■ Suha Yusuf Charitable Trust

CC NO 1137655   **ESTABLISHED** 2010
WHERE FUNDING CAN BE GIVEN Worldwide.
WHO CAN BENEFIT Registered charities.
WHAT IS FUNDED General charitable purposes.
TRUSTEES Ms Vivienne Clyde-Eckhardt; S Kornfeld.
HOW TO APPLY In writing to the correspondent.
WHO TO APPLY TO Ms Vivienne Clyde-Eckhardt, Trustee, 29 Montpelier Square, London SW7 1JY *Tel* 020 7581 1544

■ Zephyr Charitable Trust

CC NO 1003234 **ESTABLISHED** 1991
WHERE FUNDING CAN BE GIVEN UK and worldwide.
WHO CAN BENEFIT Organisations.
WHAT IS FUNDED The trust's grants are particularly targeted towards three areas: enabling lower income communities to be self-sustaining; the protection and improvement of the environment; providing relief and support for those in need, particularly from medical conditions or social or financial disadvantage.
WHAT IS NOT FUNDED No grants to individuals, expeditions or scholarships.
TYPE OF GRANT Mainly annual 'subscriptions' decided by the trustees.
RANGE OF GRANTS £500–£3,500.
SAMPLE GRANTS Beneficiaries during the year included: Friends of the Earth Trust; Medical Foundation for the Victims of Torture (£2,500 each); Organic Research Centre – Elm Farm; Hearing Research Trust (Deafness Research UK), UNICEF and Womankind (£2,000 each); Margaret Pyke Trust and MERLIN (Medical Emergency Relief International) (£1,500 each).
FINANCES *Year* 2009–10 *Income* £45,533 *Grants* £48,000 *Assets* £1,334,155
TRUSTEES Elizabeth Breeze; Marigo Harries; David Baldock; Donald I Watson.
HOW TO APPLY In writing to the correspondent. The trustees usually meet to consider grants in July each year. Unsolicited applications are unlikely to be successful, since the trust makes annual donations to a list of beneficiaries. However, the trust stated that unsolicited applications are considered on a quarterly basis by the trustees and very occasional support is given. Telephone applications are not accepted.
WHO TO APPLY TO The Trust Administrator, Luminary Finance LLP, PO Box 135, Longfield, Kent DA3 8WF

■ The Marjorie and Arnold Ziff Charitable Foundation

CC NO 249368 **ESTABLISHED** 1964
WHERE FUNDING CAN BE GIVEN UK, with a preference for Yorkshire, especially Leeds and Harrogate.
WHO CAN BENEFIT There are no restrictions regarding which organisations can benefit.
WHAT IS FUNDED This trust likes to support causes that will provide good value for the money donated by benefiting a large number of people, as well as encouraging others to make contributions to the work. This includes a wide variety of schemes that involve the community at many levels, including education, public places, the arts and helping people who are disadvantaged.
WHAT IS NOT FUNDED No grants to individuals.
TYPE OF GRANT Capital costs and building work are particularly favoured by the trustees.
SAMPLE GRANTS The University of Leeds (£1.25 million); United Jewish Israel Appeal (£67,000); Leeds Jewish Welfare Board (£34,000); Leeds International Pianoforte Competition and Maccabi GB (£13,000 each); the Chief Rabbinate Charitable Trust and Wellington College (£10,000 each); Lifeline for

the Old and Western Marble Arch Synagogue (£6,000 each); Aish Hatorah UK Limited, Donisthorpe Hall and Leeds Lubavitch (£5,000 each); Community Security Trust (£3,000); Keren Roi and YABC – Club for Young People (£2,000 each); United Synagogue and Yorkshire Chaplaincy Board (£1,000 each); Marie Curie Cancer Care, The Place2Be (£500 each); Friends of Roundhay Park (£200); and Havens Christian Hospice and The Anne Frank Trust (£50 each).
FINANCES *Year* 2009–10 *Income* £624,591 *Grants* £1,495,599 *Assets* £4,877,482
TRUSTEES Dr Marjorie E Ziff; Michael A Ziff; Edward M Ziff; Mrs Ann L Manning.
HOW TO APPLY In writing to the correspondent. Replies will only be given to a request accompanied by an sae. Please note that funds available from the trust are limited and requests not previously supported are unlikely to be successful. Initial telephone calls are welcome but please note the foregoing comments.
WHO TO APPLY TO Ann McGookin, Secretary, Town Centre House, The Merrion Centre, Leeds LS2 8LY *Tel* 0113 222 1234

■ Stephen Zimmerman Charitable Trust

CC NO 1038310 **ESTABLISHED** 1994
WHERE FUNDING CAN BE GIVEN UK.
WHO CAN BENEFIT Jewish organisations.
WHAT IS FUNDED Jewish causes.
SAMPLE GRANTS Previous beneficiaries have included: British ORT, Cancer Research, CIS Development Fund, London Youth, Jewish Association of Business Ethics, Jewish Care, Norwood Ltd, RNIB, United Jewish Israel Appeal and United Synagogue.
FINANCES *Year* 2009–10 *Grants* £132,415 *Assets* £93,735
TRUSTEES Mrs L J Zimmerman; M J P Marks and S Zimmerman.
HOW TO APPLY The trust does not respond to unsolicited applications.
WHO TO APPLY TO S Zimmerman, Trustee, 35 Stormont Road, London N6 4NR *Tel* 020 7518 3849

■ The Zochonis Charitable Trust

CC NO 274769 **ESTABLISHED** 1977
WHERE FUNDING CAN BE GIVEN UK, particularly Greater Manchester, and overseas, particularly Africa.
WHO CAN BENEFIT Registered charities only.
WHAT IS FUNDED General charitable purposes, with some preference for education and the welfare of children.
WHAT IS NOT FUNDED No grants for individuals.
TYPE OF GRANT One-off and recurrent.
RANGE OF GRANTS £2,000–£150,000.
SAMPLE GRANTS Cancer Research UK and Concert Worldwide – Haiti Emergency Appeal (£150,000 each); Bolton School and the Smile Train (£100,000 each); Greater Manchester High Sheriff's Trust (£77,500); Withington Girl's School (£75,000); The Police Foundation (£60,000); CAFOD (£50,000); Manchester YMCA (£35,000); KIDS (£30,000); Barnabus (£20,000); The Missing Foundation (£15,000); Children's Safety Education Foundation and After Adoption (£10,000 each); Action for Children and the Royal Veterinary College (£5,000 each); Welfare Ambulance Association (£3,000); and the Wildlife Trust (£2,000).

FINANCES *Year* 2009–10 *Income* £4,005,535
Grants £2,648,593 *Assets* £137,734,193
TRUSTEES Sir John Zochonis; Christopher Nigel
Green; Archibald G Calder; Joseph J Swift.
HOW TO APPLY In writing to the correspondent.
WHO TO APPLY TO Ruth Barron, c/o Cobbetts LLP,
58 Mosley Street, Manchester M2 3HZ
Tel 0845 165 5270 *Fax* 0845 166 6733
email ruth.barron@cobbetts.com

■ The Zolfo Cooper Foundation

CC NO 1134913   ESTABLISHED 2010
WHERE FUNDING CAN BE GIVEN Not defined. In
practice, UK.
WHO CAN BENEFIT Registered charities.
WHAT IS FUNDED General charitable purposes.
TRUSTEES Simon Freakley; Anne O'Keefe; Anne-
Marie Laing; Peter Saville.
OTHER INFORMATION The trustees are all partners at
Zolfo Cooper, the international provider of
corporate advisory and restructuring services,
formerly known as Kroll Corporate Advisory and
Restructuring. Simon Freakley is also a trustee
of Grange Park Opera, which aims to advance
education through the promotion, support and
encouragement of the art of music and drama
and in particular of opera.
HOW TO APPLY In writing to the correspondent.
WHO TO APPLY TO Simon Freakley, Trustee, Zolfo
Cooper LLP, 10 Fleet Place, London EC4M 7RB
Tel 020 7332 5000 *Fax* 020 7332 5001

■ Zurich Community Trust (UK) Limited

CC NO 266983   ESTABLISHED 1973
WHERE FUNDING CAN BE GIVEN UK and overseas.
Mainly focused around the company's main
office locations in Wiltshire, Hampshire and
Gloucestershire. Other areas include
Birmingham, Brighton, Cardiff, Glasgow, Leeds,
London, Manchester, Nottingham, Reigate,
Southampton, Sutton, Watford and Wilmslow.
WHO CAN BENEFIT Registered charities, voluntary
organisations and non-governmental
organisations that help people who are
disadvantaged achieve a better quality of life by
moving from dependence to independence.
WHAT IS FUNDED National programmes that create
sustainable change, tackle issues in
disadvantaged areas or work with disadvantaged
groups of older people, such as those who are
homeless or abused. Projects aiming to break
the cycle of generational drug abuse by focusing
on children and the family. Work with children
under 18 years of age who are disadvantaged.
Work to deal with mental health issues and
youth. Relief of poverty in India.
WHAT IS NOT FUNDED No grants made for: Statutory
organisations (including mainstream schools
and hospitals), unless exclusively for a special
needs unit; Fundraising events including
appeals or events for national charities;
Expeditions, exchanges or study tours;
Playgroups and mother and toddler groups,
unless for special needs groups; Medical
research, animal welfare charities, conservation
or environmental projects; Sports clubs, village
halls, political or religious organisations
(including the upkeep and repair of places of
worship); or Advertising or sponsorship
connected with charitable events or appeals.

TYPE OF GRANT One-off, or partnership grants for
three to five years; core costs; project costs;
revenues; salaries; seed funding; capital.
RANGE OF GRANTS Local grants: £100–£10,000;
partnership grants: £20,000–£100,000.
SAMPLE GRANTS Young People's Mental Health
(£484,000); Breaking the Cycle (Addaction)
(£207,000); India Programme (£113,000);
Children's Hospices UK, Phillippine Community
Trust (£100,000 each); Calvert Trust (£68,000);
Hope and Homes for Children (£63,000);
Foundation for Conductive Education, Canine
Partners (£40,000 each); NSPCC (ChildLine)
and Marie Curie Cancer Care (£25,000 each).
FINANCES *Year* 2010 *Income* £4,582,000
Grants £2,312,000 *Assets* £3,257,000
TRUSTEES T P Culling; A C Gillies; E Hopkins;
I N Lovett; A Moore; M J Brennan; S Lewis.
OTHER INFORMATION The trust also runs a
programme called the Employee Involvement
Programme.
HOW TO APPLY In the first instance, visit the trust's
website and follow the links to check eligibility
and download the guidelines and application
forms.
WHO TO APPLY TO Pam Webb, Head of Zurich
Community Trust (UK), PO Box 1288, Swindon,
Wiltshire SN1 1FL *Tel* 01793 502450
Fax 01793 506982 *email* pam.webb@zct.org.uk
Website www.zurich.org.uk